standard catalog of FIREARMS

by Ned Schwing & Herbert Houze

4th Edition

Published by:

700 E. State Street • Iola, WI 54990-0001
Telephone: 715/445-2214

Library of Congress Catalog Number: 90-62405

ISBN: 0-87341-278-8

Printed in the United States of America

ACKNOWLEDGEMENTS

Kenneth Wilkinson and Kermit Feuge gave us the benefit of their knowledge of firearms collecting based on many years of practical experience.

John Dougan, Ruger expert, who supplied us with information on the Great Western Arms Co.

Ottis Spigelmyer shared with us his in-depth knowledge of Remington arms.

Don Combs and Larry Orr helped a great deal by sharing their years of experience with Winchester rifles and shotguns.

Thanks to Smith & Wesson experts Roy Jinks, of Smith & Wesson, who wrote the introduction to that section in this book.

Thanks to Dan Brdlik, whose countless hours of research this book was based upon.

C.W. Slagle, of Scottsdale, Arizona, for his expertise in antique firearms.

Thanks to John Kronschnabl, advertising manager of *Gun List* magazine (Krause Publications), for his assistance throughout the year.

Thanks to Eric M. Larson for his knowledgeable information on Harrington & Richardson (H&R) Handy guns.

A special thanks to all the manufacturers and importers who supplied us with information and photographs on their products.

Thanks to the Lew Horton Distributing Company for their invaluable information on Colt Custom Shop products and Smith & Wesson Performance Center products.

Thanks to Jerry Cummings of Manawa, Wisconsin and William "Pete" Harvey of Falmouth, Massachusetts, who contributed photos and research information.

Thanks to all the readers who have taken the time to contact the editors with corrections, omissions and additional information.

PHOTO CREDITS

John Gallo, president of Butterfield and Butterfield auction house in San Francisco, made available a wealth of fine photographs and other auction information that has improved the quality of this publication. Through the efforts of Butterfield's, firearms collecting has reached a level of interest on par with the fine art world.

Thanks to the Milwaukee Public Museum, 800 W. Wells St., Milwaukee, WI 53233; and the Buffalo Bill Historical Center, Cody Firearms Museum, P.O. Box 1000, Cody, WY 82414, for supplying us with photographs.

Many thanks to the following who lent us their firearms to photograph for this book:

Chip Johnson of Direct Firearms, St. Joseph, Missouri
C. Roy Jones of C. Roy's Gunsmithing, Kaiser, Missouri
Mike and Wanda Moutray of Mike's Gun Sales, Grant City, Missouri
Will Parsons of Parsons Gun Shop
Joe Lech of Ironwork Armco, Raytown, Missouri
Guns of the World, Kansas City, Missouri
J.M. Stanley of Stan's Gun Shop, Joplin, Missouri
H.L. Hoeflicker of HLH Enterprises, Shawnee Mission, Kansas
S.T. Sinclair
Pat Morgan
William H. Lehman of B & B Guns, Brighton, Colorado
James D. McKenzie and Samuel Baum of Kentucky Rifle, Union City, Pennsylvania
Dean Parr of Dean's Gun Shop, St. Joseph, Missouri
E.K. Tryon of Philadelphia, Pennsylvania
Bob's Gun Rack of Lee's Summit, Missouri
Pat McWilliams
J.M. Stanley
Ken Waughtal of Merriam, Kansas
Armond Beetch of Quapaw, Oklahoma
Jim Rankin
Eric M. Larson

INTRODUCTION

Ever since the invention of the first firearm, man has been fascinated by them. First used as an instrument of war and later as a means of acquiring food, firearms quickly became an object of admiration and wonder.

Firearms are a deep part of our historical and technological experience. The purpose of this publication is to present to the reader a comprehensive view of firearms, focusing not only their values but also on the historical and technical side as well.

The editors' and publisher's goal is to furnish the reader with an encyclopedia of information that will enable the collector to gain additional insight into all aspects of firearms collecting. Collectors have sought to acquire firearms for a multitude of reasons. From firearms that are historically important, to firearms that were the innovators in design and function, to firearms that were admired for their grace and beauty; all of these factors are considered in this book.

This publication not only attempts to provide high quality photographs that illustrate the firearms in question, but to furnish the reader with detailed descriptions of each firearm and to break down these explanations into useful categories. A simplified grading system that is easily understandable is an additional aid to the collector. This 4th Edition is an improvement over the 3rd Edition, and the editors and publishers have made a commitment to improve each subsequent edition in a significant fashion. Some firearm categories are incomplete. Time and space constraints have not allowed us to make each category definitive, but that is our goal in ensuing editions.

We believe that the reader will benefit from the information presented in this book, not only from a pricing standpoint but as a reference source as well.

GRADING SYSTEM

In the opinion of the editors all grading systems are subjective. It is our task to offer the collector and dealer a measurement that most closely reflects a general consensus on condition. The system we present seems to come closest to describing a firearm in universal terms. We strongly recommend that the reader acquaint himself with this grading system before attempting to determine the correct price for a particular firearm's condition. Remember, condition determines price.

NIB-New in Box
This category can sometimes be misleading. It means that the firearm is in its original factory carton with all of the appropriate papers. It also means the firearm is new; that it has not been fired and has no wear. This classification brings a substantial premium for both the collector and shooter.

Excellent
Collector quality firearms in this condition are highly desirable. The firearm must be in at least 98 percent condition with respect to blue wear, stock or grip finish, and bore. The firearm must also be in 100 percent original factory condition without refinishing, repair, alterations or additions of any kind. Sights must be factory original as well. This grading classification includes both modern and antique (manufactured prior to 1898) firearms.

Very Good
Firearms in this category are also sought after both by the collector and shooter. Firearms must be in working order and retain approximately 92 percent metal and wood finish. It must be 100 percent factory original, but may have some small repairs, alterations, or non-factory additions. No refinishing is permitted in this category. Both modern and antique firearms are included in this classification.

Good
Modern firearms in this category may not be considered to be as collectable as the previous grades, but antique firearms are considered desirable. Modern firearms must retain at least 80 percent metal and wood finish, but may display evidence of old refinishing. Small repairs, alterations, or non-factory additions are sometimes encountered in this class. Factory replacement parts are permitted. The overall working condition of the firearm must be good as well as safe. The bore may exhibit wear or some corrosion, especially in antique arms. Antique firearms may be included in this category if their metal and wood finish is at least 50 percent original factory finish.

Fair
Firearms in this category should be in satisfactory working order and safe to shoot. The overall metal and wood finish on the modern firearm must be at least 30 percent and antique firearms must have at least some original finish or old re-finish remaining. Repairs, alterations, non-factory additions, and recent refinishing would all place a firearm in this classification. However, the modern firearm must be in working condition, while the antique firearm may not function. In either case the firearm must be considered safe to fire if in a working state.

Poor
Neither collectors nor shooters are likely to exhibit much interest in firearms in this condition. Modern firearms are likely to retain little metal or wood finish. Pitting and rust will be seen in firearms in this category. Modern firearms may not be in working order and may not be safe to shoot. Repairs and refinishing would be necessary to restore the firearm to safe working order. Antique firearms will have no finish and will not function. In the case of modern firearms their

principal value lies in spare parts. On the other hand, antique firearms in this condition may be used as "wall hangers" or as an example of an extremely rare variation or have some kind of historical significance.

Pricing Sample Format

NIB	Exc.	V.G.	Good	Fair	Poor
550	450	400	350	300	200

Pricing

Unfortunately for shooters and collectors, there is no central clearing house for firearms prices. The prices given in this book are designed as a guide, not as a quote. This is an important distinction because prices for firearms vary with the time of the year and geographical location. For example, interest in firearms is at its lowest point in the summer. People are not as interested in shooting and collecting at this time of the year as they are in playing golf or taking a vacation. Therefore, prices are depressed slightly and guns that may sell quickly during the hunting season or the winter months may not sell well at all during this time of year. Geographical location also plays an important part in pricing. For instance, a Winchester Model 70 in a .264 caliber will bring a higher price in the Western states than along the Eastern seaboard. Smaller gauges and calibers seem to be more popular along both coasts and mid-sections of the United States than in the more open western sections of the country.

It is not practical to list prices in this book with regard to time of year or location. What is given is a reasonable price based on sales at gun shows, auction houses, Gun List prices, and information obtained from knowledgeable collectors and dealers. The firearms prices listed in this book are retail prices and may bring slightly more or less depending on the variables discussed above. If you choose to sell your gun to a dealer you will not receive the retail price but a wholesale price based on the markup that particular dealer needs to operate.

One final note. In some cases the price paid for a particular gun may seem too high or too low to the collector. Many times we have heard the expression, "He paid too much for that gun." The price paid for a firearm is based on what a willing buyer and willing seller can agree upon. If someone pays a price that someone else considers too high, then that is a subjective matter based on personal opinion and does not enter into our decision to price guns at a certain level. If the price paid was done so willingly, then that is the price of the gun. Collectors often complain that the prices of firearms in their collecting field are too high. Our reply would be that it is better to have prices going up than in the other direction.

In the final analysis, the prices listed here are given to assist the shooter and collector in pursuing their hobby with a better understanding of what is going on in the marketplace. If this book can expand one's knowledge, then it will have fulfilled its purpose.

Additional Considerations

As stated in the pricing section, this publication offers a general guide to prices. There are many factors which may affect the value of a firearm. We have attempted to be as comprehensive as possible but we cannot cover all possible factors which may influence the worth of any given firearm. Some of these circumstances will be discussed so that the shooter and collector will have a better idea of how certain factors may affect prices.

Firearms have been admired and coveted, not only for their usefulness, but also for their grace and beauty. Since the beginning of the 19th century, firearms' makers have adorned their guns with engraving, fine woods, or special order features that set their products apart from the rest. There is no feasible way to give the collector every possible variation of the firearms presented in this book. However, in a general way certain special factors will significantly influence the price of a firearm.

Perhaps the most recognizable special feature collectors agree affects the price of a firearm is engraving. The artistry, beauty, and intricate nature of engraving draw all collectors toward it. But, firearms engraving is a field unto itself requiring years of experience to determine proper chronological methods and the ability to identify the engraver in question. Factory engraving generally brings more of a premium than after-market engraving. To be able to determine factory work is a difficult task full of pitfalls. In some cases, factories like Colt and Winchester may have records to verify original factory engraving work. Whereas, other manufacturers such as Parker, Remington, or Savage do not have these records. Whenever a firearm purchase is to be made with respect to an engraved gun, it is in the collector's best interest to secure an expert opinion and/or a factory letter prior to the purchase. Engraved firearms are expensive. A mistake could cost the collector thousands of dollars; proceed with caution.

The 18th century was also a time when pistols and rifles were purchased by or given to historically important individuals. Firearms have also been an important part of significant historical events such as the Battle of the Little Bighorn or the Battle of Bull Run or some other meaningful event in our nation's history. Many of these firearms are in museums where the public can enjoy, see and appreciate them. Others are in private collections which seldom, if ever, are offered for sale. If the collector should ever encounter one of these historically important firearms, it cannot be stressed strongly enough to secure an expert determination as to authenticity. Museum curators are perhaps the best source of information for these types of firearms. As with engraved guns, historical firearms are usually very expensive, and without documentation their value is questionable.

Special features and variations are also a desirable part of firearms collecting. As with engraving, special order guns can bring a considerable premium. The Colt factory has excellent records regarding their firearms and will provide the collector with a letter of authenticity. Winchester records are not as comprehensive, but rifles made prior to 1908 may have documentation. Other firearm manufacturers either do not have records or do not provide the collector with documentation. This leaves the collector in a difficult position. Special order sights, stocks, barrel lengths, calibers, and so forth must be judged on their own merits. As with other factors an expert should be consulted prior to purchase. Sometimes this can be difficult. Experienced collectors, researchers, and museums will generally provide the kind of information a collector needs before purchasing a special order or unique firearm.

Perhaps the best advice is for the collector to take his time. Do not be in a hurry and don't allow yourself to be rushed into making a decision. Learn as much as possible about the firearms you are interested in collecting or shooting. Try to keep current with prices through the *Gun List* and this publication. Go to gun shows, not just to buy or sell but to observe and learn. Firearms collecting is a rewarding hobby. Firearms are part of our nation's history and represent an opportunity to learn more about their role in that American experience. If done skillfully, firearms collecting can be a profitable hobby as well.

PRICING PANEL

Bob Anderson
Civil war era U.S. military
406 N. Derbyshire
Arlington Heights, IL 60004

David Bichrest
Winchester Lever Action rifles
49 Charlonate Drive
Gray, ME 04039
207-657-4706

Kevin Cherry
Winchester And Colt Commemoratives
3402 West Wendover Avenue
Greensboro, NC 27407
919-854-4182

Don Criswell
Winchester Model 21 shotguns
Parker shotguns
P.O. Box 277
Yorba Linda, CA 92686
714-970-5934

John Diemer
Belgium Browning shotguns and rifles
3304 Mayfield Court
Winston-Salem, NC 27104
919-760-0257

Richard Freer
Belgium Browning shotguns
Winchester pre-64 shotguns
8928 Spring Branch Drive
Houston, TX 77080
713-467-3016

Rod Fuller
Browning shotguns and rifles
Weatherby Rifles
Rt. #1, Box 177
Grant, NE 69140
308-352-4080

Ed Harlow
Colt and Winchester collectables
242 W. Main Street
Fredericksburg, TX 78624
210-997-7510

Rick Kennerknecht
Randall pistols
P.O. Box 903
Casper, WY 82602
307-235-2136

Dave Kidd
Winchester Models 85, 86, 90 & 06
Box 662
Big Sandy, MT 59520
406-378-3121

James King
Winchester Lever Action rifles
Sharps
Colt Single Action Army 1st Generation
P.O. Box 70577
Albany, GA 31708
912-436-0397

Roy Marcot
Spencer and antique Remingtons
425 Honeysuckle Lane
San Ramon, CA 94583
510-736-1471

Duke McCaa
Colt Single Action
Hi-Standard
Kimber
5243 Gulf Breeze Parkway
Gulf Breeze, FL 32561
904-932-4867

Gale Morgan
Luger and Mauser pistols
Pre-WWI Pistols
P.O. Box 72
Lincoln, CA 95648
916-645-1720

Jim Rankin
Walther pistols
3615 Anderson Road
Coral Gables, FL 33134
305-446-1792

Chad Hiddleson
Ruger
1300 16th Street
Perry, IA 50220

Dan Sheil
Merkel shotguns and rifles
9240 Southwest 140 Street
Miami, FL 33176
305-253-5984

Don Stika
Cezh pistols
Bruno and Mauser sporting rifles
Mannlicher rifles
P.O. Box 882
Bensenville, IL 60106
707-766-4617

Mike Stucklager
Antique S&W pistols
Stevens and Sharps
3017 10th Avenue South
Great Falls, MT 59405
406-761-4346

Orv Reichert
World War II-era semi-automatic pistols
P.O. Box 5232
W. Pittsburg, CA 94565
510-458-9122

Bob Swanson
Modern semi-automatic
pistols, rifles, and shotguns
6171 N. Foothills Dr.
Tuscon, AZ 85718
602-299-3454

Allan Wilson
Winchester Model 70
RR2 Box 84A
W. Lebanon, NH 03784
603-298-8085

WHAT TO DO BEFORE YOU BUY A GUN: ADVICE FOR ALL

So you want to buy a gun. For the veteran shooter or collector, the series of events leading up to a purchase is almost taken for granted. You know what you want and all you have to do is find the type and style at the price you want to pay. But what about the beginner or the experienced hand who is branching off into new territory? We all need to be reminded, from time to time, of certain steps we need to take to make a successful purchase; one that we will be happy with for a long time.

If you are about to purchase a handgun, rifle, or shotgun for practical reasons, the one recommendation that should *always* be kept in mind is to read about the types of firearms you might be interested in and the conditions that they are intended for. You wouldn't want to buy a trap gun if you are going to hunt ducks; or a .22 auto pistol to hunt brown bear in Alaska. There are almost as many opinions on what to use for any given hunting or shooting situation as there are hunters and shooters, but reading about the guns is a good place to start. Next, ask your friends what they use and why. Are they happy with the quality, performance, and reliability of the gun they use? If so, why? Ask a lot of "whys." If you are able, try to test fire the gun. That is a good start, or, better yet, use the gun under actual shooting conditions.

Remember, much of what you read and hear boils down to personal preference on the part of the user and nothing more. Occasionally, a rifle or shotgun or pistol may not fit you, may be too heavy or too light. These are all factors you should strive to find out before you buy; not after.

Where you buy is also important. Most towns and cities have at least one gun store with a competent, knowledgeable staff that is able to offer sound advice and help if you are in the market for what they carry in stock. Of course, they want to sell you a gun, so you have to keep that fact in mind. Buying a gun at a gun show is another approach that works for many people. This technique works best when you have already made up your mind what you want. Before you buy a gun at a gun show, make sure that it is what you want and it is in safe operating condition. Buy from a reputable dealer. If you get home and the gun doesn't work as it should, make sure you can return it in the same condition as when you purchased it. You can also buy a gun through the mail from publications such as *Gun List*. This avenue has its bumps in the road as well. You must purchase the gun through a licensed FFL holder. Buy from a reliable person. Ask for references and inquire about the seller. Bad reputations usually precede disreputable people. Make sure you have at least a three-day inspection period after you receive the gun to make up your mind.

For the collector, the options are similar but the circumstances are a bit more complicated. The collecting of arms, whether they be military or sporting, American or foreign, modern or antique, can be an extremely rewarding experience. It does, however, like any other collecting field, have its pitfalls. Many of these can be avoided by simply following a tried and true set of guidelines; *read, look, touch, compare, question, and read some more*. Before you buy, learn as much as you can. Read about your interest, and look and handle as many examples as possible. Ask questions about finish, markings, grips, stocks, barrel lengths, and so on. Take what you see and review what you have already read; it will calrify many of your questions. For example, you can read about Winchester's stock finish used before 1915 and think you understand the difference between shellac and a finish with chemical compounds; but you really don't know the difference until you see it and feel it.

When at last you are ready to make a purchase, investigate the seller's reputation and always demand a detailed receipt noting the make, model, serial number, special features, and so forth. Disreputable sellers are less likely to provide you with such a receipt than honest dealers. When you inquire about a particular dealer, ask collectors, not other dealers. Don't get in a hurry. You should also determine whether the seller will allow you to return the item should it not be genuine in any respect. If you follow the above steps and ask for help from an expert or knowledgeable collector, even if a fee is involved, your risk will be minimized. The expenditure of a few dollars to ensure an item's authenticity is money well spent should the item not be as advertised. In certain cases, antique firearms can be authenticated by factory letters. Some Winchesters and Colts can be "lettered" in this manner. Inquire if this can be done and have it so before you buy. If in doubt about the firearm or the seller, don't buy.

Another opportunity where collectors can purchase firearms is at auction. Though many fine pieces can be acquired in this way, extreme caution must be exercised. Since auctioneers only act as an agent for the seller, items are sold "as is," and purchases are final. Consequently it is absolutely necessary to examine material offered for sale before purchasing to ensure its authenticity. If you cannot attend an auction personally, secure the services of a trusted representative to perform the examination. To avoid becoming caught in the excitement of an auction, set the amount you are willing to pay beforehand and stick to it. As with any purchase, caution and prudence must be exercised.

Whether you are a shooter or collector and whatever approach you take, there are two keys that you should always keep in mind; *let knowledge and patience be your guide.*

TO THE BUYERS OF SEMI-AUTOMATIC FIREARMS

As the 4th Edition of the *Standard Catalog of Firearms* goes to press, the political climate in this country regarding gun control is becoming volatile. The passage of the Brady Bill has brought forth more calls for gun control with the result that a bill before Congress titled the "Public Safety and Recreational Firearms Use Protection Act" prohibits the manufacture, transfer, or possession of a number of semi-automatic assault weapons. The pending bill would also ban detachable magazines above 10 rounds for rifles and pistols as well as magazine extensions for shotguns holding over five rounds. Some of these so called assault weapons are mentioned by name and others are defined by their features.

At the present time, the passage of this bill in its current form and content is uncertain, and by the time this edition of the *Catalog* is released for sale, some type of new gun control may have passed Congress. The result of this possible legislation is a general alarm in the gun and shooting community. Prices for semi-automatic firearms have risen dramatically and will most likely continue to rise until this legislation is resolved. A potential buyer should be aware of these conditions and understand that the prices of certain firearms in this publication **do not** reflect the current or future political climate regarding gun control and its effect on prices or particular classes of firearms.

The Editors

CONTENTS

A.A.
Azanza & Arrizabalaga
Eibar, Spain

Pistols by this manufacturer are readily identifiable by the presence of the trademark "AA" on their frames.

A.A.

A 7.65mm caliber semi-automatic pistol with a 9-shot magazine. The slide marked "Modelo 1916 Eibar (Espana)."

Exc.	V.G.	Good	Fair	Poor
110	90	75	50	25

Reims

A 6.35mm or 7.65mm caliber semi-automatic pistol. The slide marked "1914 Model Automatic Pistol Reims Patent".

Exc.	V.G.	Good	Fair	Poor
100	80	65	45	25

A.A.A.
Aldazabal
Eibar, Spain

Modelo 1919

A 7.65mm semi-automatic pistol.

Exc.	V.G.	Good	Fair	Poor
90	80	60	40	25

A & R SALES SOUTH
El Monte, California

45 Auto

An alloy-frame version of the Colt Model 1911 semi-automatic pistol.

NIB	Exc.	V.G.	Good	Fair	Poor
225	200	175	150	125	100

Mark IV Sporter

A semi-automatic copy of the M-14 military rifle. Manufactured in .308 cal. (7.65mm Nato) only.

NIB	Exc.	V.G.	Good	Fair	Poor
300	275	250	225	175	150

AFC
Auguste Francotte
Liege, Belgium

This was one of the most prolific makers of revolvers in Liege during the last half of the 19th century. It is estimated that over 150 different revolvers were made and marketed by them before they were forced out of business by the German occupation of 1914. Francotte produced many variations from Tranter copies to pinfires, early Smith & Wesson designs to the 11mm M1871 Swedish troopers revolver. They made break-open revolvers and produced only one semi-auto, a 6.35mm blowback design. A good portion of their pistols were produced for the wholesale market and were sold under other names. These particular revolvers will bear the letters "AF" stamped somewhere on the frame. Because of the vast number and variety of pistols produced by this company, cataloging and pricing is beyond the scope of this or any general reference book. It is suggested that any examples encountered be researched on an individual basis. The lone semi-auto, produced in 1912, can be priced rather easily since it is the only one the company ever manufactured.

Semi-Auto

A 6.35mm, 6-shot detachable magazine pocket pistol with blue finish. This model was marked "Francotte Liege."

Exc.	V.G.	Good	Fair	Poor
250	220	190	150	100

A. J. ORDNANCE

This is a delayed blowback action that is unique in that every shot was double action. This pistol was chambered for the .45 ACP cartridge and had a 3.5" stainless-steel barrel with fixed sights and plastic grips. The detachable magazine held 6 shots, and the standard finish was matte blue. Chrome plating was available and would add approximately 15 percent to the values given.

NIB	Exc.	V.G.	Good	Fair	Poor
500	475	425	350	275	200

AMAC
American Military Arms Corporation
formerly
Iver Johnson
Jacksonville, Arkansas

The Iver Johnson Arms Co. was founded in 1871 in Fitchsburg, Massachusetts. It was one of the oldest and most successful of the old-line arms companies on which our modern era has taken its toll. In 1984 the company moved to Jacksonville, Arkansas; and in 1987 it was purchased by the American Military Arms Corporation. This company has released some of the older designs as well as some new models. The original Iver Johnson line will be listed under its own heading later in this text.

U.S.Carbine .22

This is a semi-automatic, military-style carbine that is patterned after the M1 of WWII fame. It is chambered for the .22 l.r. cartridge, has an 18.5" barrel and features military-style peep sights and a 15-shot detachable magazine.

NIB	Exc.	V.G.	Good	Fair	Poor
175	150	120	100	75	50

Wagonmaster Lever Action Rifle

This model is chambered for the .22 rimfire cartridge, has an 18.5" barrel and is styled after the Win. 94. The stock has a straight grip; and the forend, a barrel band. There are adjustable sights and a tube magazine that holds 15 l.r. cartridges.

NIB	Exc.	V.G.	Good	Fair	Poor
175	150	120	100	75	50

Wagonmaster .22 Magnum

This model is the same as the Wagonmaster except that it is chambered for the .22 rimfire magnum.

NIB	Exc.	V.G.	Good	Fair	Poor
190	160	130	110	75	50

Targetmaster Pump Action Rifle

This model is a slide- or pump-action that is chambered for the .22 rimfire cartridges. It has an 18.5" barrel with adjustable sights and a straight-grip stock. It holds 12 l.r. cartridges.

NIB	Exc.	V.G.	Good	Fair	Poor
175	150	120	100	75	50

Li'L Champ Bolt Action Rifle

This model is a scaled-down single shot that is chambered for the .22 rimfire cartridges. It has a 16.25" barrel, adjustable sights, a molded stock, and nickel-plated bolt. This model is 33" overall and is designed to be the ideal first rifle for a young shooter.

NIB	Exc.	V.G.	Good	Fair	Poor
100	75	60	45	35	20

M1 .30 Cal. Carbine

A military-style carbine styled after the M1 of WWII fame. It is chambered for the .30 Carbine cartridge and has an 18" barrel with military-style sights and hardwood stock. There are detachable 5-, 15-, and 30-round magazines available.

NIB	Exc.	V.G.	Good	Fair	Poor
265	245	200	175	140	90

Paratrooper .30 Carbine

This model is similar to the M1 model with a folding stock.

NIB	Exc.	V.G.	Good	Fair	Poor
300	265	225	200	165	125

Enforcer .30 Carbine

This is a 9.5" pistol version of the M1 Carbine. It has no buttstock.

NIB	Exc.	V.G.	Good	Fair	Poor
350	300	265	225	185	140

Long Range Rifle System

This is a specialized long-range, bolt-action rifle chambered for the .50 Cal. Browning Machinegun cartridge. It has a 33" barrel and a special muzzle brake system. A custom order version in the .338/416 caliber is also available.

NIB	Exc.	V.G.	Good	Fair	Poor
8500	7000	5000	3500	2500	2000

TP-22 and TP-25

This model is a compact, double-action, pocket automatic that was styled after the the Walther TP series. Chambered for either the .22 rimfire or the .25 centerfire cartridges, it has a 2.75" barrel, fixed sights and black plastic grips. The detachable magazine holds 7 shots and the finish is either blue or nickel-plated. The nickel-plated version is worth 10 percent more than the blue (shown).

NIB	Exc.	V.G.	Good	Fair	Poor
200	175	145	110	85	50

AMAC -22 Compact or 25 Compact

This is a compact, single-action, semi-automatic pocket pistol that is chambered for the .22 rimfire or the .25 ACP cartridge. It has a 2" barrel, 5-shot magazine, plastic grips, and blue or nickel finish. The nickel finish is 10 percent higher in cost than the blue (shown).

NIB	Exc.	V.G.	Good	Fair	Poor
150	125	100	80	55	35

AMT
Arcadia Machine and Tool
Irwindale, California

Lightning

A single-action, semi-automatic, .22 caliber pistol. Available with barrel lengths of 5" (Bull only), 6.5", 8.5", 10.5" and 12.5" (either Bull or tapered), and adjustable sights, as well as the trigger. The grips of checkered black rubber. Manufactured between 1984 and 1987, this model resembled the Ruger.

Exc.	V.G.	Good	Fair	Poor
250	210	175	125	100

Bull's Eye Regulation Target

As above, with a 6.5" vent-rib bull barrel, wooden target grips, and an extended rear sight. Manufactured in 1986 only.

Exc.	V.G.	Good	Fair	Poor
350	300	250	200	150

Baby Automag

Similar to the above with an 8.5 inch ventilated rib barrel, and Millett adjustable sights. Approximately 1,000 were manufactured.

Exc.	V.G.	Good	Fair	Poor
400	350	285	225	175

Automag II

A stainless-steel, semi-automatic .22 Magnum Pistol. Available with 3.5", 4.5", and 6" barrel lengths and Millett adjustable sights, grips of black, grooved, plastic. Was first manufactured in 1987.

NIB	Exc.	V.G.	Good	Fair	Poor
270	225	175	125	100	80

Automag III

This semi-automatic pistol is chambered for the .30 Carbine cartridge and the 9mm Winchester Magnum cartridge. Barrel length is 6.37" and overall length is 10.5". The magazine capacity is 8 rounds. Fitted with Millett adjustable rear sight and carbon fiber grips. Stainless steel finish. Pistol weighs 43 oz.

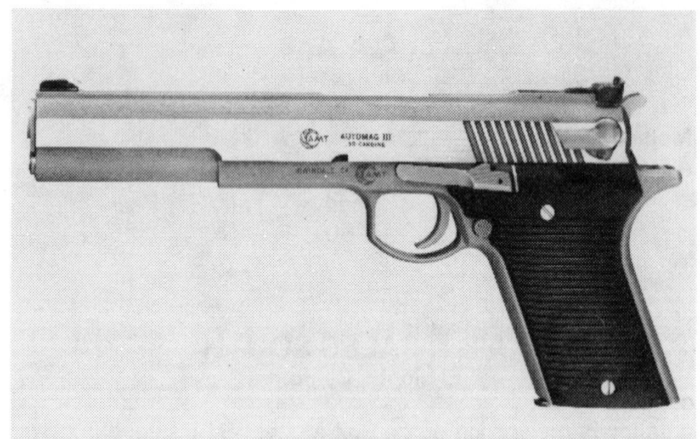

NIB	Exc.	V.G.	Good	Fair	Poor
350	300	250	200	150	125

Automag IV

Similar in appearance to the Automag III this pistol is chambered for the .45 Winchester Magnum. Magazine capacity is 7 rounds and weight is 46 oz.

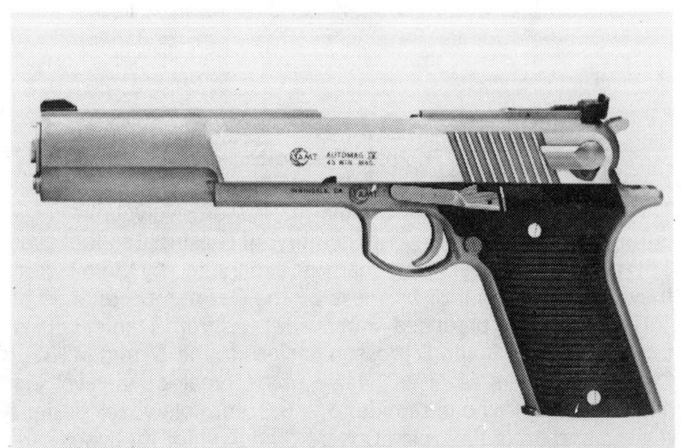

NIB	Exc.	V.G.	Good	Fair	Poor
500	450	400	350	300	200

Automag V

Introduced in 1993 this model is similar in appearance to the Automag models but is chambered for the .50 caliber cartridge. A limited production run of 3000 pistol s with special serial number from "1 of 3000 to 3000 of 3000". Barrel length is 6.5" and magazine capacity is 5 rounds. Weighs 46 oz.

NIB	Exc.	V.G.	Good	Fair	Poor
725	600	500	400	300	200

Back Up Pistol

This is a small semi-automatic pocket pistol chambered for the .22 Long Rifle and the .380 ACP cartridges. This is fitted with a 2.5" barrel and is offered with either black plastic or walnut grips. Originally manufactured by TDE, then Irwindale Arms Inc., it is now currently produced by AMT.

NIB	Exc.	V.G.	Good	Fair	Poor
200	175	150	125	100	85

.380 Back Up II

Introduced in 1993 this pistol is similar to the Back Up model but with the addition of a double safety and extended finger grip on the magazine.

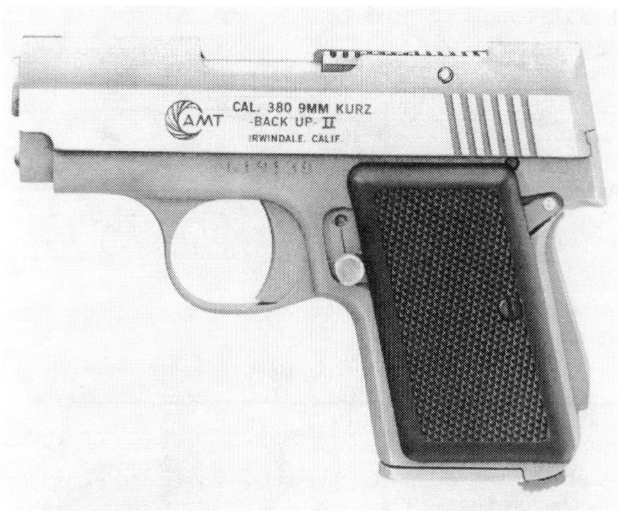

NIB	Exc.	V.G.	Good	Fair	Poor
200	175	150	125	100	85

Hardballer/Government Model

This model is similar to the Colt Gold Cup .45 ACP. It is offered in two versions. The first has fixed sights and rounded slide top while the second has adjustable Millett sights and Matte rib. Magazine capacity is 7 rounds. Wraparound rubber grips are standard. Long grip safety, beveled magazine well, and adjustable trigger are common to both variations. Weight is 38 oz.

Hardballer

NIB	Exc.	V.G.	Good	Fair	Poor
400	350	300	250	200	150

Government Model

NIB	Exc.	V.G.	Good	Fair	Poor
350	300	250	200	150	100

Hardballer Longslide

Similar to the Hardballer Model but fitted with a 7" barrel. Pistol weighs 46 oz.

NIB	Exc.	V.G.	Good	Fair	Poor
425	375	325	275	225	175

On Duty

This semi-automatic pistol features a double action only trigger action or double action with decocker and is chambered for the 9mm, .40S&W, or .45 ACP calibers. Barrel length is 4.5" and overall length is 7.75". The finish is a black anodized matte finish. Carbon fiber grips are standard. Furnished with 3-dot sights. Weighs 32 oz.

NIB	Exc.	V.G.	Good	Fair	Poor
350	300	250	200	150	100

Skipper

Identical to the Hard Baller with a 1" shorter barrel and slide, discontinued in 1984.

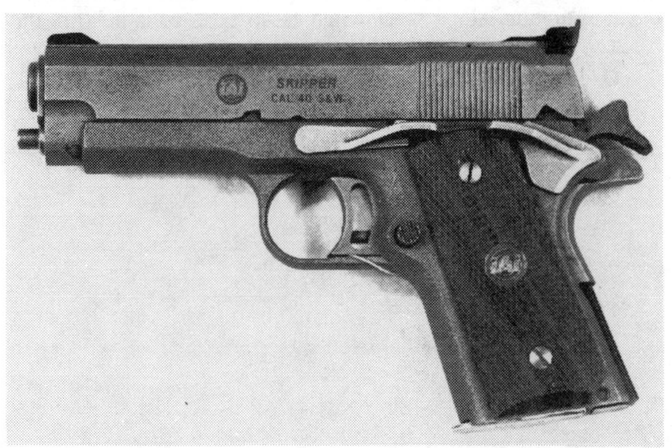

Exc.	V.G.	Good	Fair	Poor
375	325	275	225	200

Combat Skipper
Similar to the Colt Commander. Discontinued in 1984.

Exc.	V.G.	Good	Fair	Poor
350	300	250	200	175

Lightning Rifle
Patterned after the Ruger 10/22, this rifle has a 22" barrel and a 25-round, detachable magazine with a folding stock. Introduced in 1986.

NIB	Exc.	V.G.	Good	Fair	Poor
275	225	175	150	125	100

Small Game Hunter
As above with a full stock and 10-round magazine. Introduced in 1986.

NIB	Exc.	V.G.	Good	Fair	Poor
275	225	175	150	125	100

Small Game Hunter II
This semi-automatic rifle is chambered for the .22 Long Rifle cartridge. Stock is a checkered black matte nylon and is fitted with a removable recoil pad for ammo, cleaning rod, and knife. Rotary magazine holds 10 rounds. Stainless steel action and barrel. Barrel is a heavy weight target type 22" long. Weight is 6 lb.

NIB	Exc.	V.G.	Good	Fair	Poor
225	200	175	150	125	100

Hunting Rifle
This semi-automatic rifle is chambered for the .22 Rimfire Magnum cartridge. Stock is checkered black matte nylon. Other features are similar to the Small Game Hunter II including weight.

NIB	Exc.	V.G.	Good	Fair	Poor
350	300	250	200	150	125

Magnum Hunter
Introduced in early 1993 this new addition to the AMT line is chambered for the .22 Magnum cartridge and is fitted with a 22" accurized barrel. Barrel and action are stainless steel. It comes standard with a 5 round magazine and composite stock but a laminated stock is available as an extra as is a 10 round magazine.

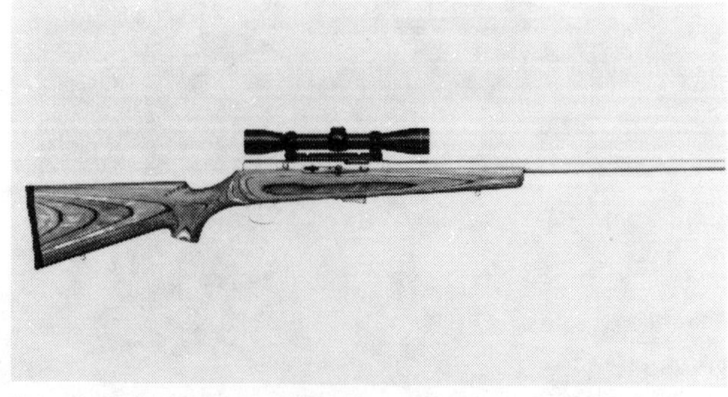

NIB	Exc.	V.G.	Good	Fair	Poor
400	350	300	250	200	150

A-SQUARE
Madison, Indiana

Hannibal Grade
Utilizing the P-17 Enfield action, with a 22" to 26" barrel, this rifle is chambered for various calibers from .270 up to and including the .458 Magnum. Blued with a checkered walnut pistol grip stock. Introduced in 1986.

NIB	Exc.	V.G.	Good	Fair	Poor
1600	1400	1000	850	750	500

Caesar Grade
Utilizing a Remington Model 700 action and chambered for the same cartridges as the above with the exception that A-Square proprietary cartridges are not available. Also made in the left-hand version. Introduced in 1986.

NIB	Exc.	V.G.	Good	Fair	Poor
1650	1450	1050	900	800	500

ATCSA
Armas De Tiro Y Casa
Eibar, Spain

Colt Police Positive Copy
A .38 caliber 6 shot revolver resembling a Colt Police Positive.

Exc.	V.G.	Good	Fair	Poor
150	125	100	60	40

Target Pistol
A .22 caliber single shot target pistol utilizing a revolver frame.

Exc.	V.G.	Good	Fair	Poor
200	175	140	100	65

AGUIRRE Y ARANZABAL (AYA)
Eibar, Spain

Side x Side Shotguns
Matador Side x Side
A 12, 16, 20, 28 or .410 bore boxlock double barrel shotgun with 26", 28" or 30" barrels, single selective trigger and automatic ejectors. Blued with a walnut stock. Manufactured from 1955 to 1963.

28 gauge and .410—Add 20 %.

Exc.	V.G.	Good	Fair	Poor
475	450	375	300	250

Matador II Side x Side
As above, in 12 or 20 gauge with a ventilated rib.

Exc.	V.G.	Good	Fair	Poor
500	460	390	300	250

Matador III Side x Side
As above, with 3" chambers.

NIB	Exc.	V.G.	Good	Fair	Poor
1235	950	800	700	550	400

Bolero Side x Side
As above, with a non-selective single trigger and extractors. Manufactured until 1984.

Exc.	V.G.	Good	Fair	Poor
450	380	300	250	200

Iberia Side x Side
A 12 or 20 gauge Magnum boxlock double barrel shotgun with 26", 28" or 30" barrels, double triggers and extractors. Blued with a walnut stock. Manufactured until 1984.

Exc.	V.G.	Good	Fair	Poor
575	480	375	285	225

Side x Sides

Iberia II Side x Side

Similar to the above, in 12 or 16 gauge with 28" barrels and 2 3/4" chambers. Manufactured in 1984 and 1985.

NIB	Exc.	V.G.	Good	Fair	Poor
575	500	425	335	250	200

Model 106 Side x Side

A 12, 16, or 20 gauge boxlock double barrel shotgun with 28" barrels, double triggers and extractors. Blued with a walnut stock. Manufactured until 1985.

NIB	Exc.	V.G.	Good	Fair	Poor
585	525	450	350	300	225

Model 107-LI Side x Side

As above, with the receiver lightly engraved and an English style stock. In 12 or 16 gauge only.

NIB	Exc.	V.G.	Good	Fair	Poor
750	675	525	465	375	275

Model 116 Side x Side

A 12, 16 or 20 gauge sidelock double barrel shotgun with 27" to 30" barrels, double triggers and ejectors. Engraved, blued with a walnut stock. Manufactured until 1985.

NIB	Exc.	V.G.	Good	Fair	Poor
1125	1000	800	675	600	475

Model 117 Side x Side

As above, with 3" chambers.

NIB	Exc.	V.G.	Good	Fair	Poor
1075	875	725	625	550	475

Model 117 "Quail Unlimited" Side x Side

As above in 12 gauge only with 26" barrels and the receiver engraved "Quail Unlimited of North America". 42 were manufactured.

Exc.	V.G.	Good	Fair	Poor
1500	1200	875	750	625

Model 210 Side x Side

An exposed hammer, 12 or 16 gauge, boxlock shotgun with 26" to 28" barrels and double triggers. Blued with a walnut stock. Manufactured until 1985.

Exc.	V.G.	Good	Fair	Poor
800	575	485	395	325

Model 711 Boxlock Side x Side

A 12 gauge boxlock double barrel shotgun with 28" or 30" barrels having ventilated ribs, single selective trigger and automatic ejectors. Manufactured until 1984.

Exc.	V.G.	Good	Fair	Poor
900	800	700	550	450

Model 711 Sidelock Side x Side

As above, with sidelocks. Manufactured in 1985 only.

Exc.	V.G.	Good	Fair	Poor
1000	900	765	625	500

Senior Side x Side

A custom order 12 gauge double barrel sidelock shotgun, gold inlaid and engraved. Made strictly to individual customer's specifications.

Exc.	V.G.	Good	Fair	Poor
15000	12500	9000	7000	4750

Over/Unders

Model 79 "A" O/U

A 12 gauge boxlock over/under double barrel shotgun with 26", 28" or 30" barrels, single selective trigger and automatic ejectors. Blued with a walnut stock. Manufactured until 1985.

Exc.	V.G.	Good	Fair	Poor
1250	1050	925	750	650

Model 79 "B" O/U

As above, with a moderate amount of engraving.

Exc.	V.G.	Good	Fair	Poor
1350	1150	950	800	675

Model 79 "C" O/U

As above, with extensive engraving.

Exc.	V.G.	Good	Fair	Poor
2000	1800	1500	1150	975

Model 77 O/U

As above, patterned after the Merkel shotgun.

Exc.	V.G.	Good	Fair	Poor
3000	2700	2150	1750	1500

Coral "A" O/U

A 12 or 16 gauge over/under boxlock double barrel shotgun with 26" or 28" barrels having ventilated ribs, double triggers and automatic ejectors. Fitted with a Kersten cross bolt. Manufactured until 1985.

Exc.	V.G.	Good	Fair	Poor
1250	900	725	600	500

Coral "B" O/U

As above, with an engraved French case hardened receiver.

Exc.	V.G.	Good	Fair	Poor
1400	1150	800	675	550

CURRENTLY IMPORTED SHOTGUNS
Importer-Armes De Chasse
Chadds Ford, PA

Sidelock side by side

AYA sidelock shotguns use the Holland and Holland system. They feature double triggers, articulated front trigger, cocking indicators, bushed firing pins, replaceable firing pins, replaceable hinge pins, and chopper lump barrels. Frame and sidelocks are case colored. These shotguns weigh between 5 and 7 pounds depending on gauge and barrel length. Barrel lengths are offered in 26", 27", 28", and 29" depending on gauge. All stocks are figured walnut with hand checkering and oil finish. These guns are available with several extra cost options that may effect price. Also influencing price of new guns is the fluctuating dollar in relation to Spanish currency.

Model No. 1

This model is offered in 12 gauge and 20 gauge with special English scroll engraving. Fitted with automatic ejectors and straight grip stock with exhibition quality wood.

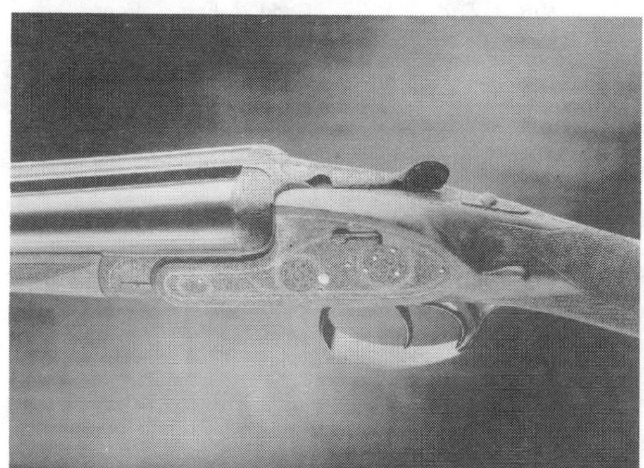

NIB	Exc.	V.G.	Good	Fair	Poor
5000	4000	3500	2500	1750	1000

Model No. 2

The Model 2 is offered in 12, 16, 20, and 28 gauge as well as .410 bore. It has automatic ejectors and straight grip select walnut stock.

NIB	Exc.	V.G.	Good	Fair	Poor
2500	1600	1250	750	600	450

Model No. 53
Chambered for 12, 16, and 20 gauge, this model features three locking lugs and side clips. It also has automatic ejectors and straight grip stock.

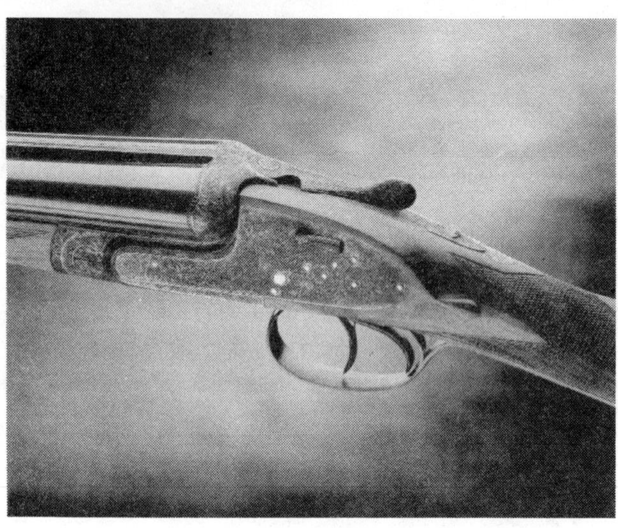

NIB	Exc.	V.G.	Good	Fair	Poor
3500	2750	2250	1750	1250	750

Model No. 56
This model is available in 12 gauge only and features three locking lugs, side clips, special wide action body, and raised matted rib. Select walnut straight grip stock.

NIB	Exc.	V.G.	Good	Fair	Poor
5500	4500	3500	2750	2000	1250

Model XXV-SL
Offered in 12 gauge and 20 gauge only this model is fitted with a Churchill type rib. Automatic ejectors and select straight grip walnut stock are standard.

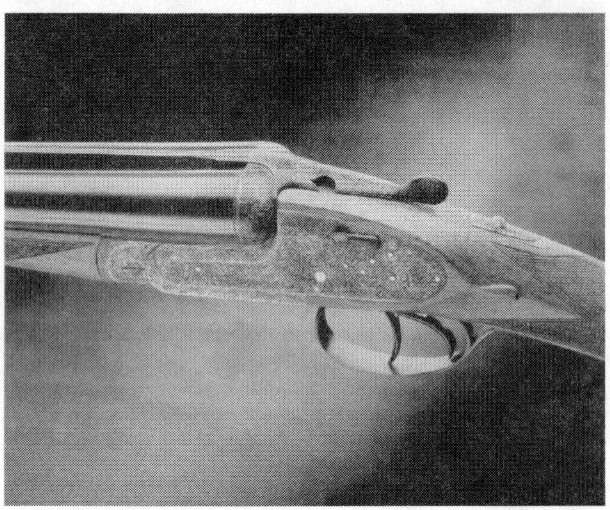

NIB	Exc.	V.G.	Good	Fair	Poor
3000	2500	2000	1250	750	500

Boxlock Side by Side
These AYA guns utilize a Anson and Deeley system with double locking lugs with detachable cross pin and separate trigger plate that gives access to the firing mechanism. Frame is case colored. The barrels are chopper lump, firing pins are bushed, automatic safety and automatic ejectors are standard. Barrel lengths are offered in 26", 27", and 28" depending on gauge. Weights are between 5 and 7 pounds depending on gauge.

Model XXV-BL
This model is available in 12 and 20 gauge only. The select walnut stock is hand checkered with straight grip stock.

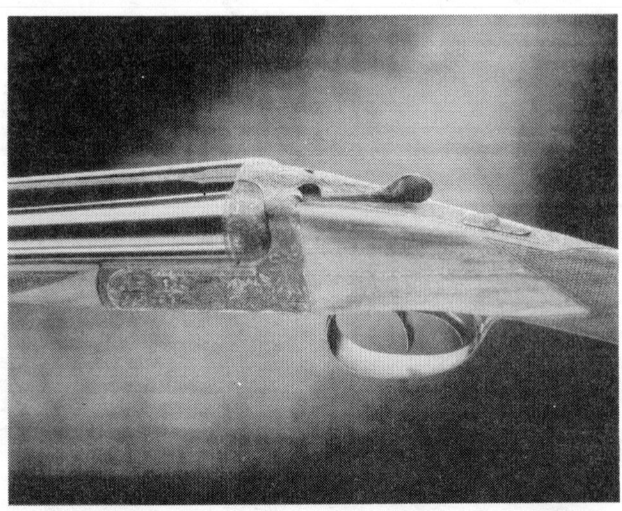

NIB	Exc.	V.G.	Good	Fair	Poor
2300	1750	1250	850	650	450

Model No. 4
This model is available in 12, 16, 20, and 28 gauge as well as .410 bore. It is fitted with select hand checkered walnut stock with straight grip. Light scroll engraving on this model.

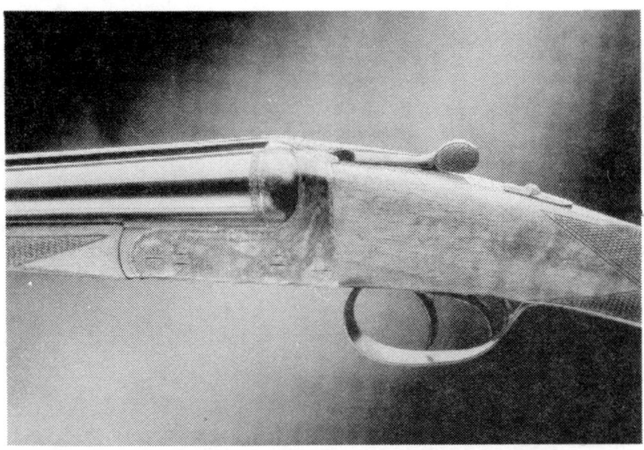

NIB	Exc.	V.G.	Good	Fair	Poor
1300	900	750	650	550	400

Model No. 4 Deluxe
Same as above but with select walnut stock and slightly more engraving coverage.

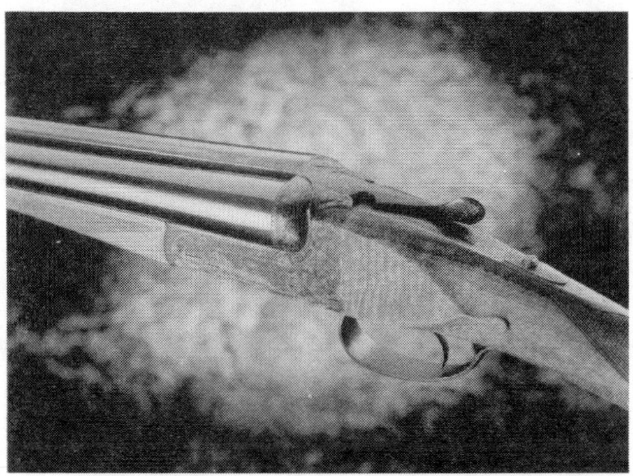

NIB	Exc.	V.G.	Good	Fair	Poor
2500	2000	1500	1000	750	500

Over and Under
These AYA shotguns are similar in design and appearance to the Gebruder Merkel over and under sidelocks with three part forend, Kersten cross bolt, and double under locking lugs.

Model No. 37 Super
This model is available in 12 gauge only with ventilated rib, automatic ejectors, internally gold plated sidelocks. Offered with three different types of engraving patterns: ducks, scroll, or deep cut engraving.

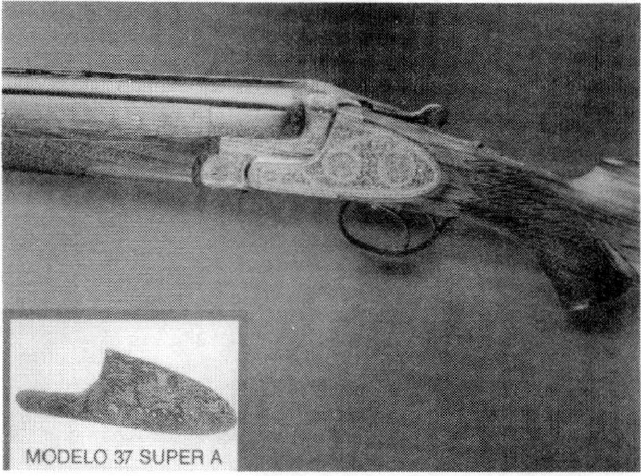

NIB	Exc.	V.G.	Good	Fair	Poor
11000	8500	5000	3500	2000	1000

Model Augusta
This is the top-of-the-line AYA model offered in 12 gauge only. It features presentation wood and deep cut scroll engraving.

NIB	Exc.	V.G.	Good	Fair	Poor
20000	15000	8000	4500	3500	1500

NOTE: For extra cost options add approximately:
Pistol grip-$90
Rubber recoil pad-$190
Left hand gun-$775
Length of pull longer than 15"-$125
Select wood-$235
Deluxe Wood-$550
Single non-selective trigger-$400
Single selective trigger-$600
Chrome lined barrels-$140
Churchill rib-$375
Raised rib-$180
Extra set of barrels-$1500

ABADIE
Liege, Belgium

System Abadie Model 1878
A 9.1mm double-action revolver with a 6-shot cylinder, octagonal barrel and integral ejector rod.

Exc.	V.G.	Good	Fair	Poor
250	225	175	125	90

System Abadie Model 1886
A heavier version of the above.

Exc.	V.G.	Good	Fair	Poor
225	200	150	110	75

ABBEY, F.J. & CO.
Chicago, Illinois

The Abbey Brothers produced a variety of percussion rifles and shotguns which are all of individual design. The prices listed below represent what a plain F.J. Abbey & Company might realize.

Rifle

Exc.	V.G.	Good	Fair	Poor
650	525	375	200	125

Shotgun

Exc.	V.G.	Good	Fair	Poor
775	650	425	275	150

ABBEY, GEORGE T.

Utica, New York, and Chicago, Illinois

George T. Abbey originally worked in Utica, New York from 1845 to 1852. He moved to Chicago in 1852 and was in business until 1874. He manufactured a wide variety of percussion and cartridge firearms. The values listed below represent those of his most common products.

Single Barrel .44 Cal.

Exc.	V.G.	Good	Fair	Poor
700	575	450	335	225

Side x Side Double Barrel

Exc.	V.G.	Good	Fair	Poor
1250	1000	800	525	375

Over/Under Double Barrel

Exc.	V.G.	Good	Fair	Poor
1500	1285	900	700	450

ACHA

Domingo Acha
Vizcaya, Spain

Acha Model 1916

A 7.65mm caliber semi-automatic pistol with internal hammer. Normally marked "F de Acha Hrs C 7.65."

Exc.	V.G.	Good	Fair	Poor
200	160	125	90	65

Atlas

A 6.35mm caliber semi-automatic pistol marked either "Domingo Acha y Cia" or "Pistolet automatique 6.35 Atlas."

Exc.	V.G.	Good	Fair	Poor
150	110	85	60	40

Looking Glass

A 6.35mm caliber semi-automatic pistol marked "Looking Glass."

Exc.	V.G.	Good	Fair	Poor
200	160	125	90	65

ACME

SEE--Davenport Arms Co., Maltby Henley & Co., and Merwin & Hulbert & Co.

ACME ARMS

New York, New York

A tradename found on .22, .32 caliber revolvers and 12 gauge shotguns marketed by the Cornwall Hardware Company.

.22 Revolver

A 7-shot single-action revolver.

Exc.	V.G.	Good	Fair	Poor
250	210	175	125	100

.32 Revolver

A 5-shot single-action revolver.

Exc.	V.G.	Good	Fair	Poor
260	225	200	150	110

Shotgun

A 12 gauge double barrel shotgun with external hammers.

Exc.	V.G.	Good	Fair	Poor
250	210	175	125	100

ACME HAMMERLESS

Made by Hopkins & Allen
Norwich, Connecticut

Acme Hammerless

A .32 or .38 caliber 5-shot revolver with either exposed hammer or enclosed hammer. Sometimes known as the "Forehand 1891."

Exc.	V.G.	Good	Fair	Poor
135	110	90	60	35

ACTION

Eibar, Spain
Maker-- Modesto Santos

Action

A 6.35mm or 7.65mm semi-automatic pistol marked on the slide "Pistolet Automatique Modele 1920." Often found bearing the tradename "Corrientes" as well as the maker's trademark "MS".

Exc.	V.G.	Good	Fair	Poor
175	150	120	90	60

ACTION ARMS LTD.

Philadelphia, Pennsylvania
Importers of the Uzi and Galil for Israeli Military Industries.

AT-84, AT-88

A 9mm or .41 Action Express caliber semi-automatic pistol with a 4.75" barrel and either 15-shot (9mm) or 10-shot (.41) magazine. Blued or chrome plated with walnut grips.

NIB	Exc.	V.G.	Good	Fair	Poor
600	500	425	350	300	275

AT-84P, AT-88P

As above, with a 3.7" barrel and smaller frame.

NIB	Exc.	V.G.	Good	Fair	Poor
700	600	525	450	400	350

AT-88H

As above with a 3.4" barrel and smaller frame.

NIB	Exc.	V.G.	Good	Fair	Poor
600	500	425	350	300	275

Timber Wolf Carbine

Introduced in 1989 this slide action carbine features a 18.5" barrel with adjustable rear sight and blade front sight. Chambered for the .357 Magnum or .38 Special cartridges it is offered in either blue or hard chrome finish. Weight is approximately 5.5 lb. Built in Israel by Israel Military Industries.

NIB	Exc.	V.G.	Good	Fair	Poor
450	400	300	200	150	100

Galil Model AR

A 5.56mm or 7.62x54mm semi-automatic rifle with either a 16.1" barrel (5.56mm) or 19" barrel (7.62x54mm). Parkerized with a folding stock.

Galil Model ARM

As above, with a folding bipod and wooden handguard.

Hadar II

As above, with a walnut pistol grip stock and furnished only in 7.62mm.

Sniper Rifle

The Model AR with a heavy 20" barrel in 7.62mm, adjustable cheek piece, bipod, telescopic sight and walnut stock.

Uzi Carbine Model B

A 9mm, .41 Action Express or .45 caliber semi-automatic carbine with a 16.1" barrel, folding metal stock and adjustable sights.

Uzi Model A
Essentially as above.

Uzi Mini Carbine
As above, with a 19.75" barrel in 9mm or .45 caliber.

Uzi Pistol
A 9mm or .45 caliber semi-automatic pistol with a 4.5" barrel.

ADAMS
Deane, Adams & Deane
London, England
London Armoury Co. (After 1856)

Revolvers based upon Robert Adams' patents were manufactured by the firm of Deane, Adams & Deane. Although more technically advanced than the pistols produced by Samuel Colt, Adams' revolvers were popular primarily in England and the British Empire.

Adams Model 1851 Self-Cocking Revolver
A .44 caliber double-action percussion revolver with a 7.5" octagonal barrel and 5-shot cylinder. The barrel and frame are blued, the cylinder case hardened and the grips are walnut. The top strap is marked "Deane, Adams and Deane 30 King William St. London Bridge." This revolver does not have a hammer spur and functions only as a double action.

Exc.	V.G.	Good	Fair	Poor
1300	1050	850	625	400

Adams Pocket Revolver
As above, in .31 caliber with a 4.5" barrel.

Exc.	V.G.	Good	Fair	Poor
950	800	575	400	300

Beaumont-Adams Revolver
As above, fitted with a Tranter Patent loading lever and the hammer made with a spur.

Exc.	V.G.	Good	Fair	Poor
1300	1050	850	625	400

ADAMY GEBRUDER
Suhl, Germany

Over/Under Shotgun
A 12 or 16 gauge double barrel over/under shotgun with 26" to 30" barrels, double triggers and a walnut stock.

Exc.	V.G.	Good	Fair	Poor
1850	1600	1275	875	700

ADIRONDACK ARMS CO. OR A.S. BABBITT CO.
Plattsburgh, New York

Orvil M. Robinson Patent Rifle
The Robinson tube-fed repeating rifle was made in New York between 1870 and 1874. The early models, 1870-1872, are marked "A.S. Babbitt"; the later models, 1872-1874, "Adirondack Arms Co." The Company was sold to Winchester in 1874, but they never produced the Robinson after that date. The rifle has been found in two styles: The first with small fingers on the hammer to cock and operate the mechanism; the second with buttons on the receiver to retract the bolt and cock the hammer. The rifle was made in .44 cal. with an octagonal barrel usually found in 26" or 28" length. The frames were predominantly brass; but some iron frames have been noted, and they will bring a premium of approximately 25 percent. The barrel and magazine tube have a blued finish.

First Model

Exc.	V.G.	Good	Fair	Poor
2400	2050	1450	775	600

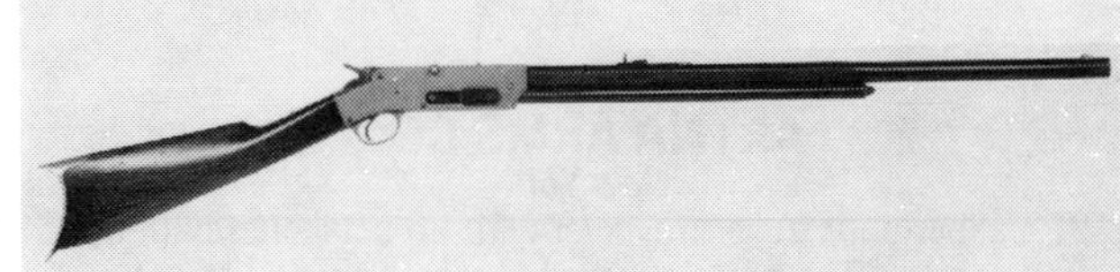

Courtesy Buffalo Bill Historical Center, Cody, Wyoming.

Second Model

Exc.	V.G.	Good	Fair	Poor
2150	1700	1100	650	500

ADLER
Engelbrecht & Wolff
Blasii, Germany

An extremely rare and unusually designed semi-automatic pistol adapted for the 7.25mm Adler cartridge. Produced in very limited numbers. Prospective purchasers are advised to secure a qualified appraisal prior to acquisition.

Courtesy James Rankin.

Courtesy James Rankin.

Exc.	V.G.	Good	Fair	Poor
7500	5000	2500	1000	500

ADVANTAGE ARMS U.S.A., INC.
Distributed by Wildfire Sports
St. Paul, Minnesota

Model 422

A .22 or .22 Magnum caliber 4 barrel derringer with 2.5" barrels. Entirely made of an aluminum alloy. Finished in either blue or nickel-plate. Manufactured in 1986 and 1987.

NIB	Exc.	V.G.	Good	Fair	Poor
165	150	125	100	85	70

AETNA ARMS CO.
New York

A .22 caliber spur trigger revolver with an octagonal barrel and 7-shot cylinder. The barrel marked "Aetna Arms Co. New York". Manufactured from approximately 1870 to 1880.

Exc.	V.G.	Good	Fair	Poor
250	225	185	135	100

AFFERBACH, W. A.
Philadelphia, Pennsylvania

This maker is known to have produced copies of Henry Derringer's percussion pocket pistols. Though uncommon, their values would be approximately as listed below.

Exc.	V.G.	Good	Fair	Poor
775	700	500	375	250

AGNER (SAXHOJ PRODUCTS INC.)
Copenhagen, Denmark
Importer: Beeman Arms
Santa Rosa, California

Model M 80

A .22 caliber single shot stainless-steel target pistol with a 5.9" barrel, adjustable sights and walnut grips. This pistol is fitted with a dry fire mechanism. Also available in a left-hand version. Imported from 1981 to 1986.

Exc.	V.G.	Good	Fair	Poor
1200	1050	900	700	500

AGUIRRE
Eibar, Spain

Basculant

A 6.35mm semi-automatic pistol marked on the slide "Cal. 6.35 Automatic Pistol Basculant".

Exc.	V.G.	Good	Fair	Poor
150	125	100	75	45

LeDragon

As above, with the slide marked "Cal. 6.35 Automatic Pistol LeDragon" and a stylized dragon molded into the grips.

Exc.	V.G.	Good	Fair	Poor
150	125	100	75	45

AIR MATCH
Importer: Kendall International
Paris, Kentucky

Air Match 500

A .22 caliber single shot target pistol with a 10.5" barrel, adjustable sights and adjustable front mounted counter weights. Blued with walnut grips. Imported from 1984 to 1986.

Exc.	V.G.	Good	Fair	Poor
700	575	475	400	300

AJAX ARMY
Unknown

Single Action

A spur-trigger, single-action, solid-frame revolver that was chambered for the .44 rimfire cartridge. It had a 7" barrel and was blued with walnut grips. It was manufactured in the 1880s.

Exc.	V.G.	Good	Fair	Poor
575	500	425	310	175

ALAMO RANGER
Spain

Alamo Ranger

A typical low-quality, early Spanish copy of the Colt Police Positive, chambered for the .38 cal. centerfire, and the cylinder held 6 shots. The finish was blued; grips were checkered hard rubber. The maker of this pistol is unknown.

Exc.	V.G.	Good	Fair	Poor
150	125	100	75	45

ALASKA
SEE--Hood Firearms Co.
Norwich, Connecticut

ALDAZABAL
Eibar, Spain
Aldazabal, Leturiondo & CIA.

Aldazabal

Another typical low-quality, "Eibar"-type semi-automatic. It was a Browning blowback copy, chambered for the 7.65mm cartridge. It had a 7-shot detachable magazine and blued finish with checkered wood grips. This company ceased production before the Spanish Civil War.

Exc.	V.G.	Good	Fair	Poor
175	135	95	65	40

ALERT
SEE--Hood Firearms Co.
Norwich, Connecticut

ALEXIA
SEE--Hopkins & Allen
Norwich, Connecticut

ALFA
SEE--Armero Especialistas Reunides
Eibar, Spain

ALKARTASUNA FABRICA DE ARMAS
Guernica, Spain

This company began production during the World War I to help Gabilondo y Urresti supply sidearms to the French. After the hostilities ceased, they continued to produce firearms under their own name. They manufactured the typical poor-quality, unimaginative weapons usually associated with Spain during this era. They produced a number of variations in both 6.35mm and 7.65mm marked "Alkar." Collector interest is very thin. The factory burned down in 1920, and by 1922 business had totally ceased.

Exc.	V.G.	Good	Fair	Poor
200	175	135	95	50

ALLEN, ETHAN
Grafton, Massachusetts

The company was founded by Ethan Allen in the early 1800s. It became a prolific gunmaking firm that evolved from Ethan Allen to Allen & Thurber, as well as the Allen & Wheelock Company. It was located in Norwich, Connecticut, and Worchester, Massachusetts, as well as Grafton. It eventually became the Forehand & Wadsworth Company in 1871 after the death of Ethan Allen. There were many and varied firearms produced under all of the headings described above. If one desires to collect Ethan Allen firearms, it would be advisable to educate oneself, as there are a number of fine publications available on the subject. The basic models and their values are as follows:

First Model Pocket Rifle
Manufactured by Ethan Allen in Grafton, Massachusetts. It was a bootleg-type, under-hammer, single shot pistol chambered for .31 percussion. Larger-caliber versions have also been noted. It had barrel lengths from 5" to 9" that were part-octagon in configuration. It had iron mountings and was blued with walnut grips. The barrel was marked, "E. Allen/ Grafton/Mass." as well as "Pocket Rifle/Cast Steel/ Warranted." There were approximately 2,000 manufactured from 1831 to 1842.

Exc.	V.G.	Good	Fair	Poor
750	375	275	200	175

Second Model Pocket Rifle
A rounded-frame, round-grip version of the First Model.

Exc.	V.G.	Good	Fair	Poor
900	575	375	275	225

Bar Hammer Pistol
A double-action pistol with a top-mounted bar hammer. It was chambered for .28 to .36 caliber percussion. The half-octagon barrels were from 2" to 10" in length. They screwed out of the frame so it was possible to breech load them. The finish was blued with rounded walnut grips. They were marked, "Allen & Thurber/Grafton Mass." There were approximately 2,000 manufactured between the early 1830s and 1860.

Exc.	V.G.	Good	Fair	Poor
900	750	550	425	350

Tube Hammer Pistol
This version was similar to the Bar Hammer with a curved hammer without a spur. There were only a few hundred manufactured between the early 1830s and the early 1840s.

Exc.	V.G.	Good	Fair	Poor
1000	850	675	525	400

Side Hammer Pistol
A single shot, target-type pistol that was chambered for .34, .41, and .45 caliber percussion. It had a part-octagon barrel that was from 6" to 10" in length. There was a wooden ramrod mounted under the barrel. This model had a good-quality rear sight that was adjustable. The ornate triggerguard had a graceful spur at its rear. The finish was blued with a rounded walnut grip. The barrel was marked, "Allen & Thurber, Worchester." There were approximately 300 manufactured in the late 1840s and early 1850s.

Exc.	V.G.	Good	Fair	Poor
500	375	300	225	175

Center Hammer Pistol
A single-action chambered for .34, .36, or .44 percussion. It had a half-octagon barrel from 4" to 12" in length. It had a centrally mounted hammer that was offset to the right side to allow for sighting the pistol. The finish was blued with walnut grips. It was marked, "Allen & Thurber, Allen Thurber & Company." Some specimens are marked, "Allen & Wheelock." There were several thousand manufactured between the late 1840s and 1860.

Exc.	V.G.	Good	Fair	Poor
350	250	200	150	125

Double Barrel Pistol
A SxS, double-barrel pistol with a single trigger. It was chambered for .36 caliber percussion with 3" to 6" round barrels. The finish was blued with walnut grips. Examples with a ramrod mounted under the barrel have been noted. The flute between the barrels was marked, "Allen & Thurber," "Allen Thurber & Company," or "Allen & Wheelock." There were approximately 1,000 manufactured in the 1850s.

Exc.	V.G.	Good	Fair	Poor
375	275	225	175	135

Allen & Wheelock Center Hammer Pistol
A single-action pocket pistol chambered for .31 to .38 caliber percussion. It had octagon barrels from 3" to 6" in length. The finish was blued with square-butt walnut grips. The barrel was marked, "Allen & Wheelock." There were approximately 500 manufactured between 1858 and 1865.

Exc.	V.G.	Good	Fair	Poor
350	300	250	185	145

Allen Thurber & Company Target Pistol
A deluxe, single-action target pistol that was chambered for .31 or .36 caliber percussion. It had a heavy, octagon barrel that was from 11" to 16" in length. There was a wooden ramrod mounted underneath the barrel. The mountings were of German silver, and there was a detachable walnut stock with a deluxe, engraved patchbox. This weapon was engraved, and the barrel was marked, "Allen Thurber & Co./Worchester/Cast Steel." This firearm was furnished in a fitted case with the stock, false muzzle, and various accessories. It was considered to be a very high grade target pistol in its era. The values shown are for a complete-cased outfit. There were very few manufactured in the 1850s.

Exc.	V.G.	Good	Fair	Poor
4000	3450	2800	1850	900

Ethan Allen Pepperboxes
During the period from the early 1830s to the 1860s, this company manufactured over 50 different variations of the revolving, pepperbox-type pistol. They were commercially quite successful and actually competed successfully with the Colt revolving handguns for more than a decade. They were widely used throughout the United States, as well as in Mexico, and during our Civil War. They are widely collectible because of the number of variations that exist. The potential collector should avail

himself of the information available on the subject. These pepperboxes can be divided into three categories.

No. 1--Manufactured from the 1830s until 1842, at Grafton, Massachusetts.

No. 2--Manufactured from 1842 to 1847, at Norwich, Connecticut.

No. 3--Manufactured from 1847 to 1865, at Worchester, Massachusetts.

There are a number of subdivisions among these three basic groups that would pertain to trigger type, size, barrel length etc. It would be impossible to cover all 50 of these variations in a text of this type. We strongly suggest that qualified, individual appraisal be secured if contemplating a transaction. The values of these pepperbox pistols in excellent condition would be between $500 and $2,800.

Large Frame Pocket Revolver

A double-action pocket revolver that was chambered for .34 caliber percussion. It had an octagon barrel from 3" to 5" in length. There were no sights. The 5-shot, unfluted cylinder was game scene-engraved. The finish was blued with rounded walnut grips. It had a bar-type hammer. This was the first conventional revolver manufactured by this company, and it was directly influenced by the pepperbox pistol for which Ethan Allen had become famous. It was marked, "Allen & Wheelock" as well as "Patented April 16, 1845." There were approximately 1,500 manufactured between 1857 and 1860.

Courtesy Milwaukee Public Museum, Milwaukee, Wisconsin.

Exc.	V.G.	Good	Fair	Poor
750	550	325	210	165

Small Frame Pocket Revolver

This version was similar to the Large Frame Pocket Revolver except chambered for .31 caliber percussion, with a 2" to 3.5" octagon barrel. It was slightly smaller in size, finished and marked the same. There were approximately 1,000 made between 1858 and 1860.

Exc.	V.G.	Good	Fair	Poor
400	325	195	150	110

Side Hammer Belt Revolver

A single-action revolver chambered for .34 caliber percussion. It had an octagon barrel from 3" to 7.5" in length. It featured a hammer that was mounted on the right side of the frame and a 5-shot, engraved, unfluted cylinder. The cylinder access pin is inserted from the rear of the weapon. The finish is blued with a case-colored hammer and triggerguard and flared-butt walnut grips. It is marked, "Allen & Wheelock." There were two basic types. Values for the early model, of which 100 were manufactured between 1858 and 1861, are as follows:

Exc.	V.G.	Good	Fair	Poor
800	700	575	400	285

Standard Model

The second type was the Standard Model, with a spring- loaded catch on the triggerguard as opposed to a friction catch on the early model. There were approximately 1,000 manufactured between 1858 and 1861.

Courtesy Milwaukee Public Museum, Milwaukee, Wisconsin.

Exc.	V.G.	Good	Fair	Poor
550	475	400	325	200

Side Hammer Pocket Revolver

This version was chambered for .28 caliber percussion and had a 2" to 5" octagon barrel. The frame was slightly smaller than the belt model.

Courtesy Milwaukee Public Museum, Milwaukee, Wisconsin.

Early Production, 100 Manufactured

Exc.	V.G.	Good	Fair	Poor
700	525	450	375	225

Standard Production, 1,000 Manufactured

Exc.	V.G.	Good	Fair	Poor
500	400	300	225	190

Side Hammer Navy Revolver

This was a large-frame, military-type revolver that was similar to the Side Hammer Belt Model, chambered for .36 caliber percussion. It features an octagon, 5.5" to 8" barrel with a 6-shot, engraved cylinder. There was an early-production type with a friction catch on the triggerguard. There were approximately 100 manufactured between 1858 and 1861.

Exc.	V.G.	Good	Fair	Poor
1250	1000	800	500	350

Standard Model, 1,000 Manufactured

Exc.	V.G.	Good	Fair	Poor
1000	850	600	325	250

Center Hammer Army Revolver

A large, military-type, single-action revolver that was chambered for .44 caliber percussion. It had a 7.5", half-octagon barrel and a 6-shot, unfluted cylinder. The hammer was mounted in the center of the frame. The finish was blued with a case-colored hammer and triggerguard and walnut grips. The barrel was marked, "Allen & Wheelock. Worchester, Mass. U.S./Allen's Pt's. Jan. 13, 1857. Dec. 15, 1857, Sept. 7, 1858." There were approximately 700 manufactured between 1861 and 1862.

Courtesy Milwaukee Public Museum, Milwaukee, Wisconsin.

Courtesy Milwaukee Public Museum, Milwaukee, Wisconsin.

Exc.	V.G.	Good	Fair	Poor
1000	800	650	425	300

Center Hammer Navy Revolver

Similar to the Army Revolver except chambered for .36 caliber percussion with a 7.5", full-octagon barrel. Examples have been noted with 5", 6", or 8" barrels. Otherwise, it was similar to the Army model.

Exc.	V.G.	Good	Fair	Poor
1100	900	750	525	425

Center Hammer Percussion Revolver

A single-action revolver chambered for .36 caliber percussion. It had an octagonal, 3" or 4" barrel with a 6-shot, unfluted cylinder. The finish was blued with walnut grips. This model supposedly was made for the Providence, Rhode Island, Police Department and has become commonly referred to as the "Providence Police Model." There were approximately 700 manufactured between 1858 and 1862.

Exc.	V.G.	Good	Fair	Poor
600	500	400	300	200

Lipfire Army Revolver

A large, military-type, single-action revolver that was chambered for the .44 lipfire cartridge. It had a 7.5", half-octagon barrel with a 6-shot, unfluted cylinder that had notches at its rear for the cartridge lips. The finish was blued with a case-colored hammer and triggerguard and square-butt walnut grips. The barrel was marked, "Allen & Wheelock, Worchester, Mass." It resembled the Center Hammer Percussion Army Revolver. There were two basic variations, with a total of 250 manufactured in the early 1860s.

Early Model Top Hinged Loading Gate

Exc.	V.G.	Good	Fair	Poor
900	800	625	500	350

Late Model Bottom Hinged Loading Gate

Exc.	V.G.	Good	Fair	Poor
825	700	575	450	300

Lipfire Navy Revolver

Similar to the Army model, except chambered for the .36 lipfire cartridge, with an octagonal, 4", 5", 6", 7.5", or 8" barrel. There were approximately 500 manufactured in the 1860s.

Exc.	V.G.	Good	Fair	Poor
900	800	675	450	350

Lipfire Pocket Revolver

A smaller version chambered for the .32 lipfire cartridge, with an octagonal, 4", 5", or 6" barrel. There were approximately 200 manufactured in the early 1860s.

Exc.	V.G.	Good	Fair	Poor
750	625	500	400	300

.32 Side Hammer Rimfire Revolver

A single-action, spur-trigger, pocket revolver chambered for the .32-caliber rimfire cartridge. It had octagonal barrels from 3" to 5" in length. The finish was blued with flared-butt, walnut grips. It was marked, "Allen & Wheelock Worchester, Mass." There were three variations with a total of approximately 1,000 manufactured between 1859 and 1862.

First Model--Rounded Top Strap

Exc.	V.G.	Good	Fair	Poor
500	425	350	265	200

Second Model--July 3, 1860 Marked on Frame

Exc.	V.G.	Good	Fair	Poor
450	375	300	225	185

Third Model--1858 and 1861 Patent Dates

Exc.	V.G.	Good	Fair	Poor
350	300	225	150	110

.22 Side Hammer Rimfire Revolver

A smaller version of the .32 revolver, chambered for the .22 rimfire cartridge. It has octagonal barrels from 2.25" to 4" in length. It has a 7-shot, unfluted cylinder. There were approximately 1,500 manufactured between 1858 and 1862. There were many variations.

Early Model First Issue--Access Pin Enters from Rear

Exc.	V.G.	Good	Fair	Poor
450	375	300	200	125

Second Issue--Access Pin Enters from Front

Exc.	V.G.	Good	Fair	Poor
475	400	325	225	150

Third Issue--Separate Rear Sight

Exc.	V.G.	Good	Fair	Poor
650	525	425	300	200

Fourth to Eighth Issue--Very Similar, Values the Same

Exc.	V.G.	Good	Fair	Poor
350	300	250	175	100

Single Shot Center Hammer

A single shot derringer-type pistol that was chambered for the .22-caliber rimfire cartridge. It had part-octagon barrels from 2" to 5.5" in length that swung to the right side for loading. Some had automatic ejectors; others did not. The frame was either brass or iron with birdshead or squared-butt walnut grips. It was marked, "Allen & Wheelock" or "E. Allen & Co." There were very few manufactured in the early 1860s.

Early Issue

Full-length, octagon barrel and a round, iron frame. It is rarely encountered.

Exc.	V.G.	Good	Fair	Poor
425	375	300	225	150

Standard Issue--Squared Butt or Birdshead

Exc.	V.G.	Good	Fair	Poor
375	300	250	200	125

.32 Single Shot Center Hammer

A larger-frame pocket pistol chambered for the .32 rimfire cartridge. It has a part-octagon or full-octagon barrel of 4" or 5" in length. It swung to the right side for loading. Otherwise, this model was similar to the .22-caliber version.

Exc.	V.G.	Good	Fair	Poor
400	325	275	200	150

Vest Pocket Derringer

A small pocket pistol chambered for the .22 rimfire cartridge. It had a 2", part-octagon barrel that swung to the right-hand side for loading. The cartridges were manually extracted. It featured a brass frame with a blued or plated barrel and walnut, birdshead grips. The barrel was marked, "Allen & Co. Makers." This was an extremely small firearm, and there were approximately 200 manufactured between 1869 and 1871.

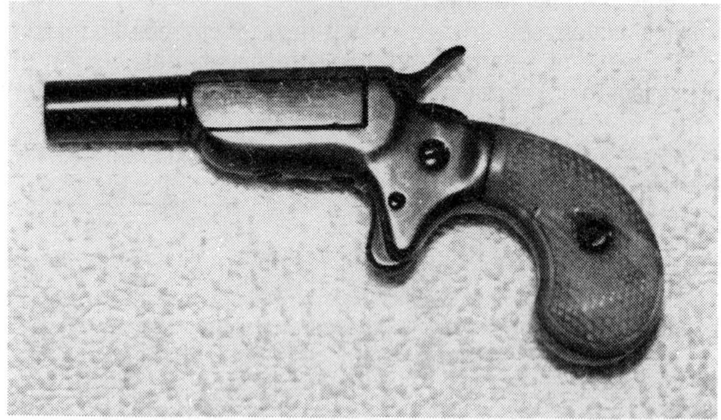

Exc.	V.G.	Good	Fair	Poor
350	300	250	200	150

.32 Derringer

Similar to the Vest Pocket Version, larger in size, and chambered for the .32 rimfire cartridge. It had a part-octagon barrel from 2" to 4" in length that swung to the right for loading. This version featured an automatic extractor. The barrel was marked, "E. Allen & Co. Worchester, Mass." This was a very rare firearm, made between 1865 and 1871.

Exc.	V.G.	Good	Fair	Poor
800	725	600	450	350

.41 Derringer

The same size and configuration as the .32-caliber model except it was chambered for the .41 rimfire cartridge with barrel lengths of 2.5" to 2.75" in length. The markings were the same. There were approximately 100 manufactured between 1865 and 1871.

Exc.	V.G.	Good	Fair	Poor
600	525	400	325	250

Center Hammer Muzzle-loading Rifle

A single-shot rifle chambered for .44 caliber percussion. It had a 36" round barrel with an octagonal breech. It had a center-mounted hammer that was offset to the right for sighting. It had iron mountings. The finish was browned with a case-colored lock. There was a ramrod mounted under the barrel. It had a walnut buttstock with a crescent buttplate and no forearm. There were approximately 100 manufactured in the 1850s.

Exc.	V.G.	Good	Fair	Poor
800	725	600	375	300

Side Hammer Muzzle-loading Rifle

Similar to the Center Hammer model, with the hammer mounted on the right side of the lock. It was chambered for .38 caliber percussion, with an octagon barrel from 28" to 32" in length. It is occasionally found with a patchbox. The barrel is browned with a case-colored lock and a walnut stock with crescent buttplate. There were several hundred manufactured from the early 1840s to the 1860s.

Exc.	V.G.	Good	Fair	Poor
950	875	750	500	350

Combination Gun

Either an Over/Under or SxS rifle chambered for 12 gauge and .38 caliber percussion. The barrels were from 28" to 34" in length. It had two hammers and double triggers with a ramrod mounted either beneath or on the right side of the barrels. The finish was browned with a walnut stock. Examples with a patchbox have been noted. Production was very limited, with the Over/Under versions worth approximately 10 percent more than the SxS values given. They were manufactured between the 1840s and the 1860s.

Exc.	V.G.	Good	Fair	Poor
1500	1350	1000	750	600

Side Hammer Breech-loading Rifle

A unique rifle chambered for .36 to .50 caliber percussion. It was offered with various-length, part-octagon barrels. It had an unusual breech mechanism that was activated by a rotating lever which resembled a water faucet. The barrel was browned with a case-colored lock and a walnut stock. It was marked, "Allen & Wheelock/ Allen's Patent July 3, 1855." There were approximately 500 manufactured between 1855 and 1860.

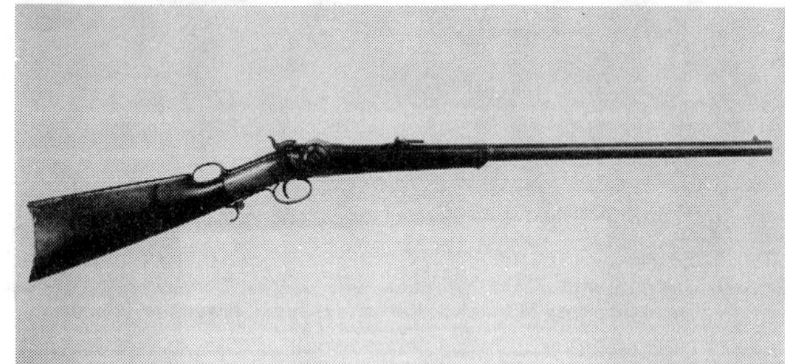

Courtesy Buffalo Bill Historical Center, Cody, Wyoming.

Exc.	V.G.	Good	Fair	Poor
900	775	600	375	300

Drop Breech Rifle

This single-shot rifle was chambered for the .22 through the .44 rimfire cartridges. It had a part-octagon barrel from 23" to 28" in length. The breech was activated by the combination trigger-guard action lever. Opening the breech automatically ejected the empty cartridge. The external hammer was manually cocked, and it featured an adjustable sight. The barrel was blued with a case-colored frame and a walnut stock. It was marked, "Allen & Wheelock/ Allen's Pat. Sept. 18, 1860." There were approximately 2,000 manufactured between 1860 and 1871.

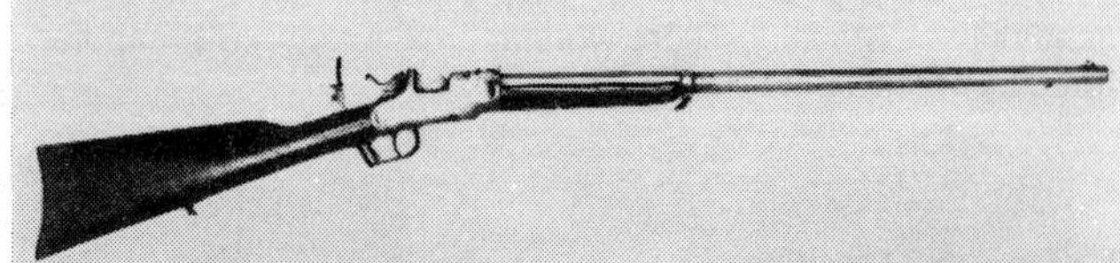

Courtesy Milwaukee Public Museum, Milwaukee, Wisconsin.

Exc.	V.G.	Good	Fair	Poor
400	325	250	175	135

Lipfire Revolving Rifle

A six-shot, cylinder-type rifle chambered for the .44-caliber lipfire cartridge. It had an unfluted cylinder with slots at its rear to allow for the cartridge lips. The round barrels were 26" to 28" in length with an octagon breech. The finish was blued with a case-colored frame and a walnut buttstock. This model was not marked with the maker's name. There were approximately 100 manufactured between 1861 and 1863.

Courtesy Buffalo Bill Historical Center, Cody, Wyoming.

Exc.	V.G.	Good	Fair	Poor
9500	8750	7000	5000	3250

Double Barrel Shotgun
A SxS gun chambered for 10 or 12 gauge. The barrel length was 28". It was loaded by means of a trapdoor-type breech that had a lever handle. The finish was blued with checkered walnut stock. There were a few hundred manufactured between 1865 and 1871.

Exc.	V.G.	Good	Fair	Poor
650	575	450	300	225

ALLEN & THURBER
SEE--Ethan Allen

ALLEN & WHEELOCK
SEE--Ethan Allen

ALLEN FIREARMS
Santa Fe, New Mexico
SEE--Aldo Uberti

ALL RIGHT F. A. CO.
Lawrence, Massachusetts

Little All Right Palm Pistol
Squeezer-type pocket pistol invented by E. Boardman and A. Peavy in 1876, was made in .22 cal. and had a 5-shot cylinder with a 1-5/8" or 2-3/8" barrel. The barrel is octagonal with a tube on top of it which houses the sliding trigger. The finish is nickel. The black hard rubber grips have "Little All Right" & "All Right Firearms Co., Manufacturers Lawrence, Mass. U.S.A." molded into them. There were several hundred produced in the late 1870s.

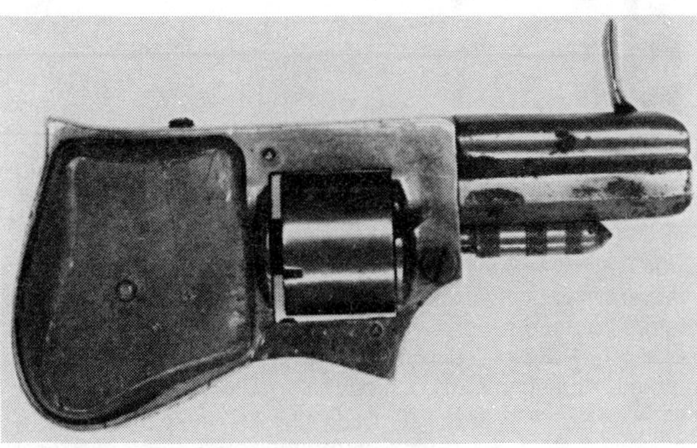

Courtesy Milwaukee Public Museum, Milwaukee, Wisconsin.

Exc.	V.G.	Good	Fair	Poor
900	800	650	500	400

ALPHA ARMS CO.
Flower Mound, Texas

Alpha Arms Co. produced high-grade bolt-action rifles on a semi-custom basis. It manufactured a number of standard models but offered many options at additional cost. Some of these options were custom sights and finishes and an octagonal barrel. These extra features would add to the value of the models listed. This company operated from 1983 until 1987.

Alpha Jaguar Grade I
Built on a Mauser-type action with barrel lengths from 20" to 24". It was chambered for most calibers between .222 Rem. and .338 Win. Mag. The stock was made from a synthetic laminated material that the company called Alphawood. This model was introduced in 1987 and only produced that year.

Exc.	V.G.	Good	Fair	Poor
900	750	550	425	325

Jaguar Grade II
Similar to the Grade I with a Douglas Premium barrel.

Exc.	V.G.	Good	Fair	Poor
1000	850	650	525	400

Jaguar Grade III
Has the Douglas barrel plus a hand-honed trigger and action and a three-position safety like the Winchester Model 70.

Exc.	V.G.	Good	Fair	Poor
1200	1000	850	700	500

Jaguar Grade IV
Has all the features of the Grade III with a specially lightened action and sling-swivel studs.

Exc.	V.G.	Good	Fair	Poor
1300	1100	950	800	600

Alpha Grand Slam
Features the same high quality as the Jaguar models and is available in a left-hand model. It has a fluted bolt, laminated stock, and a matte blue finish.

Exc.	V.G.	Good	Fair	Poor
1200	1000	850	700	500

Alpha Custom
Similar to the Grand Slam with a select grade stock.

Exc.	V.G.	Good	Fair	Poor
1500	1275	1000	750	500

Alpha Alaskan
Similar to the Grand Slam but chambered for the .308 Win., .350 Rem.Mag., .358 Win. and the .458 Win. Mag. It features all stainless-steel construction.

Exc.	V.G.	Good	Fair	Poor
1500	1275	1000	750	500

Alpha Big - Five
Similar to the Jaguar Grade IV chambered for the .300 Win Mag., .375 H&H Mag. and the .458 Win. Mag. It had a reinforced through-bolt stock to accommodate the recoil of the larger caliber cartridges for which it was chambered. It also had a decelerator recoil pad. This model was manufactured in 1987 only.

Exc.	V.G.	Good	Fair	Poor
1600	1375	1100	850	600

ALSOP, C.R.
Middletown, Connecticut

This firearms manufacturer made revolvers during 1862 and 1863. They made two basic models, the Navy and the Pocket model. Some collectors consider the Alsop to be a secondary U.S. martial handgun, but no verifying government contracts are known to exist.

First Model Navy Revolver
A .36 cal. revolver with a 3.5", 4.5", 5.5", or 6.5" barrel length and a 5-shot cylinder. It has a blued finish, wood grips, and a peculiar hump in its backstrap. The first model has a safety device which blocks the spur trigger. This device is found on serial numbers 1-100. Markings are as follows: "C.R. Alsop Middletown, Conn. 1860 & 1861" on the barrel. The cylinder is marked "C.R. Alsop" & "Nov.26th, 1861"; the sideplate, "Patented Jan. 21st,1862."

Exc.	V.G.	Good	Fair	Poor
2250	1800	1300	1000	800

Standard Model Navy Revolver
Exactly the same as the First Model without the safety device. They are serial numbered 101 to 300.

Exc.	V.G.	Good	Fair	Poor
1900	1500	1100	800	600

Pocket Model Revolver
A .31 cal. 5-shot revolver with spur trigger, 4" round barrel, blued finish, and wood grips. It is very similar in appearance to the Navy model but smaller in size. It is marked "C.R. Alsop Middletown, Conn. 1860 & 1861" on the barrel. The cylinder is marked "C.R. Alsop Nov. 26th, 1861." They are serial numbered 1-300.

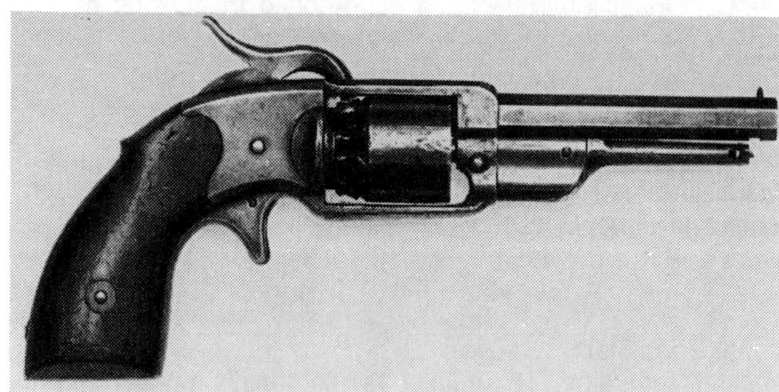

Courtesy Milwaukee Public Museum, Milwaukee, Wisconsin.

Exc.	V.G.	Good	Fair	Poor
850	725	600	450	350

AMERICAN ARMS
Garden Grove, California

Eagle .380
This pistol was a stainless-steel copy of the Walther PPKS. It was a semi-auto blowback that was chambered for the .380 ACP. It was double-action and had a 3.25" barrel and a 6-shot detachable magazine. An optional feature was a black teflon finish that would increase the value by 10 percent. This company ceased production in 1985.

Exc.	V.G.	Good	Fair	Poor
275	225	195	150	125

AMERICAN ARMS CO.
Boston, Massachusetts

The history of American Arms is rather sketchy, but it appears the company was formed in 1853 as the G. H. Fox Co. and then became the American Tool & Machine Co. in 1865. In 1870 they formed a new corporation called American Arms Company with George Fox as the principle stockholder. This corporation was dissolved in 1873; a second American Arms Co. was incorporated in 1877 and a third in 1890. It is unclear if these corporations had essentially the same owners, but George H. Fox appears as a principle owner in two of the three. One could assume that financial problems forced them to bankrupt one corporation and reorganize under another. American Arms manufactured firearms in Boston Massachusetts from 1866 until 1893. In 1893 they moved to Bluffton Alabama and manufactured guns until 1901.

Fox Model "Swing Out" Hammer Double.
Manufactured from 1870 to 1884, designed by George H. Fox not to be confused with A. H. Fox. This model is unusual in that the barrel swings to the right for loading and the barrel release is located on the tang. It comes in 10 and 12 gauge, 26", 28", 30" and 32", with twist, Damascus or laminated barrels. Early production models have conventional soldered together barrels. Later variations after 1878 feature a unique design in that the barrels are dovetailed together. These guns could be ordered with several options and choices of finish; this would add premium value to a particular gun.

Exc.	V.G.	Good	Fair	Poor
1000	900	600	300	150

Semi-Hammerless Double
Manufactured from 1892 to 1901. This model features a cocking lever that cocks an internal firing pin. It comes in 12 gauge with 30" twist barrels.

Exc.	V.G.	Good	Fair	Poor
750	650	450	250	150

Whitmore Model Hammerless Double
Manufactured from 1890 to 1901. It comes in 10, 12, and 16 gauge with 28", 30" or 32" twist, laminated or Damascus barrels. It is marked Whitmore's Patent.

Exc.	V.G.	Good	Fair	Poor
750	700	650	250	150

Semi-Hammerless Single Barrel
Manufactured from 1882 to 1901. It comes in 10, 12, and 16 gauge with 28", 30" or 32" twist or Damascus barrel.

Exc.	V.G.	Good	Fair	Poor
700	600	400	200	100

Top Break Revolvers

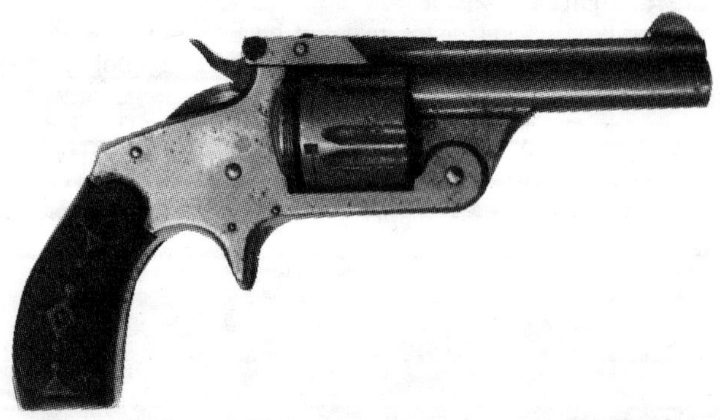

Courtesy Milwaukee Public Museum, Milwaukee, Wisconsin.

Spur Trigger — Single Action Five Shot Revolver. These revolvers were made between 1883 and 1887 in .38 S&W only. They feature an unusual manual ring extractor and double fluted cylinder. They are nickel plated with hard rubber grips and are marked "American Arms Company Boston Mass."

Exc.	V.G.	Good	Fair	Poor
200	175	125	65	45

Standard Trigger Double Action Model 1886 Revolver.
This model has a standard trigger and triggerguard, comes in .32 short and .38 S&W with a 3.5 inch barrel, in blue or nickel finish. The early models are equipped with the ring extractor and double fluted cylinder. Later variations have a standard star extractor and single fluted cylinder.

Exc.	V.G.	Good	Fair	Poor
200	175	125	65	45

Hammerless Model 1890 Double Action.
These guns were manufactured from 1890 to 1901. It has an adjustable single or double-stage trigger pull and several unusual safety devices. It comes in .32 and .38 S&W with a 3.25" ribbed barrel, fluted cylinder, nickel finish, hard rubber grips with logo and ivory or mother of pearl grips. It is marked "American Arms Co. Boston/Pat. May 25, 1886." The top strap is marked "Pat. Pending" on early models and "Pat's May 25'86/Mar 11'89/June 17'90:" on later models.

Exc.	V.G.	Good	Fair	Poor
225	200	150	110	75

American Arms Co. manufactured a two-barrel derringer-style pocket pistol. The barrels were manually rotated to load and fire the weapon. The pistol had a nickel-plated brass frame, blued barrels, and walnut grips. The markings were as follows: "American Arms Co. Boston, Mass." on one barrel and "Pat. Oct. 31,1865" on the other barrel. There were approximately 2,000-3,000 produced between 1866 and 1878.

Combination .22 cal. R.F. and .32 cal. R.F.
A two-caliber combination with 3" barrel, square butt only. The most common variation.

Exc.	V.G.	Good	Fair	Poor
500	425	325	265	200

.32 cal. R.F., both barrels
3" barrel with square butt.

Courtesy Milwaukee Public Museum, Milwaukee, Wisconsin.

Exc.	V.G.	Good	Fair	Poor
600	525	425	350	265

.32 cal. R.F. both barrels
2-5/8" barrel with birdshead grips.

Exc.	V.G.	Good	Fair	Poor
625	550	450	375	295

.38 cal.R.F. both barrels
2-5/8" barrel with birdshead grips. A very rare variation.

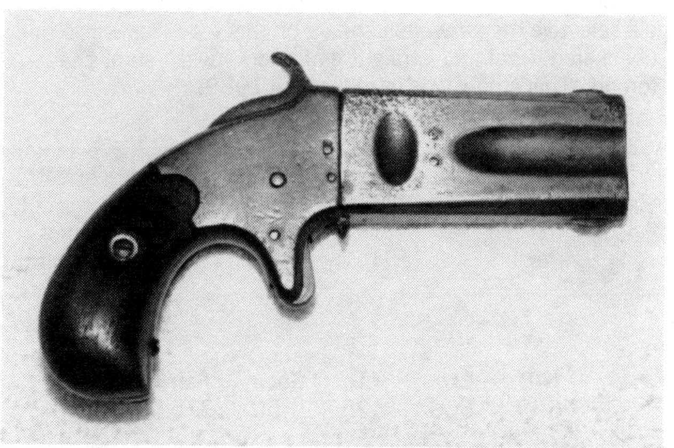

Exc.	V.G.	Good	Fair	Poor
750	675	525	450	325

.41 cal. R.F. both barrels
2-5/8" barrel with square butt only.

Exc.	V.G.	Good	Fair	Poor
800	700	600	500	400

AMERICAN ARMS, INC.
No. Kansas City, Missouri

Basically an importer of firearms: shotguns from Spain, rifles from Yugoslavia, and handguns from Germany and Yugoslavia. They also manufacture in the U.S.A. There are certain rifles that they are no longer allowed to import because of the Bush administration's ban on foreign semi-automatic rifles. These weapons are listed for reference but are not priced due to the extreme fluctuations in values as this is written.

Shotguns Side x Side
Gentry - York
These two designations cover the same model. Prior to 1988 this model was called the York. In 1988 the receiver was case-colored and the designation was changed to the Gentry. This model was chambered for 12, 20, and 28 gauge and .410. It had chrome-lined barrels from 26" -30" in length, double triggers, 3" chambers, and automatic ejectors. The boxlock action featured scroll engraving, and the walnut stock was hand-checkered. It was introduced in 1986.

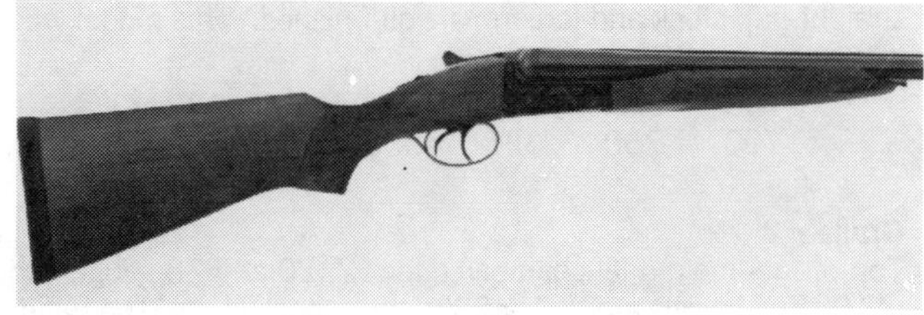

NIB	Exc.	V.G.	Good	Fair	Poor
469	425	375	300	210	165

Shotgun
A 10 gauge with 3.5" chambers and 32" barrels. It featured a scroll-engraved, chromed boxlock action and double triggers. It was imported from Spain in 1986 only.

Exc.	V.G.	Good	Fair	Poor
450	375	285	200	150

Brittany
Chambered for 12 and 20 gauge with 27" or 25" barrels with screw-in choke tubes. It had a solid matted rib and a case-colored, engraved boxlock action. Automatic ejectors and a sin-

gle selective trigger were standard on this model as was a hand-checkered, walnut, straight-grip stock with semi-beavertail forend. This model was introduced in 1989.

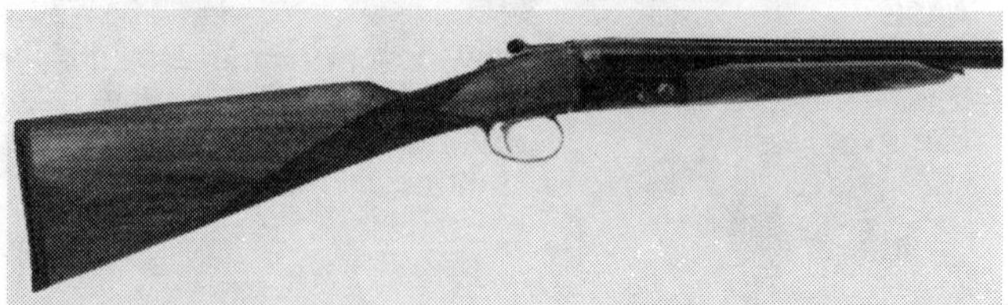

NIB	Exc.	V.G.	Good	Fair	Poor
650	600	525	450	375	275

Turkey Special

A utilitarian model designed to be an effective turkey hunting tool. It is chambered for the Magnum 10 and 12 gauges and has 26" barrels. The finish is parkerized, and the stock is also finished in a non-glare matte. Sling-swivel studs and a recoil pad are standard. This model was introduced in 1987.

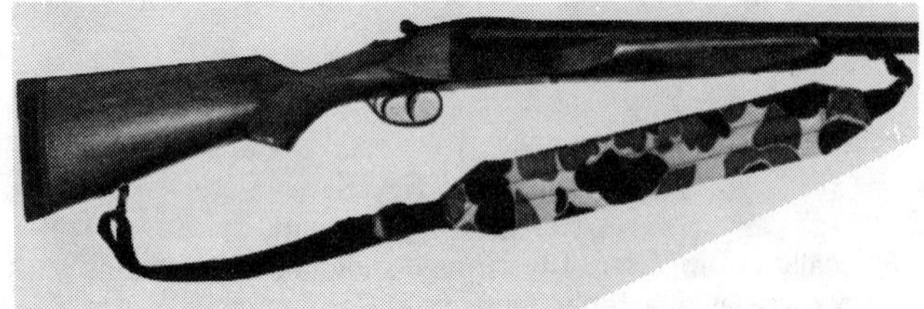

NIB	Exc.	V.G.	Good	Fair	Poor
425	375	325	300	250	150

Waterfowl Special

This model is similar to the Turkey Special but chambered for the 10 gauge only. It is furnished with a camouflaged sling. It was introduced in 1987.

NIB	Exc.	V.G.	Good	Fair	Poor
525	475	425	350	250	150

Derby

Chambered for the 12, 20, and 28 gauge and the .410. It has 26" or 28" barrels with 3" chambers and automatic ejectors. Either double or single selective triggers are offered, and the sidelock action is scroll engraved and chromed. The checkered straight-grip stock and forearm are oil-finished. This model was introduced in 1986.

NIB	Exc.	V.G.	Good	Fair	Poor
790	700	625	500	375	200

Grulla #2

Top-of-the-line model chambered for 12, 20 and 28 gauge and .410. The barrels are 26" or 28" with a concave rib. The hand-fitted full sidelock action is extensively engraved and case-colored. There are various chokes, double triggers, and automatic ejectors. The select walnut, straight-grip stock and splinter forend is hand-checkered and has a hand-rubbed oil finish. This model was introduced in 1989.

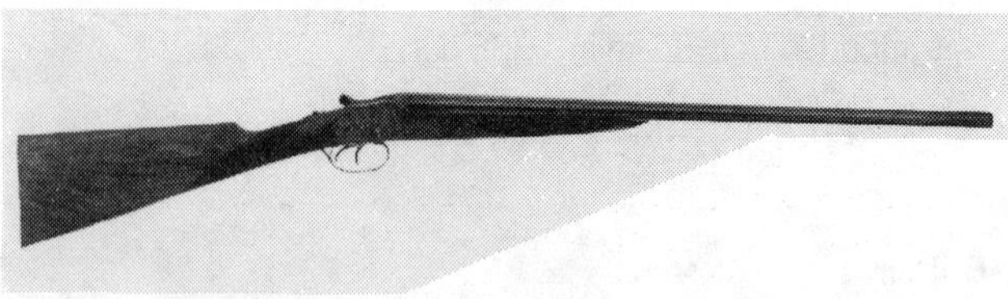

NIB	Exc.	V.G.	Good	Fair	Poor
2100	1850	1650	1400	1000	500

Shotguns Over/Under

F.S. 200

A trap or skeet model that was chambered for 12 gauge only. It had 26" Skeet & Skeet barrels or 32" full choke barrels on the trap model. The barrels were separated and had a vent rib. The boxlock action had a Greener crossbolt and was either black or matte chrome-plated. It featured a single selective trigger, automatic ejectors, and a checkered walnut pistol-grip stock. The F.S. 200 was imported in 1986 and 1987 only.

Exc.	V.G.	Good	Fair	Poor
675	575	465	350	250

F.S. 300

Similar to the F.S. 200 with lightly engraved side plates and a 30" barrel offered in the trap grade. It was imported in 1986 only.

Exc.	V.G.	Good	Fair	Poor
800	675	565	450	250

F.S. 400

Similar to the F.S. 300 with an engraved, matte chrome-plated receiver. It was imported in 1986 only.

Exc.	V.G.	Good	Fair	Poor
1100	950	800	650	250

F.S. 500

Similar to the F.S. 400 with the same general specifications. It was not imported after 1985.

Exc.	V.G.	Good	Fair	Poor
1150	1000	850	700	250

Waterfowl Special

Chambered for the 12 gauge Magnum with 3.5" chambers. It has 28" barrels with screw-in choke tubes. There are automatic ejectors and a single selective trigger. The finish is parkerized with a matte finished stock, sling swivels, and camouflaged sling and a recoil pad. It was introduced in 1987.

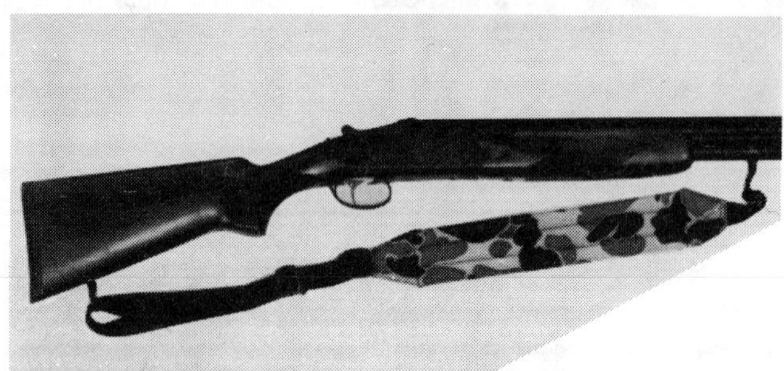

NIB	Exc.	V.G.	Good	Fair	Poor
525	475	425	375	350	250

Waterfowl 10 Gauge

The same as the Waterfowl Special but is chambered for the 10 gauge Magnum with double triggers.

NIB	Exc.	V.G.	Good	Fair	Poor
625	575	525	475	450	375

Turkey Special

Similar to the Waterfowl Special 10 gauge with a 26" barrel with screw-in choke tubes.

NIB	Exc.	V.G.	Good	Fair	Poor
525	475	425	375	350	275

Lince

Chambered for the 12 and 20 gauge and had 26" or 28" barrels with 3" chambers and various chokes. The boxlock action had a Greener crossbolt and was either blued or polished and chrome-plated. The barrels were blued with a ventilated rib. It had a single selective trigger and automatic ejectors. The Lince was imported in 1986 only.

Exc.	V.G.	Good	Fair	Poor
500	425	350	300	225

Silver Model
Similar to the Lince with a plain, unengraved, brushed-chrome-finished receiver. It was imported in 1986 and 1987.

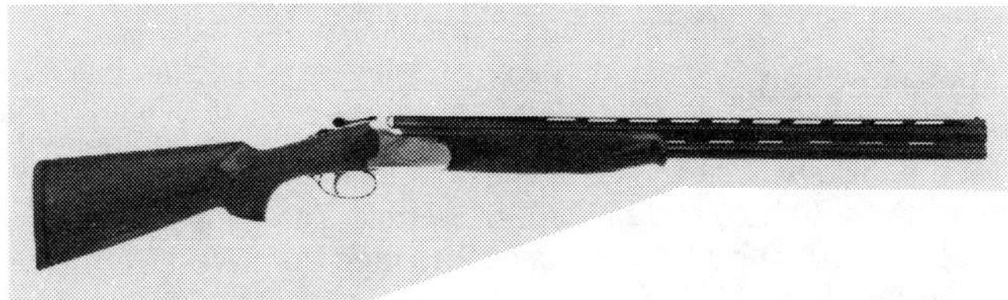

Exc.	V.G.	Good	Fair	Poor
500	425	350	300	225

Silver I
Similar to the Silver but is available in 28 gauge and .410, as well as 12 and 20 gauge. It also has a single selective trigger, fixed chokes, extractors, and a recoil pad. It was introduced in 1987.

NIB	Exc.	V.G.	Good	Fair	Poor
440	400	325	275	210	175

Silver II
Similar to the Silver II with screw-in choke tubes, automatic ejectors, and select walnut. It was introduced in 1987.

NIB	Exc.	V.G.	Good	Fair	Poor
580	525	450	375	300	250

Bristol
Chambered for 12 and 20 gauge. It has various barrel lengths with a vent rib and screw-in choke tubes. The chambers are 3", and the chrome-finished action is a boxlock with Greener crossbolt and gamescene-engraved side plates. There are automatic ejectors and a single selective trigger. It was introduced in 1986, and in 1989 the designation was changed to the Sterling.

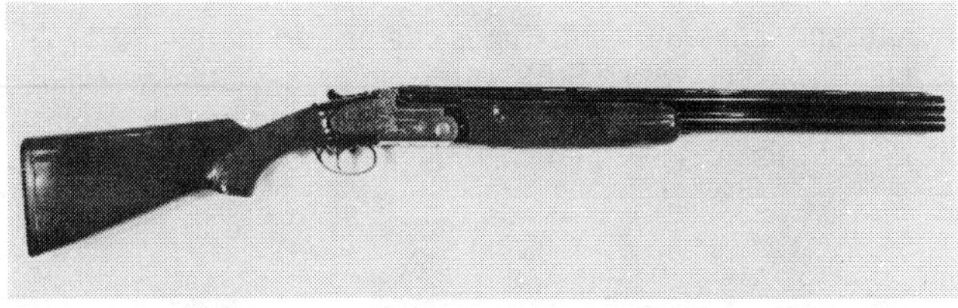

NIB	Exc.	V.G.	Good	Fair	Poor
825	750	675	500	400	300

Sir
Chambered for the 12 and 20 gauge with 3" chambers, various barrel lengths and chokings and a ventilated rib. The chrome-finished sidelock action has a Greener crossbolt and is engraved with a gamescene. There are automatic ejectors and a single selective trigger. This model was imported in 1986.

Exc.	V.G.	Good	Fair	Poor
875	750	625	500	300

Royal
Chambered for the 12 and 20 gauge. It is manufactured in various barrel lengths and chokes with a vent rib and 3" chambers. The chrome-finished sidelock action has a Greener crossbolt and is profusely scroll-engraved. It has automatic ejectors and a single selective trigger. The select pistolgrip walnut stock is hand-checkered and oil-finished. This model was imported in 1986 and 1987.

Exc.	V.G.	Good	Fair	Poor
1500	1275	1000	800	400

Excelsior
Similar to the Royal with extensive deep relief engraving and gold inlays. This model was imported in 1986 and 1987.

Exc.	V.G.	Good	Fair	Poor
1750	1500	1200	875	450

Single Barrel Shotguns
AASB
The standard single-barrel, break-open, hammerless shotgun. It is chambered for 12 and 20 gauge and .410. It has a 26" barrel with various chokes and 3" chambers. It has a pistol-grip stock and a matte finish. It was introduced in 1988.

NIB	Exc.	V.G.	Good	Fair	Poor
100	85	75	60	45	25

Campers Special
Similar to the standard model with a 21" barrel and a folding stock. It was introduced in 1988.

NIB	Exc.	V.G.	Good	Fair	Poor
107	95	85	70	50	35

Single Barrel Shotguns
Youth Model
Chambered for the 20 gauge and .410 and has a 12.5" stock with a recoil pad. It was introduced in 1989.

NIB	Exc.	V.G.	Good	Fair	Poor
115	100	80	65	50	35

Slugger
This version has a 24" barrel with rifle sights. It is chambered for the 12 and 20 gauge and has a recoil pad.

NIB	Exc.	V.G.	Good	Fair	Poor
115	100	80	65	50	35

10 Gauge Model
Chambered for the 10 gauge 3.5" Magnum. It has a 32" full choke barrel and a recoil pad. This model was introduced in 1988.

NIB	Exc.	V.G.	Good	Fair	Poor
150	135	100	85	60	45

Combo Model
Similar in appearance to the other single-barrel models but is offered in an interchangeable-barreled rifle/shotgun combination--the 28" barreled .22 Hornet and the 12 gauge, or the 26" barreled .22 l.r. and 20 gauge. This Model was furnished with a fitted hard case to hold the interchangeable barrels. It was introduced in 1989.

NIB	Exc.	V.G.	Good	Fair	Poor
235	200	175	145	110	75

Rifles
Model ZCY .223
A gas-operated, semi-automatic rifle that is chambered for the .223. It is the civilian version of the Yugoslavian Military rifle and was never actually imported --only advertised. This is another model that would have wildly fluctuating values; and if one were to be located for sale, it would be a market-will-bear situation. It is important to note that these inflated figures that have been attached to these "Assault" rifles are not true values and could cause serious grief to those who pay them should the market stabilize or ultimate sale of them be banned. These rifles are listed for reference purposes only. An independent appraisal should be secured if a transaction is contemplated.

Model ZCY .308
Essentially the same rifle as the ZCY .223—only it is chambered for the .308 cartridge. This Model was imported in 1988 only.

AKY 39
The semi-automatic version of the Soviet AK-47 as it is manufactured by Yugoslavia. It is offered with folding Tritium night sights and a wooden fixed stock. It was imported in 1988 and is now banned from further importation.

AKF 39
The same rifle as the AKY 39 with a metal folding stock.

AKC 47

Basically the same rifle as the AKY 39 without the Tritium night sights. Importation is no longer allowed.

AKF 47

The same rifle as the AKC 47 with a metal folding stock.

EXP-64 Survival Rifle

A .22 caliber, semi-automatic takedown rifle. It is self-storing in a floating, oversized plastic stock. The rifle has a 21" barrel with open sights and a crossbolt safety. There is a 10 shot detachable magazine. Importation by American Arms began in 1989.

NIB	Exc.	V.G.	Good	Fair	Poor
165	150	125	95	75	50

SM-64 TD Sporter

A .22 l.r. semi-automatic with a takedown 21" barrel. It has adjustable sights and a checkered hardwood stock and forend. Importation commenced in 1989.

NIB	Exc.	V.G.	Good	Fair	Poor
150	135	110	85	65	45

Handguns

Model TT Tokarev

The Yugoslavian version of the Soviet Tokarev chambered for 9mm Parabellum and with a safety added to make importation legal. It has a 4.5" barrel, 9-shot magazine and a blued finish with checkered plastic grips. Importation began in 1988.

NIB	Exc.	V.G.	Good	Fair	Poor
290	265	225	175	140	100

Model ZC-.380

A scaled-down version of the Tokarev that is chambered for the .380 ACP. It has a 3.5" barrel and holds 8 shots. The finish and grips are the same as on the full-sized version. Importation from Yugoslavia began in 1988.

NIB	Exc.	V.G.	Good	Fair	Poor
290	265	225	175	140	100

Model EP-.380

A high-quality, stainless-steel pocket pistol that is chambered for the .380 ACP cartridge. It is a double-action semi-automatic that holds 7 shots and has a 3.5" barrel. The grips are checkered walnut. This pistol has been imported from West Germany since 1988.

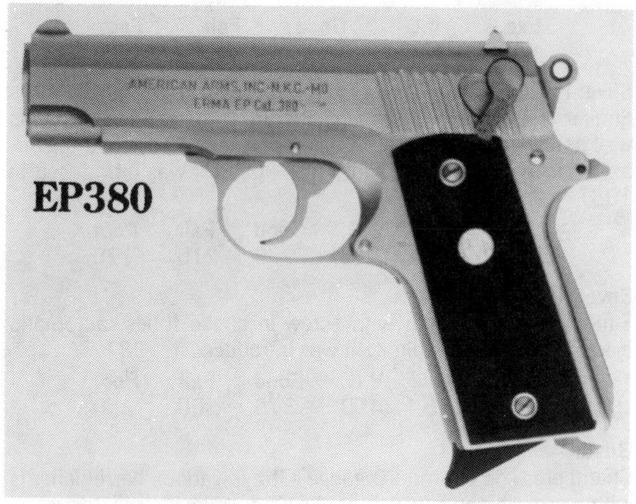

NIB	Exc.	V.G.	Good	Fair	Poor
450	400	350	275	225	175

Model PK-22

A domestic semi-automatic that is chambered for the .22 l.r. It is a double action with a 3.5" barrel and an 8-shot finger extension magazine. It is made of stainless steel and has black plastic grips. This model is manufactured in the U.S.A. by American Arms.

NIB	Exc.	V.G.	Good	Fair	Poor
200	175	150	125	100	75

Model PX-22

A compact version of the PK-22 with a 2.75" barrel and a 7-shot magazine. Manufacture commenced in 1989.

NIB	Exc.	V.G.	Good	Fair	Poor
190	175	150	130	110	75

AMERICAN BARLOCK WONDER

SEE—Crescent Arms Co.

AMERICAN DERRINGER CORP.

Waco, Texas

Model 1 Derringer

Fashioned after the Remington O/U derringer this is a high quality, rugged pistol. It is built from high tensile strength stainless steel. There are over 60 different rifle and pistol calibers to choose from on special order. The upper barrel can be chambered different from the lower barrel on request. Available in a high polish finish of a satin finish. Offered with rosewood, bacote, walnut, or blackwood grips. Ivory, bonded Ivory, stag, or pearl are available at extra cost. Overall length is 4.8", barrel length is 3", width across the frame is .9", width across the grip is 1.2". typical weight is 15 oz in .45 caliber. All guns are furnished with French fitted leatherette case. Prices are determined by caliber.

Caliber:.22 Long Rifle through .357 Mag. and .45 ACP

NIB	Exc.	V.G.	Good	Fair	Poor
210	180	150	125	100	75

Calibers: .41 Mag., .44-40, .44 special, .44 Mag., .45 Long Colt, .410 bore, .22 Hornet, .223 Re., 30-30, and .47-70 Gov't.

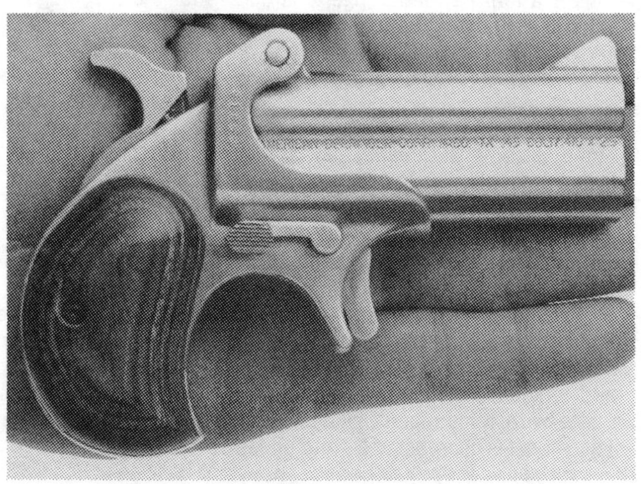

NIB	Exc.	V.G.	Good	Fair	Poor
300	275	250	200	150	100

Model 1 Texas Commemorative

Built with a solid brass frame and stainless steel barrel. Dimensions are same as Model 1. Grips are Stag or Rosewood and offered in .45 Colt, .44-40, or .38 Special. Barrels marker," Made in the 150th Year of Texas Freedom". Limited to 500 pistols in each caliber.

Caliber: .38 Special

NIB	Exc.	V.G.	Good	Fair	Poor
185	150	125	100	80	70

Calibers: .45 Colt and .44-40

NIB	Exc.	V.G.	Good	Fair	Poor
275	250	200	150	125	100

Deluxe Engraved

Special serial number engraved on back strap.

NIB	Exc.	V.G.	Good	Fair	Poor
900	750	550	350	250	150

Model 1 Lady Derringer

Similar to the Model 1 but chambered for the .38 Special, .32 Magnum, .22 Long Rifle, or .22 Rimfire Magnum. Offered in two grades.

Deluxe Grade

High polished stainless steel with scrimshawed ivory grips with Cameo or Rose design.

NIB	Exc.	V.G.	Good	Fair	Poor
200	175	150	125	100	75

Deluxe Engraved Grade

Same as above but hand engraved in 1880's style.

NIB	Exc.	V.G.	Good	Fair	Poor
650	550	500	450	250	150

Model 1 125th Anniversary Commemorative

Built to commemorate the 125th anniversary of the derringer,1866 to 1991. Similar to the Model 1 but marked with the patent date December 12, 1865. Brass frame and stainless steel barrel. Chambered for .440-40, .45 Colt, or .38 Special.

NIB	Exc.	V.G.	Good	Fair	Poor
275	250	225	175	125	100

Deluxe Engraved

NIB	Exc.	V.G.	Good	Fair	Poor
650	550	500	450	250	150

Model 2-Pen Pistol

Introduced in 1993 this is a legal pistol that cannot be fired from its pen position but requires that it be pulled apart and bent 80 degrees to fire. Made from stainless steel it is offered in .22 LR, .25 ACP, and .32 ACP. The length in pen form is 5.6" and in pistol form is 4.2". Barrel length is 2". Diameter varies from 1/2" to 5/8". Weight is 5 oz.

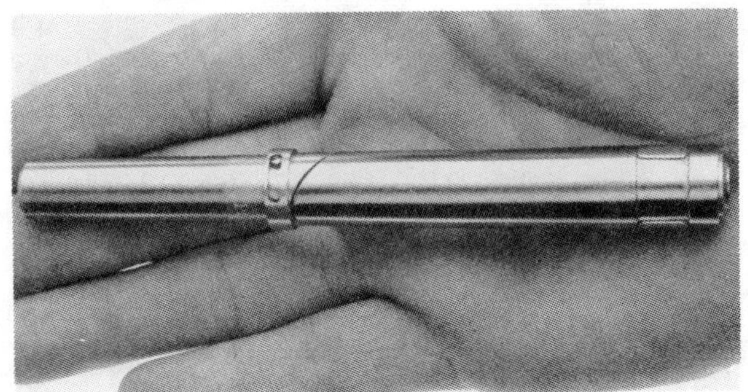

NIB	Exc.	V.G.	Good	Fair	Poor
225	175	135	115	100	85

Model 3
This model is a single barrel derringer. Barrel length is 2.5" and swing down to load. Frame and barrel are stainless steel. Offered in .38 Special or .32 Magnum. Weighs about 8 oz. Production of this model has been temporary halted.

NIB	Exc.	V.G.	Good	Fair	Poor
120	100	85	75	65	50

Model 4
Similar in appearance to the Model 3 but fitted with a 4.1" barrel. Overall length is 6" and weight is about 16.5 oz. Chambered for 3" .410 bore, .45 Long Colt, .44 Magnum, ot .357 Magnum.

NIB	Exc.	V.G.	Good	Fair	Poor
325	300	275	250	200	125

Model 4-Alaskan Survival Model
Similar to the Model 4 but with upper barrel chambered for .45-70 and lower barrel for .45 LC or .410. Both barrels can also be chambered for .44 Magnum or .45-70. Comes with oversize Rosewood grips.

NIB	Exc.	V.G.	Good	Fair	Poor
350	300	250	200	150	100

Model 6
This double barrel derringer is fitted with a 6" barrel chambered for the .45LC or .410 bore. Weighs about 21 oz. Rosewood grips are standard. Optional calibers are .357 Magnum or .45 ACP. Oversize grips are optional and add about $35 to value.

NIB	Exc.	V.G.	Good	Fair	Poor
350	300	250	200	150	100

High Standard Double Action Derringer
This double barrel derringer is chambered for the .22 Long Rifle or .22 Magnum cartridge. Its barrel length is 3.5" and overall length is 5.125". Weighs approximately 11 oz. The finish is blue with black grips. Production temporarily halted.

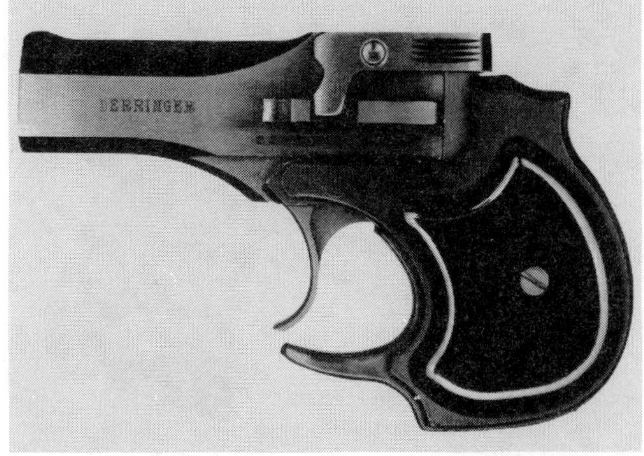

NIB	Exc.	V.G.	Good	Fair	Poor
170	150	125	100	85	75

DA 38 Double Action Derringer
This is a two barrel model featuring a double action trigger. Overall length is 4.9" and barrel length is 3". Weights is about 15 oz. Chambered for .38 Special, .357 magnum, (mm Luger, and .40S&W. Finish is satin stainless. Grip is made from aluminum. Grips are Rosewood or walnut.

NIB	Exc.	V.G.	Good	Fair	Poor
225	200	175	150	125	100

MINI COP-4 SHOT
This is a four barrel derringer chambered for the .22 Magnum Rimfire cartridge. Production is temporarily halted.

NIB	Exc.	V.G.	Good	Fair	Poor
310	285	250	225	175	125

COP-4 SHOT
Same as above but chambered for the .357 Magnum cartridge. Production is temporarily halted.

NIB	Exc.	V.G.	Good	Fair	Poor
375	350	325	300	225	150

Model 7 Derringer
Manufactured as a backup gun for police officers. The frame and barrels are made of aircraft aluminum alloy; the other parts are stainless-steel. This gun weighs 7.5 ounces. Its appearance and function are similar to the Model 1. The finish is a grey matte with thin, matte-finished grips of rosewood or bacote. This model is chambered for and priced as follows:

.32 S&W Long/.32 Magnum

NIB	Exc.	V.G.	Good	Fair	Poor
170	140	120	100	80	50

.38 S&W and .380 ACP

NIB	Exc.	V.G.	Good	Fair	Poor
170	140	120	100	80	50

.22 L.R. and .38 Special

NIB	Exc.	V.G.	Good	Fair	Poor
170	140	120	100	80	50

.44 Special

NIB	Exc.	V.G.	Good	Fair	Poor
425	400	375	325	265	200

Model 10 Derringer

Similar to the Model 1 with a frame of aluminum alloy and all other parts, including the barrels, stainless-steel. It has a grey matte finish and thin grips of rosewood or bacote. It weighs 10 ounces and is chambered for the .45 ACP or the .45 Colt.
.45 Colt—Add 10%.

NIB	Exc.	V.G.	Good	Fair	Poor
220	195	175	140	110	80

Model 11 Derringer

A stainless steel barrel and all other parts aluminum. It weighs 11 ounces and is chambered for the .38 Special. The grips and finish are the same as on the Model 10.

NIB	Exc.	V.G.	Good	Fair	Poor
180	165	135	110	85	60

Semmerling LM-4

This gun has been in production for approximately 10 years, built by various companies. This latest offering by American Derringer may, with the right marketing and manufacturing approach, be the one that makes a commercial success of this fine firearm concept. The LM-4 was designed as the ultimate police backup/defense weapon. It is a manually operated, 5-shot repeater only 5.2" long, 3.7" high, and 1" wide. It is chambered for the .45 ACP and is undoubtedly the smallest 5-shot .45 ever produced. The LM-4 is made of a special tool steel and is either blued or, at extra cost, hard chrome-plated. A stainless-steel version is also available. The LM-4 is not a semi- automatic, although it physically resembles one. The slide is flicked forward and back after each double-action squeeze of the trigger. This weapon is virtually hand-built and features high visibility sights and a smooth trigger. It is an extremely limited-production item, and the company produces only two per week. The price and availability may fluctuate, so the company should be contacted for accurate figures. The values for the guns produced before American Derringer's involvement will be found in the section dealing with the Semmerling. These values are for the latest production by American Derringer. There is a 12- to 14-month waiting period for delivery, and the manufacturer's suggested list price is $1,250. Prices listed below reflect supply and demand.
Hard Chrome—Add $200.00.
Stainless-Steel—Add 35%.

NIB	Exc.	V.G.	Good	Fair	Poor
3250	3000	2700	2250	1600	1250

AMERICAN F.A. MFG. CO., INC.
San Antonio, Texas

This company operated between 1972 and 1974, producing a .25 ACP pocket pistol and a stainless-steel .38 Special derringer. A .380 auto was produced on an extremely limited basis.

American .25 Automatic

A small, blowback, semi-automatic pocket pistol that was chambered for the .25 ACP cartridge. It had a 2" barrel and was made of either stainless-steel or blued carbon steel. The grips were of plain uncheckered walnut, and the detachable magazine held 7 shots. It was manufactured until 1974.
Stainless Steel—Add 20%.

Exc.	V.G.	Good	Fair	Poor
175	150	125	100	75

American .380 Automatic

Similar to the .25 except larger. The barrel was 3.5", and the gun was made in stainless-steel only. The grips were of smooth walnut, and it held 8 shots. There were only 10 of these .380's manufactured between 1972 and 1974. They are extremely rare, but there is little collector base for this company's products, and the value is very difficult to estimate.

Exc.	V.G.	Good	Fair	Poor
600	550	475	375	300

American .38 Special Derringer

A well-made, stainless-steel O/U derringer that was similar in appearance and function to the old Remington O/U. It had 3" barrels, that pivoted upward for loading. This gun was a single-action that had an automatic selector and a spur trigger. The smooth grips were of walnut. There were approximately 3,500 manufactured between 1972 and 1974.

Exc.	V.G.	Good	Fair	Poor
200	180	150	125	90

AMERICAN GUN CO.
Norwich, Connecticut
Crescent Firearms Co.--Maker
H. & D. Folsom Co.--Distributor

Side x Side Shotgun

A typical trade gun made around the turn of the century by the Crescent Firearms Co. to be distributed by H. & D. Folsom. These are sometimes known as "Hardware Store Guns," as that is where many were sold. This particular gun was chambered for 12, 16, and 20 gauges and was produced with or without external hammers. The length of the barrels varied, as did the chokes. Some were produced with Damascus barrels; some, with fluid steel. The latter are worth approximately 25 percent more.

Exc.	V.G.	Good	Fair	Poor
200	175	150	125	100

AMERICAN HISTORICAL FOUNDATION

Richmond, Virginia

The American Historical Foundation is a private organization which commissions historical commemorative in conjunction with leading manufacturers and craftsmen around the world. The values listed below show the Foundation's original issue prices and the last known retail price. Secondary market sales are infrequent and are difficult to confirm. The American Historical Foundation sells only direct and not through dealers or distributors. Nevertheless, the last retail price can be useful to both the buyer and seller when neither is compelled to buy or sell. When applicable, a separate price will be given for a display case. Issues that have been sold out will be so stipulated.

The collector should be aware that these firearms are valuable for their beauty and historical significance. AHF commemorative are more collectable if they remain in the exact same condition in which they were issued; new, unfired, and with all of the original packing material and papers.

PISTOLS:

40th Anniversary Commemorative Ruger Mark II

Chambered for the .22 Long Rifle this pistol features a 24-karat gold etched receiver and barrel with gold plating on small component parts, polymer ivory grips with both red and black Ruger medallions. Manufactured by Strum, Ruger Co. and limited to 950 units. Serial numbers 40th1 through 40th950.

Original Issue Price: $995
Current Issue Price: $1095

Display Case Original Issue Price: $119
Current Issue Price: $149

Airborne Jubilee Model 1911A1

Chambered for the .45 ACP cartridge and finished with a high polish blue with etched commemorative inscriptions. Selected parts are gold plated. Manufactured by Auto-Ordnance Corp. and limited to 500 units.

Original Issue Price: $995
Current Issue Price: $1095

Display Case Original Price: $119
Current Issue Price: $149

Allied Victory Browning HI-Power

This Browning manufactured 9mm pistol features 24-karat gold plating, checked walnut grips with cloisonne medallion. The slide has deeply etched inscriptions and scenes. An extra magazine and cleaning rod are also gold plated. Issue limited to 500 units.

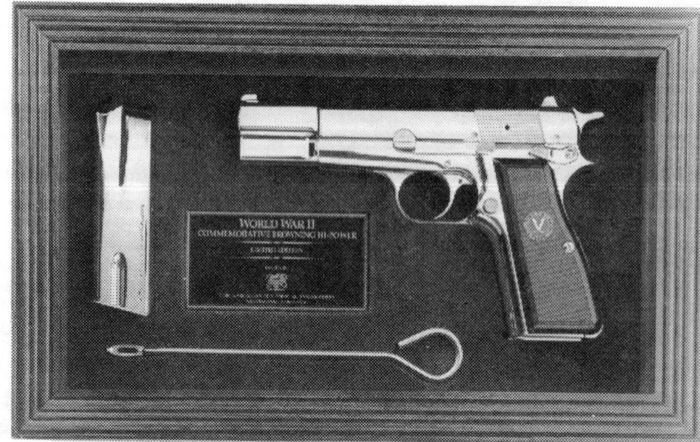

Current Issue Price: $1795
Display Case Current Issue Price: $179

Armed Forces Model 1911A1

This is a set of four Model 1911A1s representing each of the U.S. armed forces branches. Each pistol is chambered for the .45 ACP and features custom designed etchings and grips of different woods and medallions. Manufactured by Auto-Ordnance Corp. and limited to 1911 sets.

Original Issue Price: $995
Current Issue Price: $1095

Display Case Original Issue Price: $85
Current Issue price: $149

Armed Forces Ruger

Chambered for the .22 Long Rifle cartridge and fitted with a bull barrel it is available in the four military branches: Army, Navy, Marine, and Air Force. Each features a high polish blue finish with 24-karat gold foliate motif covering the full length of the barrel and receiver. There are twelve gold plated parts. A cloisonne medallion is featured in the wooden grips. Manufactured by Strum, Ruger Co. this issue is limited to 250 pistols per service branch.

Current Issue Price: $1095
Display Case Current Issue Price: $139

D-Day Commemorative Model 1911A1

This .45 ACP caliber pistol has gold plated parts, polymer ivory grips with medallions, and are serially numbered DDAY0001 through DDAY1000. Built by Auto-Ordinance Corp. and limited to 1000 units.

Original Issue Price: $995
Current Issue Price: $1095

Display Case Original Issue Price: $85
Current Issue Price: $149

ETO Luger

This European Theater of Operations commemorative issue used original P.08 Lugers manufactured by Eurfort, Simpson & Co.. The collector's edition has a contrasting mirror and matte blue finish. Etched tributes and gold gilt are applied. Six component parts are gold plated and the grips are of select walnut with high gloss finish. This edition is limited to 750 units.

Current Issue Price: $1795
Display Case Current Issue Price: $179

Deluxe Edition has 24-karat gold plating with oak leaf scroll engraving with 75 percent coverage. This Deluxe Edition is limited to 10 units.

Original Issue Price: $3995
Display Case Original Price: $179

Five Star General Series

This M15 is chambered for the .45 ACP cartridge. This is an ongoing series commemorating the five star generals of World War II. Editions are limited to 500. The blue finish has a contrasting high mirror and matte finish with seven gold plated component parts. Millett sights are fitted. Etched commemorative markings with 24-karat gold infill. First in series honors General Eisenhower and the second in the series is for General MacArthur. Manufactured by Auto Ordinance Corp.

Current Issue Price: $1295
Display Case Current Issue Price: $149

Smith & Wesson Tactical Competition

Chambered for the .40 S&W cartridge this pistol was built by the Performance Center at Smith & Wesson. It has a match grade barrel with custom tuned action and hand fitted. The slide and frame are hand engraved with a high polish blue while the frame top is a blue matte. Compensated.
Deluxe Edition limited to 10 units.

Last Issue Price: $3795
Sold Out

Collector Edition limited to 40 units
Current Issue Price: $2795

UZI Pistol
Chambered for the 9mm Parabellum cartridge the receiver and barrel are 24-karat gold plated with hand engraving. Produced by the AHF custom shop and limited to 100 units. Includes display case.

Last Issue Price: $2495
Sold Out

Vietnam War Limited Edition 1911A1
Chambered for the .45 ACP cartridge this Auto Ordinance pistol features an etched frame with high polish blue finish. Slide has 24-karat gold etchings and small parts are gold plated.

Original Issue Price: $1095

Display Case Original Issue Price: $85
Current Issue Price: $149

World War II Colt .45 Series
There are twelve .45s in this series each commemorating a major campaign of WWII. They are etched and have a high blue polish. Each of the 12 pistols is limited to 250 units. Includes display case.

Current Issue Price: $995

American Eagle Hi-Power
Manufactured by Browning this 9mm pistol is etched and selectively plated with gold. Ivory polymer grips are scrimshawed with oak leaves and scroll. Serially numbered from AE001 through AE750 this issue is limited to 750 units.

Current Issue Price: $2195

Display Case Current Issue Price: $179

REVOLVERS

200th Constitution Commemorative Revolver
Chambered fo the .44 Magnum cartridge this handgun features extensive 24-karat gold inlays and etchings. Fitted with a 10" barrel and ivory polymer grips. Collector's Edition serial numbered from CC001 through CC950. Manufactured by Wesson Firearms and limited to 950 units.

Collector's Edition Original Price: $995
Collector's Edition Last Issue Price: $1295
Sold Out

Deluxe Museum Edition serial numbered CD001 through CD500. Limited to 500 units.

Deluxe Museum Edition Original Issue Price: $1295
Deluxe Museum Edition Last Issue Price: $1595
Sold Out

1847 Model Walker
This revolver is the second issue in the "Samuel Colt Golden Tribute Collection". Limited to 950 units.

Original Issue Price: $1895
Current Issue Price: $2195

Display Case Original Issue Price: $229
Current Issue Price: $249

American Deer Hunter Commemorative
Chambered for .44 Magnum and fitted with a 10" barrel. The Deluxe Trophy Edition features a deeply blued finish with 24-karat gold plated hammer, trigger, front sight, cylinder release, and grip screws. Grips are Herrett finger groove. Serial numbered DEER001T through DEER250T. Manufactured by Wesson Firearms and limited to 250 units.

Original Issue Price: $1995

Display Case Original Issue Price: $149
Current Issue Price: $179

Sportsman's Edition is a field grade version with high polish blue finish and gold gilt etching on barrel. Serial number DEER001S through DEER750S. Limited to 750 units.

Original Issue Price: $995
Current Issue Price: $1095

Display Case Original Issue Price: $149
Current Issue Price: $179

Civil War Colt Dragoons
Chambered for .44 caliber cartridge this revolver is available in either Union Model with hand engraved and 24-karat gold plating or Confederate Model with hand engraved and silver plated. Limited to 125 units of each.

Last Issue price: $2495
Sold Out

Jefferson Davis Model 1851 Navy
Patterned after the Colt 1851 Navy pistol presented to Jefferson Davis in 1858 this handgun is chambered for the .36 caliber cartridge and features hand engraving with sterling silver plated selected parts. Comes complete with detachable shoulder stock. Manufactured by A. Uberti and limited to 250 units.

Current Issue Price: $2995

Col. J.S. Mosby Model 1860 Army
This is a stainless steel revolver chambered for the .44 caliber cartridge. It is hand engraved with selected 24-karat gold plated parts. Manufactured by Colt and limited to 150 units.

Last Issue Price: $2495
Sold Out

Old West Sheriffs Model Colt
This Colt single action army is chambered for the .45 Long Colt cartridge. The ivory cylinder pin is custom made and there are three areas of 24-karat gold inlay on a blue finish which is extensively hand engraved. The ivory grips are scrimshawed. An AHF custom shop edition limited to only 10 units. Includes display case.

Current Issue Price: $10995

General Patton Single Action Army
Fitted with a 5.5" barrel and chambered for the .45 Long Colt, this handgun features a silver plated finish with extensive scroll hand engraving. Polymer grips combined with ivory and lanyard ring. Serial numbered P001 through P2500. Manufactured by A. Uberti and limited to 2500 units.

Original Issue Price: $1495
Last Issue Price: $1895

Display Case Last Issue Price: $169

Teddy Roosevelt Single Action Army
Hand engraved with 24-karat gold inlay of Roosevelt's initials on left recoil shield this SAA is chambered for the .44-40 caliber cartridge. Entire gun is 24-karat and sterling silver plated. Manufactured by A. Uberti and limited to 750 units.

Original Issue Price: $1995

Display Case Original Issue Price: $149
Current Issue Price: $179

Texas Patterson
This is a hand engraved 24-karat gold plated 5 shot pistol chambered for the .36 caliber cartridge. It is the first issue of the "Samuel Colt Golden Tribute Collection". Manufactured by D. Pedersoll of Italy and limited to 950 units.

Original Issue Price: $1495
Current Issue Price: $2195

Display Case Original Issue Price: $225
Current Issue Price: $259

Second Amendment Commemorative Revolver
Manufactured by Wesson Firearms this pistol is chambered for the .44 Magnum and fitted with a 10" barrel. Grips are walnut with medallions. Collector's Edition limited to 1500 units and is fully etched with blued frame and barrel. Small parts are gold plated. Serial numbered 2AC0001 through 2AC1500

Collector's Edition Original Issue Price: $1295
Collector's Edition Current Issue Price: $1695

Display Case Original Issue Price: $149
Current Issue Price: $179

Deluxe Museum Edition features a fully etched frame and barrel with all parts gold plated. Serial numbered 2AD001 through 2AD750. Limited to 750 units.

Deluxe Museum Edition Original Issue Price: $1595
Deluxe Museum Edition Current Issue Price: $1895

Display Case Original Issue Price: $149
Current Issue Price: $179

J.E.B. Stuart LeMat
Chambered for .44 caliber cartridge this nine shot revolver also includes a single shot .65 caliber shotgun barrel. Finish is blued with selective etching and 24-karat gold plating. Manufactured by Navy Arms and limited to 500 units.

Original Issue Price: $2195
Current Issue Price: $2695

Display Case Original Issue Price: $179
Current Issue Price: $225

Wild Bill Hickok Model 1851 Navy
Reproduction of 1851 Navy revolver chambered for .36 caliber cartridge. Hand engraved with sterling silver plating. Manufactured by A. Uberti and limited to 500 units.

Current Issue Price: $1995

Display Case Original Issue Price: $119
Current Issue Price: $179

World War II Commando Enfield
This is a No.2 Mark I Enfield revolver. The flats are polished to high mirror blue finish while the recessed areas are matte finished. Etched commemorative markings and 24-karat gold filling. A walnut display and Commando knife are included. Limited to 250 units.

Current Issue Price: $995

American Flag Tribute
Two hand built editions honoring the American flag.; A Wesson Arms .44 Magnum and a Strum, Ruger Co. .22. Each edition features a 10" target length barrel with the entire pledge of Allegiance etched and selectively plated in gold. Each has ivory polymer grips and is serially numbered AF0001 through AF1000.

.44 Magnum
Current Issue Price: $1495

Display Case Current Issue Price: $179

Ruger .22
Current Issue Price: $1095
Display Case Current Issue Price: $179

Smith & Wesson 629 Tactical
Chambered for the .44 magnum this pistol was built by the S&W Performance Center. It features a compensation port across the top of the barrel and a machined expansion chamber inside the muzzle. The frame is hand engraved. This is the first 3" barrel Model 629 ever made. The edition is limited to 25 units. Shooters case included.

Current Issue Price: $2795
Sold Out

Smith and Wesson 629 Hunter
Built by the S&W Performance Center this 6" Mag-na-ported barrel revolver has hand engraved frame and Nikon scope. Edition is limited to 50 units.

Current Issue Price: $3795

Patton .357
This hand engraved Smith & Wesson .357 Magnum Model 27 is available in two editions: the Deluxe Edition and Collector's Edition. The Deluxe Edition is plated in Sterling Silver and has full hand engraving. It is limited to 100 units and is serially numbered from P001D through P100D.

Deluxe Edition
Current Issue Price: $2495
Display Case Current Issue Price: $195

Collector Edition has a high blue polish with the cylinder silver plated and etched with Patton's military units, insignia, and rank. This edition is limited to 950 units and is serially numbered from P001C through P950C.

Current Issue Price: $995

Display Case Current Issue Price: $195

North/South 3rd Model Dragoons
This .44 caliber revolver is offered in either the blued North Model or French Grayed South Model. Two editions are available: the Deluxe and the Collector. The Deluxe Edition is manufactured by Colt and features hand engraving and gold inlays. Limited to 50 models of North and South each. Serially numbered from USA01D through USA50D or CSA01D through CSA50D.

Current Issue Price: $2495
Display Case Current Issue Price: $179

Collector Edition is hand engraved and built by the Italian firm Uberti. Limited to 250 units of both the North and South models. Serially numbered from USA001C through USA250C or CSA001C through CSA250C.
Current Issue Price: $1595
Display Case Current Issue Price: $179

The Old West Gambler
This .45LC 3" barrel revolver is silver plated and hand engraved. Ivory polymer are scrimshawed. A compartmentalized display case with playing cards, dice, chips, and flask are included.

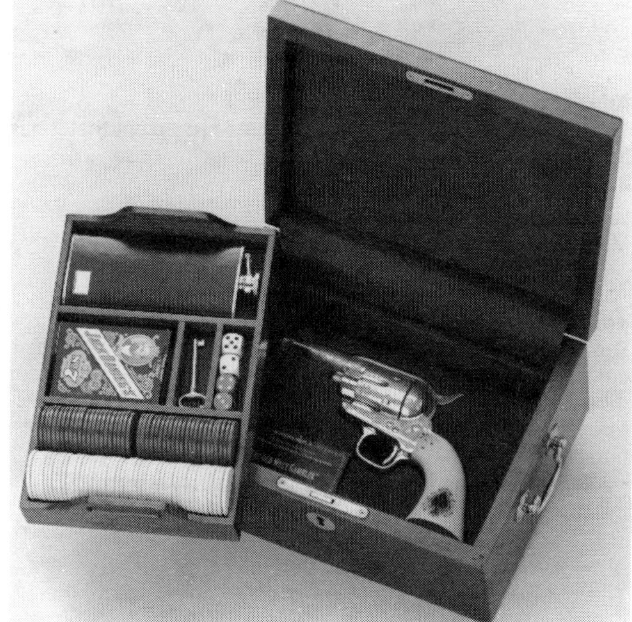

Current Issue Price: $2195

Wyatt Earp Single Action Army
The Uberti built 7.5" barrel revolver is chambered for the .45 LC and features nickel plating and etching and gold infilled banner. Fitted with walnut grips. Limited to 750 units and serially numbered from WE001 through WE750.

Current Issue Price: $1595

Display Case Current Issue Price: $179

RIFLES AND CARBINES

50 States Henry
A faithful copy of the famous repeating rifle chambered for the .44-40. This is the rare iron frame version with blued finish inlaid with 24-karat gold. The receiver, upper and lower tangs, buttplate, loading lever, barrel and hammer are hand engraved in addition to the 70"s of gold inlaid borders. The magazine follower, trigger, and breech block are gold plated. The stock is select walnut. Manufactured by A. Uberti and limited to 2 rifles per state with a limit of 100 units. Each rifle is marked with the state's outline and motto.

Current Issue Price: $11995

Display Case Current Issue Price: $499

1885 Deer Hunter
This Browning copy of the Winchester Model 1885 is chambered for the .45-70 cartridge. The receiver is french grayed with custom designed hand engraving. Collector Issue limited to 100 units.

Collector Original Issue Price: $2975

Civil War Commemorative Henrys:
Similar to the Constitution Henry with choice of either Abraham Lincoln with hand engraved brass frame with gold plating and blued barrel or Jefferson Davis with hand engraved brass frame with silver plating and brown barrel. Manufactured by A. Uberti and limited to 250 of each model.

Original Issue Price: $3495
Current Issue Price: $3995

Display Case Current Issue Price: $249

Constitution Commemorative Henry
Patterned after the Henry rifle with brass frame and hand engraved 24-karat plating. Manufactured by A. Uberti and limited to 200 units.

Last Issue Price: $2395
Sold Out

Display Case Original Issue Price: $249

ETO/PTO Thompson
A semi-automatic reproduction of the Model 1927A1 Thompson chambered for the .45 ACP. Special roll markings with gold infill. Stocks are made form select walnut and have a high polish with two cloisonne medallions. There are five gold plated component parts including the Cutts Compensator. Manufactured by Auto-Ordnance and limited to 500 for each theater of operation.

Current Issue Price: $1595
Display Case Current Issue Price: $249

Korean War Semi-Auto Thompson
Chambered for the .45 ACP this model is also available in full auto for Class III license holders. Special finish select walnut stock and forearm. Multiple gold plated parts. Serial numbered from KW0001 through KW1500. There were 2000 manufactured in 1984. Manufactured by Auto-Ordnance and limited to 1500 units.

Last Issue Price: $1195
Display Case Last Issue Price: $225

Law Enforcement Thompson
This set contains a policeman and sheriff model with gold etchings and gilting. Deluxe walnut stocks are fitted with custom medallions. Manufactured by Auto-Ordnance and limited to 1500 of each model.

Current Issue Price: $1595

Display Case Original Issue Price: $225
Current Issue Price: $249

M16 Airborne
This rifle is chambered for the .223 caliber cartridge and features hand engraving and gold plated selected parts. the Specially finish stock has a heavy textured black finish. Issue limited to 950 units.

Original Issue Price: $2495
Last Issue Price: $2795

Display Case Original Issue Price: $225
Last Issue Price: $249

M16 Vietnam War Commemorative
This issue commemorates the Vietnam War veteran. It is chambered for the .223 cartridge, is hand engraved, and has gold plated small parts.. A bipod is included. Serial numbered from VN0001 through VN1000. Issue limited to 1000.

Last Issue Price: $1995
Sold Out

Display Case Last Issue Price: $225

Model 1861 Springfield Musket
Issued to commemorate the 125th anniversary of the Civil War this rifle is a .58 caliber. Selected parts are hand engraved and gold plated. Select grade walnut stock. Manufactured by Ezechiele and Rino Chiappa and limited to 125 units.

Original Issue Price: $3495

Display Case Original Issue Price: $295
Current Issue Price: $399

Special Forces MAC-10
Chambered for the .45 ACP this semi-automatic commemorates the 25th anniversary of the Mac-10.

Original Issue Price: $1195
Current Issue Price: $1595

Display Case Original Issue Price: $169

Vietnam M14 Rifle
Chambered for the .308 Win. cartridge this rifle is manufactured by Federal Ordnance. It features gold etching

and gilted metal parts. Issue is limited to 500 units for each of two editions.

Collector's Edition Original Issue Price: $2195
Collector's Edition Last Issue Price: $2495

Deluxe Museum Edition Original Issue Price: $2495
Deluxe Museum Edition Last Issue Price: $2895

Display Case: $249 either edition.

Winchester Model 94
This issue commemorates the centennial of the closing of the American West. Chambered for the .30-30 cartridge the Collector Edition features 8 gold plated parts with walnut stocks fitted with custom medallions. One side of the receiver is hand engraved. Limited to 750 units.

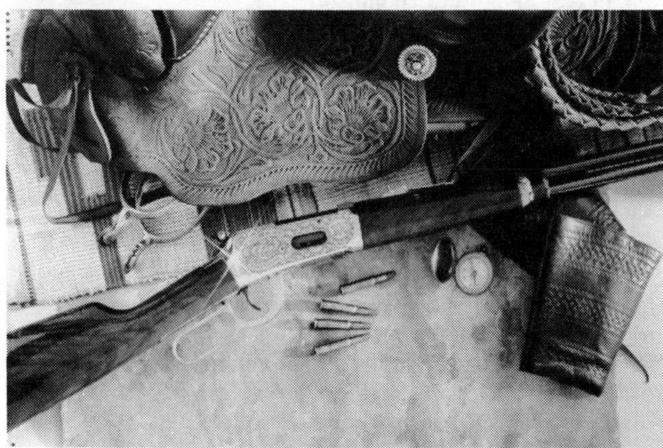

Original Issue Price: $1795
Last Issue Price: $1895

Display Case Original Issue Price: $249
Last Issue Price: $299

Deluxe Museum Edition features extensive hand engraving. Stocks are custom walnut by Fajen with rounded style butt plate which is also engraved and gold plated. Issue is limited to 250 units.

Deluxe Original Issue Price: $2495
Current Issue Price: $2895

Display Case Original Issue Price: $225
Current Issue Price: $249

World War II Springfield
Original WWII bolt action Model 1903 Springfield chambered for the .30-06 cartridge features a deeply blued finish on receiver and bolt with contrasting mirror and satin finishes on small parts. Stock is custom made. Issue limited to 500 units.

Original Issue Price: $1495
Current Issue Price: $1695

Display Case Original Issue Price: $249

World War II Garand Rifle
These original WWII Garand rifles are chambered for the .30-06 cartridge and feature gold plated parts with a high polish blue. Released in 1984 and serial numbered from WW0001 through WW2500. Limited to 2500 units.

Original Issue Price: $1695
Current Issue Price: $1895

Display case Original Issue Price: $225
Current Issue Price: $249

Airborne Golden Jubilee Thompson
This issue commemorates the 50th anniversary of the Airborne. It features special etchings and medallions. Manufactured by Auto Ordnance Corp. and limited to 500 units.

Last Issue Price: $1995

Display Case Last Issue Price: $249

American Armed Forces
This is a semi-automatic carbine version that has gold plated small parts and several gold inlays. Serial numbered from UZI001 through UZI1500. Includes detachable shoulder stock. Limited to 1500 units.

Last Issue Price: $2195
Sold Out

Armed Forces M16s
This issue is similar to the Vietnam War M16 except that it has four models to commemorate the four branches of service. Limited to 100 units for each branch.

Last Issue Price: $2995
Many branches sold out.

Display Case Last Issue Price: $249

Armed Forces Semi-Auto Thompson
Semi-Auto reproduction of the military Thompson sub-machine gun. Special finish high grade walnut, gold plated parts. Four models to commemorate the four service branches. Manufactured by Auto-Ordnance and limited to 750 for each service branch.

Current Original Issue Price: $1895
Current Issue Price: $1995

Airborne Golden Jubilee M1A1 Carbine
This issue uses an original WWII carbine chambered for the .30 caliber carbine cartridge. It features a folding stock, special commemorative etchings and gold plated selective parts. Limited to 500 carbines.

Current Issue Price: $1295

Display Case Current Issue Price: $249

SHOTGUNS

Annual Federal Duck Stamp Browning Shotguns
For the year 1991/1992 three grades were available in the Browning over and under shotgun. Hand engraved with gold inlays each is commissioned on an individual basis to customer specifications.

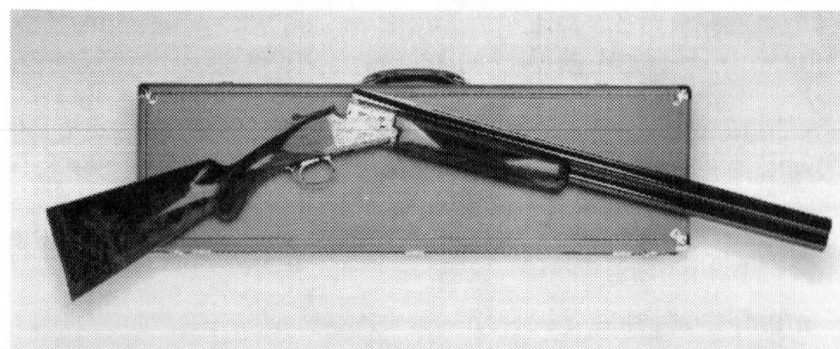

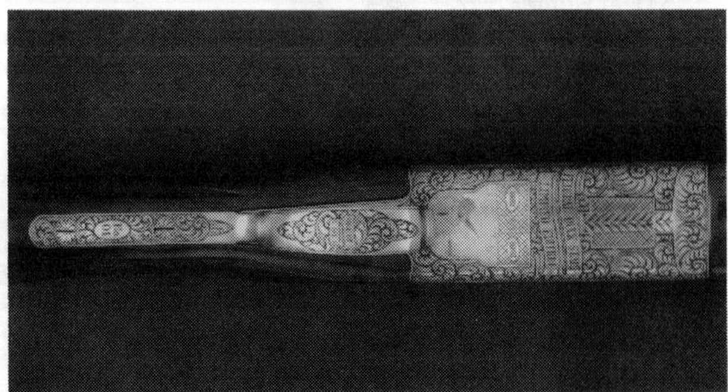

B-25 Edition limited to 50 guns.
Original Issue price: $14500
Current Issue Price: $14995

B-125 Edition limited to 100 guns.
Original Issue Price: $9995
Current Issue Price: $10495

Citori Edition limited to 200 guns.
Original Issue Price: $4995
Current Issue Price: $5495

For the year 1992/1993 the same three grades are available.

B-25 Edition limited to 50 guns.
Original Issue Price: $14500
Current Issue Price: $14995

B-125 Edition limited to 100 guns.
Original Issue Price: $9995
Current Issue Price: $10495

Auto-5 Magnum Edition limited to 250 guns.
Current Issue Price: $2495

French Revolution Shotgun
This is a custom made shotgun built by Renata Gamba. They are hand engraved and signed by Cesare Giovnelli. The left side of the receiver shows the storming of the Bastille and the right side shows the march on Versailles. Limited to 200 guns. Display case included in price.

Last Issue Price: $10995

Vietnam War Combat Shotgun
Manufactured by Savage this 12 gauge shotgun has a hand engraved receiver with gold plated small parts. Produced in 1988 and serial numbered from VN001 through VN750. Limited to 750 guns.

Last Issue Price: $1595
Sold Out

Display Case Last Issue Price: $249

Generals Ulysses S. Grant Henry and Robert E. Lee Henry
This quality Uberti copy of the rare iron frame repeating rifle is chambered for the .44-40. It is hand engraved and selectively gold plated. Limited to 250 units per General.

Current Issue Price: $2495
Display Case Current Issue Price: $299

Vietnam Tribute Colt M16
This model is the Match HBAR version and is chambered for the .223 cartridge. It is etched and gold gilt infilled. This issue commemorates the Vietnam veteran and has eleven component parts gold plated. Serially number from VT0001 through VT1500 this issue is limited to 1500 units.

Current Issue Price: $1995

Display Case Current Issue Price: $249

AMERICAN INDUSTRIES
Cleveland, Ohio

Calico M-100
A semi-automatic carbine that has a 16.1" barrel with a flash suppressor. It is chambered for the .22 l.r. and features a folding stock, full shrouding hand-guards, a 100-round capacity, helical feed, and detachable magazine. It features an ambidextrous safety, pistol grip storage compartment, and a black finished alloy frame and adjustable sights. This model was introduced in 1986.

NIB	Exc.	V.G.	Good	Fair	Poor
300	275	250	210	175	140

Calico M-100S Sporter
Similar to the Model 100 with a futuristically styled walnut buttstock and forearm. This model is also known as the M-105.

NIB	Exc.	V.G.	Good	Fair	Poor
319	290	265	225	185	150

Calico M-900
A black polymer-stocked rifle that is similar to the M-100S, chambered for the 9mm Parabellum. It has a delayed blowback action and features a stainless-steel bolt and alloy receiver. The cocking handle is non-reciprocating, and the rear sight is fixed with an adjustable front. There is a 50-round magazine standard and a 100-round capacity model optional. This model was introduced in 1989.

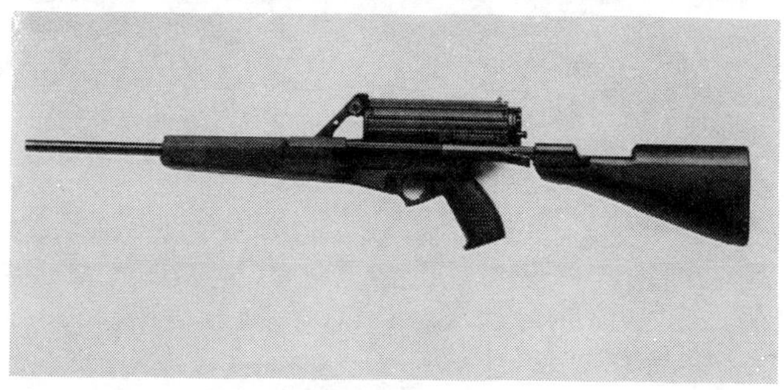

NIB	Exc.	V.G.	Good	Fair	Poor
460	410	365	300	265	240

Calico M-950 Pistol
Similar to the Model 900 rifle with a 6" barrel and no shoulder stock.

NIB	Exc.	V.G.	Good	Fair	Poor
443	400	345	285	250	200

Calico M-100P

Similar to the M-100 .22 rimfire with a 6" barrel with muzzle brake and no shoulder stock. This is also known as the M-110.

NIB	Exc.	V.G.	Good	Fair	Poor
250	225	195	150	125	100

AMERICAN INTERNATIONAL

Salt Lake City, Utah

A/K/A American Research & Development

American 180 Carbine

This firearm, imported from Austria, is a semi-automatic, 16.5"-barreled carbine chambered for the .22 l.r. The sights are adjustable, and the stock is made of high-impact plastic. The unique drum magazine holds 177 rounds and is affixed to the top of the receiver. There is a select-fire version available for law enforcement agencies only and an optional laser lock sight system. This firearm was discontinued and recently has become available again from Feather Industries in Boulder, Colorado. It is now known as the SAR-180.

Exc.	V.G.	Good	Fair	Poor
675	600	525	400	275

N.P. AMES PISTOLS

Springfield, Massachusetts

Overall length- 11-5/8"; barrel length- 6"; caliber- .54. Markings: on lockplate, forward of hammer "N.P. AMES/SPRINGFIELD/MASS", on tail, either & "U S N" or "U S R" over date; on barrel, standard U.S. Navy inspection marks. N.P. Ames of Springfield, Massachusetts received a contract from the U.S. Navy in September 1842 for the delivery of 2000 single shot muzzleloading percussion pistols. All are distinguished by having a lock mechanism that lies flush with the right side of the stock. On the first 300 Ames pistols, this lock terminates in a point; the balance produced were made with locks with a rounded tail. This "box lock" had been devised by Henry Nock in England, and was adapted to the U.S. Navy for the percussion pistols they ordered from Ames and Derringer. In addition to the 2000 pistols for the Navy, the U.S. Revenue Cutter Service purchased 144 (distinguished by the "U S R" marks) for the forerunner of the U.S. Coast Guard. The latter command triple the price over the "U S N" marked pistols, while the Navy pistols with pointed tails quadruple the value.

Courtesy Milwaukee Public Museum, Milwaukee, Wisconsin.

Courtesy Milwaukee Public Museum, Milwaukee, Wisconsin.

Exc.	V.G.	Good	Fair	Poor
1200	900	750	600	450

AMES SWORD CO.

Chicopee Falls, Massachusetts

Turbiaux Le Protector

Ames Sword Co. became one of three U.S. companies that produced this unique, French palm-sqeezer pistol. The design consists of a round disk with a protruding barrel on one side and a lever on the other. The disk contains the cylinder that holds either seven 8mm rimfire or ten 6mm rimfire cartridges. The barrel protrudes between the fingers, and the lever trigger is squeezed to fire the weapon. The design was patented in 1883 and sold successfully in France into the 1890s. In 1892 Peter Finnegan bought the patents and brought them to Ames Sword. He contracted with them to produce 25,000 pistols for the Minneapolis Firearms Company. After approximately 1,500 were delivered, Finnegan declared insolvency, and after litigation, Ames secured the full patent rights. The Ames company produced Protector Revolvers until at least 1917.

(See Chicago Firearms Co. and Minneapolis Firearms Co.)

Exc.	V.G.	Good	Fair	Poor
600	525	450	350	265

ANCION & CIE

(of Liege, Belgium

See—French Military Firearms)

ANCION MARX

Liege, Belgium

This company began production in the 1860s with a variety of cheaply made pinfire revolvers. They later switched to solid-frame, centerfire, "Velo-Dog" type revolvers chambered for 5.5mm or 6.35mm. They were marketed in various countries under many different trade names. Some of the names that they will be found under are Cobalt, Extracteur, LeNovo, Lincoln, and Milady. The quality of these revolvers is quite poor; and collector interest, almost non-existent. Values do not usually vary because of trade names.

Exc.	V.G.	Good	Fair	Poor
150	125	100	65	45

ANDERSON
Anderson, Texas

Anderson Under Hammer Pistol

An unmarked, under hammer percussion pistol that was chambered for .45 caliber. It had a 5" part-round/part- octagonal barrel with an all steel, sawhandle-shaped frame. There was a flared butt with walnut grips. The finish was blued. There is very little information on this pistol, and its origin is strongly suspected but not confirmed.

Exc.	V.G.	Good	Fair	Poor
425	375	325	250	200

ANDRUS & OSBORN
Canton, Connecticut

Andrus & Osborn Under Hammer Pistol

This pistol is of the percussion type and chambered for .25 caliber. The part-round/part-octagonal barrel is 6" long and features small silver star inlays along its length. The barrel is marked "Andrus & Osborn/Canton Conn." with an eagle stamped beside it. It is marked "Cast Steel" near the breech. The grips are of walnut, and the finish is browned. Active 1863 to 1867.

Exc.	V.G.	Good	Fair	Poor
425	375	300	225	160

ANSCHUTZ
Ulm, Germany
Importer--Precision Sales International,Westfield, Massachusetts

Mark 10 Target Rifle

A single-shot, bolt-action rifle that is chambered for the .22 l.r. cartridge. It has a 26" heavy barrel with adjustable target-type sights. The finish was blued, and the walnut target stock had an adjustable palm rest. It was manufactured between 1963 and 1981.

Exc.	V.G.	Good	Fair	Poor
350	300	250	210	150

Model 1407

Similar to the Mark 10 but is furnished without sights. It was known as the "I.S.U." model. It was discontinued in 1981.

Exc.	V.G.	Good	Fair	Poor
375	325	275	235	175

Model 1408

A heavier-barrelled version of the Model 1407.

Exc.	V.G	Good	Fair	Poor
375	325	275	235	175

Model 1411

Designed specifically to be fired from the prone position.

Exc.	V.G.	Good	Fair	Poor
350	300	250	210	150

Model 1413 Match

A high-grade, competition version with a heavy target barrel that is furnished without sights. The walnut stock has an adjustable cheekpiece.

Exc.	V.G.	Good	Fair	Poor
550	500	450	400	275

Model 1418 Mannlicher

A hunting rifle with a full-length, Mannlicher- type stock made with hand-checkered walnut.

Exc.	V.G.	Good	Fair	Poor
625	575	500	450	325

Model 1418/19

A lower-priced sporter model that was formerly imported by Savage Arms.

Exc.	V.G.	Good	Fair	Poor
300	250	200	150	125

Model 184

A high-grade, bolt-action sporting rifle chambered for the .22 l.r. cartridge. It has a 21.5" barrel with a folding-leaf sight. The finish is blued with a checkered walnut, Monte Carlo stock with a Schnabel forend. It was manufactured between 1963 and 1981.

Exc.	V.G.	Good	Fair	Poor
375	335	280	220	150

Model 54 Sporter

A high-grade, bolt-action sporting rifle chambered for the .22 l.r. cartridge. It has a 24", tapered round barrel and a 5-shot detachable magazine. It features a folding leaf-type rear sight. The finish is blued with a checkered walnut, Monte Carlo stock. It was manufactured between 1963 and 1981.

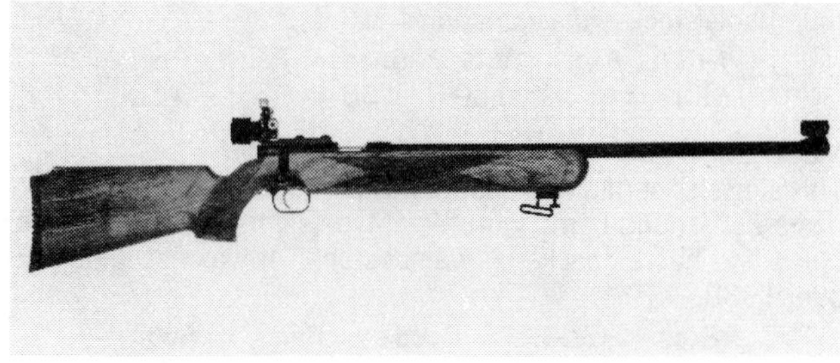

Exc.	V.G.	Good	Fair	Poor
650	575	500	350	250

Model 54M

This version is chambered for the .22 rimfire Magnum cartridge.

Exc.	V.G.	Good	Fair	Poor
700	600	525	375	275

Model 141

A bolt-action sporter chambered for the .22 l.r. cartridge. It has a 23" round barrel with a blued finish and walnut, Monte Carlo stock. It was manufactured between 1963 and 1981.

Exc.	V.G.	Good	Fair	Poor
350	300	250	200	150

Model 141M

Chambered for the .22 rimfire Magnum cartridge.

Exc.	V.G.	Good	Fair	Poor
375	325	275	225	175

Model 153

A bolt-action sporting rifle chambered for the .222 Remington cartridge. It has a 24" barrel with folding-leaf rear sight. The finish is blued with a checkered, French walnut stock featuring a rosewood forend tip and pistol grip cap. It was manufactured between 1963 and 1981.

Exc.	V.G.	Good	Fair	Poor
575	500	385	300	240

Model 153-S

This version was offered with double-set triggers.

Exc.	V.G.	Good	Fair	Poor
625	550	435	350	275

Model 64

A single shot, bolt-action rifle that is chambered for the .22 l.r. cartridge. It has a 26" round barrel and is furnished without sights. The finish is blued, and the walnut, target-type stock featured a beaver-tail forearm and adjustable buttplate. It was manufactured between 1963 and 1981.

Exc.	V.G.	Good	Fair	Poor
350	300	250	200	150

Model 64MS

This version was designed for silhouette shooting and has a 21.25" barrel, blued finish, and a target-type, walnut stock with a stippled pistol grip.

Exc.	V.G.	Good	Fair	Poor
650	600	525	400	300

Model 54.18MS

A high-grade silhouette rifle chambered for the .22 l.r. cartridge. It has a 22" barrel and a match-grade action with fully adjustable trigger. It is furnished without sights. The finish is blued with a target-type, walnut stock.

NIB	Exc.	V.G.	Good	Fair	Poor
1212	1100	950	750	475	375

Model 54.MS REP

A repeating rifle with a 5-shot, detachable magazine with a thumbhole stock with vented forearm.

NIB	Exc.	V.G.	Good	Fair	Poor
1650	1450	1150	900	675	450

Model 2000 MK

This single shot rifle was chambered for the .22 l.r. cartridge. It has a 26", round barrel with target-type sights. The finish was blued and has a checkered walnut stock. It was not imported after 1988.

Exc.	V.G.	Good	Fair	Poor
350	300	250	200	140

Model 1403D

A single shot target rifle chambered for the .22 l.r. cartridge. It has a 26" barrel and is furnished without sights. It has a fully adjustable trigger and a blued finish with a walnut, target-type stock.

NIB	Exc.	V.G.	Good	Fair	Poor
700	650	575	500	375	250

Model 1803D

A high-grade target rifle chambered for the .22 l.r. cartridge. It has a 25.5" heavy barrel with adjustable target sights. It features an adjustable trigger. The finish is blued with a light-colored wood stock with dark stippling on the pistol grip and forearm. The stock features an adjustable cheekpiece and buttplate. It was introduced in 1987.

NIB	Exc.	V.G.	Good	Fair	Poor
810	750	675	600	475	350

Model 1808ED Super

A single shot, running-bore type rifle that is chambered for the .22 l.r. cartridge. It has a 32.5" barrel furnished without sights. The finish is blued with a heavy, target-type walnut stock. It is furnished with barrel weights.

NIB	Exc.	V.G.	Good	Fair	Poor
1300	1200	1050	900	625	500

Model 1910 Super Match II

A very high-grade, single shot target rifle chambered for the .22 l.r. cartridge. It has a 27.25" barrel and is furnished with diopter-type target sights. The finish is blued with a walnut, thumbhole stock with adjustable cheekpiece and buttplate.

NIB	Exc.	V.G.	Good	Fair	Poor
2000	1800	1550	1400	1000	700

Model 1911 Prone Match

This version has a stock designed specifically for firing from the prone position.

NIB	Exc.	V.G.	Good	Fair	Poor
1600	1450	1050	800	550	450

Model 1913 Super Match

A virtually hand-built, match target rifle. It is chambered for the .22 l.r. cartridge and features a single shot action. It has adjustable, diopter-type sights on a 27.25" heavy barrel. This is a custom made gun that features every target option conceivable. The finish is blued with a fully adjustable walnut stock.

NIB	Exc.	V.G.	Good	Fair	Poor
2200	2000	1400	1000	700	600

Model 1827B Biathlon

A repeating, bolt-action target rifle chambered for the .22 l.r. cartridge. It is specially designed for the biathlon competition. Production is quite limited and on a custom basis.

NIB	Exc.	V.G.	Good	Fair	Poor
1750	1500	1050	800	550	475

Model 1433D

This is a centerfire version of the Model 54 target rifle chambered for the .22 Hornet. It is a special-order item and features a set trigger and a 4-round, detachable magazine. The finish was blued with a full-length, Mannlicher stock. It was discontinued in 1986.

Exc.	V.G.	Good	Fair	Poor
1000	850	750	550	375

Bavarian 1700

A classic-style sporting rifle chambered for the .22 l.r., .22 rimfire Magnum., .22 Hornet, and the .222 Remington cartridges. It features a 24" barrel with adjustable sights. It has a detachable magazine and a blued finish with a checkered, walnut, European-style stock. It was introduced in 1988.

NIB	Exc.	V.G.	Good	Fair	Poor
2000	850	725	525	450	335

Model 520/61

A blowback-operated, semi-automatic rifle that is chambered for the .22 l.r. cartridge. It has a 24" barrel and a 10-round, detachable magazine. The finish is blued with a checkered walnut stock. This rifle was discontinued in 1983.

Exc.	V.G.	Good	Fair	Poor
275	200	155	130	100

Model 525 Sporter

This semi-automatic rifle was chambered for the .22 l.r. cartridge. It has a 24" barrel with adjustable sights and a 10-round, detachable magazine. The finish is blued with a checkered, Monte Carlo-type stock. It was introduced in 1984. A carbine version with a 20" barrel was originally offered but was discontinued in 1986.

NIB	Exc.	V.G.	Good	Fair	Poor
435	400	350	300	195	145

Exemplar

A bolt-action pistol that is built on the Model 64 Match Action. It is chambered for the .22 l.r. cartridge and has a 10" barrel with adjustable sights and a 5-shot, detachable magazine. It features an adjustable, two-stage trigger with the receiver grooved for attaching a scope. The walnut stock and forend are stippled. It was introduced in 1987.

NIB	Exc.	V.G.	Good	Fair	Poor
400	365	275	210	185	150

Exemplar XIV

Similar to the standard Exemplar with a 14" barrel. It was introduced in 1988.

NIB	Exc.	V.G.	Good	Fair	Poor
405	370	280	215	190	150

Exemplar Hornet

Chambered for the .22 Hornet cartridge. It was introduced in 1988.

NIB	Exc.	V.G.	Good	Fair	Poor
750	675	580	500	400	275

ANTI GARROTTER

English

Percussion belt pistol, marked Balls Pat.. steel oval is 7 inches long and the barrel protrudes 1 1/2 inches, approximately 45 caliber. A cord runs from the lock up and through the sleeve and is fired by pulling the cord.

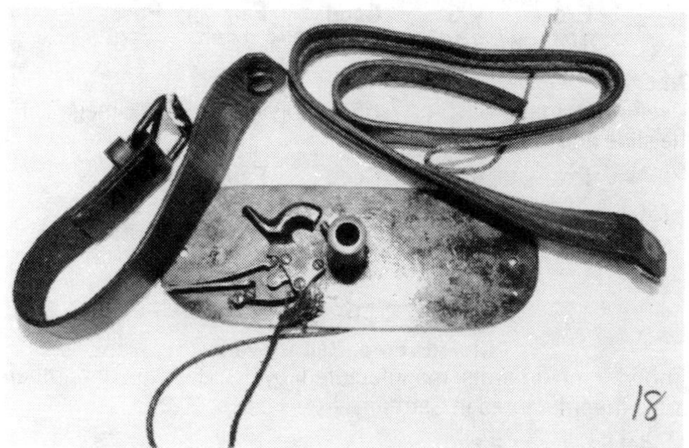

Exc.	V.G.	Good	Fair	Poor
5500	4500	1500	800	300

APACHE

Eibar, Spain

SEE--Ojanguren Y Vidosa

APALOZO HERMANOS

Zumorraga, Spain

Spanish manufacturer from approximately 1920 to 1935. Their trademark, a dove-like bird is normally found impressed into the grips.

Apaloza

Copy of a Colt Police Positive Revolver.

Exc.	V.G.	Good	Fair	Poor
150	125	100	65	45

Paramount

Copy of the Model 1906 Browning chambered for the 6.35mm. Standard marking, "Paramount Cal. .25" normally found on the slide.

Exc.	V.G.	Good	Fair	Poor
150	125	100	65	45

Triomphe

The slide is inscribed "Pistolet Automatique Triomphe Acier Comprime."

Exc.	V.G.	Good	Fair	Poor
150	125	100	65	45

ARIZAGA, G.

Eibar, Spain

Spanish manufacturer during the first half of the Twentieth Century.

Arizaga

7.65mm semi-automatic pistol.

Exc.	V.G.	Good	Fair	Poor
150	125	100	65	45

Mondial

Resembling a Savage semi-automatic pistol externally, this model is based on John M. Browning's design. Examples are known with and without a grip safety. The grips are stamped with an owl in a circle trademark and "Mondial".

Exc.	V.G.	Good	Fair	Poor
175	140	110	75	50

Pinkerton

Arizaga's standard model known to exist with a cartridge counter. Slide is marked "Pinkerton Automatic 6.35"

Exc.	V.G.	Good	Fair	Poor
135	110	80	55	35

Warwinck

As above but chambered for 7.65mm cartridges, the slide is marked "Automatic Pistol 7.65 Warwinck".

Exc.	V.G.	Good	Fair	Poor
175	140	110	75	50

ARIZMENDI

Eibar, Spain

Originally founded in the 1890s, the company was reformed in 1914 and manufactured semi-automatic pistols.

Singer

Chambered for both the 6.35mm and 7.65mm. Manufactured from 1913 onward. Standard markings include the trademark "AG" with a crown and crescent on the slide and frame.

Exc.	V.G.	Good	Fair	Poor
150	125	100	65	45

Teuf - Teuf

A 7.65mm semi-automatic pistol marked "Automatic Teuf Teuf Pistol 7.65mm."

Exc.	V.G.	Good	Fair	Poor
150	125	100	65	45

Walman

Chambered for 6.35, 7.65, and 9mm short. This pistol is normally marked "American Automatic Pistol Walman Patent".

Exc.	V.G.	Good	Fair	Poor
150	125	100	65	45

Arizmendi

Solid-frame, folding-trigger revolver chambered for 7.65mm or .32 caliber revolver. Normal markings are the trademark "FA" and a circled five pointed star.

Exc.	V.G.	Good	Fair	Poor
140	110	90	50	25

Boltun

The 6.35mm version is marked "Automatic Pistol Boltun Patent", while the 7.65mm model is marked "Automatic Pistol Boltun Patent Marca Registrada 7375 Cal. 7.65."

Exc.	V.G.	Good	Fair	Poor
150	125	100	65	45

Puppy

A variation of the "Velo-Dog" revolver with the barrel stamped "Puppy" and the frame bearing the "FA" trademark.

Exc.	V.G.	Good	Fair	Poor
140	110	80	50	35

Pistolet Automatique

Normal markings include the "FA" trademark.

Exc.	V.G.	Good	Fair	Poor
150	125	100	65	45

Kaba Spezial

This pistol is normally marked "Pistol Automatique Kaba Spezial," with the "Kaba" cast into the grips.

Exc.	V.G.	Good	Fair	Poor
150	125	100	65	45

Roland

Chambered for 6.35 and 7.65mm cartridges, this model was manufactured during the 1920s.

Exc.	V.G.	Good	Fair	Poor
150	125	100	65	45

Ydeal
Patterned after the Model 1906 Browning pistol. It is chambered for the 6.35mm or 7.65mm cartridges. Standard markings are "Pistolet Automatique Ydeal" and "Ydeal" cast in the grips.

Exc.	V.G.	Good	Fair	Poor
150	125	100	65	45

ARIZMENDI ZULAICA
Eibar, Spain

Cebra
A semi-automatic 7.65mm pistol, the slide marked "Pistolet Automatique Cebra Zulaica Eibar," together with the letters "AZ" in an oval.

Exc.	V.G.	Good	Fair	Poor
150	125	100	65	40

Cebra Revolver
Copy of a Colt Police Positive revolver marked "Made in Spain" with the word "Cebra" cast in the grips.

Exc.	V.G.	Good	Fair	Poor
140	110	80	50	25

ARMALITE, INC.
Costa Mesa, California

AR-17 Shotgun
A gas-operated semi-automatic 12 gauge shotgun, with a 24" barrel and interchangeable choke tubes. The receiver and the barrel are made of an aluminum alloy, with an anodized black or gold finish. The stock and forearm are of plastic. Approximately 2,000 were manufactured during 1964 and 1965.

Exc.	V.G.	Good	Fair	Poor
550	475	400	300	225

AR-7 Explorer Rifle
A .22 l.r. semi-auto carbine with a 16 inch barrel. The receiver and barrel are partially made of an alloy. The most noteworthy feature of this model is that it can be disassembled and the component parts stored in the plastic stock. Manufactured between 1959 and 1973.

Exc.	V.G.	Good	Fair	Poor
100	85	70	60	45

AR-7 Custom
As above with a walnut cheekpiece stock, manufactured between 1964 and 1970.

Exc.	V.G.	Good	Fair	Poor
160	135	100	80	60

AR-180
A gas-operated, semi-automatic rifle chambered for the .223 or 5.56mm cartridge. The AR-180 is the civilian version of the AR-18 which is fully automatic. It is a simple and efficient rifle that was tested by various governments and found to have potential. This rifle was also manufactured by Howa Machinery Ltd. and Sterling Armament Co. of England.

NIB	Exc.	V.G.	Good	Fair	Poor
750	700	650	550	450	300

ARMAS DE FUEGO
Guernica, Spain

Believed to have been in business from 1920 to 1924.

Alkar
A 6.35mm copy of the Model 1906 Browning pistol distinguishable by eight slots cut into the left side of the grip.

Exc.	V.G.	Good	Fair	Poor
175	145	100	75	50

ARMERO ESPECIALISTAS
Eibar, Spain

Alfa
"Alfa" was a trademark given a number of revolvers based upon both Colt and Smith & Wesson designs in calibers ranging from .22 to .44.

Exc.	V.G.	Good	Fair	Poor
175	145	110	75	50

Omega
A semi-automatic 6.35 or 7.65mm pistol marked "Omega" on the slide and grips.

Exc.	V.G.	Good	Fair	Poor
175	145	110	75	50

ARMES DE CHASSE
Chadds Ford, Pennsylvania

Importer of firearms manufactured by P. Beretta, and other arms manufactured in Germany.

Model EJ
An over/under Anson & Deeley action 12 gauge shotgun with double triggers as well as automatic ejectors. Blued barrels, silver finished receiver and checkered walnut stock. Manufactured in Germany and introduced in 1989.

NIB	Exc.	V.G.	Good	Fair	Poor
1000	950	800	650	500	425

Model EU
As above with a ventilated-rib barrel and a nonselective single trigger. Introduced in 1989.

NIB	Exc.	V.G.	Good	Fair	Poor
1200	1150	1000	850	600	475

Highlander
A side-by-side double-barrel 20 gauge shotgun with a boxlock action. Available in various barrel lengths and choke combinations, with double triggers and manual extractors. Blued with a checkered walnut stock. Manufactured in Italy and introduced in 1989.

NIB	Exc.	V.G.	Good	Fair	Poor
675	625	500	375	300	225

Chesapeake
As above but chambered for the 3.5", 12 gauge shell. The bores are chrome-lined and suitable for steel shot. Fitted with automatic ejectors and double triggers. Manufactured in Italy, it was introduced in 1989.

NIB	Exc.	V.G.	Good	Fair	Poor
775	725	600	475	400	300

Balmoral
English style straight grip 12, 16, or 20 gauge boxlock shotgun, fitted with false sideplates. Receiver and sideplates case hardened, the barrels blued. Fitted with a single trigger and automatic ejectors. Manufactured in Italy and introduced in 1989.

NIB	Exc.	V.G.	Good	Fair	Poor
800	725	625	500	425	325

Model 70E
A 12, 16, or 20 gauge side-by-side shotgun fitted with 27" or 28" barrels. The action based upon the Anson & Deeley design with a Greener crossbolt. The receiver is casehardened, barrels are blued and the walnut stock checkered. Manufactured in Germany and introduced in 1989.

NIB	Exc.	V.G.	Good	Fair	Poor
815	775	625	500	425	350

Model 74E
As above with gamescene engraving and more fully figured walnut stock. Introduced in 1989.

NIB	Exc.	V.G.	Good	Fair	Poor
1000	925	775	625	500	400

Model 76E
As above with engraved false sideplates and fully figured walnut stock. Introduced in 1989.

NIB	Exc.	V.G.	Good	Fair	Poor
1500	1450	1075	900	750	500

ARMINEX LTD.
Scottsdale, Arizona

Tri-Fire
A semi-automatic pistol chambered for 9mm, .38 Super or .45 ACP cartridges. Available with conversion units that add approximately $130 if in excellent condition. Fitted with 5", 6", or 7" stainless-steel barrels. Presentation cases were available at an extra cost of $48. Approximately 250 were manufactured from 1981 to 1985.

Exc.	V.G.	Good	Fair	Poor
400	350	275	225	175

Target Model
As above with a 6" or 7" barrel.

Exc.	V.G.	Good	Fair	Poor
450	400	325	275	200

ARMINIUS
SEE—Friedrich Pickert
Zella-Mehlis, Germany
Hermann Weirauch
Melrichstadt, Germany
F.I.E.
Hialeah, Florida

ARMITAGE INTERNATIONAL, LTD.
Seneca, South Carolina

Scarab Skorpion
A blowback-operated, semi-automatic pistol, patterned after the Czechoslovakian Scorpion submachine gun. Chambered for the 9mm cartridge with a 4.6" barrel having military-type sights. Fitted with a 32-round, detachable box magazine. The standard finish is matte black and the grips are of plastic.

NIB	Exc.	V.G.	Good	Fair	Poor
285	250	200	150	125	95

ARMS CORPORATION OF THE PHILIPPINES
Armscor Precision
Foster City, California

Armscor Precision is an importer of a variety of firearms made in the Philippines.

Shotguns

Model 30D
A slide-action 12 gauge shotgun fitted with either 28"or 30" barrels with various chokes. The magazine holds 6 cartridges.

NIB	Exc.	V.G.	Good	Fair	Poor
225	200	165	135	100	75

Model 30DG
As above with a 20" barrel, fitted with rifle sights and an 8-shot magazine.

NIB	Exc.	V.G.	Good	Fair	Poor
225	200	165	135	100	75

Model 30R
As above with shotgun bead sights.

NIB	Exc.	V.G.	Good	Fair	Poor
225	200	165	135	100	75

Model 30RP
As above with an auxiliary black composition pistol-grip and an 18.5" barrel.

NIB	Exc.	V.G.	Good	Fair	Poor
225	200	165	135	100	75

Rifles

Model M14P
A .22 caliber bolt-action rifle fitted with a 23" barrel, open sights, and a 5-shot detachable magazine. Stock of mahogany.

NIB	Exc.	V.G.	Good	Fair	Poor
110	95	75	50	35	25

Model M14D
As above with an adjustable rear sight and checkered stock. Manufactured in 1987 only.

NIB	Exc.	V.G.	Good	Fair	Poor
120	100	85	65	45	25

Model M1500
A .22 Magnum bolt-action rifle fitted with a 21.5" barrel, open sights, 5-shot magazine and checkered mahogany stock.

NIB	Exc.	V.G.	Good	Fair	Poor
145	120	100	80	60	35

Model M1600
A .22 caliber copy of the U.S.M16 rifle having an 18" barrel and a detachable 15-round magazine.

NIB	Exc.	V.G.	Good	Fair	Poor
125	100	80	60	40	25

Model M1600R
As above with a stainless-steel collapsible stock and shrouded barrel.

NIB	Exc.	V.G.	Good	Fair	Poor
135	110	90	70	50	35

Model M1600C
As above with a 20" barrel and fiberglass stock.

NIB	Exc.	V.G.	Good	Fair	Poor
135	110	90	70	50	35

Model M1600W
As above with a mahogany stock.

NIB	Exc.	V.G.	Good	Fair	Poor
135	110	90	70	50	35

Model M1800
A .22 Hornet bolt-action rifle fitted with a 23" barrel, 5-shot magazine and a mahogany Monte Carlo style stock.

Exc.	V.G.	Good	Fair	Poor
150	125	100	75	50

Model M20P
A .22 caliber 15-shot semi-automatic rifle fitted with a 20.75" barrel, open sights and plain mahogany stock.

NIB	Exc.	V.G.	Good	Fair	Poor
95	80	65	50	35	25

Model M2000
As above with adjustable sights and a checkered stock.

Exc.	V.G.	Good	Fair	Poor
80	60	50	35	25

Model MAK22S
A .22 caliber semi-automatic rifle resembling the Russian AKA-47. Barrel length of 18.5", 15-round magazine and mahogany stock.

NIB	Exc.	V.G.	Good	Fair	Poor
175	150	125	100	75	50

Model MAK22F

As above with a folding stock.

NIB	Exc.	V.G.	Good	Fair	Poor
200	175	145	110	85	65

Handguns

Model M100

A double-action, swingout-cylinder revolver chambered for .22, .22 Magnum, and the .38 Special cartridges. Having a 4" ventilated-rib barrel. Six-shot cylinder and adjustable sights. Blued with checkered mahogany grips.

NIB	Exc.	V.G.	Good	Fair	Poor
200	175	150	110	80	50

ARMSCORP OF AMERICA

Baltimore, Maryland

Rifles

M-14R

A civilian version of the U.S.M14 rifle manufactured from new and surplus parts. Introduced in 1986.

M-14 National Match

As above but built to A.M.T.U. MIL specifications. Introduced in 1987.

FAL

A civilian version of the FN FAL rifle assembled from new and Argentine surplus parts. Introduced in 1987.

M36 Israeli Sniper Rifle

A specialized weapon built upon the Armscor M-14 receiver in the Bullpup style. Barrel length 22" and of free floating design for accuracy, chambered for the .308 cartridge. There is an integral flash suppressor and a bipod. It is furnished with a 20-shot detachable magazine. This civilian version was first offered for sale in 1989.

Expert Model

A .22 caliber semi-automatic rifle with a 21" barrel, open sights, and 10-shot magazine. Introduced in 1989.

NIB	Exc.	V.G.	Good	Fair	Poor
225	200	175	145	100	80

Handguns

Hi-Power

An Argentine-made version of the Browning semi-automatic pistol chambered for 9mm with a 4.75" barrel. Matte finished with checkered synthetic grips. Introduced in 1989.

NIB	Exc.	V.G.	Good	Fair	Poor
425	385	325	280	245	200

Detective HP - Compact

As above with a 3.5" barrel.

NIB	Exc.	V.G.	Good	Fair	Poor
475	425	350	310	275	225

SD 9

An Israeli-made 9mm double-action semi-automatic pistol with a 3" barrel. Assembled extensively from sheet-metal stampings. Loaded chamber indicator and 6-round magazine. This model is also known as the Sirkus, SD9 manufactured by Sirkus Industries in Israel. Introduced in 1989.

NIB	Exc.	V.G.	Good	Fair	Poor
350	300	260	210	165	120

P 22

A copy of the Colt Woodsman .22 caliber semi-automatic pistol available with either 4" or 6" barrels and a 10 shot magazine. Finish blued, grips of checkered hardwood. Introduced in 1989.

NIB	Exc.	V.G.	Good	Fair	Poor
200	175	135	100	75	50

AROSTEGUI

Eibar, Spain

Azul, Royal

This semi-automatic pistol is a first-rate copy of the Mauser Model C96, and is very collectible.

Exc.	V.G.	Good	Fair	Poor
1100	950	800	675	500

E.A.

A 6.35mm semi-automatic pistol copied after the Model 1906 Browning. The frame is marked with the letters "EA" in a circle and a retriever is molded in the grips.

Exc.	V.G.	Good	Fair	Poor
175	150	100	75	50

Velo-Dog

A folding trigger 5.5mm or 6.35mm revolver bearing the trademark "EA" on the grips.

Exc.	V.G.	Good	Fair	Poor
125	100	75	50	30

ARRIETA S.L. ELQOLBAR

Spain

Importer—Morton's Ltd.

Lexington, Kentucky

This company produces a wide variety of double-barrel shotguns in a price range from $450 to above $14,000. It is recommended that highly engraved examples as well as small bore arms be individually appraised.

490 Eder

A double barrel boxlock shotgun with double triggers and extractors. Discontinued in 1986.

Exc.	V.G.	Good	Fair	Poor
460	420	335	275	200

500 Titan

A Holland & Holland-style sidelock double-barrel shotgun with French casehardened and engraved locks. Double triggers on extractors. No longer imported after 1986.

Exc.	V.G.	Good	Fair	Poor
560	520	435	375	300

501 Palomara

As above, but more finely finished. Discontinued in 1986.

Exc.	V.G.	Good	Fair	Poor
700	625	550	425	350

505 Alaska

As above, but more intricately engraved. Discontinued in 1986.

Exc.	V.G.	Good	Fair	Poor
800	775	625	500	400

510 Montana

A Holland & Holland-style sidelock double barrel shotgun with the internal parts gold plated.

NIB	Exc.	V.G.	Good	Fair	Poor
2200	2000	1750	1250	900	600

550 Field

As above, without the internal parts being gold plated.

NIB	Exc.	V.G.	Good	Fair	Poor
2200	2000	1750	1250	900	600

557 Standard

As above, but more finely finished.

NIB	Exc.	V.G.	Good	Fair	Poor
2600	2400	2000	1500	1100	675

558 Patria

As above, but more finely finished.

NIB	Exc.	V.G.	Good	Fair	Poor
2650	2450	2050	1550	1150	700

560 Cumbre

As above, but featuring very intricate engraving.

NIB	Exc.	V.G.	Good	Fair	Poor
2800	2600	2200	1700	1200	800

570 Lieja

NIB	Exc.	V.G.	Good	Fair	Poor
3000	2800	2400	1800	1300	850

575 Sport

NIB	Exc.	V.G.	Good	Fair	Poor
3000	2800	2400	1800	1300	850

578 Victoria

This model is engraved in the English manner with floral bouquets.

NIB	Exc.	V.G.	Good	Fair	Poor
3300	3000	2500	1900	1375	900

585 Liria

As above, but more finely finished.

NIB	Exc.	V.G.	Good	Fair	Poor
3800	3500	3000	2400	1600	1100

588 Cima

NIB	Exc.	V.G.	Good	Fair	Poor
3800	3500	3000	2400	1600	1100

590 Regina

NIB	Exc.	V.G.	Good	Fair	Poor
4000	3500	3000	2500	1750	1100

595 Principe

As above, but engraved with relief-cut hunting scenes.

NIB	Exc.	V.G.	Good	Fair	Poor
6000	5500	4500	3750	2500	1750

600 Imperial

This double-barrel shotgun has a self-opening action.

NIB	Exc.	V.G.	Good	Fair	Poor
5300	4750	4000	3250	2000	1500

601 Tiro

As above, but nickel-plated.

NIB	Exc.	V.G.	Good	Fair	Poor
6500	6000	5000	3950	2750	1950

801

A detachable sidelock, self-opening action, double-barrel shotgun engraved in the manner of Churchill.

NIB	Exc.	V.G.	Good	Fair	Poor
9000	8000	7200	5000	3250	2400

802

As above, with Holland & Holland-style engraving.

NIB	Exc.	V.G.	Good	Fair	Poor
9000	8000	7200	5000	3250	2400

803

As above, with Purdey-style engraving.

NIB	Exc.	V.G.	Good	Fair	Poor
6000	5500	4500	3750	2500	1750

875

A custom manufactured sidelock, double-barrel shotgun built solely to the customer's specifications.

NIB	Exc.	V.G.	Good	Fair	Poor
14000	12000	8500	6750	5500	4500

ARRIZABALAGA

Eibar, Spain

Arrizabalaga

A 7.65mm semi-automatic pistol with a 9-shot magazine and a lanyard ring fitted to the butt.

Exc.	V.G.	Good	Fair	Poor
150	125	100	65	40

Campeon

A 6.35mm or 7.65mm semi-automatic pistol with the slide marked "Campeon Patent 1919" and the plastic grips "Campeon".

Exc.	V.G.	Good	Fair	Poor
150	125	100	65	40

Sharpshooter

A 6.35mm, 7.65mm or 9mm Corto (short) semi-automatic pistol fitted with a cocking lever. The barrel tips up for cleaning or when using the pistol as a single shot.

Exc.	V.G.	Good	Fair	Poor
300	275	200	160	125

JoLoAr

As above, but chambered for either the 9mm Bergman Bayard or .45ACP cartridges.

Note: The .45 caliber version is worth approximately 40% more than the values listed below.

Exc.	V.G.	Good	Fair	Poor
300	275	200	160	125

ASCASO

Cataluna, Spain

A copy of the Astra Model 400. The barrel marked "F. Ascaso Tarrassa" in an oval.

Exc.	V.G.	Good	Fair	Poor
300	250	200	150	100

ASHEVILLE ARMORY

Asheville, North Carolina

Enfield Type Rifle

A .58 caliber percussion rifle with a 32.5" barrel and full stock secured by two iron barrel bands. Finished in the white, brass triggerguard and buttplate with a walnut stock. The lockplate is marked "Asheville, N.C." Approximately 300 were made in 1862 and 1863. Prospective purchasers are advised to secure a qualified appraisal prior to acquisition.

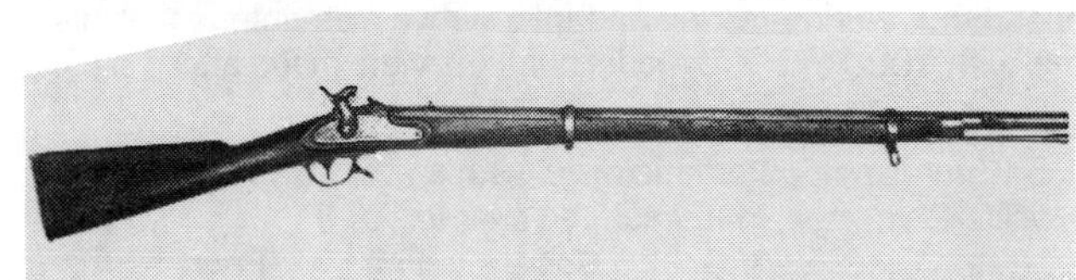

Courtesy Milwaukee Public Museum, Milwaukee, Wisconsin.

Exc.	V.G.	Good	Fair	Poor
6500	5000	3500	2000	1500

PETER & WILLIAM ASHTON

Middletown, Connecticut

Ashton Under Hammer Pistol

A .28 to .38 caliber single shot percussion revolver with 4" or 5" half-octagonal barrels marked "P.H. Ashton" or "W. Ashton." Blued or browned with walnut grips. Active 1850s.

Exc.	V.G.	Good	Fair	Poor
550	450	375	275	200

H. ASTON/H. ASTON & CO. PISTOLS

Middleton, Connecticut

Overall length- 14"; barrel length- 8- 1/12"; caliber- .54. Markings: on lockplate, forward of hammer "U S/H. ASTON" or "U S/H. ASTON & CO.," on tail "MIDDTN/CONN/(date)"; on barrel, standard government inspection marks. Henry Aston of Middleton, Connecticut received a contract from the U.S. War Department in February 1845 for 30,000 single shot percussion pistols. These were delivered between 1846 and 1852, after which Ira N. Johnston continued production under a separate contract. Three thousand of these pistols were purchased for Navy usage and many of these were subsequently marked with a small anchor on the barrel near the breech. These Navy purchases will command a slight premium.

Courtesy Milwaukee Public Museum, Milwaukee, Wisconsin.

Exc.	V.G.	Good	Fair	Poor
1250	1100	900	600	400

ASTRA-UNCETA SA

Guernica, Spain

Astra is a brand name placed on guns built by Esperanza y Unceta and then Unceta y Cia. This Spanish company has now incorporated its trade name into its corporate name and is now know as Astra-Unceta SA. The firm under the direction of Don Pedron Unceta and Don Juan Esperanza began business in Eibar on July 17, 1908 and moved to Guernica in 1913. The Astra trademark was adopted on November 25, 1914. Esperanza began production of the Spanish army's Campo Giro pistol in 1913. The Model 1921 was marketed commercially as the Astra 400. After the Spanish Civil War Uncerta was one of only four handgun companies permitted to resume manufacturing operations. An interesting and informative side-note is that pistols with 1000 to 5000 model numbers were made after 1945.

Victoria

A 6.36mm semi-automatic pistol with a 2.5" barrel. Blued with black plastic grips. Manufactured prior to 1913.

Exc.	V.G.	Good	Fair	Poor
300	250	200	150	100

Astra 1911

As above, renamed in November of 1914 and chambered additionally for the 7.65mm cartridge.

Exc.	V.G.	Good	Fair	Poor
250	200	175	100	75

Astra 1924

A 6.35mm semi-automatic pistol with a 2.5" barrel. The slide marked "Esperanza y Unceta Guernica Spain Astra Cal 6.35 .25." Blued with black plastic grips.

Exc.	V.G.	Good	Fair	Poor
225	175	125	100	75

Astra 100

A different tradename for the Model 1911 in 7.65mm caliber.

Exc.	V.G.	Good	Fair	Poor
275	225	200	150	100

Astra 200

A 6.35mm semi-automatic pistol with a 2.5" barrel and 6-shot magazine fitted with a grip safety. Also known as the "Firecat" in the United States. Manufactured from 1920 to 1966.

Exc.	V.G.	Good	Fair	Poor
250	200	175	100	75

Astra 400 or Model 1921

A 9x23 Bergman caliber semi-automatic pistol with a 6" barrel. Blued with black plastic grips. This model was adopted for use by the Spanish Army. Approximately 106,000 were made prior to 1946.

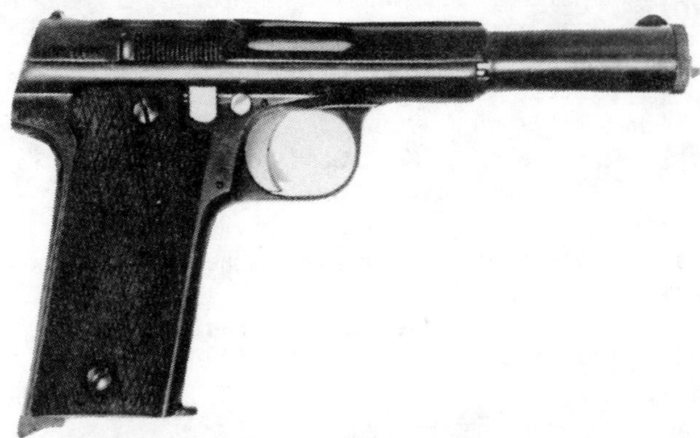

Exc.	V.G.	Good	Fair	Poor
200	150	100	75	40

Astra 300

As above, in 7.65mm or 9mm short. Those used during World War II by German forces bear Waffenamt marks. Approximately 171,000 were manufactured prior to 1947.
Nazi-Proofed—Add 25%.

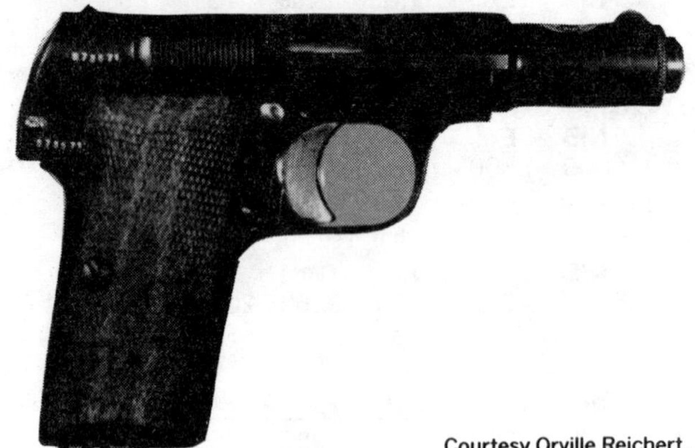

Courtesy Orville Reichert.

Exc.	V.G.	Good	Fair	Poor
325	275	225	175	100

Astra 600

Similar to the Model 400, but in 9mm Parabellum. In 1943 and 1944 approximately 10,500 were manufactured. A further 49,000 were made in 1946 and commercially sold.

Exc.	V.G.	Good	Fair	Poor
300	250	200	150	100

Astra 700

The Model 400 in 7.65mm caliber. Approximately 4,000 were made in 1926.

Exc.	V.G.	Good	Fair	Poor
500	450	400	300	200

Astra 800
Similar to the Model 600 with an external hammer and loaded chamber indicator. Blued with plastic grips having the tradename "Condor" cast in them. Approximately 11,400 were made from 1958 to 1969.

Exc.	V.G.	Good	Fair	Poor
1000	850	750	500	400

Astra 900
A copy of the Mauser Model C96 semi-automatic pistol. Blued with walnut grips.

Exc.	V.G.	Good	Fair	Poor
2000	1750	1250	750	500

Astra 1000
A post-war version of the Model 200 with a 4" barrel and 12-shot magazine.

Exc.	V.G.	Good	Fair	Poor
500	450	400	300	200

Astra 2000
As above, in .22 or 6.35mm caliber without a grip safety and with an external hammer. Blued with plastic grips.

Exc.	V.G.	Good	Fair	Poor
300	250	200	150	100

Astra 3000
The Model 300 in 7.65mm or 9mm short with a 6- or 7-shot magazine and loaded chamber indicator. Manufactured from 1948 to 1956.

Exc.	V.G.	Good	Fair	Poor
350	300	250	200	150

Astra 4000
As above, with an external hammer and also chambered in .22 caliber. Blued with plastic grips.

Exc.	V.G.	Good	Fair	Poor
250	225	200	150	100

Astra 5000
A .22, 7.65mm or 9mm short semi-automatic pistol(resembling a Walther PP Pistol) with a 3.5" barrel. Blued, chrome-plated or stainless-steel with plastic grips. Also available with a 6" barrel as a sport model. Introduced in 1965.

Exc.	V.G.	Good	Fair	Poor
300	250	200	150	100

Astra 7000
An enlarged version of the Model 2000 in .22 caliber.

Exc.	V.G.	Good	Fair	Poor
275	250	225	150	100

Constable A-60
A .380 caliber double-action semi-automatic pistol with a 3.5" barrel, adjustable sights and 13-shot magazine. Blued with plastic grips. Introduced in 1986.

NIB	Exc.	V.G.	Good	Fair	Poor
300	250	200	150	100	75

Astra A-80
A .38 Super, 9mm or .45 caliber double-action semi-automatic pistol with a 3.75" barrel and either a 9- or 15-shot magazine depending upon the caliber. Blued or chrome-plated with plastic grips. Introduced in 1982.

NIB	Exc.	V.G.	Good	Fair	Poor
400	350	300	250	200	150

Astra A-90
As above, in 9mm or .45 caliber only. Introduced in 1986.

NIB	Exc.	V.G.	Good	Fair	Poor
400	350	300	250	200	150

Astra Cadix
A .22 or .38 Special double-action swing-out cylinder revolver with a 4" or 6" barrel and either 9- shot or 5-shot cylinder. Blued with plastic grips. Manufactured from 1960 to 1968.

Exc.	V.G.	Good	Fair	Poor
175	150	125	90	70

.357 D/A Revolver
As above, in .357 Magnum caliber with a 3", 4" 6" or 8.5" barrel, adjustable sights and 6-shot cylinder. Blued or stainless-steel with walnut grips. Manufactured from 1972 to 1988.
Stainless-Steel—Add 10%.

Exc.	V.G.	Good	Fair	Poor
250	225	200	150	100

.44/.45 D/A Revolver
As above, in .41 Magnum, .44 Magnum or .45 ACP caliber with 6" or 8.5" barrels and a 6-shot cylinder. Blued or stainless-steel with walnut grips. Manufactured from 1980 to 1987.
Stainless-Steel—Add 25%.

Exc.	V.G.	Good	Fair	Poor
350	300	250	200	150

Terminator
As above, in .44 Special or .44 Magnum with a 2.75" barrel, adjustable sights and 6-shot cylinder. Blued or stainless-steel with rubber grips.
Stainless-Steel Version—Add 10%.

Exc.	V.G.	Good	Fair	Poor
350	300	250	200	150

Convertible Revolver
Similar to the .357 D/A revolver but accompanied by a cylinder chambered for 9mm cartridges. Barrel length 3". Blued with walnut grips. Introduced in 1986.

Exc.	V.G.	Good	Fair	Poor
300	250	200	150	100

CURRENTLY IMPORTED PISTOLS
Importer-European American Armory
Hialeah, FL

Model A-100

This semi-automatic service pistol is chambered for the 9mm Parabellum, .40S&W, or .45 ACP cartridges. The trigger action is double action for the first shot single action for follow-up shots. Equipped with a decocking lever. The barrel is 3.8" long and the overall length is 7.5". Magazine capacity for the 9mm is 17 rounds, .40S&W is 13 rounds, while the .45 holds 9 rounds. A blue or nickel finish is standard. Weight is approximately 34 oz.

NIB	Exc.	V.G.	Good	Fair	Poor
400	350	300	250	200	100

NOTE: Add $35 for nickel finish.

Model A-70

This is a light weight semi-automatic pistol chambered for the 9mm cartridge or .40S&W cartridge. It is fitted with 3-dot combat sights. The barrel is 3.5" long and the magazine capacity is 8 rounds for 9mm and 7 rounds for the .40S&W. Black plastic grips and blue finish are standard. Weight is 29 oz.

NIB	Exc.	V.G.	Good	Fair	Poor
325	275	225	175	150	100

NOTE: Add $35 for nickel finish.

Model A-75

Introduced in 1993 this model features all of the standard features of the Model 70 plus selective double or single trigger action and decocking lever. Offered in blue or nickel finish.

NIB	Exc.	V.G.	Good	Fair	Poor
375	325	250	200	150	100

NOTE: Add $35 for nickel finish.

AUER, B.

Louisville, Kentucky

Auer Pocket Pistol

A .60 caliber percussion pocket pistol with a 4" octagonal barrel and a long tang extending well back along the grip. Browned, silver furniture and a checkered walnut stock. The lock is marked "B. Auer". Produced during the 1850s.

Exc.	V.G.	Good	Fair	Poor
1750	1500	700	500	450

AUGUSTA MACHINE WORKS

Augusta, Georgia

1851 Colt Navy Copy

A .36 caliber percussion revolver with an 8" barrel and 6-shot cylinder. Unmarked except for serial numbers with either 6 or 12 stop cylinder slots. Blued with walnut grips. Prospective purchasers are advised to secure a qualified appraisal prior to acquisition.

Exc.	V.G.	Good	Fair	Poor
7500	6500	4500	3250	2000

AUSTRALIAN AUTOMATIC ARMS LTD.

Tasmania, Australia

Importer—North American Sales International, Inc.

Midland, Texas

SAR

A 5.56mm semi-automatic rifle with a 16.25" or 20" barrel, 5-shot or 20-shot magazine, black plastic stock and forend. Imported from 1986 to 1989.

SAP

A 10.5" barrelled pistol version of the above. Imported from 1986 to 1989.

SP

A sporting rifle version of the SAR, fitted with a wood stock and 5-shot magazine. Introduced in 1989.

AUSTRIAN MILITARY FIREARMS

The end of the Napoleonic Wars found the Army of the Austria-Hungarian Empire armed with a variety of flintlock firearms. The foot troops carried either the M1798 or the M1807 musket or the M1807 yager rifle. The mounted forces were armed with either the M1798 dragoon carbine, the M1798 Hussar carbine, the M1798 rifled cavalry carbine, the M1781 Cuirassier musketoon, and the M1798 pistol. In 1828 a new flintlock musket superseded the M1798 pattern, only to be modified again in 1835. In the latter years, however, the Austrian military also began experimenting with a variation of the percussion system invented by Giuseppe Console, utilizing a small elongated copper cylinder filled with fulminate. In 1840, the flintlock muskets adopted in 1835 were adapted to a variation of this percussion system as modified by Baron von Augustin. This system was made army-wide in 1842 with the adoption of a new musket and yager rifle with locks specifically manufactured for the Augustin tubelocks. In 1849, a new rifle replaced the M1842 pattern; both of these rifles were based on the Devilgne chambered breech. In 1850, a cavalry carbine and a horse pistol were added to the tubelock series. All of these arms were either .69 or .71 caliber. The tubelock, however, was shortlived; in 1854, Austria abandoned the tubelock system in favor of standard percussion cap then widely used by the armies of Europe. At the same time it adopted a new smaller caliber (.54) which it applied to the new M1854 rifle-musket and the M1855 yager rifle. A horse pistol based on the same system (Lorenz's compressed, elongated ball) was adopted in 1859.

Large numbers of the Austrian longarms were imported to the United States in the first two years of the American Civil War. Beginning in 1863, the Confederate States also imported large numbers of the M1854 series rifle-muskets. Most of the tubelocks first being modified to standard percussion in Belgium before importation, arms of prime interest to American collectors, accordingly demand higher prices.

In 1867, the Austria-Hungarian Empire adopted two different breechloading mechanisms and the self-contained metallic cartridge. Those muzzleloading arms deemed acceptable for alteration (the M1854 series of rifle-muskets and rifles) were adapted to the Wanzel system. Newly made arms (the M1867 rifle) were made in conformity with Werndl's breechloading design.

During the period within the scope of this catalog, Austrian arms were generally made on contract with the major gunmakers in and near Vienna ("Wien" in Austrian). These makers usually marked their products with their name upon the barrel of the arm, near the breech. The major makers included BENTZ, FERD. FRUWIRTH (who also simply marked his arms "F. F."), CARL HEISER, JOSEF JESCHER, ANNA OSTERLIEN, PIRKO, TH. ROTTME, G. SCHLAGER, TH. SEDERE, F. UMFAURER, WANZEL, and ZEILINGER (with the "Z" usually backwards). Lockplates were marked with the government ownership mark (a small double-headed eagle) and the date of manufacture (deleting the number "1" from the year, such as "847" for "1847".) Since the arms were not interchangeable, mating numbers are usually found on all the metal parts.

Austrian Musket, M1828

Overall length-57-3/4"; barrel length-42-1/2"; caliber-.69. Basically following the pattern of the French M1822 musket, this arm still accepted the quadrangular M1799 bayonet, distinguished by having a solid socket with a hook ring at its rear, like the Prussian bayonet for the M1808 musket.

Exc.	V.G.	Good	Fair	Poor
800	700	650	550	400

Austrian Musket, M1835

Overall length-57-3/4"; barrel length-42-1/2"; caliber-.69. The M1835 musket follows the pattern of the Austrian M1807 musket, but is adapted for the Consule tubelock percussion system, which essentially replaced the frizzen and pan with a hinged tube retainer. This arm still uses the M1799 quadrangular bayonet.

Exc.	V.G.	Good	Fair	Poor
1000	750	700	600	450

Austrian Musket, M1840

Overall length-57-3/4"; barrel length-42-1/2; caliber-.69. The M1840 musket was manufactured in flint. Its primary differences from the M1828 musket lies in its furniture (mainly the front band) and the bayonet attachment, which consists of a lug beneath the barrel and an elongated hook projecting from the forend of the stock to accept the new M1840 quadrangular bayonet. The bayonet is distinguished by having a straight slot in its socket, closed by a bridge.

Exc.	V.G.	Good	Fair	Poor
950	850	750	600	450

Austrian Musket, M1842

Overall length-57-3/4"; barrel length-42-1/2"; caliber-.69 (.71) The M1842 musket was manufactured in Augustin tubelock. Its main distinction from the M1840 flintlock musket is the lock, which in addition to having the integral hinged tubelock mechanism in lieu of the frizzen, has a distinctly rounded rear tail. Although 25,000 of these muskets were imported into the United States for use by Fremont's forces in Missouri in 1861, many were subsequently altered to percussion. The Cincinnati contractors, Hall, Carroll & Co. or Greenwood & Co. accounted for 10,000 of these arms, all of which were altered to percussion by means of the cone-in-barrel system. These were also rifled and a portion of them sighted with a long range rear sight similar to the Enfield P1853 rifle-musket. Many of the balance were subsequently sent to the Frankfort Arsenal in Philadelphia, where they were subcontracted to Henry Leman of Lancaster for alteration to standard percussion. Those altered by Leman are distinguished by having a new breechpiece with integral bolster, the latter with a cleanout screw through its face. In addition to the 25,000 imported for Fremont, the firm of M, Boker & Co. of New York imported approximately 8,000 Austrian M1842 muskets which it had altered to percussion in Belgium. The French method of adding a reinforced bolster to the top right-hand side of the barrel was used. Many of those were also rifled and sighted in the manner of the French adaptations fashionable in Europe. George Heydecker of New York City imported another 4,000 in 1863 which were seized in transit to Canada, reputedly for delivery to Mexican republican forces.

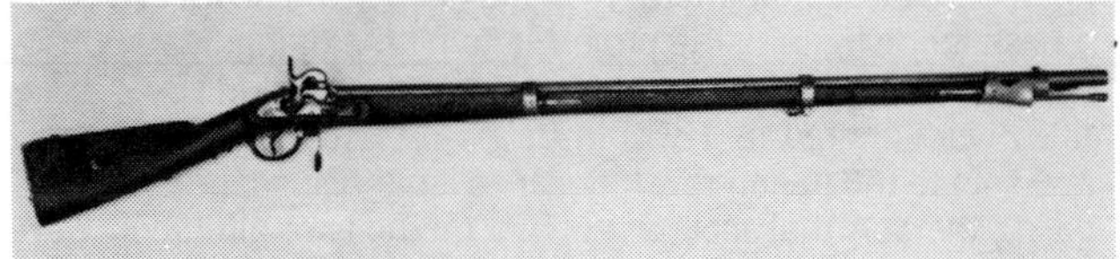

Courtesy Milwaukee Public Museum, Milwaukee, Wisconsin.

In original tubelock!

Exc.	V.G.	Good	Fair	Poor
1250	950	900	850	650

Altered to percussion (Cincinnati contractors)

Exc.	V.G.	Good	Fair	Poor
600	550	500	450	350

Altered to percussion (Leman)

Exc.	V.G.	Good	Fair	Poor
500	450	400	350	275

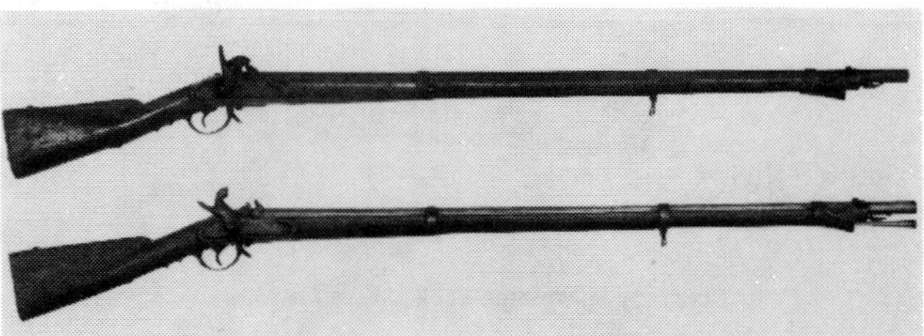

Courtesy Milwaukee Public Museum, Milwaukee, Wisconsin.

Altered to percussion and rifled (Boker)

Exc.	V.G.	Good	Fair	Poor
500	450	375	325	250

Austrian M1844 "Extra Corps" Musketoon

Overall length-48-3/8"; barrel length-33-1/2"; caliber-.69 (.71) Is essentially a shortened version of the Austrian M1842 musket. In original Augustin tubelock, it is virtually unknown. Most of the production is thought to have been purchased by arms speculators at the beginning of the American Civil War and altered to standard percussion in Liege, Belgium. The Belgian alteration followed the second pattern adopted by that government to alter arms to percussion and consisted of brazing a "lump" of metal to the upper right hand side of the barrel, into which a cone was threaded. The arms so altered were also rifled and sighted. The sights either copied the Austrian M1854 rifle-musket folding sight or the French "ladder" rear sight using the pattern utilized on the M1829 rifled cavalry musketoon. Over 10,000 of these arms were imported into the United States in 1861-1862 by Herman Boker & Co. of New York City.

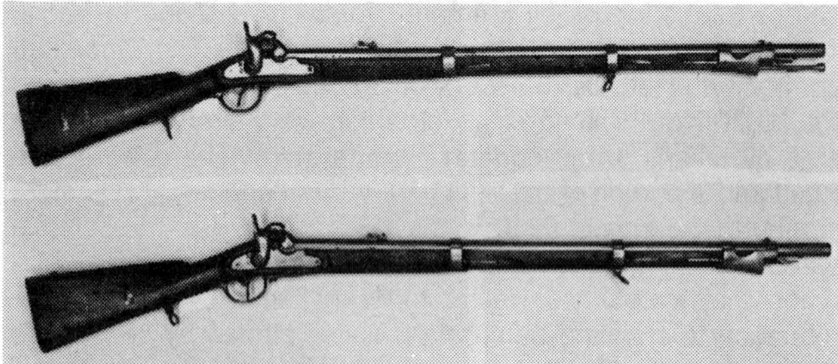

Courtesy Milwaukee Public Museum, Milwaukee, Wisconsin.

Altered to percussion and rifled (Boker)

Exc.	V.G.	Good	Fair	Poor
450	400	325	275	225

Austrian M1842 yager rifle

Overall length-48-1/4"; barrel length-33-1/4"; caliber-.69/.71. The Austrian M1842 yager rifle ("Kammer Busche") was originally manufactured in tubelock for the rifle battalions of the Austrian Army. Its bore terminated in a Delvigne breech, i.e. a chamber of lesser diameter than the caliber whose lip served as a base for disfiguring the projectile to fill the rifling. Made obsolete by the Thouvenin and Minie systems, many M1842 yager rifles were altered in 1860 in Belgium to standard percussion and sold to the Italian revolutionaries led by Giuseppe Garibaldi, giving the gun that nickname. Two methods of alteration were applied. One, the "Belgian" system, brazed a "lump" of iron to the upper right surface of the breech, which was tapped for a standard percussion cone. The other, the "Prussian," involved fitting the breech with a new barrel section incorporating a new bolster. At least 500 of these altered arms were imported into the United States during the American Civil War, where they (and the M1849 yager rifles similarly altered) were called "Garibaldi Rifles."

Courtesy Milwaukee Public Museum, Milwaukee, Wisconsin.

Exc.	V.G.	Good	Fair	Poor
450	400	350	250	175

Austrian M1849 yager rifle

Overall length-48"; barrel length-33-1/4"; caliber-.71. The successor to the M1842 Austrian "Kammerbusche," the M1849 model is distinguished by having its barrel wedge fastened rather than retained by bands. Both the M1842 and the M1849 yager rifles were adapted to socket bayonets having long straight knife blades; both socket types were slotted. That of the M1842 was secured to the barrel by the same method as the M1842 Austrian musket; that of the M1849, however, locked onto a lug on the right side of the barrel and was secured by a rotating ring on the back of the socket. Adapted to standard percussion in the same manner as the M1842 yager rifles, more than 25,000 were sold to the U.S. War Department in 1862 and 1863.

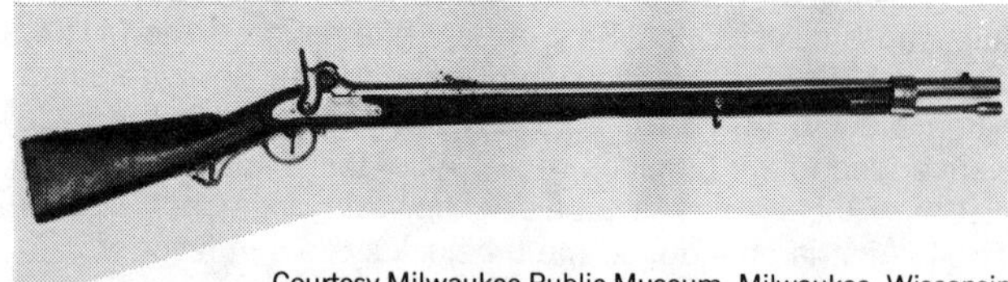

Courtesy Milwaukee Public Museum, Milwaukee, Wisconsin.

Exc.	V.G.	Good	Fair	Poor
450	400	350	275	200

Austrian M1850 horse pistol

Overall length-16"; barrel length-8-7/8"; caliber-.69. A bulky brass mounted pistol with lanyard ring, this arm was made originally in tubelock. However, a small quantity appear to have been altered to standard percussion locks in Liege, Belgium. In the process the double-strapped front bands of the original were removed and the forestock cut away to adapt the stock to an iron ramrod. (In Austrian service the ramrod was hung from the crossbelt of the mounted trooper.) Quantities imported into the United States are uncertain but may have been included among the 346 foreign horse pistols purchased by the U.S. War Department from P.S. Justice in 1861.

Exc.	V.G.	Good	Fair	Poor
400	350	300	225	150

Austrian M1850 carbine

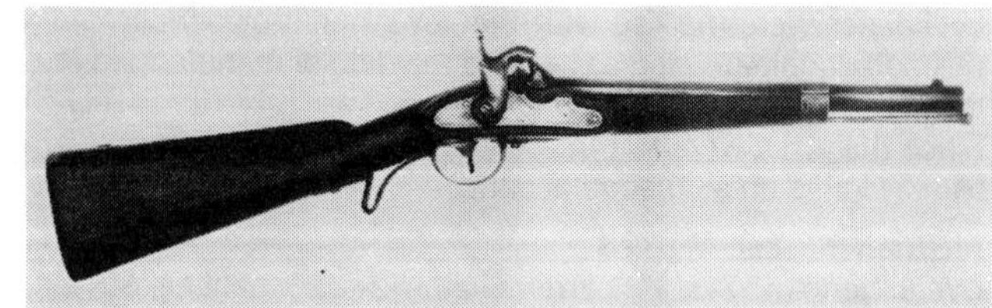

Courtesy Milwaukee Public Museum, Milwaukee, Wisconsin.

Overall length-30"; barrel length-14-1/2"; caliber-.71. Originally manufactured in tubelock for Austrian cavalry service, this large caliber, short-barrelled rifled carbine (12-groove rifling) saw service in the United States when 10,000 were purchased by U.S. purchasing agent George Schuyler in 1861. Those purchased for U.S. service, however, had been altered in Liege, Belgium for standard percussion locks in the same manner that the Austrian M1842 and M1849 yager rifles had been altered.

M1854 rifle-musket (The "Lorenz")

Overall length-52"; barrel length-37-1/4"; caliber-.54 (and .58). Adopted in 1854 as a replacement for its smoothbore muskets, the Austrian M1854 rifle-musket was made in three variants. The standard infantry arm had a simple block sight for mass volley fire. The rifles for the "rear rank" men were similar but with a folding leaf sight with windows graduated to 900 paces. A similar sight was also applied to the rifles for sharpshooter battalions, which also had a cheekpiece built into the buttstock. The quadrangular socket bayonet locked onto the front sight, whose sides were angled to accept the diagonal slot in the bayonet's socket. The Austrian M1854 rifle-musket was the second most prolifically imported arm during the American Civil War, with some 89,000 being imported into the Confederacy and more than 175,000 into the Union. Thousands of the latter were bored up to .58 caliber before being imported.

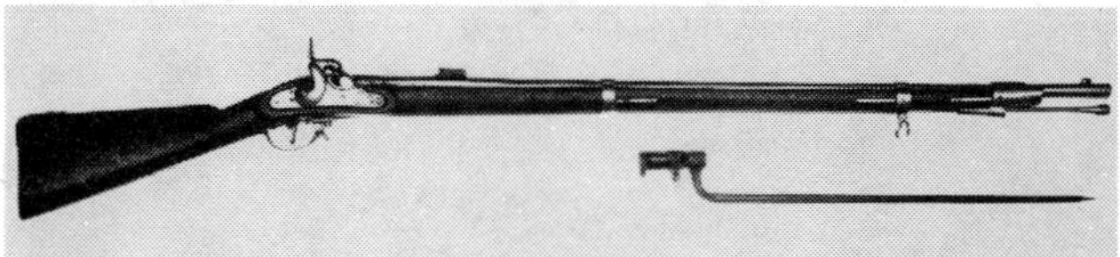

Courtesy Milwaukee Public Museum, Milwaukee, Wisconsin.

Exc.	V.G.	Good	Fair	Poor
600	550	450	300	250

M1854 yager rifle

Overall length-43"; barrel length-28"; caliber-.54. Designed for the rifle battalions of the Austrian army to replace the M1842 and M1849 rifles, the M1854 yager rifles are distinguished by having an octagonal, wedge-fastened barrel turned round near the muzzle to accept a socket bayonet with a long straight knife blade. An angled lug on the turned section engaged the diagonal slot in the bayonet's socket. The rear sight for these rifles is unusual, consisting of a curved slide that traverses two upright walls and can be locked with a turn key on its right side for various ranges up to 900 paces. These rifles were made for Austrian service without provision for a ramrod (that device being affixed to a crossbelt of the individual soldier). But the approximately 2,500 that were imported for U.S. service during the American Civil War were adapted for a ramrod by inletting a channel under the forestock.

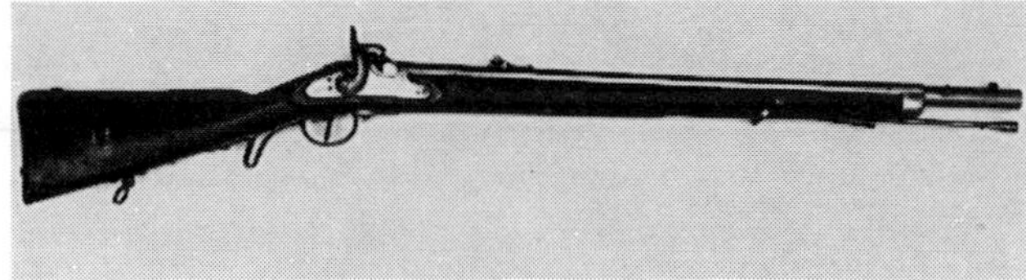

Courtesy Milwaukee Public Museum, Milwaukee, Wisconsin.

Exc.	V.G.	Good	Fair	Poor
700	600	500	275	200

Austrian M1859 horse pistol

Overall length- 16" (less stock); barrel length- 10-3/8"; caliber-54. The M1850 tubelock pistol was replaced in the Austrian service in 1859 with a new standard percussion rifled horse pistol firing the Lorenz "compression" elongated ball. Like the U.S. M1855 horse pistol, this new pistol had a detachable shoulder stock so that it could be used as a carbine. Like its predecessors, no provision was made for a ramrod, which continued to be attached to a belt crossing the trooper's torso.

Exc.	V.G.	Good	Fair	Poor
500	450	350	250	275

Austrian M1854/67 "Wanzel" alteration to breechloader

Overall length-52-1/4"; barrel (bore) length; 34-1/2"; caliber-.54. The "Wanzel" breechloading mechanism applied to the Austrian M1854 rifle-muskets is much like the Allin "trapdoor" applied in the U.S. to longarms during the period 1865-1873. A breechblock that hinges forward upon the barrel is released by a lever on the right side of the block, permitting insertion of a brass cartridge. In the process of altering these arms to breechloaders the sling swivels were moved from the middle band and triggerguard bow to the middle of the forestock and the buttstock.

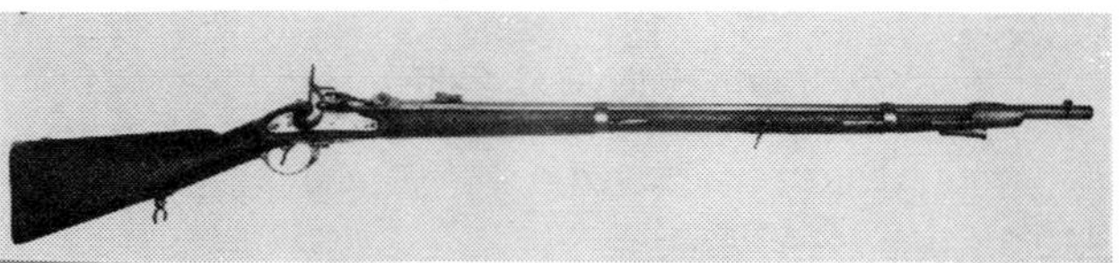

Courtesy Milwaukee Public Museum, Milwaukee, Wisconsin.

Exc.	V.G.	Good	Fair	Poor
400	350	300	275	225

Austrian M1867 "Werndl" breechloading rifle

Overall length-48-1/4"; barrel (bore) length-31-1/4"; caliber-11 mm, in 1867 the Austrian military adopted the breechloading system that had been invented by Joseph Werndl, director of the Austrian armory at Steyr. The breech of Werndl's design is rotated by means of a lever on its left side to expose the chamber for loading and extraction of cartridges. WERNDL apppears on the top of the barrel in recognition of the designer's invention. In 1888 the Werndl rifles were superseded by the Mannlicher smokeless powder arms.

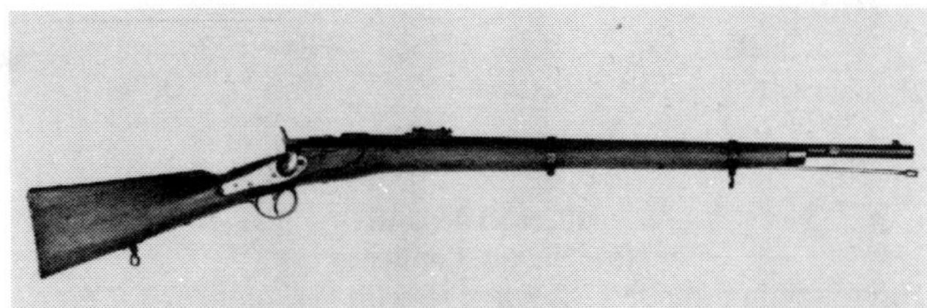

Courtesy Milwaukee Public Museum, Milwaukee, Wisconsin.

Exc.	V.G.	Good	Fair	Poor
450	400	350	250	200

AUTO MAG

Various Manufacturers

This popular stainless steel semi-automatic pistol was developed by the Sanford Arms Company of Pasadena, California in the 1960s and was chambered for a Special cartridge known as the .44AMP which had a 240 grain .44 caliber bullet. Production of this arm has been carried out by a number companies over the past 30 years. It is believed that less than 10,000 have been produced by the eight manufacturers involved.

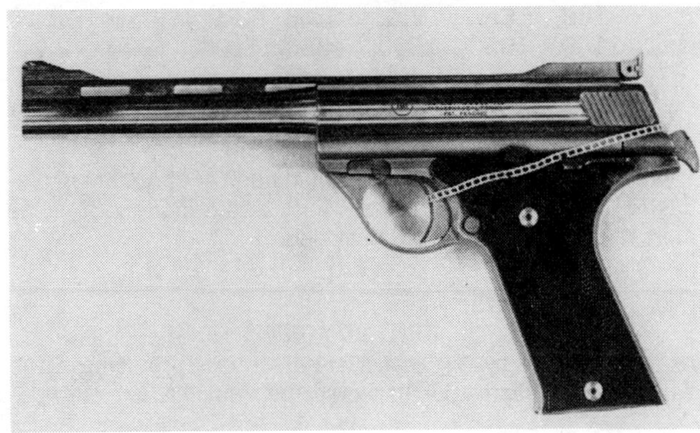

AUTO MAG CORP.

Pasadena, California

Serial number range A0000 through A3300, made with a 6.5" vent-rib barrel, chambered in .44AMP only.

NIB	Exc.	V.G.	Good	Fair	Poor
1850	1500	1250	1000	800	650

TDE CORP.
North Hollywood, California

Serial number range A3400 through AO5015, made with a 6.5" vent-rib barrel, chambered in .44AMP and .357AMP.

.44AMP

NIB	Exc.	V.G.	Good	Fair	Poor
2000	1850	1500	1250	1000	800

.357AMP

NIB	Exc.	V.G.	Good	Fair	Poor
2050	1900	1550	1300	1050	850

TDE CORP.
El Monte, California

Serial number range AO5016 through AO8300, 6.5" vent-rib barrel standard. Also available in 8" and 10" barrel lengths chambered for .44AMP and .357AMP.

.44AMP

NIB	Exc.	V.G.	Good	Fair	Poor
1800	1650	1300	1050	800	650

.357AMP

NIB	Exc.	V.G.	Good	Fair	Poor
1600	1450	1100	850	650	500

HIGH STANDARD
New Haven, Connecticut

High Standard made 132 guns, all with "H" prefix serial numbers.

NIB	Exc.	V.G.	Good	Fair	Poor
2300	2000	1750	1300	1000	850

TDE—OMC

This is known as the solid-bolt or "B" series. The serial-number range is B00001 through B00370. Either 6.5" vent-rib or 10" tapered barrels are available.

NIB	Exc.	V.G.	Good	Fair	Poor
2000	1850	1500	1250	1000	800

AMT "C" SERIES

There were 100 guns produced in this series. The first 50 were serial numbered with a "C" prefix. The second 50 were serial numbered "LAST 1" through "LAST 50." They were available with a 6.5" vent-rib or 10" tapered barrel.

NIB	Exc.	V.G.	Good	Fair	Poor
2100	1950	1600	1350	1100	900

L. E. JURRAS CUSTOM

This custom maker produced a limited number of Auto Mag pistols in 1977. These arms are worth approximately 35-50% more than standard production models.

KENT LOMONT

As pistols made by this maker are essentially prototypes, it is advised that potential purchasers secure a qualified appraisal.

AUTO ORDNANCE CORP.
West Hurley, New York

1911 A1

A 9mm, .38 Super or .45 caliber, copy of the Colt Model 1911 A1.

NIB	Exc.	V.G.	Good	Fair	Poor
350	325	275	225	175	135

ZG-51 "Pit Bull"

A reduced-size version of the above, with a 3.5" barrel in .45 caliber. Introduced in 1988.

NIB	Exc.	V.G.	Good	Fair	Poor
375	295	250	225	200	175

1927 A1 Standard

A semi-automatic version of the Thompson submachine gun, chambered for the .45 ACP cartridge with a 16" barrel. Blued with walnut stock. Manufactured till 1986.

Exc.	V.G.	Good	Fair	Poor
575	500	425	300	275

1927 A1 Deluxe

As above, with a finned barrel, adjustable sights, pistol-grip forearm, and a 50-round drum magazine costing an additional $140. The violin shaped carrying case adds approximately $115 to the values listed below.

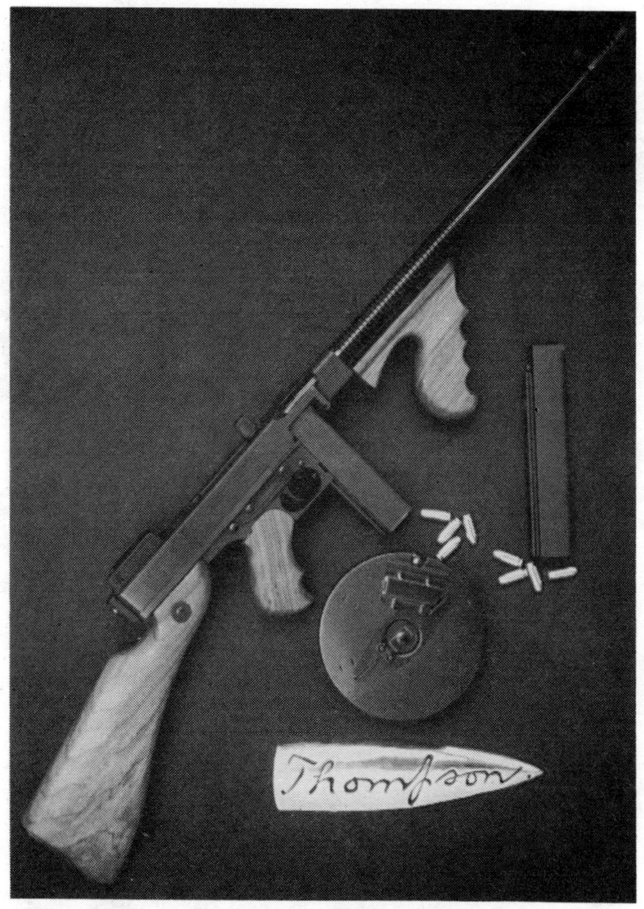

NIB	Exc.	V.G.	Good	Fair	Poor
725	650	575	500	350	300

1927 A1C

As above, with an aluminum alloy receiver. Introduced in 1984.

NIB	Exc.	V.G.	Good	Fair	Poor
635	600	525	400	325	275

1927 A5

A reduced-size version of the Model 1927 A1 with a 13" finned barrel, aluminum alloy receiver and no shoulder stock.

NIB	Exc.	V.G.	Good	Fair	Poor
625	575	500	375	300	250

1927 A3

A .22 caliber variation of the Model 1927 A1 with a 16" barrel and aluminum alloy receiver.

NIB	Exc.	V.G.	Good	Fair	Poor
485	450	400	350	275	225

AUTO POINTER

Yamamoto Co.
Tokyo, Japan

Auto - Pointer Shotgun

A 12 or 20 gauge semi-automatic shotgun with 26", 28" or 30" barrels and an aluminum alloy frame. Blued with a checkered walnut stock. Originally imported by Sloan's but no longer available.

Exc.	V.G.	Good	Fair	Poor
325	275	225	175	125

AZPIRI

Eibar, Spain

Avion

A 6.35mm semi-automatic pistol copied after the model 1906 Browning. Marked "Pistolet Automatique Avion Brevete." Manufactured from 1914 to 1918.

Exc.	V.G.	Good	Fair	Poor
200	175	125	95	65

Colon

As above, in 6.35mm caliber and marked "Automatic Pistol Colon".

Exc.	V.G.	Good	Fair	Poor
150	125	100	75	50

B

BSA GUNS LTD.
Birmingham, England
Birmingham Small Arms

Established in 1861, this firm has produced a wide variety of firearms over the years. The more common of these arms which are currently available in the United States are as follows:

No. 12 Cadet Martini

A .310 caliber single shot Martini action rifle with a 29" barrel, adjustable sights and straight-gripped walnut stock. Approximately 80,000 were manufactured from 1911 to 1913. Many of those imported into the United States were altered to .22 caliber.

Exc.	V.G.	Good	Fair	Poor
350	300	250	175	125

Centurian Match Rifle

As above, in .22 caliber with a 24" barrel, adjustable sights and a pistol-grip walnut stock.

Exc.	V.G.	Good	Fair	Poor
450	400	350	275	200

Model 13 Sporter

As above, in .22 Hornet with hunting sights.

Exc.	V.G.	Good	Fair	Poor
400	350	300	225	150

Martini International Match

As above, with a heavy match barrel, ISU style sights and a match stock. Manufactured from 1950 to 1953.

Exc.	V.G.	Good	Fair	Poor
425	375	325	250	175

Martini International Light

As above, with a 26" barrel of lighter weight.

Exc.	V.G.	Good	Fair	Poor
425	375	325	250	175

Martini International ISU

As above, meeting ISU specifications with a 28" barrel. Manufactured from 1968 to 1976.

Exc.	V.G.	Good	Fair	Poor
500	450	400	325	250

Bolt Actions

Royal

A bolt-action sporting rifle manufactured in a variety of calibers and a 24" barrel, with a checkered French walnut stock.

Exc.	V.G.	Good	Fair	Poor
350	300	250	200	150

Majestic Deluxe

A .22 Hornet, .222, .243, 7x57mm, .308 or .30-06 bolt action sporting rifle with a 22" barrel, having a folding rear sight and a checkered walnut stock with a Schnabel forend tip. Imported from 1959 to 1965.

Exc.	V.G.	Good	Fair	Poor
350	300	250	200	150

Majestic Deluxe Featherweight

As above, in .270 or .458 Magnum with a thinner barrel.

Exc.	V.G.	Good	Fair	Poor
350	300	250	200	150

Monarch Deluxe

As above, drilled and tapped for telescopic sight and also available in a heavy barrelled varmint version in .222 or .243 caliber. Imported from 1966 to 1974.

Exc.	V.G.	Good	Fair	Poor
375	325	275	225	175

Herters U9

The firm of Herters, Inc. of Waseca, Minnesota, imported BSA rifle actions beginning in 1965 which were used for custom made rifles.

Commencing in 1986, BSA began production of a new line of bolt action sporting rifles on the Model CF-2 action. The standard production models are as follows:

Sporter/Classic

A hunting rifle available in a variety of calibers with a checkered walnut stock. Introduced in 1986.

Exc.	V.G.	Good	Fair	Poor
350	325	275	200	150

Varminter

As above, with a matte-finished heavy barrel in .222, .22-250 or .243 caliber. Introduced in 1986.

Exc.	V.G.	Good	Fair	Poor
325	275	225	175	135

Stutzen Rifle

As above, with a 20.5" barrel and a Mannlicher style stock.

Exc.	V.G.	Good	Fair	Poor
375	350	300	225	175

Regal Custom

As above, with an engraved receiver, checkered walnut stock and an ebony forend. Imported only in 1986.

Exc.	V.G.	Good	Fair	Poor
850	800	700	550	400

CFT Target Rifle

A .308 caliber single shot version of the above with a 26.5" barrel and adjustable sights. Imported only in 1987.

Exc.	V.G.	Good	Fair	Poor
650	600	550	400	300

BABCOCK, MOSES
Charlestown, Massachusetts

Babcock Under Hammer Cane Gun

A .52 caliber percussion cane gun having a 27" barrel and overall length of approximately 33". Folding trigger, under hammer with a wood handle. The hammer is marked "Moses Babcock / Charlestown." Active 1850s and 1860s.

Exc.	V.G.	Good	Fair	Poor
400	350	300	250	200

BABBIT, A. S.
Plattsburgh, New York

SEE—Adirondack Arms

BACON ARMS CO.

Norwich, Connecticut

Bacon Arms operated from 1862 until 1891. They have become known primarily for the production of cheaply made, solid-frame, rim-fire revolvers known as "Suicide Specials." Bacon manufactured and sold under a number of different trademarks. They were: Bacon, Bonanza, Conqueror, Express, Gem, Governor, Guardian, and Little Giant. Collector interest is low, and values for all trademarks are quite similar.

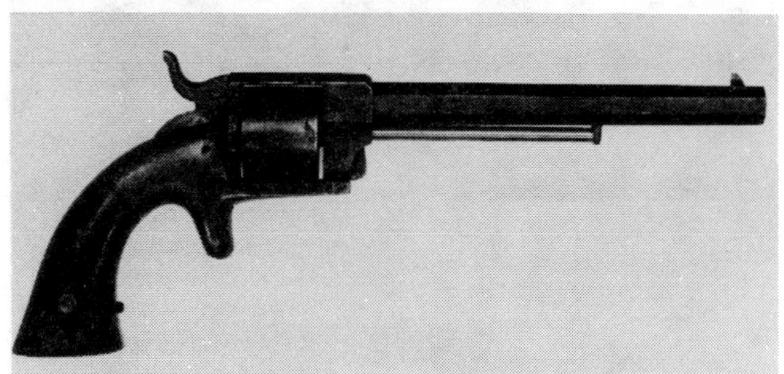

Courtesy Milwaukee Public Museum, Milwaukee, Wisconsin.

Exc.	V.G.	Good	Fair	Poor
150	125	90	65	35

BAFORD, ARMS, INC.

Bristol, Tennessee
C. L. Reedy & Assoc.—Distributors
Melbourne, Florida

Thunder Derringer

A .410 bore or .44 Special single shot pistol with 3" interchangeable barrels and a spur trigger. Additional interchangeable barrels are chambered in calibers from .22 to 9mm. Also available with a scope. Blued with a walnut grip. Introduced in 1988.

NIB	Exc.	V.G.	Good	Fair	Poor
130	115	100	80	65	45

Fire Power Model 35

A 9mm semi-automatic pistol with a 4.75" barrel, Millett adjustable sights and 14-shot magazine. Fitted with a combat safety and hammer, and Pachmayr grips. Stainless-steel. Introduced in 1988.

NIB	Exc.	V.G.	Good	Fair	Poor
495	450	375	300	250	175

BAIKAL

U.S.S.R.
Commercial Trading Imports
Bloomington, Minnesota

Baikal IJ-27E1C

A 12 or 20 gauge Magnum over/under shotgun with 26" skeet-skeet or 28" modified-full ventilated rib barrels, single selective trigger and extractors. Blued with a walnut stock.

Mfg. List Price
$449.95

Baikal TOZ - 34

A 12 or 28 gauge double-barrel shotgun with 26" or 28" barrels, double triggers, cocking indicators and extractors. Blued with a checkered walnut stock. This model was also available with a silver-plated receiver.

Mfg. List Price
$465.95

Model MC-8-0

A 12 gauge double barrel shotgun with 26" skeet-skeet or 28" full-modified barrels, hand fitted action and engraved receiver.

Mfg. List Price
$2,295.00

Model MC-5-105

The Model TOZ-34 with an engraved receiver.

Mfg. List Price
$1,325.00

Model MC-7

As above, with a relief engraved receiver.

Mfg. List Price
$2,695.00

Model MC-109

A custom made over/under shotgun with detachable sidelocks. Produced in very limited quantities and most often to the purchaser's specifications.

Mfg. List Price
$3,695.00

BAILONS GUNMAKERS, LTD.

Birmingham, England

Most of the products of this company are produced strictly on custom order.

Hunting Rifle

A bolt-action sporting rifle produced in a variety of calibers with a 24" barrel having open sights, double-set triggers and a 3- or 4-shot magazine. Blued with a well figured walnut stock. The values listed below are for a standard grade rifle.

NIB	Exc.	V.G.	Good	Fair	Poor
1850	1700	1450	1100	900	700

BAKER GAS SEAL

London, England

A .577 caliber percussion revolver with a 6.5" octagonal barrel and 6-shot cylinder. When the hammer is cocked, the cylinder is forced forward tightly against the barrel breech, thus creating a gas seal. Blued, casehardened with walnut grips.

Exc.	V.G.	Good	Fair	Poor
750	675	600	475	400

BAKER GUN & FORGING CO.

Batavia, New York

Though not well known today, this company produced a variety of exceptionally well made shotguns which were highly prized in their day.

Note: Values listed are for fluid steel-barrelled examples unless otherwise indicated. Damascus barrelled guns are generally worth approximately 60 percent to 75 percent of these figures. On the higher-grade guns where it was available, a single-trigger would add approximately $200 to $250.

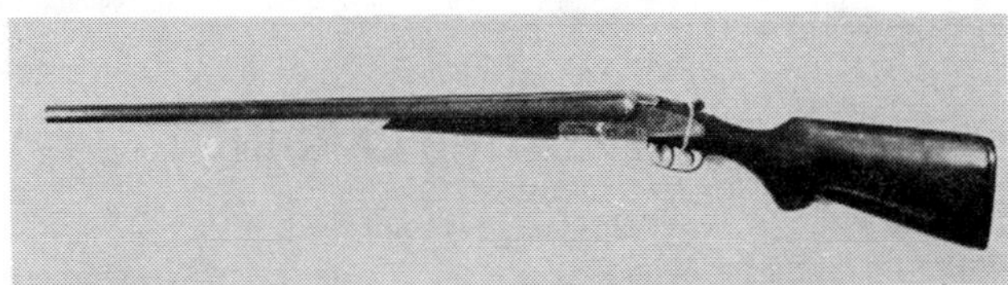

Batavia Special

A 12, 16 or 20 gauge sidelock double-barrel shotgun with 26", 28", 30" or 32" barrels, double triggers and extractors. Blued, casehardened with a walnut stock.

Exc.	V.G.	Good	Fair	Poor
400	325	275	225	175

Batavia Leader

As above, but more finely finished.

Exc.	V.G.	Good	Fair	Poor
500	425	375	325	275

Black Beauty Special

As above, with an engraved receiver and finely figured walnut stock. Also available with automatic ejectors.

Exc.	V.G.	Good	Fair	Poor
850	750	675	500	375

Batavia Ejector

As above, but more finely finished.

Exc.	V.G.	Good	Fair	Poor
900	800	725	550	425

Baker S Grade

As above, with more extensive engraving.

Exc.	V.G.	Good	Fair	Poor
1050	975	875	650	525

Baker R Grade

As above, with even a better finish.

Exc.	V.G.	Good	Fair	Poor
1300	1175	1050	800	650

Paragon Grade

As above, built strictly on custom order. All features to the customer's specifications.

Exc.	V.G.	Good	Fair	Poor
1800	1675	1500	1250	975

Expert Grade

As above, with automatic ejectors.

Exc.	V.G.	Good	Fair	Poor
2500	2200	1900	1600	1000

Deluxe Grade

The Baker Gun & Forging Company's best shotgun produced in very limited quantities and solely upon custom order. Prospective purchasers are advised to secure a qualified appraisal prior to acquisition.

Exc.	V.G.	Good	Fair	Poor
4000	3400	2950	2100	1500

BAKER, M.A.

Fayetteville, North Carolina

Percussion Rifle

A .52 caliber single shot percussion rifle with a 36" round barrel and a full stock secured by three barrel bands. Altered from the U.S. Model 1817 Rifle. The barrel breech marked "N. Carolina" and the lockplate "M.A. Baker/Fayetteville, N.C." Finished in the white with a walnut stock. Prospective purchasers are advised to secure a qualified appraisal prior to acquisition.

Exc.	V.G.	Good	Fair	Poor
4500	3800	3250	2500	1750

BALL REPEATING CARBINE

Lamson & Co.
Windsor, Vermont

Ball Repeating Carbine

A .50 caliber lever-action repeating carbine with a 20.5" round barrel and 7-shot magazine. The receiver is marked "E.G. Lamson & Co./Windsor, Vt./U.S./Ball's Patent/June 23, 1863/Mar. 15, 1864." Blued, casehardened with a walnut stock. Late production examples of this carbine have been noted with browned or bright barrels. In excess of 1,500 were made between 1864 and 1867.

Courtesy Milwaukee Public Museum, Milwaukee, Wisconsin.

Exc.	V.G.	Good	Fair	Poor
1250	1050	900	750	500

BALLARD PATENT ARMS
(until 1873; after 1875, see MARLIN)

On Nov. 5, 1861, C.H. Ballard of Worcester, Massachusetts received a patent for a breechloading mechanism that would remain in production for nearly thirty years. Ballard patented a breechblock that tilted down at its front to expose the breech by activating the lever/triggerguard. During the twelve years that followed, Ballard rifles, carbines, and shotguns were produced by five interrelated companies. Four of these were successive: Ball & Williams, R. Ball & Co. (both of Worcester, Massachusetts), Merrimack Arms & Manufacturing Co. and Brown Manufacturing Company (both of Newburyport, Massachusetts). These four companies produced Ballard arms in a successive serial range (1 through approximately 22,000), all marked upon the top of the frame and the top of the barrel where it joins the frame. In 1863, another company, Dwight, Chapin & Company of Bridgeport, Connecticut also produced Ballard rifles and carbines in a larger frame size, but in a different serial range (1 through about 1,900), usually marked on the left side of the frame below the agents' mark. The large frame carbines and rifles were produced to fulfill a U.S. War Department contract initially for 10,000 of each, subsequently reduced to 1,000 of each, issued to Merwin & Bray, the sole agents for the Ballard patent arms between 1862 and 1866. Most of the production during this period concentrated on military contracts, either for the U.S. War Department or the state of Kentucky, although the state of New York also purchased 500 for its state militia.

Ballard (Ball & Williams) sporting rifles, first type. (serial nos. 1-100)

Barrel length-24"; caliber .38 rimfire. Markings: BALL & WILLIAMS/Worcester, Mass., and BALLARD'S PATENT/Nov. 5, 1861 on octagonal barrel.

The distinctive feature of the earliest production of the Ballard rifles is the presence of an internal extractor conforming to the patent specifications. After approximately 100 rifles, this feature was dropped in favor of a manual extractor located under the barrel.

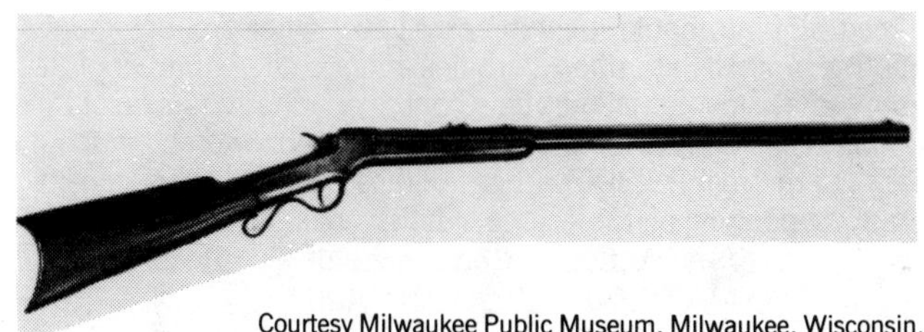
Courtesy Milwaukee Public Museum, Milwaukee, Wisconsin.

Exc.	V.G.	Good	Fair	Poor
1500	1200	1000	800	450

Ballard (Ball & Williams) sporting rifles, second type (serial nos. 200-1600, and 1600 through 14,000, interspersed with martial production)

Barrel length- 24", 28" or 30", usually octagonal, but part round/part-octagonal as well; calibers .32, .38, and .44 rimfire. Markings: BALL & WILLIAMS/Worcester, Mass., BALLARD'S PATENT/Nov. 5, 1861, and MERWIN & BRAY, AGT'S/ NEW YORK, on facets of barrel until about serial no. 9000, thereafter the patent name and date on the right side of the frame and the manufacturer and agents on the left side of the frame. On early production (200 to 1500), the extractor knob is smaller and crescent shaped. Early production (prior to about serial no. 10,000) have solid breechblocks; after that number breechblocks are made in two halves. A few of these arms were made with bronze frames to facilitate engraving and plating. These should command a higher premium

Exc.	V.G.	Good	Fair	Poor
750	700	500	350	200

Ballard (Ball & Williams) sporting rifles, third type (serial nos. 14,000 to 15,000)

These arms are essentially the same as the second type in characteristics but have Merwin & Bray's alternate percussion mechanism built into the breechblock. The hammer is accordingly marked on the left side "PATENTED JAN. 5, 1864."

Exc.	V.G.	Good	Fair	Poor
750	700	500	350	200

Ballard (Ball & Williams) military carbines. (serial nos. 1500 through 7500, and 8500 through 10,500)

Overall length-37-1/4"; barrel (bore) length-22"; caliber-.44 rimfire. Markings: same as Ballard/Ball & Williams sporting rifles, second type. Additional marks on U.S. War Department purchases include inspector's initials "MM" or "GH" on left side of frame, and "MM" on barrel, breechblock, buttplate, and on left side of buttstock in script within an oval cartouche. Three thousand of the earlier production (serial nos. 1700 through about 5000) of these carbines were sold to the state of Kentucky under an August 1862 contract extended in April 1863. In November 1863, Kentucky contracted for an additional one thousand carbines. In the interim, the state of New York purchased 500 for distribution to its militia. The U.S. War Department ordered 5,000 under a contract signed in January of 1864, but Ball & Williams delivered only 1,500 (serial nos. noted in range of 9800 through 10,600) while concentrating production on their more lucrative Kentucky contract. Another 600 of the federal contract were partially inspected (serial nos. about 6500 to 7100-MM in cartouche in stock only) but were rejected because the barrels had been rifled prior to proofing; these were sold to Kentucky in September 1864 on an open market purchase. The carbines marked with federal inspection marks usually bring a premium.

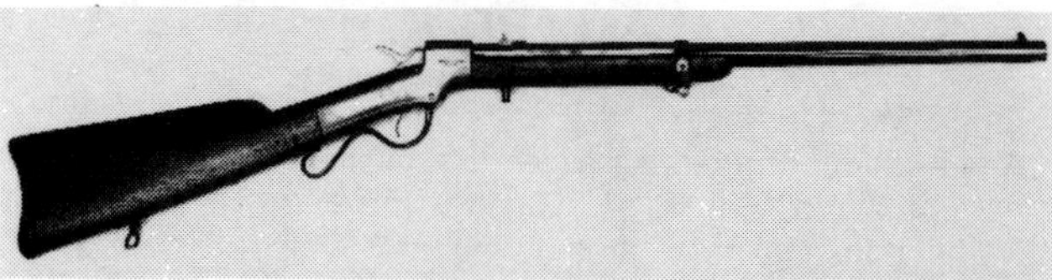
Courtesy Milwaukee Public Museum, Milwaukee, Wisconsin.

Exc.	V.G.	Good	Fair	Poor
600	500	400	350	275

Ballard (Ball & Williams) "Kentucky" half-stock rifles

Overall length- 45-3/8"; barrel (bore) length- 30"; caliber- .44 rimfire. These half-stock rifles bear the standard Ball & Williams markings upon their barrels and in addition have the state ownership mark ("KENTUCKY") on the barrel forward of the rear sights. A total of 1,000 (serial nos. about 7100 through 8550) were contracted for by Kentucky in November 1863 and delivered between January and April 1864.

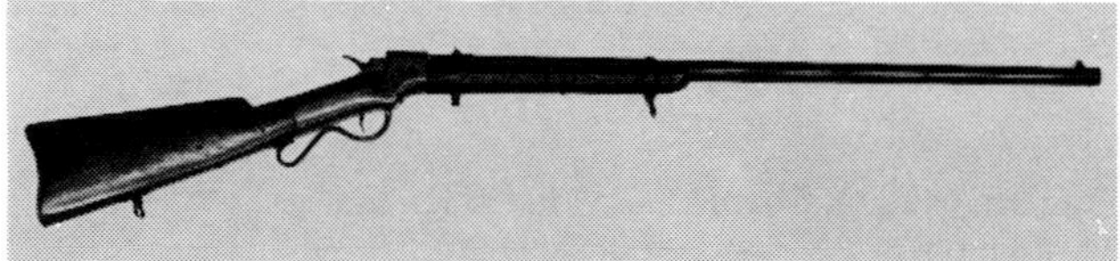
Courtesy Milwaukee Public Museum, Milwaukee, Wisconsin.

Exc.	V.G.	Good	Fair	Poor
700	600	450	375	275

Ballard (Ball & Williams) "Kentucky" full stock rifles

Overall length-45-1/4"; barrel (bore) length-30"; caliber-.46 rimfire. Marked on the frame with standard Ball & Williams manufacturer (left), agent (left), and patent (right) markings, these rifles are additionally distinguished by the state ownership mark "KENTUCKY" stamped into the top of the frame near the breech. Kentucky contracted for 3,000 of these arms in November 1863, initially in .56 caliber. However, by mutual consent of the state and the contractors, in February 1864, the caliber of the arms was changed to .46, and all deliveries were made in this caliber, beginning in July 1864 and continuing until March 1865 (serial nos. 10,400 to 14,500).

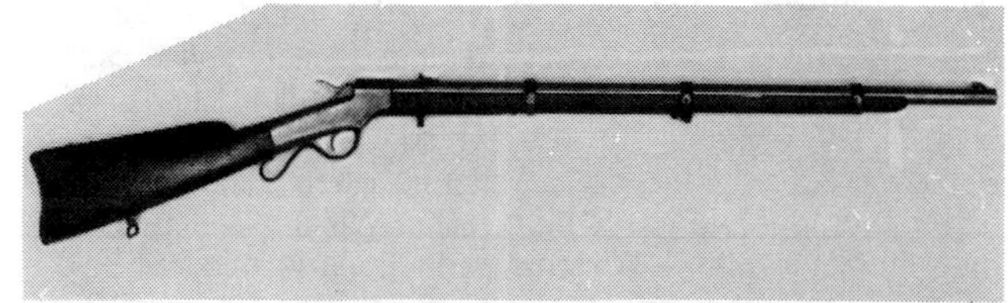
Courtesy Milwaukee Public Museum, Milwaukee, Wisconsin.

Exc.	V.G.	Good	Fair	Poor
650	600	475	350	250

Ballard (Dwight, Chapin & Co.) carbines

Overall length-37-3/4"; barrel (bore) length-22"; caliber-.56 rimfire. Markings: On left side of round-topped frame "BALLARD'S PATENT/NOV. 5 1861"; on right side of frame "DWIGHT, CHAPIN & CO./BRIDGEPORT CONN." (through serial no. about 125, deleted after that number) over "MERWIN & BRAY/AGT'S N.Y." over serial no. Inspection letters "D" frequently appear on carbines with the Dwight, Chapin, & Co. markings, indicative of preliminary inspection by E.M. Dustin, of the U.S. Ordnance Department.

Often mistaken as early Ballard production from a fictitious Fall River, Massachusetts factory, these carbines and their complementing rifles were in fact not placed into production until 1863, as evident by the split, two-piece breechblocks. Both carbines and rifles originated from a contract entered into between the U.S. War Department and Merwin & Bray in October 1862 for 10,000 of each arm, subsequently reduced to 1,000 of each by the Commission on Ordnance and Ordnance Stores. Because Ball & Williams facilities were tied up with Kentucky contracts, Merwin & Bray turned to the small parts maker of Dwight, Chapin & Co. in Bridgeport, Connecticut. Although they tooled for production, they fell short of scheduled delivery dates, and although about 100 carbines had been inspected, no deliveries were accepted (due to caliber problems) by the U.S. government, effectively bankrupting Dwight, Chapin & Co. The completed carbines and unfinished parts were sent to Worcester and assembled by Ball & Williams, and Merwin & Bray sold all 1,000 carbines in Kentucky in April 1864 on an open market purchase.

Courtesy Milwaukee Public Museum, Milwaukee, Wisconsin.

Exc.	V.G.	Good	Fair	Poor
650	600	450	350	275

Ballard (Dwight, Chapin & Co.) full-stock rifle

Overall length-53" barrel (bore) length-30"; caliber-.56 rimfire. Markings: same as Dwight, Chapin & Co. carbines, but none found with "DWIGHT, CHAPIN & CO./BRIDGEPORT, CONN." stamping above agents marks. The history of these rifles is the same as the .56 caliber carbines, with serial nos. interspersed in the production of the carbines (1 through 1850). Evidently only about 650 of the rifles were completed of the 1,000 set up. Of these, 35 were sold to a U.S. agent in Florida in February 1864 and 600 to Kentucky in April 1864 with the 1,000 carbines.

Exc.	V.G.	Good	Fair	Poor
750	700	500	400	300

Ballard (R. Ball) & Co. sporting rifles

Overall length-varies according to barrel length; barrel (bore) length usually 24", 28", and 30"; calibers- .32, .38, .44, and .46 rimfire. Markings: The frame markings of R. Ball & Co. rifles are similar to Ball & Williams production, only eliminating the Ball & Williams marking on the left side. Cartridge size, e.g. "No. 44", usually also stamped upon the top of the barrel or frame. Merwin & Bray's patent alternate ignition device usually present with left side of hammer usually marked "PATENTED JAN. 5, 1864." Serial numbers (which follow in sequence with Ball & Williams production. i.e. after no. about 15,800) appear on top of barrel and top of frame. After William Williams withdrew from the Ball & Williams partnership in mid-1865, the business continued under the name of R. Ball & Co., with Richard Ball's son-in-law, E.J. Halstead, in charge after the former's paralytic stroke in the fall of 1865.

Ballard (R. Ball) & Co. carbines

Overall length-37¼" barrel (bore) length-22" caliber-.44 rim fire. Markings: same as R. Ball & Co. sporting rifles; "No. 44" on top of frame near breech.

Although firm evidence is elusive, approximately 1,000 of these carbines were manufactured in anticipation of a Canadian contract, which never came to fruition. Serial nos. are interspersed with sporting rifles, in the 16,400 through 17,700 range. All are equipped with the Merwin & Bray dual ignition block.

Exc.	V.G.	Good	Fair	Poor
550	500	400	300	250

Ballard (Merrimack Arms & Manufacturing Co.) sporting rifles

Overall length-varies with barrel length; usual barrel lengths-24", 28"; 30"; calibers-.22, .32, .44. .46, .50 rimfire. Markings: left side of frame marked with both manufacturing and patent marks, "MERRIMACK ARMS & MFG. CO./NEWBURYPORT, MASS." over "BALLARD'S PATENT/ NOV. 5, 1861". Caliber usually marked on top of barrel or frame, e.g. "No. 38" together with serial no. Left side of hammer marked "PATENTED JAN. 5, 1864" if breech fitted with Merwin & Bray's alternate ignition device. In the spring of 1866, Edward Bray of Brooklyn, New York and former partner of Joseph Merwin purchased the Ballard machinery from R. Ball & Co. and set up a new plant in Newburyport, Massachusetts, primarily for the production of sporting rifles. The glut of surplus arms on the market following the American Civil War, however, forced him into bankruptcy in early 1869, after producing only about 2,000 Ballard rifles, carbines and a limited number of 20 gauge shotguns. Serial numbers continue in the sequence of the Ball & Williams/R. Ball & Co. production (serial numbers about 18,000 through 20,300). Prices of these rifles will vary considerably depending on the degree of finish or engraving.

Exc.	V.G.	Good	Fair	Poor
1500	1200	900	400	275

Ballard (Merrimack Arms & Manufacturing Co.) carbines

Overall length-37-1/4"; barrel (bore) length-22"; caliber-.44 rimfire. Markings: same as Merrimack Arms & Mfg. Co. sporting rifles. In March 1866, the state of New York purchased 100 Ballard carbines (serial numbers about 18,500 to 18,600) for use of its prison guards. In January 1870, an additional 70 (serial numbers 19,400 to 19,500) were purchased from New York City arms merchants Merwin, Hulbert & Co. to arm guards at Sing Sing Prison. Between these two purchases Merrimack Arms & Mfg. Co. had shortened its new "tangless" frames by 1/8", the prime distinction between the two purchases. Despite the rarity of both types of carbines, they do not command high prices.

Exc.	V.G.	Good	Fair	Poor
450	400	350	275	225

Ballard (Brown Manufacturing Co.) sporting rifles

Dimensions: same as Merrimack Arms & Mfg. Co. sporting rifles. Markings: left side of frame marked with manufacturer, "BROWN MFG. CO. NEWBURYPORT, MASS." over patent, "BALLARD'S PATENT/ NOV. 5, 1861." Serial no. on top of barrel and frame. Upon the failure of Merrimack Arms & Manufacturing Company in early 1869, the plant was purchased by John Hamilton Brown, who continued producing Ballard patent rifles until 1873 in a serial range consecutive with that of its three predecessors (Ball & Williams, R. Ball & Co., and Merrimack Arms & Mfg. Co.) Approximately 2,000 Ballard arms were produced during the period of Brown's manufacture of the Ballard (serial numbers about 20,325 through 22,100.) Brown made Ballards tend to exhibit finer finishing than earlier produced rifles, accounting for their average higher value. Special features, such as breakdown facility and side extractors (on .22 cal. rifles) will also positively affect the prices.

Exc.	V.G.	Good	Fair	Poor
1500	1250	850	450	275

Ballard (Brown Mfg. Co.) full-stock military rifles

Overall length-52-1/2" barrel (bore) length-30"; caliber-.46 rimfire. Markings: The same as Brown Mfg. Co. sporting rifles, with the addition of the caliber marking, "No. 46", on the top of the barrel forward of the rear sight. The cause for the production of the Ballard/Brown military rifle has yet to be determined, but it has been speculated that they were possibly manufactured in anticipation of a sale to France during the Franco-Prussian War. In any event, the sale was not culminated, and many, if not most, of the estimated 1,000 produced were "sporterized" by shortening the forestock and sold by commercial dealers in the United States. Serial numbers concentrate in the 20,500 through 21,600 range, with sporting rifles interspersed in the sequence. Rifles that have not been sporterized command a premium.

Exc.	V.G.	Good	Fair	Poor
550	475	375	300	225

BALLARD, C. H.

Worcester, Massachusetts

Single Shot Derringer

A .41 caliber rimfire spur trigger single shot pistol with a 2.75" barrel marked "Ballard's". Blued with silver-plated frame and walnut grips. Manufactured during the 1870s.

Iron Frame Model—Add 25%.

Exc.	V.G.	Good	Fair	Poor
375	325	250	200	165

BALLESTER-MOLINA
SEE—Hafdasa

BARNETT
SEE—English Military Firearms

BARRET F.A. MFG. CO.
Murfreesboro, Tenessee

Model 82 Rifle

A .50 caliber Browning semi-automatic rifle with a 37" barrel and 11-shot magazine. The barrel fitted with a muzzle brake, and the receiver with a telescope. Approximate weight 35 lbs. Parkerized. Manufactured from 1985 to 1987.

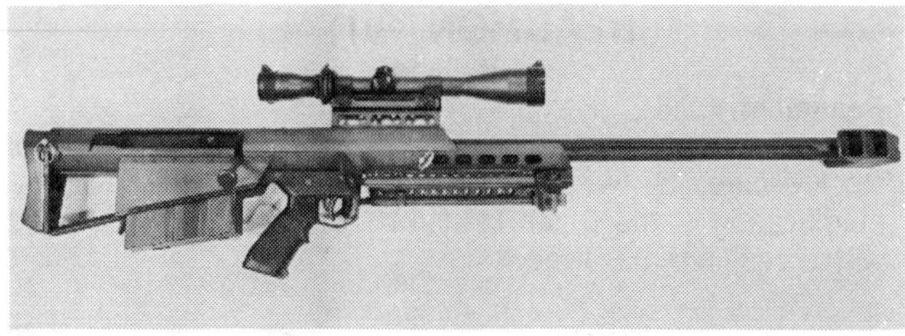

Exc.	V.G.	Good	Fair	Poor
3900	3500	2900	2250	1750

Model 82A1

As above, with a 33" barrel and a 10X telescope.

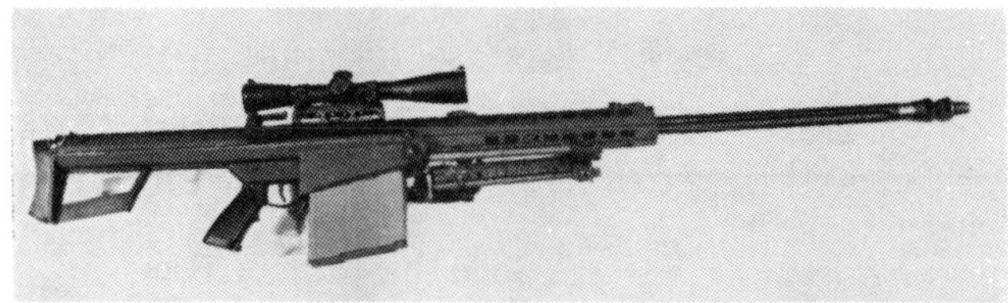

Exc.	V.G.	Good	Fair	Poor
5800	5000	4000	2950	2100

BARRETT, J. B. and A.B. & CO.
Wytheville, Virginia

Barrett Muskets and Rifled Muskets

Overall length- 57 3/4"; barrel length 41 1/2" - 42"; caliber-.69. Markings: Although the Barretts placed no marks of their own on their alterations, most were effected on Virginia Manufactory muskets, whose lockplates are marked "VIRGINIA/Manufactory" forward of the hammer and "RICHMOND/(date)" on the tail.

For many years collectors considered the adaptations of Hall rifles and carbines from breechloaders to muzzleloaders to be the product of J.B. Barrett & Co. of Wytheville. Recent evidence, however, confirms that those adaptations were actually effected in Danville, Virginia by another firm (see READ & WATSON). Nevertheless, the Barretts of Wytheville did adapt arms during the early years of the American Civil War. The adaptation, effected almost exclusively upon Virginia Manufactory flintlock muskets consisted of percussioning by means of the cone-in-barrel and rifling of the barrels with seven narrow grooves. In 1861 and 1862, the Barretts percussioned a total of 1250 muskets, of which 744 were rifled.

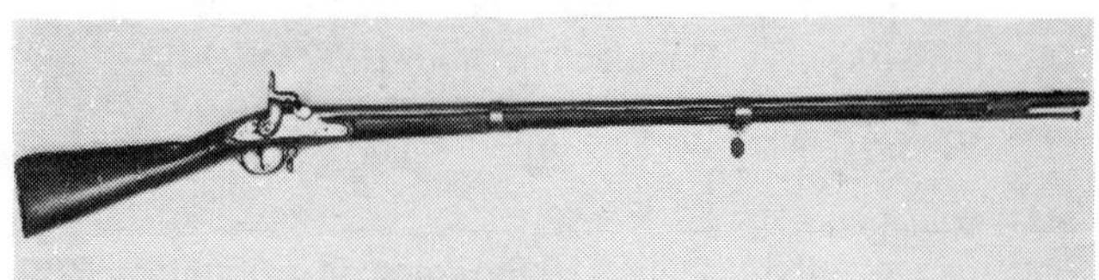

Courtesy Milwaukee Public Museum, Milwaukee, Wisconsin.

Exc.	V.G.	Good	Fair	Poor
2700	2300	1800	1200	700

BAR-STO PRECISION MACHINE
Burbank, California

Bar-Sto 25

A .25 caliber semi-automatic pistol with a brushed stainless-steel receiver and slide. Walnut grips. Produced in 1974.

Exc.	V.G.	Good	Fair	Poor
200	175	150	125	100

BASCARAN
Eibar, Spain

Martian

A 6.35mm or 7.65mm caliber semi-automatic pistol. The slide is marked "Automatic Pistol Martian". Blued with black plastic grips having the monogram "MAB" cast in them.

Exc.	V.G.	Good	Fair	Poor
225	175	135	100	75

Thunder

As above, in 6.35mm caliber. The slide is not marked, but the tradename "Thunder" is cast in the grips.

Exc.	V.G.	Good	Fair	Poor
250	200	165	125	90

BAUER F. A. CORP.
Fraser, Michigan

Bauer 25 Automatic

A .25 caliber semi-automatic pistol made of stainless-steel with a 2.5" barrel and 6 shot magazine. Walnut or imitation pearl grips. Manufactured from 1972 to 1984.

Exc.	V.G.	Good	Fair	Poor
200	175	150	110	80

The Rabbit

A .22 caliber by .410 bore combination rifle/shotgun, with a tubular metal stock. Manufactured between 1982 and 1984.

Exc.	V.G.	Good	Fair	Poor
135	110	100	75	50

BAYARD
SEE--Pieper, H. & N.
Herstal, Belgium

BAYONNE, MANUFACTURE D'ARMES
Bayonne, France
A/K/A MAB

MAB Modele A
A 6.35mm semi-automatic pistol with a 2" barrel. Blued with black plastic grips having the monogram "MAB" cast in them. Manufactured from 1921 to date.

Exc.	V.G.	Good	Fair	Poor
175	150	125	100	75

MAB Modele B
Similar to the above, with the slide marked "Pistolet Automatique MAB Brevete." Manufactured from 1932 to 1949.

Exc.	V.G.	Good	Fair	Poor
250	225	200	150	110

MAB Modele C
Patterned after the Model 1910 Browning, in 7.65mm or .380 ACP. Manufactured after 1933.

Exc.	V.G.	Good	Fair	Poor
235	210	175	135	110

MAB Modele D currently imported by CIA
As above, with a 4" barrel. Manufactured from 1933 to date.

Exc.	V.G.	Good	Fair	Poor
175	150	125	100	75

MAB Modele E
Similar to the above, in 6.35mm caliber. Introduced in 1949.

Exc.	V.G.	Good	Fair	Poor
235	210	175	135	100

MAB Modele F
Similar to the Model B, but with interchangeable barrels from 2.65" to 7.25" in length and in .22 caliber.

Exc.	V.G.	Good	Fair	Poor
210	185	150	110	85

MAB Modele GZ
Manufactured by Arizmendi of Eibar, Spain, and in 7.65mm caliber. The slide marked "Echasa Eibar (Espana) Cal. .32 Modelo GZ-MAB Espanola."

Exc.	V.G.	Good	Fair	Poor
210	185	150	110	85

MAB Modele R
Similar to the Model D, with an external hammer and in 7.65mm or 7.65mm long caliber.

Exc.	V.G.	Good	Fair	Poor
285	250	200	150	110

MAB Modele R Para
As above, in 9mm caliber.

Exc.	V.G.	Good	Fair	Poor
400	350	300	225	150

MAB Modele PA-15
As above, with a 15 shot magazine.

Exc.	V.G.	Good	Fair	Poor
400	350	300	225	150

Modele "Le Chasseur"
The Model F with an external hammer and in .22 caliber. Offered in a variety of barrel lengths and sight styles. Introduced in 1953.

Exc.	V.G.	Good	Fair	Poor
225	200	175	145	100

Note: MAB pistols that were sold in the U.S.A. were retailed by the Winfield Arms Company of Los Angeles, California, and are marked "Made in France for WAC." This does not affect values to any appreciable degree.

BEATTIE, J.
London, England

Beattie Gas Seal Revolver
A .42 caliber single-action percussion revolver with a 6.25" octagonal barrel. When the hammer is cocked, the cylinder is forced forward against the barrel breech, thus, effecting a gas seal. Blued, casehardened with walnut grips.

Exc.	V.G.	Good	Fair	Poor
4250	3950	3250	2700	2200

BEAUMONT
Maastrict, Netherlands

1873 Dutch Service Revolver, Old Model
A 9.4mm double-action 6-shot revolver weighing 2 lbs. 12 oz.

Exc.	V.G.	Good	Fair	Poor
250	225	185	145	100

1873 Dutch Service Revolver, New Model
As above, with a 6-shot cylinder.

Exc.	V.G.	Good	Fair	Poor
250	225	185	145	100

1873 KIM, Small Model
As above, with an octagonal barrel and 5-shot cylinder.

Exc.	V.G.	Good	Fair	Poor
265	240	200	150	110

BEAUMONT, ADAMS
SEE--Adams

BEAUMONT-VITALI
Holland

Beaumont-Vitali
An 11mm caliber bolt-action rifle with a 30" barrel and full stock secured by two barrel bands. Essentially this rifle is a modification of the Dutch Model 1871 single shot rifle fitted with a Vitali box magazine.

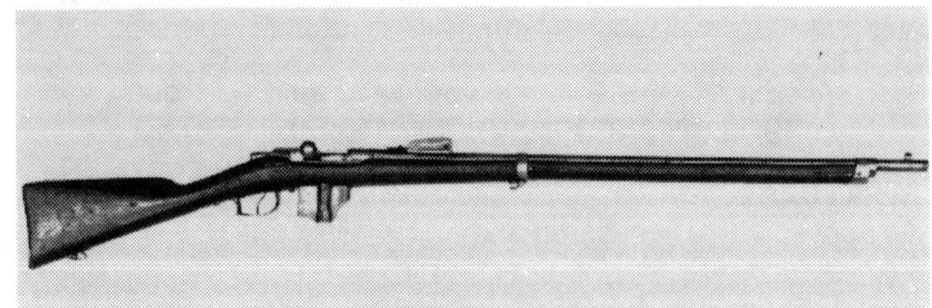

Courtesy Milwaukee Public Museum, Milwaukee, Wisconsin.

Exc.	V.G.	Good	Fair	Poor
200	175	125	90	65

BECKER AND HOLLANDER
Suhl, Germany

Beholla
A 7.65mm caliber semi-automatic pistol produced under contract for the German War Department. The right side of the slide is marked "Becker U Hollander Waffenbau Suhl" and the left side "Selbstlade Pistol Beholla Cal. 7.65."

Exc.	V.G.	Good	Fair	Poor
300	275	225	175	125

BEEMAN PRECISION ARMS, INC.
Santa Rosa, California

Although primarily known as an importer and retailer of airguns, Beeman Precision Arms, Inc. has marketed several firearms.

MP-08

A .380 caliber semi-automatic pistol with a 3.5" barrel and 6-shot magazine, resembling the German Luger. Blued. Introduced in 1968.

NIB	Exc.	V.G.	Good	Fair	Poor
390	350	300	210	175	110

P-08

As above, in .22 caliber with an 8-shot magazine and walnut grips. Introduced in 1969.

NIB	Exc.	V.G.	Good	Fair	Poor
390	350	300	210	175	110

SP Standard

A .22 caliber single shot target pistol with 8" to 15" barrels. Fitted with adjustable sights and walnut grips. Imported in 1985 and 1986.

NIB	Exc.	V.G.	Good	Fair	Poor
225	200	175	150	125	100

SP Deluxe

As above, with a walnut forend.

Exc.	V.G.	Good	Fair	Poor
250	225	200	175	125

BEERSTECHER, FREDERICK
Philadelphia, Pennsylvania(1846-1856)
Lewisburg, Pennsylvania (1857-1868)

Superposed Load Pocket Pistol

A .41 caliber superimposed load percussion pistol with an average barrel length of 3", German silver mounts and walnut stock. The hammer is fitted with a moveable twin striker head so that the first charge in the barrel can be fired and then the second fired. The lock is normally marked "F. Beerstecher's/Patent 1855". Prospective purchasers are advised to secure a qualified appraisal prior to acquisition.

Exc.	V.G.	Good	Fair	Poor
5000	4500	4000	3000	2500

BEHOLLA
SEE—Becher and Hollander

BEISTEGUI, HERMANOS
Eibar, Spain

Beistegui "RUBY"

A 7.65mm caliber semi-automatic pistol copied after the Ruby. The slide marked "1914 Model Automatic Pistol Beistegui Hermanos Eiber (Espana)."

Exc.	V.G.	Good	Fair	Poor
200	150	125	80	50

Bulwark #1

The Bulwark is a fixed-barrel, external-hammer, blowback semi-automatic chambered for the 7.65mm cartridge. It bears no external markings except the monogram "B&H" molded into the grips.

Exc.	V.G.	Good	Fair	Poor
150	125	100	75	50

Bulwark #2

A copy of the Browning .25 caliber semi-automatic pistol. The slide marked "Fabrique de Armes de Guerre de Grand Precision Bulwark patent Depose No. 67259."

Exc.	V.G.	Good	Fair	Poor
150	125	100	75	50

Libia

As above, with the mark "Libia".

Exc.	V.G.	Good	Fair	Poor
150	125	100	75	50

BENELLI
Italy
Importer—Heckler & Koch
Chantilly, Virginia

Shotguns

Model SL-121 V

This is a semi-automatic 12 gauge with 3" chambers and various barrel lengths and chokes. It has a black anodized alloy receiver and was discontinued in 1985.

NIB	Exc.	V.G.	Good	Fair	Poor
475	450	400	350	300	225

Model SL 121 Slug

This model is similar to the SL-121 V with a 21" cylinder-bore barrel and rifle sights. It too was discontinued in 1985.

NIB	Exc.	V.G.	Good	Fair	Poor
475	450	400	350	300	225

Model SL-123 V

This model has the improved, fast, third-generation action. Otherwise it resembles the earlier SL-121.

NIB	Exc.	V.G.	Good	Fair	Poor
500	475	425	350	300	225

Model SL201

This is a 20 gauge with a 26", improved cylinder barrel. It is similar in appearance to the SL-123.

NIB	Exc.	V.G.	Good	Fair	Poor
500	475	425	350	300	225

M3 Super 90

This is an improved version of the Benelli pump action and semi-automatic inertia recoil system. The shotgun can be converted from pump to semi-automatic by turning a spring loaded ring located a the end of the forearm. It has a rotating bolt system and is chambered for 12 gauge, with a 3" chamber. This model has a 19.75" barrel with cylinder bore and rifle sights with a 7 round tubular magazine. It has a matte black finish and a black fiberglass pistol grip stock and forearm. This model was introduced in 1986.

NIB	Exc.	V.G.	Good	Fair	Poor
800	750	700	600	450	300

M3 Super 90 Folding Stock

Same as above but furnished with a folding tubular steel stock.

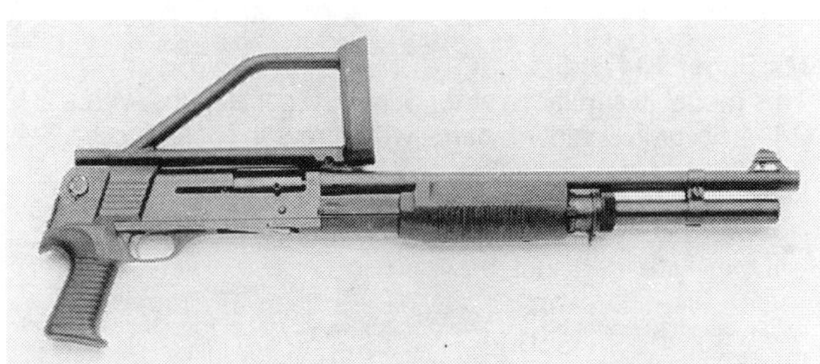

NIB	Exc.	V.G.	Good	Fair	Poor
950	900	800	700	550	350

M1 Super 90 Tactical

This is a semi-automatic 12 gauge shotgun with an inertia recoil system. It features a 18.5" plain barrel with 3 screw in choke tubes. Available in either standard polymer stock or pistol grip stock. Ghost ring sights are standard. Gun weighs 6.5 lbs. First introduced in 1993.

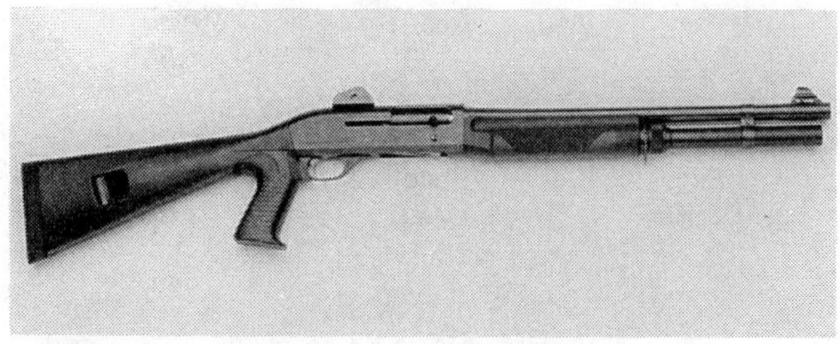

NIB	Exc.	V.G.	Good	Fair	Poor
625	575	525	450	350	275

M1 Super 90 Defense Gun

Comes standard with polymer pistol grip stock, 19.75" barrel, plain sights, or ghost ring sights. Offered in 12 gauge only. Weighs 7.1 lbs.

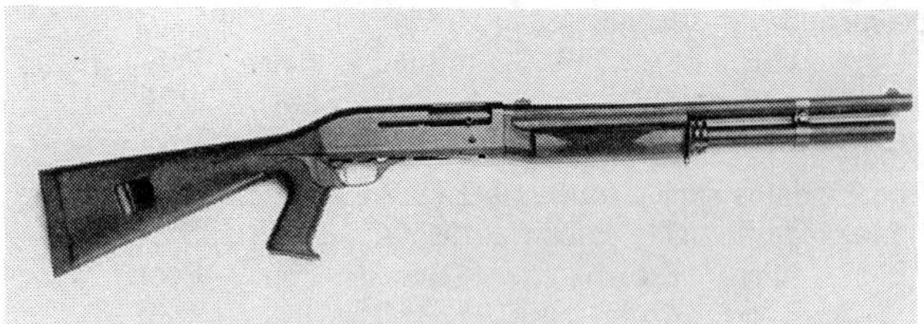

NIB	Exc.	V.G.	Good	Fair	Poor
625	575	525	450	350	275

M1 Super 90 Slug Gun

Equipped with a standard black polymer stock with 19.75" plain barrel. Fitted with a 7 shot magazine. Ghost ring sights are an option. Weighs 6.7 lbs.

NIB	Exc.	V.G.	Good	Fair	Poor
625	575	525	450	350	275

M1 Super 90 Entry Gun

This model is fitted with a black polymer pistol grip stock with 14" plain barrel. Magazine holds 5 shells. Plain or ghost ring sights available. **CAUTION: Restricted sale, class III Transfer required.**

NIB	Exc.	V.G.	Good	Fair	Poor
700	650	600	500	400	300

M1 Super 90 Field

This model is similar to other Super 90 series guns with a 21", 24",26", or 28" vent rib barrel with screw-in choke tubes.

NIB	Exc.	V.G.	Good	Fair	Poor
600	550	500	400	350	275

M1 Super 90 Sporting Special

INtroduced in 1993 this 12 gauge shotgun is similar to the Super 90 with the addition of non-reflective surfaces, 18.5" plain barrel with 3 choke tubes(IC, Mod, Full). The gun is fitted with ghost ring sights.

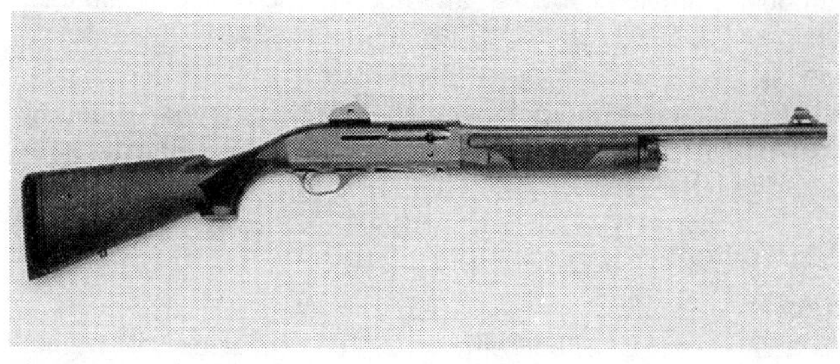

NIB	Exc.	V.G.	Good	Fair	Poor
625	575	525	425	375	300

Montefeltro Super 90

Introduced in 1987, this model is similar to the Super 90 Field with a checkered walnut stock and forearm with gloss finish. Offered with 21", 24", 26", or 28" vent rib barrel. Available in 12 gauge only with 3" chambers. This shotgun offered in left hand model also.

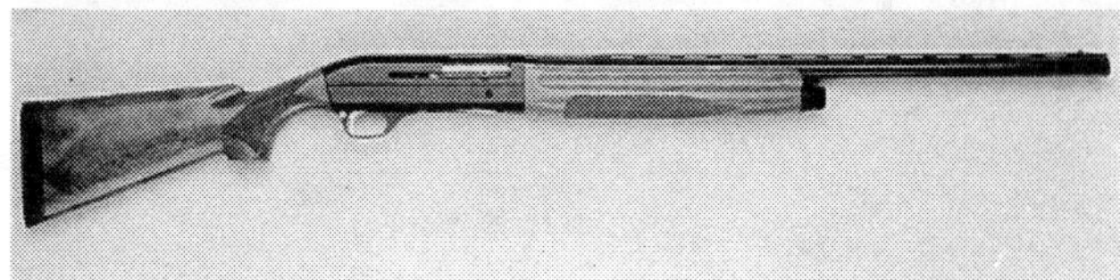

NIB	Exc.	V.G.	Good	Fair	Poor
650	600	550	450	350	250

Montefelto 20 Gauge

Introduced in 1993, this model features a walnut checkered stock with 26" vent rib barrel. Gun weighs 5.75 lbs.

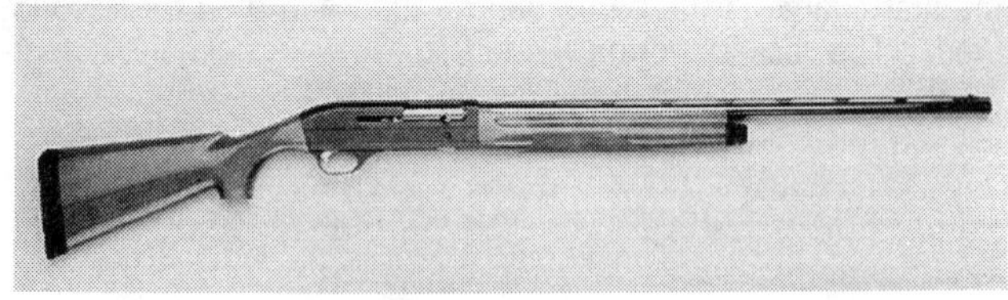

NIB	Exc.	V.G.	Good	Fair	Poor
650	600	550	450	350	250

Super Black Eagle

This model is similar to the Montefeltro Super 90 Hunter with a polymer or walnut stock and forearm. It is offered with a 24",26", or 28" vent rib-barrel with 5 screw-in choke tubes. Chambered for 12 gauge from 2 3/4" to 3 1/2". It was introduced in 1989. The 24" barrel was introduced in 1993.

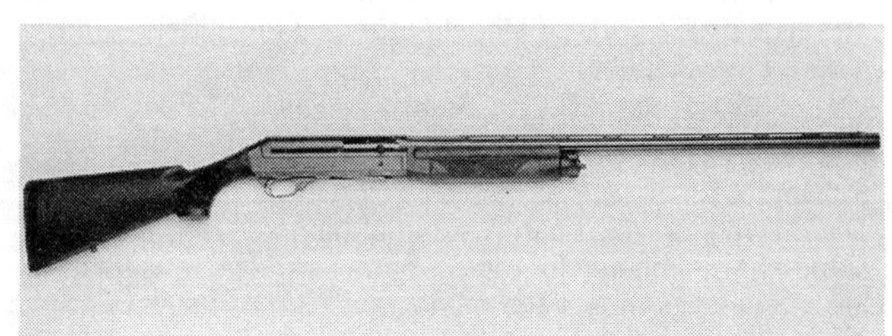

NIB	Exc.	V.G.	Good	Fair	Poor
875	800	750	600	500	350

Super Black Eagle Custom Slug Gun

This 12 gauge model has a 24" rifled barrel with 3" chamber. It comes standard with matte metal finish. Gun weighs 7.6 lbs.

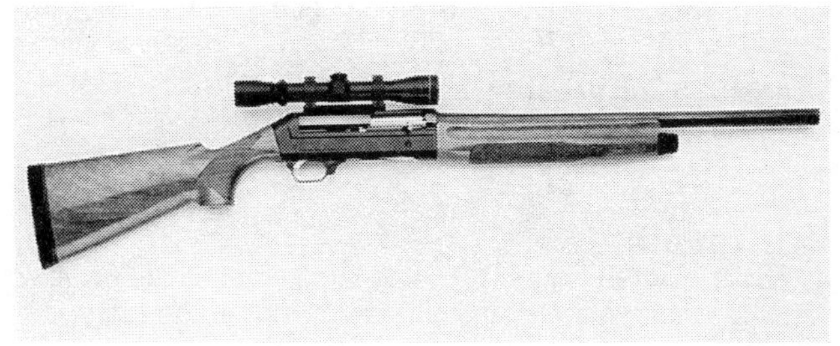

NIB	Exc.	V.G.	Good	Fair	Poor
875	800	750	600	500	350

Black Eagle Competition Gun

Offered in 12 gauge only this model is fitted with an etched receiver, mid rib bead, competition stock, and 5 screw in choke tubes. Available in either 26" or 28" vent rib barrel. The upper receiver is steel while the lower receiver is lightweight alloy. Weighs 7.3 lbs.

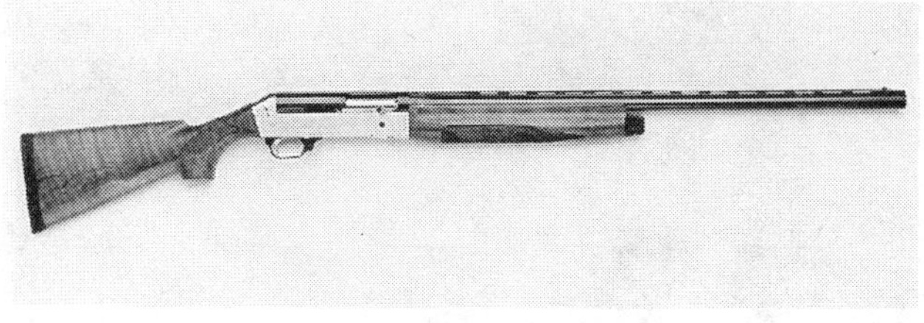

NIB	Exc.	V.G.	Good	Fair	Poor
875	800	750	600	500	350

Handguns

Model B-76

This is an all-steel, double-action semi-automatic chambered for the 9mm Parabellum. It has a 4.25" barrel, fixed sights, and an 8-round detachable magazine.

NIB	Exc.	V.G.	Good	Fair	Poor
450	400	350	300	200	100

Model B-76S

This is the target version of the B-76. It has a 5.5" barrel, adjustable sights, and target grips.

NIB	Exc.	V.G.	Good	Fair	Poor
550	500	400	300	200	100

Model B-77

This Model is similar to the B-76 except that it is chambered for the .32 ACP.

NIB	Exc.	V.G.	Good	Fair	Poor
350	300	250	200	150	100

Model B-80

This is another Model similar to the B-76 except that it is chambered for the .30 Luger cartridge.

NIB	Exc.	V.G.	Good	Fair	Poor
400	350	300	200	150	100

Model B-80S

This is the target version of the B-80 with a 5.5" barrel and adjustable sights. It also features target grips.

NIB	Exc.	V.G.	Good	Fair	Poor
500	450	400	300	200	100

BENSON FIREARMS

Seattle, Washington

SEE--Aldo Uberti

Formerly the importer of the fine Italian Uberti firearms. Their arrangement ended in 1989, and these guns are now imported by Uberti U.S.A., Inc.

BENTLEY, JOSEPH

Birmingham, England

Bentley Revolver

A .44 caliber double-action percussion revolver with a 7" barrel and 5-shot cylinder. Blued, casehardened with walnut grips.

Exc.	V.G.	Good	Fair	Poor
3500	3000	2500	1850	1200

BENTZ

SEE—Austrian Military Firearms

BERETTA, DR. F.

Brescia, Italy

Black Diamond Field Grade

A boxlock over/under shotgun produced in a variety of gauges and barrel lengths with single triggers and automatic ejectors. Blued, French casehardened with a walnut stock.

NIB	Exc.	V.G.	Good	Fair	Poor
975	850	700	575	450	375

The above model is produced in four embellished grades as follows:

Grade One

NIB	Exc.	V.G.	Good	Fair	Poor
1450	1300	1000	850	600	500

Grade Two

NIB	Exc.	V.G.	Good	Fair	Poor
2100	1850	1600	1250	1000	800

Grade Three

NIB	Exc.	V.G.	Good	Fair	Poor
3000	2750	2200	1850	1500	1150

Grade Four

NIB	Exc.	V.G.	Good	Fair	Poor
4000	3750	3200	2850	2500	2150

Gamma Standard

A 12, 16 or 20 gauge boxlock over/under shotgun with 26" or 28" barrels, single trigger and automatic ejectors. Blued, French casehardened with a walnut stock. Imported from 1984 to 1988.

Exc.	V.G.	Good	Fair	Poor
400	375	300	225	150

Gamma Deluxe

As above, but more finely finished.

Exc.	V.G.	Good	Fair	Poor
600	575	500	400	250

Gamma Target

As above, in a trap or skeet version. Imported from 1986 to 1988.

Exc.	V.G.	Good	Fair	Poor
550	500	450	375	300

America Standard

A .410 bore boxlock over/under shotgun with 26" or 28" barrels. Blued, French casehardened with a walnut stock. Imported from 1984 to 1988.

Exc.	V.G.	Good	Fair	Poor
300	275	225	185	150

America Deluxe

As above, but more finely finished.

Exc.	V.G.	Good	Fair	Poor
375	325	275	220	175

Europa

As above, with a 26" barrel and engraved action. Imported from 1984 to 1988.

Exc.	V.G.	Good	Fair	Poor
275	250	185	150	125

Europa Deluxe
As above, but more finely finished.

Exc.	V.G.	Good	Fair	Poor
375	350	285	250	225

Francia Standard
A .410 bore boxlock double-barrel shotgun with varying barrel lengths, double triggers and manual extractors. Blued with a walnut stock. Imported from 1986 to 1988.

Exc.	V.G.	Good	Fair	Poor
240	210	185	150	125

Alpha Three
A 12, 16 or 20 gauge boxlock double-barrel shotgun with 26" or 28" barrels, single triggers and automatic ejectors. Blued, French casehardened with a walnut stock. Imported from 1984 to 1988.

Exc.	V.G.	Good	Fair	Poor
400	350	300	225	150

Beta Three
A single-barrel, break-open, field-grade gun chambered for all gauges and offered with a ventilated rib barrel from 24" to 32" in length. The receiver chrome-plated, and the stock of walnut. Imported from 1985 to 1988.

Exc.	V.G.	Good	Fair	Poor
150	135	110	75	50

BERETTA, PIETRO
Brescia, Italy
IMPORTER — Beretta U.S.A. Corp.
Accokeek, Maryland

Fabbrica d'Armi Pierto Beretta, of Gardone Val Trompia, near Milan, Italy is one of the worlds oldest industrial concerns. A leading maker of sporting, military, and civilian firearms this firm has been in existence for almost 500 years. Founded by Bartolomeo Beretta, a master gunbarrel maker, in 1526 his son Giovannino followed his father's footsteps and subsequent generations have developed this firm into a world wide success. Beretta manufactured its first pistol, the Model 1915, in 1915 as a wartime project.

Spread over 500,000 square feet and employing 2,200 employees this old world firm captured the United States military contract in 1985 for its standard issue sidearm, the Model 92F. These pistols are currently manufactured at Beretta U.S.A.'s plant in Maryland. esides the affiliate in the United States, Beretta has three other located in France, Greece, and Rome.

The American affiliate was formed in 1977 to handle U.S. demand. A year later it began to manufacture some firearms, namely the Model 92F. At the present time Beretta has delivered over 250,000 Model 92F pistols to the U.S. military.

Model 1910
A 6.35mm caliber semi-automatic pistol with 2" barrel, fixed sights and 7-shot magazine. Blued with walnut grips. Manufactured between 1910 and 1934.

Exc.	V.G.	Good	Fair	Poor
300	275	200	150	100

Model 1915
A 7.65mm caliber semi-automatic pistol with 3.5" barrel, fixed sights and 8 shot magazine. Blued with walnut grips. The slide is marked "Pietro Beretta Brescia Casa Fondata nel 1680 Cal. 7.65mm Brevetto 1915." Manufactured between 1915 and 1919.

Exc.	V.G.	Good	Fair	Poor
295	270	200	150	100

Model 1915 2nd Variation
As above, in 9mm Glisenti caliber.

Exc.	V.G.	Good	Fair	Poor
375	325	250	200	125

Model 1915/1919
As above, with an improved version that incorporated a new barrel-mounting method and a longer cutout in the top of the slide.

Courtesy Orville Reichert.

Exc.	V.G.	Good	Fair	Poor
300	275	200	150	100

Model 1919
Similar to Model 1915, in 6.35mm caliber. Manufactured between 1920 and 1939.

Exc.	V.G.	Good	Fair	Poor
300	275	200	150	100

Model 1923
A 9mm caliber semi-automatic pistol with 4" barrel and 8-shot magazine. Blued with steel grips. The slide is marked, "Brev 1915-1919 Mlo 1923." Manufactured from 1923 to 1935.

Exc.	V.G.	Good	Fair	Poor
450	400	325	225	150

Model 1931
A 7.65mm caliber semi-automatic pistol with 3.5" barrel and open-top slide. Blued with walnut grips and marked, "RM" separated by an anchor.

Exc.	V.G.	Good	Fair	Poor
350	325	250	200	150

Model 1934

As above, with 9mm short caliber. The slide is marked, "P. Beretta Cal. 9 Corto-Mo 1934 Brevet Gardone VT." This inscription is followed by the date of manufacture that was given numerically, followed by a Roman numeral that denoted the year of manufacture on the Fascist calendar which began in 1922. Examples are marked, "RM" (Navy), "RE" (Army), "RA" (Air Force), and "PS" (Police). Manufactured between 1934 and 1959.

Courtesy Orville Reichert.

Exc.	V.G.	Good	Fair	Poor
300	275	200	150	100

Model 1935

As above, in 7.65mm caliber. Post-war versions are known. Manufactured from 1935 to 1959.

Courtesy Orville Reichert.

Exc.	V.G.	Good	Fair	Poor
275	250	200	150	100

Model 318

An improved version of the old Model 1919 with the butt reshaped to afford a better grip. Chambered for the .25 ACP cartridge and has a 2.5" barrel. Variety of finishes with plastic grips. In the United States it is known as the "Panther." Manufactured between 1935 and 1946.

Exc.	V.G.	Good	Fair	Poor
275	250	200	150	100

Model 418

As above, with a rounded grip and a cocking indicator. It is known as the "Bantam" in the U.S. Introduced in 1947.

Exc.	V.G.	Good	Fair	Poor
225	200	175	135	90

Model 420

An engraved and chrome-plated Model 418.

Exc.	V.G.	Good	Fair	Poor
325	300	275	200	150

Model 421

An engraved, gold-plated Model 418 with tortoise-shell grips.

Exc.	V.G.	Good	Fair	Poor
475	425	325	250	185

Model 948

A .22 l.r. version of the Model 1934. It has either a 3.5" or 6" barrel.

Exc.	V.G.	Good	Fair	Poor
190	165	135	100	75

Model 949 Olympic Target

A .22 caliber semi-automatic pistol with 8.75" barrel, adjustable sights and muzzle break. Blued with checkered, walnut grips. Manufactured from 1959 to 1964.

Exc.	V.G.	Good	Fair	Poor
700	650	550	400	250

Model 950

A .22 caliber semi-automatic pistol with 2.25" barrel hinged at the front and could be pivoted forward for cleaning or loading, making this either a semi-auto or single-shot pistol. Blued with plastic grips. Introduced in 1955. A 4" barrel version also available. This model is known as the "Minx" in the U.S.

Exc.	V.G.	Good	Fair	Poor
150	135	110	85	50

Model 950B

As above, in .25 caliber, known as the "Jetfire" in the United States.

Exc.	V.G.	Good	Fair	Poor
150	135	110	85	50

Model 951

A 9mm caliber semi-automatic pistol with 4.5" barrel and fixed sights. Blued with plastic grips. It is also known as the "Brigadier." Manufactured from 1952 to present day.

Exc.	V.G.	Good	Fair	Poor
300	225	200	175	125

Model 70

The Model 948 with cross-bolt safety, hold-open device, and a push-button magazine release. There are a number of subvariations available chambered for the .22 l.r., .32 ACP, and the .380 ACP cartridges. Available with a 3.5" or 6" barrel and has a detachable magazine. Also known as the "Puma" or the "Cougar." It was introduced in 1958 and discontinued in 1985.

Exc.	V.G.	Good	Fair	Poor
250	200	175	125	85

Model 101

Another name for the Model 70T pistol.

Exc.	V.G.	Good	Fair	Poor
250	225	175	150	100

Model 20

A .25 ACP double-action pistol with 2.5" barrel and 9-shot magazine. Blued with either walnut or plastic grips. Discontinued in 1985.

Exc.	V.G.	Good	Fair	Poor
175	150	125	90	75

Model 21

This small frame semi-automatic pistol, chambered for the .22 Long Rifle or .25 ACP cartridge, features a 2.4" tip-up barrel with fixed sights and a magazine capacity of 8 rounds(.25 ACP) or 7 rounds(.22L.R.). Comes with either plastic or walnut grips and a deluxe version with gold line engraving. Pistol weighs about 11.5 oz depending on caliber.

Standard model

NIB	Exc.	V.G.	Good	Fair	Poor
200	175	150	125	100	75

Gold Engraved Model

NIB	Exc.	V.G.	Good	Fair	Poor
250	200	175	150	100	75

Model 71 (Jaguar)

Similar to above model and chambered for .22 L.R. cartridge. Frame is alloy and is fitted with a 3.5" barrel. Barrels with 6" lengths are encountered but have more value and are known as Model 72.

Exc.	V.G.	Good	Fair	Poor
225	200	175	125	100

Model 72-6" barrel

NIB	Exc.	V.G.	Good	Fair	Poor
350	300	275	225	150	125

Model 90

A double-action, semi-automatic pocket pistol with a 3.5" barrel and 8-round magazine. Manufactured from 1969 to 1983.

Exc.	V.G.	Good	Fair	Poor
275	250	200	150	125

Model 92

A 9mm caliber double-action, semi-automatic pistol with a 5" barrel, fixed sights and a 16-round, double-stack magazine. Blued with plastic grips. Introduced in 1976 and is now discontinued.

Exc.	V.G.	Good	Fair	Poor
400	375	300	250	200

Model 92SB-P

As above, but with a polished finish. Manufactured from 1980 to 1985.

Exc.	V.G.	Good	Fair	Poor
450	425	350	300	225

Model 92SB Compact

As above, with a 4.3" barrel and a shortened grip frame that holds a 14-shot magazine. Either blued or nickle-plated with wood or plastic grips. The nickle version would be worth an additional 15 percent. The wood grips would add $20 to the value. Introduced in 1980 and discontinued in 1985.

Exc.	V.G.	Good	Fair	Poor
475	450	400	350	275

Model 92FS

The current production Model 92 chambered for the 9mm Parabellum cartridge. Barrel length is 4.9" and rear sight is a 3-dot combat drift adjustable. The magazine capacity is 15 rounds. This semi-automatic pistol features and double or single action operation. The safety is manual type. The frame is a light alloy sand blasted and anodized black. The barrel slide is steel. Grips are plastic checkered with black matte finish. Equipped with spare magazine cleaning rod, and hard carrying case. Pistol weighs 34.4 oz empty.

NIB	Exc.	V.G.	Good	Fair	Poor
450	400	350	300	200	150

Model 96FS

Identical to Model 92Fs but fitted with a 10 round magazine and chambered for the .40 S&W. Introduced in 1992.

NIB	Exc.	V.G.	Good	Fair	Poor
450	400	350	300	200	150

Model 92/96FS Inox

Same as above except the barrel, slide, trigger, extractor, and other components are made of stainless steel. the frame is made of lightweight anodized aluminum alloy.

NIB	Exc.	V.G.	Good	Fair	Poor
550	500	450	350	300	200

Model 92/96FS Centurion

Chambered for either the 9mm or .40 S&W this model features a 4.3" barrel but yet retains a full grip to accommodate a 15 round magazine(9mm) or 10 rounds(.40 S&W). Pistol weighs approximately 33.2 oz. Introduced in 1993. Black sandblasted finish.

NIB	Exc.	V.G.	Good	Fair	Poor
450	400	350	300	200	150

Model 92F

A 9mm Parabellum caliber double action semi-automatic pistol with a 4.9" barrel, fixed sights and a 15-shot double-stack magazine with an extended base. Matte-blued finish with walnut or plastic grips. Introduced in 1984.

NIB	Exc.	V.G.	Good	Fair	Poor
450	400	350	300	200	150

Model 92F Compact

As above, with a 4.3" barrel and a 13-shot magazine.

NIB	Exc.	V.G.	Good	Fair	Poor
450	400	350	300	200	150

Model 92 FS Compact "Type M"

Essentially the same as the Model 92FS Compact but with the exception of a single column magazine that holds 8 rounds and reduces the grip thickness of the pistol. Pistol weighs 30.9 oz.

NIB	Exc.	V.G.	Good	Fair	Poor
450	400	350	300	200	150

Model 92 Deluxe

Identical dimensions to the full size Model 92Fs with the addition of gold plated engraved frame with gold plated extra magazine in fitted leather presentation hard case. Grips are walnut briar with gold initial plate. Introduced in 1993.

NIB	Exc.	V.G.	Good	Fair	Poor
3750	3000	2000	1000	750	500

Model 92/96D

Same specifications as the standard Model 92 and Model 96 except that this variation has no visible hammer and is double action only. This model has no manual safety. Pistol weighs 33.8 oz.

NIB	Exc.	V.G.	Good	Fair	Poor
425	375	325	275	200	150

Model 92 Competition Conversion Kit

The kit includes a 7.3" barrel with counter weight and elevated front sight, semi-automatic, walnut grips, and fully adjustable rear sight. Comes in special carrying case with the basic pistol.

Kit Price Only:

NIB	Exc.	V.G.	Good	Fair	Poor
500	350	300	200	150	100

Model 84

This is a small semi automatic pistol chambered for the .380 cartridge. It has a double column magazine that holds 13 rounds. Offered in blue or nickel finish. Grips are checkered black plastic or checkered wood.

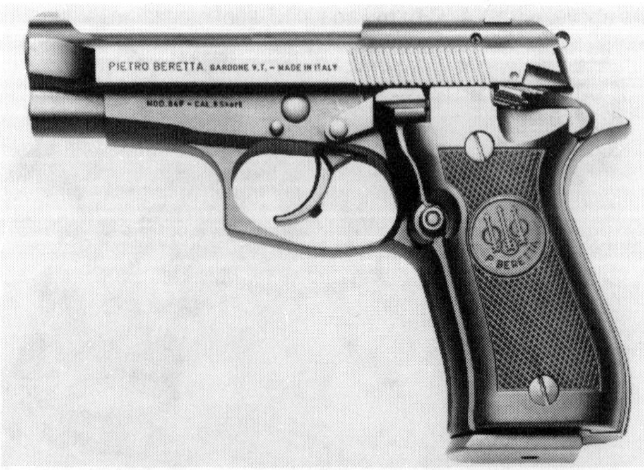

NIB	Exc.	V.G.	Good	Fair	Poor
425	385	325	275	200	150

Model 85

Similar in appearance to the Model 84 but features a single column magazine with a capacity of 8 rounds. Available in blue or nickel finish. Grips are checkered black plastic. Pistol weighs 22 oz.

NIB	Exc.	V.G.	Good	Fair	Poor
425	385	325	275	200	150

Model 86

This .380 ACP semi-automatic pistol has a 4.4" tip-up barrel. Magazine capacity is 8 rounds. Furnished with checkered wood grips. Pistol weighs 23 oz.

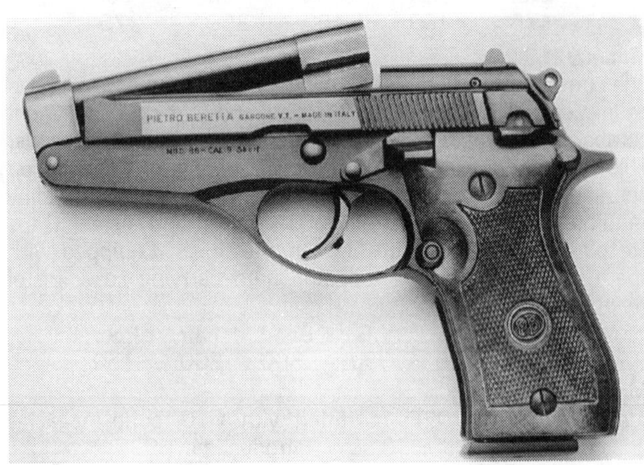

NIB	Exc.	V.G.	Good	Fair	Poor
425	385	325	275	200	150

Model 87

A .22 caliber double-action, semi-automatic target pistol with a 3.8" or 6" barrel, adjustable sights with a 7-shot magazine. Blued with checkered walnut grips. Introduced in 1986.

NIB	Exc.	V.G.	Good	Fair	Poor
450	400	350	300	225	150

Model 89

A .22 caliber, semi-automatic target pistol with adjustable sights, and 10-shot, detachable magazine. Matte finish with hand-fitting walnut grips. Introduced in 1988.

NIB	Exc.	V.G.	Good	Fair	Poor
625	575	500	400	275	200

Model 950 BS

A .22 or .25 ACP caliber semi-automatic pistol with pivoting, 2.5" or 4" barrels and either a 6- or 8-shot magazine. Either blued or nickle-plated with black plastic grips. The nickle-plated version is worth an extra 15 percent.

NIB	Exc.	V.G.	Good	Fair	Poor
150	125	100	75	60	45

AR-70

A .222 or .223 caliber, semi-automatic rifle with a 17.7" barrel, adjustable diopter sights, and a 5, 8, or 30-shot magazine. Black epoxy finish with a synthetic stock.

Model 500 Custom

A bolt-action sporting rifle chambered for a variety of calibers with a 24" barrel, open sights, three action lengths and a 3- or 4-shot magazine. Blued with a checkered walnut stock.

500 Custom

Exc.	V.G.	Good	Fair	Poor
600	525	400	325	275

This model was offered in five grades:

Model 500S

Exc.	V.G.	Good	Fair	Poor
625	550	425	350	300

Model 500DL

Exc.	V.G.	Good	Fair	Poor
1400	1250	1000	775	650

Model 500DEELL

Exc.	V.G.	Good	Fair	Poor
1600	1450	1200	975	800

Model 500DEELLS

Exc.	V.G.	Good	Fair	Poor
1625	1475	1225	1000	825

Model 501

501 Deluxe

A .243 or .308 caliber bolt-action rifle with a 23" barrel, furnished without sights and a 6-shot magazine. Blued with a checkered walnut stock. It was discontinued in 1986. It was offered in the same variations as the Model 500 series-501S, 501DL, 501DLS, 501EELL, and 501EELLS. The values for this series are the same as for the 500 series rifles.

Model 502

A .270, 7mm Remington Magnum, and the .30-06 caliber bolt action rifle with a 24" barrel, without sights and a 5-shot magazine. Blued with a checkered walnut stock. Discontinued in 1986. It is also available in the same variations as the Model 500 and the Model 501 but is valued at approximately 10 percent higher in each variation.

Model S689

A 9.3x74R or the .30-06 caliber over/under rifle with a boxlock action, 23" ribbed barrels and express-type sights. Blued, case-hardened or nickle-plated with checkered walnut stock. Double triggers and automatic ejectors.

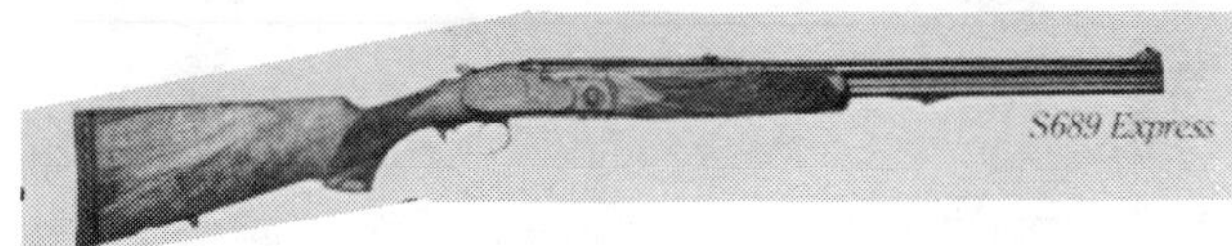
S689 Express

NIB	Exc.	V.G.	Good	Fair	Poor
4950	3750	2750	1800	1250	1000

SSO Express

A .375 Holland & Holland and .458 Winchester Magnum caliber Over/Under, double-barrel rifle with 23" barrels, folding express sights, double triggers, and automatic ejectors. Furnished with a fitted case. This firearm is available on a custom-order basis and should be individually appraised.

NIB	Exc.	V.G.	Good	Fair	Poor
18000	13000	9500	6500	5000	4000

SSO5 Express

A more finely finished version of the above.

NIB	Exc.	V.G.	Good	Fair	Poor
20000	15000	11000	8500	7000	5500

SHOTGUNS

Beretta shotguns are marked with a symbol or O stamping to indicate the type of fixed choke in the barrel or barrels. Usually this stamping is on the side of the barrel in the rear near the receiver on semi-automatics and near the ejectors on double barrel shotguns. Beretta shotguns with screw-in Mobilchoke tubes will have notches cut in them to indicate the amount of choke placed in the tube.

Fixed Chokes & Beretta Mobilchoke Designations		Mobilchoke Rim Notches
0(*)	F(Full)	I
00(**)	IM(Improved Modified)	II
000(***)	M(Modified)	III
0000(****)	IC(Improved Cyl.)	IIII
C0000(C****)	CL(Cylinder)	IIIII
SK	SK(Skeet)	No Notches

The BL series of Over/Under shotguns were manufactured between 1968 and 1973. They are chambered for 12 or 20 gauge and were offered with 26", 28", or 30" vent-ribbed barrels with various choke combinations. They feature boxlock actions and were offered with either single or double triggers, and manual extractors or automatic ejectors. The finishes are blued with checkered walnut stocks. The configurations differ basically in the quality of materials and workmanship and the degree of ornamentation.

BL-1

Exc.	V.G.	Good	Fair	Poor
500	450	350	225	150

BL-2

Exc.	V.G.	Good	Fair	Poor
425	375	300	250	200

BL-2/S (Speed Trigger)

Exc.	V.G.	Good	Fair	Poor
450	400	325	275	225

BL-2 Stakeout (18" Barrel)

Exc.	V.G.	Good	Fair	Poor
400	350	275	225	175

BL-3

Exc.	V.G.	Good	Fair	Poor
600	550	475	425	350

BL-3 Competition

Exc.	V.G.	Good	Fair	Poor
650	600	525	475	400

BL-4

Exc.	V.G.	Good	Fair	Poor
800	750	650	525	425

BL-4 Competition

Exc.	V.G.	Good	Fair	Poor
850	800	700	575	450

BL-5

Exc.	V.G.	Good	Fair	Poor
900	850	725	575	450

BL-5 Competition

Exc.	V.G.	Good	Fair	Poor
950	900	775	600	475

BL-6 (Sidelock)

Exc.	V.G.	Good	Fair	Poor
1250	1150	1000	850	675

BL-6 Competition

Exc.	V.G.	Good	Fair	Poor
1300	1200	1050	900	725

Model S55B

A 12 or 20 gauge Over/Under shotgun with 26", 28", or 30" ventilated-rib barrels, various choke combinations and boxlock action with a single selective trigger and extractors. Blued with a checkered walnut stock.

Exc.	V.G.	Good	Fair	Poor
550	500	400	325	275

Model S56 E

As above, but more finely finished.

Exc.	V.G.	Good	Fair	Poor
600	550	450	375	325

Model S58 Competition

As above, with either 26" or 30" barrels, wide vent ribs and competition-type stocks.

Exc.	V.G.	Good	Fair	Poor
700	650	550	475	400

Silver Snipe

A 12 or 20 gauge Over/Under shotgun with 26", 28", or 30" barrels, boxlock action with a double trigger and extractors. Blued with a checkered walnut stock. Manufactured from 1955 through 1967. A single selective trigger version with ventilated rib and automatic ejectors would be worth approximately 50 percent additional.

Exc.	V.G.	Good	Fair	Poor
400	375	325	275	200

Golden Snipe

As above with a ventilated rib and automatic ejectors. If it has a single selective trigger, add 10 percent.

Exc.	V.G.	Good	Fair	Poor
675	600	500	350	275

Model 57 E

As above, but more finely finished. Manufactured between 1955 and 1967.

Exc.	V.G.	Good	Fair	Poor
825	775	600	475	350

ASEL Model

A 12 or 20 gauge Over/Under shotgun with 26", 28", or 30" ventilated rib barrel with various choke combinations. Single selective trigger and automatic ejectors. Blued with a checkered pistolgrip stock. Manufactured between 1947 and 1964.

Exc.	V.G.	Good	Fair	Poor
1350	1150	850	575	450

Model 409 PB

A 12, 16, 20, and 28 gauge boxlock, double-barrel shotgun with 27", 28", or 30" barrels with double triggers and extractors and various choke combinations. Blued with a checkered walnut stock. Manufactured between 1934 and 1964.

Exc.	V.G.	Good	Fair	Poor
775	700	625	500	375

Model 410 E

As above, but more finely finished.

Exc.	V.G.	Good	Fair	Poor
900	825	650	500	425

Model 410

As above, with a 32" full-choke barrel. Blued with a checkered walnut stock. Introduced in 1934.

Exc.	V.G.	Good	Fair	Poor
1000	925	750	600	525

Model 411 E

The Model 410 with false sideplates and more heavily engraved. Manufactured between 1934 and 1964.

Exc.	V.G.	Good	Fair	Poor
1200	1125	950	800	725

Model 424

A 12 and 20 gauge boxlock shotgun with 26" or 28" barrels, double triggers, various choke combinations, and extractors. Blued with a checkered walnut stock. In 20 gauge it is designated the Model 426 and would be worth an additional $100.

Exc.	V.G.	Good	Fair	Poor
950	875	675	500	425

Model 426 E

As above, with silver inlays and heavier engraving, single selective trigger and automatic ejectors. Not imported after 1983.

Exc.	V.G.	Good	Fair	Poor
1150	1075	875	700	600

Model 625

A 12 or 20 gauge boxlock, double-barrel shotgun with 26", 28", or 30" barrels, various choke combinations, double triggers and extractors. Moderately engraved and blued with a checkered walnut grip. Imported between 1984 and 1986.

Exc.	V.G.	Good	Fair	Poor
800	750	600	500	400

Silver Hawk

A 10 or 12 gauge boxlock, double-barrel shotgun with 30" barrels, double triggers and extractors. Blued with a silver-finished receiver and a checkered walnut stock. The 10 gauge version would be worth an additional 20 percent. Discontinued in 1967.

Exc.	V.G.	Good	Fair	Poor
500	450	375	250	200

SO-5 Trap

A premium grade Beretta over and under shotgun built for competition Trap shooting. Available in 12 gauge with 30" vent rib barrels standard. Barrels in 28" and 32" may be special ordered. Receiver is silver with light scroll engraving. The stock is select highly figured walnut with pistol grip and offered in International or Monte Carlo dimensions. Special trap rubber recoil pad is furnished. Weighs 8 lbs., 2 oz. Furnished with leather case and tools.

NIB	Exc.	V.G.	Good	Fair	Poor
12000	8000	5000	3500	2500	1500

SO-5 Trap 2 BBL Set

NIB	Exc.	V.G.	Good	Fair	Poor
15500	11000	8500	6000	4500	2500

SO-5 Skeet

Same general specifications as above but furnished to skeet dimensions. Offered in 12 gauge only with 26" or 28" vent rib barrels choked sheet. Weighs 7 lbs., 8 oz.

NIB	Exc.	V.G.	Good	Fair	Poor
12000	8000	5000	3500	2500	1500

SO-5 Sporting Clays

Offered in 12 gauge only with choice of 28" or 30" barrels; 26" on special order. Sporting clay dimension walnut stock with pistol grip and rubber recoil pad. Weighs 7 lbs., 8oz.

NIB	Exc.	V.G.	Good	Fair	Poor
12000	8000	5000	3500	2500	1500

SO-6

This is a premium grade Beretta that is available in several different configurations similar to the SO 5. Available in 12 gauge only. It features a true side lock action, single selective or non-selective trigger, fixed or screw-in choke tubes. The receiver is offered either in silver finish or case hardened without engraving. The walnut is highly select walnut with fine line checkering. A choice of pistol grip or straight grip is offered. Supplied with a leather fitted hard case. Weighs about 7 lbs., 4 oz. depending on barrel length.

SO-6 Trap

NIB	Exc.	V.G.	Good	Fair	Poor
16500	12000	8000	5000	3500	2000

SO-6 Skeet

NIB	Exc.	V.G.	Good	Fair	Poor
16500	12000	8000	5000	3500	2000

SO-6 Sporting Clays

NIB	Exc.	V.G.	Good	Fair	Poor
16500	12000	8000	5000	3500	2000

SO-6 EELL

A higher grade in the SO 6 series that features a silver receiver with custom engraving with scroll or game scenes. Gold inlays are available on request. Choice of barrel lengths from 26" to 30". All of the same features of the SO 6, but with higher fit and finish. Offered in 12 gauge only.

NIB	Exc.	V.G.	Good	Fair	Poor
26000	20000	12500	8000	5000	2500

SO-7

One of Beretta's best-grade, sidelock, double-barrel shotgun. It is elaborately engraved and has the highest grade walnut in the stock.

Exc.	V.G.	Good	Fair	Poor
8500	7850	6750	5500	4500

SO-2 O/U

A 12 gauge Over/Under shotgun with 26", 28", or 30" ventilated-rib barrels, sidelock action, various choke combinations, single selective trigger and automatic ejectors. Introduced in 1948.

Exc.	V.G.	Good	Fair	Poor
5000	4500	3850	3000	2250

SO-9

This model Over/Under is Beretta's highest grade. Offered in 12, 20, and 28 gauge, and .410 bore. The true side lock(removable) receiver is highly engraved with scroll or game scenes by Italy's finest craftsmen. Barrel lengths are offered from 26" to 30" with solid hand filed rib. The walnut stock is the finest available with either pistol grip or straight grip. Stock dimensions to customers request. A custom fitted leather with accessories is supplied with gun.

NIB	Exc.	V.G.	Good	Fair	Poor
28500	23500	18500	10000	5000	2500

SS06

This is a premium grade side lock over and under express rifle. Equipped with double triggers. It is offered in 9.3x74R, .375 H&H Magnum, and .458 Win. Magnum. It is fitted with a 24" barrel with express sights. Claw mounts and Ziess are available from the factory. The receiver is case colored with light scroll engraving. Special select walnut is used in the stock and forearm with fine line checkering. Stock comes with cheek piece and rubber recoil pad. Furnished with leather case. Rifle weighs about 11 lbs.

NIB	Exc.	V.G.	Good	Fair	Poor
21000	15000	10000	7500	3500	2500

SS06 EELL

Offered in the same calibers as above but furnished with hand engraved game scenes with gold inlays. Walnut stock is special select briar with fine diamond line checkering.

NIB	Exc.	V.G.	Good	Fair	Poor
23000	17500	12500	10000	4500	3000

Model 452

This is a premium grade side by side shotgun fitted with slide locks(removable). Offered in 12 gauge only with 26", 28", or 30" solid rib barrels. The receiver is a highly polished silver finish without engraving. Triggers may be double, single selective, or single non-selective. The stock and forearm are special select walnut with fine line checkering with a choice of pistol or straight grip. Comes with leather hard case. Weighs about 6 lbs., 13 oz.

NIB	Exc.	V.G.	Good	Fair	Poor
22000	17000	12500	8500	4500	2500

Model 452 EELL

Same as above but furnished with fine scroll or game scene engraving. The highest grade of walnut is furnished for the stock and forearm. Leather case with accessories furnished.

NIB	Exc.	V.G.	Good	Fair	Poor
31000	27500	19500	12000	7500	3500

Model 455

This is a premium grade side by side express rifle with slide locks. Available in the following calibers: .375 H&H Magnum, .458 Win. Magnum, .470 Nitro Express, .500 Nitro Express, and .416 Rigby. The receiver is case colored without engraving and the walnut stock is highly figured with fine line checkering. Comes supplied with express sights. Claw mounts and Zeiss

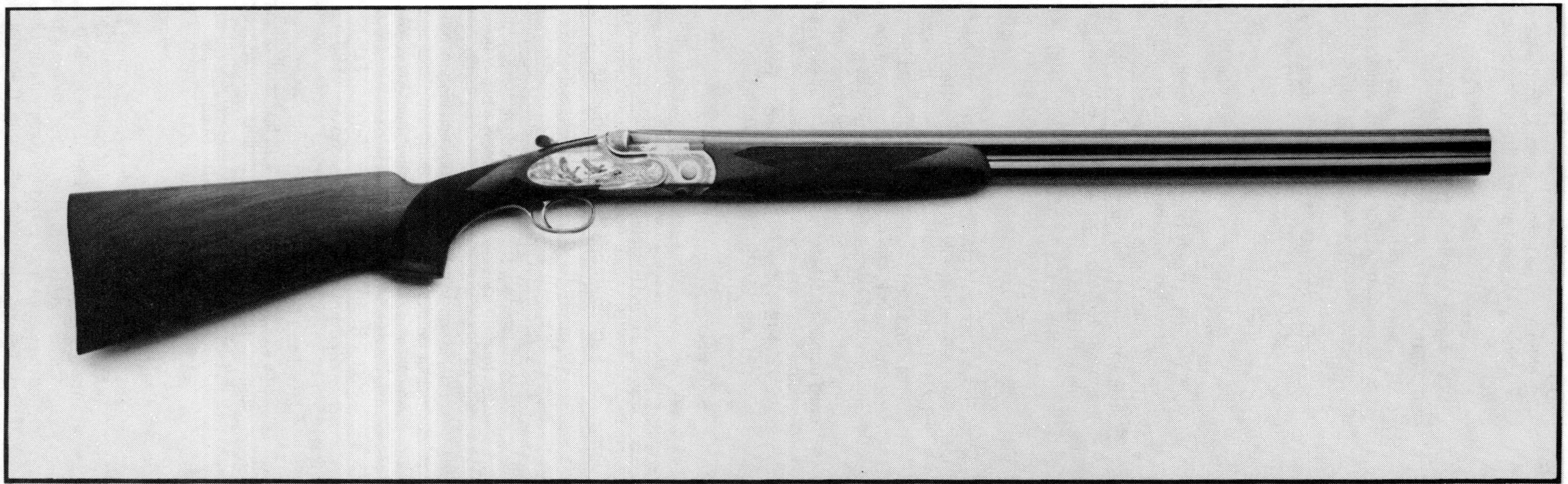

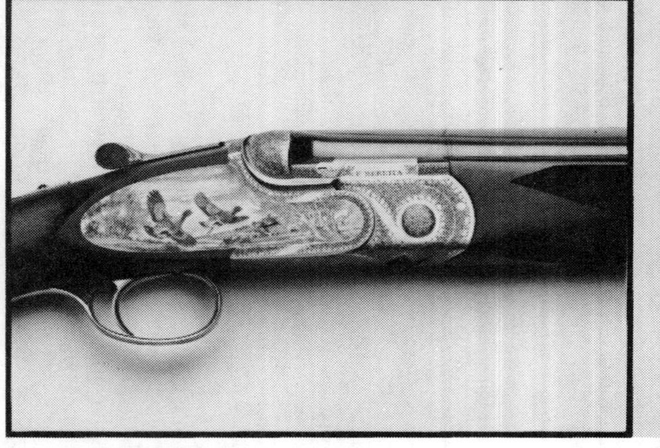

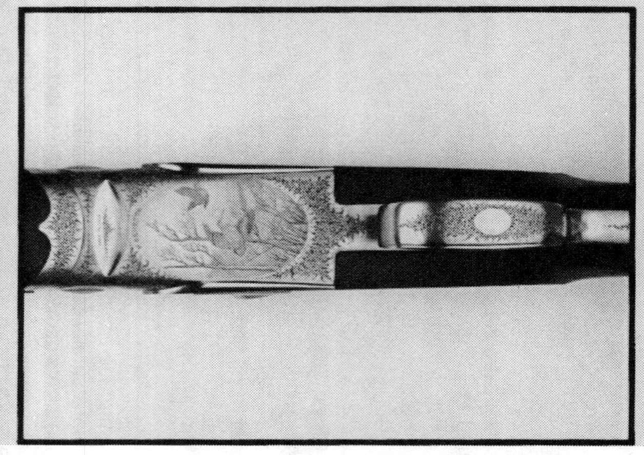

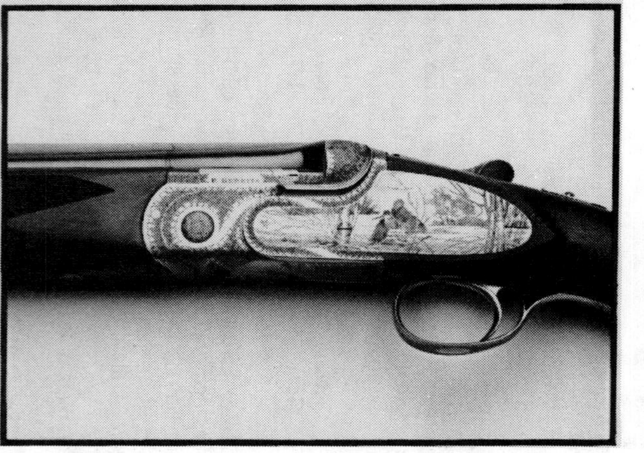

BERRETA PREMIUM GRADES

Shown above: The Beretta SO9 20 gauge Over/Under shotgun. Beretta Premium Grades feature hand detachable sideplates. European walnut stocks and fore-ends, Boehler high-nickel antinit steel barrels, true sidelock actions, closed receivers and a variety of engraving patterns.

scope offered at customers request only on .375, .458, and .416. Weighs about 11 lbs.

NIB	Exc.	V.G.	Good	Fair	Poor
36000	30000	22500	15000	9500	4500

Model 455 EELL

Same as above model but furnished with case colored game scene engraving with gold inlays. Walnut briar stock with fine diamond line checkering. Supplied with leather case and accessories.

NIB	Exc.	V.G.	Good	Fair	Poor
47000	37500	27500	17500	9500	4500

Model 682

This is a high grade, quality built Over/Under shotgun. Offered in 12 and 20 gauge, it is also available in some configurations in 28 gauge and .410 bore with barrel lengths from 26" to 34" depending on the type of shooting required. It is fitted with single selective trigger and automatic ejectors. Barrels are fitted with ventilated rib and various fixed or screw-in choke combinations are available. The stock is a high grade walnut with fine checkering in stock dimensions to fit the function of the gun. The frame is silver with light scroll borders on most models. This model covers a wide variety of applications and these are listed below by grade and/or function:

682 Super Skeet

This model is offered in 12 gauge only with 28" vent rib barrels choked skeet and skeet. Single selective trigger and auto ejectors are standard. This Super Skeet features ported barrels and adjustable length of pull and drop. A fitted hard case is standard. Gun weighs 7 lbs 8 oz.

NIB	Exc.	V.G.	Good	Fair	Poor
2300	1850	1500	1250	950	750

682 Skeet

This is the standard 12 gauge Skeet model which features a choice of 26" or 28" vent rib barrels choked skeet and skeet. Walnut stock is of International dimensions with special skeet rubber recoil pad. Gun is supplied with hard case. Weighs 7lb. and 8 oz.

NIB	Exc.	V.G.	Good	Fair	Poor
2000	1850	1500	1250	950	700

682 4 BBL Set

This skeet gun is fitted with 4 barrels in 12, 20, 28 gauge, and .410 bore. Each barrel is 28", choked skeet and skeet, and fitted with a vent rib.

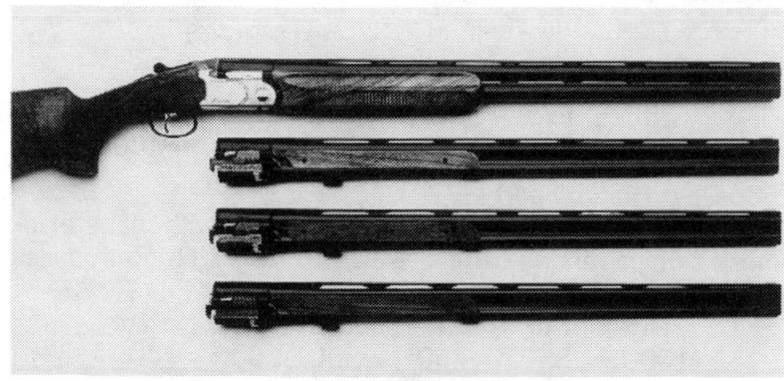

NIB	Exc.	V.G.	Good	Fair	Poor
4500	4000	3500	3000	2000	11250

682 Super Sporting

Built for Sporting Clays this 12 gauge or 20 gauge model features ported barrel and adjustable length of pull and drop. Fitted with 28" or 30" vent barrel with screw-in chokes; fixed chokes on special order. Checkered walnut stock with pistol grip and recoil pad. Supplied with case. Introduced in 1993. Weight of 12 gauge is 7 lbs, 8 oz. and 20 gauge weighs 6lbs, 3 oz.

NIB	Exc.	V.G.	Good	Fair	Poor
2300	1850	1500	1250	950	750

682 Sporting

The standard version of the 12 gauge or 20 gauge Super Sporting model with a choice of 28" or 30 " vent rib barrel with screw-in chokes. Checkered walnut stock with recoil pad. Introduced in 1993.

NIB	Exc.	V.G.	Good	Fair	Poor
2000	1850	1500	1250	950	700

682 Sporting Combo

Similar to the 682 Sporting with the addition of two 12 gauge 28" and 30" barrel fitted with screw-in chokes. Supplied with hard case.

NIB	Exc.	V.G.	Good	Fair	Poor
2800	2500	2250	1750	1250	950

682 Super Trap

This 12 gauge Trap model(a 20 gauge set of barrels is available on special order) features ported 30" or 32" ventilated rib barrels with either fixed or screw-in chokes. Automatic ejectors are standard as is a single non-selective trigger. The checkered walnut stock can be adjusted for length of pull and drop of comb and is offered in either Monte Carlo or International dimensions. Weight is approximately 8 lbs, 6 oz.

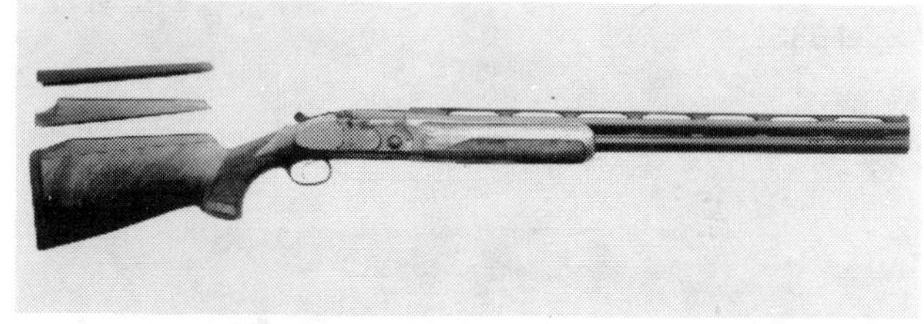

NIB	Exc.	V.G.	Good	Fair	Poor
2300	1850	1500	1250	950	700

682 Top Single Super Trap

Same as the Super Trap but available in a single barrel configuration of either 32" or 34".

NIB	Exc.	V.G.	Good	Fair	Poor
2400	1950	1600	1350	950	700

682 Top Combo Super Trap

This configuration features a single barrel and a Over/Under barrel both interchangeable. The combinations are: 30",32" and 30", 34".

NIB	Exc.	V.G.	Good	Fair	Poor
3000	2750	2250	1750	1250	950

682 Trap

This model is the standard variation Beretta Trap gun. This 12 gauge comes standard with 30" vent rib barrels. However, 28" and 32" barrel can be special ordered. Fixed or screw-in chokes are available. The 3-position sliding trigger allows for adjustable length of pull. A checkered walnut stock with recoil pad is standard. Stock is available in either Monte Carlo or International dimensions. Customer has choice of either sliver or black receiver. Comes cased.

NIB	Exc.	V.G.	Good	Fair	Poor
2000	1750	1500	1250	900	650

682 Top Single Trap

This 12 gauge single barrel trap gun is available in 32" or 34" vent rib barrel.

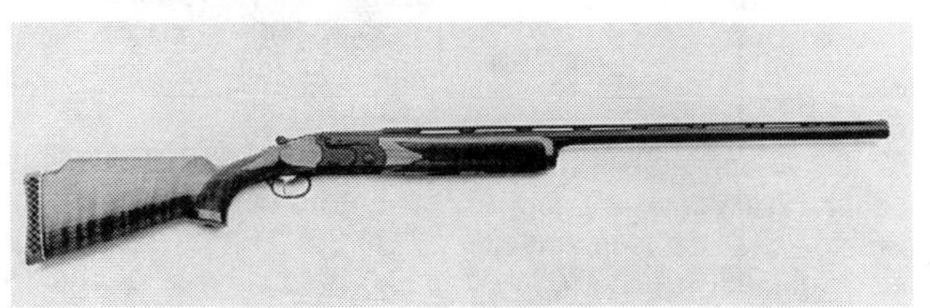

NIB	Exc.	V.G.	Good	Fair	Poor
2100	1750	1500	1250	900	700

682 Mono Combo Trap

A special configuration that features a single barrel with vent rib set to place single barrel in bottom position of what would normally be an Over/Under set-up. A second barrel that is an Over/Under is also provided as part of the set. Single barrel is 34" and the Over/Under set is 32" in length.

NIB	Exc.	V.G.	Good	Fair	Poor
2700	2350	1850	1350	950	700

682 Top Combo

This trap combination features a standard placement single barrel with an interchangeable Over/Under barrel. Barrel are available in 30", 32"; 30", 34"; and 32", 34". Barrel are fitted with ventilated rib.

NIB	Exc.	V.G.	Good	Fair	Poor
2700	2350	1850	1350	950	700

Model 685

A Lower-priced Over/Under chambered for 12 or 20 gauge with 3" chambers, a satin-chromed boxlock action with a single trigger and extractors. Not imported after 1986.

Exc.	V.G.	Good	Fair	Poor
650	600	500	375	275

Model 686

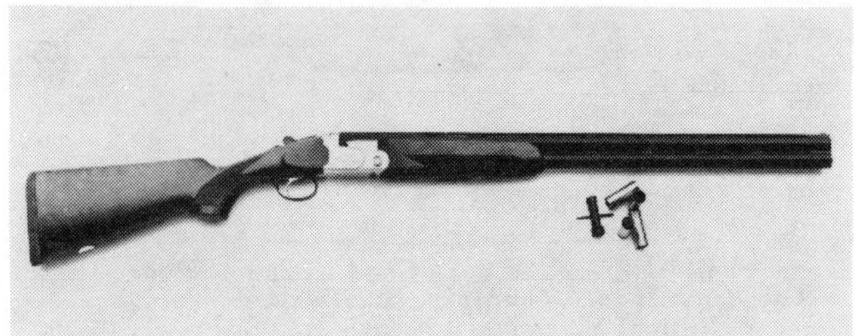

This Beretta Over/Under shotgun is available in a number of different configurations. This basic model features a a ventilated rib barrels from 24" to 30"; 30" being a special order. Screw-in chokes or fixed chokes are available. All configurations are offered in 12 gauge and 20 gauge with 28 gauge and .410 bore available in special order only. The gun is fitted with checkered American walnut stock with black rubber recoil pad and special grip cap. Some models have silver receiver with scroll engraving and others have black receivers with gold filled contours.

686 Ultra Light Onyx

This model features a black anodized light alloy receiver accented with an engraved gold-filled "P. Beretta" signature. Available in 12 gauge only with 26" or 28" vent rib barrels. Chokes are either fixed or screw-in type. Weighs 5 lbs., 11 oz.

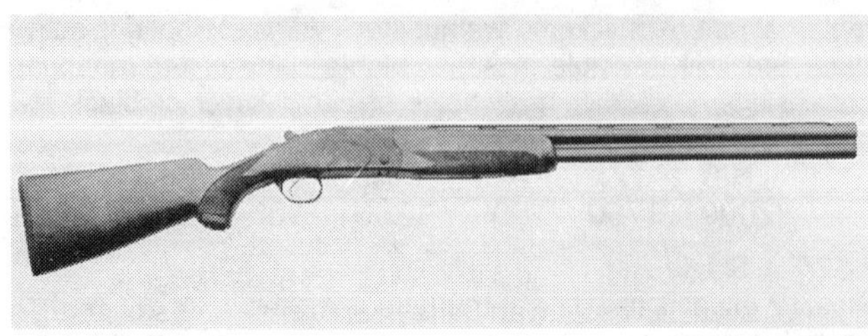

NIB	Exc.	V.G.	Good	Fair	Poor
1050	850	750	600	500	400

686 Onyx

Similar in appearance to the Ultra Light Onyx, but available in either 12 gauge or 20 gauge with vent rib barrel lengths from 26" to 28". Chambers are either 3" or 3.5". Checkered walnut stock offered in pistol grip or straight grip. Choice of chokes types. Weight of 12 gauge 6 lbs., 13 oz.; 20 gauge 6 lbs., 3 oz.

NIB	Exc.	V.G.	Good	Fair	Poor
950	850	750	650	500	400

686 Onyx 2 BBL Set

Same as above but supplied with a 20 gauge 28" vent rib barrel and a 28 gauge 26" vent rib barrel.

NIB	Exc.	V.G.	Good	Fair	Poor
1450	1250	1000	800	650	500

686 Silver Receiver

This model is the basic 686. It features a plain semi-matte silver receiver and is available in either 12 or 20 gauge; 28 gauge available on special order. Vent rib barrels are offered in lengths from 24" to 30" with fixed chokes or choke tubes.

NIB	Exc.	V.G.	Good	Fair	Poor
950	850	750	650	500	400

686 L

Same as above but furnished with a scroll engraved silver receiver. Offered in 28 gauge with 26" or 28" vent rib barrels. Gun weighs 5 lbs., 5 oz.

NIB	Exc.	V.G.	Good	Fair	Poor
950	850	750	650	500	400

686 EL

This model is available in 12 gauge or 20 gauge with 26" or 28" vent rib barrels. The receiver is silver with scroll engraving and fitted with side plates. A fitted hard case comes with the gun.

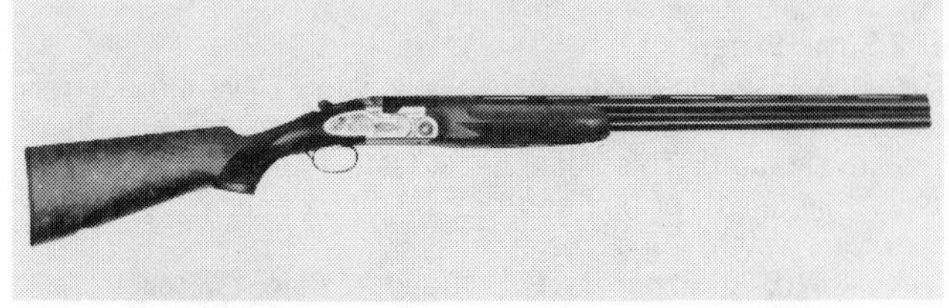

NIB	Exc.	V.G.	Good	Fair	Poor
1550	1250	1000	800	700	550

686 Hunter Sport

A Sporting Clays 12 gauge or 20 gauge shotgun that features a silver receiver with scroll engraving. Wide 12.5mm target rib. Radiused recoil pad. Offered in 26" or 28" vent rib barrels with screw-in chokes. Offered for the first time in 1993.

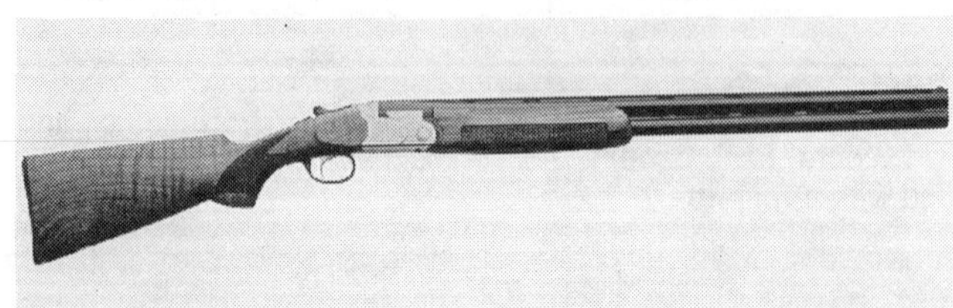

NIB	Exc.	V.G.	Good	Fair	Poor
1000	850	750	600	500	400

686 Onyx Hunter Sport

Same as above but offered in 12 gauge only with matte black finish on receiver and barrels. Weighs 6 lbs., 13 ox. Introduced in 1993.

NIB	Exc.	V.G.	Good	Fair	Poor
1000	850	750	600	500	400

686 Sporting Combo

Same specifications as the Hunter Sport with the addition of an interchangeable 30" 12 gauge barrel.

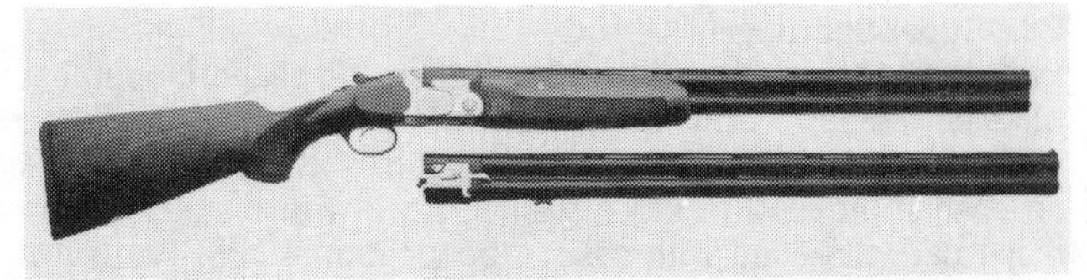

NIB	Exc.	V.G.	Good	Fair	Poor
1800	1500	1250	1000	800	550

Model 687

This model is similar to the Model 686 but in a slightly more ornate version.

687 L

This model is offered in 12 gauge or 20 gauge with 26" or 28" vent rib barrels. The box lock receiver is scroll engraved with game scenes. Auto ejectors and double or single triggers are offered.

NIB	Exc.	V.G.	Good	Fair	Poor
1300	1100	950	800	650	500

687 Sporting

A Sporting Clays version available in 12 or 20 gauge with 28" or 30" barrels.

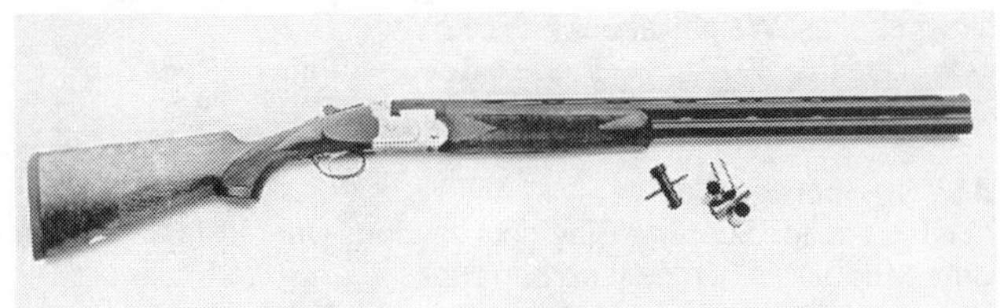

NIB	Exc.	V.G.	Good	Fair	Poor
1600	1400	1100	900	750	550

687 Sporting Combo

Offered in 12 gauge only with two sets of 12 gauge interchangeable vent rib barrels in 28" and 30".

NIB	Exc.	V.G.	Good	Fair	Poor
2400	2100	1850	1500	1150	800

687 EL

This model is offered with scroll engraved gold inlaid game animals. Fitted with side plates. The stock is highly figured walnut with fine line checkering. Available in 12, 20, 28 gauge or .410 bore in 26" or 28" vent rib barrels with screw-in chokes. Comes with fitted hard case. Weights for 12 gauge: 6 lbs, 13 oz.; 20 gauge: 6 lbs., 3 oz.; 28/.410: 5 lbs., 5 oz..

687 EL 12 gauge and 20 gauge

NIB	Exc.	V.G.	Good	Fair	Poor
2150	1850	1500	1250	950	700

687 EL 28/.410

NIB	Exc.	V.G.	Good	Fair	Poor
2500	2250	1850	1450	1100	800

687 EL Sporting

A Sporting Clays model chambered for 12 gauge and fitted with 28" or 30" vent rib barrels. Offered new in 1993. Comes with fitted hard case.

NIB	Exc.	V.G.	Good	Fair	Poor
2400	2150	1750	1350	1000	700

687 EELL

Same as above, including gauge and barrel offerings, but furnished with more fully figured walnut and finer checkering. Fitted with slide plates that are scroll engraved with fine cut game scenes. This grade is also available in a straight grip English stock version in 20 gauge as well as a Combo set of 20 gauge and 28 gauge interchangeable 26" barrels. All 687 EELL models are fitted with hard case.

687 EELL 12 and 20 gauge

NIB	Exc.	V.G.	Good	Fair	Poor
3200	2850	2250	1500	1000	800

687 EELL 28 gauge and .410 bore

NIB	Exc.	V.G.	Good	Fair	Poor
3750	3500	3000	2250	1500	1000

687 EELL Combo

NIB	Exc.	V.G.	Good	Fair	Poor
3500	3250	2750	2000	1500	1000

687 Skeet

Same as above with the addition of a skeet configuration. A 12 gauge version is offered with 28" vent rib barrels choked skeet and skeet. Weighs about 7 lbs., 8 oz.. A 4 barrel set is also offered with interchangeable 12, 20, 28 gauge, and .410 bore barrels choked skeet and skeet.

687 EELL 12 gauge

NIB	Exc.	V.G.	Good	Fair	Poor
3200	2850	2250	1500	1000	800

687 EELL 4 BBL Set

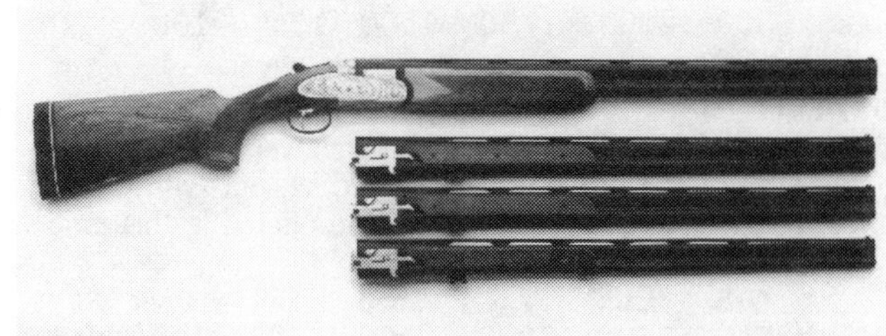

NIB	Exc.	V.G.	Good	Fair	Poor
5750	5000	4500	3750	2500	1500

687 EELL Sporting

A Sporting Clays version of the 687 EELL in 12 gauge only with 28" vent rib barrels fitted with screw-in chokes.

NIB	Exc.	V.G.	Good	Fair	Poor
3500	3000	2500	2000	1500	1000

687 EELL Trap

This model is fitted with either International or Monte Carlo trap stock dimensions. Offered in 12 gauge with 30" vent rib barrels fixed or screw-in choke tubes. Weighs about 8 lbs., 6 oz.

NIB	Exc.	V.G.	Good	Fair	Poor
3500	3000	2500	2000	1500	1000

687 EELL Top Combo

A single barrel trap gun with choice of one single barrel set and one Over/Under steel rod barrel in either 30" and 32" or 32" and 34".

NIB	Exc.	V.G.	Good	Fair	Poor
4000	3500	3000	2250	1500	1000

Model 626 Field Grade

A 12 or 20 gauge boxlock double-barrel shotgun with a 26" or 28" barrel, various choke combinations, single-trigger and automatic ejectors. Engraved, blued with a checkered walnut stock. Imported between 1984 and 1988.

Exc.	V.G.	Good	Fair	Poor
900	825	700	575	475

626 Onyx

This model is a box lock side by side shotgun offered in 12 gauge and 20 gauge. With choice of 26" or 28" solid rib barrels with screw-in chokes. Double triggers are standard but single trigger is available on request. Receiver is anti-glare black matte finish. Stock is walnut with hand checkering and pistol grip. The 12 gauge weighs 6 lbs., 13 oz. and the 20 gauge weighs 6 lbs., 13 oz.

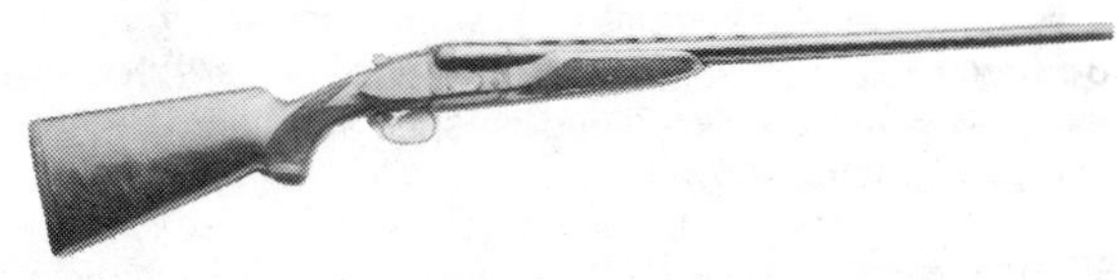

NIB	Exc.	V.G.	Good	Fair	Poor
1250	950	850	750	500	400

627 EL

This model is offered in 12 gauge only with choice of 26" or 28" solid rib barrels. The walnut is highly figured and fine cut checkered. The receiver is silver with slide plates engraved with scroll. Comes with hard case.

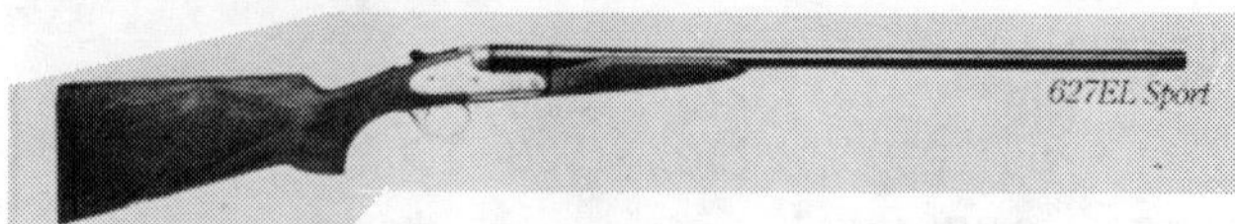

627EL Sport

NIB	Exc.	V.G.	Good	Fair	Poor
2500	2000	1750	1500	1250	1000

627 EELL

Same as above but fitted with scroll engraved side plates with game scenes. Walnut is highly figured walnut with fine line checkering. A straight grip stock is also offered in this model. comes with hard case.

NIB	Exc.	V.G.	Good	Fair	Poor
3750	3500	3000	2500	1500	1000

Model 451 Series

A custom order sidelock shotgun. The lowest-priced version would be worth approximately $6,000 in excellent condition; and the top-of-the-line model, approximately $25,000. Prospective purchasers are advised to secure a qualified appraisal prior to acquisition.

Model FS-1

A single-barrel boxlock shotgun in all gauges and a 26" or 28", full-choke barrel. Blued with a checkered walnut stock. This Model was also known as the "Companion."

Exc.	V.G.	Good	Fair	Poor
250	225	175	125	90

TR-1 Trap

A 12 gauge, single-barrel boxlock trap gun, 32" ventilated-rib, full-choke barrel. Blued with a checkered, Monte Carlo stock. Manufactured between 1968 and 1971.

Exc.	V.G.	Good	Fair	Poor
275	250	200	150	100

TR-2 Trap

As above, with a high, competition-type vent rib. It was manufactured between 1969 and 1973.

Exc.	V.G.	Good	Fair	Poor
300	275	225	175	125

Mark II Trap

A 12 gauge, boxlock single-barrel trap shotgun with a 32" or 34", full-choke barrel, competition-type rib and automatic ejector. Blued with a checkered, Monte Carlo type, walnut stock. Manufactured between 1972 and 1976.

Exc.	V.G.	Good	Fair	Poor
700	625	525	450	375

Model ASE 90

This is a competition trap model Over/Under shotgun. It features a trigger lock assembly that is removable in the field so a spare can be used in the event of failure.The single non-selective trigger has a three way adjustment. The ventilated rib is wide and the side ribs are also ventilated. Walnut stock and forearms are interchangeable. Special trap recoil pad is standard. Receiver is silver with gold inlays or blued on special order. The ASE 90 weighs about 8 lbs., 6 oz.

ASE 90 Pigeon

Equipped with 28" barrels choked Improved Modified and Full.

NIB	Exc.	V.G.	Good	Fair	Poor
5750	5250	4500	4000	3000	1500

ASE 90 Trap

Comes standard with 30" vent rib barrels

NIB	Exc.	V.G	Good	Fair	Poor
5750	5250	4500	4000	3000	1500

ASE 90 Gold X Trap Combo

Introduced in 1993 this set features a single barrel and interchangeable over and under barrels in 30" and 32" and 30" and 34" combinations.

NIB	Exc.	V.G	Good	Fair	Poor
6750	6250	5500	5000	3000	1500

ASE 90 Skeet

This model is a skeet version of the ASE 90 series. Features the same basic specifications as the trap model but configured for competition skeet. Offered in 12 gauge only with 28" skeet and skeet chokes. Weighs about 7 lbs., 11 oz.

NIB	Exc.	V.G.	Good	Fair	Poor
5750	5250	4500	4000	3000	1500

ASE 90 Sporting Clay

Configured for Sporting Clay competition. Offered in 12 gauge only with 28" or 30" cent rib barrels.

NIB	Exc.	V.G.	Good	Fair	Poor
5750	5250	4500	4000	3000	1500

Model SL-2

A 12 gauge slide action shotgun, 26", 28", or 30", ventilated-rib barrels with various chokes. Blued with a checkered walnut stock. Manufactured between 1968 and 1971.

Exc.	V.G.	Good	Fair	Poor
350	300	250	200	150

Pigeon Series

As above, in three grades.

Silver Pigeon

Exc.	V.G.	Good	Fair	Poor
300	250	200	150	110

Gold Pigeon

Exc.	V.G.	Good	Fair	Poor
450	400	300	250	200

Ruby Pigeon

Exc.	V.G.	Good	Fair	Poor
600	550	450	375	275

AL Series

A 12 or 20 gauge semi-automatic shotgun with 26", 28", or 30" barrels and various choke combinations. Blued with a checkered walnut stock. Manufactured between 1969 and 1976.

AL-1

Exc.	V.G.	Good	Fair	Poor
400	375	300	225	150

AL-2

Exc.	V.G.	Good	Fair	Poor
350	300	250	175	125

AL-2 Competition

Exc.	V.G.	Good	Fair	Poor
400	350	300	225	175

AL-2 Magnum

Exc.	V.G.	Good	Fair	Poor
425	375	325	250	200

AL-3

Exc.	V.G.	Good	Fair	Poor
400	350	300	225	175

AL-3 Deluxe Trap

Exc.	V.G.	Good	Fair	Poor
775	700	600	500	425

Model 301

Improved version of the AL Series manufactured between 1977

and 1982. It is also available as a slug gun with a 22" barrel with rifle sights.

Exc.	V.G.	Good	Fair	Poor
400	350	300	225	175

Model 1200 Field Grade

A 12 gauge semi-automatic shotgun, 28" ventilated-rib barrel, screw-in choke tubes and a 4-round, tubular magazine. Matte-blued with either a checkered walnut or black synthetic stock. Introduced in 1984.

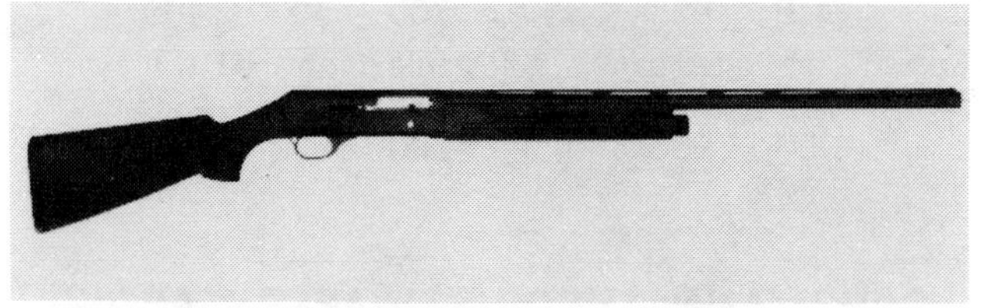

NIB	Exc.	V.G.	Good	Fair	Poor
585	525	425	325	250	200

Model 1200 Magnum (3" Chamber)

NIB	Exc.	V.G.	Good	Fair	Poor
585	525	425	325	250	200

Model 1200 Riot (20" Cyl. Bore Barrel)

NIB	Exc.	V.G.	Good	Fair	Poor
585	525	425	325	250	200

Model 1201

This 12 gauge semi-automatic shotguns has a short recoil system and features a synthetic stock with matte black finish and lightweight alloy receiver. Available in two basic configurations: the Field grade with choice of 24", 26", and 28" vent rib barrel with screw-in chokes and Riot models with 20" plain cylinder choked barrel with either full stock or pistol grip only stock(introduced in 1993). Field Grade weighs about 6 lbs. 12 oz. and the Riot model about 6 lbs. 5 oz.

Field Grade

NIB	Exc.	V.G.	Good	Fair	Poor
450	400	350	300	200	150

Riot Model

NIB	Exc.	V.G.	Good	Fair	Poor
500	450	400	350	250	175

Model 302

A 12 or 20 gauge semi-automatic shotgun using 2.75" or 3" shells interchangeably, various barrel lengths and screw-in choke tubes. Blued with a checkered walnut stock. Manufactured between 1982 and 1987.

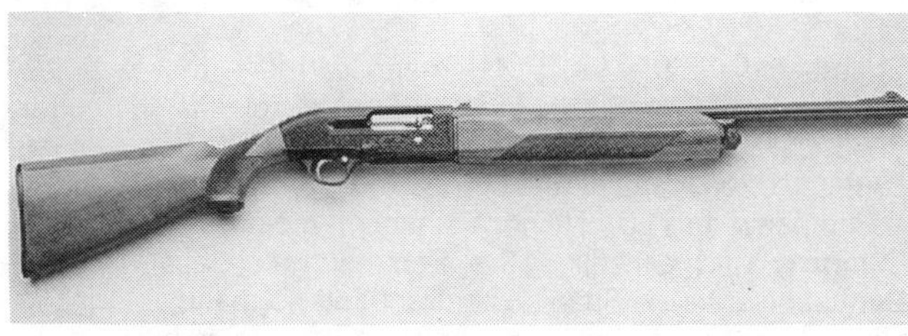

Exc.	V.G.	Good	Fair	Poor
400	350	275	200	150

Model 302 Super Lusso

As above, with a heavily engraved receiver and goldplated, contrasting parts. Presentation-grade walnut was used for the hand-checkered stock. Discontinued in 1986.

Exc.	V.G.	Good	Fair	Poor
2150	2000	1600	1050	850

Model Vittoria

This semi-automatic 12 gauge shotgun was introduced to the Beretta product line in 1993. It has a short recoil operation and is offered with a 24" or 26" vent rib barrel with screw-in chokes. A 24" rifled choke tube version for slugs is also available. A non-reflective matte finish is put on all wood and metal surfaces. Equipped with sling swivels and walnut stock. Weighs about 7 lbs.

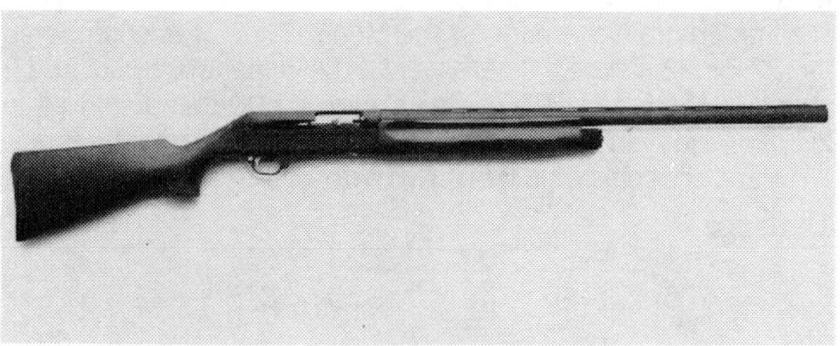

NIB	Exc.	V.G.	Good	Fair	Poor
600	550	500	400	350	250

A-303 Series

A 12 or 20 gauge semi-automatic shotgun, 26", 28", 30", or 32" ventilated rib barrels with screw-in choke tubes. Blue with a checkered walnut stock. Introduced in 1987. The various models offered differ slightly in configuration and/or quality of materials.

Model A-303

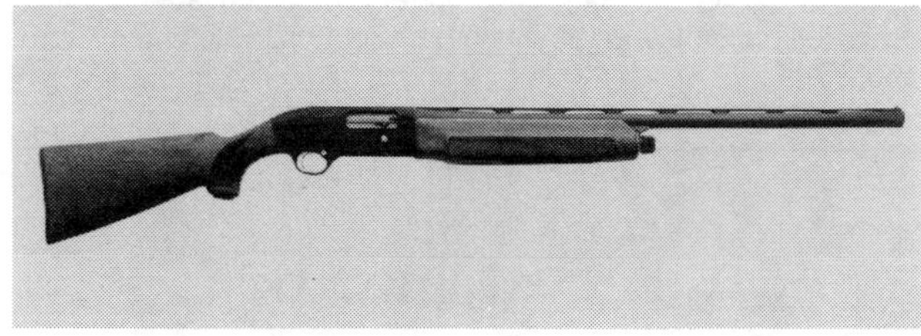

NIB	Exc.	V.G.	Good	Fair	Poor
650	600	475	375	300	250

Model A-303 Upland (24" Barrel)

NIB	Exc.	V.G.	Good	Fair	Poor
680	650	525	425	350	300

Model A-303 Sporting Clays

NIB	Exc.	V.G.	Good	Fair	Poor
735	700	575	475	400	350

Model A-303 Competition (Trap or Skeet)

NIB	Exc.	V.G.	Good	Fair	Poor
675	650	530	425	350	300

Model A-303 Slug Gun (22" Barrel with Sights

NIB	Exc.	V.G.	Good	Fair	Poor
680	650	525	425	350	300

Model 303 Youth Gun

This version of the Model 303 is available in 20 gauge with a shorter length of pull, 13.5", than standard. It is fitted with a rubber recoil pad, screw-in choke tubes, and checkered walnut stock.

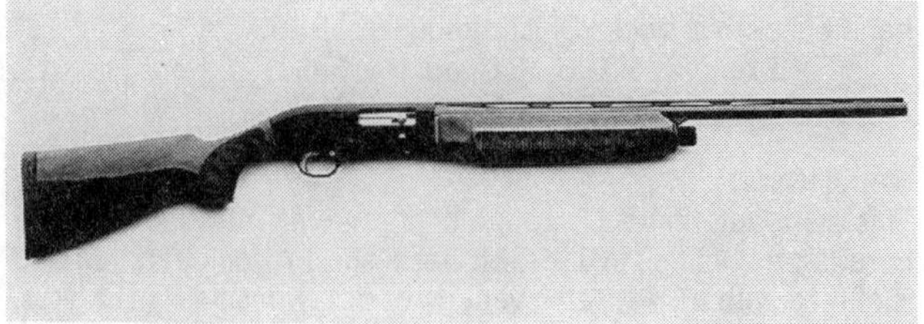

NIB	Exc.	V.G.	Good	Fair	Poor
500	450	400	300	250	200

Model A-303 Ducks Unlimited

A commemorative version of the Model 303. It is chambered for 12 or 20 gauge. There were 5,500 manufactured in 12 gauge in 1986 and 1987. There were 3,500 manufactured in 20 gauge in 1987 and 1988. These are commemorative firearms and are collectible when NIB with all furnished materials.

12 Gauge

NIB	Exc.	V.G.	Good	Fair	Poor
575	500	425	325	275	225

20 Gauge

NIB	Exc.	V.G.	Good	Fair	Poor
675	600	525	425	375	325

Model 390

This series of 12 gauge semi-automatic shotguns features a self compensating gas operating recoil system. All loads from target to 3" magnums can be used in the same gun. The Field model features an anodized light alloy receiver with scroll engraved side plates and matte black receiver top. Magazine capacity is 3 rounds. Checkered walnut stock with recoil pad. Available in vent rib barrel lengths from 24" to 30" with 32" on special request. A 22" or 24" slug plain barrel is also available. Chokes are fixed or screw-in at customer's option. Shotgun weighs about 7 lbs.

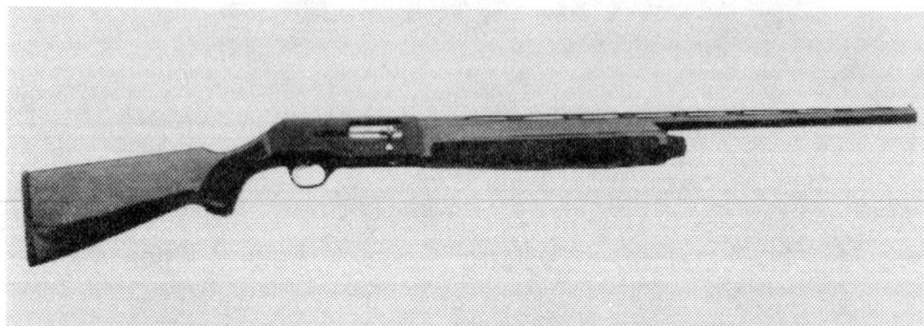

Field Grade

NIB	Exc.	V.G.	Good	Fair	Poor
550	500	450	350	300	250

Slug Gun

NIB	Exc.	V.G.	Good	Fair	Poor
550	500	450	350	300	250

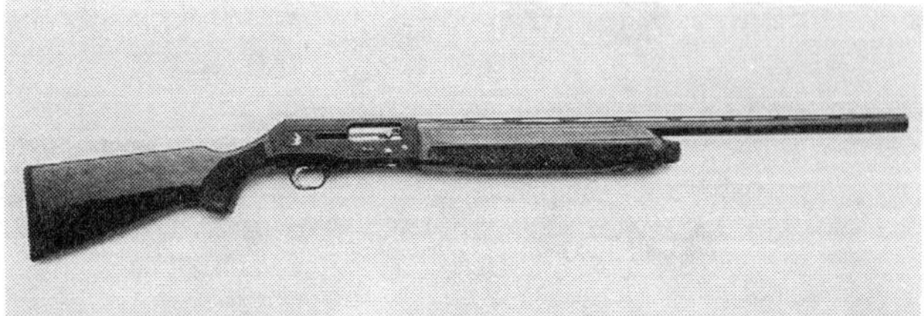

Deluxe Grade-Gold filled game animals and select walnut stock.

NIB	Exc.	V.G.	Good	Fair	Poor
750	700	650	550	450	350

Waterfowl/Turkey Model-Matte Finish

NIB	Exc.	V.G.	Good	Fair	Poor
550	500	450	350	300	250

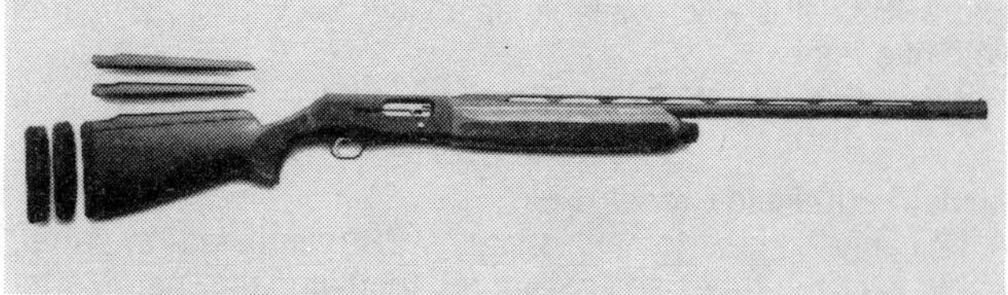

Super Trap-Ported barrels, adjustable comb and L.O.P.

NIB	Exc.	V.G.	Good	Fair	Poor
975	925	850	700	500	400

Super Skeet-Ported barrels, adjustable comb and L.O.P.

NIB	Exc.	V.G.	Good	Fair	Poor
950	900	825	700	500	400

BERGMANN, THEODOR WAFFENFABRIK

Suhl, Germany

Model 1894—Bergmann Schmeisser

A 5mm or 8mm caliber semi-automatic pistol. Extremely rare. This model was not made commercially and is rarely encountered today. A very compact pistol that features a folding trigger. The 5mm version would be worth approximately 50 percent additional.

Exc.	V.G.	Good	Fair	Poor
4000	3600	2500	1600	900

Model 1896

Similar to the Model 1894 with the recoil spring located inside the butt instead of beneath the barrel. The magazine has two slots machined in its cover and holds five rounds. Chambered for the 5mm and 6.5mm cartridges.

Exc.	V.G.	Good	Fair	Poor
2000	1750	1250	950	500

Model 1896 No. 3

As above, without the folding trigger and with the addition of an extractor.

Exc.	V.G.	Good	Fair	Poor
2000	1750	1250	950	500

Model 1896 No. 4

As above, in 8mm Bergman caliber. Approximately 200 manufactured.

Exc.	V.G.	Good	Fair	Poor
2200	1950	1400	1100	750

Model 1897 No. 5

A locked-breech, semi-automatic pistol chambered for the 7.8mm Bergman cartridge. This version has a box magazine that is located in front of the triggerguard similar to that found on a C/96 Mauser. It is detachable but could be loaded with a stripper clip.

Exc.	V.G.	Good	Fair	Poor
2500	2250	1600	1300	850

Model 1899 No. 6

Similar to the No. 5 with the early, side-loaded magazine. It was chambered for the 8mm cartridge and later chambered for the 7.5mm.

Exc.	V.G.	Good	Fair	Poor
2500	2250	1600	1300	850

Mars

Chambered for the 9mm Bergmann cartridge that was also known as the 9mm Largo in Spain, this pistol was adopted by the Spanish army as their service pistol in 1905. Bergman had contracted the manufacture of this model to the firm of Schilling & Company. In 1904 Heinrich Krieghoff took over the Schilling Company and cancelled the Bergmann contract. This left Bergmann with the Spanish contract and no manufacturing facility. He attempted to manufacture this model in his own factory but failed, and the Mars was licensed to the firm of Pieper in Liege, Belgium.

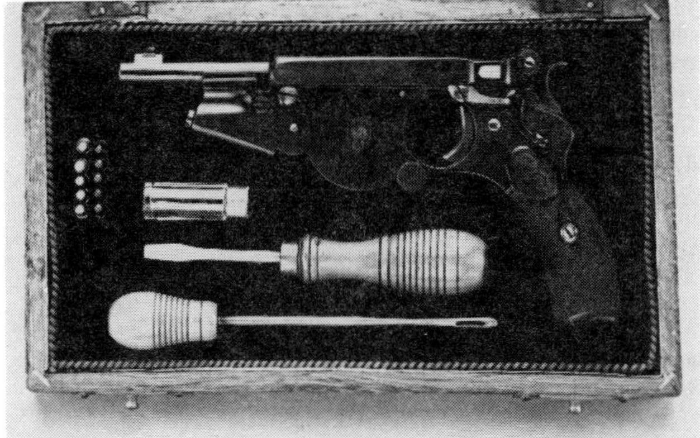
Courtesy Butterfield & Butterfield, San Francisco, California.

Exc.	V.G.	Good	Fair	Poor
8000	7000	3500	2000	1500

In 1921 the company firm was sold to a group headed by the firm of Lignose, and they began manufacture of the Lignose one-handed pistol that is covered in its own section of this text.

Model 2

Similar to the 1906 Browning. Is a 6.35mm caliber semi-automatic pistol with a 2.5" barrel. Blued with plastic grips.

Exc.	V.G.	Good	Fair	Poor
300	250	175	110	80

No. 3

As above, with a 9-round, detachable magazine.

Exc.	V.G.	Good	Fair	Poor
300	250	175	110	80

Bergmann-Erben

A 7.65mm caliber semi-automatic pistol with a 3.5" barrel and double-action lock. Blued with plastic grips. Manufactured between 1937 and 1939.

Exc.	V.G.	Good	Fair	Poor
350	300	225	150	110

Bergmann-Erben Model 2

As above, in 6.35mm caliber. Manufactured between 1937 and 1939.

Exc.	V.G.	Good	Fair	Poor
350	300	225	150	110

BERN, WAFFENFABRIK

Bern, Switzerland

The Swiss Military Arsenal in Bern produced a variety of military arms for that country's armed forces. A total of 47,732 Parabellum semi-automatic pistols were made there, most of which were in 7.65mm caliber.

Swiss Ordnance Revolver M 1878

A 10.4mm caliber double-action revolver with an octagonal barrel and 6-shot cylinder. The left sideplate of this revolver is hinged so that it may be swung forward to clean the lockwork. The grips are impressed with the Swiss Cross.

Exc.	V.G.	Good	Fair	Poor
800	700	575	450	375

M1872/78

A 10.4mm rimfire or 10.4mm centerfire Chamelot-Delvigne revolver.

Exc.	V.G.	Good	Fair	Poor
500	450	375	300	250

Model 1882

A 7.5mm revolver similar in appearance to the Model 1878.

Exc.	V.G.	Good	Fair	Poor
300	250	200	150	125

Model 1889

As above, with a more acutely angled butt and an improved sideplate release mechanism.

Exc.	V.G.	Good	Fair	Poor
300	250	200	150	125

Pistol 06 W+F (Model 06/24)

A Swiss made copy of the German Model 1900/06 Luger semi-automatic pistol, marked "Waffenfabrik Bern." On top of the breech there is a Swiss Cross.

Exc.	V.G.	Good	Fair	Poor
2500	2100	1800	1500	1000

Pistol 1929

Similar to the above, with the exception that the toggle finger pieces are smooth, the grip frame is uncurved, safety lever is a flat configuration and the grip safety is of inordinate size. Fitted with plastic grips.

Exc.	V.G.	Good	Fair	Poor
2100	1700	1500	1200	750

BERNARDELLI, VINCENZO

Brescia, Italy

Aspen Outfitting Co., Aspen, Colorado

Established in the 1870s, this company originally manufactured military arms and only entered the commercial sporting arms market in 1928.

Vest Pocket Model

Similar to the Walther Model 9, in a 6.35mm caliber semi-automatic pistol with a 2.25" barrel, and 5-shot magazine. An extended 8-shot version was also available. Blued with plastic grips. Manufactured between 1945 and 1948.

Exc.	V.G.	Good	Fair	Poor
275	225	155	100	75

Pocket Model

As above, in 7.65mm caliber. This model was also offered with extended barrels that protruded beyond the end of the slide. Introduced in 1947.

Exc.	V.G.	Good	Fair	Poor
275	200	150	100	75

Baby Model

As above, in .22 short or long rifle. Manufactured between 1949 and 1968.

Exc.	V.G.	Good	Fair	Poor
275	200	150	100	75

Sporter Model

A .22 caliber semi-automatic pistol with 6", 8", or 10" barrels and adjustable sights. Blued with walnut grips. Manufactured between 1949 and 1968.

Exc.	V.G.	Good	Fair	Poor
300	225	175	125	100

Revolvers

A .22 rimfire and .32 caliber double-action revolver with 1.5", 2", or 5" barrels. A .22 caliber, 7" barrel version with adjustable sights also available. Manufactured between 1950 and 1962.

Exc.	V.G.	Good	Fair	Poor
200	150	125	100	75

Model 60

A .22, .32 ACP or .380 ACP caliber semi-automatic pistol with a 3.5" barrel and fixed sights. Blued with plastic grips. Manufactured since 1959.

Exc.	V.G.	Good	Fair	Poor
225	175	150	125	90

Model 68

A .22 rimfire caliber semi-automatic pistol with a 2" barrel and 6 shot magazine. Blued with plastic grips.

Exc.	V.G.	Good	Fair	Poor
150	125	100	75	50

Model 80

A .22 or .380 ACP caliber semi-automatic pistol with a 3.5"

barrel and adjustable sights. Blued with plastic grips. Imported between 1968 and 1988.

Exc.	V.G.	Good	Fair	Poor
190	165	125	100	80

Model USA

A .22, .32 ACP or .380 ACP caliber semi-automatic pistol with a 3.5" barrel, adjustable sights, steel frame and a loaded-chamber indicator. Blued with plastic grips.

NIB	Exc.	V.G.	Good	Fair	Poor
290	250	200	150	110	90

Model AMR

As above, with a 6" barrel.

NIB	Exc.	V.G.	Good	Fair	Poor
310	275	225	150	110	90

Model 69

A .22 caliber semi-automatic target pistol with a 6" heavy barrel, and a 10 shot magazine. Blued with checkered walnut grips.

NIB	Exc.	V.G.	Good	Fair	Poor
460	400	325	225	175	125

Model PO10

A .22 caliber, single-action, semi-automatic target pistol with a 6" barrel, target sights and an adjustable trigger. Matte-black finish with stippled walnut grips. Introduced in 1989.

NIB	Exc.	V.G.	Good	Fair	Poor
525	475	400	300	225	150

Model PO18

A 7.65mm or 9mm Parabellum caliber, double-action, semi-automatic pistol with a 4.75" barrel and a 16-shot, double-stack, detachable magazine. All-steel construction, blued with plastic grips. Walnut grips are available for an additional $40. Introduced in 1985.

NIB	Exc.	V.G.	Good	Fair	Poor
450	400	350	275	200	150

Model PO18 Compact

As above, with a 4" barrel and a shorter grip frame with a 14-shot, double-column magazine. Introduced in 1989.

NIB	Exc.	V.G.	Good	Fair	Poor
525	475	400	300	225	175

Model 115 Series

A 12 gauge Over/Under, boxlock, double-barrel shotgun with various barrel lengths and choke combinations, single triggers and automatic ejectors.

Model 115

NIB	Exc.	V.G.	Good	Fair	Poor
1925	1750	1250	900	750	600

Model 115S

NIB	Exc.	V.G.	Good	Fair	Poor
2500	2250	1500	1200	900	700

Model 115L

NIB	Exc.	V.G.	Good	Fair	Poor
3200	2950	2200	1900	1500	1100

Model 115E

NIB	Exc.	V.G.	Good	Fair	Poor
5200	4800	4200	3500	2500	1850

Model 115 Trap

NIB	Exc.	V.G.	Good	Fair	Poor
2200	1950	1400	950	750	600

Model 115S Trap

NIB	Exc.	V.G.	Good	Fair	Poor
2700	2450	1900	1450	1150	900

Model 115E Trap

NIB	Exc.	V.G.	Good	Fair	Poor
5250	4800	4200	3500	2500	1850

Model 190 Series

A 12 gauge, Over/Under shotgun with various barrel lengths and choke combinations, a single selective trigger and automatic ejectors. Engraved and silver-finished with a checkered walnut stock. Introduced in 1986. The various versions differ in the degree of ornamentation and quality of materials utilized in construction.

Model 190

NIB	Exc.	V.G.	Good	Fair	Poor
1050	950	750	600	475	400

Model 190MC

NIB	Exc.	V.G.	Good	Fair	Poor
1150	1050	850	700	575	500

Model 190 Special

NIB	Exc.	V.G.	Good	Fair	Poor
1350	1150	950	800	675	600

Model 190 Combo Gun

A .243, 308 or .30-06 caliber and 12, 16 or 20 gauge combination Over/Under rifle shotgun with a boxlock action, double triggers and automatic ejectors. Blued with a checkered walnut stock. Introduced in 1989.

NIB	Exc.	V.G.	Good	Fair	Poor
1325	1125	925	775	650	575

Orione Series

A 12 gauge boxlock Over/Under shotgun with various barrel lengths and choke combinations. Finishes and triggers were optional, as were extractors or automatic ejectors.

Orione

NIB	Exc.	V.G.	Good	Fair	Poor
1400	1200	1000	800	700	625

Orione S

NIB	Exc.	V.G.	Good	Fair	Poor
1425	1225	1025	825	725	650

Orione L

NIB	Exc.	V.G.	Good	Fair	Poor
1550	1350	1200	900	800	700

Orione E

NIB	Exc.	V.G.	Good	Fair	Poor
1650	1450	1300	1000	900	800

S. Uberto 1 Gamecock

A 12, 16, 20 or 28 gauge boxlock double-barrel shotgun with either 25.75" or 27.5" barrels, various chokes, double triggers and extractors. Automatic ejectors were available and would be worth a 20 percent premium. Blued with a checkered stock.

Exc.	V.G.	Good	Fair	Poor
1200	1050	900	700	500

Brescia

A 12, 16 or 20 gauge sidelock double-barrel shotgun with exposed hammers, various barrel lengths, choke combinations, a sidelock action, double triggers, and manual extractors. Blued with an English-style, checkered walnut stock.

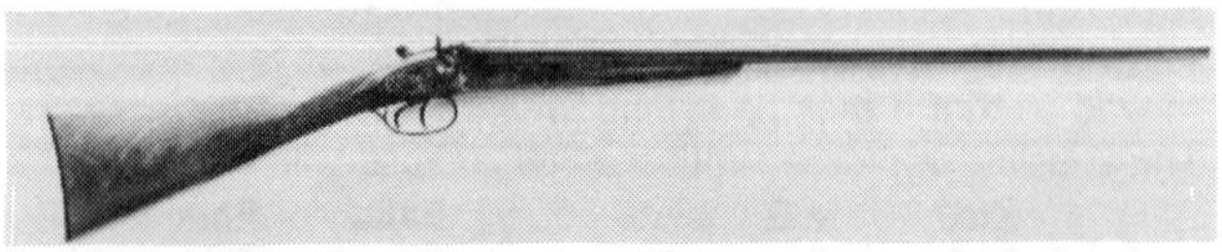

NIB	Exc.	V.G.	Good	Fair	Poor
1840	700	550	450	375	325

Italia

This is a higher-grade version of the Brescia.

NIB	Exc.	V.G.	Good	Fair	Poor
2050	950	700	600	475	425

Italia Extra

This is the highest grade hammer gun that Bernardelli produces.

NIB	Exc.	V.G.	Good	Fair	Poor
4900	2800	2250	1750	1000	750

Uberto Series

A 12, 16, 20 or 28 gauge, Anson & Deeley boxlock double-barrel shotgun with various barrel lengths and choke combinations. The increased value of the various models is dependent on the degree of engraving, options, and quality of materials and workmanship utilized in their construction.

S. Uberto 1

NIB	Exc.	V.G.	Good	Fair	Poor
1200	1000	850	675	550	475

S. Uberto 1E

NIB	Exc.	V.G.	Good	Fair	Poor
1635	1400	1250	1000	850	600

S. Uberto 2

NIB	Exc.	V.G.	Good	Fair	Poor
1600	1350	1200	950	800	550

S. Uberto 2E

NIB	Exc.	V.G.	Good	Fair	Poor
1675	1400	1250	1000	850	600

S. Uberto F.S.

NIB	Exc.	V.G.	Good	Fair	Poor
1750	1500	1300	1100	850	625

S. Uberto F.S.E.

NIB	Exc.	V.G.	Good	Fair	Poor
1835	1600	1450	1200	1000	800

Roma Series

Similar to the S. Uberto Series with false sideplates. The values of the respective variations result from the degree of ornamentation and quality of materials and workmanship utilized in their construction.

Roma 3

NIB	Exc.	V.G.	Good	Fair	Poor
900	850	750	650	550	450

Roma 3E

NIB	Exc.	V.G.	Good	Fair	Poor
1250	1000	900	700	600	500

Roma 4

NIB	Exc.	V.G.	Good	Fair	Poor
1400	1300	1150	900	800	600

Roma 4E

NIB	Exc.	V.G.	Good	Fair	Poor
1400	1300	1150	900	800	600

Roma 6

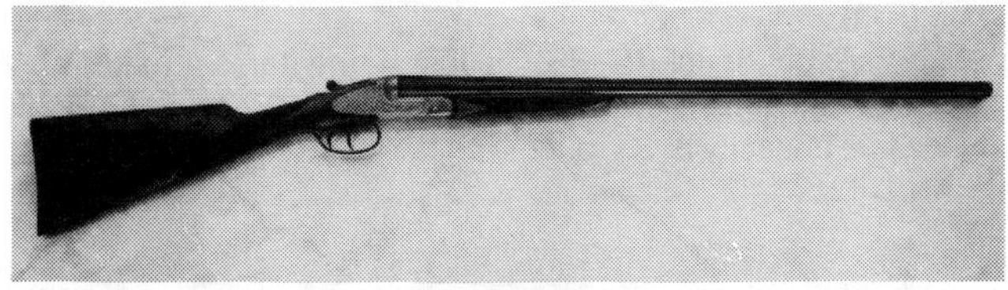

NIB	Exc.	V.G.	Good	Fair	Poor
1500	1250	950	850	700	600

Roma 6E

NIB	Exc.	V.G.	Good	Fair	Poor
1500	1250	950	850	700	600

Elio

A 12 gauge, boxlock double-barrel shotgun with various barrel lengths and choke combinations, lightweight frame, double triggers and extractors. Scroll-engraved, silver finished receiver, blued barrels and a select, checkered walnut stock.

NIB	Exc.	V.G.	Good	Fair	Poor
1600	1400	1250	1000	850	600

Elio E

As above, with automatic ejectors.

NIB	Exc.	V.G.	Good	Fair	Poor
1700	1500	1350	1100	950	675

Hemingway

As above, with coin-finished receiver, engraved with hunting scenes, 23.5" barrels, double triggers and a select, checkered walnut stock.

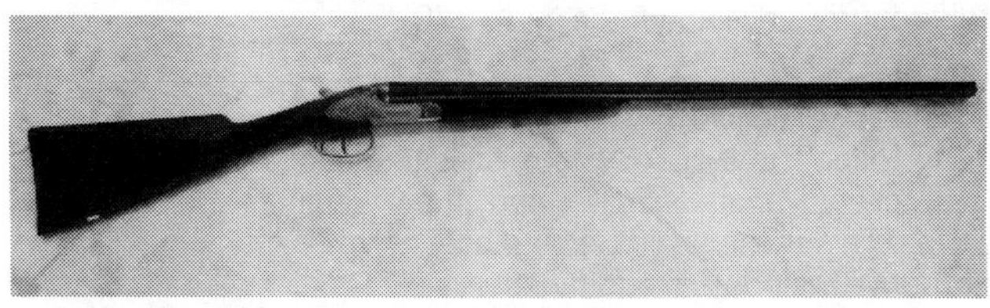

NIB	Exc.	V.G.	Good	Fair	Poor
1850	1600	1450	1200	1000	725

Las Palomas Pigeon

As above, in 12 gauge.

NIB	Exc.	V.G.	Good	Fair	Poor
3800	3200	2650	2100	1650	1450

Holland V.B. Series

A 12 or 20 gauge sidelock, shotgun with various barrel lengths, detachable Holland & Holland-type locks, single triggers, and automatic ejectors. The various models listed below vary in the amount of engraving and the quality of their wood. Prospective purchasers are advised to secure a qualified appraisal prior to acquisition.

Holland V.B. Liscio

NIB	Exc.	V.G.	Good	Fair	Poor
6000	5500	4250	3650	3000	2450

Holland V.B. Inciso

NIB	Exc.	V.G.	Good	Fair	Poor
7000	6500	5250	4650	4000	3450

Holland V.B. Lusso

NIB	Exc.	V.G.	Good	Fair	Poor
8750	8200	7000	5650	4500	3750

Holland V.B. Extra

NIB	Exc.	V.G.	Good	Fair	Poor
15000	13000	10500	7500	5250	4400

Holland V.B. Gold

NIB	Exc.	V.G.	Good	Fair	Poor
35000	30000	22500	15000	12500	10000

BERNARDON MARTIN

St. Etienne, France

1907/8 Model

A 7.65mm caliber semi-automatic pistol. The left side of the slide is marked "Cal. 7.65mm St. Etienne." The trademark "BM" is molded into the grips.

Exc.	V.G.	Good	Fair	Poor
325	295	225	185	150

1908/9 Model

As above, with a grip safety.

Exc.	V.G.	Good	Fair	Poor
325	295	225	185	150

Occasionally the Bernardon Martin pistol will be noted with the word "Hermetic" stamped on the slide in letters that do not match the other markings on the weapon.

BERNEDO, VINCENZO

Eibar, Spain

BC

A 6.35mm caliber semi-automatic pistol, having a completely exposed barrel. The slide marked "Pistolet Automatique Bernedo Patent No. 69952."

Exc.	V.G.	Good	Fair	Poor
250	225	175	125	75

BERSA

Ramos Mejia, Argentina
Importer—Eagle Imports

The firm Fabrica de Armas Bersa SA has been selling pistols in this country since about the mid 1970's.

Model 644

This model is a blowback pocket pistol chambered for the .22 Long Rifle. The trigger system is single action. Barrel length is 3.5", overall length is 6.57", and empty weight is approximately 28 oz. This is the basic Bersa model from which its other models derive their design and function.

NIB	Exc.	V.G.	Good	Fair	Poor
200	175	150	125	100	75

Model 622

Similar to the Model 644 but with a slightly longer barrel.

NIB	Exc.	V.G.	Good	Fair	Poor
200	175	150	125	100	75

Model 23

A .22 rimfire caliber, double-action, semi-automatic pistol with a 3.5" barrel and 10-shot detachable magazine. Either blued or satin nickel-plated with checkered walnut grips.

NIB	Exc.	V.G.	Good	Fair	Poor
225	200	150	125	100	75

Model 223

As above, with a squared trigger guard and nylon grips. Imported after 1988.

Exc.	V.G.	Good	Fair	Poor
225	185	135	100	75

Model 224

As above, with a 4" barrel. Imported after 1988.

Exc.	V.G.	Good	Fair	Poor
225	185	135	100	75

Model 225

As above, with a 5" barrel. Discontinued in 1986.

Exc.	V.G.	Good	Fair	Poor
225	185	135	100	75

Model 226

As above, with a 6" barrel. Discontinued in 1988.

Exc.	V.G.	Good	Fair	Poor
225	185	135	100	75

Model 323

A .32 ACP caliber single-action semi-automatic pistol, with a 3.5" barrel, fixed sights and a 7-shot detachable magazine. Blued with molded plastic grips. Not imported after 1986.

Exc.	V.G.	Good	Fair	Poor
150	125	100	75	50

Model 383

As above, in .380 caliber. Discontinued in 1988.

Exc.	V.G.	Good	Fair	Poor
175	150	125	90	75

Model 383 DA

A .380 ACP caliber double-action semi-automatic pistol with a 3.5" barrel and 7-shot magazine. Blued with checkered walnut grips. Not imported after 1988.

Exc.	V.G.	Good	Fair	Poor
200	150	125	100	75

Model 83

The new designation for the Model 383. Introduced in 1988.

NIB	Exc.	V.G.	Good	Fair	Poor
225	200	150	125	100	75

Model 85

As above, with a double-column magazine. Introduced in 1988.

NIB	Exc.	V.G.	Good	Fair	Poor
275	250	200	150	100	75

Model 97

This model is a slightly larger version of the Model 644 chambered for the 9mm Short.

NIB	Exc.	V.G.	Good	Fair	Poor
200	175	150	125	100	75

Model 86

Similar to the Model 85 .380 caliber but features a matte blue or satin nickel finish, wrap around rubber grips, and 3-dot sight. Magazine capacity is 13 rounds.

NIB	Exc.	V.G.	Good	Fair	Poor
295	250	225	200	150	100

Thunder 9

Introduced in 1993 this model is a double action 9mm pistol that features ambidextrous safety, reversible extended magazine release, ambidextrous slide release, adjustable trigger stop, combat style hammer, 3-dot sights, and matte blue finish. Magazine capacity is 15 rounds.

NIB	Exc.	V.G.	Good	Fair	Poor
335	300	250	200	150	100

BERTHIER

French State

The Berthier bolt-action rifle was adopted as the French service rifle in 1890 and was made in two styles: a Carbine with a 17.5" barrel, and a rifle with a 31.5" barrel. Both were chambered for the 8mm Lebel cartridge and originally had 3-shot magazines. After WWI, many of these arms were modified so that a 5-shot magazine could be used.

Berthier Carbine

Exc.	V.G.	Good	Fair	Poor
275	250	175	125	75

Berthier Rifle

Exc.	V.G.	Good	Fair	Poor
250	225	150	100	50

BERTRAND, JULES

Liege, Belgium

Le Novo

A 6.35mm caliber double-action revolver. Manufactured in the 1890s. The only identifying markings are the "JB" trademark on the grips.

Exc.	V.G.	Good	Fair	Poor
100	75	50	35	20

Lincoln

As above, in 7.65mm caliber.

Exc.	V.G.	Good	Fair	Poor
100	75	50	35	20

LeRapide

A 6.35mm caliber, semi-automatic pistol marked "Man Gr/d'Armes et Munitions Cal. Browning 6.35 LeRapide." The grips are marked "LeRapide" and "JB."

Exc.	V.G.	Good	Fair	Poor
125	100	75	50	25

BERTUZZI

Brescia, Italy
Importer-- New England Arms
Kittery Point, Maine

Shotguns Over/Under

Zeus

A 12 gauge sidelock shotgun with automatic ejectors, single selective trigger, and deluxe checkered walnut stock. Custom order in various barrel lengths and chokes. Engraved. Rarely seen on the used gun market.

NIB	Exc.	V.G.	Good	Fair	Poor
10000	8500	6500	4500	3500	2500

Zeus Extra Lusso

As above, but available on special order only.

NIB	Exc.	V.G.	Good	Fair	Poor
15000	12000	8500	6000	4500	3500

Shotguns SxS

Orione

A 12-gauge boxlock shotgun with Anson & Deeley through bolt, in various barrel lengths and chokes, single selective trigger and automatic ejectors. Hand-checkered, walnut stock with a semi-beavertail forearm.

NIB	Exc.	V.G.	Good	Fair	Poor
3500	3000	2500	1850	1500	1000

Best Quality Sidelock

A custom order sidelock shotgun in various gauges with barrel lengths and chokes to suit the customer. Extensively engraved with a walnut stock.

NIB	Exc.	V.G.	Good	Fair	Poor
7500	7000	6000	4500	3500	2500

BIGHORN ARMS CO.

Watertown, South Dakota

Target Pistol

A .22 caliber single shot pistol resembling a semi-automatic. Ventilated-rib barrel 6" in length. Stock of molded plastic.

Exc.	V.G.	Good	Fair	Poor
150	125	100	85	65

Shotgun

A single shot 12 gauge shotgun with a 26" barrel. Blued with a plastic stock.

Exc.	V.G.	Good	Fair	Poor
100	85	65	50	30

BIGHORN RIFLE CO.

Orem, Utah

Bighorn Rifle

Custom order in any caliber, double-barrel, bolt-action rifle with optional barrel lengths and finishes. Double trigger and walnut stock.

Exc.	V.G.	Good	Fair	Poor
2000	1750	1500	1250	950

BILHARZ, HALL, & CO. CONFEDERATE CARBINES

During the American Civil War, the Southern Confederacy made valiant but often futile efforts to produce small arms for its forces. The small firm of Bilharz, Hall, & Co. of Pittsylvania Court House (currently Chatham), Virginia exemplifies one such effort to furnish the Confederate cavalry with arms. Unfortunately, because their arms were never marked with the name of the manufacturer, they have been mistaken for the products of other small arms makers of the Confederacy.

Bilharz, Hall & Co. breechloading ("Rising Breech") carbine
Overall length- 40"; barrel length- 21"; caliber- .54. Markings: either "P" or "P/CS" on upper left side of barrel and top of rising breech. The peculiar feature of this carbine is the manner in which the breechblock exposes the chamber. A box-like chamber at the rear of the barrel rises vertically to expose the chamber for a paper cartridge by activating the lever/triggerguard mechanism. Only 100 of this type were delivered to the Confederacy in September 1862. Two types of front sight blades are known, but neither affects the value.

Courtesy Milwaukee Public Museum, Milwaukee, Wisconsin.

Exc.	V.G.	Good	Fair	Poor
10000	8500	6500	5000	3500

Bilharz, Hall & Co. muzzleloading carbine
Overall length- 37-1/2"; barrel length- 22"; caliber- .58. Markings: "P/CS" on upper left of barrel near breech; "CSA" on top near breech. Modeled after the Springfield U.S. M1855 rifle-carbine, the Bilharz, Hall & Co. muzzleloading carbine has often been mistakenly identified as a product of D.C. Hodgkins & Sons of Macon, Georgia. Serial numbers (found internally) belie that identification. Instead these arms are part of deliveries made to Richmond from the middle of 1863 until March 1864. Serial numbers, noted in excess of 700, suggest that about 1,000 were produced. Two basic types, the earlier (through serial number 300) were made with brass nosecaps; the later type (about serial number 310 through at least 710) have pewter nosecaps on the short forestock; neither type affects value.

Exc.	V.G.	Good	Fair	Poor
9500	8250	6000	4500	3000

BILLINGHURST, WILLIAM
Rochester, New York

W. Billinghurst Under Hammer Pistol
This pistol is somewhat different than most of the under hammers encountered. The barrels are 12" to 18" in length and of a heavy octagonal construction. They are chambered from .30 to .38 caliber and utilize the percussion ignition system. Higher grade versions feature a part-round barrel, and it is important to note that no two pistols are alike. These pistols were furnished with detachable shoulder stocks, and a good many were cased with telescopic sights and false muzzles. This is a very high quality weapon; and if encountered with the optional accessories, it would definitely warrant an individual appraisal. This firearm was manufactured in the 1850s and 1860s.
Shoulder Stock—Add 50%-75%.

Exc.	V.G.	Good	Fair	Poor
1450	1200	850	650	500

BILLINGS
Location Unknown

Billings Pocket Pistol
A .32 rimfire caliber single shot spur trigger pistol with a 2.5" round barrel and an unusually large grip. The barrel is stamped "Billings Vest Pocket Pistol Pat. April 24, 1866." Blued with walnut grips. Manufactured between 1865 and 1868.

Exc.	V.G.	Good	Fair	Poor
750	675	525	400	275

BINGHAM LTD.
Norcross, Georgia

PPS 50
A .22 rimfire caliber semi-automatic rifle patterned after the Soviet PPSH submachine gun with 16" barrel and a 50-round drum magazine. Blued, walnut or beech stock with a vented handguard. Manufactured between 1976 and 1985.

Exc.	V.G.	Good	Fair	Poor
250	210	175	125	85

AK-22
A .22 rimfire caliber semi-automatic rifle patterned after the Soviet AK-47 with either a 15- or 29-shot magazine. Walnut or beech stock. Manufactured between 1976 and 1985.

Exc.	V.G.	Good	Fair	Poor
200	165	135	100	75

Bantam
A .22 rimfire or .22 rimfire Magnum caliber bolt-action rifle with an 18.5" barrel. Manufactured between 1976 and 1985.

Exc.	V.G.	Good	Fair	Poor
100	85	70	50	35

BISMARCK
Location Unknown

Bismarck Pocket Revolver
A .22 caliber spur trigger revolver with a 3" round-ribbed barrel and a 7-shot, unfluted cylinder. Brass frame and the remainder was plated with rosewood grips. The barrel is marked "Bismarck." Manufactured in the 1870s.

Exc.	V.G.	Good	Fair	Poor
325	250	200	150	90

BITTERLICH, FRANK J.
Nashville, Tennessee

A .41 caliber single shot percussion pistol in a variety of octagonal barrel lengths, German silver mounts, walnut stock. The barrel and locks are marked "Fr.J. Bitterlich/Nashville, Tenn." Produced between 1861 and 1867.

Exc.	V.G.	Good	Fair	Poor
1150	1000	875	700	550

BITTNER, GUSTAV
Wieport, Bohemia

Bittner
A 7.7mm Bittner caliber self-loading pistol with a 4.5" barrel. The bolt containing the firing pin is fully mounted within the frame and is operated by the finger lever trigger. Manufactured in 1893. Less than 500 were made.

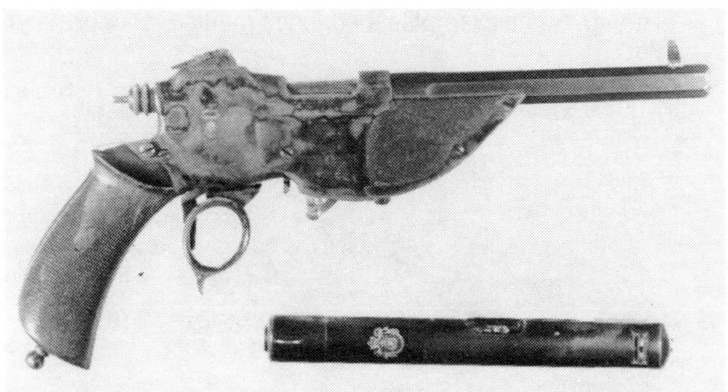

Exc.	V.G.	Good	Fair	Poor
4000	3000	1750	1200	500

BLAKE, J. H.
New York, New York

Blake Bolt Action Rifle

A .30-40 Krag caliber bolt-action rifle with a 30" barrel, and a 7-shot magazine. The stock is secured by three barrel bands. Blued with a walnut stock. Manufactured between 1892 and 1910.

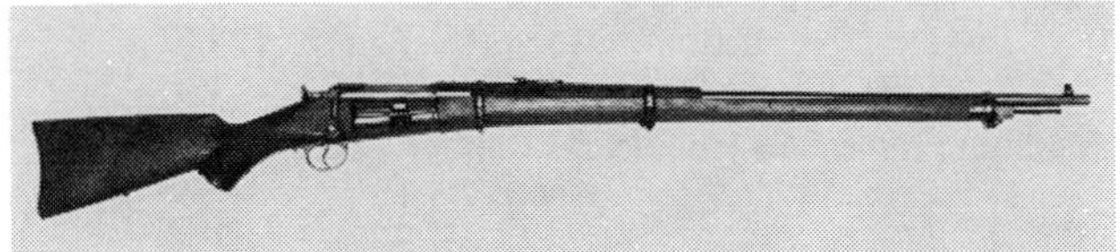

Courtesy Milwaukee Public Museum, Milwaukee, Wisconsin.

Exc.	V.G.	Good	Fair	Poor
750	675	500	375	275

BLANCH, JOHN
London, England

Blanch Percussion Pistol

A .69 caliber single shot, percussion pistol with a 5" Damascus barrel. Engraved frame and hammer with a walnut grip. Manufactured in the 1830s.

Exc.	V.G.	Good	Fair	Poor
2650	2450	2025	1850	1550

BLAND, THOMAS & SONS
London, England

Thomas Bland & Sons manufactured a wide variety of firearms including double barrel rifles, shotguns and pistols. One of their most unusual products was a 4-barrelled pistol having hinged barrels, a rotating firing pin and a double action lock. Most were chambered for the .455 Ely cartridge.

Exc.	V.G.	Good	Fair	Poor
2450	2000	1750	1250	900

BLASER JAGDWAFFEN
West Germany

Model K77

A single shot rifle chambered in a variety of calibers with a 24" barrel and silver plated as well as engraved receiver. Walnut stock. Introduced in 1988.

Extra Barrels—Add $750 Per Barrel.

NIB	Exc.	V.G.	Good	Fair	Poor
2300	2050	1575	1300	950	750

Model R-84

A bolt-action sporting rifle chambered in a variety of calibers with either a 23" or 24" barrel. Interchangeable barrels are available for this model. Walnut stock. Imported beginning in 1988.

NIB	Exc.	V.G.	Good	Fair	Poor
1600	1475	1100	850	750	600

Ultimate Bolt Action

As above, with a silver-plated and engraved receiver as well as a set trigger.

NIB	Exc.	V.G.	Good	Fair	Poor
1500	1300	1050	825	700	575

Special Order Ultimate

The above model is available in a variety of finishes and degrees of decoration as follows:

Ultimate Deluxe

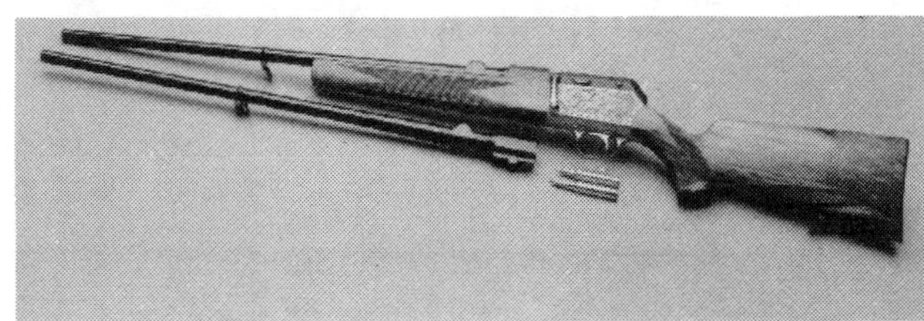

NIB	Exc.	V.G.	Good	Fair	Poor
1600	1400	1150	925	800	675

Ultimate Super Deluxe

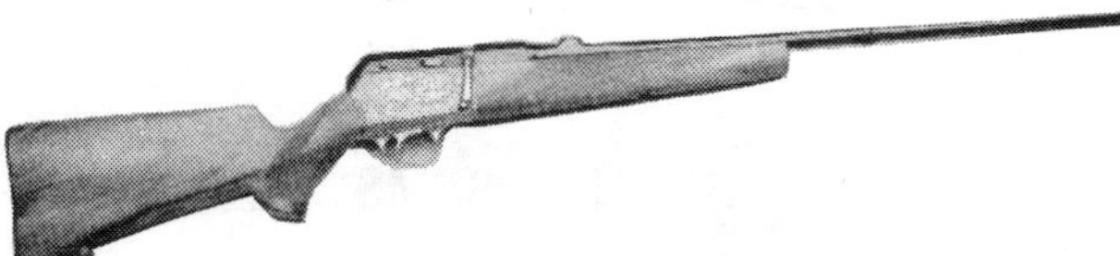

NIB	Exc.	V.G.	Good	Fair	Poor
4050	3750	3250	2500	2000	1750

Ultimate Exclusive

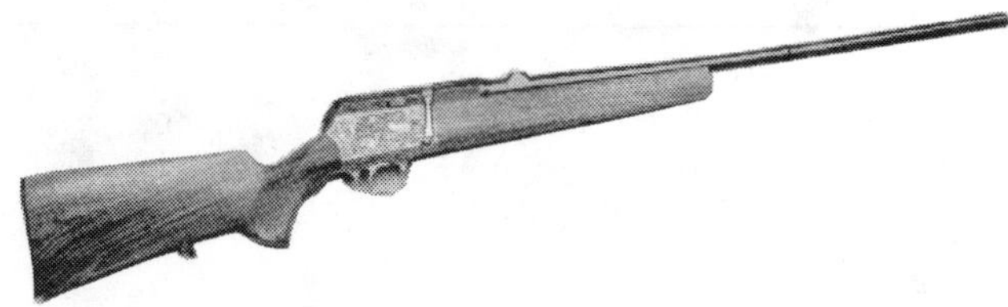

NIB	Exc.	V.G.	Good	Fair	Poor
5700	5250	4500	3750	2600	2000

Ultimate Super Exclusive

NIB	Exc.	V.G.	Good	Fair	Poor
8900	8250	7100	5000	4250	3700

Ultimate Royal

NIB	Exc.	V.G.	Good	Fair	Poor
11500	10000	7500	6000	5200	4500

Note: Extra interchangeable-caliber barrels for the above rifles are available at $700 to $1,200 per barrel depending on the grade.

BLISS, F. D.

New Haven, Connecticut

Bliss Pocket Revolver

A .25 caliber spur trigger revolver with a 3.25" octagon barrel, 6-shot magazine, and a square butt. Blued with either hard rubber or walnut grips. The barrel is stamped "F.D. Bliss New Haven, Ct." There was an all-brass framed version made very early in the production, and this model would be worth approximately 50 percent more than the values listed here for the standard model. Approximately 3,000 manufactured circa 1860 to 1863.

Exc.	V.G.	Good	Fair	Poor
350	300	250	175	125

BLISS & GOODYEAR

New Haven, Connecticut

Pocket Model Revolver

A .28 caliber percussion revolver with a 3" octagonal barrel, 6-shot magazine, unfluted cylinder and a solid frame with a removable sideplate. Blued with a brass frame and walnut grips. Approximately 3,000 manufactured in 1860.

Exc.	V.G.	Good	Fair	Poor
475	425	350	275	175

BLISSETT

SEE—English Military Firearms

BLUNT & SYMS

New York, New York

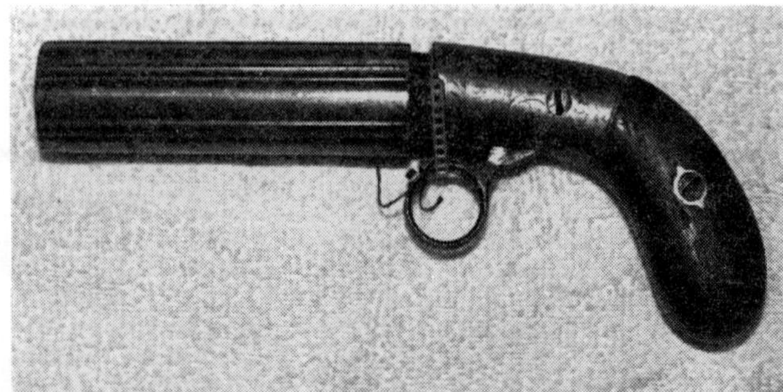

Under Hammer Pepperbox

Pepperboxes produced by Blunt & Syms are noteworthy for the fact that they incorporate a ring trigger cocking/revolving mechanism and a concealed under hammer. They were produced in a variety of calibers and the standard finish was blued. Normally these pistols are found marked simply "A-C" on the face of the barrel group. Some examples though are marked "Blunt & Syms New York".

This firm was in business from approximately 1837 to 1855.

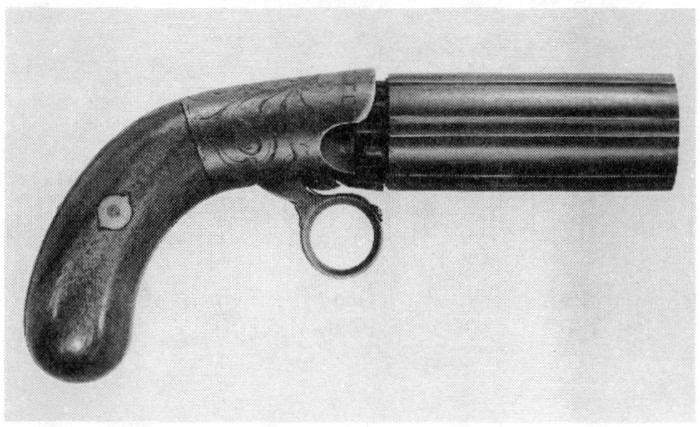

Small Frame Round Handle .25-.28 Caliber

Exc.	V.G.	Good	Fair	Poor
450	400	350	275	175

Medium Frame Round Handle .31 Caliber

Exc.	V.G.	Good	Fair	Poor
400	350	300	225	150

Round Handle Dragoon .36 Caliber

Exc.	V.G.	Good	Fair	Poor
750	650	550	400	300

Medium Frame Saw Handle .31 Caliber

Exc.	V.G.	Good	Fair	Poor
500	450	400	325	250

Saw Handle Dragoon .36 Caliber

Exc.	V.G.	Good	Fair	Poor
800	700	600	425	350

Dueling Pistol

A .52 caliber percussion single shot pistol with an octagonal barrel normally of 9" length. Steel furniture with a walnut stock. Barrel marked "B&S New York/Cast Steel".

Exc.	V.G.	Good	Fair	Poor
800	700	600	425	350

A .36 caliber single shot percussion pistol with a 6" half octagonal barrel and a bar hammer. Blued or browned with walnut grips. Marked as above.

Exc.	V.G.	Good	Fair	Poor
400	325	275	200	150

Side Hammer Pocket Pistol

A .31 or .35 caliber single shot percussion pistol with a 2.5" to 6" octagonal barrel. Blued with walnut grips.

Exc.	V.G.	Good	Fair	Poor
425	350	300	225	175

Side Hammer Belt Pistol

As above, in calibers ranging from .36 to .44 with barrel lengths of 4" or 6".

Exc.	V.G.	Good	Fair	Poor
500	425	375	300	250

Ring Trigger Pistol

A .36 caliber percussion single shot pistol with a 3" to 5" half octagonal barrel and a ring trigger. Blued with walnut grips.

Exc.	V.G.	Good	Fair	Poor
450	375	325	250	200

Double Barrel Pistol

A .36 to .44 caliber percussion double barrel pistol with 7.5" barrels and walnut grips. A ring trigger variation of this model is known.

Exc.	V.G.	Good	Fair	Poor
475	400	350	275	225

Double Barrel Under Hammer Pistol

As above, with two under hammers and in .34 caliber with 4" barrels.

Exc.	V.G.	Good	Fair	Poor
500	425	375	300	250

Derringer Style Pistol

A .50 caliber single shot percussion pistol with a 3" barrel, German silver mounts and a walnut stock. The lock is marked "Blunt & Syms/New York".

Exc.	V.G.	Good	Fair	Poor
900	750	600	475	350

BODEO

Italian Service Revolver

System Bodeo Modello 1889 (Enlisted Model)

A 10.4mm caliber revolver with a 4.5" octagonal barrel, and 6-shot cylinder. This revolver was adopted as the Italian Service Revolver in 1889 and was replaced by the Glisenti in 1910. Manufactured by various Italian Arms companies.

Exc.	V.G.	Good	Fair	Poor
200	175	150	100	75

Modello 1889 (Officers Model)

Essentially the same as the enlisted man's model with a round barrel, non-folding trigger, and conventional triggerguard.

Exc.	V.G.	Good	Fair	Poor
200	175	150	100	75

BOLUMBURO, G.

Eibar, Spain

A 6.35 and 7.65mm caliber semi-automatic pistol under the trade names: Bristol, Giralda, Gloria, Marina, Regent, and Rex. The values on these would be quite similar, and they may be regarded the same.

Exc.	V.G.	Good	Fair	Poor
150	110	85	65	35

BOND

SEE—English Military Firearms

BOOM

SEE—Shattuck, C.S.

Hatfield, Massachusetts

BORCHARDT

Berlin, Germany

Waffenfabrik Lowe

DWM

A 7.65mm semi-automatic pistol with a 6.5" barrel and an 8-shot magazine. Blued with walnut grips and a detachable walnut shoulder stock. This pistol was designed by Hugo Borchardt and was manufactured by Ludwig Lowe of Berlin. It is the immediate predecessor of the Luger. Later models were manufactured by DWM. Prospective purchasers should secure a qualified appraisal prior to acquisition.

Lowe Manufacture—Add 15%.

Exc.	V.G.	Good	Fair	Poor
12500	9000	7000	5000	2000

BORSIG

East Germany

The Borsig is the East German version of the Soviet Makarov pistol. It is a double-action, chambered for the Soviet 9X18mm cartridge. Its appearance is nearly identical to the Makarov.

Exc.	V.G.	Good	Fair	Poor
200	175	150	100	75

BOSS & CO.

London, England

The firm of Boss & Co. has been in the firearms business since 1832 and enjoys a reputation for producing some of the finest shotguns in the world. The prices of these guns are quite high, and setting a value in a publication of this nature is nearly impossible. There are not enough bought and sold to give an accurate market value. There were less than 10,000 manufactured ever, and anyone contemplating purchase should secure an individual and expert appraisal. For reference purposes we list the basic models and their prices.

Side x Side

This is a custom order shotgun available in any gauge with barrel lengths and chokes to the customer's specifications. It has automatic ejectors and either a single or double trigger. The stock is made of the best-grade walnut and made to order with or without a pistol grip. The small-gauge guns would bring a sizeable premium as few were made.

Exc.	V.G.	Good	Fair	Poor
15000	13500	10000	8000	5500

Over/Under

The O/U was built to order and is similar in quality to the Side x Side.

Exc.	V.G.	Good	Fair	Poor
20000	17500	15000	10000	7500

The following is applicable to both models:

20 Gauge—Add 25%.
28 Gauge—Add 40%.
.410—Add 50%.
Cased with Accessories—Add $1000.

BOSWELL, CHARLES

London, England

One of England's more established makers of best-quality rifles and shotguns. In 1988 the company was purchased by an American consortium and the Cape Horn Outfitters of Charlotte, North Carolina was appointed their sole agent.

Double Rifle, Boxlock

A .300 Holland & Holland, .375 Holland & Holland or .458 Winchester Magnum double-barrel boxlock rifle with double triggers and a walnut stock. Other features were made to the customer's specifications. A .600 Nitro Express version was also available.

.600 Nitro Express—Add 25%.

Exc.	V.G.	Good	Fair	Poor
40000	32500	25000	17500	12500

Double Rifle, Sidelock

As above, with Holland & Holland-style-sidelocks.

.600 Nitro Express—Add 25%.

Exc.	V.G.	Good	Fair	Poor
55000	40000	30000	20000	17500

Shotgun, Boxlock

A boxlock double-barrel shotgun produced in a variety of gauges, barrel lengths and degrees of decoration.

.28 Gauge and .410—Add 20%.

Exc.	V.G.	Good	Fair	Poor
8500	7000	5500	4000	3000

Shotgun, Sidelock

As above, with Holland & Holland-style-sidelocks.
.28 Gauge and .410—Add 20%.

Exc.	V.G.	Good	Fair	Poor
9500	8000	6500	5000	3750

BOSWORTH, B. M.

Warren, Pennsylvania

Bosworth Under Hammer Pistol

A .38 caliber single shot percussion pistol with an under hammer and a 6" half octagonal barrel. The frame is marked "BM Bosworth". Browned with brass grips forming part of the frame. Made circa 1850 to 1860.

Exc.	V.G.	Good	Fair	Poor
500	425	350	275	200

BRAENDLIN ARMOURY

London, England

A .450 caliber 8-barrel pistol with hinged barrels, rotating firing pin and double-action lock. Manufactured during the 1880s.

Exc.	V.G.	Good	Fair	Poor
5000	4500	3500	2750	2000

BRAND

E. Robinson, Maker
New York

Brand Breech Loading Carbine

A .50 rimfire caliber carbine with a 22" barrel secured by one barrel band. The frame is marked "Brand's Patent July 29,1862/E. Robinson Manfr/New York." This carbine was produced in very limited numbers, primarily for trial purposes.

Exc.	V.G.	Good	Fair	Poor
2000	1750	1500	1150	800

BREDA, ERNESTO

Milan, Italy
Importer—Diana Imports Co.
San Francisco, California

Andromeda Special

A 12 gauge boxlock shotgun with various barrel lengths and chokes, single selective triggers and automatic ejectors. Engraved, satin-finished with checkered walnut stock.

Exc.	V.G.	Good	Fair	Poor
700	650	550	425	300

Vega Special

A 12 gauge boxlock Over/Under shotgun with 26" or 28" barrels, various choke combinations, single selective trigger and automatic ejectors. Engraved and blued with a checkered walnut stock.

Exc.	V.G	Good	Fair	Poor
650	600	500	375	275

Vega Special Trap

As above with a competition-styled stock and 30" or 32" barrels with full chokes.

Exc.	V.G.	Good	Fair	Poor
1150	900	750	500	350

Sirio Standard

Similar to the Vega with extensive engraving and a higher degree of finishing. There is a 28"-barreled skeet version available in this model.

Exc.	V.G.	Good	Fair	Poor
2250	2000	1750	1250	1000

Standard Semi-Automatic

A 12 gauge semi-automatic shotgun with 25" or 27" ventilated rib barrels, screw-in choke tubes, an engraved receiver, and checkered walnut stock.

Exc.	V.G.	Good	Fair	Poor
325	275	225	175	125

Grade I

As above, with more engraving and finer wood.

Exc.	V.G.	Good	Fair	Poor
550	475	325	225	175

Grade II

A more elaborately engraved version of the Grade I.

Exc.	V.G.	Good	Fair	Poor
675	600	450	375	250

Grade III

The most deluxe version in this line with select walnut and extensive engraving.

Exc.	V.G.	Good	Fair	Poor
875	800	650	575	450

Magnum Model

Same as the standard, 12 gauge Magnum.

Exc.	V.G.	Good	Fair	Poor
475	400	350	275	200

Gold Series Antares Standard

A 12 gauge semi-automatic shotgun with a 25" or 27" ventilated-rib barrel and screw-in choke tubes. Blued with a checkered walnut stock.

Exc.	V.G.	Good	Fair	Poor
500	400	350	275	225

Gold Series Argus

As above, with alloy frame.

Exc.	V.G.	Good	Fair	Poor
525	425	375	300	250

Gold Series Aries

As above, except in 12 gauge Magnum.

Exc.	V.G.	Good	Fair	Poor
550	450	400	325	275

BREN 10

Dornaus & Dixon Inc.
Huntington Beach, California

Manufactured from 1983 until 1986.

Standard Bren 10

A 10mm caliber double-action semi-automatic pistol with a 5" barrel and 11-shot magazine. Stainless frame and satin-blued slide. Manufactured between 1983 and 1986.

NIB	Exc.	V.G.
1350	1100	800

M & P Model

As above, with a matte black finish.

NIB	Exc.	V.G.
1350	1000	800

Pocket Model

As above, with a 4" barrel and 9-shot magazine.

NIB	Exc.	V.G.
1300	1150	850

Dual-Master Presentation Model

As above, with a .45 caliber, extra barrel and slide and a fitted walnut case.

NIB	Exc.	V.G.
1750	1500	1050

Marksman Model

Similar to the Standard Model but in .45 caliber. There were

250 manufactured for the "Marksman Shop" in Chicago, Illinois.

NIB	Exc.	V.G.
1100	1000	750

Initial Commemorative
There were supposed to be 2,000 of these manufactured in 1986, but no one knows how many were actually produced. They are chambered for the 10mm and have a high-gloss blue finish with 22 kt. gold-plated details. The grips are laser engraved, and the whole affair is furnished in a walnut display case.

NIB	Exc.	V.G.
3000	2500	2000

BRETTON
Ste. Etienne, France
Importers--Quality Arms, Inc.
Houston, Texas
Mandall Shooting Supplies
Scottsdale, Arizona

Baby Standard
A 12 or 20 gauge O/U shotgun with various barrel lengths and choke combinations and double triggers. Blued, checkered walnut stock.

NIB	Exc.	V.G.	Good	Fair	Poor
800	725	625	500	425	375

Deluxe Grade
A 12, 16 and 20 gauge O/U shotgun. Engraved, coin-finished receiver with walnut stock.

NIB	Exc.	V.G.	Good	Fair	Poor
1000	900	750	600	500	425

BRIGGS, H. A.
Norwich, Connecticut

Briggs Single Shot Pistol
A .22 caliber single shot spur trigger pistol with a 4" part-round/part-octagonal barrel with a downward rotating breech block. Blued with walnut grips. Frame is marked "H.A. Briggs/Norwich, Ct." Manufactured in the 1850s and 1860s.

Exc.	V.G.	Good	Fair	Poor
750	600	525	400	275

BRIXIA
Brescia, Italy

Model 12
A commercial version of the Model 1910 Glisenti in 9mm caliber. The only markings are the monogram "MBT" cast in the grips.

Exc.	V.G.	Good	Fair	Poor
375	325	275	200	150

BRNO ARMS
(BOLT ACTION RIFLES)
Uhersky Brod, Czech Republic
Importer—Action Arms
Philadelphia, PA

Brno rifles are built in the same factory as CZ pistols.

ZH-Series
A double barrel O/U boxlock series of shotguns with interchangeable barrels in shotgun and rifle configurations, of various lengths, double triggers and automatic ejectors. The models listed below represent the different gauges and/or calibers offered.

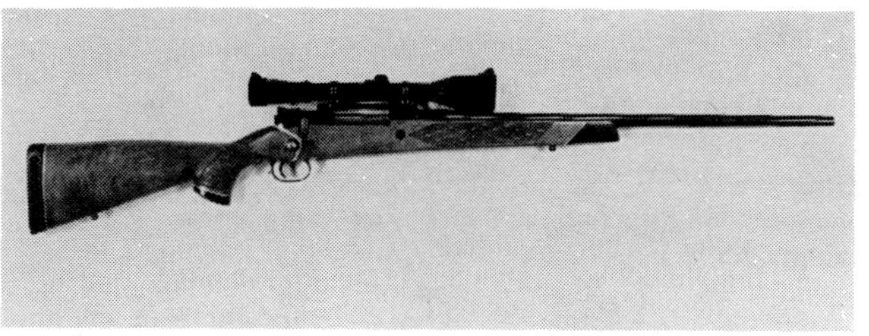

ZH-300

NIB	Exc.	V.G.	Good	Fair	Poor
700	600	500	350	300	225

ZH-301

Exc.	V.G.	Good	Fair	Poor
650	525	425	350	275

ZH-302

Exc.	V.G.	Good	Fair	Poor
600	550	425	350	275

ZH-303

Exc.	V.G.	Good	Fair	Poor
650	550	425	350	275

ZH-304

Exc.	V.G.	Good	Fair	Poor
800	650	500	425	375

ZH-305

Exc.	V.G.	Good	Fair	Poor
800	700	550	425	375

ZH-306

Exc.	V.G.	Good	Fair	Poor
850	750	550	450	400

ZH-321

Exc.	V.G.	Good	Fair	Poor
625	525	400	350	300

ZH-324

Exc.	V.G.	Good	Fair	Poor
775	650	500	425	375

Model 300 Combo
The model ZH-300 with 8 interchangeable barrels in a fitted case. Introduced in 1986.

NIB	Exc.	V.G.	Good	Fair	Poor
5000	4250	3500	2250	1750	1250

Model 500
The model ZH-300 with acid etched decoration, automatic ejectors and in 12 gauge.

NIB	Exc.	V.G.	Good	Fair	Poor
775	650	500	400	350	275

CZ-581
A 12 gauge O/U double barrel boxlock shotgun with 28" ventilated-rib barrels, single-trigger, and automatic ejectors. Blued with a walnut stock.

NIB	Exc.	V.G.	Good	Fair	Poor
750	650	550	450	400	325

CZ-584
A combination 12 gauge/7x57Rmm, .222 or .308 caliber O/U combination rifle/shotgun with 24.5" ventilated-rib barrels, single-triggers and automatic ejectors. Blued with a walnut stock. Discontinued in 1986.

Exc.	V.G.	Good	Fair	Poor
1250	1000	850	650	550

ZP-49
A 12 gauge sidelock double-barrel shotgun with double triggers and automatic ejectors. Blued with a walnut stock. Imported in 1986 only.

Exc.	V.G.	Good	Fair	Poor
650	550	475	350	300

ZP-149

As above, without engraving.

NIB	Exc.	V.G.	Good	Fair	Poor
600	550	475	350	300	250

ZP-349

As above, with the buttstock having a cheekpiece and the forend of beavertail form.

Exc.	V.G.	Good	Fair	Poor
550	450	350	275	225

Hornet Sporter

A .22 Hornet caliber bolt-action rifle with a 23" barrel, express sights and double set triggers. Blued with a walnut stock.

Exc.	V.G.	Good	Fair	Poor
1000	900	800	650	500

Model 21H

A 6.5x57mm, 7x57mm or 8x57mm caliber bolt-action sporting rifle with a 28.5" barrel, express sights and double set triggers. Blued with a walnut stock.

Exc.	V.G.	Good	Fair	Poor
950	850	750	600	475

Model 22F

As above, with a Mannlicher-style stock.

Exc.	V.G.	Good	Fair	Poor
1200	1000	850	650	500

Model I

A .22 caliber bolt-action rifle with a 22.75" barrel having folding leaf rear sights. Blued with a walnut stock.

Exc.	V.G.	Good	Fair	Poor
600	500	400	325	250

Model II

As above, with a more finely figured walnut stock.

Exc.	V.G.	Good	Fair	Poor
650	550	450	375	275

ZKM-452

As above, with a 25" barrel and either a 5- or 10-shot magazine. Blued with a beechwood stock.

Exc.	V.G.	Good	Fair	Poor
250	200	175	125	100

ZKM-452D

As above, with a walnut, Monte Carlo-style stock.

Exc.	V.G.	Good	Fair	Poor
350	300	225	150	120

ZKB 680

A .22 Hornet or .222 caliber bolt-action rifle with a 23.5" barrel, double set triggers and 5-shot magazine. Blued with a walnut stock.

NIB	Exc.	V.G.	Good	Fair	Poor
650	550	450	350	275	175

ZKK 600

Offered in 7x57mm, 7x64mm, .270, or .30-06. Features a Mauser type bolt action with controlled feed, non-rotating extractor, and dove-tailed receiver in three action lengths.

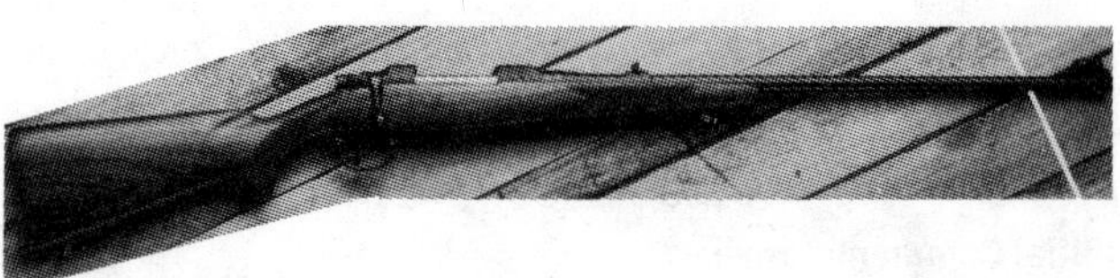

NIB	Exc.	V.G.	Good	Fair	Poor
600	525	450	400	325	250

NOTE: Add $100 to prices for pop-up receiver sight which was discontinued in 1977.

ZKK 601

As above, in .243 or .308 caliber.

NIB	Exc.	V.G.	Good	Fair	Poor
600	525	450	400	325	250

ZKK 602

As above, in .300 Holland & Holland, .375 Holland & Holland or .458 Winchester Magnum.

NIB	Exc.	Good	Good	Fair	Poor
750	675	525	500	425	325

CZ-511

A .22 caliber semi-automatic rifle with adjustible sights. Blued with a walnut stock. Discontinued in 1986.

Exc.	V.G.	Good	Fair	Poor
400	350	250	175	125

Model 581

Similar to the above, but more finely finished.

Exc.	V.G.	Good	Fair	Poor
600	525	450	400	325

Model 537

This bolt action rifle is chambered for the .270, .308, and .30-06 cartridges. The rear sight is adjustable and the stock is checkered walnut. Barrel length is 23.6". Magazine capacity is 5 rounds. Weight is approximately 7.9 lb.

NIB	Exc.	V.G.	Good	Fair	Poor
385	310	275	225	175	125

Model 527

This bolt action model is chambered for the .22 Hornet, .222 Rem., and the .223 Rem. The rear sight is adjustable and the checkered stock is walnut. Barrel length is 23.6" and magazine capacity is 5 rounds. Weight is approximately 6.2 lb.

NIB	Exc.	V.G.	Good	Fair	Poor
315	250	225	200	175	125

Super Express Rifle

An O/U sidelock double barrel rifle, with 23.5" barrels, double triggers and automatic ejectors. Engraved, blued with a walnut stock. Available in 6 grades as below:

Standard Model

NIB	Exc.	V.G.	Good	Fair	Poor
4500	3750	3000	2500	1750	1250

Grade I

NIB	Exc.	V.G.	Good	Fair	Poor
6500	5500	4750	4500	3600	3250

Grade II

NIB	Exc.	V.G.	Good	Fair	Poor
5500	4750	4000	3500	2750	2250

Grade III

NIB	Exc.	V.G.	Good	Fair	Poor
5250	4500	3950	3250	2750	2250

Grade IV

NIB	Exc.	V.G.	Good	Fair	Poor
5000	4000	3500	3000	2500	2250

Grade V

NIB	Exc.	V.G.	Good	Fair	Poor
4500	3850	3000	2600	2000	1600

Grade VI

NIB	Exc.	V.G.	Good	Fair	Poor
4600	3950	3100	2750	2100	1750

BRONCO

SEE--Arizmendi
Eibar, Spain

BROOKLYN F. A. CO.

Brooklyn, New York

Slocum Pocket Revolver

A .32 caliber spur trigger revolver with a 3" round barrel. The frame is silver-plated brass and scroll engraved; the remainder is either blued or plated with walnut grips. The barrel is marked "B.A. Co. Patented April 14, 1863." Approximately 10,000 were manufactured in 1863 and 1864. The cylinder has five individual tubes that slide forward to open for loading and then for ejecting the spent cartridges.

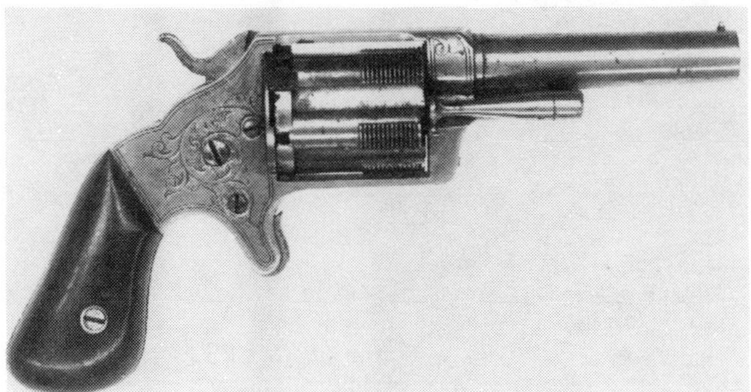

Exc.	V.G.	Good	Fair	Poor
350	300	225	150	100

Slocum Unfluted Cylinder Pocket Revolver

As above, but in .22 or .32 caliber with 5- or 7-shot cylinder. Approximately 250 were manufactured in .32 rimfire and 100 in .22 rimfire.

.22 Caliber—Add 25%.

Exc.	V.G.	Good	Fair	Poor
450	400	325	250	200

BROWN MANUFACTURING CO.

Newburyport, Massachusetts
SEE—also Ballard

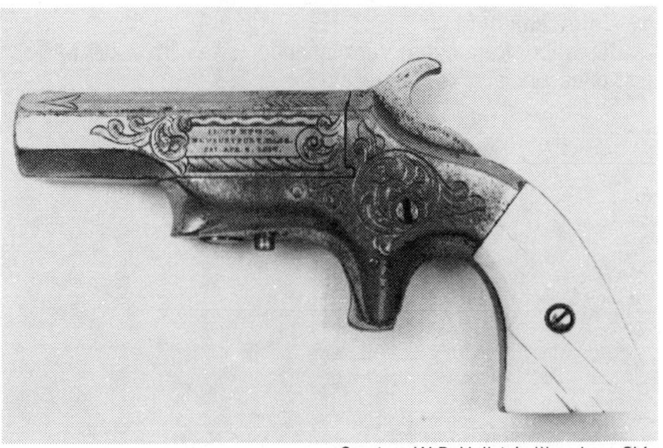

Courtesy W.P. Hallstein III and son Chip.

Southerner Derringer

A .41 caliber spur trigger single shot pocket pistol with a pivoted 2.5" or 4" octagonal barrel marked "Southerner". Silver plated or blued with walnut grips. This pistol was manufactured by the Merrimack Arms Co. from 1867 to 1869 and by the Brown Manufacturing Co. from 1869 to 1873.

Brass Framed 2.5" Barrel

Exc.	V.G.	Good	Fair	Poor
350	300	225	175	125

Iron Frame 2.5" Barrel (Brown Mfg. Only)

Exc.	V.G.	Good	Fair	Poor
375	325	250	200	150

Brass Frame 4" Barrel

Exc.	V.G.	Good	Fair	Poor
750	650	550	425	300

Brown Mfg. Co./Merrill Patent breechloading rifles

Overall length-54-3/4"; barrel (bore) length- 35"; caliber- .577. Markings: On breechblock-bolt mechanism, "BROWN MFG. CO. NEWBURYPORT, MASS./PATANTED OCT. 17, 1871." The patent issued to George Merrill in 1871, permitted the Brown Manufacturing Co. to alter probably up to 1,000 English P1853 rifle-muskets to a single shot breechloading system. The large bolt handle projecting upward at the end of the breech readily distinguishes these arms.

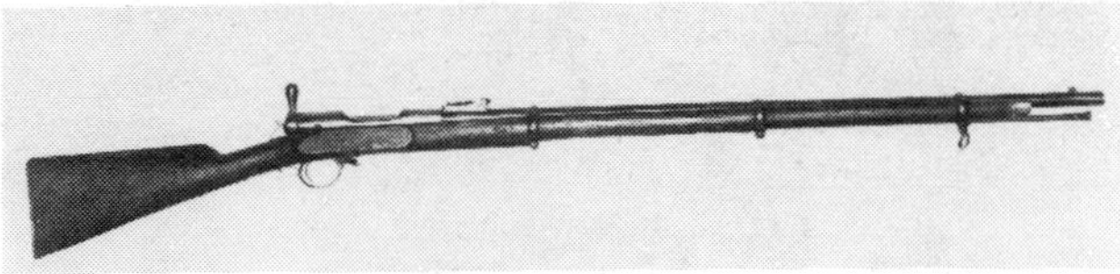

Courtesy Milwaukee Public Museum, Milwaukee, Wisconsin.

Exc.	V.G.	Good	Fair	Poor
950	750	500	400	275

BROWN PRECISION, INC.

Los Molinos, California

Although known as a manufacturer of stocks, this company also produces custom order rifles.

High Country Standard

A .243 to .30-06 bolt-action rifle with a 22" barrel and kevlar stock.

Gray Camo Stock, Stainless Barrel and Leupold 2.5 x 10 Scope—Add $650.

NIB	Exc.	V.G.	Good	Fair	Poor
985	925	775	575	450	375

Open Country Varmint Rifle

Similar to the above, with a heavy barrel. Introduced in 1989.

NIB	Exc.	V.G.	Good	Fair	Poor
1100	1000	850	650	500	400

Law Enforcement Model

A .308 caliber Remington Varmint action rifle with a 20" barrel, Zeiss telescope and kevlar stock.

NIB	Exc.	V.G.	Good	Fair	Poor
1050	950	800	600	450	375

Pro-Hunter

A .375 Holland & Holland or .458 Winchester Magnum bolt action rifle. Blued, electroless nickel-plated or teflon coated.

NIB	Exc.	V.G.	Good	Fair	Poor
1800	1700	1450	1250	1000	750

Custom Winchester Model 70

A .270 or .30-06 bolt-action rifle with a 22" featherweight barrel and kevlar stock.

NIB	Exc.	V.G.	Good	Fair	Poor
600	525	450	350	300	250

Blaser Rifle

Built on the Camex-Blaser action with a Brown Precision stock.

NIB	Exc.	V.G.	Good	Fair	Poor
1400	1250	1000	750	650	500

BROWNING

BROWNING ARMS CO.
Ogden, Utah

Contrary to popular belief, the firm of Browning Arms has actually manufactured only one gun in its long and colorful history. This was the Model 1878 single shot rifle, which was actually the first gun that the prolific inventor John M. Browning patented. This firm was founded in 1880 as J. M. Browning & Bro. in Ogden, Utah. John Browning is considered by many to be the greatest firearms genius of all time. He created 80 firearms designs and held 128 individual patents. He sold designs to Winchester, Stevens, Remington, and Colt, as well as to the Belgian firm of Fabrique Nationale (FN). He was directly responsible for designing many of the firearms with which we have come to be familiar, including the 1911 Colt Government Model, the 1885 Winchester Single Shot (evolved from the Model 1878 that was actually Browning-manufactured), the Models 1886, 1892, 1894, and 1895 Lever Action Rifles, as well as the Model 1897 Shotgun. He was also directly responsible for producing the Model 1935 Hi-Power which achieved worldwide service pistol acceptance. In the 1890s Browning had difficulty dealing with the American arms corporations, so he went to Europe and established a lasting relationship with the firm of Fabrique Nationale in Herstal, Belgium. This agreement has lasted to this day, and many of the firearms sold under the Browning banner are still produced at FN. In the early 1970s, the Browning corporation contracted with the firm of B. C. Miroku in Japan and has since marketed guns produced by them. One should be cognizant of the fact that in the opinion of many experts Miroku-produced Browning firearms are as high in quality as any others produced; collector interest dictates greater values on the Belgian-manufactured versions.

Early Semi-Automatic Pistols

In the period between 1900 and the development of the Model 1935 Hi-Power Pistol, Browning had a number of semi-automatic pistols manufactured by Fabrique Nationale of Herstal, Belgium. They were the Models 1900, 1903, 1905, 1910, 1922, the Baby, and the 1935 Model Hi-Power. These firearms will be listed in more detail with their respective values in the Fabrique Nationale section of this text.

Hi-Power Modern Production

This version of the FN Model 1935 is quite similar in appearance to the original described in the FN section. It is chambered for the 9mm Parabellum cartridge and has a 4.75" barrel. It has a double column, 35-round, detachable box magazine and is blued with checkered walnut grips. It has fixed sights and has been produced in its present configuration since 1954. An adjustable-sight version is also available and would be valued at approximately 10 percent higher. A matte-nickle version is also available and would be worth approximately 5 percent additional.

NIB	Exc.	V.G.	Good	Fair	Poor
475	400	350	300	275	200

Hi-Power-.30 Luger

This version is similar to the standard Hi-Power except that it is chambered for the .30 Luger cartridge. There were approximately 1,500 imported between 1986 and 1989. The slide is marked "FN." The Browning-marked versions are quite rare and worth approximately 10 percent additional.

Exc.	V.G.	Good	Fair	Poor
475	400	350	275	200

Tangent Sight Model

This version is similar to the standard Hi-Power with the addition of an adjustable rear sight calibrated to 500 meters. There were approximately 7,000 imported between 1965 and 1978. If the grip frame is slotted to accept a detachable shoulder stock, add approximately 20 percent to the value; but be wary of fakes.

Exc.	V.G.	Good	Fair	Poor
750	675	500	400	300

Renaissance Hi-Power

This is a heavily engraved version with a matte-silver finish. It features synthetic-pearl grips and a goldplated trigger. The adjustable-sight version would be worth approximately 5 percent additional. Import on this model ended in 1980.

NIB	Exc.	V.G.	Good	Fair	Poor
1200	1050	800	600	500	400

Cased Renaissance Set

This features one example of a fully engraved and silver-finished .25 ACP "Baby," one .380 ACP Pistol, and one Hi-Power. The set is furnished in a fitted walnut case and was imported between 1955 and 1969.

NIB	Exc.	V.G.	Good	Fair	Poor
3500	3000	2500	2150	1750	1250

Louis XVI Model

This is a heavily engraved Hi-Power pistol that features a leaf-and-scroll pattern. It is satin-finished and features checkered walnut grips. It is furnished in a fitted walnut case. To realize its true potential, this pistol must be NIB. It was not imported after 1984.

NIB	Exc.	V.G.	Good	Fair	Poor
1000	875	750	600	500	400

Hi-Power Centennial Model

This version is similar to the standard fixed-sight Hi-Power but is chrome-plated with the inscription, "Browning Centennial/1878-1978" engraved on the slide. It is furnished with a fitted case. There were 3,500 manufactured in 1978. As with all commemorative pistols, in order to realize its collector potential, this Model should be NIB with all supplied material.

NIB	Exc.	V.G.	Good	Fair	Poor
800	525	450	400	350	275

Hi-Power Captain

This is a new verions of the Hi-Power model fitted with tangent sights. Introduced in 1993. Furnished with walnut grips. Weighs about 32 oz.

NIB	Exc.	V.G.	Good	Fair	Poor
475	400	350	300	250	200

Hi-Power Practical

First introduced in 1993 this version is furnished with a blued slide and chrome frame. Has Pachmayr wraparound rubber grips, round style serrated hammer, and removable front sight. As available with adjustable sights. Weighs 36 oz.

NIB	Exc.	V.G.	Good	Fair	Poor
475	400	350	300	250	200

Hi-Power Silver Chrome Model

Furnish in hard chrome and fitted with wraparound Pachmayr rubber grips. Weighs 36 oz.

NIB	Exc.	V.G.	Good	Fair	Poor
450	375	325	275	225	200

Hi-Power Mark III

The pistol has a matte blued finish with low profile fixed sights, and two piece molded grips with thumb rest. Weighs 32 oz.

NIB	Exc.	V.G.	Good	Fair	Poor
380	325	275	225	200	175

BDA-380

This is a double-action, semi-automatic pistol chambered for the .380 ACP cartridge. It features a 3.75" barrel with a 14-round, double-stack, detachable magazine. The finish is either blued or nickle-plated with smooth walnut grips. This pistol was manufactured in Italy by Beretta and introduced in 1982. Add 5 Percent for Nickle Finish.

NIB	Exc.	V.G.	Good	Fair	Poor
450	375	325	275	200	150

Model BDA

This is a double-action, semi-automatic pistol manufactured for Browning by Sig-Sauer of Germany. It is identical to the Sig-Sauer Model 220. It is chambered for 9mm Parabellum, .38 Super, and the .45 ACP cartridges. The .38 Super would be worth approximately 30 percent additional.

Exc.	V.G.	Good	Fair	Poor
500	425	375	300	235

BDM Pistol

This is a double-action, semi-automatic pistol chambered for the 9mm cartridge. The pistol is fitted with a selector switch that allows the shooter to choose between single action model or double action mode. It features a 4.75" barrel with adjustable rear sight. The magazine capacity is 15 rounds. Weighs 31 oz.

NIB	Exc.	V.G.	Good	Fair	Poor
560	500	450	400	300	200

Nomad

This is a blowback-operated, semi-automatic pistol chambered for the .22 l.r. cartridge. It was offered with a 4.5" or 6.75" barrel. It has a 10-round, detachable magazine with adjustable sights and all-steel construction. The finish is blued with black plastic grips. It was manufactured between 1962 and 1974 by FN.

Exc.	V.G.	Good	Fair	Poor
300	250	200	150	100

Challenger
This is a more deluxe target pistol chambered for the .22 l.r. cartridge. It was offered with a 4.5" or 6.75" barrel and has a 10-round magazine. It is constructed entirely of steel and has adjustable sights. The finish is blued with a gold-plated trigger and checkered, wrap-around, walnut grips. It was manufactured between 1962 and 1975 by FN.

Exc.	V.G.	Good	Fair	Poor
375	300	250	200	140

Renaissance Challenger
This version is fully engraved with a satin-nickle finish and a fitted walnut case.

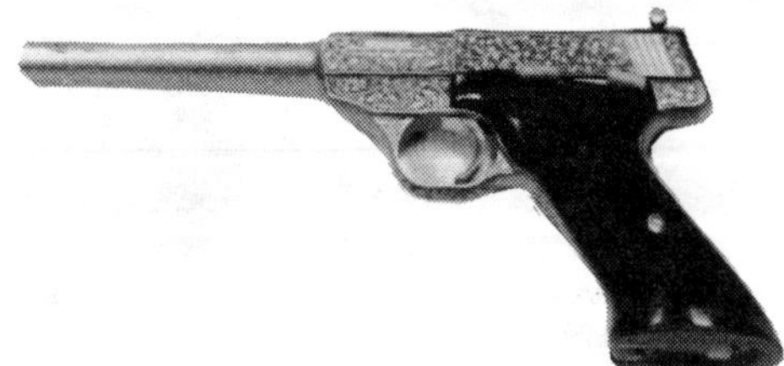

NIB	Exc.	V.G.	Good	Fair	Poor
1000	850	600	500	350	275

Gold Line Challenger
This version is blued and has a gold-inlaid line around the outer edges of the pistol. It was cased.

NIB	Exc.	V.G.	Good	Fair	Poor
1400	1250	1000	750	500	350

Challenger II
This is a blowback-operated, semi-automatic pistol chambered for the .22 l.r. cartridge. It has a 6.75" barrel with an alloy frame. The finish is blued with phenolic impregnated hardwood grips. This pistol was manufactured between 1975 and 1982 in Salt Lake City, Utah.

Exc.	V.G.	Good	Fair	Poor
250	225	175	140	100

Challenger III
This version features a 5.5" bull barrel with adjustable sights. It was manufactured between 1982 and 1985 in Salt Lake City, Utah. A 6.75", tapered-barrel version was also available and known as the Sporter.

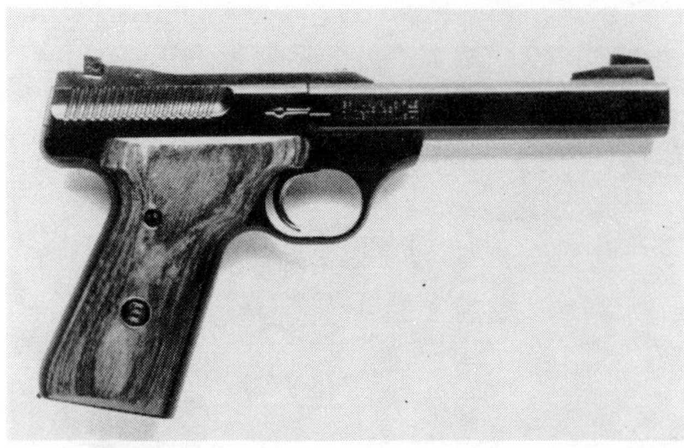

Exc.	V.G.	Good	Fair	Poor
225	200	150	125	90

Medalist
This is a high-grade, semi-automatic target pistol chambered for the .22 l.r. cartridge. It has a 6.75", vent-rib barrel with adjustable target sights. It was supplied with three barrel weights and a dry-fire-practice mechanism. The finish is blued with target-type, thumbrest, walnut grips. It was manufactured between 1962 and 1975 by FN. There were four additional high-grade versions of this pistol that differed in the degree of ornamentation.

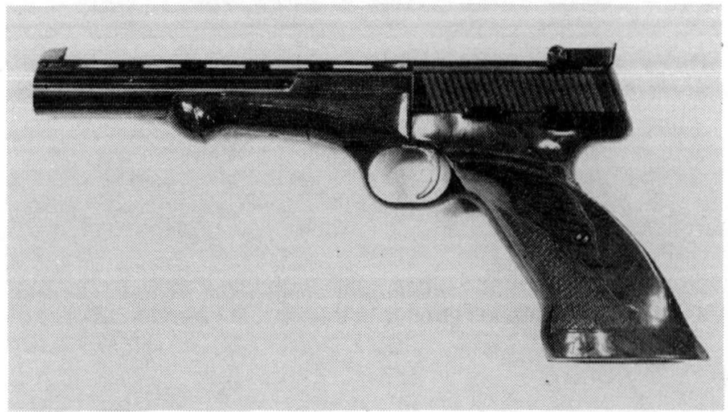

NIB	Exc.	V.G.	Good	Fair	Poor
800	650	575	475	375	250

Gold Line Medalist—407 Produced in 1963

NIB	Exc.	V.G.	Good	Fair	Poor
1750	1600	1250	1000	750	500

Renaissance Medalist

NIB	Exc.	V.G.	Good	Fair	Poor
2200	2150	1800	1500	1200	950

Browning Collector's Edition—Non-Engraved, 38 Manufactured

NIB	Exc.	V.G.	Good	Fair	Poor
1500	1250	1000	750	500	400

Browning Collector's Edition—Engraved, 22 Manufactured

NIB	Exc.	V.G.	Good	Fair	Poor
2500	2250	2000	1750	1400	1100

Buck Mark

This is a blowback-operated, semi-automatic pistol chambered for the .22 l.r. cartridge. It has a 5.5" bull barrel with adjustable sights. It has an 11-round, detachable magazine and is matte-blued with skip-line checkered synthetic grips. It was introduced in 1985.

NIB	Exc.	V.G.	Good	Fair	Poor
210	175	150	135	110	85

Buck Mark Plus

This version is similar to the standard with plain wood grips. It was introduced in 1987.

NIB	Exc.	V.G.	Good	Fair	Poor
250	210	185	150	120	100

Buck Mark Varmint

This version has a 9.75" bull barrel with a full length ramp to allow scope mounting. It has no sights. It was introduced in 1987.

NIB	Exc.	V.G.	Good	Fair	Poor
320	285	250	200	175	125

Buck Mark Silhouette

This version features a 9.75" bull barrel with adjustable sights.

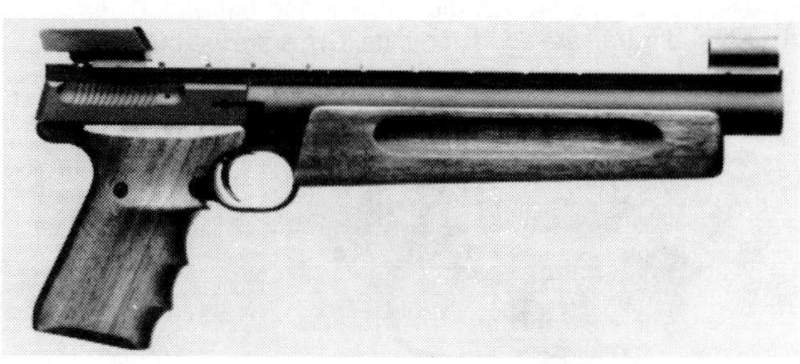

NIB	Exc.	V.G.	Good	Fair	Poor
350	325	285	220	185	140

Buck Mark 22 Micro

This version of the Buck Mark 22 is fitted with a 4" bull barrel. Available in blue, matte blue, or nickel finish. Also available in Micro Plus variation with walnut grips. Weighs 32 oz.

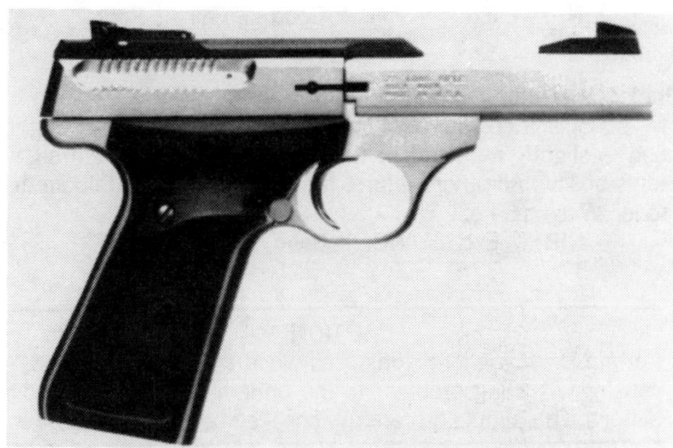

NIB	Exc.	V.G.	Good	Fair	Poor
200	175	150	125	100	70

Micro Plus

NIB	Exc.	V.G.	Good	Fair	Poor
225	200	175	150	125	90

Buck Mark 5.5

This .22 caliber pistol has a 5.5" heavy bull barrel fitted with target sights. It is offered in three separate models.

5.5 Blued Target

This version has a blued finish, contoured walnut grips, target sights. Weighs 35.5 oz.

NIB	Exc.	V.G.	Good	Fair	Poor
300	275	250	200	150	100

5.5 Gold Target

Same as above but has a gold anodized frame and top rib. Slide is blue. Walnut grips.

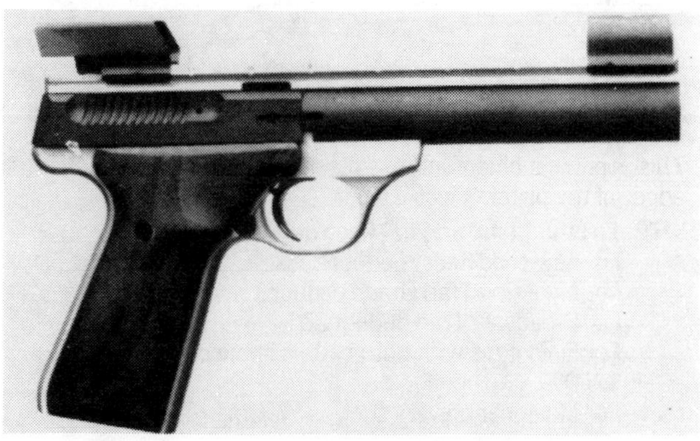

NIB	Exc.	V.G.	Good	Fair	Poor
325	300	275	225	175	125

5.5 Field

Same action and barrel as the Target Model but with adjustable field sights. Sights are hoodless. Slide and barrel is blued while the rib and frame are anodized blue. Grips are walnut.

NIB	Exc.	V.G.	Good	Fair	Poor
300	275	250	200	150	100

Buck Mark Unlimited Match

This pistol is fitted with a 14" barrel with top rib. The front sight hood is slightly rearward of the muzzle for a maximum sight radius of 15". All other features are the same as the Silhouette model. Weighs 64 oz.

NIB	Exc.	V.G.	Good	Fair	Poor
375	325	275	225	175	125

CAUTION

Certain Browning long guns used wood that was salt-cured, causing a rusting problem to the underside of barrels and actions. This should be carefully checked before purchase.

Superposed Shotgun

This series of Over/Under, double-barrel shotguns is chambered for all gauges and is offered with vent-rib barrels from 26.5" to 32" in length. It features various choke combinations. This shotgun is built on a boxlock action and features either double or single selective triggers and automatic ejectors. There were a number of versions offered that differ in the amount of ornamentation and the quality of the materials and workmanship utilized in manufacture. Values for small-bore models are generally higher. This series was introduced in 1931 and is manufactured by FN.

20 Gauge—Add 20%.
28 Gauge—Add 50%.
.410—Add 20%.

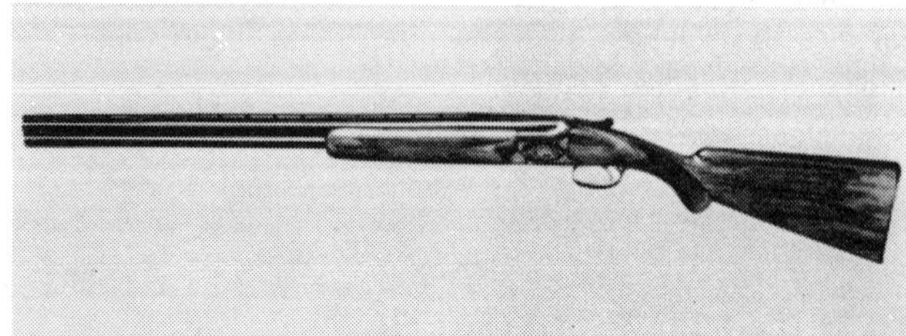

NOTE: For short tang and flat knob deduct 20%.
For new style Skeet deduct 20%.
For Lightning Trap Grade deduct 15%.
For Broadway Trap deduct 20%.
For Field guns with both barrels choked Skeet deduct 10%.
For Master engravers such as Watrin, Vrankan, J. Baerten, or Funkin add 10%.
For recoil pads or shorter than standard stocks deduct 25%.

Grade I

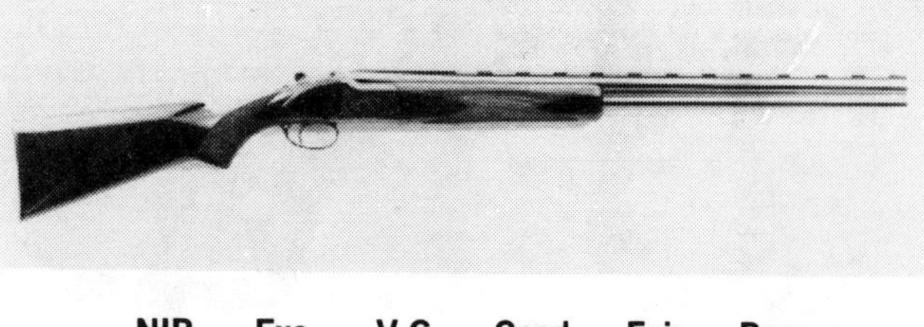

NIB	Exc.	V.G.	Good	Fair	Poor
1400	1250	900	650	500	400

Grade I Lightning

NIB	Exc.	V.G.	Good	Fair	Poor
1550	1350	900	650	500	400

Grade I Magnum

NIB	Exc.	V.G.	Good	Fair	Poor
1550	1350	1100	900	750	525

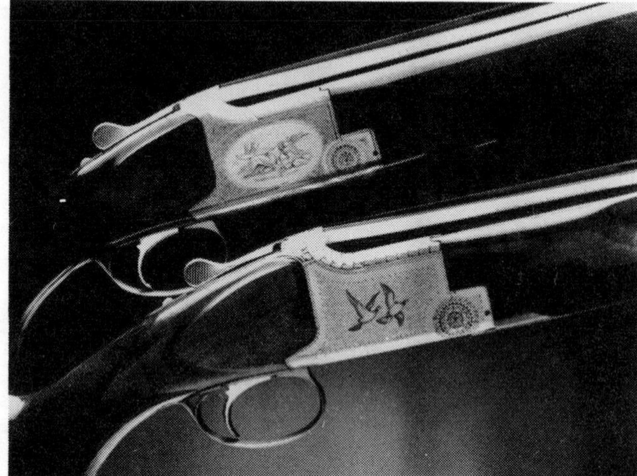

Pigeon Grade

NIB	Exc.	V.G.	Good	Fair	Poor
2500	2250	1750	1200	850	500

Grade III

NIB	Exc.	V.G.	Good	Fair	Poor
3000	2500	2250	1500	900	600

Pointer Grade

NIB	Exc.	V.G.	Good	Fair	Poor
3000	2500	2250	1500	900	600

Grade IV

NIB	Exc.	V.G.	Good	Fair	Poor
3750	3200	2850	2000	1250	700

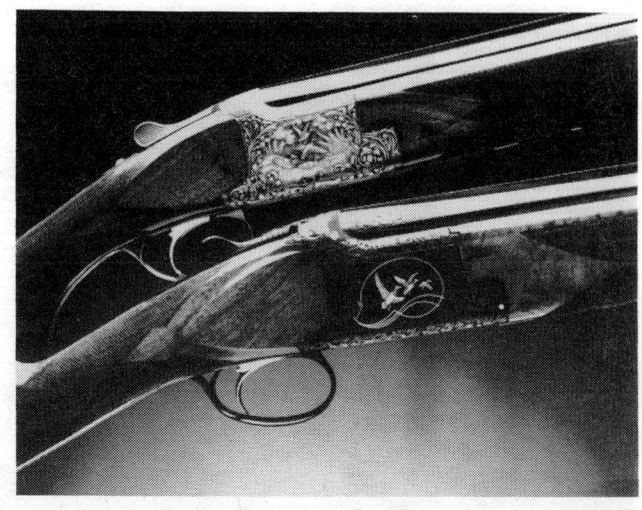

Diana Grade

NIB	Exc.	V.G.	Good	Fair	Poor
4000	3500	3000	2000	1250	700

Midas Grade

NIB	Exc.	V.G.	Good	Fair	Poor
5000	4500	4000	2500	1500	900

Grade VI

NIB	Exc.	V.G.	Good	Fair	Poor
7000	5500	4750	3000	2000	1000

The following superposed shotguns were manufactured between 1977 and 1984 by FN in Belgium. The following models differ in the amount of ornamentation and the quality of materials and workmanship utilized in construction. Additional values for small-bore chamberings are similar to the early superposed models listed previously. This series was also available in a superlight configuration. The following values would be increased approximately 25 percent for this lightweight variation.

Presentation 1

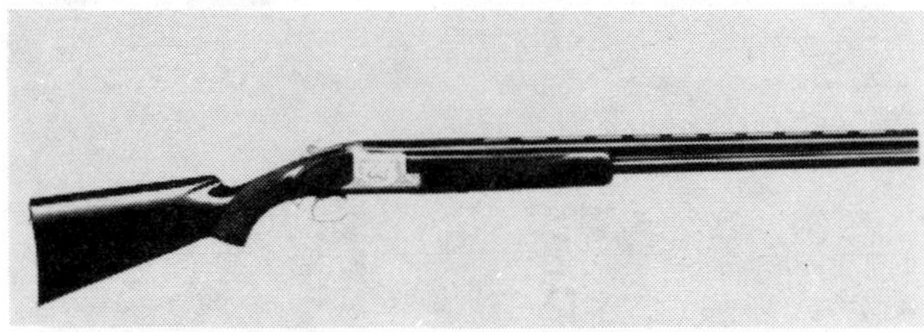

Exc.	V.G.	Good	Fair	Poor
2750	2250	1750	900	400

Presentation 1 Gold-Inlaid

Exc.	V.G.	Good	Fair	Poor
3500	2650	2150	900	400

Presentation 2

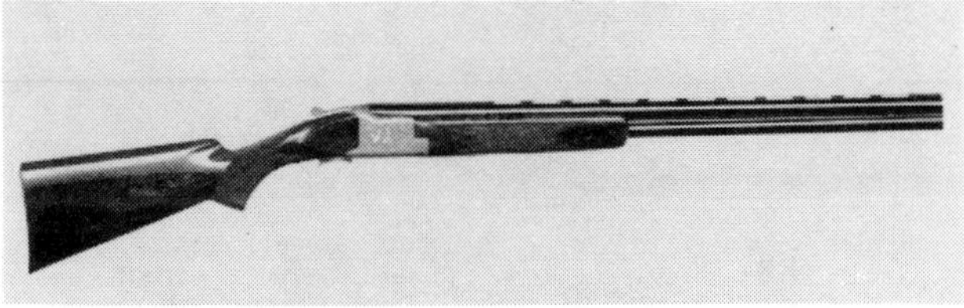

Exc.	V.G.	Good	Fair	Poor
2950	2600	2100	900	400

Presentation 2 Gold-Inlaid

Exc.	V.G.	Good	Fair	Poor
4000	3250	2750	1200	500

Presentation 3

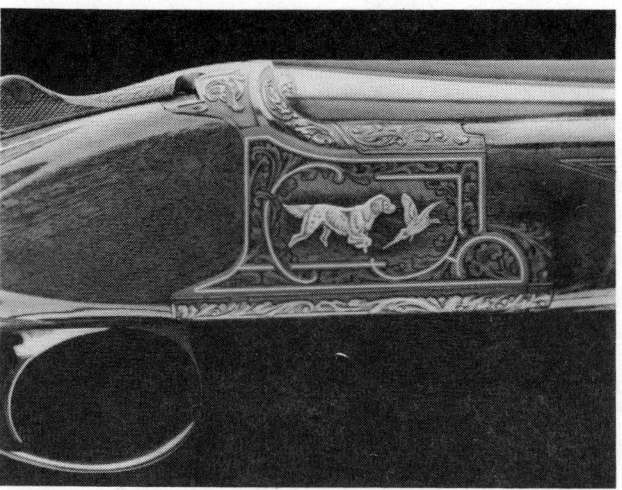

Exc.	V.G.	Good	Fair	Poor
5500	4500	3800	1500	600

Presentation 4

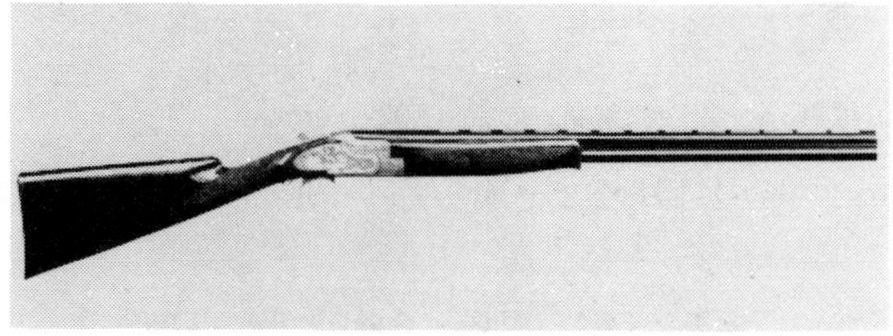

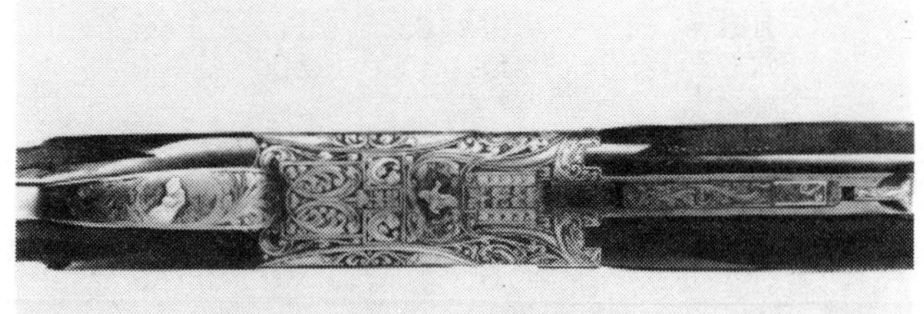

Exc.	V.G.	Good	Fair	Poor
6500	5000	4000	2000	900

Superlight

This model was first introduced in 1967 and is found in 12, 20, and 28 gauge as well as .410 bore. It was offered in 26.5" barrel lengths with 28" barrels available on special order. It features a rounded frame and straight grip stock with vent rib barrels. Regular production on the Superlight ended in 1976 for the grades listed below. Production did continue for the Superlight in the P series begun in 1977.

NOTE: For 20 gauge guns add a 20% premium.
For 28 gauge guns add a 50% premium.
For .410 bore guns add 20% premium.

Grade I

NIB	Exc.	V.G.	Good	Fair	Poor
1800	1500	900	650	500	400

Pigeon Grade

NIB	Exc.	V.G.	Good	Fair	Poor
3100	2750	1900	1200	850	500

Pointer Grade

NIB	Exc.	V.G.	Good	Fair	Poor
3750	3000	2500	1500	900	600

Diana Grade

NIB	Exc.	V.G.	Good	Fair	Poor
5000	4250	3500	2000	1250	700

Midas Grade

NIB	Exc.	V.G.	Good	Fair	Poor
6500	5250	4000	2500	1500	900

1981 Mallard Issue

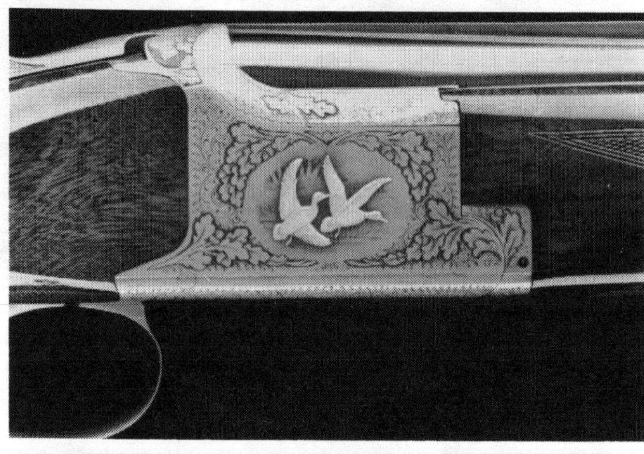

NIB	Exc.	V.G.	Good	Fair	Poor
5000	4250	3500	3000	2500	2000

1982 Pintail Issue

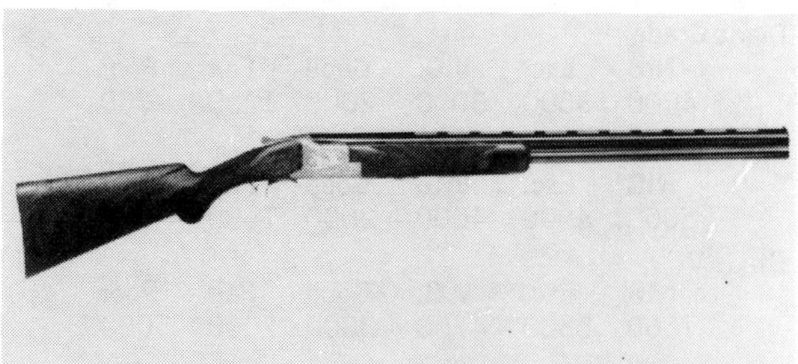

NIB	Exc.	V.G.	Good	Fair	Poor
5500	4250	3500	3000	2500	2000

1983 Black Duck Issue

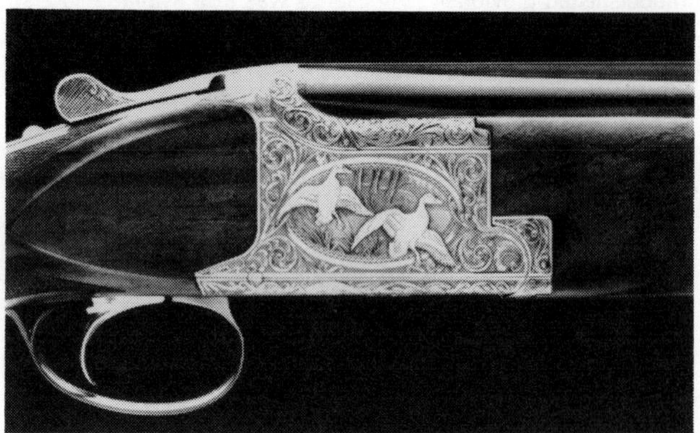

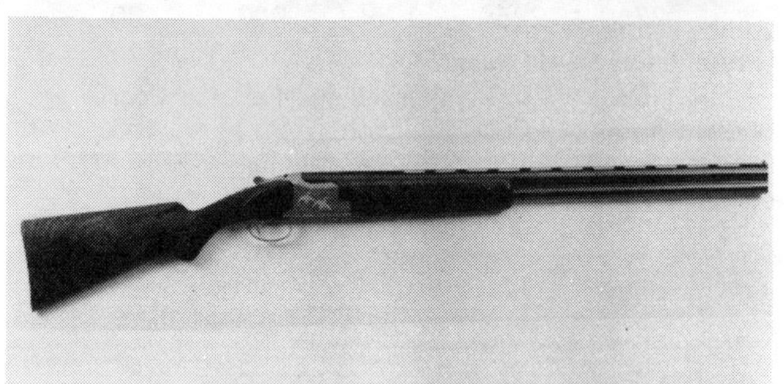

NIB	Exc.	V.G.	Good	Fair	Poor
5500	4250	3500	3000	2500	2000

Liege

This is an Over/Under shotgun chambered for 12 gauge. It was offered with 26.5", 28", or 30" vent-rib barrels with various choke combinations. It features a boxlock action with a non-selective single trigger and automatic ejectors. The finish is blued with a checkered walnut stock. There were approximately 10,000 manufactured between 1973 and 1975.

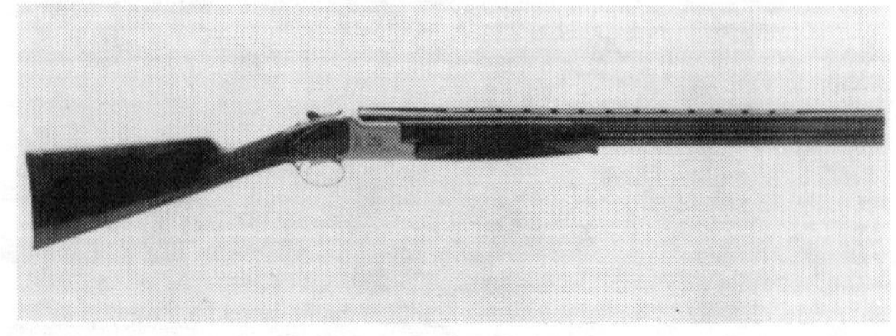

Exc.	V.G.	Good	Fair	Poor
800	700	600	425	350

B 27

This modified version of the Liege was imported into the U.S. without the Browning Arms Company markings. It was offered in a number of variations that differed in the amount of ornamentation and quality of materials and workmanship utilized. It features the same action as the Liege Over/Under gun.

Standard

Exc.	V.G.	Good	Fair	Poor
750	675	550	450	375

Grade II Deluxe

Exc.	V.G.	Good	Fair	Poor
875	750	575	475	400

Grand Deluxe

Exc.	V.G.	Good	Fair	Poor
1100	900	700	600	500

Deluxe Trap

Exc.	V.G.	Good	Fair	Poor
750	650	475	400	375

Deluxe Skeet

Exc.	V.G.	Good	Fair	Poor
850	750	550	450	375

City of Liege Commemorative—250 Manufactured

NIB	Exc.	V.G.	Good	Fair	Poor
1150	1000	850	750	650	550

ST-100

This is an Over/Under trap gun that features separated barrels with an adjustable point of impact. It is chambered for 12 gauge and has a 30" or 32" barrel with full choke and a floating ventilated rib. It features a single trigger and automatic ejectors. The finish is blued with a checkered walnut stock. It was manufactured by FN between 1979 and 1983. It was not marked "Browning."

Exc.	V.G.	Good	Fair	Poor
2200	2000	1750	1400	1000

Citori Series

This is an Over/Under, double-barrel shotgun chambered for all gauges and offered with vent-rib barrels of 26" through 30" in length. It has a boxlock action with a single selective trigger and automatic ejectors. The various grades differ in the amount of ornamentation and the quality of materials and workmanship utilized in construction. This series is manufactured in Japan by B. C. Miroku and was introduced in 1973.

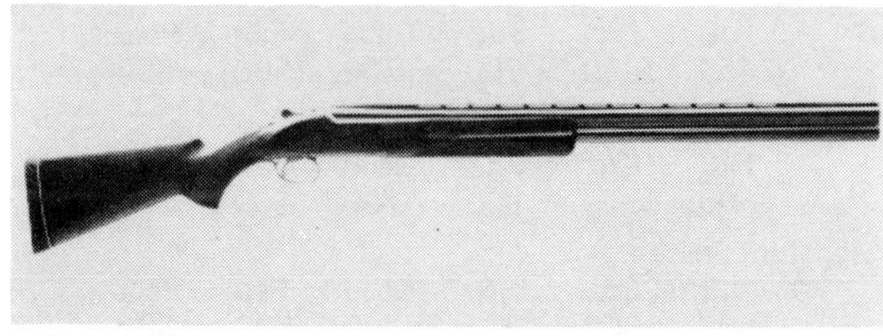

Grade I

NIB	Exc.	V.G.	Good	Fair	Poor
900	800	725	550	425	300

Upland Special—Grade I

Offered with straight grip stock and 24" rib barrels. Available in 12 gauge or 20 gauge. Weighs 6 lbs., 11 oz. in 12 gauge and 6 lbs in 20 gauge.

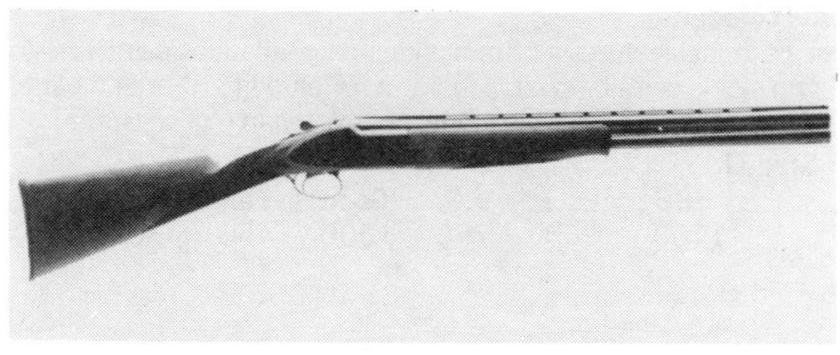

NIB	Exc.	V.G.	Good	Fair	Poor
935	850	700	600	400	300

Grade II—Discontinued 1983

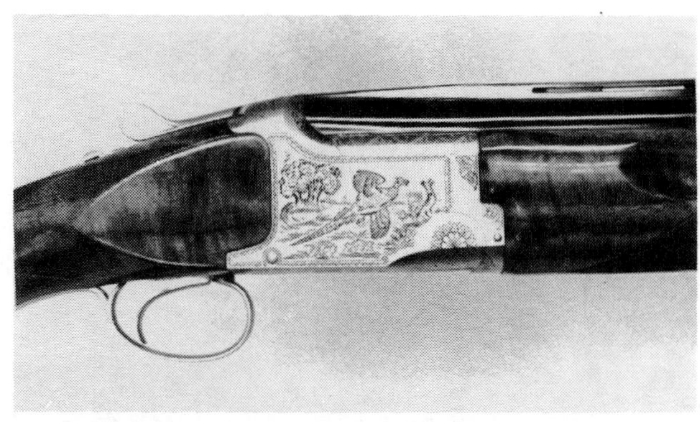

Exc.	V.G.	Good	Fair	Poor
950	800	675	550	400

Grade III—Choke Tubes

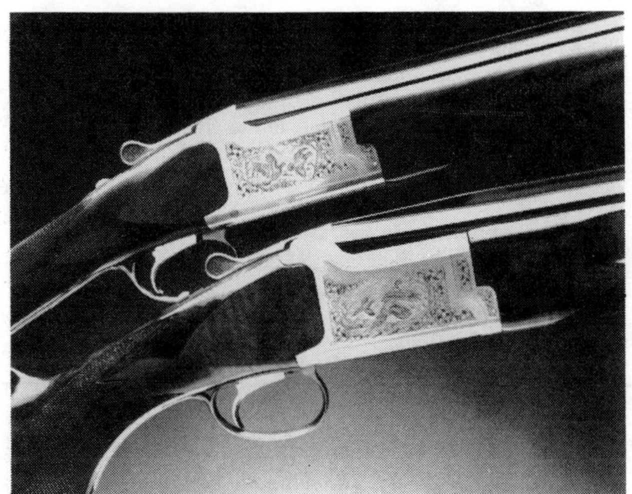

NIB	Exc.	V.G.	Good	Fair	Poor
1400	1250	950	775	650	400

Grade V—Discontinued 1984

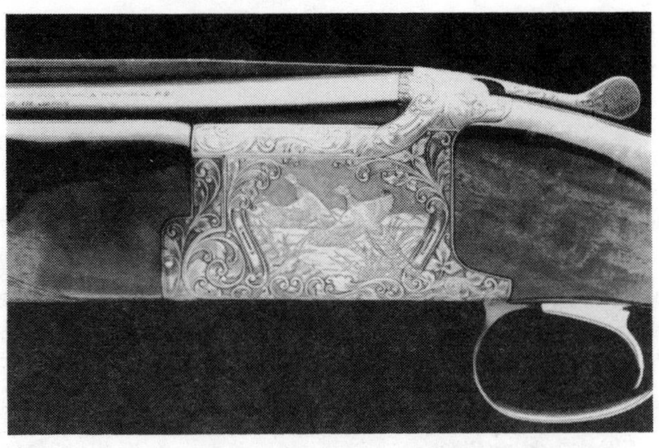

Exc.	V.G.	Good	Fair	Poor
1400	1250	950	750	400

Grade VI—Choke Tubes

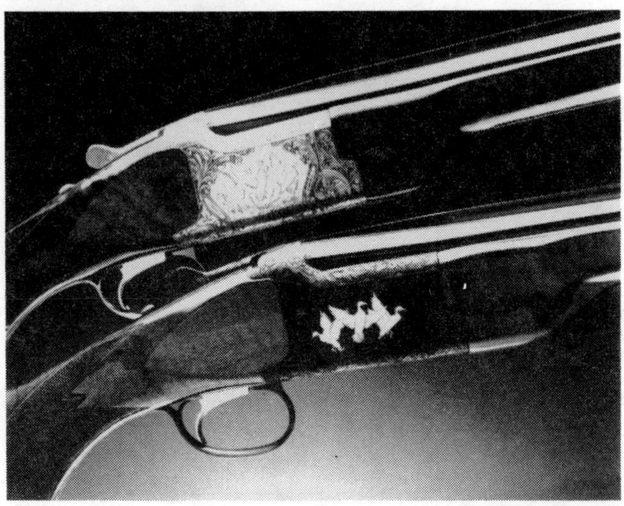

NIB	Exc.	V.G.	Good	Fair	Poor
1750	1500	1200	1000	750	500

Citori Lightning
This is a lightweight version that features a slimmer profile and has a checkered, round-knob, pistol-grip stock. It is offered in all gauges and in the same barrel lengths as the standard Citori. It features screw-in choke tubes known as invectors. It was introduced in 1988. The models differ in the amount of ornamentation and quality of materials and workmanship utilized.

Grade I

NIB	Exc.	V.G.	Good	Fair	Poor
995	850	700	575	450	375

Grade III

NIB	Exc.	V.G.	Good	Fair	Poor
1400	1250	950	775	650	500

Grade VI

NIB	Exc.	V.G.	Good	Fair	Poor
1750	1500	1200	1000	750	500

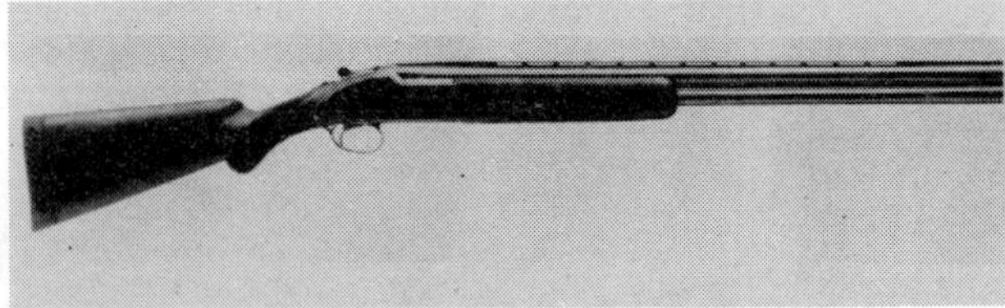

Citori Sporting Clays
Specifically design for Sporting Clays shooting. Offered in 12 gauge only, each model is back-bored, ported and fitted with Invector-Plus choke tubes. Barrels are chromed plated. Receiver is blued with gold inscription. Pigeon Grade has gold detailing and high grade gloss walnut stock. Signature Grade features a red and black print on the stock with gold decals. Trigger is adjustable to three length of pull positions. Comes with three interchangeable trigger shoes. Each model is fitted with rubber recoil pad.

Lightning Sporting Model
This model features a rounded pistol grip and Lightning forearm with choice of high or low vent rib. Chambered for 3" shells. Offered in 28" or 30" barrels. Weighs about 8.5 lbs.

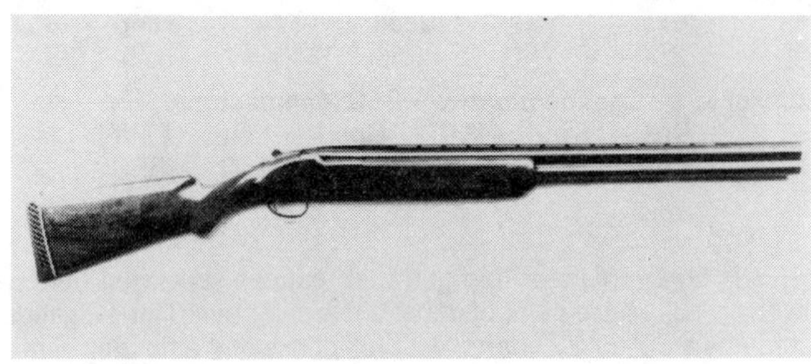

NIB	Exc.	V.G.	Good	Fair	Poor
1100	900	750	600	450	300

Pigeon Grade

NIB	Exc.	V.G.	Good	Fair	Poor
1200	1000	800	650	450	300

Citori Plus
This model features an adjustable point of impact from 3" to 12" above point of aim. Receiver on Grade I is blued with scroll engraving. Walnut stock is adjustable and forearm is a modified beavertail style. Available in 30" or 32" barrels which are back-bored and ported. Non-ported barrels are optional. Weighs about 9 lbs., 6 oz.

Grade I

NIB	Exc.	V.G.	Good	Fair	Poor
1450	1250	900	700	500	300

Pigeon Grade

NIB	Exc.	V.G.	Good	Fair	Poor
1600	1350	900	700	500	300

Signature Grade

NIB	Exc.	V.G.	Good	Fair	Poor
1500	1300	900	700	500	300

Trap Combination Set
This version is offered in Grade I only and features a 34" single barrel and a 32" set of Over/Under barrels. It is furnished in a fitted case and has been discontinued.

Exc.	V.G.	Good	Fair	Poor
1200	1050	950	800	700

GTI Model
This model features a 13mm wide rib, ventilated side ribs, pistol grip stock, semi-beavertail forearm. Offered in 28" or 30" barrel. Weighs about 8 lbs. This model not offered in Pigeon Grade.

Grade I

NIB	Exc.	V.G.	Good	Fair	Poor
1100	900	750	600	450	300

Signature Grade

NIB	Exc.	V.G.	Good	Fair	Poor
1100	900	750	600	450	300

Citori Superlight

This is a lighter-weight version of the Citori chambered for all gauges and offered with the same features as the Lightning Series. The grades differ in the amount of ornamentation and quality of materials and workmanship utilized. This series was introduced in 1983.

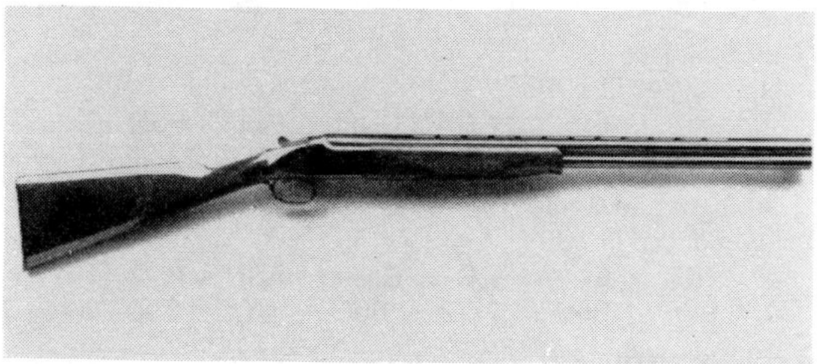

Micro Lightning

Offered in 20 gauge only and has reduced dimensions for smaller shooters. Available with 24" vent rib barrels. Weighs 6 lbs., 3 oz.

NIB	Exc.	V.G.	Good	Fair	Poor
950	850	700	600	400	300

Gran Lightning

This is essentially a Grade I Lightning with a high grade select walnut stock with satin finish. Receiver and barrels are blued. Offered in 12 gauge and 20 gauge with choice of 26" or 28" vent rib barrels. Choke tubes standard. Weighs about 8 lbs. in 12 gauge and 6 lbs., 11 oz. in 20 gauge.

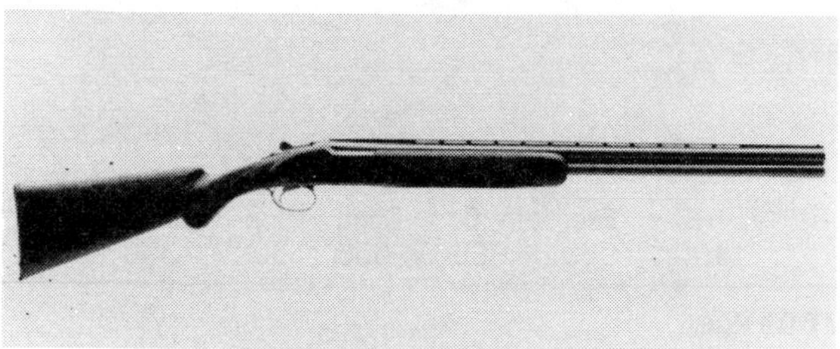

NIB	Exc.	V.G.	Good	Fair	Poor
1250	1000	800	650	450	300

Grade I

NIB	Exc.	V.G.	Good	Fair	Poor
1000	900	750	500	425	350

Grade III

NIB	Exc.	V.G.	Good	Fair	Poor
1400	1300	1050	750	550	450

Grade V—Discontinued 1984

Exc.	V.G.	Good	Fair	Poor
1450	1350	1100	800	500

Grade VI

NIB	Exc.	V.G.	Good	Fair	Poor
1800	1600	1300	1000	800	500

Citori Skeet

This series of guns was chambered for all gauges and was designed for competition skeet shooting. It is similar to the standard Citori with a high-post target rib and 26" or 28" barrels. The versions differ in the amount of engraving and the quality of materials and workmanship utilized.

Grade I

NIB	Exc.	V.G.	Good	Fair	Poor
1000	925	750	550	425	350

Grade II—Discontinued 1983

Exc.	V.G.	Good	Fair	Poor
1000	900	750	500	400

Grade III

NIB	Exc.	V.G.	Good	Fair	Poor
1500	1350	1050	750	550	475

Grade V—Discontinued 1984

Exc.	V.G.	Good	Fair	Poor
1500	1200	900	750	500

Grade VI

NIB	Exc.	V.G.	Good	Fair	Poor
2000	1750	1200	900	800	500

3 Gauge Set

Consist of 20 gauge, 28 gauge, and .410 bore interchangeable 28" vent rib barrels.

Grade I

NIB	Exc.	V.G.	Good	Fair	Poor
2100	1950	1700	1250	900	700

Grade III

NIB	Exc.	V.G.	Good	Fair	Poor
2500	2250	1900	1400	1100	800

Grade VI

NIB	Exc.	V.G.	Good	Fair	Poor
2950	2500	2000	1500	1200	900

4 Gauge Set

This set has a 12 gauge, 20 gauge, 28 gauge, and .410 bore interchangeable vent rib barrels in either 26" or 28" lengths.

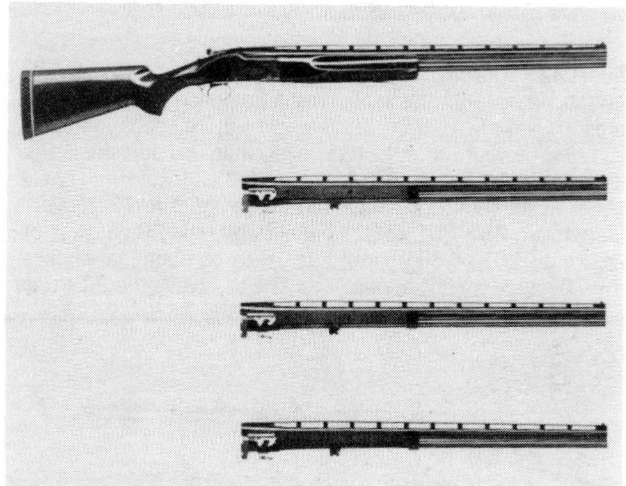

Grade I

NIB	Exc.	V.G.	Good	Fair	Poor
2950	2500	2250	1700	1250	900

Grade III

NIB	Exc.	V.G.	Good	Fair	Poor
3400	2900	2500	1900	1350	900

Grade VI

NIB	Exc.	V.G.	Good	Fair	Poor
3800	3300	2900	2250	1400	950

Citori Trap

This version is similar to the standard Citori, offered in 12 gauge only with 30" or 32" barrels. It features a high rib and a Monte Carlo-type stock with recoil pad. The versions differ as to the amount of ornamentation and the quality of materials and workmanship utilized.

Grade I

NIB	Exc.	V.G.	Good	Fair	Poor
1000	900	750	550	425	350

Plus Trap—Adjustable Rib and Stock

NIB	Exc.	V.G.	Good	Fair	Poor
1500	1350	1000	750	600	500

Grade II—Discontinued 1983

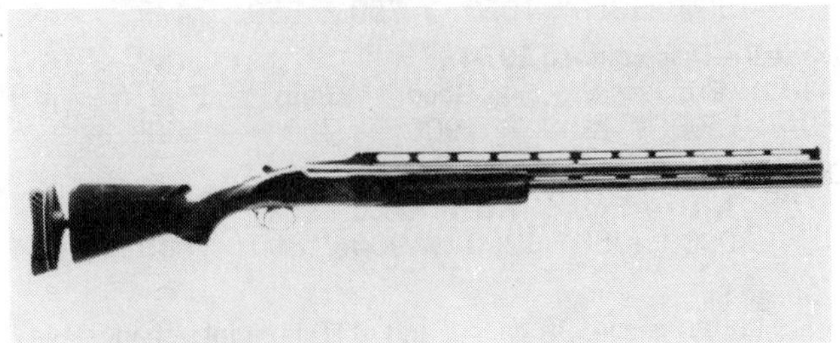

Exc.	V.G.	Good	Fair	Poor
1000	850	675	450	350

Grade III

NIB	Exc.	V.G.	Good	Fair	Poor
1500	1350	1000	750	600	500

Grade V—Discontinued 1984

Exc.	V.G.	Good	Fair	Poor
1400	1250	900	650	450

Grade VI

NIB	Exc.	V.G.	Good	Fair	Poor
2100	1800	1550	1250	1000	800

Signature Grade

NIB	Exc.	V.G.	Good	Fair	Poor
1150	950	800	600	450	300

Model 325 Sporting Clays

Introduced in 1993 this model has a European design that features a grayed receiver scroll engraved, Schnabel forearm, 10mm wide vent rib, three interchangeable and adjustable trigger shoes, back-bore barrel that are ported and fitted with choke tubes. Available in 12 gauge and 20 gauge. The 12 gauge is offered with 28", 30", or 32" barrels while the 20 gauge is offered with 28" or 30" barrel fitted with conventional chokes. The 12 gauge weighs about 7 lbs., 14 oz., while the 20 gauge weighs about 6 lbs., 12 oz.

325 Sporting Clays

NIB	Exc.	V.G.	Good	Fair	Poor
1350	1200	900	700	450	300

BT-99

This is a break-open, single-barrel trap gun chambered for 12 gauge only. It is offered with a 32" or 34", vent-rib barrel with screw-in choke tubes. It features a boxlock action with automatic ejectors. The finish is blued with a checkered walnut stock and beavertail forearm. It was introduced in 1971 by B. C. Miroku.

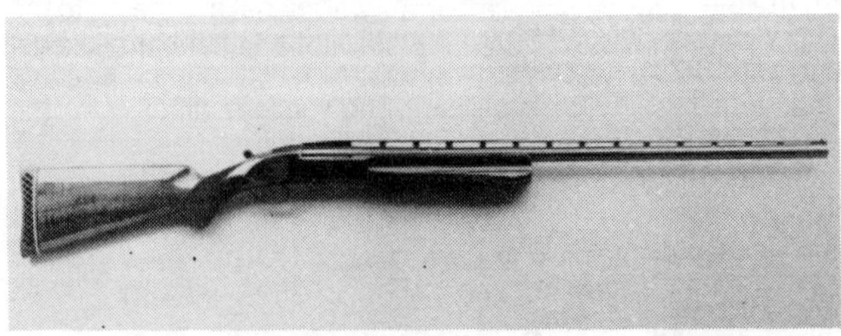

NIB	Exc.	V.G.	Good	Fair	Poor
1000	850	675	500	400	350

Citori Plus Combo

This model features a single barrel trap and an interchangeable Over/Under set of barrels. Other features are similar to Citori Plus Grade I. Barrel combinations are 32" O/U with 34" single barrel or 30" O/U barrel with 32" or 34" single barrel.

NIB	Exc.	V.G.	Good	Fair	Poor
2500	2100	1750	1100	700	450

BT-99 Stainless

First introduced in 1993.

NIB	Exc.	V.G.	Good	Fair	Poor
1275	1150	900	700	550	350

BT-99 Signature Grade

First introduced in 1993.

NIB	Exc.	V.G.	Good	Fair	Poor
975	850	700	600	500	300

BT-99 Pigeon Grade

First introduced in 1993.

NIB	Exc.	V.G.	Good	Fair	Poor
1100	950	800	650	500	300

BT-99 Plus

This version features an adjustable vent-rib and a recoil-reduction system. It has an adjustable stock and recoil pad, as well as a backboard barrel. It was introduced in 1989.

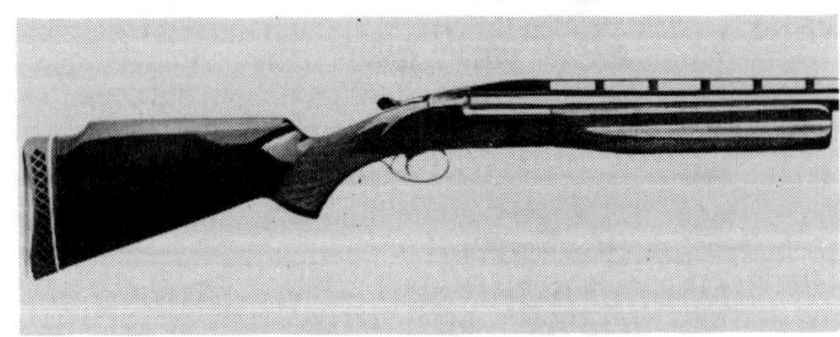

NIB	Exc.	V.G.	Good	Fair	Poor
1350	1200	900	700	500	300

BT-99 Plus Stainless—Grade I

Same as standard version but offered in Stainless Steel. First introduced in 1993. Available in 32" and 34" barrels. Weighs about 8 lbs., 11 oz.

NIB	Exc.	V.G.	Good	Fair	Poor
1600	1350	900	700	500	350

BT-99 Plus—Pigeon Grade

NIB	Exc.	V.G.	Good	Fair	Poor
1500	1200	900	800	550	350

BT-99 Plus—Signature Grade

NIB	Exc.	V.G.	Good	Fair	Poor
1400	1100	850	700	500	300

BT-99 Plus Micro
A slightly reduced dimensions and offered in barrel lengths form 28" to 34". Weighs about 8 lbs., 6 oz.

NIB	Exc.	V.G.	Good	Fair	Poor
1350	1100	900	700	500	300

BT-99 Plus—Pigeon Grade

NIB	Exc.	V.G.	Good	Fair	Poor
1500	1200	900	800	550	350

BT-99 Plus—Signature Grade

NIB	Exc.	V.G.	Good	Fair	Poor
1400	1150	900	750	500	300

Recoilless Trap
First introduced in 1993 this model features an advanced design that eliminates recoil up to 72 percent. The receiver is a special bolt action single shot. Receiver is black anodized. It is fitted with a adjustable ventilated rib so the point of impact can be moved. Adjustable length of pull. The Standard model is a 12 gauge with 30" barrel while the Micro Model is fitted with 27" barrels. Choke tubes are supplied. Standard Model weighs 9 lbs., 1 oz., while the Micro Model weighs 8 lbs., 10 oz.

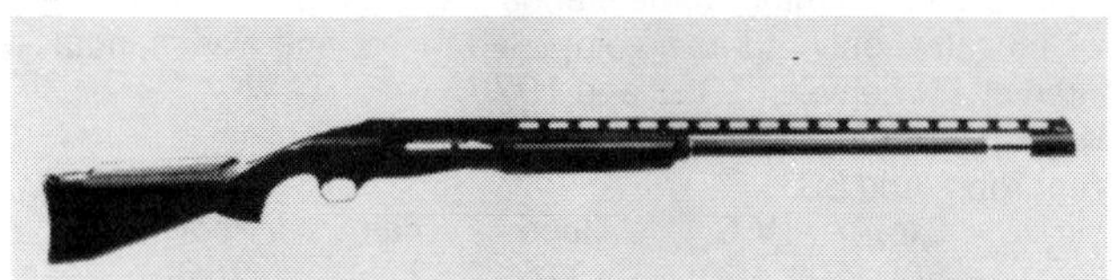

NIB	Exc.	V.G.	Good	Fair	Poor
1500	1300	900	700	500	350

BSS
This is a SxS, double-barrel shotgun chambered for 12 or 20 gauge. It was offered with a 26", 28", or 30" barrel with various choke combinations. It features a boxlock action and automatic ejectors. Early guns had a nonselective single trigger; late production, a selective trigger. The finish is blued with a checkered walnut stock and beavertail forearm. It was manufactured between 1971 and 1988 by B. C. Miroku.
Single-Selective Trigger—Add 20%.
20 Gauge—Add 10%.

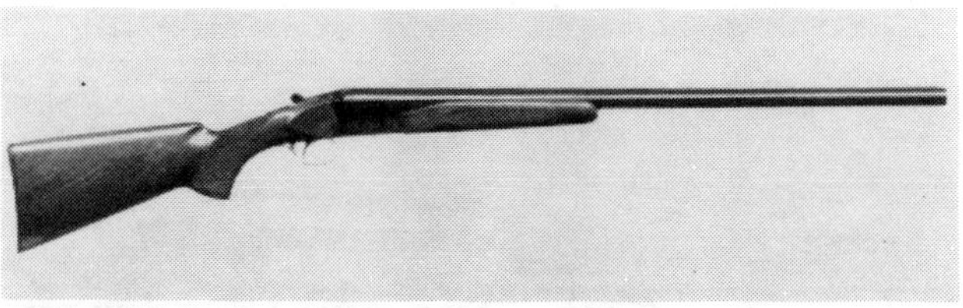

Exc.	V.G.	Good	Fair	Poor
650	575	400	300	200

BSS Sporter
This version features an English-style, straight-grip stock and a splinter forearm. The stock was oil-finished. It was offered with a 26" or 28" barrel.

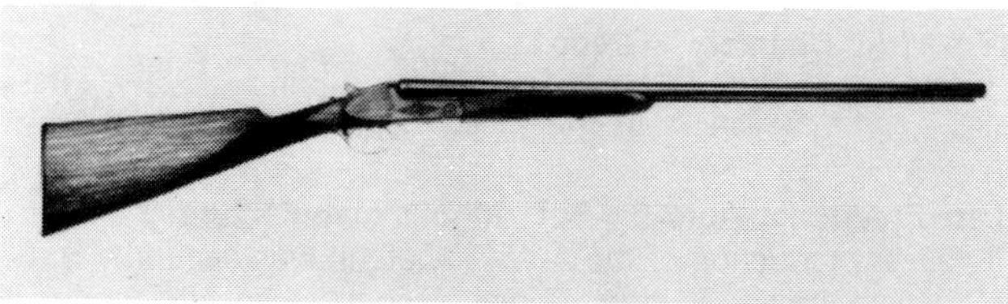

Exc.	V.G.	Good	Fair	Poor
750	650	450	350	250

BSS Grade II
This version features gamescene engraving and a satin, coin-finished receiver. It was discontinued in 1983.

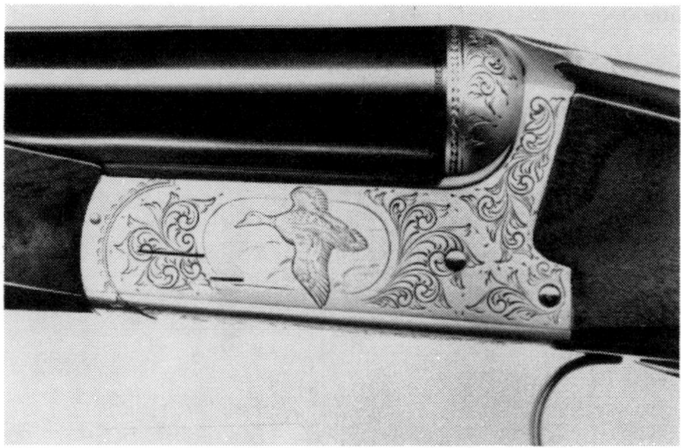

Exc.	V.G.	Good	Fair	Poor
1250	1000	750	600	400

BSS Sidelock
This version features an engraved sidelock action and was offered in 12 or 20 gauge. It was offered with a 26" or 28" barrel and has a straight-grip stock and splintered forearm. It was manufactured in Korea between 1983 and 1988.

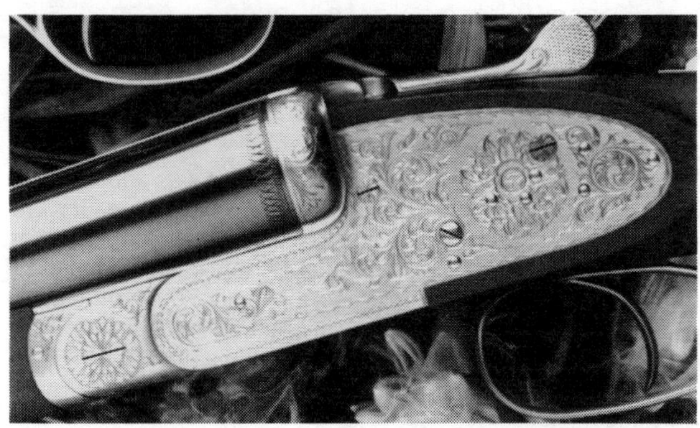

Exc.	V.G.	Good	Fair	Poor
2250	1750	1250	800	500

BSS Sidelock

NOTE: Add 20% to above prices for 20 gauge guns.

Early Production Auto-5
This series of recoil-operated, semi-automatic shotguns was designed by John M. Browning and was offered in 12 or 16 gauge. The barrel lengths were 26", 28", 30", or 32" with various chokes and ribs. It has a unique, square-back action that has become instantly recognizable. The finish is blued with a checkered, walnut, round-knob stock. The various versions differ in the amount of ornamentation, type of rib, and quality of materials and workmanship utilized in construction. This series was manufactured in Belgium by FN between 1903 and 1939. The first example appeared in the United States in 1923. Pre-WWII 16 gauge guns had 2-9/16" chambers; early models should be inspected by a qualified gunsmith before firing.

NOTE: For 16 gauge not converted to 2 3/4" chamber deduct 25 percent. Original pre-war barrels were serial numbered to the gun. Prices given below are for guns with original barrels serial numbered to the gun.

Grade I—Plain Barrel

Exc.	V.G.	Good	Fair	Poor
450	400	300	250	150

Grade I—Matte Rib

Exc.	V.G.	Good	Fair	Poor
550	500	375	300	175

Grade I—Vent Rib

Exc.	V.G.	Good	Fair	Poor
650	600	475	375	200

Grade II—Plain Barrel

Exc.	V.G.	Good	Fair	Poor
1050	975	750	550	425

Grade II—Matte Rib

Exc.	V.G.	Good	Fair	Poor
1300	1175	850	650	500

Grade II—Vent Rib

Exc.	V.G.	Good	Fair	Poor
1600	1450	1200	950	750

Grade III—Plain Barrel

Exc.	V.G.	Good	Fair	Poor
2500	2250	1850	1450	1000

Grade III—Matte Rib

Exc.	V.G.	Good	Fair	Poor
2750	2500	2000	1600	1250

Grade III—Vent Rib

Exc.	V.G.	Good	Fair	Poor
3000	2750	2250	1800	1500

Grade IV—Plain Barrel

Exc.	V.G.	Good	Fair	Poor
4000	3750	3250	2750	2400

Grade IV—Matte Rib

Exc.	V.G.	Good	Fair	Poor
4200	3950	3450	3000	2600

Grade IV—Vent Rib

Exc.	V.G.	Good	Fair	Poor
4400	4100	3750	3200	2750

American Browning Auto-5

This recoil-operated, semi-automatic shotgun was another variation of the early-production Auto-5. It was chambered for 12, 16, or 20 gauge and was manufactured by the Remington Company for Browning. It is quite similar to Remington's Model 11 Shotgun but features the Browning logo and a different type of engraving. There were approximately 45,000 manufactured between 1940 and 1942.

Vent Rib—Add 20%.
20 Gauge—Add 10%.

Exc.	V.G.	Good	Fair	Poor
450	350	300	200	170

Mid-Production Auto-5—FN Manufacture

Standard Weight

This version of the recoil-operated, semi-automatic Auto-5 shotgun was manufactured by FN in Belgium between 1952 and 1976. It was offered in 12 or 16 gauge with 26" through 32" barrels with various chokes. The finish is blued with a checkered walnut stock and a black buttplate that was marked "Browning." Some will be found with roundknob pistol grips. The flatbottom variation was introduced in 1967.

Plain Barrel

Exc.	V.G.	Good	Fair	Poor
425	375	300	250	175

Matte Rib

Exc.	V.G.	Good	Fair	Poor
450	400	325	275	200

Vent Rib

Exc.	V.G.	Good	Fair	Poor
500	450	350	300	250

Auto-5 Lightweight

This version was chambered for 12 or 20 gauge and featured a lighter-weight, scroll-engraved receiver. It was manufactured between 1952 and 1976 by FN.

Vent Rib—Add 20%.

Exc.	V.G.	Good	Fair	Poor
450	400	325	275	200

Auto-5 Magnum

This version featured 3" chambers and was offered with 26" through 32", full-choke barrels. It was manufactured between 1958 and 1976 by FN.

Vent Rib—Add 20%.

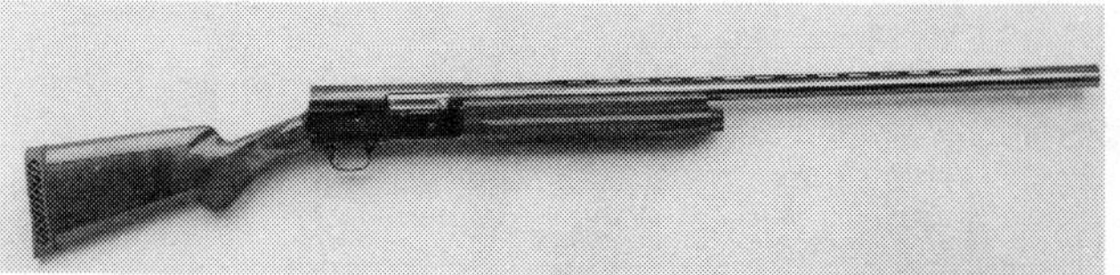

Exc.	V.G.	Good	Fair	Poor
550	500	425	325	250

Auto-5 Skeet

This version is similar to the Lightweight Model, chambered for 12 or 20 gauge with a 26" or 28", vent-rib, skeet-choked barrel.

Exc.	V.G.	Good	Fair	Poor
550	500	425	325	250

Auto-5 Trap Model

This version is similar to the standard-weight model except chambered for 12 gauge only, with a 30", vent-rib, full-choke barrel. It was manufactured by FN until 1971.

Exc.	V.G.	Good	Fair	Poor
525	475	400	300	225

Sweet Sixteen

This version is similar to the standard-weight and is chambered for 16 gauge only. It has a goldplated trigger and was manufactured by FN between 1953 and 1976.

Matte Rib—Add 25%.
Vent Rib—Add 50%.

Exc.	V.G.	Good	Fair	Poor
500	450	375	275	200

Buck Special

This version features a 24", cylinder-bore barrel with adjustable rifle sights. It was manufactured by FN between 1958 and 1976.

Exc.	V.G.	Good	Fair	Poor
550	500	425	325	250

Two Millionth Commemorative

This version commemorated the two millionth Auto-5 shotgun produced by FN. It was engraved with a special high-polish blue finish and high-grade, checkered walnut in the stock. It was furnished in a fitted case along with a book on the Browning Company. There were 2,500 manufactured between 1971 and 1974. As with all commemoratives, it must be NIB to realize its top potential.

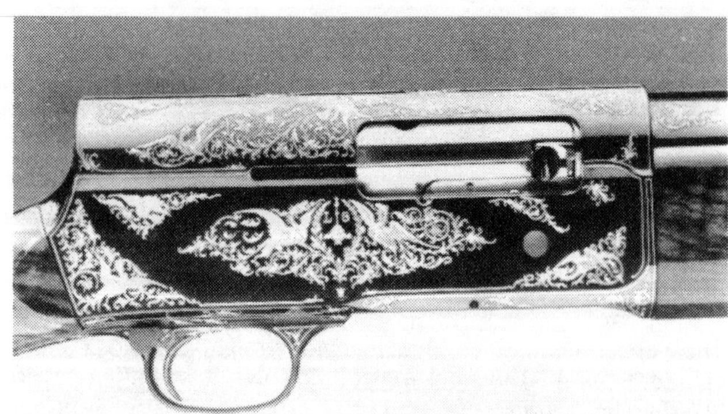

NIB	Exc.	V.G.	Good	Fair	Poor
1200	950	800	500	350	250

Late Production Auto-5—B. C. Miroku Manufacture

In 1976 production of the Auto-5 shotgun was begun by B. C. Miroku in Japan. This move was accomplished after approximately 2,750,000 Auto-5 shotguns were manufactured by FN in Belgium between 1903 and 1976. The Japanese manufactured guns in the opinion of many knowledgeable people show no less quality or functionality but are simply not as desirable from a collector's standpoint. The variations and their values are as follows:

Auto-5 Light 12

This version is chambered for 12 gauge only and is offered with a lightweight receiver. The barrel has a vent-rib and choke tubes. It was introduced in 1986.

NIB	Exc.	V.G.	Good	Fair	Poor
685	600	500	400	300	225

Auto-5 Light 20

This version is similar to the Light 12 except chambered for 20 gauge only.

NIB	Exc.	V.G.	Good	Fair	Poor
685	600	500	400	300	225

Auto-5 Magnum

This version features 3" chambers and is offered with 26", 28", 30", or 32" barrels. It was introduced in 1976 by Miroku.

NIB	Exc.	V.G.	Good	Fair	Poor
700	600	500	400	300	225

Auto-5 Buck Special

This version has a 24" barrel cylinder-bored with adjustable sights. It was introduced by Miroku in 1976.

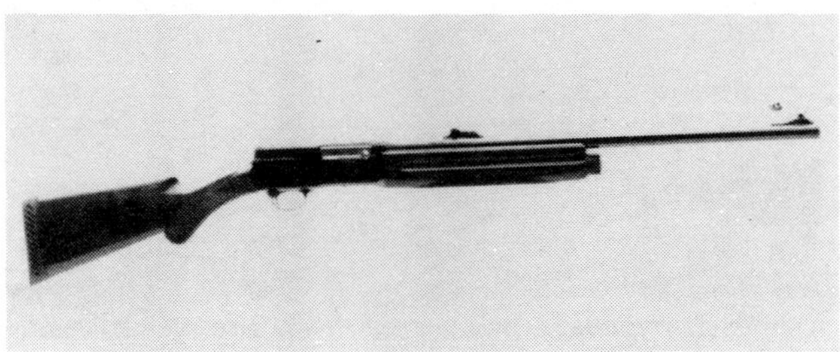

NIB	Exc.	V.G.	Good	Fair	Poor
685	600	500	400	300	225

Auto-5 Skeet

This is a competition model that features 26" or 28", skeet-bored barrels with a vent-rib. It was manufactured between 1976 and 1983 by Miroku.

Exc.	V.G.	Good	Fair	Poor
450	400	350	250	200

Sweet Sixteen

This version is similar to the Belgian-produced Sweet Sixteen but is offered standard with a vent-rib and screw-in invector choke tubes. It was introduced in 1987 by Miroku.

NIB	Exc.	V.G.	Good	Fair	Poor
685	600	500	400	300	225

A-5 DU 50th Anniversary

This was a high-grade version of the Auto-5 produced to commemorate the fiftieth anniversary of Ducks Unlimited. It is highly engraved and features high-gloss bluing and a fancy checkered walnut stock. There were approximately 5,500 manufactured by Miroku in 1987. They were auctioned by the Ducks Unlimited chapters to raise money for the organization; and because of this fact, it is difficult to furnish an accurate value. This is a commemorative firearm and, as such, must be NIB with all furnished materials to command premium collector value. We furnish what we feel is a general value.

NIB	Exc.	V.G.	Good	Fair	Poor
1100	950	750	500	350	250

A-5 DU Sweet Sixteen

This was a special version of the Miroku-manufactured Sweet Sixteen that was auctioned by the Ducks Unlimited chapters in 1988. There were 5,500 produced. All specifications and cautions that were furnished for the 50th Anniversary gun also apply here.

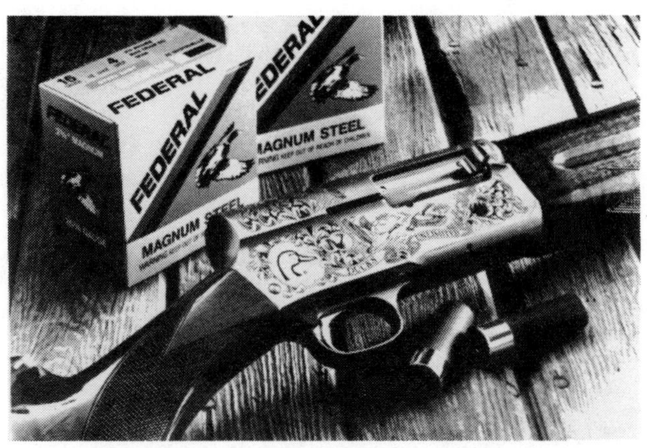

NIB	Exc.	V.G.	Good	Fair	Poor
1100	950	750	500	350	250

Auto-5 Classic

This is a special limited edition series of A-5 shotguns built in 12 gauge only. The Classic is engraved with game scenes on a silver gray receiver. 5,000 of these guns were manufactured in 1984. The Gold Classic is similar in appearance but features gold inlays and is limited to 500 guns.

Classic

NIB	Exc.	V.G.	Good	Fair	Poor
1150	950	750	650	500	300

Gold Classic

NIB	Exc.	V.G.	Good	Fair	Poor
4000	3000	2500	2000	1000	500

Auto-5 Light Buck Special

This model is a lightweight version of the Buck Special. Chambered for the 2 3/4" shell and fitted with a 24" vent rib barrel. Conventional choked for slug or buckshot. Barrel has adjustable rear sight and ramp front sight. Weighs 8 lbs.

NIB	Exc.	V.G.	Good	Fair	Poor
550	475	400	300	225	150

Auto-5 Stalker

New for 1993 this model is available in either a lightweight version or a Magnum version. The Light Stalker is available in 12 gauge with either 26" or 28" barrel with choke tubes. The Magnum Stalker is offered in 12 gauge (3" chamber) with 28" or 30" barrel and choke tubes. The Light Stalker weighs 8 lbs., 4 oz. and the Magnum Stalker weighs 8 lbs., 11 oz.

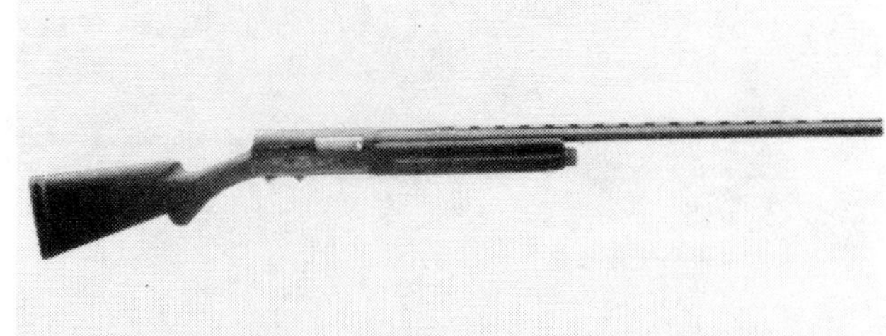

Light Stalker

NIB	Exc.	V.G.	Good	Fair	Poor
575	500	425	325	250	150

Magnum Stalker

NIB	Exc.	V.G.	Good	Fair	Poor
575	500	425	325	250	150

Double Automatic Shotgun

This is a short recoil-operated, semi-automatic shotgun chambered for 12 gauge only. It was offered with a 26", 28", or 30" barrel that was either plain or vent-ribbed. It has various chokes. The receiver is steel, and the finish is blued with a checkered

walnut stock. The tubular magazine holds only two shots--hence its name. It was manufactured between 1952 and 1971.
Vent Rib—Add 25%.

Exc.	V.G.	Good	Fair	Poor
450	400	325	250	200

Twelvette Double Auto
This version is similar to the Double Automatic except that it has an aircraft aluminum alloy frame color-anodized in either blue, silver, green, brown, or black. Red-, gold-, or royal blue-colored receivers were the rarest colors and would command approximately a 15 percent premium. It was offered with either a plain or vent-rib barrel. There were approximately 65,000 produced between 1952 and 1971.
Vent Rib—Add 25%.

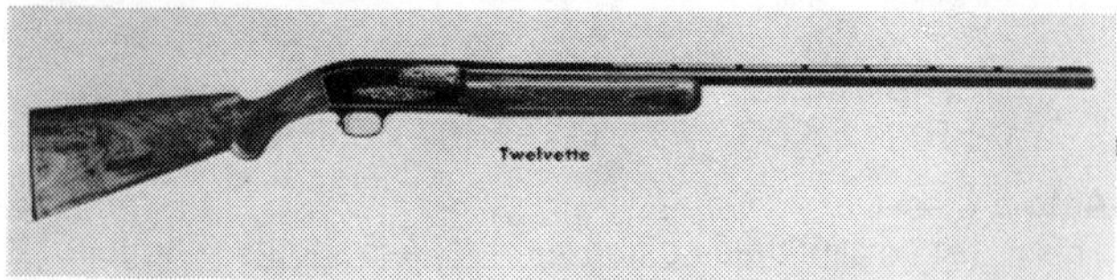

Exc.	V.G.	Good	Fair	Poor
500	425	350	275	225

Twentyweight Double Auto
This version is similar in all respects to the Twelvette except that it is three-quarters of a pound lighter and was offered with a 26.5" barrel. It was manufactured between 1952 and 1971.
Vent Rib—Add 25%.

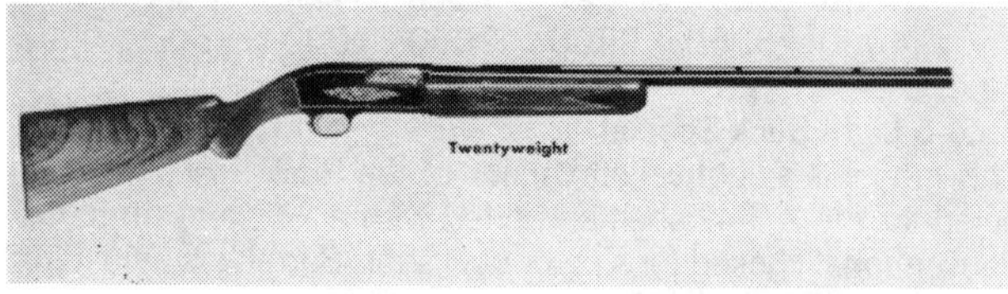

Exc.	V.G.	Good	Fair	Poor
485	435	375	300	250

B-2000
This is a gas-operated, semi-automatic shotgun chambered for 12 or 20 gauge and offered with a 26", 28", or 30", vent-rib barrel with various chokes. The finish is blued with a checkered walnut stock. This shotgun was assembled in Portugal from parts that were manufactured by FN in Belgium. There were approximately 115,000 imported between 1974 and 1983.

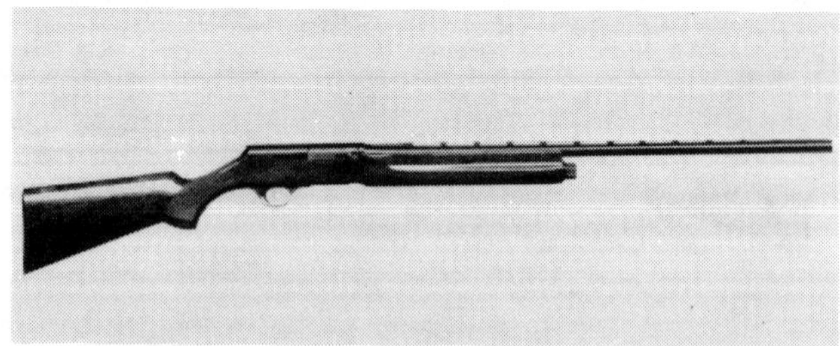

Exc.	V.G.	Good	Fair	Poor
385	325	300	250	150

B-2000 Magnum
This version features 3" chambers and was offered standard with a recoil pad.

Exc.	V.G.	Good	Fair	Poor
425	350	325	275	175

B-2000 Buck Special
This version has a 24", cylinder-bored barrel with rifle sights.

Exc.	V.G.	Good	Fair	Poor
400	340	300	250	175

B-2000 Trap
This version has a 30", full-choke barrel with a floating rib and a Monte Carlo-type trap stock.

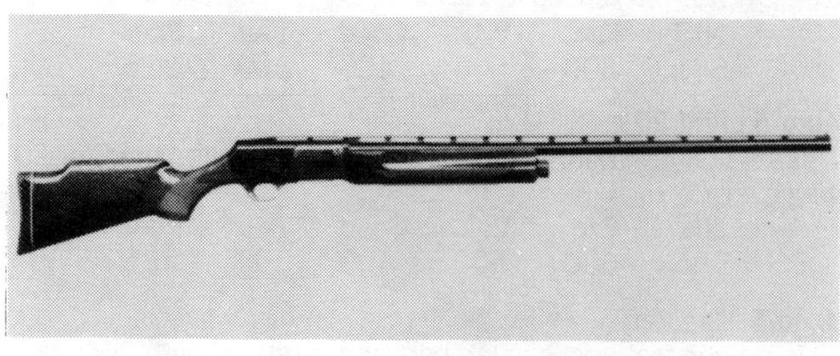

Exc.	V.G.	Good	Fair	Poor
400	340	300	250	175

B-2000 Skeet
This version features a 26", skeet-bored barrel with a floating vent-rib and a skeet-type stock.

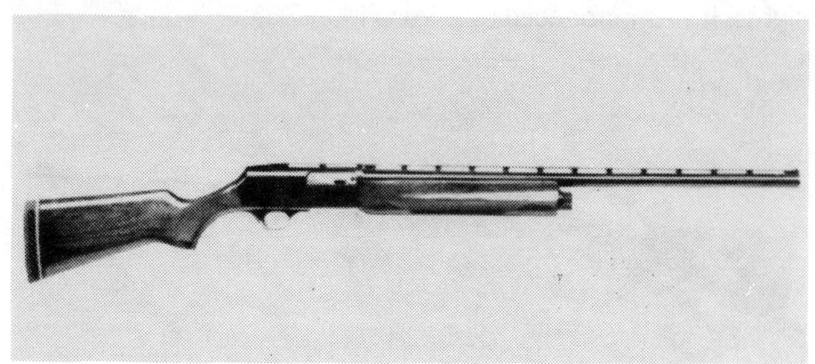

Exc.	V.G.	Good	Fair	Poor
400	340	300	250	175

Model B-80
This is a gas-operated, semi-automatic shotgun chambered for 12 or 20 gauge. It features 3" Magnum potential by simply exchanging the barrel. It features various-length barrels and was offered with screw-in Invector chokes as of 1985. The receiver is either steel or lightweight aluminum alloy. The finish is blued with a checkered walnut stock. This gun was assembled in Portugal from parts manufactured by Beretta in Italy. It was manufactured between 1981 and 1988.

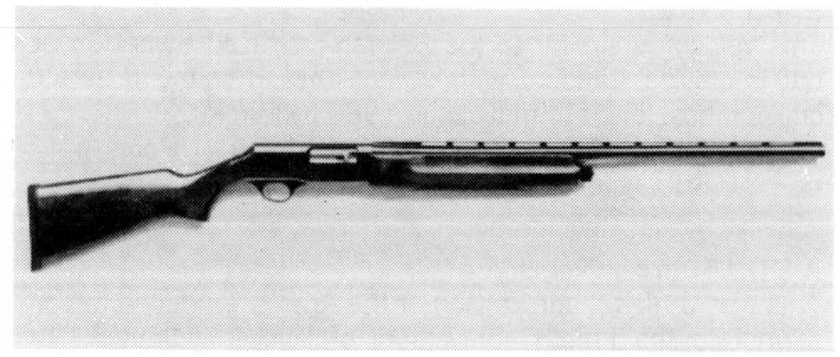

Exc.	V.G.	Good	Fair	Poor
450	400	350	300	200

Model B-80 Buck Special
This version features a 24", cylinder-bored barrel with rifle sights. It was discontinued in 1984.

Exc.	V.G.	Good	Fair	Poor
450	400	350	300	200

Model B-80 DU Commemorative
This version was produced to be auctioned by American Ducks Unlimited chapters. In order to realize the collector potential, it must be NIB with all supplied materials. Values supplied are general.

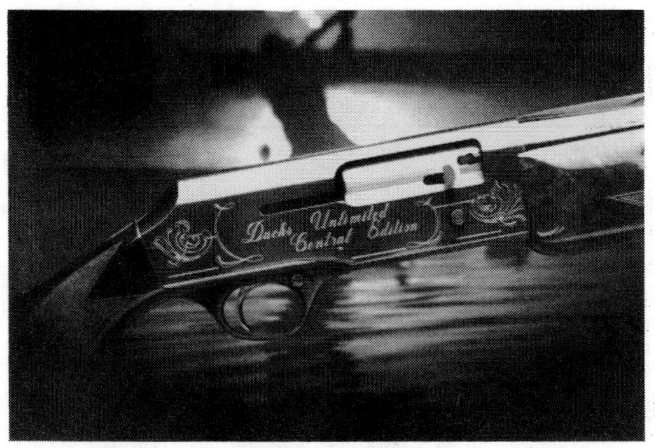

NIB	Exc.	V.G.	Good	Fair	Poor
900	700	500	375	300	250

Model Gold 10

Introduced for the first time in 1993 this is a gas operated 5-shot semi-automatic shotgun chambered for the 10 gauge shell. Offered with 26", 28", or 30" vent rib barrel. The standard model has a walnut stock, blued receiver and barrel while the Stalker model is fitted with a graphite composite stock with non-glare finish on receiver and barrel. Both models are fitted with choke tubes. Weighs about 10 lbs., 10 oz.

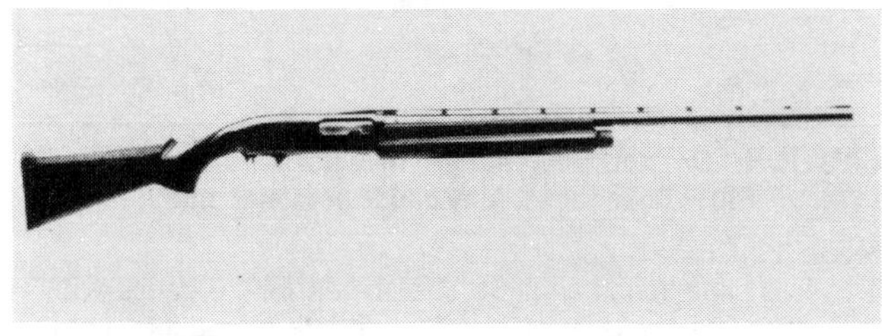

NIB	Exc.	V.G.	Good	Fair	Poor
725	650	550	450	300	150

Stalker Model

NIB	Exc.	V.G.	Good	Fair	Poor
725	650	550	450	300	150

A-500

This is a self-adjusting, gas-operated, semi-automatic shotgun chambered for 12 gauge only. It is offered with 26", 28", or 30" barrels with a vent-rib and screw-in Invector choke tubes. It has 3" chambers and can fire any load interchangeably. The finish is blued with a checkered walnut stock and recoil pad. It features light engraving. It was introduced in 1987.

NIB	Exc.	V.G.	Good	Fair	Poor
560	490	425	350	275	225

A-500G Sporting Clays

This gas operated version is designed for Sporting Clays and features a choice of 28" or 30" vent rib barrel with semi-gloss finish with gold lettering "Sporting Clays". Ventilated recoil pad standard. Weighs about 8 lbs.

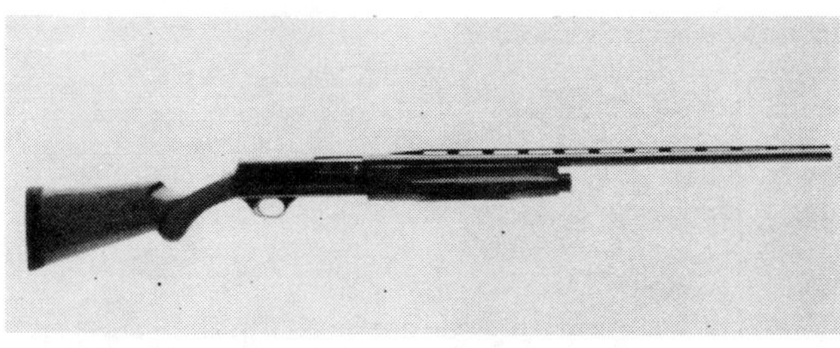

NIB	Exc.	V.G.	Good	Fair	Poor
520	425	350	300	200	150

A-500R Hunting Model

Similar in appearance to the A-500G with the exception that this model operates on a short recoil design. The butt stock features a full pistol grip. Available with 26", 28", or 30" vent rib barrels. Choke tubes standard. Weighs about 7 lbs., 13 oz.

NIB	Exc.	V.G.	Good	Fair	Poor
475	385	300	250	200	150

A-500R Buck Special

Same as Hunting model with the addition of adjustable rear sight and contoured front ramp sight with gold bead. Choke tubes standard as is 24" barrel. Weighs 7 lbs., 11 oz.

NIB	Exc.	V.G.	Good	Fair	Poor
500	425	350	300	225	150

BPS Model

This is a slide action shotgun chambered for 10, 12, or 20 gauge. It is offered with various-length, vent-rib barrels with screw-in Invector chokes. It features 3" Magnum chambers and a bottom-ejection system that effectively makes it ambidextrous. It has double slide bars and a 5-shot tubular magazine. It is constructed of all steel. It was introduced by B. C. Miroku in 1977.

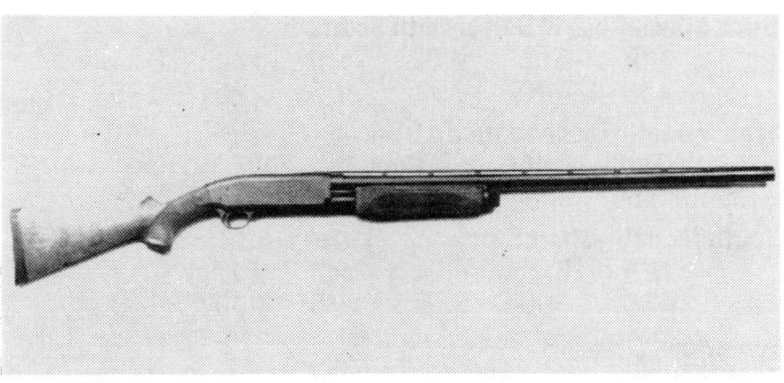

Field Grade

NIB	Exc.	V.G.	Good	Fair	Poor
435	390	325	275	200	150

Magnum Model—10 or 12 Gauge, 3.5" Chambers

NIB	Exc.	V.G.	Good	Fair	Poor
510	450	375	325	250	200

Upland Special—22" Barrel, Straight Stock

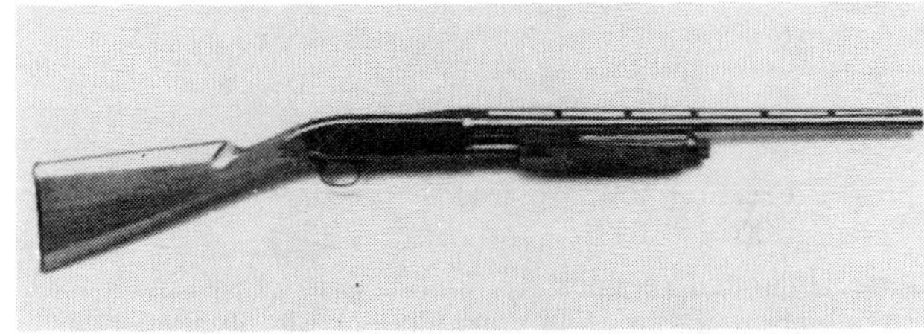

NIB	Exc.	V.G.	Good	Fair	Poor
435	390	325	275	200	150

Stalker Model—Matte Finish, Black Stock

NIB	Exc.	V.G.	Good	Fair	Poor
435	390	325	275	200	150

Pigeon Grade

Furnished in 12 gauge only with high grade walnut stock and gold trimmed receiver.

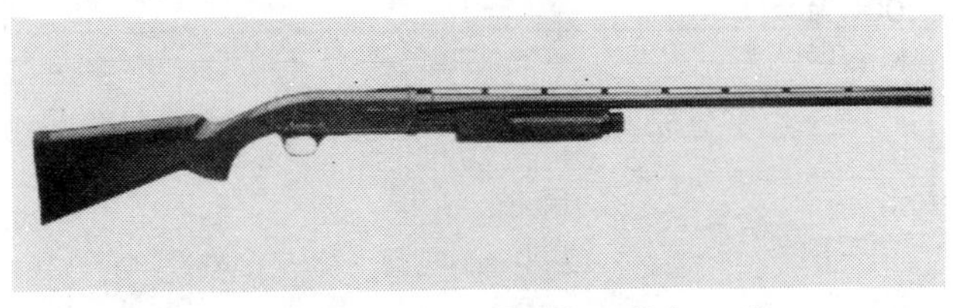

NIB	Exc.	V.G.	Good	Fair	Poor
450	400	300	225	175	125

Game Gun

Offered in 12 gauge only this model is available in either a Turkey Special or a Deer Special. Both have 20.5" plain barrel and drilled and tapped receivers. The stock is walnut. The Turkey gun is fitted with an extra full choke. The Deer gun has a special rifled choke tube for slugs. Both weigh about 7 lbs., 7 oz.

NIB	Exc.	V.G.	Good	Fair	Poor
250	200	175	125	100	50

Buck Special—24" Barrel With Sights

NIB	Exc.	V.G.	Good	Fair	Poor
450	400	350	300	225	175

Trap Model—Discontinued 1984

Exc.	V.G.	Good	Fair	Poor
375	325	275	200	150

Youth Model—Short Stock, 22" Barrel

NIB	Exc.	V.G.	Good	Fair	Poor
435	390	325	275	200	150

Waterfowl Deluxe

This version is chambered for 12 gauge with a 3" chamber and features an etched receiver with a gold-plated trigger. Otherwise, it is similar to the standard BPS.

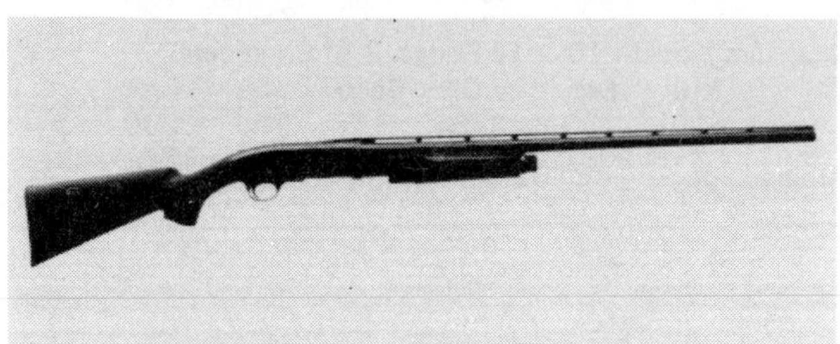

Exc.	V.G.	Good	Fair	Poor
600	525	425	325	250

Ducks Unlimited Versions

These were limited-edition guns produced to be auctioned by Ducks Unlimited. They were furnished with a case and must be NIB with furnished materials to realize their collector potential.

NIB	Exc.	V.G.	Good	Fair	Poor
650	525	425	325	250	175

BROWNING CHOKE TUBE SELECTION

12 Gauge Invector-Plus for Back-Bored Guns

Rim Notches	Pattern w/Lead Shot	Pattern w/Steel Shot
Knurled	X-Full Turkey	Do not use
I	Full	Do not use
II	Imp. Modified	Full
III	Modified	Full
IIII	Imp. Cylinder	Modified
IIIII	Skeet	Imp. Cylinder
No Notches	Cylinder	Cylinder

10 Gauge Invector

Rim Notches	Pattern w/Lead Shot	Pattern w/Steel Shot
Knurled	X-Full Turkey	Do not use
I	Full	Do not use
II	Modified	Full
III	Imp. Modified	Modified

16 Gauge Invector

Rim Notches	Pattern w/Lead Shot	Pattern w/Steel Shot
I	Full	Do not use
II	Modified	Full
III	Imp. Cylinder	Modified
IIII	Skeet	Imp. Cylinder
No Notches	Cylinder	Imp. Cylinder

20 Gauge Invector

Rim Notches	Pattern w/Lead Shot	Pattern w/Steel Shot
I	Full	Full
II	Modified	Imp. Modified
III	Imp. Cylinder	Modified
IIII	Skeet	Modified
No Notches	Cylinder	Imp. Cylinder

CAUTION: Do not interchange Invector choke tubes with Invector-Plus choke tubes. May cause personal injury.

Model 12-Grade I

This is a slide-action shotgun chambered for 20 gauge with a 26", modified-choke, vent-rib barrel. It is a reproduction of the Winchester Model 12 shotgun. It has a 5-round, tubular magazine with a floating, high-post rib. It has a takedown feature and is blued with a walnut stock. Introduced in 1988, total production will be limited to 8,500 guns.

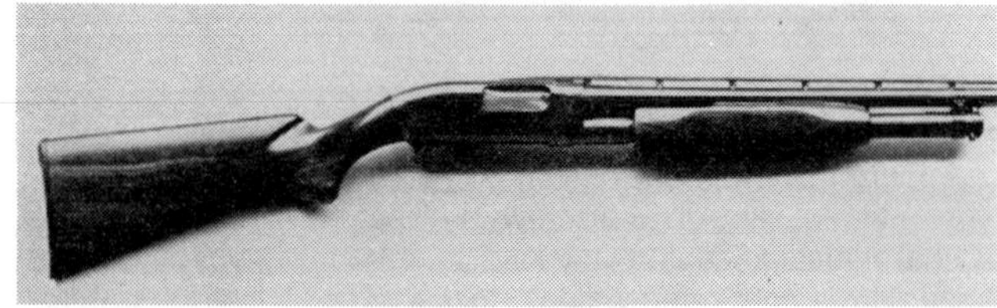

NIB	Exc.	V.G.	Good	Fair	Poor
725	650	575	475	400	300

Model 12-Grade V

This is an extensively engraved version of the Grade I Model 12. It features a select walnut stock with deluxe checkering and a high-gloss finish. There are gold inlays. It was introduced in 1988, and production will be limited to 4,000 guns.

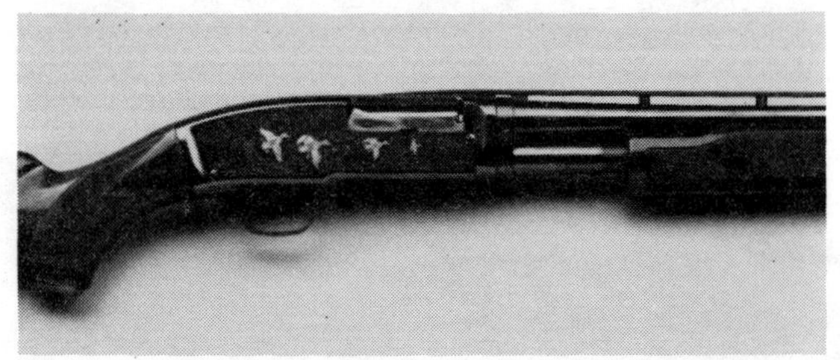

NIB	Exc.	V.G.	Good	Fair	Poor
1200	1050	900	750	500	350

Limited Edition Model 42

A new version of the .410 bore pump shotgun that was last produced by Winchester in 1963. Available in two grades both fitted with 26" vent rib barrels. The Grade I features a plain blued receiver with walnut stock. The Grade V features a blued receiver with scroll engraving and gold inlays. Both models are choked full and weigh 6 lbs., 4 oz.

Grade I

NIB	Exc.	V.G.	Good	Fair	Poor
650	600	500	400	300	200

Grade V

NIB	Exc.	V.G.	Good	Fair	Poor
1050	900	700	500	350	200

High-Power Bolt Action Rifle

This was a high-grade, bolt-action sporting rifle manufactured by FN in Belgium. It was built on either a Mauser or a Sako action and chambered for a number of popular calibers from the .222 Remington up to the .458 Winchester Magnum. There were three basic grades that differed in the amount of ornamentation and the quality of materials and workmanship utilized. Certain calibers are considered to be rare and will bring a premium from collectors of this firearm. We recommend securing a qualified appraisal on these rifles if a transaction is contemplated. We furnish general values only.

NOTE: From 1960 through 1966 Mauser actions with long extractors were featured. These Mauser actions will bring a premium depending on caliber. From 1967 on, Supreme actions with short extractors were used. *Only* .30-06 and .270 calibers continued with long extractor Mauser actions. **CAUTION:** for buyer and seller alike some rare calibers may be worth as much as 100 percent or more over prices listed below for rare calibers such as .284 Win. and .257 Roberts.

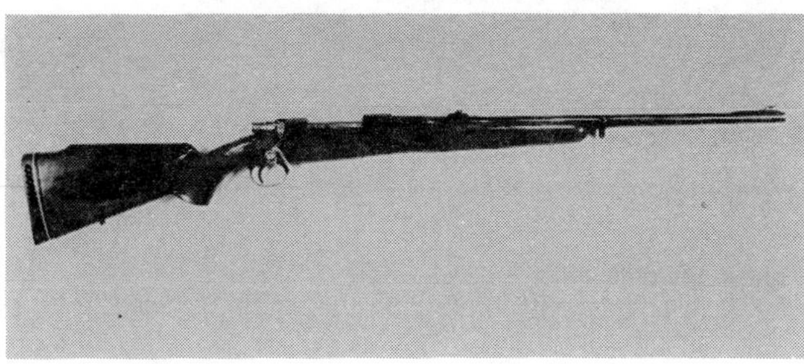

Safari Grade—Standard Model, Standard Calibers

Exc.	V.G.	Good	Fair	Poor
800	675	525	400	300

Medallion Grade—Scroll Engraved

Exc.	V.G.	Good	Fair	Poor
1500	1250	1000	750	500

Olympian Grade—Extensive Engraving

Exc.	V.G.	Good	Fair	Poor
2250	2000	1750	1450	1000

Model BBR

This is a bolt-action sporting rifle chambered for various popular calibers. It has a 24" barrel with an adjustable trigger and fluted bolt. It features a detachable magazine under the floorplate and was furnished without sights. The finish is blued with a checkered, walnut, Monte Carlo stock. It was manufactured between 1978 and 1984 by Miroku.

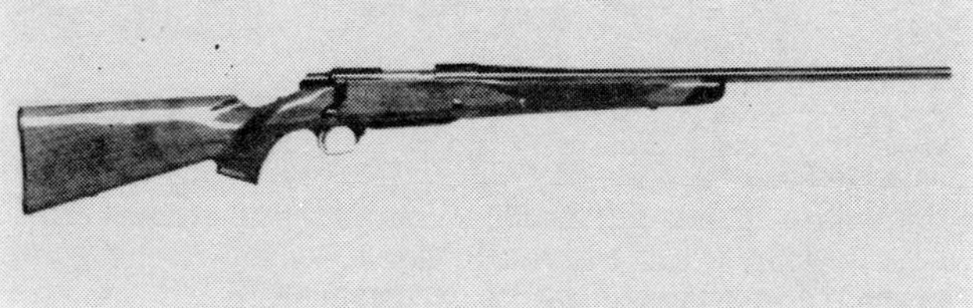

Exc.	V.G.	Good	Fair	Poor
475	400	350	275	200

A-Bolt Hunter

This is the current bolt-action rifle manufactured by B. C. Miroku. It is chambered for various popular calibers and offered with a 22", 24", or 26" barrel. It has either a short or long action, an adjustable trigger, and a detachable box magazine that is mounted under the floorplate. It is furnished without sights and is blued with a checkered walnut stock. It was introduced in 1985.

NIB	Exc.	V.G.	Good	Fair	Poor
450	400	350	300	250	200

Composite Stalker

Supplied with composite stock and matte finish bluing. Offered in .338 Win. Mag., .300 Win. Mag., 7mm Rem. Mag., .25-06, .270, .280, .30-06.

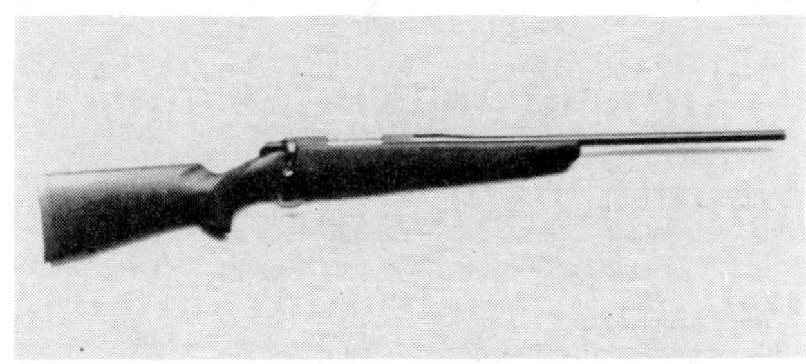

NIB	Exc.	V.G.	Good	Fair	Poor
400	350	300	250	200	150

Stainless Stalker

This version is chambered for the .270, .30-06, and the 7mm Remington Magnum cartridges. It is constructed of stainless-steel and has a black, painted wood stock. It was introduced in 1987.

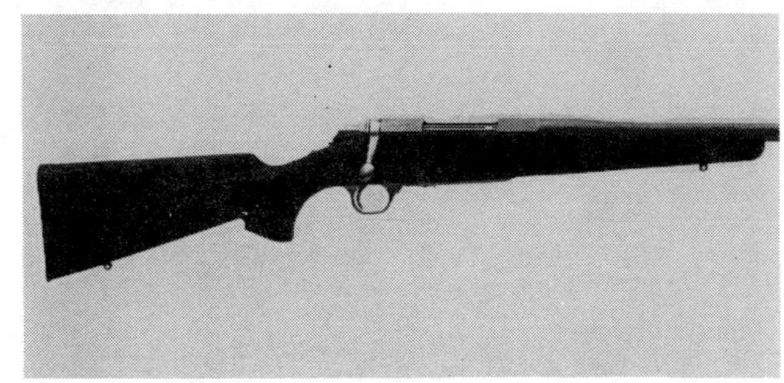

NIB	Exc.	V.G.	Good	Fair	Poor
580	525	450	350	300	250

Euro-Bolt

First introduced in 1993 this A-Bolt variation features a rounded bolt shroud, Mannilicher style bolt handle, continental style stock with cheek piece, Schnabel style forearm. The finish is a low luster blue. Offered in .270, 30-06, and 7mm Rem. Mag. calibers. Weighs about 7 lbs.

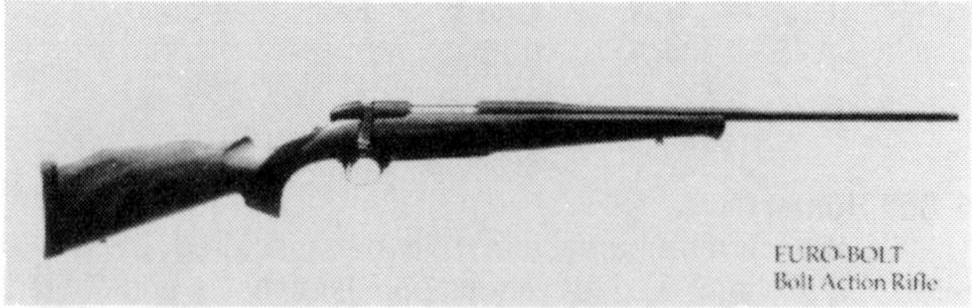

NIB	Exc.	V.G.	Good	Fair	Poor
550	500	450	350	250	150

Medallion Model

This is a deluxe version of the A-Bolt Hunter with a high-polish blue finish and a select walnut stock with rosewood pistol-grip cap and forend tip.

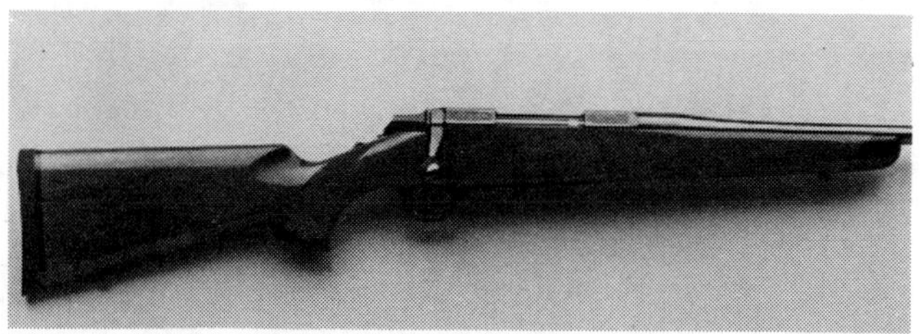

NIB	Exc.	V.G.	Good	Fair	Poor
525	475	400	350	300	250

Gold Medallion

This version has a fancy-grade walnut stock with a cheekpiece. It is lightly engraved and has gold-inlaid letters. It was introduced in 1988.

NIB	Exc.	V.G.	Good	Fair	Poor
690	625	550	450	400	325

Big Horn Sheep Issue

This is a high-grade version of the A-Bolt chambered for the .270 cartridge. It features a deluxe skip-line checkered walnut stock with a heavily engraved receiver and floorplate. It has two gold sheep inlays. There were 600 manufactured in 1986 and 1987.

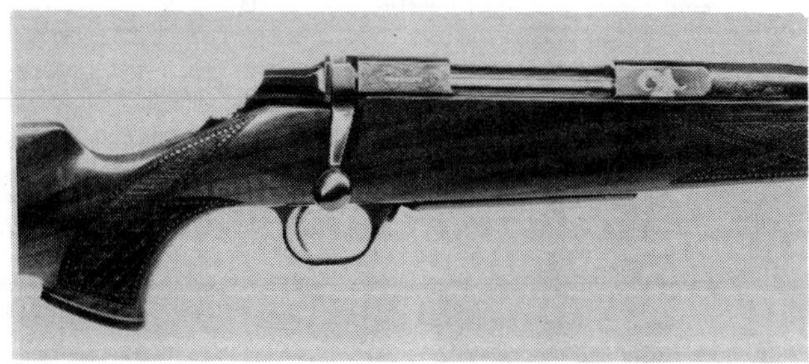

NIB	Exc.	V.G.	Good	Fair	Poor
1050	800	600	450	400	325

Pronghorn Issue

This is a deluxe version of the A-Bolt chambered for the .243 cartridge. It is heavily engraved and gold inlaid and features a presentation-grade walnut stock with skipline checkering and pearl-inlaid borders. There were 500 manufactured in 1987.

NIB	Exc.	V.G.	Good	Fair	Poor
1300	1000	750	500	400	325

Micro-Medallion Model

This is a smaller version of the A-Bolt Hunter chambered for popular cartridges that fit a short action. It has a 20" barrel without sights and a 3-round magazine. It was introduced in 1988.

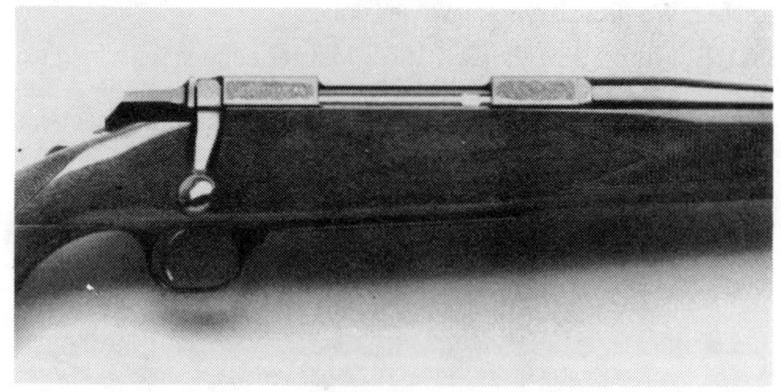

NIB	Exc.	V.G.	Good	Fair	Poor
525	475	400	350	300	250

Grade I A-Bolt .22

This is a bolt-action sporting rifle chambered for the .22 l.r. or .22 Magnum cartridges. It features a 60-degree bolt and a 22" barrel available either with or without open sights. It has a 5-round, detachable magazine and an adjustable trigger. The finish is blued with a checkered walnut stock. It was introduced in 1986.

.22 Magnum—Add 15%.

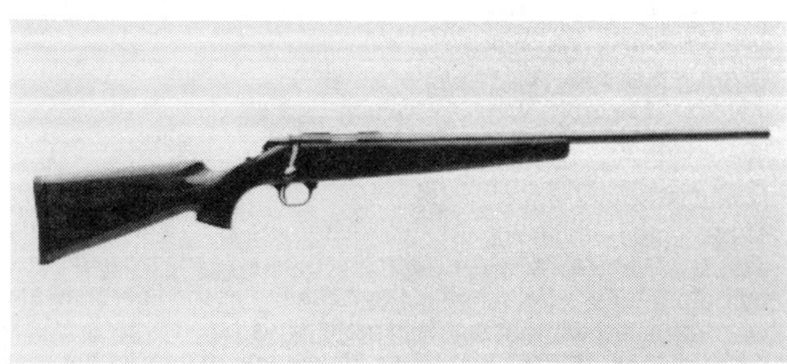

NIB	Exc.	V.G.	Good	Fair	Poor
340	275	210	150	125	100

Gold Medallion A-Bolt .22

This deluxe, high-grade version features a select stock with rosewood pistol-grip cap and forend tip. It is lightly engraved and has gold-filled letters. It was introduced in 1988.

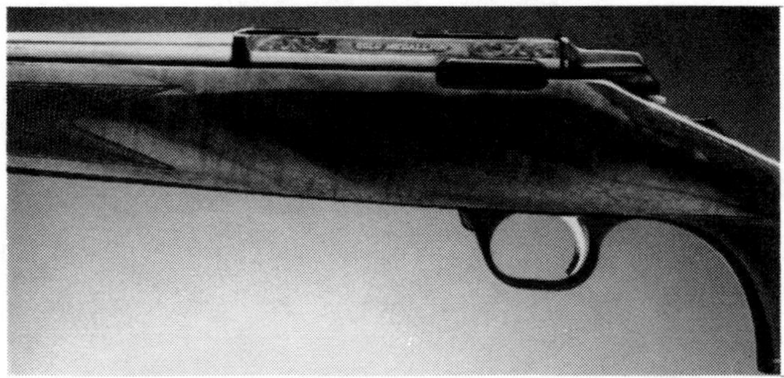

NIB	Exc.	V.G.	Good	Fair	Poor
450	400	350	300	225	175

T-Bolt Model T-1

This is a unique, straight-pull, bolt-action sporting rifle chambered for the .22 l.r. cartridge. It has a 22" barrel with open sights and a 5-round magazine. The finish is blued with a plain walnut stock. It was manufactured between 1965 and 1974 by FN.

Exc.	V.G.	Good	Fair	Poor
300	275	225	150	100

T-Bolt Model T-2

This version is similar to the T-1 with a select, checkered walnut stock and a 24" barrel.

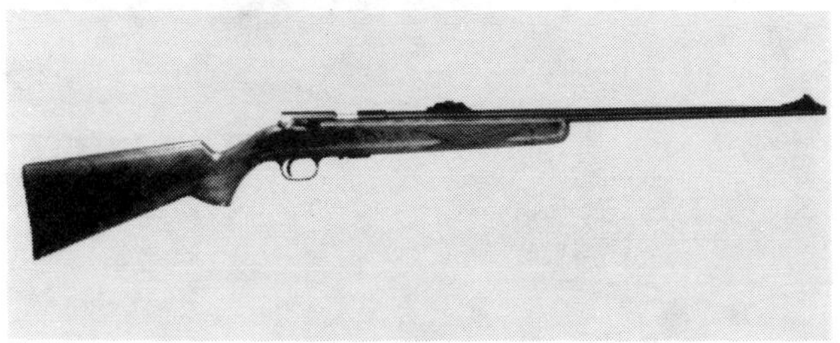

Exc.	V.G.	Good	Fair	Poor
400	325	250	200	150

Trombone Model

This is a slide-action rifle chambered for the .22 l.r. cartridge. It has a 24" barrel with open sights and a takedown design. It has a tubular magazine and a hammerless action. There were approximately 150,000 manufactured by FN between 1922 and 1974. Approximately 3,200 were imported by Browning in the 1960s. They are marked with either the FN barrel address or the Browning Arms address. The Browning marked guns are worth approximately 20 percent additional. The values given are for FN-marked guns.

NIB	Exc.	V.G.	Good	Fair	Poor
750	550	500	450	375	275

BPR-22

This is a short-stroke, slide action rifle chambered for the .22 Magnum cartridge. It has a 20.25" barrel with open sights and an 11-round, tubular magazine. The finish is blued with a checkered walnut stock. It was manufactured between 1977 and 1982.

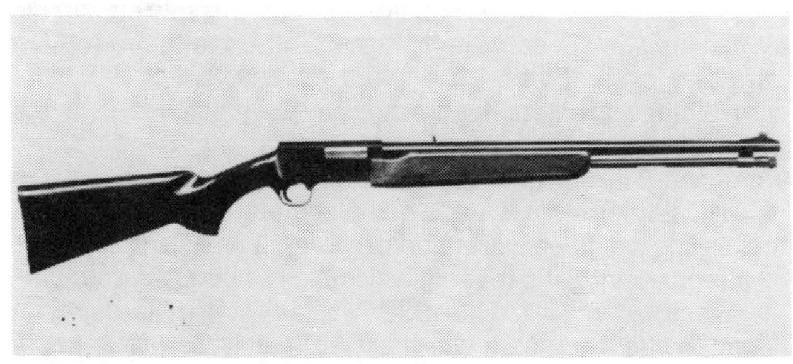

Exc.	V.G.	Good	Fair	Poor
275	200	150	125	95

BPR-22 Grade II

This version is engraved and has a select walnut stock.

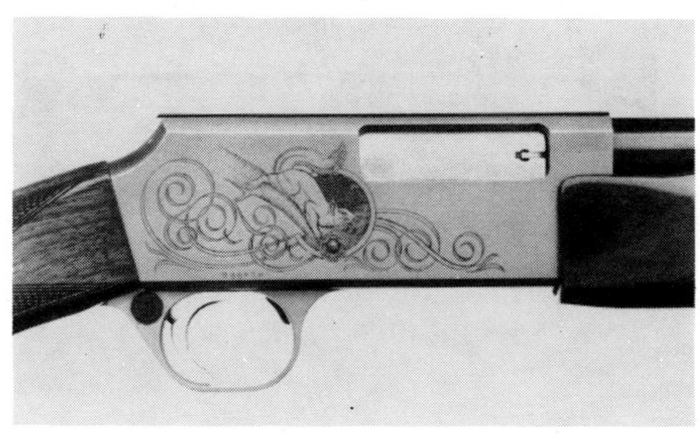

Exc.	V.G.	Good	Fair	Poor
375	300	250	200	125

.22 Semi-Auto

This is a blowback-operated, semi-automatic rifle chambered for the .22 rimfire cartridge. It features a take-down barrel design with a 19.25" barrel and an 11-round, tubular magazine inside the buttstock. It is loaded through a hole in the middle of the buttstock. The finish is blued with a checkered walnut stock and beavertail forearm. This lightweight, compact firearm was manufactured by FN between 1914 and 1976. There are a number of versions that differ in the amount of ornamentation and the quality of materials and workmanship utilized.

.22 Short Only—Add 15%.

Early Wheel Sight—Add 15%.

NOTE: For .22 Short Grade I add 15%.
For .22 Short Grade II add 300%.
For .22 Short Grade III add 500%.

Grade I

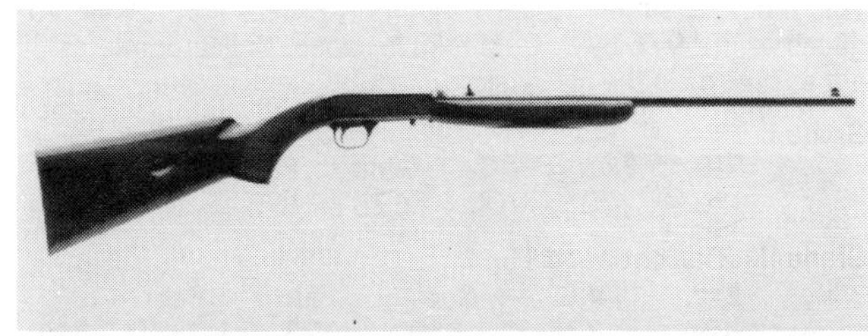

NIB	Exc.	V.G.	Good	Fair	Poor
400	350	300	250	200	125

Grade II—Satin Chromed Receiver

NIB	Exc.	V.G.	Good	Fair	Poor
750	700	600	400	300	200

Grade III—Coin Finished

NIB	Exc.	V.G.	Good	Fair	Poor
1500	1250	1050	600	400	300

.22 Semi-Auto (Miroku Mfg.)

This model is similar to the Belgian FN except that it was produced as of 1976 by B. C. Miroku in Japan. Collector interest is not as high as in the FN version.

Grade I

NIB	Exc.	V.G.	Good	Fair	Poor
330	280	200	175	125	100

Grade II—Discontinued 1984

Exc.	V.G.	Good	Fair	Poor
425	375	300	225	150

Grade III—Discontinued 1983

Exc.	V.G.	Good	Fair	Poor
700	625	500	400	250

Grade VI—Gold Inlaid

NIB	Exc.	V.G.	Good	Fair	Poor
675	600	500	425	325	275

BAR-22

This is a blowback-operated, semi-automatic rifle chambered for the .22 l.r. cartridge. It has a 20.25" barrel with open sights and a 15-round, tubular magazine. It features a polished, lightweight alloy receiver. It was finished in blue with a checkered walnut stock. It is manufactured between 1977 and 1985 by Miroku.

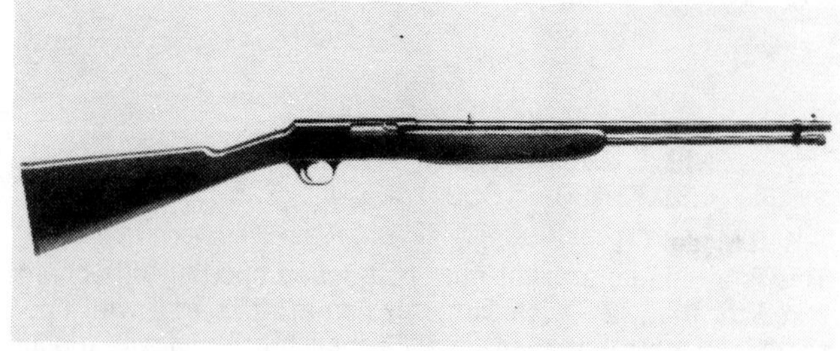

Exc.	V.G.	Good	Fair	Poor
225	175	150	125	90

BAR-22 Grade II

This is a deluxe version with an engraved, silver-finished receiver. It has a select walnut stock. It was discontinued in 1985.

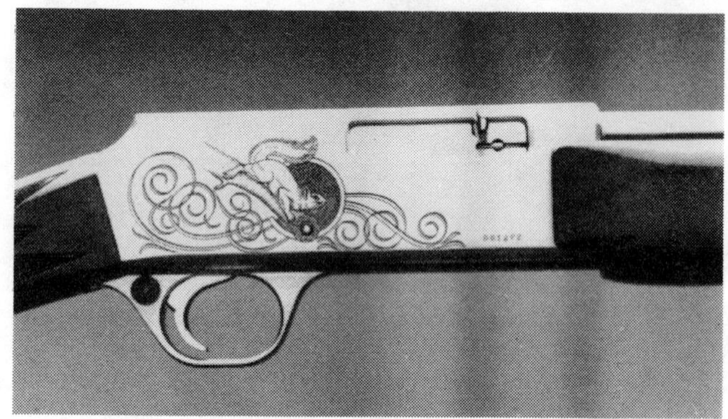

Exc.	V.G.	Good	Fair	Poor
300	250	200	150	120

Patent 1900 High Power

This is a semi-automatic sporting rifle chambered for the .35 Remington cartridge. It is similar in configuration to the Remington Model 8 rifle. It has a 22" barrel with open sights and a 5-round, integral magazine. The finish is blued with a plain walnut stock. There were approximately 5,000 manufactured between 1910 and 1931. A deluxe model with a ribbed barrel and checkered walnut stock was also available and would be worth approximately 15 percent additional.

Exc.	V.G.	Good	Fair	Poor
675	600	500	375	300

BAR High Power Rifle

This is a gas-operated, semi-automatic sporting rifle chambered for various popular calibers from the .243 up to the .338 Magnum cartridges. It was offered with either a 22" or 24" barrel with folding leaf sight. The finish is blued with a checkered walnut stock. The various grades offered differed in the amount of ornamentation and the quality of materials and workmanship utilized. Earlier models were manufactured in Belgium by FN; these guns would be worth approximately 15 percent additional over the current guns that are assembled in Portugal from parts manufactured by FN. The .338 Magnum model is rarely encountered and would be worth approximately 25 percent additional. The values furnished are for current production, Portugese-assembled guns. This model was introduced in 1967.

Grade I

NIB	Exc.	V.G.	Good	Fair	Poor
600	525	450	350	300	225

Grade I Magnum

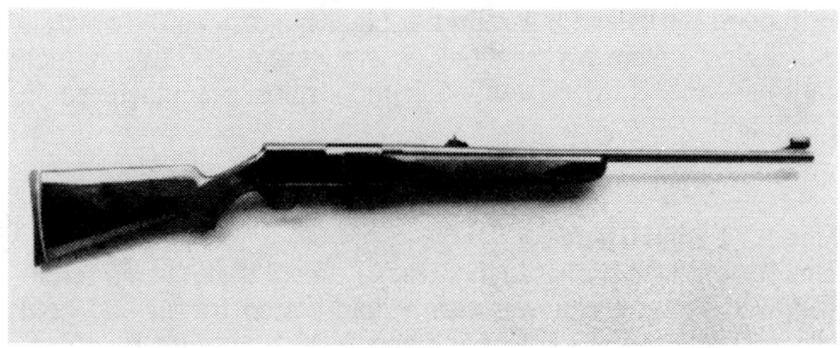

NIB	Exc.	V.G.	Good	Fair	Poor
650	575	500	400	350	250

Grade II—Discontinued 1974

Exc.	V.G.	Good	Fair	Poor
700	625	550	425	325

Grade II Magnum—Discontinued 1974

Exc.	V.G.	Good	Fair	Poor
775	700	625	500	400

Grade III—Discontinued 1984

Exc.	V.G.	Good	Fair	Poor
900	825	700	600	500

Grade III Magnum—Discontinued 1984

Exc.	V.G.	Good	Fair	Poor
950	875	750	650	550

Grade IV—Gamescene Engraved

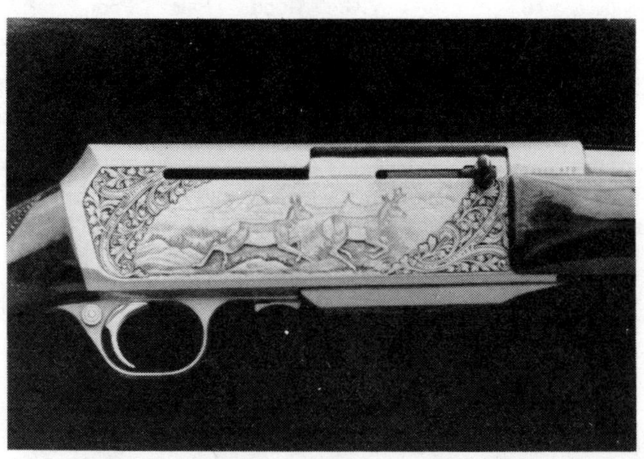

Exc.	V.G.	Good	Fair	Poor
1250	1050	900	800	650

Grade IV Magnum—Discontinued 1984

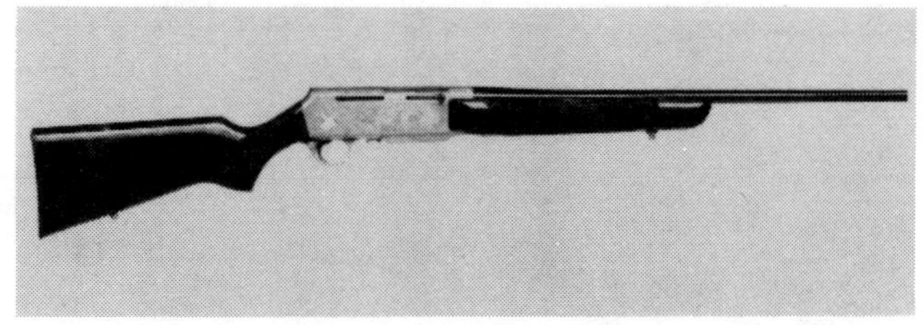

Exc.	V.G.	Good	Fair	Poor
1375	1175	1000	900	700

Grade V—Gold Inlaid, Discontinued 1974

Exc.	V.G.	Good	Fair	Poor
3200	2850	2500	1600	1200

Grade V Magnum—Discontinued 1974

Exc.	V.G.	Good	Fair	Poor
3500	3000	2750	1850	1500

North American Deer Rifle Issue

This is a deluxe version of the BAR chambered for .3006 only. It features an engraved, silver-finished receiver and a deluxe, checkered walnut stock. There were 600 produced and furnished with a walnut case and accessories. This model was discontinued in 1983. As with all commemoratives, it must be NIB to command premium values.

NIB	Exc.	V.G.	Good	Fair	Poor
3600	2750	2000	1500	1200	800

BAR Mark II Safari Rifle

This is an improved version of the BAR first introduced by Browning in 1967. Announced in 1993 this Mark II design uses a new gas system with a newly designed buffering system to improve realibility. This model also has a new bolt release lever, a new easily removable trigger assembly. Available with or without sights. Walnut stock with full pistol grip and recoil pad on Magnum gun are standard. The receiver is blued with scroll engraving. Rifles with Magnum calibers have a 24" barrel while standard calibers are fitted with a 22" barrel. Available in .243, .308, .270, 30-06, 7mm Rem. Mag., .270 Weatherby Mag., .300 Win. Mag., .338 Win. Mag. Standard calibers weigh about 7 lbs., 9 oz. and Magnum calibers weigh about 8 lbs., 6 oz.

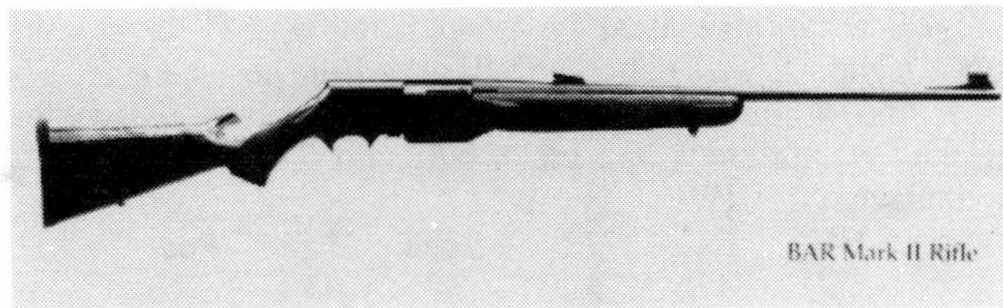
BAR Mark II Rifle

NIB	Exc.	V.G.	Good	Fair	Poor
525	450	400	350	250	150

BL-22 Grade I

This is a lever-action rifle chambered for the .22 rimfire cartridge. It has an 18" barrel with a tubular magazine and a folding leaf rear sight. It is a Western-style firearm that features an exposed hammer. The finish is blued with a walnut stock. It was introduced in 1970 by Miroku.

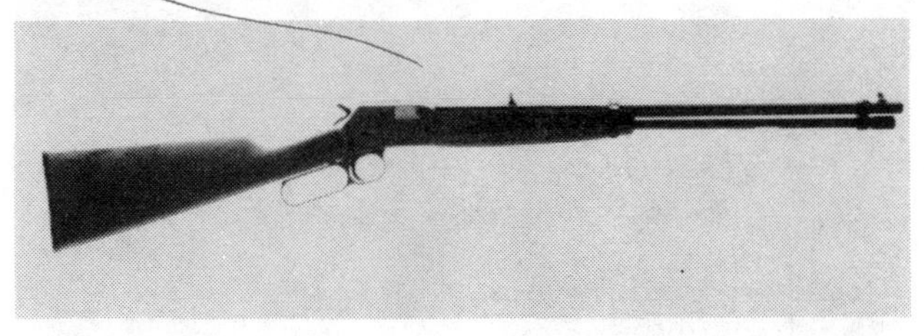

NIB	Exc.	V.G.	Good	Fair	Poor
285	225	200	150	125	100

BL-22 Grade II

This version is similar with a scroll-engraved receiver and a checkered, select walnut stock.

NIB	Exc.	V.G.	Good	Fair	Poor
325	250	225	175	150	125

Model 81 BLR

This is a contemporarily designed, lever-action sporting rifle chambered for various popular calibers from .22-250 up to .358 Winchester. It has a 20" barrel with adjustable sights. It features a 4-round, detachable magazine and a rotary locking bolt. The finish is blued with a checkered walnut stock and recoil pad. It was introduced in 1971 and manufactured that year in Belgium. In 1972 manufacture moved to Miroku in Japan. The Belgian manufactured version is worth approximately 20 percent additional.

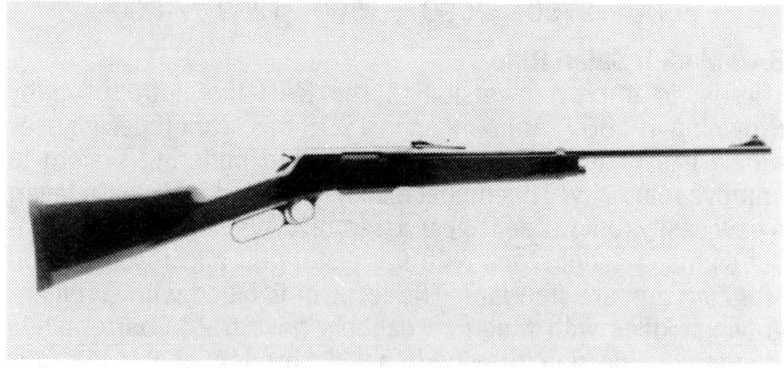

NIB	Exc.	V.G.	Good	Fair	Poor
475	400	325	275	200	150

Model 65 Grade I

This was a limited-edition, lever-action rifle chambered for the .218 Bee cartridge. It has a tapered, round, 24" barrel with open sights. It was patterned after the Winchester Model 65 rifle. It has a 7-round, tubular magazine. The finish is blued with a plain walnut stock and metal buttplate. There were 3,500 manufactured in 1989.

NIB	Exc.	V.G.	Good	Fair	Poor
550	475	400	325	250	175

Model 65 High Grade

This is a deluxe version that features a silver-finished, scroll-engraved receiver with gold animal inlays and a gold-plated trigger. It features a select, checkered walnut stock. There were 1,500 manufactured in 1989.

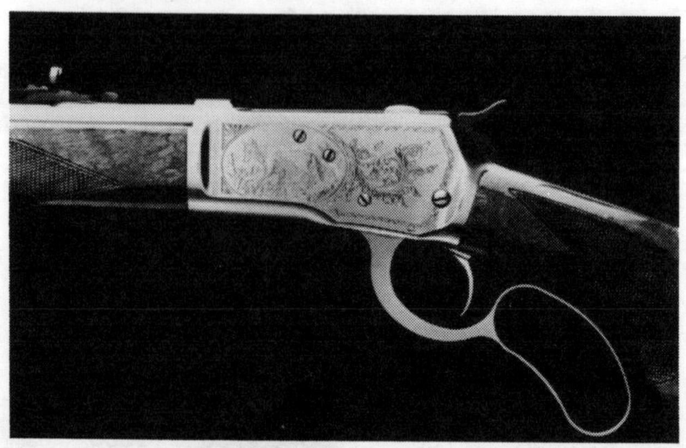

NIB	Exc.	V.G.	Good	Fair	Poor
850	750	600	500	400	275

Model 71 Grade I

This was a reproduction of the Winchester Model 71, chambered for the .348 cartridge. It has either a 20" or 24" barrel with open sights and a 4-round, tubular magazine. The finish is blued with a plain walnut stock. There were 4,000 twenty-inch carbines and 3,000 twenty-four-inch rifles manufactured in 1986 and 1987.

Exc.	V.G.	Good	Fair	Poor
595	500	400	300	225

Model 71 High Grade

This version was similar to the Grade I except that it had a scroll-engraved, grayed receiver with a gold-plated trigger and gold inlays. There were 3,000 rifles and 3,000 carbines manufactured in 1986 and 1987.

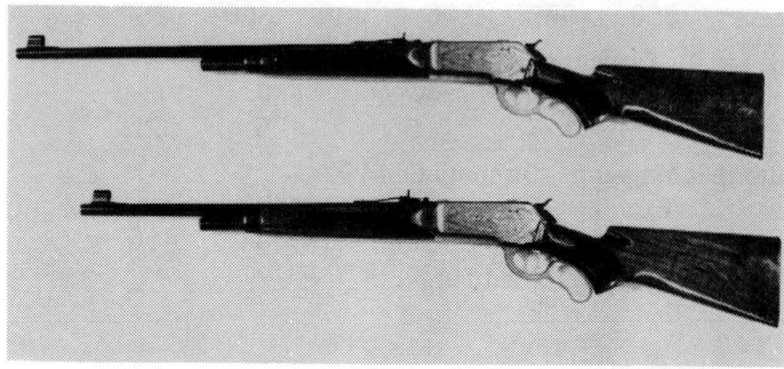

Exc.	V.G.	Good	Fair	Poor
900	750	600	500	400

Model 1885

This is a single shot rifle with falling block action and octagonal free floating barrel. The stock is a high grade walnut with straight grip and recoil pad. Furnished with 28" barrel it is offered in the following calibers: .223, 22-250, .270, 30-06, 7mm Rem. Mag., 45-70 Gov't. Weighs about 8 lbs., 12 oz.

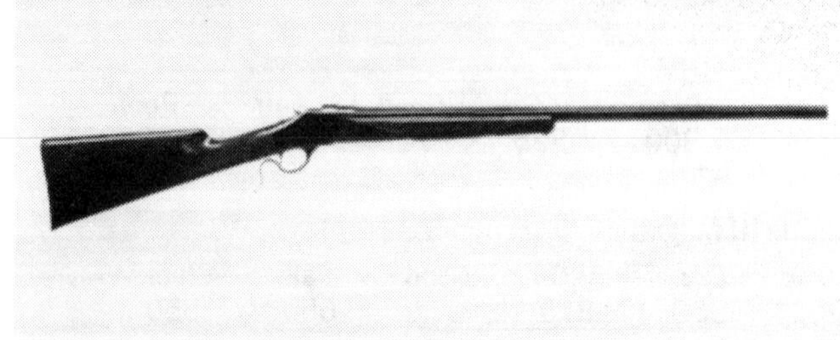

NIB	Exc.	V.G.	Good	Fair	Poor
650	600	500	400	300	200

Model 1886 Grade I

This was a lever-action sporting rifle patterned after the Model 1886 Winchester rifle. It was chambered for the .45-70 cartridge and has a 26", octagonal barrel with a full-length, tubular magazine. The finish is blued with a walnut stock and crescent buttplate. There were 7,000 manufactured in 1986.

Exc.	V.G.	Good	Fair	Poor
750	675	550	425	300

Model 1886 High Grade
This deluxe version of the Model 1886 features gamescene engraving with gold accents and a checkered, select walnut stock. "1 of 3,000" is engraved on the top of the barrel. There were 3,000 manufactured in 1986.

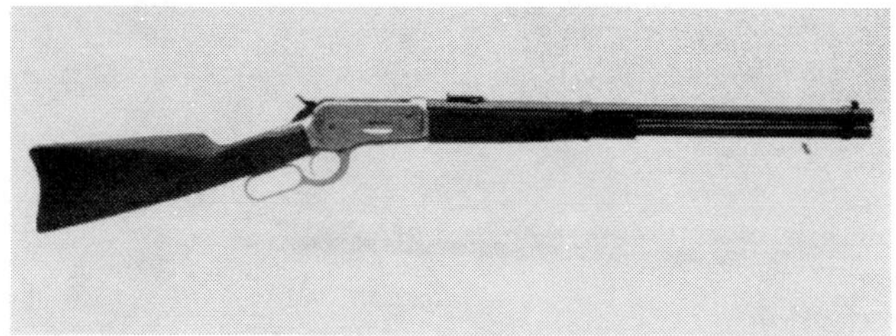

NIB	Exc.	V.G.	Good	Fair	Poor
1000	900	800	650	500	425

Model 1886 Montana Centennial
This version is similar to the High Grade with a different engraving pattern designed to commemorate the centennial of the State of Montana. There were 2,000 manufactured in 1986. As with all commemoratives, it must be NIB with all supplied materials to command collector interest.

NIB	Exc.	V.G.	Good	Fair	Poor
950	850	750	600	450	375

B-92 Carbine
This is a lever-action sporting rifle patterned after the Winchester Model 92. It was chambered for the .357 Mag. and the .44 Mag. cartridges. It has a 20" barrel with an 11-round, tubular magazine. The finish is blued with a walnut stock. It was discontinued in 1986.

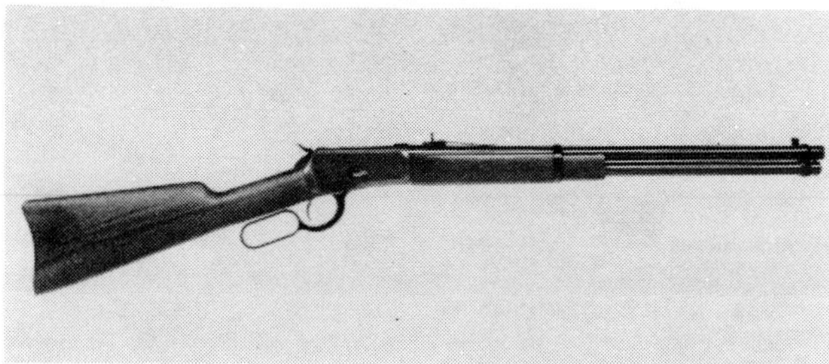

Exc.	V.G.	Good	Fair	Poor
275	225	195	150	120

Model 1895 Grade I
This is a lever-action sporting rifle chambered in .30-.40 Krag and the .30-06 cartridge. It was patterned after the Model 1895 Winchester rifle. It has a 24" barrel and a 4-round, integral box magazine. It has a buckhorn rear sight and a blade front. The finish is blued with a walnut stock. There were 6,000 manufactured in .30-06 and 2,000 chambered for the .30-40 Krag. It was manufactured in 1984.

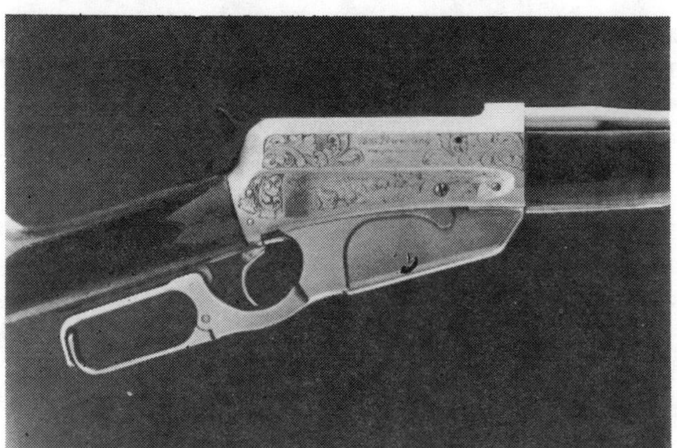

Exc.	V.G.	Good	Fair	Poor
600	525	450	375	275

Model 1895 High Grade
This is the deluxe engraved version of the Model 1895. It has gold-inlaid gamescenes and a gold-plated trigger and features a checkered select walnut stock. There were 2,000 produced in 1984--1,000 in each caliber.

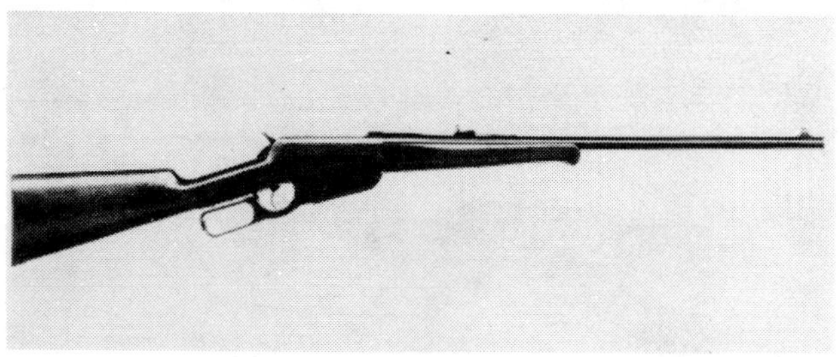

Exc.	V.G.	Good	Fair	Poor
1000	900	700	575	400

Express Rifle
This is an Over/Under, superposed rifle chambered for the .270 Winchester or the .30-06 cartridges. It has 24" barrels with folding express sights and automatic ejectors. It features a single trigger. The receiver is engraved and is finished in blue with a deluxe checkered walnut stock. It was discontinued in 1986.

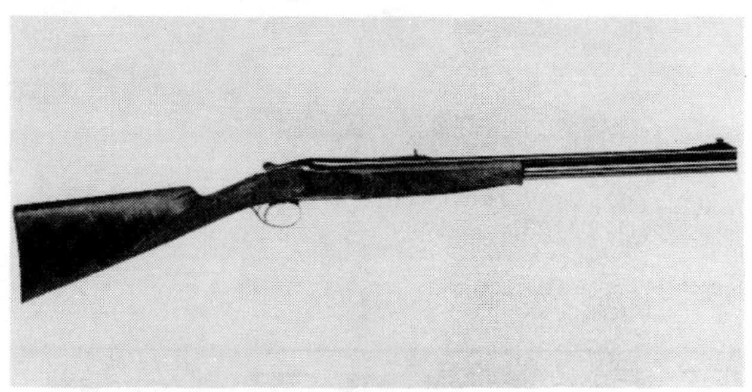

Exc.	V.G.	Good	Fair	Poor
2000	1800	1500	1100	800

Continental Set
This consists of an Express Rifle chambered for the .30-06 cartridge and furnished with an extra set of 20 gauge, Over/Under barrels. The shotgun barrels are 26.5" in length. There is a single trigger, automatic ejectors, and a heavily engraved receiver. The select walnut stock is hand-checkered and oil-finished. It was furnished with a fitted case. There were 500 manufactured in 1986.

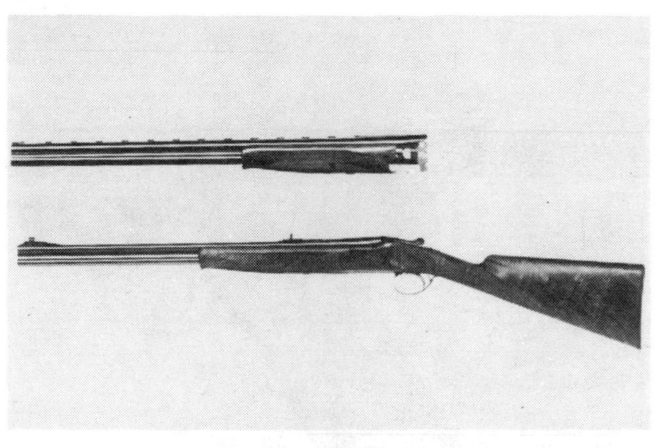

Exc.	V.G.	Good	Fair	Poor
3000	2750	2200	1750	1000

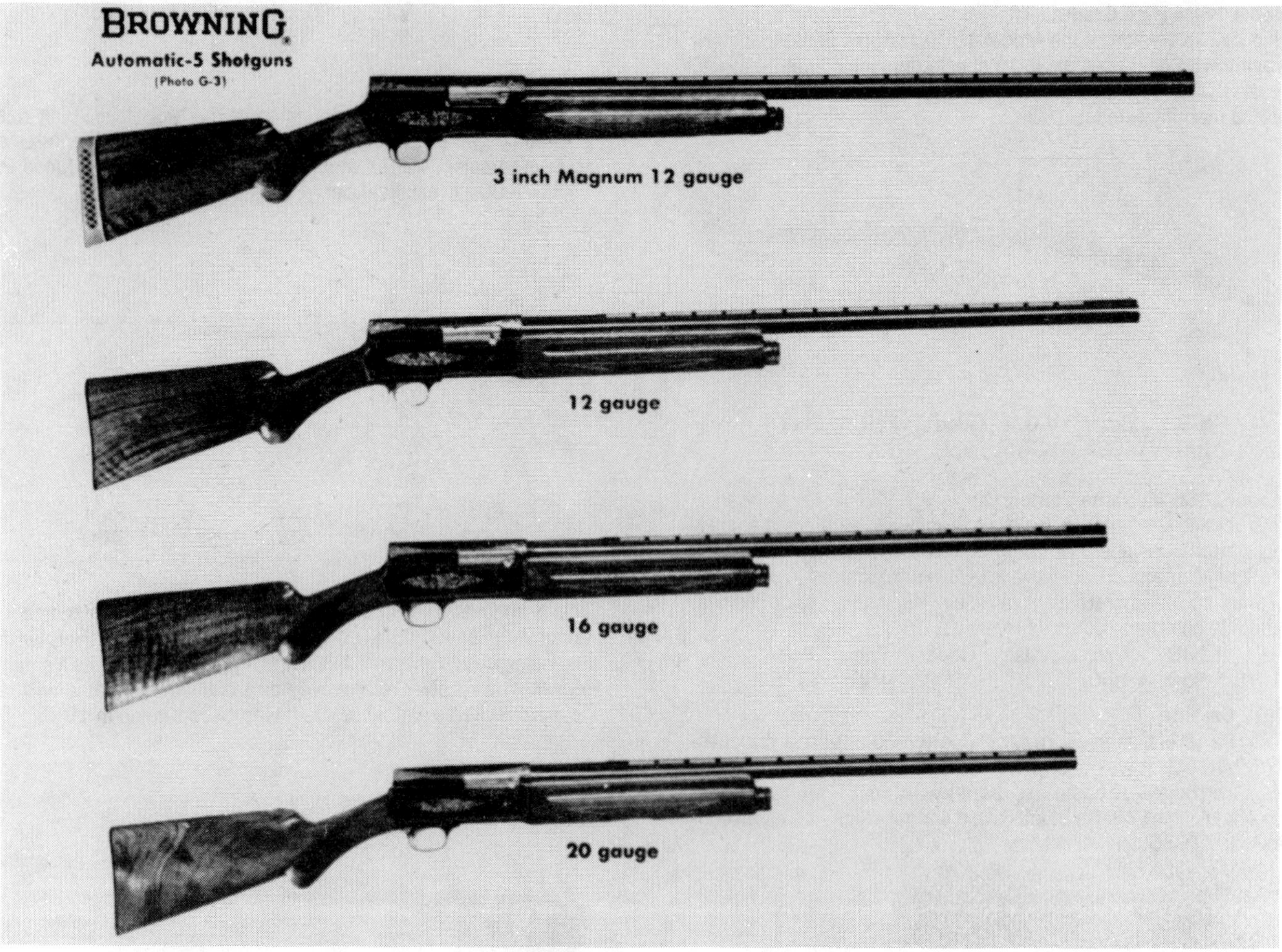

BROWNING
Automatic-5 Shotguns
(Photo G-3)
3 inch Magnum 12 gauge
12 gauge
16 gauge
20 gauge

Challenger
Medalist
Nomad
BROWNING
.22 Automatic Pistols
(Photo G-15)

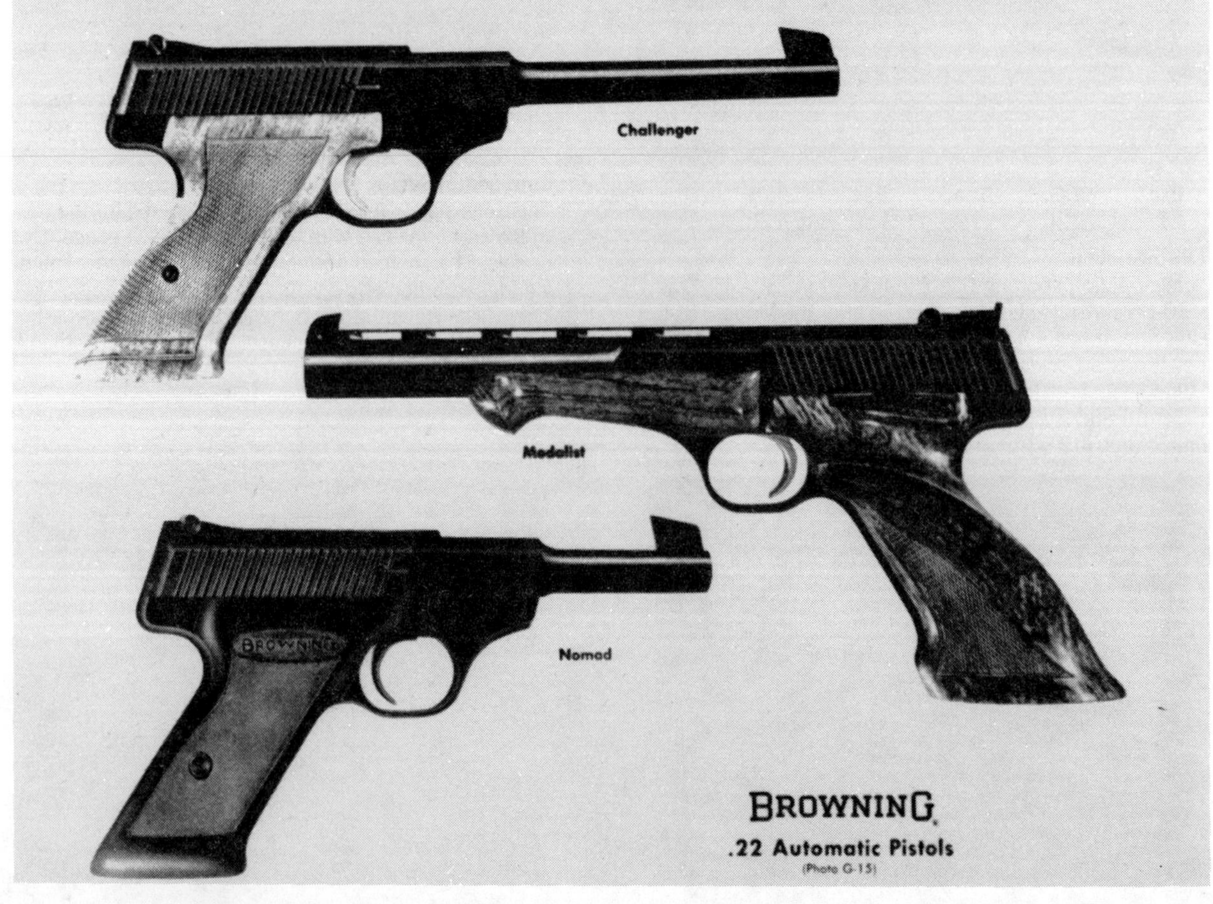

BROWNING
Automatic Pistols
(Photo G-8)

Top 9mm

Center .380 caliber

Bottom .25 caliber

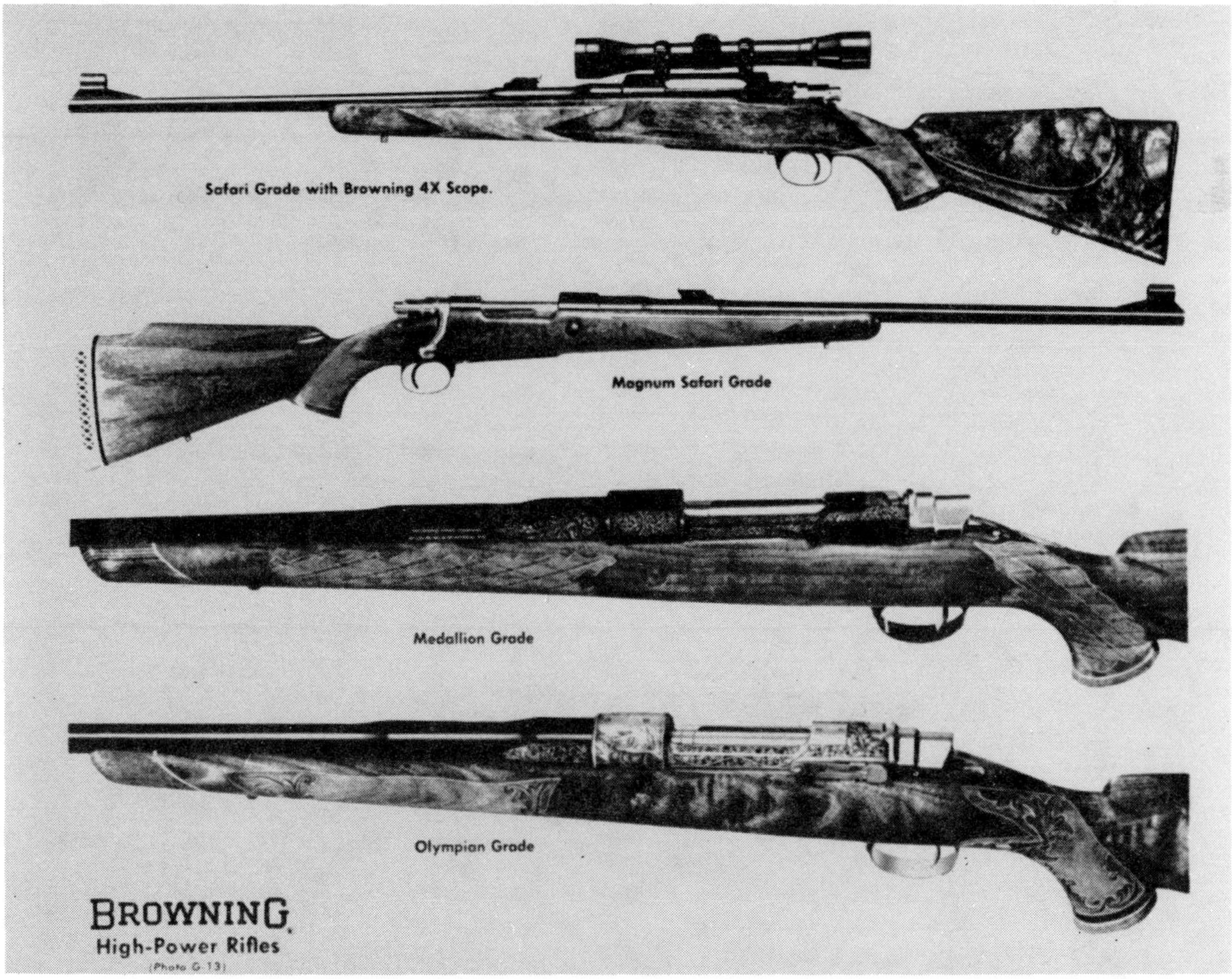

Safari Grade with Browning 4X Scope.

Magnum Safari Grade

Medallion Grade

Olympian Grade

BROWNING
High-Power Rifles
(Photo G-13)

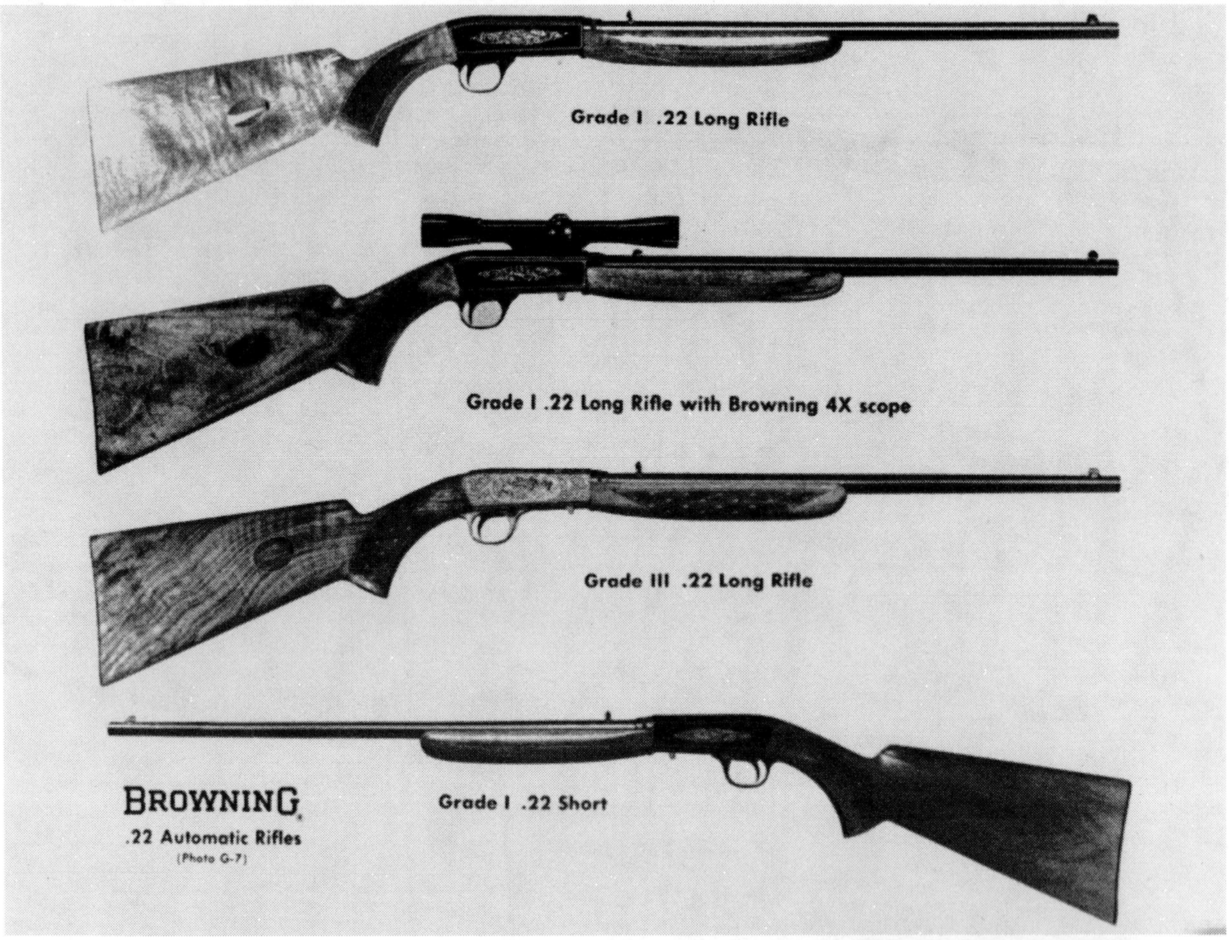

Grade I .22 Long Rifle

Grade I .22 Long Rifle with Browning 4X scope

Grade III .22 Long Rifle

Grade I .22 Short

BROWNING
.22 Automatic Rifles
(Photo G-7)

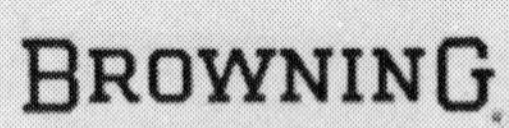

AUTOMATIC RIFLE

Grade II

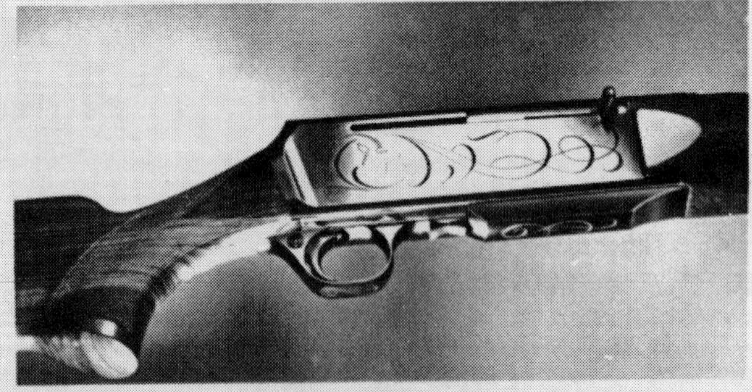

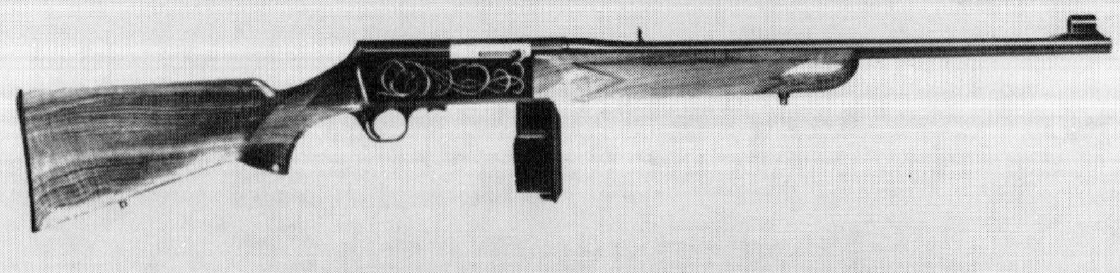

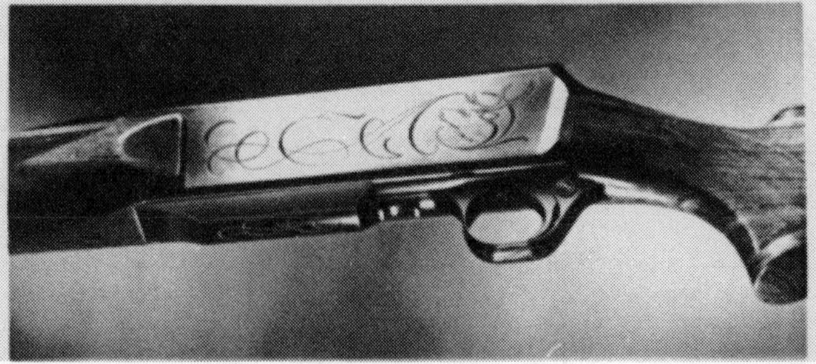

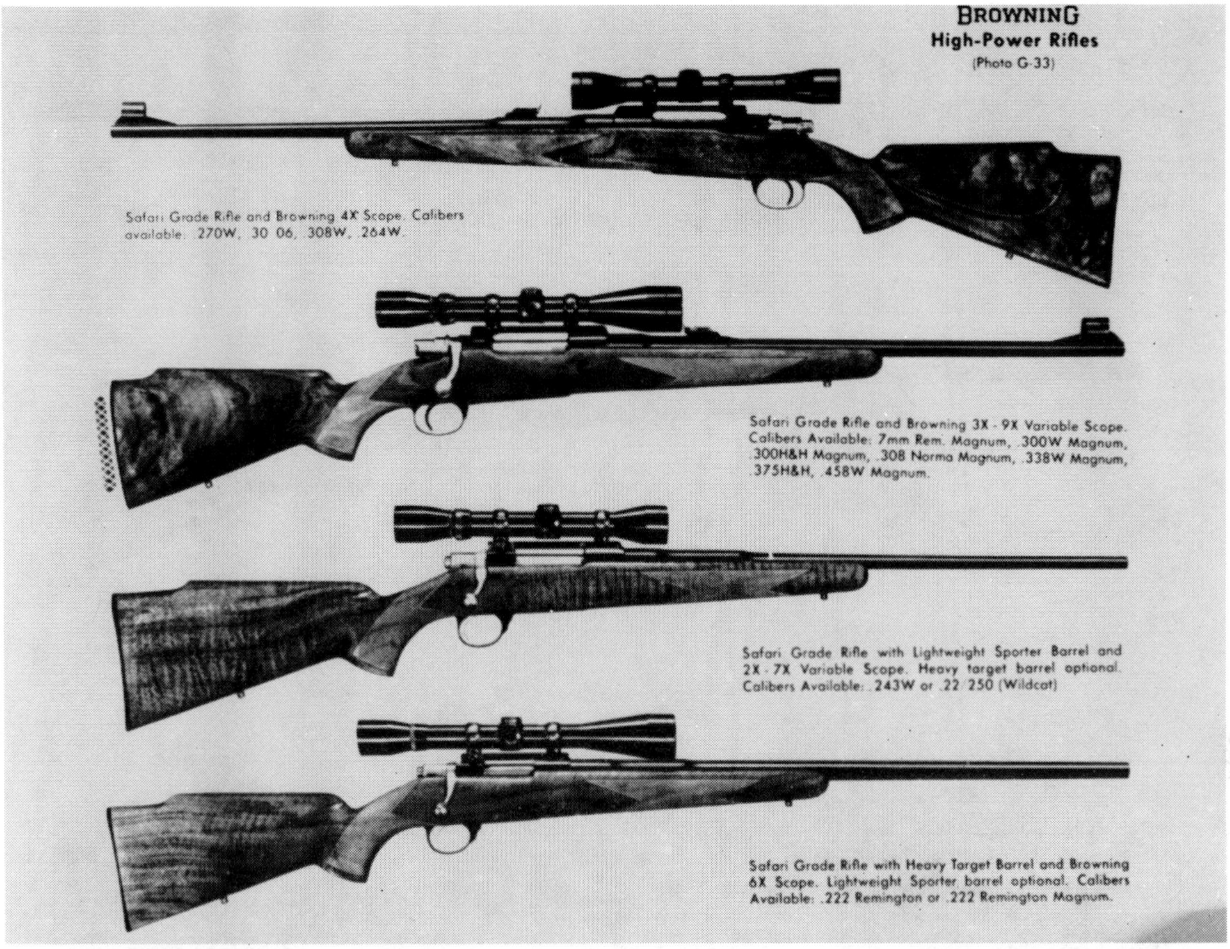

BROWNING
High-Power Rifles
(Photo G-33)

Safari Grade Rifle and Browning 4X Scope. Calibers available: .270W, .30 06, 308W, .264W.

Safari Grade Rifle and Browning 3X - 9X Variable Scope. Calibers Available: 7mm Rem. Magnum, .300W Magnum, .300H&H Magnum, .308 Norma Magnum, .338W Magnum, .375H&H, .458W Magnum.

Safari Grade Rifle with Lightweight Sporter Barrel and 2X - 7X Variable Scope. Heavy target barrel optional. Calibers Available: .243W or .22/250 (Wildcat)

Safari Grade Rifle with Heavy Target Barrel and Browning 6X Scope. Lightweight Sporter barrel optional. Calibers Available: .222 Remington or .222 Remington Magnum.

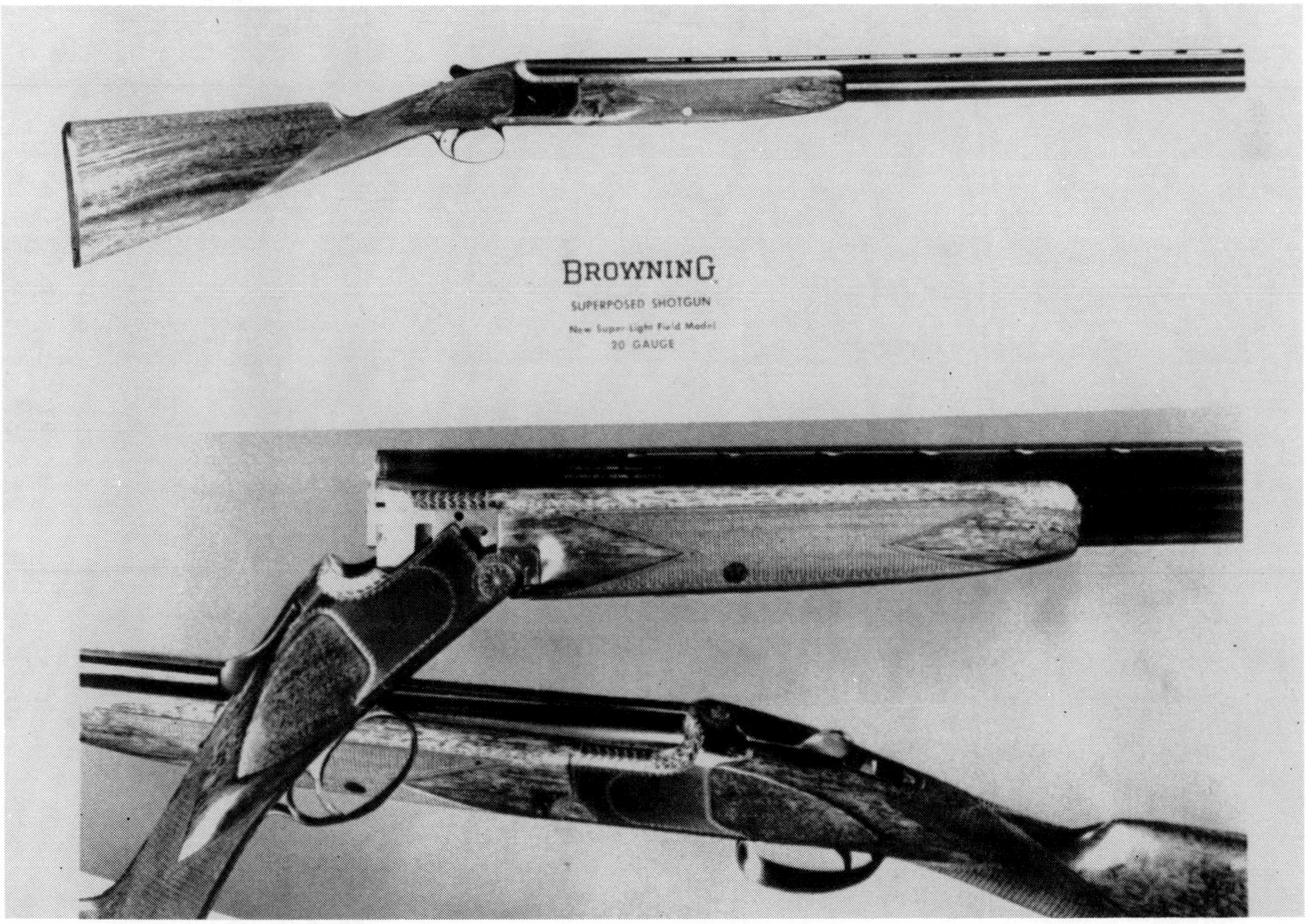

BROWNING
SUPERPOSED SHOTGUN
New Super-Light Field Model
20 GAUGE

T-2
T-1 with Browning 4X .22 Riflescope
BROWNING
T-BOLT .22 CALIBER BOLT ACTION RIFLE
An entirely new concept in bolt action design.

(Photo G-37)

BRUCE & DAVIS
Webster, Massachusetts

Double Barreled Pistol

A .36 caliber double-barrel percussion pistol with 3" to 6" round barrels. The barrel rib marked "Bruce & Davis". Blued with walnut grips. Manufactured during the 1840s.

Exc.	V.G.	Good	Fair	Poor
450	375	300	200	150

BRUCHET
Ste. Etienne, France

Model A Shotgun

A 12 or .410 bore sliding action shotgun with double triggers, and automatic ejectors. The barrel lengths and chokes are to customer specifications. Produced on a limited basis (50 per year) since 1982.

Base Price as Follows; Add 25 Percent Per Grade.

NIB	Exc.	V.G.	Good	Fair	Poor
1995	1800	1550	1250	1000	750

Model B

As above, with a finer finish and a spring assisted action opener. Imported since 1982.

NIB	Exc.	V.G.	Good	Fair	Poor
5800	5000	4250	3250	2500	1850

BRUFF, R.P.
New York, New York

Bruff Pocket Pistol

A .41 caliber single shot percussion pistol with 2.5" to 3" barrels The pistol is marked "R.P.Bruff NY" in an arch and "Cast Steel." German silver with a checkered walnut stock. Manufactured between 1861 and 1870.

Exc.	V.G.	Good	Fair	Poor
1500	1000	500	400	300

BUCO
Germany

Buco Gas Pistol

This odd firearm looks more like a telescope than a pistol. It is chambered for a 10.55mm gas cartridge and is a single shot. Overall it is approximately 5.5" long in its open or cocked position. The barrel is smooth bore and 3.75" in length. This pistol has no sights and no safety—one simply pulls the inner tube back much like extending a telescope, unscrews the end cap, inserts the round, and screws the cap back into place. When it is needed, a thumbnail is used to depress the sear and fire the pistol. They are marked on the end cap "Buco DRGM." No more information is available as to quantity or year of manufacture.

Exc.	V.G.	Good	Fair	Poor
300	250	200	150	100

BUDISCHOWSKY
Mt. Clemens, Michigan

TP-70

A .22 or .25 ACP caliber semi-automatic pistol with a 2.5" barrel, fixed sights and 6-shot magazine. Stainless-steel with plastic grips. Manufactured between 1973 and 1977.

.22 Rimfire Caliber

NIB	Exc.	V.G.	Good	Fair	Poor
475	425	350	300	225	150

.25 ACP Caliber

NIB	Exc.	V.G.	Good	Fair	Poor
400	325	250	200	175	125

Note: After 1977 Norton Arms produced this pistol; values are approximately 40 percent less than those made by Budischowsky.

BULLARD REPEATING ARMS CO.
Springfield, Massachusetts

Designed by James H. Bullard, the following rifles were manufactured in competition with those produced by the Whitney Arms Company and the Winchester Repeating Arms Company. Approximately 12,000 were made between 1886 and 1890.

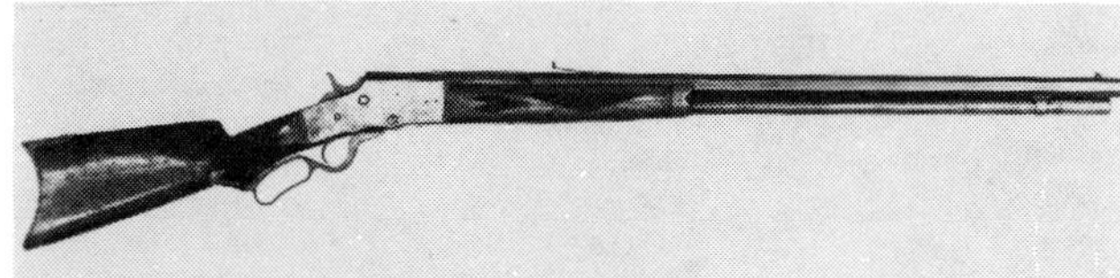

Courtesy Milwaukee Public Museum, Milwaukee, Wisconsin.

Small Frame

A .32-40 and .38-45 caliber lever-action rifle with a 26" octagonal barrel and either a half- or full-length magazine tube. Blued or casehardened with a walnut stock. The receiver is stamped "Bullard Repeating Arms Company/Springfield, Mass., U.S.A.Pat. Aug.16, 1881." The caliber is marked on top of the frame.

Exc.	V.G.	Good	Fair	Poor
2000	1500	750	600	475

Large Frame

A .40-75 through .45-85 caliber lever-action rifle with 28" octagonal barrel. Other features and markings as above. Can be custom ordered in .50-95 and .50-115.

Exc.	V.G.	Good	Fair	Poor
2500	1500	950	800	650

Carbine

A .45-70 caliber lever-action rifle with a 22" round barrel and a sliding dust cover on the receiver. Marking and finish as above.

Exc.	V.G.	Good	Fair	Poor
4500	3500	2750	2000	1500

Musket

A .45-70 caliber lever-action rifle with a 30" round barrel with a full-length stock secured by two barrel bands. There is a rod under the barrel, military sights, and the same sliding cover on the receiver as found on the Carbine. There have been examples noted without the manufacturer's markings.

Exc.	V.G.	Good	Fair	Poor
4000	3250	2750	2000	1500

BULLDOG SINGLE SHOT PISTOL
Connecticut Arms & Manufacturing Co.
Naubuc, Connecticut

Bulldog

A .44 or .50 caliber single shot spur trigger pistol with 4" or 6" barrels, and a pivoting breechblock that moves to the left for loading. Blued, casehardened and stamped "Connecticut Arms & Manf. Co. Naubuc Conn. Patented Oct. 25, 1864." There were only a few hundred manufactured, and the .50 caliber, 6" barrelled versions would be worth an additional 40 percent. Produced between 1866 and 1868.

Exc.	V.G.	Good	Fair	Poor
400	325	275	200	150

BURGESS GUN CO.

Buffalo, New York
ALSO SEE—Colt and Whitney

One of the most prolific 19th century designers was Andrew Burgess who established his own company in 1892. The Burgess Gun Company manufactured slide action shotguns and rifles operated by a unique pistol grip prior to their being purchased by the Winchester Repeating Arms Company in 1899. Arms based on Burgess' patents were manufactured by a variety of American gunmakers. Serial numbers for all Burgess shotguns begin at 1000.

12 Gauge Slide Action Shotgun

A 12 gauge slide action shotgun with a 28" or 30" barrel. Blued with a walnut stock. This model was available with 6 grades of engraving. The values listed below are for the standard, plain model.

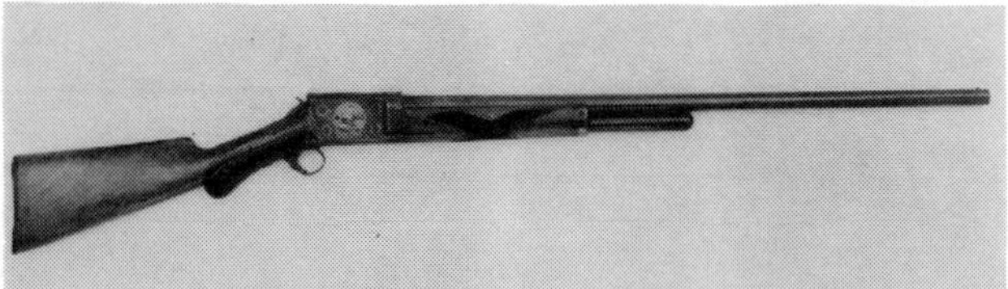

Burgess engraving grades (1-4)

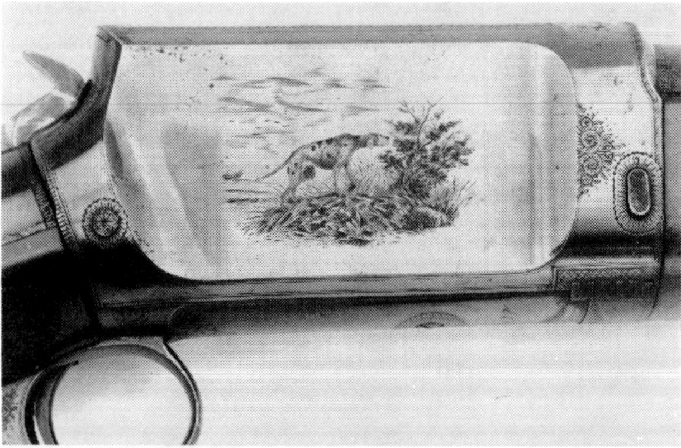

Exc.	V.G.	Good	Fair	Poor
1500	1250	750	250	175

Folding Shotgun

As above, with a 19.5" barrel which is hinged so that it may be folded back against the buttstock.

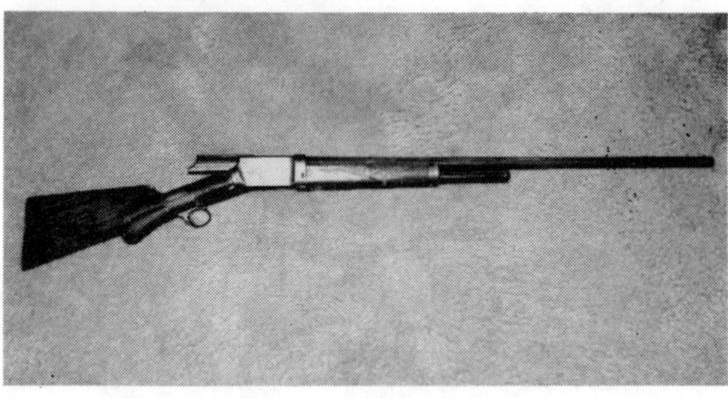

Exc.	V.G.	Good	Fair	Poor
2000	1500	750	400	300

Slide Action Rifle

An extremely rare rifle based upon the shotgun design described above. Manufactured in at least 3 calibers with varying barrel lengths. Blued with a walnut stock.

Exc.	V.G.	Good	Fair	Poor
3500	2750	1500	1250	900

BURGSMULLER, K.

Kreiensen, Germany

Burgo

The Rohm RG10 under another name. It is a poor quality, inexpensive, .38 caliber revolver. The examples marketed by Burgsmuller are so marked.

Exc.	V.G.	Good	Fair	Poor
125	100	75	50	25

Regent

The Regent is a .22 caliber revolver that resembles the Colt Police Positive in appearance. It is of a higher quality than the Burgo. The manufacturer is not known.

Exc.	V.G.	Good	Fair	Poor
150	125	100	75	50

BURNSIDE RIFLE CO.

Providence, Rhode Island
Bristol Firearms Co.
Bristol, Rhode Island

This is a very historically desirable firearm for Civil War collectors as the designer, Ambrose E. Burnside, was to become a well known Union general. The rifle, of which there were four distinct models, was used quite extensively in the Civil War.

This carbine was manufactured first by the Bristol Firearms Co., which made the entire production of the first model and also some of the second model. In 1862 the Burnside Firearms Co. was formed, and they produced the remainder of the second models and all of the third and fourth models. Production ceased entirely in 1865.

Burnside Carbine 1st Model

This model was produced by Bristol and was chambered for the .54 caliber. It is a breechloader that uses the percussion ignition system but features a cartidge of sorts made of copper, and a tape priming device that was located inside the frame. It has a 22" round barrel with no forend and a walnut stock with inspector's cartouche. The finish is blued and case-colored, and the frame is stamped "Burnside's/Patent/March 25th/1856." There were approximately 250 1st Models manufactured.

Exc.	V.G.	Good	Fair	Poor
4000	3500	3000	2000	1200

2nd Model

The 2nd Model features an improved breech-block opening mechanism located inside the triggerguard. The barrel is 21" long, and the other features are similar to the 1st Model. They are marked either "Bristol Firearm Co." or "Burnside Rifle Co./Providence-R.I." The barrel is marked "Cast Steel 1861," and some of the breech-block devices are marked "G.P.Foster Pat./April 10th 1860." There were approximately 1,500 2nd Models manufactured in 1861 and 1862.

Courtesy Milwaukee Public Museum, Milwaukee, Wisconsin.

Exc.	V.G.	Good	Fair	Poor
2500	2000	1500	1000	650

3rd Model

This model differs from the 2nd Model in that it has a forend with a barrel band and a slightly modified hammer. The markings are the same as the Burnside-manufactured 2nd Models. There were approximately 2,000 produced in 1862.

Exc.	V.G.	Good	Fair	Poor
1250	1000	800	600	450

4th Model

This model differs from the others in that it features a hinged breech that permits simpler loading of the oddshaped Burnside percussion cartridge. The frame is marked "Burnside's Patent/Model of 1864." The other features are similar to the 3rd Model. There were approximately 50,000 manufactured between 1862 and 1865.

Courtesy Milwaukee Public Museum, Milwaukee, Wisconsin.

Exc.	V.G.	Good	Fair	Poor
1200	950	750	550	400

BUSHMASTER FIREARMS INC.

North Windham, Maine

Bushmaster Pistol

A .223 caliber semi-automatic pistol with an 11.5" barrel and 30-shot magazine. Early models had alloy frames; later models, steel. Parkerized, and walnut stock. Manufactured since 1974. Price volatility requires individual appraisals.

Bushmaster Rifle

As above, with an 18.5" barrel and either a wood stock or a folding metal one. Price volatility requires individual appraisals.

BUTLER, WM. S.

Rocky Hill, Connecticut

Butler Single Shot Pistol

A .36 caliber single shot percussion pocket pistol with a 2.5" barrel and the frame and grip made in one piece. The frame marked "Wm. S. Butler's Patent/Patented Feb.3,1857."

Exc.	V.G.	Good	Fair	Poor
400	325	250	200	150

BUTTERFIELD, JESSE

Philadelphia, Pennsylvania

Butterfield Army Revolver

A .41 caliber revolver with a 7" octagonal barrel, an unfluted 5-shot cylinder and features a special priming device, a disk which was loaded in front of the triggerguard. A brass frame, blued with walnut grips. The frame is stamped "Butterfield's Patent Dec.11,1855/Phila." Approximately 650 manufactured in 1861 and 1862.

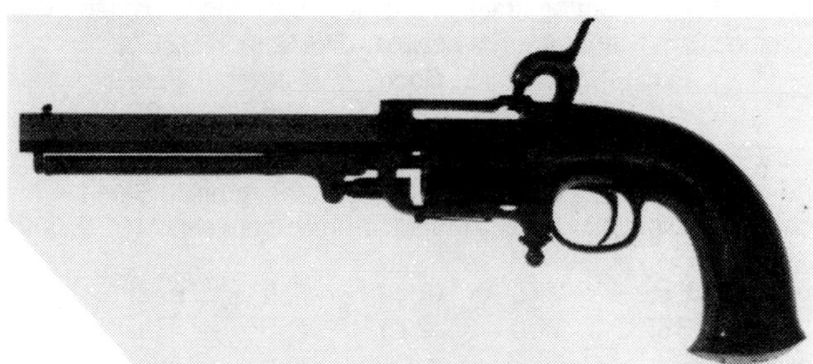

Courtesy Milwaukee Public Museum, Milwaukee, Wisconsin.

Exc.	V.G.	Good	Fair	Poor
2000	1800	1500	1250	900

Butterfield Pocket Pistol

A .41 caliber single shot percussion pistol with a 2" to 3.5" barrel. German silver with walnut stocks. The lock is marked "Butterfield's/Patent Dec 11,1855." Extremely rare. Manufactured in the 1850s.

Exc.	V.G.	Good	Fair	Poor
5000	4650	4000	3000	2500

CZ

(Ceska Zbrojovka)
Uhersky Brod, Czech Republic

Established by Karel Bubla and Alois Tomiska in 1919. This company later merged with Hubertus Engineering Company. In 1949 the company was nationalized.

Fox

A 6.35mm caliber semi-automatic pistol with a 2.5" barrel, tubular slide, a folding trigger and no triggerguard. Blued with plastic grips. Manufactured between 1919 and 1926.

Exc.	V.G.	Good	Fair	Poor
325	250	200	125	90

CZ 1922

As above with a conventional trigger and guard. Blued with checkered plastic grips. Manufactured between 1926 and 1936.

Exc.	V.G.	Good	Fair	Poor
350	300	225	150	100

CZ 1924

The first military pistol produced by CZ. It is a locked-breech pistol with a 3.5" rotating barrel chambered for the 9mm short cartridge, external hammer and a magazine safety. It features a rounded slide and is blued with a wrap-around walnut grip. The slide is marked, "Ceska Zbrojovka A.S. v Praze."

Exc.	V.G.	Good	Fair	Poor
400	350	275	175	100

A limited number of pistols have been noted marked, "CZ 1925" and "CZ 1926." There are various minor design changes on each model, and it is conjectured that they were prototypes that were manufactured on the road to the production of the less complicated, blowback-operated CZ 1927 pistol.

CZ 1927

A semi-automatic pistol chambered for the 7.65mm cartridge, marked the same as the CZ 1924, but the cocking grooves on the slide are cut vertically instead of sloped as on the earlier model. This model was blued with checkered, wrap-around, plastic grips. This version remained in production during the German occupation of Czechoslovakia between 1939 and 1945. Occupation pistols are marked, "Bohmische Waffenfabrik AG in Prag." After the War, these pistols continued in production until 1951. There were over 500,000 manufactured.

Nazi-Proofed—Add 50%.

Courtesy Orville Reichert.

Exc.	V.G.	Good	Fair	Poor
300	250	200	125	100

CZ 1936

A 6.35mm caliber semi-automatic pistol with 2.5" barrel, and double-action-only lockwork. Discontinued in 1940 because of wartime production.

Exc.	V.G.	Good	Fair	Poor
250	225	175	100	75

CZ 1938

This very odd pistol has been rated as one of the worst military-service pistols ever manufactured. It is chambered for the 9mm short cartridge and has a 4.65" barrel. Except for a few examples with a conventional sear and exposed hammer, it is double-action only and very difficult to fire accurately. It utilizes an 8-round, detachable box magazine; and the slide is hinged at the muzzle to pivot upward for ease of cleaning and disassembly. It is well made and well finished but is as large in size as most 9mm Parabellum pistols. Production began in 1938, and the Germans adopted it as the "Pistole Mod 39" on paper; but it is doubtful that any were actually used by the German army. It now appears that the P39(t), which is the Nazi designation, were all sent to Finland and a large number with "SA" (Finnish) markings have recently been surplused along with their holsters.

Exc.	V.G.	Good	Fair	Poor
400	350	300	225	150

CZ 45

This model is a small .25 caliber(6.35mm) pocket pistol which is double action only. It was produced and sold after WWII. It is a modified version of the CZ 36. Approximately 60,000 were built between 1945 and 1949.

Exc.	V.G.	Good	Fair	Poor
300	250	200	150	100

CZ 1950

This is a blowback-operated, semi-automatic, double action pistol chambered for the 7.65mm cartridge. It is patterned after the Walther Model PP with a few differences. The safety catch is located on the frame instead of the slide; and the triggerguard is not hinged, as on the Walther. It is dismantled by means of a catch on the side of the frame. Although intended to be a military pistol designed by the Kratochvil brothers, it proved to be underpowered and was adopted by the police. There were very few released on the commercial market.

Exc.	V.G.	Good	Fair	Poor
150	135	125	100	75

Model 1970

This model was an attempt to correct dependability problems with the Model 50. There is little difference to see externally between the two except for markings and the grip pattern. Production began during the 1960s and ended in 1983.

Exc.	V.G.	Good	Fair	Poor
400	350	300	225	175

CZ 1952 currently imported by CIA

Since the Czechoslovakian army was not happy with the underpowered CZ 1950 pistol, they began using Soviet weapons until 1952, when this model was designed. It was designed for a new cartridge known as the 7.62mm M48. It was similar to the Soviet cartridge but loaded to a higher velocity. This is a double-action, semi-automatic pistol with a 4.5" barrel. It has a locked breech that utilizes two roller cams. This was an excellent pistol that has been replaced by the Soviet Makarov, a pistol that is decidedly inferior to it.

Exc.	V.G.	Good	Fair	Poor
350	300	250	200	125

CURRENTLY IMPORTED CZ PISTOLS
Importer-Action Arms
Philadelphia, PA

CZ 75

Designed by the Koucky brothers in 1975, this model bears little resemblance to previous CZ pistols. Considered by many to be the best pistol ever to come from the Czech Republic. Chambered for the 9mm Parabellum cartridge it is copied in many countries. This pistol has a breech lock system utilizing a Browning style cam. The slide rides on the inside of the slide rails. Magazine capacity is 15 rounds, barrel length is 4.72", overall length is 8", and the empty pistol weighs 34.5 oz. Offered in black paint, matte or polished blue finish.

NIB	Exc.	V.G.	Good	Fair	Poor
375	325	250	200	150	100

CZ 75 Compact

Introduced in 1992 this is a compact version of the CZ 75. The barrel length is 3.9", the overall length is 7.3", and the weight is about 32 oz. Offered in black paint, matte or polished blue finish.

NIB	Exc.	V.G.	Good	Fair	Poor
375	325	250	200	150	100

CZ 85

This model is similar in appearance to the CZ 75 but offers some new features such as ambidextrous safety and slide stop levers, squared trigger guard, adjustable sight, and ribbed slide. Caliber ,magazine capacity, and weight are same as CZ 75.

NIB	Exc.	V.G.	Good	Fair	Poor
475	425	350	300	225	150

CZ 85-Combat

Similar to the CZ 85 but with the addition of adjustable sights, walnut grips, round hammer, and free dropping magazine.

NIB	Exc.	V.G.	Good	Fair	Poor
550	500	400	300	225	150

CZ 83

This is a fixed barrel .380 caliber pistol. It features a ambidextrous safety and magazine catch behind the trigger guard. the pistol is stripped bu means of a hinged trigger guard. Barrel length is 3.8", overall length is 6.8", and weight is about 23 oz.

NIB	Exc.	V.G.	Good	Fair	Poor
350	300	250	200	150	100

NOTE: In 1993 Action Arms has introduced Special Editions of the above pistols. This Special Edition consist of special finishes for currently imported CZ pistols. There are high polish blue, nickel, Chrome, Gold, and a combination of the above finishes. These Special Edition finishes may effect price and the buyer and seller should be aware of the initial extra cost which added between $100 and $250 to the cost of the pistol when new.

CABANAS, INDUSTRIAS S.A.

Aguilas, Mexico

This company manufactures a variety of bolt-action single shot rifles which utilize .22 caliber blanks to propel a .177 caliber pellet.

Mini-82 Youth

NIB	Exc.	V.G.	Good	Fair	Poor
75	65	50	40	30	20

R-83 Larger Youth

NIB	Exc.	V.G.	Good	Fair	Poor
85	75	60	50	40	30

Safari

NIB	Exc.	V.G.	Good	Fair	Poor
100	90	75	50	40	30

Varmint

NIB	Exc.	V.G.	Good	Fair	Poor
125	110	90	75	50	35

Espronceda IV

NIB	Exc.	V.G.	Good	Fair	Poor
125	110	90	75	50	35

Leyre

NIB	Exc.	V.G.	Good	Fair	Poor
140	125	100	85	65	50

Master

NIB	Exc.	V.G.	Good	Fair	Poor
150	130	110	100	75	60

CABELAS, INC.

Sidney, Nebraska

AYA Grade II Custom

A 12, 16, and 20 gauge boxlock shotgun in various barrel lengths and chokes, a single selective trigger, and automatic ejectors. Engraved with a hand-checkered walnut stock. This model is no longer available.

Exc.	V.G.	Good	Fair	Poor
1250	1175	950	700	575

Hemingway Model

A 12 or 20 gauge boxlock shotgun with 28" barrels, various chokes, a single selective trigger and automatic ejectors. Engraved with a hand-checkered walnut stock.

NIB	Exc.	V.G.	Good	Fair	Poor
975	900	750	600	525	450

CALICO

SEE—American Industries, Inc.
Cleveland, Ohio

CAMEX-BLASER USA, INC.

SEE—Blaser Jagwaffen
Ft. Worth, Texas

CAMPO GIRO

Eibar, Spain

Esperanza y Unceta

Model 1904

Designed by Lt. Col. Venancio Aguirre. This pistol was produced in very limited numbers. Prospective purchasers are advised to secure a qualified appraisal prior to acquisition.

Exc.	V.G.	Good	Fair	Poor
1250	1000	800	600	450

Model 1910

Similar to the above, in 9mm Largo. Tested but not adopted by the Spanish Army.

Exc.	V.G.	Good	Fair	Poor
1000	800	650	500	450

Model 1913

An improved version of the above.

Courtesy James Rankin.

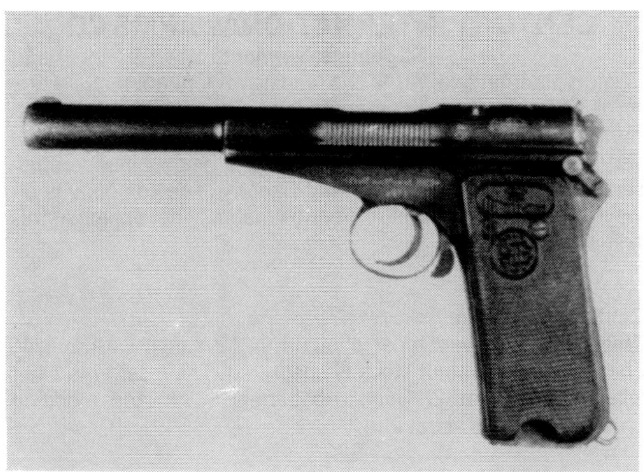

Courtesy James Rankin.

Exc.	V.G.	Good	Fair	Poor
900	750	650	500	450

Model 1913/16

An improved version of the above.

Courtesy James Rankin.

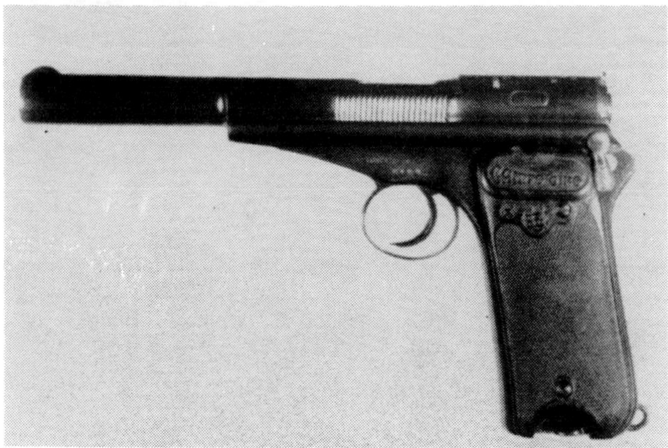

Courtesy James Rankin.

Exc.	V.G.	Good	Fair	Poor
500	450	375	300	200

CARCANO

Turin, Italy

Designed by Salvator Carcano, the Model 1891 was adopted as Italy's standard service rifle in 1892.

Fucile Modello 91

A 6.5mm caliber bolt-action rifle with a 31" barrel, 6-shot magazine, full-length stock, split bridge receiver, and a tangent rear sight with a wooden handguard and barrel bands retaining the stock.

Exc.	V.G.	Good	Fair	Poor
100	80	65	40	20

Cavalry Carbine

As above, with a shorter-barrelled, half-stocked and a folding bayonet.

Exc.	V.G.	Good	Fair	Poor
100	80	65	40	20

Fucile Modello 38

A 7.35 caliber bolt-action rifle.

Exc.	V.G.	Good	Fair	Poor
100	80	65	40	20

Cavalry Carbine

As above, with a shorter barrel, a folding bayonet and a fixed rear sight.

Exc.	V.G.	Good	Fair	Poor
125	100	80	60	40

CARD, S. W.

Unknown

Under Hammer Pistol

A .34 caliber single shot percussion pocket pistol with a 7.75" half octagonal barrel marked "S.W. Card" and "Cast Steel". Blued with walnut grips.

Exc.	V.G.	Good	Fair	Poor
400	325	275	200	125

CARLTON, M.

Haverhill, New Hampshire

Under Hammer Pistol

A .34 caliber percussion under hammer single shot pistol with a 3.5" to 7.75" half octagonal barrel marked "M.Carleton & Co." Browned with walnut grips. Active 1830s and 1840s.

Exc.	V.G.	Good	Fair	Poor
500	425	350	250	175

CASARTELLI, CARLO

Brescia, Italy

Importer—New England Arms Co.

Kittery Point, Maine

Sidelock Shotgun

Custom order sidelock shotgun that is available in any gauge, barrel length, choke, automatic ejectors and single selective trigger and choice of engraving style.

NIB	Exc.	V.G.	Good	Fair	Poor
15000	13500	10000	8250	6000	4000

Kenya Double Rifle

Custom order, full sidelock rifle that is available in all standard and magnum calibers. The customer may literally design this firearm if one desires and if one can afford it.

NIB	Exc.	V.G.	Good	Fair	Poor
30000	27000	22500	18000	13000	9000

Africa Model

A bolt-action rifle built on a square-bridge magnum Mauser action. It is chambered for the heavy magnum calibers and can be taken down for transport. The other features are on a custom order basis.

NIB	Exc.	V.G.	Good	Fair	Poor
8750	8000	7000	5750	4750	3750

Safari Model

Built on a standard Mauser bolt-action and is chambered for the non-magnum calibers.

NIB	Exc.	V.G.	Good	Fair	Poor
7000	6500	5500	4500	3250	2500

CASE WILLARD & CO.
New Hartford, Connecticut

Under Hammer Pistol
A .31 caliber single shot percussion pistol with a 3" half octagonal barrel marked "Case Willard & Co./New Hartford Conn." Blued, brass frame with walnut grips.

Exc.	V.G.	Good	Fair	Poor
450	375	300	225	150

CASPIAN ARMS, LTD.
Hardwick, Vermont

Government Model
Similar to the Colt 1911, a .45 ACP caliber semi-automatic pistol with interchangeable slides for 9mm and .38 Super available. This model features high profile sights, an adjustable trigger, carbon steel or stainless-steel and walnut grips. Manufactured since 1986.

NIB	Exc.	V.G.	Good	Fair	Poor
550	475	425	375	300	225

Model 110
A fully customized version of the Colt 1911, .45 ACP or .38 Super caliber semi-automatic pistol with all the custom features one could cram on the Government Model. Manufactured since 1988.

NIB	Exc.	V.G.	Good	Fair	Poor
900	825	700	600	475	400

Viet Nam Commemorative
Government Model engraved by J.J. Adams and nickle-plated. The walnut grips have a branch service medallion inlaid, and gold plating was available for an additional $350. There were 1,000 manufactured in 1986.

NIB	Exc.	V.G.	Good	Fair	Poor
1200	1000	800	600	475	400

CENTURY GUN CO.
Greenfield, Indiana

This was formerly a handmade revolver produced in Evansville, Indiana, and chambered for the .45-70 cartridge. This model was discontinued after only 524 were manufactured. They are now back in production as of 1986. The original guns are valued separately from the new production version.

Model 100 Revolver
A .30-30, .375 Winchester, .444 Marlin, .45-70, and .50-70 caliber revolver with barrel lengths from 6.5" to 15", 6-shot steel cylinder and a manganese bronze alloyed frame, a cross-bolt safety, adjustable sights, and walnut grips. A limited-production item, with only 600 produced since 1976. The .45-70 is considered the standard caliber, and all other calibers are custom-order only.

.45-70 Caliber

NIB	Exc.	V.G.	Good	Fair	Poor
750	700	600	500	400	325

All Other Calibers

NIB	Exc.	V.G.	Good	Fair	Poor
1600	1400	1200	1000	800	600

Original Evansville Model 100

NIB	Exc.	V.G.	Good	Fair	Poor
2500	2250	2000	1600	1250	950

CENTURY INTERNATIONAL ARMS CO.
St. Albans, Vermont

Century International Arms is a leading importer of military firearms primarily of foreign manufacture. These low cost firearms are excellent shooters and many have been restocked to make very satisfactory hunting rifles. The listing below offers a representative sample of imports from Century. The company is always providing new surplus firearms that may not appear in this edition.

Centurion Shotgun
This is a new Over/Under shotgun in 12 gauge with 2 3/4" chambers. The walnut stock is checkered. The receiver is blue. Offered in 26" or 28" vent rib barrels in full and modified chokes. Weight is about 7 lb.

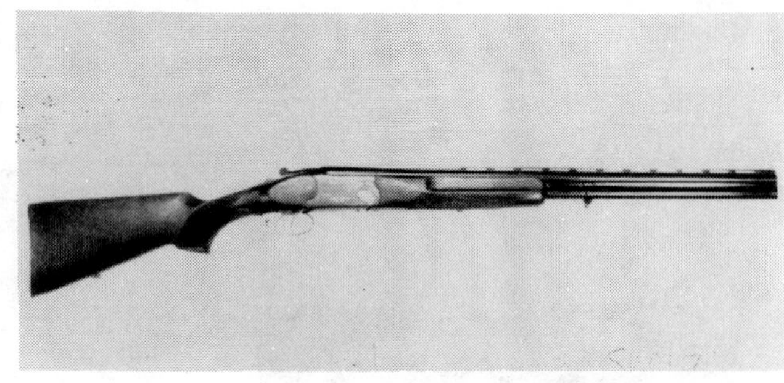

Exc.	V.G.	Good	Fair	Poor
280	225	200	175	125

Centurion 98 Sporter
This is a refinished and rebuilt on a surplus German Mauser 98 action with new commercial 22" barrel. No sights. A synthetic stock with recoil pad is standard. Chambered for .270 or .30-06. Weighs about 7 lb 13 oz.

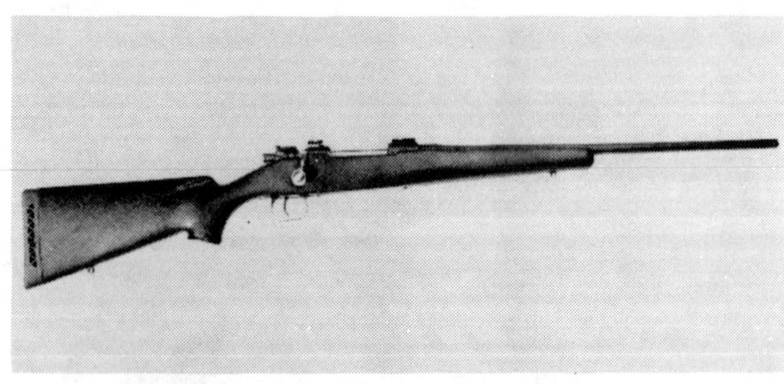

Exc.	V.G.	Good	Fair	Poor
230	200	175	150	100

Enfield Sporter No. 1 Mark III
This refinished rifle has a cut down Sporter style stock. Action and sights are original. Caliber is .303.

Exc.	V.G.	Good	Fair	Poor
120	80	60	50	40

Enfield Sporter No. 4 Mark I
Similar to above with cut down stock. Caliber .303.

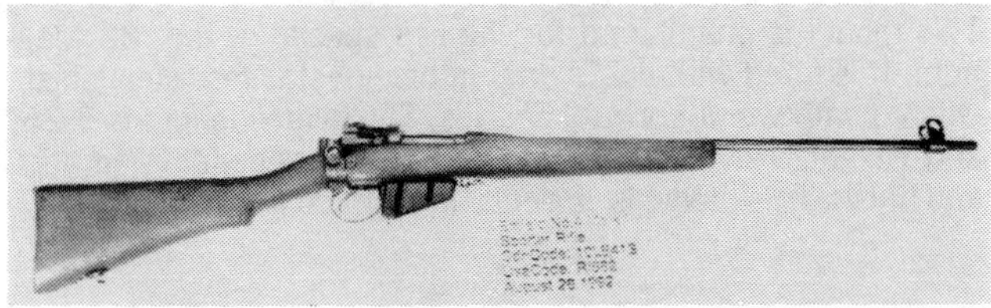

Exc.	V.G.	Good	Fair	Poor
120	80	60	50	40

With new Walnut Stock

Exc.	V.G.	Good	Fair	Poor
160	125	100	75	50

TOZ-17
An original Russian rifle chambered for the .22 Long Rifle. Has a 21" barrel and 5 round magazine. Checkered stock and iron sights. Weighs about 5.4 lb.

Exc.	V.G.	Good	Fair	Poor
120	80	60	50	40

TOZ-17-1
Same as above with hooded front sight and tangent rear sight. Receiver is grooved for scope mount.

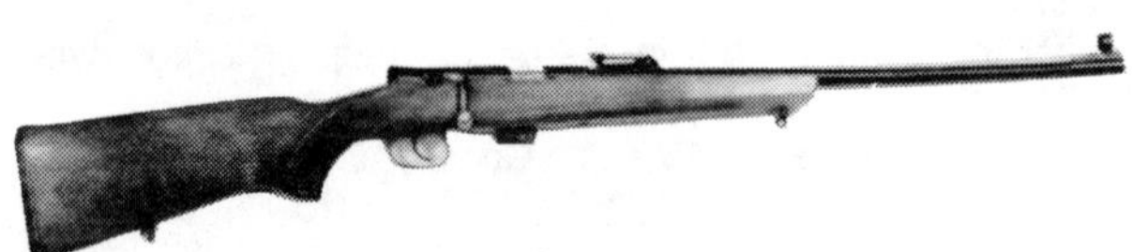

Exc.	V.G.	Good	Fair	Poor
80	65	50	40	35

Mexican Mauser Model 1910 Sporter
This rifle has been converted from a military rifle to a sporter by cutting down the stock. The metal is refinished and the barrel has been rebored and rechambered for the .30-06 cartridge. The box magazine holds 5 rounds. Barrel is 23" and rifle weighs about 8 lb.

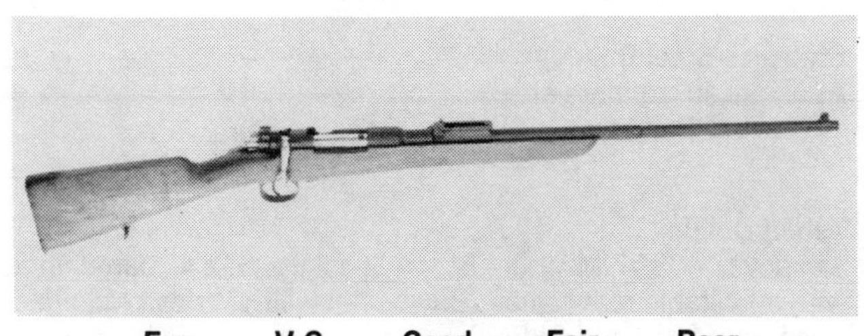

Exc.	V.G.	Good	Fair	Poor
175	140	125	100	75

FAL Sporter
This is a refinished FAL receiver and barrel installed in a synthetic thumbhole stock. The flash suppressor and bayonet lug have been removed. Barrel is 20.75" and weight is approximately 10 lb.

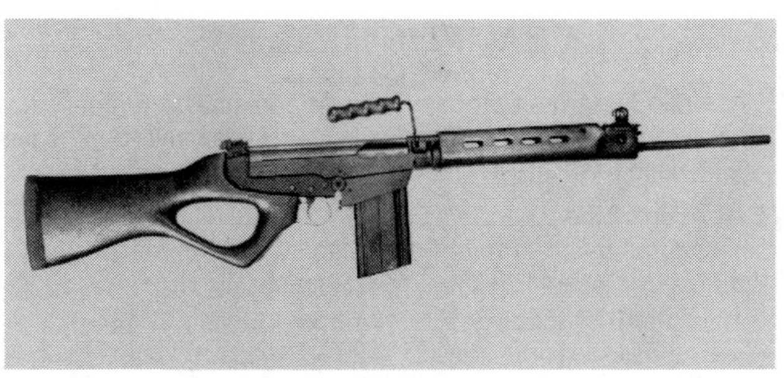

Exc.	V.G.	Good	Fair	Poor
500	350	300	250	150

CETME
Madrid, Spain

Cetme Autoloading Rifle
A .308 caliber semi-automatic rifle with a fluted chamber, a 17.74" barrel, an aperture rear sight and a 20-round detachable magazine. Black with a military-style wood stock. Price volatility requires individual appraisals.

CHAMELOT-DELVIGNE
Liege, Belgium

Model 1871 Belgian Troopers Revolver
A large, solid-frame weapon chambered for the 11mm centerfire cartridge.

Exc.	V.G.	Good	Fair	Poor
400	325	250	175	125

Model 1872 Swiss
This model, also known as the "Schmidt," had some modifications in the lockwork. It was chambered for the 12mm rimfire, 9mm rimfire, and the 10.4mm rimfire for the Swiss. The Italian army used it chambered for the 10.4 centerfire cartridge.

Exc.	V.G.	Good	Fair	Poor
800	625	550	400	300

Model 1873
The Netherlands used the Model 1873, chambered for the 9.4mm centerfire, as an officer's revolver. The French had it chambered in 11mm centerfire for the enlisted troopers.

Exc.	V.G.	Good	Fair	Poor
275	250	200	150	100

Model 1874
The Model 1874 was used by French officers and was chambered for 11mm centerfire.

Exc.	V.G.	Good	Fair	Poor
300	275	225	175	125

Model 1872/78 Swiss
This Model designation signifies a recall of the Swiss Schmidt version. The 10.4mm centerfire caliber was standardized, and all Model 1872 revolvers still in service were converted and remarked.

Exc.	V.G.	Good	Fair	Poor
475	425	350	275	225

Model 1879 Italian
The Italian army used the Model 1879 chambered for the 10.4mm centerfire as its officers' revolver.

Exc.	V.G.	Good	Fair	Poor
225	175	150	110	80

CHAMPLIN FIREARMS
Enid, Oklahoma

Champlin Firearms Company manufactures custom order rifles built to the customer's specifications. Prospective purchasers are advised to secure a qualified appraisal prior to acquisition.

Bolt Action Rifle

These arms featured round or octagonal barrels, set triggers, a variety of sights and well figured walnut stocks.

NIB	Exc.	V.G.	Good	Fair	Poor
5500	4500	3500	2900	2200	1500

CHAPMAN C.
Unknown

Chapman Rifle

This very rare Confederate weapon was patterned after the U.S. Model 1841. It is chambered for .58 caliber and utilizes the percussion ignition system. The round barrel is 33" long, with a full-length stock and two barrel bands. The mountings are brass, and the stock is walnut. "C.Chapman" was stamped on the lock. This weapon was manufactured somewhere in the Confederate States of America during the Civil War, but little else is known.

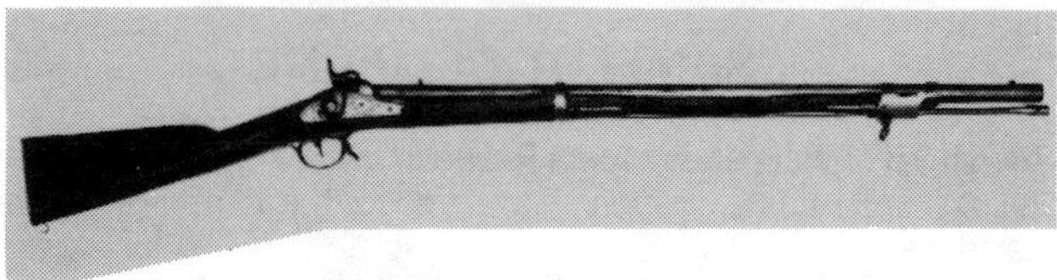

Courtesy Milwaukee Public Museum, Milwaukee, Wisconsin.

Exc.	V.G.	Good	Fair	Poor
6000	5000	4000	2500	1750

CHAPMAN, G. & J.
Philadelphia, Pennsylvania

Chapman Pocket Revolver

A .32 caliber revolver with a 4" round barrel and 7 shot cylinder. The frame is made of brass while the barrel and cylinder are of steel. The barrel is marked "G.& J. Chapman/Philada/Patent Applied For/1861." Manufactured during the 1860's.

Exc.	V.G.	Good	Fair	Poor
600	525	450	325	250

CHAPIUS
France

RG Progress

A 12, 16, or 20 gauge boxlock shotgun. Most options are available on order.

NIB	Exc.	V.G.	Good	Fair	Poor
2500	2250	2000	1800	1250	900

RG Express Model 89

A 7 X 65R, 8 X 57 JRS, 9.3 X 74R, and .375 Holland & Holland caliber sidelock, double-barrelled shotgun. The other features are at the customer's order.

NIB	Exc.	V.G.	Good	Fair	Poor
6500	5750	4800	4000	3250	2500

CHARLEVILLE
("Manufre Royle de Charleville")
SEE—French Military Firearms)

CHARTER ARMS, CORP.
Ansonia, CT

Police Undercovers

This model is chambered for the .38 special or the .32 Magnum. It is fitted with a 2" barrel in blue or stainless steel finish. Offered with walnut or rubber grips. The overall length is 6.25" and weight is between 16 oz. and 19 oz. depending on grips and finish. This model is currently in production.

NIB	Exc.	V.G.	Good	Fair	Poor
225	200	175	150	100	75

Undercover Stainless-Steel

As above, in stainless-steel.

NIB	Exc.	V.G.	Good	Fair	Poor
275	250	225	175	125	100

Undercoverette

As above, with a thinner grip and in .32 S&W.

Exc.	V.G.	Good	Fair	Poor
175	150	125	100	75

Pathfinder

Similar to the above, but in .22 or .22 magnum caliber with a 2", 3" or 6" barrel with adjustable sights.

NIB	Exc.	V.G.	Good	Fair	Poor
225	200	175	150	100	75

Pathfinder Stainless-Steel

As above, in stainless-steel.

NIB	Exc.	V.G.	Good	Fair	Poor
290	275	200	175	125	100

Bulldog

Similar to the Undercover model, but in .44 Special caliber with a 2.5" or 3" barrel and 5-shot cylinder.

NIB	Exc.	V.G.	Good	Fair	Poor
235	200	175	150	125	100

Stainless-Steel Bulldog

As above, in stainless-steel.

NIB	Exc.	V.G.	Good	Fair	Poor
285	250	225	175	150	110

Target Bulldog

As above, in .357 Magnum or .44 Special with a 4" barrel fitted with adjustable rear sights. Blued with walnut grips. Manufactured from 1986 to 1988.

NIB	Exc.	V.G.	Good	Fair	Poor
200	185	160	145	110	80

Bulldog Pug

Chambered for the .44 Special cartridge it is fitted with a 2.5" barrel. Available with walnut or Neoprene grips in blue or stainless steel finish with choice of spur or pocket hammer the cylinder holds 5 rounds. Overall length is 7" and weight is between 20 oz. and 25 oz. depending on grip and finish. This model is currently in production.

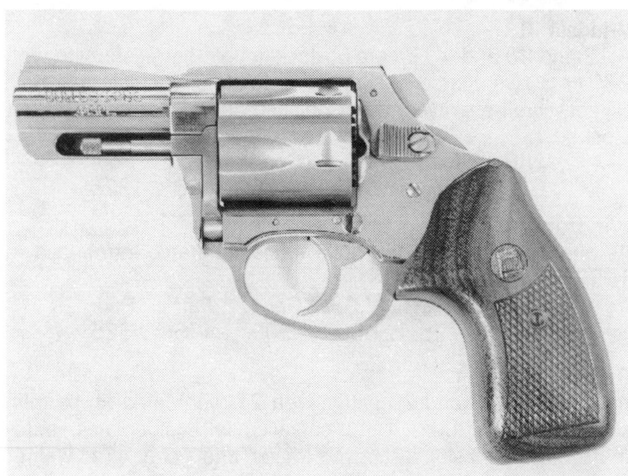

NIB	Exc.	V.G.	Good	Fair	Poor
250	200	175	150	100	75

Stainless-Steel Bulldog Pug

As above, in stainless-steel.

NIB	Exc.	V.G.	Good	Fair	Poor
300	250	225	175	150	125

Bulldog Tracker

As above, with a 2.5", 4" or 6" barrel in .357 Magnum only.

NIB	Exc.	V.G.	Good	Fair	Poor
250	225	200	165	140	110

Police Bulldog

As above, in .32 H&R Magnum, .38 Special or .44 Special with a 3.5" or 4" barrel.

NIB	Exc.	V.G.	Good	Fair	Poor
235	200	175	150	125	100

Stainless-Steel Police Bulldog

As above, in stainless-steel and available also in .357 Magnum.

NIB	Exc.	V.G.	Good	Fair	Poor
285	250	210	175	145	110

Off Duty

Chambered for the .38 Special or .22 Long Rifle this revolver is fitted with a 2" barrel. Offered with either walnut or rubber grips in blue or stainless steel finish with choice of spur or pocket hammer. Weight of the .38 special version is between 17 oz. and 23 oz. depending on grip and finish. The .22 LR version weighs between 19 oz. and 22 oz. The overall length is 4.75". This model is currently in production. A nickel finish with rubber grips is also offered.

NIB	Exc.	V.G.	Good	Fair	Poor
185	150	125	100	75	60

Pit Bull

A 9mm Federal, .38 Special or .357 Magnum caliber double-action revolver with a 2.5", 3.5" or 4" barrel. Blued with rubber grips.

NIB	Exc.	V.G.	Good	Fair	Poor
285	250	200	175	125	90

Explorer II Pistol

A .22 caliber semi-automatic pistol with 6", 8" or 10" barrels. Available with a camo, black, silver or gold finish and plastic grips. Discontinued in 1986.

NIB	Exc.	V.G.	Good	Fair	Poor
110	95	75	65	45	25

Model 40

A .22 caliber double-action semi-automatic pistol with a 3.5" barrel and 8-shot magazine. Stainless-steel with plastic grips. Manufactured from 1984 to 1986.

Exc.	V.G.	Good	Fair	Poor
250	225	200	150	100

Model 79K

A .32 or .380 caliber double-action semi-automatic pistol with a 3.5" barrel and 7-shot magazine. Stainless-steel with plastic grips. Manufactured from 1986 to 1988.

Exc.	V.G.	Good	Fair	Poor
325	300	250	180	125

Model 42T

A .22 caliber semi-automatic pistol with a 6" barrel and adjustable sights. Blued with walnut grips. Manufactured in 1984 and 1985.

NIB	Exc.	V.G.	Good	Fair	Poor
500	450	400	325	275	200

AR - 7 Explorer Rifle

A .22 caliber semi-automatic rifle with a 16" barrel, 8-shot magazine and hollow plastic stock which can house the barrel when detached.

NIB	Exc.	V.G.	Good	Fair	Poor
150	125	100	80	60	40

CHASSEPOT
French Military

MLE 1866

An 11mm caliber bolt-action rifle with a 32" barrel, a full-length walnut stock held on by two barrel bands, a cleaning rod mounted under the barrel and a bayonet lug that allows the attaching of a brass-handled, saber-type bayonet. White with a walnut stock.

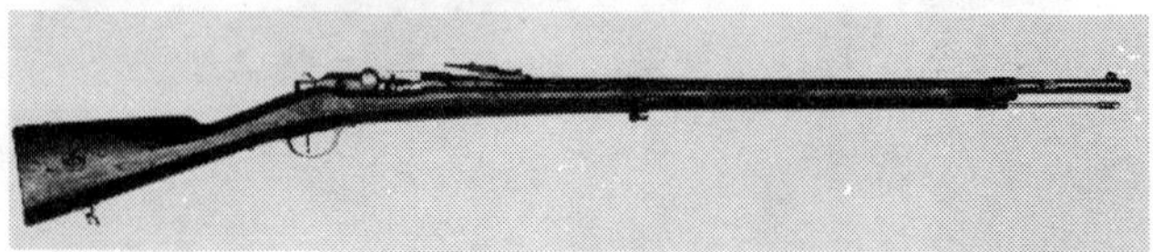

Courtesy Milwaukee Public Museum, Milwaukee, Wisconsin.

Exc.	V.G.	Good	Fair	Poor
275	225	175	125	100

CHICAGO F. A. CO.
Chicago, Illinois

Protector Palm Pistol

A .32 caliber radial cylinder revolver designed to fit in the palm of the hand and to be operated by a hinged lever mounted to the rear of the circular frame. The sideplates are marked "Chicago Firearms Co., Chicago,Ill." and "The Protector". Blued with hard rubber grip panels or nickle-plated with pearl grip panels. Manufactured by the Ames Manufacturing Company.

Standard Model Nickle-Plated/Black Grips

Exc.	V.G.	Good	Fair	Poor
800	600	450	350	250

Blued Finish—Add 30%.
Pearl Grips—Add 15%.

CHIPMUNK, INC.
Medford, Oregon

Chipmunk Single Shot Rifle

A .22 or the .22 rimfire magnum caliber bolt-action rifle with 16.25" barrel, and open sights.

NIB	Exc.	V.G.	Good	Fair	Poor
130	110	100	80	60	40

Deluxe Chipmunk

As above, with a hand-checkered walnut stock.

NIB	Exc.	V.G.	Good	Fair	Poor
180	160	135	100	80	50

Silhouette Pistol

A .22 caliber bolt-action pistol with a 14.5" barrel, open sights and rear pistol-grip walnut stock.

NIB	Exc.	V.G.	Good	Fair	Poor
150	125	100	80	60	40

CHURCHILL
Importer—Ellet Bros.
Chapin, South Carolina

Windsor I

A 10, 12, 16, 20, 28 and .410 bore Anson & Deeley double barrel boxlock shotgun with barrel lengths from 23" through 32", various choke combinations, double triggers and extractors. Scroll-engraved, silver-finished, with checkered walnut pistol grip and forend.

NIB	Exc.	V.G.	Good	Fair	Poor
650	600	500	400	300	200

Windsor II

As above, in 10, 12, and 20 gauge only with automatic ejectors. Not imported after 1987.

Exc.	V.G.	Good	Fair	Poor
600	550	450	350	250

Windsor VI

As above with sidelocks. Chambered for 12 and 20 gauge only with automatic ejectors. Not imported after 1987.

Exc.	V.G.	Good	Fair	Poor
800	750	650	500	350

Royal

A 12, 20, 28 and .410 bore boxlock double-barrel shotgun with various barrel lengths and chokes, double triggers and extractors. Casehardened with checkered walnut stock. Introduced in 1988.

NIB	Exc.	V.G.	Good	Fair	Poor
550	500	425	350	275	200

Over/Unders

Monarch

A 12, 20, 28 or .410 bore Over/Under shotgun with a boxlock action, 25", 26", or 28" ventilated-rib barrels, either double or a single selective trigger, extractors, and a checkered walnut stock.

NIB	Exc.	V.G.	Good	Fair	Poor
530	475	425	375	300	225

Windsor III

A 12 and 20 and .410 bore boxlock double-barrel shotgun with 27" or 30 ventilated-rib barrels, extractors, a single selective trigger, scroll-engraved, silver finished and a checkered walnut stock.

NIB	Exc.	V.G.	Good	Fair	Poor
625	575	525	475	400	325

Windsor IV

As above, with screw-in choke tubes standard. Introduced in 1989.

NIB	Exc.	V.G.	Good	Fair	Poor
850	775	650	500	425	325

Regent

As above, in 12 and 20 gauge with 27" ventilated-rib barrels, screw-in choke tubes, scroll-engraved false sideplates, automatic ejectors, a single selective trigger, and a checkered walnut stock. Not imported after 1986.

Exc.	V.G.	Good	Fair	Poor
750	650	550	450	350

Regent II

As above with finer overall finishing.

NIB	Exc.	V.G.	Good	Fair	Poor
1100	1000	850	750	500	375

Regent Shotgun Rifle Combination

A .222, .223, .243, .270, .308, or .30-06 caliber/12 gauge Over/Under rifle/shotgun with a 25" ventilated-rib, automatic ejectors and single selective trigger. Silver finished, scroll-engraved with a checkered walnut stock.

NIB	Exc.	V.G.	Good	Fair	Poor
925	825	725	600	450	400

Windsor Grade Semi-Automatic

A 12 gauge semi-automatic shotgun with 26", 28", or 30" ventilated-rib barrels and screw-in choke tubes. An etched and anodized alloy receiver with a checkered walnut stock.

NIB	Exc.	V.G.	Good	Fair	Poor
425	375	325	275	225	175

Windsor Grade Slide Action
A 12 gauge slide action shotgun with a 26" through 30" ventilated-rib barrel, various chokes, double slide rails, and an anodized alloy receiver. Checkered walnut stock. Discontinued in 1986.

Exc.	V.G.	Good	Fair	Poor
400	375	300	250	175

Rifles
Highlander
A .25-06 through .300 Winchester Magnum caliber bolt-action rifle with a 22" barrel, with or without sights, a 3-shot magazine, and a checkered walnut stock.

NIB	Exc.	V.G.	Good	Fair	Poor
460	420	375	300	250	200

Regent
As above, with a with Monte Carlo-style comb and cheekpiece. Discontinued in 1988.

Exc.	V.G.	Good	Fair	Poor
550	500	425	350	275

CHURCHILL, E. J. LTD.
London, England

One of One Thousand Rifle
A .270 to .458 Magnum caliber bolt-action rifle with 24" barrel and a select French walnut stock with a trap pistol-grip cap and recoil pad. Only 100 produced for the 20th anniversary of Interarms in 1973.

Exc.	V.G.	Good	Fair	Poor
15000	12500	10000	7000	5500

Premier Over/Under Shotgun
A 12, 16, and 20 gauge sidelock Over/Under shotgun with barrel lengths from 25" through 32", any choke combination, automatic ejectors and single selective triggers. Engraved with walnut stock.

Exc.	V.G.	Good	Fair	Poor
17500	15000	12500	8000	5000

Premier Side x Side
As above, in the side-by-side configuration. Available in all gauges and as a double rifle in most popular calibers at a higher cost.
Double Rifle—Add 40%.

Exc.	V.G.	Good	Fair	Poor
17500	15000	12500	8000	5000

Imperial
The second quality side x side made by this company; and made-to-order available in all gauges, barrel lengths, and chokes. It was also made as a double rifle in most calibers at extra cost.
Double Rifle—Add 40%.

Exc.	V.G.	Good	Fair	Poor
13000	11000	9000	6500	4000

Field Model
The third quality sidelock, side x side shotgun available in 12 gauge only, with all other features available on order.

Exc.	V.G.	Good	Fair	Poor
9000	8000	6000	4500	3000

Hercules
The best quality boxlock side x side. Available in any gauge and barrel length. All other options were available on request. There were some produced as small caliber double rifles.
Double Rifle—Add 40%.

Exc.	V.G.	Good	Fair	Poor
9000	8000	6000	4500	3000

Utility Model
The 2nd quality boxlock—available with custom features similar to the Hercules.

Exc.	V.G.	Good	Fair	Poor
6000	5000	3500	2500	2000

Crown
The third quality boxlock and was available with many custom features.

Exc.	V.G.	Good	Fair	Poor
4000	3000	2500	1750	1200

CHYLEWSKI, WITOLD
Austria

A .635mm caliber semi-automatic pistol, marked "Brevete Chylewski" and bears the name Neuhausen on the left side of the pistol. Approximately 1,000 were made between 1910 and 1918.

Exc.	V.G.	Good	Fair	Poor
850	750	675	500	375

CIMARRON F. A. MFG. CO.
SEE—Aldo Uberti

CLAPP, HOFFMAN & CO.
CLAPP, GATES & CO. RIFLES.
Alamance, North Carolina

Clapp, Hoffman & Co. and its successor, Clapp, Gates & Co., both of Alamance (Guilford County), North Carolina, entered into several contracts with the state of North Carolina for the delivery of rifles. These contracts included an escalator clause which allowed the contractors to charge costs plus a percentage. Under their contracts, Clapp, Gates & Co. delivered 1,078 rifles in four varieties, before the state bought out the balance of the contract in 1864 due to the exorbitant prices caused by inflation.

Overall length- Types I, II, & III- 51-1/4" to 52", Type IV- varies between 46-1/2" and 51"; barrel length- Types I, II, & III- 35-1/4" to 36", Type IV- varies between 31-1/4" and 35-7/8"; caliber- Types I, II, & III- .50; Type IV- .577. Markings: none. Despite the absence of makers marks, the Clapp, Gates & Co. products are readily distinguished by their part-round, part-octagonal (octagonal section on Types I to III, about 4" long, 4-3/4" to 5-1/2" on Type IV rifles) barrels having only a slightly raised bolster projecting from the upper right quarter. This small bolster accommodates the boxlock that distinguished the first 100 rifles produced. This gave way to a standard percussion lock on subsequent production, which required that the hammer bend sharply to the left to strike the cone. Type I and Type II rifles were adapted to a "footprint" saber bayonet lug on the right side of the barrel; Types III and IV also had a saber bayonet lug on the right side of the barrel but of the standard pattern. Types III and IV are distinguished by their caliber, the former being .50, the latter .577. Prices reflect Type II through IV production; Type I (while extant) has never been offered for sale and would presumably bring a significantly higher premium.

Exc.	V.G.	Good	Fair	Poor
11000	9500	8250	5500	4000

CLARK, F. H.
Memphis, Tennessee

Pocket Pistol
A .41 caliber single shot percussion pistol with a 3.5" to 5" barrel, German silver mounts and end cap, and the barrel is stamped "F.H.Clark & Co./Memphis." Manufactured in the 1850s and 1860s.

Exc.	V.G.	Good	Fair	Poor
1250	1100	950	750	500

CLASSIC DOUBLES
Tochigi City, Japan
Importer—Classic Doubles International
St. Louis, Missouri

Importer of the Japanese shotgun formerly imported by Winchester as the Model 101 and Model 23. These Models were discontinued by Winchester in 1987.

Model 201 Classic
A 12 or 20 gauge boxlock double-barrel shotgun with 26" ventilated-rib barrels, screw-in choke tubes single selective trigger and automatic ejectors. Blued with checkered walnut stock and beavertail forearm.

NIB	Exc.	V.G.	Good	Fair	Poor
2200	1950	1700	1500	1250	900

Model 201 Small Bore Set
As above, with a smaller receiver and two sets of barrels chambered for 28 gauge and .410. The barrels are 28" in length.

NIB	Exc.	V.G.	Good	Fair	Poor
3650	3200	2750	2250	1750	1250

Model 101 Classic Field Grade I
A 12 or 20 gauge Over/Under shotgun with 25.5" or 28" ventilated-rib barrels, screw-in choke tubes, automatic ejectors and a single-selective trigger. Engraved, blued with checkered walnut stock.

NIB	Exc.	V.G.	Good	Fair	Poor
1900	1750	1500	1250	1000	700

Classic Field Grade II
As above, in 28 gauge and .410, highly engraved with a coin-finished receiver and a deluxe walnut stock with a round-knob pistol-grip and fleur-de-lis checkering.

NIB	Exc.	V.G.	Good	Fair	Poor
2200	2000	1750	1500	1250	900

Classic Sporter
As above, in 12 gauge only with 28" or 30" barrels, ventilated-rib and screw-in choke tubes. The frame is coin-finished with light engraving and a matted upper surface to reduce glare. The stock is select walnut. This model was designed for "Sporting Clays."

NIB	Exc.	V.G.	Good	Fair	Poor
2000	1800	1500	1250	1000	700

Waterfowl Model
As above with 30" barrels having 3" chambers, vent rib, and screw-in choke tubes. The overall finish is a subdued matte with light engraving.

NIB	Exc.	V.G.	Good	Fair	Poor
1500	1350	1000	850	650	500

Classic Trap Over/Under
Designed for competition trap shooting with 30" or 32" barrels having a ventilated center and top rib, automatic ejectors, screw-in choke tubes, and a single trigger. Blued with light engraving and a walnut stock in straight or Monte Carlo style.

NIB	Exc.	V.G.	Good	Fair	Poor
1900	1750	1500	1250	1000	700

Classic Trap Single
As above, with a single 32" or 34" barrel.

NIB	Exc.	V.G.	Good	Fair	Poor
2000	1800	1500	1250	1000	700

Classic Trap Combo
As above, with a single barrel and a set of Over/ Under barrels.

NIB	Exc.	V.G.	Good	Fair	Poor
2800	2500	2000	1750	1250	1000

Classic Skeet
As above, with 27.5" barrels.

NIB	Exc.	V.G.	Good	Fair	Poor
1900	1750	1500	1250	1000	700

Classic Skeet 4 Gauge Set
As above, furnished with four sets of barrels chambered for 12, 20, 28 gauge, and .410.

NIB	Exc.	V.G.	Good	Fair	Poor
3700	3000	2500	2250	1850	1500

CLEMENT, CHAS.
Liege, Belgium

Model 1903
A 5.5mm Clement semi-automatic pistol.

Exc.	V.G.	Good	Fair	Poor
600	500	450	375	300

Model 1907
As above, but in 6.35mm amd 7.65mm caliber.

Exc.	V.G.	Good	Fair	Poor
350	300	250	200	150

Model 1908
As above with grip frame and a repositioned magazine release.

Exc.	V.G.	Good	Fair	Poor
450	400	350	300	250

Model 1910
Redesigned version of the above with the barrel and housing all one piece. This unit is held in position by the triggerguard.

Courtesy Orville Reichert.

Exc.	V.G.	Good	Fair	Poor
450	400	350	300	250

Model 1912
A .635mm caliber semi-automatic rifle marked "Clement's Patent"; others, "Model 1912 Brevet 243839."

Exc.	V.G.	Good	Fair	Poor
750	650	550	400	325

Revolver copy of the Colt Police Positive. It was chambered for .38 caliber.

Exc.	V.G.	Good	Fair	Poor
275	250	200	125	90

CLERKE PRODS.
Santa Monica, California

Hi-Wall

A copy of the Winchester Model 1885 High Wall rifle with the action activated by a lever, and the receiver is case-colored. This rifle is chambered for almost all of the modern calibers and features a 26" barrel and a walnut stock with a pistol-grip and a Schnabel forend. It was manufactured between 1972 and 1974.

Exc.	V.G.	Good	Fair	Poor
275	250	200	150	100

Deluxe Hi-Wall

As above, with a half-round/half-octagonal barrel, select walnut stock, and a recoil pad. It was manufactured between 1972 and 1974.

Exc.	V.G.	Good	Fair	Poor
325	300	250	200	150

CLIFTON ARMS
Grand Prairie, Texas

Although this company primarily is a manufacturer of composite laminated stocks, they will on special order build custom rifles. Due to the unique nature of each rifle, a qualified appraisal is necessary.

COBRAY INDUSTRIES
Atlanta, Georgia
S.W.D., Inc.

M 11 Pistol

A 9mm caliber semi-automatic pistol. It fires from the closed bolt and is made of steel stampings with a parkerized finish. It is patterned after, though a good deal smaller than, the Ingram Mac 10. It is currently out of production and impossible to accurately price. If purchase or sale is contemplated, please check local values.

M 11 Carbine

As above, with a 16.25" shrouded barrel and a telescoping metal shoulder stock.

Terminator Shotgun

A single shot 12- or 20-gauge shotgun which fires from an open-bolt position. The cocked bolt is released to slam home on the shell when the trigger is pulled. The 18" barrel is cylinder-bored. There is a telescoping wire stock and the finish is parkerized.

Exc.	V.G.	Good	Fair	Poor
125	100	80	60	40

COCHRAN TURRET
C. B. Allen
Springfield, Massachusetts

Under Hammer Turret Rifle

A .36 or .40 caliber percussion radial cylinder rifle with 31" or 32" octagonal barrels and walnut stocks. The barrel marked "Cochrans/Many/Chambered/&/Non Recoil/Rifle" and the top strap "C.B. Allen / Springfield." These rifles were produced in the variations listed below. Manufactured during the late 1830s and 1840s.

1st Type

Fitted with a circular top strap secured by two screws. Serial numbered from 1 to approximately 30.

Exc.	V.G.	Good	Fair	Poor
6500	5750	5000	3750	2500

2nd Type

Fitted with a rectangular hinged top strap, the locking catch of which serves as the rear sight. Serial numbered from approximately 31 to 155.

Exc.	V.G.	Good	Fair	Poor
6000	5250	4500	3250	2000

3rd Type

As above, with a smaller hammer and a plain triggerguard.

Exc.	V.G.	Good	Fair	Poor
6000	5250	4500	3250	2000

Pistol

Action similar to above with 4" to 7" barrels.

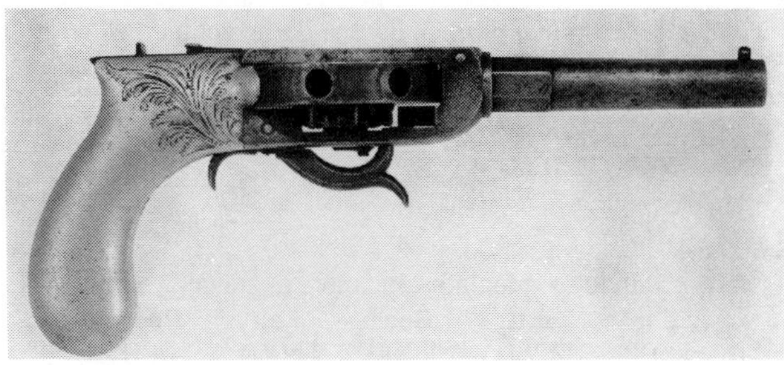

Exc.	V.G.	Good	Fair	Poor
10000	7500	6000	4500	3500

COFER, T. W.
Portsmouth, Virginia

Cofer Navy Revolver

A .36 caliber spur trigger percussion revolver with a 7.5" octagonal barrel and 6-shot cylinder. The top strap is marked "T.W. Cofer's/Patent." and the barrel "Portsmouth, Va." This revolver was manufactured in very limited quantities during the Civil War. Prospective purchasers are advised to secure a qualified appraisal prior to acquisition.

Exc.	V.G.	Good	Fair	Poor
30000	27500	20000	15000	10000

COGSWELL
London, England

Cogswell Pepperbox Pistol

A .47 caliber 6-shot percussion pepperbox with casehardened barrels, German silver frame and walnut grips. Normally marked "B. Cogswell, 224 Strand, London" and "Improved Revolving Pistol."

Exc.	V.G.	Good	Fair	Poor
2500	2000	1750	1250	750

COGSWELL & HARRISON, LTD.
London, England

Markor

A 12, 16, or 20 gauge boxlock double-barrel shotgun with 27" or 30 " barrels, various chokes, automatic ejectors and double triggers. The English-style straight stock is select walnut. This model is no longer manufactured.

Auto Ejectors—Add 20%.

Exc.	V.G.	Good	Fair	Poor
1500	1400	1200	950	700

Huntic

As above, with ejectors, a single selective trigger (optional) and a 25" barrel was offered.

Exc.	V.G.	Good	Fair	Poor
3600	3400	3000	2500	2000

Regency Model

A 12, 16, or 20 gauge Anson and Deeley boxlock double-barrel shotgun with 26", 28", or 30" barrels, various chokes, double triggers, automatic ejectors, and an English-style stock. This model has been manufactured since 1970.

Exc.	V.G.	Good	Fair	Poor
3250	2850	2400	1750	1400

Ambassador Model

As above, with false sideplates and a higher degree of engraving.

Exc.	V.G.	Good	Fair	Poor
4000	3500	3000	2500	2000

Rex

A 12, 16, or 20 gauge boxlock double-barrel shotgun with 25", 27.5", or 30" barrels, automatic ejectors, double triggers, and an English-style stock. It is no longer made.

Exc.	V.G.	Good	Fair	Poor
1750	1500	1250	1000	750

Sandhurst

As above, with false sideplates and more engraving.

Exc.	V.G.	Good	Fair	Poor
2500	2250	2000	1500	1000

Konor

Similar to the Sandhurst with more elaborate engraving and a fancier grade stock. Single selective triggers are available for an additional 15 percent.

Exc.	V.G.	Good	Fair	Poor
2900	2600	2250	1850	1500

Primic

A 12, 16, and 20 gauge sidelock shotgun with various barrel lengths and chokes, hand-detachable full sidelocks, automatic ejectors, and double triggers. A single selective trigger was available for an additional charge. English-style, walnut stock.

Exc.	V.G.	Good	Fair	Poor
6000	5000	3750	2500	2000

Victor

Similar to the above, but made solely to custom order.

Exc.	V.G.	Good	Fair	Poor
10000	8750	6250	4500	2750

COLT

(COLT, next page)

(COLT, from page 153)

COLTS PATENT FIREARMS MANUFACTURING COMPANY

Hartford, Connecticut

Of all the American firearms manufacturers, perhaps the best known is the Colt Company. Indeed, this recognition is so widespread that some popular writers have used the name Colt to indicate a revolver or semi-automatic pistol.

Originally founded in 1836 as the Patent Arms Manufacturing Company (Paterson, New Jersey) to produce percussion revolvers designed by Samuel Colt, the concern was initially a failure. However, the company formed in 1847 to manufacture revolvers of an improved form was a success. Even after Samuel Colt's death in 1862, his company thrived. With the introduction of the Model 1873 Single Action Army Revolver, the myth of the Colt became part of the American legend for that revolver was to be used by adventurers, cowboys, farmers, soldiers and a host of others for better than 70 years.

In 1897 the Colt's Patent Fire Arms Manufacturing Company entered into an agreement with John M. Browning to produce self-loading pistols of his design. One result of this association was to be the .45 caliber Model 1911 Semi-Automatic Pistol, which was the standard issue sidearm of the U.S. Armed Forces from 1911 to the late 1980s.

Because of their romance, form and variation, Colt revolvers, pistols and longarms are most sought after by collectors. Due to this, however, caution should be exercised and the opinion of experts should be sought when the purchase of rare or pristine examples is contemplated.

COLT PATERSON MODELS

Paterson, New Jersey

Pocket or Baby Paterson Model 1

The Paterson was the first production revolver manufactured by Colt. It was first made in 1837. The Model 1 or Pocket Model is the most diminutive of the Paterson line. The revolver is serial numbered in its own range, #1 through #500. The numbers are not visible without dismantling the revolver. The barrel lengths run from 1.75" to 4.75". The standard model has no attached loading lever. The chambering is .28 caliber percussion and it holds five shots. The finish is all blued, and the grips are varnished walnut. It has a roll-engraved cylinder scene, and the barrel is stamped "Patent Arms Mfg. Co. Paterson N.J.-Colt's Pt."

Exc.	V.G.	Good	Fair	Poor
12500	10000	7000	4000	2750

Belt Model Paterson #2

The Belt Model Paterson is a larger revolver with a straight-grip and an octagonal barrel that is 2.5" to 5.5" in length. It is chambered for .31 caliber percussion and holds five shots. The finish is all blued, with varnished walnut grips and no attached loading lever. It has a roll-engraved cylinder scene, and the barrel is stamped "Patent Arms Mfg. Co. Paterson N.J. Colt's Pt." The serial number range is #1-#850 and is shared with the #3 Belt Model. It was made from 1837-1840.

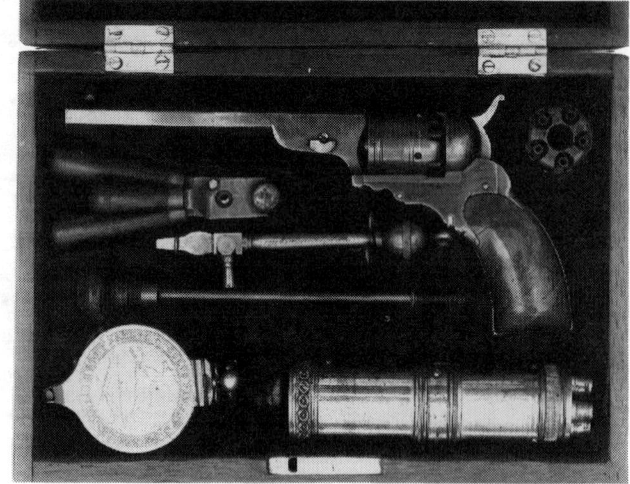

Courtesy Buffalo Bill Historical Center, Cody, Wyoming.

Exc.	V.G.	Good	Fair	Poor
12500	10000	7000	4000	2750

Belt Model Paterson #3

This revolver is quite similar to the Model #2 except that the grips are curved outward at the bottom to form a more hand-filling configuration. They are serial numbered in the same #1-850 range. Some attached loading levers have been noted on this Model, but they are extremely rare and would add approximately 35 percent to the value.

Exc.	V.G.	Good	Fair	Poor
11500	9500	6500	3500	2500

Ehlers Model Pocket Paterson

John Ehlers was a major stockholder and treasurer of the Patent Arms Mfg. Co. when it went bankrupt. He seized the assets and inventory. These revolvers were Pocket model Patersons that were not finished at the time. Ehlers had them finished and marketed them. They had an attached loading lever, and the abbreviation "M'g Co." was deleted from the barrel stamping. There were 500 revolvers involved in the Ehlers variation totally, and they were produced from 1840-1843.

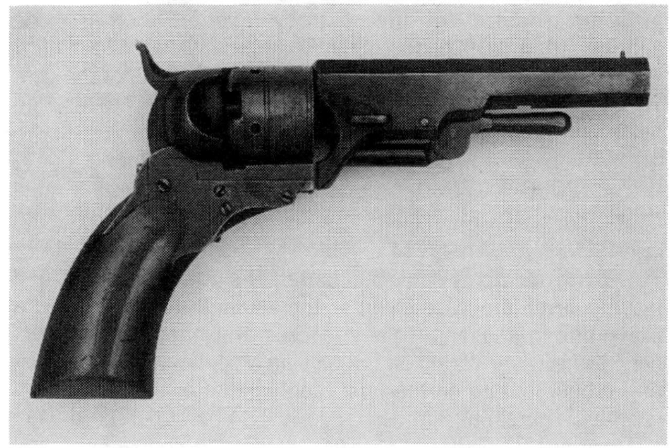

Exc.	V.G.	Good	Fair	Poor
13500	11000	8000	5000	3500

Ehlers Belt Model Paterson
The same specifications apply to this larger revolver as they do to the Ehlers Pocket Model. It falls within the same 500 revolver involvement and is very rare.

Exc.	V.G.	Good	Fair	Poor
12500	10000	7000	4000	2750

Texas Paterson Model #5
This is the largest and most sought after of the Paterson models. It is also known as the Holster model. It has been verified as actually seeing use by both the military and civilians on the American frontier. It is chambered for .36 caliber percussion, holds five shots, and has an octagonal barrel that ranges from 4" to 12" in length. It has been observed with and without the attached loading lever, but those with it are rare. The finish is blued, with a case-colored hammer. The grips are varnished walnut. The cylinder is roll-engraved; and the barrel is stamped "Patent Arms Mfg. Co. Paterson, N.J. Colts Pt." Most Texas Patersons are well used and have a very worn appearance. One in excellent or V.G. condition would be highly prized. A verified military model would be worth a great deal more than standard, so qualifed appraisal would be essential. The serial number range is #11,000, and they were manufactured from 1838-1840. The attached loading lever brings approximately a 25 percent premium.

Exc.	V.G.	Good	Fair	Poor
28500	22500	15000	8500	7500

COLT REVOLVING LONG GUNS 1837-1847

First Model Ring Lever Rifle
This was actually the first firearm manufactured by Colt; the first revolver appeared a short time later. There were 200 of the First Models made in 1837 and 1838. The octagonal barrel of the First Model is 32" long and browned, while the rest of the finish is blued. The stock is varnished walnut with a cheekpiece inlaid with Colt's trademark. The ring lever located in front of the frame is pulled to rotate the 8-shot cylinder and cock the hammer. The rifle is chambered for .34, .36, .38, .40, and .44 caliber percussion. The cylinder is roll-engraved, and the barrel is stamped "Colt's Patent/Patent Arms Mfg. Co., Paterson, N.Jersey." This Model has a top strap over the cylinder. They were made both with and without an attached loading lever. The latter is worth approximately 10 percent more.

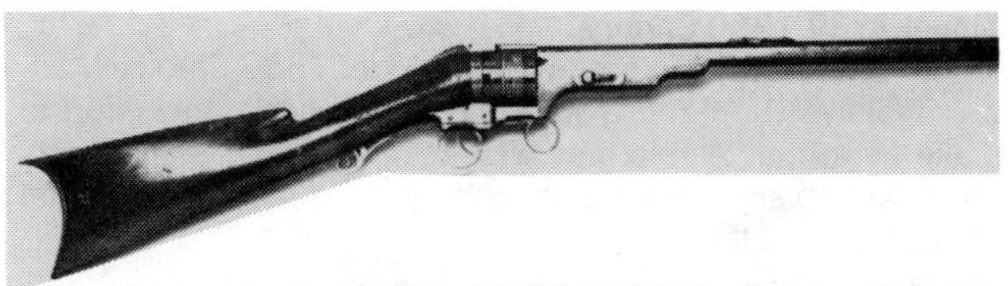

Courtesy Butterfield & Butterfield, San Francisco, California.

Exc.	V.G.	Good	Fair	Poor
11000	8000	6500	5000	3500

Second Model Ring Lever Rifle
This Model is quite similar in appearance to the First Model. Its function is identical. The major difference is the absence of the top strap over the cylinder. It had no trademark stamped on the cheekpiece. The Second Model is offered with a 28" and a 32" octagonal barrel and is chambered for .44 caliber percussion, holding 8 shots. There were approximately 500 produced from 1838-1841. The presence of an attached cheekpiece would add approximately 10 percent to the value.

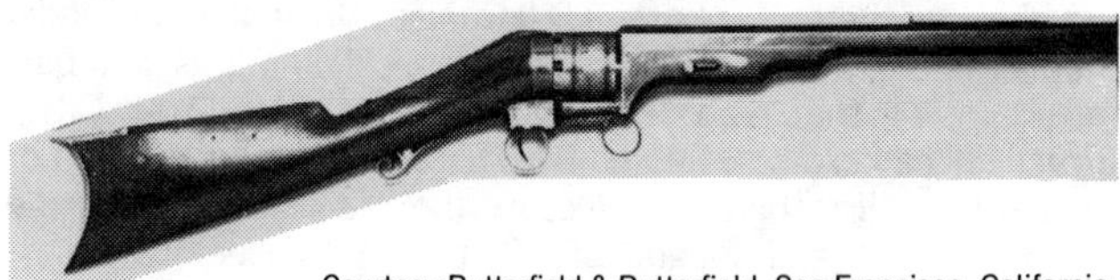

Courtesy Butterfield & Butterfield, San Francisco, California.

Exc.	V.G.	Good	Fair	Poor
11000	8000	6500	5000	3500

Model 1839 Carbine
This Model has no ring but features an exposed hammer for cocking and rotating the 6-shot cylinder. It is chambered for .525 smoothbore and comes standard with a 24" round barrel. Other barrel lengths have been noted. The finish is blued, with a browned barrel and a varnished walnut stock. The cylinder is roll-engraved, and the barrel is stamped "Patent Arms Mfg. Co. Paterson, N.J.-Colt's Pt." There were 950 manufactured from 1838-1841. Later variations of this Model are found with the attached loading lever standard, and earlier models without one would bring approximately 25 percent additional. There were 360 purchased by the military and stamped "WAT" on the stock. These would be worth twice what a standard model would bring. Anyone considering the purchase of one would be well advised to proceed with extreme caution.

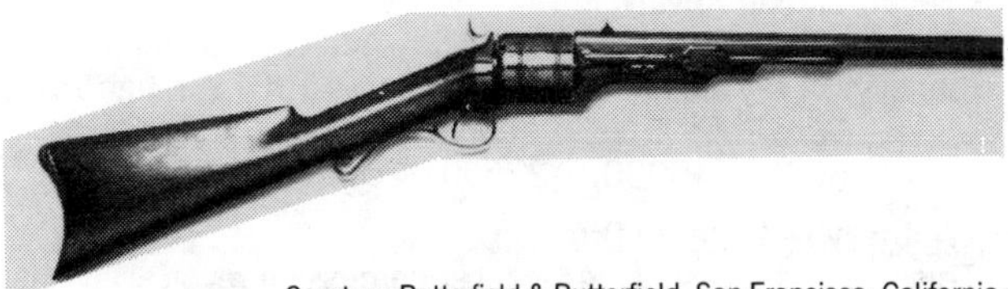

Courtesy Butterfield & Butterfield, San Francisco, California.

Exc.	V.G.	Good	Fair	Poor
8500	7000	5000	4000	3250

Model 1839 Shotgun
This Model is quite similar in appearance to the 1839 Carbine. It is chambered for 16 gauge and holds six shots. It has a Damascus pattern barrel, and the most notable difference is a 3.5" (instead of a 2.5") long cylinder. There were only 225 of these made from 1839-1841. The markings are the same as on the Carbine.

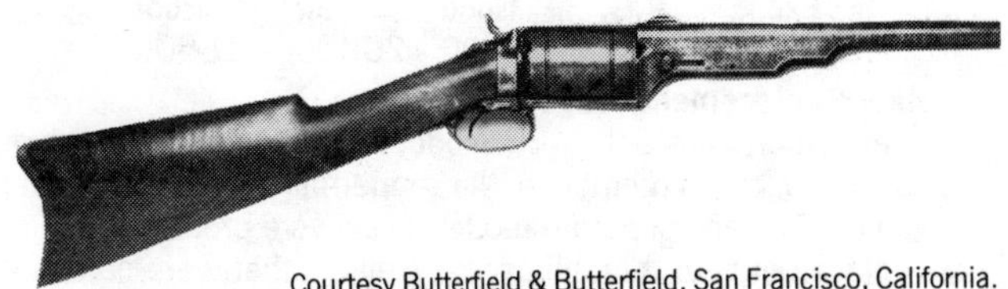

Courtesy Butterfield & Butterfield, San Francisco, California.

Exc.	V.G.	Good	Fair	Poor
7500	6000	4500	3500	2750

Model 1839/1850 Carbine

In 1848 Colt acquired a number of Model 1839 Carbines (approximately 40) from the State of Rhode Island. In an effort to make them marketable they were refinished and the majority fitted with plain cylinders (brightly polished) having integral ratchets around the arbor hole.

Barrel length 24"; caliber .525; barrel browned; cylinder polished; frame blued; furniture casehardened; walnut stock varnished.

Exc.	V.G.	Good	Fair	Poor
8500	7000	5000	4000	3250

WALKER-DRAGOON MODELS

Hartford, Connecticut

Walker Model Revolver

The Walker is a massive revolver. It weighs 4 pounds 9 ounces and has a 9" part-round/part-octagonal barrel. The cylinder holds six shots and is chambered for .44 caliber percussion. There were 1,000 Walker Colts manufactured in 1847, and nearly all of them saw extremely hard use. Originally this model had a roll-engraved cylinder, military inspection marks, and barrel stamping that read "Address Saml. Colt-New York City." Practically all examples noted have had these markings worn or rusted beyond recognition. Because the Walker is perhaps the most desirable and sought after Colt from a collector's standpoint and because of the extremely high value of a Walker in any condition, qualified appraisal is definitely recommended. These revolvers were serial numbered A, B, C and D Company 1-220, and E Company 1-120.

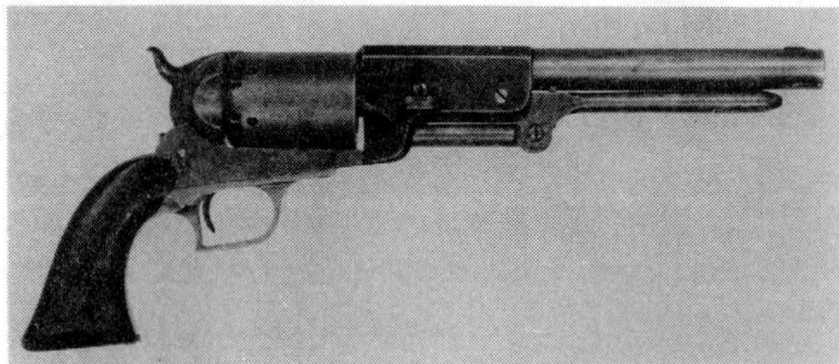

Courtesy Buffalo Bill Historical Center, Cody, Wyoming.

Exc.	V.G.	Good	Fair	Poor
70000	50000	30000	22500	20000

Civilian Walker Revolver

This model is identical to the military model but has no martial markings. They are found serial numbered 1001 through 1100.

Exc.	V.G.	Good	Fair	Poor
65000	45000	27500	20000	18500

Whitneyville Hartford Dragoon

This is a large, 6-shot, .44-caliber percussion revolver. It has a 7.5" part-round/part-octagonal barrel. The frame, hammer, and loading lever are case-colored. The remainder is blued, with a brass triggerguard and varnished walnut grips. There were only 240 made in late 1847. The serial numbers run from 1100-1340. This model is often referred to as a Transitional Walker. Some of the parts used in its manufacture were left over from the Walker production run. This model has a roll-engraved cylinder scene, and the barrel is stamped "Address Saml. Colt New York-City." This is an extremely rare model, and much care should be taken to authenticate any contemplated acquisitions.

Exc.	V.G.	Good	Fair	Poor
65000	45000	27500	20000	18500

Walker Replacement Dragoon

This extremely rare Colt (300 produced) is sometimes referred to as the "Fluck" in memory of the gentleman who first identified it as a distinct and separate model. They were produced by Colt as replacements to the military for Walkers that were no longer fit for service due to mechanical failures. They were large, 6-shot, .44 caliber percussion revolvers with 7.5" part-round/part-octagonal barrels. Serial numbers ran from 2216 to 2515. The frame, hammer, and loading lever are case-colored; the remainder, blued. The grips, which are longer than other Dragoons and similar to the Walkers, are of varnished walnut and bear the inspector's mark "WAT" inside an oval cartouche on one side and the letters "JH" on the other. The frame is stamped "Colt's/Patent/U.S." The letter "P" appears on various parts of the gun. This is another model that should definitely be authenticated before any acquisition is made.

Exc.	V.G.	Good	Fair	Poor
12500	7500	6000	4000	2500

First Model Dragoon

Another large, 6-shot, .44 caliber percussion revolver. It has a 7.5" part-round/part-octagonal barrel. The frame, hammer, and loading lever are case-colored; the remainder, blued with a brass grip frame and square backed triggerguard. The triggerguard is silver-plated on the Civilian Model only. Another distinguishing feature on the First Model is the oval cylinder stop notches. The serial number range is 1341-8000. There were approximately 5,000 made. The cylinder is roll-engraved; and the barrel stampings read "Address Saml. Colt, New York City." "Colt's Patent" appears on the frame. On Military Models the letters "U.S." also appear on the frame.

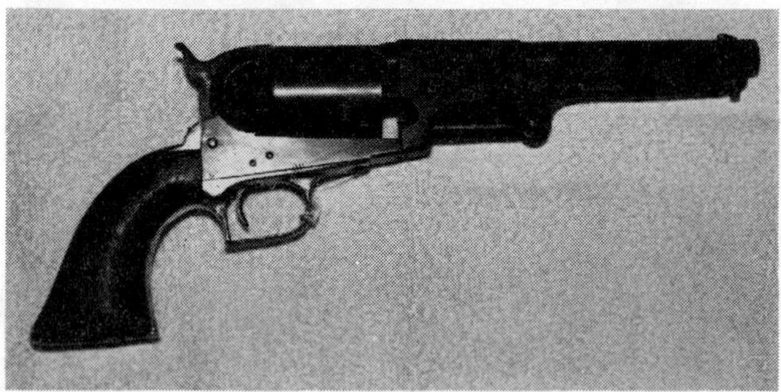

Military Model

Exc.	V.G.	Good	Fair	Poor
12500	9000	6000	3500	1500

Civilian Model

Exc.	V.G.	Good	Fair	Poor
10000	8000	4000	2000	1000

Second Model Dragoon

Most of the improvements that distinguish this model from the First Model are internal and not readily apparent. The most obvious external change is the rectangular cylinder-stop notches. This Model is serial numbered from 8000-10700, for a total production of approximately 2,700 revolvers manufactured in 1850 and 1851. There is a Civilian Model, a Military Model, and an extremely rare variation that was issued to the militias of New Hampshire and Massachusets (marked "MS."). Once again, caution is advised in acquisition.

Civilian Model

Exc.	V.G.	Good	Fair	Poor
8000	5000	3250	2000	1200

Military Model

Exc.	V.G.	Good	Fair	Poor
9000	6500	4500	2500	1500

Militia Model

Exc.	V.G.	Good	Fair	Poor
9000	6500	4500	2500	1500

Third Model Dragoon

This is the most common of all the large Colt percussion revolvers. Approximately 10,500 were manufactured from 1851 through 1861. It is quite similar in appearance to the Second Model, and the most obvious external difference is the round triggerguard. The Third Model Dragoon was the first Colt revolver available with a detachable shoulder stock. There are three basic types of stocks, and all are quite rare as only 1,250 were produced. There are two other major variations we will note--the "C.L." Dragoon, which was a militia-issued model and is very rare, and the late-issue model with an 8" barrel. These are found over serial number 18000, and only 50 were produced. Qualified appraisal should be secured before acquisition as many fakes abound.

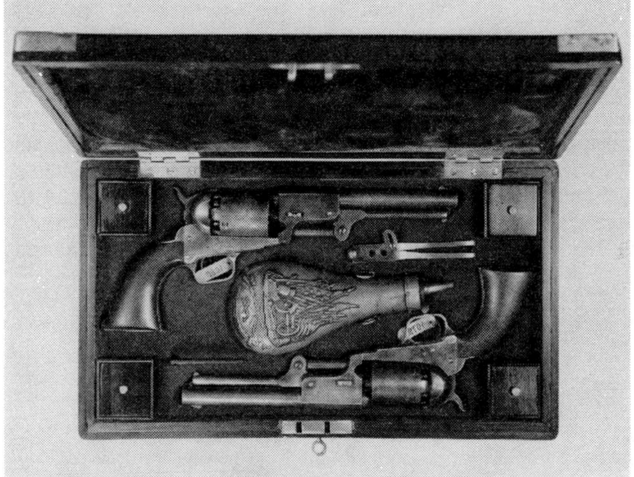

Courtesy Buffalo Bill Historical Center, Cody, Wyoming.

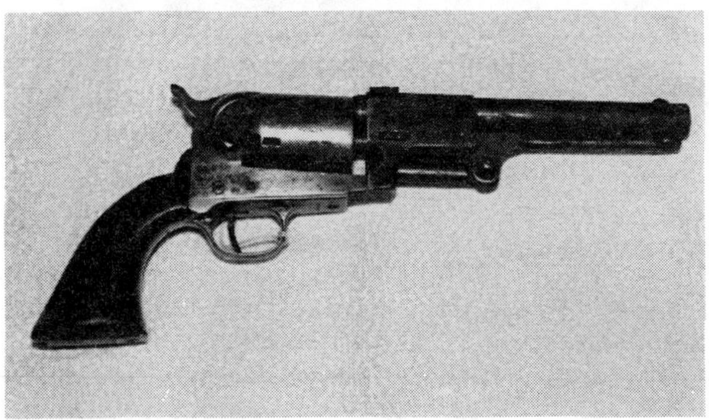

Civilian Model

Exc.	V.G.	Good	Fair	Poor
4500	3750	2750	2000	1500

Military Model

Exc.	V.G.	Good	Fair	Poor
5000	4000	3000	2500	2000

Shoulder Stock Cut Revolvers

Exc.	V.G.	Good	Fair	Poor
9000	7500	6000	4250	3500

Shoulder Stocks

Exc.	V.G.	Good	Fair	Poor
3000	2500	2000	1500	1000

C.L. Dragoon (Hand Engraved, Not Stamped)

Exc.	V.G.	Good	Fair	Poor
7000	5500	4000	3250	2500

8" Barrel Late Issue

Exc.	V.G.	Good	Fair	Poor
9000	7500	6000	4250	3500

Hartford English Dragoon

This is a variation of the Third Model Dragoon. The only notable differences are the British proofmarks and the distinct #1-700 serial-number range. Other than these two features, the description given for the Third Model would apply. These revolvers were manufactured in Hartford but were finished at Colt's London factory from 1853-1857. Some bear the hand-engraved barrel marking "Col. Colt London." Many of the English Dragoons were elaborately engraved, and individual appraisal would be a must. Two hundred revolvers came back to America in 1861 to be used in the Civil War. As with all the early Colts, caution is advised in acquisition.

Exc.	V.G.	Good	Fair	Poor
5000	4500	3500	2250	1400

Model 1848 Baby Dragoon

This is a small, 5-shot, .31-caliber percussion revolver. It has an octagonal barrel in lengths of 3", 4", 5",and 6". Most were made without an attached loading lever, although some with loading levers have been noted. The frame, hammer, and loading lever (when present) are case-colored; the barrel and cylinder, blued. The grip frame and triggerguard are silver plated brass. There were approximately 15,500 manufactured between 1847 and 1850. The serial range is between #1-5500. The barrels are stamped "Address Saml. Colt/New York City." Some have been noted with the barrel address inside brackets. The frame is marked "Colt's/Patent." The first 10,000 revolvers have the Texas Ranger/Indian roll-engraved cylinder scene; the later guns the Stagecoach Holdup scene. This is a very popular Model, and many fakes have been noted.

Attached Loading Lever—Add 15%.

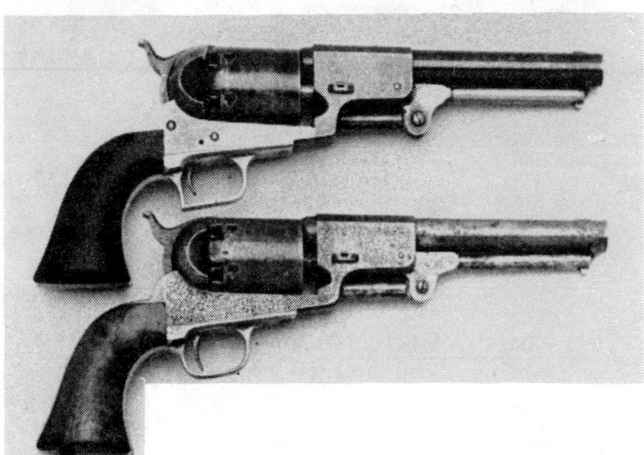

Courtesy Butterfield & Butterfield, San Francisco, California.

Courtesy Milwaukee Public Museum, Milwaukee, Wisconsin.

Texas Ranger/Indian Scene

Exc.	V.G.	Good	Fair	Poor
2500	2000	1500	1000	750

Stagecoach Holdup Scene

Exc.	V.G.	Good	Fair	Poor
3000	2500	1750	1250	1000

Model 1849 Pocket Revolver

This is a small, either 5- or 6-shot, .31 caliber percussion revolver. It has an octagonal barrel 3", 4", 5", or 6" in length. Most had loading gates, but some did not. The frame, hammer, and loading lever are case-colored; the cylinder and barrel are blued. The grip frame and round triggerguard are made of brass and silver-plated. There are both large and small triggerguard variations noted. This is the most plentiful of all the Colt percussion revolvers, with approximately 325,000 manufactured over a 23-year period, 1850-1873. There are over 200 variations of this Model, and one should consult an expert for individual appraisals. There are many fine publications specializing in the field of Colt percussion revolvers that would be helpful in the identification of the variations. The values represented here are for the standard model.

Courtesy Butterfield & Butterfield, San Francisco, California.

Exc.	V.G.	Good	Fair	Poor
2000	1750	1250	850	600

London Model 1849 Pocket Revolver

Identical in configuration to the standard 1849 Pocket Revolver, the London-made models have a higher quality finish and their own serial number range, #111,000. They were manufactured from 1853 through 1857. They feature a roll-engraved cylinder scene, and the barrels are stamped "Address Col. Colt/London." The first 265 revolvers, known as early models, have brass grip frames and small round triggerguards. They are quite rare and worth approximately 50 percent more than the standard model which has a steel grip frame and large oval triggerguard.

Exc.	V.G.	Good	Fair	Poor
2250	1850	1450	1000	800

Model 1851 Navy Revolver

This is undoubtedly the most popular revolver Colt produced in the medium size and power range. It is a 6-shot, .36-caliber percussion revolver with a 7.5" octagonal barrel. It has an attached loading lever. The basic model has a case-colored frame, hammer, and loading lever, with silver-plated brass grip frame and trigger guard. The grips are varnished walnut. Colt manufactured approximately 215,000 of these fine revolvers between 1850 and 1873. The basic Navy features a roll-engraved cylinder scene of a battle between the navies of Texas and Mexico. There are three distinct barrel stampings--serial number 174,000, "Address Saml. Colt New-York City"; serial number 74,001-101,000 "Address Saml. Colt. Hartford, Ct."; and serial number 101,001-215,000 "Address Saml. Colt New York U.S. America." The left side of the frame is stamped "Colt's/Patent" on all variations. This Model is also available with a detached shoulder stock, and values for the stocks today are nearly as high as for the revolver itself. Careful appraisal should be secured before purchase. The number of variations within the 1851 Navy model designation makes it neccessary to read specialized text available on the subject. We furnish values for the major variations but again caution potential purchasers to acquire appraisals.

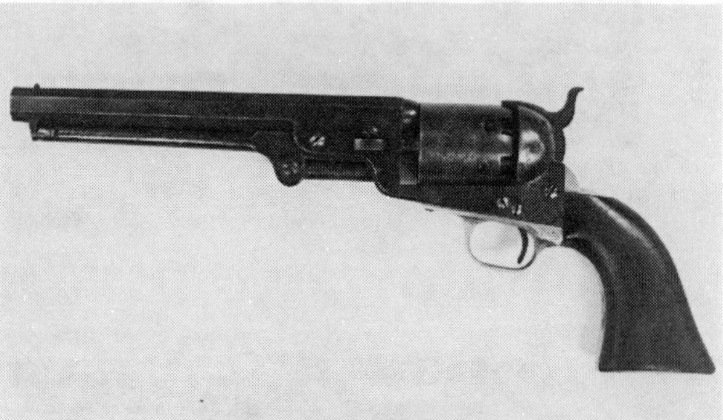

Courtesy Milwaukee Public Museum, Milwaukee, Wisconsin.

Square Back Trigger Guard Serial #1-4,200

Exc.	V.G.	Good	Fair	Poor
7500	6000	4000	2500	1500

Small Round Trigger Guard Serial #4,201-85,000

Exc.	V.G.	Good	Fair	Poor
3000	2500	2000	1500	850

Large Round Trigger Guard Serial #85,001-215,000

Exc.	V.G.	Good	Fair	Poor
2500	2000	1750	1250	750

Martial Model

"U.S." stamped on the left side of frame; inspector's marks and cartouche on the grips.

Exc.	V.G.	Good	Fair	Poor
3500	2750	2250	1750	1000

Shoulder Stock Variations

1st and 2nd Model Revolver Cut for Stock Only

Exc.	V.G.	Good	Fair	Poor
5000	4000	3000	2250	1750

Stock Only

Exc.	V.G.	Good	Fair	Poor
3500	2500	2000	1750	1250

3rd Model

Revolver Only

Exc.	V.G.	Good	Fair	Poor
4500	3250	2750	2000	1400

Stock

Exc.	V.G.	Good	Fair	Poor
2500	2000	1750	1250	850

London Model 1851 Navy Revolver

These revolvers are physically similar to the U.S.-made model with the exception of the barrel address, which reads "Address Col. Colt. London."There are also British proofmarks stamped on the barrel and cylinder. There were 42,000 made between 1853 and 1857. They have their own serial-number range, #142,000. There are two major variations of the London Navy, and again a serious purchaser would be well advised to seek qualified appraisal as fakes have been noted.

1st Model
Serial #1-2,000 with a small round brass triggerguard and grip frame. Squareback guard worth a 40 percent premium.

Exc.	V.G.	Good	Fair	Poor
3500	2750	2000	1500	750

2nd Model
Serial #2,001-42,000, steel grip frame, and large round trigger guard.

Exc.	V.G.	Good	Fair	Poor
2250	1800	1250	800	600

Model 1854 Russian Contract Musket
In 1854 Colt purchased a large number of U.S. Model 1822 flintlock Muskets which the company altered to percussion cap ignition and rifled. The reworked muskets are dated 1854 on the barrel tang and at the rear of the lockplate. In most instances the original manufactory marks, such as Springfield or Harpers Ferry at the rear of the lockplate, have been removed, while the U.S. and eagle between the hammer and bolster remain. The percussion nipple bolster is marked COLT'S PATENT. Some examples have been noted with the date 1858.

Barrel length 42"; caliber .69; lock and furniture burnished bright; walnut stock oil finished.

Exc.	V.G.	Good	Fair	Poor
2900	2500	2000	1500	750

Breech loading examples made in two styles are also known. Production of this variation is believed to have only taken place on an experimental basis.

Exc.	V.G.	Good	Fair	Poor
6500	6000	5000	2500	2000

SIDE HAMMER MODELS

Model 1855 Side Hammer "Root" Pocket Revolver
The "Root", as it is popularly known, was the only solid-frame revolver Colt ever made. It has a spur trigger and walnut grips, and the hammer is mounted on the right side of the frame. The standard finish is a case-colored frame, hammer, and loading lever, with the barrel and cylinder blued. It is chambered for both .28 caliber and .31 caliber percussion. Each caliber has its own serial number range—#1-30000 for the .28 caliber and #1-14000 for the .31 caliber. The model consists of seven basic variations, and the serious student should avail himself of the fine publications dealing with this model in depth. Colt produced the Side Hammer Root from 1855-1870.

Models 1 and 1A Serial #1-384
3.5" octagonal barrel, .28 caliber, roll-engraved cylinder, Hartford barrel address without pointing hand.

Exc.	V.G.	Good	Fair	Poor
3000	2500	1750	1250	800

Model 2 Serial #476-25000
Same as Model 1 with pointing hand barrel address.

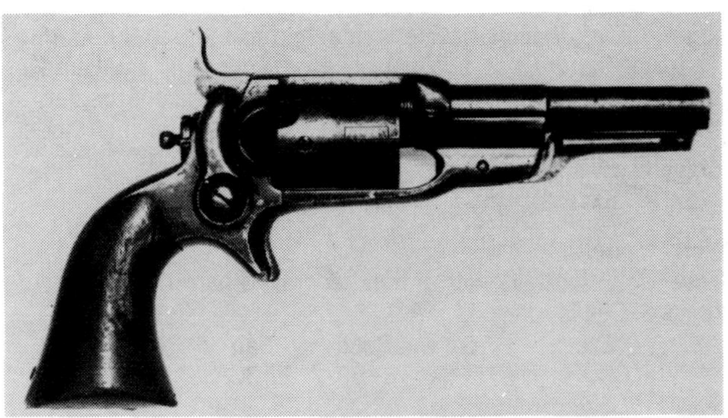

Courtesy Milwaukee Public Museum, Milwaukee, Wisconsin.

Exc.	V.G.	Good	Fair	Poor
1750	1400	1100	850	650

Model 3 Serial #25,001-#30000
Same as the Model 2 with a full fluted cylinder.

Exc.	V.G.	Good	Fair	Poor
1750	1400	1100	850	650

Model 3A and 4 Serial #1-2400
.31 caliber, 3.5" barrel, Hartford address, full fluted cylinder.

Exc.	V.G.	Good	Fair	Poor
2000	1750	1250	1000	750

Model 5 Serial #2401-8000
.31 caliber, 3.5" round barrel, address "Col. Colt New York."

Exc.	V.G.	Good	Fair	Poor
1750	1400	1100	850	650

Model 5A Serial #2,401-8000
Same as Model 5 with a 4.5" barrel.

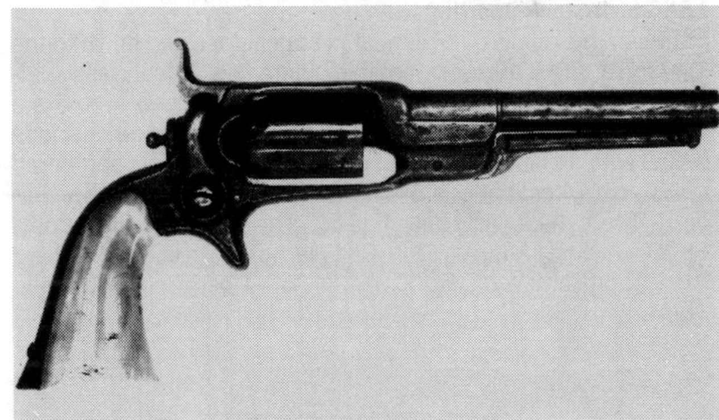

Courtesy Milwaukee Public Museum, Milwaukee, Wisconsin.

Exc.	V.G.	Good	Fair	Poor
1850	1500	1200	950	750

Models 6 and 6A Serial #8001-11074
Same as Model 5 and 5A with roll-engraved cylinder scene.

Exc.	V.G.	Good	Fair	Poor
1750	1400	1100	850	650

Models 7 and 7A Serial #11,075-14,000
Same as Models 6 and 6A with a screw holding in the cylinder pin.

Exc.	V.G.	Good	Fair	Poor
2250	2000	1600	1250	1000

SIDE HAMMER LONG GUNS

1855 Sporting Rifle, 1st Model
This is a 6-shot revolving rifle chambered for .36 caliber percussion. It comes with a 21", 24", 27", or 30" round barrel that is part octagonal where it joins the frame. The stock is walnut with either an oil or a varnish finish. The frame, hammer, and loading lever are case-colored; the rest of the metal, blued. The hammer is on the right side of the frame. The 1st Model has no

forend, and an oiling device is attached to the barrel underlug. The triggerguard has two spur-like projections in front and in back of the bow. The roll-engraved cylinder scene depicts a hunter shooting at five deer and is found only on this model. The standard stampings are " Colt's Pt./1856" and "Address S. Colt Hartford, Ct. U.S.A."

Early Model

Low serial numbers with a hand-engraved barrel marking "Address S. Colt Hartford,U.S.A."

Exc.	V.G.	Good	Fair	Poor
6000	4750	3750	2500	1750

Production Model

Exc.	V.G.	Good	Fair	Poor
4500	3500	2750	2000	1500

1855 1st Model Carbine

Identical to the 1st Model Rifle but offered with a 15" and 18" barrel.

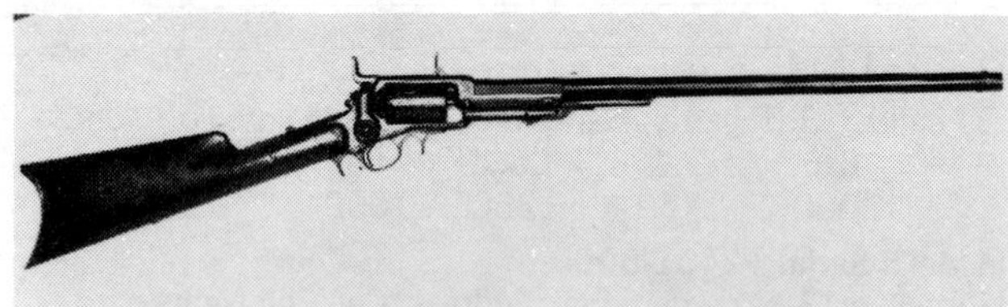

Courtesy Milwaukee Public Museum, Milwaukee, Wisconsin.

Exc.	V.G.	Good	Fair	Poor
6500	5000	4000	2750	2000

1855 Half Stock Sporting Rifle

Although this rifle is quite similar in appearance and finish to the 1st Model, there are some notable differences. It features a walnut forend that protrudes halfway down the barrel. There are two types of triggerguards—a short projectionless one or a long model with a graceful scroll. There is a 6-shot model chambered for .36 or .44 caliber or a 5-shot model chambered for .56 caliber. The cylinder is fully fluted. The markings are "Colt's Pt/1856" and "Address Col. Colt/Hartford Ct. U.S.A." There were approximately 1,500 manufactured between 1857 and 1864.

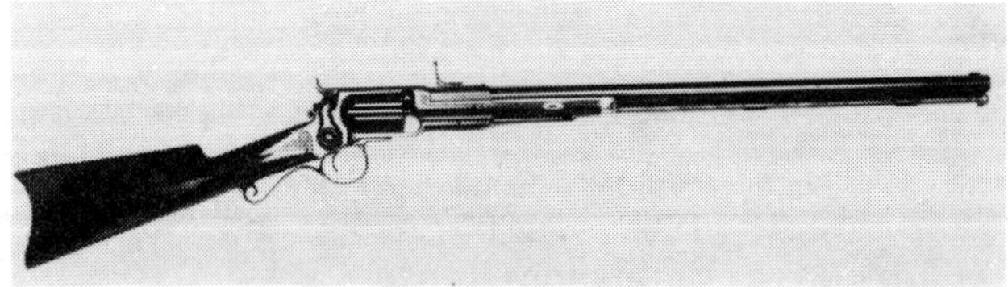

Courtesy Milwaukee Public Museum, Milwaukee, Wisconsin.

Exc.	V.G.	Good	Fair	Poor
3200	2750	2000	1500	1250

1855 Full Stock Military Rifle

This model holds 6 shots in its .44 caliber chambering and 5 shots when chambered for .56 caliber. It is another side hammer revolving rifle that resembles the Half Stock model. The barrels are round and part-octagonal where they join the frame. They come in lengths of 21", 24", 27", 31", and 37". The hammer and loading lever are case-colored; the rest of the metal parts, blued. The walnut butt stock and full length forend are oil finished, and this model has sling swivels. The cylinder is fully fluted. Military models have provisions for affixing a bayonet and military-style sights and bear the "U.S." martial mark on examples that were actually issued to the military. The standard stampings found on this model are "Colt's Pt/1856" and "Address Col. Colt Hartford, Ct. U.S.A." There were an estimated 9,300 manufactured between 1856 and 1864.

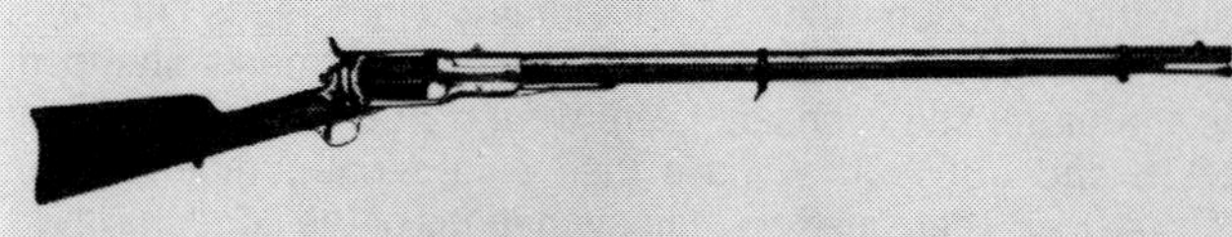

Courtesy Milwaukee Public Museum, Milwaukee, Wisconsin.

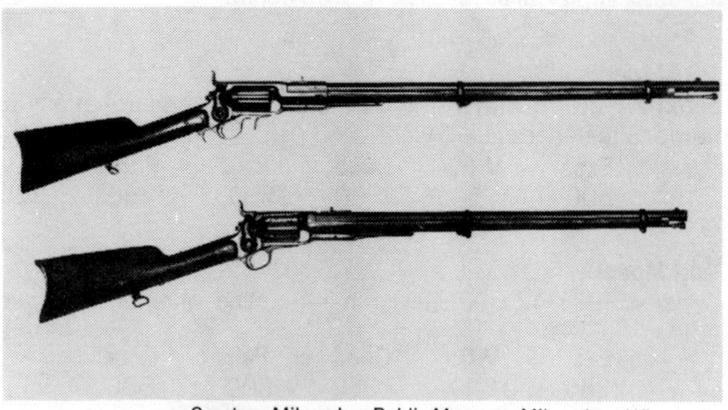

Courtesy Milwaukee Public Museum, Milwaukee, Wisconsin.

Martially Marked Models

Exc.	V.G.	Good	Fair	Poor
6000	4750	3750	2500	1750

Without Martial Markings

Exc.	V.G.	Good	Fair	Poor
4500	3500	2750	2000	1500

1855 Full Stock Sporting Rifle

This model is very similar in appearance to the Military model, with these notable exceptions. There is no provision for attaching a bayonet, there are no sling swivels, and it has sporting-style sights. The buttplate is crescent shaped. This model has been noted chambered for .56 caliber in a 5-shot version and chambered for .36, .40, .44, and .50 caliber in the 6-shot variation. They are quite scarce in .40 and .50 caliber and will bring a 10 percent premium. The standard markings are "Colt's Pt/1856" and "Address Col. Colt/Hartford Ct. U.S.A." Production on this model was quite limited (several hundred at most) between the years 1856 and 1864.

Exc.	V.G.	Good	Fair	Poor
4000	3000	2250	1750	1250

Model 1855 Revolving Carbine

This Model is very similar in appearance to the 1855 Military Rifle. The barrel lengths of 15", 18" and 21" plus the absence of a forend make the standard Carbine Model readily identifiable. The markings are the same. Approximately 4,400 were manufactured between 1856 and 1864.

Exc.	V.G.	Good	Fair	Poor
6500	5500	4000	2750	1500

Model 1855 Artillery Carbine

Identical to the standard carbine but chambered for .56 caliber only, it has a 24" barrel, full-length walnut forend, and a bayonet lug.

Exc.	V.G.	Good	Fair	Poor
7250	6500	4750	3500	2250

Model 1855 British Carbine

This is a British-proofed version with barrel lengths of up to 30". It has a brass triggerguard and buttplate and is chambered for .56 caliber only. This variation is usually found in the 10000-12000 serial number range.

Exc.	V.G.	Good	Fair	Poor
6000	5000	3500	2250	1150

Model 1855 Revolving Shotgun

This model very much resembles the Half Stock Sporting Rifle but was made with a 27", 30", 33" and 36" smoothbore barrel. It has a 5-shot cylinder chambered for .60 or .75 caliber (20 or 10 gauge). This model has a case-colored hammer and loading lever; the rest of the metal is blued, with an occasional browned barrel noted. The buttstock and forend are of walnut, either oil- or varnish-finished. This model has no rear sight and a small triggerguard with the caliber stamped on it. Some have been noted with the large scroll triggerguard; these would add 10 percent to the value. The rarest shotgun variation would be a full-stocked version in either gauge, and qualified appraisal would be highly recommended. This model is serial numbered in its own range, #1-1100. They were manufactured from 1860-1863.

.60 Caliber (20 gauge)

Exc.	V.G.	Good	Fair	Poor
4250	3500	2750	2000	1200

.75 Caliber (10 gauge)

Exc.	V.G.	Good	Fair	Poor
4000	3250	2500	1750	1500

Model 1861 Single shot Rifled Musket

With the advent of the Civil War, the army of the Union seriously needed military arms. Colt was given a contract to supply 112,500 1861-pattern percussion single shot muskets. Between 1861 and 1865, 75,000 were delivered. They have 40" rifled barrels chambered for .58 caliber. The musket is equipped with military sights, sling swivels, and a bayonet lug. The metal finish is bright steel, and the stock is oil-finished walnut. Military inspector's marks are found on all major parts. "VP" over an eagle is stamped on the breech along with a date. The Colt address and a date are stamped on the lockplate. A large number of these rifles were altered to the Snyder breech loading system for the Bey of Egypt.

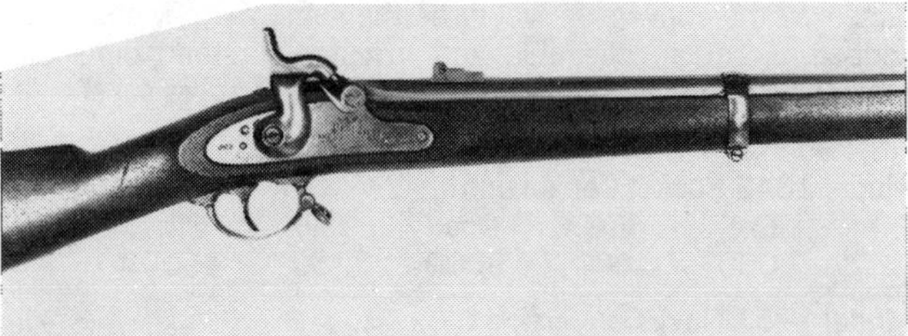

Courtesy Milwaukee Public Museum, Milwaukee, Wisconsin.

Production Model

Exc.	V.G.	Good	Fair	Poor
1500	1250	1000	750	450

Model 1860 Army Revolver

This model was the third most produced of the Colt percussion handguns. It was the primary revolver used by the Union Army during the Civil War. Colt delivered 127,156 of these revolvers to be used during those hostilities. This is a 6-shot .44 caliber percussion revolver. It has either a 7.5" or 8" round barrel with an attached loading lever. The frame, hammer, and loading lever are case-colored; the barrel and cylinder are blued. The triggerguard and front strap are brass, and the backstrap is blued steel. The grips are one-piece walnut. The early models have the barrels stamped "Address Saml. Colt Hartford Ct." Later models are stamped "Address Col. Saml. Colt New-York U.S. America." "Colt's/Patent" is stamped on the left side of the frame; ".44 Cal.," on the triggerguard. The cylinder is roll-engraved with the naval battle scene. There were a total of 200,500 1860 Army Revolvers manufactured between 1860 and 1873.

Production Model

Exc.	V.G.	Good	Fair	Poor
4000	3500	2750	2000	1500

Civilian Model

The difference between this variation and the standard Army is the three-screw instead of four-screw frame and the absence of shoulder stock attaching cuts. Civilian models are usually better finished.

Courtesy Milwaukee Public Museum, Milwaukee, Wisconsin.

Exc.	V.G.	Good	Fair	Poor
4500	4000	3250	2500	1750

Fluted Cylinder Model

Approximately 4,000 Armies were made with full fluted cylinders. They appear in the first 8,000 serial numbers.

Courtesy Milwaukee Public Museum, Milwaukee, Wisconsin.

Exc.	V.G.	Good	Fair	Poor
5000	4500	3500	2750	2000

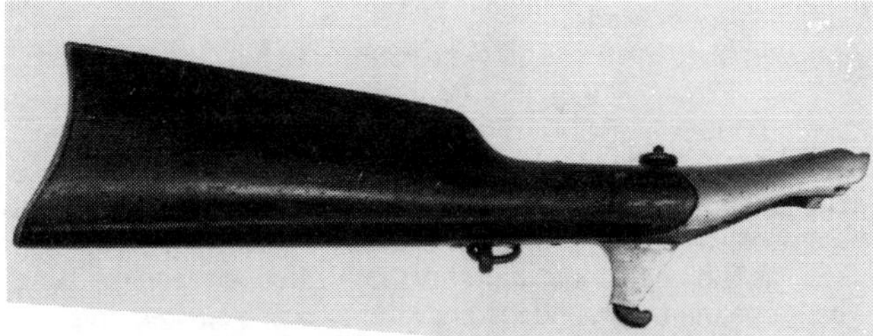

Courtesy Milwaukee Public Museum, Milwaukee, Wisconsin.

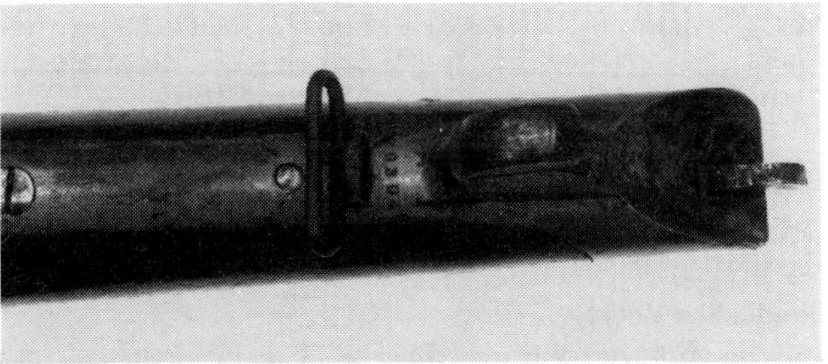

Courtesy Milwaukee Public Museum, Milwaukee, Wisconsin.

Shoulder Stock 2nd Type (Fluted Cylinder Model)

Exc.	V.G.	Good	Fair	Poor
3500	3000	2000	1500	1250

Shoulder Stock 3rd Type (Standard Model)

Exc.	V.G.	Good	Fair	Poor
2500	2000	1500	1000	750

Model 1861 Navy Revolver

This Model is a 6-shot, 7.5" round-barrelled, .36 caliber percussion revolver. The frame, hammer, and attached loading lever are case-colored. The barrel and cylinder are blued. The gripframe and triggerguard are silver-plated brass. The grips are of one-piece walnut. The cylinder has the roll-engraved naval battle scene, and the barrel stamping is "Address Col. Saml. Colt New-York U.S. America." The frame is stamped "Colts/Patent" with "36 Cal." on the triggerguard. There are not many variations within the 1861 Navy model designation, as less than 39,000 were made between 1861 and 1873.

Courtesy Butterfield & Butterfield, San Francisco, California.

Production Model

Exc.	V.G.	Good	Fair	Poor
3500	3000	2000	1250	750

Military Model

Marked "U.S." on frame, inspector's cartouche on grip. 650 were marked "U.S.N." on the butt.

Exc.	V.G.	Good	Fair	Poor
5000	4500	3500	2750	2000

Shoulder Stock Model

Only 100 3rd-type stocks were made. They appear between serial #11000-14000.

Revolver

Exc.	V.G.	Good	Fair	Poor
5500	5000	4000	3250	2250

Stock

Exc.	V.G.	Good	Fair	Poor
3000	2500	2000	1500	1250

Fluted Cylinder Model

Approximately the first 100 were made with full fluted cylinders.

Exc.	V.G.	Good	Fair	Poor
10000	8000	5500	3000	2250

Model 1862 Pocket Navy Revolver

This is a smaller, 5-shot, .36-caliber percussion revolver that resembles the configuration of the 1851 Navy. It has a 4.5", 5.5", or 6.5" octagonal barrel with an attached loading lever. The frame, hammer, and loading lever are case-colored; the barrel and cylinder, blued. The grip frame and triggerguard are silver-plated brass; and the one-piece grips, of varnished walnut. The stagecoach holdup scene is roll-engraved on the cylinder. The frame is stamped "Colt's/Patent"; and the barrel, "Address Col. Saml. Colt New-York U.S. America." There were approximately 19,000 manufactured between 1861 and 1873. They are serial numbered in the same range as the Model 1862 Police. Because a great many were used for metallic cartridge conversions, they are quite scarce today.

The London Address Model with blued steel gripframe would be worth approximately twice the value of the standard model.

Production Model

Exc.	V.G.	Good	Fair	Poor
4000	2500	1750	1250	750

Model 1862 Police Revolver

This is a very slim, attractively designed revolver that some consider to be the most aesthetically pleasing of all the Colt percussion designs. It has a 5-shot, half-fluted cylinder chambered for .36 caliber. It is offered with a 3.5", 4.5", 5.5", or 6.5" round barrel. The frame, hammer, and loading lever are casecolored; the barrel and cylinder, blued. The grip frame is silver-plated brass; and the one-piece grips, varnished walnut. The barrel is stamped "Address Col. Saml Colt New-York U.S. America"; the frame has "Colt's/Patent" on the left side. One of the cylinder flutes is marked "Pat Sept. 10th 1850." There were approximately 28,000 of these manufactured between 1861 and 1873. Many were converted to metallic cartridge use, so they are quite scarce on today's market.

The London Model would be worth approximately twice the value of the standard model.

Courtesy Milwaukee Public Museum, Milwaukee, Wisconsin.

Production Model

Exc.	V.G.	Good	Fair	Poor
4000	2500	1750	1250	750

METALLIC CARTRIDGE CONVERSIONS

Thuer Conversion Revolver

Although quite simplistic and not commercially successful, the Thuer conversion was the first attempt by Colt to convert the percussion revolvers to the new metallic cartridge system. This conversion was designed around the tapered Thuer cartridge and consists of a ring that replaced the back part of the cylinder, which had been milled off. This ring is stamped "Pat. Sep. / 15. 1868." The ejection position is marked with the letter "E." These conversions have rebounding firing pins and are milled to allow loading from the front of the revolver. This conversion was undertaken on the six different models listed below; and all other specifications, finishes, markings, etc., not directly affected by the conversion would be the same as previously described. From a collectible and investment standpoint, the Thuer Conversion is very desirable. Competent appraisal should be secured if acquisition is contemplated.

Model 1849 Pocket Conversion

Exc.	V.G.	Good	Fair	Poor
5000	4000	3000	2250	1500

Model 1851 Navy Conversion

Exc.	V.G.	Good	Fair	Poor
4000	3000	2250	1500	1250

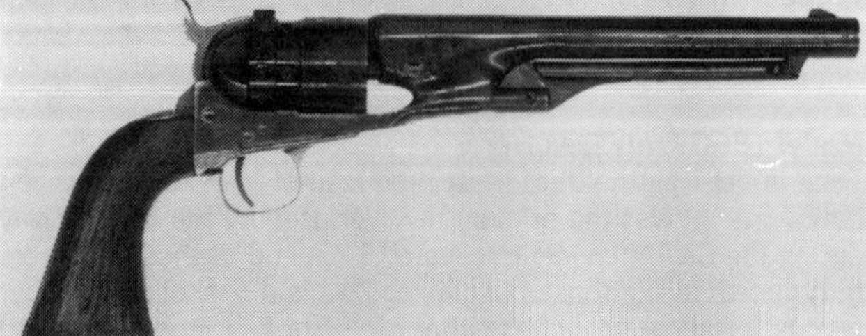

Courtesy Milwaukee Public Museum, Milwaukee, Wisconsin.

Model 1860 Army Conversion

Exc.	V.G.	Good	Fair	Poor
5000	3500	2250	1500	1250

Model 1861 Navy Conversion

Exc.	V.G.	Good	Fair	Poor
6250	5000	3500	2500	1750

Models 1862 Police Conversion

Exc.	V.G.	Good	Fair	Poor
6000	5000	3000	2250	1500

Model 1862 Pocket Navy Conversion

Exc.	V.G.	Good	Fair	Poor
6000	5000	3000	2250	1500

Richards Conversion, 1860 Army Revolver

This was Colt's second attempt at metallic cartridge conversion, and it met with quite a bit more success than the first. The Richards Conversion was designed for the .44 Colt cartridge and has a 6-shot cylinder and an integral ejector rod to replace the loading lever which had been removed. The other specifications pertaining to the 1860 Army Revolver remain as previously described if they are not directly altered by the conversion. The Richards Conversion adds a breechplate with a firing pin and its own rear sight. There were approximately 9,000 of these Conversions manufactured between 1873 and 1878.

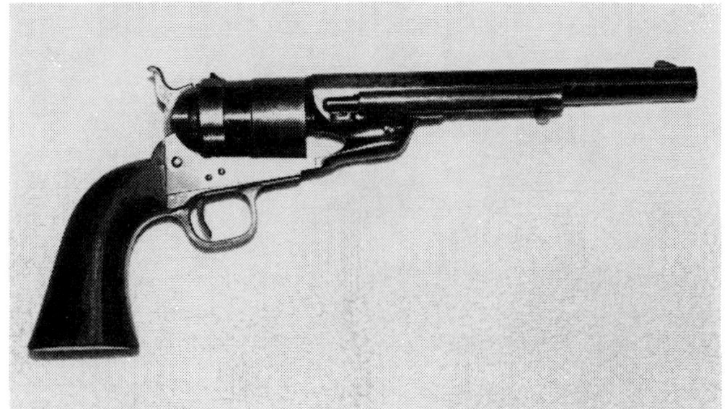

Production Model

Exc.	V.G.	Good	Fair	Poor
2500	2000	1500	1000	750

Martially Marked Variation

This variation is found with mixed serial numbers and a second set of conversion serial numbers. The "U.S." is stamped on the left side of the barrel lug, and inspector's cartouche appears on the grip.

Exc.	V.G.	Good	Fair	Poor
3250	2750	2250	1500	900

Richards-Mason Conversion, 1860 Army Revolver

This conversion is different from the Richards Conversion in a number of readily apparent aspects. The barrel was manufactured with a small lug much different in appearance than seen on the standard 1860 Army. The breechplate does not have its own rear sight, and there is a milled area to allow the hammer to contact the base of the cartridge. These Conversions were also chambered for the .44 Colt cartridge, and the cylinder holds 6 shots. There is an integral ejector rod in place of the loading lever. The barrels on some are stamped either "Address Col. Saml. Colt New-York U.S.America" or "Colt's Pt. F.A. Mfg. Co. Hartford,Ct." The patent dates 1871 and 1872 are stamped on the left side of the frame. The finish of these revolvers, as well as the grips, were for the most part the same as on the unconverted Armies; but for the first time, nickel-plated guns are found. There were approximately 2,100 of these Conversions produced in 1877 and 1878.

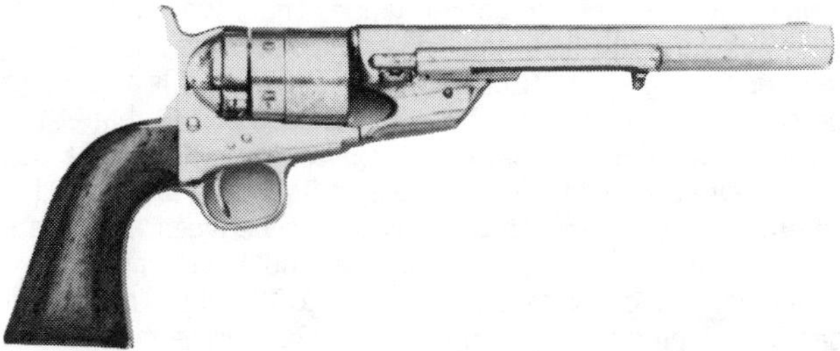

Courtesy Butterfield & Butterfield, San Francisco, California.

Exc.	V.G.	Good	Fair	Poor
2750	2250	1750	1250	750

Richards-Mason Conversions 1851 Navy Revolver

These revolvers were converted in the same way as the 1860 Army previously described, the major difference being the caliber .38, either rimfire or centerfire. Finishes are mostly the same as on unconverted revolvers, but nickel-plated guns are not rare.

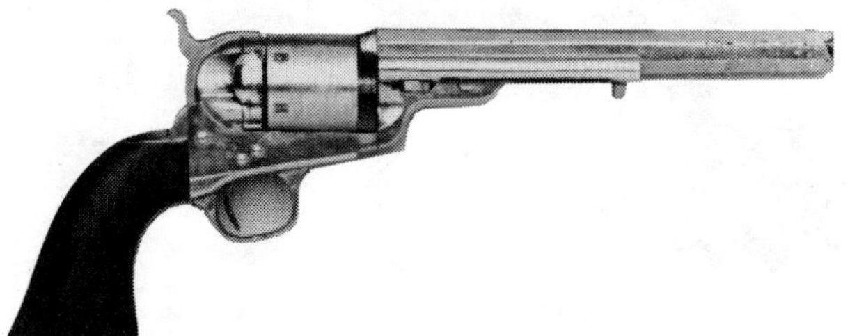

Courtesy Butterfield & Butterfield, San Francisco, California.

Production Model Serial #1-3800

Exc.	V.G.	Good	Fair	Poor
2000	1750	1250	750	600

U.S.Navy Model Serial #41000-91000 Range

"USN" stamped on butt; steel grip frame.

Exc.	V.G.	Good	Fair	Poor
2500	2000	1500	1000	750

Richards-Mason Conversion 1861 Navy Revolver

The specifications for this model are the same as for the 1851 Navy Conversion described above, with the base revolver being different. There were 2,200 manufactured in the 1870s.

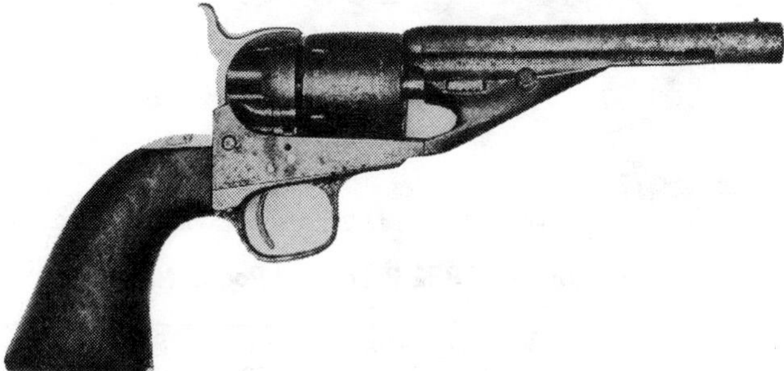

Courtesy Wallis & Wallis, Lewes, Sussex, England.

Production Model Serial #100-3300 Range

Exc.	V.G.	Good	Fair	Poor
2000	1750	1250	750	600

U.S.Navy Model #1,000-9,999 Serial Range

Exc.	V.G.	Good	Fair	Poor
2500	2000	1500	1000	750

Model 1862 Police and Pocket Navy Conversions

The conversion of these two revolver models is the most difficult to catalogue of all the Colt variations. There were approximately 24,000 of these produced between 1873 and 1880. There are five basic variations with a number of sub-variations. The confusion is usually caused by the different ways in which these were marked. Depending upon what parts were utilized, caliber markings could be particularly confusing. One must also consider the fact that many of these conversion revolvers found their way into secondary markets, such as Mexico and Central and South America, where they were either destroyed or received sufficient abuse to obliterate most identifying markings. The five basic variations are all chambered for either the .38 rimfire or the .38 centerfire cartridge. All held 5 shots, and most were found with the round roll-engraved stagecoach holdup scene. The half-fluted cylinder from the 1862 Police is quite rare on the conversion revolver and not found at all on some of the variations. The finishes on these guns were pretty much the same as they were before conversion, but it is not unusual to find nickel-plated specimens. The basic variations are as follows.

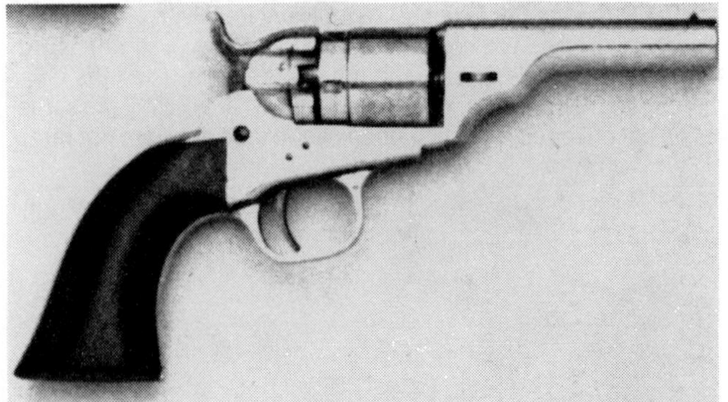

Courtesy Butterfield & Butterfield, San Francisco, California.

Round Barrel Pocket Navy with Ejector

Exc.	V.G.	Good	Fair	Poor
2500	2000	1500	1000	750

3.5" Round Barrel Without Ejector

Exc.	V.G.	Good	Fair	Poor
1750	1250	1000	650	500

4.5" Octagonal Barrel

Exc.	V.G.	Good	Fair	Poor
2000	1750	1250	750	600

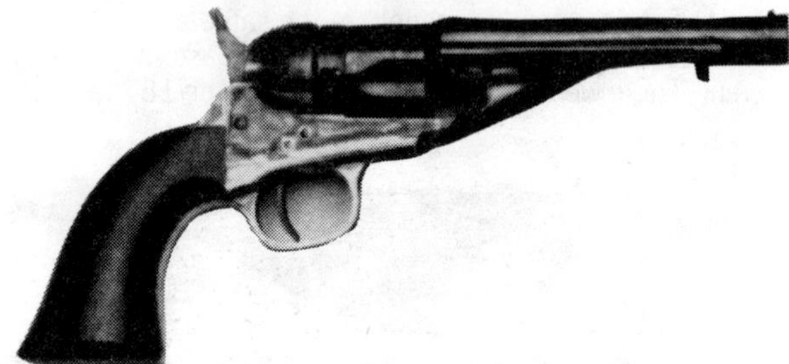

Courtesy Butterfield & Butterfield, San Francisco, California.

Standard Configuration 1862 Police and Pocket Navy

Half-fluted cylinder—Add 20%.

Exc.	V.G.	Good	Fair	Poor
2000	1750	1250	750	600

Round Barrel Model, with Ejector

Exc.	V.G.	Good	Fair	Poor
2500	2000	1500	1000	750

Model 1871-1872 open Top Revolver

This Model was the first revolver Colt manufactured especially for a metallic cartridge. It was not a conversion. The frame, 7.5"or 8" round barrel, and the 6-shot cylinder were produced for the .44 rimfire metallic cartridge. The gripframe and some internal parts were taken from the 1860 Army and the 1851 Navy. Although this Model was not commercially successful and was not accepted by the U.S. Ordnance Department, it did pave the way for the Single Action Army which came out shortly thereafter and was an immediate success. This Model is all blued, with a casecolored hammer. There are some with silverplated brass grip frames, but most are blued steel. The one-piece grips are of varnished walnut. The cylinder is roll-engraved with the naval battle scene. The barrel is stamped "Address Col. Saml. Colt New-York U.S.America." The later-production revolvers are barrel stamped "Colt's Pt. F.A.Mfg. Co. Hartford, Ct. U.S.A." The first 1,000 revolvers were stamped "Colt's/Patent." After that, 1871 and 1872 patent dates appeared on the frame. There were 7,000 of these revolvers manufactured in 1872 and 1873.

1860 Army Gripframe

Exc.	V.G.	Good	Fair	Poor
8500	7000	5500	3000	1500

1851 Navy Gripframe

Exc.	V.G.	Good	Fair	Poor
9000	7500	6000	3500	1750

DERRINGERS AND POCKET REVOLVERS

First Model Derringer

This is a very small all-metal single shot. It is chambered for the .44 rimfire cartridge. The 2.5" barrel pivots to the left and downward for loading. This model is engraved with a scroll pattern and has been noted blued, silver, or nickel-plated. The barrel is stamped "Colt's Pt. F.A. Mfg. Co./Hartford Ct. U.S.A/ No.1." ".41 Cal." is stamped on the frame under the release catch. There were approximately 6,500 of this model manufactured from 1870-1890. It was the first single shot pistol Colt produced.

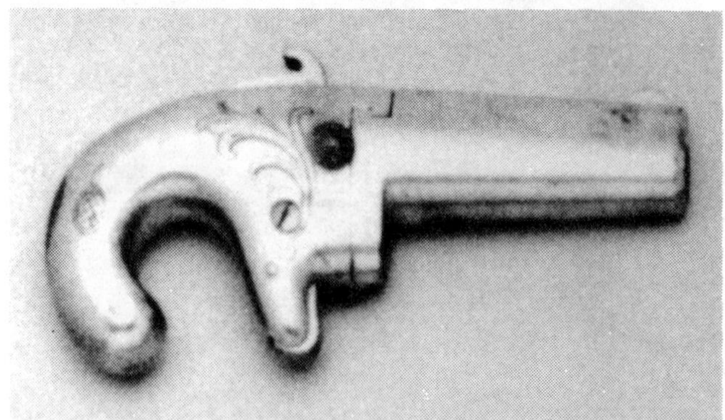

Courtesy Butterfield & Butterfield, San Francisco, California.

Exc.	V.G.	Good	Fair	Poor
1000	750	600	400	250

Second Model Derringer

Although this model has the same odd shape as the First Model, it is readily identifiable by the checkered varnished walnut grips and the "No 2" on the barrel after the address. It is also .41 rimfire and has a 2.5" barrel that pivots in the same manner as the First Model. There were approximately 9,000 of these manufactured between 1870 and 1890.

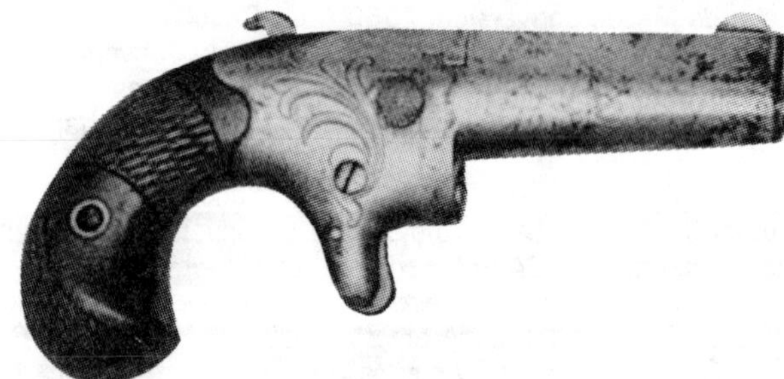

Courtesy Wallis & Wallis, Lewes, Sussex, England.

Exc.	V.G.	Good	Fair	Poor
750	500	450	300	150

Third Model Derringer

This model was designed by Alexander Thuer who was also responsible for Colt's first metallic cartridge conversion. It is often referred to as the "Thuer Model" for this reason. It is also chambered for the .41 rimfire cartridge and has a 2.5" barrel that pivots to the right (but not down) for loading. The Third Model has a more balanced appearance than its predecessors, and its commercial success (45,000 produced between 1875 and 1910) reflects this. The barrel on this model is stamped "Colt" in very small block letters on the first 2,000 guns. The remainder of the production features the "COLT" in large italicized print. The ".41 Cal." is stamped on the left side of the frame. This model will be found with the barrel blued or plated in either silver or nickel and the bronze frame plated. The grips are varnished walnut.

Courtesy Butterfield & Butterfield, San Francisco, California.

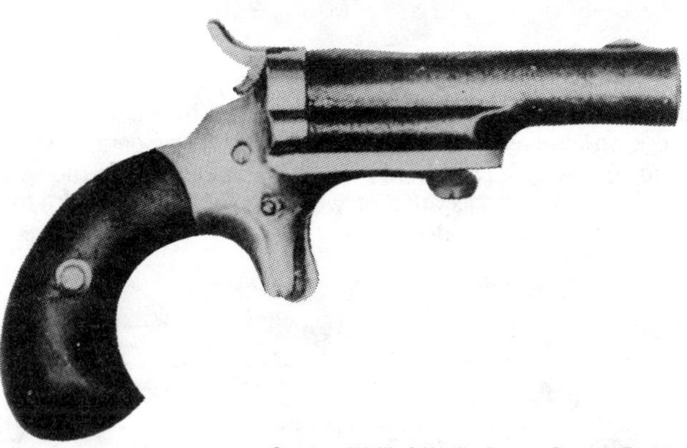

Courtesy Wallis & Wallis, Lewes, Sussex, England.

First Variation, Early Production

This has a raised area on the underside of the frame through which the barrel screw passes, and the spur is not angled. Small block "colt" lettering on barrel.

Exc.	V.G.	Good	Fair	Poor
2000	1750	1250	750	500

First Variation, Late Production

This is similar to Early Production but has large Italicized "COLT" on barrel.

Exc.	V.G.	Good	Fair	Poor
1250	850	650	450	250

Production Model

Exc.	V.G.	Good	Fair	Poor
600	500	400	300	200

House Model Revolver

There are two basic versions of this model. They are both chambered for the .41 rimfire cartridge. The 4-shot version is known as the "Cloverleaf" due to the shape of the cylinder when viewed from the front. Approximately 7,500 of the nearly 10,000 House revolvers were of this 4-shot configuration. They are offered with a 1.5" or 3" barrel. The 1.5" length is quite rare, and some octagonal barrels in this length have been noted. The 5-shot round-cylinder version accounts for the rest of the production. It is found with serial numbers over 6100 and is offered with a 2-7/8" length barrel only. This Model is stamped on the top strap "Pat. Sept.19, 1871." This Model has brass frames that were sometimes nickel-plated. The barrels are found either blued or plated. The grips are varnished walnut or rosewood. There were slightly fewer than 10,000 of both variations manufactured from 1871-1876.

Cloverleaf with 1.5" Barrel

Exc.	V.G.	Good	Fair	Poor
1000	800	650	500	350

Courtesy Buffalo Bill Historical Center, Cody, Wyoming.

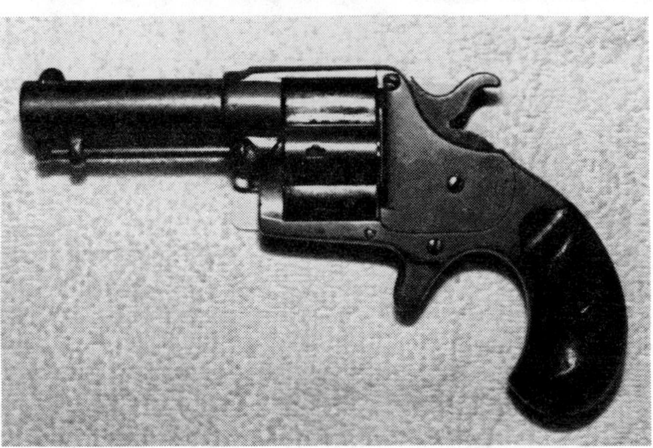

Cloverleaf with 3" Barrel

Exc.	V.G.	Good	Fair	Poor
850	700	500	400	250

Courtesy Milwaukee Public Museum, Milwaukee, Wisconsin.

House Pistol with 5-Shot Round Cylinder

Exc.	V.G.	Good	Fair	Poor
1150	1000	750	600	450

Open Top Pocket Revolver

This is a .22-caliber rimfire, 7-shot revolver that was offered with either a 2-3/8" or a 2-7/8" barrel. The model was a commercial success, with over 114,000 manufactured between 1871 and 1877. There would undoubtedly have been a great deal more sold had not the cheap copies begun to flood the market at that time, forcing Colt to drop this model from the line. This revolver has a silver or nickel-plated brass frame and a nickel-plated or blued barrel and cylinder. The grips are varnished walnut. The cylinder bolt slots are found toward the front on this model. "Colt's Pt. F.A. Mfg. Co./Hartford, Ct. U.S.A." is stamped on the barrel and ".22 Cal." on the left side of the frame.

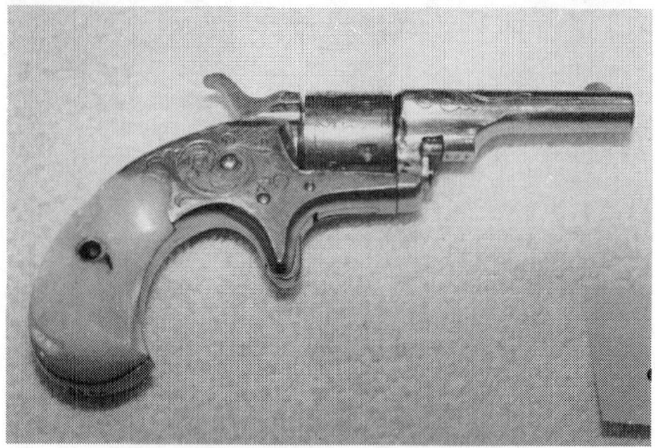

Early Model With Ejector Rod

Exc.	V.G.	Good	Fair	Poor
650	550	450	300	175

Production Model Without Ejector Rod

Exc.	V.G.	Good	Fair	Poor
500	400	350	250	125

New Line Revolver .22

This was the smallest framed version of the five distinct New Line Revolvers. It has a 7-shot cylinder and a 2.25" octagonal barrel. The frame is nickel-plated, and the balance of the revolver is either nickel-plated or blued. The grips are of rosewood. There were approximately 55,000 of these made from 1873-1877. Colt also stopped production of the New Lines rather than try to compete with the "Suicide Specials." "Colt New .22" is found on the barrel; and ".22 Cal.," on the frame. The barrel is also stamped "Colt's Pt. F.A. Mfg.Co./Hartford, Ct. U.S.A."

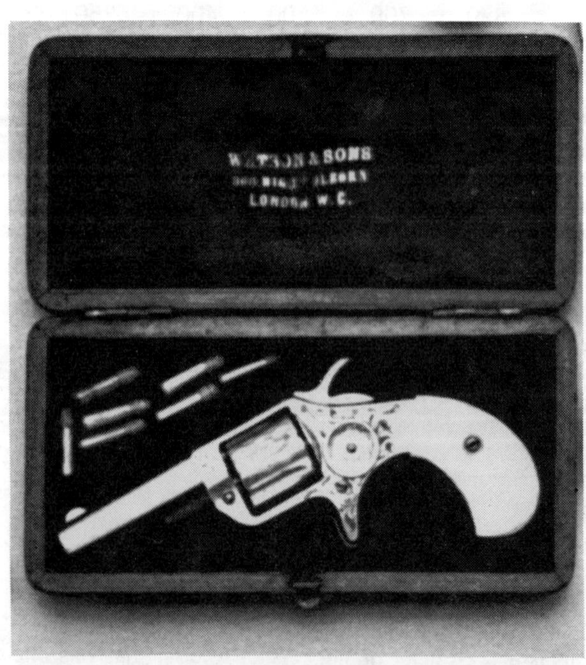

Courtesy Butterfield & Butterfield, San Francisco, California.

1st Model

Short cylinder flutes.

Exc.	V.G.	Good	Fair	Poor
550	450	400	350	200

2nd Model

Long cylinder flutes.

Exc.	V.G.	Good	Fair	Poor
500	400	350	250	125

New Line Revolver .30

This is a larger version of the .22 New Line. The basic difference is the size, caliber, caliber markings, and the offering of a blued version with casecolored frame. There were approximately 11,000 manufactured from 1874-1876.

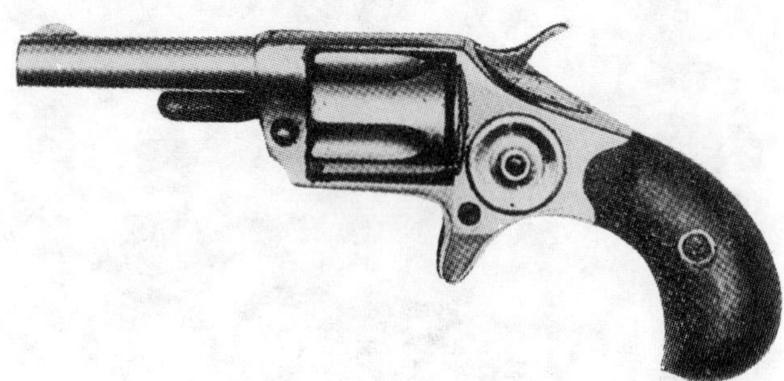

Courtesy Wallis & Wallis, Lewes, Sussex, England.

Exc.	V.G.	Good	Fair	Poor
600	500	400	300	250

New Line Revolver .32

This is the same basic revolver as the .30 caliber except that it is chambered for the .32-caliber rimfire and .32-caliber centerfire and is so marked. There were 22,000 of this model manufactured from 1873-1884. This model was offered with the very rare 4" barrel, and this variation would be worth nearly twice the value of a standard model.

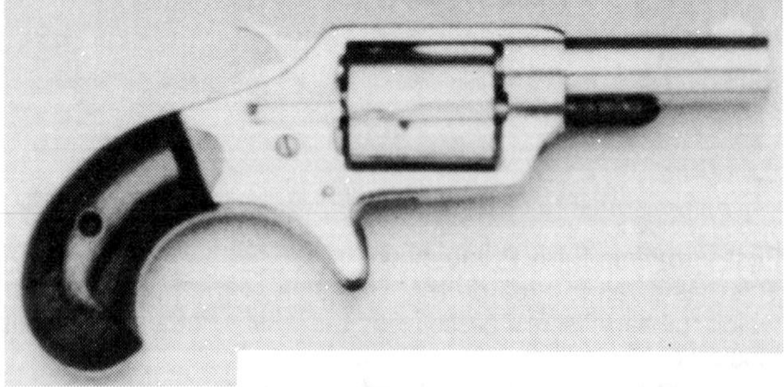

Courtesy Butterfield & Butterfield, San Francisco, California.

Exc.	V.G.	Good	Fair	Poor
500	400	300	250	200

New Line Revolver .38

There were approximately 5,500 of this model manufactured between 1874 and 1880. It is chambered for either the .38 rimfire or .38 centerfire caliber and is so marked. This model in a 4" barrel would also bring twice the value.

Exc.	V.G.	Good	Fair	Poor
600	500	400	300	250

New Line Revolver .41

This is the "Big Colt," as it was sometimes known in advertising of its era. It is chambered for the .41 rimfire and the .41 centerfire and is so marked. The large caliber of this variation makes this the most desirable of the New Lines to collectors. There were approximately 7,000 of this model manufactured from 1874-1879. A 4"-barrelled version would again be worth a 100 percent premium.

Exc.	V.G.	Good	Fair	Poor
600	500	400	300	250

New House Model Revolver

This Revolver is similar to the other New Lines except that it features a square butt instead of the birds head configuration, a 2.25" round barrel without ejector rod, and a thin loading gate. It is chambered for the .32 (rare), .38, and the .41 centerfire cartridges. The finish was either full nickel-plated or blued, with a casecolored frame. The grips are walnut, rosewood or (for the first time on a Colt revolver) checkered hard rubber, with an oval around the word "Colt." The barrel address is the same as on the other New Lines. The frame is marked "New House," with the caliber. There were approximately 4,000 manufactured between 1880-1886. .32 Caliber Model Would Bring a 10 Percent Premium.

Exc.	V.G.	Good	Fair	Poor
1000	800	650	450	300

New Police Revolver

This was the final revolver in the New Line series. It is chambered for .32, .38, and .41 centerfire caliber. The .32 and .41 are quite rare. It is offerred in barrel lengths of 2.25", 4.5", 5.5", and 6.5". An ejector rod is found on all but the 2.5" barrel. The finish is either nickel or blued and case-colored. The grips are hard rubber with a scene of a policeman arresting a criminal embossed on them; thusly the model became known to collectors as the "Cop and Thug" model. The barrel stamping is as the other New Lines, and the frame is stamped "New Police .38." There were approximately 4,000 of these manufactured between 1882-1886.

The .32 and .41 Caliber Versions of This Model Will Bring a 40-50 Percent Premium.

Courtesy Milwaukee Public Museum, Milwaukee, Wisconsin.

Exc.	V.G.	Good	Fair	Poor
1000	800	650	450	300

COLT'S SINGLE ACTION ARMY REVOLVER

The Colt Single Action Army, or Peacemaker as it is sometimes referred to, is one of the most widely collected and recognized firearms in the world. With few interruptions or changes in design, it has been manufactured from 1873 until the present. It is still available on a limited production basis from the Colt Custom Shop. The variations in this model are myriad. It has been produced in 30 different calibers and barrel lengths from 2.5" to 16", with 4.75", 5.5", and 7.5" standard. The standard finish is blued, with a casecolored frame. Many are nickel-plated. Examples have been found silver- and gold-plated, with combinations thereof. The finest engravers in the world have used the SAA as a canvas to display their artistry. The standard grips from 1873-1883 were walnut, either oil-stained or varnished. From 1883 to approximately 1897, the standard grips were hard rubber with eagle and shield. After this date, at serial number 165000, the hard rubber grips featured the Rampant Colt. Many special-order grips were available, notably pearl and ivory, which were often checkered or carved in ornate fashion. The variables involved in establishing values on this model are extreme. Added to this, one must also consider historical significance, since the SAA played a big part in the formative years of the American West. Fortunately for those among us interested in the SAA, there are a number of fine publications available dealing exclusively with this model. It is my strongest recommendation that they be acquired and studied thoroughly to prevent extremely expensive mistakes. The Colt factory records are nearly complete for this model, and research should be done before acquisition of rare or valuable specimens.

For our purposes we will break down the Single Action Army production as follows:

Antique or Black Powder, 1873-1898, serial #1-175000
The cylinder axis pin is retained by a screw in the front of the frame.

Pre-War, 1899-1940, serial #175001-357859
The cylinder axis pin is retained by a spring-loaded button through the side of the frame. This method is utilized on the following models, as well.

Post-War 2nd Generation, 1956-1978, serial #0001SA-99999SA

3rd Generation, 1978-Present, serial #SA1001-

A breakdown of production by caliber will follow the chapter. It is important to note that the rarer calibers and the larger calibers bring higher values in this variation.

ANTIQUE SINGLE ACTION ARMY REVOLVER

1st Year Production "Pinched Frame" 1873 Only

It is necessary to categorize this variation on its own. This is one of the rarest and most interesting of all the SAAs—not to mention that it is the first. On this model the top strap is pinched or constricted approximately one half inch up from the hammer to form the rear sight. The highest surviving serial number having this feature is #156, the lowest #1. From these numbers, it is safe to assume that the first run of SAAs were all pinched-frame models; but there is no way to tell how many there were, since Colt did not serial number the frames in the order that they were manufactured. An educated guess would be that there were between 50 and 150 pinched frame guns in all and that they were all made before mid-July 1873. The reason for the change came about on the recommendation of Capt. J. R. Edie, a government inspector who thought that the full fluted top strap would be a big improvement in the sighting capabilities of the weapon. The barrel length of the first model is 7.5"; the standard caliber, .45 Colt; and the proper grips were of walnut. The front sight blade is German silver. Needless to say, this model will rarely be encountered; and if it is, it should never be purchased without competent appraisal.

Exc.	V.G.	Good	Fair	Poor
15000	11000	7500	5000	4000

Early Military Model 1873-1877

The serial number range on this first run of military contract revolvers extends to #24000. The barrel address is in the early script style with the #symbol preceding and following. The frame bears the martial marking "US," and the walnut grips have the inspector's cartouche stamped on them. The front sight is steel as on all military models; the barrel length, 7.5". The caliber is .45 Colt, and the ejector rod head is the bullseye or donut style with a hole in the center of it. The finish features the military polish and case-colored frame, with the remainder blued. Authenticate any potential purchase; many spurious examples have been noted.

Exc.	V.G.	Good	Fair	Poor
10000	7500	6000	3750	2250

Early Civilian Model 1873-1877

This model is identical to the Early Military Model but has no military acceptance markings or cartouches. Some could have the German silver front sight blade. The early bullseye ejector rod head is used on this Model. The Civilian Model has a higher degree of polish than is found on the military models, and the finish on these early models could be plated or blued with a case-colored frame. The grips are standard one-piece walnut. Ivory-grip models are worth a premium.

Exc.	V.G.	Good	Fair	Poor
8500	6000	4000	2500	1750

.44 Rimfire Model 1875-1880

This model was made to fire the .44 Henry Rimfire Cartridge. It was to be used as a compatible companion sidearm to the Henry and Winchester 1866 rifles that were used extensively during this era. However, this was not the case; and the .44 Rimfire was doomed to economic failure as soon as it appeared on the market. By that time, it had already been established that large-caliber centerfire cartridges were a good deal more efficient than their rimfire counterparts. The large-caliber rimfires were deemed obsolete before this Colt ever hit the market. The result of this was that Colt's sales representatives sold most of the production to obscure Banana Republics in South and Central America, where this model received much abuse. Most had the original 7.5" barrels cut down; and nearly all were denied even the most basic maintenance, making the survival rate of this model quite low. All this adds to its desirability as a collector's item and makes the risk of acquiring a fake that much greater. This model is unique in that it was the only SAA variation to have its own serial-number range, starting with #1 and continuing to #1892, the latest known surviving specimen. The block style barrel markings were introduced during this production run. At least 90 of these revolvers were converted by the factory to .22 rimfire, and one was shipped chambered for .32 rimfire.

Exc.	V.G.	Good	Fair	Poor
10000	7500	6000	3750	2250

Late Military Model 1878-1891

The later Military Models are serial numbered to approximately #136000. They bear the block-style barrel address without the #prefix and suffix. The frames are marked "US," and the grips have the inspector's cartouche. The finish is the military-style polish, case-colored frame; and the remainder, blued. Grips are oil-stained walnut. On the military marked Colts, it is imperative that potential purchases be authenticated as many fakes have been noted.

Exc.	V.G.	Good	Fair	Poor
5000	4000	3000	2250	1500

Artillery Model 1895-1903

A number of "US" marked SAAs were returned either to the Colt factory or to the Springfield Armory, where they were altered and refinished. These revolvers have 5.5" barrels and any combination of mixed serial numbers. They were remarked by the inspectors of the era and have a case-colored frame and a blued cylinder and barrel. Some have been noted all blued within this variation. This model, as with the other military marked Colts, should definitely be authenticated before purchase. Some of these revolvers fall outside the 1898 antique cutoff date that has been established by the government and, in our experience, are not quite as desirable to investors. They are generally worth approximately 20 percent less.

Exc.	V.G.	Good	Fair	Poor
3000	2500	2250	1750	1250

London Model

These SAAs were manufactured to be sold through Colt's London Agency. The barrel is stamped "Colt's Pt.F.A. Mfg. Co. Hartford, Ct. U.S.A. Depot 14 Pall Mall London." This model is available in various barrel lengths. They are generally chambered for .45 Colt, .450 Boxer, .450 Eley, .455 Eley, and rarely .476 Eley, the largest of the SAA chamberings. A good many of these London Models were cased and embellished, and they should be individually appraised. This model should be authenticated as many spurious examples have been noted.

Exc.	V.G.	Good	Fair	Poor
3000	2500	2250	1750	1250

Frontier Six-Shooter 1878-1882

Several thousand SAAs were made with the legend "Colt's Frontier Six Shooter" acid-etched into the left side of the barrel instead of being stamped. This etching is not very deep, and today collectors will become ecstatic if they discover a specimen with mere vestiges of the etched panel remaining. These acid-etched SAAs are serial numbered #45000-65000. They have various barrel lengths and finishes, but all are chambered for the .44-40 caliber.

Exc.	V.G.	Good	Fair	Poor
9000	7500	5000	2500	1500

Sheriff's or Storekeeper's Model 1882-1898

This model was manufactured with a short barrel (2.5"-4.75"). Most have 4" barrels. It features no ejector rod or housing, and the frame is made without the hole in the right forward section to accommodate the ejector assembly. The Sheriff's or Storekeeper's Model is numbered above serial #73000. It was manufactured with various finishes and chambered for numerous calibers. This model continued after 1898 into the smokeless or modern era. Examples manufactured in the prewar years are worth approximately 20 percent less. Although faking this model is quite difficult, it has been successfully attempted.

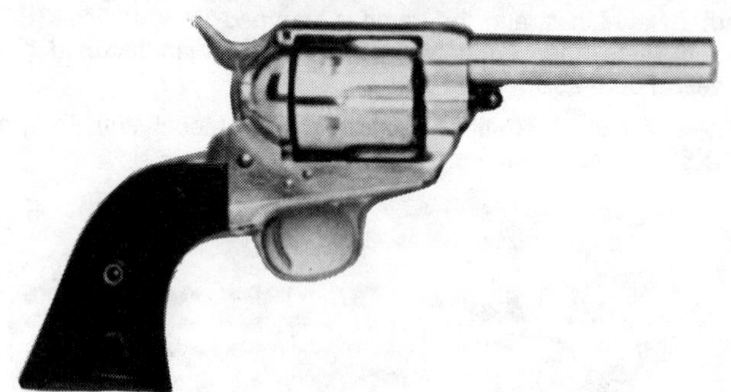

Courtesy Butterfield & Butterfield, San Francisco, California.

Exc.	V.G.	Good	Fair	Poor
12500	10000	7500	4500	2500

Flattop Target Model 1888-1896

This model is highly regarded and sought after by collectors. It is not only rare (only 925 manufactured) but is an extremely attractive and well finished variation. It is chambered for 22 different calibers from .22 rimfire to .476 Eley. The .22 rimfire, .38 Colt, .41 and .45 Colt are the most predominant chamberings. The 7.5" barrel length is the most commonly encountered. The serial number range is between #127000-162000. Some have been noted in higher ranges. The finish is all blued, with a case-colored hammer. The checkered grips are either hard rubber or walnut. The most readily identifying feature of the flattop i.e. the lack of a groove in the top strap and the sight blade dovetailed into the flattop. The front sight has a removable blade insert. The values given are for a standard production model chambered for the calibers previously mentioned as being the most common. It is important to have other calibers individually appraised as variance in values can be quite extreme.

Exc.	V.G.	Good	Fair	Poor
15000	12500	8500	5000	3750

Bisley Model 1894-1915

This model was named for the target range in Great Britain, where their National Target Matches were held since the nineteenth century. The model was designed as a target revolver with an odd humped-back grip that was supposed to better fill the hand while target shooting. It is also easily identified by the wide low profile hammer spur, the wide trigger, and the name "Bisley" stamped on the barrel. The Bisley production fell within the serial number range #165000-331916. There were

44,350 made. It was offered in 16 different chamberings from .32 Colt to .455 Eley. The most common calibers were .32-20, .38-40, .41, .44-40, and .45 Colt. The barrel lengths are 4.75", 5.5", and 7.5". The frame and hammer are case-colored; the remainder, blued. Smokeless powder models produced after 1899 utilized the pushbutton cylinder pin retainer. The grips are checkered hard rubber. This model was actually designed with English sales in mind; and though it did sell well over there, American sales accounted for most of the Bisley production. The values we provide here cover the standard calibers and barrel lengths. Rare calibers and/or other notable variations can bring greatly fluctuating values, and qualified appraisals should be secured in such cases.

Bisleys manufactured from 1898-1915 are worth approximately 20 percent less.

Exc.	V.G.	Good	Fair	Poor
3500	3000	2000	1250	750

Bisley Model Flattop Target 1894-1913

This model is quite similar to the Standard Bisley Model, with the flattop frame and dovetailed rear sight feature. It also has the removable front sight insert. It has an all-blued finish with case-colored hammer only and is available with a 7.5" barrel. Smokeless powder models produced after 1899 utilized the pushbutton cylinder pin retainer. The calibers are the same as the standard Bisley. Colt manufactured 976 of these revolvers. The advice regarding appraisal would also apply.

Exc.	V.G.	Good	Fair	Poor
8000	7000	4500	2500	1750

Standard Civilian Production Models 1876-1898

This final designated category for the black powder or antique SAA's includes all the revolvers not previously categorized. They have barrel lengths from 4.75", 5.5", and 7.5" and are chambered for any one of 30 different calibers. The finishes could be blued, blued and case-colored, or plated in nickle, silver, gold, or combinations thereof. Grips could be walnut, hard rubber, ivory, pearl, stag, or bone. The possibilities are endless. The values given here are for the basic model, and we again strongly advise securing qualified appraisal when not completely sure of any model variation.

Exc.	V.G.	Good	Fair	Poor
7500	5500	3500	2000	1000

At this time it is important to note that the Colt's Single Action Army Revolvers we have discussed to this point are in the antique category as established by our Federal Government. The arbitrary cutoff date of 1898 has been established, and any weapon made prior to this date is considered an antique and, as such, not subject to the restraints placed on collectors and dealers by the Gun Control Act of 1968. This is important because firearms falling into this category will usually bring higher values due to the demand by pure investors who do not relish paperwork on collectible investments. There will be those who disagree with me on this line of reasoning, but my experience tells me that it is correct.

PREWAR SINGLE ACTION ARMY REVOLVER 1899-1940

Standard Production Prewar Models

The 1899 cutoff has been thoroughly discussed, but it is interesting to note that the actual beginning production date for smokeless models was 1900. The Prewar Colts are, all in all, quite similar to the antiques—the finishes, barrel lengths, grips, etc. Calibers are also similar, with the exception of the obsolete ones being dropped and new discoveries added. The most apparent physical difference between the smokeless powder and black powder models is the previously discussed method of retaining the cylinder axis pin. The prewar Colts utilized the springloaded button through the side of the frame. The black powder models utilized a screw in the front of the frame. The values we furnish for this model designation are for these standard models only. The serial number range on the Prewar SAAs is 175001-357859. Note that any variation can have marked effects on value fluctuations, and qualified appraisal should be secured.

Exc.	V.G.	Good	Fair	Poor
5000	4000	3000	2000	1000

Long Fluted Cylinder Model 1913-1915

Strange as it may seem, the Colt Company has an apparent credo they followed to never throw anything away. That credo was never more evident than with this model. These Long Flute Cylinders were actually left over from the Model 1878 Double Action Army Revolvers. Someone in the hierarchy at Colt had an inspiration that drove the gunsmiths on the payroll slightly mad: to make these cylinders fit the SAA frames. There were 1,478 of these Long Flutes manufactured. They are chambered for the .45 Colt, .38-40, .32-20, .41 Colt, and the .44 Smith & Wesson Special. They were offered in the three standard barrel lengths and were especially well polished, having what has been described as Colt's "Fire Blue" on the barrel and cylinder. The frame and hammer are casecolored. They are fitted with checkered hard rubber grips and are particularly fine examples of Colt's craft.

Exc.	V.G.	Good	Fair	Poor
6000	4500	3500	2500	1500

POSTWAR SINGLE ACTION ARMY REVOLVER

Standard Postwar Model 1956-1975

In 1956 the shooting and gun-collecting fraternity succeeded in convincing Colt that there was a market for a re-introduced SAA. The revolver was brought back in the same external configuration. The only changes were internal. The basic specifications as to barrel length and finish availability were the same. The calibers available were .38 Special, .357 Magnum, .44 Special, and .45 Colt. The serial number range of the re-introduced 2nd Generation, as it is sometimes known, Colt is #0001SA-73000SA. Values for the standard postwar Colts are established by four basic factors: caliber (popularity and scarcity), barrel length, finish, and condition. Shorter barrel lengths are generally more desirable than the 7.5". The .38 Special is the rarest caliber, but the .45 Colt and .44 Special are more sought after than the .357 Magnum. Special feature revolvers, such as the 350 factory-engraved guns produced during this period, must be individually appraised. The ivory situation in the world today has become quite a factor, as ivory grips are found on many SAAs. We will attempt to take these factors into consideration and evaluate this variation as accurately and clearly as possible. Remember as always, when in doubt secure a qualified appraisal.

4.75" Barrel— Add 25%.
5.5" Barrel—Add 15%.
Nickle Finish—Add 20%.
Ivory Grips—Add $250.

Values for 7.5" Barrel Model

.38 Special

NIB	Exc.	V.G.	Good	Fair	Poor
1250	1050	850	750	650	550

.357 Magnum

NIB	Exc.	V.G.	Good	Fair	Poor
1000	800	725	650	600	550

.44 Special

NIB	Exc.	V.G.	Good	Fair	Poor
1600	1250	950	850	750	650

.45 Colt

NIB	Exc.	V.G.	Good	Fair	Poor
1500	1150	950	850	750	650

Sheriff's Model 1960-1975

Between 1960 and 1975, there were approximately 500 Sheriff's Models manufactured. They have 3" barrels and no ejector rod assemblies. The frames were made without the hole for the ejector rod to pass through. They were blued, with case-colored frames; 25 revolvers were nickle-plated and would bring a sizeable premium if authenticated. The barrels are marked "Colt Sheriff's Model." The serial number has an "SM" suffix. They are chambered for the .45 Colt cartridge.

Nickle Finish—Add 20%.

NIB	Exc.	V.G.	Good	Fair	Poor
1500	1200	1000	750	600	500

Buntline Special 1957-1975

The "Buntline Special" was named after a dime novelist named Ned Buntline, who supposedly gave this special long barrel revolver to Wyatt Earp. The story is suspected to be purely legend as no Colt records exist to lend it credence. Be that as it may, the Colt factory decided to take advantage of the market and produced the 12" barrelled SAA from 1957-1974. There were approximately 3,900 manufactured. They are chambered for the .45 Colt cartridge and are offered in the blued and case-colored finish. Only 65 Buntlines are nickle-plated, making this an extremely rare variation that definitely should be authenticated before purchase. Walnut grips are the most commonly noted, but they are also offered with the checkered hard rubber grips. The barrels are marked on the left side "Colt Buntline Special .45."

Nickle Finish—Add 60%.

NIB	Exc.	V.G.	Good	Fair	Poor
1000	800	650	550	400	350

New Frontier 1961-1975

The New Frontier is readily identified by its flattop frame and adjustable sight. It also has a very high front sight. Colt manufactured approximately 4,200 of them. They are chambered for the .357 Magnum, .45 Colt, .44 Special (255 produced), and rarely (only 49 produced) in .38 Special. The 7.5" barrel length is by far the most common, but the 4.75" and 5.5" barrels are also offered. The standard finish is case-colored and blued. Nickle-plating and full blue are offered but are rarely encountered. Standard grips are walnut. The barrel is stamped on the left side "Colt New Frontier S.A.A." The serial has the "NF" suffix.

4.75" Barrel—Add 25%.
5.5" Barrel—Add 20%.
Full Blue—Add 50%.
.38 Special—Add 50%.
.44 Special—Add 30%.

NIB	Exc.	V.G.	Good	Fair	Poor
750	650	500	450	400	300

New Frontier Buntline Special 1962-1967

This model is very rare, as Colt only manufactured 70 during this five-year period. They are similar to the standard Buntline, with a 12" barrel. They are chambered for .45 Colt only.

NIB	Exc.	V.G.	Good	Fair	Poor
1500	1200	1000	750	600	500

THIRD GENERATION SINGLE ACTION ARMY 1976-1981

In 1976 Colt made some internal changes in the SAA. The external configuration was not altered. The serial number range began in 1976 with #80000SA, and in 1978 #99999SA was reached. At this time the suffix became a prefix, and the new serial range began with #SA01001. This model's value is determined in much the same manner as was described in the section on the 2nd Generation SAAs. Caliber, barrel length, finish, and condition are once again the four main determining factors. The prevalence of special-order guns was greater during this period, and many more factory-engraved SAAs were produced. Colt's Custom Shop was quite active during this period. We feel that it is not advisable to undertake evaluation of specially embellished guns and strongly advise that competent appraisal be secured on any firearms that deviate from the standard. There are, quite frankly, too many fraudulent Colt SAAs out there; and the financial risks are great.

4.75" Barrel—Add 25%.
5.5" Barrel—Add 10%.
Nickle Plated—Add 10%.
Ivory Grips—Add $250.

Values with 7.5" Barrel

.357 Magnum

NIB	Exc.	V.G.	Good	Fair	Poor
800	600	550	450	350	300

.44-40

NIB	Exc.	V.G.	Good	Fair	Poor
1000	750	650	550	450	400

.44-40 Black Powder Frame (Screw Retaining Cylinder Pin)

NIB	Exc.	V.G.	Good	Fair	Poor
1250	1000	800	650	550	450

.44 Special

NIB	Exc.	V.G.	Good	Fair	Poor
850	650	600	500	400	350

.45 Colt

NIB	Exc.	V.G.	Good	Fair	Poor
850	650	600	500	400	350

Sheriff's Model 3rd Generation

This Model is very similar to the 2nd Generation Sheriff's Model. The serial number and the fact that this model is also chambered for the .44-40 are the only external differences. Colt offered this model with interchangeable cylinders—.45 Colt/.45 ACP or .44-40/.44 Special—available in 3" barrel, blued and case-colored finish standard.

Interchangeable Cylinders—Add 30%.
Nickle Finish—Add 10%.
Ivory Grips—Add $250.

NIB	Exc.	V.G.	Good	Fair	Poor
850	700	650	550	450	400

Buntline Special 3rd Generation

This is the same basic configuration as the 2nd generation with the 12" barrel. Standard finish blued and case-colored, it is chambered for .45 Colt and has checkered hard rubber grips.

Nickle Finish—Add 10%.

NIB	Exc.	V.G.	Good	Fair	Poor
850	700	600	500	400	350

New Frontier 3rd Generation

This model is very similar in appearance to the 2nd Generation guns. The 3rd Generation New Frontiers have five-digit serial numbers; the 2nd Generation guns, four-digit numbers. That and the calibers offered are basically the only differences. The 3rd Generations are chambered for the .44 Special and .45 Colt

and are rarely found in .44-40. Barrel lengths are 7.5" standard, with the 4.75" and 5.5" rarely encountered.
.44-40—Add 20%.
4.75" Barrel—Add 35%.
5.5" Barrel—Add 25%.

NIB	Exc.	V.G.	Good	Fair	Poor
650	550	450	400	300	250

CURRENT PRODUCTION SINGLE ACTION ARMY 1982-PRESENT

Standard Single Action Army

The SAA, it is sad to note, has all but faded from the firearms picture. They are currently available as a special-order custom shop proposition. The cost is great; and the availability, low. The heyday of one of the most venerable firearms of them all is pretty much at an end. The current SAAs are available in only .44-40, .44 Special, and .45 Colt. Barrels are available in 3" through 10" lengths. The finishes are nickle-plated and blued, with case-colored frames. A number of optional finishes are available on request. Grips are available on a custom order basis. This model is available on special-order only.

The minimum order that the Colt custom shop will accept is $1,095 at retail, so anyone desiring to own a new Colt SAA must order options, as the base price of a new gun won't be acceptable.
Nickle Finish—Add $125.
Royal Blue Finish—Add $200.
Mirror Brite Finish—Add $225.
Gold Plate—Add $365.
Silver Plate—Add $365.
Class A Engraving—Add $875.
Class B Engraving—Add $1,200.
Class C Engraving—Add $1,500.
Class D Engraving—Add $1,750.
Buntline Engraving—Add 15%.

NIB	Exc.	V.G.	Good	Fair	Poor
1150	1000	600	450	400	300

SCOUT MODEL SINGLE ACTION ARMY

New Frontier Scout 1958-1972

This is a scaled-down version of the SAA that is chambered for the .22 l.r. with an interchangeable .22 Magnum cylinder. It is offered with a 4.25", 4.75", or a 9.5" barrel. The frame is alloy; and the finish, either blued or nickle-plated. The grips are hard rubber.
9.5" Buntline—Add 50%.
Extra cylinder—Add 10%.
Nickle Plated—Add 10%.

NIB	Exc.	V.G.	Good	Fair	Poor
300	250	200	175	125	90

Peacemaker Scout 1970-1977

This model is quite similar to the New Frontier Scout, with a steel case-colored frame. The barrel lengths offered are 4.75", 6", or 7.5". It also has an interchangeable .22 Magnum cylinder.

NIB	Exc.	V.G.	Good	Fair	Poor
325	275	225	200	150	100

Colt Single Action Army Production Breakdown by Caliber Antique and Pre-War

CALIBER	SAA	FLATTOP SAA	BISLEY	FLATTOP BISLEY
.22 R.F.	107	93	0	0
.32 R.F.	1	0	0	0
.32 Colt	192	24	160	44
.32 S&W	32	30	18	17
.32-44	2	9	14	17
.32-20	29,812	30	13,291	131
.38 Colt	1,011	122	412	96
(1914)	-	-	-	-
.38 Colt	1,365	0	0	0
(1922)	-	-	-	-
.38 S&W	9	39	10	5
.38 Colt Sp.	82	7	0	0
.38 S&W Sp.	25	0	2	0
.38-44	2	11	6	47
.357 Mag.	525	0	0	0
.380 Eley	1	3	0	0
.38-40	38,240	19	12,163	98
.41	16,402	91	3,159	24
.44 SmBr.	15	0	1	0
.44 R.F.	1,863	0	0	0
.44 Germ.	59	0	0	0
.44 Russ.	154	51	90	62
.44 S&W	24	51	29	64
.44 S&W Sp.	506	1	0	0
.44-40	64,489	21	6,803	78
.45 Colt	150,683	100	8,005	97
.45 SmBr.	4	0	2	0
,45 ACP	44	0	0	0
.450 Boxer	729	89	0	0
.450 Eley	2,697	84	5	0
.455 Eley	1,150	37	180	196
.476 Eley	161	2	0	0
Total	**310,386**	**914**	**44,350**	**976**

The above chart covers the production by caliber of the Single Action Army Revolvers manufactured between 1873 and 1940. These are the antique and the pre-war firearms. This chart readily informs us as to which are the rare calibers.

Scout Model SAA

This is basically a scaled-down version of the SAA chambered for the .22 l.r. cartridge. This model is offered with a 4.75", 6", or 7" barrel. The earlier production has case-colored frames with the remainder blued; later production is all blued. Grips are checkered hard rubber. This model was discontinued in 1986.

NIB	Exc.	V.G.	Good	Fair	Poor
250	200	175	150	100	75

Anyone wishing to procure a factory letter authenticating a Single Action Army should do so by writing to: COLT HISTORIAN, P.O. BOX 1868, HARTFORD, CT 06101. There is a charge of $35 per serial number for this service. If Colt cannot provide the desired information, $10 will be refunded. Enclose the Colt model name, serial number, and your name and address, along with the check.

COLT ANTIQUE LONG ARMS

Berdan Single Shot Rifle

This is a very scarce rifle on today's market. There were approximately 30,200 manufactured, but nearly 30,000 of them were sent to Russia. This rifle was produced from 1866-1870. It is a trapdoor-type action chambered for .42 centerfire. The standard model has a 32.5" barrel; the carbine, 18.25". The finish is blued, with a walnut stock. This rifle was designed and the patent held by Hiram Berdan, Commander of the Civil War "Sharpshooters" Regiment. This was actually Colt's first cartridge arm. The 30,000 rifles and 25 half-stocked carbines that were sent to Russia were in Russian Cyrillic letters. The few examples made for American sales have Colt's name and Hartford address on the barrel.

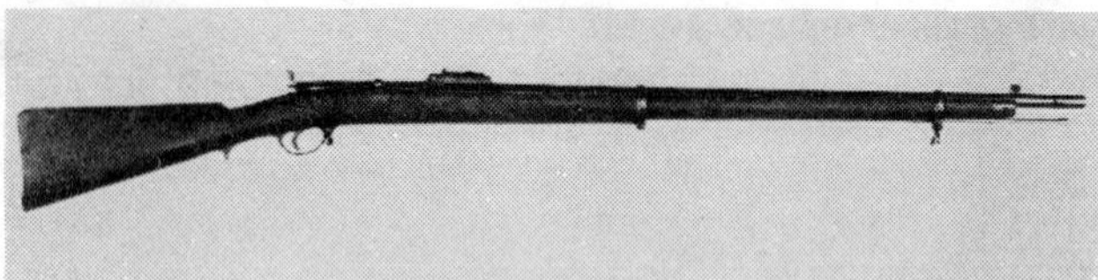

Courtesy Milwaukee Public Museum, Milwaukee, Wisconsin.

Rifle Russian Order, 30,000 Manufactured

Exc.	V.G.	Good	Fair	Poor
1500	1250	1000	650	450

Carbine Russian Order, 25 Manufactured

Exc.	V.G.	Good	Fair	Poor
4500	3750	3000	2000	1500

Rifle U.S. Sales, 100 Manufactured

Exc.	V.G.	Good	Fair	Poor
2750	2000	1750	1250	1000

Carbine U.S. Sales, 25 Manufactured

Exc.	V.G.	Good	Fair	Poor
5000	4000	3500	2500	2000

Colt-Franklin Military Rifle

This is a rifle that was not a successful venture for Colt. The patents were held by William B. Franklin, a vice president of the company. This was a bolt-action rifle with a primitive, gravity-fed box magaine. It is chambered for the .45-70 government cartridge, has a 32.5" barrel, and is blued, with a walnut stock. The rifle has the Colt Hartford barrel address and is stamped with an eagle's head and U.S. inspector's marks. There were only 50 of these rifles produced, and it is believed that they were prototypes intended for government sales. This was not to be, and production ceased after approximately 50 were manufactured in 1887 and 1888.

Exc.	V.G.	Good	Fair	Poor
4500	3750	3000	2000	1500

Colt-Burgess Lever Action Rifle

This represented Colt's only attempt to compete with Winchester for the lever-action rifle market. It is said that when Winchester started to produce revolving handguns for prospective marketing, Colt dropped the Burgess from their line. This rifle is chambered for .44-40. It has a 25.5" barrel and a 15-shot tubular magazine. The Carbine version has a 20.5" barrel and 12-shot magazine. The finish is blued, with a case-colored hammer and lever. The stock is walnut with an oil finish. The Colt Hartford address is on the barrel, and "Burgess Patents" is stamped on the bottom of the lever. There were 3,775 rifles manufactured—1,219 with round barrels and 2,556 with octagonal barrels. There were also 2,593 Carbines. The Burgess was produced from 1883-1885.

Courtesy Buffalo Bill Historical Center, Cody, Wyoming.

Rifle, Octagonal Barrel

Exc.	V.G.	Good	Fair	Poor
1750	1400	1000	750	550

Rifle, Round Barrel

Exc.	V.G.	Good	Fair	Poor
2000	1650	1250	950	750

Carbine

Exc.	V.G.	Good	Fair	Poor
2250	1850	1500	1250	950

Baby Carbine, Lighter Frame and Barrel (RARE)

Exc.	V.G.	Good	Fair	Poor
2750	2000	1750	1500	1150

Lightning Slide Action, Medium Frame

This was the first slide action rifle Colt produced. It is chambered for .32-20, .38-40, and .44-40 and was intended to be a companion piece to the SAAs in the same calibers. The rifle has a 26" barrel with 15-shot tube magazine; the carbine, a 20" barrel with 12-shot magazine. The finish is blued, with case-colored hammer; the walnut stock is oil-finished; and the forend, usually checkered. The Colt name and Hartford address are stamped on the barrel along with the patent dates. There were approximately 89,777 manufactured between 1884 and 1902.

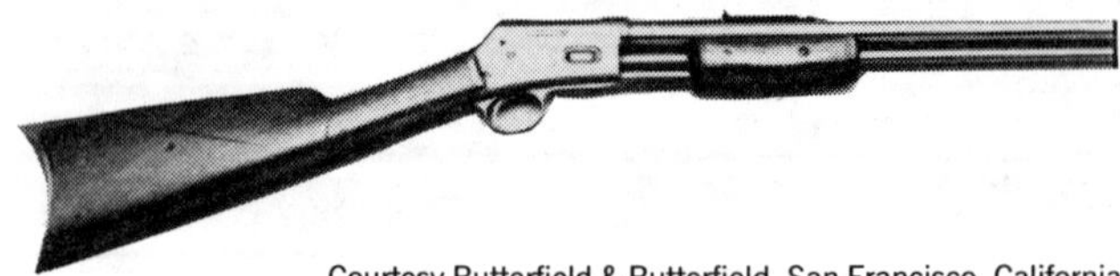

Courtesy Butterfield & Butterfield, San Francisco, California.

Rifle

Exc.	V.G.	Good	Fair	Poor
1500	1250	950	650	400

Carbine

Exc.	V.G.	Good	Fair	Poor
2000	1500	1250	800	500

Military Rifle or Carbine

.44-40 caliber, short magazine tube, bayonet lug, and sling swivels.

Exc.	V.G.	Good	Fair	Poor
4500	3500	2750	2000	1500

Baby Carbine, 1 lb., Lighter Version of Standard Carbine

Exc.	V.G.	Good	Fair	Poor
4500	3500	2750	2000	1500

San Francisco Police Rifle
.44-40 caliber, #SFP 1-SFP401 on bottom tang.

Exc.	V.G.	Good	Fair	Poor
2000	1500	1250	800	500

Lightning Slide Action Small Frame
This is a very well-made rifle and the first of its type that Colt manufactured. It is chambered for the .22 Short and Long. The standard barrel length is 24"; the finish, blued with a case-colored hammer. The stock is walnut; some were checkered; some, not. The barrel is stamped with the Colt name and Hartford address and the patent dates. There were 89,912 manufactured between 1887 and 1904.

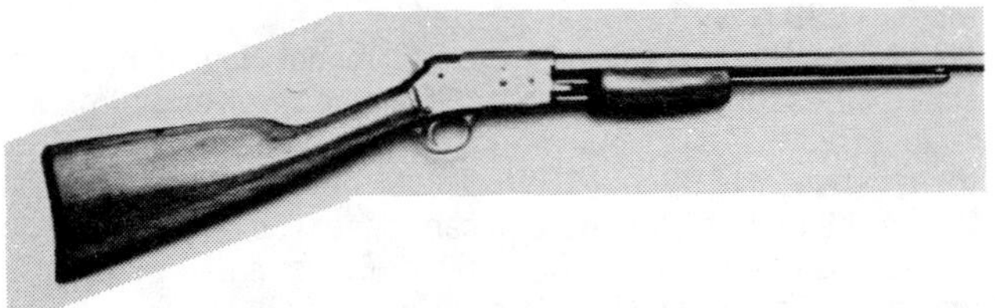

Courtesy Butterfield & Butterfield, San Francisco, California.

Exc.	V.G.	Good	Fair	Poor
1000	850	700	500	300

Lightning Slide Action, Large Frame
This rifle is similar in appearance to the Medium Frame Lightning, though larger in size. It is chambered in larger rifle calibers of the era, from .38-56 up to .50-95 Express. The larger calibers are more desirable from a collector's standpoint. The rifle has a 28" barrel; the carbine, a 22" barrel. The finish is blued, with a case-colored hammer. The stock is oiled walnut; the forend, checkered. The Colt name and Hartford address are stamped on the barrel along with the patent dates. This rifle is quite large and has come to be known as the "Express Model." Colt manufactured 6,496 between 1887 and 1894.

Rifle, 28" Octagonal Barrel

Exc.	V.G.	Good	Fair	Poor
2500	2000	1500	750	500

Rifle, 28" Round Barrel

Exc.	V.G.	Good	Fair	Poor
2750	2250	1750	1000	600

Carbine, 22" Barrel

Exc.	V.G.	Good	Fair	Poor
3500	3000	2250	1500	750

Baby Carbine, 22" Barrel 1lb. Lighter

Exc.	V.G.	Good	Fair	Poor
8500	7500	6000	3000	1750

Model 1878 Double Barrel Shotgun
This Model is chambered in 10 or 12 gauge and has 28", 30", or 32" barrels. It is a sidelock double-trigger hammer gun with case-colored locks and breech. The barrels are browned Damacus-patterned. The checkered walnut stock is varnished or oil-finished. The Colt's Hartford address is stamped on the barrel rib; and Colt's name, on the lock. This has been regarded as one of the finest shotguns made in America, although Colt had difficulty competing with the less expensive European imports of the day. They ceased production after only 22,690 were manufactured between 1878 and 1889.
Fully Engraved Model—Add 80%.

Exc.	V.G.	Good	Fair	Poor
3500	3000	2250	1250	650

Model 1883 Double Barrel Shotgun
This model is a hammerless boxlock, chambered for 10 or 12 gauge. The barrels are 28", 30", or 32"; and it features double triggers. The frame and furniture are case-colored; the barrels, browned with Damascus pattern. The checkered walnut stock is varnished or oil-finished. Colt's Hartford address is stamped on the barrel rib. "Colt" is stamped on each side of the frame. Again, as in the Model 1878, this is rated as one of the finest of all American-made shotguns. There were many special orders, and they require individual appraisal. Colt manufactured 7,366 of these guns between 1883 and 1895.
Fully Engraved Model—Add 80%.

Exc.	V.G.	Good	Fair	Poor
3800	3250	2500	1500	750

Double Barrel Rifle
This is one of the rarest of all Colt fireams and is a prize for the Colt collector. There were only 35 of these guns manufactured. They were said to be the special interest of Caldwell Hart Colt, Samuel Colt's son, who was an avid arms collector. It is said that most of the 35 guns produced wound up in his collection or those of his friends. This gun is chambered for .45-70 or one of the larger variations thereof. It is an exposed hammer sidelock with double triggers. The locks, breech, and furniture are case-colored; the barrels, browned or blued. The barrels are 28" in length, and the checkered stock was oil-finished or varnished walnut. The barrel rib is stamped with the Colt name and Hartford address. The locks are also stamped "Colt." One must exercise extreme caution in dealing with this model as there have been Model 1878 Shotguns converted into double rifles. Colt manufactured the 35 guns over the period 1879-1885.

Courtesy Butterfield & Butterfield, San Francisco, California.

Exc.	V.G.	Good	Fair	Poor
15000	12500	8500	6500	5000

COLT DOUBLE ACTION REVOLVERS

Model 1877 "Lightning" and "Thunderer"
The Model 1877 was Colt's first attempt at manufacturing a double-action revolver. It shows a striking resemblance to the Single Action Army. Sales on this model were brisk, with over 166,000 produced between 1877 and 1909. Chambered for two different cartridges, the .38 Colt, known as the "Lightning"; and .41 Colt, as the "Thunderer." The standard finishes are blued, with case-colored frame and nickle plate. The birdshead grips are of checkered rosewood on the early guns and hard rubber on the majority of the production run. The barrel lengths most often encountered are 2.5" and 3.5" without an ejector rod, and 4.5" and 6" with the rod. Other barrel lengths from 1.5" through 10" were offered. The Model 1877 holds 6 shots in either caliber. There were quite a few different variations found within this model designation. Values furnished are for the standard variations. Antiques made before 1898 would be more desirable from an investment standpoint.
.41 Caliber "Thunderer"—Add 10%.
Over 7" Barrel—Add 10%.
London Barrel Address—Add 20%.
.32 Caliber—Add 25%.
Rosewood Grips—Add 10%.

Without Ejector, 2.5" and 3.5" Barrel

Exc.	V.G.	Good	Fair	Poor
1500	1200	750	500	350

With Ejector, 4.5" and 6" Barrel

Exc.	V.G.	Good	Fair	Poor
1750	1500	1000	750	450

Model 1878 "Frontier"

This model is a large and somewhat ungainly looking revolver. It has a solid frame with a removable triggerguard. The cylinder does not swing out, and there is a thin loading gate. It has birdshead grips made of checkered hard rubber; walnut would be found on the early models. The finish is either blued and casecolored or nickle-plated. The Model 1878 holds 6 shots, and the standard barrel lengths are 4.75", 5.5", and 7.5" with an ejector assembly and 3", 3.5", and 4" without. The standard chamberings for the Model 1878 are .32-20, 38-40, .41 Colt, .44-40, and .45 Colt. This model was fairly well received because it is chambered for the large calibers that were popular in that era. Colt manufactured 51,210 between 1878 and 1905. Antique models made before 1898 would be more desirable from an investment standpoint.

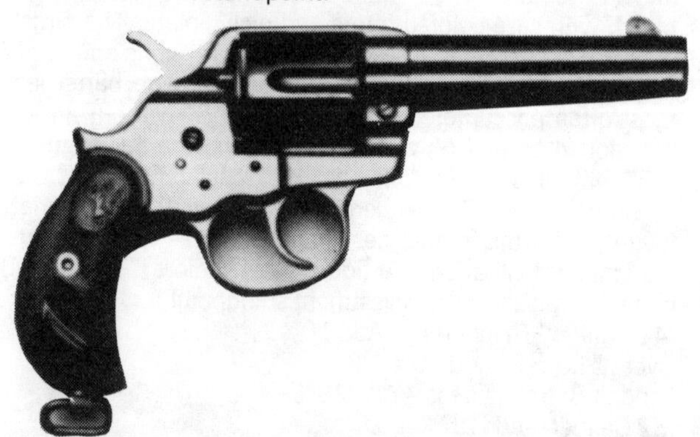

Courtesy Butterfield & Butterfield, San Francisco, California.

Model 1878 "Frontier" Standard

Exc.	V.G.	Good	Fair	Poor
1500	1200	750	500	350

Model 1902

This is a U.S. Ordnance contract Model 1878. It has a 6" barrel and is chambered for .45 Colt. The finish is blued, and there is a lanyard swivel on the butt. This model bears the U.S. inspector's marks. It is sometimes referred to as the Philippine or the Alaskan model. The triggerguard is quite a bit larger than standard.

Exc.	V.G.	Good	Fair	Poor
1750	1500	1000	700	500

Model 1889 Navy

The 1889 Navy is a very important model from a historical standpoint as it was the first double-action revolver Colt manufactured with a swingout cylinder. They produced 31,000 of them between 1889 and 1894. The Model 1889 is chambered for the .38 Colt and the .41 Colt cartridges. The cylinder holds 6 shots. It is offered with a 3", 4.5", or 6" barrel; and the finish was either blued or nickle-plated. The grips are checkered hard rubber with the "Rampant Colt" in an oval molded into them. The patent dates 1884 and 1888 appear in the barrel marking, and the serial numbers are stamped on the butt.

3" Barrel—Add 20%.

Exc.	V.G.	Good	Fair	Poor
950	750	650	450	200

U.S. Navy Model

This variation has a 6" barrel, is chambered for .38 Colt, and is offered in blued finish only. "U.S.N." is stamped on the butt. Most of the Navy models were altered at the Colt factory to add the Model 1895 improvements. An original unaltered specimen would be worth as much as 50 percent premium over the altered values shown.

Courtesy Butterfield & Butterfield, San Francisco, California.

Exc.	V.G.	Good	Fair	Poor
1000	800	700	500	250

Model 1892 "New Army and Navy"

This Model is very similar in appearance to the 1889 Navy. The main differences are improvements to the lockwork function. It has double bolt stop notches, a double cylinder locking bolt, and shorter flutes on the cylinder. The .38 Smith & Wesson and the .32-20 were added to the .38 Colt and .41 Colt chamberings. The checkered hard rubber grips are standard, with plain walnut grips found on some contract series guns. Barrel lengths and finishes are the same as described for the Model 1889. The patent dates 1895 and 1901 appear stamped on later models. Colt manufactured 291,000 of these revolvers between 1892 and 1907. Antiques before 1898 are more desirable from an investment standpoint.

3" Barrel—Add 20%.

Exc.	V.G.	Good	Fair	Poor
400	350	300	200	100

U.S. Navy Model

Exc.	V.G.	Good	Fair	Poor
550	450	400	300	200

Courtesy Butterfield & Butterfield, San Francisco, California.

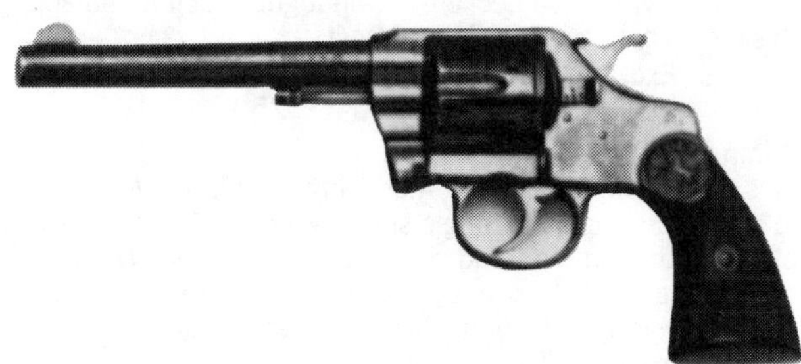
Courtesy Butterfield & Butterfield, San Francisco, California.

U.S. Army Model

Exc.	V.G.	Good	Fair	Poor
500	400	350	250	150

Model 1905 Marine Corps

This model is a variation of the New Army and Navy Model. It was derived from the late production with its own serial range #10001-10926. With only 926 produced between 1905 and 1909, it is quite rare on today's market and is eagerly sought after by Colt Double Action collectors. This model is chambered for the .38 Colt and the .38 Smith & Wesson Special cartridges. It holds 6 shots, has a 6" barrel, and is offered in a blued finish only. The grips are checkered walnut and are quite different than those found on previous models. "U.S.M.C." is stamped on the butt;, patent dates of 1884, 1888, and 1895 are stamped on the barrel. One hundred twenty-five of these revolvers were earmarked for civilian sales and do not have the Marine Corps markings; these will generally be found in better condition. Values are very similar.

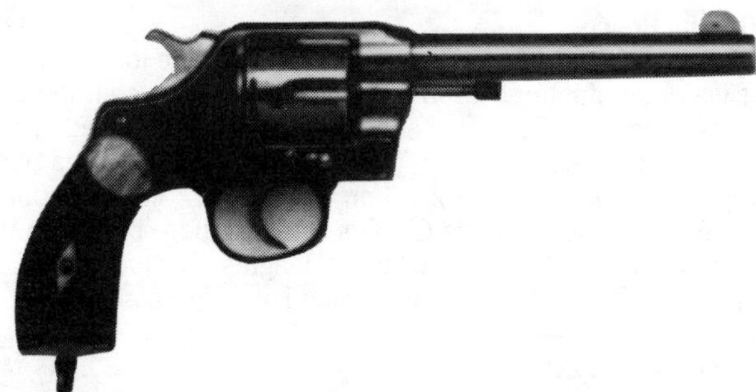
Courtesy Butterfield & Butterfield, San Francisco, California.

Exc.	V.G.	Good	Fair	Poor
750	650	500	350	200

New Service Model

This model was in continual production from 1898 through 1944. It is chambered for 11 different calibers—.38 Special, .357 Magnum, .38-40, .44 Russian, .44 Special, .44-40, .45ACP, .45 Colt, .450 Eley, .455 Eley, and .476 Eley. It is offered in barrel lengths from 2" to 7.5", either blued or nickle-plated. Checkered hard rubber grips were standard until 1928, and then checkered walnut grips were used with an inletted Colt medallion. This was the largest swingout cylinder double-action revolver that Colt ever produced, and approximately 356,000 were manufactured over the 46 years they were made. There are many different variations of this revolver, and one should consult a book dealing strictly with Colt for a thorough breakdown and description.

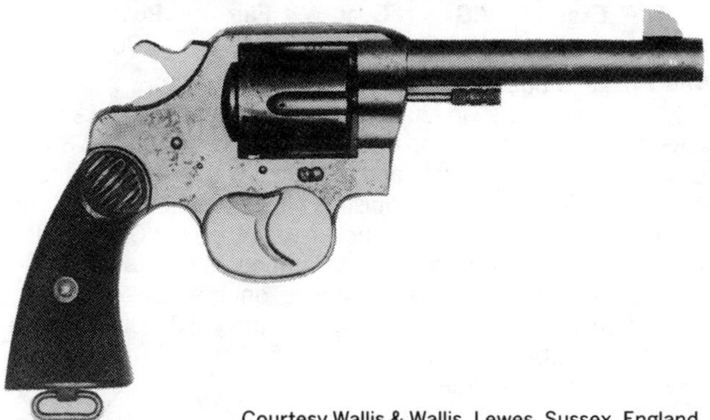
Courtesy Wallis & Wallis, Lewes, Sussex, England.

Early Model, #1-12000

Exc.	V.G.	Good	Fair	Poor
850	750	600	350	250

Early Model Target, #6000-15000

Checkered walnut grips, flattop frame, 7.5" barrel.

Exc.	V.G.	Good	Fair	Poor
900	800	650	400	300

Improved Model, #21000-32500

Has internal locking improvements.

Exc.	V.G.	Good	Fair	Poor
600	500	400	300	200

Improved Target Model, #21000-32500

Exc.	V.G.	Good	Fair	Poor
750	650	500	350	250

U.S.Army Model 1909, #30000-50000

5.5" barrel, .45 Colt, walnut grips, "U.S. Army Model 1909" on butt.

Exc.	V.G.	Good	Fair	Poor
600	500	400	300	200

U.S.Navy Model 1909, #30000-50000

Same as above with "U.S.N." on butt.

Exc.	V.G.	Good	Fair	Poor
850	750	600	350	250

U.S. Marine Corps Model 1909, #30000-50000

Checkered walnut rips,·"U.S.M.C." on butt.

Exc.	V.G.	Good	Fair	Poor
1500	1200	800	650	450

U.S. Army Model 1917, #150000-301000

Smooth walnut grips, 5.5" barrel, .45ACP and .45 Colt, model designation stamped on butt.

Exc.	V.G.	Good	Fair	Poor
550	450	400	300	225

Model 1917 Civilian, #335000-336000

Approximately 1,000 made in .45ACP only from Army parts over-run. No military markings.

Exc.	V.G.	Good	Fair	Poor
900	800	650	400	300

Late Model New Service, #325000-356000

Checkered walnut grips and internal improvements.

Exc.	V.G.	Good	Fair	Poor
600	500	400	300	200

Shooting Master, #333000-350000

Round butt, checkered walnut grips with Colt medallion, 6" barrel, "Colt Shooting Master" on barrel, flattop frame with target sights.

Exc.	V.G.	Good	Fair	Poor
900	800	650	400	300

Magnum Model New Service, Over #340000

.357 Magnum, .38 Special.

Exc.	V.G.	Good	Fair	Poor
500	400	350	250	200

New Pocket Model

This was the first swingout-cylinder, double-action pocket revolver made by Colt. It is chambered for .32 Colt and .32 Smith & Wesson. It holds 6 shots and is offered with barrel lengths of 2.5", 3.5", 5", and 6". The finish is blued or nickle-plated, and the grips are checkered hard rubber with the oval Colt molded into them. "Colt's New Pocket" is stamped on the frame. 1884 and 1888 patent dates are stamped on the barrel of later-production guns. There were approximately 30,000 of these manufactured between 1893 and 1905. Antiques made before 1898 are more desirable.

Early Production Without Patent Dates—Add 25%.

5" Barrel—Add 10%.

Exc.	V.G.	Good	Fair	Poor
400	350	300	250	150

Pocket Positive

Externally this is the same revolver as the New Pocket, but it has the positive lock feature. It was manufactured between 1905 and 1940.

Exc.	V.G.	Good	Fair	Poor
400	375	275	225	125

New Police Model

This model appears very similar to the New Pocket Model. The frame is stamped "New Police." It is chambered for the .32 Colt, .32 Colt New Police, and .32 Smith & Wesson cartridges. The barrel lengths are 2.5", 4", and 6". The finishes are blued or nickle-plated. Colt manufactured 49,500 of this model from 1896-1907. The New York City Police Department purchased 4,500 of these revolvers, and the backstraps are so marked. There was also a target model of this revolver, which features a 6" barrel with a flattop frame and target sights, of which 5,000 were produced.

New York Police Marked—Add 10%.

Target Model—Add 20%.

Exc.	V.G.	Good	Fair	Poor
300	250	200	150	100

Police Positive

This is externally the same as the New Police with the addition of the positive lock feature and two new chamberings—the .38 New Police and the .38 Smith & Wesson. They were manufactured from 1905-1947.

Exc.	V.G.	Good	Fair	Poor
350	300	250	200	150

Police Positive Target

This is basically the same as the New Police Target with the positive lock feature. It is chambered in .22 l.r., as well as the other cartridges offered in the earlier model.

Exc.	V.G.	Good	Fair	Poor
550	500	400	300	200

Police Positive Special

This model is very similar to the Police Positive but has a slightly larger frame to accept the longer cylinder needed to chamber more powerful cartridges such as the .38 Special, in addition to the original chamberings. They were manufactured from 1907-1973.

Exc.	V.G.	Good	Fair	Poor
300	275	225	150	100

Army Special Model

This is a heavier-framed improved version of the New Army and Navy revolver. It is chambered for the .32-20, .38 Colt, .38 Smith & Wesson, and .41 Colt. It is offered with a 4", 4.5", 5", and 6" barrel. The finish is blued or nickle-plated, and the grips are checkered hard rubber. The serial number range is #291000-540000, and they were manufactured between 1908-1927.

Exc.	V.G.	Good	Fair	Poor
350	300	250	200	150

Officer's Model Target 1st Issue

This revolver is chambered for the .38 Special cartridge. It has a 6" barrel and is blued. It has a flattop frame with adjustable target sights. Colt manufactured this model from 1904-1908.

Exc.	V.G.	Good	Fair	Poor
550	450	350	300	200

Officer's Model Target 2nd Issue

This model is very similar to the 1st Issue but is offered in .22 l.r. and .32 Police Positive caliber, as well as in .38 Special. It also is furnished with a 4", 4.5", 5", 6", and 7.5" barrel in .38 Special only. It has checkered walnut grips. Colt manufactured this model between 1908 and 1940.

Exc.	V.G.	Good	Fair	Poor
500	400	300	250	150

Camp Perry Single Shot

This model was created by modifying an Officer's Model frame to accept a special flat single shot "cylinder." This flat chamber pivots to the left side and downward for loading. The pistol is chambered for .22 l.r. and is offered with an 8" or 10" barrel. The finish is blued, with checkered walnut grips. The name "Camp Perry Model" is stamped on the left side of the chamber; the caliber is on the barrel. Colt named this model after the site of the U.S. Target competition held annually at Camp Perry, Ohio. They manufactured 2,525 of these between 1920 and 1941.

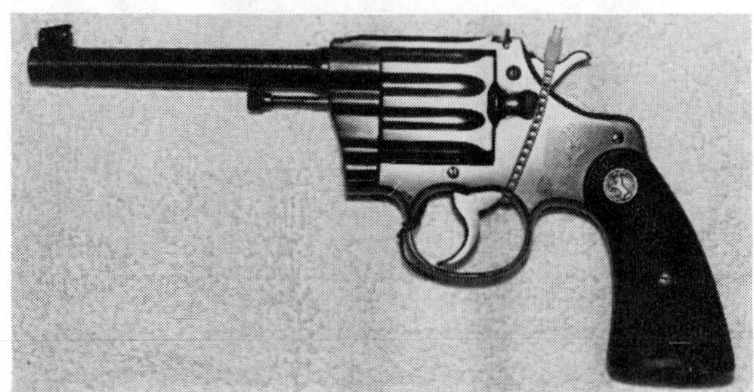

Exc.	V.G.	Good	Fair	Poor
1250	1000	750	500	350

Official Police

This was a very popular revolver in the Colt line for many years. It was manufactured from 1927 to 1969. It is chambered for .32-20 and .41 Colt. These calibers were discontinued in 1942 and 1930, respectively. The .38 Special was chambered throughout the entire production run, and .22 l.r. was added in 1930. This model holds 6 shots, has a square butt, and is offered with 2", 4", 5", and 6" barrel lengths. The grips are checkered walnut. The finish is either blued or nickle-plated.

Nickle-plated—Add 10%.

.22 l.r.—Add 20%.

Exc.	V.G.	Good	Fair	Poor
350	300	250	200	150

Commando Model

This model, for all intents and purposes, is an Official Police chambered for .38 Special, with a 2", 4", or 6" barrel. This Model is parkerized and stamped "Colt Commando" on the barrel. There were approximately 50,000 manufactured between 1942-1945 for use in WWII.

Exc.	V.G.	Good	Fair	Poor
300	275	225	150	100

Marshall Model

This is an Official Police that is marked "Colt Marshall" on the barrel and has an "M" suffix in the serial number. It has a 2" or 4" barrel and a round butt. The finish is blued. There were approximately 2,500 manufactured between 1954 and 1956.

Exc.	V.G.	Good	Fair	Poor
500	400	300	250	150

Bankers Special

The Bankers Special is a 2"-barrelled, easily concealed revolver. It was designed with bank employees in mind. It is chambered for .38 Special and was offered in blued finish. The grips are rounded but full-sized, and Colt utilized this feature in advertising this model. The U.S. Postal Service equipped its railway mail clerks with this model. There were approximately 35,000 manufactured between 1926 and 1943.

Exc.	V.G.	Good	Fair	Poor
500	400	300	250	150

Detective Special 1st Issue

This model is actually a duplication, as it is nothing more than a Police Positive Special with a 2" barrel standard. It was originally chambered for .32 New Police, .38 New Police, (which were discontinued) and .38 Special, which continued until the end of the production run. The finish is blued, and it is offered with wood or plastic grips. There were over 400,000 manufactured between 1926 and 1972.

Exc.	V.G.	Good	Fair	Poor
375	300	250	175	100

Detective Special 2nd Issue

This is basically a modernized, streamlined version of the 1st issue. It is very similar except that it has a 2" or 3" barrel with a shrouded ejector rod and wraparound checkered walnut grips and is chambered for .38 Special. It was finished in blue or nickle plate.

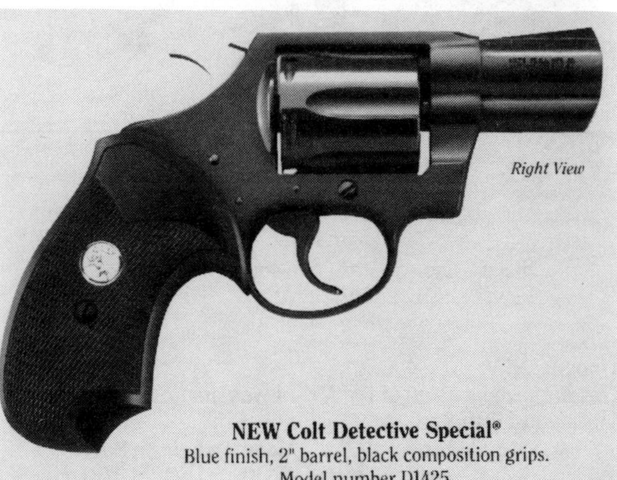

NEW Colt Detective Special®
Blue finish, 2" barrel, black composition grips.
Model number D1425.

Exc.	V.G.	Good	Fair	Poor
350	275	225	150	100

Add $25 for nickel finish.

Cobra 1st Issue

The Cobra is simply an alloy-framed lightweight version of the Detective Special. It weighs only 15 ounces. The Cobra is chambered for .32, .38 Special, and .22 l.r. This model is available in either a round butt or square butt version with a 4" barrel only. They were manufactured between 1950 and 1973.

Exc.	V.G.	Good	Fair	Poor
350	275	225	150	100

Cobra 2nd Issue

The same as the 1st Issue in .38 Special only, this is streamlined with wraparound walnut grips and shrouded ejector rod.

Exc.	V.G.	Good	Fair	Poor
300	250	200	125	100

Agent 1st Issue

This revolver is basically the same as the 1st Issue Cobra with a shortened grip frame. This was done to make the Agent more concealable. Colt manufactured the Agent 1st Issue from 1955-1973.

Exc.	V.G.	Good	Fair	Poor
300	250	200	125	100

Agent L.W. 2nd Issue

This is a streamlined version with the shrouded ejector rod. In the last four years of its production, it was matte finished. Colt manufactured this model between 1973 and 1986.

Exc.	V.G.	Good	Fair	Poor
250	200	175	125	100

Border Patrol

This model is quite rare, as Colt manufactured only 400 of them in 1952. It is basically a Police Special with a heavy 4" barrel. It is chambered for the .38 Special and was built to be very strong. The finish is blued and serial numbered in the 610000 range.

Exc.	V.G.	Good	Fair	Poor
750	650	500	400	250

Air Crewman Special

This model was especially fabricated for the Air Force to be carried by their pilots for protection. It is extremely lightweight at 11 ounces. The frame and the cylinder are made of aluminum alloy. It has a 2" barrel and is chambered for the .38 Special. The finish was blued, with checkered walnut grips. There were approximately 1,200 manufactured in 1951, and they are marked "U.S." or "A.F."

Exc.	V.G.	Good	Fair	Poor
1200	800	500	400	250

Courier

This is another version of the Cobra. It features a shorter gripframe and a 3" barrel. This model is chambered for .32 and .22 rimfire. There were approximately 3,000 manufactured in 1955 and 1956.

.22 Rimfire—Add 20%.

Exc.	V.G.	Good	Fair	Poor
850	750	600	500	350

Trooper

This model was designed specifically by Colt to fill the need for a large, heavy-duty, powerful revolver that was accurate. The Trooper filled that need. It was offered with a 4" or 6" barrel and blued or nickle finishes with checkered walnut grips. The Trooper is chambered for the .38 Special/.357 Magnum, and there is a .22 rimfire version for the target shooters. This model was manufactured between 1953 and 1969.

Exc.	V.G.	Good	Fair	Poor
300	250	200	150	100

Colt .357 Magnum

This is a deluxe version of the Trooper. It is offered with a special target wide hammer and large target-type grips. The sights are the same as Accro target model. It features a 4" or 6" barrel and a blued finish and was manufactured between 1953 and 1961. There were less than 15,000 produced.

Exc.	V.G.	Good	Fair	Poor
400	350	300	200	150

Diamondback

This model is a medium-frame, duty-type weapon suitable for target work. It has the short frame of the Detective Special with the ventilated-rib 2.5", 4", or 6" barrel. It is chambered for .38 Special and .22 rimfire for the target shooters. The finish is blued or nickle-plated, with checkered walnut grips. The Diamondback features adjustable target sights, wide target hammer, and a steel frame. It was manufactured between 1966 and 1986.

Nickle Finish—Add 15%.

NIB	Exc.	V.G.	Good	Fair	Poor
400	375	300	250	200	150

NOTE: For .22 caliber-2" barrel add $200. If finish is nickel add $500.

Viper

This is an alloy-framed revolver chambered for the .38 Special. It has a 4" barrel and was manufactured between 1977 and 1984. The Viper is essentially a lightweight version of the Police Positive.

NIB	Exc.	V.G.	Good	Fair	Poor
275	225	200	175	125	100

Python

The Python is the Cadillac of the Colt double-action line. It has been manufactured since 1955 and is still the flagship of the Colt line. It is chambered for the .357 Magnum cartridge, holds 6 shots, and has been offered in barrel lengths of 2.5", 3", 4", 6", and 8". This revolver is offered finished in high polished Colt Royal Blue, nickle-plate, matte-finish stainless-steel, or what is known as "The Ultimate"—a high polished stainless-steel. The 3" barrel, as well as the nickle-plating, has been discontinued. The grips are checkered walnut. It is possible that the nickle-plated specimens may bring a 10 percent premium. In my experience this is not always the case as many potential purchasers have a definite preference for the blued finish.

NIB	Exc.	V.G.	Good	Fair	Poor
750	550	450	350	275	225

Matte Stainless Steel

NIB	Exc.	V.G.	Good	Fair	Poor
825	650	550	450	350	275

"The Ultimate"

NIB	Exc.	V.G.	Good	Fair	Poor
875	675	575	475	375	300

Python .38 Special

This is an 8"-barrelled Python chambered for the .38 Special only. It was a limited-production venture that was not a success. It was offered in blue only.

Exc.	V.G.	Good	Fair	Poor
500	400	325	275	225

Python Hunter

The Hunter was a special 8" .357 Magnum Python with an extended eye relief Leupold 2X scope. The grips are neoprene with gold Colt medallions. The revolver, with mounted scope and accessories, was fitted into a Haliburton extruded aluminum case. The Hunter was manufactured in 1981 only.

NIB	Exc.	V.G.	Good	Fair	Poor
1000	800	650	500	400	300

Metropolitan MK III

This revolver is basically a heavier-duty version of the Official Police. It is chambered for .38 Special and fitted with a 4" heavy barrel. It is finished in blue only and was manufactured from 1969-1972.

NIB	Exc.	V.G.	Good	Fair	Poor
200	175	150	125	100	75

Lawman MK III

This model is offered chambered for the .357 Magnum with a 2" or 4" barrel. It has checkered walnut grips and is either blued or nickel-plated. Colt manufactured the Lawman between 1969 and 1983.

Exc.	V.G.	Good	Fair	Poor
275	250	200	150	100

Lawman MK V

This is an improved version of the MK III. It entailed a redesigned grip, a shorter lock time, and an improved double action. It was manufactured from 1982-1985.

NIB	Exc.	V.G.	Good	Fair	Poor
300	250	225	175	125	90

Trooper MK III

This revolver was intended to be the target-grade version of the MK III series. It is offered with a 4", 6", or 8" vent-rib barrel with a shrouded ejector rod similar in appearance to the Python. It is chambered for the .22 l.r. and the .22 Magnum, as well as .357 Magnum. It features adjustable target sights, checkered walnut target grips, and is either blued or nickle-plated. This model was manufactured between 1969 and 1983.

NIB	Exc.	V.G.	Good	Fair	Poor
325	275	250	200	150	100

Trooper MK V

This improved version of the MK III was manufactured between 1982 and 1985.

NIB	Exc.	V.G.	Good	Fair	Poor
325	275	250	200	150	100

Boa

This is basically a deluxe version of the Trooper MK V. It has all the same features plus the high polished blue found on the Python. Colt manufactured 1,200 of these revolvers in 1985, and the entire production was purchased and marketed by Lew Horton Distributing Company in Southboro, Massachusetts.

NIB	Exc.	V.G.	Good	Fair	Poor
450	400	350	300	250	150

Peacekeeper

This model was designed as a duty-type weapon with target capabilities. It is offered with a 4" or 6" barrel chambered for .357 Magnum. It features adjustable sights and neoprene combat-style grips and has a matte blued finish. This model was manufactured between 1985 and 1987.

NIB	Exc.	V.G.	Good	Fair	Poor
300	275	225	200	150	100

King Cobra

This model has become the workhorse of the Colt revolver line. The King Cobra has a forged steel frame and barrel and a full-length ejector rod housing. The barrel is fitted with a solid rib. This mode is equipped with an adjustable, white outline rear sight and a red insert front sight. Colt black neoprene combat-style grips are standard.

Blued

NIB	Exc.	V.G.	Good	Fair	Poor
325	300	250	200	150	100

Stainless Steel

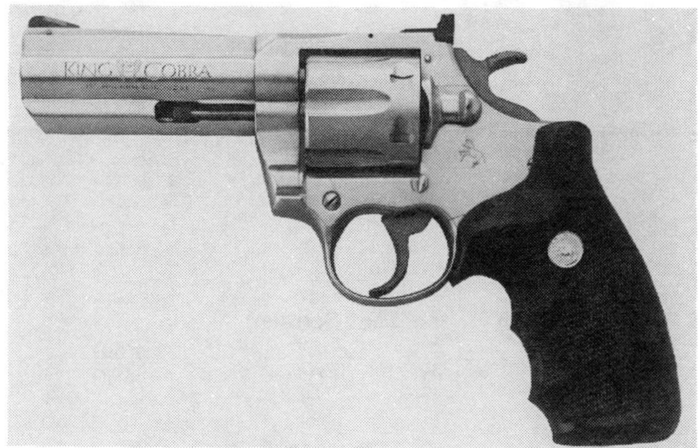

NIB	Exc.	V.G.	Good	Fair	Poor
375	325	300	250	200	125

High Polish Stainless Steel

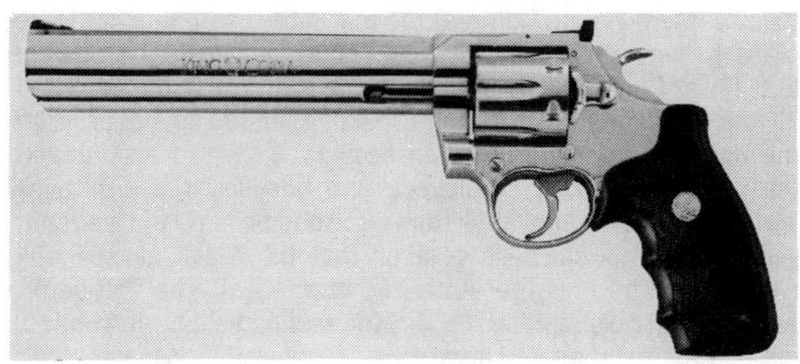

NIB	Exc.	V.G.	Good	Fair	Poor
400	350	300	250	200	125

Anaconda

This double-action .44 Magnum revolver was introduced in 1990. It is offered with 4", 6", or 8" barrel lengths. The 4" model weighs 47 ozs., the 6" model weighs 63 ozs., and the 8" model weighs 59 ozs. The Anaconda holds 6 rounds and is available with a matte stainless steel finish. For 1993 a new chambering in .45 Colt was offered for the Anaconda. This model wqas offered only with a 6" barrel in a matte stainless steel finish.revolver chambered for the .44 Remington Magnum cartridge. It is currently offered with a 6" barrel and adjustable red-insert front and white-outline rear sights. It is constructed of matte-finished stainless-steel and has black neoprene finger-groove grips with gold Colt medallions. At this writing, prices are not yet available.

.44 Magnum

NIB	Exc.	V.G.	Good	Fair	Poor
425	390	350	300	250	200

.45 Colt

NIB	Exc.	V.G.	Good	Fair	Poor
450	410	350	300	250	200

COLT SEMI-AUTOMATIC PISTOLS

The Colt Firearms Co. was the first of the American gun manufacturers to take the advent of the semi-automatic pistol seriously. This pistol design was becoming popular among European gunmakers in the late 1880s and early 1900s. In the United States, however, the revolver was firmly ensconced as the accepted design. Colt realized that if the semi-auto could be made to function reliably, it would soon catch on. The powers that be at Colt were able to negotiate with some of the noted inventors of the day, including Browning, and to secure or lease the rights to manufacture their designs. Colt also encouraged the creativity of their employees with bonuses and incentives and, through this innovative thinking, soon became the leader in semi-auto pistol sales—a position that they have never really relinquished to any other American gun maker. The Colt semi-automatic pistols represent a very interesting field for the collector of Colt handguns. There were many variations with high enough production to make it worthwhile to seek them out. There are a number of fine books on the Colt semi-automatics, and anyone wishing to do so will be able to learn a great deal about them. Collector interest is very high in this field, and values are definitely on the rise.

Model 1900

This was the first of the Colt automatic pistols. It was actually a developmental model with only 3,500 being produced. The Model 1900 was not really a successful design. It was quite clumsy and out of balance in the hand and was not as reliable in function as it should have been. This Model is chambered for the .38 Rimless smokeless cartridge. It has a detachable magazine that holds seven cartridges. The barrel is 6" in length. The finish is blued, with a case-colored hammer and safety/sight combination. The grips are either plain walnut, checkered walnut, or hard rubber. This pistol is a Browning design, and the left side of the slide is stamped "Browning's Patent" with the 1897 patent date. Colt sold 200 pistols to the Navy and 200 to the Army for field trials and evaluation. The remaining 3,300 were sold on the civilian market. This model was manufactured from 1900-1903.

Civilian Model with Sight/Safety Combination—Add 40%.

Standard Civilian Production

Exc.	V.G.	Good	Fair	Poor
3000	2500	1500	900	500

U.S. Navy Military Model

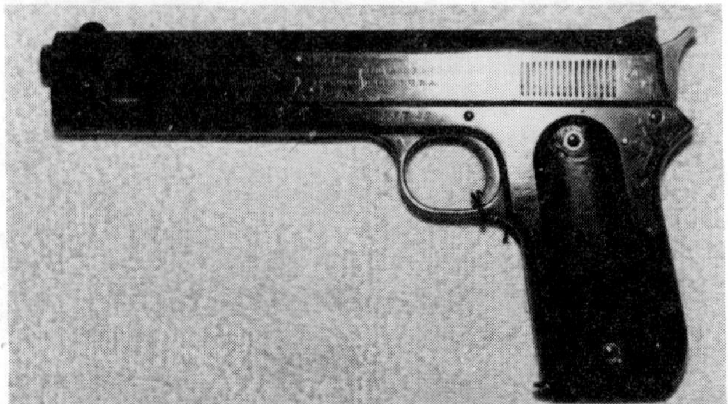

Exc.	V.G.	Good	Fair	Poor
5500	5000	3000	1750	1000

U.S. Army Military Model

Exc.	V.G.	Good	Fair	Poor
4750	3750	2200	1250	750

Model 1902 Sporting Pistol

This model is chambered for the .38 Rimless smokeless cartridge. It has a 7-round detachable magazine and a 6" barrel and is blued, with checkered hard rubber grips featuring the "Rampant Colt" molded into them. The most notable features of the 1902 Sporting Model are the rounded butt, rounded hammer spur, dovetailed rear sight, and the 1897-1902 patent dates. Colt manufactured approximately 7,500 of these pistols between 1903 and 1908.

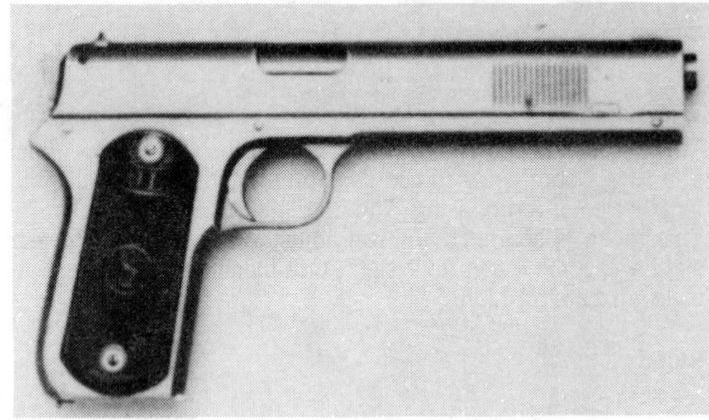

Exc.	V.G.	Good	Fair	Poor
2750	2000	1250	750	450

Model 1902 Military Pistol

This model is a somewhat larger, heavier pistol than the 1902 Sporting Pistol. It has the same .38 ACP chambering and 6" barrel, but the detachable magazine holds 8 rounds. The grip of this model is larger and squared off, and it has a lanyard swivel on the butt. There were approximately 18,000 manufactured between 1902 and 1929.

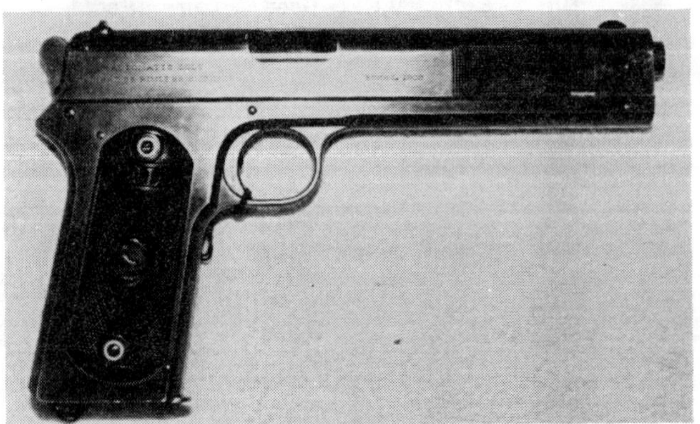

Early Model with Front of Slide Serrated

Exc.	V.G.	Good	Fair	Poor
2750	2000	1250	750	450

Standard Model with Rear of Slide Serrated

Exc.	V.G.	Good	Fair	Poor
2500	1750	1000	500	400

U.S. Army Marked, #15001-15200 with Front Serrations

Exc.	V.G.	Good	Fair	Poor
6000	5000	2750	1500	800

Model 1903 Pocket Pistol

This was the first automatic pocket pistol Colt produced. It is essentially identical to the 1902 Sporting Model with a shorter slide. The barrel length is 4.5", and it is chambered for the .38 Rimless smokeless cartridge. It is blued, with a case-colored hammer, with checkered hard rubber grips that have the "Rampant Colt" molded into them. The detachable magazine holds 7 rounds. There were approximately 26,000 manufactured between 1903 and 1929.

Exc.	V.G.	Good	Fair	Poor
950	750	450	300	200

Model 1903 Hammerless, .32 Pocket Pistol

Courtesy Orville Reichert.

This was the second pocket automatic Colt manufactured. It was another of John Browning's designs, and it developed into one of Colt's most successful pistols. This pistol is chambered for the .32 ACP cartridge. Initially the barrel length was 4"; this was shortened to 3.75". The detachable magazine holds 8 rounds. The standard finish is blue, with quite a few nickle-plated. The early model grips are checkered hard rubber with the "Rampant Colt" molded into them. Many of the nickle-plated pistols had pearl grips. In 1924 the grips were changed to checkered walnut with the Colt medallions. The name of this Model can be misleading as it is not a true hammerless but a concealed hammer design. It features a slide stop and a grip safety. Colt manufactured 572,215 civilian versions of this pistol and approximately 200,000 more for military contracts. This Model was manufactured between 1903 and 1945.

Early Model 1897 Patent Date— Add 40%.
Nickle Plated With Pearl Grips—Add $100.
4" Barrel to #72,000—Add 20%.

Exc.	V.G.	Good	Fair	Poor
550	500	450	300	200

U.S. Military Model

Serial prefix M, marked "U.S. Property" on frame, parkerized finish.

Exc.	V.G.	Good	Fair	Poor
750	600	400	300	250

Model 1908 Hammerless .380 Pocket Pistol

This model is essentially the same as the .32 Pocket Pistol, chambered for the more potent .380 ACP, also known as the 9mm Browning short. Other specifications are the same. Colt manufactured approximately 138,000 in this caliber for civilian sales. An unknown number were sold to the military.

Standard Civilian Model

Nickle with Pearl Grips—Add $100.

Exc.	V.G.	Good	Fair	Poor
650	550	475	350	250

Military Model

Serial prefix M, marked "U.S. Property" on frame, parkerized finish.

Exc.	V.G.	Good	Fair	Poor
900	750	650	500	300

Model 1908 Hammerless .25 Pocket Pistol

This was the smallest automatic Colt made. It is chambered for the .25 ACP cartridge, has a 2" barrel, and is 4.5" long overall. It weighs a mere 13 ounces. This is a true pocket pistol. The detachable magazine holds 6 shots. This model was offered in blue or nickle-plate, with grips of checkered hard rubber and checkered walnut on later versions. This model has a grip safety, slide lock, and a magazine disconnector safety. This was another Browning design, and Fabrique Nationale manufactured this pistol in Belgium before Colt picked up the rights to make it in the U.S. This was a commercial success by Colt's standards, with approximately 409,000 manufactured between 1908 and 1941.

Courtesy Orville Reichert.

Civilian Model

Exc.	V.G.	Good	Fair	Poor
400	350	300	200	100

Military Model

"U.S. Property" marked on right frame. Very rare.

Exc.	V.G.	Good	Fair	Poor
1000	750	600	450	300

Model 1905 .45 Automatic Pistol

The Spanish American War and the experiences with the Moro's in the Philippine campaign taught a lesson about stopping power or the lack of it. The United States Army was convinced that they needed a more powerful handgun cartridge. This led Colt to the development of a .45-caliber cartridge suitable for the semi-automatic pistol. The Model 1905 and the .45 Rimless round were the result. In actuality, this cartridge was not nearly powerful enough to satisfy the need, but it led to the development of the .45 ACP. Colt believed that this pistol/cartridge combination would be a success and was geared up for mass production. The Army actually bought only 200 of them, and the total production was approximately 6,300 from 1905 to 1911. The pistol has a 5" barrel and detachable 7-shot magazine and is blued, with a case-colored hammer. The grips are checkered walnut. The hammer was rounded on the first 3,600 pistols and was changed to a spur hammer on the later models. The right side of the slide is stamped "Automatic Colt/ Calibre 45 Rimless Smokeless." This model was not a commercial success for Colt—possibly because it has no safety whatsoever except for the floating inertia firing pin. The 200 military models have grip safeties only. A very small number (believed to be less than 500) of these pistols were grooved to accept a shoulder stock. The stocks were made of leather and steel and made to double as a holster. These pistols have been classified "Curios and Relics" under the provisions of the Gun Control Act of 1968.

Civilian Model

Exc.	V.G.	Good	Fair	Poor
1500	1200	800	550	300

Military Model, Serial #1-201

Known as the 1907 Contract Pistol, it has a lanyard loop, a loaded chamber indicator, and a grip safety and bears the inspector's initials "K.M."

Exc.	V.G.	Good	Fair	Poor
2250	1750	1250	750	450

COLT 1911

The Colt Government Model is one of the most recognizable handguns in the world. Its popularity is second only to the Single Action Army among firearm collectors in the world today. It was this pistol that established Colt as the leader among handgun manufacturers. Arguably the advent of this fine pistol was timely from a historic point of view. It appeared just in time for the beginning of WWI and was able to prove its worth on the battlefields of Europe and the Pacific in both WWI and WWII. This was undoubtedly John Browning's crowning achievement, as this pistol shall always be the most respected of the Colt Auto line. There were over 200 factory variations and the production run from 1911, and still going strong, is unsurpassed. There were approximately 336,000 civilian and 2,695,212 military versions of the 1911 and 1911A1 manufactured to this point. This model was used in WWI, WWII, the Korean War and Vietnam. Its recent replacement still stirs controversy from some knowledgeable quarters. There are a number of excellent books specializing in this firearm, and one interested in collecting this pistol will have no trouble gaining an education in the field.

Model 1911 Automatic Pistol Commercial Series

The commercial or civilian version of the 1911 is readily recognized by the "C" prefix in the serial number. This variation commenced production in 1911 with serial number C1 and was replaced in 1925 by its successor, the 1911A1 at serial number C130000. The 1911 is a large-frame semi-automatic with a 5" barrel. The finish is a high polish blue with checkered walnut grips. The grips feature a raised diamond around the screw holes. The 1911 has a thin front sight blade, long trigger, short spur on the hammer, and the grip safety. The mainspring housing is flat, and there is no relief cut on the frame behind the trigger. The pistol is chambered for the .45 ACP and has a 7-round detachable magazine. The words "Government Model" were not stamped on this pistol until the 1911A1 Series after 1946. There are a number of variations of this Model. We list the major ones and advise those interested in collecting to procure one of the excellent volumes available on this pistol.

Early Models 1897,1902,1905 and 1911 Patent Dates
Serial numbers through C4500
3 Digit Serial Number—Add 20%.
2 Digit Serial Number—Add 40%.

Exc.	V.G.	Good	Fair	Poor
1350	1000	750	500	400

Standard 1911 Pistol

Exc.	V.G.	Good	Fair	Poor
1150	850	600	400	300

Argentine Contract

This is part of the commercial serial range and falls between numbers C110000 and C130000. The pistols are marked "Pistola Automatica Sistema Colt, Calibre 11.25mm, Modelo 1916." They bear the Argentine Crest and were manufactured between 1917 and 1925.

Exc.	V.G.	Good	Fair	Poor
950	750	550	400	300

1911 Russian Order

This variation is chambered for .45ACP and has the Russian version of "Anglo Zakazivat" stamped on the frame. There were 14,500 of these blued pistols manufactured in 1915-1916. They are found between serial numbers C50000 and C85000.

This variation is rarely encountered today, as they did go to Russia and a lot has happened over there since. One should be extremely cautious and secure qualified appraisal if contemplating a purchase, as fakes have been noted.

Exc.	V.G.	Good	Fair	Poor
2500	1750	1250	650	400

WWI British Contract

This series is chambered for the British .455 cartridge and is so marked on the right side of the slide. The British "Broad Arrow" proofmark will also be found. These pistols were made in 1915-1916 and have their own serial range W10001 through W21000. They are commercial series pistols.

Exc.	V.G.	Good	Fair	Poor
1500	1000	750	550	450

Model 1911 Automatic Pistol, Military Series

The military Model 1911 is basically identical to the commercial series except for the markings that appear on the military version. They both have the blued finish and the diamond-checkered walnut grips. The serial-number range on 1911 military pistols falls between 1 and 629500 with no prefix. They were manufactured by other subcontractors as well as by Colt and are listed with appropriate values. The standard frame stamping is "United States Property," The right side of the slide is marked "Model of 1911" followed by "U.S.Army", "U.S.Navy," or "U.S.M.C." They were manufactured between 1912 and 1925.

Courtesy Milwaukee Public Museum, Milwaukee, Wisconsin.

Colt Manufacture

U.S. Army marked throughout serial range.
Below Serial #10000—Add 10%.

Exc.	V.G.	Good	Fair	Poor
1150	1000	750	550	450

U.S. Navy Marked

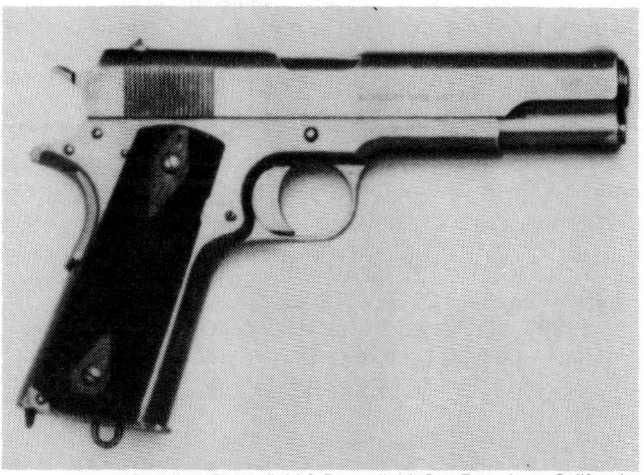

Courtesy Butterfield & Butterfield, San Francisco, California.

Exc.	V.G.	Good	Fair	Poor
1500	1000	750	550	450

U.S.M.C. Marked

Approximately 13,500 produced in appropriate serial range.

Exc.	V.G.	Good	Fair	Poor
1500	1000	750	550	450

Springfield Armory Manufacture

There were approximately 25,767 pistols produced by the Springfield Armory. They are within serial number 72751 and #133186. These pistols have the Springfield Eagle and the U.S. Ordnance Flaming Bomb stamped on the frame and slide.

Exc.	V.G.	Good	Fair	Poor
1250	900	700	500	400

Springfield Armory D.C.M. Model

There were fewer than 100 of these pistols produced for sale through the Department of Civilian Marksmanship before the beginning of WWI. They are marked "NRA" on the frame. Expert authentication should be secured on this pistol!

Exc.	V.G.	Good	Fair	Poor
2500	1850	1250	800	600

Remington-UMC Manufacture

There were 21,676 of these pistols produced in 1918 and 1919. They have their own serial-number range #1-21676 and are stamped "Remington UMC" on the slide.

Exc.	V.G.	Good	Fair	Poor
1250	900	700	500	400

North American Arms Co. Manufacture

This is the rarest variation of the military Colt 1911. Only 100 were produced in Quebec, Ontario, during 1918. These pistols are not serial numbered. A small number, used for record-keeping, can be found on some of the pistols. It appears on the slide just after the serrations end. These pistols are also not marked "U.S Property." One must be very wary of fakes when dealing with this model, as it is extremely desirable to collectors.

Exc.	V.G.	Good	Fair	Poor
10000	7500	6000	400	2750

British RAF Rework

These pistols were made from the British Contract pistols left at the end of WWI. They were simply refinished and stamped by hand "RAF" on the left side of the frame.

Exc.	V.G.	Good	Fair	Poor
1250	900	700	500	400

Arsenal Reworked 1911 Military Models

After WWI the Armed Forces still had a need for handguns. It is estimated that over 50 percent of the 1911s went home in duffel bags as war souvenirs with the returning "Doughboys." The remaining 1911s were sent to Augusta Arsenal, Rock Island Arsenal, or Springfield Armory, where they were refurbished as needed. These guns were parkerized and bear the initials of the arsenal that reworked them, "AA", "RIA," or "SA".

Exc.	V.G.	Good	Fair	Poor
750	650	500	350	250

Norwegian Automatisk Pistol Model 1912

Norway had been seriously considering the adoption of a semi-automatic pistol since 1904, when they established the "Permanent Gun Commission" to test the offerings available at that time. Eventually, after much testing and debate, including the Norwegian Parliament's involvement, the Colt 1911 was settled on. Due to legal ramifications around John Browning's involvement with Fabrique Nationale, the Norwegian government had to negotiate with F.N. instead of Colt. They desired to acquire the rights to manufacture the pistol themselves under license and not merely to purchase it outright. In 1917 the negotiations were complete, and the "Kongsberg Vapenfabrikk" delivered the first pistol. There were 500 pistols in the initial order. They have Norwegian acceptance markings and are designated "M/1912." In all other respects, they are identical to the Colt Model 1911. The last of the "M/1912" pistols was manufactured in 1919.

Exc.	V.G.	Good	Fair	Poor
1200	900	700	550	400

Norwegian Automatisk Pistol Model 1914

In 1919 the Norwegian service pistol was changed slightly. The slide lock lever was enlarged and extended downward, and the hammer spur was made slightly longer. The reasoning behind these modifications was to make the pistol easier to handle. Whether it accomplished this goal or not is debatable. The new model is marked "11.25m/m Aut.Pistol M/1914" on the left side of the slide. Production on the M/1914 continued until the early 1930s. Approximately 20,000 were manufactured.

Exc.	V.G.	Good	Fair	Poor
900	675	600	400	200

Pistole 657(n)-Norw. 14-

After Nazi Germany occupied Norway, the "Kongsberg Vapenfabrikk" was put into operation to produce the M/1914 to be issued to occupation troops. This production ceased in 1943, after approximately 10,000 pistols were produced. The above designation was assigned by the German Heereswaffenamt. These pistols do not exhibit the Norwegian crown cypher; and some, though not all, bear the WAA German Ordnance Office acceptance mark.

Exc.	V.G.	Good	Fair	Poor
900	675	600	400	200

MODEL 1911A1 SEMI-AUTOMATIC PISTOL

The Model 1911-A1 was manufactured by Colt until 1971 when it was replaced by the Series 70 Government Model. This modification involved a slightly heavier slide and a modified collet barrel bushing. In 1983 Colt introduced the Series 80 models which had the additional passive firing pin safety lock. The half-cock notch was also redesigned. At the beginning of 1992 another change was made to the Model 1911-A1 model in the form of an enhanced pistol. Included were the Government models, the Commander, the Officer's model, the Gold Cup, and the Combat Elite. These modifications are the result of Colt's desire to meet the shooters demand for a more "customized" pistol. The Model 1911-A1 may be the most modified handgun in the world. Colt chose some of the most popular modifications to perform on their new enhanced models. They include beavertil safety grip, a slotted Commander style hammer, a relief cut under the trigger guard, a beveled magazine well, a slightly longer trigger, a flat-top rib, and angled slide serrations.

Model 1911A1 Automatic Pistol Commercial Series

It is said that the period between the two wars saw the finest of the Colt Automatics produced. The 1911A1 was known as the "Government Model" in its civilian configuration; and with the exception of the fit, finish, and markings, it was identical to the military models. The "C" prefix still designated the commercial series and did so until 1950, when it was changed to a suffix. The "Government Model" is polished and blued. It has checkered walnut grips. There were a number of different commercial models manufactured. We individually list them.

Pre-WWII Commercial

These pistols were manufactured by Colt from 1925-1942. They fall within the #C130000-C215000 serial range.

Exc.	V.G.	Good	Fair	Poor
1250	900	700	500	350

Post WWII Commercial

Produced 1946-1969. "C" prefix until 1950, when it was changed to a suffix. Approximately 196,000 manufactured.

Exc.	V.G.	Good	Fair	Poor
650	550	450	350	250

Super .38 1929 Model

This pistol is identical in outward physical configuration to the .45 ACP Colt Commercial. It is chambered for the .38 Super cartridge and has a magazine that holds 9 rounds. The right side of the slide is marked "Colt Super .38 Automatic" in two lines, followed by the "Rampant Colt."

Exc.	V.G.	Good	Fair	Poor
1750	1450	1000	700	600

Super Match .38 1935 Model

Only 5,000 of these specially fit and finished target-grade pistols were manufactured. They have Stevens adjustable sights, and the top surfaces are matte-finished to reduce glare. Twelve hundred of these pistols were purchased and sent to Britain in 1939, at the then costly rate of $50 per unit.

Exc.	V.G.	Good	Fair	Poor
3000	2250	1700	1100	800

1st Model National Match .45

This pistol was produced so that Colt would have a factory-produced target-grade pistol for the 1932 National Matches at Camp Perry. The pistol was made up of specially selected hand-honed and fitted parts. It has a special "Match" grade barrel. The first pistols had fixed sights, but shortly thereafter the "Stevens Adjustable Rear Target Sight" was used. The right side of the slide is marked "National Match." This Model possessed exceptional shooting qualities. It was produced until 1941.

Exc.	V.G.	Good	Fair	Poor
1500	1250	950	650	450

Ace Model .22 Pistol

In 1930 Colt purchased advertising which, in effect, requested the shooting public to let the company know if they would be interested in a .22 rimfire pistol built similar to the Government Model. The response must have been positive because in 1931 the Colt Ace appeared on the market. The Ace uses the same frame as the Government Model with a modified slide and a heavy barrel. It is chambered for .22 l.r. The size is the same as the larger-caliber version, and the weight is 36 ounces. The operation is straight blowback. The Ace has a 10-round detachable magazine and features the "Improved Ace Adjustable Target Sight." The markings on the left side of the slide are the same as on the Government Model; the right side reads "Colt Ace 22 Long Rifle." At first the Army purchased a few pistols (totalling 206) through 1936. It was found, however, that the function of the Ace was less than perfect, as the .22 rimfire lacked the power to consistently and reliably blow back the slide. Approximately 11,000 Ace pistols were manufactured, and in 1941 they were discontinued.

Exc.	V.G.	Good	Fair	Poor
1800	1500	1200	700	500

Service Model Ace .22 R.F. Pistol

In 1937 Colt introduced this improved version of the Ace Pistol. It utilizes a floating chamber invented by David "Carbine" Williams, the firearm's designer who invented the M1 carbine while serving time on a southern chain gang. This loading chamber gave the Service Model Ace the reliability and "feel" that the public wanted. The serial number is prefixed by the letters "SM." The external configuration is the same as the Ace, and the slide is marked "Colt Service Model Ace .22 Long Rifle." Colt sold some to the Army and some on a commercial basis. There was a total of 13,000 manufactured before production ceased in 1944.

Exc.	V.G.	Good	Fair	Poor
1700	1450	1100	800	600

Conversion Units .22/.45, .45/.22

In 1938 Colt released a .22-caliber conversion unit. With this kit, one who already owned a Government Model could simply switch the top half and fire inexpensive .22 rimfire ammunition. The unit consists of a slide marked "Service Model Ace", barrel with floating chamber, ejector, slide lock, recoil spring, and 10-shot magazine. The Conversion Units feature the Stevens Adjustable Rear Sight. Later that same year, a kit to convert the

Service Model Ace to .45 ACP was offered. In 1942 production of these units ceased. The .22 kit was reintroduced in 1947; the .45 kit was not brought back.

Prewar Service Model Ace Conversion Unit

Exc.	V.G.	Good	Fair	Poor
1050	800	550	450	350

.45/.22 Conversion Unit

Exc.	V.G.	Good	Fair	Poor
350	300	250	200	150

Postwar .22 Conversion Unit

Exc.	V.G.	Good	Fair	Poor
300	275	250	200	150

Drake National Match Pistols

In the 1950s, Springfield Armory used some of these specially machined and hardened slides to construct highly accurate pistols for the Camp Perry Competition. The slides have "NM" and a number on the left side and the Drake name on the right. The "NM" number also appears on the barrel, and the bushing and "NM" is stamped on the triggerguard. "SA" (designating Springfield Armory) is stamped on the frame, along with the letter "S" on the barrel link. These high-grade pistols have either adjustable sights or high-profile fixed sights. They are quite scarce and should be authenticated.

Exc.	V.G.	Good	Fair	Poor
950	750	600	450	400

National Match Reworks

These pistols were hand fitted by government armorers for use by the U.S. shooting teams. They have the letters "NM" on all the parts and are either blued or parkerized with target-type sights.

Exc.	V.G.	Good	Fair	Poor
800	700	600	450	350

Gold Cup National Match

This model is chambered for the .45 ACP, features the flat mainspring housing of the 1911, and has a matchgrade barrel and bushing. The parts were hand fitted to target tolerances, and the slide has an enlarged ejection port. The trigger is the long version with an adjustable trigger stop, and the sights are adjustable target type. The finish is blued, with checkered walnut grips and gold medallions. The slide is marked "Gold Cup National Match," and the serial number is prefixed by the letters "NM." This pistol was manufactured from 1957 until 1970.

Exc.	V.G.	Good	Fair	Poor
700	800	550	450	350

Gold Cup MKIII National Match

This pistol is identical to the Gold Cup .45 except that it is chambered for the .38 Mid-Range Wad Cutter round. It was manufactured from 1961 until 1974.

Exc.	V.G.	Good	Fair	Poor
750	700	600	450	350

Foreign Contract Commercial Pistols

Mexican Contract Pistols

These pistols were manufactured before 1927. They are marked "Ejercito Mexicano," which translates to "Mexican Army." They have the "C" serial-number prefix, and most were well-used.

Exc.	V.G.	Good	Fair	Poor
900	750	600	500	350

Argentine Contract Pistols

These pistols were delivered to Argentina in 1927. The right side of the slide is marked with the two-line inscription "Ejercito Argentino Colt .Cal.45 Mod. 1927." There is also the Argentine National Seal and the "Rampant Colt." Colt enjoyed a profitable relationship with Argentina through the late 1920s, delivering approximately 10,000 pistols before failing to meet a delivery date in the early 1930s. This brought about the licensing of the Argentine Government to manufacture the Colt Pistol on their own.

Exc.	V.G.	Good	Fair	Poor
550	500	400	300	200

Model 1911A1 Automatic Pistol Military Model

As WWII loomed on the horizon and Germany's intentions became ever clearer, it became apparent that we would have an escalated need for weapons once again in this century. We were, however, now better able to fill this need than we had been the time before. Our gun manufacturers had already tooled up and were producing guns for the British "Lend Lease Program." Our Government awarded contracts to Colt, Remington-Rand, Ithaca, Union Switch & Signal, and Singer. Their collective efforts resulted in the manufacture of approximately 2,000,000 1911A1s. These pistols were used not only in WWII but in the Korean and Vietnam Wars.

It is only recently that the 1911A1 has been replaced, controversially, as our Nation's Service Pistol. Regardless of who manufactured these 1911A1s, they all have 5" barrels and 7-round detachable magazines and are chambered for the .45 ACP cartridge. All but the earliest Colt-produced guns are parkerized and have brown checkered plastic grips. The first 1911A1s produced were a bright polished blue with checkered walnut grips. The authenticity of a WWII 1911A1 can be checked by comparing the manufacturer to the assigned serial number chart that appears at the end of this chapter. There are a number of fine publications that specialize in this model, and the serious student should acquire them and learn.

Colt Manufacture

These pistols were produced from 1924 through 1945. They commenced with serial number 700000, and there were approximately 1,627,000 manufactured.

Early Models with Polished and Blued Finish—Add 100%.

Exc.	V.G.	Good	Fair	Poor
600	500	400	300	250

Remington-Rand Manufacture

Approximate production 948,905; 1943-1945.

Exc.	V.G.	Good	Fair	Poor
600	500	400	300	250

Ithaca Manufacture

Approximate production 441,557; 1943-1945.

Exc.	V.G.	Good	Fair	Poor
650	550	450	350	300

Union Switch & Signal Manufacture

Approximate production 55,100; 1943 only.

Exc.	V.G.	Good	Fair	Poor
1200	1000	800	500	400

Singer Manufacture

Five hundred produced in 1942 only. Exercise caution if contemplating purchase, as the extreme rarity of this model has encouraged fakery.

Exc.	V.G.	Good	Fair	Poor
10000	7500	5500	4500	3500

MKIV Series 70 Government Model

This model is essentially a newer version of the 1911A1. It has the prefix "70G" from 1970-1976, "G70" from 1976-1980, and "70B" from 1980-1983, when production ceased. This Model is offered in blue or nickle-plate and has checkered walnut grips with the Colt medallion. It is chambered for .45 ACP, .38 Super, 9mm, and 9mm Steyr (foreign export only).

NIB	Exc.	V.G.	Good	Fair	Poor
600	500	400	300	250	200

MKIV Series 70 Gold Cup National Match

This is the newer version of the 1957 National Match. It features a slightly heavier slide and Colt Elliason sights. The chambering is .45 ACP only. The Accurizer barrel and bushing was introduced on this model. It was manufactured form 1970-1983.

NIB	Exc.	V.G.	Good	Fair	Poor
700	600	500	400	300	250

Colt Enhanced Government Models

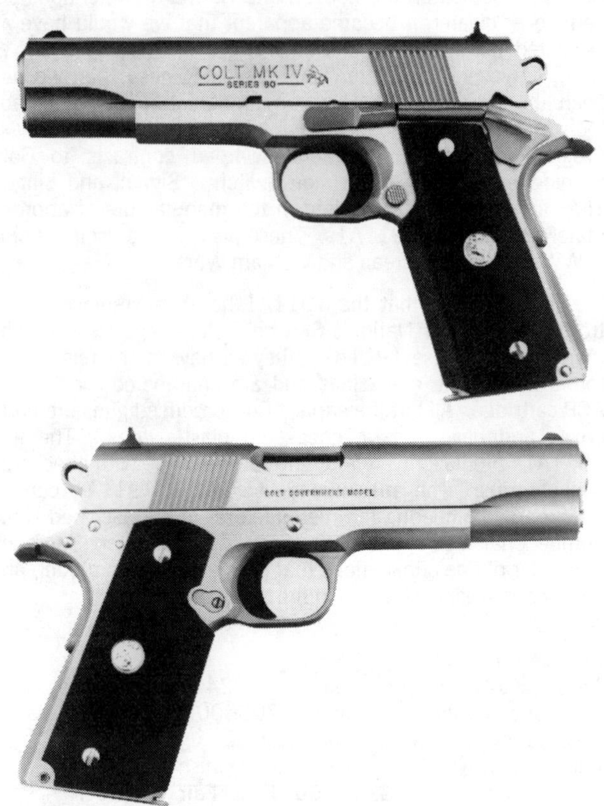

In 1992 Colt introduced a new set of features for its Model 1911A1 series pistols. These new features include: a flattop slide, angled rear slide serrations, scalloped ejection port, combat style hammer, beavertail grip safety, relief cut under trigger guard, and long trigger. The models that are affected by this new upgrade are the: Delta Elite, Combat Elite, Government model, Combat Commander, Lightweight Commander, Officer's ACP, Officer's ACP Lightweight.

Commander

This is a shortened version of the Government Model. It has a 4.25" barrel, a lightweight alloy frame, and a rounded spur hammer. The total weight of the Commander is 27.5 ounces. The serial number has the suffix "LW." The Commander is chambered for the .45 ACP, 9mm, and .38 Super. The latter two have been discontinued. Some were chambered for 7.65 Parabellum for export only. The Commander was introduced in 1949 and is still being manufactured.

NIB	Exc.	V.G.	Good	Fair	Poor
550	450	400	350	300	200

Combat Commander

The Combat Commander was produced in response to complaints from some quarters about the excessive recoil and rapid wear of the alloy-framed Commander. This model is simply a Commander with a steel frame. The Combat Commander weighs 32 ounces and is offered in blue or satin nickle with walnut grips.

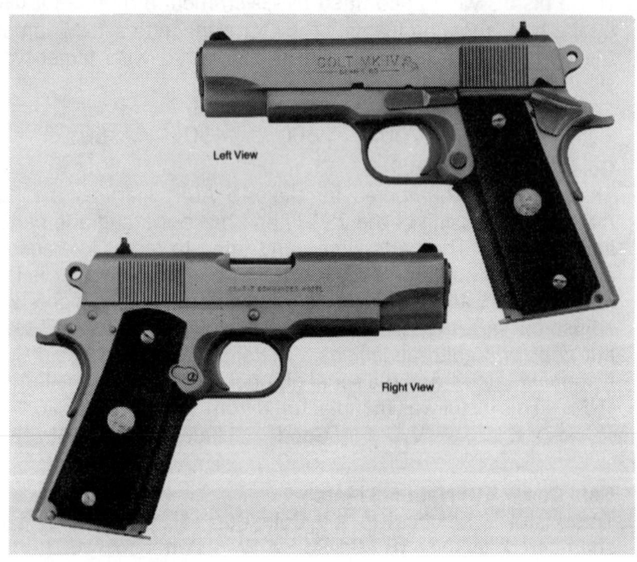

NIB	Exc.	V.G.	Good	Fair	Poor
600	500	450	375	300	200

MKIV Series 80 Government Model

This model was introduced in 1983. It is, for all purposes, the same externally as the Series 70. The basic difference is the addition of the new firing pin safety on this model.

Blued

NIB	Exc.	V.G.	Good	Fair	Poor
600	500	400	350	300	250

Nickel Plated

Exc.	V.G.	Good	Fair	Poor
550	450	375	300	250

Stainless Steel

NIB	Exc.	V.G.	Good	Fair	Poor
625	575	475	400	325	275

Polished Stainless Steel

NIB	Exc.	V.G.	Good	Fair	Poor
700	600	500	450	350	300

Colt 1991A1

Introduced in 1992 this Colt government model is designed to resemble the original GI service issue Government model. Offered in .45 ACP, a 5" barrel, 7 round magazine, black composition grips, and a special Parkerized finish.

NIB	Exc.	V.G.	Good	Fair	Poor
370	300	250	200	150	125

M1991A1 Commander

Chambered for the .45 ACP this model has all of the same features as the standard M1991A1 with a slightly shorter 4.25" barrel.

Left View

Right View

NIB	Exc.	V.G.	Good	Fair	Poor
370	300	250	200	150	125

M1991A1 Compact

Chambered for the .45 ACP this model has a 3.25" barrel. It is 1.5" shorter than the standard M1991A1 model and .375" shorter in height. Its magazine holds 6 rounds.

Left View

Right View

NIB	Exc.	V.G.	Good	Fair	Poor
370	300	250	200	150	125

MKIV Series 80 Gold Cup National Match

Externally the same as the Series 70 Gold Cup with the new firing pin safety.

Blued

NIB	Exc.	V.G.	Good	Fair	Poor
700	600	500	450	350	250

Stainless Steel

NIB	Exc.	V.G.	Good	Fair	Poor
775	650	550	500	400	300

Polished Stainless Steel

NIB	Exc.	V.G.	Good	Fair	Poor
825	700	600	550	450	350

Officers ACP

This is a shortened version of the Government Model. It has a 3.5" barrel and weighs 37 ounces. It is chambered for the .45 ACP only and has checkered walnut grips. The Officers ACP was introduced in 1985.

Blued

NIB	Exc.	V.G.	Good	Fair	Poor
550	450	350	325	250	200

Matte Blued

NIB	Exc.	V.G.	Good	Fair	Poor
525	425	325	300	225	200

Satin Nickle (Discontinued 1985)

Exc.	V.G.	Good	Fair	Poor
400	300	250	200	150

Stainless Steel

NIB	Exc.	V.G.	Good	Fair	Poor
625	500	400	350	300	250

Lightweight Officers ACP

This is an alloy-framed version that weighs 24 ounces. It was introduced in 1986.

NIB	Exc.	V.G.	Good	Fair	Poor
600	500	400	375	300	200

Delta Gold Cup

Introduced in 1992 the Delta Gold Cup is chambered for the 10MM, features a 5" barrel, stainless steel finish, adjustable Accro sights, special trigger, and black rubber wraparound stocks. Features all of the new "Enchanced" model features.

NIB	Exc.	V.G.	Good	Fair	Poor
800	750	650	550	400	200

Delta Elite

This model is chambered for the 10mm Norma cartridge. It is offered in blue or stainless steel. The grips are black neoprene with the Delta medallion. It features a high-profile three-dot combat sight system. The Delta Elite was introduced in 1987.

Blued

NIB	Exc.	V.G.	Good	Fair	Poor
550	475	375	325	300	250

Stainless Steel

NIB	Exc.	V.G.	Good	Fair	Poor
600	500	400	350	300	250

Polished Stainless Steel

NIB	Exc.	V.G.	Good	Fair	Poor
675	575	450	400	350	250

Combat Elite This is a specialized Government model that has a 5" barrel and adjustable Accro sights. It is chambered either in .45 ACP or .38 Super. It weighs 38 ozs. and has an 8-round magazine for the .45 ACP and a 9-round magazine for the .38 Super. Finish can be either blue or matte stainless steel.

NIB	Exc.	V.G.	Good	Fair	Poor
650	550	450	350	300	200

Double Eagle

This is a double-action semi-automatic pistol chambered for the 10mm Auto and the .45 ACP cartridges. It has a 5" barrel and an 8-round detachable box magazine. It is constructed of stainless-steel and has checkered black synthetic grips. The sights are fixed and utilize the three-dot system.

NIB	Exc.	V.G.	Good	Fair	Poor
500	425	350	300	250	200

Double Eagle Officer's Model

This is a compact version of the double-action Double Eagle pistol chambered for .45 ACP only.

NIB	Exc.	V.G.	Good	Fair	Poor
480	425	375	300	250	200

Double Eagle Combat Commander

Based on the standard Double Eagle design but with a slightly shorter 4.25" barrel, the Double Eagle Combat Commander fits between the standard model and the smaller Officer's Model. Available in .45 ACP and 40 S&W (1993) this model weighs about 36 ozs., holds 8-rounds, has white dot sights, and checkered Xenoy grips. The finish is matte stainless steel.

NIB	Exc.	V.G.	Good	Fair	Poor
625	550	500	400	300	200

Double Eagle First Edition

This version of the double-action Double Eagle pistol is chambered for the 10mm Auto and is furnished with a Cordura holster, double-magazine pouch, and three magazines, as well as a zippered black Cordura case.

NIB	Exc.	V.G.	Good	Fair	Poor
700	650	550	475	375	300

.380 Series 80 Government Model

This is a single-action, blowback-operated semi-automatic pistol chambered for the .380 ACP cartridge. It has a 3.25" barrel and a 7-round magazine. The sights are fixed. It is available either blued, nickle-plated, or stainless steel. It has synthetic grips and was introduced in 1985.

Nickle Finish—Add 10%.

Stainless Steel—Add 10%.

NIB	Exc.	V.G.	Good	Fair	Poor
350	300	250	200	175	125

Mustang

This is a more compact version of the .380 Government Model. It has a 2.75" barrel and a 5-round detachable magazine.

Nickle Finish—Add 10%.

Stainless Steel—Add 10%.

NIB	Exc.	V.G.	Good	Fair	Poor
350	300	250	200	175	125

Mustang Plus II

This version of the Mustang pistol features the 2.75" barrel with the longer grip frame that accommodates a 7-round magazine. It was introduced in 1988 and is offered in blue, as well as stainless steel.

Stainless Steel—Add 10%.

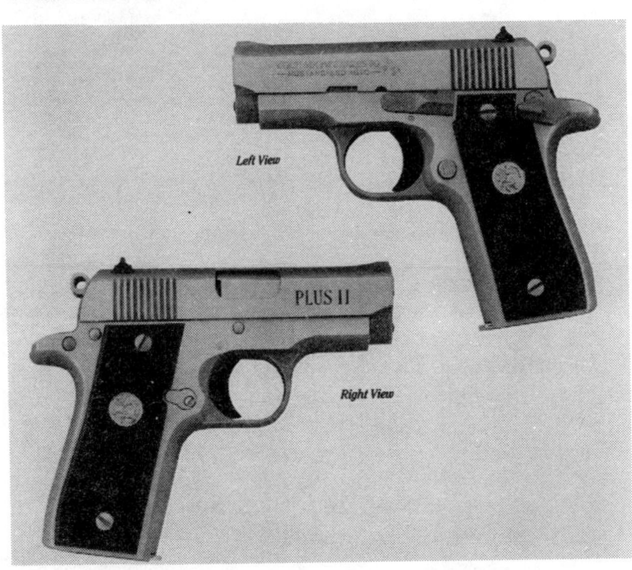

NIB	Exc.	V.G.	Good	Fair	Poor
385	300	250	200	175	125

Mustang Pocket Life

A lightweight version of the Mustang that features an aluminum-alloy receiver. The finish is blued only, and it has synthetic grips. It was introduced in 1987.

NIB	Exc.	V.G.	Good	Fair	Poor
385	300	250	200	175	125

Colt Model 2000

Introduced in 1992, the Model 2000 is a new departure for Colt from its traditional service style semi-automatic pistols. Chambered for the 9MM, the Model 2000 is a double action only pistol with a 4.5" barrel and a choice between a Polymer frame or an aluminum alloy frame. The polymer frame model weighs 29 ozs. while the aluminum alloy frame weighs 33 ozs. Grips are black composition and sights are white dot.

NIB	Exc.	V.G.	Good	Fair	Poor
450	400	350	300	250	200

.22 RIMFIRE SEMI-AUTOMATIC PISTOLS

Colt Junior Pocket Model

This diminutive unit is only 4.5" long overall and weighs 12 ounces. Colt did not manufacture this pistol but rather had it made for them by Astra in Spain. The pistol was introduced in 1958 chambered for .25 ACP. One year later a .22 Short version appeared. Both had external hammers and detachable 6-round magazines. The passage of the 1968 Gun Control Act made import of a weapon of this size illegal, so Colt discontinued its relationship with Astra. The pistol was re-introduced in 1970 as an American-made product and was produced for two more years. Production ceased in 1972. Astra also made this pistol and called it the Cub.

.22 Short—Add 25%.

NIB	Exc.	V.G.	Good	Fair	Poor
300	250	200	175	125	75

Pre-Woodsman Model

This pistol was designed by John Browning. The name Woodsman was not used until 1927, but some collectors use it to describe this pistol as it is of the same pattern. This pistol was designed for general purpose use, hunting, and informal target practice. The pistol has a 6.5" thin barrel and weighs 28 ounces. There is a 10-round detachable magazine, and the chambering is .22 Long Rifle standard velocity only. It has a concealed hammer and a sliding thumb safety. The finish is blue, with checkered plastic grips. It was manufactured between 1915 and 1927, and there were approximately 54,000 produced.

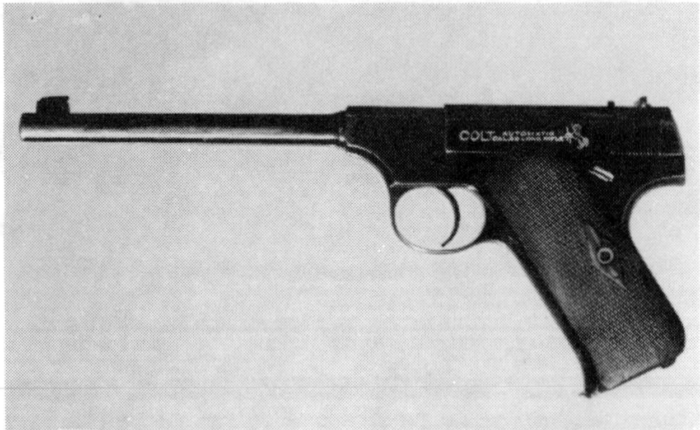

Courtesy Orville Reichert.

Exc.	V.G.	Good	Fair	Poor
750	550	450	300	200

1st Series Woodsman

This series was manufactured from 1927 until 1947. It was chambered for .22 l.r. standard velocity up to 1932. After that date it was redesigned to fire high-velocity ammunition. The mainspring housing on these high-velocity models is serrated instead of checkered. This change took place at serial number 83790. All Woodsmans after this fired high-velocity ammunition. This model is blued, with checkered wood grips; and the side of the frame is marked "The Woodsman." The 10-shot detachable magazine is released at the bottom. There were approximately 112,000 manufactured.

Sport Model, 4.5" Barrel

Exc.	V.G.	Good	Fair	Poor
750	550	450	300	200

Target Model, 6.5" Barrel

Exc.	V.G.	Good	Fair	Poor
650	475	375	275	200

1st Series Woodsman Match Target

This model has a special 6.5" heavy barrel, target sights, and longer checkered walnut target grips. The side of the receiver has a "Bullseye" and the "Match Target" designation stamped on it. There were only 16,000 of these pistols manufactured between 1938 and 1944. They are quite scarce today.

Exc.	V.G.	Good	Fair	Poor
1500	1250	850	500	400

2nd Series Woodsman

This is a totally redesigned pistol and is very different from the preceding models. It has a slide stop, a hold-open device, and a push-button magazine release behind the triggerguard. It is blued, with brown plastic grips. There were approximately 146,000 manufactured between 1948 and 1955.

Sport Model, 4.5" Barrel

Exc.	V.G.	Good	Fair	Poor
550	450	350	250	200

Target Model, 6" Barrel

Exc.	V.G.	Good	Fair	Poor
450	350	300	200	150

Match Target Model, 4.5" Barrel

Exc.	V.G.	Good	Fair	Poor
700	600	500	400	300

Match Target Model, 6" Barrel

Exc.	V.G.	Good	Fair	Poor
600	500	400	300	250

3rd Series Woodsman

This model is very similar to the 2nd Series except that the magazine catch is located at the bottom of the grip. It was manufactured from 1955-1960 with black plastic grips and from 1960-1977 with checkered walnut.

Sport Model, 4.5" Barrel

Exc.	V.G.	Good	Fair	Poor
400	300	250	175	125

Target Model, 6" Barrel

Exc.	V.G.	Good	Fair	Poor
375	325	250	175	125

Match Target Model, 4.5" Barrel

Exc.	V.G.	Good	Fair	Poor
500	400	300	200	150

Match Target, 6" Barrel

Exc.	V.G.	Good	Fair	Poor
450	350	300	200	150

Challenger Model

This pistol is simply a Woodsman with less expensive grips and sights. It has either a 4.5" or a 6" barrel, fixed sights, no hold-open device, and a bottom magazine release. It is chambered for .22 l.r. The production ran to 77,000. It was manufactured between 1950 and 1955.

Exc.	V.G.	Good	Fair	Poor
350	300	250	200	150

Huntsman Model

The only difference between the Huntsman and the Challenger is that the Huntsman utilizes a 3rd Series frame. The Huntsman had black plastic grips until 1960 and checkered walnut after that. There were approximately 100,000 manufactured between 1955 and 1977.

Exc.	V.G.	Good	Fair	Poor
300	250	200	150	100

Targetsman Model

This is essentially the Huntsman with adjustable target sights and a thumbrest grip. It is offered with a 6" barrel only. There were approximately 65,000 manufactured between 1959 and 1977.

Exc.	V.G.	Good	Fair	Poor
350	300	250	200	150

SERIAL NUMBERS ASSIGNED TO M1911 AND 19211A1 CONTRACTORS

Year	Serial No.	Manufacturer
1912	1-500	Colt
	501-1000	Colt USN
	1001-1500	Colt
	1501-2000	Colt USN
	2001 2500	Colt
	2501-3500	Colt USN
	3501-3800	Colt USMC
	3801-4500	Colt
	4501-5500	Colt USN
	5501-6500	Colt
	6501-7500	Colt USN
	7501-8500	Colt
	8501-9500	Colt USN
	9501-10500	Colt
	10501-11500	Colt USN
	11501-12500	Colt
	12501-13500	Colt USN
	13501-17250	Colt
1913	17251-36400	Colt
	36401-37650	Colt USMC
	37651-38000	Colt
	38001-44000	Colt USN
	44001-60400	Colt
1914	60401-72570	Colt
	72571-83855	Springfield
	83856-83900	Colt
	83901-84400	Colt USMC
	84401-96000	Colt
	96001-97537	Colt
	97538-102596	Colt
	102597-107596	Springfield
1915	107597-109500	Colt
	109501-110000	Colt USN
	110001-113496	Colt
	113497-120566	Springfield
	120567-125566	Colt
	125567-133186	Springfield
1916	133187-137400	Colt
1917	137401-151186	Colt
	151187-151986	Colt USMC
	151987-185800	Colt
	185801-186200	Colt USMC
	186201-209586	Colt
	209587-210386	Colt USMC
	210387-215386	Colt Frames
	215387-216186	Colt USMC
	216187-216586	Colt
	216587-216986	Colt USMC
1918	216987-217386	Colt USMC
	217387-232000	Colt
	232001-233600	Colt USN
	233601-594000	Colt
1918	1-13152	Rem-UMC
1919	13153-21676	Rem-UMC
	594001-629500	Colt
	629501-700000	Winchester (Assigned)
1924	700001-710000	Colt
1937	710001-712349	Colt
1938	712350-713645	Colt
1939	713646-717281	Colt USN
1940	717282-721977	Colt
1941	721978-756733	Colt
1942	756734-800000	Colt
	S800001-S800500	Singer
	800501-801000	H&R (Assigned)
1943	801001-958100	Colt
	958101-1088725	U.S. S.& S.
	1088726-1208673	Colt
	1208674-1279673	Ithaca

SERIAL NUMBERS ASSIGNED TO M1911 AND 19211A1 CONTRACTORS

Year	Serial No.	Manufacturer
1943	1279674-1279698	Augusta Arsenal (Renumber)
	1279699-1441430	Remington-Rand
	1441431-1471430	Ithaca
	1471431-1609528	Remington-Rand
1944	1609529-1743846	Colt
	1743847-1890503	Ithaca
	1890504-2075103	Remington-Rand
1945	2075104-2134403	Ithaca
	2134404-2244803	Remington-Rand
	2244804-2380013	Colt
	2380014-2619013	Remington-Rand
	2619014-2693613	Ithaca

COLT MODERN LONG ARMS

Colteer I-22

This is a single shot bolt-action rifle chambered for .22 l.r. or .22 Magnum. It has a plain uncheckered walnut stock, 20" barrel, and adjustable sights. There were approximately 50,000 manufactured between 1957 and 1966.

Exc.	V.G.	Good	Fair	Poor
250	200	175	125	90

Stagecoach

This is a semi-automatic, saddle ring carbine. It is chambered for .22 l.r. and has a 16.5" barrel and a 13-shot tubular magazine. The stock is fancy walnut, and the receiver has the stagecoach holdup scene roll-engraved on it. There were approximately 25,000 manufactured between 1965 and 1975.

Exc.	V.G.	Good	Fair	Poor
300	250	200	150	100

Courier

This model is very similar to the Stagecoach, with a pistolgrip stock and beavertail forearm. It was manufactured between 1970 and 1975.

Exc.	V.G.	Good	Fair	Poor
250	200	175	125	90

Colteer

This is a less expensive version of the Stagecoach. It features a 19.5" barrel, has a 15-shot tubular magazine, and is stocked in a plainer grade walnut. There is no roll engraving. Approximately 25,000 were manufactured between 1965 and 1975.

Exc.	V.G.	Good	Fair	Poor
250	200	175	125	90

Colt "57" Bolt Action Rifle

This rifle was manufactured for Colt by the Jefferson Mfg. Co of New Haven, Connecticut. It utilizes a Fabrique Nationale Mauser action and has a checkered American walnut stock with a Monte Carlo comb. The rifle is offered with adjustable sights. It is chambered for .243 or .30-06. There is also a deluxe version that features higher-grade wood. There were approximately 5,000 manufactured in 1957.

Deluxe Version—Add 20%.

Exc.	V.G.	Good	Fair	Poor
550	450	350	300	225

Coltsman Bolt Action Rifle

The Coltsman was manufactured for Colt by Kodiak Arms. It utilizes either a Mauser or Sako action. The rifle is offered in .243, .308, .30-06, and .300 Winchester Magnum. It has a barrel length of 22", 24" in the Magnum chambering. The stock is checkered American walnut. There were approximately 10,000 manufactured between 1958 and 1966. There is a deluxe version that features a higher-grade, skipline-checkered walnut stock and rosewood forend tip; this is called "The Coltsman Custom."

Coltsman Custom—Add 50%.

Exc.	V.G.	Good	Fair	Poor
650	550	450	350	250

Coltsman Pump Shotgun

This model was manufactured by Jefferson Arms, utilizing an aluminum alloy frame made by Franchi. It is chambered for 12, 16, and 20 gauge and has a 26" or 28" plain barrel. There were approximately 2,000 manufactured between 1961 and 1965.

Exc.	V.G.	Good	Fair	Poor
350	300	275	200	150

Semi-Auto Shotgun

The Semi-Auto Shotgun was manufactured for Colt by the firm of Luigi Franchi in Italy. It features an aluminum alloy receiver and is chambered for 12 or 20 gauge. The barrel length is 26", 28", 30", or 32"-either vent-rib or plain. A deluxe version, "The Custom Auto," features a fancy walnut stock and a hand engraved receiver. There were approximately 5,300 manufactured between 1962 and 1966.

Custom Auto—Add 25%.

Exc.	V.G.	Good	Fair	Poor
375	325	300	225	175

Double Barrel Shotgun

During 1961 and 1962. Colt had approximately 50 side-by-side shotguns made for them by a French gun manufacturer. They have the Colt name on the breech area of the barrels and are in the 467000-469000 serial range. There is very little information available on this gun, and Colt never went past the test-market stage.

Exc.	V.G.	Good	Fair	Poor
1000	750	650	500	400

Colt Sauer Bolt Action Rifle

This is a very high quality and unique rifle manufactured for Colt by the firm of J.P. Sauer & Son of Germany. The rifle features a non-rotating bolt that makes the Colt Sauer action smoother functioning than most. It has a 24" barrel, skipline-checkered walnut stock with rosewood forend tip, pistol grip cap, and recoil pad. There are five basic configurations: the Standard Action, chambered for .25-06, .270 Winchester, and .30-06; the Short Action, chambered for .22-250, .243 Winchester, and .308 Winchester; the Magnum Action, chambered for .7mm Remington Magnum, .300 Winchester Magnum, and .300 Weatherby Magnum; also the "Grand Alaskan" and the "Grand African," heavier versions chambered for .375 Holland & Holland Magnum and 458 Winchester Magnum, respectively. These rifles were all discontinued by Colt in 1985.

Colt Sauer Short Action

Exc.	V.G.	Good	Fair	Poor
900	750	500	400	350

Standard Action—Add $50.
Magnum Action—Add $200.
"Grand Alaskan"—Add $400.
"Grand African"—Add $450.

Colt Sauer Drilling

This is a rather unique firearm and one with which many American enthusiasts are not familiar—a 3-barrelled gun. It features a side-by-side shotgun in 12 gauge over a .30-06 or .243 rifle barrel. The name was based on the German word for three, as this is where the concept was developed. They are quite popular in Europe where the game preserve style of hunting is prevalent but have little use in America where our hunting seasons don't often overlap. This drilling has 25" barrels and pop-up sights for the rifle barrel and is nicely engraved. It was discontinued by Colt in 1985.

Exc.	V.G.	Good	Fair	Poor
3500	2750	2000	1500	1100

Colt-Sharps Rifle

Introduced in 1970 as the last word in sporting rifles, the Colt-Sharps is a falling-block action that was advertised as a modern Sharps-Borchardt. This undertaking was first-class all the way. The finish is high polish blue with a deluxe-grade hand-checkered walnut stock and forend. This rifle is chambered for .17 Remington, .22-250, .243, .25-06, 7mm Remington Magnum, .30-06, and .375 Holland & Holland Magnum; and it was offered cased with accessories. This model was manufactured between 1970 and 1977.

Exc.	V.G.	Good	Fair	Poor
2500	2000	1600	1200	750

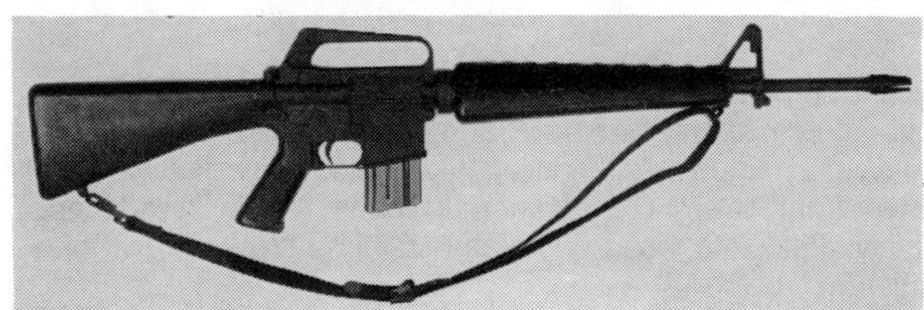

AR-15 Sporter (Model #6000)
A semi-automatic rifle firing from a closed bolt was introduced into the Colt product line in 1964. Similar in appearance and function to the military version; the M-16. Chambered for the .223 cartridge. It is fitted with a standard 20" barrel with no forward assist, no case deflector, but with a bayonet lug. Weighs about 7.5 lbs. Dropped from production in 1985.

NIB	Exc.	V.G.	Good	Fair	Poor
750	675	600	500	400	300

AR-15 Sporter w/collapsible stock (Model #6001)
Same as above but fitted with a 16" barrel and folding stock. Weighs approximately 5.8 lbs. Introduced in 1978 and discontinued in 1985.

NIB	Exc.	V.G.	Good	Fair	Poor
850	775	700	600	450	300

AR-15 Carbine (Model #6420)
Introduced in 1985 this model has a 16" standard weight barrel. All other features are the same as the previous discontinued AR-15 models. This version was dropped from the Colt product line in 1987.

NIB	Exc.	V.G.	Good	Fair	Poor
1100	900	800	650	450	300

AR-15 9mm Carbine (Model #6450)
Same as above but chambered for 9mm cartridge. Weighs 6.3 lbs.

NIB	Exc.	V.G.	Good	Fair	Poor
1050	900	800	650	450	300

AR-15A2 (Model #6500)
Introduced in 1984 this was an updated version with a heavier barrel and forward assist. The A1 sight was still utilized. Weighs approximately 7.8 lbs.

NIB	Exc.	V.G.	Good	Fair	Poor
950	875	800	650	450	300

AR-15A2 Govt. Model Carbine (Model #6520)
Added to the Colt line in 1988 this 16" standard barrel carbine featured for the first time a case deflector and the improved A2 rear sight. Discontinued in 1990. Weighs about 5.8 lbs.

NIB	Exc.	V.G.	Good	Fair	Poor
1050	900	800	650	450	300

AR-15A2 Gov't Model (Model #6550)
This model was introduced in 1988 is the rifle equivalent to the Carbine. It features the heavier 20" A2 barrel, forward assist, case deflector, but still retains the bayonet lug. Weighs about 7.5 lbs. Discontinued in 1990.

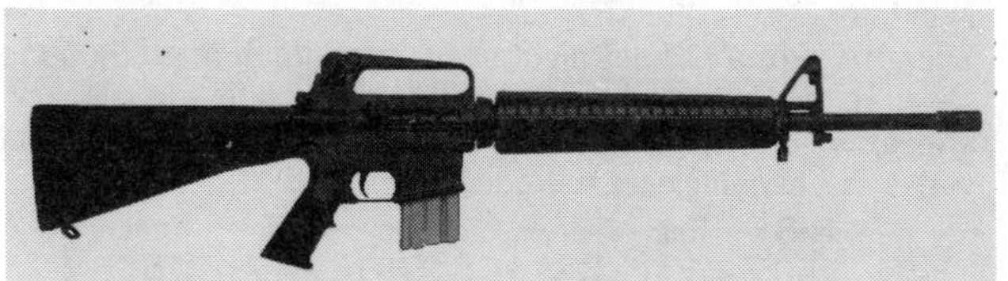

NIB	Exc.	V.G.	Good	Fair	Poor
950	875	800	650	500	300

AR-15A2 H-Bar (Model #6600)
Introduced in 1986 this version features a special 20" heavy barrel. All other features are the same as the A2 series of AR-15s. Discontinued in 1991. Weighs about 8 lbs.

NIB	Exc.	V.G.	Good	Fair	Poor
1100	950	800	650	450	300

AR-15A2 Delta H-Bar (Model #6600DH)
Same as above but fitted with a 3x9 scope and detachable cheek piece. Dropped from the Colt line in 1990. Weighs about 10 lbs.

NIB	Exc.	V.G.	Good	Fair	Poor
1500	1350	900	700	500	300

Sporter Lightweight Rifle
This lightweight model has a 16" barrel and is finished in a matte black. It is available in either a .223 Rem caliber (Model #6530) which weighs 6.7 lbs. a (Model #6430) 9MM caliber weighing 7.1 lbs., or a (Model #6830) 7.65x39MM which weighs 7.3 lbs. The .223 is furnished with two five-round box magazines as is the 9MM and 7.65x39MM. A cleaning kit and sling are also supplied with each new rifle. The butt stock and pistol grip are made of durable nylon and the handguard is reinforced fiberglass and aluminum lined. The rear sight is adjustable for windage and elevation. These newer models are referred to simply as Sporters and are <u>not</u> fitted with a bayonet lug.

NIB	Exc.	V.G.	Good	Fair	Poor
725	650	550	450	350	300

NOTE: The Model 6830 will bring about $25 less than the above prices.

Sporter Target Model Rifle (Model #6551)
This 1991 model is a full size version of the Lightweight rifle. The Target rifle weighs 7.5 lbs. and has a 20" barrel. Offered in .223 Rem caliber only with target sights adjustable to 800 meters. New rifles are furnished with two 5 rounds box magazines, sling and cleaning kit.

NIB	Exc.	V.G.	Good	Fair	Poor
675	600	500	400	300	250

Sporter Match H-Bar (Model #6601)
This 1991 variation of the AR-15 is similar to the Target model but has a 20" heavy barrel chambered for the .223 caliber. This model weighs 8 lbs. and has target type sights adjustable out to 800 meters. Supplied with two 5-round box magazines, sling, and cleaning kit.

NIB	Exc.	V.G.	Good	Fair	Poor
750	675	550	450	350	300

Sporter Match Delta H-Bar (Model #6601DH)
Same as above but supplied with a 3x9 scope. Weighs about 10 lbs. Discontinued in 1992.

NIB	Exc.	V.G.	Good	Fair	Poor
650	600	500	400	300	250

Sporter Competition H-Bar (Model #6700)
Introduced in 1992, the Competition H-Bar is available in .223 caliber with a 20" heavy barrel counteredbored for accuracy. The carry handle is detachable with target sights. With the carry handle removed the upper receiver is dovetailed and grooved for Weaver style scope rings. This model weighs approximately 8.5 lbs. New rifles are furnished with two 5 round box magazines, sling, and cleaning kit.

NIB	Exc.	V.G.	Good	Fair	Poor
800	725	600	450	350	300

Sporter Competition H-Bar Select w/scope (Model #6700CH)
This variation, also new for 1992, is identical to the Sporter Competition with the addition of a factory mounted scope. The rifle has also been selected for accuracy and comes complete with a 3-9X rubber armored variable scope, scope mount, carry handle with iron sights, and nylon carrying case.

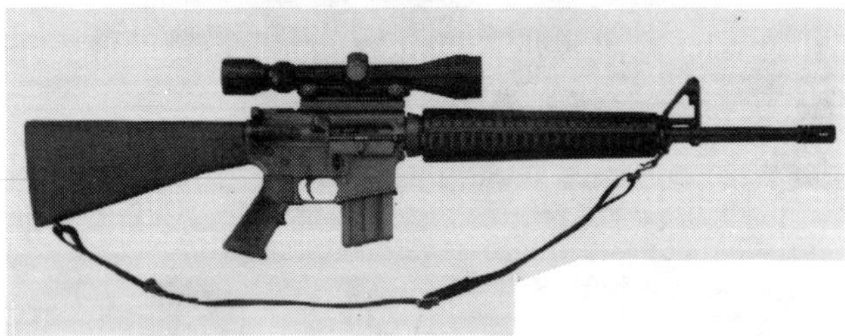

NIB	Exc.	V.G.	Good	Fair	Poor
700	625	500	400	300	250

COLT CUSTOM SHOP

The Colt Custom Shop has developed several models over the years that are available to the public. The basis of these offerings are standard Colt models upgraded to perform special functions.

Special Combat Government Model (Competition)
This is a competition ready model. Chambered for the .45 ACP it comes fitted with a skeletized trigger, upswept grip safety, custom tuned action, polished feed ramp, throated barrel, flared ejection port, cutout commander hammer, two 8-round magazines, hard chromed slide and receiver, extended thumb safety, Bomar rear sight, Clark dovetail front sight, and flared magazine funnel. The pistol has been accurized and is shipped with a certified target.

NIB	Exc.	V.G.	Good	Fair	Poor
1450	1100	800	500	300	200

Special Combat Government Model (Carry)
This model has all of the same features as the competition model except that it has a royal blue finish, special bar-dot night sights, ambidextrous safety. It has also been accurized and shipped with a certified target.

NIB	Exc.	V.G.	Good	Fair	Poor
1250	900	700	400	300	200

Gold Cup Commander
Chambered for the .45 ACP and has the following features: heavy duty adjustable target sights, beveled magazine well, serrated front strap, checkered mainspring housing, wide grip safety, Palo Alto wood grips, and stainless steel or royal blue finish.

NIB	Exc.	V.G.	Good	Fair	Poor
650	550	450	350	250	150

Ultimate Python
Custom tuned action with both Elliason and Accro sighting systems. Both rubber and Walnut grips are included. Bright stainless steel or royal blue finish. Available only with 6" barrel.

NIB	Exc.	V.G.	Good	Fair	Poor
1000	850	750	600	400	250

Custom Anaconda
Custom tuned action, Magna-ported barrel, with Elliason rear sight. The contoured trigger is polished smooth. Comes with Pachmayr grips and brushed stainless steel finish.

NIB	Exc.	V.G.	Good	Fair	Poor
650	575	500	400	300	200

Anaconda Hunter
Comes with a Leupold 2X scope, heavy duty mounts, cleaning accessories, both walnut and rubber grips, in a hard case. Furnished only with an 8" barrel.

NIB	Exc.	V.G.	Good	Fair	Poor
975	900	800	600	400	250

Limited Class .45 ACP
Designed for tactical competition. Supplied with a parkerized matte finish, lightweight composite trigger, extended ambidextrous safety, upswept grip safety, beveled magazine well, accurized, and shipped with a signed target. Introduced in 1993.

NIB	Exc.	V.G.	Good	Fair	Poor
750	675	600	450	300	200

Compensated Model .45 ACP
This competition pistol has a hard chrome receiver, bumper on magazine, extended ambidextrous safety, blue slide with full profile BAT compensator, Bomar rear sight, and flared funnel magazine well. Introduced in 1993.

NIB	Exc.	V.G.	Good	Fair	Poor
1850	1350	900	650	400	250

Nite Lite .380
Supplied with a bar-dot night sight, special foil mark on barrel slide, Teflon coated alloy receiver, stainless slide, high capacity grip extension magazine, and a standard magazine. Shipped with a soft carrying case. Introduced in 1993.

NIB	Exc.	V.G.	Good	Fair	Poor
450	400	325	275	225	150

The following is a list of special edition Colt pistols and revolvers produced by the Colt Custom Shop exclusively for distributor Lew Horton. These handguns are listed to provide the reader with an idea of the number of limited edition Colt's sold by Lew Horton and the year they were produced with the retail price.

Because of the limited numbers built it is difficult to furnish accurate prices for the secondary market.

Model	Qty. Built	Year Made	Retail Price
Horse Pistol, SAA	100	1983	$1100.00
Ultimate Officer's .45ACP	500	1989	777.00
Lt. Commander .45ACP	800	1985	590.00
Combat Cobra 2 1/2"	1000	1987	500.00
Lady Colt (MKIV .380ACP)	1000	1989	547.00
Night Commander .45ACP	250	1989	725.00
El Presidente .38 Super	350	1990	800.00
El Comandante .38 Super	500	1991	800.00
El General .38 Super	500	1991	850.00
El Capitan	500	1991	875.00
Colt Boa-4" & 6"	600	1985	525.00
El Dorado	750	1992	1099.00
El Coronel	750	1993	899.00
El Teniente	400	1992	1036.00
Classic Gold Cup	300	1993	1849.95
Night Officer	350	1993	679.95
El Presidente Premier Edition	10	1993	3000.00

COLT COMMEMORATIVES

The field of commemoratives can be fascinating and frustrating, depending on one's point of view. For someone who collects things from purely an aesthetic sense, commemoratives are quite desirable. Most are embellished and have had great care put into their fit and finish. They are attractively cased, and the proliferation of them makes acquisition relatively simple except from a financial standpoint. On the other hand, the collector who has an eye for the investment potential of his collections has found that the commemorative market has been soft and as investments they historically have not done well. The reason for this is twofold. The limited production appeal is not always what it seems. Many times the amounts produced are greater than one would consider limited. It is also a fact that if one fires a commemorative, its collectibility is gone. Even excessive handling can cause this problem. This means that since the majority of these firearms are kept new in the original boxes, the supply will usually outstrip the demand.

Very few commemoratives are ever lost or worn out. Collectors who seek firearms for their historic significance are usually not interested in the commemoratives, as even though they may have been issued to commemorate a specific historic person or event, they are not a part of the era and are regarded as "instant" collectibles. In some areas one will find that the Colt Commemoratives are not as desirable, saleable, or expensive as the plain out of the box versions. This is especially true in the Single Action Army models. We list the commemoratives made by Colt in chronological order. Remember that the prices reflect new-in-the-box as it came from the factory—all papers, books, etc., intact and included. We also include the issue price for comparison. If the model with which you are concerned has been fired or is not in its original casing or box, deduct as much as 50 percent from these prices. It is interesting to note that in some areas shooters are taking advantage of the soft commemorative market and are buying SAAs at lower prices than the plain 3rd Generation guns—then shooting them. This can perhaps have a positive effect on appreciation.

COLT COMMEMORATIVES

1961	Issue	NIB	Amount Mfg.
Geneseo,IL. 125th Anniv. Derringer	$ 28	$ 650	104
Sheriff's Model (Blue & Case)	130	1995	478
Sheriff's Model (Nickle)	140	5000	25
Kansas Statehood Scout	75	350	6,201
125th Anniv. Model SAA .45	150	895	7,390
Pony Express Cent. Scout	80	450	1,007
Civil War Cent. Pistol	75	175	24,114
1962			
Rock Island Arsenal Cent. Scout	$ 39	$ 250	550
Columbus, OH. Sesquicent. Scout	100	550	200
Ft. Findlay,OH. Sesquicent. Scout	90	650	110
Ft. Findlay Cased Pair	185	2500	20
New Mex. Golden Anniv. Scout	80	375	1,000
Ft. McPherson,Nebraska Cent. Derringer	29	395	300
West Virginia Statehood Cent. Scout	75	350	3,452

COLT COMMEMORATIVES

1963	Issue	NIB	Amount Mfg.
West Virginia Statehood Cent. SAA .45	$ 150	$ 950	600
Ariz. Terr. Cent. Scout	75	350	5,355
Ariz. Terr. Cent. SAA .45	150	950	1,280
Carolina Charter Tercent. Scout	75	350	300
Carolina Charter tercent. 22/45 Comb.	240	1195	251
H.Cook 1 To 100 22/45 Comb.	275	1595	100
Ft. Stephenson,Oh. Sesquicent. Scout	75	550	200
Battle of Gettysburg Cent. Scout	90	350	1,019
Idaho Terr. Cent. Scout	75	350	902
Gen. J.H.Morgan Indiana Raid Scout	75	650	100
Cherry's 35th Anniv. 22/45 Comb.	275	1595	100
Nevada Statehood Cent. Scout	75	350	3,984
Nevada Statehood Cent. SAA .45	150	950	1,688
Nevada Statehood Cent. 22/45 Comb.	240	1295	189
Nev.Statehood Cent.22/45 W/extra Cyls.	350	1395	577
Nevada Battle Born Scout	85	350	981
Nevada Battle Born SAA .45	175	1195	80
Nevada Battle Born 22/45 Comb.	265	2595	20
Montana Terr. Cent. Scout	75	350	2,300
Montana Terr. Cent. SAA .45	150	950	851
Wyoming Diamond Jubilee Scout	75	350	2,357
General Hood Cent. Scout	75	350	1,503
New Jersey Terrcent. Scout	75	350	1,001
New Jersey Terrcent SAA .45	150	950	250
St.Louis Bicent. Scout	75	350	802
St.Louis Bicent. SAA .45	150	950	200
St.Louis Bicent 22/45 Comb.	240	1295	250
California Gold Rush Scout	80	375	500
Pony Express Pres. SAA .45	250	1095	1,004
Chamizal Treaty Scout	85	350	450
Chamizal Treaty SAA .45	170	1295	50
Chamizal Treaty 22/45 Comb.	280	1995	50
Col. Sam Colt Sesquicent. SAA .45	225	950	4,750
Col. Sam Colt Deluxe SAA .45	500	1950	200
Col. Sam Colt Special Deluxe SAA .45	1000	2950	50
1964			
Wyatt Earp Buntline SAA .45	$ 250	$1795	150
1965			
Oregon Trail Scout	$ 75	$ 350	1,995
Joaquin Murietta 22/45 Comb.	350	1595	100
Forty Niner Miner Scout	85	350	500
Old Ft. Des Moines Reconst. Scout	90	350	700
Old Ft. Des Moines Reconst. SAA.45	170	995	100
Old Ft. Des Moines Reconst. 22/45 Comb.	290	1595	100
Appomattox Cent. Scout	75	350	1,001
Appomattox Cent.SAA .45	150	850	250
Appomattox Cent. 22/45 Comb.	240	1295	250
General Meade Campaign Scout	75	350	1,197
St. Augustine Quadracent. Scout	85	350	500
Kansas Cowtown Series Wichita Scout	85	350	500
1966			
Kansas Cowtown Series Dodge City Scout	$ 85	$ 350	500
Colorado Gold Rush Scout	85	375	1,350
Oklahoma Territory Scout	85	350	1,343
Dakota Teritory Scout	85	350	1,000
General Meade SAA .45	165	950	200
Abercrombie & Fitch Trailblazer N.Y.	275	995	200
Abercrombie & Fitch Trailblazer Chic.	275	995	100
Abercrombie & Fitch Trailblazer S.F.	275	995	100
Kansas Cowtown Series Abilene Scout	95	350	500
Indiana Sesquicent Scout	85	350	1,500
Pony Express 4-Square Set .45 4 Guns	1,400	4395	N/A
California Gold Rush SAA .45	175	1195	130
1967			
Lawman Series Bat Masterson Scout	$ 90	$ 350	3,000
Lawman Series Bat Masterson SAA .45	180	1200	500

COLT COMMEMORATIVES

1967	Issue	NIB	Amount Mfg.
Alamo Scout	85	350	4,250
Alamo SAA .45	165	850	750
Alamo 22/45 Comb.	265	1295	250
Kansas Cowtown Series Coffeyville Scout	95	350	500
Kansas Trail Series Chisolm Trail Scout	100	350	500
WWI Series Chateau Thierry .45 Auto	200	695	7,400
WWI Series Chateau thierry Deluxe	500	1350	75
WWI Series Chateau thierry Sp. Deluxe	1000	2750	25
1968			
Nebraska Cent. Scout	$ 100	$ 350	7,001
Kansas Trail Series Pawnee Trail Scout	110	350	501
WWI Series Belleau Wood .45 Auto	200	695	7,400
WWI Series Belleau Wood Deluxe	500	1350	75
WWI Series Belleau Wood Sp. Deluxe	1000	2750	25
Lawman Series Pat Garrett Scout	110	350	3,000
Lawman Series Pat Garrett SAA .45	220	995	500
1969			
Gen. Nathan B. Forrest Scout	$ 110	$ 350	3,000
Kansas Trail Series Santa Fe Trail Sct.	120	350	501
WWI Ser. 2nd Battle of Marne .45Auto	220	695	7,400
WWI Ser. 2nd Battle of Marne Deluxe	500	1350	75
WWI Ser. 2nd Battle of Marne Sp.Del.	1000	2750	25
Alabama Sesquicent. Scout	110	350	3,001
Alabama Sesquicent. SAA .45	N/A	15000	1
Golden Spike Scout	135	350	11,000
Kansas Trail Ser. Shawnee Tr. Scout	120	350	501
WWI Ser. Meuse- Argonne .45 Auto	220	695	7,400
WWI Ser. Meuse- Argonne Deluxe	500	1350	75
WWI Ser. Meuse- Argonne Sp. Deluxe	1000	2750	25
Arkansas Terr. Sesquicent. Scout	110	350	3,500
Lawman Ser. Wild Bill Hickok Scout	117	350	3,000
Lawman Ser. Wild Bill Hickok SAA .45	220	995	500
California Bicent. Scout	135	350	5,000
1970			
Kansas Ft. Ser. Ft. Larned Scout	$ 120	$ 350	500
WWII Ser. European Theatre	250	695	11,500
WWII Ser. Pacific Theatre	250	695	11,500
Texas Ranger SAA .45	650	1795	1,000
Kansas Ft. Ser. Ft. Hays Scout	130	350	500
Marine Sesquicent. Scout	120	350	3,000
Missouri Sesquicent. Scout	125	350	3,000
Missouri Sesquicent. SAA .45	220	795	900
Kansas Ft. Ser. Ft. Riley Scout	130	350	500
Lawman Ser. Wyatt Earp Scout	125	395	3,000
Lawman Ser. Wyatt Earp SAA .45	395	1650	500
1971			
NRA Centenial SAA .45	$ 250	$ 995	5,000
NRA Centenial SAA .357 Mag.	250	795	5,000
NRA Centenial Gold Cup .45 Auto	250	850	2,500
U.S.Grant 1851 Navy	250	595	4,750
Robt. E. Lee 1851 Navy	250	595	4,750
Lee - Grant Set 1851 Navies	500	1350	250
Kansas Ft. Ser. Ft. Scott Scout	130	350	500
1973			
Florida Terr. Sesquicent. Scout	$ 125	$ 350	2,001
Arizona Ranger Scout	135	350	3,001
1974			
Peacemaker Centenial SAA .45	$ 300	$ 1095	1,500
Peacemaker Centenial SAA .44-40	300	1095	1,500
Peacemaker Centenial Cased Set	625	2250	500
1975			
USS Texas Special Edition .45 Auto Not Factory Issued	$ N/A	$1000	500

COLT COMMEMORATIVES

1976	Issue	NIB	Amount Mfg.
U.S. Bicentenial Set	$1695	$1895	1,776
1977			
2nd Amendment .22	$ 195	$ 325	3,020
U.S.Cavalry 200th Anniversary Set	995	1250	3,000
1978			
Statehood 3rd Model Dragoon	$12500	$ 6995	52
1979			
Ned Buntline SAA N.F. .45	$ 895	$ 795	3,000
Ohio President's Spec.Edit. .45 Auto	N/A	800	250
Tombstone Cent. .45 Auto	$ 550	$ 650	300
1980			
Drug Enforcement Agency .45 Auto	$ 550	$1100	910
Olympics Ace Spec. Edition .22	1000	1150	200
Heritage Walker .44 Percussion	1495	950	1,847
1981			
John M. Browning .45 Auto	$1100	$ 795	3,000
1982			
John Wayne SAA	$ 2995	$ 1995	3,100
John Wayne SAA Deluxe	10000	7500	500
John Wayne SAA Presentation	20000	12000	100
1983			
Buffalo Bill Wild West Show Cent SAA	$1350	$1250	500
Armory Model Limited Prod. SAA .45 (not a true commemorative)	1125	1495	500
1984			
1st Edition Govt. Model .380 ACP	$ 425	$ 400	1,000
Duke Frontier .22	475	475	1,000
Winchester /Colt SAA.44-40	N/A	1995	4,000
USA Edition SAA .44-40	4995	2995	100
Kit Carson New Frontier .22	550	450	1,000
2nd Edition Govt. Model .380 ACP	525	400	1,000
Officer's ACP Commencement Issue	700	600	1,000
Theodore Roosevelt SAA .44-40	1695	1500	500
No Amer. Oilmen Buntline SAA .45	3900	3500	200
1986			
150th Anniversary SAA .45	$1595	$1400	1,000
150th Anniv. Engraving Sampler	1613	2500	N/A
150th Anniv. Engraving Sampler.45 Auto	1155	1000	N/A
Texas 150th Sesquicent. Sheriff's .45	836	1095	N/A
Mustang 1st Edition .380 ACP	475	395	1,000
Officer's ACP Heirloom Edition	1575	1550	N/A
Klay-Colt 1851 Navy	1850	1850	150
Klay-Colt 1851 Navy Engraved Edit.	3150	3150	50
Double Diamond Set .357 & .45 Auto	1575	1595	1,000
1987			
Combat Elite Custom Edition .45 Auto	$ 900	$ 750	500
12th Man Spirit of Aggieland .45 Auto	950	750	999
1989			
Snake Eyes Ltd. Edit. 2-2.5" Pythons	$2950	$1895	500

REPRODUCTION COLT PERCUSSION REVOLVERS

Walker

Made from 1979 to 1981; serial numbers 1200-4120 and 32256 to 32500.

NIB	Exc.	V.G.
800	750	500

Walker Heritage Model

NIB
900

First Model Dragoon

Made from 1980 to 1982; serial numbers 24100-34500.

NIB	Exc.	V.G.
375	300	100

Second Model Dragoon
Made from 1980 to 1982; serial numbers as above.

NIB	Exc.	V.G.
375	300	100

Third Model Dragoon
Made from 1980 to 1982; serial numbers as above.

NIB	Exc.	V.G.
375	300	100

Model 1848 Pocket Pistol
Made in 1981; serial numbers 16000-17851.

NIB	Exc.	V.G.
350	300	100

Model 1851 Navy Revolver
Made from 1971 to 1978; serial numbers 4201-25100 and 24900-29150.

NIB	Exc.	V.G.
450	400	325

Model 1861 Army Revolver
Made from 1978 to 1982; serial numbers 201000-212835.

NIB	Exc.	V.G.
550	500	475

Model 1861 Navy Revolver
Made during 1980 and 1981; serial numbers 40000-43165.

NIB	Exc.	V.G.
500	450	400

Model 1862 Pocket Pistol
Made from 1979 to 1984; serial numbers 8000-58850.

NIB	Exc.	V.G.
400	350	300

Model 1862 Police Revolver
Made from 1979 to 1984; serial numbers in above range.

NIB	Exc.	V.G.
450	400	300

NOTE: The above revolvers were manufactured in a variety of styles (cylinder form, stainless steel, etc.) which effect prices. Factory engraved examples command a considerable premium over the prices listed above.

COLUMBIA ARMORY
Columbia, Tennessee

A tradename applied to a variety of cartridge revolvers made by John T. Smith Company of Rock Falls, Connecticut. The value for these arms in all variations is as follows.

Exc.	V.G.	Good	Fair	Poor
150	125	100	75	50

COLUMBUS F. A. MFG. CO.
Columbus, Georgia

Columbus Revolver
A .36-caliber double-action percussion revolver with a 6-shot, unfluted cylinder and a 7.5" octagonal barrel. Similar in appearance to the 1851 Colt Navy. The pistol is browned steel, with brass gripstraps and walnut grips. The barrel is marked "Columbus Fire Arms Manuf. Co/Columbus Ga." 100 revolvers were manufactured in 1863 and 1864.

Exc.	V.G.	Good	Fair	Poor
15000	12500	10000	7500	5000

COMBLAIN
Belgium and Brazil

Single Shot Rifle
A 11x53Rmm caliber rifle with a falling block action. Manufactured both in a hammerless and hammer version. Full stock secured by two barrel bands.

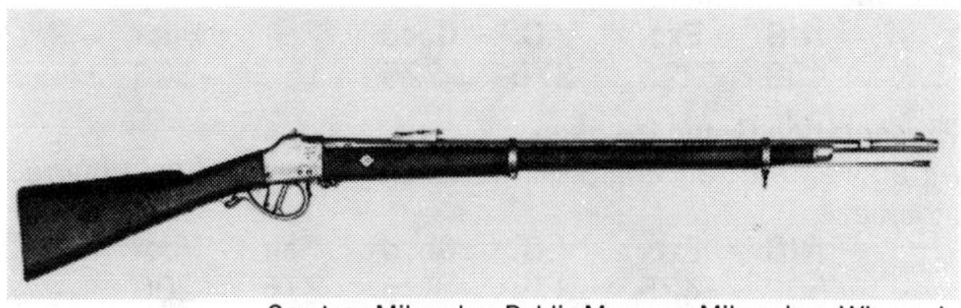

Courtesy Milwaukee Public Museum, Milwaukee, Wisconsin.

Exc.	V.G.	Good	Fair	Poor
750	650	500	350	250

COMMANDO ARMS
Knoxville, Tennessee

Formerly known as Volunteer Enterprises. The name change took place in 1978.

Mark III Carbine
A .45 ACP caliber semi-automatic rifle with a 16.5" barrel, a peep rear sight and a vertical foregrip. Manufactured between 1969 and 1976.

Exc.	V.G.	Good	Fair	Poor
300	275	225	175	125

Mark 9 Carbine
As above, in 9mm caliber.

Exc.	V.G.	Good	Fair	Poor
300	275	225	175	125

Mark .45
The new designation for the Mark III after the company changed its name.

Exc.	V.G.	Good	Fair	Poor
300	275	225	175	125

CONNECTICUT ARMS CO.
Norfolk, Connecticut

Pocket Revolver
A .28 caliber spur trigger revolver with 3" octagonal barrel, 6 shot unfluted cylinder, using a cup-primed cartridge and loads from the front of the cylinder. There is a hinged hook on the side of the frame under the cylinder that acts as the extractor. Silver-plated brass, blued with walnut grips. The barrel is marked "Conn. Arms Co. Norfolk, Conn." Approximately 2,700 manufactured in the 1860s.

Exc.	V.G.	Good	Fair	Poor
300	275	225	150	100

CONNECTICUT VALLEY ARMS CO.
Norcross, Georgia

Express Rifle
A .50 caliber double barrel percussion rifle with 28" barrels. Blued with a walnut stock.
Deluxe Version—Add 100%.

NIB	Exc.	V.G.	Good	Fair	Poor
525	450	400	350	300	225

Over/Under Rifle
A .50 caliber double-barrel Over/Under rifle with 26" barrels. Blued with a walnut stock.

NIB	Exc.	V.G.	Good	Fair	Poor
575	500	450	400	350	275

Hawken Rifle
A .50 caliber with a 28" octagonal barrel, double set triggers and a walnut stock.

NIB	Exc.	V.G.	Good	Fair	Poor
400	325	275	225	150	100

Presentation Grade Hawken
As above, with an engraved lock, patchbox and finely figured stock.

NIB	Exc.	V.G.	Good	Fair	Poor
500	425	375	325	275	200

Pennsylvania Long Rifle
A .50 caliber flintlock rifle with a 40" octagonal barrel, double set triggers and a walnut stock.

NIB	Exc.	V.G.	Good	Fair	Poor
475	400	350	300	250	175

Kentucky Rifle
A .45 caliber percussion rifle with a 33.5" octagonal barrel and walnut stock.

NIB	Exc.	V.G.	Good	Fair	Poor
275	225	175	150	100	75

Mountain Rifle
A .50 or .54 caliber percussion half-stock rifle.

NIB	Exc.	V.G.	Good	Fair	Poor
300	225	175	125	100	75

Blazer Rifle
A .50 caliber percussion rifle with a 28" octagonal barrel and walnut stock.

NIB	Exc.	V.G.	Good	Fair	Poor
150	125	100	85	65	45

Brittany II Shotgun
A .410 bore double-barrel percussion shotgun with 24" barrels, double triggers and a walnut stock.

NIB	Exc.	V.G.	Good	Fair	Poor
170	150	125	100	75	50

Trapper Shotgun
A 12 gauge percussion single barrel shotgun with a 28" barrel threaded for choke tubes and a walnut stock.

NIB	Exc.	V.G.	Good	Fair	Poor
225	200	175	150	100	75

PISTOLS

Siber
A .45 caliber percussion pistol patterned after the Swiss Siber.

NIB	Exc.	V.G.	Good	Fair	Poor
400	325	275	225	150	100

Kentucky
A .45 caliber single shot percussion pistol with a 10" barrel and walnut stock.

NIB	Exc.	V.G.	Good	Fair	Poor
140	125	100	80	60	40

Philadelphia Derringer
A .45 caliber single shot percussion pistol with a 3.25" barrel and walnut stock.

NIB	Exc.	V.G.	Good	Fair	Poor
75	65	50	40	30	20

Sheriff's Model
A .36 caliber percussion revolver, nickle-plated with walnut grips.

NIB	Exc.	V.G.	Good	Fair	Poor
225	200	175	150	125	100

3rd Model Dragoon

NIB	Exc.	V.G.	Good	Fair	Poor
225	200	175	150	125	100

Colt Walker Replica

NIB	Exc.	V.G.	Good	Fair	Poor
275	250	225	200	175	150

Remington Bison

NIB	Exc.	V.G.	Good	Fair	Poor
250	225	200	175	150	125

Pocket Police

NIB	Exc.	V.G.	Good	Fair	Poor
135	110	100	85	65	45

Wells Fargo

NIB	Exc.	V.G.	Good	Fair	Poor
165	145	125	100	75	50

1851 Navy

NIB	Exc.	V.G.	Good	Fair	Poor
135	110	100	85	65	45

1861 Navy

NIB	Exc.	V.G.	Good	Fair	Poor
150	135	110	90	75	50

1860 Army

NIB	Exc.	V.G.	Good	Fair	Poor
220	200	175	150	125	100

1858 Remington

NIB	Exc.	V.G.	Good	Fair	Poor
175	150	125	100	75	50

1858 Remington Target
As above, but fitted with adjustable sights.

NIB	Exc.	V.G.	Good	Fair	Poor
235	200	175	125	100	75

CONSTABLE, R.

Philadelphia, Pennsylvania

Pocket Pistol
A single shot percussion pistol with a 3" round or octagonal barrel. German-silver mounts and walnut stock. These pistols are marked "R.Constable Philadelphia" and were manufactured during the late 1840s and 1850s.

Exc.	V.G.	Good	Fair	Poor
1500	1000	450	350	250

CONTENTO/VENTUR

Importer—Ventura
Seal Beach, California

This high-grade, double-barrel shotgun is no longer imported.

Side By Side

Model 51
A 12, 16, 20, 28 and .410 bore boxlock double barrel shotgun with 26", 28", 30", and 32" barrels, various chokes, extractors and double triggers. Checkered walnut stock.

Exc.	V.G.	Good	Fair	Poor
400	350	300	225	150

Model 52
As above in 10 gauge.

Exc.	V.G.	Good	Fair	Poor
500	450	400	325	250

Model 53
As above, with scalloped receiver, automatic ejectors and available with a single selective trigger.
Single-Selective Trigger—Add 25%.

Exc.	V.G.	Good	Fair	Poor
475	425	375	300	225

Model 61
A 12 or 20 gauge Holland & Holland sidelock shotgun with various barrel lengths and chokes, automatic ejectors, cocking indicators, a floral engraved receiver, a checkered, walnut stock.

Exc.	V.G.	Good	Fair	Poor
875	800	750	600	450

Model 65

As above, but more finely finished.

Exc.	V.G.	Good	Fair	Poor
1150	1000	850	700	550

Contento Over/Under

A 12 gauge Over/Under shotgun with 32" barrels, screw-in choke tubes, a high ventilated-rib, automatic ejectors, and a standard single selective trigger. Checkered, with Monte Carlo walnut stock.

Exc.	V.G.	Good	Fair	Poor
1050	900	750	600	500

Mark 2

As above, with an extra single barrel and fitted in a leather case.

Exc.	V.G.	Good	Fair	Poor
1350	1200	1050	900	800

Mark 3

As above, but engraved with a finely figured walnut stock.

Exc.	V.G.	Good	Fair	Poor
1600	1500	1250	1100	950

Mark 3 Combo

As above, with an extra single barrel and fitted in a leather case.

Exc.	V.G.	Good	Fair	Poor
2800	2600	2250	1750	1300

CONTINENTAL

RWM

Cologne, Germany

Continental Pocket Pistol

A 6.35mm caliber semi-automatic pistol with a 2" barrel, internal hammer, and a 7-shot detachable magazine. Blued with plastic grips, and the slide is marked "Continental Kal.6.35."

Exc.	V.G.	Good	Fair	Poor
210	185	145	110	75

CONTINENTAL ARMS CO.

Liege, Belgium

Double Rifle

A .270, .303, .30-40, .30-06, .348, 375 H&H, .400 Jeffreys, .465, .475, .500, and .600 Nitro Express caliber Anson & Deeley boxlock double-barreled rifle with 24" or 26" barrels, and double triggers. Checkered walnut stock.

Exc.	V.G.	Good	Fair	Poor
5000	4500	3750	3000	2250

CONTINENTAL ARMS CO.

Norwich, Connecticut

Pepperbox

A .22 caliber 5 barrel pepperbox with a spur trigger and 2.5" barrels marked "Continental Arms Co. Norwich Ct. Patented Aug. 28, 1866." Some examples of this pistol are to be found marked "Ladies Companion".

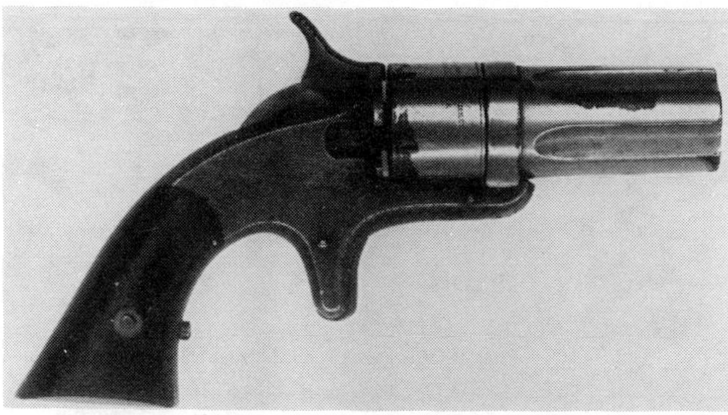

Courtesy Milwaukee Public Museum, Milwaukee, Wisconsin.

Exc.	V.G.	Good	Fair	Poor
600	525	475	375	300

COOK & BROTHERS RIFLES AND CARBINES

New Orleans

In early 1861, Ferdinand W.C. Cook and his brother, Francis L. Cook, both English emigres, joined to form Cook & Brother in New Orleans to manufacture rifles and carbines following the English P1853 series for the newly seceded state of Louisiana and its neighbors. Between June 1861 and the federal occupation of New Orleans in April 1862, this firm produced about 200 cavalry and artillery carbines and about 1000 rifles. Having successfully moved the armory's machinery before federal occupation, the firm continued manufacture of rifles in Selma, Alabama during 1862, probably completing another 1000 rifles with the New Orleans lock markings from the parts brought with them. Reestablished in Athens, Georgia in early 1863, the firm continued to build both carbines and rifles, manufacturing more than 5500 above the New Orleans production through 1864. The firm's products were clearly among the best small arms made within the Confederacy

Cook & Brothers rifles (New Orleans & Selma production)

Overall length- 48 3/4"; barrel length- 33"; caliber- .58. Markings: representation of a Confederate flag ("Stars & Bars") and "COOK & BROTHER/N.O./1861 (or) 1862" on lock; same usually on barrel, together with serial number and "PROVED" near breech. Rifles in the early production have long range rear sights and unusual two piece block and blade front sights as well as an integral bayonet lug with guide on right side of barrel. Later production utilizes a brass clamping ring for the bayonet, a block open rear sight and a simple block and blade front sight. Earlier production will claim a premium if in good condition.

Courtesy Milwaukee Public Museum, Milwaukee, Wisconsin.

Exc.	V.G.	Good	Fair	Poor
8500	7500	5500	4500	3000

Cook & Brothers carbines (New Orleans production)

Overall length- 40" (artillery), 37" (cavalry); barrel length- 24" (artillery), 21"-21-1/2"; caliber- .58. Markings: As on Cook & Brothers rifles (New Orleans production) artillery and cavalry carbines were produced in New Orleans in a separate serial range from the rifles. Total production is thought not to have exceeded 225, divided evenly between 1861 and 1862 dates. In addition to the overall and barrel lengths, the main difference between the artillery and cavalry carbines is the manner in which they were carried. The former bears standard sling rings on the upper band and the triggerguard strap, the latter has a bar with a ring on the left side of the stock. Both are exceedingly rare.

Exc.	V.G.	Good	Fair	Poor
10,000	9000	7500	6500	5000

Cook & Brothers rifles (Athens production)

Overall length- 49"; barrel length- 33"; caliber- .58. Markings: representation of a Confederate flag ("Stars & Bars") and "COOK & BROTHER/ATHENS GA./date (1863 or 1864), and serial number on lock; "PROVED" on barrel near breech; serial number on various metal parts. After reestablishing their plant at Athens, Georgia in the spring of 1863, Cook & Brother continued to manufacture rifles in a consecutive serial range after their New Orleans/Selma production (beginning about serial no. 2000) and continued to make arms well into 1864 (through at least serial number 7650) until Sherman's Army threatened the plant and necessitated the employment of its work force in a military capacity as the 23rd Battalion Georgia State Guard.

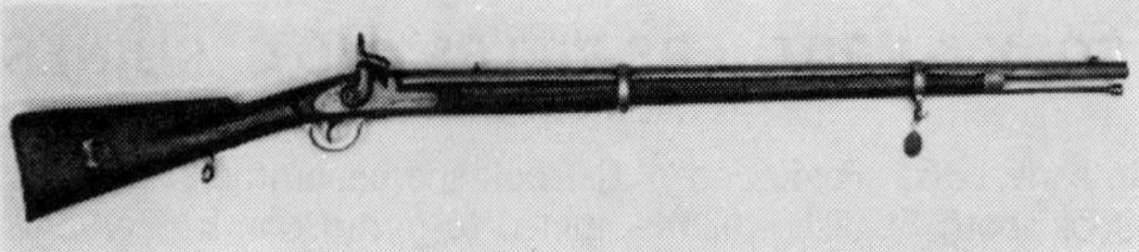

Courtesy Milwaukee Public Museum, Milwaukee, Wisconsin.

Exc.	V.G.	Good	Fair	Poor
5500	4750	4250	3500	2750

Cook & Brothers carbines (Athens Production)

Overall length- 40" (artillery) or 37" (cavalry); barrel lengths- 24" (artillery) or 21"-21 112" (cavalry); caliber- .58. Markings: same as on Athens production rifles. Artillery and cavalry carbines were manufactured in the same serial range as the Athens production rifles (about 2000 through 7650). As in New Orleans production, the artillery and cavalry carbines are distinguished from one another by their respective lengths. Unlike New Orleans/Selma production, however, some of the cavalry carbines are mounted with sling swivels of the artillery style, while others bear the sling ring on the left side and additionally have a swivel ring to secure the ramrod.

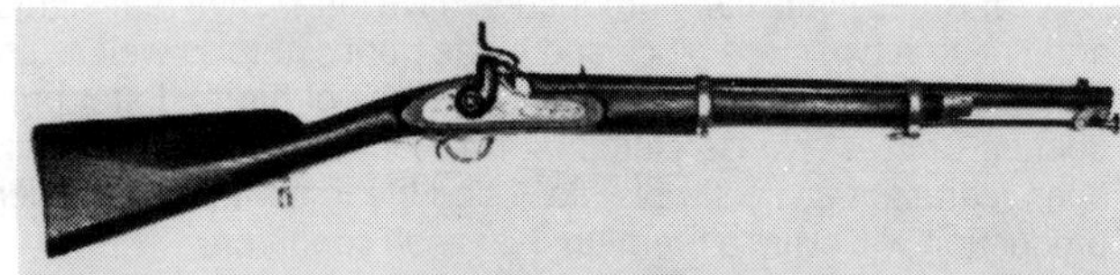

Courtesy Milwaukee Public Museum, Milwaukee, Wisconsin.

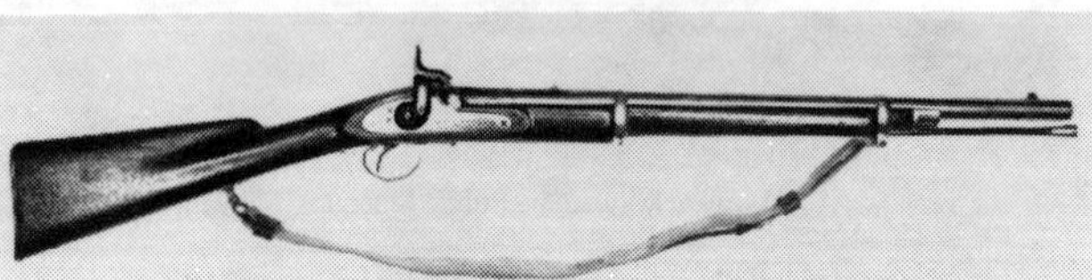

Courtesy Milwaukee Public Museum, Milwaukee, Wisconsin.

Exc.	V.G.	Good	Fair	Poor
8500	7500	6000	4500	4000

COONAN ARMS CO.

St. Paul, Minnesota

Model A

A .357 Magnum semi-automatic pistol with a 5" barrel, a 7-shot, detachable magazine, and fixed sights. Stainless steel with walnut grips. Introduced in 1981 and discontinued at in 1984.

NIB	Exc.	V.G.	Good	Fair	Poor
625	600	525	450	400	325

Model B

An improved version of the above with a linkless barrel system, extended grip safety, enclosed trigger bar, and a more contoured grip. A 6" barrel is available, as are adjustable sights, as extra cost options. A .38 Special conversion is also available. Introduced in 1985.

6" Barrel—Add $40.

Bomar Adjustable Sights—Add $130.

.38 Special Conversion—Add $40.

NIB	Exc.	V.G.	Good	Fair	Poor
680	650	600	525	450	375

Comp I

As above, with an attached compensator and a stippled front grip strap. Introduced in 1989.

NIB	Exc.	V.G.	Good	Fair	Poor
1350	1200	1000	850	700	500

Comp I Deluxe

As above, with a blued stainless steel slide, checkered grip straps, and a finer finishing.

NIB	Exc.	V.G.	Good	Fair	Poor
1650	1350	1150	950	800	600

COOPER, J. M. & CO.

Philadelphia, Pennsylvania

Pocket Revolver

A .31-caliber percussion double action revolver with 4", 5" or 6" octagonal barrel, and a 6-shot unfluted cylinder. Blued with walnut grips. During the first two years of production they were made in Pittsburgh, Pennsylvania, and were so marked. Approximately 15,000 were manufactured between 1864 and 1869.

Pittsburgh-Marked Models—Add 20%.

Courtesy Milwaukee Public Museum, Milwaukee, Wisconsin.

Courtesy Milwaukee Public Museum, Milwaukee, Wisconsin.

Exc.	V.G.	Good	Fair	Poor
1500	1000	500	250	150

COOPERATIVA OBRERA
Eibar, Spain

Longines

A 7.65mm caliber semi-automatic pistol. The slide is marked "Cal. 7.65 Automatic Pistol Longines."

Exc.	V.G.	Good	Fair	Poor
225	175	150	110	85

COPELAND, FRANK
Worcester, Massachusetts

Copeland Pocket Revolver .22

A .22 cartridge spur trigger revolver with a 2.5" barrel, 7-shot magazine, an unfluted cylinder and lock notches on the front. Frame is brass, blued walnut or rosewood grips. The barrel marked "F.Copeland,Worcester, Mass." Manufactured in the 1860's.

Exc.	V.G.	Good	Fair	Poor
275	225	175	125	100

Copeland .32 Revolver

A .32-caliber spur trigger revolver with a 5-shot fluted cylinder and an iron frame. Nickel-plated. The barrel marked "F. Copland, Sterling, Mass." Manufactured in the 1860's.

Exc.	V.G.	Good	Fair	Poor
250	200	150	100	75

COSMI, A. & F.
Torrette, Italy
Importer—New England Arms
Kittery Pt., Maine

Semi-Automatic

A 12 and 20 gauge semi-automatic shotgun with various barrel lengths and chokes, an 8-shot magazine, and a ventilated-rib This is basically a custom-built, made-to-order gun. There is a standard and a deluxe model, with the differences being in the degree of embellishment.

Standard Model

NIB	Exc.	V.G.	Good	Fair	Poor
4000	3750	3250	2850	2200	1750

Deluxe Model

NIB	Exc.	V.G.	Good	Fair	Poor
5000	4750	4250	3500	2750	2000

COSMOPOLITAN ARMS CO.
Hamilton, Ohio

Breech Loading Rifle

A .52 single shot percussion rifle with a 31" round barrel. The frame marked "Cosmopolitan Arms Co. Hamilton O. U.S./Gross Patent." Blued with a walnut buttstock. Approximately 100 were made between 1859 and 1862.

Exc.	V.G.	Good	Fair	Poor
1500	1300	1000	750	500

COWLES & SON
Chicopee, Massachusetts

Single Shot

A .22 or .30 caliber single shot spur trigger pistol with a 3.25" round barrel. Silver-plated brass frame, blued with walnut grip. Approximately 200 manufactured in 1865.

Exc.	V.G.	Good	Fair	Poor
250	225	175	125	100

CARL PHILLIP CRAUSE MUSKETS AND RIFLES
Herzberg, Germany

Carl Phillip Crause (who signed his products only with his last name) operated a gun manufactory in Herzberg on the Harz in the northwestern German kingdom of Hannover from the close of the Napoleonic Wars until 1857. The main production of his factory was devoted to military arms for Hannover and the surrounding principalities. Weapons of his manufacture included the Brunswick M1835 and M1848 rifles, the Hannovarian M1850 and M1854 rifle-muskets and yager rifles, and the M1840 and M1849 rifle-muskets of the Hanseatic League (a coalition of the north German states of Oldenberg, Hamburg, Bremen, and Lubeck). The latter two arms were subsequently altered to accept the elongated projectiles popular during the 1850s, and a few thousand evidently were imported into the United States and saw service during the American Civil War.

Hanseatic League M1840 rifled musket

Overall length- 55-1/2"; barrel length- 40-1/4"; caliber- .70. Markings: on lockplate forward of hammer, "Crause in Herzberg" in script, the "s" in the archaic form, appearing as an "f." Of the 6000 muskets of this type made, approximately half were sent to the United States in 1861 during the arms crisis that accompanied the outbreak of the American Civil War. A total of 2680 of these were issued to Ohio and at least one regiment (the 56th Ohio) was armed with these rifled muskets. These arms were misidentified during the period as being Saxon due to the similarity of the large squared off foresection of the lockplate.

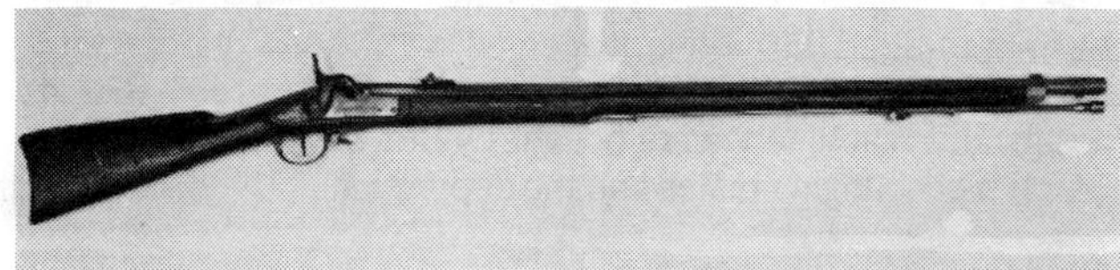

Courtesy Milwaukee Public Museum, Milwaukee, Wisconsin.

Exc.	V.G.	Good	Fair	Poor
775	650	475	375	250

Oldenberg M1849 rifled musket

Overall lengths- 55-1/2"-56-5/8" (long version), 49-1/2 (short version); barrel lengths- 39" - 39-1/8" (long version), 33" (short version); caliber- .69-.72 (rifled) Markings: "Crause in Herzberg" inscribed in script on the backstrap of the hammer housing, the "s" in archaic form, appearing as an "f." Nicknamed the "Cyclops" because its large, center hung hammer is pierced with a large window that served as its rear sight, a few hundred of these clumsy rifled muskets may have been intermixed with the shipments of "Saxon" muskets imported in 1861 or 1862 into the United States during the American Civil War.

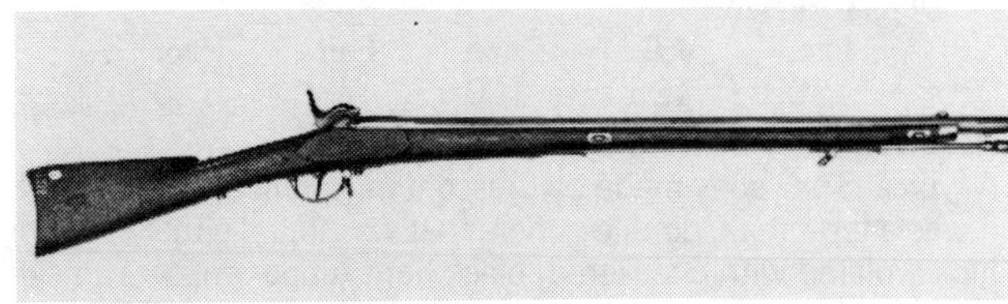

Courtesy Milwaukee Public Museum, Milwaukee, Wisconsin.

Exc.	V.G.	Good	Fair	Poor
700	600	500	350	225

CRESCENT F. A. CO.
Norwich, Connecticut

This company manufactured good quality, inexpensive side-by-side and single barrel shotguns and was founded in 1893. They were bought by the H & D Folsom Arms Company of New York, importers and distributors of firearms and sporting goods.

After the purchase of Crescent, the Folsom Company was able to offer a complete range of shotguns, imported English, French, Belgium, and American made Crescents. By the turn of the century Crescent Arms produced huge quantities of "Hardware Guns". They produced guns under direct contract to distributors, mail order houses and hardware distributors with any brand name the customer requested. Crescent also produced guns for its parent company, as Folsom house brands that were sold to customers that didn't want their own brand name.

By the late 1890's Crescent was producing basically five grades of double barrel shotguns offering a model for most tastes. #2641 was a double bolt, top lever action, barlock with armory steel barrels and low circular hammers. This model came in 12 gauge only with either 30 or 32-inch Belgian made Damascus barrels, the rest is American made. #2650 this model is the same as 2641 but it has Damascus Belgian made barrels and was better finished. #2660 was also the same as 2641 however, it was fitted with American made Damascus barrels. #2655 was of the same basic design and was fitted with twist barrels with a Deeley & Edge snap fore end. It has engraving on the trigger guard and locks and is somewhat better finished. #2665 has much more and better quality engraving, but was essentially the same as #2655. In 1904 Crescent added hammerless models with fluid steel barrels but they still offered the same line with a choice of hammers or not. Basically Crescent was able to mix and match barrel steels, engraving, checkering, wood and finish to provide a model for most tastes and still use the same basic design by changing the components. Various models could be ordered in 12, 16, 20, and 28 gauge, adn .410.

The Crescent/Folsom Arms Company continued this type of business until 1930 when it merged with Davis-Warner Arms Corp. and became the Crescent-Davis Arms Corp. In 1932 its assets and machinery were bought by Stevens Arms Company, a victim of changing tastes and the depression.

Doubles

12 and 16 Gauge

Exc.	V.G.	Good	Fair	Poor
200	175	150	125	100

20 Gauge

Exc.	V.G.	Good	Fair	Poor
300	275	225	175	140

28 Gauge and .410

Exc.	V.G.	Good	Fair	Poor
400	350	300	250	200

Single Shot

Made in 12, 16, 20, and 28 gauge and .410. Barrel lengths were 26", 28", 30" and 32", with various chokes. It had an exposed hammer, fluid steel barrel, and walnut pistol grip stock.

Exc.	V.G.	Good	Fair	Poor
150	125	100	75	50

Revolver

A typical S&W copy made by Crescent in Norwich, Connecticut. It was a top-break, double-action, that was found either blued or nickel-plated with checkered, black hard rubber grips. The cylinder held 5 shots and was chambered for the .32 S&W cartridge.

Exc.	V.G.	Good	Fair	Poor
175	150	125	85	40

Brand names used by Crescent Arms

American Bar Lock Wonder made for Sears, Roebuck & Co.
American Boy made for Townley Metal & Hardware Co.
American Gun Co. (H & D Folsom house brand)
American Gun Company of New York
American Nitro
Armory Gun Co.
Baker Gun Co. (if no foreign proof marks)
T. Barker New York—if a sidelock hammerless double.
Bellmore Gun Co.
Berkshire No. 3000 made for Shapleigh Hardware Co. of St. Louis, MO
Black Beauty—hammerless doubles
Bluefield Clipper
Bluegrass Arms Co. made for Belknap Hardware Co. of Louisville, KY
Blue Whistler
Bridge Black Prince
Bridge Gun Co.
Bridge Gun Works
Bridgeport Arms Co. (if no foreign proof marks)
Bright Arms Co.
Canadian Belle
Carolina Arms Co. made for Smith Wadsworth Hardware Co. of Charlotte, NC
Caroline Arms
Central Arm Co. made for Shapleigh Hardware Co. of St. Louis, MO
Chatham Arms Co
Cherokee Arms Co. made for C.M. McClung Co. of Knoxville, TN
Chesapeake Gun Co
Chicago Long Range Wonder 1908-1918 made for Sears, Roebuck & Co. of Chicago, IL
Colonial
Columbian New York Arms Co.
Compeer made for Van Camp Hardware & Iron Co. of Indianapolis, IN
Connecticut Arms Co.
Crescent Fire Arms Co.
Creve Cour (if no foreign proof marks) made for Isaac Walker Hardware Co. of Peoria, IL
Cruso
Daniel Boone Gun Co. made for Belknap Hardware Co. of Louisville, KY
Delphian Arms Co. (some models without foreign proof marks) made for Supplee-Biddle Hardware Co. of Philadelphia, PA
Delphian Manufacturing Co. (some models)
Diamond Arms Co. (some models) made for Shapleigh Hardware Co. of St. Louis, MO
Dunlap Special made for Dunlap Hardware Co. of Macon, GA
E. C. Mac made for E. C. Meacham Arms Co. of St. Louis, MO
Elgin Arms Co. made for Strauss & Schram and Fred Biffar & Co. both of Chicago, IL
Empire Arms Co. made for Sears, Roebuck & Co. of Chicago, IL
Empire State Arms Co.
Enders Oakleaf made for Shapleigh Hardware Co. of St. Louis, MO
Enders Special Service made for Shapleigh Hardware Co.
Enders Royal Service made for Shapleigh Hardware Co.
Essex made for Belknap Hardware Co. of Louisville, KY
Excel made for Montgomery Ward & Co. of Chicago, IL
Farwell Arms Co. made for Farwell, Ozmun & Kirk of St. Paul, MN
Faultless made for John M. Smythe Co. of Chicago, IL
Faultless Goose Gun made for John M. Smyth Co. of Chicago, IL

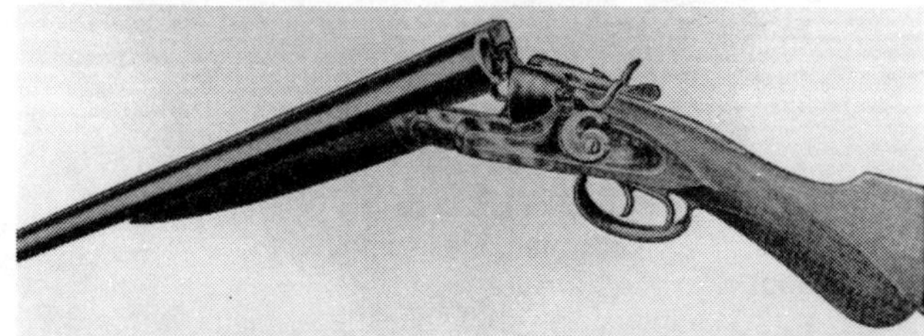

The Field after 1894
Folsom Arms Co. (also used by H & D Folsom on Belgian imports)

F. F. Forbes (H & D Folsom house brand)
Fort Pitt Arms Co.
Fremont Arms Co. (also used on Belgian imports)
Gold Medal Wonder
Greenfield (some models) made for Hibbard, Spencer, Bartlett & Co. of Chicago, IL
H.B.C. (some models) made for Hudson's Bay Co. of Canada.
H.S.B. & Co. (some models) made for Hibbard, Spencer, Bartlett & Co. of Chicago, IL
Hanover Arms Co. (if no foreign proof marks)
S. H. Harrington (if no foreign proof marks)
Hartford Arms Co. made for both Simmons Hardware and Shapleigh Hardware Co. of St. Louis, MO
Harvard (H & D Folsom house brand)
Hermitage (some models) made for Grey-Dusley Hardware Co. of Nashville, TN
Hip Spe Bar (some models) made for Hibbard, Spencer, Bartlett & Co. of Chicago, IL
Hibbard (some models) made for Hibbard, Spencer, Bartlett & Co. of Chicago, IL
Howard Arms Co. made for Fred Biffar & Co. of Chicago, IL
Hudson (some models) made for Hibbard, Spencer, Bartlett & Co. of Chicago, IL
Hunter made for Belknap Hardware Co. Louisville, KY
Interstate Arms Co. made for Townley Metal & Hardware Co. of Kansas City, MO
Jackson Arms Co. made for C. M. McClung & Co. of Knoxville, TN
Joseph Arms Co. Norwich, Conn.
K K and Keen Kutter (some models) made for Shapleigh Hardware Co. of St. Louis, MO
Kingsland Special and Kingsland 10 Star made for Geller, Ward & Hasner of St. Louis, MO
Kirk Gun Co. made for Farwell, Ozmun & Kirk of St. Paul, MN
Knickerbocker (up to 1915, H & D Folsom house brand)
Knockabout (before 1925) made for Montgomery Ward & Co. of Chicago, IL
Knoxall (only hammerless doubles)
Laclede Gun Co.
Lakeside made for Montgomery Ward & Co. of Chicago, IL
Leader Gun Co. made for Charles Williams Stores of New York, NY
Lee's Special and Lee's Munner Special made for Lee Hardware Co. of Salina, KS
Long Range Marvel, Long Range Winner, and Long Range Wonder made between 1893 to 1909 for Sears, Roebuck & Co. of Chicago, IL
F. A. Loomis
Massachusetts Arms Co. made before 1920 for Blish, Mizet and Silliman Hardware Co. of Atchison, KS
Mears (if no foreign proof marks)
Metropolitan made for Siegal-Cooper Co. of New York, NY
Minnesota Arms Co. made for Farwell, Ozmun, Kirk & Co. of St. Paul, MN
Mississippi Arms Co. St. Louis (some models) made for Shepleigh Hardware Co. of St. Louis, MO
Mississippi Valley Arms Co. (some models) made for Shapleigh Hardware Co. of St. Louis, MO
Mohawk made for Glish, Mizet and Lilliman Hardware Co. of Atchinson, KS
R. Murdock, National Firearms Co. (some models)
National Arms Co. hammer Doubles (without foreign proof marks) and hammerless doubles made for May Hardware Co. of Washington, D.C. and Moskowitz and Herbach Co. of Philadelphia, PA
New Britain Arms Co.'s Monarch
New Elgin Arms Co.
New Empire
New England (some models after 1914) made for Sears, Roebuck & Co.
New England Arms Co. (some models)
Newport Model CN made for Hibbard, Spencer, Bartlett and Co. of Chicago
Newport Model WN (some models) made for Hibbard, Spencer, Bartlett and Co. of Chicago
New Rival made for Van Camp Hardware and Iron Co. of Indianapolis, IN
New York Arms Co. made for Garnet Carter Co. of Chattanooga, TN
New York Machine Made (some models)
New York Match Gun (some models)
New York Nitro Hammerless
Nitro Bird made for Conover Hardware Co. of Kansas City, MO
Nitro Hunter made for Belknap Hardware Co. of Louisville, KY
Nitro King 1908 to 1917 made for Sears, Roebuck & Co. of Chicago, IL
Not-Noc Manufacturing Co. made for Belknap Hardware Co. of Louisville, KY and Canton Hardware Co. of Canton, OH
Osprey made for Lou J. Eppinger, Detroit, MI
Oxford made for Belknap Hardware Co. of Louisville, KY

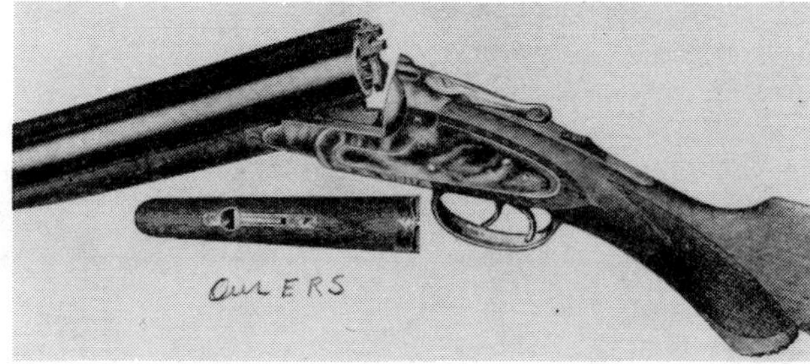

Peerless (H & D Folsom house brand)
Perfection made for H. G. Lipscomb & Co. of Nashville, TN
Piedmont made for Piedmont Hardware Co. of Danville, PA
Pioneer Arms (if no foreign proof marks) made for Kruse and Baklmann Hardware Co. of Cincinnati, OH

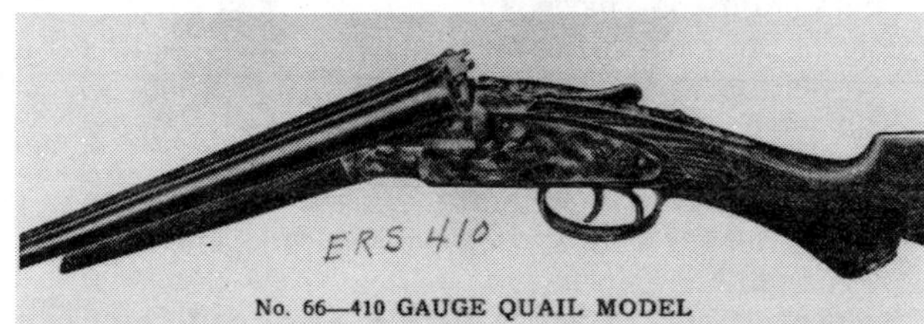

No. 66—410 GAUGE QUAIL MODEL

Quail (H & D Folsom house brand)
Queen City made for Elmira Arms Co. of Elmira, NY
Red Chieftan (model 60) made for Supplee Biddle Hardware Co. of Philadelphia, PA
Rev-O-Noc (some models) made for Hibbard, Spencer, Bartlett & Co. of Chicago, IL

Rich-Con made for Richardson & Conover Hardware Co.
Charles Richter (some models) made for New York Sporting Goods Co. of New York, NY
Rickard Arms Co. made for J. A. Rickard Co. of Schenectady, NY
Rival (some models) made for Van Camp Hardware and Iron Co. of Indianapolis, IN

Rocket Special
Royal Service made for Shapleigh Hardware Co. of St. Louis, MO
Rummel Arms Co. made for A. J. Rummel Arms Co. of Toledo, OH
Ruso (if no foreign proof marks)
St. Louis Arms Co. (sidelock hammerless doubles) made for Shapleigh Hardware Co. of St. Louis, MO
Seminole (hammerless) unknown

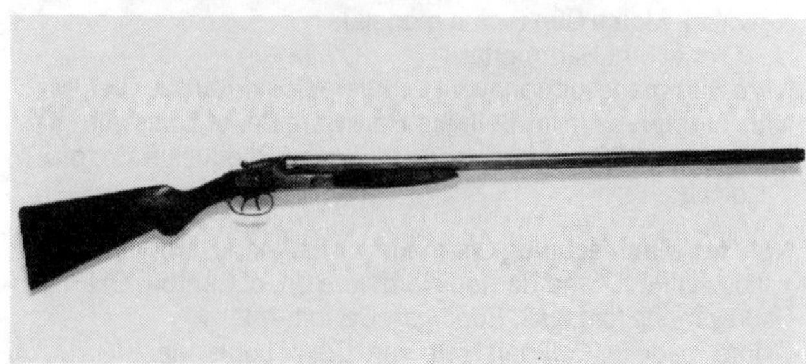

Shue's Special made for Ira M. Shue of Hanover, PA
Smithsonian (some models)
John M. Smythe & Co. made for John M. Smythe Hardware Co. of Chicago, IL
Southern Arms Co. (some models)
Special Service made for Shapleigh Hardware Co. of St. Louis, MO
Spencer Gun Co. made for Hibbard, Spencer, Bartlett & Co. of Chicago, IL
Sportsman (some models) made for W. Bingham & Co. of Cleveland, OH
Springfield Arms Co. used until 1930. (H & D Folsom house brand). This brand was also used by Stevens and James Warner guns.
Square Deal made for Stratton, Warren Hardware Co. of Memphis, TN
Star Leader (some models)
State Arms Co. made for J. H. Lau & Co. of New York, NY
Sullivan Arms Co. made for Sullivan Hardware Co. of Anderson, SC
Superior (some models) made for Paxton & Gallagher Co. of Omaha, NE
Syco (some models) made for Wyeth Hardware Co. of St. Joseph, MO
Ten Star & Ten Star Heavy Duty (if no foreign proof marks) made for Geller, Ward & Hasner Co. of St. Louis, MO
Tiger (if no foreign proof marks) made for J. H. Hall & Co. of Nashville, TN
Townley's Pal and Townley's American Boy made for Townley Metal & Hardware Co. of Kansas City, MO
Trap's Best made for Watkins, Cottrell Co. of Richmond, VA
Triumph (some models) made for Sears, Roebuck & Co. of Chicago, IL
Tryon Special (some models) made for Edward K. Tryon Co. of Philadelphia, PA
U. S. Arms Co. (if no foreign proof marks) made for Supplee-Biddle Hardware Co. of Philadelphia, PA
U. S. Field
Utica Firearms Co. (some models) made for Simmons Hardware Co. of St. Louis, MO

Victor & Victor Special made for Hibbard, Spencer, Bartlett & Co. of Chicago, IL
Virginia Arms Co. made for Virginia-Carolina Co. of Richmond, VA
Volunteer (some models) made for Belknap Hardware Co. of Louisville, KY
Vulcan Arms Co. made for Edward K. Tryon Co. of Philadelphia, PA
Warren Arms Co. (if no foreign proof marks)
Washington Arms Co. (some models)
Wauregan (some models)
Wautauga (some models) made for Wallace Hardware Co. Morristown, TN
Wildwood made for Sears, Roebuck & Co. of Chicago, IL
Wilkinson Arms Co. (if no foreign proof marks) made for Richmond Hardware Co. of Richmond, VA
Wilshire Arms Co. made for Stauffer, Eshleman & Co. of New Orleans, LA
Winfield Arms Co. (H & D Folsom house brand)
Winoca Arms Co. made for Jacobi Hardware Co. of Philadelphia, PA
Witte Hardware Co. (some models) made for Witte Hardware Co. of St. Louis, MO
Wolverine Arms Co. made for Fletcher Hardware Co. of Wilmington, NC
Worthington Arms Co. made for George Worthington Co. of Cleveland, OH

CRISPIN, SILAS
New York, New York

Crispin Revolver

A .32 Crispin caliber 5- or 6-shot revolver produced in very limited quantities. Some are marked "Smith Arms Co., New York City. Crispin's Pat. Oct.3,1865." The most noteworthy feature of these revolvers is that the cylinder is constructed in two pieces so that the belted Crispin cartridge can be used. It is believed that these revolvers were only made on an experimental basis, between 1865 and 1867.

Exc.	V.G.	Good	Fair	Poor
4500	4250	3750	3000	2500

CRUCELEGUI, HERMANOS
Eibar, Spain

A 5mm, 6.35mm, 7.65mm, and 8mm caliber double-action revolver. The tradenames used were; Puppy, Velo-Mith, Le-Brong, Bron-Sport, C.H., and Brong-Petit.

Exc.	V.G.	Good	Fair	Poor
125	100	80	60	35

CUMMINGS, O. S.

Lowell, Massachusetts

Cummings Pocket Revolver

A .22 caliber spur trigger revolver with a 3.5" ribbed round barrel, and a 7-shot fluted cylinder. Nickel-plated with rosewood grip. The barrel is stamped "O.S. Cummings Lowell, Mass." Approximately 1,000 manufactured in the 1870s.

Exc.	V.G.	Good	Fair	Poor
250	225	175	150	125

CUMMINGS & WHEELER

Lowell, Massachusetts

Pocket Revolver

Similar to the Cummings Pocket Revolver with subtle differences—such as the length of the flutes on the cylinder and the size and shape of the grip. The barrel is slightly longer and is marked "Cummings & Wheeler, Lowell, Mass."

Exc.	V.G.	Good	Fair	Poor
275	250	200	150	125

CUSTOM GUN GUILD

Doraville, Georgia

Wood Model IV

A falling block single shot rifle produced in a number of popular calibers with barrel lengths from 22" to 28". The stock of select checkered walnut. This is a very lightweight rifle, at approximately 5.5 lbs. It was manufactured for one year only, 1984, and is not often encountered on today's market.

Exc.	V.G.	Good	Fair	Poor
3000	2750	2500	1750	1000

D (anchor) C

(probably either "Dejardine & Cie," "L. Demousse & Cie," or "DeFooze & Cie," all of Liege, Belgium
SEE—English Military Firearms

NIB	Exc.	V.G.	Good	Fair	Poor
250	200	175	125	100	75

D.W.M.

Berlin, Germany
ALSO SEE—Luger & Borchardt

Model 22

A 7.65mm caliber semi-automatic pistol with 3.5" barrel. Blued with walnut grips; later changed to plastic grips. Approximately 40,000 manufactured between 1921 and 1931.

Exc.	V.G.	Good	Fair	Poor
750	675	500	400	350

DAEWOO

Korea

Max I

A 5.56mm caliber semi-automatic rifle with an 18" barrel, gas-operated rotary bolt action, magazines interchangeable with those from the M-16. Black. Introduced in 1985, but is no longer imported.

Max II

This rifle is quite similar to the Max I with a folding composite stock.

DAISY

Rogers, Arkansas

V/L Rifle

A .22 combustible cartridge single shot rifle with an 18" barrel and plastic stock. Cartridge is ignited by compressed air. Manufactured during 1968 and 1969. It is believed that less than 20,000 were made.

NIB	Exc.	V.G.	Good	Fair	Poor
125	100	85	75	50	25

V/L Presentation Model

As above, with a walnut stock. Approximately 4,000 were made in 1968 and 1969.

NIB	Exc.	V.G.	Good	Fair	Poor
175	150	125	100	75	50

V/L Cased Presentation Model

As above, with a gold plaque inlaid in the stock and with a fitted case containing three hundred VL cartridges.

DAKIN GUN CO.

San Francisco, California

Model 100

A 12 and 20 gauge boxlock double-barrel shotgun with 26" or 28" barrels, various chokes, extractors and double triggers. Engraved, blued, with a checkered walnut stock. Manufactured in the 1960s.

Exc.	V.G.	Good	Fair	Poor
350	325	280	210	150

Model 147

As above, with ventilated-rib barrels.

Exc.	V.G.	Good	Fair	Poor
400	375	225	250	175

Model 160

As above with a single selective trigger.

Exc.	V.G.	Good	Fair	Poor
450	400	350	300	250

Model 215

As above, but more finely finished.

Exc.	V.G.	Good	Fair	Poor
950	850	700	500	425

Model 170

A 12, 16, and 20 gauge Over/Under shotgun with 26" or 28" ventilated-rib barrels, various chokes, and double triggers. Blued and lightly engraved. Discontinued in the 1960s.

Exc.	V.G.	Good	Fair	Poor
500	425	350	275	

DAKOTA ARMS, INC.

Sturgis, South Dakota

This company was formed by Don Allen, Inc., and H. L. Grisel, Inc. Both were fine craftsmen in the field of custom rifles. They offer four basic models with a number of options to fit the customers' needs or wants. The workmanship and materials are of the highest quality. They have been in business since 1987.

Dakota 76 Classic

A .257 Roberts, .270 Winchester, .280 Remington, .3006, 7mm Remington Magnum, .338, .300 Winchester Magnum, and the .458 Winchester Magnum bolt-action rifle with a 23" barrel, and Mauser-type extractor. Checkered walnut stock. Manufactured in 1987.

NIB	Exc.	V.G.	Good	Fair	Poor
2000	1850	1650	1400	950	750

Safari Grade

As above, in .375 Holland & Holland and .458 Winchester Magnum with an ebony forend tip, one-piece magazine assembly and features open sights.

NIB	Exc.	V.G.	Good	Fair	Poor
3000	2750	2450	2000	1350	1000

Alpine Grade

As above, but lighter in weight and chambered for .22-250, .243, .6mm, 250-3000, 7mm/08, .308, and .358. Introduced in 1989.

NIB	Exc.	V.G.	Good	Fair	Poor
1850	1750	1400	1250	850	500

African Grade

As above in .416 Rigby, with walnut especially selected for strength, with crossbolts through the stock.

NIB	Exc.	V.G.	Good	Fair	Poor
3500	3250	2750	2450	1500	1250

DALY, CHARLES

Dayton, Ohio

An importer successively of German, Japanese and Italian shotguns and combination guns.

Charles Daly, Early Prussian Guns

Commanidor Over/Under Model 100

A boxlock Over/Under Ansonn & Deeley action shotgun chambered all gauges, choice of barrel length and chokes, double triggers (standard) or single selective trigger. Blued with a checkered walnut stock. Manufactured in Belgium in the late 1930s.

Exc.	V.G.	Good	Fair	Poor
500	450	375	275	220

Commanidor Over/Under Model 200

As above, with a better-grade walnut stock.

Exc.	V.G.	Good	Fair	Poor
650	600	500	375	275

Superior Side x Side

As above, with an Anson & Deeley boxlock action and double triggers. Blued with a walnut stock. Not manufactured after 1933.

Exc.	V.G.	Good	Fair	Poor
1000	850	650	450	400

Empire Side x Side

As above, but engraved with a better grade of walnut.

Exc.	V.G.	Good	Fair	Poor
2500	2000	1750	1250	1000

Diamond Grade Side x Side

A deluxe version of the above.

Exc.	V.G.	Good	Fair	Poor
5000	4500	3750	3000	2250

Regent Diamond Grade Side x Side

A custom order version of the above.

Exc.	V.G.	Good	Fair	Poor
5500	4750	4000	3250	2500

Empire Over/Under

A 12, 16 and 20 gauge Anson & Deeley boxlock shotgun with choice of barrel length and choke, double triggers and automatic ejectors. Engraved with fine quality scrollwork and walnut stock. Discontinued in 1933.

Exc.	V.G.	Good	Fair	Poor
2250	2000	1500	1150	900

Diamond Grade Over/Under

As above, but more finely finished.

Exc.	V.G.	Good	Fair	Poor
5000	4500	3750	3000	2250

Sextuple Single Barrel Trap

Empire Grade

A 12 gauge boxlock single barrel shotgun with 30"-34" full-choke barrels, a ventilated-rib and automatic ejectors. The action features six locking lugs and is very strong. Engraved with a walnut stock. Manufactured after 1933.

Exc.	V.G.	Good	Fair	Poor
2500	2250	1850	1500	1150

Regent Diamond Grade

As above, with more engraving and a better-grade walnut stock.

Exc.	V.G.	Good	Fair	Poor
3500	3250	2850	2500	1750

Drillings

Superior Grade Drilling

A 12, 16, and 20 gauge Over/Under rifle/shotgun with a rifle barrel in .25-20, .25-35, or .30-30 running beneath them. Engraved with a walnut stock. Not manufactured after 1933.

Exc.	V.G.	Good	Fair	Poor
2500	2250	1800	1450	1000

Diamond Grade Drilling

As above, with more engraving and a better grade of walnut in the stock.

Exc.	V.G.	Good	Fair	Poor
4500	4000	3750	3000	2400

Regent Diamond Grade Drilling

As above, with elaborate engraving and the highest quality walnut stock.

Exc.	V.G.	Good	Fair	Poor
5500	5000	4500	4000	3400

Charles Daly, B. C. Miroku Guns

Empire Grade Side By Side

A 12, 16, and 20 gauge Anson and Deeley boxlock shotgun with 26", 28", and 30" barrels, various chokes, extractors and a single trigger. Blued with a checkered walnut stock. Manufactured between 1968 and 1971.

Add 10% for Ventilated-Rib Barrels and/or 20 Gauge.

Exc.	V.G.	Good	Fair	Poor
550	500	450	375	300

Superior Grade Single Barrel Trap

A 12 gauge boxlock shotgun with 32" or 34" ventilated rib barrels, full choke, and automatic ejector. Blued with Monte Carlo walnut stock. Manufactured between 1968 and 1976.

Exc.	V.G.	Good	Fair	Poor
550	500	450	350	300

Over/Unders

A 12, 20, and 28 gauge and .410 Bore boxlock shotgun with 26", 28", and 30" barrels with ventilated ribs. Various choke combinations were offered with single selective triggers and automatic ejectors. Blued with checkered walnut stocks. The differences between the grades are the degree and quality of the engraving and the grade of walnut used for the stock. The smaller-bore guns bring a premium as follows. Manufactured between 1963 and 1976 by B. C. Miroku.

20 Gauge—Add 10%.
28 Gauge—Add 20%.
.410—Add 30%.

Venture Grade

Exc.	V.G.	Good	Fair	Poor
550	500	450	375	300

Venture Grade Skeet or Trap

Offered with either 26" Skeet & Skeet or 30" full choke.

Exc.	V.G.	Good	Fair	Poor
575	525	475	375	300

Field Grade
Chambered for 12 and 20 gauge only.

Exc.	V.G.	Good	Fair	Poor
650	575	500	425	325

Superior Grade

Exc.	V.G.	Good	Fair	Poor
750	675	600	525	400

Superior Grade Trap

Exc.	V.G.	Good	Fair	Poor
650	575	500	425	325

Diamond Grade

Exc.	V.G.	Good	Fair	Poor
1000	900	750	600	500

Diamond Grade Trap or Skeet
With either 26" Skeet & Skeet or 30" full choke barrels and Monte Carlo stocks.
Wide Rib—Add 5%.

Exc.	V.G.	Good	Fair	Poor
1050	950	800	650	550

Charles Daly, Italian Manufacture
Manufactured by the firm of Breda in Milan, Italy. The semi-automatic "Novamatic" was produced in 1968. All other models began Italian production in 1976.

Novamatic Lightweight
A 12 gauge semi-automatic shotgun with a 26" or 28" ventilated-rib barrel and screw-in choke tubes. The receiver is alloy, with checkered walnut stock. Imported under the Daly name in 1968 only.

Exc.	V.G.	Good	Fair	Poor
300	275	225	175	125

Novamatic Trap
As above, with a Monte Carlo stock and a 30" full choke barrel.

Exc.	V.G.	Good	Fair	Poor
350	300	250	200	150

Charles Daly Field Grade Over/Under
A 12 and 20 gauge Over/Under shotgun with 26" or 28" chrome-lined ventilated-rib barrels with a crossbolt boxlock action, single selective trigger, and extractors. Blued with a stamped checkered walnut stock. Introduced in 1989.

Exc.	V.G.	Good	Fair	Poor
450	400	350	275	225

Charles Daly Deluxe Over/Under
As above with automatic ejectors, screw-in choke tubes, and a silver-finished receiver. The walnut stock is handcheckered. Introduced in 1989.

Exc.	V.G.	Good	Fair	Poor
650	600	500	400	300

Diamond Grade Over/Under
As above in 12 and 20 gauge Magnum with various barrel lengths and screw-in choke tubes, single trigger, automatic ejectors, and select walnut stock. Discontinued in 1968.

Exc.	V.G.	Good	Fair	Poor
700	625	550	400	325

Diamond Grade Trap or Skeet
As above, with 26" or 30" barrels. Available in 1989 after the Field model was discontinued.

Exc.	V.G.	Good	Poor
1000	900	750	400

Presentation Grade Over/Under
As above, with a Purdy-type boxlock action and engraved false sideplates. The stock is of deluxe French walnut. Discontinued in 1986.

Exc.	V.G.	Good	Fair	Poor
1000	900	750	500	400

Superior II O/U
A 12 and 20 gauge Over/Under shotgun with 26" or 28" ventilated rib barrels, various chokes, single trigger, and automatic ejectors. Engraved, blued with a walnut stock. Discontinued in 1988.

Exc.	V.G.	Good	Fair	Poor
675	600	500	375	300

Superior Grade Side x Side
A 12 and 20 gauge boxlock double barrel shotgun with 26" or 28" barrels, various chokes, a boxlock action, and single trigger. Blued, with a walnut stock.

Exc.	V.G.	Good	Fair	Poor
500	425	375	300	225

Charles Daly Automatic
A 12 gauge Magnum semi-automatic shotgun with 26" or 28" ventilated rib barrels, screw-in choke tubes and a 5-shot magazine. There is a slug gun available with rifle sights. Checkered walnut grip in two versions—a pistol grip and an English-style straight grip. The choke-tube model would be worth a 10% premium.

Exc.	V.G.	Good	Fair	Poor
375	325	275	225	150

DAN ARMS OF AMERICA
Allentown, Pennsylvania

These are Italian-made shotguns manufactured by Silmer and imported by Dan Arms of America. They are no longer produced as of 1988.

Side x Sides
Field Grade
A boxlock shotgun chambered for all gauges with 26" or 28" barrels, various choke combinations, double triggers and extractors. Blued with a walnut stock.

Exc.	V.G.	Good	Fair	Poor
300	265	225	150	125

Deluxe Field Grade
As above, with a single trigger and automatic ejectors.

Exc.	V.G.	Good	Fair	Poor
450	400	325	250	200

Over/Unders
Lux Grade I
A 12 and 20 gauge Over/Under shotgun with a 26", 28" or 30" ventilated-rib barrels, double triggers and extractors. Blued finish with a walnut stock.

Exc.	V.G.	Good	Fair	Poor
275	250	200	150	100

Lux Grade II
As above, in 12 gauge only with a single trigger.

Exc.	V.G.	Good	Fair	Poor
325	300	250	200	150

Lux Grade III
As above, in 20 gauge only with automatic ejectors.

Exc.	V.G.	Good	Fair	Poor
400	325	275	225	175

Lux Grade IV
As above in 12 gauge only with screw-in choke tubes.

Exc.	V.G.	Good	Fair	Poor
450	375	325	275	200

Silver Snipe
A 12 or 20 gauge shotgun manufactured to custom order with engraved false sideplates and a select walnut stock.

Exc.	V.G.	Good	Fair	Poor
1250	1000	800	600	450

DANCE & BROTHERS CONFEDERATE REVOLVERS
Columbia, Texas

J.H., G.P., and D.E. Dance began production of percussion revolvers for the Confederate States of America in Columbia,

Texas in mid-1862, moving to Anderson, Texas in early 1864. Based on surviving serial numbers, the combined output at both places did not exceed 350 pistols. Most of these were in the "Army" (.44 caliber) size but a limited number of "Navy" (.36 caliber) were also manufactured. Nearly all are distinguished by the absence of a "recoil shield" on the frame behind the cylinders. As Colt M1851 "Navy" revolvers closely resemble the Dance Navy revolvers, great care must be exercised in examining revolvers purported to be Dance Navies.

.44 Caliber

Exc.	V.G.	Good	Fair	Poor
7500	6500	5000	3750	3000

.36 Caliber

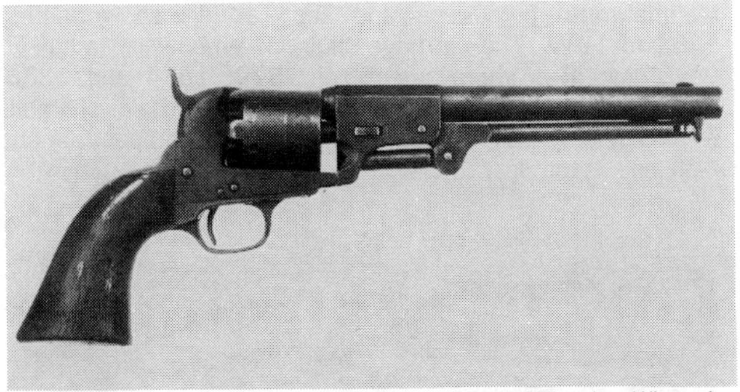

Courtesy Milwaukee Public Museum, Milwaukee, Wisconsin.

Exc.	V.G.	Good	Fair	Poor
10000	8500	7500	5000	3500

C DANDOY/A LIEGE

(SEE—French Military Firearms)

DANSK INDUSTRII SYNDIKAT

Copenhagen, Denmark

Schouboe 1903

A 7.65mm caliber semi-automatic pistol. Production ended in 1910, with less than 1,000 manufactured.

Exc.	V.G.	Good	Fair	Poor
4000	3500	3000	2500	2000

Model 1907

An 11.35mm caliber semi-automatic pistol designed to fire a 55-grain, copper-aluminum-and-wood projectile at a velocity of 1625 ft./sec. 500 were manufactured before production stopped in 1917.

Exc.	V.G.	Good	Fair	Poor
5000	4500	4000	3500	3000

Combination holster/shoulder stocks were made for this model, but are extremely rare. If present with a pistol, they would add approximately 40% to the value.

DARDICK CORP.

Hamden, Connecticut

Perhaps one of the most unusual firearms to have been designed and marketed in the United States during the 20th Century. It utilizes "tround" which is a triangular plastic case enclosing a cartridge. The action of these arms consists of a revolving carrier which brings the trounds from the magazine into line with the barrel. Discontinued in 1962.

Series 1100 (3" barrel)

Chambered in .38 Dardick only.

Exc.	V.G.	Good	Fair	Poor
750	650	550	400	350

Series 1500 (6" barrel)

Chambered for the .22, .30, and the .38 Dardick.

Exc.	V.G.	Good	Fair	Poor
950	850	750	600	500

A carbine conversion kit consisting of a long barrel and shoulder stock was available and would bring a premium of $250 to $400 depending on the condition.

DARLING, B. & B. M.

Belingham, Massachusetts

Darling Pepperbox Pistol

A .30 caliber percussion 6-shot pepperbox with 3.25" length barrels. Blued with walnut grips. This is one of the rarest American pepperboxes and copies are known to have been made. Consequently, prospective purchasers are advised to secure a qualified appraisal prior to acquisition. Manufactured during the late 1830s.

Exc.	V.G.	Good	Fair	Poor
5000	3500	1400	1000	750

DARNE, S. A.

St. Etienne, France

Darne Side x Side Shotguns

A 12, 16, 20 or 28 gauge sliding breech double-barrel shotgun manufactured in a variety of barrel lengths and with numerous optional features. Manufactured from 1881 to 1979.

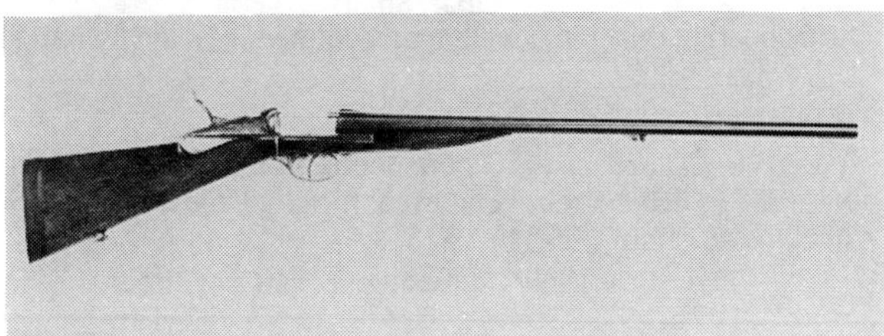

Model R11

Exc.	V.G.	Good	Fair	Poor
1000	900	750	600	450

Model R15

Exc.	V.G.	Good	Fair	Poor
2500	2000	1750	1500	1000

Model V19

Exc.	V.G.	Good	Fair	Poor
3250	3000	2750	2250	1750

Model V22

Exc.	V.G.	Good	Fair	Poor
3750	3500	3000	2500	2000

Model V Hors Series No. 1

Exc.	V.G.	Good	Fair	Poor
4500	4000	3750	3250	2500

DAUDETEAU
St. Denis, France

Model 1896

A 6.5mm caliber bolt-action rifle with a 26" barrel, full length stock secured by two barrel bands and a fixed magazine. Blued with a walnut stock.

Exc.	V.G.	Good	Fair	Poor
200	175	150	100	75

DAVENPORT FIRE ARMS CO.
Norwich, Connecticut

Single Barrel Shotgun

A 10, 12, 16 or 20 gauge side hammer single barrel shotgun with 26" to 36" barrels and extractors. Blued, case hardened with a walnut stock. Manufactured from approximately 1880 to 1915.

Exc.	V.G.	Good	Fair	Poor
200	150	125	100	75

8 Gauge Goose Gun

As above, in 8 gauge.

Exc.	V.G.	Good	Fair	Poor
300	250	200	150	100

Falling Block Single Shot Rifle

A .22, .25 or .32 rimfire single shot rifle with a 24" round barrel and exposed hammer. Blued with a walnut stock. The barrel marked "The W.H. Davenport Fire Arms Co. Norwich, Conn. U.S.A. Patented Dec. 15, 1891." Manufactured between 1891 and 1910.

Exc.	V.G.	Good	Fair	Poor
550	500	425	325	250

DAVIDSON F. A.
Eibar, Spain

Arms bearing this name were manufactured in Spain by Fabrica De Armas.

Model 63B

A 12, 16, 20, 28 or .410 bore double barrel boxlock shotgun with 25" to 30" barrels. Engraved, nickel-plated with a walnut stock. Made from 1963 to 1976.

Exc.	V.G.	Good	Fair	Poor
275	225	200	150	125

Model 69 SL

A 12 or 20 gauge sidelock double-barrel shotgun with 26" or 28" barrels and finished as above.

Exc.	V.G.	Good	Fair	Poor
400	350	300	225	150

Stagecoach Model 73

A 12 or 20 gauge Magnum sidelock double barrel shotgun with 20" barrels and exposed hammers.

Exc.	V.G.	Good	Fair	Poor
275	225	175	150	125

DAVIS, A. JR.
Stafford, Connecticut

Under Hammer Pistol

A .31 caliber single shot under hammer percussion pistol with a 7.5" half octagonal barrel and brass frame. The grips of maple and formed with a bottom tip. The top strap marked "A.Davis Jr./Stafford Conn."

Exc.	V.G.	Good	Fair	Poor
400	350	300	225	175

DAVIS, N.R. & CO.
DAVIS, N.R. & SONS
Freetown and Assonet, Massachusetts

Manufaturer of percussion, and later, cartridge shotguns from 1853 to 1917. The cartridge shotguns embodied Nathan R. Davis' patented improvements of 1879, 1884 and 1886. Though only made in plain, serviceable grades, Davis shotguns were extremely well made and lived up to the company's motto "As Good as the Best".

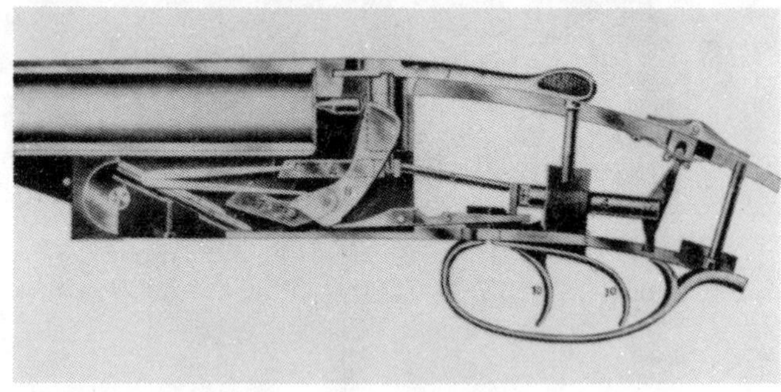

Grade A, B and BS Hammerless Shotguns

Made in 12 or 16 gauge with 28", 30" or 32" barrels.

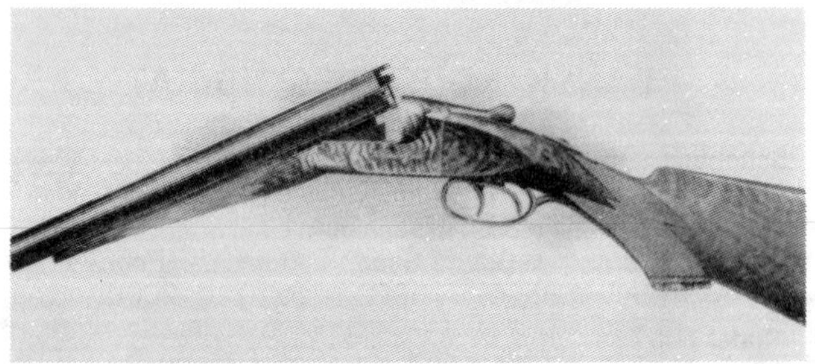

Exc.	V.G.	Good	Fair	Poor
750	600	400	200	100

Grade C Hammerless Shotgun

Made in 10 gauge with 30" or 32" barrels.

Exc.	V.G.	Good	Fair	Poor
750	600	400	200	100

Grade D and DS Hammer Shotguns

Made in 12 or 16 gauge with 28", 30" or 32" barrels.

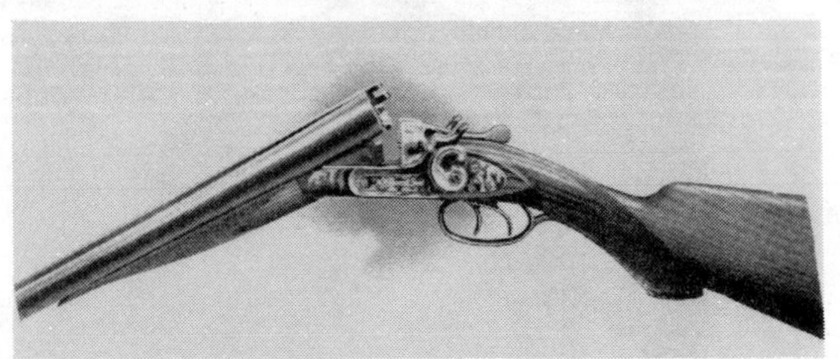

Exc.	V.G.	Good	Fair	Poor
750	600	400	200	100

Grade E and F Single Barrel Shotguns
Made in 12 or 16 gauge with 30" or 32" barrels.

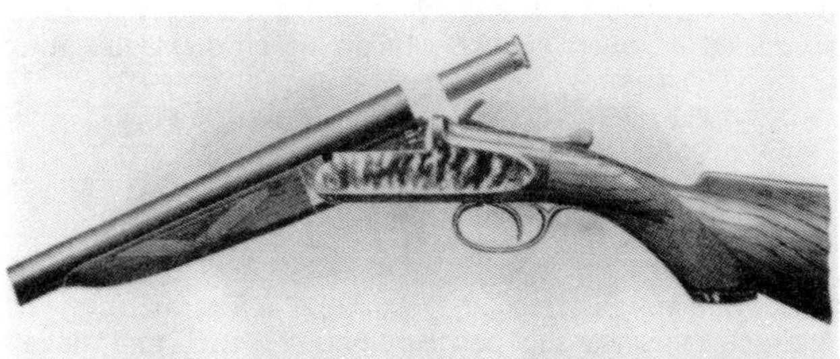

Exc.	V.G.	Good	Fair	Poor
250	200	100	75	50

DAVIS & BOZEMAN
Central, Alabama

Pattern 1841 Rifle
A .58 caliber single shot percussion rifle with a 33" round barrel, full walnut stock, 2 barrel bands, brass furniture and an iron ramrod. The lock marked "D. & B. Ala." as well as the serial number and date of manufacture. Prospective purchasers are advised to secure a qualified appraisal prior to acquisition.

Exc.	V.G.	Good	Fair	Poor
5500	4750	4000	3250	2500

DAVIS INDUSTRIES
Chino, California

D-22 Derringer
A .22, .22 WMR, .25 ACP and .32 ACP caliber double barrel Over/Under Derringer with 2.4" barrels. Black teflon or chrome plated finish with laminated wood grips.

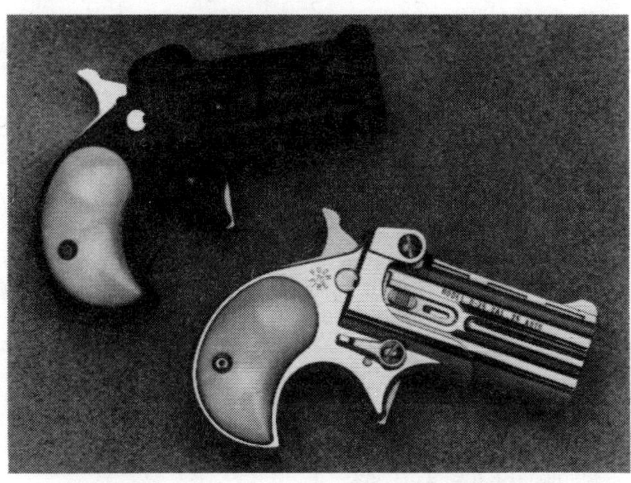

NIB	Exc.	V.G.	Good	Fair	Poor
70	60	45	35	30	20

P-32
A .32 caliber semi-automatic pistol with a 2.8" barrel and 6-shot magazine. Black teflon or chrome-plated finish with laminated wood grips.

NIB	Exc.	V.G.	Good	Fair	Poor
85	75	60	45	35	25

P-380
As above, in .380 caliber.

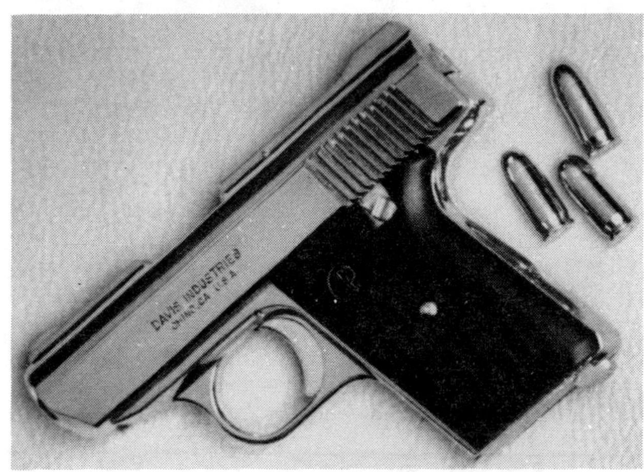

NIB	Exc.	V.G.	Good	Fair	Poor
100	80	65	50	40	30

DAVIS-WARNER ARMS CORPORATION
Norwich, Connecticut

Established in 1917, when N.R. Davis & Sons purchased the Warner Arms Company. Manufactured shotguns, as well as revolvers and semi-automatic pistols. Ceased operations in 1930. The Crescent Arms Company purchased the proprietary rights to the name and briefly assembled shotguns under the name (probably from parts acquired in the purchase) until Crescent was in turn purchased by J.C. Stevens.

Initially, the Davis-Warner shotguns were identical to those made by Davis, (see preceding entry), but they subsequently made a Davis Grade B.S. Hammerless, Davis-Warner Expert and Davis Grade D.S. The pistols made by the company included .32 caliber revolvers and two Browning Patent semi-automatics made in Belgium for the company.

Davis Grade B.S. Hammerless Shotgun
Made in 12, 16, or 20 gauge with 28", 30" or 32" barrels.

Exc.	V.G.	Good	Fair	Poor
750	600	400	200	100

Davis-Warner Expert Hammerless
Made in 12, 16, or 20 gauge with 26", 28", 30" or 32" barrels.

Exc.	V.G.	Good	Fair	Poor
750	600	400	200	100

Davis-Warner Swing Out Revolver

Double action .32 caliber revolver with a 5" or 6" barrel.

Exc.	V.G.	Good	Fair	Poor
150	125	100	75	50

Davis-Warner Semiautomatic Pistols

Browning Patent .25 ACP, .32 ACP or .380 caliber pistols.

Exc.	V.G.	Good	Fair	Poor
300	250	175	125	75

Warner Infallibe Semiautomatic Pistol

Freyberg Patent .32 ACP.

Exc.	V.G.	Good	Fair	Poor
300	250	175	125	75

DAW, G.H.

London, England

Daw Revolver

A .38 caliber double-action percussion revolver with a 5.5" barrel marked "George H. Daw, 57 Threadneedle St. London, Patent No.112." Blued, with walnut grips. Manufactured in the 1860's.

Exc.	V.G.	Good	Fair	Poor
3500	3000	2500	1850	1400

DEANE, ADAMS & DEANE

London, England

SEE—Adams

DEANE-HARDING

London, England

Deane-Harding Revolver

A .44 caliber percussion revolver with a 5.25" barrel and 5-shot cylinder. Blued, case-hardened with walnut grips. Manufactured during the late 1850s.

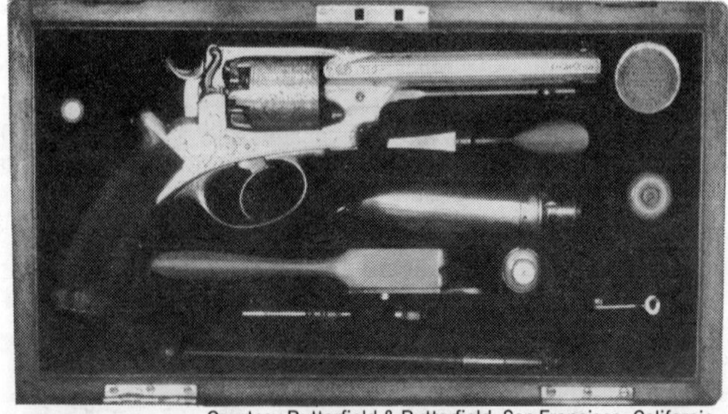

Courtesy Butterfield & Butterfield, San Francisco, California.

Exc.	V.G.	Good	Fair	Poor
2500	2000	1750	1250	800

DECKER, WILHELM

Zella St. Blasii, Germany

A 6.35mm double-action revolver with a 6-shot cylinder and concealed hammer. Blued with plastic grips. Manufactured prior to 1914.

Exc.	V.G.	Good	Fair	Poor
900	800	700	500	350

DEMIRETT, J.

Montpelier, Vermont

Under Hammer Pistol

A .27 caliber single shot percussion pistol with 3" to 8" barrels and an under hammer. The barrel marked "J. Demerrit / Montpelier / Vermont." Blued with maple, walnut or stag horn grips. Active from 1866 to the mid-1880s.

Exc.	V.G.	Good	Fair	Poor
750	675	500	400	300

DEMRO

Manchester, Connecticut

XF-7 Wasp Carbine

A 9mm or .45 caliber semi-automatic carbine with a 16.5" barrel and folding stock.

Exc.	V.G.	Good	Fair	Poor
350	300	250	200	150

T.A.C. Model 1

As above, with a fixed stock.

Exc.	V.G.	Good	Fair	Poor
350	300	250	200	150

DERINGER REVOLVER AND PISTOL CO.

Philadelphia, Pennsylvania

After Henry Deringer's death, his name was used by I.J. Clark who manufactured rimfire revolvers on Charles Foehl's patents between 1870 and 1879.

Deringer Model I

A .22 caliber spur trigger revolver with a hinged octagonal barrel and 7 shot cylinder. Manufactured circa 1873.

Exc.	V.G.	Good	Fair	Poor
400	350	275	200	150

Deringer Model II

As above, with a round barrel and also available in .32 caliber.

Exc.	V.G.	Good	Fair	Poor
375	325	250	175	150

Centennial 1876

A .22, .32 or .38 caliber solid frame revolver.

Exc.	V.G.	Good	Fair	Poor
400	350	275	200	150

HENRY DERINGER RIFLES AND PISTOLS

Philadelphia, Pennsylvania

Henry Deringer Sr. and his son, Henry Jr., were well established in Philadelphia by the close of the War of 1812, having made both sporting and military rifles at that place since the turn of the century. Henry Jr. continued in the gun trade until the outbreak of the American Civil War, primarily producing flintlock and percussion military rifles, at least 2,500 "Northwest guns" and 1,200 rifles for the Indian trade, a few percussion martial pistols, but most importantly the percussion pocket pistols that became so popular that they took on his misspelled name as a generic term, the "derringers."

Deringer U.S. M1814 military rifle

Overall length- 48-1/2"; barrel length- 32-3/4"; caliber- .54. Markings: on lockplate, "U S/H. DERINGER/PHILADA", on top flat of barrel, "H. DERINGER/PHILADA" and standard U.S. proofmarks. The U.S. M1814 rifle is distinguished by its part octagonal barrel, whose bands were secured by wedge-shaped spring bands, and the distinctive finger ridges on the triggerguard strap. Henry Deringer Sr. received a contract for 2,000 of these rifles in 1814, but delivered only 50 that year, devoting his resources instead to a more lucrative Pennsylvania state contract for rifles.

Exc.	V.G.	Good	Fair	Poor
2000	1850	1600	1200	850

Deringer U.S. M1817 military rifle (Types I & II)

Overall length- 51-1/4"; barrel length- 36"; caliber- .54. Markings: on lockplate, "U S/H. DERINGER/PHILADA" forward of cock, date on tail; standard U.S. proofmarks on barrel. The U.S. M1817 "common" rifle followed much of the same design elements as its predecessor, the U.S. M1814 rifle; however, the barrel is fully round with its bands secured by full band springs, and on the earlier production, the finger ridges on the triggerguard strap were eliminated in favor of a plain strap formed into a handgrip. On the 6,000 rifles manufactured under his 1840 contract, Deringer eliminated the "pistol grip" in favor of a plain strap, distinguishing Type II production from Type I. As one of the four major contractors for the U.S. M1817 rifle, Deringer produced a total of 11,000 rifles for the U.S. War Department. Many of the rifles from first two contracts (2,000 in 1821, 3,000 in 1823) were distributed to southern states under the 1808 Militia Act. Accordingly, Deringer M1817 rifles altered to percussion by traditional southern methods may generate a premium.

(in flintlock)

Exc.	V.G.	Good	Fair	Poor
1950	1800	1500	1200	800

(altered to percussion)

Exc.	V.G.	Good	Fair	Poor
950	800	700	550	400

Deringer original percussion martial rifles (Types I & II).

Overall length- 51-1/4"; barrel length- 36"; caliber- .54. Markings: Type I- on lockplate forward of hammer "DERINGER/PHILA"; also known to exist with standard U.S. M1817 lock markings and barrel marks; Type II- on lockplate forward of hammer "U S"/DERINGER/PHILADELA" or "DERINGER/PHILADELA" and same on top of barrel.

Although the Type I rifle of this series appears at first glance to be a late contract rifle altered to percussion by means of the cone-in-barrel method, in fact it is an original percussion rifle made by Deringer from modified spare parts that remained after the completion of his 1840 contract. The Type II rifle also evidences having been made from modified parts; however, its cone is set in an elongated bolster brazed to the right side of the barrel. Speculation concerning these rifles is rampant; however, the available evidence indicates that Deringer produced about 600 of these most likely produced at the beginning of the American Civil War.

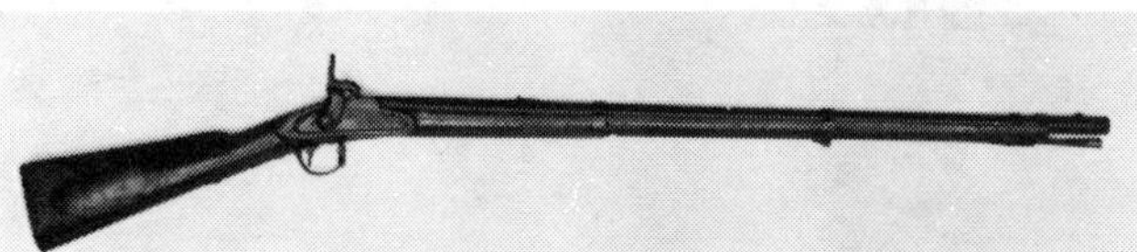

Courtesy Milwaukee Public Museum, Milwaukee, Wisconsin.

Exc.	V.G.	Good	Fair	Poor
1200	1100	900	650	450

Deringer original percussion rifle-muskets

Overall length- 57-3/4"; barrel length- 42"; caliber- .69. Markings: on lock forward of hammer, "U S/DERINGER/PHILADELA". Just as the original percussion rifle appears to be an altered arm, the rare Deringer rifle-muskets at first appear to have been flintlocks. However, these arms are original percussion, having been made from spare or rejected parts from the U.S. M1816 muskets. The brazed bolsters are identical in style to that of the Type II original percussion rifles made by Deringer. Barrels are rifled with seven grooves, and the barrels accordingly bear a rear sight. Deringer probably assembled a hundred of these rifles in 1861 to arm some company of Pennsylvania's early war regiments.

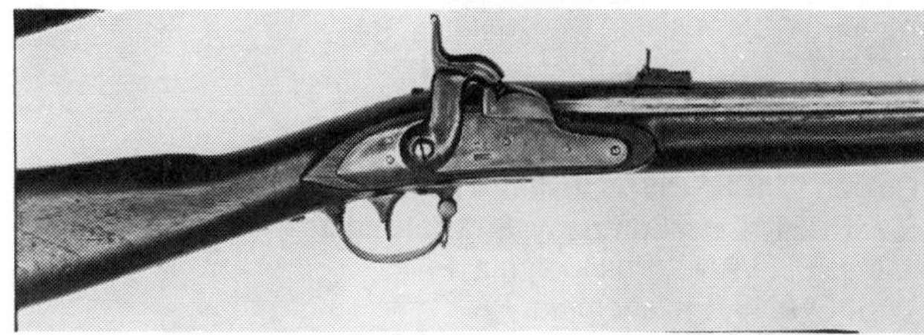

Courtesy Milwaukee Public Museum, Milwaukee, Wisconsin.

Exc.	V.G.	Good	Fair	Poor
1200	1100	900	650	450

Deringer U.S. Navy contact "boxlock" pistols

Overall length- 11-5/8"; barrel length- 6"; caliber- .54. Markings: on lockplate, "U S/DERINGER/PHILADELIA" or merely "DERINGER/PHILADEL'A" in center, the tail either plain or marked "U.S.N./(date)"; barrels sometimes marked with U.S. Navy inspection marks.

Deringer was granted a contract with the U.S. Navy in 1845 for 1200 of the new "boxlock" percussion pistols also made by Ames. All of these appear to have been delivered. From the extra parts, Deringer is thought to have assembled several hundred extra pistols, some of which he rifled. The latter bring a premium, even though quantities remain enigmatic.

Exc.	V.G.	Good	Fair	Poor
1800	1600	1400	1100	750

Deringer percussion pocket pistols

Overall length- varies with barrel length; barrel length- 1-1/2" to 6" in regular 1/8" gradiants; caliber- .41 (usually, other calibers known) Markings: "DERINGER/PHILADELA" on back-action lock and rear section of top barrel flat; "P" impressed in circle with serrated edges on left side of breech; agent marks occasionally on top of barrel.

The most famous of Henry Deringer's products, an estimated 15,000 were produced between the Mexican War through the Civil War, usually in pairs. The popularity of the pistol is attested in the large number of imitations and the nickname "Derringer" applied to them, even when clearly not Deringer's products. Prices can fluctuate widely based on agent marks occasionally found on barrel. Care is advised in purchasing purported "true" derringers.

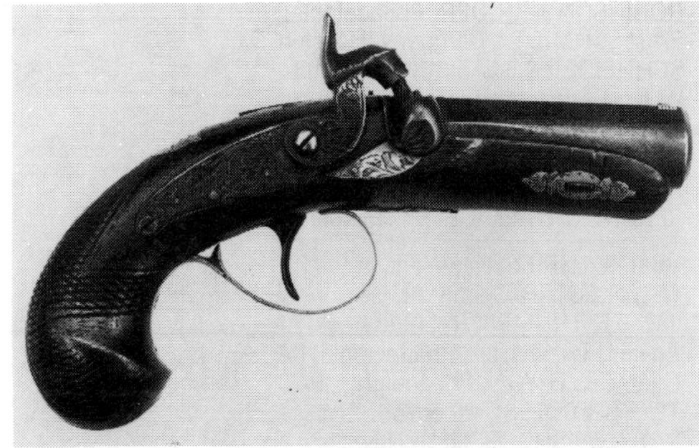

Courtesy Milwaukee Public Museum, Milwaukee, Wisconsin.

Exc.	V.G.	Good	Fair	Poor
2200	2000	1600	1200	800

Principle maker of Deringer style pocket pistols

William AFFLERBACH, Philadelphia, PA
Balthaser AUER, Louisville, KY
Frederick BEERSTECHER, Philadelphia and Lewisburg, PA
Franz J. BITTERLICH, Nashville, TN

BLUNT & SYMS, New York, NY
Richard P. BRUFF, New York, NY
Jesse S. BUTTERFIELD, Philadelphia, PA
Daniel CLARK, Philadelphia, PA
Richard CONSTABLE, Philadelphia, PA
DELONG & SON, Chattanooga, TN
MOSES DICKSON, Louisville, KY
Horace E. DIMICK, St. Louis, MO
Gustau ERICHSON, Houston, TX
B.J. EUSTACE & Company, St. Louis, MO
James E. EVANS, Philadelphia, PA
W.S. EVANS, Philadelphia, PA
FIELD, LANGSTROTH & Company, Philadelphia, PA
Daniel FISH, New York, NY
FOLSOM BROTHERS & Company, New Orleans, LA
August G. GENEZ, New York, NY
George D.H. GILLESPIE, New York, NY
Frederick G. GLASSICK, Memphis, TN
James GOLCHER, Philadelphia, PA
Joseph GRUBB & Company, Philadelphia, PA
John H. HAPPOLDT, Charlestown, SC
John M. HAPPOLDT, Columbus, George and Charlestown, SC
HAWS & WAGGONER, Columbia, SC
HODGKINS & SONS, Macon, GA
Louis HOFFMAN, Vicksburg, MS
HYDE & GOODRICH, New Orleans, LA
Joseph JACOB, Philadelphia, PA
William W. KAYE, Philadelphia, PA
Benjamin KITTERIDGE, Cincinnati, OH
Peter W. KRAFT, Columbia, SC
John KRIDER, Philadelphia, PA
Jacob KUNTZ, Philadelphia, PA
Martille La FITTE, Natchitoches, LA
A. Frederichk LINS, Philadelphia, PA
C. LOHNER, Philadelphia, PA
John P. LOWER, Denver, CO
A.R. MENDENHALL, Des Arc, AK
John MEUNIER, Milwaukee, WI
William D. MILLER, New York, NY
MURPHY & O'CONNELL, New York, NY
------ NEWCOMB, Natchez, MS
Charles A. OBERTEUFFER, Philadelphia, PA
Stephen O'DELL, Natchez, MS
Henry C. PALMER, St. Louis, MO
R. PATRICK, New York, NY
REID & TRACY, New York, NY
William ROBERTSON, Philadelphia, PA
ROBINSON & KRIDER, Philadelphia, PA
Ernst SCHMIDT & Company, Houston, TX
SCHNEIDER & GLASSICK, Memphis, TN
W.A. SEAVER, New York, NY
Paul J. SIMPSON, New York, NY
SLOTTER & Company, Philadelphia, PA
Patrick SMITH, Buffalo, NY
SPRANG & WALLACE, Philadelphia, PA

Adam W. SPIES, New York, NY
Casper SUTER, Selma, AL
Jacob F. TRUMPLER, Littler Rock, AK
Edward TRYON, Jr., Philadelphia, PA
George K. TRYON, Philadelphia, PA
TUFTS & COLLEY, New York, NY
WOLF, DASH & FISHER, New York, NY
Alfred WOODHAM, New York, NY
Andrew WURFFLEIN, Philadelphia, PA
John WURFFLEIN, Philadelphia, PA

Agent Names Found On Deringer Pocket Pistols
W.C. ALLEN, San Francisco, CA
W.H. CALHOUN, Nashville, TN
CANFIELD & BROTHERS, Baltimore, MD
F.H. CLARK & CO., Memphis, TN
COLEMAN & DUKE, Cahaba, AL
M.W. GALT & BROTHER, Washington, DC
J.B. GILMORE, Shreveport, LA
A.B. GRISWOLD, & CO., New Orleans, LA
HYDE & GOODRICH, New Orleans, LA
LULLMAN & VIENNA, Memphis, TN
A.J. MILLSPAUGH, Shreveport, LA
H.G. NEWCOMB, Natchez, MS
A.J. PLATE, San Francisco, CA
J.A. SCHAFER, Vicksburg, MS
S.L. SWETT, Vicksburg, MS
A.J. TAYLOR, San Francisco, CA
WOLF & DURRINGER, Louisville, KY

DESERT EAGLE

Imported by Magnum Research
Minneapolis, Minnesota

The Desert Eagle is a semi-automatic gas operated pistol chambered for the .357 Magnum, .41 Magnum, .44 Magnum, and .50 Action Express. It is produced by Israel Military Industries. The pistols are furnished with a standard 6" barrel but 10" and 14" interchangeable barrels are offered as options. Also available are these interchangeable barrels that are Mag-Na-Ported. The standard material used for frame is steel, but stainless and aluminum are also available. The standard finish for these pistols are black oxide but custom finishes are available on special order. These special finishes are: gold, stainless steel, satin nickel, bright nickel, polished blue, camo, matte chrome, polished chrome, brushed chrome, and matte chrome with gold. All of these special order finishes as well as the optional barrels will affect the prices of the pistols. Prices listed here will reflect standard pistols only.

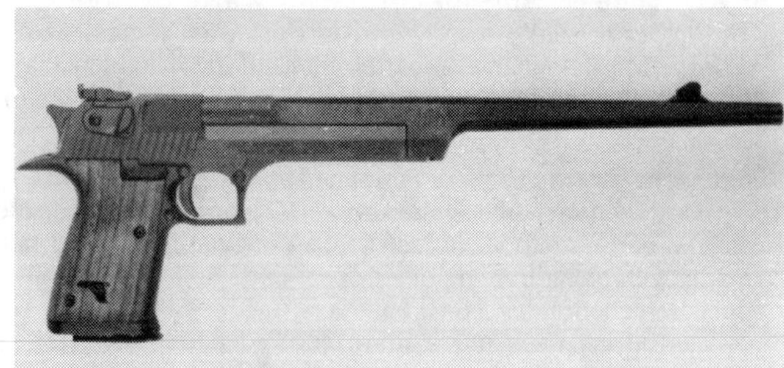

Desert Eagle .357 Magnum

Standard with 6" barrel and black oxide finish. Magazine capacity is 9 rounds. Standard weight is 58 oz.

NIB	Exc.	V.G.	Good	Fair	Poor
650	600	550	500	400	250

Desert Eagle .41 Magnum/.44 Magnum

Standard barrel length is 6" with black oxide finish. Magazine capacity is 8 rounds. Weight for standard pistol is 63 oz.

NIB	Exc.	V.G.	Good	Fair	Poor
750	700	600	550	450	275

Desert Eagle .50 Action Express

Standard barrel length is 10" with black oxide finish. Magazine capacity is 7 rounds. Standard weight is 72 oz.

NIB	Exc.	V.G.	Good	Fair	Poor
1200	950	800	700	600	375

Baby Eagle

The Baby Eagle is a smaller version of the Desert Eagle. It is an all steel construction, extra long slide rail, nylon grips, combat style trigger guard, ambidextrous thumb safety, decocking safety. It is a double action design and available in 9mm, .40 S&W, .41 Action Express. Standard finish is black oxide but matte chrome and brushed are offered as optional finishes. Fixed sights are standard. Fixed night sights an adjustable night sights are options.

Baby Eagle 9mm

Fitted with a 4.7" barrel and black oxide finish this model has a magazine capacity of 16 rounds. Empty weight is 35 oz.

NIB	Exc.	V.G.	Good	Fair	Poor
450	400	350	300	250	200

Baby Eagle .40 S&W

Supplied with 4.7" barrel and black oxide finish it has a magazine capacity of 10 rounds. Empty weight is 35 oz.

NIB	Exc.	V.G.	Good	Fair	Poor
450	400	350	300	250	200

Baby Eagle .41 Action Express

This model also has a 4.7" barrel and black oxide finish. Magazine capacity is 11 rounds. Empty weight is 35 oz.

NIB	Exc.	V.G.	Good	Fair	Poor
450	400	350	300	250	200

Mountain Eagle

This semi-automatic pistol is chambered for the .22 Long Rifle cartridge. It features a 6.5" barrel with adjustable rear sight. The grip is a one piece molded plastic, checkered with raised side panels. The magazine capacity is 15 rounds with 20 round magazine available as an option. A black oxide finish is standard. The pistol weighs 21 oz.

NIB	Exc.	V.G.	Good	Fair	Poor
200	175	150	125	100	75

Mountain Eagle-Target Edition

Similar to the standard Mountain Eagle but fitted with an 8" accurized barrel, two-stage target trigger, jeweled bolt, adjustable sights with three interchangeable blades, and range case.

NIB	Exc.	V.G.	Good	Fair	Poor
250	200	175	150	125	85

Lone Eagle

This is a single shot rotating breech pistol designed to fire centerfire cartridges. The standard finish is a black oxide blue luster. The barrel is drilled and tapped for scope mounts. Standard barrel length is 14". Fixed, adjustable, or silhouette sights are offered as options. Stock assembly is made from Lexan. The handgun is offered in the following calibers: 22-250, .223, .22 Hornet, .243, .30-30, .30-06, .308, .357 Mag., .358 Win., .35 Rem., .44 Mag., .444 Marlin, 7mm-08, 7mm Bench Rest. Weighs between 4 lb. 3 oz. to 4 lbs. 7 oz. depending on caliber.

NIB	Exc.	V.G.	Good	Fair	Poor
325	300	275	250	200	125

DESTROYER CARBINE
Spain

Destroyer Carbine
A 9mm Bayard caliber bolt-action rifle with a 20" barrel and 7-shot magazine. Full length stock with 2 barrel bands.

Exc.	V.G.	Good	Fair	Poor
175	125	90	65	35

DETONICS MANUFACTURING CORP.
Bellevue, Washington

This company manufactured semi-automatic pistols based upon the Colt Model 1911.

Mark I
A .45 caliber semi-automatic pistol with a 3.25" barrel and 6-shot magazine. Matte blued with walnut grips. Discontinued in 1981.

Exc.	V.G.	Good	Fair	Poor
500	450	400	300	200

Mark II
As above, with satin nickle-plated finish. Discontinued in 1979.

Exc.	V.G.	Good	Fair	Poor
500	400	350	300	225

Mark III
As above, with hard chrome plating. Discontinued in 1979.

Exc.	V.G.	Good	Fair	Poor
550	450	400	350	275

Mark IV
As above, with polished blue finish. Discontinued in 1981.

Exc.	V.G.	Good	Fair	Poor
550	450	400	350	275

Combat Master
The Mark I in 9mm, .38 Super or .45 caliber.

NIB	Exc.	V.G.	Good	Fair	Poor
925	775	600	500	425	350

Combat Master Mark V
As above, in stainless steel with a matte finish. Discontinued in 1985.

Exc.	V.G.	Good	Fair	Poor
750	600	500	400	300

Combat Master Mark VI
As above, with adjustable sights and the sides of the slide polished. 1,000 were made in .451 Detonics Magnum caliber.

.451 Detonics Magnum—Add 40%.

NIB	Exc.	V.G.	Good	Fair	Poor
800	725	650	550	450	350

Combat Master Mark VII
As above, without sights.

.451 Detonics Magnum—Add 40%.

NIB	Exc.	V.G.	Good	Fair	Poor
900	800	750	650	550	450

Military Combat MC2
As above, in 9mm, .38 Super or .45 caliber with fixed sights, dull finish and Pachmayr grips. Discontinued in 1984.

NIB	Exc.	V.G.	Good	Fair	Poor
625	575	500	425	350	275

Scoremaster
As above, in .45 or .451 Detonics Magnum with a 5" or 6" barrel, Millet sights and a grip safety.

NIB	Exc.	V.G.	Good	Fair	Poor
1150	1000	850	650	500	400

Janus Competition Scoremaster
As above, in .45 caliber with a compensated barrel. Introduced in 1988.

NIB	Exc.	V.G.	Good	Fair	Poor
1650	1450	1250	1000	750	500

Servicemaster
As above, with a 4.25" barrel, interchangeable sights and matte finish. Discontinued in 1986.

Exc.	V.G.	Good	Fair	Poor
900	750	600	400	325

Pocket 9
A 9mm double action semi-automatic pistol with a 3" barrel and 6-shot magazine. Matte finish stainless steel. Discontinued in 1986.

Exc.	V.G.	Good	Fair	Poor
400	350	275	225	175

DEUTSCHE WERKE
Erfurt, Germany

Ortgies
A 7.65mm or 9mm short semi-automatic pistol marked on the slide "Deutsche Werke Erfurt". The walnut grips inlaid with a brass medallion cast with an ornate "D".

6.35mm

Exc.	V.G.	Good	Fair	Poor
250	225	175	125	90

DEVISME, F. P.
Paris, France

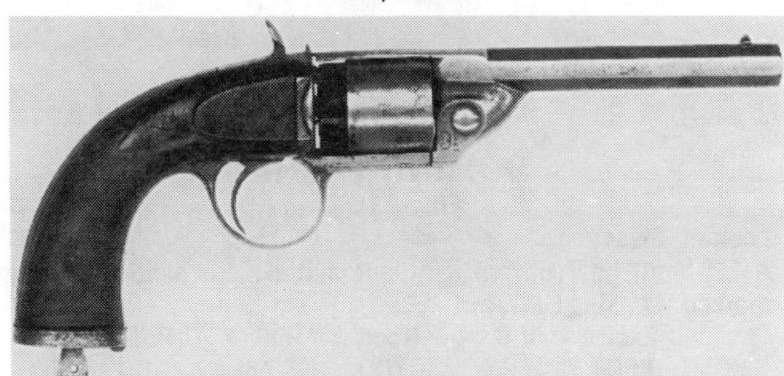

One of the more popular French gunsmiths of the mid 19th Century, F. P. Devisme manufactured a wide variety of firearms including single shot percussion pistols, double-barrel percussion rifles and shotguns, percussion revolvers and cane guns. After 1858 this maker manufactured cartridge weapons of the same style as his percussion arms. The quality of all of his products is uniformly high and it is impossible to provide generalized price guide. Prospective purchasers are advised to secure a qualified appraisal prior to acquisition.

DICKINSON

SEE—Dickinson, E.L.

DICKINSON, E. L. & J.

Springfield, Massachusetts

Ranger

A .32 caliber spur trigger revolver with a 6-shot cylinder.

Exc.	V.G.	Good	Fair	Poor
200	175	150	110	80

Single Shot

A .32 caliber single shot pistol with a 3.75" hinged barrel, silver plated brass frame, blued barrel and walnut grips.

Exc.	V.G.	Good	Fair	Poor
400	350	300	225	150

DICKSON, NELSON & CO.

Dawson, Georgia

Dickson, Nelson Rifle

A .58 caliber single shot percussion rifle with a 34" barrel, full stock secured by 2 barrel bands, brass furniture and iron loading rod. The lock marked "Dickson/Nelson & Co./C.S." as well as "Ala." and the date of manufacture. Prospective purchasers are advised to secure a qualified appraisal prior to acquisition. A carbine version of this arm is known and has a 24" barrel.

Exc.	V.G.	Good	Fair	Poor
5000	4500	4000	3500	2750

DIMICK, H. E.

St. Louis, Missouri

While this maker is primarily known for half stock Plains Rifles, he also manufactured a limited number of percussion pistols. These vary in length, caliber, stock form and type of furniture. The values listed below should only be used as a rough guide. Prospective purchasers should secure a qualified appraisal prior to acquisition. Active 1849 to 1873.

Exc.	V.G.	Good	Fair	Poor
3000	2000	1500	1150	900

DOMINGO ACHA

Eibar, Spain

Looking Glass

A 6.35mm or 7.65mm semi-automatic pistol with the slide marked "Looking Glass".

Exc.	V.G.	Good	Fair	Poor
150	125	100	75	50

DOMINO

Brescia, Italy
Importer—Mandall Shooting Supplies
Scottsdale, Arizona

Model OP 601 Match Pistol

A .22 caliber short semi-automatic pistol with a 5.6" vented barrel, target sights, adjustable and removable trigger. Blued with adjustable walnut grips.

NIB	Exc.	V.G.	Good	Fair	Poor
1300	1150	1000	800	625	450

Model SP 602 Match Pistol

As above, in .22 l.r. caliber.

NIB	Exc.	V.G.	Good	Fair	Poor
1300	1150	1000	800	625	450

DORNHAUS & DIXON

Huntington Beach, California

SEE—Bren 10

DORNHEIM, G. C.

Suhl, Germany

Gecado

A 6.35mm or 7.65mm semi-automatic pistol bearing the name "Gecado" on the slide. Marketed by G.C. Dornheim.

Exc.	V.G.	Good	Fair	Poor
200	150	125	75	50

DREYSE

SEE—Rheinmetall

DRISCOLL, J. B.

Springfield, Massachusetts

Single Shot Pocket Pistol

A small pistol chambered for .22 rimfire. It has a 3.5" octagonal barrel that pivots downward for loading after a trigger-like hook under the breech is pulled. It has a spur trigger, silver-plated brass frame, and a blued barrel. The square butt is flared at the bottom, and the grips are walnut. There were approximately 200 manufactured in the late 1860s.

Exc.	V.G.	Good	Fair	Poor
350	300	250	200	150

DUBIEL ARMS CO.

Sherman, Texas

Established in 1975 by Joseph Dubiel and Dr. John Tyson. They are engaged in the manufacture of high quality, custom-built, bolt-action rifles. The rifles are constructed from patented Dubiel actions that feature a 5-lug bolt locking mechanism and a 36-degree bolt rotation. They are chambered for all calibers from .22-250 through .458 Winchester Magnum. Barrel lengths, weights, and stock styles are made to the customer's order. Douglas Premium barrels and Canjar triggers are used, and there are six basic stock designs available. The rifles are guaranteed to group in 1.5" at 100 yards with factory ammunition. The values listed are basic retail prices, and appraisal should be secured as options will drastically affect prices.

NIB	Exc.	V.G.	Good	Fair	Poor
2500	2250	2000	1750	1500	1200

DUMOULIN
Herstal, Belgium
IMPORTER—MIDWEST GUNSPORT
Zebulon, North Carolina

The guns produced by Ernest Dumoulin are essentially handmade to the customer's order. They are of the highest quality, both in materials and workmanship. There are many options available that have a tremendous impact on value fluctuations. The models and values listed here are base prices. If a sale or purchase is contemplated, individual competent appraisal should be secured.

Shotguns

Europa Model

A side-by-side double barrel chambered for 12, 20, and 28 gauge and .410 bore. It is available in any length barrel and choke combination, with an Anson & Deeley boxlock action and automatic ejectors. One has the option of double or single-selective triggers and a choice of six different moderate engraving patterns. The select walnut stock is oil-finished. This model was introduced in 1989.

Basic Values

NIB	Exc.	V.G.	Good	Fair	Poor
3350	3100	2750	2250	1800	1400

Leige Model

A side-by-side double chambered for 12, 16, 20, and 28 gauge. It is similar to the Europa, with a greater degree of finish and more engraving. The walnut is of a higher grade. This model was introduced in 1986.

NIB	Exc.	V.G.	Good	Fair	Poor
5300	5000	4500	4000	3500	3000

Continental Model

A side by side chambered for 12, 20, and 28 gauge and .410. Barrel lengths and chokes are on a custom-order basis. This is a true sidelock action with automatic ejectors and choice of triggers. There are six different engraving patterns, and the stock is made of high grade, hand-checkered, oil-finished walnut. This model was introduced in 1989.

NIB	Exc.	V.G.	Good	Fair	Poor
7500	7000	6500	5750	5000	4200

Etendart Model

A side by side chambered for 12, 20, and 28 gauge. This best grade side by side is built on a purely made-to-order basis. It is profusely engraved and uses exhibition grade walnut in its stock. There are 12 different engraving patterns from which to choose, and the cost is according to embellishments chosen. Values given here are for the basic model.

NIB	Exc.	V.G.	Good	Fair	Poor
14500	12500	10000	8000	6000	4500

Superposed Express International

An Over/Under chambered for 20 gauge and is furnished with a set of rifle barrels in the customer's choice of seven calibers. The walnut is of a deluxe grade, and engraving is available at extra cost. This is a made-to-order gun, and the value here is for the most basic model. This gun was discontinued in 1985.

Exc.	V.G.	Good	Fair	Poor
2500	2250	1750	1250	1000

Boss Royal Model

The best grade Over/Under, chambered for 12, 20, and 28 gauge. It is a full sidelock gun that is made to the customer's specification using the finest materials and workmanship available. This model was introduced in 1987.

NIB	Exc.	V.G.	Good	Fair	Poor
18500	15000	12500	10000	8000	6750

Eagle Model Combination Gun

This model has a rifle barrel or the shotgun barrel which is chambered for 12 or 20 gauge. The rifle calibers available are .22 Hornet, .222 Remington, .222 Remington Magnum, 6mm, .243, .25-06, .30-06, 6.5 X 57R, 7 X 57R, 8 X 57JRS, and 9.3 X 74R. The action is a boxlock with automatic ejectors, and the other specifications are on a custom-order basis. This model was introduced in 1989.

NIB	Exc.	V.G.	Good	Fair	Poor
2750	2500	2000	1750	1250	1000

Double Rifles

Europa I

A made-to-order, Over/Under, double-barrelled rifle available in the same calibers as the Eagle Combination gun. It has an Anson & Deeley boxlock and all other options to the customer's specifications.

NIB	Exc.	V.G.	Good	Fair	Poor
5000	4750	4000	3500	2900	2250

Continental I Model

A more deluxe Over/Under rifle with a true sidelock action. The calibers are the same as the Europa. The specifications are to the customer's order with 12 engraving patterns to choose from at extra cost. This model was introduced in 1989.

NIB	Exc.	V.G.	Good	Fair	Poor
8500	7800	7000	5500	4500	3750

Pionnier Express Rifle

A side-by-side double rifle chambered for the .22 Hornet through the .600 Nitro Express. It has the Anson & Deeley boxlock action and is quite deluxe throughout. The specifications are to the customer's order, and there are basically 12 models available (P-I through P-XII). The differences among these models are in the degree of ornamentation and quality of the walnut used for the stock. The prices of these models would have to be ascertained through appraisal, as a book of this nature could not possibly consider the variables that one could encounter with a gun of this type. Values range from approximately $8,000 to $12,000 for the basic models.

Aristocrat Model

A low-profile single shot chambered for all calibers up to .375 Holland & Holland. This is a deluxe, made-to-order rifle with exhibition-grade walnut and 12 engraving patterns available.

Exc.	V.G.	Good	Fair	Poor
9000	8000	7000	5500	4800

Bolt Action Rifles

Centurion Model

A custom-order rifle built on a Mauser or Sako action and chambered for all calibers from .270 to .458 Winchester Magnum. The barrel lengths available were 21.5", 24", and 25.5"; and there were many engraving options from which to choose. The stock is of deluxe French walnut, with rosewood forend tip and pistolgrip cap. This rifle was discontinued in 1986.

Exc.	V.G.	Good	Fair	Poor
675	600	500	400	325

Centurion Classic

Similar to the Mauser-actioned Centurion chambered for the non-Magnum calibers only. The walnut used for the stock is a better grade.

NIB	Exc.	V.G.	Good	Fair	Poor
1500	1350	1100	900	650	550

Diane

A more deluxe version of the Centurion Classic.

NIB	Exc.	V.G.	Good	Fair	Poor
1550	1400	1150	950	700	600

Amazone

A 20"-barrelled, full-length stocked, upgraded version of the Diane.

NIB	Exc.	V.G.	Good	Fair	Poor
1750	1600	1250	1000	750	600

Bavaria Deluxe

Similar to the Centurion, with the same barrel lengths and calibers available. The engraving styles available are more deluxe. This model was discontinued in 1985.

NIB	Exc.	V.G.	Good	Fair	Poor
1900	1750	1500	1250	1000	750

Safari Model
Similar to the Bavaria Deluxe, but it is chambered for the heavy Magnum calibers only.

NIB	Exc.	V.G.	Good	Fair	Poor
2400	2000	1750	1500	1250	1000

Safari Sportsman
Built on a Magnum Mauser action and is chambered for the .375 Holland & Holland, .404 Jeffreys, .416 Rigby, and the .505 Gibbs. This is a true big game rifle that was made available in 1986.

NIB	Exc.	V.G.	Good	Fair	Poor
4000	3750	3250	2750	2500	2000

African Pro
A more deluxe version of the Safari Sportsman, with a folding-leaf rear sight, hooded front sight, and an ebony or buffalo horn forend tip.

NIB	Exc.	V.G.	Good	Fair	Poor
4800	4500	4000	3250	2750	2500

NOTE: Again we feel it is important to note that all values furnished in this section are estimates based on the most basic model in each designation. There are many options that will radically affect the values, and a competent appraisal should be secured if a sale or purchase is contemplated.

DURLOV
Czech Republic

This company was part of the national co-operative under Communists rule when the Czech Republic was part of Czechoslovakia. The company was formed in 1948. The company specialized in low-cost but well made rimfire target pistols.

Durlov Model 70 Standard
This model is a bolt action single shot pistol chamberd for the .22 Long Rifle. A knob at the rear of the frame opened the bolt. When the bolt is closed the firing pin is cocked. The barrel is 9.75" long with an adjustable front sight for windage. The rear sight is adjustable for elevation. Wooden wrap around grips with thumbrest are standard. Weighs about 44 oz.

Exc.	V.G.	Good	Fair	Poor
250	200	175	100	75

Durlov Model 70 Special
Same as above but with the addition of a set trigger.

Exc.	V.G.	Good	Fair	Poor
300	250	200	150	100

Durlov Model 75
This model features a set trigger, better sights, and grip. The rear sight is fully adjustable.

Exc.	V.G.	Good	Fair	Poor
350	300	250	200	150

Pav
This target pistol was introduced in 1963. It is an inexpensive pistol with a fixed front sight and a notch for the rear sight. Like the other models above it is also a single shot chambered for the .22 Long Rifle cartridge. The barrel is 10.25" and weighs about 35 oz.

Courtesy Orville Reichert.

Exc.	V.G.	Good	Fair	Poor
175	150	100	75	50

DUSEK, F.
Opocno, Czechoslovakia

Dusek commenced business in the mid-1920s and continued to make firearms through WWII. They manufactured pistols for Nazi Germany under the contract code "aek." After the War the communists took over, and Dusek's designs were relegated to the CZ factory.

Duo
Introduced in 1926, this 6.35mm pistol is based on the 1906 Browning design. It has a 2.25" barrel and 6-shot detachable magazine. The Duo was very successful from a commercial standpoint and was exported throughout the world. During WWII the slide markings were in German; and the name "Eblen", Dusek's German sales agent, may sometimes be found on the slide. The Duo may also be found marked Ideal, Jaga, and Singer.

Nazi-marked examples will bring a 25 percent premium.

Exc.	V.G.	Good	Fair	Poor
225	200	150	100	80

Perla
This 6.35mm pistol has a fixed barrel and open-topped slide. It resembles a Walther design and is striker-fired. The slide is marked "Automat Pistole Perla 6.35mm"; the grips, "Perla 6.35." Dusek made this model from the early 1930s until WWII.

Exc.	V.G.	Good	Fair	Poor
225	200	150	100	80

E.M.F. CO., INC.

Santa Ana, California

SEE—Uberti, Aldo

An importer and distributer of quality Italian-made reproduction firearms. Their offerings are listed in the section dealing with Aldo Uberti firearms.

EAGLE ARMS CO.

New Haven, Connecticut

SEE—Plant Manufacturing Co.

ECHAVE & ARIZMENDI

Eibar, Spain

Founded in 1911 and produced the usual poor-quality, early Spanish semi-automatic pistols. They did improve their quality later on and were permitted to return to gun manufacturing after the Spanish Civil War. They were one of the few pistol makers to survive this period. They imported many models, and their products are not particularly of interest to collectors.

Basque, Echasa or Dickson Special Agent

These two pistols are the same under different names. They are chambered for 7.65mm and are double-action, blowback-operated, semi-automatic copies of the Walther PP. The disassembly methods and the quality are the two differences. The finish is blued, and the grips are checkered wood. The slides are marked either "Basque" or "Echasa" and "Made in Spain Cal. .32."

Exc.	V.G.	Good	Fair	Poor
200	150	125	100	75

Bronco

A copy of the Browning 1906 chambered for 7.65mm and 6.35mm. It has a grip safety and is marked "1918 Model Automatic Pistol Bronco Patent No. 66130." This model was manufactured at the end of WWI.

Exc.	V.G.	Good	Fair	Poor
150	125	100	75	50

Echasa

Similar to the 6.35mm Bronco, without a grip safety. It is marked "Model 1916."

Exc.	V.G.	Good	Fair	Poor
150	125	100	75	50

Fast

Similar to the Echasa except that it is chambered for the .22 l.r. and the 9mm short, as well as the 7.65mm and the 6.35mm. There is one version that is chrome-plated with white plastic grips.

Exc.	V.G.	Good	Fair	Poor
175	150	125	100	75

Lightning

A renamed version of the Bronco in 6.35mm.

Exc.	V.G.	Good	Fair	Poor
150	125	100	75	50

Lur Panzer

A copy of the Luger toggle-lock action, chambered for .22 rimfire. This is an almost exact copy except for a different trigger assembly and a less robust mainspring. It is marked "Lur Cal.22 LR Made in Spain." The plastic grips have "Panzer" molded into them.

Exc.	V.G.	Good	Fair	Poor
225	200	150	125	100

Pathfinder

The 6.35mm Bronco with another name for export purposes.

Exc.	V.G.	Good	Fair	Poor
150	125	100	75	50

Protector

Similar to the Echasa, chambered for 6.35mm. There is a slight difference in the triggerguard and the magazine catch. The grips have molded flowers and the caliber in a circle.

Exc.	V.G.	Good	Fair	Poor
150	125	100	75	50

Selecta

Similar to the Protector, chambered for 7.65mm.

Exc.	V.G.	Good	Fair	Poor
150	125	100	75	50

ECHEVERRIA, STAR-BONIFACIO SA

Eibar, Spain

An old-line Spanish company that survived the Spanish civil war. It was founded in 1908 by Jean Echeverria, but the early records of the company were lost during the civil war. The early pistols the company produced were patterned after the Mannlicher designs, and the tradename Star was the closest thing to Steyr that could be used. After the close of WWI, the company began production of the open-topped slide Star for which they have become known. They also produced a large 1911-type pistol that was successful. During the civil war, the plant was damaged and the company records destroyed; but after the cessation of hostilities, they were one of only three gun companies that were allowed to remain in business. They survive to this day and are known for the manufacture of quality firearms.

Star Model 1908

The first pistol produced under the Star banner. It is a Mannlicher copy that is chambered for 6.35mm. It has a 3" fixed barrel and an open-topped slide. The detachable magazine holds 8 shots. The finish is blued, and the grips are checkered plastic. The slide is marked "Automatic Pistol Star Patent."

Exc.	V.G.	Good	Fair	Poor
275	250	200	150	100

Star Model 1914

Similar to the model 1908, with a 5" barrel and larger grips that have the Star name molded into them. This model was the first to have the six-pointed star surrounded by rays of light (that became the Star trademark) stamped on its slide.

Exc.	V.G.	Good	Fair	Poor
275	250	200	150	100

Star Model 1919

Also a copy of a Mannlicher design and differs from its predecessors chiefly in the way the pistol is disassembled. This model has a spring catch at the top of the triggerguard. This model also has a small spur on the hammer, and the magazine release was relocated to a button behind the triggerguard instead of a catch at the bottom of the butt. This model was chambered for 6.35mm, 7.65mm and 9mm short, with various barrel lengths offered. The maker's name, as well as the Star trademark, is stamped into the slide. This model was produced until 1929.

Exc.	V.G.	Good	Fair	Poor
275	250	200	150	100

Modelo Militar

Represents the first pistol Star produced that was not a Mannlicher design copy. This model was copied from the Colt 1911. It was chambered initially for the 9mm Largo in hopes of securing a military contract. When this contract was awarded to Astra, Star chambered the Model 1919 for the .38 Super and the .45 ACP and put it on the commercial market. This model is like the Colt 1911—it has a Browning-type swinging link and the same type of lock up. However there is no grip safety, and the thumb safety functions differently. This model was produced until 1924.

Exc.	V.G.	Good	Fair	Poor
275	250	200	175	125

Star Model A

A modification of the Model 1919, chambered for the 7.63 Mauser, 9mm Largo, and the .45 ACP cartridge. The slide is similar in appearance to the 1911 Colt, and the spur hammer has a small hole in it. Early models had no grip safety, but later production added this feature. Some models are slotted for addition of a shoulder stock.

Exc.	V.G.	Good	Fair	Poor
250	225	175	150	100

Star Model B

Similar to the Model A except that it is almost an exact copy of the Colt 1911. It is chambered for 9mm parabellum and has a spur hammer with no hole. This model was introduced in 1928.

Courtesy Orville Reichert.

Exc.	V.G.	Good	Fair	Poor
275	250	200	175	125

Star Model C

The Model B chambered for the 9mm Browning Long cartridge. It was manufactured in the 1920s.

Exc.	V.G.	Good	Fair	Poor
225	175	150	125	90

Star Model CO

A pocket pistol similar to the early open-topped Star pistols. It is chambered for the 6.35mm cartridge, and the finish is blued with checkered plastic grips that bear the Star name and logo. This model was manufactured between 1930 and 1957.

Exc.	V.G.	Good	Fair	Poor
200	150	125	100	75

Star Model D

A medium-sized pistol that is similar in appearance to a smaller Model A. It is chambered for the .9mm short cartridge and was called the "Police and Pocket Model" after it was adopted by the Spanish police. It was manufactured between 1930 and 1941.

Exc.	V.G.	Good	Fair	Poor
200	175	150	110	80

Star Model E

A pocket pistol chambered for the 6.35mm cartridge. It has a 2.5" barrel and an external hammer. The detachable magazine holds 5 rounds, and the finish is blued with checkered plastic grips. This model was manufactured between 1932 and 1941.

Exc.	V.G.	Good	Fair	Poor
200	175	150	110	80

Star Model F

The first of the .22 caliber Star pistols. It has a 4" barrel, a 10-shot magazine, and fixed sights. The finish is blued, and the plastic grips are checkered. This model was manufactured between 1942 and 1967.

Exc.	V.G.	Good	Fair	Poor
175	150	125	100	75

Star Model F Target

Similar to the Model F, with a 6" barrel.

Exc.	V.G.	Good	Fair	Poor
225	200	175	150	110

Star Model F Sport

Has a 5" barrel and was also manufactured between 1962 and 1967.

Exc.	V.G.	Good	Fair	Poor
200	175	150	125	100

Star Model F Olympic

Has a 6" barrel and adjustable sights. It is furnished with a muzzle brake and barrel weights. It was manufactured between 1942 and 1967.

Exc.	V.G.	Good	Fair	Poor
275	225	175	150	125

Star Model F Olympic Rapid Fire

Similar to the Olympic but is chambered for .22 short only.

Exc.	V.G.	Good	Fair	Poor
275	225	175	150	125

Star Model FR

Has an adjustable sight and a slide stop. The 4" barrel is heavier, with flattened sides. It was manufactured between 1967 and 1972.

Exc.	V.G.	Good	Fair	Poor
185	165	145	125	100

Star Model FRS

Similar to the Model FR, with a 6" barrel. It is also available chrome-plated with white checkered plastic grips. It was introduced in 1967 and is still in production.

Exc.	V.G.	Good	Fair	Poor
185	165	145	125	100

Star Model FM

A heavier-framed version of the Model FRS. It has a 4.5" barrel and is available in blue or chrome-plated. It was introduced in 1972 and is still made.

Exc.	V.G.	Good	Fair	Poor
185	165	145	125	100

Star Model H

Similar to the old Model CO—only larger in size. It is chambered for the 7.65mm cartridge and was manufactured between 1932 and 1941.

Exc.	V.G.	Good	Fair	Poor
165	145	125	100	75

Star Model HF

A pocket-sized version of the Model F chambered for .22 short. It has a 2.5" barrel and is quite scarce on today's market.

Exc.	V.G.	Good	Fair	Poor
200	175	150	125	100

Star Model HN

Simply the Model H chambered for the 9mm short cartridge. It was manufactured and discontinued at the same time as the Model H was.

Exc.	V.G.	Good	Fair	Poor
175	150	125	100	75

Star Model I

An improved version of the Model H with a 4" barrel and a recontoured grip. It was chambered for 7.65mm and was produced until 1941. After the war it was resumed and survived until the mid-1950s, when it was replaced by the modernized Model IR which would be valued approximately the same.

Exc.	V.G.	Good	Fair	Poor
150	125	100	75	60

Star Model M

Similar to the Model B, chambered for the .38 Auto cartridge.

Exc.	V.G.	Good	Fair	Poor
175	150	125	100	75

Star Model P

The postwar version of the Model B, chambered for the .45 ACP cartridge.

Exc.	V.G.	Good	Fair	Poor
250	225	300	150	125

Star Model CU "Starlet"

Similar to the Model CO, with an alloy frame that was anodized in black, blue, gray, green, or gold. It has a steel slide that is blued or chrome-plated. It has checkered, white plastic grips and is chambered for the .25ACP cartridge. It has a 2.5" barrel, fixed sights, and a 5-shot magazine. This model was introduced in 1975 and was not imported after 1986.

Exc.	V.G.	Good	Fair	Poor
175	150	125	100	75

Star Model BKS "Starlight"

The smallest locked-breech automatic chambered for the 9mm cartridge at the time. It has an alloy frame and a 4.25" barrel. It is similar in appearance to a scaled-down Colt 1911 without a grip safety. It has an 8-shot magazine and is either blued or chrome-plated, with checkered plastic grips. This model was manufactured between 1970 and 1981.

Exc.	V.G.	Good	Fair	Poor
250	225	200	150	125

Star Model PD

Chambered for the .45 ACP cartridge and has a 4" barrel. It has an alloy frame and a 6-shot magazine and adjustable sights and is blued with checkered walnut grips. It was introduced in 1975.

NIB	Exc.	V.G.	Good	Fair	Poor
400	325	275	225	175	125

Star Model BM

A steel-framed 9mm that is styled after the Colt 1911. It has an 8-shot magazine and a 4" barrel. It is available either blued or chrome-plated.

NIB	Exc.	V.G.	Good	Fair	Poor
335	300	250	200	150	125

Star Model BKM

Similar to the BM, with an alloy frame.

NIB	Exc.	V.G.	Good	Fair	Poor
375	325	275	225	175	125

Star Model 28

The first of Star's Super 9's. It is a double-action semi-automatic chambered for the 9mm Parabellum cartridge. It has a 4.25" barrel and a steel frame. The magazine holds 15 shots. The construction of this pistol was totally modular, and it has no screws at all in its design. It is blued with checkered synthetic grips and was manufactured in 1983 and 1984.

NIB	Exc.	V.G.	Good	Fair	Poor
415	375	325	275	225	175

Star Model 30M

An improved version of the Model 28, that is quite similar in appearance. It was introduced in 1985.

NIB	Exc.	V.G.	Good	Fair	Poor
450	350	300	250	200	125

Star Model 30/PK

Similar to the Models 28 and 30M, with a lightweight alloy frame.

NIB	Exc.	V.G.	Good	Fair	Poor
450	350	300	250	200	125

ECHEVERRIA
(Star)
IMPORTER—INTERARMS
Alexandria, Virginia

Megastar

This is a double-action semi-automatic pistol chambered for the 10mm or .45 ACP cartridge. It features a three position ambidextrous selective decocking lever, rubber grips, combat style trigger guard slotted hammer, and checkered mainspring housing. Barrel length is 4.6" and the magazine capacity is 12 rounds. Available in either blue or starvel (brushed chrome). The pistol weighs 47.6 ozs.

NIB	Exc.	V.G.	Good	Fair	Poor
500	450	350	250	200	100

Firestar-M/43, M/40, and M45
This is a compact large caliber semi-automatic pistol offered in 9mm, the M43, .40 S&W, the M40, and the .45 ACP, the M45. It features an ambidextrous safety, steel frame and slide, checkered rubber grips. The barrel is 3.4" on the M43 and M40 and 3.6" on the M45. Choice of finish siblue or starvel (brushed chrome). A finger rest magazine is optional. Weight for the M43 and M40 is 30 ozs. while the M56 weighs 35 ozs.

NIB	Exc.	V.G.	Good	Fair	Poor
350	300	250	200	150	100

Starfire Model 31P
This model evolved from the Models 28 and 30. It is chambered for either the 9mm Parabellum or .40 S&W. The trigger action is double-action/single-action. Barrel length is 3.9". It is fitted with a two position safety/decocking lever. The magazine capacity for the 9mm is 15 rounds while the .40 S&W holds 11 rounds. The pistol weighs 39 ozs.

NIB	Exc.	V.G.	Good	Fair	Poor
425	350	300	250	200	100

Starfire Model 31PK
Similar to the Model 31P but built on an alloy frame. Chambered for 9mm only with a 15 round magazine capacity. Weight is 30 ozs.

NIB	Exc.	V.G.	Good	Fair	Poor
400	350	300	250	200	100

ECLIPSE
Pittsburgh, Pennsylvania
Enterprise Gun Works

Single Shot Derringer
This pocket pistol was made by the firm of James Bown & Son, doing business as the Enterprise Gun Works. It is chambered for .22 or .32-caliber rimfire cartridges. A few in .25 rimfire have been noted and would add approximately 25 percent to the values listed. The barrel is 2.5" in length and is part-round/part-octagonal. It pivots sideways for loading. It has a spur trigger and a birdshead grip. The barrel is stamped "Eclipse." It is made of nickle-plated iron, with walnut grips. There were approximately 10,000 manufactured between 1870 and 1890.

Exc.	V.G.	Good	Fair	Poor
200	175	150	100	75

84 GUN CO.
Eighty Four, Pennsylvania

In business for a brief time in the early 1970s. They produced three basic bolt-action rifles—each in four grades that differ in amounts of embellishment and grades of wood. There is very little known about this company and their products. An accurate appraisal with hands-on would be the only proper way to place a value on these rifles as there are not enough traded in to establish correct values in a book of this nature. The basic models are as follows.

Classic Rifle
Grade 1—Grade 4 available
450--1600

Lobo Rifle
Grade 1—Grade 4 available
425--2500

Pennsylvania Rifle
Grade 1—Grade 4 available
425--2500

ELGIN CUTLASS

Springfield, Massachusetts

Manufactured by two companies--C. B. Allen of Springfield, Massachusetts, and Morill, Mosman and Blair of Amherst, Massachusetts. It is a unique pistol that has an integral knife attachment affixed to the gun barrel. It was designed and patented by George Elgin and simultaneously produced by the two companies. The inspiration for this weapon was supposedly Jim Bowie, who at that time had made a name as a knife fighter with his large "Bowie" knife. The blades for these pistols were supplied by N. P. Ames of the famed Ames Sword Co. These pistols are much sought after, and one must excercise caution as fraudulent examples have been noted.

C. B. Allen-Made Pistols

U.S. Navy Elgin Cutlass Pistol

Chambered for .54 caliber percussion and has a 5" octagonal smooth-bore barrel. The Bowie-style blade is 11" long by 2" wide and is forged together with the triggerguard and the knuckle guard that protects the grip. The handle is walnut. This pistol was issued to the U.S. Navy's Wilkes-South Sea Exploration Expedition, and the markings are "C.B.Allen / Springfield / Mass." "Elgin's Patent" and the letters "CB", "CBA" along with the date 1837. If the sheath that was issued with this knife pistol is included and in sound condition, it would add approximately $700 to the value. There were 150 manufactured for the U.S. Navy in 1838.

Exc.	V.G.	Good	Fair	Poor
12500	10000	8000	6500	4750

Civilian Model

Chambered for .35 or .41 caliber percussion and has a 4" octagonal barrel with a 7.5"-10" knife blade. It has a round triggerguard but does not have the knuckle bow across the grip, as found on the military model. They are marked "C.B.Allen Springfield, Mass." Blades marked "N.P.Ames" have been noted. There were approximately 100 manufactured in 1837.

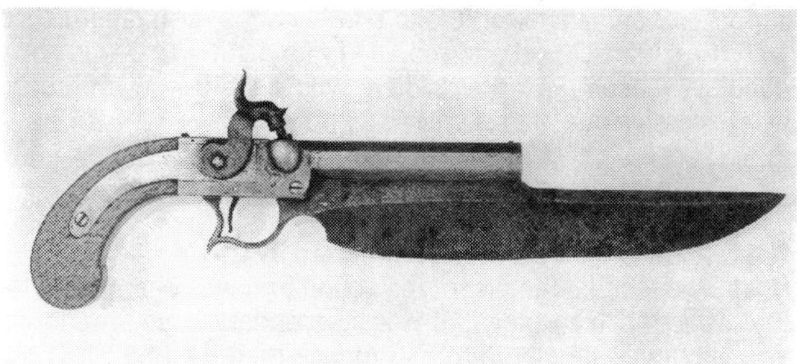

Exc.	V.G.	Good	Fair	Poor
5000	4500	3750	3250	2750

Morill, Mosman and Blair-Made Pistols

Small Model

The main difference in the pistols of the two makers is that this model has a round barrel and a square-back triggerguard that comes to a point at the rear. This version is chambered for .32 caliber percussion and has a 2.75" barrel. The knife blade is 7.5" in length and is screwed to the frame. This model is unmarked except for a serial number. The number produced is unknown, and they were manufactured in 1837.

Exc.	V.G.	Good	Fair	Poor
4000	3500	2750	2250	1750

Large Model

Chambered for .36 caliber percussion and has a 4" round barrel and a 9" knife blade. The pistol is usually marked "Cast Steel" and serial numbered. The blade is etched with an American eagle, stars, and an urn with flowers. "Elgin Patent" is etched in the center. This model was also manufactured in 1837.

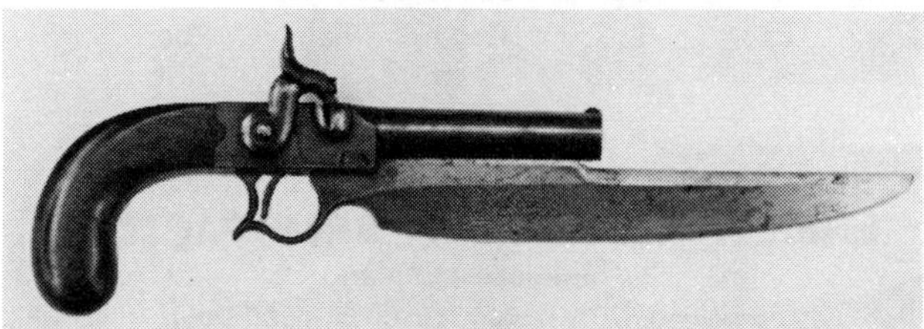

Courtesy Milwaukee Public Museum, Milwaukee, Wisconsin.

Exc.	V.G.	Good	Fair	Poor
4000	3500	3000	2500	2000

ELLS, JOSIAH

Pittsburgh, Pennsylvania

Pocket Revolver

Three distinct variations of this percussion revolver. They are chambered for .28 and .31 caliber and have 6-shot unfluted cylinders. They have been noted with 2.5", 3", and 3.75" octagonal barrels.

Model 1

The first model has an open-topped frame and is chambered for .28 caliber. The cylinder holds 5 or 6 shots, and the hammer is of the bar type. It was offered with a 2.5" or 3" barrel. The markings are "J.Ells; Patent;1854." There were approximately 625 manufactured between 1857 and 1859.

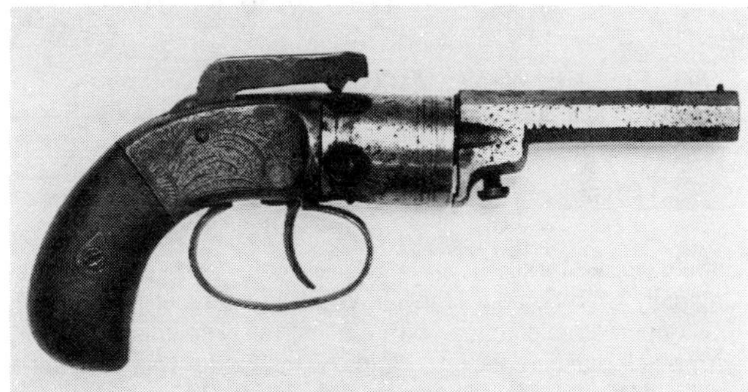

Courtesy Milwaukee Public Museum, Milwaukee, Wisconsin.

Exc.	V.G.	Good	Fair	Poor
450	400	325	275	200

Model 2

The second model is similar to the first, with a solid-topped frame. They have 5-shot cylinders and 3.75" long barrels. There were approximately 550 manufactured.

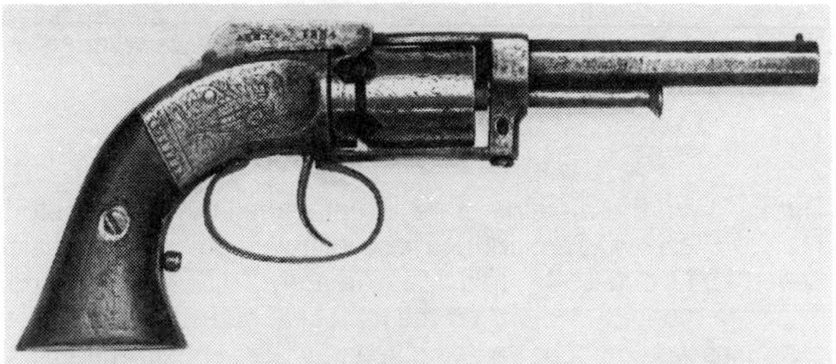

Courtesy Milwaukee Public Museum, Milwaukee, Wisconsin.

Exc.	V.G.	Good	Fair	Poor
450	400	325	275	200

Model 3

The third model is radically different from its forerunners. It has a closed-top frame and a conventional spur-type hammer that strikes from the right side. It functions either as a double-or single-action. It is chambered for .28 caliber and has a 5-shot cylinder and a 3.75" barrel. There were only about 200 manufactured between 1857 and 1859.

Exc.	V.G.	Good	Fair	Poor
575	550	425	375	300

ENFIELD ROYAL SMALL ARMS FACTORY

Middlesex, England

In 1879 the British Army needed revolvers, and the Royal Small Arms Factory was commissioned to produce them. The result was that on August 11, 1880, the Enfield Mark I was accepted for duty.

Enfield Mark I Revolver

A 6-shot, hinged-frame, break-open revolver. It has an odd ejection system—when the barrel is pulled down, the cylinder moves forward; and the extractor plate remains in place, retaining the spent cartridges. This revolver is chambered for the .476 cartridge and has a 6-shot cylinder. The barrel is 6" long, and the finish is blued with checkered walnut grips.

Exc.	V.G.	Good	Fair	Poor
250	225	175	140	100

Enfield Mark 2

The Mark 2 is similar externally, with some design improvements—such as a rounded front sight, taper-bored cylinders, an integral top strap, and plain grips. The Mark 2 was introduced in 1881 and was replaced by the Webley Mark I in 1887.

Exc.	V.G.	Good	Fair	Poor
250	225	175	140	100

Enfield-Produced Webley Mark 6

This model is identical to the Webley-produced versions. It is of .455 caliber and is stamped "Enfield" on the frame.

Exc.	V.G.	Good	Fair	Poor
225	200	175	140	100

Enfield No. 2 Mark I

Originally chambered for the .38 Webley Special. It is a 6-shot, break-open double action, with a 5" barrel. The finish is blued, with black plastic checkered grips. This model was actually a modified Webley design and was adopted in 1932. In 1938 the bullet was changed from a 200-grain lead "soft-nosed" to a 178-grain jacketed, in response to pressure from the Geneva Conference.

Exc.	V.G.	Good	Fair	Poor
200	175	150	125	100

Enfield No. 2 Mark I*

The same as the Mark I with the hammer spur and single-action lockwork omitted in response to the Royal Tank Regiment's fear that the spur would catch on the tank as the crews were entering and exiting their confines.

Exc.	V.G.	Good	Fair	Poor
225	200	175	150	125

During WWII these pistols were manufactured by Albion Motors Ltd. of Glasgow, Scotland. These pistols were produced between 1941 and 1943, and approximately 24,000 were made. They are marked "Albion" on the right side of the frame. These examples would not be valued differently than Enfield-made pistols. Enfield pistols with the marking "SM" or "SSM" will also be noted, and this refers to various parts produced by Singer Sewing Machine Company of England. These pistols were assembled at Enfield. Used until 1957, when the FN-Browning GP35 semi-automatic pistol replaced them.

Enfield Rifles

Lee-Enfield Mark I

Chambered for the .303 cartridge and has a 30" barrel. The attached box magazine holds 10 rounds, and the sights are military-styled. The stock is full-length walnut, and there is a cleaning rod beneath it. There are two barrel bands and a bayonet lug. This model was manufactured between 1895 and 1899.

Exc.	V.G.	Good	Fair	Poor
250	225	200	150	100

Lee-Enfield Mark I*

A Mark 3 Martini Henry with a .303-caliber barrel fitted to it. It was introduced in 1899.

Exc.	V.G.	Good	Fair	Poor
250	225	200	150	100

Lee-Enfield Mark I**

Simply the Mark I with no attached cleaning rod. It was introduced in 1899.

Exc.	V.G.	Good	Fair	Poor
250	225	200	150	100

Lee-Enfield Mark II SMLE

The Mark I converted by fitting a shorter and lighter barrel, modifying the action to accept a stripper clip, and fitting new sights. The letters SMLE stand for Short Magazine, Lee-Enfield. It was introduced in 1903.

Exc.	V.G.	Good	Fair	Poor
225	200	175	150	100

SMLE Mark III currently imported by CIA

Chambered for .303 British and has a 25" barrel with a 10-round magazine. The magazine has a cut off, and the sights are military-styled. The action is modified to accept a stripper clip and automatically eject it when the bolt is closed. This model was introduced in 1907.

Exc.	V.G.	Good	Fair	Poor
150	100	85	60	30

SMLE No. 5 Mark I

Also known as the Jungle Carbine. It is chambered for the .303 British cartridge and has a 20.5" barrel with an attached flash suppressor and a shorter forend and handguard. It is furnished with a rubber buttpad and modified rear sight. This was not a popular weapon with the soldiers who carried it as the recoil was excessive due to the lighter weight.

Exc.	V.G.	Good	Fair	Poor
300	250	225	175	125

No. 3 Mark I P1914 currently imported by CIA

Built on a modified Mauser-type action and was chambered for the .303 British cartridge. It was a secondary-issue arm during WWI and was simpler to mass-produce than the SMLE. These rifles were also produced in the U.S.A. by Remington and Winchester.

Exc.	V.G.	Good	Fair	Poor
170	120	90	65	35

SMLE No. 4 Mark I currently imported by CIA

An improved version that featured a stronger action with an aperture sight and was easier to mass produce. It was issued in 1939 and was used during WWII. There is a cased and scoped Sniper model of this variation.

Exc.	V.G.	Good	Fair	Poor
150	100	85	60	30

Sniper Model Cased

Exc.	V.G.	Good	Fair	Poor
750	650	550	425	350

No .3 Mark I

A single-shot, bolt-action training rifle that is chambered for the .22 rimfire cartridge.

Exc.	V.G.	Good	Fair	Poor
350	325	275	200	150

ENFIELD AMERICAN, INC.
Atlanta, Goergia

MP-45

A blowback-operated, semi-automatic assault pistol chambered for the .45 ACP cartridge. It was offered with a barrel length of 4.5" through 18.5". The long barrel features a shroud. The finish is parkerized, and there were four different magazines available in 10, 20, 30, and 50-round capacities. This firearm was manufactured in 1985 only.

Exc.	V.G.	Good	Fair	Poor
300	275	225	175	125

ENGLISH MILITARY FIREARMS
Enfield, England

Until the establishment of the Royal Armory at Enfield in 1816, the government of England relied solely upon the contract system to obtain small arms for its naval and military forces. Even after the Enfield Armory began is first major production in 1823, the contractors continued to dominate the production of arms for the military. These contractors were concentrated in two major cities, Birmingham and London. Although a number of makers from Birmingham were capable of manufacturing arms, "lock, stock, and barrel," and of assembling them, most of the makers of that city specialized in the making of specific parts, which could be assembled into complete arms on the "factory system" then prevalent in Liege. When the English War Department was the purchaser, the parts were usually delivered to the Tower of London for assembly. Most military arms made in Birmingham accordingly are seldom marked with a single maker's name. Rather they bear the English crown and the name "TOWER" on the lock. Those barrels that passed proof at Birmingham after 1813 were marked with the view and proof marks derived from Ketland's only proofmarks; these consisted of a pair of crowned, crossed scepters, one pair of which had the letter "V" in the lower quarter and the other of which had the letters "B," "C," and "P" respectively in the left, right, and lower quarters. In contrast, the arms manufactured at London were almost always completed by their manufacturers, and bear their names usually upon the lockplates and barrels. The London gunmakers also marked their barrels with a pair of proofmarks, consisting of a crown over a "V" and a crown over an intertwined "G" and "P." Prominent martial arms makers in the London trade through the 1860s included, "BOND," "BARNETT," "BLISSETT," "GREENER," "HOLLIS & SONS," "LONDON ARMORY CO," "KERR," "PARKER, FIELD & SONS," "PRITCHETT," "POTTS & HUNT," "ROBERT WHEELER," "WILSON & CO.," and "YEOMANS." (It should be noted that most of these London makers also manufactured sporting and other trade arms, which will bear similar marks.) During the period of transition from the contract system to the reliance upon the works at Enfield (roughly 1816 through 1867), the arms themselves underwent major transitions, first from flintlock to percussion ignition systems and then from smoothbore to rifled bore, first in large and then in small bore sizes. The major infantry types include:

New Land Pattern musket

Overall length- 58 1/2"; barrel length- 42"; caliber- .75. The mainstay of the British Army during the Napoleonic Wars, this flintlock arm continued, primarily, in service until 1838, with major quantities (5,000 from each) being ordered from Enfield and from the contractors as late as 1823.

Ex.	V.G.	Good	Fair	Poor
2200	2000	1500	850	600

Pattern of 1839 (P1839) musket

Overall length- 55"; barrel length- 39"; caliber- .76. In 1838 the British War Department contracted for the parts for 30,000 new flintlock arms. However, before these arms could be assembled, the War Department adopted the percussion system of ignition and ordered that these arms be made as percussion. Obsolete by 1861, large numbers were purchased by the Southern Confederacy and imported for use in the American Civil War. Arms with firm evidence of Confederate military usage increases the value of the arm considerably.

Ex.	V.G.	Good	Fair	Poor
950	850	500	450	350

Pattern of 1842 (P1842) musket (and rifled musket)

Overall length- 55"; barrel length- 39 1/4"; caliber- .75. The first English-made as percussion musket to be issued to the Line regiments of the British Army, continued in production through the Crimean War. The final production (1851-1855) of 26,400 were made with rifled barrel and a long range rear sight soldered to the barrel, very similar in configuration to that of the P1851 rifle-musket. These rifled versions of the P1842 musket will command a premium.

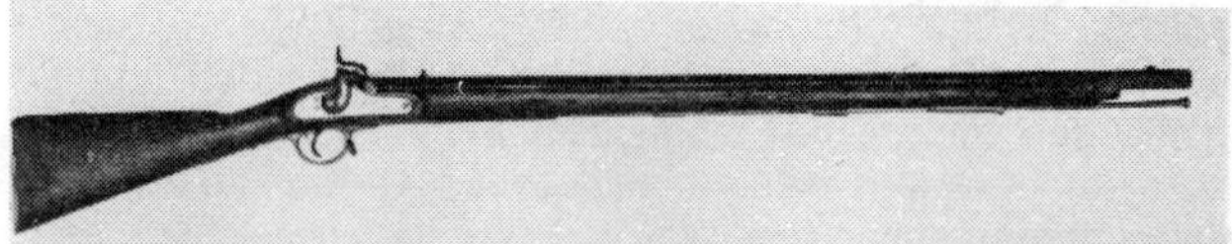

Courtesy Milwaukee Public Museum, Milwaukee, Wisconsin.

Ex.	V.G.	Good	Fair	Poor
900	850	650	450	350

"Brunswick" rifles (first model or P1837) and (second model or P1845)

Overall length- 46 1/2" (P1837), 45 3/4" (P1845); barrel length- 33" (P1837), 30" (P1845); caliber- .704. The "Brunswick" rifle differed from its predecessors (the "Baker rifle") adopted for the English "Rifle Brigade" in having a large bore cut with only two spiraling grooves. These grooves engaged a specially cast ball having a raised belt circumventing it. The first model of the "Brunswick rifle" adopted in 1837 is primarily distinguished by having a "backaction" percussion lock, which continued in production until 1844 despite having been officially changed to the standard "barlock" in 1841. Those made after 1844 bear the standard percussion lock. The value of these rifles is enhanced by virtue of the importation of at least 2,000 (probably first model variants) into the Southern Confederacy during the American Civil War. (It should be noted that Russia also adopted a variant of the "Brunswick" style rifle, having them made in Liege, Belgium (and so marked with Liege proofmarks). These rifles are distinguished by having a distinctive rear sight with an adjustable arcing ladder.)

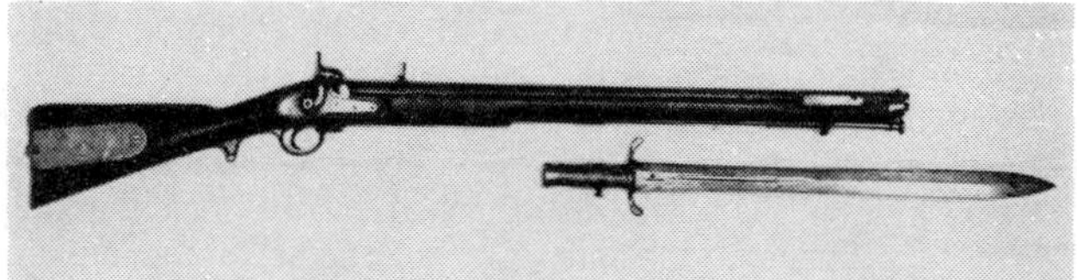

Courtesy Milwaukee Public Museum, Milwaukee, Wisconsin.

Ex.	V.G.	Good	Fair	Poor
1250	1100	900	700	450

Pattern of 1851 (P1851) rifle-musket

Overall length- 55"; barrel length- 39"; caliber- .702. With the success of the "Minie ball" projectile in France, England in 1851 adopted its first production rifle-musket. Externally resembling the P1842 musket, the P1851 is distinguished by the long range rear sight soldered to the barrel and its smaller caliber (.70) rifled bore. Approximately 35,000 were manufactured until 1855, with a substantial number being imported to the United States during the early years of the American Civil War.

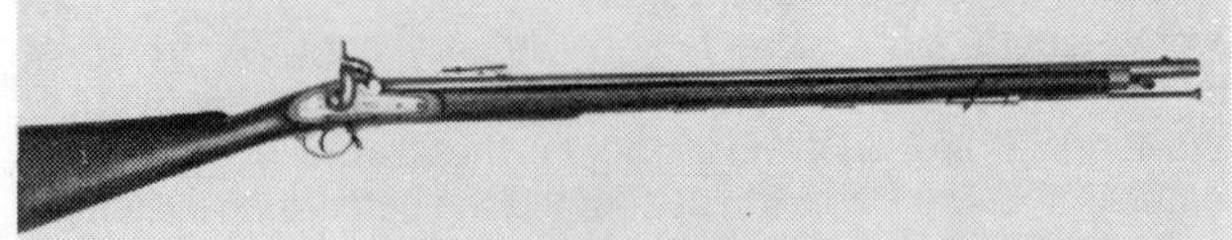

Courtesy Milwaukee Public Museum, Milwaukee, Wisconsin.

Ex.	V.G.	Good	Fair	Poor
1500	1250	1000	700	450

Pattern of 1853 (P1853) rifle-musket (first through fourth types)

Overall length- 55" (54" on fourth type); barrel length- 39"; caliber- .577. The P1853 rifle-musket underwent several changes during the span of its production. The earliest type (first model) was made with clamping bands. Due to problems with the bands slipping, the bands were modified in late 1855 to solid, spring fastened (second model), the upper wider than the other two. However, in 1858 the government reverted to clamping bands continuing production in this style through 1863. Those made at Enfield after 1859 were one inch shorter in the buttstock, but the contractors continued to deliver them in 55 inch length well into the 1860s. The fourth model is distinguished by the "Baddeley patent" clamping barrel bands, wherein the screwheads are recessed into the bands. The third model saw the greatest production, with more than 600,000 being imported into the north and about 300,000 into the south during the American Civil War. P1853 rifle-muskets with early Confederate importation marks on the stock and butt plate will command a premium if authentic.

Courtesy Milwaukee Public Museum, Milwaukee, Wisconsin.

Ex	V.G.	Good	Fair	Poor
1300	950	650	450	350

American made copies of the English P1853 rifle-musket

Three firms during the period from 1855 through 1862 produced copies of the P1853 rifle-musket, Robbins & Lawrence of Windsor, Vermont; Orison Blunt of New York City; and John Moore of New York City. All three types command a premium over the standard imported muskets and may be distinguished as follows:

Robbins & Lawrence P1853 rifle-muskets

During the Crimean War, Robbins & Lawrence received a contract for 25,000 P1853 rifle-muskets of the second model. Due to production delays, the company had delivered only 10,400 when the war ended. Due to the penalties for non-deliveries, Robbins & Lawrence declared bankruptcy. An additional 5,600 arms were made on the firms machinery while in receivership by the "Vermont Arms Co." before the machinery was sold to Sharps and Eli Whitney, Jr. The Robbins & Lawrence-made P1853 rifle-muskets are distinguished by the lock marking "WINDSOR" beneath the date (such as "1856") on the forward part of the lock and by non-English proofmarks on the barrel. Many of these arms saw service in the American Civil War, with Alabama obtaining several hundred in 1861. Arms with confirmed southern usage will bring substantial premiums.

Ex.	V.G.	Good	Fair	Poor
2000	1800	1300	850	600

Orison Blunt P1853 rifle-muskets

At the beginning of the Civil War, Orison Blunt of New York City attempted to produce a copy of the P1853 rifle-musket but with a 40-inch barrel and in .58 caliber. After making several hundred, his proposed contract with the U.S. War Department was declined. Nevertheless, in mid-1862, it is thought that about 1,000 of his rifle-muskets were purchased by the U.S. government and sent to Illinois to arm volunteers. Blunt "Enfields" are distinguished by two distinct markings. While most lockplates are totally unmarked, a few are known with the mark "UNION" on the forward part of the lockplate and an eagle impressed into the rounded tail. More importantly, Blunt barrels bear an oval with the letters "DP/B" near the breech. (Note: Not all P1853 rifle-muskets with 40-inch barrels were made by Blunt; Birmingham and Liege contractors supplied the Spanish government with a 40-inch barrel copy of the P1853 English rifle-musket as well, and some of these were diverted to the American market during the Civil War. These are usually distinguished by the letter "C" in a diamond near the breech of the barrel surrounded by proofmarks.)

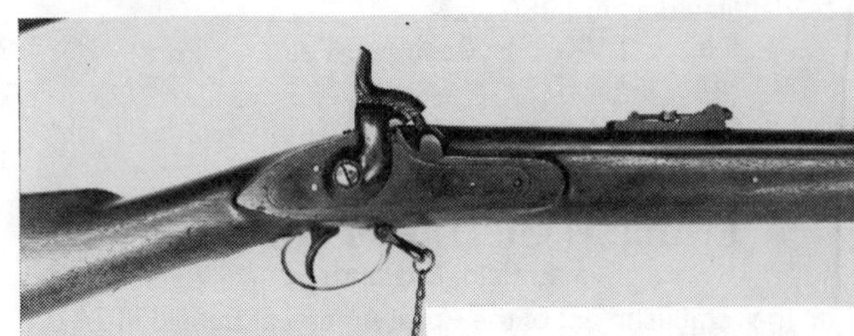

Courtesy Milwaukee Public Museum, Milwaukee, Wisconsin.

Ex.	V.G.	Good	Fair	Poor
1200	1100	1000	750	475

John P. Moore P1853 rifle-muskets

During the American Civil War arms merchant John P. Moore of New York City received a contract for the delivery of 20,000 P1853 rifle-muskets, supposedly to be made in the United States. In fact, most of his contract was made in Birmingham, England, with only 1,080 completely made in the United States. These are distinguished by having an unusual script proofmark on the barrel near the breech instead of the standard Birmingham crossed scepters. These script letters have been interpreted as either "V LB" or "EP I" depending on how they are read. All of Moore's P1853 deliveries bear a distinctive lock marking, consisting of the date forward of the hammer ("1861," "1862," or "1863") and an eagle perched on a shield on the tail. The shield bears the letter "M" in its chief. Moore also delivered 999 short rifles (33" barrels) with the same lock markings. Likewise, all of the barrels on the Moore P1853 rifle-musket contract are serially numbered, either on the forward side near the muzzle or on the side of the bayonet lug/front sight. Because the Moore rifles have been misidentified as a product of a North Carolina arms merchant, they tend to command higher prices than are warranted by their numbers.

Ex.	V.G.	Good	Fair	Poor
1100	1000	850	600	450

"Brazilian Naval Rifle"

Overall length- 48"; barrel length- 32"; caliber- .58. Markings: on lockplate forward of hammer "D (anchor) C"; the same mark stamped in the wood and metal in various places on the rifle; on barrel, same mark and Liege proofmarks (an oval encompassing the letters E/LG/(star). Although neither made for the English government nor in England, this rifle copies so many features of the English P1856 series rifles (see next page) as to be easily mistaken for it. The major differences consist of a longer (3⅜") sight base than the English rifles and a front band/nosecap that also serves as the ramrod funnel. These Liege made rifles were supposedly made for the Brazilian government, but at the beginning of the American Civil War they were diverted to the United States, about 10,000 being imported. To show their new ownership, a brass shield bearing the U.S. coat of arms was screwed into the wrist of the stock.

Courtesy Milwaukee Public Museum, Milwaukee, Wisconsin.

Ex.	V.G.	Good	Fair	Poor
800	725	650	450	275

Patterns of 1856, 1858, 1860, and 1861 (P1856, P1858, P1860, P1861) Sergeant's rifles

Overall length- 49"; barrel length- 33"; caliber- .577. The four variations of the short rifle adopted for sergeants in the British Army in 1856 are relatively minor. The P1856 is mainly distinguished by having a short (112") key forward of the saber bayonet lug on the right side of the barrel. The P1858 rifle moved this lug to the forward band, permitting the extension of the length of the forestock. (A brass furnished rifle also without the key but with the lug on the barrel was also adopted in 1858 for the Navy; it is distinguished by having its rear sling swivel attached to the triggerguard bow instead of the tail of the triggerguard strap.) The P1860 rifle differed from its predecessors by having five groove rifling instead of three groove. The introduction of a new gunpowder in 1861 permitted the resighting of the ladder on the P1861 rifle to 1250 yards instead of the 1100 yards that had been previously used. Significant quantities of these rifles were purchased by both belligerents during the American Civil War; those with proven southern history will command a premium.

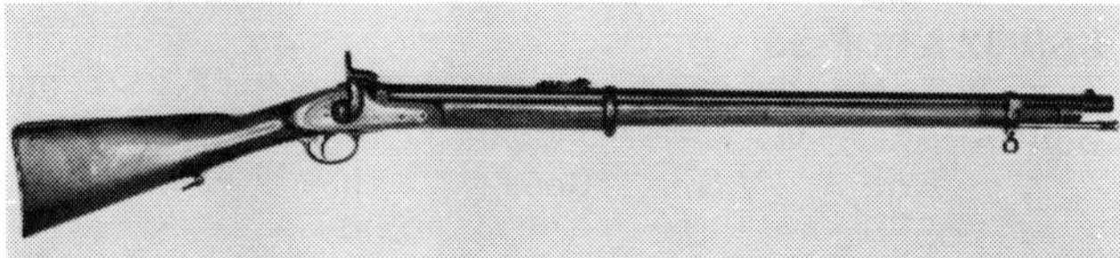

Courtesy Milwaukee Public Museum, Milwaukee, Wisconsin.

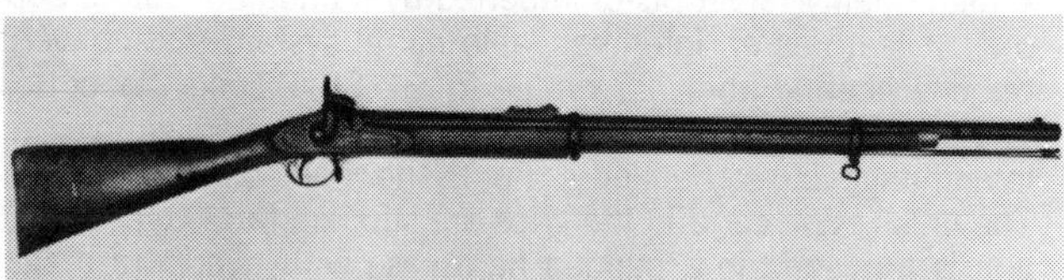

Courtesy Milwaukee Public Museum, Milwaukee, Wisconsin.

Ex.	V.G.	Good	Fair	Poor
1250	1050	800	650	450

Pattern of 1853 (P1853) artillery carbine (first, second, and third models)

Overall length- 40"; barrel length- 24"; caliber- .577. Designed for the gunners of the Royal Artillery, this carbine was meant to be slung over the shoulder and accordingly has a sling swivel on the upper band and upon a lug inset into the buttstock. The first model (adopted in 1853), like the sergeant's rifle has a 1/2" key forward of the saber bayonet lug on the right side of the barrel; in addition to other minor improvements, this key was eliminated in the second model, adopted in 1858. In 1861, a third model was adopted, having five groove rifling and improved rear sight. Approximately 1000 of the latter type saw service in the American Civil War. Carbines with Confederate stock and buttplate markings will command a premium.

Courtesy Milwaukee Public Museum, Milwaukee, Wisconsin.

Ex.	V.G.	Good	Fair	Poor
1100	950	700	550	400

Patterns of 1856 (P1856) and Pattern of 1861 (P1861) cavalry carbines

Overall length- 37" (P1856), 36-1/2" (P1861) barrel length- 21"; caliber- .577. Due to inadequacies in the various breechloading carbines tried by the British mounted service, in 1856 the War Department adopted a muzzleloading carbine incorporating the features of the P1853 series small arms. The earlier version had three groove rifling and a small rear sight with two leaves. In 1861 this was replaced by a larger ladder sight and five groove rifling adopted. More than 6,000 P1856 carbines were imported by the Southern Confederacy during the Civil War to make up for the inadequate supply of carbines. Carbines with verifiable Southern history will command a premium.

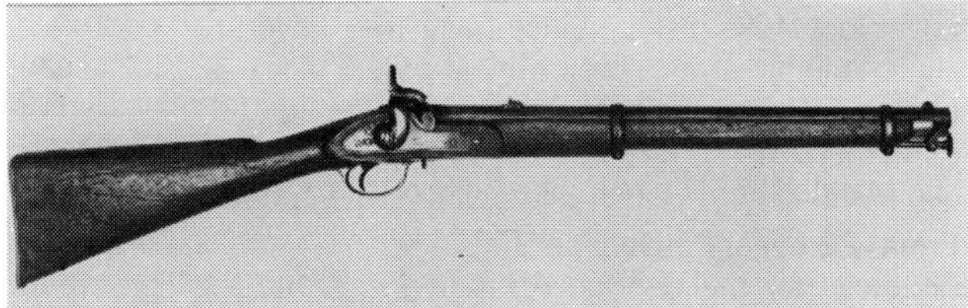

Courtesy Milwaukee Public Museum, Milwaukee, Wisconsin.

Ex.	V.G.	Good	Fair	Poor
975	850	725	600	375

ERA

Brazil

Era Double Barrel Shotgun

An inexpensive shotgun chambered for 12 and 20 gauge, as well as .410. It was offered with 26", 28", or 30" barrels with various choke combinations. It has double triggers and extractors, with a checkered hardwood pistol-grip stock. This gun is also available as a Quail model with a 20" barrel and as a Riot model with an 18" barrel. These two models are not offered in .410 bore.

Exc.	V.G.	Good	Fair	Poor
175	150	125	100	75

Era Over/Under Shotgun

Chambered for 12 or 20 gauge, with 28" ventilated-rib barrels that were choked full and modified. It is a boxlock with double triggers, extractors, and a hardwood stock. It was also offered in a trap model and a skeet model chambered for 12 gauge only and appropriately choked. These latter two models would be worth a 10 percent premium over the values shown.

Exc.	V.G.	Good	Fair	Poor
300	275	250	200	150

ERICHSON, G.

Houston, Texas

Erichson Pocket Pistol

A very close copy of the Philadelphia-style Henry Deringer. It is chambered for .45-caliber percussion and has a 3.25" barrel. The mountings are German silver and not engraved; the stock is walnut. The hammer is deeply fluted; and the forend, carved. The barrel is marked "G.Erichson / Houston, Texas." The number produced is unknown, but examples are scarce. They were manufactured in the 1850s and 1860s.

Exc.	V.G.	Good	Fair	Poor
4000	3000	2000	1500	1000

ERMA WERKE WAFFENFABRIK

Erfurt, Germany
Post-War
Dachau, Germany

Known primarily as a manufacturer of submachine guns, but they are also in the handgun and rifle business. In 1933 they answered the German Army's need for an inexpensive practice weapon by producing a .22 rimfire conversion unit for the Luger pistol. This was marketed commercially and was available for many years. The success of this unit led the company to produce other inexpensive target and plinking pistols. After the war they were reorganized in the western sector and resumed submachine gun production. In 1964 they returned to the sporting firearms business with the introduction of their .22 rimfire Luger-look-alike pistol. Since then, they have produced many like-quality firearms. They were imported by Excam of Hialeah, Florida. This association is now terminated, and they are currently imported by Beeman Precision in Santa Rosa, California, and Mandell Shooting Supplies in Scottsdale, Arizona.

Erma .22 Luger Conversion Unit

Produced for the German Army in 1933 and then became a successful commercial item. It would turn a standard 9mm or 7.65mm Luger into an inexpensive-to-shoot .22 rimfire. The unit consists of a barrel insert, a breech block, and toggle unit with its own lightened recoil spring, and a .22 magazine. This unit was furnished with a wooden box. There were many different sized units to fit various caliber and barrel-length Lugers, but all used the same parts and concept. These units have become very desirable to Luger collectors.

Exc.	V.G.	Good	Fair	Poor
500	425	350	275	200

.22 Target Pistol (Old Model)

An inexpensive, blowback-operated, semi-automatic pistol chambered for the .22 rimfire cartridge. This model has a 4" barrel and an open-topped slide. The frame is made from a cast zinc alloy, and there is an external hammer. There are adjustable sights, and balance weights were available. This pistol was manufactured in 1936.

Exc.	V.G.	Good	Fair	Poor
250	225	175	125	100

.22 Target Pistol (New Model)

An improved version of the Old Model, that features a new grip angle and a magazine and takedown device which is like that of the Luger. There were interchangeable barrels and three basic models--the "Sport," "Hunter," and the "Master." The difference was the length of the barrels --4", 5", and 6", respectively. These pistols were manufactured between 1937 and 1940, when they were discontinued due to Erma's involvement in the war effort.

Exc.	V.G.	Good	Fair	Poor
275	250	200	150	125

KGP-Series

Made to resemble the Luger quite closely. They utilized the mechanical features of the .22 conversion unit and developed a pistol around it. There are many different versions of this pistol chambered for .22 rimfire, .32 ACP, and .380 ACP. The original designation was the KGP-68; but the Gun Control Act of 1968 required that a magazine safety be added, and the model was redesignated the KGP-68A. The last designations for the three calibers are KGP-22, KGP-32, and KGP-38. These pistols were manufactured between 1964 and 1986, and their values are as follows.

KGP-68

A 4" barrel and is chambered for the .32 ACP and the .380 ACP cartridges. It has a 6-shot magazine and an anodized alloy receiver. This model is also known as the Beeman MP-08.

Exc.	V.G.	Good	Fair	Poor
175	150	125	100	75

KGP-69

A .22 rimfire version of this series, with an 8-shot magazine capacity. It is also known as the Beeman P-08.

Exc.	V.G.	Good	Fair	Poor
175	150	125	100	75

ET-22 Luger Carbine

A rare firearm. According to some estimates only 375 were produced. It features a 11.75" barrel and is chambered for the .22 rimfire cartridge. It has an artillery Luger-type rear sight and checkered walnut grips, with a smooth walnut forend. The pistol was furnished with a red felt lined, black leatherette case.

Exc.	V.G.	Good	Fair	Poor
400	350	300	200	150

KGP-22

The later version of the KGP-69 chambered for .22 rimfire.

Exc.	V.G.	Good	Fair	Poor
350	300	250	200	125

KGP-32 & KGP-38

These two designations are the later versions of the KGP-68 and 68A.

Exc.	V.G.	Good	Fair	Poor
350	300	250	200	125

ESP 85A

A high quality target pistol imported by Mandall Shooting Supply. It features an interchangable barrel system that converts the chambering from .22 rimfire to .32 S&W Long Wadcutter. The barrels are both 6" in length, and there are adjustable and interchangeable sights and a 5-or 8-shot detachable magazine. The finish is blued, and the grips are stippled target types. The gun is furnished in a padded hard case with two extra magazines and takedown tools. This unit was introduced in 1989.

NIB	Exc.	V.G.	Good	Fair	Poor
1100	1000	850	700	550	450

RX-22

A .22 rimfire copy of the Walther PPK. It has a 3.25" barrel, an 8-shot detachable magazine, and a blued finish with checkered black plastic grips. It was assembled in the U.S.A. from parts made in West Germany. It was discontinued in 1986.

Exc.	V.G.	Good	Fair	Poor
200	175	150	125	100

Revolvers

ER-772 Match

A target revolver chambered for the .22 rimfire and has a 6" shrouded barrel with a solid rib. The swing-out cylinder holds 6 shots, and the sights are adjustable. The finish is blued, with stippled target grips. This model was introduced in 1989.

NIB	Exc.	V.G.	Good	Fair	Poor
500	450	400	350	250	200

ER-773 Match

Similar to the ER-772 except that it is chambered for the .32 S&W long cartridge.

NIB	Exc.	V.G.	Good	Fair	Poor
500	450	400	350	250	200

ER-777

Basically a similar revolver to the ER-773 except that it has a 4.5" or 5" barrel and is chambered for the .357 Magnum cartridge. The revolver is larger and has standard sport grips. This model was also introduced in 1989.

NIB	Exc.	V.G.	Good	Fair	Poor
500	450	400	350	250	200

Rifles

EMI .22

A semi-automatic .22 rimfire version of the M1 Carbine. It has an 18" barrel and a 15-round magazine. It was manufactured between 1966 and 1976.

Exc.	V.G.	Good	Fair	Poor
200	175	150	125	100

EG-72, EG-722

A 15-shot slide action carbine chambered for .22 rimfire, with a 18.5" barrel and open sights. The finish is blued, and it was manufactured between 1970 and 1985.

Exc.	V.G.	Good	Fair	Poor
135	110	100	75	50

EG-712, EG-73

A lever copy of the Winchester 94 Carbine chambered for the .22 rimfire or the .22 rimfire Magnum (EG-73). It has an 18.5" barrel and holds 15 shots in a tubular magazine. It was manufactured between 1973 and 1985.

Exc.	V.G.	Good	Fair	Poor
200	175	150	125	100

ERQUIAGA

Eibar, Spain

Another Spanish company that commenced business during WWI as a subcontractor on the French "Ruby" contract. They manufactured the usual poor-quality, 7.65mm Eibar-type pistol.

Fiel

The tradename found on the Ruby subcontract pistol described above. It is marked "Erquiaga y Cia Eibar Cal. 7.65 Fiel."

Exc.	V.G.	Good	Fair	Poor
175	150	125	100	75

Fiel 6.35

After the end of WWI, a 1906 Browning copy was made. It is chambered for the 6.35mm cartridge. The markings are "Automatic Pistol 6.35 Fiel No.1." Later models had "EMC" molded into the grip.

Exc.	V.G.	Good	Fair	Poor
150	125	100	75	50

Marte

Another poor-quality "Eibar"-type pistol that is chambered for the 6.35mm and that was made in the early 1920s.

Exc.	V.G.	Good	Fair	Poor
150	125	100	75	50

ERRASTI, A.

Eibar, Spain

Errasti manufactured a variety of inexpensive yet serviceable pistols from the early 1900s until the Spanish Civil War.

Velo-Dog

Usual cheap solid frame folding trigger revolvers one associates with the model designation. They were chambered in 5.5mm and 6.35mm and were made in the early 1900s.

Exc.	V.G.	Good	Fair	Poor
150	125	100	75	50

M1889

In 1915-1916 Errasti produced the 10.4mm Italian army service revolver. The quality was reasonably good. They were marked "Errasti Eiber" on the right side of the frame.

Exc.	V.G.	Good	Fair	Poor
200	175	150	100	75

Errasti

Two "Eibar" type Browning copies were made under this tradename. One was chambered for the 6.35mm, the other the 7.65mm. They were both marked "Automatic Pistol Errasti."

Exc.	V.G.	Good	Fair	Poor
150	125	100	75	50

Errasti Oscillante

Manufactured in the 1920s, these revolvers were copied from the Smith & Wesson Military & Police design. They were chambered for the .32, .38, and .44 calibers with the .38 being the most frequently encountered.

Exc.	V.G.	Good	Fair	Poor
150	125	100	75	50

Dreadnaught, Goliath and Smith Americano

These three trade-names were found on a group of poor quality nickle-plated revolvers. They were made from 1905 through 1920 and were obvious copies of the Iver Johnson design. They had break-open actions, ribbed barrel, and were chambered for .32, .38, and .44 calibers. They are scarce today, as most have long since fallen apart.

Exc.	V.G.	Good	Fair	Poor
150	125	100	75	50

ESCODIN, M.

Eibar, Spain

This company made a Smith & Wesson revolver copy from 1924 through 1931. It is chambered for the .32 and the .38 Special. The only marking is a coat of arms stamped on the left side of the frame.

Exc.	V.G.	Good	Fair	Poor
150	125	100	75	50

ESPIRIN, HERMANOS

Eibar, Spain

Euskaro

This very poor-quality, often unsafe revolver was manufactured from 1906 until WWI. They are copies of the Iver Johnson-design break-open actions, chambered for .32, .38, and .44. This product epitomizes the worst Eibar had to offer during the pre-civil war era.

Exc.	V.G.	Good	Fair	Poor
125	100	75	50	25

EUROARMS OF AMERICA

Winchester, Virginia

An importer of black powder muzzle-loading firearms, primarily replicas of early American weapons.

Revolvers

1851 Navy

A replica of the Colt revolver chambered for .36 or .44 caliber percussion. It has a squareback, silver-plated triggerguard and a 7.5" barrel.

NIB	Exc.	V.G.	Good	Fair	Poor
135	125	110	80	65	45

1851 Navy Police Model

Chambered for .36 caliber with a 5-shot, fluted cylinder and a 5.5" barrel.

NIB	Exc.	V.G.	Good	Fair	Poor
135	125	110	80	65	45

1851 Navy Sheriff's Model

A 5" barrelled version of the Navy Model.

NIB	Exc.	V.G.	Good	Fair	Poor
110	100	80	60	50	35

1851 "Schneider & Glassick" Navy

A replica of the Confederate revolver chambered for .36 or .44 caliber percussion.

NIB	Exc.	V.G.	Good	Fair	Poor
110	100	80	60	50	35

1851 "Griswold & Gunnison" Navy

A replica of this Confederate revolver chambered for .36 or .44 caliber percussion.

NIB	Exc.	V.G.	Good	Fair	Poor
110	90	75	60	40	25

1862 Police

A replica of the Colt Model 1862 chambered for .36 caliber percussion, with a 7.5" barrel and a steel frame.

NIB	Exc.	V.G.	Good	Fair	Poor
150	125	110	90	65	45

1860 Army

A replica of the Colt revolver chambered for .44 caliber percussion. It was offered with a 5" or 8" barrel.

NIB	Exc.	V.G.	Good	Fair	Poor
150	125	100	75	50	30

1861 Navy

A replica of the Colt revolver chambered for .36 caliber percussion.

NIB	Exc.	V.G.	Good	Fair	Poor
160	135	110	80	60	40

1858 Remington Army or Navy

Replicas of the Remington percussion revolvers chambered for .26 or .44 caliber.

NIB	Exc.	V.G.	Good	Fair	Poor
175	150	125	100	75	50

Rifles

The following rifles are modern replicas of early American and British firearms. They are of good quality and are quite serviceable. There is little collector interest, and we list them along with their values.

Cook & Brother Carbine

NIB	Exc.	V.G.	Good	Fair	Poor
375	325	250	100	150	100

1863 J.P. Murray

NIB	Exc.	V.G.	Good	Fair	Poor
360	310	225	175	125	100

1853 Enfield Rifled Musket

NIB	Exc.	V.G.	Good	Fair	Poor
400	350	300	250	175	125

1858 Enfield Rifled Musket

NIB	Exc.	V.G.	Good	Fair	Poor
375	325	250	200	150	100

1861 Enfield Musketoon

NIB	Exc.	V.G.	Good	Fair	Poor
350	300	225	175	125	90

1803 Harper's Ferry

NIB	Exc.	V.G.	Good	Fair	Poor
500	425	350	300	225	150

1841 Mississippi Rifle

NIB	Exc.	V.G.	Good	Fair	Poor
475	400	325	275	200	125

Pennsylvania Rifle

NIB	Exc.	V.G.	Good	Fair	Poor
300	250	225	200	150	100

Hawken Rifle

NIB	Exc.	V.G.	Good	Fair	Poor
300	250	200	150	100	80

Cape Gun

NIB	Exc.	V.G.	Good	Fair	Poor
400	350	275	225	175	125

Buffalo Carbine

NIB	Exc.	V.G.	Good	Fair	Poor
400	350	300	250	175	100

1862 Remington Rifle

NIB	Exc.	V.G.	Good	Fair	Poor
300	250	225	200	125	60

Zouave Rifle

NIB	Exc.	V.G.	Good	Fair	Poor
325	275	225	175	125	90

Shotguns

Duck Gun

A single-barrelled percussion fowling piece chambered for 8, 10, or 12 gauge. It has a 33" smooth-bore barrel and a case-colored hammer and lock. The stock is walnut with brass mountings. This model was introduced in 1989.

NIB	Exc.	V.G.	Good	Fair	Poor
400	350	300	250	175	100

Double Barrel Shotgun

A side-by-side, chambered for 12 gauge percussion. It has 28" barrels with engraved locks and a walnut stock.

NIB	Exc.	V.G.	Good	Fair	Poor
425	375	325	275	200	125

EUROPEAN AMERICAN ARMORY CORP.

Importers
Hialeah, Florida

Witness Pistols

These quality pistols are produced by Tanfoglio, an Italian firm, and imported into the U.S. by European American Armory. These handguns are based on the CZ design and offer many features that are sought after by the shooter such as: competition sights, double-action/single-action trigger system, and internal firing pin lock. The firm was founded by Giuseppe Tanfoglio after WWII. He formed a partnership with Antonio Sabbati and began to manufacture small caliber pistols. During the 1960s the firm also produced derringers and Colt SAA copies. In 1980 the Tanfoglio company decided to enter the service pistol market and copied the respected Czech CZ design. The Tanfoglio company currently produces the P9 series for Springfield Armory and the Desert Eagle line for IMI. In 1993 EAA converted from two frame sizes to one and redesigned the trigger guard and beavertail. This redesigned frame enables all of the different caliber slide assemblies to be interchangeable with one frame This new configuration will begin to appear in mid 1993. The buyer should be aware that the EAA Custom Shop offers a wide variety of accessories for its pistols, such as compensators, hammers, ported barrels, grips, etc., that will effect price.

EAA Witness Standard

Available in 9mm, .41AE, 40S&W, and .45 ACP with 4.5" barrel. Magazine capacity: 9mm-16 rounds, .41AE-11 rounds, .40S&W-12 rounds, .45 ACP-10 rounds. Offered in blue, chrome, two-tone, and stainless steel. Weighs approximately 33 oz.

Old Configuration

NIB	Exc.	V.G.	Good	Fair	Poor
385	325	275	225	175	125

New Configuration

NIB	Exc.	V.G.	Good	Fair	Poor
385	325	275	225	175	125

NOTE: For Chrome, two-tone, and stainless steel add 5% to above prices. Pistols chambered for .45ACP add 10%.

EAA Witness Subcompact

Offered in the same calibers as the standard model but fitted with a 3.66" barrel and shorter grip. Magazine capacity: 9mm-13 rounds, .41AE-9 rounds, .40S&W-9 rounds, .45 ACP-8 rounds. Weighs about 30 oz.. Offered in blue, chrome, two-tone, and stainless steel.

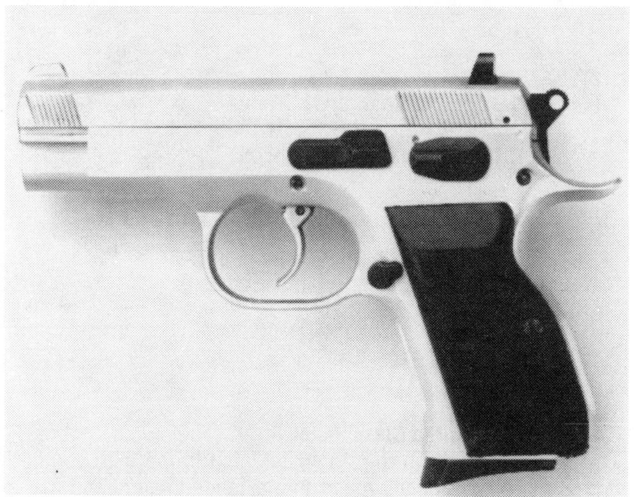

Old Configuration

NIB	Exc.	V.G.	Good	Fair	Poor
385	325	275	225	175	125

New Configuration

NIB	Exc.	V.G.	Good	Fair	Poor
385	325	275	225	175	125

NOTE: For Chrome, two-tone, and stainless steel add 5% to above prices. Pistols chambered for .45ACP add 10%.

EAA Witness Carry Comp

This model is offered in 9mm, .41AE, .40S&W, and .45 ACP. It features a 1" steel compensator. The barrel is 4.1" long. Overall length is the same as the standard model as is magazine capacity. Offered in blue or blue chrome finish. Weighs 34 oz.

Old Configuration

NIB	Exc.	V.G.	Good	Fair	Poor
500	450	375	325	250	175

New Configuration

NIB	Exc.	V.G.	Good	Fair	Poor
500	450	375	325	250	175

NOTE: For .45 ACP add 15% to above prices.

EAA Witness Combo 9/40

This model offers a 9mm conversion kit, a .40S&W conversion kit. These kit consist of a slide, barrel, recoil spring and guide, and magazine. Available in standard or subcompact size in blue, chrome,or two-tone finish.

NIB	Exc.	V.G.	Good	Fair	Poor
550	475	400	350	275	175

NOTE: For Chrome or two-tone finish add 5% to above prices.

EAA Witness Sport L/S

This model features a longer slide for its 4.75" barrel. Offered in 9mm, .41 AE, .40S&W, and .45 ACP. Magazine capacity: 9mm-19 rounds, .41AE-13 rounds, .40S&W-14 rounds, and .45 ACP-11 rounds. This model is also fitted with adjustable rear sight and extended safety. Available in two-tone finish. Weighs about 34.5 oz. A ported barrel is offered as an option.

Old Configuration

NIB	Exc.	V.G.	Good	Fair	Poor
625	550	500	400	300	200

New Configuration

NIB	Exc.	V.G.	Good	Fair	Poor
625	550	500	400	300	200

NOTE: For 45 ACP add 10% to prices.

EAA Witness Sport

This model is built on the standard Witness frame with the addition of an adjustable rear sight and extended safety. Offered in 9mm, .41AE, .40S&W, .45 ACP in standard model magazine capacity. Weighs 33 oz. Available in two-tone finish.

Old Configuration

NIB	Exc.	V.G.	Good	Fair	Poor
550	475	400	300	200	150

New Configuration

NIB	Exc.	V.G.	Good	Fair	Poor
550	475	400	300	200	150

NOTE: For .45 ACP add 10% to above prices.

EAA Witness Silver Team Match

This is designed as a competition pistol. It is fitted with a 5.25" barrel. It has the following features: dual chamber compensator, single action trigger, extended safety, competition hammer, paddle magazine release, checkered walnut grips, and adjustable rear sight or drilled and tapped for scope mount. Offered in 9mm-19 rds., .40S&W-14 rds., .41AE-13 rds., .45ACp-11 rds., and 9x21. Finish is blue and weight is approximately 34 oz.

NIB	Exc.	V.G.	Good	Fair	Poor
900	800	700	600	450	300

EAA Witness Gold Team Match

This is a full race competition pistol with tripe chamber compensator, beavertail grip safety, beveled magazine well, adjustable rear sight or drilled and tapped for scope mount, extended safety and magazine release, competition hammer, square trigger guard, checkered front and back strap, competition grips, and hard chrome finish. Same barrel length, magazine capacity, and calibers as the Silver Team Match. Weighs 38 oz.

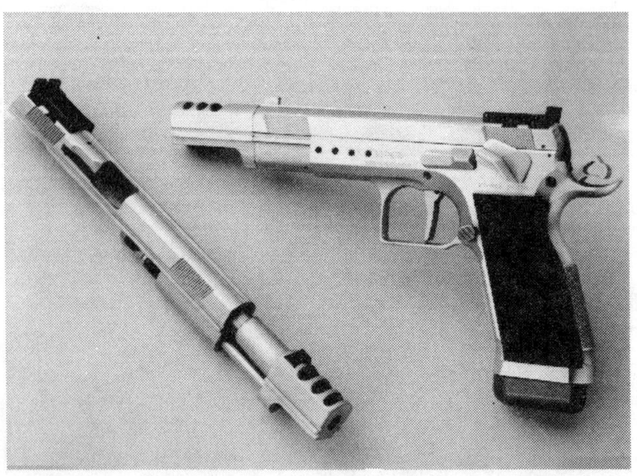

NIB	Exc.	V.G.	Good	Fair	Poor
1600	1250	900	750	600	400

EAA Witness Limited Class Pistol

This model is built on the Witness Match frame with competition grips, high capacity magazine, extended safety and magazine release, single action trigger, long slide with adjustable rear sight, and match grade barrel. Offered in 9mm, .40S&W, .38 Super, and .45 ACP with blue finish.

NIB	Exc.	V.G.	Good	Fair	Poor
900	775	650	550	400	300

EAA Witness Multi Class Pistol Package

This package consist of one Witness Limited Class pistol with a complete unlimited class top half. The top half is made up of a standard length slide with super sight, recoil guide and spring, match grade competition barrel(threaded for compensator), and a dual chamber compensator. Available in 9mm, .40S&W, 9x21, .45 ACP, 9x23,, and .38 Super. Finish is blue.

NIB	Exc.	V.G.	Good	Fair	Poor
1500	1200	850	600	300	200

NOTE: Any of the above EAA Witness pistol can be supplied with double-action only triggers at no additional charge.

OTHER EAA IMPORTED FIREARMS

EAA Big Bore Bounty Hunter

This model is a single action revolver made in Germany. It features 3 position hammer, forged barrel, and walnut grips. Offered in .357 Mag., .45 Long Colt, and .44 Mag. in 4.5", 5.5", or 7.5" barrel lengths. Choice of finish include blue or case colored frame, chrome, gold, or blue and gold.

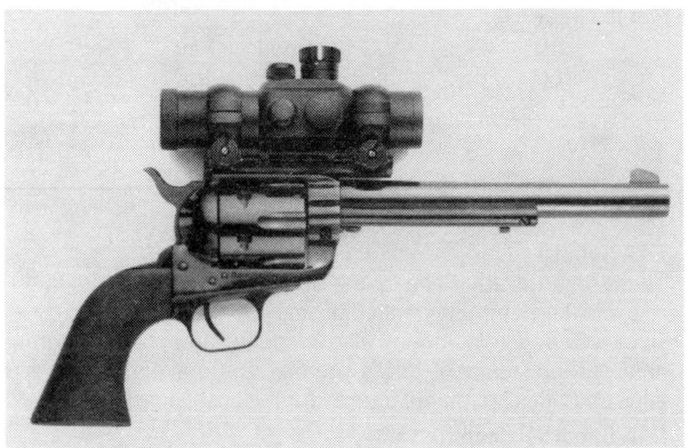

NIB	Exc.	V.G.	Good	Fair	Poor
300	225	175	150	125	100

NOTE: For Chrome, gold, or blue and gold finish add 20%.

EAA Small Bore Bounty Hunter

This is a single action .22 caliber revolver. It has wood grips and is available in blue or blue and brass finish. Barrel lengths are 4.75", 6", and 9". It is chambered for .22 Long Rifle or .22 Winchester Rimfire Magnum.

NIB	Exc.	V.G.	Good	Fair	Poor
150	125	100	90	70	60

EAA F.A.B. 92 Pistol

This model is a semi-automatic pistol similar to the Witness, but fitted with a hammer drop safety and slide mounted safety, that is both a double-action or single-action. It is available in either a full size (33 oz) or compact size(30 oz). The full size version has a 4.5" barrel while the compact is fitted with a 3.66" barrel. Offered in 9mm or .40S&W in blue, two-tone, or chrome finish.

NIB	Exc.	V.G.	Good	Fair	Poor
350	275	225	175	125	100

EAA European Standard Pistol

This is a single-action semi-automatic pistol with external hammer, slide grip serrations, wood grips, and single column magazine. The barrels length is 3.2" and overall length is 6.5". Chambered for .22 Long Rifle, 380 ACP, .32 ACP. The magazine capacity is 10 rounds for the .22 LR, 7 rounds for .380, and 7 rounds for .32. Offered in blue, blue/chrome, chrome, blue/gold. Weighs 26 oz.

NIB	Exc.	V.G.	Good	Fair	Poor
165	135	110	95	75	50

EAA European Target Pistol

This model features adjustable rear sight, external hammer, single action trigger, walnut target grips, and adjustable weight system. Chambered for .22 Long Rifle. Offered in blue finish and weighs 40 oz.

NIB	Exc.	V.G.	Good	Fair	Poor
325	275	225	175	150	100

EAA Windicator Standard Grade

This German built model is a double action revolver chambered for the .22 Long Rifle, .22 Winchester Rimfire Magnum, .32 H&R, and .38 Special. It is offered in 2", 4", and 6" barrel lengths. The cylinder capacity for the .22 LR/.22WRM is 8 rds., .32 H&R is 7 rds., and the .38 Special is 6 rds. The cylinder is unfluted. Finish is blue.

NIB	Exc.	V.G.	Good	Fair	Poor
185	140	120	95	75	60

EAA Windicator Basic Grade

This model is chambered for the .38 Special or the .357 Magnum with 2" barrel. The fluted cylinder holds 6 rounds. Finish is blue.

NIB	Exc.	V.G.	Good	Fair	Poor
175	130	110	85	65	50

EAA Windicator Tactical Grade

This model is similar in appearance to the standard grade but is chambered for the .38 Special with 2" or 4" barrel. The 4" barrel has an integral compensator. Finish is blue.

2" Barrel

NIB	Exc.	V.G.	Good	Fair	Poor
190	150	125	100	80	60

4" Barrel

NIB	Exc.	V.G.	Good	Fair	Poor
250	200	150	125	100	75

EAA Windicator Target Grade

This model has the following special features: adjustable trigger pull, walnut grips, adjustable rear sight, drilled and tapped for scope mount, target hammer, adjustable trigger stop. Fitted with 6" target barrel. Chambered for .22LR, .38 Special, .357 Mag. Blue finish.

NIB	Exc.	V.G.	Good	Fair	Poor
350	275	225	200	150	100

EAA PM2 Shotgun

This is a pump action 12 gauge shotgun with 6-round box magazine. Barrel length is 20" and finish is either blue or Chrome. Stock is black composite. Weight is 6.8 lb. This model was discontinued in 1993.

NIB	Exc.	V.G.	Good	Fair	Poor
450	350	300	250	200	150

NOTE: Add $100 for optional night sights.

EAA HW 60 Rifle

This is German made target rifle is chambered for the .22 Long Rifle. It features a adjustable trigger and other target and match grade components. The barrel length is 26.8", the stock is stippled walnut, and the finish is blue. Weighs approximately 10.8 lb.

Target Grade

NIB	Exc.	V.G.	Good	Fair	Poor
670	575	500	400	300	200

Match Grade

NIB	Exc.	V.G.	Good	Fair	Poor
760	650	550	450	350	250

EAA Sabatti

These firearms are made by the Sabatti firm in Gardone, Italy. It is a old line company, having been in the firearms business since 1674. The company also produces and supplies component parts to many of Italy's premier gun makers. These shotguns and rifles are manufactured for the cost conscience buyer.

EAA Sabatti Falcon

This is a field grade Over/Under shotgun with checkered walnut stock with pistol grip, boxlock action, double triggers, and extractors. Offered in 12 or 20 gauge with 3" chambers. Also available in 28 gauge and .410 bore with 26" or 28" barrels. Barrel lengths are available in 26", 28", or 30". Chokes are fixed.

NIB	Exc.	V.G.	Good	Fair	Poor
575	425	400	350	300	250

28/.410

NIB	Exc.	V.G.	Good	Fair	Poor
625	480	425	375	325	275

EAA Sporting Clay Basic

This model features a single selective trigger, extractors, checkered walnut stock with pistol grip, extra wide rib, and blued receiver with scroll engraving. Offered in 12 gauge only with 28" fixed choke barrel.

NIB	Exc.	V.G.	Good	Fair	Poor
350	275	250	200	150	100

EAA Sporting Clay Pro

This model is similar to the basic sporting clay model with the addition of a select walnut stock, screw in choke tubes, automatic ejectors, recoil pad. Comes with hard shell case.

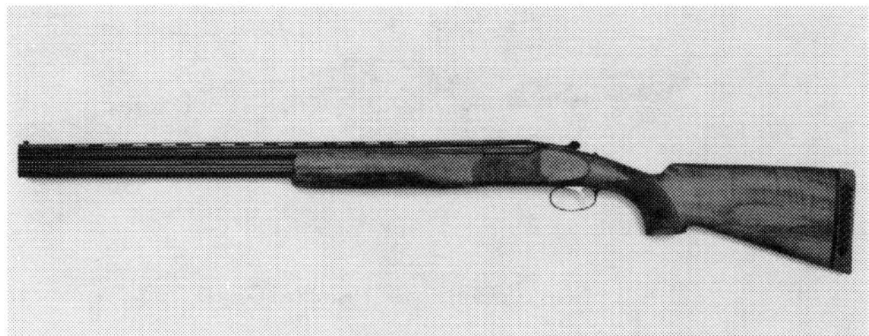

NIB	Exc.	V.G.	Good	Fair	Poor
950	720	650	550	450	300

EAA Sporting Clay Pro Gold

Same as above but with gold inlay receiver.

NIB	Exc.	V.G.	Good	Fair	Poor
1000	750	650	550	450	300

EAA Saba

This model is a side by side shotgun that features an engraved silver box lock receiver, double or single triggers, selective ejectors, solid raied matted rib, and select European walnut checkered stock. Offered in 12, 20, and 28 gauge as well as .410 bore. Barrel length are 26" or 28" with fixed chokes.

NIB	Exc.	V.G.	Good	Fair	Poor
775	600	500	400	300	250

EAA Rover 870

This is a high quality bolt action rifle. The walnut stock is checkered with rubber recoil pad. Adjustable rear sight and receiver is drilled and tapped for scope mount. Barrel length is 22". Chambered for the following cartridges: .22-250, .243, .25-06, .270, .308, .30-06, 7mm Rem. Mag., .300 and .338 Win. Mag.

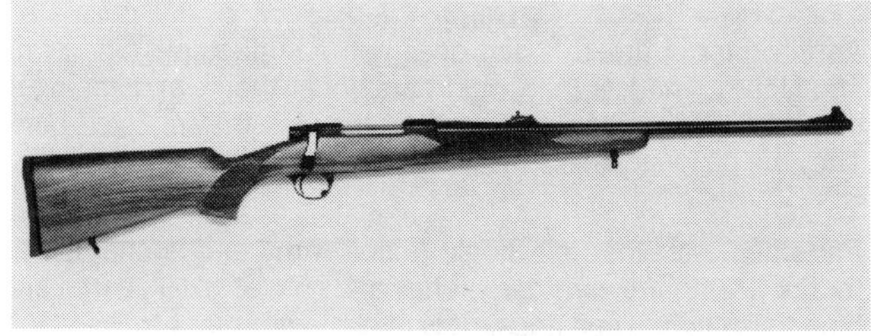

NIB	Exc.	V.G.	Good	Fair	Poor
560	425	375	300	200	125

EAA SP 1822

This Sabatti rifle is chambered for the .22 Long Rifle. It is a semi-automatic carbine with a two piece stock and adjustable stock.

NIB	Exc.	V.G.	Good	Fair	Poor
200	150	125	100	85	60

EAA SP 1822H

This a heavy barrel version of the above model without sights. The receiver is fitted with scope mount base.

NIB	Exc.	V.G.	Good	Fair	Poor
200	150	125	100	85	60

EAA SP 1822TH

This variation also has a heavy barrel without sights but with base mounts. A one piece Bell and Carlson thumb hole stock is the feature of this model.

NIB	Exc.	V.G.	Good	Fair	Poor
350	260	225	175	125	90

EAA Benelli Silhouette Pistol

This is a specialized competition pistol with a semi-automatic action. The stocks are match type walnut with stippling. The palm shelf is adjustable.The barrel is 4.3" long. Fully adjustable sights. It is chambered for the .22 Long Rifle, .22 Short, and the .32WC. Supplied with loading tool and cleaning rod. The .22 Caliber version weighs 38.5 oz. Overall length is 11.7".

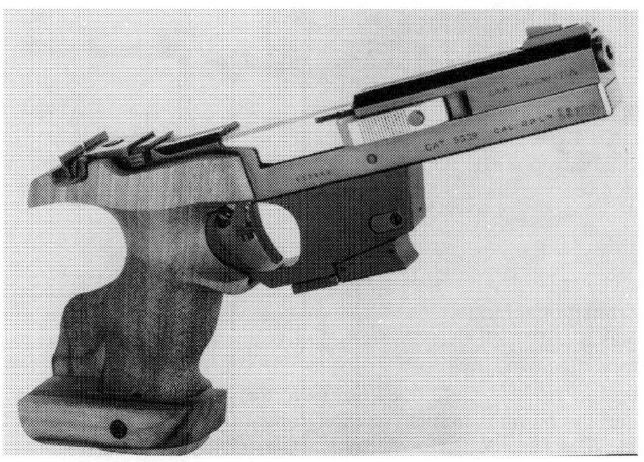

NIB	Exc.	V.G.	Good	Fair	Poor
1850	1250	950	750	600	400

EAA Astra Pistol

see Astra

EVANS REPEATING RIFLE CO.

Mechanic Falls, Maine

Lever Action Rifle

This rifle is totally unique for a number of reasons. It holds the most rounds of any repeating rifle that did not have a detachable magazine, with capacities up to 38 rounds on some models. This rifle was chambered for its own cartridge—the .44 Evans—of which there were two versions: a 1" cartridge in the "Old Model" and the "Transition Model" and a 1.5" cartridge in the "New Model." The finish on these rifles is blued, with nickle-plated levers and buttplates noted on some examples. The stocks are walnut. There were approximately 12,250 of all models manufactured between 1873 and 1879.

Old Model

This variation is chambered for the 1" .44 Evans cartridge and has a buttstock that covers only the top half of the revolving 34-shot magazine located in the butt of the rifle. The butt plate appears as if it is reversed, and the markings on the "Old Model" are "Evans Repeating Rifle/ Pat. Dec. 8, 1868 & Sept. 16, 1871." There are three versions of the Old Model as follows. They were manufactured between 1874 and 1876 and serial numbered 1-500.

Military Musket

This version has a 30" barrel, with 2 barrel bands and provisions for a bayonet. There were only 50 estimated manufactured.

Exc.	V.G.	Good	Fair	Poor
1500	1250	900	750	500

Sporting Rifle

Approximately 300 of this model produced with a 26", 28", or 30" octagonal barrel.

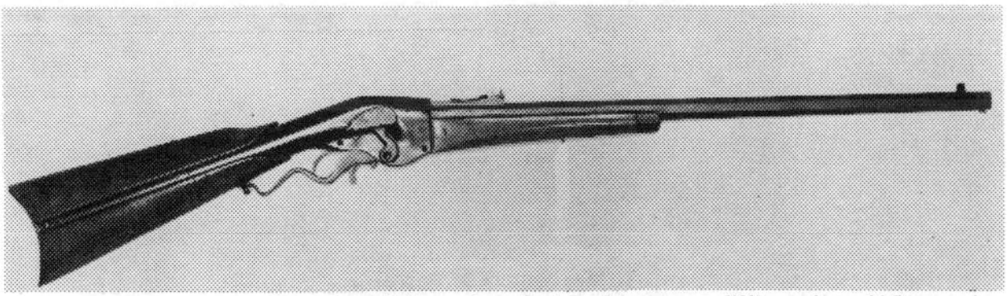

Courtesy Milwaukee Public Museum, Milwaukee, Wisconsin.

Exc.	V.G.	Good	Fair	Poor
1100	900	750	500	400

Carbine

This variation has a 22" barrel, with one barrel band and a sling swivel. There were 150 produced.

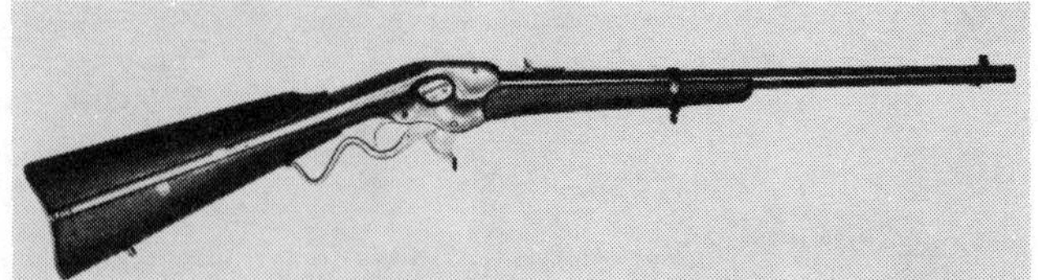

Courtesy Milwaukee Public Museum, Milwaukee, Wisconsin.

Exc.	V.G.	Good	Fair	Poor
1350	1150	800	650	550

Transitional Model

Has a buttstock that covers both the top and bottom of the rotary magazine, with an exposed portion in the middle of the butt. The butt plate does not have the backward appearance, and the barrel is marked "Evans Repeating Rifle Mechanic Falls Me./Pat Dec. 8, 1868 & Sept. 16, 1871." This version was manufactured in 1876 and 1877 and was serial numbered between 500-2185, for a total of approximately 1,650 manufactured.

Military Musket

Has a 30" barrel and two barrel bands. 150 were produced.

Exc.	V.G.	Good	Fair	Poor
1150	950	800	600	450

Carbine

450 of these produced, with a 22" barrel and one barrel band.

Exc.	V.G.	Good	Fair	Poor
1000	800	650	500	375

Sporting Rifle

Has a 26", 28", or 30" barrel. There were 1,050 produced.

Exc.	V.G.	Good	Fair	Poor
800	600	475	350	275

"Montreal Carbine"

A special issue marked "Montreal," sold by R. H. Kilby, Evans' Canadian sales agent. There were between 50 and 100 produced.

Exc.	V.G.	Good	Fair	Poor
1150	950	800	600	450

New Model

Approximately 10,000 of the New Model produced, chambered for the 1.5" .44 Evans cartridge with a magazine capacity reduced to 28. The frame was redesigned and rounded at the top, and the forend fit flush to the receiver. The lever and hammer are streamlined, and there is a dust cover over the loading gate. The markings are the same as on the Transitional Model with "U.S.A." added to the last line. This version was not serial numbered, and any numbers found are assembly numbers only.

Military Musket

3,000 produced, with a 30" barrel and two barrel bands.

Courtesy Butterfield & Butterfield, San Francisco, California.

Exc.	V.G.	Good	Fair	Poor
1000	800	650	500	375

Carbine

4,000 produced with a 22" barrel, one barrel band, and a sling swivel.

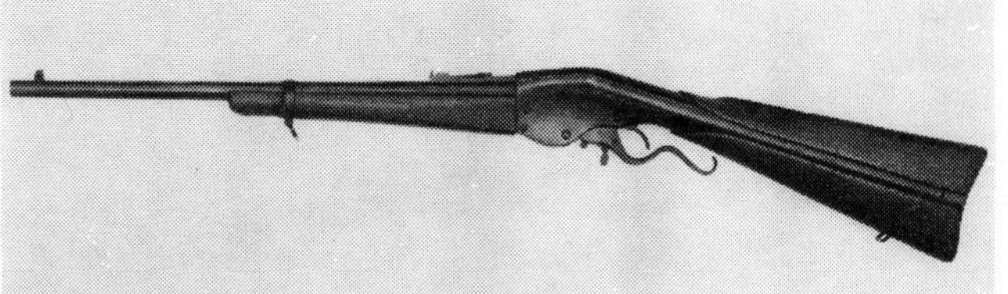

Courtesy Buffalo Bill Historical Center, Cody, Wyoming.

Exc.	V.G.	Good	Fair	Poor
850	750	600	450	400

Sporting Rifle

3,000 produced with 26", 28", or 30" octagonal barrels.

Exc.	V.G.	Good	Fair	Poor
650	550	450	375	275

EVANS, J. E.

Philadelphia, Pennsylvania

Evans Pocket Pistol

A copy of the Philadelphia-made Henry Deringer pistol and is chambered for .41 caliber. It utilizes the percussion ignition system and has barrels from 2.5" to 3" in length. The stock is of walnut with a checkered grip, and the mountings are scroll-engraved German silver. The barrel is marked "J.E.Evans Philada." These pistols were manufactured in the 1850s.

Exc.	V.G.	Good	Fair	Poor
1750	1000	550	450	350

EXCAM

Hialeah, Florida

An importer of firearms and does not manufacture. The Erma and Uberti products they import are under their own heading in this book. The other products that they import are listed here. They are no longer in business.

TA 76

Patterned after the Colt Single Action Army and is chambered for the .22 rimfire cartridge. It has a 4.75", 6", or 9" barrel and blue finish with wood grips. It is offered with brass triggerguard and backstrap and also offered chrome-plated. A combo model with an extra .22 Magnum cylinder is available and would add 10% to the listed values.

Exc.	V.G.	Good	Fair	Poor
90	75	65	40	25

TA 38 Over/Under Derringer

A 2-shot derringer patterned after the Remington Derringer. It is chambered for the .38 Special cartridge, has 3" barrels that pivot upward for loading, and is blued with checkered nylon grips. This model was discontinued in 1985.

Exc.	V.G.	Good	Fair	Poor
90	75	65	40	25

TA 90

A double-action, semi-automatic copy of the CZ-75 which some experts rate as the finest combat handgun in the world. It is chambered for the 9mm parabellum and has a 4.75" barrel. It is constructed of steel and is finished with a matte blue or chrome with checkered wood or rubber grips. The detachable magazine holds 15 rounds.

NIB	Exc.	V.G.	Good	Fair	Poor
415	380	325	275	200	150

BTA-90B

A compact version of the TA 90, that has a 3.5" barrel and a 12-round detachable magazine. It is similar in all other respects to the standard model, with rubber grips only.

NIB	Exc.	V.G.	Good	Fair	Poor
425	400	350	300	225	175

TA 90 SS
A competition version of the TA 90, that is similar to the standard model except that it is compensated and features adjustable sights. It is offered either blued or chrome-plated and was introduced in 1989.

NIB	Exc.	V.G.	Good	Fair	Poor
650	575	500	400	325	225

TA 41, 41C, and 41 SS
This series of pistols is identical to the TA 90 series except that they are chambered for the .41 Action Express cartridge. Their values are about 10 percent higher than the 9mm versions. They were introduced in 1989.

Warrior Model W 722
A double-action revolver chambered for the .22 rimfire and the .22 rimfire magnum with an interchangeable cylinder. It has a 6" barrel, adjustable sights, and an 8-shot cylinder capacity. It is blued, with checkered plastic grips. This model was not imported after 1986.

Exc.	V.G.	Good	Fair	Poor
100	75	50	35	20

Model W 384
A double-action revolver chambered for the .38 Special cartridge, with a 4" or 6" vent-rib barrel, blued finish, and plastic grips. It was discontinued in 1986.

Exc.	V.G.	Good	Fair	Poor
150	125	100	75	50

Model W 357
Similar to the W 384 except that it is chambered for the .357 Magnum cartridge. It was discontinued in 1986.

Exc.	V.G.	Good	Fair	Poor
200	150	125	100	75

Targa GT 26
A blowback-operated, semi-automatic pistol chambered for the .25 ACP cartridge. It has a 2.5" barrel and a 6-shot detachable magazine. It is finished in blue or matte chrome, with a choice of alloy or steel frame. The grips are wood.

Steel Frame Version

NIB	Exc.	V.G.	Good	Fair	Poor
110	90	75	50	40	30

Alloy Frame Version

NIB	Exc.	V.G.	Good	Fair	Poor
70	60	50	35	30	25

GT 22
A semi-automatic pistol chambered for the .22 l.r. cartridge. It has a 4" barrel, fixed sights, and a 10-round magazine. It is available either blued or matte chrome-plated and has wooden grips.

NIB	Exc.	V.G.	Good	Fair	Poor
200	175	150	125	90	70

GT 22 T
Similar to the GT 22, with a 6" barrel and adjustable target-type sights.

NIB	Exc.	V.G.	Good	Fair	Poor
225	200	175	150	100	75

GT 32
A blowback-operated semi-automatic pistol chambered for the .32 ACP cartridge. It has a 7-round magazine and is either blued or matte chrome-plated with wood grips.

NIB	Exc.	V.G.	Good	Fair	Poor
200	175	150	125	90	75

GT 380
Similar to the GT 32 except that it is chambered for the .380 ACP cartridge.

NIB	Exc.	V.G.	Good	Fair	Poor
215	185	175	135	110	85

GT 380 XE
Similar to the the GT 380, with an 11- shot, high-capacity, detachable magazine.

NIB	Exc.	V.G.	Good	Fair	Poor
225	200	185	150	125	100

EXEL ARMS OF AMERICA
Gardner, Massachusetts
SEE—Lanber
Laurona & Ugartechia

This firm was engaged in the import of Spanish shotguns. They ceased importing them in 1967, and the specific models will be found listed under the manufacturers' names.

F.A.S.
Italy
Importer—Beeman Prec. Arms
Santa Rosa, California
Osbourne's
Cheboygan, Michigan

Model 601
A high-grade, competition target pistol chambered for the .22 short cartridge. It is a semi-automatic, with a 5.5" barrel and adjustable target sights. The detachable magazine holds 5 rounds, and the finish is blued with wraparound target grips. This model was discontinued in 1988.

Exc.	V.G.	Good	Fair	Poor
1000	900	750	575	400

Model 602
Similar to the Model 601 except that it is chambered for the .22 l.r. It was discontinued in 1987.

Exc.	V.G.	Good	Fair	Poor
950	850	700	525	350

Model 603
Chambered for the .32 S&W Wadcutter cartridge and features adjustable grips. It was discontinued in 1987.

Exc.	V.G.	Good	Fair	Poor
950	850	700	525	350

FEG (FEGYVERGYAR)
Budapest, Hungary
Importer—Century International Arms Co.
St. Albans, Vermont

Rudolf Frommer was a first-class engineer who became associated with Fegyvergyar in 1896. In 1900 he became the manager and held that position until his retirement in 1935. He died one year later in 1936. His designs were successful and prolific. They were used militarily and sold on the commercial market as well.

Model 1901
An odd pistol that was not successful at all. It was chambered for an 8mm cartridge that was the forerunner of the 8mm Roth-Steyr. It has a long, slender barrel, which was actually a collar with the barrel within. It has a rotary bolt and external hammer and is recoil-operated. There is a 10-round integral magazine, and it is loaded from the top via a stripper clip. This pistol was manufactured from 1903 to 1905.

Exc.	V.G.	Good	Fair	Poor
1750	1500	1250	1000	750

Model 1906
An improved version of the 1901, chambered for the 7.65mm Roth cartridge. It is, for all intents and purposes, the same action; but on later models a detachable 10-round magazine was adopted. It was manufactured between 1906 and 1910 in small quantity.

Exc.	V.G.	Good	Fair	Poor
1500	1350	1100	850	675

Model 1910
The final version in this series of pistols and is similar with the addition of a grip safety.

Exc.	V.G.	Good	Fair	Poor
1250	1000	900	700	500

Model "Stop"
Introduced in 1912 and took a whole new approach compared to any of the pistols this company had produced to that point. It is still unconventional as it uses two recoil springs in a tube above the barrel and resembles an air pistol in this way. It is chambered for 7.65mm or 9mm short and has a 3.75" barrel. The detachable magazine holds 7 rounds, and the sights are fixed. This locked-breech action, semi-automatic pistol was a commercial success. It was used widely by the Austro-Hungarian military during WWI. It was manufactured between 1912 and 1920.

Exc.	V.G.	Good	Fair	Poor
275	225	200	150	100

Baby Model
A smaller version of the Stop that was designed as a pocket pistol with a 2" barrel and chambered for the same calibers. It was manufactured at the same time as the Stop Model.

Exc.	V.G.	Good	Fair	Poor
275	225	175	125	100

Lilliput
This pocket pistol is chambered for 6.35mm and outwardly resembles the Baby. It is actually a simple, blowback-operated, semi-automatic pistol and was a good deal less complex to produce. This model was introduced in 1921.

Exc.	V.G.	Good	Fair	Poor
250	200	150	125	75

Model 1929
A blowback-operated semi-automatic chambered for the 9mm short cartridge. It has an external hammer; and the barrel was retained, as the Browning was, by four lugs. This was a simple and reliable pistol, and it was adopted by the military as a replacement for the Stop. This model was manufactured between 1929 and 1937.

Exc.	V.G.	Good	Fair	Poor
225	190	175	125	100

Model 1937
An improved version of the Model 1929 and was the last of Frommer's designs. It appeared a year after his death. This model is similar to the Model 1929, with a grooved slide to make cocking easier. It was adopted as the M1937 by the Hungarian Military, and in 1941 the German government ordered 85,000 pistols chambered for 7.65mm to be used by the Luftwaffe. These pistols were designated the "P Mod 37 Kal 7.65." They were also marked "jhv," which was the German code for the Hungarian company. These German pistols also have a manual safety, which is not found on the Hungarian military version and bears the Waffenamt acceptance marks. This model was manufactured from 1937 until the end of WWII.

Nazi Proofed 7.65mm Version

Exc.	V.G.	Good	Fair	Poor
275	250	200	150	100

9mm Short Hungarian Military Version

Exc.	V.G.	Good	Fair	Poor
250	225	175	125	90

Model R-9

A copy of the Browning Hi-Power semi-automatic pistol. It is chambered for 9mm parabellum and has a 4.75" barrel. The frame is steel, and the finish is blued with checkered wood grips. The detachable magazine holds 13 shots, and the sights are fixed. This model was imported in 1986 and 1987 only.

Exc.	V.G.	Good	Fair	Poor
275	225	200	150	125

Model PPH

A copy of the Walther PP, chambered for the .380 ACP cartridge. It is a double-action semi-automatic with a 3" barrel, alloy frame, and a blued finish, with thumbrest checkered plastic grips. It was imported in 1986 and 1987 only.

Exc.	V.G.	Good	Fair	Poor
225	175	150	110	90

Model B9R

This semi-automatic pistol is chambered for the .380 ACP cartridge and fitted with a 4" barrel, it features double or single action trigger operation. The frame is alloy and weighs about 25 oz. Magazine capacity is 15 rounds.

NIB	Exc.	V.G.	Good	Fair	Poor
225	200	175	150	125	90

Model AP9

Chambered for the .380 ACP this pistol is a copy of the Walther PP. It has a aluminum alloy frame and a magazine capacity of 7 rounds. The barrel is 3.94" in length and the pistol is 6.89" overall. The trigger is double action.

Exc.	V.G.	Good	Fair	Poor
135	100	85	70	55

Model PA63

Same as above but chambered for the 9mm Makarov(9x18mm) cartridge.

Exc.	V.G.	Good	Fair	Poor
125	90	75	60	50

Model FP9

This model is a copy of the Browning Hi-Power pistol. Chambered for the 9mm Luger cartridge. It features a walnut checkered grip with blue finish. Barrel is 5" and overall length is 8". The top of the slide features a full length ventilated rib with fixed sights. Weighs 35 oz. Magazine capacity is 14 rounds.

NIB	Exc.	V.G.	Good	Fair	Poor
215	175	150	125	90	70

Model P9R

This is similar to the model above and follows the Browning Hi-Power lines with the exception of the ventilated rib. Barrel length is 4.66" and the pistil is offered in blue or chrome finish. Magazine capacity is 15 rounds.

Blue

NIB	Exc.	V.G.	Good	Fair	Poor
225	200	150	125	90	70

Chrome

NIB	Exc.	V.G.	Good	Fair	Poor
250	225	175	150	120	80

Model P9RK

Similar to model above but fitted with 4.12" barrel and 7.5" overall length. Finger grooves on front strap and back strap is serrated. Weighs about 34 oz.

NIB	Exc.	V.G.	Good	Fair	Poor
230	200	150	125	90	70

F.I.E.
Hialeah, Florida

Firearms Import and Export, was engaged in the business of importing the Franchi shotgun (which is listed under its own heading) and the Arminius revolver (which is made in Germany). They were also distributors for the Titan semi-automatic pistols, which are manufactured in the U.S.A. They were also importing a series of 9mm pistols from Italy that are produced by Tanfoglio and known as the TZ series. F.I.E. is no longer in business.

TZ 75

A copy of the CZ 75 Czechoslovakian combat pistol produced by Tanfoglio in Italy. It is a 9mm, double-action semi-automatic with a 4.75" barrel, all-steel construction, fixed sights, and a 15-shot magazine. It is offered either blued or matte chrome plated, with wood or rubber grips.

NIB	Exc.	V.G.	Good	Fair	Poor
440	400	350	300	225	150

TZ 75 Series 88

An improved version that is also chambered for the .41 Action Express cartridge. It has a firing pin safety and can be carried cocked and locked. There are a few other minor changes. It was introduced in 1988.

NIB	Exc.	V.G.	Good	Fair	Poor
460	425	375	325	250	175

KG-99

A blowback-operated, semi-automatic assault pistol chambered for the 9mm parabellum cartridge. It has a 36-round magazine. It was discontinued in 1984.

Exc.	V.G.	Good	Fair	Poor
450	400	350	250	175

Spectre Assault Pistol

An assault-type semi-automatic pistol chambered for the 9mm parabellum. It has a 30-or 50-round magazine available. It was introduced in 1989.

NIB	Exc.	V.G.	Good	Fair	Poor
650	575	475	400	300	200

Titan II .22

A semi-automatic pistol chambered for the .22 l.r. It has a 10-shot magazine and a blued finish with walnut grips. It is made in the U.S.A.

NIB	Exc.	V.G.	Good	Fair	Poor
155	125	100	75	50	25

Titan E32

A single-action, blowback-operated, semi-automatic pistol that was chambered for the .32 ACP and is now chambered for the .380 ACP cartridge. The finish is blue or chrome-plated, and the grips are walnut.

NIB	Exc.	V.G.	Good	Fair	Poor
225	200	150	125	100	75

Super Titan II

Similar to the Titan except that it has a 12-round, high-capacity magazine.

NIB	Exc.	V.G.	Good	Fair	Poor
250	225	200	150	100	75

Titan 25

A smaller version of the Titan Series chambered for the .25 ACP cartridge. It is blued or chrome-plated.

NIB	Exc.	V.G.	Good	Fair	Poor
75	65	50	40	30	20

Titan Tigress

Similar to the Titan 25 except that it is gold-plated and cased.

NIB	Exc.	V.G.	Good	Fair	Poor
165	145	125	100	50	30

D38 Derringer

A 2-shot, Over/Under, Remington-style derringer chambered for the .38 Special cartridge. It is chrome-plated and was dropped from the line in 1985.

Exc.	V.G.	Good	Fair	Poor
75	60	45	30	20

D86 Derringer

A single-shot derringer with a 3" barrel. It is chambered for the .38 Special cartridge and is chrome-plated. There is an ammunition storage compartment in the butt and a transfer bar safety that makes it safer to carry. This model was introduced in 1986.

NIB	Exc.	V.G.	Good	Fair	Poor
95	80	65	50	35	20

There is a series of single-action, .22-caliber revolvers that were patterned after the Colt Single Action Army. They were manufactured in the U.S.A. or Brescia, Italy. They are inexpensive and of fair quality. The differences between these models are basically barrel lengths, type of sights, and finish. They all are chambered for the .22 l.r. and have interchangeable .22 magnum cylinders. We list them for reference purposes.

Cowboy

NIB	Exc.	V.G.	Good	Fair	Poor
100	80	70	50	35	20

Gold Rush

NIB	Exc.	V.G.	Good	Fair	Poor
175	150	125	100	75	50

Texas Ranger

NIB	Exc.	V.G.	Good	Fair	Poor
100	85	75	50	35	20

Buffalo Scout

NIB	Exc.	V.G.	Good	Fair	Poor
95	80	70	50	35	20

Legend S.A.A.

NIB	Exc.	V.G.	Good	Fair	Poor
125	110	85	65	50	30

Hombre

A single-action made in Germany by Arminius. It is patterned after the Colt Single Action Army revolver. The Hombre is chambered for the .357 Magnum, .44 Magnum, and .45 Colt cartridges. It is offered with a 5.5", 6", or 7.5" barrel, case-colored frame, and blued barrel and cylinder, with smooth walnut grips. The backstrap and triggerguard are offered in brass and will bring a 10 percent premium.

NIB	Exc.	V.G.	Good	Fair	Poor
250	225	200	175	110	75

Arminius Revolvers

522TB

A swing-out cylinder, double-action revolver chambered for the

.22 rimfire cartridge. It has a 4" barrel and is blued with wood grips.

NIB	Exc.	V.G.	Good	Fair	Poor
150	125	100	75	50	30

722

Similar to the 522, with an 8-shot cylinder and a 6" barrel. It is available with a chrome finish.

NIB	Exc.	V.G.	Good	Fair	Poor
150	125	100	75	50	30

532TB

A 7-shot, double-action revolver chambered for the .32 S&W cartridge. It has a 4" barrel and adjustable sights and is finished in either blue or chrome.

NIB	Exc.	V.G.	Good	Fair	Poor
160	130	110	80	60	40

732B

Similar to the 532TB, with a 6" barrel and fixed sights. It was discontinued in 1988.

NIB	Exc.	V.G.	Good	Fair	Poor
120	100	80	65	50	35

Standard Revolver

A double-action, swing-out cylinder revolver chambered for .32 Magnum or .38 Special. It has a 4" or 6" barrel and fixed sights and is blued with wood grips. This model is made in the U.S.A. and was introduced in 1989.

NIB	Exc.	V.G.	Good	Fair	Poor
125	100	75	50	35	20

Models 384TB and 386TB

These two models are double-action chambered for the .38 Special cartridge. The 384 has a 4" barrel; and the 386, a 6" barrel. They are available in blue or chrome plate and were discontinued in 1985.

NIB	Exc.	V.G.	Good	Fair	Poor
185	160	140	110	85	60

Model 357TB

Similar to the 384TB except that it is chambered for the .357 Magnum cartridge and is offered with a 3", 4", or 6" barrel.

NIB	Exc.	V.G.	Good	Fair	Poor
250	225	175	125	90	75

222, 232, and 382TB

These models are double-action swing-out cylinder revolvers chambered for .22 rimfire, .32 S&W, and .38 Special. They are 2"-barrelled snub-nosed revolvers, with either blued or chrome-plated finishes. They were discontinued in 1985.

Exc.	V.G.	Good	Fair	Poor
125	100	75	50	25

Model 3572

A similar revolver to the 382TB except that it is chambered for the .357 Magnum cartridge. It was discontinued in 1984.

Exc.	V.G.	Good	Fair	Poor
225	200	175	125	100

Shotguns and Rifle

Model 122

A bolt-action rifle chambered for .22 rimfire, with a 21" barrel and adjustable sights. It has a 10-shot magazine and a walnut Monte Carlo stock. It was introduced in 1986.

Exc.	V.G.	Good	Fair	Poor
110	95	75	50	25

Single Shot

Brazilian made and chambered for 12 or 20 gauge and .410. It is a single-barrelled break open, with 25" through 30" barrel and various chokes. It is blued with a wood stock and was introduced in 1985.

Exc.	V.G.	Good	Fair	Poor
100	80	60	45	25

S.O.B.

Similar to the single shot, with an 18.5" barrel and a pistol grip instead of a standard stock. This model was discontinued in 1984.

Exc.	V.G.	Good	Fair	Poor
100	80	60	45	25

Sturdy Over/Under

Chambered for 12 and 20 gauge and has 3" chambers and 28" vent-rib barrels with various chokes. This is an Over/Under with double triggers and extractors. The frame is engraved and silver finished. It was manufactured in Italy by Maroccini and imported between 1985 and 1988.

Exc.	V.G.	Good	Fair	Poor
300	275	225	175	150

Brute

A side-by-side chambered for 12 and 20 gauge and .410. It has 19" barrels, double triggers, and extractors. It has a wood stock and was dropped from the line in 1984.

Exc.	V.G.	Good	Fair	Poor
200	175	125	100	75

SPAS-12

A unique shotgun in that it can function as a pump or an automatic with the touch of a button. It is a paramilitary-type shotgun chambered for 12 gauge, with a 21.5" barrel and a 9-shot tube magazine. It has an alloy receiver and a folding stock. The finish is all black. This model is manufactured by Franchi in Italy.

NIB	Exc.	V.G.	Good	Fair	Poor
600	575	500	450	300	150

Law-12

A paramilitary-type, 12-gauge, semi-automatic shotgun that is gas-operated and has a 9-shot tube magazine. The barrel is 21.5" in length and choked cylinder bore. It has a military special black finish and a black synthetic stock.

NIB	Exc.	V.G.	Good	Fair	Poor
425	375	325	275	200	150

SAS-12

A paramilitary-type, slide-action shotgun chambered for 12 gauge. It has a 21.5" barrel, choked cylinder bore. The finish is similar to the LAW-12, and it is manufactured by Franchi in Italy.

NIB	Exc.	V.G.	Good	Fair	Poor
350	325	300	250	200	150

F & T

(Falise & Trappman of Liege, Belgium)

SEE—French Military Firearms

FABARM

Brescia, Italy

Importer—St. Lawrence Sales, Inc.

Lake Orion, Michigan

Semi-Automatic Shotguns

Ellegi Standard

A gas-operated, semi-automatic shotgun chambered for 12 gauge. It has a 28" vent-rib barrel with choice of choke. The receiver is blue anodized alloy with a photo-etched gamescene, and the stock and forearm are checkered walnut. This model was introduced in 1989.

NIB	Exc.	V.G.	Good	Fair	Poor
700	625	525	450	350	250

The Ellegi Model is available in six other configurations. The differences are in the barrel length and choke, type of choke tubes, and finish. Basically the guns are quite similar to the standard model. These variations are as follows.

Ellegi Multichoke

NIB	Exc.	V.G.	Good	Fair	Poor
700	625	525	450	350	250

Ellegi Innerchoke

NIB	Exc.	V.G.	Good	Fair	Poor
725	650	550	475	375	275

Ellegi Magnum

NIB	Exc.	V.G.	Good	Fair	Poor
725	650	550	475	375	275

Ellegi Super Goose

NIB	Exc.	V.G.	Good	Fair	Poor
800	725	625	550	450	350

Ellegi Slug

NIB	Exc.	V.G.	Good	Fair	Poor
775	700	600	525	425	325

Ellegi Police

NIB	Exc.	V.G.	Good	Fair	Poor
575	500	450	400	300	225

Slide Action Shotguns

Model S.D.A.S.S.

Chambered for 12 gauge with a 3" chamber. It is offered with a 20" or 24.5" barrel threaded for external choke tubes. This model has an 8-shot tube magazine, twin action bars, an alloy receiver, and a matte black finish. It is a defensive-type shotgun and has been imported since 1989.

NIB	Exc.	V.G.	Good	Fair	Poor
500	450	400	350	250	175

The Special Police and the Martial Model are variations of the basic slide action and differ in barrel length and choke. The Police Model has a shrouded barrel.

Special Police

NIB	Exc.	V.G.	Good	Fair	Poor
525	475	425	350	275	200

Martial Model

NIB	Exc.	V.G.	Good	Fair	Poor
475	425	375	300	225	175

Single Shot Shotguns

Omega Standard

Has an alloy receiver and is chambered for 12 and 20 gauge, as well as .410. It has 26" or 28" barrels with various chokes. The finish is black with a beech stock. It was introduced in 1989.

NIB	Exc.	V.G.	Good	Fair	Poor
150	125	100	75	50	40

Omega Goose Gun

Chambered for 12 gauge only, with a 35.5" full-choke barrel.

NIB	Exc.	V.G.	Good	Fair	Poor
160	140	125	100	75	50

Side x Side Shotguns

Beta Model

This double barrel is chambered for 12 gauge only, with choice of barrel length and choke. It has a boxlock action with false side plates. It has a single trigger and automatic ejectors, and the finish is blued with a checkered, select walnut stock. This model was introduced in 1989.

NIB	Exc.	V.G.	Good	Fair	Poor
925	850	750	600	450	300

Beta Europe

A deluxe version that features single selective triggers and a gamescene-engraved, coin-finished receiver. The stock is the straight English style with a splinter forend. This model was introduced in 1989.

NIB	Exc.	V.G.	Good	Fair	Poor
1750	1500	1250	1000	750	500

Over/Under Shotguns

Field Model

Chambered for 12 gauge and has 29" vent-rib barrels with various chokes. The receiver is coin-finished, and the stock is checkered walnut. This Model was discontinued in 1985.

NIB	Exc.	V.G.	Good	Fair	Poor
900	700	600	500	400	300

Gamma Field

Chambered for 12 or 20 gauge and is offered with 26", 28", or 29" vent-rib barrels and various choke combinations. Screw-in choke tubes are available and would be worth a 10 percent premium. This model has a boxlock, coin-finished receiver that is moderately engraved and a checkered walnut stock.

NIB	Exc.	V.G.	Good	Fair	Poor
925	850	775	650	500	350

Gamma Paradox Gun

Chambered for 12 gauge only, and the top barrel is rifled for accurate placement of slugs. The barrels are 25" long with vent rib, and the bottom barrel has three screw-in choke tubes. This model has a single selective trigger and automatic ejectors. The finish is similar to the Field Model. It was introduced in 1989.

NIB	Exc.	V.G.	Good	Fair	Poor
1000	900	825	750	600	450

Gamma Trap or Skeet

Competition-grade guns with either a 27.5" barrel with five screw-in choke tubes on the skeet model or a 29" barrel with screw-in trap chokes. Both models feature single selective triggers and automatic ejectors; and the trap model has a Monte Carlo stock. They have moderately engraved, coin-finished boxlock actions and were introduced in 1989.

NIB	Exc.	V.G.	Good	Fair	Poor
1000	900	825	750	600	450

Gamma Sporting Competition Model

Designed for Sporting Clays and is chambered for 12 gauge only. The 29" barrel has a wide rib and is furnished with five screw-in choke tubes. It has a single selective trigger, automatic ejectors, and a checkered walnut stock with a competition recoil pad. It is finished like the skeet and trap models and was introduced in 1989.

NIB	Exc.	V.G.	Good	Fair	Poor
1000	900	825	750	600	450

FABBRI ARMI

Gardone V.T., Italy
Importer--New England Arms
Kittery Point, Maine

Fabbri Armi currently manufactures one of the best shotguns in the world. They are available as a custom made- to-order item, and they are not often seen in the used gun market. The values for guns of this nature and quality are impossible to accurately establish in a book of this nature as there are so many options and conditions that make the prices fluctuate greatly. We give an estimate figure as a base starting point but strongly urge individual appraisal should a transaction involving one of these fine firearms be contemplated.

Side x Side Shotgun

Chambered for 12 or 20 gauge with all other features on a custom-order basis.

NIB	Exc.	V.G.	Good	Fair	Poor
22500	20000	17500	12500	8500	6000

Over/Under Shotgun

Chambered for 12 or 20 gauge with all other features on a custom-order basis.

NIB	Exc.	V.G.	Good	Fair	Poor
25000	22500	20000	15000	10000	7500

FABRIQUE NATIONALE

Herstal, Belgium

In 1889 Fabrique Nationale (or FN) was founded by a group of Belgian investors for the purpose of manufacturing Mauser rifles for the Belgian army. This was to be accomplished under license from Mauser, with the technical assistance of Kudwig Loewe of Berlin. A few years later, in the 1890s, John Browning arrived in Europe seeking a manufacturer for his semi-automatic shotgun. He had severed his ties with Winchester after a disagreement. This led to a long association that worked out extremely well for both parties. Later Browning became associated with Colt, and the world market was divided—with the Eastern Hemisphere going to FN and the Western Hemisphere to Colt.

In this section, we list arms that bear the FN banner. The FN-manufactured firearms produced under the Browning banner are listed in the Browning section of this book.

Model 1900

A blowback-operated semi-automatic pistol chambered for the 7.65mm cartridge. It has a 4" barrel and fixed sights and is blued with molded plastic grips. This model is notorious as the pistol that was used to assassinate Archduke Ferdinand, an event that touched off WWI. It was manufactured between 1899 and 1910. This model is referred to as the "Old Model."

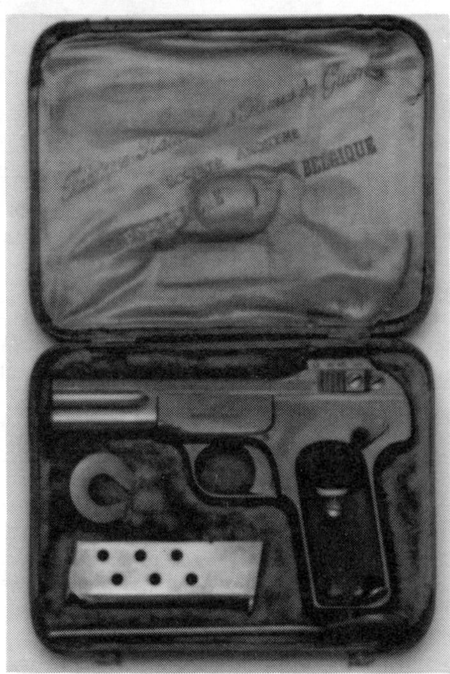

Courtesy Butterfield & Butterfield, San Francisco, California.

Exc.	V.G.	Good	Fair	Poor
350	325	275	200	150

Model 1903

A considerable improvement over the Model 1900. It is also a blowback-operated semi-automatic; but the recoil spring is located under the barrel, and the firing pin travels through the slide after being struck by a hidden hammer. The barrel is held in place by five locking lugs that fit into five grooves in the frame. This pistol is chambered for the 9mm Browning long cartridge and has a 5" barrel. The finish is blued with molded plastic grips, and the detachable magazine holds 7 rounds. There is a detachable shoulder stock/holster along with a 10-round magazine that was available for this model. These accessories are extremely rare and if present would make the package worth approximately five times that of the pistol alone. There were approximately 58,000 manufactured between 1903 and 1939. This model was one of the Browning patents that the Eibar Spanish gunmakers did so love to copy because of the simplicity of the design.

Exc.	V.G.	Good	Fair	Poor
475	425	375	275	175

Model 1906

A smaller version of the Model 1903, designed to be a pocket pistol and chambered for the 6.35mm cartridge. It became known as the "Vest Pocket" model and was also the basis for many Eibar copies. It has a 2.5" barrel and was produced in two distinct variations. The first variation had no safety lever or slide lock and relied on the grip safety. The second variation, that occurred at approximately serial number 100000, added this safety lever and slide lock, which helped simplify dismantling of the pistol. This model was available either blued or nickle-plated. The plated models would bring a 10 percent premium. There were approximately 1,086,100 manufactured between 1906 and 1959.

1st Variation Under Serial Number 100000

Exc.	V.G.	Good	Fair	Poor
350	300	250	200	125

2nd Variation Over Serial Number 100000

Exc.	V.G.	Good	Fair	Poor
300	275	200	175	100

Model 1910 "New Model"

Chambered for 7.65mm and 9mm short. It has a 3.5" barrel, is blued, and has molded plastic grips. The principal difference between this model and its predecessors is that the recoil spring on the Model 1910 is wrapped around the barrel. This gives the slide a more graceful tubular appearance instead of the old slab-sided look. This model has the triple safety features of the 1906 Model 2nd variation and is blued with molded plastic grips. This model was adopted by police forces around the world. It was manufactured between 1912 and 1954.

Courtesy Orville Reichert.

Exc.	V.G.	Good	Fair	Poor
350	300	250	175	125

Model 1922

Similar to the Model 1910, with a longer 4.5" barrel and correspondingly longer slide. This model was a military success, and approximately 200,000 were produced during the WWII German occupation of Belgium in 1940-1944. These pistols that bear the Waffenamt acceptance marks, are known as the "Pistole Modell 626(b)," and are chambered for 7.65mm only. These pistols would bring a 10 percent premium. There were also contracts from France, Yugoslavia, and Holland, as well as Belgian military versions. They were manufactured between 1912 and 1959.

Exc.	V.G.	Good	Fair	Poor
275	225	175	125	100

"Baby" Model

A smaller and lighter version of the Model 1906. It is chambered for the 6.35mm cartridge and has a 2" barrel. There is no grip safety or slide lock on this model, and it appears to be more square in shape than the Model 1906. This model was offered in blue, with molded plastic grips. Early models have the word "Baby" molded into the grips; post-1945 versions do not. There is also a nickle-plated version with pearl grips. There were over 500,000 of these manufactured between 1931 and 1983.

Courtesy Orville Reichert.

Courtesy Orville Reichert.

Exc.	V.G.	Good	Fair	Poor
400	325	300	225	150

Model 1935

The last design from John Browning and was developed between 1925 and 1935. This pistol is known as the Model 1935, the P-35, High-Power or HP, and also as the GP (which stood for "Grand Puissance") and was referred to by all those names at one time or another. The HP is essentially an improved version of the Colt 1911 design. The swinging link was replaced with a fixed cam, which was less prone to wear. It is chambered for the 9mm Parabellum and has a 13-round detachable magazine. The only drawback to the design is that the trigger pull is not as fine as that of the 1911, as there is a transfer bar instead of a stirrup arrangement. This is necessary due to the increased magazine capacity resulting in a thicker grip. The barrel is 4.75" in length. It has an external hammer with a manual and a magazine safety and was available with various finishes and sight options and was furnished with a shoulder stock. The Model 1935 was used by many countries as their service pistol as such there are many variations. We list these versions and their approximate values. There are books available specializing in this model, and it would be beneficial to gain as much knowledge as possible if one contemplates acquisition of this fine and highly collectible pistol.

Pre-War Commercial Model

Found with either a fixed sight or a sliding tangent rear sight and is slotted for a detachable shoulder stock. It was manufactured from 1935 until 1940.

Wood Holster Stock—Add 50%.

Fixed Sight Version

Exc.	V.G.	Good	Fair	Poor
600	525	475	375	275

Tangent Sight Version

Exc.	V.G.	Good	Fair	Poor
1000	850	675	550	400

Prewar Military Contract

The Model 1935 was adopted by many countries as a service pistol, and they are as follows.

Belgium

Exc.	V.G.	Good	Fair	Poor
1200	1050	900	600	375

Canada and China (See John Inglis & Company)

Denmark

Exc.	V.G.	Good	Fair	Poor
1250	1100	950	650	400

Great Britain

Exc.	V.G.	Good	Fair	Poor
1150	1000	850	550	325

Estonia

Exc.	V.G.	Good	Fair	Poor
1200	1050	900	600	375

Holland

Exc.	V.G.	Good	Fair	Poor
1250	1100	950	650	400

Latvia

Exc.	V.G.	Good	Fair	Poor
1500	1350	1050	775	500

Lithuania

Exc.	V.G.	Good	Fair	Poor
1250	1100	950	650	400

Romania

Exc.	V.G.	Good	Fair	Poor
1500	1350	1050	775	500

German Military Pistole Modell 640(b)

In 1940 Germany occupied Belgium and took over the FN plant. The production of the Model 1935 continued, with Germany taking the output. The FN plant was assigned the production code "ch," and many thousands were produced. The finish on these Nazi guns runs from as fine as the Prewar Commercial series to downright crude, and it is possible to see how the war was progressing for Germany by the finish on their weapons.

One must be cautious with some of these guns as there have been fakes noted with their backstraps cut for shoulder stocks, producing what would appear to be a more expensive variation. Individual appraisal should be secured if any doubt exists.

Fixed Sight Model

Exc.	V.G.	Good	Fair	Poor
500	450	400	300	250

Tangent Sight Model—50,000 Manufactured

Courtesy Orville Reichert.

Courtesy Orville Reichert.

Exc.	V.G.	Good	Fair	Poor
800	750	700	550	400

Captured Prewar Commercial Model

These pistols were taken over when the plant was occupied. They are slotted for stocks and have tangent sights. There were few produced between serial number 48,000 and 52,000. All noted have the Waa 613 Nazi proof mark. Beware of fakes!

Exc.	V.G.	Good	Fair	Poor
1500	1400	1150	750	500

Postwar Military Contract

Manufactured from 1946, and they embody some design changes—such as improved heat treating and barrel locking. Pistols produced after 1950 do not have barrels that can interchange with the earlier model pistols. The earliest models have an "A" prefix on the serial number and do not have the magazine safety. These pistols were produced for many countries, and there were many thousands manufactured.

Fixed Sight

Exc.	V.G.	Good	Fair	Poor
475	425	375	300	250

Tangent Sight

Exc.	V.G.	Good	Fair	Poor
750	675	575	400	300

Slotted and Tangent Sight

Exc.	V.G.	Good	Fair	Poor
1150	1050	750	500	400

Postwar Commercial Model

Introduced in 1950 and in 1954. Those imported into the U.S.A. are marked Browning Arms Co. These pistols have the commercial polished finish.

Fixed Sight

Exc.	V.G.	Good	Fair	Poor
500	425	350	300	250

Tangent Sight

Exc.	V.G.	Good	Fair	Poor
750	650	500	400	350

Slotted and Tangent Sight

Exc.	V.G.	Good	Fair	Poor
1200	1100	800	550	450

WARNING: A large number of counterfeit FN Hi-Power's have been shipped to the United States possibly from the Balkans. The slides are marked just like the FN originals but the fit and finish is of poor quality. These pistols are missing numerous small proof stamps and markings normally found on FN pistols. These counterfeits have a serial number on the front of the grip strap with a single letter prefix. All are fitted with the late style extractor. Metal finish is either a military matte blue or a commercial high gloss blue.

Rifles

Model 1889

The Mauser rifle that FN was formed to manufacture. It is chambered for 7.65mm and has a 30.5" barrel. The magazine holds 5 rounds. The unique feature which set the Belgian rifle apart from the Mausers made by other countries is the thin steel tube that encases the barrel. The sights are of the military type. The finish is blued, with a walnut stock.

Exc.	V.G.	Good	Fair	Poor
275	250	200	125	100

Model 1949

A gas-operated semi-automatic rifle chambered for 7x57, 7.92mm, and .30-06. It has a 23" barrel and military-type sights. The integral magazine holds 10 rounds. The finish is blued, and the stock is walnut. This is a very well-made gun that was actually designed before WWII. When the Germans were in the process of taking over Belgium, a group of FN engineers fled to England and took the plans for this rifle with them, preventing the German military from acquiring a very fine weapon. This model was introduced in 1949, after hostilities had ceased. This model was sold on contract to Egypt, chambered for 7.92mm; to Venezuela, chambered for 7x57; and to Columbia and Indonesia, chambered for the .30-06. The Egyptian model has recently been imported in large numbers and is worth approximately 20 percent less.

.30-06 caliber—Add 20%.

Exc.	V.G.	Good	Fair	Poor
400	350	300	225	150

Model 30-11 Sniper Rifle

Chambered for the 7.62 NATO cartridge. It has a 20" heavy barrel and Anschutz sights. There is a flash suppressor mounted on the muzzle. It is built on a highly precision-made Mauser bolt action fed by a 9-round, detachable box magazine. The walnut stock is rather unique in that the butt is made up of two parts, with the rear half being replaceable to suit the needs of different-sized shooters. It is issued with a shooting sling, bipod, and a foam-lined carrying case. This is a very rare firearm on the commercial market as it was designed and sold to the military and police markets.

Exc.	V.G.	Good	Fair	Poor
5000	4500	3500	2750	2000

FN-L.A.R.

A gas-operated, semi-automatic version of the famous FN battle rifle. This weapon has been adopted by more free world countries than any other. It is chambered for the 7.62 NATO or .308 and has a 21" barrel with an integral flash suppressor. The sights are adjustable with an aperture rear, and the detachable box magazine holds 20 rounds. The stock and forearm are made of wood or a black synthetic. This model has been discontinued by the company and is no longer manufactured. Sadly, this is another firearm that has been affected by the assault rifle hysteria; and it is virtually impossible to accurately place a cash value on it. If one is contemplating a transaction, qualified appraisal should be secured.

Heavy Barrelled Model

Similar to the L.A.R. except that the barrel is much heavier in diameter, and there is a bipod furnished. The forend is shorter than on the standard model, and it is made of wood. This model was also discontinued in 1988 and also cannot accurately be appraised in a book of this nature.

Paratroopers Model

Similar rifle to the standard L.A.R., with an 18" barrel and a folding stock. There is also a model that has the standard 21" barrel. This model should also be individually appraised due to radical market fluctuations.

FNC

A lighter-weight assault-type rifle chambered for the 5.56mm cartridge. It is a gas-operated semi-automatic with a 18.5" barrel. It has a 30-round box magazine and is black, with either a fixed or folding stock. This model was also discontinued by FN. The same problem with fluctuating values applies to this weapon as to the L.A.R., and we strongly advise that one researches the market in a particular geographic location as prices can fluctuate radically.

Sporting Rifles

Musketeer

A bolt-action rifle built on the Mauser action chambered for various popular cartridges. It has a 24" barrel and is blued, with a checkered walnut stock. It was manufactured between 1947 and 1963.

Exc.	V.G.	Good	Fair	Poor
400	375	325	225	150

Deluxe Sporte

A higher-grade version of the Musketeer with the same general specifications. It was also manufactured between 1947 and 1963.

Exc.	V.G.	Good	Fair	Poor
500	450	400	300	200

FN Supreme

Chambered for the popular standard calibers and has a 24" barrel with an aperture sight and a checkered walnut stock. It was manufactured between 1957 and 1975.

Exc.	V.G.	Good	Fair	Poor
550	500	450	350	225

Supreme Magnum Model

Similar to the standard Supreme except that it is chambered for .264 Win. Mag., 7mm Rem. Mag., and .300 Win. Mag. It is furnished with a recoil pad and was manufactured between the same years as the standard model.

Exc.	V.G.	Good	Fair	Poor
600	550	500	400	250

FAIRBANKS, A. B.

Boston, Massachusetts

Fairbanks All Metal Pistol

This odd pistol was produced of all metal, with a one-piece cast brass frame and handle and an iron barrel and lock system. It is chambered for .33 caliber and utilizes the percussion ignition system. The barrel lengths noted are of 3" to 10". The barrels are marked "Fairbanks Boston.Cast Steel." They were manufactured between 1838 and 1841.

Exc.	V.G.	Good	Fair	Poor
350	300	250	200	150

FALCON FIREARMS

Northridge, California

Portsider

A copy of the Colt 1911 built for a lefthanded individual. It is constructed of stainless steel and is similar in all other respects to the Colt. It was introduced in 1986.

NIB	Exc.	V.G.	Good	Fair	Poor
575	500	425	375	300	225

Portsider Set

A matching serial numbered pair consisting of a lefthanded and a righthanded version of this model. It was cased, and there were only 100 manufactured in 1986 and 1987.

NIB	Exc.	V.G.	Good	Fair	Poor
1400	1250	1000	750	600	475

Gold Falcon

The frame was machined from solid 17-karat gold. The slide is stainless steel, and the sights have diamond inlays. It was engraved to the customer's order, and there were only 50 manufactured.

NIB	Exc.	V.G.	Good
30000	25000	20000	15000

FAMARS, A. & S.

Brescia, Italy

The Famars shotgun is one of the world's finest and is available on a custom-order basis. This makes it quite difficult to accurately establish values in a book of this nature. Each individual gun must be appraised if a transaction is contemplated as the array of options available makes the values fluctuate greatly. They manufacture two basic models, and we list them and give an estimated value in their basic form only.

External Hammer Shotgun

A double-barrelled, side by side, with external hammers and double triggers. All other features are custom-ordered.

Exc.	V.G.	Good	Fair	Poor
7500	7000	6000	4000	2750

Sidelock Shotgun

A side by side, with hand-detachable sidelocks. All other features are custom ordered.

Exc.	V.G.	Good	Fair	Poor
10000	8500	7500	5000	3500

FARQUHARSON, JOHN

London, England

Not a gunmaker but the designer of what is perhaps the finest single shot action ever developed. It was patented on May 25, 1872, and has been used as the basis for some of the world's best single shot rifles manufactured by top English gunmakers throughout the years. There will be references to this action under sections dealing with these makers.

FARROW ARMS CO.

Holyoke, Massachusetts
Mason, Tennessee

Farrow Falling Block Rifle

Designed by W.M. Farrow, a target shooter who had worked on the Ballard rifles for the Marlin company. The Farrow rifles are chambered for various calibers and have barrel lengths from 28"-36" of octagonal configuration. They feature tang sights and are either all blued or have a nickle-plated receiver. The stocks are walnut. There were two grades offered that varied according to the grade of wood used. These rifles are quite scarce on today's market, and the number manufactured between 1885 and 1900 is unknown.

No. 1 Model

Fancy walnut with checkering and a Schutzen buttplate.

Exc.	V.G.	Good	Fair	Poor
4500	4000	3500	3000	1750

No. 2 Model

Plainer wood and no checkering.

Exc.	V.G.	Good	Fair	Poor
3750	3000	2750	2250	1400

FAYETTEVILLE ARMORY PISTOLS AND RIFLES

Fayetteville, North Carolina

In 1861, the U.S. Arsenal at Fayetteville, North Carolina was seized by the officials of that state and later turned over to the government of the Confederate States of America. While still controlled by the state of North Carolina, a number of inferior flintlock arms were altered at the arsenal from flint to percussion, including a number of U.S. M1836 pistols and U.S. M1819 Hall rifles (the latter also shortened and remodeled into cavalry carbines). In accordance with an agreement between the governors of Virginia and North Carolina, the rifle machinery seized at the former U.S. Armory at Harpers Ferry, Virginia was also sent to Fayetteville, where in 1862 the Confederacy began the construction of rifles modeled after the the U.S. M1855 rifle. Production continued until 1865 when the advance of Sherman's Armies necessitated the evacuation of the armory.

Fayetteville Armory Percussion Pistols (U.S. M1836 pistols, altered)

Overall length- 13-3/4"; barrel length- 8-1/2"; caliber- .54. Markings: (same as U.S. M1836 contact pistols, i.e. the locks either marked with eagle head over "A. WATERS/MILBURY MS./(date)" or "US/R. JOHNSON/MIDDN CONN./(date)" and various barrel proofmarks; also occasionally marked "N. CAROLINA".

The Fayetteville Armory altered approximately 900 U.S. M1836 pistols from flintlock to percussion. These arms were altered by enlarging the flint touchhole and screwing in a cylindrical drum in place of the pan and frizzen. The distinguishing feature of the Fayetteville alteration is the clean-out screw at the faced of the cylinder and the "S" shaped hammer, not unlike that used on post-1862 dated rifles.

Courtesy Milwaukee Public Museum, Milwaukee, Wisconsin.

Exc.	V. G.	Good	Fair	Poor
2300	2000	1750	1200	900

Fayetteville Armory Rifles (Types I through IV)

Overall length- 49-3/8"; barrel length- 33"; caliber- .58. Markings: on barrel, an eagle over "C.S.A./FAYETTEVILLE" forward of the hammer and the date on the rounded tail. "CSA" also found on buttplates; date on top of barrel; proofmarks (eaglehead, "V" and "P") on left quarter of barrel near breech.

From 1862 to early 1865, the Fayetteville Armory produced four variants of the old U.S. M1855 rifle on the machinery that had been lent to North Carolina by Virginia after its capture in April 1861. The earliest 1862 production (Type I) utilized unmilled lockplates captured at Harpers Ferry and are distinguished by having a "hump" (where the Maynard priqer would have been milled) that extends to the arc of the hammer. Type II production utilized the newly made locks received from Richmond during the balance of 1862; they had a relatively low "hump" whose upper surface matched the contour of the stock. By the end of 1862, Fayetteville was producing its own lock, the plate of which resembled the U.S. M1861 rifle-musket, but with a distinctive "S" shaped hammer. This lock distinguishes both type III and type IV production. All rifles made through 1863 continued to bear a saber bayonet lug on the right side of the barrel. In 1864, however, this was eliminated in favor of a triangular socket bayonet. The absence of the saber bayonet lug and remodeled front sight distinguishes type IV production. Because the barrel machinery went to Richmond, production at Fayetteville was continually hindered, seldom reaching more than 300 per month in the three years that the Fayetteville rifle was manufactured. (Note: The rarity of Type I production will usually generate a premium for that variant.)

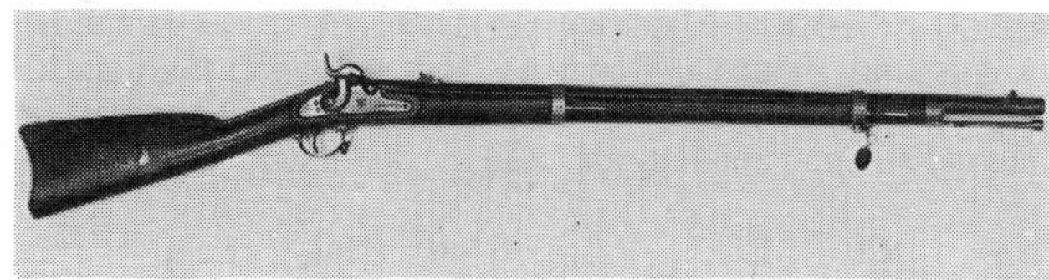

Courtesy Milwaukee Public Museum, Milwaukee, Wisconsin.

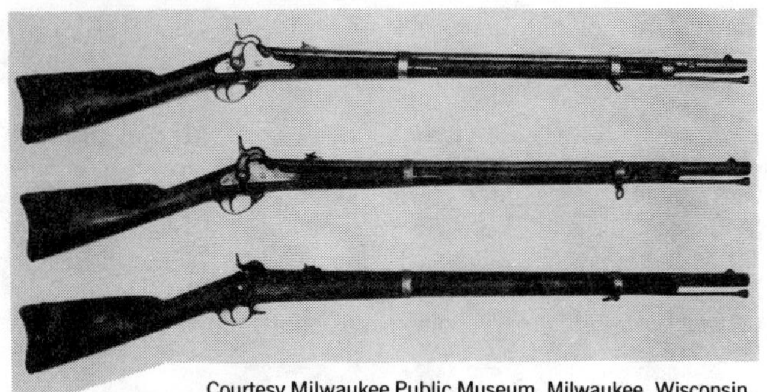

Courtesy Milwaukee Public Museum, Milwaukee, Wisconsin.

Exc.	V.G.	Good	Fair	Poor
6500	5500	4750	4250	3750

FEATHER INDUSTRIES, INC.

Boulder, Colorado

AT-22

A blowback-operated semi-automatic chambered for the .22 l.r. cartridge. It has a removable, shrouded 17" barrel and a folding metal stock. There are adjustable sights, and the finish is black. There is a detachable 20-round magazine. This model was introduced in 1986.

NIB	Exc.	V.G.	Good	Fair	Poor
250	200	175	150	110	75

AT-9

Similar to the AR-22 except that it is chambered for the 9mm parabellum cartridge and has a 16" barrel and 32-round magazine. It was introduced in 1988.

NIB	Exc.	V.G.	Good	Fair	Poor
325	275	250	225	175	125

KG-9

A 9mm, semi-automatic assault rifle that was introduced in 1989.

NIB	Exc.	V.G.	Good	Fair	Poor
575	500	425	375	300	250

KG-22

Similar in appearance to the KG-9 except that it is chambered for .22 l.r. and has a 20-round detachable magazine. It was introduced in 1989.

NIB	Exc.	V.G.	Good	Fair	Poor
300	275	225	175	125	100

SAR-180

The current incarnation of the old American 180, which was manufactured in Austria a number of years ago. It is chambered for .22 l.r. and has a 17.5" barrel. It is a blowback-operated semi-automatic that has a 165-round drum magazine that sits on top of the action on the flat side. The rear sight is adjustable, and the finish is blued with a walnut stock, pistol grip, and forend. This model was revived by Feather Industries in 1989.

NIB	Exc.	V.G.	Good	Fair	Poor
500	450	400	350	275	200

Mini-AT

A blowback-operated semi-automatic pistol chambered for the .22 l.r. cartridge. It is a 5.5"-barrelled version of the AT-22 rifle and has a 20- round magazine. This model was manufactured between 1986 and 1989.

NIB	Exc.	V.G.	Good	Fair	Poor
350	200	175	150	125	100

Guardian Angel

A 2-shot, Over/Under, derringer-styled pistol. It is chambered for the 9mm parabellum and can be converted to fire the .38 Super cartridge. It is constructed of stainless steel and has an internal hammer and fully enclosed trigger. It was introduced in 1988.

NIB	Exc.	V.G.	Good	Fair	Poor
150	125	100	75	50	40

FEDERAL ENGINEERING CORP.

Chicago, Illinois

XC-220

A blowback-operated, semi-automatic rifle chambered for the .22 l.r. cartridge. It has a 16.5" barrel and a steel receiver that is blued. The stock is black synthetic. This model was introduced in 1984.

NIB	Exc.	V.G.	Good	Fair	Poor
350	300	275	225	175	125

XC-450

Similar in appearance to the XC-220 except that it is chambered for the .45 ACP cartridge. It has a 30-round detachable magazine.

NIB	Exc.	V.G.	Good	Fair	Poor
600	525	450	400	300	250

XC-900

A 9mm parabellum version of the same basic firearm. It has a 32-round magazine and was introduced in 1984.

NIB	Exc.	V.G.	Good	Fair	Poor
550	500	425	350	275	200

FEDERAL ORDNANCE, INC.

South El Monte, California

An importer as well as a manufacturer that basically fabricates new and custom firearms out of existing older military parts. The firearms they import are military surplus weapons that will be covered in their own sections of this book. The firearms covered here are of Federal Ordnance manufacture.

M-14 Semi-Automatic

A semi-automatic version of the M-14 service rifle. It is constructed of a newly manufactured receiver that has no selector and select surplus G.I. parts. The rifle is refinished to original specifications and furnished with a 20-round magazine and either a wood or fiberglass stock. This model was introduced in 1986. Although this model is a battle rifle and falls into the category affected by the wild price fluctuations we have been experiencing, prices for this gun have stayed fairly stable due to a fairly constant supply. This model has been manufactured since 1986.

Exc.	V.G.	Good	Fair	Poor
650	600	550	450	375

Model 714 Broomhandle Mauser

A remanufactured C96-type pistol chambered for 7.63mm or 9mm parabellum. It utilizes a new manufactured frame and surplus parts. It features a 10-round detachable magazine, adjustable sights, and walnut grips. A Bolo Model with a smaller grip was produced in 1988 only.

NIB	Exc.	V.G.	Good	Fair	Poor
850	750	650	500	250	100

Model 713 Mauser Carbine

A 16"-barrelled version of the Mauser with a fixed walnut stock. It has a standard magazine and is chambered for 7.63mm or 9mm parabellum. It is refinished and was introduced in 1987.

Exc.	V.G.	Good	Fair	Poor
1250	1000	900	700	575

Model 713 Deluxe

Chambered for 7.63mm and has a 16" barrel with a detachable shoulder stock made of deluxe walnut. It has been modified to accept detachable magazines and is furnished with two 20-shot units. It has a 1000-meter adjustable sight and is furnished in a fitted leather case. There were only 1,500 manufactured in 1986.

NIB	Exc.	V.G.	Good	Fair	Poor
2000	1750	1500	1250	1000	800

Standard Broomhandle
A refurbished surplus C-96 Mauser pistol with a new 7.63mm or 9mm barrel. All springs are replaced, and the entire gun is refinished. It is furnished with a shoulder stock/holster of Chinese manufacture.

NIB	Exc.	V.G.	Good	Fair	Poor
725	650	525	450	350	275

Ranger 1911A1
Federal Ordnance's version of the 1911A1 Colt service pistol. It is made of all steel, is chambered for .45 ACP, and has checkered walnut grips. It was introduced in 1988.

NIB	Exc.	V.G.	Good	Fair	Poor
440	375	325	275	225	150

FEINWERKBAU
Oberndorf, Germany
Importer--Beeman Precision Arms
Santa Rosa, California

Known predominately for the production of high quality, extremely accurate air rifles and pistols. They also produce some of the most accurate target .22-caliber firearms in the world today. These firearms are listed.

Model 2000 Universal
A single-shot, bolt-action target rifle chambered for the .22 rimfire cartridge. It has a 26.5" barrel with adjustable aperture sights and a fully adjustable trigger. There were four different stock configurations offered with stippled pistol grips and forearms. An electronic trigger was available as a $450 option. This model was discontinued in 1988.

Exc.	V.G.	Good	Fair	Poor
1200	1050	850	650	550

Mini 2000
Has a 22" barrel, and the electronic trigger was available at the additional cost.

Exc.	V.G.	Good	Fair	Poor
1000	850	750	550	450

Running Boar Rifle
Has a thumbhole stock with an adjustable cheekpiece and is furnished without sights. It was specially designed for the offhand Running Boar Competitions.

Exc.	V.G.	Good	Fair	Poor
1200	1050	850	650	550

Match Rifle
Has a 26.75" barrel and an adjustable cheekpiece stock.

Exc.	V.G.	Good	Fair	Poor
1100	950	750	550	450

Model 2600 Ultra Match Free Rifle
Similar to the Model 2000, with a laminated thumbhole stock and a heavy 26" barrel, fully adjustable sights, and trigger. It is offered with an electronic trigger for an additional $400. This model was introduced in 1986.

NIB	Exc.	V.G.	Good	Fair	Poor
1400	1200	1000	850	650	550

FEMARU
Budapest, Hungary

Hungary became a communist sattelite in the mid-1950s. At this time the Femaru company was designated to replace the firm of Fegyvergyar as the official Hungarian arms manufacturer. The products are of good quality.

Hege
A complete copy of the Walther PP. It is chambered for the 7.65mm and manufactured to be sold by Hegewaffen of Germany. The slide is so marked, along with a Pegasus in a circle. The designation "AP 66 Cal.7.65" also appears. The pistol was intended for export sales in the U.S. and other western countries.

Exc.	V.G.	Good	Fair	Poor
250	225	175	125	100

Tokagypt
15,000 of these pistols were built in 1958, under contract for the Egyptian army. It is a modified version of the Soviet TT-33 Tokarev chambered for the 9mm parabellum with a safety added. This is a very well-made, serviceable pistol; and it is difficult to understand why Egypt renigged on the contract. The balance were sold commercially—some under the trademark "Firebird."

Exc.	V.G.	Good	Fair	Poor
400	350	275	200	125

Walam
Another Walther PP copy of excellent quality chambered for the 9mm short or .380 ACP. Egypt was also to be the recipient of this contract, but again they mysteriously cancelled. The pistols were sold on the commercial market—some designated Model 48.

Exc.	V.G.	Good	Fair	Poor
250	225	175	125	100

FERLIB
Gardone V.T., Italy
Importers—Quality Arms
Houston, Texas
New England Arms
Kittery Point, Maine

Model F.VI
A high-grade, side-by-side shotgun chambered for all gauges and is essentially custom-ordered. It is available in various barrel lengths and chokes and has an Anson and Deeley boxlock action, double triggers, and automatic ejectors. The action is case-colored, and the stock is hand-checkered select walnut. Single selective triggers are available for an additional $375.
28 Gauge and .410—Add 10%.

NIB	Exc.	V.G.	Good	Fair	Poor
3800	3500	2800	2250	1700	1450

Model F.VII
Has a scroll-engraved, coin-finished frame but otherwise is similar to the Model F.VI. Single trigger option and small gauge premium are the same.

NIB	Exc.	V.G.	Good	Fair	Poor
5000	4250	3750	3000	2400	1950

Model F.VII/SC
A more deluxe version with gold inlays and a gamescene-engraved receiver. Options and premium are the same.

NIB	Exc.	V.G.	Good	Fair	Poor
6100	5500	4500	3750	2800	2250

Model F.VII Sideplate
Features false sideplates that are completely covered with gamescene engraving. This model is standard with a single-selective trigger, but the small gauge premium is applicable.

NIB	Exc.	V.G.	Good	Fair	Poor
5500	5000	4250	3500	2750	2200

Model F.VII/SC Sideplate
The false sideplate model with gold inlays accenting the full coverage engraving.
28 Gauge and .410—Add 10%.

NIB	Exc.	V.G.	Good	Fair	Poor
7200	6500	5250	4500	3500	2750

Hammer Gun
Features a boxlock action with external hammers. Its other features are custom ordered to the purchaser's specifications.

NIB	Exc.	V.G.	Good	Fair	Poor
2900	2500	1850	1500	1000	750

FERRY, ANDREWS & CO.
Stafford, Connecticut

Under Hammer Pistol

This boot pistol is chambered for .36 caliber percussion and has a 3" part-round / part-octagonal barrel. They are very similar to the other under hammer pistols that were produced in Connecticut and Massachusetts. The topstrap was marked "Andrews Ferry & Co." The number manufactured is unknown. They were produced in the 1850s.

Exc.	V.G.	Good	Fair	Poor
400	350	300	225	125

FIALA ARMS COMPANY
New Haven, Connecticut

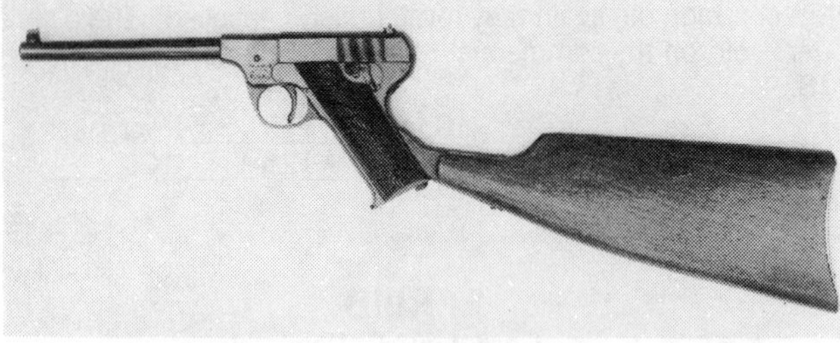

Fiala Target Pistol

A different type of pistol than what is commonly encountered. Outwardly it resembles a semi-automatic Colt Woodsman; in actuality it is a manually operated firearm that must be cycled by hand after every shot. It was chambered for the .22 rimfire and was offered with interchangeable barrels in lengths of 3", 7.5", and 20". The finish is blued, and the grips are checkered walnut. They are marked "Fiala Arms and Equipment Co. Inc. / New Haven Conn. / Patents Pending." This pistol was furnished with a detachable shoulder stock in a leather trunk case that held the gun, three barrels, stock, and cleaning tools. The government has classified this pistol with its stock as a "Curio and Relic"; and in its complete state it is a very desirable collectible.

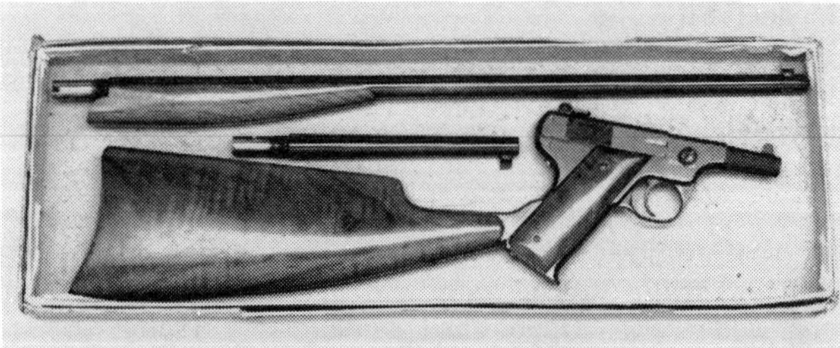

Courtesy Butterfield & Butterfield, San Francisco, California.

Complete, Three barrels, Stock, Tools, and Case

Exc.	V.G.	Good	Fair	Poor
1250	1100	850	675	550

Gun Only

Exc.	V.G.	Good	Fair	Poor
500	425	350	250	150

FINNISH LION
Valmet, Sweden

ISU Target Rifle

A single shot, bolt-action rifle chambered for the .22 rimfire cartridge. It has a 27" heavy barrel and a target stock with accessories. It features target adjustable sights and was manufactured between 1966 and 1977.

Exc.	V.G.	Good	Fair	Poor
350	300	250	200	125

Champion Free Rifle

Has a 29" heavy barrel and double-set triggers. Otherwise it is similar to the ISU model. It was manufactured between 1965 and 1972.

Exc.	V.G.	Good	Fair	Poor
600	525	450	375	275

Match Rifle

Similar to the Champion rifle, with a thumbhole stock and an adjustable butt plate. It was manufactured between 1937 and 1972.

Exc.	V.G.	Good	Fair	Poor
500	425	350	275	200

FIOCCHI OF AMERICA, INC.
Ozark, Missouri

SEE—Pardini and A. Zoli

Imports the above firearms, and they are listed in their own respective sections.

FIREARMS INTERNATIONAL
Washington, D.C.

SEE—Star

Was once the importer of the Star Model D as it was sold in the U.S.A. They also imported various other .25- caliber Colt copies that are not considered collectible and that would be valued in the $150-and-under range.

FOEHL C.
Philadelphia, Pennsylvania

Foehl Derringer

A .41 caliber percussion single shot pistol with a 2" barrel, German silver mounts and a walnut stock. The lock marked "C. Foehl".

Exc.	V.G.	Good	Fair	Poor
750	700	600	450	300

FOEHL & WEEKS
Philadelphia, Pennsylvania

Columbian

A .32 or .38 caliber revolver marked with the patent date "20 January 1891".

Exc.	V.G.	Good	Fair	Poor
150	125	100	75	50

Columbian Automatic

A .38 caliber revolver with a hinged barrel and cylinder assembly.

Exc.	V.G.	Good	Fair	Poor
175	150	125	100	75

Perfect

As above, with a concealed hammer and also in .32 caliber.

Exc.	V.G.	Good	Fair	Poor
175	150	125	100	75

FOGARTY
American Repeating Rifle Co.
Boston, Massachusetts

Fogarty Repeating Rifle and Carbine

A limited number of repeating rifles and carbines based upon Valentine Fogarty's patents were produced between 1866 and 1867. The calibers of these arms varies and the normal barrel lengths are 20" and 28". Blued, casehardened with walnut stocks. The American Repeating Rifle Company was purchased by the Winchester Repeating Arms Company in 1869. Prospective purchasers are advised to secure a qualified appraisal prior to acquisition.

Rifle

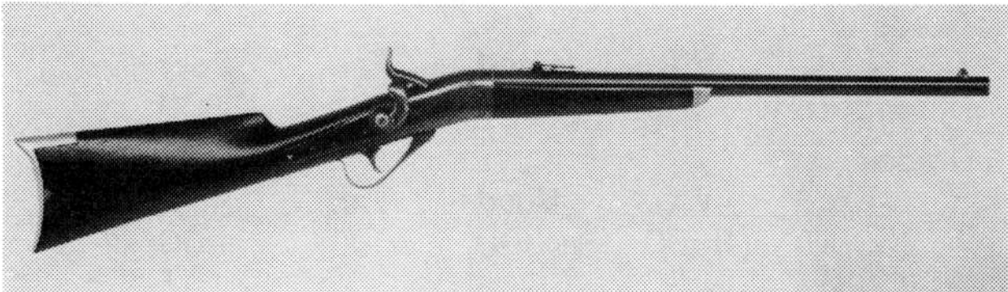

Courtesy Buffalo Bill Historical Center, Cody, Wyoming.

Exc.	V.G.	Good	Fair	Poor
2000	1850	1600	1250	950

Carbine

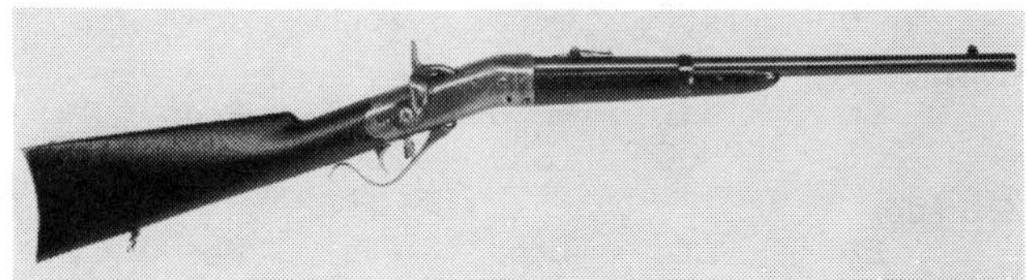

Courtesy Buffalo Bill Historical Center, Cody, Wyoming.

Exc.	V.G.	Good	Fair	Poor
2500	2375	2000	1600	1250

FOLSOM, H.

St. Louis, Missouri

SEE—Crescent Arms Co.

Derringer

A .41 caliber single shot percussion pocket pistol with a 2.5" barrel, German silver mounts and a walnut stock. The barrel marked "H. Folsom".

Exc.	V.G.	Good	Fair	Poor
650	575	450	350	275

FOREHAND & WADSWORTH

Worcester, Massachusetts

Established in 1871 and operated under the above name until 1890 when it became the Forehand Arms Company. Hopkins & Allen purchased the company in 1902.

Single Shot Derringer

A .22 caliber single shot pocket pistol with a 2" half octagonal pivoted barrel, spur trigger and nickle or silver plated frame. Walnut grips. The barrel marked "Forehand & Wadsworth Worcester".

Exc.	V.G.	Good	Fair	Poor
300	250	200	150	100

Single Shot .41 Derringer

As above in .41 caliber with a 2.5" round barrel.

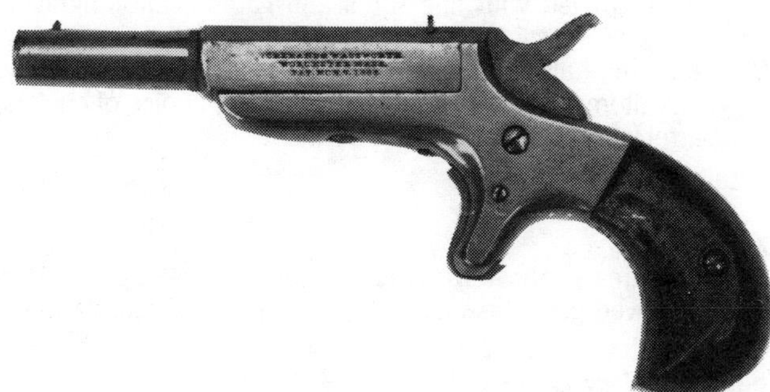

Courtesy Milwaukee Public Museum, Milwaukee, Wisconsin.

Exc.	V.G.	Good	Fair	Poor
450	400	325	250	200

Side Hammer .22

A .22 caliber spur trigger revolver with a 2.25" to 4" octagonal barrel and 7 shot cylinder. Blued or nickle-plated with walnut grips.

Exc.	V.G.	Good	Fair	Poor
300	250	200	150	100

Center Hammer

A .32 caliber spur trigger revolver with a 3.5" octagonal barrel and 6-shot cylinder. Blued or nickle-plated with rosewood or walnut grips. The top strap commonly found marked "Terror".

Courtesy Milwaukee Public Museum, Milwaukee, Wisconsin.

Exc.	V.G.	Good	Fair	Poor
350	300	150	175	125

Old Model Army Single Action Revolver

A .44 Russian caliber revolver with a 7.5" round barrel and 6-shot cylinder. The barrel marked "Forehand & Wadsworth, Worchester, Mass. U.S. Patd. Oct. 22, '61, June 27, '71 Oct. 28, '73." Blued with walnut grips. Approximately 250 were manufactured between 1872 and 1878.

Exc.	V.G.	Good	Fair	Poor
750	675	575	450	300

New Model Army Single Action Revolver

Similar to the above, with a 6.5" barrel and half-cock notch on the hammer. Approximately 250 were made between 1878 and 1882.

Exc.	V.G.	Good	Fair	Poor
650	575	475	350	225

Double Action Revolver

A .32 or .38 caliber double-action revolver with a 3.5" barrel and 6-shot cylinder. The .32 caliber version marked "Forehand & Wadsworth Double Action", and the .38 caliber "American Bulldog". Manufactured from 1871 to 1890.

Exc.	V.G.	Good	Fair	Poor
250	225	175	125	75

British Bulldog

A solid frame double-action revolver similar to the above.

Exc.	V.G.	Good	Fair	Poor
250	225	175	125	90

British Bulldog .44

As above in .44 S&W caliber with a 5" barrel and 5-shot cylinder.

Exc.	V.G.	Good	Fair	Poor
275	250	175	125	90

Swamp Angel

A .41 caliber single action revolver with a 3" barrel and 5-shot cylinder. The top strap marked "Swamp Angel".

Exc.	V.G.	Good	Fair	Poor
200	175	150	100	75

Forehand Arms Co. 1898-1902

Perfection Automatic

A .32 or .38 caliber double-action revolver with a hinged barrel and cylinder assembly. Varying barrel lengths. Blued or nickle-plated with hard rubber grips.

Exc.	V.G.	Good	Fair	Poor
200	150	100	75	50

FOWLER, B. JR.
Hartford, Connecticut

Percussion Pistol

A .38 caliber single shot percussion pistol with a 4" half octagonal barrel, iron frame and maple grips. The barrel marked "B. Fowler, Jr." Manufactured between 1835 and 1838.

Exc.	V.G.	Good	Fair	Poor
375	350	300	225	150

FOX, A. H.
Philadelphia, Pennsylvania

Ansley H. Fox established the Fox Gun Company in Baltimore, Maryland in 1896. Subsequently, he made arms under the name Philadelphia Gun Company. As of 1905, he operated under the name A. H. Fox. In 1930, this company was purchased by the Savage Arms Company who continued manufacturing all grades of Fox shotguns. As of 1942, the Savage Company only made the plainer grades.

Sterlingworth

A .12, 16 or 20 gauge boxlock double-barrel shotgun with 26", 28" or 30" barrels, double triggers and extractors. Automatic ejectors were also available and would add approximately 30% to the values listed below. Blued, case-hardened with a walnut stock. Manufactured from 1903 to 1930.

20 Gauge—Add 50%.

Exc.	V.G.	Good	Fair	Poor
1250	1000	800	500	275

Sterlingworth Deluxe

As above, with an ivory bead, recoil pad and optional 32" barrel.

20 Gauge—Add 50%.

Exc.	V.G.	Good	Fair	Poor
1450	1250	1000	700	400

SP Grade

A 12 or 20 gauge boxlock double-barrel shotgun with varying length barrels, double triggers and extractors.

20 Gauge—Add 35%.

Automatic Ejectors—Add 15%.

Exc.	V.G.	Good	Fair	Poor
1000	850	750	450	225

HE Grade

Similar to the Sterlingworth, but with 3" chambers, 30" or 32" barrels and automatic ejectors. This model is marked on the barrel "Not Warranted".

Single Selective Trigger—Add 20%.

Exc.	V.G.	Good	Fair	Poor
2400	2150	1750	1000	650

High Grade Guns A-FE

The Fox Company as well as the Savage Arms Company produced a variety of shotguns decorated in varying grades. As the value for these arms depends on the particular features of these arms, prospective purchasers are advised to secure a qualified appraisal prior to acquisition.

A Grade

Exc.	V.G.	Good	Fair	Poor
1450	1150	850	600	400

AE Grade (Automatic Ejectors)

Exc.	V.G.	Good	Fair	Poor
1750	1450	1150	900	700

BE Grade

Exc.	V.G.	Good	Fair	Poor
2800	2500	2000	1500	900

CE Grade

Exc.	V.G.	Good	Fair	Poor
3000	2600	2100	1550	950

XE Grade

Exc.	V.G.	Good	Fair	Poor
5500	5000	3500	1850	1100

DE Grade

Exc.	V.G.	Good	Fair	Poor
8500	7500	5000	3000	1500

FE Grade

Exc.	V.G.	Good	Fair	Poor
25000	18500	10000	7000	5000

Single Barrel Trapgun

A 12 gauge single barrel boxlock shotgun with 30" or 32" ventilated-rib barrels and automatic ejector. Produced in four grades as listed below.

JE Grade

Exc.	V.G.	Good	Fair	Poor
1750	1450	950	750	450

KE Grade

Exc.	V.G.	Good	Fair	Poor
2500	2000	1650	1250	750

LE Grade

Exc.	V.G.	Good	Fair	Poor
3250	2500	2000	1500	1000

ME Grade

Exc.	V.G.	Good	Fair	Poor
8000	6500	4500	3000	2000

Currently manufactured A.H. Fox shotguns

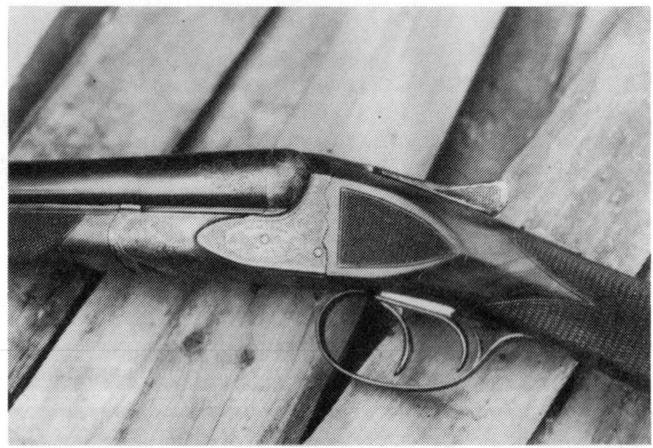

In 1993 the Connecticut Manufacturing Company of New Britain, Connecticut announced the production of the A.H. Fox shotgun in 20 gauge exclusively. The gun is hand built and constructed to the same dimensions and standards as the original Fox. The gun is offered in five grades with many standard features and several optional ones as well. Each shotgun is built to order. Because these guns are newly built and have no pricing history only manufacture's retail price will be given.

CE Grade

Receiver engraved with fine scroll and game scene engraving with Turkish Circassian walnut stock, fine line hand checkering. Choice of full, half, or straight grip with splinter forend. Double triggers, automatic ejectors, automatic safety, choice of chokes, and barrel lengths in 26, 28, and 30 inches.

Retail price: $5,650

XE Grade

Same features as above with the addition of chiseled scroll work with engraved game scenes and higher quality Circassian walnut.

Retail price: $8,500

DE Grade
Same features as above with more intricate and extensive engraving. Even higher quality wood with diamond pattern checkering.

Retail price: $12,500

FE Grade
This grade features gold inlays and distinctive scroll work. Best quality wood with very fine line diamond pattern checkering.

Retail price: $17,500

Exhibition Grade
This is the company's highest grade and features any optional detail the customer desires including custom engraving and exhibition quality wood. Each Exhibition Grade Fox will be unique and should be appraised on an individual basis.

Retail price: $25,000

FOX
SEE—Demro

FRANCHI, L.
Brescia, Italy
Importer—American Arms, Inc.
No. Kansas City, Missouri

Side x Side Shotguns

Astore
A 12 gauge boxlock shotgun manufactured in a variety of barrel lengths with double triggers and automatic ejectors. Blued with a straight walnut stock. Manufactured from 1937 to 1960.

Exc.	V.G.	Good	Fair	Poor
1000	900	750	500	350

Astore II
As above, but more finely finished.

Exc.	V.G.	Good	Fair	Poor
1250	1100	900	700	450

Astore 5
As above, but more finely finished.

Exc.	V.G.	Good	Fair	Poor
2000	1750	1250	950	600

Airone
Similar to the Astore. Manufactured during the 1940s.

Exc.	V.G.	Good	Fair	Poor
1300	1050	950	750	500

Sidelock Double Barrel Shotgun
A 12, 16 or 20 gauge sidelock double-barrel shotgun manufactured in a variety of barrel lengths with a single selective trigger and automatic ejectors. Produced in the following grades:

Condor

Exc.	V.G.	Good	Fair	Poor
7500	6500	4500	3500	2500

Imperial

Exc.	V.G.	Good	Fair	Poor
10000	8500	6000	4500	3250

Imperiales

Exc.	V.G.	Good	Fair	Poor
10500	9000	6500	5000	3500

No. 5 Imperial Monte Carlo

Exc.	V.G.	Good	Fair	Poor
15000	12500	9000	7500	5000

No. 11 Imperial Monte Carlo

Exc.	V.G.	Good	Fair	Poor
16000	13500	10000	8000	5500

Imperial Monte Carlo Extra

Exc.	V.G.	Good	Fair	Poor
20000	17500	12500	9500	7500

Over/Under Shotguns

Priti Deluxe Model
A 12 or 20 gauge Over/Under boxlock double-barrel shotgun with 26" or 28" ventilated-rib barrels, single trigger and automatic ejectors. Introduced in 1988.

NIB	Exc.	V.G.	Good	Fair	Poor
475	425	350	300	225	150

Falconet
A 12 gauge to .410 bore boxlock double-barrel shotgun with single selective trigger and automatic ejectors. The receiver was annodized in tan, ebony, or silver finishes. Manufactured from 1968 to 1975.

Silver Receiver—Add 10%.
28 Gauge and .410—Add 25%.

Exc.	V.G.	Good	Fair	Poor
550	500	425	350	250

Falconet Skeet
As above, with a 26" skeet barrel with a wide rib and the receiver case-hardened. Manufactured from 1970 to 1974.

Exc.	V.G.	Good	Fair	Poor
950	850	700	550	450

Falconet International Skeet
As above, but more finely finished.

Exc.	V.G.	Good	Fair	Poor
1000	900	750	600	475

Falconet Trap
As above, with a 30" modified and full choke barrel, and trap stock. Manufactured from 1970 to 1974.

Exc.	V.G.	Good	Fair	Poor
950	850	700	550	450

Falconet International Trap
As above, but more finely finished.

Exc.	V.G.	Good	Fair	Poor
1000	900	750	600	475

Peregrine Model 451
A 12 gauge boxlock double-barrel shotgun with 26" or 28" ventilated-rib barrels, alloy receiver, single selective trigger and automatic ejectors. Manufactured in 1975.

Exc.	V.G.	Good	Fair	Poor
600	525	450	375	275

Peregrine Model 400
As above, with a steel frame.

Exc.	V.G.	Good	Fair	Poor
650	575	500	400	300

Aristocrat
Similar to the above, with 26", 28" or 30" ventilated-rib barrels. Manufactured from 1960 to 1969.

Exc.	V.G.	Good	Fair	Poor
650	575	500	400	300

Aristocrat Magnum
As above, with 3" chambers and 32" full choke barrels.

Exc.	V.G.	Good	Fair	Poor
650	575	500	400	300

Aristocrat Silver King
As above, with a French case-hardened receiver, and available in four grades of decoration.

Exc.	V.G.	Good	Fair	Poor
750	675	575	475	350

Aristocrat Deluxe

Exc.	V.G.	Good	Fair	Poor
1000	800	675	575	400

Aristocrat Supreme

Exc.	V.G.	Good	Fair	Poor
1450	1200	850	700	575

Aristocrat Imperial

Exc.	V.G.	Good	Fair	Poor
2750	2250	1750	1250	950

Aristocrat Monte Carlo

Exc.	V.G.	Good	Fair	Poor
3500	3000	2750	2000	1500

Model 2003 Trap

A 12 gauge boxlock double-barrel shotgun with 30" or 32" ventilated-rib barrels, single selective trigger and automatic ejectors. Manufactured in 1976.

Exc.	V.G.	Good	Fair	Poor
1250	1100	800	650	500

Model 2004 Trap

A single-barrelled version of the Model 2003.

Exc.	V.G.	Good	Fair	Poor
1250	1100	800	650	500

Model 2005 Combination Trap

The Model 2003 with both a single and set of Over/Under barrels.

Exc.	V.G.	Good	Fair	Poor
2500	2200	1750	1200	950

Model 3000 "Undergun"

As above, with a single barrel fitted with a high ventilated-rib so that it fires from the lower barrel position.

Exc.	V.G.	Good	Fair	Poor
2750	2450	2000	1500	1200

Alcione Model

A 12 gauge boxlock double-barrel shotgun with 28" ventilated-rib barrels, single selective trigger and automatic ejectors.

NIB	Exc.	V.G.	Good	Fair	Poor
850	775	575	475	350	300

Alcione SL

As above, but more finely finished and with a French casehardened receiver.

Exc.	V.G.	Good	Fair	Poor
1500	1200	950	700	500

Black Magic Hunter

A 12 gauge Magnum double-barrel shotgun with 28" ventilated-rib barrels threaded for choke tubes, single selective triggers and automatic ejectors. Blued with a walnut stock. Introduced in 1989.

NIB	Exc.	V.G.	Good	Fair	Poor
1200	1050	850	700	550	450

Black Magic Lightweight Hunter

As above, with 26" barrels and 2.75" chambers gun.

NIB	Exc.	V.G.	Good	Fair	Poor
1150	1000	800	650	500	400

Semi-Automatic Shotguns

Standard Model

A 12 or 20 gauge semi-automatic shotgun with 24" to 30" ventilated-rib barrels (those made after 1989, threaded for choke tubes) and an alloy receiver. Walnut stock. Manufactured since 1950.

Magnum Model—Add 10%.

NIB	Exc.	V.G.	Good	Fair	Poor
525	475	425	350	250	175

Hunter Model

As above with an etched receiver and more finely figured wood.

Magnum Model—Add 10%.

NIB	Exc.	V.G.	Good	Fair	Poor
575	500	450	375	275	200

Eldorado

As above, but more finely finished. Manufactured from 1954 to 1975.

Exc.	V.G.	Good	Fair	Poor
475	425	325	250	175

Crown Grade, Diamond Grade, Imperial Grade

As above, with hand done engraving and finely figured walnut stocks.

Crown Grade

Exc.	V.G.	Good	Fair	Poor
1500	1250	1000	700	475

Diamond Grade

Exc.	V.G.	Good	Fair	Poor
2000	1750	1250	900	675

Imperial Grade

Exc.	V.G.	Good	Fair	Poor
2500	2250	1750	1250	950

Model 500

A 12 gauge semi-automatic shotgun with a 28" ventilated-rib barrel and walnut stock. Introduced in 1976.

Deluxe Version—Add 10%.

Exc.	V.G.	Good	Fair	Poor
350	325	275	200	150

Model 520 "Eldorado Gold"

An engraved and gold inlaid version of the above.

Exc.	V.G.	Good	Fair	Poor
1000	850	650	450	300

Model 530 Trap

The Model 500 with a 30" or 32" ventilated-rib barrel and trap stock.

Exc.	V.G.	Good	Fair	Poor
675	600	500	400	300

Prestige Model

A 12 gauge semi-automatic shotgun manufactured in a variety of barrel lengths. After 1989 the barrels threaded for choke tubes. Alloy receiver and walnut stock.

NIB	Exc.	V.G.	Good	Fair	Poor
725	675	525	450	350	275

Elite Model

As above, with an etched receiver and more finely figured stock.

NIB	Exc.	V.G.	Good	Fair	Poor
750	700	550	475	375	300

SPAS 12

A 12 gauge slide action or semi-automatic shotgun with a 21.5" barrel and 9-shot magazine. Annodized, black finish with a composition folding or fixed stock.

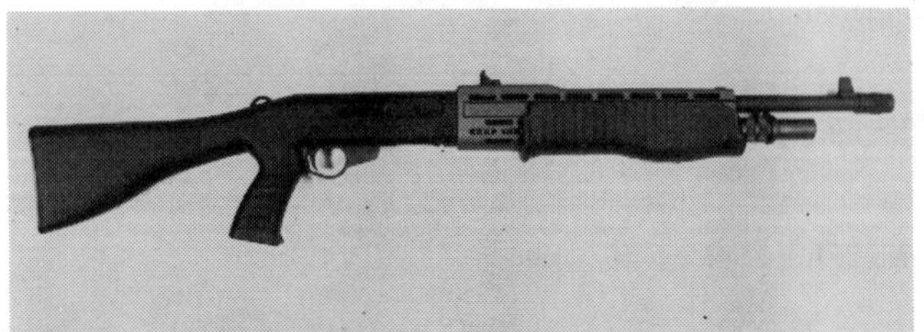

NIB	Exc.	V.G.	Good	Fair	Poor
600	575	500	450	300	150

Black Magic Game Model

A 12 gauge Magnum semi-automatic shotgun with 24" to 28" ventilated-rib barrels threaded for choke tubes, gold annodized

alloy receiver, blackened barrel and walnut stock. Also available in trap or skeet configuration.
Skeet Model—Add 20%.
Trap Model—Add 25%.

NIB	Exc.	V.G.	Good	Fair	Poor
600	550	475	400	325	225

Rifles

Centennial Semi-Automatic

A .22 caliber semi-automatic rifle with a 21" barrel, adjustable sights, alloy receiver and walnut stock. Manufactured in 1968 only.
Deluxe Engraved Model—Add 20%.

NIB	Exc.	V.G.	Good	Fair	Poor
500	350	300	250	175	125

FRANCOTTE, A.

Liege, Belgium

Jubilee

A 12, 16, 20 and 28 gauge Anson & Deeley boxlock double-barrel shotgun with various barrel lengths and chokes, automatic ejectors, double triggers and walnut stock.

Exc.	V.G.	Good	Fair	Poor
1500	1350	1100	850	700

No. 14

Exc.	V.G.	Good	Fair	Poor
2000	1850	1600	1300	1100

No. 18

Exc.	V.G.	Good	Fair	Poor
2500	2250	2000	1500	1300

No. 20

Exc.	V.G.	Good	Fair	Poor
3000	2500	2250	1750	1500

No. 25

Exc.	V.G.	Good	Fair	Poor
3500	3000	2750	2000	1750

No. 30

Exc.	V.G.	Good	Fair	Poor
4500	4000	3500	3000	2500

Eagle Grade No. 45

A finer finished Jubilee model.

Exc.	V.G.	Good	Fair	Poor
3500	3000	2500	2000	1500

Knockabout

A plain version of the Jubilee Model in 12, 16, 20, 28 and .410 bore.
20 Gauge—Add 20%.
28 Gauge—Add 30%.
.410—Add 40%.

Exc.	V.G.	Good	Fair	Poor
1250	1100	850	650	500

Sidelock Side x Side

A 12, 16, 20, and 28 and .410 bore sidelock shotgun ordered per customer's specifications. Extensive scroll engraving, deluxe walnut stock and finely checkered. The .410 will bring a premium of from $1,200—$1,500.

NIB	Exc.	V.G.	Good	Fair	Poor
12650	10000	8000	6500	5000	3500

Deluxe Sidelock Side x Side

As above, with gold-inlaid hunting scenes.

NIB	Exc.	V.G.	Good	Fair	Poor
15000	12500	10000	8000	5750	4800

FRANCOTTE, A.

Liege, Belgium

CURRENTLY IMPORTED SHOTGUNS AND RIFLES

Importer—Armes De Chasse

Chadds Ford, PA

Francotte currently imports side by side boxlock or sidelock shotguns, double rifles, and single shot rifles as well as bolt action rifles into the United States through Armes De Chasse. These shotguns and rifles are all custom built to the customers specifications. Gauge (including 24 and 32 gauge), caliber, barrel length, engraving, wood type and style are all individually produced. No two all alike. These shotguns and rifles should be individually appraised before the sale. Prices listed below reflect a range that the original buyer paid and also reflect the value of the changing dollar.

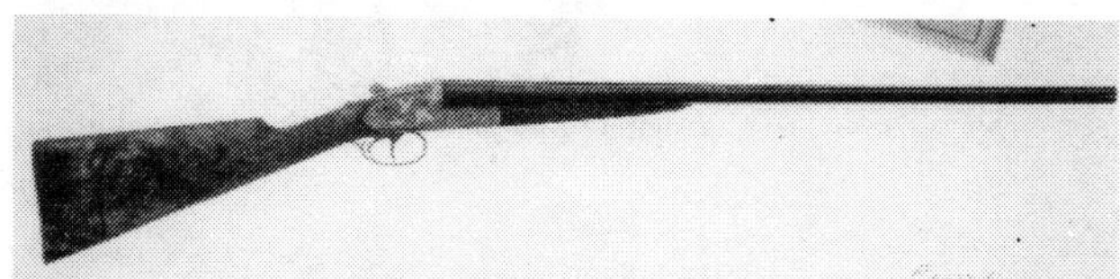

Custom Side by Side Shotguns

Available in 12, 16, 20, 28 gazuge and .410 bore in either boxlock or sidelock actions. Barrel length, engraving, wood type and style are at the customer's discretion. Retail prices range from:

Basic Boxlock with 27.5" barrels and walnut stock with double triggers in 12, 16, and 20 gauge—$16,000
Basic Boxlock in 28 gauge or .410 bore—$20,000

Basic Boxlock with 26.5" 50 28" barrels and deluxe walnut stock and double triggers in 12, 16, and 20 gauge—$20,000
Basic Boxlock in 28 gauge or .410 bore—$25,000

Prices for 24 and 32 gauge are extra.
These prices do not include engraving.

Custom Double Rifles

These custom built double rifles are offered in calibers from 9.3x74R to .470 Nitro Express in boxlock or sidelock actions. Barrel length, engraving, wood type and style are at the customer's discretion. Retail prices range from:

Prices for 24 and 32 gauge are extra.
These prices do not include engraving.

Boxlock in 9.3x74R, 8x57JRS and other European calibers—$20,000
Boxlock in .375 H&H and .470 NE—$25,000

Sidelock in 9.3x74R, etc.—$30,000
Sidelock in large calivers—$36,000

Custom Single Shot Mountain Rifles

These single shot rifles are offered in rimmed cartridges but rimless cartridge rifles can be built on special request. Barrel length, engraving, wood type and style are at the customer's discretion. Retail prices range from:

Boxlock in rimmed calibers—$15,000

Sidelock in 7x65R and 7mm Rem. Mag.—$27,000

Custom Bolt Action Rifles

These bolt action rifles utilize a Mauser 98 type action with adjustable trigger. They are offered in calibers from .17 Bee to .505 Gibbs. Barrel lengths are 21" to 24.5", engraving wood type and style are at the customers' discretion. Retail prices range from:

Standard bolt action calibers: .270, .30-06, 7x64, 8x60S and 9.3x62—$9,000
Short action calibers: .222, .223—$10,000
Magnum action calibers: 7mm Rem. Mag., .300 Win. Mag., .338 Win. Mag., .375 H&H, and .458 Win. Mag.—$15,000
African calibers: .416 Rigby, .460 Wby.,
.505 Gibbs—$15,000

NOTE: Remember that the above prices are for the basic models. They do not reflect the extensive list of options available on these custom firearms.

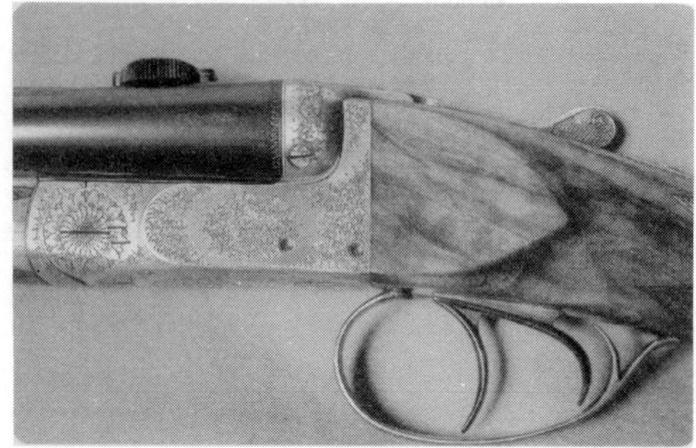

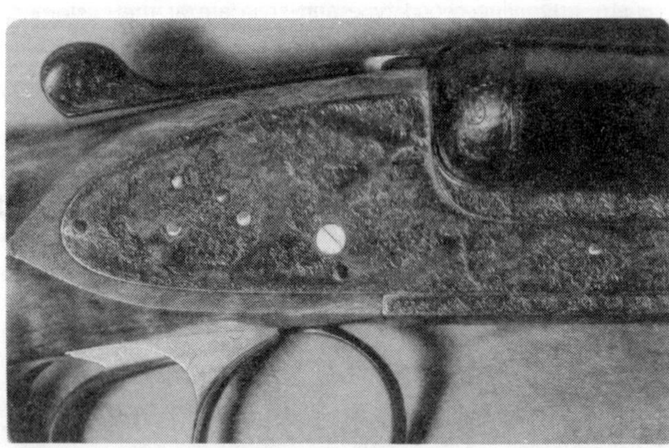

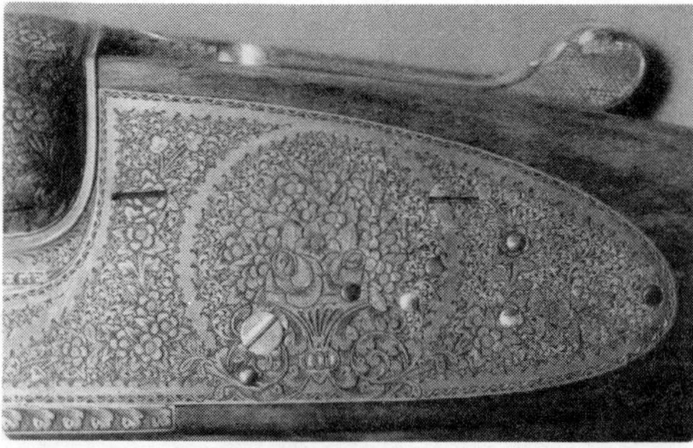

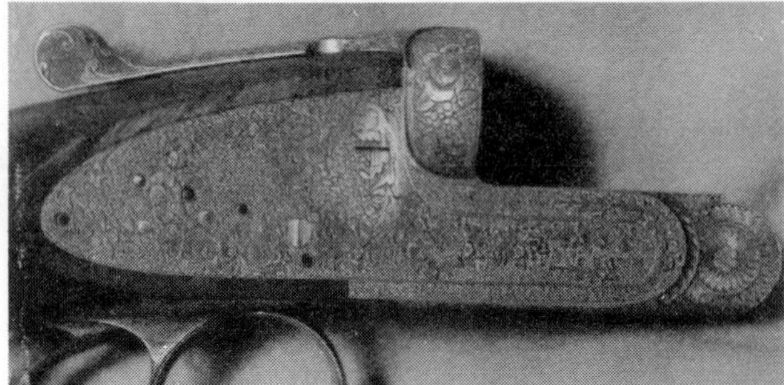

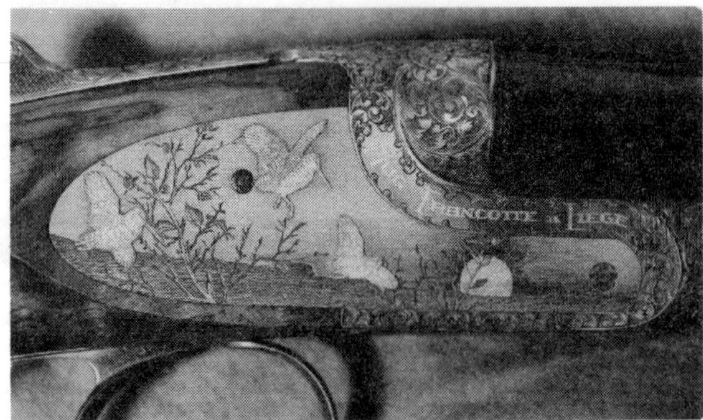

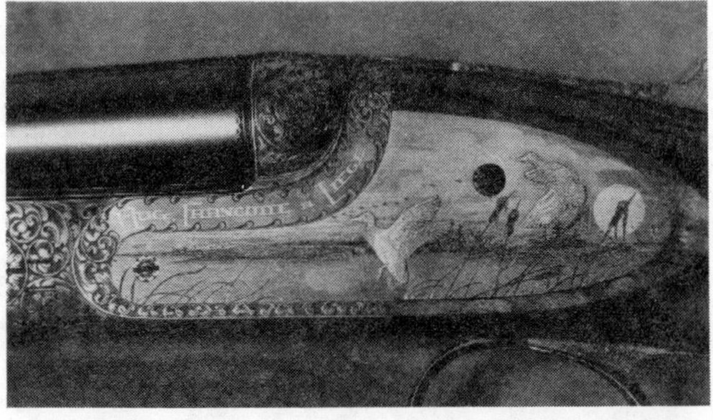

Francotte engraving patterns.

FRANKLIN, C. W.

Liege, Belgium

Manufacturer of utilitarian shotguns with either exposed or enclosed hammers. Circa 1900.

Single Barrel

Exc.	V.G.	Good	Fair	Poor
100	75	50	35	20

Damascus Barrel Double

Exc.	V.G.	Good	Fair	Poor
175	150	125	100	65

Steel Barrel Double

Exc.	V.G.	Good	Fair	Poor
200	175	150	125	90

FRANKONIA JAGD

Germany

Favorit

Chambered for various European calibers, this bolt-action rifle has a 24" barrel and set triggers. Blued, with a checkered walnut stock.

Exc.	V.G.	Good	Fair	Poor
300	275	250	175	125

Favorit Deluxe

As above, with a more finely figured stock.

Exc.	V.G.	Good	Fair	Poor
325	300	275	200	150

Safari Model

As above, in Magnum calibers.

Exc.	V.G.	Good	Fair	Poor
475	425	375	275	200

Heeren Rifle

A best quality single shot rifle with a 26" octagonal barrel, double-set triggers, and adjustable sights. Engraved with hand-checkered, high-grade walnut. Blued. Produced in a variety of calibers.

Exc.	V.G.	Good	Fair	Poor
3000	2650	2200	1700	1250

FRASER, DANIEL & SON

Edinburgh, Scotland

Established in 1871, D. Fraser & Son manufactured a variety of high quality single and double-barrel rifles and shotguns. As these arms were essentially all made to a specific customer's requirements, it is impossible to provide generalized values. Prospective purchasers are advised to secure a qualified appraisal prior to acquisition.

FRASER F. A. CROP.

Fraser, Michigan

Fraser 25 cal.

A .25 ACP caliber semi-automatic pistol with a 2.25" barrel and 6-round magazine. Stainless steel with black nylon grips. There is a 24 kt. gold-plated model that is worth approximately $100 additional.

NIB	Exc.	V.G.	Good	Fair	Poor
135	125	100	75	50	35

FREEDOM ARMS

Freedom, Wyoming

"Percussion" Mini-Revolver

A .22 caliber spur trigger revolver with 1", 1.75", or 3" barrel lengths, 5-shot cylinder and a birds head grip. Stainless steel. A belt buckle is available that houses the pistol for an additional $40.

NIB	Exc.	V.G.	Good	Fair	Poor
200	180	165	125	100	75

Patriot

As above, in .22 l.r. caliber.

NIB	Exc.	V.G.	Good	Fair	Poor
155	135	110	85	65	45

Minuteman

As above, with a 3" barrel. Discontinued in 1988.

Exc.	V.G.	Good	Fair	Poor
145	125	90	75	50

Ironsides

As above, in .22 Magnum with a 1" or a 1.75" barrel.

NIB	Exc.	V.G.	Good	Fair	Poor
175	150	125	100	80	60

Bostonian

As above, with a 3" barrel.

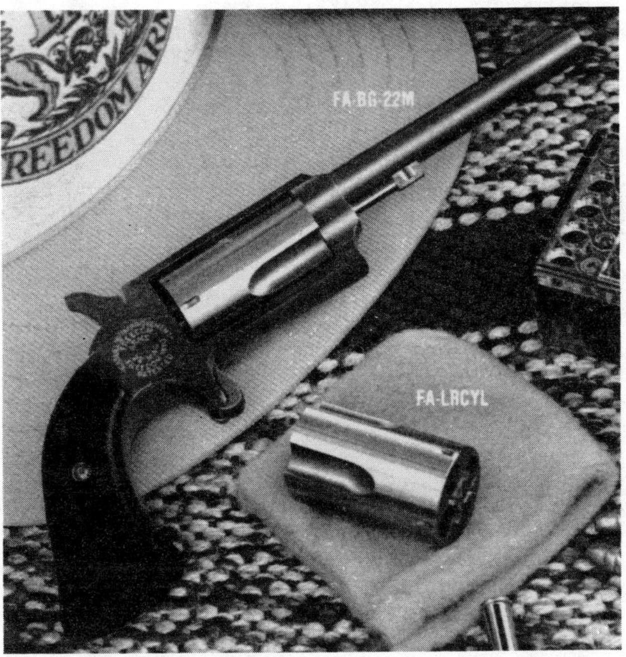

NIB	Exc.	V.G.	Good	Fair	Poor
175	150	125	100	80	60

Celebrity

As above, with the belt buckle mount for either .22 or .22 Magnum revolvers.

.22 Magnum Model—Add $25.

NIB	Exc.	V.G.	Good	Fair	Poor
325	300	250	200	150	100

Casull Field Grade

A .454 Casull Magnum revolver with a 4.75", 7.5" and a 10" barrel and standard fixed sights. Fires a 225-grain bullet Adjustable sights available as a $75 option. Matte stainless steel with black rubber "Pachmayr" grips. Introduced in 1988.

NIB	Exc.	V.G.	Good	Fair	Poor
1000	850	750	600	500	400

Casull Premier Grade

A .454 Mag., .44 Rem. Mag., .45 Win. Mag., and the .45 Colt revolver with replaceable forcing and walnut grips. The adjustable sights are an extra cost option on this model as well.

NIB	Exc.	V.G.	Good	Fair	Poor
1500	1250	950	750	650	500

Signature Edition

As above, with a highly polished finish, rosewood grips, 7.5" barrel only and a fitted case. The serial numbers are DC1—DC2000. (The DC represents Dick Casull, the designer of the firearm.) A total of 2,000 were made.

NIB	Exc.	V.G.	Good	Fair	Poor
2000	1750	1500	1250	900	600

FREEMAN, AUSTIN T.

Hoard's Armory
Watertown, New York

Freeman Army Model Revolver

A .44 caliber percussion revolver with a 7.5" round barrel and a 6-shot unfluted cylinder with recessed nipples. Blued, case-hardened rammer and hammer, and walnut grips. The frame is marked "Freeman's Pat. Dec. 9, 1862/Hoard's Armory, Watertown,N.Y." Several thousand were manufactured in 1863 and 1864.

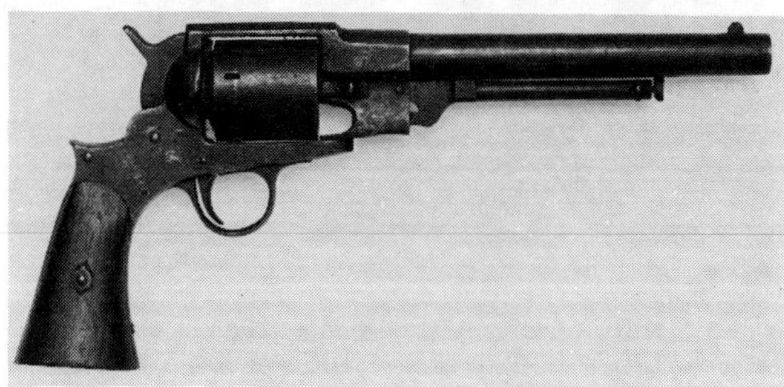

Exc.	V.G.	Good	Fair	Poor
1000	900	750	650	500

FRENCH MILITARY FIREARMS

(including copies made in Liege, Belgium)
Charleville, St. Etienne, Chatellrault,
Mutzig and Tulle Armories

Despite its defeats in the closing battles of the Napoleonic Wars, France maintained a considerable army after the conflict that continued the traditions of Napoleon's leadership and propelled itself into the forefront of 19th century arms development. The diversity of the French Army is reflected in the many variations of the firearms produced during the fifty years following 1815. Most of these firearms were the products of five major armories, the old Charleville Armory and St. Etienne works, and the newer armories at Chatellrault, Mutzig, and Tulle. The armory of manufacture was invariably inscribed in script upon the lock, usually preceeded by an abbreviation "Manuf re Roy le de" or "M re R le de" until 1848, "M re N le de" from 1848 until 1852, and "M re Imp ale de" after 1852, respectively representing, "The Royal Manufactory at . . . ," "The National Manufactory at . . .," and, "The Imperial Manufactory at . . ." In addition to these lock markings, the specific model year was usually marked upon the barrel tang, preceded by an "M". If the model had been altered, a "T" (for "transformed") was added after the date, and if subsequently remodeled, the script ("bis" was added after that (for "again"). Date of manufacture usually appears upon the barrel, and also within the pressed circle surrounding the "touch mark" on the right side of the buttstock. Numerous inspection marks also appear on the metal parts of the gun.

The arms manufactured for the French military were widely copied in Europe's major firearms center, Liege, Belgium. The Liege gun trade, however, was based on the "factory" system. Each specialist, working out of his own cottage, manufactured one type of part on subcontract and delivered it to an assembler. Many of the final assemblers in Liege did not mark their products or did so only with crowned initials. Those that did usually marked their "products" upon the lockplates. Among the better known Liege assemblers' marks during the middle of the nineteenth century were ANCION & CIE/A LIEGE, A F (A. Francotte), B F (Beuret Freres), C D (probably for Charles Dandoy), D (anchor) C (probably Dejerdine & Co., Demousse & Co., or DeFooz & Co.), D L (DeLoneux) C. DANDOY/A LIEGE, A. & CH DE LONEUX DRISKET & WAROUX, G M (Gulikers Marquinay), V. GULIKERS/A LIEGE, J L (Joseph LeMille), L (anchor) C or L. LAMBIN & CIE/LIEGE, LE MILLE/A LIEGE, P.J. MALHEREBE & CIE/LIEGE, E. MUNSEUR/LIEGE, J.A. PETRY/A LIEGE, G. SCHOPEN/A LEIGE, TANNER & CIE., T. TILKEN/A/LIEGE, AND V P (Vivario- Plombeur). It should be noted, however, that these makers produced not only copies of French arms, but also accepted contracts for arms from other European powers, notably Russia, Spain, the Piedmont, Saxony, and England. Whether marked on the lock or not, all Liege barrels were required to pass a proof of strength, and having done so were marked near their breech with a small tower and the Liege black powder proof, an oval encompassing the letters "E/LG/"(star). The main French firearms produced or copied during the muzzleloading era were:

French M1816 flintlock musket (for infantry/light infantry)

Overall length- 58-1/8"/ 56"; barrel length- 42-7/8"/ 40-1/2"; caliber-.69 This musket is basically the French M1777 musket with minor improvements. Although the French did not subsequently alter this model to percussion, the Kingdom of Wurtemberg obtained several thousand from the Charleville Armory, which were altered to percussion and then rifled and sighted after their own models of 1842 and 1855, the barrel receiving a long range French style rear sight after rifling. As many as 2,000 of these may have been imported into the United States in 1862 by Marcellus Hartley.

(in flintlock)

Exc.	V.G.	Good	Fair	Poor
2200	2000	1700	1350	700

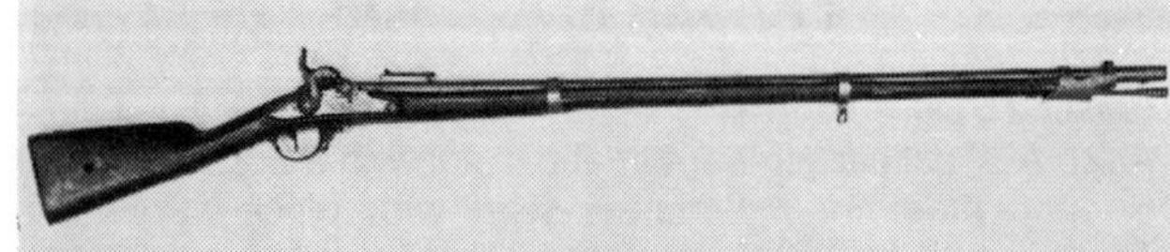

Courtesy Milwaukee Public Museum, Milwaukee, Wisconsin.

(altered to percussion, rifled and sighted)

Exc.	V.G.	Good	Fair	Poor
800	650	500	400	275

French M1822 flintlock musket (for infantry/light infantry)

Overall length- 58"/55-7/8"; barrel length- 42-5/8"/ 40-5/8" (40-5/8" for both types if "T bis"); caliber- .69 (.71 for rifled versions). The French M1822 musket in either full infantry length or the shorter version for light infantry (voltiguers), set the pattern for most of the muskets subsequently adopted by the European powers during the second quarter of the 19th century.

In the 1840s many were "transformed," i.e. altered to percussion by adding a convex bolster to the upper right side of the barrel near the breech for a cone and replacing the flintlock battery with a percussion hammer. With the adoption of the Minie ball projectile, it was determined to further upgrade these arms; however, because a new caliber had been adopted, the old barrels were deemed too thin to both enlarge and rifle. Accordingly new barrels were made in .71 caliber. The percussioned version was copied in Liege (by Ancion, Francotte, and Falise & Trapmann) for the Kingdom of Piedmont as its M1844 musket and M1860 rifle-musket. These are distinguished by the enlarged tip of the hammer spur, a peculiar rear sight added to the breech and tang, and Liege markings.

(in flintlock)

Exc.	V.G.	Good	Fair	Poor
2200	2000	1700	1350	700

(altered to percussion, and rifled)

Exc.	V.G.	Good	Fair	Poor
800	650	500	400	275

French M1822 cavalry flintlock pistol (and "T bis")

Overall length- 13-3/4"; barrel length- 7-7/8"; caliber- .69 (.71 in "T bis"). The M1822 cavalry or horse pistol served as the secondary arm of the French mounted forces, with a pair assigned to each horseman to be kept in saddle holsters astride the pommel of the saddle. Like the M1822 muskets, these were altered ("transformed") to percussion after 1842 in the same manner as the muskets. In 1860, the ordnance department decided to rifle them as well ("transformed again"- hence "T-bis") but this required a new barrel since the adoption of the new caliber (.71) precluded rifling the thin old barrels.

(in flintlock)

Exc.	V.G.	Good	Fair	Poor
900	800	600	450	375

(in percussion and rifled)

Exc.	V.G.	Good	Fair	Poor
575	525	500	375	250

French M1822 cavalry and lancer flintlock musketoons (and "T")

Overall length- 34-5/8"; barrel length- 19-5/8"; caliber- .69. The main difference between the carbines carried by the cavalry and that of the lancers was the manner of slinging, with the latter having sling rings attached to the upper band and to a projection set into the buttstock. The ramrod was carried separately, consequently there was no inletting of the forestock. After 1842, both types were altered to percussion in the same manner as the M1822 muskets and pistols.

(in flintlock)

Exc.	V.G.	Good	Fair	Poor
950	850	650	450	375

(in percussion and rifled)

Exc.	V.G.	Good	Fair	Poor
600	550	450	350	250

French M1829 artillery flintlock carbine (and "T bis")

Overall length- 37-3/4"/38-3/4" (for "T bis"); barrel length- 23-5/8"; caliber- .69/.71 (for "T bis"). The carbine for artillerists was very similar in configuration to that for the cavalry and lancers, differing primarily in having a ramrod in a channel below the barrel. After 1841, these arms were altered to percussion and after 1846 a bayonet lug with long guide was added to the right side of the barrel to accommodate the French M1847 yatagan saber bayonet. At the same time, a number of these arms were sighted, rifled, and a "tige" (a metal column or pillar) was inserted into the breech of the bore that permitted the arm to fire the Thouvenin projectile. After 1857 new barrel were manufactured that permitted the introduction of the standard Minie projectile of .71 caliber

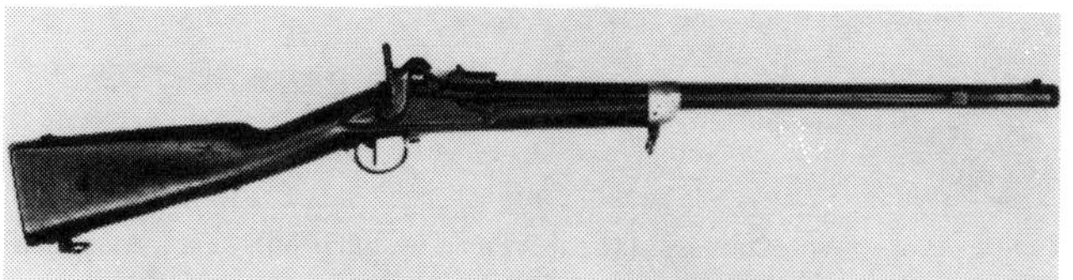

Courtesy Milwaukee Public Museum, Milwaukee, Wisconsin.

Exc.	V.G.	Good	Fair	Poor
950	850	650	450	375

(in percussion and rifled)

Exc.	V.G.	Good	Fair	Poor
600	550	450	350	250

French M1837 rifle ("carbine a la Poncharra")

Overall length- 51-5/8"; barrel length- 34-1/4"; caliber- .69. The first of the French percussion arms for the general services, the M1837 rifle was designed on the Poncharra system. In this system, a chamber of lesser diameter than the bore was affixed to the barrel. A projectile of the diameter across the lands and its "sabot" was rammed into the barrel, and upon striking the lip of the chamber theoretically expanded into the rifling.

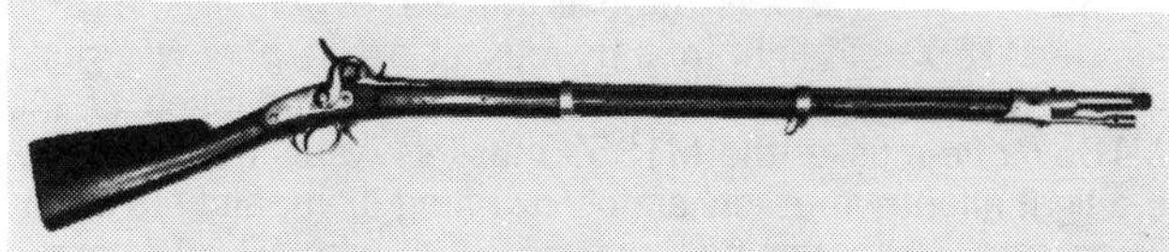

Courtesy Milwaukee Public Museum, Milwaukee, Wisconsin.

Exc.	V.G.	Good	Fair	Poor
1600	1500	1250	850	450

French M1840 rifle ("carbine de Munition")

Overall length- 48-3/8"; barrel- 32-5/8"; caliber- .71. After the success of the M1837 carbine, the rifle went into production at the armories at Mutzig and Chatellrault as the M1840 "carbine Tierry" or "carbine de munition." It was modified in 1842. The design was modified by adding a projection to the lower end of the butt plate. Herman Boker of New York City imported 25,000 of the M1840 rifles in 1862, but the slow twist of the rifling caused them to be classified as "4th class" weapons and none were issued.

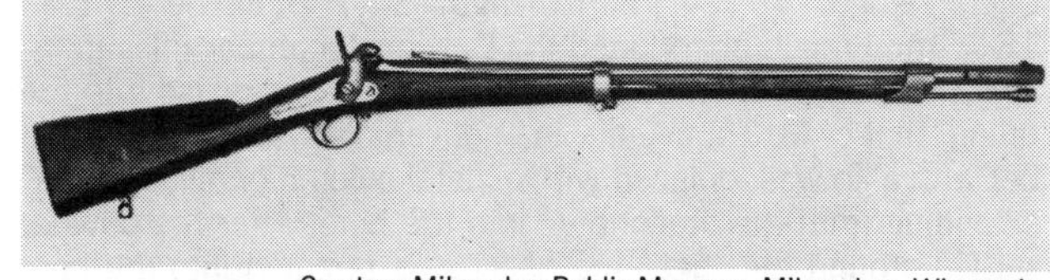

Courtesy Milwaukee Public Museum, Milwaukee, Wisconsin.

Exc.	V.G.	Good	Fair	Poor
850	750	600	450	300

French M1840 and M1842 percussion muskets (infantry/light infantry)

Overall length- 58-1/4"/55-3/4"; barrel length- 42-5/8"/40-1/2"; caliber- .71. The M1840 and M1842 muskets were the first percussion arms adopted for general infantry service in the French army, both being distinguished by employing back-action percussion locks. The M1840 was distinguished from the M1842 by having a screwed in "patent" breech integrating the bolster, while the bolster of the M1842 musket was forged integral to the barrel, both flush with the right side of the barrel. The M1842 musket was later "transformed" to the M1842T by rifling the barrel with four broad grooves. The Belgian gun trade copied the M1842T both with and without the block rear sight that stood on the breechplug tang.

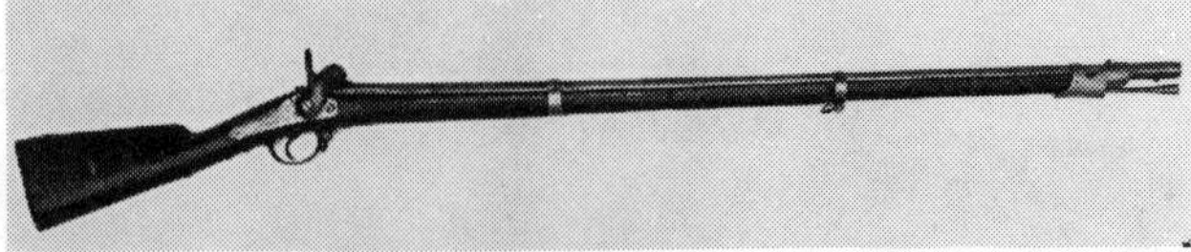

Courtesy Milwaukee Public Museum, Milwaukee, Wisconsin.

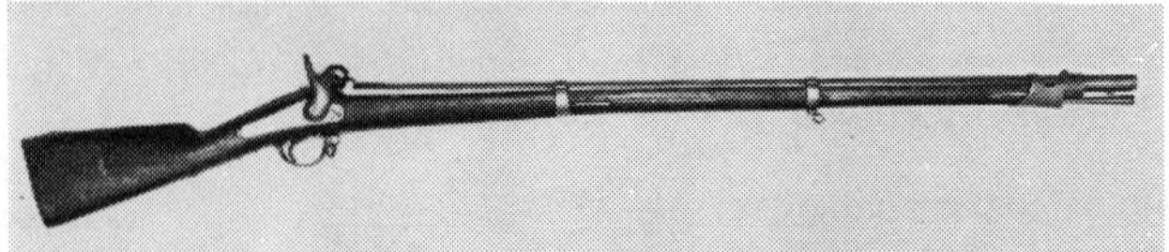

Courtesy Milwaukee Public Museum, Milwaukee, Wisconsin.

Exc.	V.G.	Good	Fair	Poor
800	700	475	400	275

French M1853 musket, M1853 "T" and M1857 rifle-muskets

Overall length- 58-1/8" (M1853 infantry musket only)/55-3/4"; barrels- 42-5/8" (M1853 only)/40-1/2"; caliber- .71. In 1853, the M1842 series of arms was modified slightly, the most visible difference being the right face of the bolster, which stands away from the right side of the barrel. After the adoption of the "Minie ball" as the main projectile of the French army, the new M1857 rifle-musket was introduced. It was essentially the same as the M1853 "T" light infantry musket but its bore was rifled with four broad grooves. Subsequent to the adoption of the M1857 rifle-musket the M1853 muskets were "transformed," the light infantry muskets simply by rifling them, and the infantry muskets by shortening them to 55-3/4" with 40-1/2" barrels and rifling them. Both types were widely copied by the Belgian gun trade, who exported thousands to the United States in 1861, many with French style long range sights affixed to the barrels.

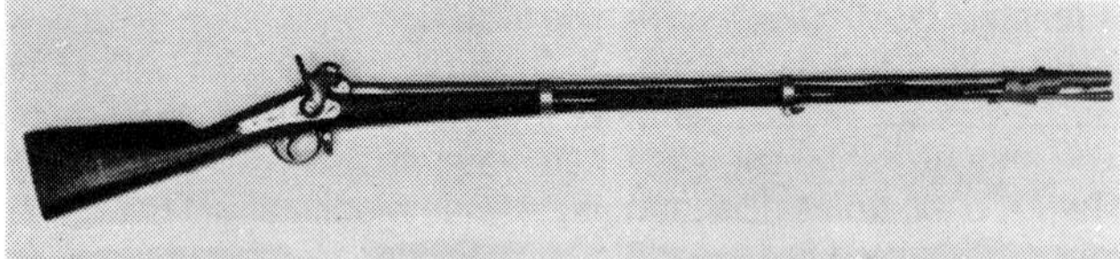

Courtesy Milwaukee Public Museum, Milwaukee, Wisconsin.

Exc.	V.G.	Good	Fair	Poor
800	700	475	425	300

French M1846 and M1853 rifles ("carbine a tige")

Overall length- 49-3/4"; barrel length- 34-1/4"; caliber- .71. In 1846 the French abandoned the Delvigne chamber rifles in favor of a different method of compressing the projectile into the rifling, that of M. Thouvenin. In Thouvenin's system, the chamber with a lip was replaced with a metal column or pillar "a tige" extending from the breechplug into the bore. After the powder settled around the "tige" the bullet was rammed into the bore and compressed against the tige to expand it into the rifling. The rifle adopted in 1853 differed from the original model adopted in 1846 only in the bolster configuration, the latter extending away from the right side of the barrel. At least a thousand Belgian made "carbines a tige" were imported into the Confederacy in 1861. Accordingly, Belgian "tige" rifles with proven Southern usage should command a premium over those without such history.

Exc.	V.G.	Good	Fair	Poor
900	800	650	475	350

French M1853 "T" and M1859 rifles ("carbine de Vincennes")

Overall length- 49-3/4"; barrel length- 34-1/4"; caliber- .71. With the adoption of the self expanding "Minie ball" in 1857, the French ordnance soon adopted a rifle which was suitable for it, the M1859 "carbine de Vincennes." Beginning in 1860, the M1853 "tige" rifles were "transformed" by the removal of the pillars from the breechplugs and fitting them with the rear sight leaves of the M1859 rifle. The M1853 "T" and M1859 French rifle was widely copied in Liege, and thousands were exported to the United States during the American Civil War, while most of the French made M1859 rifles reposed in French arsenals. Like the M1840 and M1846 and M1853 rifles, the M1859 rifle took a long yatagan blade saber bayonet that was affixed to a lug with a guide on the right side of the barrel.

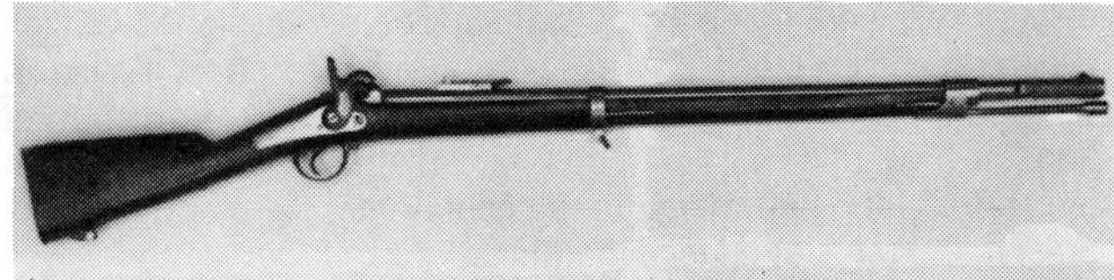

Courtesy Milwaukee Public Museum, Milwaukee, Wisconsin.

Exc.	V.G.	Good	Fair	Poor
950	875	700	525	425

FRENCH STATE

Manufactured by MAS
Etienne, France
SACM
Cholet, France
MAC
Chatellerault, France
MAT
Tulle, France

Model 1885

An 11mm caliber percussion revolver with a 5" barrel, solid frame and a 6-shot cylinder with a loading gate. Blued with checkered walnut grips.

Exc.	V.G.	Good	Fair	Poor
300	250	200	150	100

Model 1887

As above, with 8mm caliber.

Exc.	V.G.	Good	Fair	Poor
300	250	200	150	100

Model 1892

An 8mm Lebel caliber solid-frame revolver with a 5" barrel and the 6-shot cylinder. Blued, with checkered walnut grips and a lanyard swivel on the butt.

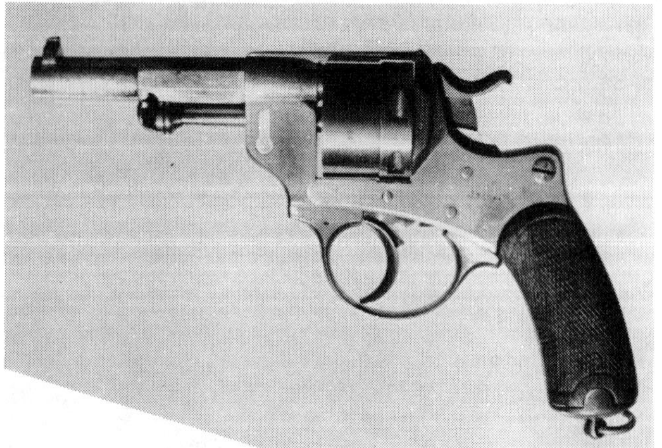

Courtesy Orville Reichert.

Exc.	V.G.	Good	Fair	Poor
225	200	175	125	75

Model 1892 "A Pompe"

As above, except that the cylinder latch is a sleeve around the ejector rod that can be moved forward to release the cylinder.

Exc.	V.G.	Good	Fair	Poor
225	200	175	125	75

MAS Model 1935A

A 7.65mm Long caliber semi-automatic pistol. Eventually became known as the Model 1935A.

German Waffenamt Model

Exc.	V.G.	Good	Fair	Poor
225	175	150	100	75

Standard Model

Exc.	V.G.	Good	Fair	Poor
175	150	125	100	75

Model 1935S

As above, with locking ribs on slide.

Exc.	V.G.	Good	Fair	Poor
175	150	125	100	75

MAS Model 1950

A 9mm Parabellum caliber semi-automatic pistol with a 9-shot magazine. Blued, with ribbed plastic grips.

Exc.	V.G.	Good	Fair	Poor
475	425	350	275	200

FRIGON
Clay Center, Kansas

An importer of guns manufactured by Marocchi located in Italy.

FT 1

A 12 gauge boxlock single-barrel shotgun with a 32" or 34" ventilated-rib barrel, full choke, automatic ejector and interchanged stock. Blued. Introduced in 1986.

NIB	Exc.	V.G.	Good	Fair	Poor
875	750	650	550	450	300

FTC

As above, with two sets of barrels (a single ventilated-rib trap barrel and a set of Over/Under ventilated-rib barrels). In a fitted case. Introduced in 1986.

NIB	Exc.	V.G.	Good	Fair	Poor
1600	1400	1150	800	650	500

FS-4

A four gauge set (12, 20, and 28 gauge and .410 bore). Introduced in 1986.

NIB	Exc.	V.G.	Good	Fair	Poor
2350	2100	1750	1500	1100	750

FROMMER
SEE—Fegyvergyar

FRUHWIRTH
Austria

M.1872 Fruhwirth System Rifle

An 11mm bolt-action rifle with a 25" barrel and 6-shot magazine. Blued with a full length walnut stock.

Exc.	V.G.	Good	Fair	Poor
350	300	250	175	100

FURR ARMS
Prescott, Arizona
J. & G. Sale, Inc.
Prescott, Arizona

In addition to producing reproductions of various cannon, this company also manufactured one-tenth to three-quarter scale reproductions of Gatling guns. Prospective purchasers are advised to secure a qualified appraisal prior to acquisition.

FYRBURG, ANDREW
Hopkinton, Massachusetts

A 3"-barrelled .32 caliber and a 3.5" .38 caliber revolver with round ribbed barrels and round butts. The grips bear the trademark, "AFCo."

Exc.	V.G.	Good	Fair	Poor
150	125	100	75	50

G M

(Gulikers Marquinay of Liege, Belgium)
SEE—French Military Firearms

GABBET - FAIRFAX, H.

Leamington Spa, England

Mars

Designed by Hugh Gabbet-Fairfax, this semi-automatic pistol was produced on an extremely limited basis by the Webley company, in 1906. The pistol was produced in two calibers; the .380 and the .45ACP. This is rare and desirable collectable and prospective purchasers are advised to acquire a qualified appraisal prior to the sale.

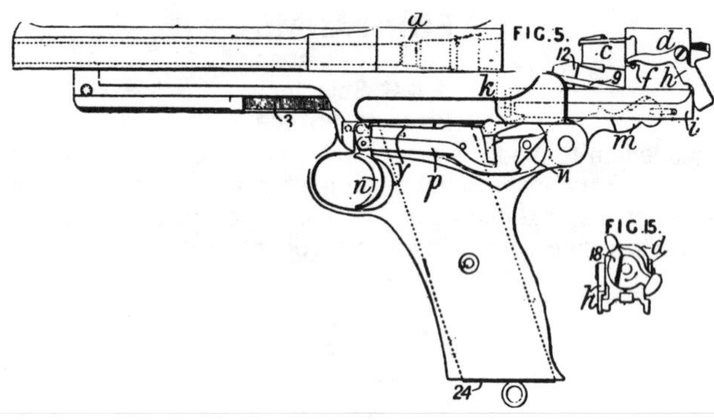

Exc.	V.G.	Good	Fair	Poor
25000	15000	9000	5000	2000

GABILONDO Y CIA

SEE—Llama

GABILONDO Y URRESTI

Guernica, Spain
Elgoibar, Spain
SEE—Llama

This Spanish firm was founded in 1904 to produce inexpensive revolvers of the Velo-Dog type. Sometime around 1909 the firm began to manufacture the Radium revolver. In 1914 the company produced a semi-automatic pistol distributed as the Ruby. This pistol soon became the mainstay of the company with orders of 30,000 pistols a month for the French army. With the end of WWI Gabilondo Y Urresti moved to Elgoeibar, Spain. The company produced a Browning 1910 replica pistol until the early 1930's. It was at this point that Gabilondo began to manufacture a Colt Model 1911 copy that became known as the Llama. For information of specific Llama models see the Llama section. The pistols listed below reflect the pre-Llama period and are so marked with the trade name of that particular model. The monogram "GC" frequently appears on the grips but not on the slide.

Velo-Dog Revolver

A 6.35mm double-action revolver with a 1.5" barrel, folding trigger and concealed hammer. Blued with walnut grips. Manufactured from 1904 to 1914.

Exc.	V.G.	Good	Fair	Poor
150	125	100	75	50

Radium

A 6.35mm caliber semi-automatic pistol with a 2.5" barrel and 6-shot magazine. The slide is marked "Fire Arms Manufacturing Automatic Pistol Radium Cal. 6.35." Produced between 1909 and 1914.

Exc.	V.G.	Good	Fair	Poor
175	150	125	100	75

Ruby

A 7.65mm caliber semi-automatic pistol. Discontinued in 1930.

Exc.	V.G.	Good	Fair	Poor
200	175	150	100	75

Bufalo

A 6.35mm, 7.65mm, and 9mm short caliber semi-autmatic pistol. Blued with black plastic grips. Marked "Automatica Piastola Espana Bufalo." The caliber is also stamped on the slide. Manufactured between 1919 and 1925 under this name and for a number of years more under different names.

Exc.	V.G.	Good	Fair	Poor
175	150	125	100	75

Danton

As above, without the grip safety. "Danton" stamped on the side. Manufactured between 1925 and 1933.

Exc.	V.G.	Good	Fair	Poor
175	150	125	100	75

Perfect

This semi-automatic pistol was chambered for the 6.35mm and 7.65mm cartridges. It was a cheap, low priced pistol marketed by Mugica. These pistols usually have the word "Perfect" on the grips. The slide may be stamped with the name MUGICA but many are not.

Exc.	V.G.	Good	Fair	Poor
225	175	150	100	75

Plus Ultra

This pistol was chambered for the 7.65mm cartridge and was built from 1925 to 1933. It had a 20 round magazine which gave the pistol an unusual appearance.

Exc.	V.G.	Good	Fair	Poor
250	200	175	125	100

GALAND, C.F.
Liege, Belgium

Galand, Galand & Sommerville, Galand Perrin
A 7mm, 9mm and 12mm caliber double-action revolver with a 6-shot cylinder, open-frame, a unique ejection system which, by means of rotating a lever downward from the triggerguard, causes the barrel and cylinder to slide forward, leaving the ejector and the spent cases behind. Circa 1870.

Exc.	V.G.	Good	Fair	Poor
350	325	275	200	150

Velo-Dog
A 5.5mm Velo-Dog caliber fixed trigger and guard double-action revolver with open-top design. Later models (.22 and 6.35mm caliber) feature folding triggers and no triggerguards.

Exc.	V.G.	Good	Fair	Poor
150	125	100	75	50

Le Novo
As above, with a concealed hammer and in 6.35mm caliber.

Exc.	V.G.	Good	Fair	Poor
200	175	125	100	75

Tue-Tue
A .22 short, 5.5mm Velo-Dog, and 6.35mm caliber double action revolver with a concealed hammer, folding trigger, and a swing-out cylinder with central extractor. Introduced in 1894.

Exc.	V.G.	Good	Fair	Poor
200	175	150	100	75

GALAND & SOMMERVILLE
Liege, Belgium
SEE—Galand

GALEF
Zabala Hermanos & Antonio Zoli
Spain

Zabala Double
A 10, 12, 16, and 20 caliber boxlock shotgun with a 22" to 30" barrel and various chokes. Hardwood stock.

Exc.	V.G.	Good	Fair	Poor
225	200	150	100	75

Companion
A folding 12 to .410 bore single shot underlever shotgun with a 28" or 30" barrel.

Exc.	V.G.	Good	Fair	Poor
125	100	75	50	25

Monte Carlo Trap
A 12 gauge underlever single shot shotgun with a 32" ventilated-rib barrel.

Exc.	V.G.	Good	Fair	Poor
200	175	150	100	75

Silver Snipe, Golden Snipe, and Silver Hawk
SEE—Antonio Zoli

GALESI, INDUSTRIA ARMI
Brescia, Italy

Founded in 1914. The company was recently renamed "Rigarmi."

Galesi
A 6.35mm caliber semi-automatic pistol. A copy of the 1906 Browning, without a grip safety. Introduced in 1914.

Exc.	V.G.	Good	Fair	Poor
230	225	175	125	100

Model 1930
A 6.35mm, 7.65mm or 9mm short caliber semi-automatic pistol. Based on the 1910 Browning design. Blued with plastic grips. The slide marked "Brevetto Mod. 1930." The prewar designation was the Model 6.

Exc.	V.G.	Good	Fair	Poor
250	225	175	125	100

Model 9
A .22 rimfire, 6.35mm, and the 7.65mm caliber semi-automatic pistol. Blue or plated. Marked "Hijo" and imported by Sloan & Co. of New York.

Exc.	V.G.	Good	Fair	Poor
175	150	125	100	75

Rigarmi
A copy of the Walther PP, in .22 l.r., 6.35mm, and the 7.65mm caliber. Finished in a variety of ways and marked "Rigarmi Brescia."

Exc.	V.G.	Good	Fair	Poor
125	100	75	50	25

GALIL
Israel Military Industries
Israel
Importer—Action Arms, Ltd.
Phiadelphia, Pennsylvania

Model AR

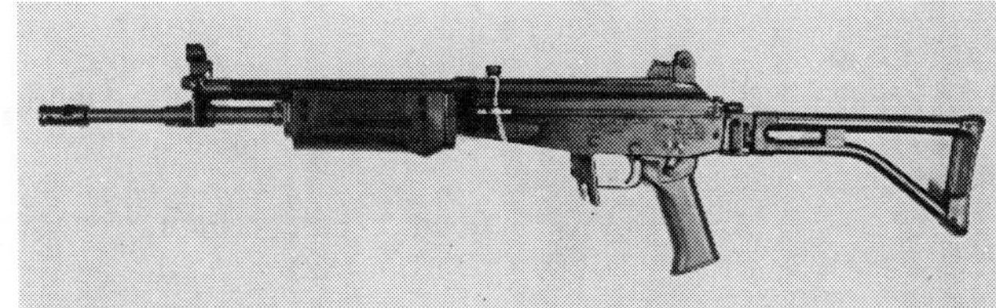

A .223 or .308 caliber semi-automatic rifle with 16" or a 19" barrels. Parkerized with the flip "Tritium" night sights and folding stock. The .308 version would be higher priced.

Model ARM
As above, with a ventilated wood handguard and a folding bipod and carrying handle.

Sniper Rifle
As above, with a 20" heavy barrel, adjustable wooden stock, and a 6X40 scope is furnished in addition to the Tritium night sights. Supplied with two 25-shot magazines and a fitted case.

Hadar II
As above, in a walnut, one-piece, thumbhole stock, an 18.5" barrel, 4-shot magazine and adjustable sight, Introduced in 1989.

NIB	Exc.	V.G.	Good	Fair	Poor
1000	900	800	650	550	450

GALLAGER

Richardson & Overman
Philadelphia, Pennsylvania

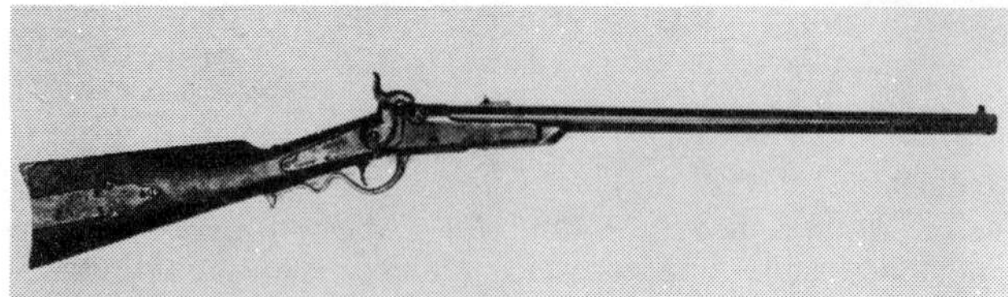

Courtesy Milwaukee Public Museum, Milwaukee, Wisconsin.

Gallager Carbine

A .50 caliber single shot percussion carbine with a 22.25" barrel, saddle ring and walnut stock. Blued and case-hardened. Approximately 23,000 were made during the Civil War.

Percussion Model

Exc.	V.G.	Good	Fair	Poor
750	675	550	450	350

As above, in .56-62 rimfire caliber. Approximately 5,000 of this model were made.

Spencer Cartridge Model

Exc.	V.G.	Good	Fair	Poor
650	575	450	350	300

GAMBA, RENATO

Gardone V. T., Italy

Shotguns Side x Side

Hunter Super

A 12 gauge Anson & Deeley boxlock double-barrel shotgun with a variety of barrel lengths and chokes, double triggers and extractors. Engraved and silver-plated.

NIB	Exc.	V.G.	Good	Fair	Poor
1500	1350	1050	850	650	500

Principessa

A 12 or 20 gauge boxlock shotgun. Engraved, checkered stock.

NIB	Exc.	V.G.	Good	Fair	Poor
2000	1850	1500	1250	900	700

Oxford 90

A 12 or 20 gauge sidelock shotgun with various barrel lengths and chokes, the Purdey locking system, double triggers, and automatic ejectors. Walnut stock.

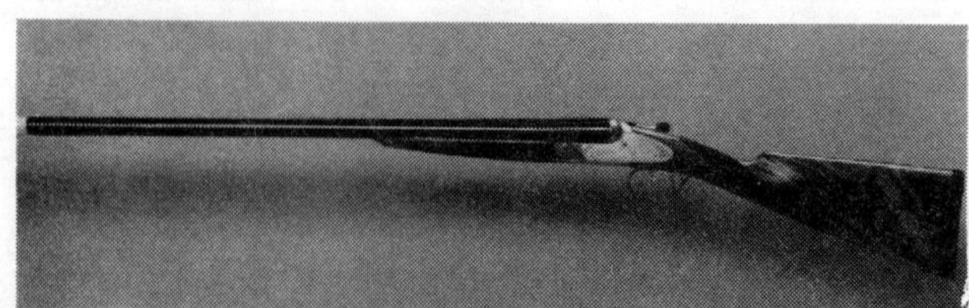

NIB	Exc.	V.G.	Good	Fair	Poor
2750	2500	2000	1750	1250	950

London

A 12 or 20 gauge Holland & Holland sidelock shotgun with various barrel lengths and chokes, double or single selective trigger, automatic ejectors. Walnut stock.

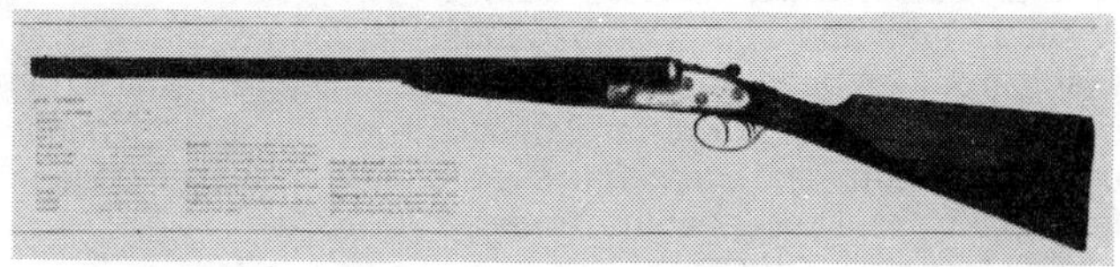

NIB	Exc.	V.G.	Good	Fair	Poor
6750	6000	5000	4000	2500	2000

London Royal

As above with engraved hunting scenes.

NIB	Exc.	V.G.	Good	Fair	Poor
8000	6500	5500	4500	3000	2500

Ambassador Golden Black

A 12 and 20 gauge Holland & Holland sidelock shotgun with various barrel lengths and chock combinations, single selective trigger, automatic ejectors, and a single gold line engraved on the barrels and the frame. Walnut stocks.

NIB	Exc.	V.G.	Good	Fair	Poor
14650	13500	10000	7500	6500	5500

Ambassador Executive

Gamba's best quality shotgun produced in 12 or 20 gauge to the customer's specifications.

NIB	Exc.	V.G.	Good	Fair	Poor
23500	20000	17500	14500	10000	7500

Over and Under Shotguns

Country Model

A 12 and 20 gauge Over/Under shotgun with 28" or 30" barrels with ventilated-rib, double triggers, extractors, and walnut stock.

NIB	Exc.	V.G.	Good	Fair	Poor
775	650	500	450	375	300

Grifone Model

A 12 and 20 gauge Over/Under shotgun with 26", 28", or 30" ventilated-rib barrels, a single selective trigger, and automatic ejectors. The boxlock action is silver-plated, with walnut stock. Available with screw-in chokes, and this would add 10% to the values.

NIB	Exc.	V.G.	Good	Fair	Poor
950	850	750	650	500	400

Europa 2000

A 12 gauge Over/Under shotgun in various barrel lengths and choke combinations, single selective trigger, and automatic ejectors. Engraved, silver-plated, boxlock action with false side-plates with walnut stock.

NIB	Exc.	V.G.	Good	Fair	Poor
1450	1250	1000	750	650	500

Grinta Trap and Skeet

A 12 gauge Over/Under shotgun with 26" skeet or 30" full-choke barrels, a single selective trigger, automatic ejectors, and some engraving. Walnut stock.

NIB	Exc.	V.G.	Good	Fair	Poor
1700	1500	1200	1000	750	500

Victory Trap and Skeet

As above, but more finely finished.

NIB	Exc.	V.G.	Good	Fair	Poor
1900	1700	1400	1200	900	700

Edinburg Match

As above, with slightly different engraving patterns.

NIB	Exc.	V.G.	Good	Fair	Poor
1950	1750	1450	1250	950	750

Boyern 88 Combination Gun

A 12 gauge combination Over/Under rifle/shotgun with double triggers, and extractors. Engraved gamescenes and coin-finished with walnut stock.

NIB	Exc.	V.G.	Good	Fair	Poor
1500	1300	1000	800	550	350

Rifles

Safari Express

A 7x65R, 9.3x74R, or .375 H&H caliber boxlock double barrel rifle with 25" barrels, open sights double triggers, automatic ejectors, and a coin-finished scroll engraved receiver. Walnut stock.

NIB	Exc.	V.G.	Good	Fair	Poor
6600	6000	5500	4750	3750	2500

Mustang

A 5.6x50, 6.5x57R, 7x65R, .222 Rem., .270 Win., or .30-06 caliber sidelock single-barrel rifle with double-set triggers, Engraved sidelock action and walnut stock.

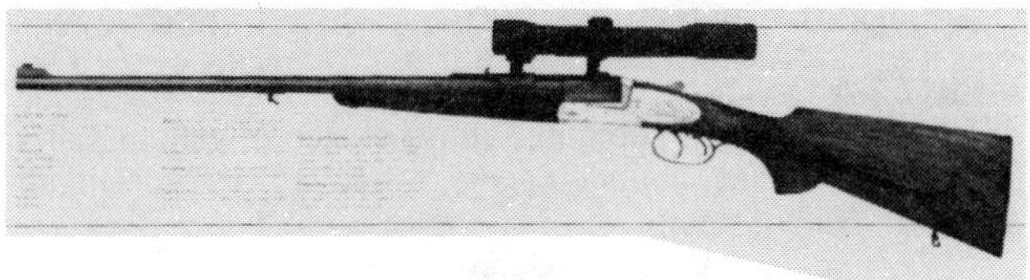

NIB	Exc.	V.G.	Good	Fair	Poor
13000	12000	10000	7500	5000	4000

RGZ 1000

7x64, .270 Win., 7mm Rem. Mag., and .300 Win. Mag. caliber Mauser 98 bolt action with a 20.5" barrel. Walnut pistol-grip stock with a cheekpiece.

NIB	Exc.	V.G.	Good	Fair	Poor
1300	1100	950	750	500	400

RGX 1000 Express

As above, with double-set triggers and a 23.75" barrel.

NIB	Exc.	V.G.	Good	Fair	Poor
1450	1250	1000	800	600	500

Pistols

SAB G90

A 7.65 parabellum or 9 mm caliber double-action semi-automic pistol with a 4.75" barrel, and 15-shot magazine. Blued or chrome-plated with walnut grips.

NIB	Exc.	V.G.	Good	Fair	Poor
675	625	550	500	350	275

SAB G91 Compact

As above, with a 3.5" barrel and a 12-shot magazine.

NIB	Exc.	V.G.	Good	Fair	Poor
695	650	600	500	400	325

Trident Fast Action

A .32 S&W or the .38 Special caliber double-action revolver with a 2.5" or 3" barrel, 6-shot cylinder and is double-actioned. Blued, with walnut grips.

NIB	Exc.	V.G.	Good	Fair	Poor
600	525	450	400	300	225

Trident Super

As above, with a 4" ventilated-rib barrel.

NIB	Exc.	V.G.	Good	Fair	Poor
650	600	525	475	325	250

Trident Match 900

As above, with 6" heavy barrel, adjustable sights and target-type, walnut grips.

NIB	Exc.	V.G.	Good	Fair	Poor
1000	900	750	600	450	300

GARAND

Various

The generic name for the U.S.M1 Rifle. See respective makers for values.

GARATE, ANITUA

Eibar, Spain

Charola

A 5.5mm Clement semi-automatic pistol with the magazine located in front of the trigger and having an exposed hammer. Normally encountered with a nickle-plated finish and composition grips.

Exc.	V.G.	Good	Fair	Poor
250	225	175	125	90

Cosmopolite

A .38 caliber copy of the Colt Police Positive. Manufactured from 1920 to 1930.

Exc.	V.G.	Good	Fair	Poor
175	150	125	100	75

El Lunar
Resembling the Colt Police Positive in 88mm Lebel caliber, this revolver was made for the French Government in 1915 and 1916.

Exc.	V.G.	Good	Fair	Poor
200	175	150	125	100

G.A.C.
A copy of the Smith & Wesson Military & Police revolver, manufactured between 1930 and 1936, in .32-20 caliber. Marked "G.A.C. Firearms Mfg. Co."

Exc.	V.G.	Good	Fair	Poor
175	150	125	100	75

Garate, Anitua
A 7.65mm caliber "Eibar" semi-automatic pistol with 8-shot magazine.

Exc.	V.G.	Good	Fair	Poor
150	125	100	75	50

Garate, Anitua
A .455 caliber double-action break-open revolver with a 5" barrel, adopted by the Royal Army in November of 1915 and known as "Pistol OP No. 1 Mark 1".

Exc.	V.G.	Good	Fair	Poor
275	250	200	150	100

La Lira
A copy of the Mannlicher Model 1901 in .32ACP caliber with removable magazine marked "System La Lira" on the breech; "Para Cartoucho Browning 7.65mm," on the barrel; and "G.A.C.," on the grips. Produced prior to WWI.

Exc.	V.G.	Good	Fair	Poor
200	175	150	125	100

L'Eclair
A 5.5mm Velo-Dog caliber folding trigger double-action revolver with 6-shot cylinder. Manufactured from 1900-1914.

Exc.	V.G.	Good	Fair	Poor
150	125	100	75	50

Sprinter
A 6.35mm caliber semi-automatic pistol marked "The Best Automatique Pistol Sprinter Patent 6.35mm Cartridge." Manufactured before WWI.

Exc.	V.G.	Good	Fair	Poor
150	125	100	75	50

Triumph
Identical to the La Lira model but marked "Triumph Automatic Pistol."

Exc.	V.G.	Good	Fair	Poor
200	175	150	125	100

GARATE, HERMANOS
Ermua, Spain

Cantabria
A 6.35mm caliber folding trigger double-action revolver with a concealed hammer, cocking spur and a short barrel resembling the slide on a semi-automatic. The name "Cantabria" is stamped on the left side.

Exc.	V.G.	Good	Fair	Poor
175	150	125	100	75

Velo-Stark
A double-action folding trigger revolver with concealed hammer.

Exc.	V.G.	Good	Fair	Poor
150	125	90	65	40

GARBI
Eibar, Spain
Importer—W. L. Moore and Co.Westlake Village, California

Model 51-A
A 12 gauge boxlock shotgun with various barrel lengths and chokes, double triggers, extractors, a case-hardened receiver, and walnut stock.

Exc.	V.G.	Good	Fair	Poor
475	450	400	300	225

Model 51-B
As above, in 16 and 20 gauge, as well as 12 gauge, with automatic ejectors, case-hardened or coin-finished receiver.

Exc.	V.G.	Good	Fair	Poor
800	725	650	500	375

Model 60-A
A 12 gauge sidelock shotgun with various barrel lengths and chokes, cocking indicators, engraved receiver and walnut stock.

Exc.	V.G.	Good	Fair	Poor
700	625	550	400	275

Model 60-B
As above, but chambered for 16 and 20 gauge as well as 12 gauge with automatic ejectors, and English-style stock.

Exc.	V.G.	Good	Fair	Poor
1250	1100	900	700	500

Model 62-A
A 12 gauge sidelock shotgun, with a choice of various barrel lengths and chokes, double triggers, extractors, and cocking indicators. Walnut stock.

Exc.	V.G.	Good	Fair	Poor
725	650	500	425	300

Model 62-B
Similar to the above, but chambered for 16 and 20 gauge as well as 12 gauge. Engraved, case-hardened or coin-finished receiver and walnut stock.

Exc.	V.G.	Good	Fair	Poor
1200	1050	850	650	450

Model 71
A 12, 16, or 20 gauge Holland & Holland sidelock shotgun with various barrel lengths and choke combinations, automatic ejectors and a single selective trigger. Engraved with fine English-style scrollwork and walnut stock. Discontinued in 1988.

Exc.	V.G.	Good	Fair	Poor
2250	2000	1800	1500	1100

Model 100
A 12, 16, or 20 gauge Holland & Holland sidelock shotgun with chopper-lump barrels, automatic ejectors, and a single trigger. Engraved in the Purdy style, with walnut stock.

NIB	Exc.	V.G.	Good	Fair	Poor
3250	3000	2500	2000	1500	1000

Model 101
As above, with floral engraving.

NIB	Exc.	V.G.	Good	Fair	Poor
4000	3750	3250	2500	2000	1750

Model 102
As above, with Holland & Holland style, engraving and also in 28 gauge. Discontinued in 1988.

Exc.	V.G.	Good	Fair	Poor
4000	3750	3200	2500	2000

Model 103A
As above with finer engraving.

NIB	Exc.	V.G.	Good	Fair	Poor
5500	5000	4500	3750	3000	2500

Model 103B
In 12, 16, 20, or 28 gauge Holland & Holland sidelock shotgun with various barrel lengths and choke combinations, chopper-lump barrels, Holland & Holland easy-opening mechanism, automatic ejectors, single selective trigger, and Purdy-type scroll engraving.

NIB	Exc.	V.G.	Good	Fair	Poor
4000	3500	3000	2500	1500	1000

Model 120
As above, with engraved hunting scenes.

NIB	Exc.	V.G.	Good	Fair	Poor
4000	3500	3000	2500	1500	1000

Model 200
As above, in Magnum gauges and with engraving.

NIB	Exc.	V.G.	Good	Fair	Poor
4500	4000	3500	3000	2000	1500

Model Special AG
A 12, 16, 20, or 28 gauge Holland & Holland sidelock shotgun with various barrel lengths and choke combinations, single selective trigger,and automatic ejectors. Large scroll engraving with walnut stock.

NIB	Exc.	V.G.	Good	Fair	Poor
7600	6800	6200	4500	3750	3200

GARCIA
SEE—Sako
Importer of Sako rifles.

GARRET, J. & F. CO.
Greensboro, North Carolina

Garrett Single Shot Pistol
A .54 caliber single shot percussion pistol with an 8.5" round barrel, swivel ramrod, walnut stock and brass mounts. Marked on the barrel breech "G.W." or "S.R." Approximately 500 were made in 1862 and 1863.

Exc.	V.G.	Good	Fair	Poor
3000	2500	2000	1500	1000

GASSER, LEOPOLD
Ottakring, Austria

M1870
An 11mm caliber double-action revolver with a 14.75" or 9.3" barrel, and 6-shot cylinder. Marked "Gasser Patent, Guss Stahl." It also bears an Austrian eagle and an apple pierced by an arrow, with the words "Schutz Mark."

Exc.	V.G.	Good	Fair	Poor
375	325	250	175	125

M1870/74
As above, with a steel frame.

Exc.	V.G.	Good	Fair	Poor
375	325	250	175	125

Gasser-Kropatschek M1876
An M1870/74 weighing 1 lb. 11 ozs. and 9mm caliber.

Exc.	V.G.	Good	Fair	Poor
300	225	175	125	100

Montenegrin Gasser
A 10.7mm caliber double-action revolver with 5" or 6" barrels, and 5-shot cylinder. Engraved, silver and gold inlay, and ivory or bone grips.

Values given are for the plain, unadorned model. Embellished models will need individual appraisal.

Exc.	V.G.	Good	Fair	Poor
400	325	250	200	150

Rast & Gasser M1898
A 8mm caliber double-action revolver with 4.75" barrel, 8-shot cylinder, solid-frame revolver with loading gate and an integral ejector rod.

Exc.	V.G.	Good	Fair	Poor
275	225	175	125	100

GATLING ARMS CO.
Birmingham, England

Established in 1888, this company remained in operation until approximately 1890. Although primarily involved with the marketing of Gatling Guns, it did market the one revolver listed below.

Dimancea
A .38 or .45 caliber double-action hammerless revolver with a 6-shot cylinder. The loading system is rather unusual—a spur that resembles a hammer is pulled down, allowing the barrel and cylinder to pivot and to be pulled forward. During this motion the empty cases are ejected and new ones could be inserted. Marked "The Gatling Arms and Ammunition Co. Birmingham"; some are also marked "Dimancea Patent."

Exc.	V.G.	Good	Fair	Poor
900	800	675	500	425

GAULOIS
St. Etienne, France
SEE—Le Francaise

GAVAGE, A.
Liege, Belgium

A 7.65mm caliber semi-automatic pistol with a fixed barrel and a concealed hammer. Similar in appearance to the Clement. Markings with "AG" molded into the grips. Some have been found bearing German Waffenamts. Manufactured from 1930s to 1940s.

Exc.	V.G.	Good	Fair	Poor
350	275	225	150	100

GAZANAGA, ISIDRO
Eibar, Spain

Destroyer M1913
A 6.35mm caliber semi-automatic pistol copied after the 1906 Browning. Produced through WWI.

Exc.	V.G.	Good	Fair	Poor
150	125	100	75	50

Destroyer M1916
A 7.65mm caliber "Eibar" design semi-automatic pistol with a 7- or 9-shot magazine. Marked "Pistolet Automatique Destroyer I Gaztanaga Eibar."

Exc.	V.G.	Good	Fair	Poor
150	125	100	75	50

Destroyer Revolver
A good quality .38 caliber copy of the Colt Police Positive.

Exc.	V.G.	Good	Fair	Poor
175	150	125	100	75

Super Destroyer
A 7.65mm caliber copy of the Walther PP. The slide is stamped "Pistola Automatica 7.65 Super Destroyer."

Exc.	V.G.	Good	Fair	Poor
175	150	125	100	75

Surete
As above in 7.65mm caliber. Marked "Cal. 7.65 Pistolet Automatique Surete" with "IG" stamped on the frame.

Exc.	V.G.	Good	Fair	Poor
175	150	125	100	75

GECO
SEE—Genschow, Gustave
Hamburg, Germany

GEHA

Germany

An altered Mauser 98 rifle rebarrelled for use with 12 gauge shotgun shells. Barrel length 26.5", military stock shortened to half length and the butt inlaid with a brass medallion marked "Geha". Manufactured from approximately 1919 to 1929.

Exc.	V.G.	Good	Fair	Poor
225	200	150	100	75

GEM

Bacon Arms Company
Norwich, Connecticut

SEE—Bacon Arms Company under their separate listing.

Gem Pocket Revolver

A .22 caliber spur trigger revolver with a 1.25" octagonal barrel. The frame is iron, engraved, nickle-plated. with walnut or ivory grips. The barrel marked "Gem." Manufactured between 1878 and 1883.

Exc.	V.G.	Good	Fair	Poor
500	450	400	300	200

GENEZ, A. G.

New York, New York

Pocket Pistol

A .41 caliber single shot percussion pistol with a 3" barrel, German silver mountings and a walnut stock. Manufactured in the 1850s and 1860s.

Exc.	V.G.	Good	Fair	Poor
2500	2000	1000	400	300

GENSCHOW, G.

Hamburg, Germany

Geco

A 6.35mm, 7.65mm, .32 long, and 8mm Lebel caliber folding trigger double-action revolver.

Exc.	V.G.	Good	Fair	Poor
150	125	100	75	50

German Bulldog

A .32, .38 and .45 caliber folding trigger double-action revolver with solid frames, integral ejector rods, and loading gates. The proofmarks indicate Belgian manufacture.

Exc.	V.G.	Good	Fair	Poor
150	125	100	75	50

GERING, H. M. & CO.

Arnstadt, Germany

Leonhardt

Identical to the "Beholla" made by Becker.

Exc.	V.G.	Good	Fair	Poor
275	250	200	150	100

GERMAN WWII SERVICE PISTOL THE P.38

Walther developed its German military service pistol, the P.38 or Model HP (Heerespistole), in 1937. It was adopted by the German military as its primary handgun in 1938. The background behind this adoption by the German military is an interesting one. In the 1930s, the German Army High Command wanted German arms manufacturers to develop a large caliber semi-automatic pistol to replace the Luger which was difficult and costly to manufacture. The Army wanted a pistol that was easy to manufacture as well as simple to assemble and disassemble. It also required a pistol that could be produced by several manufacturers if necessary and one whose parts would be interchangeable among manufacturers. Walther had just completed its Model HP for world wide distribution and had the advantage over the other German companies. The German High Command approved Walther's design with only a few mechanical changes. This designation, the P.38, was not used by Walther on its commercial guns. Production began in late 1939 for both civilian and military use. Both military and commercial versions were produced throughout the war years. The civilian pistol was referred to as the MOD HP until late in the war when a few were marked MOD P.38 to take advantage of the identity of the military pistol. In late 1942, Mauser and Spreewerke began production of the P.38. Mauser was assigned the code "BYF" and in 1945 the code was changed to "SVW". Spreewerke code was "CYQ". Late in the war the die stamp broke and the code appears as "CVQ".

The P.38 is a double-action semi-automatic pistol that is short recoil operated and fires from a locked breech by means of an external hammer. It is chambered for the 9mm Parabellum and has a 5 inch barrel. The detachable magazine holds 8 cartridges and the front sight is adjustable for windage. Initially the finish was a high quality blue, but when the war effort increased less time was spent on the finish. The P.38 was equipped with two styles of plastic grips. Early pistols have a checkered grip and later grips are the military ribbed variety; the later style is much more common. The P.38 was produced by three companies and each had its own distinct markings and variations as outlined below. Despite the large number of variations that the P.38 collector will encounter, it is important for him to be aware that there are no known documented examples of P.38s that are factory engraved, nickle-plated, have barrels that are longer or shorter than standard, or built as military presentation pistols.

Collectors should be made aware of a final note. The P.38 pistol was first adopted over 50 years ago. During that period of time the pistol has seen use all over the world. After the end of WWII several governments came into possession of fairly large quantities of P.38s and used them in their own military and police agencies. Many countries such as South Africa and Israel have reworked these older P.38s with both original and new component parts. However, the former country of East Germany was the primary source of reworked P-38s. Many of these pistols have been completely refinished and re-proofed by a number of countries. The collector should be aware of the existence of reworked P.38s and examine closely any P.38 carefully to determine if the pistol is original German military issue. These reworked pistols bring substantially lower prices than original P.38s.

Walther Commercial

The Commercial version of the P.38 is identified by commercial proofmarks of a crown over N or an eagle over N. Production started at around serial number 1000 and went through serial number 26659. This was the first of the commercial pistols and was a high-quality, well made gun with a complete inscription on the left slide. A few of these very early pistols were equipped with checkered wooden grips. The quality decreased as the war progressed. There are many variations of these commercial models and values can vary from $1,000 to $6,000. It is suggested that these pistols be appraised and evaluated by an expert.

Walther Military

Courtesy Orville Reichert.

Courtesy Orville Reichert.

0 Series

This was the first of the military P.38s and they are well made with a high polish finish. These pistols have the Walther banner and the designation P.38. The serial number began with 01 and went through about 013714. The First 0 Series has a concealed extractor and rectangular firing pin. About 1,000 First 0 Series were built. The Second 0 Series has a rectangular firing pin and standard extractor, with a production of about 2,300. The Third 0 Series has a standard firing pin and standard extractor and has the highest production with 10,000 built.

Courtesy Orville Reichert.

First Issue 0 Series

Exc.	V.G.	Good	Fair	Poor
3500	3000	2250	1500	950

Second Issue 0 Series

Exc.	V.G.	Good	Fair	Poor
3000	2500	1750	1000	750

Third Issue 0 Series

Exc.	V.G.	Good	Fair	Poor
1200	950	700	500	300

480 Code

This code was utilized by Walther in late 1940 and represents the first true military contract pistols. There were approximately 7,250 guns produced under this code. There are two sub-variations: one with a round lanyard loop and the other with a rectangular lanyard loop.

Exc.	V.G.	Good	Fair	Poor
2250	1950	1450	1000	600

"ac" Codes

This variation follows the 480 code.

"ac" (no date)

This variation has on the slide "P.38 ac" then the serial number only. This is the first use of the "ac" code by Walther. There were approximately 2,500 pistols produced with this code and is the rarest of all military P.38s.

Courtesy Orville Reichert.

Courtesy Orville Reichert.

Exc.	V.G.	Good	Fair	Poor
3000	2500	1750	1000	750

"ac40"

There are two types of "ac40s". The first variation is the ac with the 40 added, that is the 40 was hand stamped below the ac. There are about 10,000 of these produced. The second variation is the ac 40 rolled on together. There are also about

10,000 of these produced as well. The "ac" 40 added is more valuable than the standard "ac40".

"ac40" (added)

Exc.	V.G.	Good	Fair	Poor
1500	950	750	600	400

"ac40" (standard)

Exc.	V.G.	Good	Fair	Poor
1200	750	550	400	300

"ac41"

There are three variations of the "ac41". The first variation has "ac" on left triggerguard and features a high gloss blue. About 25,000 of this variation were made. The second variation, about 70,000 were produced, also has a high gloss blue but does not have "ac" on the triggerguard. The third variation features a military blue rather than a high gloss blue and had a production run of about 15,000 pistols.

"ac41" (1st variation)

Exc.	V.G.	Good	Fair	Poor
1000	750	550	400	300

"ac41" (2nd variation)

Exc.	V.G.	Good	Fair	Poor
900	600	500	400	300

"ac41" (3rd variation)

Exc.	V.G.	Good	Fair	Poor
900	600	500	400	300

"ac42"

There are two variations of the "ac42" code. The first has an eagle over 359 stamped on all small parts as do all preceeding variations and a production of 21,000 pistols. The second variation does not have the eagle over 359 stamped on small parts. This second variation has a large production run of 100,000 pistols.

Courtesy Orville Reichert.

Courtesy Orville Reichert.

"ac42" (1st variation)

Exc.	V.G.	Good	Fair	Poor
500	450	350	275	200

"ac42" (2nd variation)

Exc.	V.G.	Good	Fair	Poor
400	350	250	175	100

"ac43" Stacked Date

This code has three variations. The first is a standard date with "ac" over 43. It has an early frame and extractor cut. The second variation has the late frame and extractor cut. Both variations are frequently encountered because approximately 130,000 were built.

"ac43" (1st variation)

Exc.	V.G.	Good	Fair	Poor
400	350	250	175	100

"ac43" (2nd variation)

Exc.	V.G.	Good	Fair	Poor
400	350	250	175	100

"ac43" single line slide

This variation represents the beginning of the placement of the date on the same line with the production code. There were approximately 20,000 built in this variation.

Exc.	V.G.	Good	Fair	Poor
600	500	400	300	200

"ac44"

This variation also has the date stamped beside "ac" and is fairly common. About 120,000 were produced.

Exc.	V.G.	Good	Fair	Poor
400	350	250	200	150

Note: Add $50 for Czech (FNH) frame.

"ac45"

This code has three variations. The first has all matching numbers on a plum colored frame. About 32,000 of this first variation were produced. The second variation has a capital "A" in place of the lowercase "a". The third variation has all major parts with factory mismatched numbers, with a single eagle over 359 on the slide. The first variation is the most common of this code.

"ac45" (1st variation)

Exc.	V.G.	Good	Fair	Poor
400	350	250	200	150

"ac45" (2nd variation)

Exc.	V.G.	Good	Fair	Poor
450	375	275	250	200

"ac45" (3rd variation)

Exc.	V.G.	Good	Fair	Poor
350	300	250	200	150

Note: Add $50 for pistols with Czech barrels; barrel code "fnh".

"ac45" 0 Series

This is a continuation of the commercial pistols with a military marked slide. This series has "ac45" plus the 0 prefix serial number on the left side as well as the usual P-38 rollstamp. It may or may not have commercial proofmarks. A total of 1,800 of these "ac45" 0 Series guns were produced in 1945. They are often seen with a plum colored slide.

"ac45" 0 Series

Exc.	V.G.	Good	Fair	Poor
1200	900	700	450	325

MAUSER MILITARY

The following P.38s were produced by Mauser and are identified by various Mauser codes.

Courtesy Orville Reichert.

Courtesy Orville Reichert.

"Police" P.38

Mauser produced the only police P.38s from 1943 to 1945. More than 8,000 were produced and there are numerous subvariations and markings which greatly affect the value. An expert should be consulted. These Police P.38s are readily recognized by their appearance of an eagle over F or eagle over L to indicate police procurement.

"byf42"

Approximately 19,000 P.38s were manufactured in this variation. Some of these pistols will have a flat blue finish.

Exc.	V.G.	Good	Fair	Poor
600	500	400	300	200

"byf43"

A very common variation of the P.38 with approximately 140,000 produced.

Exc.	V.G.	Good	Fair	Poor
400	350	250	200	150

"byf44"

Another common variation with a total production of about 150,000 guns.

Exc.	V.G.	Good	Fair	Poor
400	350	250	200	150

Note: Add $100 for dual tone finish which is a combination of blue and gray components.

"svw45"

The Mauser code is changed from "byf" to "svw". This variation was produced until the end of the war when France took over production and continued through 1946. French produced guns will have a 5 point star on the right side of the slide. A large number of these French pistols have been imported thereby depressing values.

Exc.	V.G.	Good	Fair	Poor
350	300	250	200	150

SPREEWERKE MILITARY

Production of the P.38 began at Spreewerke (Berlin) in late 1942 and Spreewerke used the code "cyq" that had been assigned to it at the beginning of the war.

"cyq" (1st variation)

The first 500 of these guns have the eagle over 359 on some small parts and command a premium. Value depends on markings and an expert should be consulted for values.

"cyq" (standard variation)

There were approximately 300,000 of these pistols produced in this variation which makes them the most common of all P.38 variations.

Exc.	V.G.	Good	Fair	Poor
325	250	200	175	150

Note: If "A" or "B" prefix add $125.

"cyq" 0 Series

This variation features a 0 ahead of the serial number and only about 5,000 of these guns were produced.

Exc.	V.G.	Good	Fair	Poor
650	500	400	300	200

GERSTENBERGER & EBERWEIN

Gussenstadt, Germany

Em-Ge, G.& E., Omega & Pic

A series of poor-quality revolvers sold in the U.S.A. before

1968. .22 and .32 calibers with 2.25" barrels, and 6-shot cylinder.

Exc.	V.G.	Good	Fair	Poor
125	100	75	50	25

GEVARM
St. Etienne, France

E-1 Autoloading Rifle

A .22 caliber semi-automatic rifle with a 19" barrel, 10-shot magazine, blued with walnut grips.

Exc.	V.G.	Good	Fair	Poor
175	150	125	100	75

GIB
Eibar, Spain

10 Gauge Shotgun

A 10 gauge Magnum boxlock double-barrel shotgun with 32" matte-ribbed barrels. Case-hardened, blued with walnut grips.

Exc.	V.G.	Good	Fair	Poor
275	250	225	150	100

GIBBS
New York, New York

Gibbs Carbine

A .52 caliber single shot percussion carbine with a sliding 22" round barrel. Blued, case-hardened with a walnut stock. The lock marked with an American eagle and "Wm. F. Brooks/Manf New York/1863." The breech marked "L.H. Gibbs/Patd/Jany 8, 1856." There were only 1,050 produced.

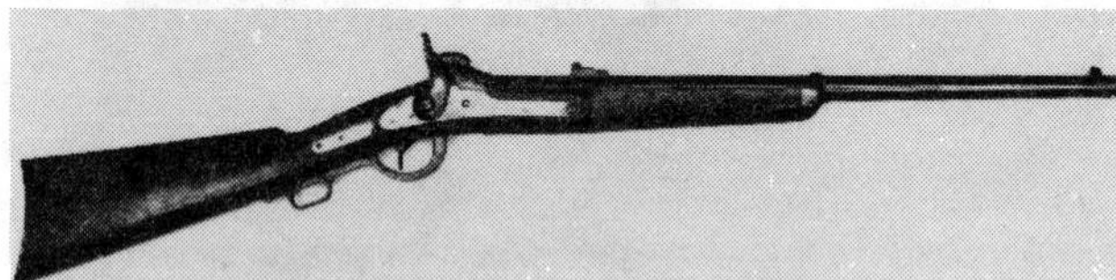

Courtesy Milwaukee Public Museum, Milwaukee, Wisconsin.

Courtesy Milwaukee Public Museum, Milwaukee, Wisconsin.

Exc.	V.G.	Good	Fair	Poor
2750	2500	2000	1500	1000

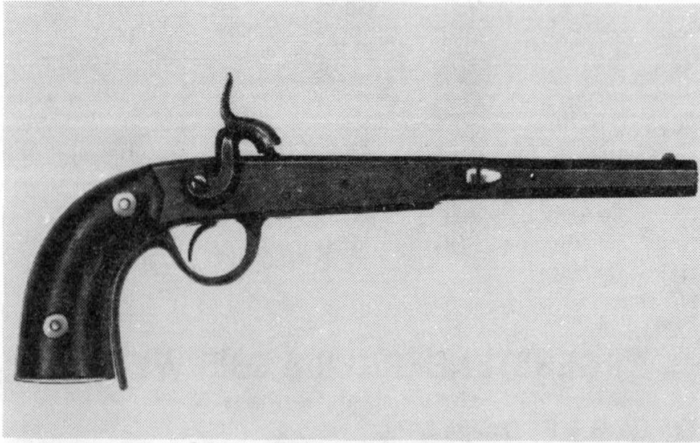

Courtesy Milwaukee Public Museum, Milwaukee, Wisconsin.

Gibbs Pistol

A caliber percussion pistol made by Hull & Thomas of Ilion, NY: - 1855 or 1856.

Exc.	V.G.	Good	Fair	Poor
2000	1750	1200	750	500

GIBBS GUNS, INC.
Greenback, Tennessee

Mark 45 Carbine

A .45 ACP caliber semi-automatic rifle with a 16.5" barrel, a 5-, 15-, 30-, or 90-shot magazine. Blued, with a walnut buttstock and forend. A nickle-plated model was available as an option and would bring approximately $25 additional. Discontinued in 1988.

NIB	Exc.	V.G.	Good	Fair	Poor
275	225	175	150	125	100

GIBBS TIFFANY & CO.
Sturbridge, Massachusetts

Under Hammer Pistol

A .28 caliber single shot percussion pistol with 3" to 8" barrels. A browned iron frame, walnut or maple pointed handle trimmed with brass. The top strap is marked "Gibbs Tiffany & Co." Active 1820 to 1838.

Exc.	V.G.	Good	Fair	Poor
500	425	350	275	175

GILLESPIE
New York, New York

Derringer Type Pocket Pistol

A .41 caliber single shot percussion pistol with a 2.5" barrel and a walnut stock. Manufactured from 1848 to 1870.

Exc.	V.G.	Good	Fair	Poor
2000	1250	750	350	250

GLAZE, W. & CO.
Columbia, South Carolina
SEE—B. & B. M. Darling

GLISENTI
Turin, Italy

Glisenti Model 1910

A 9mm Glisenti caliber semi-automatic pistol with a 3.9" barrel, fixed sights, and 7-shot magazine. Manufactured from 1910 to 1934.

Exc.	V.G.	Good	Fair	Poor
550	500	425	300	225

GLOCK
Austria
Importer—Glock Inc.
Smyrna, Georgia

Glock Inc. is an Austrian company founded by Gaston Glock in 1963. What originally began as a commercial appliance manufacturing company developed into a line of products that involved military and police products. In 1982 Glock bid on and won the right to manufacture a new state-of-the-art semi-automatic 9mm pistol for the Austrian Army. This new pistol used polymer as a basic component material along with steel. The slide is steel, while the grip and slide base are polymer. The result is a lightweight, strong, and highly reliable military and police pistol. In 1984 the Norwegian Army chose the Glock 17 as its service pistol. With its growing success in Europe, Glock established an American subsidiary in Smyrna, Georgia in 1985 to sell its Glock 17 to American police forces and civilian shooters. By 1990 over 2,700 law enforcement agencies were using the Glock pistol as a duty weapon. One of its unusual design features is a trigger-activated safety. From its introduction as the 9mm Glock 17, the company has expanded its caliber offerings to include the 10mm, .40 S&W, and the .45 ACP.

Glock 17

This model is chambered for the 9mm Parabellum cartridge. It is a double-action only semi-automatic that has a 4.49" barrel and a 17-shot detachable magazine. The empty weight of this pistol is 21.91 oz. This pistol is offered with either fixed or adjustable sights at the same retail price. The finish is black with black plastic grips. It is furnished in a plastic case with an extra magazine. This pistol was introduced in 1985 and is still currently produced.

Note: Add $80.00 if equipped with night sights.

NIB	Exc.	V.G.	Good	Fair	Poor
400	375	325	300	275	175

Glock 17L Competition Model

This version features a 6" compensated barrel and adjustable sights. The trigger is fine-tuned to provide between a 5 to 8 lbs. trigger pull. This model was introduced in 1988 and is still being manufactured. In 1990 this pistol won the I.P.S.C. World Stock Gun Championship.

NIB	Exc.	V.G.	Good	Fair	Poor
600	550	500	425	350	225

Glock 22

Almost identical in appearance to the Model 17, the Model 22 is chambered for the .40 S&W cartridge. It comes standard with a 15-round clip. It has a slightly larger and heavier slide. Weight is 22.36 oz.

Note: Add $80.00 if equipped with night sights.

NIB	Exc.	V.G.	Good	Fair	Poor
425	375	325	300	275	175

Glock 19

This is similar in appearance to the Model 17 but is a compact version with a 4" barrel and a smaller grip that will accept either a 15-round or the standard 17-round magazine that protrudes a bit. Weight for this model is 20.99 oz. empty. The grip straps on this model are serrated as they are on the other Glock models. It was introduced in 1988 and is currently in production.

Note: Add $80.00 if equipped with night sights.

NIB	Exc.	V.G.	Good	Fair	Poor
400	375	325	300	275	175

Model 23

Model 23 is chambered for the .40 S&W cartridge. Its slide is slightly heavier and larger than the Model 19. Weight is 21.67 oz. The Glock 23 magazine holds 13 rounds.

Note: Add $80.00 if equipped with night sights.

NIB	Exc.	V.G.	Good	Fair	Poor
425	375	350	325	275	175

Glock 20 and Glock 21

Both of these models are identical in physical appearance except for the caliber: the Model 20 is chambered for the 10mm cartridge while the Model 21 is chambered for the .45 ACP. Both have a barrel length of 4.60". The Model 20 has a 15-round clip and weighs 26.35 oz. while the Model 21 has a 13-round magazine and weighs 25.22 oz.

Note: Add $80.00 if equipped with night sights.

NIB	Exc.	V.G.	Good	Fair	Poor
450	400	350	300	250	200

GODDARD

SEE—B. & B. M. Darling

GOLDEN EAGLE

Tochigi, Japan
Nikko Limited

Shotguns

Golden Eagle Model 5000 Grade I

A 12 or 20 gauge Over/Under shotgun with of 26", 28", and 30" barrels with ventilated-ribs and various choke combinations, a single selective trigger and automatic ejectors. Blued, with a walnut stock that has an eagle's head inlaid into the pistol-grip cap. Manufactured between 1976 and the early 1980s.

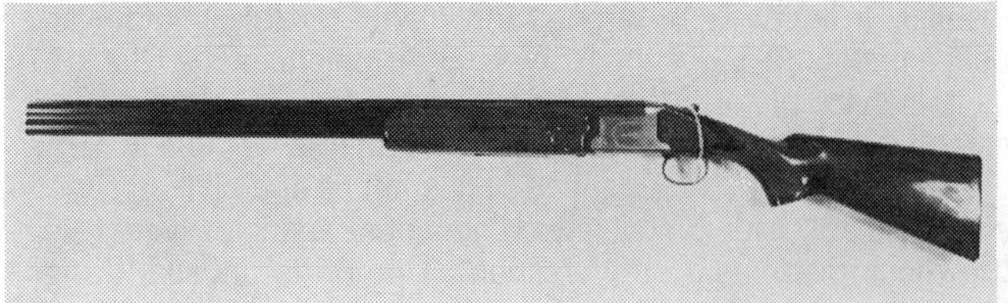

Exc.	V.G.	Good	Fair	Poor
850	750	600	475	300

Grade I Skeet

As above, with a 26" or 28" barrel having a wide competition rib.

Exc.	V.G.	Good	Fair	Poor
950	800	700	550	375

Grade I Trap

Similar to the skeet model, with a 30" or 32" barrel.

Exc.	V.G.	Good	Fair	Poor
950	800	700	550	375

Model 5000 Grade II

As above, but more finely finished with an eagle head inlaid in the receiver in gold.

Exc.	V.G.	Good	Fair	Poor
1000	850	750	600	425

Grandee Grade III

As above, but more elaborately engraved.

Exc.	V.G.	Good	Fair	Poor
2500	2000	1750	1400	1000

Rifles

Model 7000 Grade I

A Mauser bolt-action rifle chambered for all popular American calibers with a 24" or 26" barrel, walnut stock and a rosewood pistol-grip cap and forend tip.

NIB	Exc.	V.G.	Good	Fair	Poor
700	600	500	400	325	250

Model 7000 African

As above in .375 H&H and .458 Win. Mag. caliber with open sights.

NIB	Exc.	V.G.	Good	Fair	Poor
700	600	500	400	325	250

Model 7000 Grade II

As above, but engraved.

Exc.	V.G.	Good	Fair	Poor
625	550	475	375	300

GONCZ CO.
Hollywood, California

GC Carbine
A 7.63mm Mauser, 9mm Parabellum, .38 Super, and the .45 ACP caliber semi-automatic rifle with a 16.1" barrel. Black with a walnut stock. All current production models are now stainless-steel.

NIB	Exc.	V.G.	Good	Fair	Poor
450	400	325	275	200	125

GC Stainless
As above, in stainless-steel. Introduced in 1987.

NIB	Exc.	V.G.	Good	Fair	Poor
550	450	375	325	250	175

GC Collectors Edition
A limited edition with hand-polished finish.

NIB	Exc.	V.G.	Good	Fair	Poor
800	600	500	425	350	225

Halogen Carbine
The GC Carbine with a powerful light source mounted under the barrel. Chambered for 9mm and .45 ACP only.

NIB	Exc.	V.G.	Good	Fair	Poor
550	450	375	325	250	175

Laser Carbine
As above, with a laser sighting system effective to 400 yards.

NIB	Exc.	V.G.	Good	Fair	Poor
1500	1250	1000	750	650	500

GA Pistol
The GC Carbine with a 9.5" shrouded barrel and a 16- or 18-shot magazine. Black with a one-piece grip. Manufactured between 1985 and 1987.

NIB	Exc.	V.G.	Good	Fair	Poor
425	350	275	200	150	100

GAT-9 Pistol
As above, in a 9mm caliber with an adjustable trigger and hand-honed action.

NIB	Exc.	V.G.	Good	Fair	Poor
550	475	375	300	225	150

GA Collectors Edition
A hand-polished stainless-steel limited production of the above.

NIB	Exc.	V.G.	Good	Fair	Poor
750	675	600	500	400	300

GS Pistol
The Model GA with a plain 5" barrel. In 1987 pistols were made in stainless steel.

NIB	Exc.	V.G.	Good	Fair	Poor
350	275	225	175	125	75

GS Collectors Edition
A hand-polished, limited-production, stainless steel version of the GS.

NIB	Exc.	V.G.	Good	Fair	Poor
725	625	550	475	350	250

J.F. GOUDRY
Paris, France

Double action 10 shot turret pistol. Marked on barrel rib J.F. Goudry Paris and Systeme A. Norl. By raising the gate on the left side the turret can be removed and reloaded or another pre-loaded turret inserted.

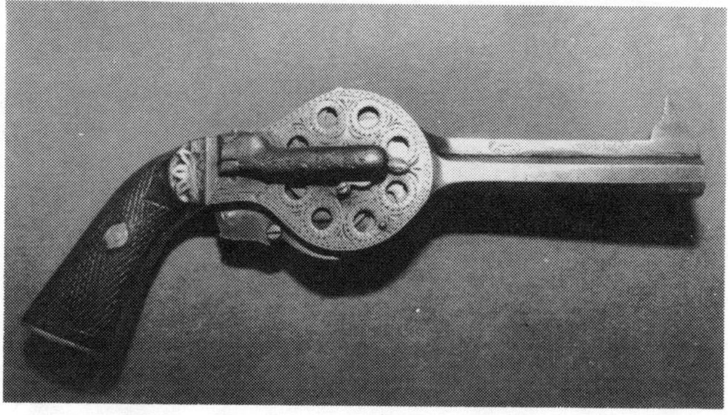

Exc.	V.G.	Good	Fair	Poor
5000	3500	3000	2000	1500

GOVERNOR
Norwich, Connecticut

Governor Pocket Revolver
A .22 caliber spur trigger revolver with a 3" barrel and 7-shot cylinder. These revolvers were made from modified Bacon pepperboxes. The top strap marked "Governor". Manufactured from approximately 1868 to 1874.

Exc.	V.G.	Good	Fair	Poor
200	175	125	75	50

GRABNER, G.
Rehberg, Austria

Kolibri
A 2.7mm and 3mm caliber semi-automatic pistol with a 3-grain bullet at approximately 500 feet per second and 5-shot magazine. Manufactured from 1914 to the 1920s.

Exc.	V.G.	Good	Fair	Poor
675	600	500	400	300

GRAND PRECISION
Eibar, Spain
A retailer of Spanish made firearms.

GRANGER, G.
St. Etienne, France
Importer—Wes Gilpin
Dallas, Texas

Side x Side Shotgun
A custom-order 12, 16, and 20 gauge boxlock double-barrel shotgun. Manufactured since 1902.

Exc.	V.G.	Good	Fair	Poor
15000	12500	10000	7500	5000

GRANT, STEPHEN
London, England

Side x Side Shotgun

This company produced very high quality firearms on a custom-order, limited-production basis. Their guns are chambered for 12, 16, and 20 gauge and are extremely scarce on today's market. The workmanship and materials were of the highest order. Manufacture has been discontinued. It is not possible to estimate the values of this rare firearm. Individual qualified appraisal should be secured.

GRAS
France

Model 1874

An 11mm caliber bolt-action rifle with a 32" barrel with a walnut stock, a barrel band and a metal tip. The bayonet is a spike blade with a wood handle and a brass butt cap.

Exc.	V.G.	Good	Fair	Poor
275	250	200	150	75

GREAT WESTERN ARMS COMPANY

A certain amount of confusion surrounds Great Western Arms Company firearms. Collectors believe that this company's Colt single action and Remington derringer look-alikes were produced in Italy or Spain and imported into the U.S. under the West Coast distributor H.Y. Hunter. In fact all major components were built of the finest alloys using investment castings and assembled in Los Angeles, California. Great Western offered an extensive variety of combinations of caliber, finish, and grips. Auxiliary cylinders were offered as well in the following chambers: .44 Special/44-40/.44 Magnum, .357/.38 Special and .45 ACP/.45 Long Colt. The company made available to its customers several grades and styles of engraving.

During the ten years that Great Western was in business the quality of its firearms was inconsistent due to uncertain management and finances. This left the company's reputation damaged and allowed Colt and Ruger to dominate the single action market. By 1961 Great Western Arms Company was no longer able to compete. Despite the company's unstable history there is a small but growing collector interest in these firearms. Approximately 22,000 single action revolvers were built and less than 3,500 derringers were manufactured from 1953 to 1961.

Standard barrel lengths were : 4 3/4, 5 1/2, and 7 1/2 inches.

Standard Calibers were: .38 Special, .357 Magnum, .357 Atomic, .44 Special, 44-40, .44 Magnum, .45 Long Colt, and .22 Long Rifle.

Standard Finishes were: Case-hardened frame and blued barrel and cylinder, or all blue finish.

Centerfire Single Action

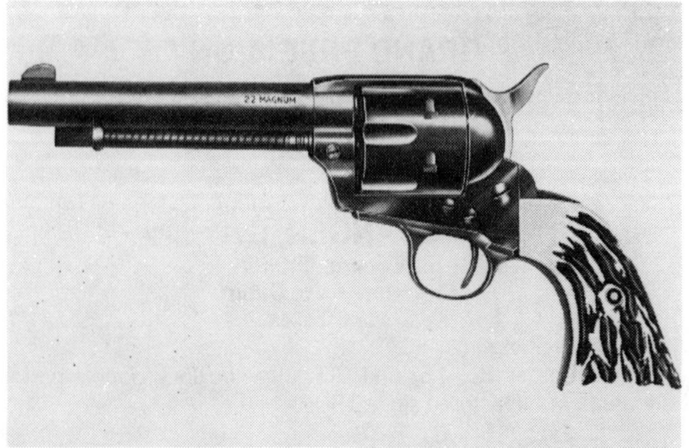

Courtesy John C. Dougan.

Courtesy John C. Dougan.

Exc.	V.G.	Good	Fair	Poor
500	425	350	250	200

.22 Long Rifle Single Action

Exc.	V.G.	Good	Fair	Poor
335	295	250	200	150

Target Model-Flattop with Micro Sights

Exc.	V.G.	Good	Fair	Poor
550	475	400	300	225

Fast Draw Model-Brass Backstrap and Triggerguard

Exc.	V.G.	Good	Fair	Poor
550	475	400	300	225

Deputy Model-4 inch Barrel with Full Length Sight Rib

Exc.	V.G.	Good	Fair	Poor
1000	850	750	650	550

Note: For calibers other than standard such as .22 Hornet, 32-20, .45 ACP, .22 Magnum, .30 Carbine add 10 percent premium.

For factory plated pistols—Add 10%.

For factory cased pistols-Add 20%.

For Sheriff's Model or Buntline Special-Add 15%.

Courtesy John C. Dougan.

For factory ivory grips add $175, for stag grips-Add $95, and for pearl grips-Add $150.

Factory engraved guns will-Add $750 to $3,500 to above prices depending on coverage.

Unassembled Kit Gun-in the White

N.I.B.	Exc.	V.G.	Good	Fair
350	300	—	—	—

Note: Assembled Kit Gun will bring between $100 and $200 depending on condition.

Derringer Model-.38 Special & .38 S&W

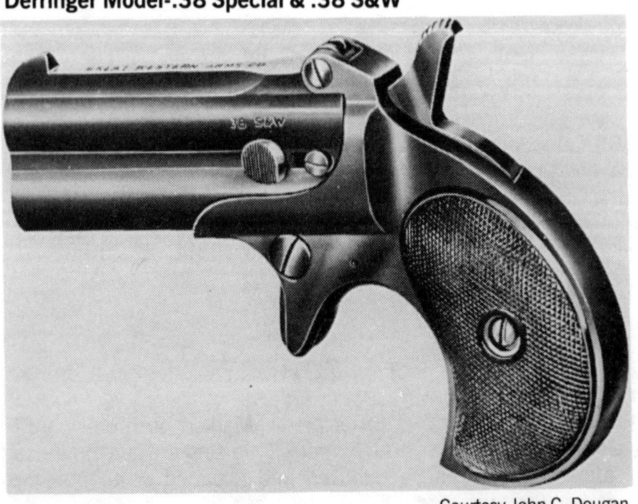

Courtesy John C. Dougan.

Exc.	V.G.	Good	Fair	Poor
300	250	200	150	100

Derringer Model-.22 Magnum RF

Exc.	V.G.	Good	Fair	Poor
400	350	250	200	150

Note: Factory Engraved Derringers add $350 to $500.

Courtesy John C. Dougan.

Courtesy John C. Dougan.

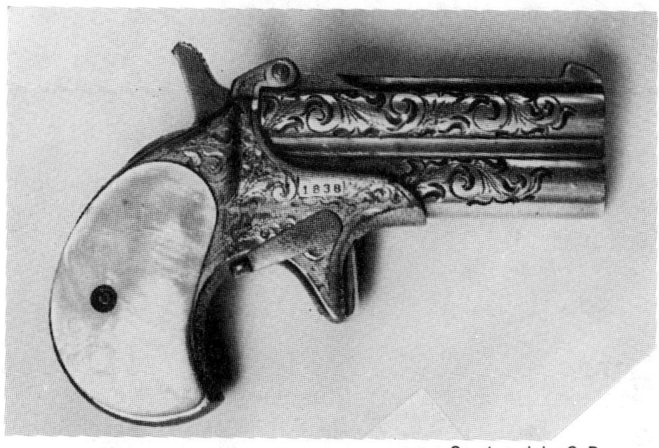

Courtesy John C. Dougan.

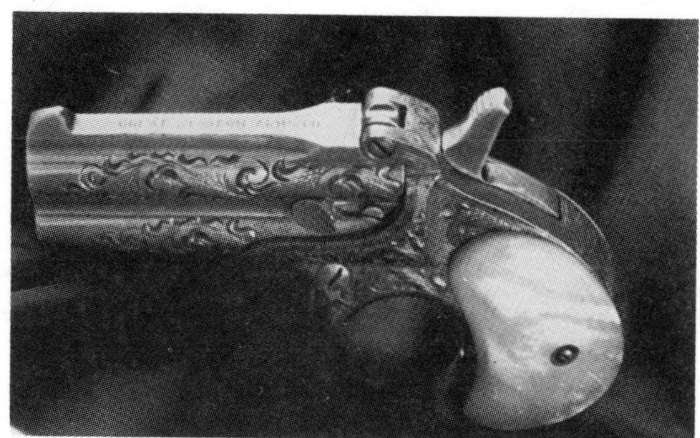

Courtesy John C. Dougan.

GREEN, E.
Cheltenham, England

Green

A .450 and .455 caliber double-action revolver, popular with its military users in the late 1800s.

Exc.	V.G.	Good	Fair	Poor
450	400	350	275	200

GREENE
Milbury, Massachusetts

Greene Breechloading Rifle

A .53 caliber single shot bolt-action percussion rifle with a 35" barrel, under hammer and full length walnut stock secured by three barrel bands. Marked "Greene's Patent/Nov. 17, 1857". Approximately 4,000 were made by the A.H. Waters Armory between 1859 and 1862.

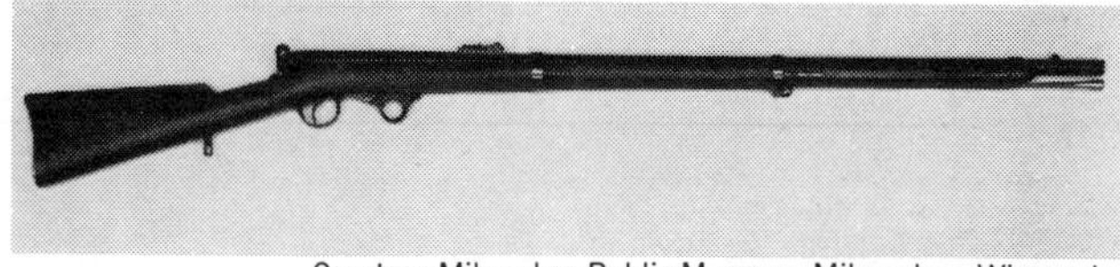

Courtesy Milwaukee Public Museum, Milwaukee, Wisconsin.

Exc.	V.G.	Good	Fair	Poor
1500	1350	1000	750	500

GREENER
See—English Military Firearms

GREENER, W. W. LTD.
Birmingham, England

General Purpose Model

A Martini action single shot 12 gauge shotgun with 26", 30" or 32" barrels. Blued, case-hardened with a walnut stock.

Exc.	V.G.	Good	Fair	Poor
350	300	250	175	125

Empire

A 12 gauge boxlock double-barrel shotgun with 2.75" or 3" chambers, 28" through 32" barrels, various choke combinatiions, double triggers, and automatic ejectors at an additional cost. Stock in either the straight style or pistol grip.

Automatic Ejectors—Add 20%.

Exc.	V.G.	Good	Fair	Poor
1750	1500	1250	1000	750

Empire Deluxe

As above, with more finely figured wood.

Automatic Ejectors—Add 20%.

Exc.	V.G.	Good	Fair	Poor
2000	1750	1500	1250	950

F35 Grade Farkiller

A 12 gauge boxlock double-barrel shotgun with 28" to 32" barrels, various choke combinations, double triggers and optional automatic ejectors. Walnut stock, in either straight or pistol grip.

Automatic Ejectors—Add 20%.

Exc.	V.G.	Good	Fair	Poor
2500	2250	2000	1500	1200

F35 Farkiller Large Bore

As above in either 8 or 10 gauge.

Automatic Ejectors—Add 20%.

Exc.	V.G.	Good	Fair	Poor
2750	2500	2250	1750	1500

Jubilee Grade DH35

A 12, 16, 20, 28 and .410 bore boxlock single barrel shotgun with a 26" to 30" barrel, various choke combinations, automatic ejectors, and double triggers. A single selective trigger available which adds approximately $500 to the value. Walnut stock in either a straight or pistolgrip stock.

Exc.	V.G.	Good	Fair	Poor
2500	2250	2000	1500	1250

Sovereign Grade DH40

As above, but more finely finished.

Exc.	V.G.	Good	Fair	Poor
2750	2500	2250	1750	1500

Crown Grade DH55

As above, with more elaborate engraving and fancier walnut.

Exc.	V.G.	Good	Fair	Poor
3500	3000	2750	2000	1750

Royal Grade DH75

The best grade Greener similar to the Crown Grade, with more engraving and the best quality of walnut.

Exc.	V.G.	Good	Fair	Poor
4500	4000	3750	3000	2750

GREIFELT & CO.

Suhl, Germany

Over/Under Shotguns

Grade No.1

A 12, 16, 20, 28 and .410 bore Anson & Deeley boxlock Over/Under shotgun with 26" to 32" ventilated-rib barrels, various choke combinations, automatic ejectors, and double triggers. A single selective trigger was available and would increase the value approximately 15 percent. Walnut stock in a straight or pistolgrip stock. The values are for the standard 12 gauge version.

28 Gauge and .410—Add 25%.

Exc.	V.G.	Good	Fair	Poor
3500	3150	2750	1750	1450

Grade No.3

Similar to the No. 1, with less engraving. Manufactured prior to WWII.

28 Gauge and .410—Add 25%.

Exc.	V.G.	Good	Fair	Poor
2750	2300	1850	1450	1000

Model 143E

The postwar version of the No. 1. Not made in 28 gauge or .410 bore.

Exc.	V.G.	Good	Fair	Poor
2500	2150	1750	1300	850

Combination Gun

A combination Over/Under rifle shotgun manufactured in all bores and a variety of rifle calibers with 24" or 26" barrels. Made prior to 1939.

Deduct 40% if rifle caliber is obsolete.

28 Gauge and .410—Add 25%.

Automatic Ejectors—Add 15%.

Exc.	V.G.	Good	Fair	Poor
5000	4500	4000	3000	2250

Side x Side Shotguns

Model 22

A 12 or 20 gauge boxlock double-barrel shotgun with 28" or 30" barrels, sideplates, double triggers and extractors. Blued, case-hardened with a walnut stock. Manufactured after 1945.

Exc.	V.G.	Good	Fair	Poor
2000	1800	1500	1200	950

Model 22E

As above, with automatic ejectors.

Exc.	V.G.	Good	Fair	Poor
2500	2200	1750	1500	1150

Model 103

A 12 and 16 gauge boxlock shotgun with a 28" or a 30" barrel, double triggers and extractors. Walnut stock with a pistol or straight English-style grip. Postwar model.

Exc.	V.G.	Good	Fair	Poor
2000	1800	1500	1200	950

Model 103E

As above, with automatic ejectors.

Exc.	V.G.	Good	Fair	Poor
2250	2000	1500	1250	1000

Drilling

A 12, 16 or 20 gauge double-barrel shotgun fitted with a rifle barrel, chambered for a variety of cartridges. Barrel length 26", boxlock action, double triggers, extractors and folding rear sight. Manufactured prior to 1939.

Deduct 40% if rifle caliber is obsolete.

20 Gauge—Add 10%.

Exc.	V.G.	Good	Fair	Poor
3500	3150	2750	2250	1750

GRENDEL, INC.

Rockledge, Florida

P-10 Pistol

A .380 caliber semi-automatic pistol with a 3" barrel, 11-shot cylinder, all-steel construction, matte-black finish with black plastic grips. It is offered in electroless nickle-plate, as well as a green teflon finish for a slightly higher price.

Green Finish—Add $5.

Electroless Nickle—Add $15.

NIB	Exc.	V.G.	Good	Fair	Poor
150	125	100	75	65	50

SRT-20F Compact Rifle

A .308 caliber bolt-action rifle with 20" finned matchgrade barrel, 9-shot magazine, a folding synthetic stock, integral bipod and no sights.

NIB	Exc.	V.G.	Good	Fair	Poor
525	475	400	325	250	150

SRT-24

As above, with a 24" barrel. Discontinued in 1988.

Exc.	V.G.	Good	Fair	Poor
450	375	300	225	125

GRIFFIN & HOWE
New York, New York

Established in 1923, this firm manufactured on custom order a variety of bolt-action sporting rifles. As these arms essentially were all built to specific customer's specifications, prospective purchasers should secure a qualified appraisal prior to purchase.

GRISWOLD & GUNNISON
Griswoldville, Georgia

1851 Navy Type

A .36 caliber percussion revolver with a 7.5" barrel and 6-shot cylinder. The frame and grip straps made of brass and the barrel as well as cylinder made of iron. Approximately 3,700 were made between 1862 and 1864, for the Confederate Government.

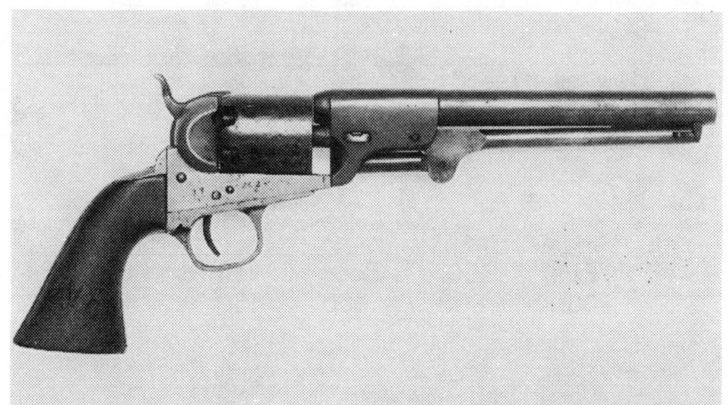

Courtesy Milwaukee Public Museum, Milwaukee, Wisconsin.

Exc.	V.G.	Good	Fair	Poor
7500	6500	5000	4000	2750

GROSS ARMS CO.
Tiffin, Ohio

Pocket Revolver

A .25 and .30 caliber spur trigger revolver with a 6" octagonal barrel, a 7-shot cylinder and marked "Gross Arms Co., Tiffin, Ohio." Blued, with walnut grips. Only a few hundred were manufactured between 1864 and 1866.

Exc.	V.G.	Good	Fair	Poor
750	700	600	475	325

GRUBB, J. C. & CO.
Philadelphia, Pennsylvania

Pocket Pistol

A .41 caliber single shot percussion pistol with various barrels lengths. German silver, walnut stock and engraved lock and triggerguard. The lock is marked "J.C.Grubb." Several hundred were manufactured between 1860 and 1870.

Exc.	V.G.	Good	Fair	Poor
1500	1000	750	375	275

GUEDES-CASTRO
Steyr, Austria

Model 1885

An 8x60mm Guedes single shot dropping block rifle with a 28" barrel, full length walnut stock and iron mounts. Made in Austria under contract for the Portuguese Army in 1885.

Exc.	V.G.	Good	Fair	Poor
500	400	350	250	125

GUIDE LAMP
Detroit, Michigan
Division General Motors

Liberator

A .45 ACP caliber single shot pistol with a 3.5" smoothbore barrel and overall length of 5.5". This pistol is made primarily of stampings and was intended to be air dropped to partisans in Europe during WWII. The hollow grip is designed to hold a packet of four extra cartridges. Originally packaged in unmarked cardboard boxes with an illustrated instruction sheet.

Exc.	V.G.	Good	Fair	Poor
500	425	375	300	225

GUION, T. F.
New Orleans, Louisiana

Pocket Pistol

A .41-caliber single shot percussion pistol with a 2.5" barrel, German silver mountings, and a walnut stock. Manufacured in the 1850s.

Exc.	V.G.	Good	Fair	Poor
2500	1750	1000	400	275

V. GULIKERS/A LIEGE
SEE—French Military Firearms

GUNWORKS LTD.
Buffalo, New York

Model 9 Derringer

An Over/Under derringer chambered in 9mm, .38 Special, .38 Super, and .357 Magnum caliber with 2.5" barrels, with a spur trigger and Millet sights. Nickle-plate, with walnut grips. Manufacturing ceased in 1986.

Exc.	V.G.	Good	Fair	Poor
125	100	90	75	50

GUSTAF, CARL
Eskilstuna, Sweden

Bolt Action Rifle

A 6.5x55, 7x64, .270, 7mm Magnum, .308, .30-06, and 9.3x62 caliber bolt-action rifle with a 24" barrel. Blued with a walnut stock in either the classic style or with a Monte Carlo cheekpiece. Manufactured between 1970 and 1977.

Exc.	V.G.	Good	Fair	Poor
500	425	350	275	200

Grade II

As above, with better walnut and a rosewood pistol grip cap and forend tip.

Exc.	V.G.	Good	Fair	Poor
600	525	450	375	300

Grade III

As above, with a high-gloss finish and a finely figured walnut stock.

Exc.	V.G.	Good	Fair	Poor
700	625	550	475	400

Deluxe Bolt Action

As above, with an engraved floorplate and triggerguard, a damascened bolt, and a high-grade French walnut stock. Manufactured between 1970 and 1977.

Exc.	V.G.	Good	Fair	Poor
800	725	650	575	500

Varmint Model

A .222, .22—250, .243, and 6.5x55 caliber bolt-action rifle with 27" barrel and a large bolt knob made of Bakelite. Furnished without open sights and has a heavy target-type stock. Manufactured in 1970 only.

Exc.	V.G.	Good	Fair	Poor
500	425	350	275	200

Grand Prix Target

A .22 caliber single-shot, bolt-action rifle with a 27" barrel and adjustable weights. Furnished without sights and with an adjustable butt target stock. Only manufactured in 1970.

Exc.	V.G.	Good	Fair	Poor
550	475	400	325	300

Model 2000

A 6.5x55, .243, .270, .308, and .30-06 caliber bolt-action rifle with a 60-percent bolt lift and a cold swaged barrel and action. Furnished with open sights, Blued, walnut stock with a Monte Carlo cheekpiece. Manufactured until 1985.

Exc.	V.G.	Good	Fair	Poor
600	500	400	300	200

GWYN & CAMPBELL

Hamilton, Ohio

Union Carbine

A .52 caliber single shot breech loading percussion carbine with a round/octagonal 20" barrel marked "Gwyn & Campbell/ Patent/1862/ Hamilton,O." Blued, case-hardened with a walnut stock. Approximately 8,500 were made between 1862 and 1865.

Courtesy Milwaukee Public Museum, Milwaukee, Wisconsin.

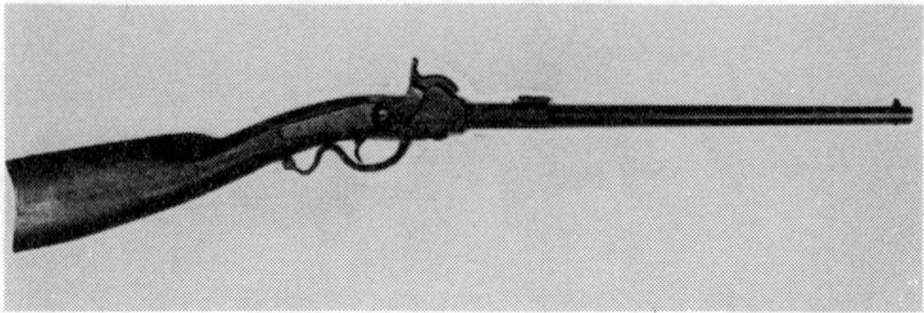

Courtesy Milwaukee Public Museum, Milwaukee, Wisconsin.

Exc.	V.G.	Good	Fair	Poor
1000	800	600	450	350

HDH, SA.
Liege, Belgium

Cobold

A 9.4mm Dutch, 10.6mm German, .38, and .45 caliber double-action revolver with solid-frame octagonal barrel and an odd safety catch that locks the cylinder.

Exc.	V.G.	Good	Fair	Poor
200	175	125	100	75

Puppy

A 5.5mm to 7.65 mm caliber folding trigger double-action revolver. Most are "Velo-Dogs".

Exc.	V.G.	Good	Fair	Poor
150	125	100	75	50

Lincoln

A .22-caliber folding trigger double-action revolver with a solid frame, imitation pearl or ivory grips, and engraving.

Exc.	V.G.	Good	Fair	Poor
150	125	100	75	50

Lincoln-Bossu

A 5.5mm or 6.35mm caliber folding trigger double action revolver ("Velo-Dog" type) with, solid-frame and hammerless.

Exc.	V.G.	Good	Fair	Poor
150	125	100	75	50

Left Wheeler

A Colt Police Positive copy in .32 or .38 caliber. The last revolver HDH manufactured.

Exc.	V.G.	Good	Fair	Poor
175	150	125	100	75

H.J.S. INDUSTRIES, INC.
Brownsville, Texas

Frontier Four Derringer

A .22 caliber four barrelled pocket pistol with 2.5" sliding barrels, stainless steel frame and barrel grip and walnut grips.

Exc.	V.G.	Good	Fair	Poor
125	100	75	50	25

Lone Star Derringer

A .38 Special caliber single shot spur trigger pistol with a 2.5" barrel. Stainless steel with wood grips.

Exc.	V.G.	Good	Fair	Poor
150	125	100	75	50

HWP INDUSTRIES
Milwaukee, Wisconsin

Sledgehammer

A .500 HWP caliber double-action revolver with a shrouded 4" barrel, 5-shot, swingout-cylinder. Stainless steel with Pachmayr grips. Introduced in 1989.

Exc.	V.G.	Good	Fair	Poor
1300	1000	900	650	450

HAENEL, C. G.
Suhl, Germany

Established in 1840, this company began to manufacture semi-automatic pistols after Hugo Schmeisser joined the firm in 1921 as its chief engineer.

Model 1

A 6.35mm caliber semi-automatic pistol with a 2.48" barrel, striker fired, a 6-shot magazine and the left side of the slide is stamped "C.G. Haenel Suhl-Schmeisser Patent." Each grip panel is marked "HS" in an oval.

Exc.	V.G.	Good	Fair	Poor
300	275	225	175	100

Model 2

As above, but shorter and lighter in weight. "Schmeisser" is molded into the grips.

Exc.	V.G.	Good	Fair	Poor
325	300	250	200	125

HAFDASA
Buenos Aires, Argentina

Ballester-Molina

A copy of the Colt Model 1911 semi-automatic pistol differing only in the absence of a grip safety, smaller grip and the finger grooves on the slide. The slide stamped "Pistola Automatica Cal. .45 Fabricado por HAFDASA Patentes Internacional Ballester Molina Industria Argentina" on the slide. Introduced in 1930s.

Exc.	V.G.	Good	Fair	Poor
475	425	325	225	150

Criolla

A .22 caliber automatic pistol, similar to the Ballester-Molina. Some were sold commercially under the trademark "La Criolla."

Exc.	V.G.	Good	Fair	Poor
1000	850	650	500	350

Hafdasa

A .22 caliber semi-automatic pistol with a tubular receiver. A true hammerless, striker-fired, with an angled grip. Markings are "HA" on the butt.

Exc.	V.G.	Good	Fair	Poor
350	325	275	200	150

Zonda

As above, but marked "Zonda".

Exc.	V.G.	Good	Fair	Poor
350	325	275	200	150

HAKIM
Egypt

A 7.92x57mm caliber semi-automatic rifle copied from the Swedish Model 42 Ljungman. Manufactured by Maadi Military and Civil Industries Co.

Exc.	V.G.	Good	Fair	Poor
250	225	200	150	100

HAHN, WILLIAM
New York, New York

Pocket Pistol

A .41 caliber single shot percussion pistol with a 2.5" round barrel, German silver mountings, and a walnut stock. Manufactured in the 1860s and 1870s.

Exc.	V.G.	Good	Fair	Poor
1500	900	500	400	300

HALE, H. J.
Bristol, Connecticut

Under Hammer Pistol

A.31 caliber single shot, under hammer percussion pistol with a 5" or 6" part-round/part-octagonal barrel and an iron frame with either a pointed or a round walnut butt. Markings read "H.J.Hale/Warranted/Cast Steel." Manufactured during the 1850s.

Exc.	V.G.	Good	Fair	Poor
600	500	400	300	200

HALE & TULLER
Hartford, Connecticut

Under Hammer Pistol

A .44 caliber single shot under hammer percussion pistol with a 6" tapered round barrel and a pointed walnut grip. Manufactured at the Connecticut State Prison between 1837 and 1840.

Exc.	V.G.	Good	Fair	Poor
600	525	450	350	250

HALL, ALEXANDER
New York, New York

Revolving Rifle

A .58 caliber percussion revolving rifle with a 15-shot open centered cylinder. The frame made of brass, the barrel and cylinder of iron and the stock of walnut. Manufactured during the 1850s in very limited quanities. Prospective purchasers should secure a qualified appraisal prior to acquisition.

Exc.	V.G.	Good	Fair	Poor
11500	9500	7500	5000	3750

HALL-NORTH
Middletown, Connecticut

Model 1840 Carbine

This carbine was manufactured by Simeon North and was chambered for .52 caliber percussion. It is a single shot, breech-loading, smoothbore with a 21" round barrel. It has a full-length stock held on by two barrel bands. There is a ramrod mounted under the barrel, and the mountings are of iron. The lock is case-hardened, and the barrel is brown. The stock is walnut. The markings are "US/S. North/Midltn/ Conn." There are two distinct variations, both produced under military contract.

Type 1 Carbine

This model has a squared, right-angled breech lever mounted on the triggerplate. There were 500 of these manufactured in 1840.

Exc.	V.G.	Good	Fair	Poor
3200	2750	2200	1600	1200

Type 2 Carbine

This variation features a curved, breech-operating lever that is known as a fishtail. There were approximately 6,000 of these manufactured from 1840 to 1843. Some have an 8" bar and ring.

Exc.	V.G.	Good	Fair	Poor
2400	1850	1400	1100	750

HAMBUSH, JOSEPH
Ferlach, Austria

Boxlock Side x Side Shotgun

A custom-order boxlock double-barrel shotgun chambered for all gauges, single selective or double trigger and automatic ejectors. It features workmanship of a very high order, and all specification could vary with the customer's wishes. Engraved with hunting scenes. This is a rare gun and is not often encountered on today's market. Pricing is only estimated as not enough are traded to provide accurate values.

Exc.	V.G.	Good	Fair	Poor
1250	1000	800	550	350

Sidelock Side x Side Shotgun

Similar to the above, but features a full sidelock action.

Exc.	V.G.	Good	Fair	Poor
2250	2000	1800	1500	1250

HAMILTON RIFLE COMPANY
Plymouth, Michigan

Manufacturer of inexpensive .22 caliber rifles established by Clarence J. Hamilton and his son Coello.

Model 27

Single shot .22 caliber rifle with stamped steel receiver. Barrel length 16"; overall length 30".

Exc.	V.G.	Good	Fair	Poor
250	200	150	100	50

Model 027

As above with a walnut stock.

Exc.	V.G.	Good	Fair	Poor
250	200	150	100	50

Military Rifle

Single shot .22 caliber rifle with a full length stock.

Exc.	V.G.	Good	Fair	Poor
350	250	150	100	50

HAMMERLI, SA

Lenzburg, Switzerland

Rifles

Model 45 Smallbore rifle

A .22 caliber bolt-action single shot, with a 27.5" heavy barrel, an aperture rear and globe target front sight and a match rifle-type thumbhole stock. Manufactured between 1945 and 1957.

Exc.	V.G.	Good	Fair	Poor
675	600	525	425	325

Model 54 Smallbore Rifle

As above, with an adjustable buttplate. Manufactured between 1954 and 1957.

Exc.	V.G.	Good	Fair	Poor
700	625	550	450	350

Model 503 Smallbore Free Rifle

Similar to the Model 54, with a free rifle style stock.

Exc.	V.G.	Good	Fair	Poor
650	575	500	400	300

Model 506 Smallbore Match Rifle.

The later version of the Smallbore target series. Manufactured between 1963 and 1966.

Exc.	V.G.	Good	Fair	Poor
700	625	650	550	450

Olympic 300 Meter

A 7x57, .30-06, or .300 H&H Magnum caliber bolt-action, single shot, rifle with a 20.5" heavy barrel, an aperture rear, globe target front sight, double-set triggers and a free rifle-type, adjustable thumbhole stock with a wide beavertail forearm and Schutzen-style buttplate. Manufactured between 1945 and 1959.

Exc.	V.G.	Good	Fair	Poor
900	800	650	500	400

Sporting Rifle

A bolt-action, single shot rifle chambered for many popular calibers (American and European), double-set triggers and a classic-style stock.

Exc.	V.G.	Good	Fair	Poor
650	575	500	400	325

Pistols

Model 100 Free Pistol

A .22 caliber single shot Martini action target pistol with an 11.5" octagonal barrel, adjustable sights, single set trigger and walnut stocks. Manufactured from 1933 to 1949.

Exc.	V.G.	Good	Fair	Poor
850	725	650	500	400

Model 101

As above, with a heavy round barrel and more sophisticated target sights. A matte-blued finish and was manufactured between 1956 and 1960.

Exc.	V.G.	Good	Fair	Poor
850	725	650	500	400

Model 102

As above, with highly polished blue finish. Manufactured between 1956 and 1960.

Exc.	V.G.	Good	Fair	Poor
850	725	650	500	400

Model 103

Similar to the Model 101, with a lighter-weight octagonal barrel, high polished blued finish. Manufactured between 1956 and 1960.

Exc.	V.G.	Good	Fair	Poor
950	825	750	600	500

Model 104

As above, with a lightweight round barrel. Manufactured between 1961 and 1965.

Exc.	V.G.	Good	Fair	Poor
750	625	550	450	350

Model 105

As above, with a redesigned stock and an improved action. Manufactured between 1962 and 1965.

Exc.	V.G.	Good	Fair	Poor
950	825	750	600	500

Model 107

As above, with an improved trigger.

Exc.	V.G.	Good	Fair	Poor
1000	900	750	600	475

Model 107 Deluxe

As above, but engraved and with a carved stock.

Exc.	V.G.	Good	Fair	Poor
1350	1250	900	800	600

Model 120-1 Free Pistol

A bolt-action, single shot pistol in .22 l.r. caliber with a a 9.9" barrel, adjustable target sights, activated for loading and cocking by an alloy lever on the side of the bolt. Blued, with checkered walnut grips.

Exc.	V.G.	Good	Fair	Poor
450	375	300	225	150

Model 120-2

As above with contoured grips.

Exc.	V.G.	Good	Fair	Poor
475	400	325	250	175

Model 120 Heavy Barrel

As above, with a 5.7" heavy barrel.

Exc.	V.G.	Good	Fair	Poor
450	375	300	225	150

Model 150

A single shot, Martini action .22 caliber pistol with an 11.25" barrel, adjustable sights, contoured grips and a single-set trigger. Blued with walnut stocks.

Exc.	V.G.	Good	Fair	Poor
1950	1800	1500	1250	1000

Model 152

As above, with an 11.25" barrel, and an electronic release trigger.

Exc.	V.G.	Good	Fair	Poor
2150	1950	1750	1500	1200

International Model 206

A .22 caliber semi-automatic pistol with a 7.5" barrel, an integral muzzle brake, adjustable sights, and walnut grips. Manufactured between 1962 and 1969.

Exc.	V.G.	Good	Fair	Poor
700	600	475	375	275

International Model 207

As above, with adjustable grips.

Exc.	V.G.	Good	Fair	Poor
725	625	500	400	300

International Model 208

A .22 caliber semi-automatic pistol with a 6" barrel, adjustable sights and an 8-shot magazine, adjustable trigger, and target grips. The barrel is drilled and tapped for the addition of barrel weights. Manufactured between 1966 and 1988.

Exc.	V.G.	Good	Fair	Poor
1750	1550	1250	1000	750

International Model 208 Deluxe

As above, with an engraved receiver, and carved grips. Discontinued in 1988.

Exc.	V.G.	Good	Fair	Poor
3000	2750	2500	2000	1500

International Model 209

A .22 short caliber semi-automatic pistol with a 4.75" barrel, a muzzle brake, adjustable target sights, and 5-shot magazine. Blued, with walnut grips. Manufactured between 1966 and 1970.

Exc.	V.G.	Good	Fair	Poor
800	700	600	450	350

International Model 210

As above, with adjustable grips.

Exc.	V.G.	Good	Fair	Poor
800	700	600	450	350

International Model 211

As above, with non-adjustable thumbrest grips.

Exc.	V.G.	Good	Fair	Poor
1750	1550	1250	1000	750

Model 212

A .22 caliber semi-automatic pistol with a 5" barrel, and adjustable sights. Blued with walnut grips.

Exc.	V.G.	Good	Fair	Poor
1500	1275	1000	750	650

Model 230

A .22 caliber semi-automatic pistol with a 6.3" barrel, a 5-shot magazine, adjustable sights and walnut grip. Manufactured between 1970 and 1983.

Exc.	V.G.	Good	Fair	Poor
700	600	500	400	300

Model 232

A .22 short caliber semi-automatic pistol with a 5" barrel, adjustable sights, and a 6-shot magazine. Contoured walnut grips. Introduced in 1984.

Exc.	V.G.	Good	Fair	Poor
1500	1300	1150	850	650

Model 280

This is the new state-of-the-art target pistol from Hammerli. It features a modular design and has a frame of carbon fiber material. It has a 4.6" barrel with adjustable sights, trigger, and grips. It is chambered for .22 l.r. or .32 Wadcutter. The magazine holds 5 rounds, and the pistol was introduced in 1988.

Exc.	V.G.	Good	Fair	Poor
1800	1500	1350	1000	800

Dakota

A single action revolver based on the Colt SAA design. It has a solid frame and is loaded through a gate. It is chambered for .22 l.r., .357 Magnum .44-40, and .45 Colt and was offered with barrel lengths of 5", 6", and 7.5". It has a 6-shot cylinder and is blued, with a brass triggerguard and walnut grips.

Exc.	V.G.	Good	Fair	Poor
150	125	100	75	50

Large Calibers

Exc.	V.G.	Good	Fair	Poor
225	175	150	125	100

Super Dakota

Similar to the Dakota but is chambered for .41 and .44 Magnum, with adjustable sights.

Exc.	V.G.	Good	Fair	Poor
250	225	175	150	100

Virginian

Basically a more deluxe version of the Dakota. It is chambered for the .357 and .45 Colt cartridge. The triggerguard and back strap are chrome plated, with the frame case-colored and the remainder blued. This model features the "Swissafe" safety system that allows the cylinder axis pin to be locked back to prevent the hammer from falling.

Exc.	V.G.	Good	Fair	Poor
275	250	200	175	125

HAMMERLI-WALTHER

Lenzburg, Switzerland

These target pistols were produced by Hammerli under license from Walther after WWII. This project continued until approximately 1963, when production was ceased.

Olympia Model 200 Type 1952

A .22 caliber semi-automatic pistol with a 7.5" barrel, a 10-shot magazine, adjustable target sights, and a blued with walnut grips. Manufactured between 1952 and 1958.

Exc.	V.G.	Good	Fair	Poor
650	575	475	375	300

Model 200 Type 1958

As above with an integral muzzle brake. Manufactured between 1958 and 1963.

Exc.	V.G.	Good	Fair	Poor
700	625	525	425	325

Model 201

A Model 200 Type 1952 with a 9.5" barrel. Manufactured between 1955 and 1957.

Exc.	V.G.	Good	Fair	Poor
650	575	475	375	300

Model 202

Similar to the Model 201, with adjustable walnut grips. Manufactured between 1955 and 1957.

Exc.	V.G.	Good	Fair	Poor
700	625	525	425	325

Model 203

Similar to the Model 200, with the adjustable grips, available with or without a muzzle brake.

Exc.	V.G.	Good	Fair	Poor
700	625	525	425	325

Model 204

A .22 caliber semi-automatic pistol with a 7.5" barrel, a muzzle brake, and barrel weights. Manufactured between 1956 and 1963.

Exc.	V.G.	Good	Fair	Poor
750	675	575	475	375

Model 205

As above, with adjustable target grips. Manufactured between 1956 and 1963.

Exc.	V.G.	Good	Fair	Poor
850	775	675	575	450

HAMMOND BULLDOG

Connecticut Arms & Mfg. Co.
Naubuc, Connecticut

Hammond Bulldog

A .44 rimfire single shot spur trigger pistol with a 4" octagonal barrel which pivots to open. Blued with checkered walnut grips. Manufactured from 1864 to approximately 1867.

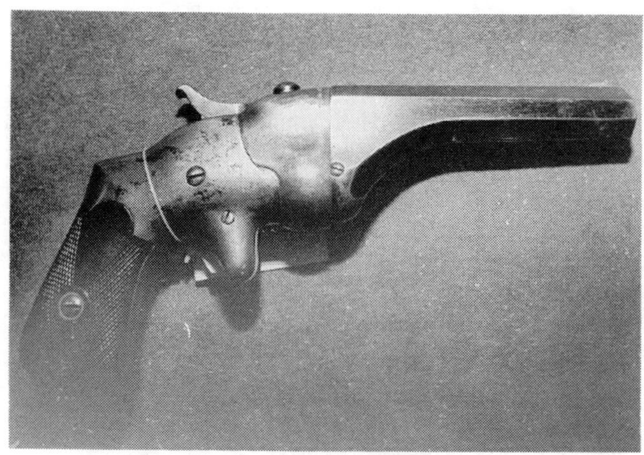

Exc.	V.G.	Good	Fair	Poor
750	600	500	375	250

HAMMOND, GRANT MFG. CO.

New Haven, Connecticut

Military Automatic Pistol

A .45 ACP caliber semi-automatic pistol with a 6.75" barrel and an 8-shot magazine. Blued, with checkered walnut grips. Marked on the right of the slide "Grant Hammond Mfg. Corp. New Haven, Conn." The left side shows the patent dates. Manufactured in 1917. As all the known specimens of this pistol exhibit differences, it is believed that they were only made as prototypes. The highest serial number known is 14.

Exc.	V.G.	Good	Fair	Poor
8500	7850	6750	5000	4000

HANKINS, WILLIAM

Philadelphia, Pennsylvania

Pocket Revolver

A .26 caliber spur trigger percussion revolver with a 3" octagonal barrel, and a 5-shot unfluted cylinder. Blued with walnut grips. Approximately 650 were manufactured in 1860 and 1861.

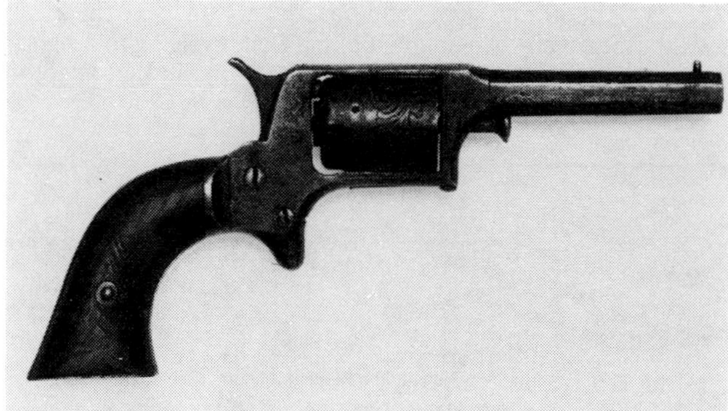

Courtesy Milwaukee Public Museum, Milwaukee, Wisconsin.

Exc.	V.G.	Good	Fair	Poor
1700	1000	550	425	275

HARPERS FERRY ARMORY MUSKETS AND CARBINES

Harpers Ferry, Virginia

Established at Harpers Ferry, Virginia in 1798 as the new nation's "Southern Armory," production finally began in 1800 and continued at the "musket works" until the facilities were seized by Virginia state militia in April, 1861. With the signing of a contract in 1819 between the government and J.H. Hall, the latter was permitted to construct a separate facility for the production of his patent breechloading rifles, which continued to be known as the "rifle works" after the discontinuation of Hall production until it too was seized by Virginia militia in 1861. The machinery of the former was sent to Richmond to be used in the manufacture of the "Richmond rifle-musket" while the rifle machinery was sent to Fayetteville, North Carolina were it was employed in making "Fayetteville rifles."

Harpers Ferry U.S. M1816 muskets (Types I to III)

Overall length- 57-3/4"; barrel length- 42"; caliber- .69. Markings: on lockplate- eagle over "US" forward of cock, "HARPERS/FERRY/(date) on tail. Barrel tang also bears the date, and barrel should show proofmarks on upper left side near breech. The 45605 (type I) muskets produced at Harpers Ferry from 1817 through 1821 were made with a lower sling swivel that was attached to a separate lug extending from the forward strap of the triggerguard. In 1822, this piece was eliminated and the balance of the production (216,116) officially known as the M1822 musket, incorporated the lower sling swivel directly to the triggerguard bow. Until 1832, these muskets were manufactured with a "browned" barrel to inhibit rusting. The brown barrels of these 107,684 muskets distinguish them as Type II production. The balance of production until 1844 (98,432) were made with bright barrel, distinguishing Type III muskets. Despite the large numbers produced, most were altered to percussion during the 1850s. Most by the "cone-in-barrel" (so-called arsenal) method. Many of these were altered again during the American Civil War, usually with a "Patent Breech," and were then rifled and sighted.

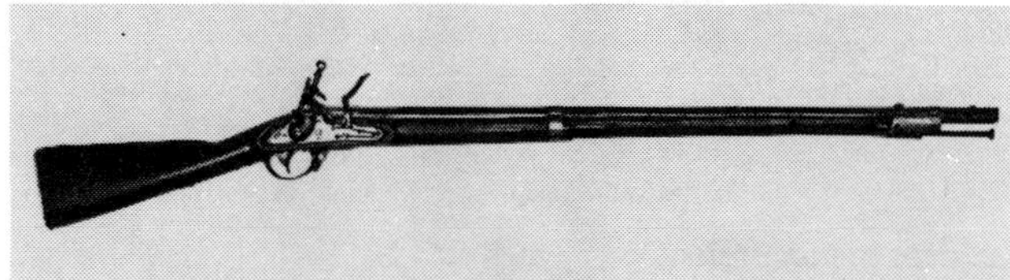

Courtesy Milwaukee Public Museum, Milwaukee, Wisconsin.

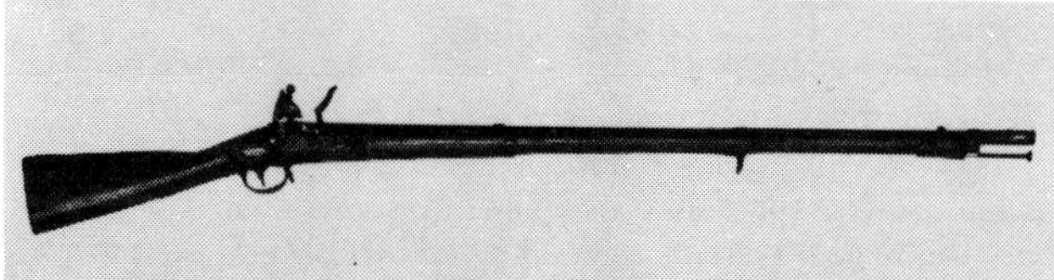

Courtesy Milwaukee Public Museum, Milwaukee, Wisconsin.

(in flintlock)

Exc.	V.G.	Good	Fair	Poor
2900	2500	1650	1100	850

(altered to percussion)

Exc.	V.G.	Good	Fair	Poor
950	875	600	450	300

Harpers Ferry U.S. M1842 musket

Overall length-57-3/4"; barrel length- 42"; caliber- .69. Markings: on lockplate, eagle over "U S" forward of hammer, "HARPERS/FERRY/(date)" on tail; barrel tang also shows date; upper left quarter of barrel near breech includes proofmarks (an eagle head, a "V", and a "P") and inspector's initials. Between 1844 and 1855, Harpers Ferry manufactured 106,629 of these smoothbore muskets, many of which were subsequently rifled and sighted; the latter will bring a slight premium.

Exc.	V.G.	Good	Fair	Poor
1200	1000	850	550	400

Harpers Ferry U.S. M1819 Hall rifle (Types I and II)

Overall length- 52-3/4"; barrel (bore) length- 32-5/8"; caliber- .52. Markings: on top of receiver, either "J.H. HALL/H. FERRY/(date)/U.S." or "J.H. HALL/U.S./(date)." The 2,000 rifles manufactured between 1824 and 1826 (Type I) are distinguished by having their barrel bands retained by band springs on the right side of the stock. The balance of production (17,680), made between 1828 and 1840, have pins driven through the bands and the stock, distinguishing Type II production. Many of these rifles were altered to percussion just before and in the early months of the American Civil War. Those with evidence of having been altered in the South will command a premium.

(in flintlock)

Exc.	V.G.	Good	Fair	Poor
1800	1600	1350	1000	750

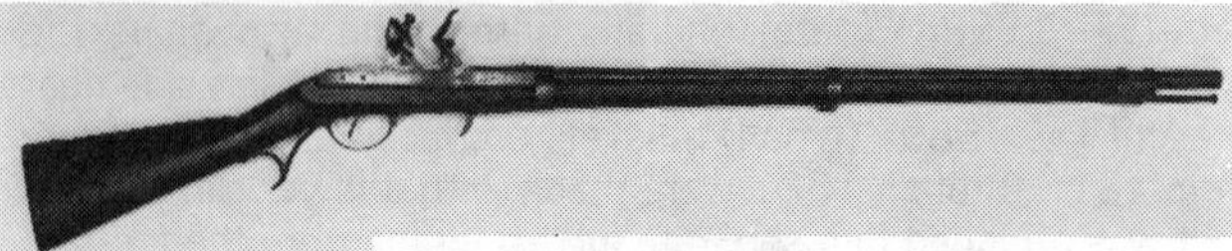

Courtesy Milwaukee Public Museum, Milwaukee, Wisconsin.

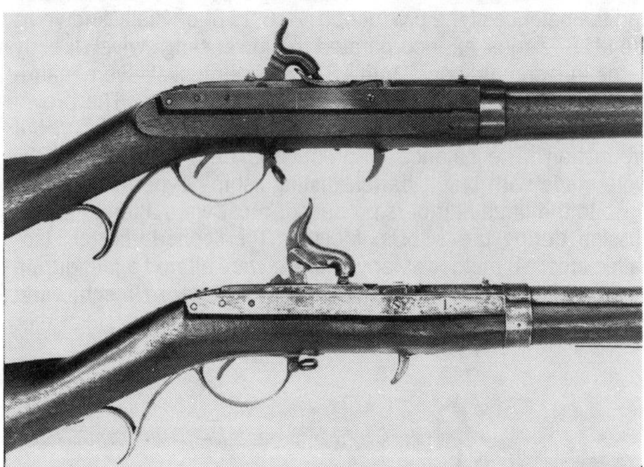

Courtesy Milwaukee Public Museum, Milwaukee, Wisconsin.

(altered to percussion)

Exc.	V.G.	Good	Fair	Poor
1550	1400	1050	800	600

Harpers Ferry U.S. M1841 Hall rifle

Overall length- 52-3/4"; barrel (bore) length- 32-5/8"; caliber- .52. Markings: on top of receiver, "HARPERS FERRY/U S/(date)." With the general adoption of the percussion system of ignition, the manufacture of Hall's rifles was changed to conform to the new system, a cone tapped directly into the breechblock substituting for the frizzen and pan, and a hammer replacing the flint cock. The newly made percussion arms also incorporated the newly adopted "fishtail" latch for levering the breechblock. Two-thirds of the 4,213 rifles made were still in storage at the arsenal when it was burned in 1861, enhancing the rarity of the arm.

Exc.	V.G.	Good	Fair	Poor
1650	1450	1100	850	650

Harpers Ferry U.S. M1836 Hall carbine (Types I & II)

Overall length- 43"; barrel (bore) length- 23"; caliber- .64. Markings: on top of receiver, "J.H. HALL/U.S./(date)." To furnish the newly raised 2nd Regiment U.S. Dragoons raised in 1836, Harpers Ferry Armory was directed to construct 1,003 Hall carbines, differing in length and caliber over the M1833 model produced by the North for the 1st Regiment, but were not ready when the unit was sent to Florida. Another 1,017 were made during 1839-1840 with the addition of a tool compartment in the buttstock, distinguishing Type II production.

Courtesy Milwaukee Public Museum, Milwaukee, Wisconsin.

Exc.	V.G.	Good	Fair	Poor
1850	1600	1350	1050	900

Harpers Ferry U.S. M1842 Hall carbine

Overall length- 40"; barrel (bore) length- 21"; caliber- .52. Markings: on top of receiver, "H. FERRY/U S/1842." To meet the needs of the U.S. Dragoons for replacement carbines, Harpers Ferry manufactured 1,001 carbines in 1842, differing only from the North M1840 (Type II - "fishtail lever") carbine by being brass instead of iron mounted.

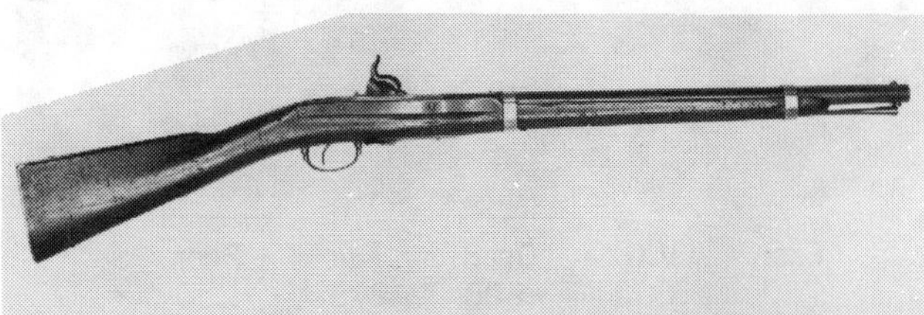

Courtesy Milwaukee Public Museum, Milwaukee, Wisconsin.

Exc.	V.G.	Good	Fair	Poor
9500	9000	8000	7000	5500

Harpers Ferry U.S. M1841 muzzleloading rifle- the "Mississippi rifle"

Overall length- 49"; barrel length- 33"; caliber- .54 (altered to .58 after 1857). Markings: on lockplate, eagle over "U S" forward of hammer; "HARPERS/FERRY/(date)" on tail; date also on tang of breechplug; inspector's initials "AW/P" or "WW/P" and proofmarks (eagle head, "V" and "P" on upper left side of barrel). With the discontinuance of production of the Hall patent arms, Hall's Rifle Works was transformed into the production of the new U.S. rifle adopted in 1841. From 1846 until 1855 a total of 25,296 were manufactured at Harpers Ferry. Approximately 10,000 of these rifles were subsequently adapted for long range firing and to saber bayonets at Harpers Ferry between 1855 and 1861. The adaptations in chronological order included the adoption of the Snell bayonet and Benton long range "screw" sight, the adoption of a saber bayonet lug with guide and the Benton sight, the adoption of the saber bayonet lug with guide and the Burton "ladder" long range sights, the adoption of the U.S. M1855 (Type I) rifle sights and bayonet lug (first in .54 and then in .58 caliber), and finally the adoption of the U.S. M1855 (Type II) rifle sights and bayonet lug (in .58 caliber). A few thousand were also adapted to the Colt revolving rifle sights and split ring bayonet adaptor in 1861-1862, but that adaptation was not restricted to Harpers Ferry made rifles.

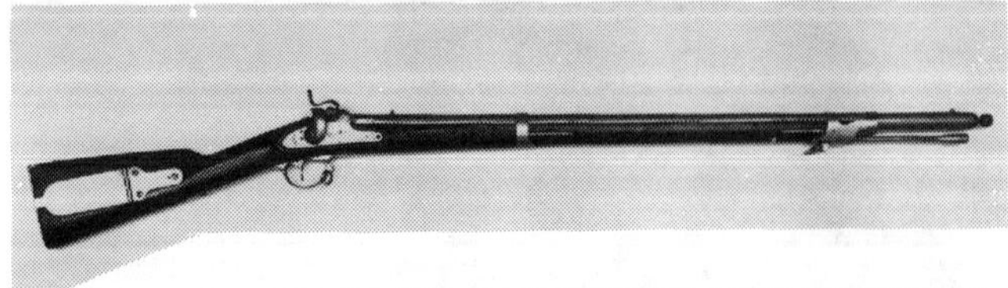

Courtesy Milwaukee Public Museum, Milwaukee, Wisconsin.

Courtesy Milwaukee Public Museum, Milwaukee, Wisconsin.

Exc.	V.G.	Good	Fair	Poor
2700	2550	1850	1400	850

Harpers Ferry U.S. M1842 musket

Overall length- 57-3/4"; barrel length- 42"; caliber- .69. Markings: on lockplate, eagle over "US" forward of hammer;

"HARPERS/FERRY/(date)" on tail; date also on tang of breechplug; inspector's initials and proofmarks on barrel near breech. Harpers Ferry manufactured a total of 106,629 of these smoothbore muskets between 1844 and 1855. Many of these muskets were subsequently rifled and sighted from 1855 to 1858 or simply rifled during the early years of the American Civil War.

Exc.	V.G.	Good	Fair	Poor
2500	2200	1600	900	600

Harpers Ferry U.S. M1855 rifle-musket (Type I & II)

Overall length- 56"; barrel length- 40"; caliber- .58. Markings: on lockplate, eagle on Maynard primer door; "U S/HARPERS FERRY" forward of hammer; date on tail; date also on top of barrel near breech plus proofmarks (eagle head, "V", and "P"). Between 1857 and 1858 Harpers Ferry produced 15,071 of these rifles, but many were still unsighted at the end of the fiscal year. This early production (Type I) is distinguished from the later production (1859-1860) by the absence of the iron "patchbox" on the right side of the buttstock, a long range rear sight, and a brass nosecap. The "patchbox" was added in 1859 together with a short base rear sight with leaves graduated to only 300 and 500 yards. The brass nosecaps were gradually phased out during 1859.

Exc.	V.G.	Good	Fair	Poor
2600	2300	1800	1100	650

Harpers Ferry U.S. M1855 rifles (Type I & II)

Overall length- 49"; barrel length- 33"; caliber- .58. Markings: on lockplate, eagle on Maynard primer door; "U S/HARPERS FERRY" forward of hammer; date on tail; date also on top of barrel near breech plus proofmarks (eagle head, "V", and "P"). Designed as the replacement of the U.S. M1841 rifle, production of the U.S. M1855 rifle began at John Hall's old "Harpers Ferry Rifle Works" in 1857. The production of 1857 and 1858 (Type I), numbering only 3,645 rifles, were all brass mounted, bore a long range rear sight on the browned barrel, and bore a "patchbox" inletted for a special crosshair figure "8" detachable front sight, though many were still without their rear sights at the end of the fiscal year due to the intervention of the Secretary of War. Most of these were never issued and were subsequently destroyed when the arsenal was set afire in April 1861 to prevent the capture of its arms by Virginia forces. The 3,771 rifles produced between 1858 and April 1861 (Type II) were all iron mounted (though a transitional period continued to utilize the brass nosecaps), eliminated the special front sight (permitting the cavity to be enlarged for greased patches), and employed a short base long range rear sight similar to that of the Type II M1855 rifle-musket.

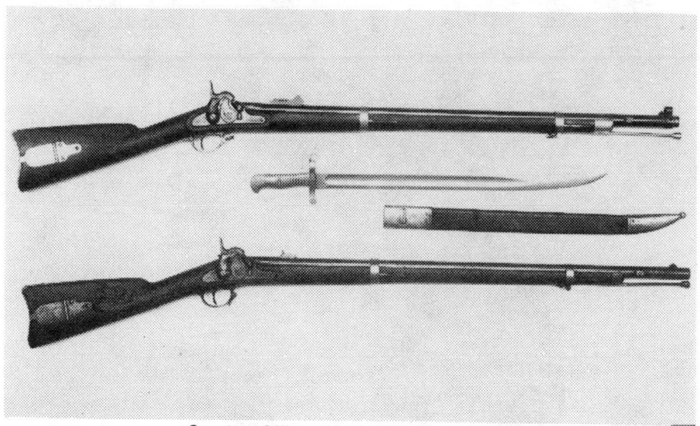

Courtesy Milwaukee Public Museum, Milwaukee, Wisconsin.

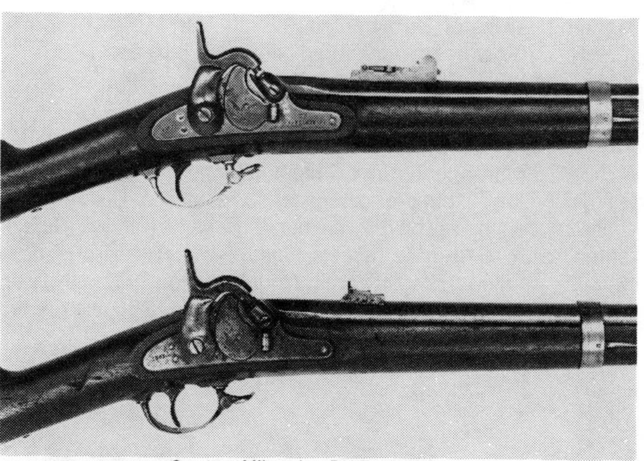

Courtesy Milwaukee Public Museum, Milwaukee, Wisconsin.

(Type I)

Exc.	V.G.	Good	Fair	Poor
26,000	16,000	10,000	8000	6500

(Type II)

Exc.	V.G.	Good	Fair	Poor
2700	2500	2100	1700	950

HARRINGTON & RICHARDSON, INC.

Worchester, Massachusetts

Established in 1877 by G. H. Harrington and W. A. Richardson. The arms originally produced by this company were marketed under the tradename Aetna.

Model No. 1

A .32 or .38 caliber spur-trigger single action revolver with a 3" octagonal barrel, solid-frame, a 7-shot or a 5-shot cylinder, depending on the caliber. Nickle-plated with checkered rubber birdshead grips. Barrel marked "Harrington & Richardson Worchester, Mass." Approximately 3,000 were manufactured in 1877 and 1878.

Exc.	V.G.	Good	Fair	Poor
300	250	200	125	75

Model 1-1/2

A .32 caliber spur-trigger, single action revolver with a 2.5" octagonal barrel and a 5-shot cylinder. Nickle-plated, round-butt rubber grips with an "H&R" emblem molded in. Approximately 10,000 were manufactured between 1878 and 1883.

Exc.	V.G.	Good	Fair	Poor
175	150	125	75	50

Model 2-1/2

As above, with a 3.25" barrel and a 7-shot cylinder. Approximately 5,000 were manufactured between 1878 and 1883.

Exc.	V.G.	Good	Fair	Poor
175	150	125	75	50

Model 3-1/2

Similar to the Model 2-1/2 except in .38 rimfire caliber with a 3.5" barrel and a 5-shot cylinder. Approximately 2,500 were manufactured.

Exc.	V.G.	Good	Fair	Poor
200	175	150	100	75

Model 4-1/2

A .41 rimfire caliber spur trigger revolver with a 2.5" barrel and a 5-shot cylinder. Approximately 1,000 were manufactured.

Exc.	V.G.	Good	Fair	Poor
250	200	175	125	90

Model 1880

A .32 or .38 S&W centerfire caliber double-action revolver with a 3" round barrel, a solid frame, and a 5- or 6-shot cylinder, depending on the caliber. Nickle-plated with hard rubber grips.

Marked "Harrington & Richardson Worchester, Mass." Approximately 4,000 were manufactured between 1880 and 1883.

Exc.	V.G.	Good	Fair	Poor
250	200	175	125	90

The American Double Action

A .32, .28 or .44 centerfire caliber double-action revolver with a 2.5", 4.5", or 6" round or octagonal barrel, a 5- or 6-shot fluted cylinder, depending on the caliber, and solid frame, Nickle-plated, with some blue models noted. The grips are of hard rubber. Marked "The American Double Action." Some noted are marked "H&R Bulldog." Approximately 850,000 were manufactured between 1883 and 1940.

Exc.	V.G.	Good	Fair	Poor
125	100	85	65	40

The Young America Double Action

A .22 rimfire or .32 S&W centerfire caliber, double-action revolver, with 2", 4.5", or 6"-round or octagonal barrels, solid frame, and a 5-shot or 7-shot cylinder, depending on the caliber. Blued or nickle-plated, with hard rubber grips. Marked "Young America Double Action" or "Young America Bulldog." Approximately 1,500,000 were manufactured between 1884 and 1941.

Exc.	V.G.	Good	Fair	Poor
125	100	85	65	40

First Model Hand Ejector

A .32 or .38 centerfire caliber double-action revolver with a 3.25" ribbed round barrel. This version does not feature the automatic ejection found on later models. Nickle-plated, with hard rubber grips. The company name is marked on the barrel. Approximately 6,000 were manufactured between 1886 and 1888.

Exc.	V.G.	Good	Fair	Poor
200	150	125	90	65

Model 1 Double Action Revolver

A .32, .32 long, and the .38 S&W caliber double action revolver with a 3.25" ribbed round barrel, and a 5- or 6-shot cylinder, depending on the caliber. Nickle-plated, with hard rubber grips. Approximately 5,000 were manufactured between 1887 and 1889.

Exc.	V.G.	Good	Fair	Poor
175	145	110	80	50

Model 2

Similar to the Model 1, with 2.5", 3.25", 4", 5", or 6" barrels. The grips feature the H&R target logo. There were approximately 1,300,000 manufactured between 1889 and 1940.

Exc.	V.G.	Good	Fair	Poor
125	100	80	65	40

Knife Model

The Model 2 with a 4" ribbed round barrel having a folding 2.25" double-edged knife mounted under the barrel. Blued or nickle-plated. Approximately 2,000 were manufactured between 1901 and 1917.

Exc.	V.G.	Good	Fair	Poor
450	400	350	250	150

Self-Loader

A 6.35mm or the 7.65mm semi-automatic pistol with a 2" or 3.5" barrel, a 6-shot or 8-shot magazine. The larger 7.65 model has a grip safety. Blued or nickle-plated with checkered, hard rubber grips that bear the H&R monogram. The slide is marked, "H&R Self-Loading" with 1907 or 1909 patent dates. Approximately 16,500 were manufactured in 6.35mm between 1912 and 1916 and 34,500 in 7.65mm manufactured between 1916 and 1924.

Courtesy Orville Reichert.

Courtesy Orville Reichert.

Courtesy Orville Reichert.

Courtesy Orville Reichert.

Exc.	V.G.	Good	Fair	Poor
300	250	200	150	100

Hunter

A .22 caliber double-action revolver with a 10" octagonal barrel and a 9-shot fluted cylinder. Blued, with checkered walnut grips.

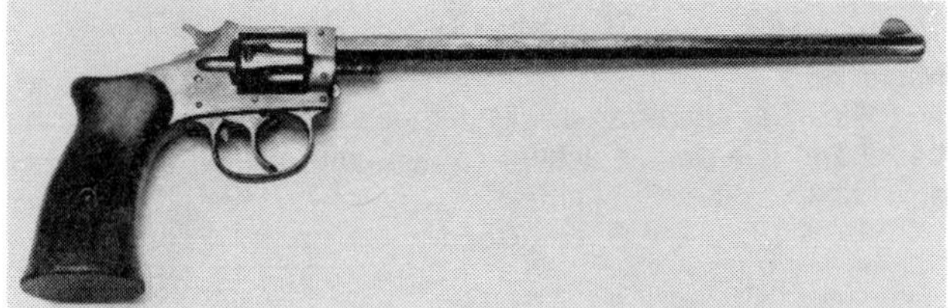
Courtesy Mike Stuckslager.

Exc.	V.G.	Good	Fair	Poor
200	150	125	100	75

Trapper

As above, with a 6" octagonal barrel and a 7-shot cylinder. Otherwise it is similar to the Hunter.

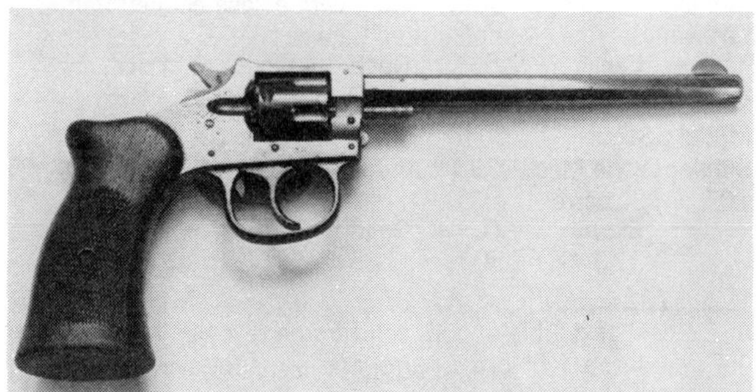
Courtesy Mike Stuckslager.

Exc.	V.G.	Good	Fair	Poor
200	150	125	100	75

Model 922 First Issue

A .22 caliber double-action revolver with a 2.5", 4", or 6" barrel. Blued, with checkered walnut grips.

Exc.	V.G.	Good	Fair	Poor
150	125	100	75	50

Target Model

A .22 l.r. or .22 rimfire Magnum caliber double-action revolver with 7-shot cylinder, a break-open frame and a 6" barrel with fixed sights. Blued, with checkered walnut grips.

Exc.	V.G.	Good	Fair	Poor
150	125	100	75	50

.22 Special

A .22 l.r. or the .22 rimfire Magnum double-action, break-open revolver with a 6" barrel and a 7-shot cylinder. Blued, with checkered walnut grips.

Exc.	V.G.	Good	Fair	Poor
175	150	125	90	65

Expert

As above, with a 10" barrel.

Exc.	V.G.	Good	Fair	Poor
150	125	100	75	50

No. 199 Sportsman

A .22 caliber single action, break-open revolver with a 6" barrel, adjustable target sights and a 9-shot cylinder. Blued, with checkered walnut grips.

Exc.	V.G.	Good	Fair	Poor
200	175	150	100	75

Ultra Sportsman

As above, but more finely finished and with a special, wide target hammer and an improved action.

Exc.	V.G.	Good	Fair	Poor
225	200	175	125	90

Defender

A .38 S&W caliber double-action, break-open revolver with a 4" or 6" barrel and fixed sights. Blued, with plastic grips.

Exc.	V.G.	Good	Fair	Poor
150	125	100	75	50

New Defender

A .22 caliber double-action, break-open revolver with a 2" barrel and a 9-shot cylinder. Blued with checkered, walnut round-butt grips.

Exc.	V.G.	Good	Fair	Poor
225	200	175	125	90

USRA Target Pistol

A single shot, break-open pistol .22 caliber, offered with a 7", 8", or 10" barrel having adjustable target sights. Blued or nickle-plated, with checkered walnut grips. Manufactured between 1928 and 1941.

Exc.	V.G.	Good	Fair	Poor
500	450	400	300	200

Model 504

A .32 H&R Magnum caliber double-action, swing-out cylinder revolver with a 4" or 6" heavy barrel, adjustable sights, and 5-shot cylinder. Blued, with either black plastic or walnut grips. Smaller version manufactureed with a 3" or 4" barrel and a round butt.

Exc.	V.G.	Good	Fair	Poor
175	150	125	90	65

Model 532

As above, but with a cylinder that has to be removed for loading. Manufactured in 1984 and 1985.

Exc.	V.G.	Good	Fair	Poor
100	75	50	40	25

Model 586

A .32 H&R Magnum caliber double-action revolver with a 4.5", 5.5", 7.5", or 10" barrel, adjustable sights and a 5-shot cylinder. Blued, with either black plastic or walnut grips.

Exc.	V.G.	Good	Fair	Poor
175	150	125	100	75

Model 603

A .22 rimfire Magnum caliber double-action revolver with a 6" flat-sided barrel and swing-out 6-shot cylinder. Blued, with smooth walnut grips.

Exc.	V.G.	Good	Fair	Poor
165	140	110	85	60

Model 604

As above, with a 6", ribbed, heavy barrel.

Exc.	V.G.	Good	Fair	Poor
175	150	125	90	65

Model 622

A .22 caliber solid-frame double-action revolver with a 2.5" or 4" barrel. Blued, with round-butt plastic grips.

Exc.	V.G.	Good	Fair	Poor
100	80	65	50	25

Model 623

As above, but nickle-plated.

Exc.	V.G.	Good	Fair	Poor
125	100	80	60	40

Model 632

As above in .32 centerfire.

Exc.	V.G.	Good	Fair	Poor
110	90	75	60	30

Model 642

As above, in .22 rimfire Magnum.

Exc.	V.G.	Good	Fair	Poor
100	80	65	50	25

Model 649

The Model 622, with a 5.5" or 7.5" barrel.

Exc.	V.G.	Good	Fair	Poor
150	125	100	75	50

Model 650

As above, but nickle-plated.

Exc.	V.G.	Good	Fair	Poor
150	125	100	75	50

Model 660

A .22 caliber solid-frame, Western-style revolver with a 5.5" barrel and is a double-action. Blued, with walnut grips. It is also known as the "Gunfighter."

Exc.	V.G.	Good	Fair	Poor
100	80	65	45	25

Model 666

A .22 or . 22 rimfire Magnum caliber double-action revolver with a 6" barrel and a 6-shot cylinder. Blued, with plastic grips. Manufactured between 1976 and 1982.

Exc.	V.G.	Good	Fair	Poor
100	80	65	45	25

Model 676

Similar to the Model 660. Blued, with a case-colored frame. It has walnut grips. Manufactured between 1976 and 1982.

Exc.	V.G.	Good	Fair	Poor
150	125	100	75	50

Model 686

Similar to the Model 660 "Gunfighter" with a 4.5", 5.5", 7.5", 10", or 12" barrel.

Exc.	V.G.	Good	Fair	Poor
175	150	125	100	75

Model 732

A .32 caliber double-action, solid-frame revolver with a swing-out cylinder, a 2.5" or 4" barrel and a 6-shot cylinder. Blued, with black plastic grips. Also known as the "Guardsman."

Exc.	V.G.	Good	Fair	Poor
125	100	80	65	45

Model 733

As above, but nickle-plated and a 2.5" barrel.

Exc.	V.G.	Good	Fair	Poor
150	125	100	75	50

Model 900

A .22 caliber solid-frame revolver with a removable cylinder, a 2.5" or 4" barrel and a 9-shot cylinder. Blued, with black plastic grips. Manufactured between 1962 and 1973.

Exc.	V.G.	Good	Fair	Poor
100	90	80	60	40

Model 901

As above, but chrome-plated with white plastic grips. Manufactured in 1962 and 1963 only.

Exc.	V.G.	Good	Fair	Poor
100	90	80	60	40

Model 903

As above, with a swing-out cylinder, a flat-sided, 6" barrel, and a 9-shot cylinder. Blued, with walnut grips.

Exc.	V.G.	Good	Fair	Poor
125	100	90	75	50

Model 904

As above, with a ribbed heavy barrel.

Exc.	V.G.	Good	Fair	Poor
150	125	100	75	50

Model 905

As above, but nickle-plated.

Exc.	V.G.	Good	Fair	Poor
165	140	110	80	65

Model 922 Second Issue

A .22 rimfire caliber solid-frame revolver with a 2.5", 4", or 6" barrel. Blued, with black plastic grips. Manufactured between 1950 and 1982.

Exc.	V.G.	Good	Fair	Poor
100	90	80	60	40

Model 923

As above, but nickle-plated.

Exc.	V.G.	Good	Fair	Poor
110	95	85	65	45

Model 925

A .38 S&W caliber double-action, break-open, hand ejector revolver with a 2.5" barrel, adjustable sights and a 5-shot cylinder. Blued, with a one-piece wrap-around grip. Manufactured between 1964 and 1984.

Exc.	V.G.	Good	Fair	Poor
150	125	100	75	50

Model 935

As above, but nickle-plated.

Exc.	V.G.	Good	Fair	Poor
150	125	100	75	50

Model 929

A .22 rimfire solid-frame, swing-out revolver with a 2.5", 4", or 6" barrel and a 9-shot cylinder. Blued, with plastic grips. It is also known as the "Sidekick". Manufactured between 1956 and 1985.

Exc.	V.G.	Good	Fair	Poor
125	100	85	65	45

Model 930

As above, but nickle-plated and not available with a 6" barrel.

Exc.	V.G.	Good	Fair	Poor
125	100	85	65	45

Model 939 Ultra Sidekick

As above, with a ventilated-rib, flat sided 6" barrel, adjustable sights, thumbrest grips and features a safety device whereby the pistol could not be fired unless it was unlocked by a furnished key. Manufactured between 1958 and 1982.

Exc.	V.G.	Good	Fair	Poor
125	100	85	65	45

Model 940

A round-barrelled version of the above.

Exc.	V.G.	Good	Fair	Poor
100	90	80	65	45

Model 949

A .22 caliber double-action, Western-type revolver with a 5.5" barrel with an ejector rod, 9-shot, gate-loaded cylinder and adjustable sights. Blued, with walnut grips. Manufactured between 1960 and 1985.

Exc.	V.G.	Good	Fair	Poor
125	100	80	65	40

Model 950

As above, but nickle-plated.

Exc.	V.G.	Good	Fair	Poor
125	100	80	65	40

Model 976

As above, with a case-hardened frame.

Exc.	V.G.	Good	Fair	Poor
100	80	65	45	30

Model 999 Sportsman

A .22 rimfire caliber double-action, break-open, self ejecting revolver with a 6" ventilated-rib barrel and adjustable sights. Blued, with walnut grips. Manufactured between 1950 and 1985.

Exc.	V.G.	Good	Fair	Poor
200	150	125	90	65

Engraved Model 999

As above, but engraved.

Exc.	V.G.	Good	Fair	Poor
425	350	300	200	125

Hammerless Double

A 10 or 12 gauge Anson & Deeley hammerless boxlock double-barrel shotgun with a 28", 30", or 32" Damascus barrels in various choke combinations, double triggers and extractors. Engraved, case-hardened and walnut stock. Four grades were available. They differ in the amount of engraving and the quality of materials and workmanship utilized. Approximately 3,500 were manufactured between 1882 and 1885.

D Grade

Exc.	V.G.	Good	Fair	Poor
650	550	425	300	175

C Grade

Exc.	V.G.	Good	Fair	Poor
750	650	500	400	275

B Grade

Exc.	V.G.	Good	Fair	Poor
900	750	600	500	350

A Grade

Exc.	V.G.	Good	Fair	Poor
2000	1750	1500	1000	550

Harrich No. 1

A 12 gauge boxlock single-barrel shotgun with a 32" or 34", ventilated-rib, full-choke barrel and automatic ejector. Engraved, blued with a checkered, walnut stock. Imported between 1971 and 1975.

Exc.	V.G.	Good	Fair	Poor
1750	1500	1150	850	650

Harrington & Richardson manufactured a series of single barrel, break-open shotguns between 1908 and 1942. They were chambered for various gauges and had various barrel lengths and chokes. The finishes were blued with walnut stocks. There is little collector interest in these guns and, if in sound condition, are desirable as shooters only. They are the Models 3, 5, 6, 7, 8, and 9, as well as a hinged-frame, folding design. Values are as follows:

Exc.	V.G.	Good	Fair	Poor
125	100	85	65	40

H&R Handy-Gun (by Eric M. Larson)

The H&R Handy-Gun is a smooth bore .410 or 28 gauge shot pistol with an 8" or 12.25" barrel, manufactured from the early 1920s until it was ruled a "firearm" in the "any other weapon" category under the National Firearms Act (NFA) of 1934. A small game gun, it was also briefly produced with an 18" barrel apparently (but unsuccessfully) to avoid NFA controls, whose registration requirements and prohibitive $200 tax on each transfer of ownership virtually destroyed the Handy-Gun's sales market. Some incomplete original H&R factory serial number records of Handy-Gun shipments, located in August 1993, indicate total production was at least 53700 and possibly 58693.

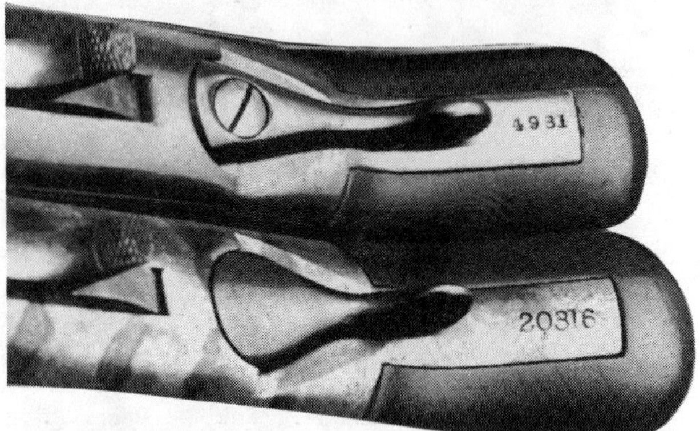

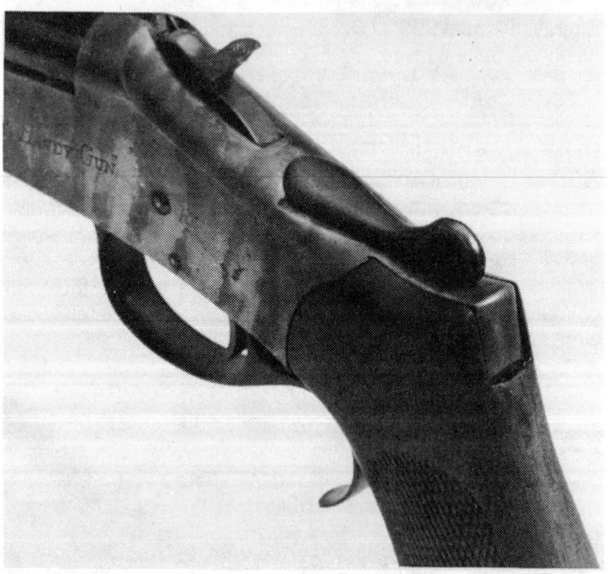

Handy-Guns are not bought and sold frequently enough to establish reliable values. Prices for rarer variations may exceed those estimated here for a typical 12.25"-barrel .410.

Exc.	V.G.	Good	Fair	Poor
450	300	250	100	75

Three smooth bore Handy-Gun models can be identified based on differences in receiver finish and markings, barrel latch levers, barrel type and markings, and trigger guard and grip. Each model can be further classified into three types. These "Models" and "Types" were defined arbitrarily, and are not classifications known to have been used elsewhere. H&R termed some late-model .410 and 28 gauge Handy-Guns as Models 141 and 128, respectively, but earlier variations were not so identified. H&R also sold the Handy-Gun as the Model 625 through H&R Arms Co., Ltd., of Drummondville, Quebec, Canada, mainly in 1947.

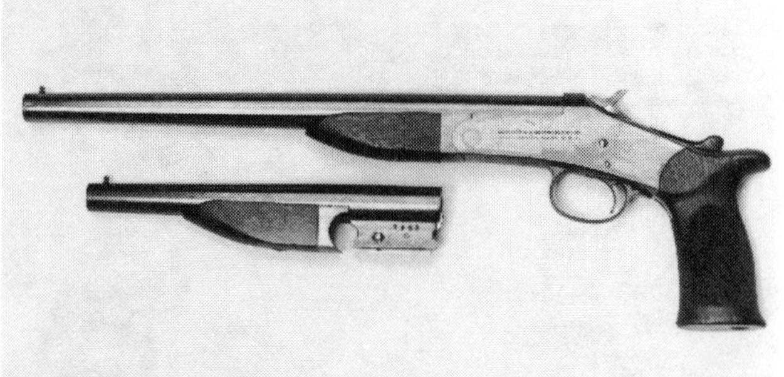

Model 1 has a blued receiver of malleable (ductile) iron, plain trigger guard, heavy cylinder bore (unchoked) barrel marked **410-12m/m or 28 GAUGE,** and checkered walnut "saw-handle" spur grip. Model 1, Type I has a 1.71" barrel latch lever secured by a screw, with apparently hand-cut knurling (termed Type A), and the left side of the receiver is stamped **Harrington & Richardson Arms Co/Worcester, Mass. U.S.A.** Model 1, Type II is the same as Model 1, Type I except for a 1.5" barrel latch lever that is not secured by a screw, with cast knurling (termed Type B). Model 1, Type III is the same as Model 1, Type II except that the H&R manufacturer's identification was moved to the right side of the receiver, and **H&R "Handy-Gun"** is stamped on the left side.

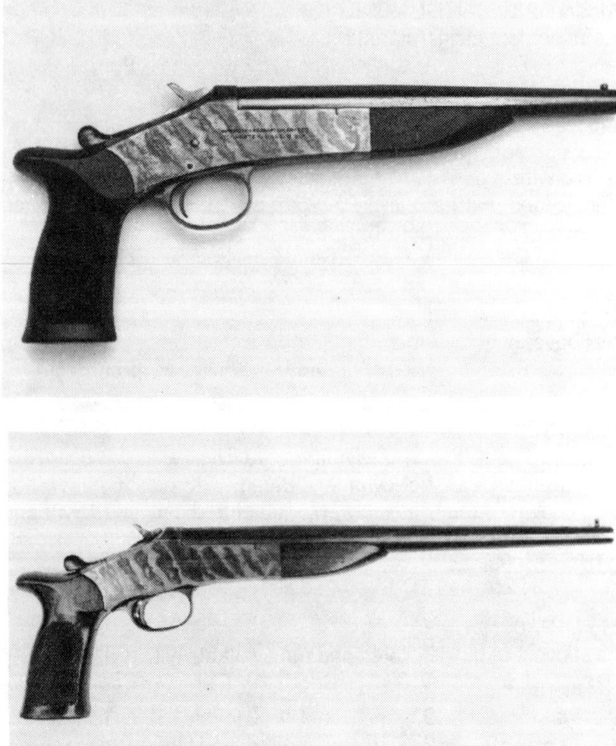

Model 2 has a receiver whose so-called "tiger stripe" finish was produced by hot cyanide dip, which resembles but is not true case-hardening. Model 2, Type I is identical to Model 1, Type III, except for its "tiger strips" finish. Model 2, Type II is identical to Model 2, Type I except that in .410, the barrel is choked and its markings are **410-12m/mCHOKE;** apparently, such changes were not made to the 28 gauge, whose variations appear to stop with Model 2, Type I. Model 2, Type III is identical to Model 2, Type II except that the barrel markings were changed to **MADE IN U.S.A. 410 GA.CHOKE,** and a 1.81" barrel latch lever with dish checkered knurling, which covers the serial number (termed Type C).

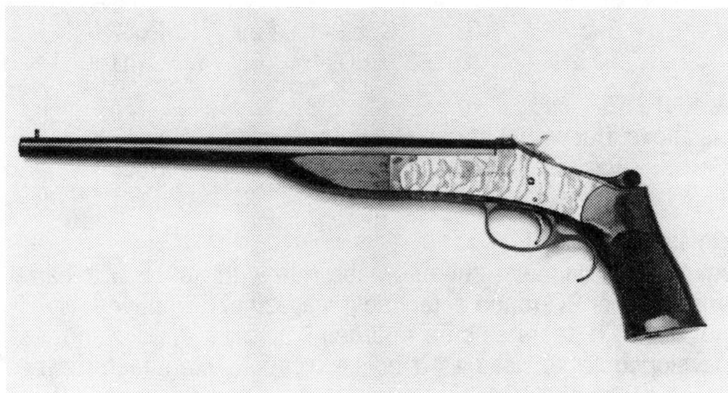

Model 3 has a flat grip mounted at a 70° angle to the barrel, in contrast to the 80° angle on Models 1 and 2, and the receiver was shortened .312", probably by grinding, to accommodate it. Model 3, Type I is identical to Model 2, Type III except for the new flat grip. Model 3, Type II is identical to Model 3, Type I except that a hook was added to the trigger guard for the middle finger to assist in stabilizing recoil. Model 3, Type III is identical to Model 3, Type II except that **3** is stamped in the lower right-hand corner of the left side of the barrel lug, to designate the barrel was H&R factory chambered for the 3" .410 shotshell of 1933. All previous .410 and 28 gauge variations are chambered only for 2.5" shells with relatively light loads.

H&R manufactured "private-branded" or "trade-branded" Handy-Guns for other distributors. One variation bears the marking **ESSEX GUN WORKS** on the left side of the receiver; another has **HIBBARD** stamped on the left, and **MODEL W.H.** on the right. Most have nickel-plated receivers, and are serial numbered within the same ranges as regular-production Handy-Guns.

No definitive factory records of serial number ranges or years of manufacture for the above variations have yet been located, and it is unknown if the .410 and 28 gauge variations were numbered separately. This data is estimated, based on serial numbers and characteristics of 347 Handy-Guns and very limited original sales records, NFA paperwork, H&R advertisements, and other sources, as follows:

Model and Type	Estimated years of manufacture	Observed serial number ranges .410 bore	28 gauge
Model 1			
Type I	Early 1920s	167 to 4981	5 to 4527
Type II	Early 1920s	5052 to 6588	5554 to 6274
Type III	Early 1920s to circa 1924	unknown to 6817	6973 to 7065
Model 2			
Type I	Circa 1924-25	8276 to 17837	10539 to 29731
Type II	Circa 1925-27	17935 to 38335	none observed
Type III	Circa 1927-30	39060 to 47528	none observed
Model 3			
Type I	Circa 1931	47642 to 48218	none observed
Type II	Circa 1932-33	48920 to 51655	none observed
Type III	Circa 1933-34	51920 to 53637	none observed

The NFA and changing transfer tax rates have significantly affected Handy-Gun sales. Effective July 1, 1945, the Congress lowered the $200 rate to $1 for firearms such as the Handy-Gun with a barrel 12" or more, based upon a June 16, 1938, law which did the same for guns such as Marble's Game Getter Gun, a firearm with 12", 15" or 18" Over/Under rifled/smooth bore barrels in .22/.44 or .22/.410, with a removable, folding stock. The Congress determined both types of guns have "legitimate uses" and the $200 rate "a severe hardship" on people who use them. In a Letter Ruling dated March 1, 1939, the Bureau of Internal Revenue exempted the 18" barrel Game Getter from the NFA.

The $200 rate for 8" barrel Handy-Gun was effective until July 1, 1960, when the Congress changed it to $5 for all NFA firearms in the "any other weapon" category. Newly discovered records indicate most Handy-Guns bearing serial numbers from 51081 to 53700 were sold in the United States and Canada in 1947, after the $200 rate was changed to $1, and the last recorded shipment was in 1957. It is likely that most of these Handy-Guns have a 12.25" barrel.

Model 3 was available with an extra-cost optional shoulder stock, and all are extremely rare. The tax rate (if the barrel is less than 18") has always been $200, because the stock causes the Handy-Gun to lose its identity as a pistol. An 18" barrel smooth bore Handy-Gun with a shoulder stock is not subject to the NFA.

The ATF classifies the Handy-Bun as a "curio or relic" because it "derives a substantial part of its monetary value from the fact that it is novel, rare or bizarre," and was manufactured at least 50 years prior to the current date, but it is still controlled as an "any other weapon" under the NFA. Curio or relic status merely allows federally licensed gun collectors to acquire Handy-Guns from licesnees and nonlicensees without regard to state of residence.

The only way any person can legally own a smooth bore Handy-Gun at this time is to apply to the Bureau of Alcohol, Tobacco and Firearms (ATF) to acquire it by a lawful transfer from its owner. Under current law an unregistered Handy-Gun cannot be registered, and ATF deems it contraband subject to immediate confiscation. Any person who possesses or receives a Handy-Gun that is not registered to him or her risks a fine of up to $10,000, up to 10 years imprisonment, and other penalties.

Under the Gun Control Act (GCA) of 1968, the Handy-Gun can be removed from NFA controls if the ATF rules it is "primarily a collector's item and is not likely to be used as a weapon." ATF has declined to do so although functionally equivalent modern firearms, such as the 10" rifled-barrel .45/.410 Thompson Contender pistol (which is not considered a crime weapon or a collector's item), have been commercially available without NFA controls for more than 25 years.

These materials are copyright © 1993 by Eric M. Larson, and printed in the *Catalog* by permission of the copyright holder. They are based on the booklet *Variations of the Smooth Bore H&R Handy-Gun* and other research for a book which seeks to comprehensively document and analyze commercially manufactured pre-NFA era smooth bore shot pistols such as the H&R Handy-Gun, .410 Stevens, Ithaca Auto & Burglar Gun, .410 Crescent-Davis and other lesser-known models, related firearms such as Marble's Game Getter Gun, and the history and consequences of their control under the NFA. The rarity of these guns, and of valid and reliable information about them, makes it impossible for anyone to complete such a book unaided. People interested in sharing information, such as photographs, factory records, advertisements and other data, or with questions about this research, should contact Eric M. Larson, P.O. Box 5497, Takoma Park, Maryland 20913, telephone (301) 270-3450. Credits for information will be gratefully negotiated and acknowledged. As in researching *Variations of the Smooth Bore H&R Handy-Gun,* all requests for confidentiality will be honored.

Topper
A single shot, break-open shotgun chambered for various gauges with various barrel lengths, chokes. Blued, with a hardwood stock. Introduced in 1946.

Exc.	V.G.	Good	Fair	Poor
110	95	75	60	40

Model 088
An external hammer single shot, break-open shotgun chambered for all gauges with various barrel lengths, chokes and an automatic ejector. Blued, with a case-colored frame and hardwood stock.

Exc.	V.G.	Good	Fair	Poor
80	65	50	40	30

Model 099
As above, but matte, electroless, nickle-plated.

Exc.	V.G.	Good	Fair	Poor
110	95	75	60	40

Model 162
A 12 or 20 gauge boxlock single shotgun with a 24" barrel with rifle sights.

Exc.	V.G.	Good	Fair	Poor
125	100	80	65	45

Model 176
A 10-gauge, 3.5" Magnum caliber boxlock single barrel shotgun with a heavy-weight 36" barrel and a full choke. Manufactured between 1977 and 1985.

Exc.	V.G.	Good	Fair	Poor
125	100	80	65	45

Model 400
A 12, 16 or 20 gauge slide action shotgun with a 28" full-choke barrel. Blued, with a hardwood stock. Manufactured between 1955 and 1967.

Exc.	V.G.	Good	Fair	Poor
150	125	100	75	50

Model 401
As above, with a variable-choke device. Manufactured between 1956 and 1963.

Exc.	V.G.	Good	Fair	Poor
175	150	125	90	65

Model 402
As above, in a .410 bore. Manufactured between 1959 and 1967.

Exc.	V.G.	Good	Fair	Poor
175	150	125	90	65

Model 440
A 12, 16, or 20 gauge slide action shotgun with a 26", 28", or 30" barrel in various shokes. Blued, with a hardwood stock. Manufactured between 1968 and 1973.

Exc.	V.G.	Good	Fair	Poor
150	125	100	75	50

Model 442
As above with a ventilated-rib barrel and a checkered stock. Manufactured between 1969 and 1973.

Exc.	V.G.	Good	Fair	Poor
175	150	125	90	65

Model 403
A .410 bore semi-automatic shotgun with a 26", full choke barrel. Blued, with a hardwood stock. Manufactured in 1964.

Exc.	V.G.	Good	Fair	Poor
200	175	150	100	75

Model 404
A 12, 20 or .410 bore boxlock double-barrel shotgun with 26" or 28" barrels, double triggers and extractors. Blued with a walnut stock. Manufactured by Rossi in Brazil and imported between 1969 and 1972.

Exc.	V.G.	Good	Fair	Poor
175	150	125	90	65

Model 1212
A 12 gauge Over/Under boxlock shotgun with 28" ventilated-rib barrels. Blued with a walnut stock. Also available with 30" barrels having 3" chambers. Manufactured by Landbar Arms of Spain and imported after 1976.

Exc.	V.G.	Good	Fair	Poor
300	250	200	150	100

Model 058
A 20 gauge, .22 Hornet, .30-30, .357 Magnum, or .44 Magnum caliber combination Over/Under rifle/shotgun. Blued, with a hardwood stock.

Exc.	V.G.	Good	Fair	Poor
125	100	80	65	40

Model 258
As above, but with a matte, electroless nickle-plate finish.

Exc.	V.G.	Good	Fair	Poor
175	150	125	90	65

Reising Model 60
A .45 ACP caliber semi-automatic rifle with an 18.25" barrel and a 12- or 20-round detachable magazine. Blued, with a walnut stock. It operates on a retarded blowback system and was developed to be used as a police weapon. Manufactured between 1944 and 1946.

Exc.	V.G.	Good	Fair	Poor
375	325	250	175	100

Model 65 Military
A .22 l.r. caliber semi-automatic rifle with a 23" barrel and Redfield peepsights. Blued, with a walnut stock. Manufactured between 1944 and 1956.

Exc.	V.G.	Good	Fair	Poor
250	200	175	125	90

Model 150
A .22 l.r. caliber semi-automatic rifle with a 20" barrel and a 5-shot magazine. Blued, with a walnut stock. Manufactured between 1949 and 1953.

Exc.	V.G.	Good	Fair	Poor
100	80	60	45	30

Model 155
This is a single-shot, break-open rifle chambered for the .44 Magnum or the .45-70 cartridge. It has a 20" barrel with fixed sights. The finish is blued, with a walnut stock. It was introduced in 1972.

Exc.	V.G.	Good	Fair	Poor
125	100	80	60	40

Model 157
As above in .22 Magnum, .22 Hornet, and the .30-30 caliber.

Exc.	V.G.	Good	Fair	Poor
125	100	80	60	40

Model 158
A .357 or .44 Magnum single shot side lever rifle with a 22" barrel. Blued, case-hardened with a walnut stock. Available with an interchangeable 26" 20 gauge barrel. Manufactured prior to 1986.

Exc.	V.G.	Good	Fair	Poor
100	80	60	45	30

Model 171
A reproduction of the Model 1873 Trapdoor Springfield Carbine with a 22" barrel. Blued, with a case-colored receiver and a walnut stock.

Exc.	V.G.	Good	Fair	Poor
300	250	200	150	100

Model 171-DL
As above, but more finely finished.

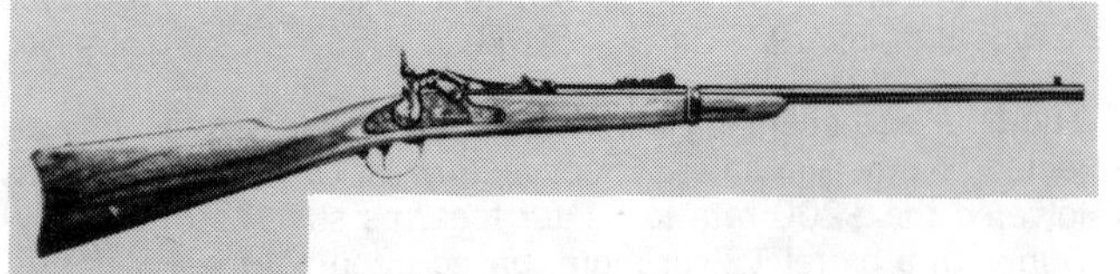

Exc.	V.G.	Good	Fair	Poor
350	300	250	200	125

Model 300 Ultra
A .22-250 up to the .300 Winchester Magnum caliber, bolt-action rifle with a 22" or 24" barrel and without sights. High-polished blue, and checkered walnut stock. Manufactured between 1965 and 1978.

Exc.	V.G.	Good	Fair	Poor
450	400	350	275	175

Model 301 Carbine
As above with an 18" barrel and a full-length, Mannlicher-style stock.

Exc.	V.G.	Good	Fair	Poor
450	400	350	275	175

Model 317 Ultra Wildcat
A .17 Rem., .17-223, .222 Rem., and the .223 Rem. caliber short Sako bolt-action rifle with a 20" barrel furnished without sights. Blued, with a checkered walnut stock. Manufactured between 1968 and 1976.

Exc.	V.G.	Good	Fair	Poor
450	400	350	275	175

Model 317P
As above, but more finely finished. Manufactured between 1968 and 1976.

Exc.	V.G.	Good	Fair	Poor
550	500	450	375	250

Model 333
The Model 300 in 7mm Mag. caliber. Manufactured in 1974.

Exc.	V.G.	Good	Fair	Poor
250	200	175	125	100

Model 340
A .243 to .308 Winchester caliber bolt-action rifle with a 22" barrel and a 5-shot magazine. Blued, with a checkered walnut stock.

Exc.	V.G.	Good	Fair	Poor
400	350	300	225	150

Model 360 Ultra Automatic
A.243 Win. and the .308 Win. caliber semi-automatic rifle with a 22" barrel, adjustable sights and a 3-shot detachable magazine. Blued, with a checkered walnut stock. Manufactured between 1965 and 1978.

Exc.	V.G.	Good	Fair	Poor
350	300	250	175	100

Model 451 Medalist
A .22 l.r. caliber bolt-action rifle with a 26" barrel, open sights and a 5-shot detachable magazine. Blued, with a walnut stock. Manufactured between 1948 and 1961.

Exc.	V.G.	Good	Fair	Poor
175	150	125	100	75

Model 700
A .22 rimfire Magnum caliber, semi-automatic rifle with a 22" barrel, adjustable sights and a 5-round, detachable magazine. Blued, with a checkered walnut stock. Manufactured between 1977 and 1985.

Exc.	V.G.	Good	Fair	Poor
225	200	150	125	85

Model 700 DL
As above, with a checkered walnut stock and with a 4X scope. Manufactured until 1985.

Exc.	V.G.	Good	Fair	Poor
300	250	200	150	100

Model 750
A .22 l.r. bolt-action single shot rifle with a 22" barrel with sights and a short stock. Blued, and the stock is hardwood.

Exc.	V.G.	Good	Fair	Poor
100	80	60	45	25

Model 865
A .22 l.r. caliber bolt-action rifle with a 22" barrel, open sights and a 5-shot magazine. Blued, with a hardwood stock.

Exc.	V.G.	Good	Fair	Poor
100	80	60	45	25

Model 5200
A .22 l.r. caliber bolt-action, single shot rifle with a 28" heavy barrel without sights, and an adjustable trigger. Blued, with a target-type walnut stock.

Exc.	V.G.	Good	Fair	Poor
400	350	300	225	125

Model 5200 Sporter
A .22 l.r. caliber bolt-action rifle with a 24" barrel, adjustable sights and a 5-shot magazine. Blued with a walnut stock. Not manufactured after 1983.

Exc.	V.G.	Good	Fair	Poor
400	350	300	225	125

100th Anniversary Officer's Model
A commemorative replica of the Officer's Model 1873 Trapdoor Springfield Rifle, with a 26" barrel. Engraved, and an anniversary plaque mounted on the stock. Blued, with a case-colored receiver and a pewter forend tip. There were 10,000 manufactured in 1971. As with all commemoratives, this model is desirable only when NIB with all supplied material.

NIB	Exc.	V.G.	Good	Fair	Poor
450	350	300	275	200	125

Custer Memorial Issue
A limited-production issue commemorating George Armstrong Custer's Battle of the Little Bighorn. Heavily engraved and gold-inlaid with a very high-grade checkered walnut stock. Furnished in a mahogany display case that included two books dealing with the subject. There were two versions produced—an Officer's Model, of which 25 were issued commemorating the 25 officers that fell with Custer, and another version commemorating the 243 enlisted men who lost their lives at the Little Bighorn. As with all commemoratives, in order to be collectible, they must be NIB with all furnished material.

Officer's Model—25 Manufactured

NIB	Exc.	V.G.	Good	Fair	Poor
2700	2000	1500	1000	600	400

Enlisted Men's Model—243 Manufactured

NIB	Exc.	V.G.	Good	Fair	Poor
1500	1000	750	500	350	250

Model 174
A plain copy of the Springfield Model 1873 Carbine in .45-70 caliber with a 22" barrel. Manufactured in 1972.

Exc.	V.G.	Good	Fair	Poor
400	350	300	250	175

Model 178
A copy of the Springfield Model 1873 rifle with a 32" barrel. Manufactured from 1973 to 1984.

Exc.	V.G.	Good	Fair	Poor
325	300	250	200	125

HARTFORD ARMS & EQUIPMENT CO.
Hartford, Connecticut

Established in 1929, this firm was purchased by the High Standard Company in 1933.

Single Shot Target
A .22 caliber single shot pistol with a 6.75" round barrel, target sights and either walnut or composition grips. The frame marked "Manfd. by the Hartford Arms and Equip. Co. Hartford,

Conn. Patented .22 cal. Long Rifle." Although this pistol resembles a semi-automatic, it is infact a single shot manually operated pistol.

Exc.	V.G.	Good	Fair	Poor
750	650	500	350	275

Repeating Pistol
Identical to the above, but a manually operated repeating pistol with a 10-shot magazine.

Exc.	V.G.	Good	Fair	Poor
750	650	500	350	275

Semi-Auto 1st Model
As above, but semi-automatic.

Exc.	V.G.	Good	Fair	Poor
700	600	450	375	300

Semi-Auto 2nd Model
As above, with a heavier barrel with flat sides.

Exc.	V.G.	Good	Fair	Poor
700	600	450	375	300

HATFIELD RIFLE COMPANY
St. Joseph, Missouri

Squirrel Rifle
A flintlock or percussion rifle in .32 to .50 caliber with a 39" barrel, double set triggers, adjustable sights, brass mounts and maple stocks. Available in a wide variety of forms which affect the values. The values listed below are for plain, standard models.

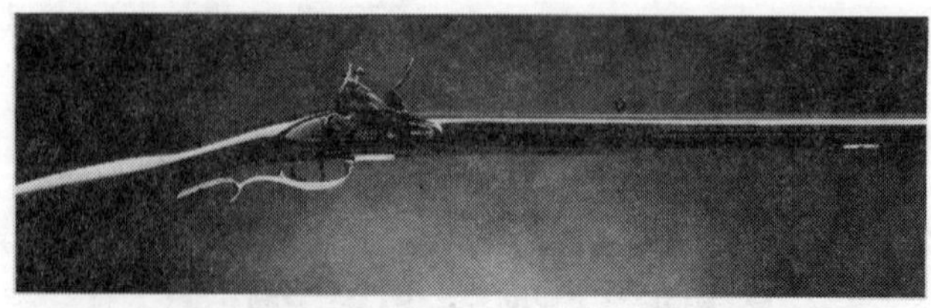

NIB	Exc.	V.G.	Good	Fair	Poor
475	400	350	300	225	150

Shotguns

Uplanded Grade I
A 20 gauge boxlock double-barrel shotgun with a 26" improved cylinder and modified barrel with a matte raised rib, single selective trigger and automatic ejectors. Case-hardened, blued with a deluxe-grade, hand-checkered walnut stock. Introduced in 1987.

NIB	Exc.	V.G.	Good	Fair	Poor
1150	1050	750	600	475	400

Uplander Pigeon Grade II
As above, with scroll engraving with a fitted leather case.

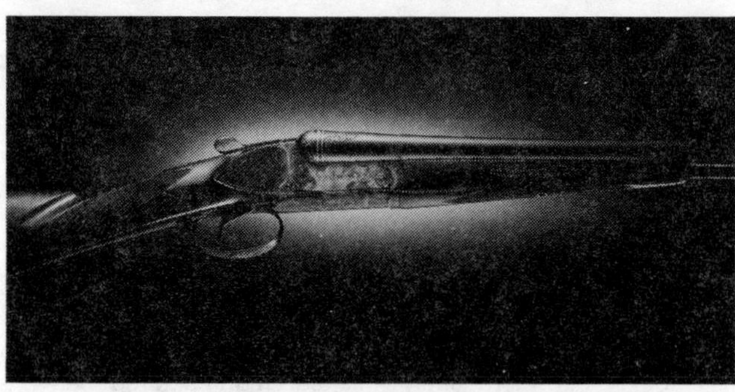

NIB	Exc.	V.G.	Good	Fair	Poor
2000	1750	1275	900	650	500

Uplander Super Pigeon Grade III
As above, with deep-relief cut engraving and a leather case.

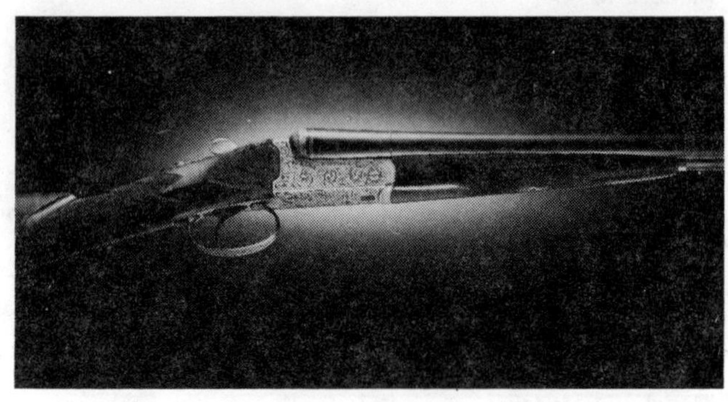

NIB	Exc.	V.G.	Good	Fair	Poor
2500	2200	1700	1400	1000	700

Uplander Golden Quail Grade IV
A gold inlaid version of the above.

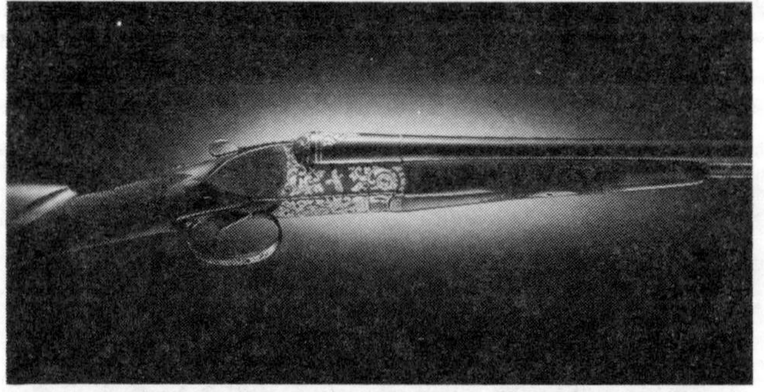

NIB	Exc.	V.G.	Good	Fair	Poor
4000	3500	2750	2000	1700	1300

Uplander Woodcock Grade V
As above, with seven 24 Kt. gold inlays and best quality engraving. Furnished with a leather case.

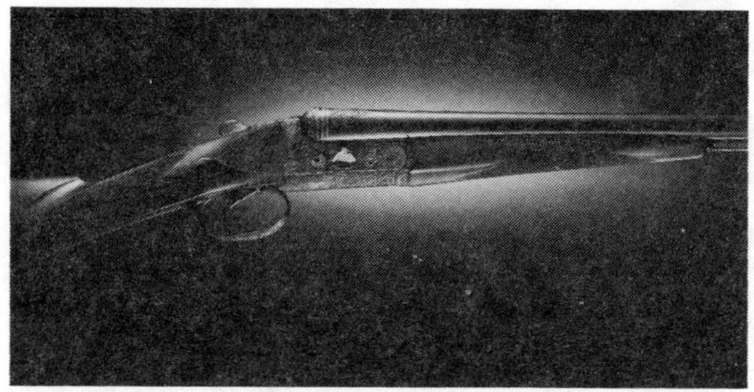

NIB	Exc.	V.G.	Good	Fair	Poor
5600	5000	4250	3500	2750	2000

HAVILAND & GUNN
Ilion, New York

Gallery Pistol

A .17 caliber rimfire single shot pistol with a 5" barrel. The barrel and frame made of one piece of iron and nickle-plated. There are no markings on these pistols whatsoever. Believed to have been made during the 1870s.

Exc.	V.G.	Good	Fair	Poor
400	350	300	225	125

HAWES
Los Angeles, California

An importer of handguns primarily made in Europe.

Courier

A .25 caliber, blowback, semi-automatic pocket pistol manufactured by Galesi.

Exc.	V.G.	Good	Fair	Poor
125	100	75	50	25

Diplomat

A .380ACP pistol with an external hammer.

Exc.	V.G.	Good	Fair	Poor
150	125	100	75	50

Trophy

A J. P. Sauer & Sohn, manufactured revolver with a swing-out cylinder and a 6" barrel. Chambered for the .22 l.r. and the .38 Special. Has adjustable sights.

Exc.	V.G.	Good	Fair	Poor
250	200	175	125	90

Medalion

As above, with a 3", 4", or 6" barrel and fixed sights.

Exc.	V.G.	Good	Fair	Poor
200	175	125	100	75

J. P. Sauer also made a Western-styled series for Hawes based in appearance on the Colt Single Action Army.

Silver City Marshal

A .22 l.r. or .22 rimfire Magnum caliber single action revolver with a 5.5" barrel, 6 shot cylinder, and fixed sights.

Exc.	V.G.	Good	Fair	Poor
125	100	75	50	25

Western Marshal

A .357 Magnum, .44 Magnum .45 Colt, .45ACP, .44-40, 9mm, .22 l.r., and .22 rimfire Magnum single action revolver with fixed sights. Blued.

Exc.	V.G.	Good	Fair	Poor
175	150	125	100	75

Chief Marshal

A .357 Magnum, .44 Magnum, and the .45 Colt caliber revolver with a 6.5" barrel, and 6-shot cylinder and adjustable sights. Blued.

Exc.	V.G.	Good	Fair	Poor
175	150	125	100	75

Texas Marshal

As above, but nickle-plated.

Exc.	V.G.	Good	Fair	Poor
185	160	135	100	75

Montana Marshal

The Western Marshal with a brass backstrap and triggerguard.

Exc.	V.G.	Good	Fair	Poor
175	150	125	100	75

Deputy Marshal

A .22 l.r. and .22 rimfire Magnum single action revolver with a 5.5" barrel, and 6-shot cylinder.

Exc.	V.G.	Good	Fair	Poor
125	100	75	50	25

Federal Marshal

A 6-shot single action revolver in .357 Magnum, .44 Magnum, and the .45 Colt caliber.

Exc.	V.G.	Good	Fair	Poor
175	150	125	100	75

HAWES & WAGGONER
Philadelphia, Pennsylvania

Pocket Pistol

A .41 caliber single shot percussion pistol with a 3" barrel, German silver mountings, and a walnut stock. Manufactured in the 1850s.

Exc.	V.G.	Good	Fair	Poor
1250	750	450	350	250

HAWKEN
St. Louis, Missouri

During the early part of the 19th century, Jacob and Samual Hawken manufactured a variety of flintlock, percussion and cartridge rifles, shotguns and pistols. They are best known, however, for half stock Plains Rifles. Though a very plain nature, these arms were recognized for their accuracy and dependability. Prospective purchasers are advised to secure a qualified appraisal prior to acquisition.

HECKLER & KOCH
Oberndorf/Neckar, Germany

At the end of WWII, the French dismantled the Mauser factory as part of their reparations; and the buildings remained idle until 1949, when firearms production was again allowed in Germany. Heckler & Koch was formed as a machine tool enterprise and occupied the vacant Mauser plant. In the early 1950's Edmund Heckler and Theodor Kock began to produce the G3 automatic rifle based on the Spanish CETME design and progressed to machine guns and submachine guns and eventually to the production of commercial civilian rifles and pistols. In 1990 the company got into financial difficulties because of a failed contract bid. In December of 1990 the French state consortium GIAT announced the purchase of Heckler and Kock, but a little more than a year later the contract was cancelled. Later in 1991 the company was purchased by Royal Ordnance of Britain.

Model 91

This rifle is recoil-operated, with a delayed-roller lock bolt. It is chambered for the .308 Winchester cartridge and has a 17.7" barrel with military style aperture sights. It is furnished with a 20-round detachable magazine and is finished in matte black with a black plastic stock. Some areas of the country have made their ownership illegal.

NIB	Exc.	V.G.	Good	Fair	Poor
1750	1250	900	750	600	300

Model 91 A3

This Model is simply the Model 91 with a retractable metal stock.

NIB	Exc.	V.G.	Good	Fair	Poor
1850	1500	1250	900	700	350

Model 93

This Model is similar to the Model 91 except that it is chambered for the .223 cartridge and has a 16.4" barrel. The magazine holds 25 rounds, and the specification are the same as for the Model 91.

NIB	Exc.	V.G.	Good	Fair	Poor
1800	1300	900	750	600	300

Model 93 A3

This is the Model 93 with the retractable metal stock.

NIB	Exc.	V.G.	Good	Fair	Poor
1850	1550	1250	900	700	350

Model 94

This is a carbine version chambered for the 9mm Parabellum cartridge, with a 16.5" barrel. It is a smaller-scaled weapon that has a 15-shot magazine.

NIB	Exc.	V.G.	Good	Fair	Poor
2400	2200	1750	1200	800	400

Model 94 A3

This model is a variation of the Model 94 with the addition of a retractable metal stock.

NIB	Exc.	V.G.	Good	Fair	Poor
2500	2300	1800	1250	800	400

Model 270

This Model is chambered for the .22 l.r. cartridge. It is a sporting-styled rifle with a 16.5" barrel. It is furnished with either a 5- or a 20-round magazine and is blued, with a checkered walnut stock. This rifle was discontinued in 1985.

NIB	Exc.	V.G.	Good	Fair	Poor
575	500	450	350	250	150

Model 300

This Model is similar to the Model 270 except that it is chambered for the .22 rimfire Magnum cartridge. It was not imported after 1988.

NIB	Exc.	V.G.	Good	Fair	Poor
650	575	450	350	250	150

Model 630

This Model is chambered for the .223 and features the same roller-delayed semi-automatic action as found on the paramilitary-type weapons. This is a sporting style rifle that has a polished blue finish and a checkered walnut stock. The barrel is 17.7" long, and the magazines offered hold either 4 or 10 rounds. Importation was discontinued in 1986.

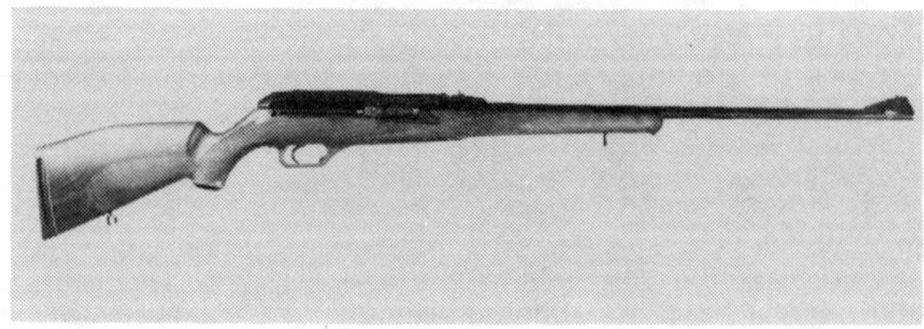

NIB	Exc.	V.G.	Good	Fair	Poor
800	725	600	450	300	150

Model 770

This Model is similar to the Model 630 except that it is chambered for the .308 Winchester cartridge and has 19.7" barrel. It was not imported after 1986.

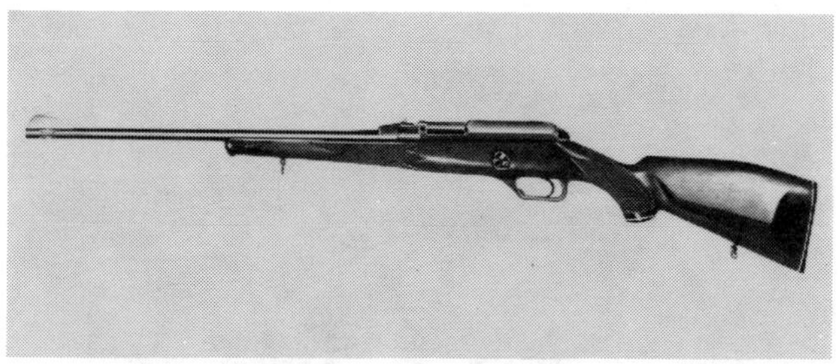

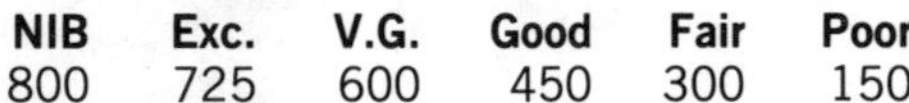

NIB	Exc.	V.G.	Good	Fair	Poor
800	725	600	450	300	150

Model 940

This Model is essentially the same as the Model 770 except that it is chambered for the .30-06 cartridge. It has a 21" barrel and was not imported after 1986.

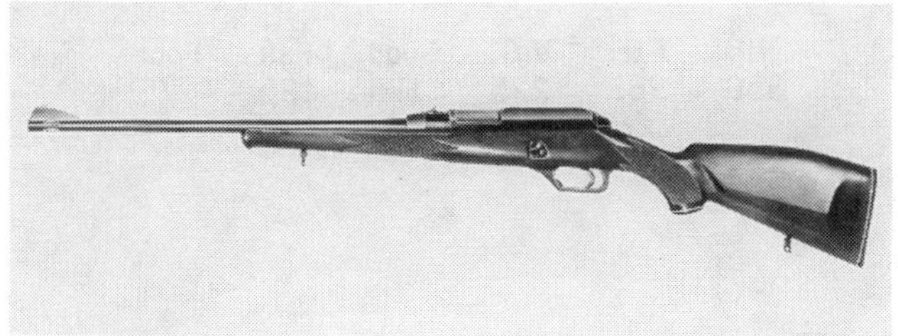

NIB	Exc.	V.G.	Good	Fair	Poor
800	725	600	450	300	150

Model SL6

This is Heckler & Koch's current sporting rifle chambered for the .223 cartridge. It has a 17.7" barrel and features the same basic action as the military versions. It has a matte black finish and a walnut stock with a vented walnut hand guard. The magazine holds 4 rounds.

NIB	Exc.	V.G.	Good	Fair	Poor
750	600	525	475	375	275

Model SL7

This Model is similar to the SL6 except that it is chambered for the .308 Winchester cartridge and has a 3- round magazine.

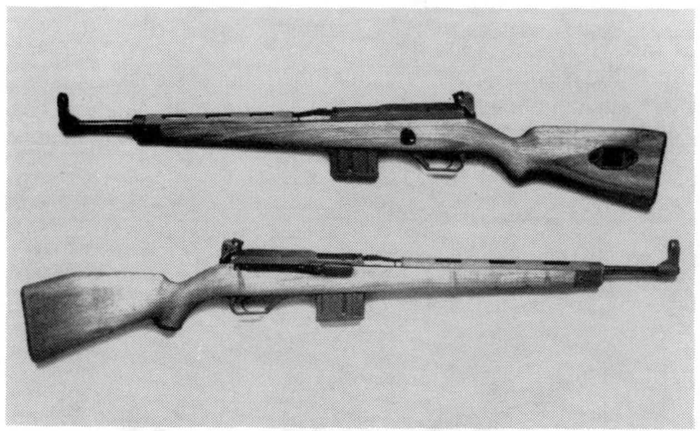

NIB	Exc.	V.G.	Good	Fair	Poor
750	600	575	475	375	275

Model SR9

This model was introduced into the U.S. market after the Federal government prohibited the importation of H&K's other semi-automatic rifles. The SR9 is similar to the HK91 but has been certified by the BATF as a sporting rifle. This model features a special thumbhole stock made of Kevlar reinforced fiberglass. The action is a delayed roller locked bolt semi-automatic design chambered for the .308 Winchester cartridge. /The barrel is 19.7" in length and features adjustable rear sight with hooded front sight. The rifle weighs 10.9 lbs.

NIB	Exc.	V.G.	Good	Fair	Poor
1200	950	850	700	500	250

Model SR9(T) Target

Similar to the standard model SR9 but with the addition of a special MSG90 adjustable butt stock, PSG1 trigger group, and a PSG1 contoured handgrip. Rifle weighs 10.6 lbs.

NIB	Exc.	V.G.	Good	Fair	Poor
1600	1300	950	800	600	300

Model SR9(TC) Target Competition

Similar to the Model SR9(T) but with the addition of the PSG1 adjustable butt stock. Rifle weighs 10.9 lbs.

NIB	Exc.	V.G.	Good	Fair	Poor
1750	1450	1050	850	650	350

PSG-1

This rifle is a high precision sniping rifle that features the delayed-roller semi-automatic action. It is chambered for the .308 Winchester cartridge and has a 5 shot magazine. Barrel length is 25.6". It is furnished with a complete array of accessories including a 6x42-power illuminated Hensholdt scope and mounting system. Rifle weighs 17.8 lbs.

NIB	Exc.	V.G.	Good	Fair	Poor
8750	7500	4500	2500	900	450

BASR Model

This is a bolt-action rifle chambered for various popular calibers. It has a stainless-steel barrel and was essentially custom built to the customer's specifications. The stock is of Kevlar. This Model is quite rare since only 100 were manufactured in 1968.

Exc.	V.G.	Good	Fair	Poor
1750	1200	900	650	400

Pistols

HK4

This is a blowback-operated semi-automatic pistol based on the Mauser HSc design. It is chambered for .22 l.r., .25 ACP, .32 ACP, and .380. These calibers were easily converted by switching the barrels, recoil springs and magazines. The rimfire model could be changed by rotating the breechface. The conversion kits were available for all calibers. The barrel is 3" long; and the finish is blued, with molded plastic thumbrest grips. This pistol was sold from 1968-1973 as the Harrington & Richardson HK4 and is so marked. It was completely discontinued in 1984.

.22 Caliber or .380 Caliber

Exc.	V.G.	Good	Fair	Poor
475	350	250	200	100

.25 Caliber or .32 Caliber

Exc.	V.G.	Good	Fair	Poor
350	300	250	200	100

Conversion Units

Exc.	V.G.	Good	Fair	Poor
150	125	90	60	30

P9

This is a single-action, delayed-blowback semi- automatic pistol chambered for 9mm or 7.65mm Parabellum. The action is based on the G-3 rifle mechanism. The barrel is 4" in length, and the pistol has an internal hammer and a thumb-operated hammer drop and recocking lever. There is also a manual safety and a loaded-chamber indicator. The finish is parkerized, and the grips are molded plastic and well contoured. It has fixed sights. This model was manufactured between 1977 and 1984.

NIB	Exc.	V.G.	Good	Fair	Poor
650	550	450	350	300	200

P9S

This model is similar to the Model P9 except that the action features a double-action capability and it is chambered for the .45 ACP and the 9mm Parabellum. This model was also manufactured between 1977 and 1984.

NIB	Exc.	V.G.	Good	Fair	Poor
700	600	500	400	300	200

P9S Target Model

This version is similar to the Model P9S, with a 5.5" barrel, adjustable sights, and an adjustable trigger. It was discontinued in 1984.

NIB	Exc.	V.G.	Good	Fair	Poor
1150	850	750	650	400	300

VP 70Z

This is a blowback-operated semi-automatic chambered for the 9mm Parabellum cartridge. It is striker-fired and double-action only. The barrel is 4.5" long, and the double-column magazine holds 18 rounds. The finish is blued, and the receiver and grip are molded from plastic. This model was discontinued in 1984.

NIB	Exc.	V.G.	Good	Fair	Poor
350	285	225	175	125	75

P7 PSP

This was the first of the squeeze-cocked H&K pistols. It is a single-action semi-automatic that is placed in the firing position by pressure on the front of the gripstrap. This moves the striker into battery; and firing is then accomplished by a single-action pressure on the trigger, releasing the grip strap cocking device and decocking the mechanism. This particular model does not have the extended finger guard on the trigger and also does not have an ambidextrous safety. It was discontinued in 1984.

NIB	Exc.	V.G.	Good	Fair	Poor
800	700	600	500	400	200

P7 M8

This is the 8-shot newer version of the "squeeze cocker." It has the heat-shield finger guard and the ambidextrous safety. It has a 4" barrel and a 3-dot sight system. The finish is matte blue or nickel with stippled black plastic grips.

NIB	Exc.	V.G.	Good	Fair	Poor
1000	900	750	650	500	300

NOTE: For night sights, introduced in 1993, add $100.

P7 M10

A new addition to the P7 series in 1993, this variation is chambered for the .40S&W cartridge. Magazine holds 10 rounds and the finish is available in either blue or nickel. Pistol weighs 2.69 lbs.

NIB	Exc.	V.G.	Good	Fair	Poor
1200	1000	800	650	500	300

NOTE: For night sights add $100.

P7 M13

This version is similar to the P7 M8 except that it has a double-column 13-shot magazine.

NIB	Exc.	V.G.	Good	Fair	Poor
1200	1000	800	650	500	300

NOTE: For night sights add $100.

P7 K3

This is the "Squeeze Cocker" chambered for either the .380 or .22 Long Rifle caliber. It has a recoil buffer that is oil-filled and a 3.8" barrel. The magazine holds 8 rounds. This model was introduced in 1988.

NIB	Exc.	V.G.	Good	Fair	Poor
1000	900	750	650	500	300

.22 Caliber Conversion Kit

This unit will convert the P7 K3 to fire the .22 Long.Rifle cartridge.

NIB	Exc.	V.G.	Good	Fair	Poor
475	400	350	300	150	75

.32ACP Caliber Conversion Kit

NIB	Exc.	V.G.	Good	Fair	Poor
200	175	150	100	75	50

SP89

Introduced in the early 1990s, this is a large frame semi-automatic pistol chambered for the 9MM cartridge. It features a 15 round magazine and a square notch rear sight with a hooded front sight. The pistol has a 4.5" barrel and is 13" overall. It weighs 4.4 lbs. In August, 1993 this model was no longer imported due to a ban on assault pistols. This ban will affect price, but to what degree is uncertain at this time.

NIB	Exc.	V.G.	Good	Fair	Poor
1500	1250	900	700	500	250

USP40

Introduced in 1993 this new semi-automatic H&H pistol features a new design that incorporates a short recoil modified Browning action. Chambered for the .40S&W cartridge this model has a 4.13" barrel and a magazine capacity of 13 rounds. It weighs 1.74 lbs. Available in 7 different variations from traditional double action to double action only and various safety locations and styles. These variants are numbered by H&K as follows:

1. DA/SA with safe position and control lever on left side of frame.
2. DA/SA with safe position and control lever on right side of frame.
3. DA/SA without safe position and decocking lever on left side of frame.
4. DA/SA without safe position and decocking lever on left side of frame.
5. DA only with safe position and safety lever on left side of frame.
6. DA only with safe position and safety lever on right side of frame.
7. DA only without control lever.

NIB	Exc.	V.G.	Good	Fair	Poor
650	550	450	350	250	150

USP9

Same as the USP40 but chambered for the 9MM cartridge. Magazine holds 16 rounds and pistol weighs 1.66 lbs. This model also has the choice of 7 variations as listed above for the USP40. New for 1993.

NIB	Exc.	V.G.	Good	Fair	Poor
600	500	400	300	225	150

HEINZELMANN, C.E.

Plochigen am Neckar, Germany

Heim

A 6.35mm semi-automatic pistol manufactured during the 1930s and marked on the frame "C.E.Heinzelmann Plochingen A.N. Patent Heim-6.35."

Exc.	V.G.	Good	Fair	Poor
750	675	550	400	300

HEISER, CARL

SEE—Austrian Military Firearms

HELFRICHT

Germany

Model 3 Pocket Pistol

A 6.35mm semi-automatic pistol with a 2" barrel and 6-shot magazine. Blued with black plastic grips having the monogram "KH" cast in them.

Exc.	V.G.	Good	Fair	Poor
450	400	350	275	200

Model 4 Pocket Pistol

As above, without the barrel extension.

Exc.	V.G.	Good	Fair	Poor
400	350	300	225	150

HENRION & DASSY
Liege, Belgium

Semi-automatic

A 6.35mm semi-automatic pistol with a 2.5" barrel and 5-shot magazine. Blued with black plastic grips. Marked "H&D".

Exc.	V.G.	Good	Fair	Poor
600	500	450	375	275

HENRY
SEE—Winchester

HENRY, ALEXANDER
Edinburgh, Scotland

Single Shot Rifle

A high-grade single shot that features a true falling-block action that is activated by a side lever on the action. It was available in the popular European cartridges of the era, and the barrel length varies from 22" to 28" in length. This rifle exhibits fine quality materials and workmanship. The select-grade walnut stock and schnabel forend are hand checkered. The finish of the rifle is scroll-engraved and blued. This company manufactured firearms from 1869 until 1895.

Exc.	V.G.	Good	Fair	Poor
2500	2250	1750	1250	800

Double Rifle

A side-by-side, double-barrelled Express Rifle chambered for the .500/450 Black Powder Express cartridge. It has Damascus barrels and double triggers. This gun is hammerless and features ornate scroll engraving as well as a high-grade hand-checkered walnut stock and forend. It was furnished with a fitted leather case and accessories. This rifle was manufactured in the 1890s.

Exc.	V.G.	Good	Fair	Poor
5000	4500	3750	2900	1850

HEROLD
Franz Jaeger
Suhl, Germany

Bolt Action Rifle

A .22 Hornet bolt-action sporting rifle with a 24" ribbed barrel, adjustable sights, double set triggers and walnut stock. Imported by Charles Daly and Stoeger Arms prior to WWII.

Exc.	V.G.	Good	Fair	Poor
1000	850	700	550	475

HERTERS
Waseca, Minnesota

An importer and retailer of European made firearms. Active until approximately 1980.

Revolvers

Guide

A .22 caliber double-action swing-out cylinder revolver with a 6" barrel and 6-shot cylinder. Blued with walnut grips.

Exc.	V.G.	Good	Fair	Poor
100	80	50	35	25

Power-Mag Revolver

A .357 Magnum, .401 Herters Power Magnum, and .44 Magnum caliber single action revolver with a 4" or 6" barrel and 6-shot cylinder. Blued, with walnut grips.

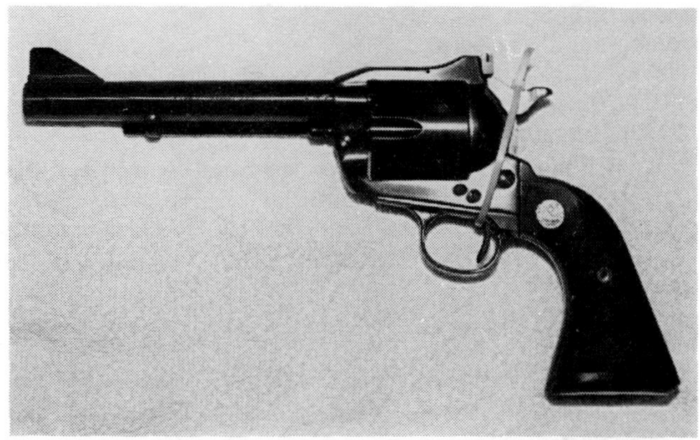

Exc.	V.G.	Good	Fair	Poor
150	125	80	60	50

Western

As above, in .22 caliber.

Exc.	V.G.	Good	Fair	Poor
85	75	60	45	25

Rifles

J-9 or U-9 Hunter

Mauser action sporting rifles manufactured in England (J-9) and Yugoslavia (U-9), with 24" barrels and Monte Carlo-style walnut stocks.

Exc.	V.G.	Good	Fair	Poor
225	185	135	100	75

J-9 or U-9 Presentation or Supreme

As above, with checkering and sling swivels.

Exc.	V.G.	Good	Fair	Poor
250	225	200	150	100

HEYM, F. W.
Suhl, Germany
Importer—Heym America
Ft. Wayne, Indiana

Established in 1934 in Suhl, Germany, this company was reestablished after WWII in Munnerstadt. Postwar arms were originally imported by Paul Jaeger of Grand Junction, Tennessee.

Single Shot Rifles

Model HR-30

Built on the Ruger No. 1 falling-block action and chambered for most calibers with a 24" round barrel or a 26" barrel in the magnum calibers. There is a quarter rib with express sights, and the single-set trigger is made by Canjar. The rifle is engraved with a gamescene motif, and the stock is deluxe, hand-checkered French walnut with a classic European-style cheekpiece. French case-hardened and blued.

Exc.	V.G.	Good	Fair	Poor
3000	2750	2250	1750	1250

Model HR-38

As above, with an octagonal barrel.

Exc.	V.G.	Good	Fair	Poor
3500	3250	2500	2000	1500

Double Rifle

Model 77B/55B Over/Under Rifle

An Over/Under rifle manufactured in a variety of calibers with 25" barrels having open sights and a boxlock action with Kersten double crossbolts. The action is heavily engraved with a gamescene motif and is silverplated. This model has double triggers, cocking indicators, automatic ejectors, and select walnut stock. The barrels machined to accept a Zeiss scope with claw mounts.

Exc.	V.G.	Good	Fair	Poor
5000	4500	4000	3250	2500

Model 55BSS

As above with sidelocks.

Exc.	V.G.	Good	Fair	Poor
9500	8500	7500	5000	3500

Model 55BF/77BF

Similar to the Model 55B, except one barrel is rifled and the other smooth in 12, 16, or 20 gauge.

Exc.	V.G.	Good	Fair	Poor
5000	4500	4000	3250	2500

Model 55BFSS

As above, with sidelocks.

Exc.	V.G.	Good	Fair	Poor
9500	8500	7500	5000	3500

Model 88 B

A large bore double-barrel boxlock rifle with 24" barrels, automatic ejectors, double triggers, and select walnut stock.

Exc.	V.G.	Good	Fair	Poor
9500	8750	7750	5500	4000

Model 88 BSS

As above with sidelocks.

Exc.	V.G.	Good	Fair	Poor
14000	12500	9500	6500	5250

Model 88 Safari

As above, but chambered for .375 Holland & Holland, .458 Winchester Magnum, .470, or .500 Nitro Express calibers with 25" barrels.

Exc.	V.G.	Good	Fair	Poor
13500	12000	9000	6000	4750

Model 22 Safety

An Over/Under combination rifle/shotgun chambered for 16 or 20 gauge over .22 Hornet, .22 WMR, .222 Remington, .222 Remington Magnum, .223, 5.6x50Rmm, 6.5x57Rmm, and 7x57Rmm with 24" barrels. Boxlock action with a single trigger, automatic ejectors, and automatic decocking mechanism. French case-hardening, blued with a walnut stock.

Exc.	V.G.	Good	Fair	Poor
2500	2000	1750	1200	900

Drillings

Model 33

A boxlock drilling manufactured in a variety of calibers and gauges with 25" barrels, double triggers and extractors. Case-hardened, blued with a walnut stock.

Exc.	V.G.	Good	Fair	Poor
6000	5000	4250	3250	2500

Model 37

As above with sidelocks.

Exc.	V.G.	Good	Fair	Poor
9500	8500	7500	6000	4250

Bolt Action Rifles

Model SR-20

A Mauser action sporting rifle manufactured in a variety of calibers with 21", 24" or 26" barrels, open sights, adjustable trigger or set trigger. Blued with a walnut stock.

NIB	Exc.	V.G.	Good	Fair	Poor
1450	1250	950	750	600	450

Model SR-20 Alpine

As above with a 20" barrel and Mannlicher stock. Introduced in 1989.

NIB	Exc.	V.G.	Good	Fair	Poor
2650	2250	1750	1250	850	600

Model SR-20 Classic Safari

As above, but chambered for .404 Jeffries, .425 Express, and the .458 Winchester Magnum with a 24" barrel having express sights. Introduced in 1989.

NIB	Exc.	V.G.	Good	Fair	Poor
3500	3000	2750	2250	1750	1450

HIGGINS, J. C.

Chicago, Illinois

The Sears, Roebuck & Company of Chicago used the tradename J. C. Higgins on the firearms and other sporting goods they sold between 1946 and 1962. Arms bearing this tradename were manufactured by a variety of American gunmakers.

HIGH STANDARD MFG. CO.

New Haven, Connecticut

Established in 1926, this company began the production of firearms in 1933 and ceased operations in 1984.

Model A

A .22 caliber semi-automatic pistol with a 4.5" or 7.5" barrel, adjustable sights and 10-shot magazine. Blued with walnut grips. Approximately 7,300 were made between 1933 and 1943.

Exc.	V.G.	Good	Fair	Poor
425	375	325	250	175

Model B

As above, with fixed sights and hard rubber grips. Approximately 65,000 manufactured between 1933 and 1942.

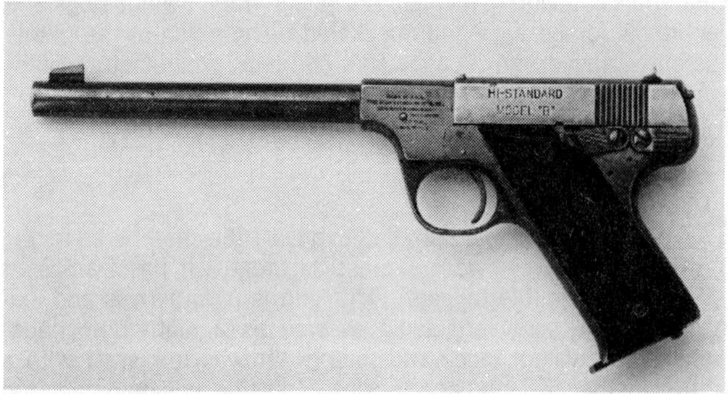

Exc.	V.G.	Good	Fair	Poor
400	350	300	225	150

U.S. Marked Model B

As above, marked "Property of U.S." on the frame. Approximately 14,000 manufactured.

Exc.	V.G.	Good	Fair	Poor
475	400	350	275	200

Model C

Similar to the Model B, but in .22 short caliber. Approximately 5,000 manufactured between 1935 and 1942.

Exc.	V.G.	Good	Fair	Poor
500	425	375	300	225

Model D

Similar to the Model A, with a heavy barrel. Approximately 2,500 were made between 1938 and 1942.

Exc.	V.G.	Good	Fair	Poor
475	400	350	275	200

Model E

The Model A with a heavy barrel and thumbrest grips. Approximately 2,500 manufactured between 1938 and 1942.

Exc.	V.G.	Good	Fair	Poor
600	550	475	375	275

Model H-A

The Model A with an exposed hammer and no external safety. Approximately 1,000 made between 1940 and 1942.

Exc.	V.G.	Good	Fair	Poor
500	425	375	300	225

Model H-B

The Model B with an exposed hammer. Approximately 25,000 manufactured between 1940 and 1954.

Exc.	V.G.	Good	Fair	Poor
475	400	350	275	200

Model H-D
The Model D with an exposed hammer and no external safety. Approximately 7,000 manufactured between 1940 and 1949.

Exc.	V.G.	Good	Fair	Poor
450	375	325	250	175

Model H-D—USA
A bull-barrelled, fixed-sight version of the Model H-D marked "Property of U.S.A." Approximately 44,000 manufactured between 1943 and 1946. The early blued guns are worth approximately 20 percent additional.

Exc.	V.G.	Good	Fair	Poor
425	350	300	225	150

Model H-D Military
Similar to the Model H-D, with the addition of an external thumb safety. Approximately 150,000 manufactured between 1946 and 1955.

Exc.	V.G.	Good	Fair	Poor
400	350	300	225	125

Model H-E
An exposed-hammer version of the Model E. Approximately 1,000 manufactured between 1940 and 1942. This is the rarest of the semi-automatic High Standard pistols.

Exc.	V.G.	Good	Fair	Poor
800	700	600	450	300

Model G
A .380 caliber semi-automatic pistol with a 5" barrel, fixed sights and lever takedown mechanism. Fitted with an exposed hammer and external safety. Blued with plastic grips. Approximately 7,400 manufactured between 1947 and 1950.

Exc.	V.G.	Good	Fair	Poor
550	450	400	275	200

Model G-B
A .22 caliber semi-automatic pistol with a 4.5" or 7.5" barrel and 10-shot magazine. Blued with plastic grips. Approximately 5,000 manufactured between 1949 and 1950. If both barrels are present, add approximately 15 percent to the value.

Exc.	V.G.	Good	Fair	Poor
425	375	325	250	150

Model G-D
As above with a heavy barrel and adjustable sights. Approximately 3,300 manufactured between 1948 and 1951. Both barrels would increase the values approximately 15 percent.

Exc.	V.G.	Good	Fair	Poor
425	375	325	250	150

Model G-E
As above, with a heavy barrel and adjustable sights. Approximately 3,000 were made in 1949 and 1950.

Exc.	V.G.	Good	Fair	Poor
600	500	400	300	200

1st Model Olympic
As above, in .22 short caliber with a lightweight alloy slide and redesigned takedown lever. Approximately 1,200 were made in 1949 and 1950.

Exc.	V.G.	Good	Fair	Poor
700	600	500	375	275

1st Model Sport King
A .22 caliber semi-automatic pistol with a 4.5" or 6.75" barrel, fixed sights. Blued with plastic grips. Manufactured between 1951 and 1958.

Exc.	V.G.	Good	Fair	Poor
375	325	250	175	100

1st Model Flite King
An alloy-framed version of the Sport King chambered for the .22 short cartridge. Manufactured between 1953 and 1958. The extra barrel would add approximately 15 percent to the value.

Exc.	V.G.	Good	Fair	Poor
350	300	225	150	100

Field King
As above with a heavy barrel. Manufactured between 1951 and 1958. The extra barrel would add approximately 15 percent to the value.

Exc.	V.G.	Good	Fair	Poor
375	325	250	175	100

Supermatic
A .22 caliber semi-automatic pistol with a 4.5" or 6.75" barrel, adjustable sights, barrel weights and 10-shot magazine. Blued with plastic grips. Manufactured between1951 and 1958.

Exc.	V.G.	Good	Fair	Poor
400	350	300	225	125

2nd Model Olympic
As above, with an alloy slide and in .22 short caliber.

Exc.	V.G.	Good	Fair	Poor
650	550	350	250	175

Duramatic
A .22 caliber semi-automatic pistol with a 4.5" or 6.5" barrel, fixed sights, screw takedown mechanism and walnut grips. Manufactured from 1954 to 1970.

Exc.	V.G.	Good	Fair	Poor
375	325	250	175	100

2nd Model Sport King
An improved version of the Sport King that was manufactured between 1958 and 1970. The extra barrel would add approximately 15 percent to the value.

Exc.	V.G.	Good	Fair	Poor
350	300	225	150	100

3rd Model Sport King
Similar to the 2nd Model but available in nickle-plate. Manufactured between 1974 and 1984.

Exc.	V.G.	Good	Fair	Poor
300	250	200	125	100

Sport King M
As above with military-style, straight grip.

Exc.	V.G.	Good	Fair	Poor
300	250	200	125	100

2nd Model Flite King

The 2nd Model Sport King with a lightweight, alloy slide and in .22 short caliber. Manufactured between 1958 and 1966.

Exc.	V.G.	Good	Fair	Poor
300	250	200	125	100

Sharpshooter

The 2nd Model Sport King with a 5.5" heavy barrel, adjustable sights and push-button takedown mechanism. Blued with brown, checkered plastic grips. Manufactured between 1971 and 1981.

Exc.	V.G.	Good	Fair	Poor
400	300	250	150	100

Supermatic Tournament

As above, with a a 5.5" or 6.75" heavy barrel, barrel weights and adjustable target-type sights. Blued with checkered walnut grips. Manufactured between 1958 and 1966.

Exc.	V.G.	Good	Fair	Poor
400	350	300	200	125

Supermatic Citation

As above, with a 5.5" bull barrel and adjustable target sights. Blued with thumbrest grips.

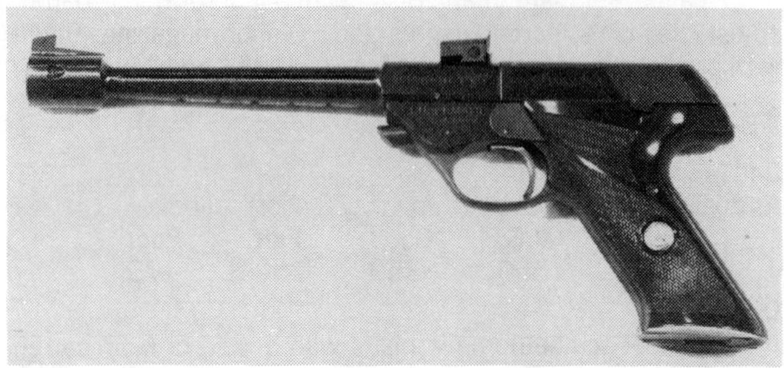

Exc.	V.G.	Good	Fair	Poor
500	450	350	250	175

Supermatic Citation Military

Similar to the Citation, except that it has the straight, military-type grip frame.

Exc.	V.G.	Good	Fair	Poor
550	450	400	250	175

Supermatic Trophy

As above, with angled grips, adjustable sights, and available with a 6.75", 8" or 10" tapered, 5.5" bull barrel or a 7.5" fluted barrel. The rear sight is mounted on the frame and straddles the slide. An adjustable trigger pull and over-travel adjustment. Blued with checkered, walnut, thumbrest grips.

10" Barrel—Add 40%.

8" Barrel—Add 25%.

Exc.	V.G.	Good	Fair	Poor
575	500	400	300	200

Supermatic Trophy Military

As above, with a military-type grip frame. Manufactured between 1965 and 1984.

Exc.	V.G.	Good	Fair	Poor
575	500	400	300	200

3rd Model Olympic

Similar to the Supermatic Trophy model with a lightweight, alloy slide and in .22 short cartridge. A straight-grip, military model is also available. Manufactured between 1963 and 1966.

Exc.	V.G.	Good	Fair	Poor
650	550	450	300	225

Olympic ISU

Similar to the Supermatic Citation, with a 6.75" or 8" barrel furnished with weights and in .22 short caliber. A military model with the straight grip is also available. The values are the same. Manufactured between 1958 and 1984.

Exc.	V.G.	Good	Fair	Poor
700	600	550	400	250

1972 Olympic Commemorative

A limited edition issued to commemorate the only American-manufactured .22 pistol used to win an Olympic Gold Medal. It is heavily engraved with gold-inlaid Olympic Rings and furnished in a fitted presentation case. It was manufactured in 1972 and, as with all commemoratives, must be NIB with all furnished material to be desirable from a collector's standpoint.

NIB	Exc.	V.G.	Good	Fair	Poor
1300	1000	750	600	500	300

1980 Olympic Commemorative

Similar to the above, with gold inlaid Olympic rings on the receiver. 1,000 were made in 1980 and have the serial number prefix USA.

NIB	Exc.	V.G.	Good	Fair	Poor
750	650	450	325	225	150

Victor

A .22 caliber semi-automatic pistol with a 4.5" or 5.5" ribbed barrel, adjustable sights, push-button or screw takedown mechanism and 10-shot magazine. Blued with walnut grips.

Exc.	V.G.	Good	Fair	Poor
600	550	425	350	175

10-X

A custom made semi-automatic target pistol hand assembled and signed by the employee who made the pistol. Available with either a push-button barrel release or an Allen screw release. Manufactured from 1982 to 1984.

Exc.	V.G.	Good	Fair	Poor
850	775	700	550	425

Sharpshooter-M

Similar to the Victor, with a 5.5" heavy barrel and adjustable sights. Manufactured from 1982 to 1984.

Exc.	V.G.	Good	Fair	Poor
350	300	250	175	100

Derringer
A .22 or .22 Magnum caliber Over/Under double-action pocket pistol with 3.5" barrels. Blued or nickle-plated with plastic grips.

Exc.	V.G.	Good	Fair	Poor
200	165	145	100	75

Silver Plated Derringer with Presentation Case

Exc.	V.G.	Good	Fair	Poor
250	200	150	125	100

Gold Plated Derringer with Presentation Case

Exc.	V.G.	Good	Fair	Poor
275	225	175	150	100

Sentinel Series
A .22 caliber double-action swing-out cylinder revolver with a 3", 4" or 6" barrel and 9-shot cylinder. Annodized aluminum frame with blue, nickle, pink or yellow finish.

Sentinel

Exc.	V.G.	Good	Fair	Poor
150	125	100	75	50

Sentinel Imperial—Adjustable Sights

Exc.	V.G.	Good	Fair	Poor
165	145	110	90	75

Sentinel Deluxe

Exc.	V.G.	Good	Fair	Poor
165	145	110	90	75

Sentinel Snub—2.5" Barrel, Round Butt

Exc.	V.G.	Good	Fair	Poor
150	125	100	75	50

Durango
A Western-style, double-action revolver in .22 caliber with a 4.5" or 5.5" barrel. Blued or nickle-plated with walnut grips. Manufactured between 1971 and 1973.

Exc.	V.G.	Good	Fair	Poor
150	125	100	75	50

Double Nine
As above, with a 5.5" barrel and alloy frame. Blued or nickle-plated with simulated ivory, ebony or staghorn grips. Manufactured from 1959 to 1984.

Exc.	V.G.	Good	Fair	Poor
150	125	100	75	50

Longhorn
As above, with a 9.5" barrel.

Exc.	V.G.	Good	Fair	Poor
200	175	125	100	75

Hombre
The Double Nine with a 4.5" barrel and steel frame.

Exc.	V.G.	Good	Fair	Poor
150	125	100	75	50

High Sierra
As above, with a 7" octagonal barrel and gold-plated back strap and triggerguard.

Exc.	V.G.	Good	Fair	Poor
200	175	125	100	75

Posse
As above, with a 3.5" barrel and a brass back strap and triggerguard. Walnut grips. Manufactured between 1961 and 1966.

Exc.	V.G.	Good	Fair	Poor
125	100	75	50	25

Natchez
As above, with rounded birdshead grips.

Exc.	V.G.	Good	Fair	Poor
125	100	75	50	25

Kit Gun
A .22 caliber double-action swing-out cylinder revolver with a 4" barrel, adjustable sights and 9-shot cylinder. Blued with walnut grips. Manufactured from 1970 to 1973.

Exc.	V.G.	Good	Fair	Poor
150	125	100	75	50

Sentinel I
Similar to the above, with a 2", 3" or 4" barrel. Blued or nickle-plated with walnut grips.

Exc.	V.G.	Good	Fair	Poor
225	175	125	100	75

Sentinel Mark IV
As above, in .22 Magnum.

Exc.	V.G.	Good	Fair	Poor
150	125	100	75	50

Sentinel Mark II
A .357 Magnum caliber double-action revolver with 2.5", 4" or 6" barrels, fixed sights, blued finish and walnut grips. Manufactured from 1974 to 1976.

Exc.	V.G.	Good	Fair	Poor
225	175	125	100	75

Sentinel Mark III
As above, with adjustable sights.

Exc.	V.G.	Good	Fair	Poor
250	200	150	125	100

Crusader
A .357 Magnum, .44 Magnum, or the .45 Colt caliber double-action, swing-out cylinder revolver with a 7.5" barrel, adjustable sights and 6-shot cylinder. Production of this model was limited.

Exc.	V.G.	Good	Fair	Poor
550	500	450	350	275

Supermatic Field Grade
A 12 gauge semi-automatic shotgun with a 28" or 30" barrel. Blued with a walnut stock. Manufactured from 1960 to 1966.

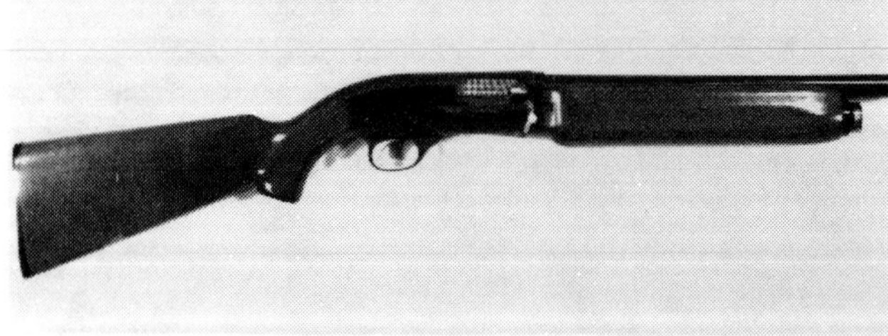

Exc.	V.G.	Good	Fair	Poor
200	175	150	100	65

Supermatic Special
As above, with a 27" barrel. Manufactured by Harrington & Richardson.

Exc.	V.G.	Good	Fair	Poor
200	175	150	100	65

Supermatic Deluxe
Similar to the Field Grade, with a ventilated-rib barrel and a checkered walnut stock. Manufactured between 1961 and 1966.

Exc.	V.G.	Good	Fair	Poor
250	200	175	125	85

Supermatic Deer Gun
As above, with a 22" barrel fitted with rifle sights and the stock having a recoil pad. Manufactured in 1965 only.

Exc.	V.G.	Good	Fair	Poor
225	175	150	100	75

Supermatic Skeet
As above, with a 26" ventilated-rib barrel which is skeet bored. Manufactured between 1962 and 1966.

Exc.	V.G.	Good	Fair	Poor
300	250	200	150	100

Supermatic Trap
As above, with a 30" barrel and trap-style stock. Manufactured between 1962 and 1966.

Exc.	V.G.	Good	Fair	Poor
250	200	150	100	75

Flite King Field Grade
A 12 or 20 gauge slide action shotgun with 26", 28" or 30" barrels. Blued with a walnut stock. Manufactured between 1960 and 1966.

Exc.	V.G.	Good	Fair	Poor
175	150	125	100	75

Flite King Special
As above, with a 27"-barrel having adjustable choke.

Exc.	V.G.	Good	Fair	Poor
175	150	125	100	75

Flite King Deluxe
As above, with a ventilated-rib barrel and a checkered walnut stock. Manufactured between 1961 and 1966.

Exc.	V.G.	Good	Fair	Poor
200	175	150	125	100

Flite King Trophy
As above, with a 27" ventilated-rib barrel with the adjustable choke. Manufactured between 1960 and 1966.

Exc.	V.G.	Good	Fair	Poor
200	175	150	125	100

Flite King Brush
As above, with an 18" or 20" cylinder-bore barrel fitted with rifle sights. Manufactured between 1962 and 1964.

Exc.	V.G.	Good	Fair	Poor
175	150	125	100	75

Flite King Brush Deluxe
As above, with an adjustable peepsight and sling swivels. Manufactured between 1964 and 1966.

Exc.	V.G.	Good	Fair	Poor
250	200	175	125	100

Flite King Skeet
As above, in 12-gauge with a 26" ventilated-rib barrel that is skeet-bored. Manufactured between 1962 and 1966.

Exc.	V.G.	Good	Fair	Poor
275	225	200	150	125

Flite King Trap
As above, with a 30" ventilated-rib, full-choke barrel and a trap-type stock with recoil pad. Manufactured between 1962 and 1966.

Exc.	V.G.	Good	Fair	Poor
250	200	175	125	100

Model 10B
A 12 gauge semi-automatic shotgun with an 18" barrel, pistol-grip stock and bullpup design. Fitted with a folding carrying handle and a flashlight attachment on the top of the receiver. Produced in limited quantities.

Exc.	V.G.	Good	Fair	Poor
650	575	450	350	250

Supermatic Shadow Seven
A 12 gauge Over/Under boxlock shotgun with 27.5" or 29.5" ventilated-rib barrels, single trigger and automatic ejectors. Blued with a walnut stock. Manufactured in Japan and imported in 1974 and 1975.

Exc.	V.G.	Good	Fair	Poor
675	600	500	425	350

Supermatic Indy
As above, with finer engraving and a better figured walnut stock. Manufactured in Japan and imported in 1974 and 1975.

Exc.	V.G.	Good	Fair	Poor
800	700	600	500	425

Supermatic Shadow
A 12 or 20 gauge (standard or Magnum) semi-automatic shotgun with 26", 28" or 30" ventilated-rib barrels. Blued with a walnut stock. Manufactured in Japan and imported in 1974 and 1975.

Exc.	V.G.	Good	Fair	Poor
350	300	275	200	125

Sport King Rifle
A .22 caliber semi-automatic rifle with a 22" barrel, open sights and tubular magazine. Blued with a walnut stock. Manufactured between 1960 and 1966.

Exc.	V.G.	Good	Fair	Poor
100	90	75	50	25

Sport King Special
As above, with a Monte Carlo-type stock and beavertail forearm.

Exc.	V.G.	Good	Fair	Poor
150	125	100	60	40

Sport King Deluxe
As above, with a checkered walnut stock. Manufactured between 1966 and 1975.

Exc.	V.G.	Good	Fair	Poor
175	150	125	100	75

Sport King Carbine
As above, with an 18" barrel and sling swivels. Manufactured between 1964 and 1973.

Exc.	V.G.	Good	Fair	Poor
175	150	125	100	75

Flite King
A .22 caliber slide action rifle with a 24" barrel, open sights and tubular magazine. Blued with a Monte Carlo-style stock. Manufactured between 1962 and 1975.

Exc.	V.G.	Good	Fair	Poor
125	100	80	60	40

Hi-Power Field Grade
A .270 or .30-06 caliber bolt-action rifle with a 22" barrel, open sights and 4-shot magazine. Blued with a walnut stock. Manufactured between 1962 and 1966.

Exc.	V.G.	Good	Fair	Poor
300	250	225	150	100

Hi-Power Deluxe
As above, with a Monte Carlo-style stock. Manufactured between 1962 and 1966.

Exc.	V.G.	Good	Fair	Poor
350	300	275	200	150

HILL, W.J.
Birmingham, England

Hill's Self Extracting Revolver
A .32 caliber double-action folding trigger revolver with a 3.75" barrel and 6-shot cylinder. Marked "Hill's Patent Self-Extractor". Blued with walnut grips.

Exc.	V.G.	Good	Fair	Poor
500	400	350	250	150

HILLIARD, D. H.
Cornish, New Hampshire

Under Hammer Pistol
A .34 caliber under hammer percussion pistol with varying barrel lengths. Blued with walnut grips. Active 1842 to 1877.

Exc.	V.G.	Good	Fair	Poor
500	400	325	250	200

HINO-KOMURA
Tokyo, Japan

A 7.65mm or 8mm Nambu semi-automatic pistol manufactured in very limited quantities between 1905 and 1912. The operation of this pistol involves pulling the muzzle forward until the slide engages a catch on the trigger assembly. Pulling the trigger at this point allows the barrel to move back and engage the cartridge nose into the chamber. Squeezing the grip safety then allows the barrel to slam back into the fixed firing pin on the breechblock. Prospective purchasers are advised to secure a qualified appraisal prior to acquisition.

Exc.	V.G.	Good	Fair	Poor
3500	3250	2750	2000	1500

HODGKINS, D. C. & SONS
Macon, Georgia

SEE—Bilharz, Hall & Co.

HOFER, P.
Ferlach, Austria

A gunmaker specializing in double-barrel rifles made strictly to custom order. Prospective purchasers should secure a qualified appraisal prior to acquisition.

HOFFMAN, LOUIS
Vicksburg, Mississippi

Pocket Pistol
A .41 caliber percussion pocket pistol with a 3" barrel, German silver mounts and walnut stock. Active 1857 to 1886.

Exc.	V.G.	Good	Fair	Poor
600	500	400	300	225

HOLDEN, C. B.
Worcester, Massachusetts

Open Frame Rifle
A .44 r.f. single shot rifle with a 28" barrel, open sights, silver plated bronze frame and walnut stock. The barrel marked "C.B. Holden Worcester-Mass." Produced in limited quantities during the mid-1860s.

Exc.	V.G.	Good	Fair	Poor
750	675	600	475	325

HOLLAND & HOLLAND, LTD.
London, England
Importer—New England Arms
Kittery Point, Maine

Established in 1835, Holland & Holland has manufactured a wide variety of shotguns and rifles during its existence. The greater part of these arms were made to custom order and, therefore, prospective purchasers are advised to secure a qualified appraisal prior to acquisition.

The following models are listed as a guide only.

Over/Under Shotguns

Old Model Royal Grade
A 12 gauge sidelock double-barrel shotgun manufactured to custom order prior to 1951.

Exc.	V.G.	Good	Fair	Poor
22000	18500	15000	11000	8500

New Model Royal Grade
As above, with a slimmer action. Manufactured from 1951 to 1960.

Exc.	V.G.	Good	Fair	Poor
25000	20000	17500	12500	10000

Royal Grade Game Gun
Currently manufactured.

Exc.	V.G.	Good	Fair	Poor
45000	38000	32500	25000	20000

Side x Side Shotguns

Northwood Boxlock
A 12 to 28 gauge boxlock double-barrel shotgun with 28" or 30" barrels, double triggers and automatic ejectors.
20 or 28 Gauge—Add 10%.
Deluxe Version with Engraving—Add 10%.

Exc.	V.G.	Good	Fair	Poor
7500	6500	5250	4000	3000

Cavalier Boxlock
As above, but made on custom order.
20 or 28 Gauge—Add 10%.
Deluxe Model with More Engraving—Add 20%.

Exc.	V.G.	Good	Fair	Poor
12500	10000	7500	5500	4500

Dominion Sidelock
A 12, 16 or 20 gauge sidelock double-barrel shotgun with double triggers and automatic ejectors.

Exc.	V.G.	Good	Fair	Poor
5000	4250	3500	2750	2000

Dominion Game Gun
The current production model, manufactured in 12 gauge only.

Exc.	V.G.	Good	Fair	Poor
30000	25000	20000	15000	10000

Royal Ejector Grade Hammerless Sidelock
Produced strictly on custom order.
20 Gauge—Add 25%.
28 Gauge—Add 35%.
.410—Add 70%.

Exc.	V.G.	Good	Fair	Poor
12500	10000	7500	6000	5000

Deluxe Model
As above, but more finely finished with a self-opening action.

Exc.	V.G.	Good	Fair	Poor
15000	12500	10000	7500	5500

Badminton Grade
As above, without the self-opener.
20 Gauge—Add 25%.
28 Gauge—Add 35%.
.410—Add 50%.

Exc.	V.G.	Good	Fair	Poor
11000	8500	7500	5500	4000

Riviera Grade
As above, with an extra set of barrels.
20 Gauge—Add 25%.
28 Gauge—Add 35%.
.410—Add 50%.

Exc.	V.G.	Good	Fair	Poor
15000	12500	10000	7500	5500

Centenary Grade
A 12 gauge (2") sidelock double-barrel shotgun.

Royal Game Gun
Holland & Holland's best quality shotgun.
20 and 28 Gauges—Add 10%.

Exc.	V.G.	Good	Fair	Poor
42500	32500	25000	17500	10000

Single Barrel Trap Gun
A 12 gauge boxlock single barrel shotgun with 30" or 32" barrel.

Standard Grade

Exc.	V.G.	Good	Fair	Poor
5000	4500	3750	2500	2000

Deluxe Grade

Exc.	V.G.	Good	Fair	Poor
7500	6500	5500	4750	3000

Exhibition Grade

Exc.	V.G.	Good	Fair	Poor
9000	8000	7000	5500	3750

Double Rifles

No. 2 Grade Double Rifle
A sidelock double-barrel rifle produced in a variety of calibers with 24" barrels, double triggers, automatic ejectors and express sights. Obsolete cartridges qould be worth less.

Exc.	V.G.	Good	Fair	Poor
15000	12500	8500	7000	6000

Royal Side x Side Rifle
Similar to the above, but more finely finished.

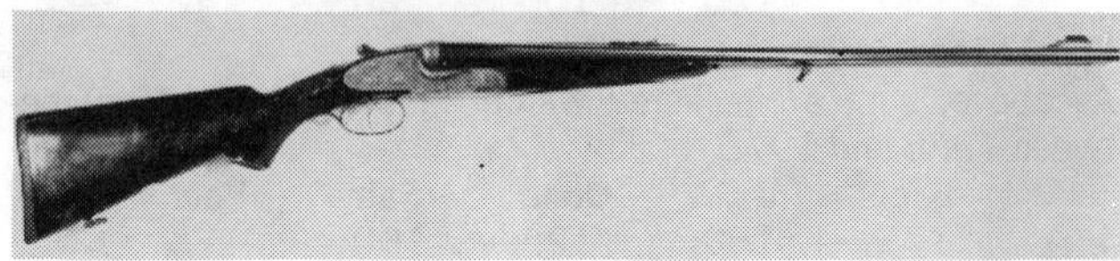

Exc.	V.G.	Good	Fair	Poor
50000	40000	30000	22500	15000

Royal Deluxe Side x Side Rifle
Holland & Holland's best quality double-barrel rifle.

Exc.	V.G.	Good	Fair	Poor
56000	45000	35000	25000	17500

H&H 700 Bore Side x Side Rifle
A .700 Holland & Holland double-barrel rifle. Currently manufactured. Due to the uniqueness of the piece, buyers should seek qualified appraisal.

Bolt Action Rifles

Best Quality Rifle
A bolt-action rifle produced in calibers up to .375 Holland & Holland with a 24" barrel, express sights and 4-shot magazine.

Exc.	V.G.	Good	Fair	Poor
7500	6500	5000	3500	2250

Deluxe Magazine Rifle
As above, but more finely finished.

Exc.	V.G.	Good	Fair	Poor
10500	8500	7000	5000	3000

HOLLIS & SONS

SEE—English Military Firearms

HOLLOWAY ARMS CO.

Ft. Worth, Texas

HAC Model 7
A 7.62x54mm semi-automatic rifle with a 20" barrel, adjustable sights, integral telescope mount and 20-shot magazine. Black annodized finish with folding stock.

HAC Model 7C
As above, with a 16" barrel.

HAC Model 7S
As above, with a heavy-barrel.

HOLMES FIREARMS
Wheeler, Arkansas

MP-22
A .22 caliber semi-automatic pistol with a 6" barrel and alloy receiver. Annodized black finish with a walnut grip. Manufactured in 1985.

NIB	Exc.	V.G.	Good	Fair	Poor
350	300	275	225	200	150

MP-83
Similar to the above, but in 9mm or .45 caliber. Manufactured in 1985.

NIB	Exc.	V.G.	Good	Fair	Poor
400	350	325	275	250	200

NOTE: Several of the Holmes pistols have been declared machine guns by the BATF because of their easy conversion to full automatic. Make sure before purchase that a Class III license is not required.

HOOD F. A. CO.
Norwich, Connecticut

A manufacturer of spur trigger .22 or .32 caliber revolvers with varying length barrels and finishes. Many of these revolvers are found stamped only with tradenames.

Exc.	V.G.	Good	Fair	Poor
200	175	125	100	75

HOPKINS & ALLEN
Norwich, Connecticut
ALSO SEE—Bacon Arms Co.
Merwin Hulbert & Co.

Established in 1868, this company produced a variety of spur trigger revolvers in .22, .32, .38 or .41 caliber often marked with tradenames such as: Acme, Blue Jacket, Captain Jack, Chichester, Defender, Dictator, Hopkins & Allen, Imperial Arms Co., Monarch, Mountain Eagle, Ranger, Tower's Police Safety, Universal, and XL.

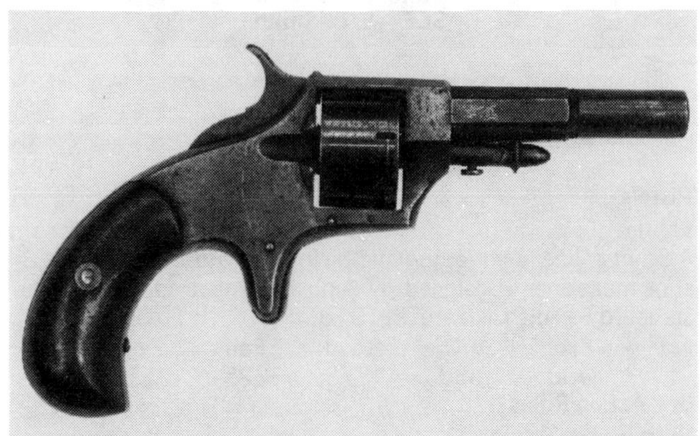

Courtesy Milwaukee Public Museum, Milwaukee, Wisconsin.

Exc.	V.G.	Good	Fair	Poor
175	150	125	100	75

Some of these revolvers are hinged frame, double-action break opens with round-ribbed barrels of various lengths. Blued or nickle-plated, with checkered plastic grips.

Exc.	V.G.	Good	Fair	Poor
150	125	100	75	50

Dictator
A .36 caliber percussion or .38rf single action revolver with a 4" barrel and 5-shot cylinder. Blued with walnut grips. The barrel marked "Dictator". Approximately 6,000 percussion revolvers were made and 5,000 rimfire.

Exc.	V.G.	Good	Fair	Poor
500	400	350	250	150

Falling Block Rifle
A .22 to .38-55 caliber single shot rifle with a 24", 26" or 28" octagonal barrel. Blued with a walnut stock. Manufactured between 1888 and 1892.

Exc.	V.G.	Good	Fair	Poor
500	400	300	225	125

Schuetzen Rifle
A .22 or .25-20 caliber single shot rifle with a 26" octagonal barrel, double-set trigger and a Schuetzen-type buttplate. Blued with a walnut stock.

Exc.	V.G.	Good	Fair	Poor
850	750	650	500	400

Navy Revolver
A .38 caliber single action revolver with a 6.5" barrel marked, "Hopkins & Allen Mfg. Co., Pat. Mar. 28, 71, Apr. 27, 75" and a 6-shot cylinder. The top strap marked, "XL Navy". Blued or nickle-plated with walnut grips. Several hundred were made between 1878 and 1882.

Exc.	V.G.	Good	Fair	Poor
500	425	350	250	175

Army Revolver
As above, in .44rf with a 4.5", 6" or 7.5" barrel. The top strap marked, "XL No. 8." Several hundred were manufactured between 1878 and 1882.

Exc.	V.G.	Good	Fair	Poor
650	575	475	325	225

Derringer
A .22 caliber single shot pistol with a hinged 1.75" barrel which pivots downwards for loading. Blued or nickle-plated with walnut, ivory or pearl grips. The frame marked, "Hopkins & Allen Arms Co., Norwich, Conn. U.S.A." Several hundred were manufactured in the 1880s and 1890s.

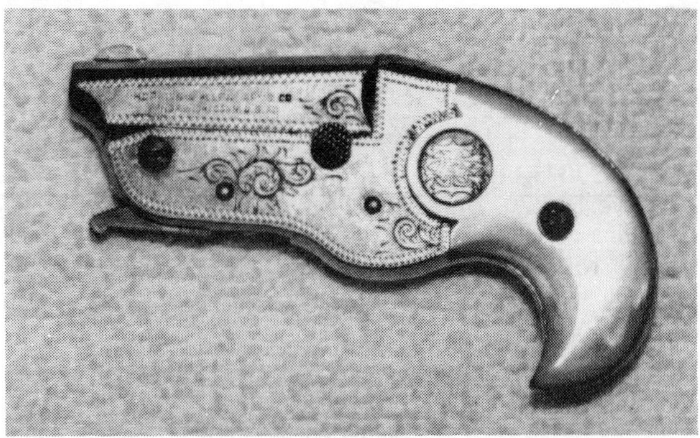

Exc.	V.G.	Good	Fair	Poor
800	700	600	475	350

HOTCHKISS
Winchester Arms Co
New Haven, Connecticut

HOWA MACHINE COMPANY
Japan

This company manufactured bolt-action rifles for Smith & Wesson until 1985 and then for Mossberg in 1986 and 1987. Presently, Howa firearms are imported by Interarms of Alexandria, Virginia.

Model 1500 Hunter
A .22-250, .223, .243, .270, 7mm Remington Magnum .308, .30-06, and .300 Winchester Magnum caliber bolt-action sporting rifle with a 22" or 24" barrel and 3-shot or 5-shot

magazine. Blued with a checkered walnut stock. Imported by Interarms in 1988 only.

NIB	Exc.	V.G.	Good	Fair	Poor
325	300	275	225	175	100

Model 1500 Trophy

As above, but with more finely figured walnut stocks and checkering. Introduced in 1988.

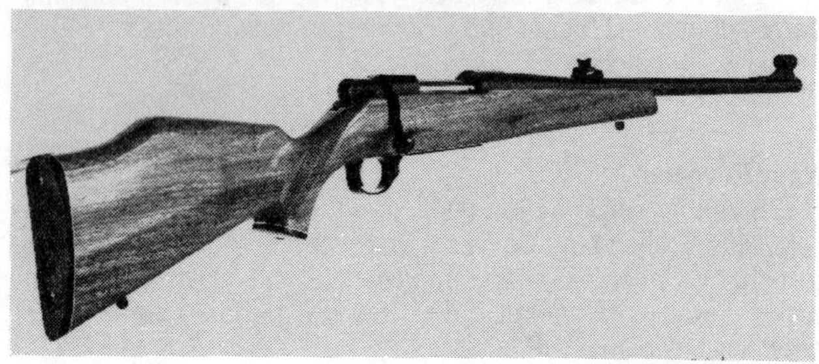

NIB	Exc.	V.G.	Good	Fair	Poor
400	350	300	250	200	150

Model 1500 Varmint

As above, in .22-250 or .223 caliber with a 24" heavy barrel. Introduced in 1988.

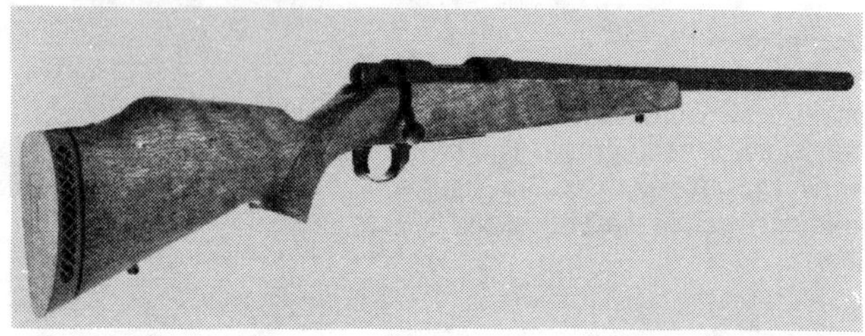

NIB	Exc.	V.G.	Good	Fair	Poor
425	375	325	275	200	150

Model 1500 Lightning

As above, in .270, 7mm Remington Magnum, and .30-06 caliber with a composition stock. Introduced in 1988.

NIB	Exc.	V.G.	Good	Fair	Poor
500	450	400	350	250	175

Realtree Camo Rifle

Introduced in 1993 this bolt action model features a composite stock, a 22" barrel. Both the metal and stock finish are a brown leaf pattern. The receiver is a mono-block system. The floorplate is hinged and the magazine holds 5 rounds. The receiver is drilled and tapped for scope mounts. Fitted with a sling swivel and recoil pad. Offered in .30-06 and .270 calibers. Weighs 8 lbs.

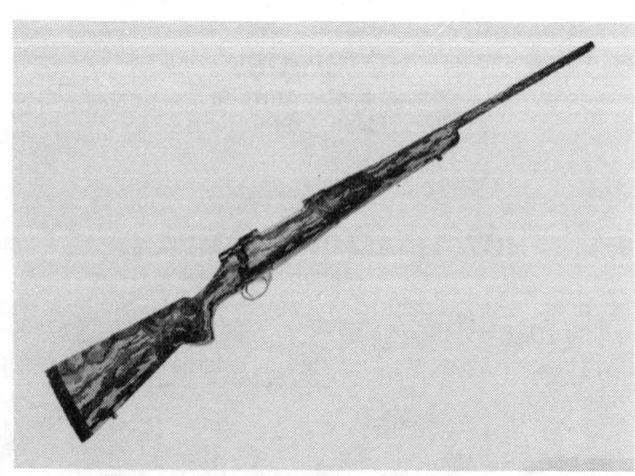

NIB	Exc.	V.G.	Good	Fair	Poor
500	450	400	350	300	200

Lighting Rifle

Introduced in 1993 this model has a black composite checkered stock with Schnabel forend. The butt stock is Monte Carlo. Offered in .223, .22-250, .243, .270, .308, .30-06, 7mm Rem. Mag., .300 and .338 Win. Mag. Weighs about 7.5 lbs.

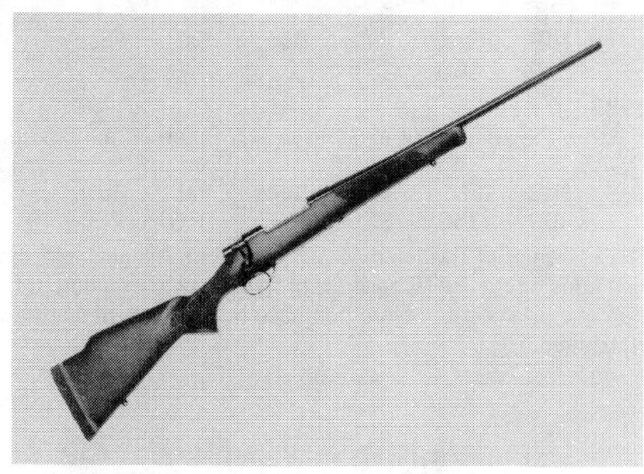

NIB	Exc.	V.G.	Good	Fair	Poor
400	350	300	250	200	125

HOWARD-WHITNEY

New Haven, Connecticut

SEE—Whitney Arms Co.

HUNT

New Haven, Connecticut

SEE—Winchester Repeating Arms Co.

HUNTER ARMS CO.

Fulton, New Tork

SEE—L. C. Smith

HUSQVARNA

Husqvarna, Sweden

Pistols

Lahti

A 9mm caliber semi-automatic pistol with a 5.5" barrel and 8-shot magazine. Designed by Aino Lahti and adopted as the standard Swedish sidearm in 1940.

Exc.	V.G.	Good	Fair	Poor
400	350	275	225	150

Bolt Action Rifles

Hi-Power

A bolt-action sporting rifle manufactured in a variety of calibers with a 24" barrel, open sights and beechwood stock. Manufactured between 1946 and 1951.

Exc.	V.G.	Good	Fair	Poor
350	300	275	200	150

Model 1100 Deluxe

As above, with a walnut stock. Manufactured between 1952 and 1956.

Exc.	V.G.	Good	Fair	Poor
450	400	325	250	200

Model 1000 Super Grade

As above, with a Monte Carlo-style stock. Manufactured between 1952 and 1956.

Exc.	V.G.	Good	Fair	Poor
450	400	325	250	200

Model 3100 Crown Grade
A bolt-action sporting rifle manufactured in a variety of calibers with a 24" barrel, walnut stock with a black composition forend tip and pistol grip cap. Manufactured between 1954 and 1972.

Exc.	V.G.	Good	Fair	Poor
475	425	350	300	250

Model 4100 Lightweight
As above, with a Schnabel forend tip. Manufactured between 1954 and 1972.

Exc.	V.G.	Good	Fair	Poor
475	425	350	300	250

Model 456
As above, with a full length Mannlicher-style stock. Manufactured between 1959 and 1970.

Exc.	V.G.	Good	Fair	Poor
400	350	300	250	200

Model 6000
The Model 4100 with express folding sights and a finely figured walnut stock. Manufactured between 1968 and 1970.

Exc.	V.G.	Good	Fair	Poor
500	400	350	300	200

Model 9000 Crown Grade
A bolt-action sporting rifle manufactured in a variety of calibers with a 23.5" barrel, open sights, adjustable trigger and walnut stock. Manufactured in 1971 and 1972.

Exc.	V.G.	Good	Fair	Poor
475	425	350	300	250

Model 8000 Imperial Grade
As above, with an engraved magazine floor plate, machine jeweled bolt and finely figured walnut stock. Manufactured in 1971 and 1972.

Exc.	V.G.	Good	Fair	Poor
600	550	475	400	300

HY-HUNTER, INC.
Burbank, California

Chicago Cub
A .22 caliber folding trigger double-action revolver with a 2" barrel and 6-shot cylinder.

Exc.	V.G.	Good	Fair	Poor
50	40	30	25	20

Detective
A .22 or .22WMR caliber double-action revolver with a 2.5" barrel and 6-shot cylinder. Blued with plastic grips.

Exc.	V.G.	Good	Fair	Poor
65	50	40	30	25

Frontier Six Shooter
A .22 or .22WMR caliber single action revolver with a 6-shot cylinder.

Exc.	V.G.	Good	Fair	Poor
75	65	50	40	30

Frontier Six Shooter
As above, in .357 Magnum, .44 Magnum or .45 Colt.

Exc.	V.G.	Good	Fair	Poor
125	100	85	75	50

Maxim
A .25 caliber semi-automatic pistol with a 2" barrel and 5-shot magazine.

Exc.	V.G.	Good	Fair	Poor
75	65	50	40	30

Militar
A .22, .32 or .380 caliber double-action semi-automatic pistol with a 4" barrel and 6-shot magazine.

Exc.	V.G.	Good	Fair	Poor
100	80	60	50	40

Stingray
A .25 caliber semi-automatic pistol with a 2.5" barrel and 5-shot magazine.

Exc.	V.G.	Good	Fair	Poor
75	65	50	40	30

Panzer
A .22 caliber semi-automatic pistol with a 4" barrel and 7-shot magazine.

Exc.	V.G.	Good	Fair	Poor
75	65	50	40	30

Stuka
Similar to the above.

Exc.	V.G.	Good	Fair	Poor
75	65	50	40	30

Automatic Derringer
A .22 caliber Over/Under pocket pistol patterned after the Remington Double Derringer.

Exc.	V.G.	Good	Fair	Poor
50	40	30	25	20

Accurate Ace
A .22 caliber Flobert action pistol.

Exc.	V.G.	Good	Fair	Poor
50	40	30	25	20

Favorite
A .22 or .22WMR caliber copy of the Steven's single shot pistol with a 6" barrel and nickle-plated frame.

Exc.	V.G.	Good	Fair	Poor
100	80	70	50	25

Gold Rush Derringer
A .22 caliber spur trigger single shot pistol with a 2.5" barrel.

Exc.	V.G.	Good	Fair	Poor
50	40	30	25	20

Target Model
A .22 or .22WMR bolt-action single shot pistol with a 10" barrel, adjustable sights and walnut grip.

Exc.	V.G.	Good	Fair	Poor
50	40	30	25	20

HYDE & SHATTUCK
Hatfield, Massachusetts

Queen Derringer
A .22 caliber spur trigger single shot pistol with a 2.5" half octagonal barrel. Blued or nickle-plated with walnut grips. The barrel normally marked "Queen", but sometimes "Hyde & Shattuck". Manufactured between 1876 and 1879.

Exc.	V.G.	Good	Fair	Poor
300	250	200	150	100

HYPER
Jenks, Oklahoma

Single Shot Rifle
A custom made falling block action single shot rifle manufactured in a variety of calibers, barrel lengths, barrel types, and stock styles. As these rifles were made to custom order, prospective purchasers should secure a qualified appraisal prior to acquisition. Manufactured until 1984.

Exc.	V.G.	Good	Fair	Poor
2500	2000	1750	1450	1250

I

IAB
Brescia, Italy
Industria Armi Bresciane

Imported by Puccinelli & Co. of San Anselmo, California, and by Sporting Arms International of Indianola, Mississippi.

S-300
A 12 gauge boxlock single barrel trap gun with 30" or 32" barrels having a wide ventilated-rib and walnut trap-style stock.

Exc.	V.G.	Good	Fair	Poor
1500	1250	1000	850	650

C-300 Combo
A 12 gauge Over/Under boxlock double-barrel shotgun with 30" or 32" barrels, single selective trigger, automatic ejectors, trap-style walnut stock, accompanied by two extra single barrels.

Exc.	V.G.	Good	Fair	Poor
2500	2250	1850	1500	1250

C-300 Super Combo
As above, but more finely finished.

Exc.	V.G.	Good	Fair	Poor
3000	2750	2250	1750	1500

IGA
Veranopolis, Brazil
Importer—Stoeger Industries
Hackansack, New Jersey

Single Barrel Shotgun
A 12, 20 or .410 bore single barrel shotgun with an exposed hammer, 28" barrel and hardwood stock.

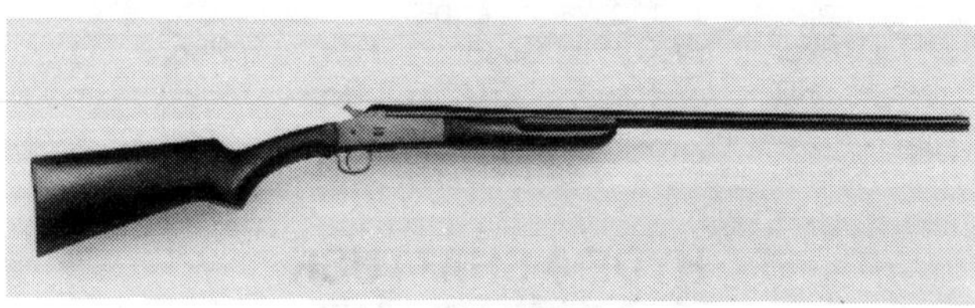

NIB	Exc.	V.G.	Good	Fair	Poor
110	90	75	50	40	30

Single Barrel Shotgun-Youth Model
Offered in 20 gauge and .410 bore this model features a 22" barrel and shorter than standard butt stock. Weighs 5 lbs.

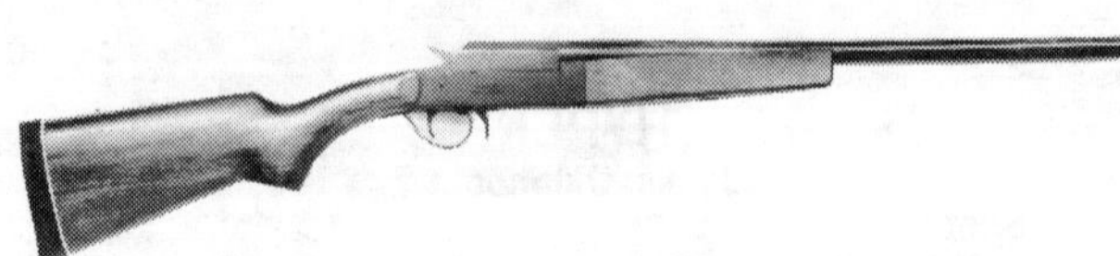

NIB	Exc.	V.G.	Good	Fair	Poor
120	100	80	60	50	35

Coach Gun
A 12 or 20 gauge boxlock double-barrel shotgun with 20" barrels, double triggers and extractors. Blued with a hardwood stock.

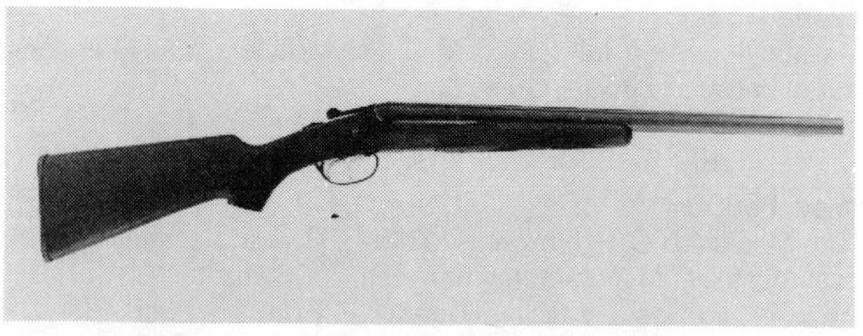

NIB	Exc.	V.G.	Good	Fair	Poor
285	225	175	150	100	75

Standard Side x Side-Uplander Model
Offered in 12, 20, 28 gauge, and .410 bore with 26" and 28" barrels. Checkered hardwood stock with pistol grip or straight grip in 20 gauge only. Weighs 6.75 lbs.

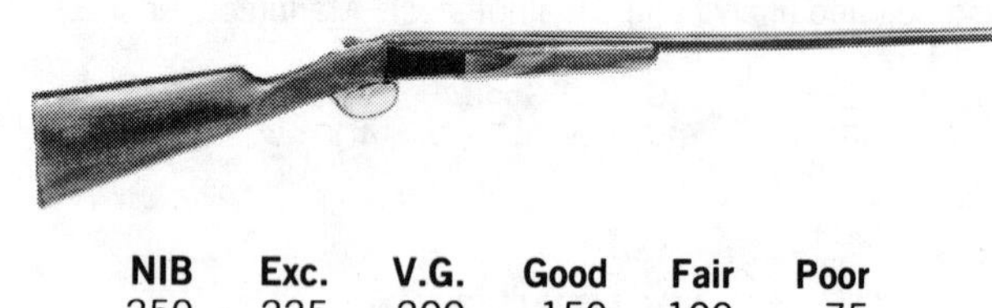

NIB	Exc.	V.G.	Good	Fair	Poor
250	225	200	150	100	75

Standard O/U-Condor I
This model is offered in 12 or 20 gauge with 26" or 28" barrels. Fitted with extractors and single trigger. Choke tubes are standard. Checkered hardwood stock with pistol grip and recoil pad. Weighs 8 lbs.

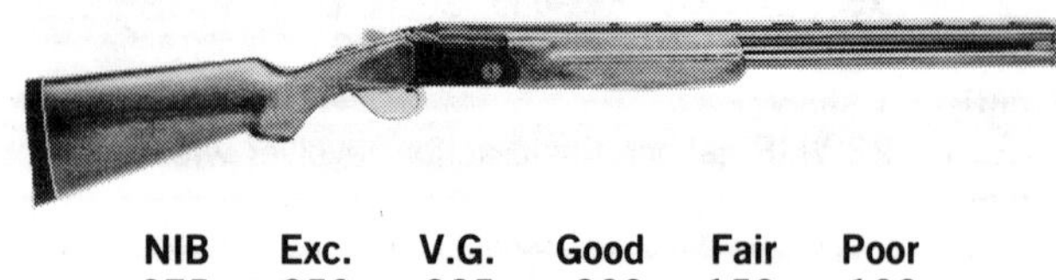

NIB	Exc.	V.G.	Good	Fair	Poor
275	250	225	200	150	100

Condor II
Same as above but with double triggers and plastic butt plate.

NIB	Exc.	V.G.	Good	Fair	Poor
275	225	200	150	100	75

Deluxe O/U-ERA 2000
Offered in 12 gauge only with 26" or 28" barrels. Fitted with single trigger and extractors. Choke tubes are standard. Barrels are chrome lined and stock is hand checkered.

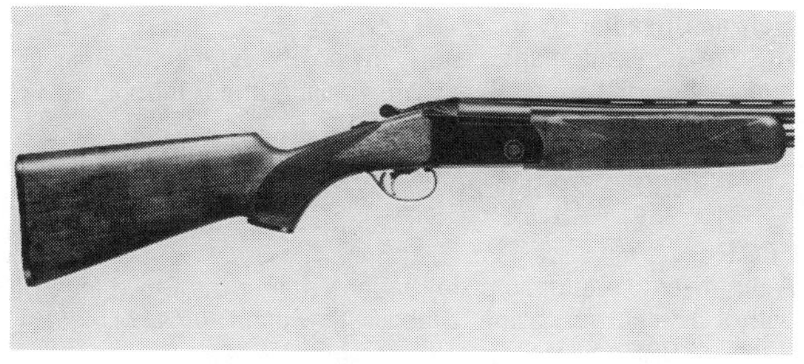

NIB	Exc.	V.G.	Good	Fair	Poor
375	325	275	225	175	125

I.G.I.
Zingone de Tressano, Italy
Italguns International

Domino SP602

A .22 caliber semi-automatic target pistol with a 6" barrel and 5-shot magazine (which is inserted into the action from the top), adjustable trigger and customized grips.

Exc.	V.G.	Good	Fair	Poor
800	700	600	450	350

Domino OP601

As above, but in .22 short caliber.

Exc.	V.G.	Good	Fair	Poor
800	700	600	450	350

INDIAN ARMS CORP.
Detroit, Michigan

Indian Arms .380

A .380 caliber semi-automatic pistol with a 3.25" barrel and 6-shot magazine. Made of stainless steel and finished either in the white or blued with walnut grips. Manufactured from 1975 to 1977.

Exc.	V.G.	Good	Fair	Poor
375	325	275	175	100

INGLIS, JOHN & COMPANY
Toronto, Canada

This firm manufactured Browning Pattern 35 semi-automatic pistols for both the Canadian and Chinese governments.

Chinese Contract Pattern .35

A 9mm semi-automatic pistol with a 5" barrel and 13-shot magazine. Black annodized finish with black plastic grips, sliding tangent rearsight and the rear of the grip slotted for a shoulder stock. Manufactured in 1944 and 1945.

Wooden Shoulder Stock—Add $200.

Exc.	V.G.	Good	Fair	Poor
1750	1500	1250	800	700

Note: Pistols of this type have been imported in large quantities and are available at low cost. The values listed above, however, are for examples not stamped with an importer's tradename or trademark.

Canadian Military

Mk. 1 No. 1

Identical to the Chinese contract but with all markings in English.

Wooden Shoulder Stock—Add $200.

Exc.	V.G.	Good	Fair	Poor
1200	1000	800	600	450

Mk. 1 No. 2

As above, with a fixed rear sight and the grip strap not slotted for a shoulder stock.

Exc.	V.G.	Good	Fair	Poor
600	500	450	350	250

Mk. 1 No. 2

As above, with the grip strap slotted for a shoulder stock. As this variation can be made from a standard Mk. 1 No. 2, caution is advised prior to purchase.

Exc.	V.G.	Good	Fair	Poor
1200	1000	800	600	450

INDUSTRIA ARMI GALESI
Brescia, Italy
SEE—Galesi

INGRAM
Atlanta, Georgia
Military Armament Corp.

MAC 10

A 9mm or .45 caliber semi-automatic pistol with a 5.75" barrel and 32-shot magazine. Annodized with plastic grips.

Accesory Kit (Barrel Extension and Extra Magazine)—Add 20%.

Exc.	V.G.	Good	Fair	Poor
800	700	600	500	400

MAC 10A1

As above, but firing from a closed bolt.

Accessory Kit—Add 20%.

Exc.	V.G.	Good	Fair	Poor
400	350	300	250	150

MAC 11

As above, but in .380 caliber.

Accessory Kit—Add 20%.

Exc.	V.G.	Good	Fair	Poor
700	600	500	400	300

INTERARMS
Alexandria, Virginia

An importer of arms made by Howa Machine, Star, Walther, and Rossi.

Rifles

Mark X Viscount

Bolt-action sporting rifle made in a variety of calibers with a 24" barrel, open sights, adjustable trigger and magazine holding either 3 or 5 cartridges. Manufactured in Yugoslavia. Blued with a walnut stock.

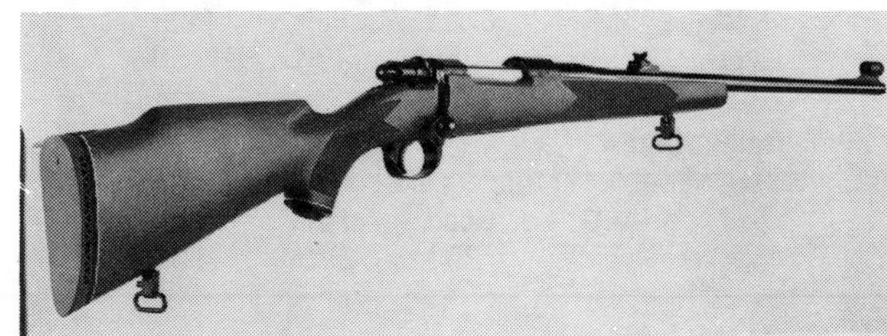

NIB	Exc.	V.G.	Good	Fair	Poor
350	300	250	200	175	125

Mark X Lightweight

As above, with a 20" barrel and composition stock. Introduced in 1988.

NIB	Exc.	V.G.	Good	Fair	Poor
350	300	250	200	175	125

Mini Mark X

As above, with a short action in .223 caliber only with a 20" barrel, open sights, adjustable trigger and 5-shot magazine. Introduced in 1987.

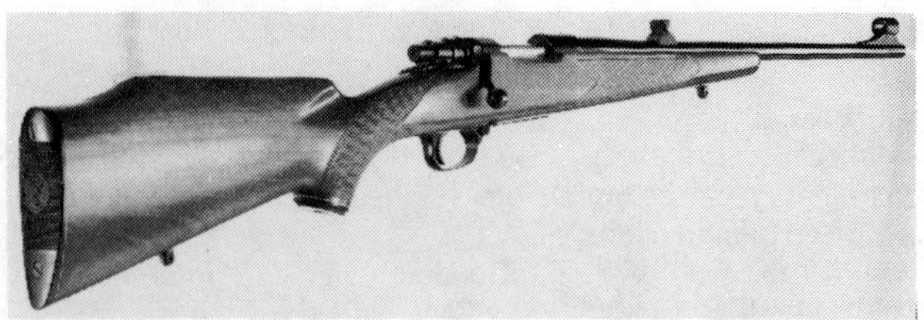

NIB	Exc.	V.G.	Good	Fair	Poor
350	300	250	200	175	125

Mark X American Field
As above, with a finely figured walnut stock, ebony forend tip, pistol grip cap, sling swivels and recoil pad. Introduced in 1984.

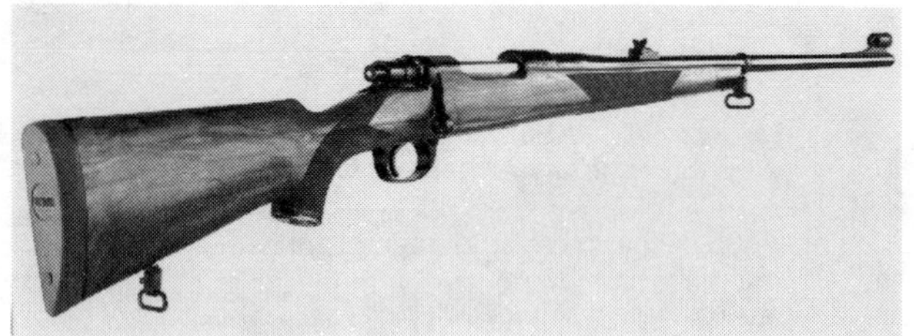

NIB	Exc.	V.G.	Good	Fair	Poor
450	400	350	300	250	175

Whitworth Express Rifle
A .375 Holland & Holland or .458 Winchester Magnum bolt action sporting rifle with a 24" barrel, express sights and 3-shot magazine. Blued with a walnut stock. Introduced in 1974.

NIB	Exc.	V.G.	Good	Fair	Poor
550	500	450	350	250	200

Whitworth Mannlicher Carbine
A .243, .270, .7x57mm, .308, and the .30-06 caliber bolt-action rifle with a 20" barrel, open sights, sling swivels and a full length stock. Manufactured between 1984 and 1987.

Exc.	V.G.	Good	Fair	Poor
450	400	350	250	200

Cavalier
A bolt-action sporting rifle made in a variety of calibers with a modern styled stock having a rollover cheekpiece. Discontinued.

Exc.	V.G.	Good	Fair	Poor
325	275	250	200	150

Mannlicher Carbine
As above, with a 20" barrel and full length stock. Discontinued.

Exc.	V.G.	Good	Fair	Poor
325	275	250	200	150

Continental Carbine
As above, with double set triggers. Discontinued.

Exc.	V.G.	Good	Fair	Poor
350	300	250	200	150

Alaskan Model
Similar to the Mark X, in .375 Holland & Holland or .458 Winchester Magnum with a 24" barrel. Discontinued in 1985.

Exc.	V.G.	Good	Fair	Poor
450	400	350	300	200

22-ATD
A .22 caliber semi-automatic rifle with a 19.4" barrel, open sights and 11-shot magazine. Blued with a hardwood stock. Manufactured by Norinco. Introduced in 1987.

NIB	Exc.	V.G.	Good	Fair	Poor
125	100	80	60	50	40

Helwan Brigadier
A 9mm semi-automatic pistol with a 4.5" barrel, fixed sights and 8-shot magazine. Blued with plastic grips. Introduced in 1988.

NIB	Exc.	V.G.	Good	Fair	Poor
260	225	200	175	125	100

FEG R-9
A 9mm semi-automatic pistol patterned after the Browning 35 with a 13-shot magazine. Blued with walnut grips. Manufactured in 1986 and 1987.

Exc.	V.G.	Good	Fair	Poor
275	225	185	145	100

FEG PPH
A .380 caliber double action semi-automatic pistol with a 3.5" barrel and 6-shot magazine. Blued with plastic grips.

Exc.	V.G.	Good	Fair	Poor
200	175	150	125	100

Virginian Dragoon
A .44 Magnum single action revolver with a 6", 7.5", 8.75" or 12" barrel, adjustable sights and 6-shot cylinder. Originally made in Switzerland and then in the U.S.A. Discontinued in 1984.

Exc.	V.G.	Good	Fair	Poor
200	150	125	100	75

Stainless Dragoon
As above, in stainless-steel.

Exc.	V.G.	Good	Fair	Poor
225	175	150	125	100

Virginian .22 Convertible
As above, in .22 caliber with a 5.5" barrel.

Exc.	V.G.	Good	Fair	Poor
175	150	125	100	75

Virginian Stainless .22 Convertible
As above, in stainless-steel.

Exc.	V.G.	Good	Fair	Poor
200	175	150	100	80

Mauser Parabellum Karabiner
A 9mm caliber semi-automatic carbine with an 11.75" barrel and detachable shoulder stock. Fitted in a leather case. Only 100 were imported into the United States and this arm is subject to BATF registration.

NIB	Exc.	V.G.	Good	Fair	Poor
6500	5750	5000	4000	3000	2250

Mauser Parabellum Cartridge Counter
A reproduction of the cartridge counter Luger. Fitted in a leather case with only 100 units imported into the United States.

NIB	Exc.	V.G.	Good	Fair	Poor
3600	3000	2500	2000	1500	1000

INTERDYNAMICS OF AMERICA
Miami, Florida

KG-9
A 9mm caliber semi-automatic pistol with a 3" barrel and 36-shot magazine. Manufactured from 1981 and 1983.

Exc.	V.G.	Good	Fair	Poor
700	625	575	500	400

KG-99
As above, with a barrel shroud. Manufactured from 1981 and 1984.

Exc.	V.G.	Good	Fair	Poor
275	225	175	125	100

KG-99 Stainless
As above, in stainless-steel. Manufactured in 1984.

Exc.	V.G.	Good	Fair	Poor
325	275	225	150	125

KG-99M
A more compact version of the above. Manufactured in 1984.

Exc.	V.G.	Good	Fair	Poor
210	185	165	145	100

INTRATEC USA, INC.
Miami, Florida

TEC-9
A 9mm caliber semi-automatic pistol with a 5" shrouded barrel and 36-shot magazine. Introduced in 1985.

NIB	Exc.	V.G.	Good	Fair	Poor
225	200	175	150	125	100

TEC-9C
As above, with a 16" barrel and a folding stock. Manufactured in 1987.

Exc.	V.G.	Good	Fair	Poor
250	225	200	150	100

TEC-9M
As above, with a 3" barrel and 20-shot magazine. Also made in stainless-steel.

NIB	Exc.	V.G.	Good	Fair	Poor
250	200	175	150	100	75

TEC-22 "Scorpion"
Similar to the above, but in .22 caliber with a 4" barrel and 30-shot magazine.

NIB	Exc.	V.G.	Good	Fair	Poor
175	150	125	100	75	50

TEC-38
A .38 caliber Over/Under double-action derringer with 3" barrels. Manufactured between 1986 and 1988.

Exc.	V.G.	Good	Fair	Poor
125	100	80	65	45

IRVING, W.
New York, New York

Single Shot Derringer
A .22 caliber spur trigger single shot pistol with a 2.75" half octagonal barrel. Silver plated brass frame, blued barrel and rosewood grips. The barrel marked "W. Irving". Manufactured in the 1860s.

The .32 caliber variation has a 3" barrel and is worth approximately 40% more than the values listed below.

Exc.	V.G.	Good	Fair	Poor
500	400	300	200	125

Pocket Revolver

1st Model
A .31 caliber spur trigger percussion revolver with a 3" octagonal barrel, 6-shot cylinder and brass frame. The barrel marked "W. Irving". Approximately 50 were made between 1858 and 1862.

Exc.	V.G.	Good	Fair	Poor
700	600	500	350	250

2nd Model
A .31 caliber percussion revolver with a 4.5" round barrel, loading lever and either brass or iron frame. The barrel marked "Address W.Irving. 20 Cliff St. N.Y." Approximately 600 manufactured with a brass frame and 1500 with a frame of iron. The brass-frame version will bring a premium of about 35 percent.

Exc.	V.G.	Good	Fair	Poor
550	500	400	300	200

IRWINDALE ARMS, INC.
Irwindale, California
SEE—AMT

ISRAELI MILITARY INDUSTRIES
Israel

Civilian firearms manufactured by this firm are retailed by Action Arms Limited and Magnum Research.

ITHACA GUN CO.
Ithaca, New York

Established in 1883 by William H. Baker as the WH Baker & Company Gunworks, the company was renamed in 1889 after Baker's death.

Crass Model
A 10 or 12 gauge exposed hammer Damascus barrelled shot-

gun with double triggers, extractors and a walnut stock. Approximately 77,000 manufactured between 1893 and 1903.

Exc.	V.G.	Good	Fair	Poor
750	675	600	500	350

Lewis Model

An improved version of the above, manufactured until 1906.

Exc.	V.G.	Good	Fair	Poor
750	675	600	500	350

Marien Model

An improved version of the above, manufactured between 1906 and 1908.

Exc.	V.G.	Good	Fair	Poor
750	675	600	500	350

Flues Model

Similar to the above. Manufactured from 1908 to 1926.

Exc.	V.G.	Good	Fair	Poor
700	550	500	450	350

Hammerless Double

*A 10, 12, 16, 20 or .410 bore boxlock double-barrel shotgun with 26", 28", 30" or 32" barrels, double triggers and extractors. Also available with a variety of options as listed below:
Non-selective Single Trigger—Add $150
Single selective Trigger—Add $200
Ventilated-Rib—Add $200
Vent-Rib, High-grade Models—Add $350
Automatic Ejectors—Add 35%.
Beavertail Forearm—Add $175.

Those arms manufactured prior to 1925 are not considered safe to fire with modern ammunition.

The values listed below are for 12- and 16-gauge guns.

20-gauge guns are worth approximately 20 percent additional.

10-gauge, 20-gauge, and .410 guns are worth approximately 100 percent additional.

Field Grade

Exc.	V.G.	Good	Fair	Poor
1000	850	650	450	250

Grade No. 2

Exc.	V.G.	Good	Fair	Poor
1500	1250	950	650	350

Grade No. 3

Exc.	V.G.	Good	Fair	Poor
1750	1500	1000	650	350

28-gauge and .410 bore models are extremely rare in the following configurations. Prospective purchasers should secure a qualified appraisal prior to acquisition.

Grade No. 4E—Auto Ejectors

Exc.	V.G.	Good	Fair	Poor
3250	2750	2000	1250	550

Grade No. 5E—Auto Ejectors

Exc.	V.G.	Good	Fair	Poor
4000	3250	2500	1500	750

Grade No. 6E—Auto Ejectors

Exc.	V.G.	Good	Fair	Poor
4750	4000	3000	1750	900

Grade No. 7E—Auto Ejectors

Exc.	V.G.	Good	Fair	Poor
9500	8000	5500	3500	1850

$1,000 Grade

Similar to the Model 7E Grade, but more finely finished. Manufactured before WWII. Prospective purchasers should secure a qualified appraisal prior to acquisition.

Exc.	V.G.	Good	Fair	Poor
12500	10000	7000	4000	2500

$2,000 Grade

An even finer finished shotgun. Prospective purchasers should secure a qualified appraisal prior to acquisition.

Exc.	V.G.	Good	Fair	Poor
12500	10000	7000	4000	2500

Sousa Grade

Ithaca's finest shotgun of which only 11 were made. Prospective purchasers should secure a qualified appraisal prior to acquisition.

Single Barrel Trap Guns

A 12 gauge boxlock single barrel shotgun with 30", 32" or 34" ventilated-rib barrels and automatic ejector. Produced in a variety of grades. Examples made prior to 1921 have serial numbers under 400,000 and are known as Flues Models. Prospective purchasers should secure a qualified appraisal prior to acquisition.

Victory Grade

Exc.	V.G.	Good	Fair	Poor
1000	800	675	500	400

Knick Model

Exc.	V.G.	Good	Fair	Poor
1400	1100	850	650	550

No. 4E

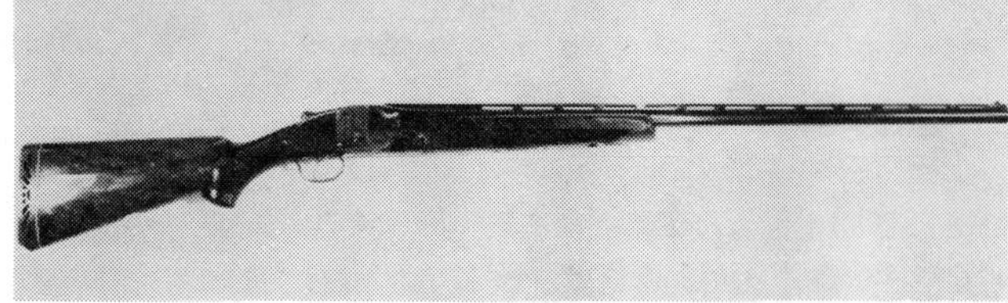

Exc.	V.G.	Good	Fair	Poor
1500	1000	850	750	650

No. 7E

Exc.	V.G.	Good	Fair	Poor
4000	3050	2500	2000	1600

$5,000 Grade

Exc.	V.G.	Good	Fair	Poor
9500	8250	6750	5500	4750

Sousa Grade

Prospective purchasers should secure a qualified appraisal prior to acquisition.

Century Grade Trap

A 12 gauge boxlock single barrel shotgun with a 32" or 34" ventilated-rib barrel and automatic ejector. Blued with a walnut stock. Manufactured by SKB during the 1970s.

Exc.	V.G.	Good	Fair	Poor
600	500	450	350	300

Century II

As above, with a Monte Carlo-style stock.

Exc.	V.G.	Good	Fair	Poor
650	550	500	400	350

5E Grade

A 12 gauge boxlock single barrel shotgun with 32" or 34" ventilated-rib barrels, engraved action and finely figured walnut stock. Manufactured between 1925 and 1986. Production was resumed in 1988.

NIB	Exc.	V.G.	Good	Fair	Poor
7500	3500	2500	2000	1750	1450

Dollar Grade

As above, but built only on custom order. Production was resumed in 1988.

NIB	Exc.	V.G.	Good	Fair	Poor
10000	6000	5000	4250	3250	2500

Model 66

A 20 or .410 bore single shot shotgun with a 24" barrel. Blued with a walnut stock. Manufactured from 1963 to 1978.

Exc.	V.G.	Good	Fair	Poor
125	100	75	50	25

Model 66 RS
As above, in 20 gauge with a 22" barrel fitted with rifle sights.

Exc.	V.G.	Good	Fair	Poor
150	125	100	75	50

Model 37 Featherlight
A 12, 16, or 20 gauge slide action shotgun with a 26", 28" or 30" barrel and 4-shot magazine. Blued with a walnut stock. Originally made from 1937 to 1986 and reintroduced by Ithaca as the Model 87.

Exc.	V.G.	Good	Fair	Poor
275	250	200	150	100

Model 37V—Vent-Rib

Exc.	V.G.	Good	Fair	Poor
325	300	250	200	150

Model 37D—Deluxe

Exc.	V.G.	Good	Fair	Poor
350	325	275	225	175

Model 37DV—Deluxe, Vent-Rib

Exc.	V.G.	Good	Fair	Poor
400	350	300	250	200

Model 37 Magnum—3" Chamber

Exc.	V.G.	Good	Fair	Poor
325	300	250	200	150

Model 37 Ultralite—English Stock

Exc.	V.G.	Good	Fair	Poor
350	300	250	225	175

Model 37 Bicentennial
A commemorative version of the Model 37 in 12 gauge. Engraved and fitted in a case together with a pewter belt buckle. A total of 1,776 were made in 1976.

NIB	Exc.	V.G.	Good	Fair	Poor
400	350	300	250	200	125

Model 37 Ducks Unlimited Commemorative

NIB	Exc.	V.G.	Good	Fair	Poor
375	300	250	200	175	100

Model 37 2500 Series Centennial
A commemorative Model 37 12 gauge shotgun with silver-plated parts. Manufactured between 1980 and 1984.

NIB	Exc.	V.G.	Good	Fair	Poor
600	550	500	400	300	175

Model 37 $1,000 Grade
The Model 37 with an engraved receiver, gold inlays and a well-figured walnut stock. Manufactured between 1937 and 1940.

Exc.	V.G.	Good	Fair	Poor
6000	5000	4000	3000	2250

Model 37 $5,000 Grade
As above, but more extensively engraved and gold inlaid. Manufactured from 1947 to 1967.

Exc.	V.G.	Good	Fair	Poor
5500	4500	3500	2500	2000

Model 87 Magnum
A 12 or 20 gauge Magnum slide action shotgun with a 25" barrel fitted with screw-in choke tubes, ventilated-rib which is similar to the Model 37. Blued with a walnut stock.

NIB	Exc.	V.G.	Good	Fair	Poor
300	250	200	175	125	100

The Model 87 was manufactured in the following styles as of 1989:

Model 87 Field Grade—Economy Model

NIB	Exc.	V.G.	Good	Fair	Poor
300	250	200	175	125	100

Model 87 Camo

NIB	Exc.	V.G.	Good	Fair	Poor
400	350	350	250	200	150

Model 87 Turkey Gun

NIB	Exc.	V.G.	Good	Fair	Poor
250	200	175	125	100	75

Model 87 Deluxe

NIB	Exc.	V.G.	Good	Fair	Poor
400	350	300	250	200	150

Model 87 Ultralite

NIB	Exc.	V.G.	Good	Fair	Poor
300	250	200	175	125	100

Model 87 Ultralite Deluxe

NIB	Exc.	V.G.	Good	Fair	Poor
400	350	300	250	200	150

Model 87 Supreme Grade

NIB	Exc.	V.G.	Good	Fair	Poor
700	600	500	400	300	200

Model 87 Deerslayer

NIB	Exc.	V.G.	Good	Fair	Poor
250	200	175	125	100	75

Model 87 Deluxe Deerslayer

NIB	Exc.	V.G.	Good	Fair	Poor
350	300	250	200	175	150

Monte Carlo Deerslayer II

NIB	Exc.	V.G.	Good	Fair	Poor
450	400	350	300	200	175

Model 87 Military & Police

NIB	Exc.	V.G.	Good	Fair	Poor
250	200	175	125	100	75

Model 51 Series
A 12 or 20 gauge semi-automatic shotgun with 26", 28" or 30" ventilated-rib barrels. Blued with a walnut stock. Manufactured from 1970 to 1985 as follows:

Model 51A Standard—Plain Barrel
Vent-Rib—Add $100.

Exc.	V.G.	Good	Fair	Poor
275	225	200	150	100

Model 51A Magnum—3" Chamber
Vent-Rib—Add $100.

Exc.	V.G.	Good	Fair	Poor
300	250	225	175	125

Model 51A Waterfowler—Matte Finished

Exc.	V.G.	Good	Fair	Poor
425	375	325	250	175

Model 51A Deerslayer

Exc.	V.G.	Good	Fair	Poor
325	275	225	150	100

Model 51A Turkey Gun

Exc.	V.G.	Good	Fair	Poor
325	275	225	150	100

Model 51A Supreme Trap

Exc.	V.G.	Good	Fair	Poor
425	375	325	250	175

Model 51A Supreme Skeet

Exc.	V.G.	Good	Fair	Poor
450	400	350	275	200

Model 51 Ducks Unlimited Commemorative

NIB	Exc.	V.G.	Good	Fair	Poor
475	400	375	325	275	200

Model 51 Presentation—Engraved Receiver

NIB	Exc.	V.G.	Good	Fair	Poor
1500	1250	1000	750	500	300

Mag-10 Series
A 10 gauge Magnum semi-automatic shotgun manufactured in a variety of barrel lengths, styles and finishes. Manufactured from 1975 to 1986 in as follows:

Standard Grade

Exc.	V.G.	Good	Fair	Poor
750	700	650	500	400

Standard Vent-Rib Grade

Exc.	V.G.	Good	Fair	Poor
850	775	700	550	450

Deluxe Vent-Rib Grade

Exc.	V.G.	Good	Fair	Poor
1000	850	775	600	500

Supreme Grade

Exc.	V.G.	Good	Fair	Poor
1200	1050	850	700	600

Roadblocker—Military and Police Model

Exc.	V.G.	Good	Fair	Poor
650	575	500	400	300

Presentation Grade—Engraved, Gold-Inlaid, 200 Made

NIB	Exc.	V.G.	Good	Fair	Poor
1875	1500	1100	900	750	600

National Wild Turkey Federation—1985 Manufacture

NIB	Exc.	V.G.	Good	Fair	Poor
850	700	600	550	450	350

Shotguns manufactured by Perazzi and Japanese firms which were marketed by Ithaca are listed under the respective manufacturer's name.

Model X5-C

A .22 caliber semi-automatic rifle with a 7-shot magazine. Blued with a walnut stock. Manufactured between 1958 and 1964.

Exc.	V.G.	Good	Fair	Poor
100	80	70	60	45

Model X-15

Similar to the above, but manufactured between 1964 and 1967.

Exc.	V.G.	Good	Fair	Poor
100	80	70	60	45

Model 49 Saddlegun

A .22 caliber lever action single shot rifle with an 18.5" barrel, fixed sights, alloy receiver and hardwood stock. Manufactured between 1961 and 1978.

Exc.	V.G.	Good	Fair	Poor
125	100	70	60	45

Model 72 Saddlegun

A .22 or .22 Magnum caliber lever action rifle with an 18.5" barrel, tubular magazine, open sights and walnut stock. Made by Erma in Germany between 1973 and 1978.

Exc.	V.G.	Good	Fair	Poor
275	225	175	125	75

LSA-55 or 65 Series

A bolt action sporting rifle manufactured in a variety of calibers and barrel lengths by Tikka of Finland. Imported between 1969 and 1977 in the following models:

LSA-55 Standard

Exc.	V.G.	Good	Fair	Poor
400	350	300	250	175

LSA-55 Deluxe

Exc.	V.G.	Good	Fair	Poor
425	375	325	275	200

LSA-55 Varmint—Heavy Barrel

Exc.	V.G.	Good	Fair	Poor
450	400	350	300	225

LSA-65—Long Action

Exc.	V.G.	Good	Fair	Poor
400	350	300	250	175

LSA-65 Deluxe

Exc.	V.G.	Good	Fair	Poor
425	375	325	275	200

LSA-55 Turkey Gun

A 12 gauge by .22 Remington caliber Over/Under combination rifle/shotgun with 24.5" barrels, double triggers, exposed hammer and walnut stock. Manufactured in Finland by Tikka between 1970 and 1981.

Exc.	V.G.	Good	Fair	Poor
600	525	450	350	275

X-Caliber

A .22 to .44 Magnum caliber single shot pistol with 10" or 15" barrels featuring a dual firing pin system so that interchangeable barrels could be used. The Model 20 blued, the Model 30 teflon coated. Introduced in 1988.

NIB	Exc.	V.G.	Good	Fair	Poor
275	225	200	175	145	100

IVER JOHNSON ARMS, INC.

Middlesex, New Jersey
ALSO SEE—AMAC

Established in 1883 in Fitchburg, Massachussets, this company has produced a wide variety of firearms during its existance.

Tradename Revolvers

A series of spur trigger revolvers were made by Iver Johnson bearing only the tradenames such as those that follow: Encore, Eclipse, Favorite, Tycoon, and Eagle. In general, the value for these revolvers is as follows:

Exc.	V.G.	Good	Fair	Poor
125	100	75	50	25

Safety Automatic Double Action

A .22, .32CF or .38CF caliber double-action revolver produced in a variety of barrel lengths with or without exposed hammers. Manufactured between 1893 and 1950.

Exc.	V.G.	Good	Fair	Poor
150	125	100	75	50

Model 1900

A .22 to .38 caliber double-action revolver with a 2.5", 4.5" or 6" barrel. Blued or nickle-plated with rubber grips and no cartridge ejecting system. Manufactured between 1900 and 1947.

Exc.	V.G.	Good	Fair	Poor
150	125	100	75	50

Safety Cycle Automatic

Similar to the Safety Automatic with a 2" barrel.

Exc.	V.G.	Good	Fair	Poor
150	125	100	75	50

Petite

A .22 short caliber double-action folding trigger revolver with a 1" barrel and 7-shot cylinder. Nickle-plated with rubber grips. Introduced in 1909.

Exc.	V.G.	Good	Fair	Poor
250	200	175	125	75

Supershot Sealed 8

A .22 caliber double-action revolver with a 6" barrel and counter bored 8-shot cylinder. Blued with rubber grips. Manufactured from 1919 to 1957.

Exc.	V.G.	Good	Fair	Poor
150	125	100	50	25

Protector Sealed 8

As above, with a 2.5" barrel.

Exc.	V.G.	Good	Fair	Poor
150	125	100	50	25

Supershot 9

Similar to the Supershot Sealed 8 with a 9-shot uncounter bored cylinder. Manufactured between 1929 and 1949.

Exc.	V.G.	Good	Fair	Poor
150	125	100	50	25

Trigger Cocker Single Action

A .22 caliber single action revolver with a 6" barrel and 8-shot counter bored cylinder. Blued with walnut grips. Manufactured between 1940 and 1947.

Exc.	V.G.	Good	Fair	Poor
150	125	100	50	25

.22 Target Single Action
As above, with adjustable sights and adjustable grips. Manufactured between 1938 and 1948.

Exc.	V.G.	Good	Fair	Poor
150	125	100	75	50

Model 844
A .22 caliber double-action revolver with a 4.5" or 6" barrel, adjustable sights and an 8-shot cylinder. Manufactured in the 1950s.

Exc.	V.G.	Good	Fair	Poor
125	100	75	50	25

Model 855
As above, but single action with a 6" barrel. Manufactured in the 1950s.

Exc.	V.G.	Good	Fair	Poor
125	100	75	50	25

Model 55A Sportsmen Target
A .22 caliber single action revolver with a 4.75" or 6" barrel, fixed sights and 8-shot cylinder. Blued with walnut grips.

Exc.	V.G.	Good	Fair	Poor
100	75	65	50	25

Model 55S-A Cadet
A .22 to .38 caliber single action revolver with a 2.5" barrel and fixed sights. Blued with plastic grips. Introduced in 1955.

Exc.	V.G.	Good	Fair	Poor
100	75	65	50	25

Model 57A Target
As above, with a 4.5" or 6" barrel and adjustable sights. Manufactured between 1955 and 1975.

Exc.	V.G.	Good	Fair	Poor
100	75	65	50	25

Model 66 Trailsman
A .22 caliber double-action revolver with a 6" barrel, adjustable sights and 8-shot cylinder. Blued with walnut grips. Manufactured between 1958 and 1975.

Exc.	V.G.	Good	Fair	Poor
100	75	65	50	25

Model 67 Viking
As above, with a safety hammer.

Exc.	V.G.	Good	Fair	Poor
100	75	65	50	25

Model 50
A .22 or .22 Magnum single action revolver with a 4.75" or 6" barrel, 8-shot cylinder and either fixed or adjustable sights. Also known as the Sidewinder. Manufactured between 1961 and 1975.

Exc.	V.G.	Good	Fair	Poor
100	75	65	50	25

American Bulldog
A .22 to .38 caliber double-action revolver with a 2.5" or 4" barrel and adjustable sights. Blued or nickle-plated with plastic grips. Manufactured between 1974 and 1976.

Exc.	V.G.	Good	Fair	Poor
125	100	75	50	25

Rookie
A .38 caliber revolver with a 4" barrel and 5-shot cylinder. Blued or nickle-plated with plastic grips.

Exc.	V.G.	Good	Fair	Poor
125	100	75	50	25

Cattleman Series
Manufactured by Aldo Uberti and listed under that name in this book.

Model X300 Pony
A .380 semi-automatic pistol with a 3" barrel and 6-shot magazine. Blued with plastic grips. Introduced in 1975.

Exc.	V.G.	Good	Fair	Poor
175	150	125	100	75

Trailsman
A .22 caliber semi-automatic pistol with a 4.5" or 6" barrel and 10-shot magazine. Blued with plastic or walnut grips.

Exc.	V.G.	Good	Fair	Poor
175	150	125	100	75

TP Pistol
A .22 or .25ACP caliber double-action semi-automatic pistol with a 2.8" barrel and 7-shot magazine. Blued or nickle-plated with plastic grips.

Exc.	V.G.	Good	Fair	Poor
195	150	125	100	75

Champion
A single barrel shotgun manufactured in a variety of gauges as well as .44 or .45 caliber with 26" to 32" barrels, external hammers and automatic ejectors. Blued with a walnut stock. Manufactured between 1909 and 1956.

Exc.	V.G.	Good	Fair	Poor
125	100	75	50	25

Matted Rib Grade
As above, in 12, 16 or 20 gauge with a matte-rib barrel. Manufactured between 1909 and 1948.

Exc.	V.G.	Good	Fair	Poor
150	125	100	75	50

Trap Grade
As above, in 12 gauge with a 32" ventilated-rib barrel. Manufactured between 1909 and 1942.

Exc.	V.G.	Good	Fair	Poor
275	225	175	125	100

Hercules Grade
A boxlock double-barrel shotgun manufactured in a variety of gauges with 26" to 32" barrels, double triggers and extractors. Blued with a walnut stock.
Automatic Ejectors—Add 15%.
Single Selective Trigger—Add 15%.

Exc.	V.G.	Good	Fair	Poor
550	450	375	300	250

Skeeter Model
As above, but more finely finished. Discontinued in 1946.

Exc.	V.G.	Good	Fair	Poor
1100	950	700	500	375

Super Trap
A 12 gauge boxlock single barrel shotgun with a 32" barrel, and extractors. Discontinued in 1942.

Exc.	V.G.	Good	Fair	Poor
1100	950	700	500	375

Silver Shadow
A 12 gauge boxlock Over/Under shotgun with a 26" or 28" ventilated-rib barrels, double triggers and extractors. Blued with a walnut stock. Also available with a single trigger which would increase the values listed below by approximately 25%. Manufactured in Italy and imported by Iver Johnson.

Exc.	V.G.	Good	Fair	Poor
350	300	275	200	150

IXL

New York, New York

Pocket Revolver

A .31 caliber double-action percussion revolver with a 4" octagonal barrel and 6-shot cylinder. Blued with walnut grips. The barrel marked "IXL N.York." Approximately 750 were made without hammer spurs and 150 with side mounted hammers during the 1850s.

Exc.	V.G.	Good	Fair	Poor
750	500	350	275	150

Navy Revolver

As above in .36 caliber. Approximately 100 were made with both center and side mounted hammers during the 1850s.

Exc.	V.G.	Good	Fair	Poor
1500	1250	750	500	400

Courtesy Milwaukee Public Museum, Milwaukee, Wisconsin.

J

JACQUEMART, JULES
Liege, Belgium

Le Monobloc
A 6.35mm semi-automatic pistol with a 2" barrel and 6-shot magazine. The slide marked "Le Monobloc/Pistolet Automatique/Brevette." Blued with composition grips. Production ceased in 1914.

Exc.	V.G.	Good	Fair	Poor
350	300	250	200	125

JACQUITH, ELIJAH
Brattleboro, Vermont

Revolving Under Hammer Rifle
An extremely rare .40 caliber percussion revolving rifle with a 34" round-octagonal barrel and 8-shot cylinder. It is believed that approximately 25 of these rifles were made in 1838 and 1839. The barrel marked "E. Jaquith Brattleboro. Vt." Prospective purchasers should secure a qualified appraisal prior to acquisition.

Exc.	V.G.	Good	Fair	Poor
8000	7000	5500	4000	3000

JAGER WAFFENFABIK
Suhl, Germany

Jager Semi-automatic Pistol
A 7.65mm caliber semi-automatic pistol with a 3" barrel and 7-shot magazine. Largely made from steel stampings. Blued with plastic grips. The slide marked "Jager-Pistole DRP Angem." Approximately 5,500 were made prior to 1914.

Exc.	V.G.	Good	Fair	Poor
400	300	250	175	100

JAPANESE STATE MILITARY WEAPONS
Japan

Murata Type 20
An 8mm caliber bolt-action rifle with a 32" barrel, 8-shot tubular magazine and full length stock secured by two barrel bands.

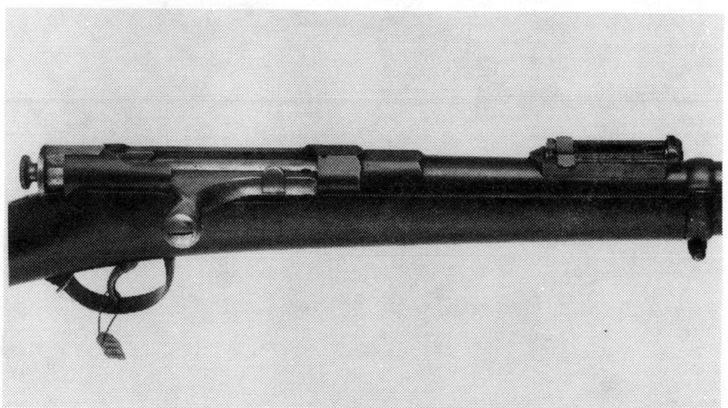

Courtesy Buffalo Bill Historical Center, Cody, Wyoming.

Exc.	V.G.	Good	Fair	Poor
300	250	200	125	75

Murata Shotgun
A smoothbore modification of the Type 20 made during the 1920s for export.

Exc.	V.G.	Good	Fair	Poor
150	125	100	75	50

Arisaka Type 30 Rifle
A 6.5mm Arisaka caliber bolt-action rifle with a 31.5" barrel, 5-shot magazine and full length stock secured by two barrel bands. Manufactured from 1897 to 1905.

Exc.	V.G.	Good	Fair	Poor
175	150	125	90	65

Arisaka Type 30 Carbine
As above, with a 19" barrel and no upper hand guard.

Exc.	V.G.	Good	Fair	Poor
175	150	125	90	65

Arisaka Type 38 Rifle
6.5mm Arisaka caliber bolt-action rifle with a 31.5" barrel, 5-shot magazine and large bolt handle. Full length stock secured by two barrel bands. Manufactured from 1905 to 1911.

Exc.	V.G.	Good	Fair	Poor
175	150	125	90	65

Arisaka Type 38 Carbine
As above, with a 19" barrel and no upper hand guard.

Exc.	V.G.	Good	Fair	Poor
200	175	150	125	85

Arisaka Type 44 Carbine
As above, with an 18.5" barrel and folding bayonet.

Exc.	V.G.	Good	Fair	Poor
250	200	150	100	75

Japanese "Siamese Mauser" Rifle
A modified Mauser in 8x52Rmm caliber manufactured during the 1920s for the Siamese Government.

Exc.	V.G.	Good	Fair	Poor
125	100	80	60	40

Arisaka Type 97 "Sniper's Rifle"
The Type 38 with a 4-power telescope and a bipod. Introduced in 1937.

Exc.	V.G.	Good	Fair	Poor
350	300	250	175	125

Arisaka Type 99 Rifle
A 7.7mm caliber bolt-action rifle with a 25" barrel and full length stock secured by two barrel bands. Fitted with a monopod.

Courtesy Buffalo Bill Historical Center, Cody, Wyoming.

Exc.	V.G.	Good	Fair	Poor
150	125	100	80	60

Type 99 Parachute Rifle
As above, with a stock hinged at the wrist.

Exc.	V.G.	Good	Fair	Poor
300	250	225	175	125

Type 2 Parachute Rifle
Similar to the above, with a sliding wedge release for the folding butt.

Exc.	V.G.	Good	Fair	Poor
300	250	225	175	125

Type 99 Takedown Rifle
As above, but with the barrel and forend detachable from the receiver unit.

Exc.	V.G.	Good	Fair	Poor
250	200	175	125	80

Type 99 "Snipers Rifle"
The standard Type 99 with a 25.5" barrel and 4-power telescope.

Exc.	V.G.	Good	Fair	Poor
350	300	250	200	125

Type 5 Semi-automatic Rifle
A 7.7mm semi-automatic rifle patterned after the U.S. M1. Made at the Kure Navel Arsenal in 1945. It is believed that approximately 75 were made. Prospective purchasers should secure a qualified appraisal prior to acquisition.

Type 26 Revolver
A 9mm caliber double-action hinged barrel revolver with a 6-shot cylinder. As this pistol does not have a hammer spur, it only functions in double-action. Manufactured from 1893 to 1924.

Exc.	V.G.	Good	Fair	Poor
550	400	300	200	125

4th Year Type Nambu Pistol
This is a quality built semi-automatic pistol chambered for the 8mm cartridge. It is fitted with a 4.7" barrel and has a magazine capacity of 8 rounds. It can be identified by the grip safety located on the front strap. The early models, serial numbers 1 to 2450, are known as "Grandpa" to collectors. Later pistols are known as "Papa" Nambu. The values shown here are only approximate. Different variations may bring different prices and an appraisal is recommended. Pistols with original wooden stocks are worth considerably more.

Exc.	V.G.	Good	Fair	Poor
1000	800	650	450	350

Baby Nambu
As above, with a 3.5" barrel. 7mm cartridge.

Courtesy Buffalo Bill Historical Center, Cody, Wyoming.

Exc.	V.G.	Good	Fair	Poor
2250	2000	1500	1000	750

14th Year Type Nambu Pistol
Similar to the 4th Year Type but without a grip safety and with grooved grips and a larger triggerguard. Manufactured until 1945.

Courtesy Orville Reichert.

Courtesy Orville Reichert.

Exc.	V.G.	Good	Fair	Poor
475	400	350	250	175

Type 94 Pistol
An 8mm caliber semi-automatic pistol with a 3.3" barrel and 6-shot magazine. Manufactured from 1937 to 1945.

Courtesy Orville Reichert.

Courtesy Orville Reichert.

Exc.	V.G.	Good	Fair	Poor
325	275	225	175	125

JEFFERY, W. J. & CO. LTD.
London, England

This company produced very high quality shotguns and rifles. Their products have been used by wealthy sportsmen for many years. They produced guns under their own banner and also as contractors for other distributors. They made the guns sold by the Army & Navy Departmant Store in London. Guns of this type were basically custom-ordered and as such are extremely hard to evaluate on a general basis. We supply an estimated value for a standard model but strongly urge that one secure an individual appraisal if a transaction is contemplated.

Shotguns
Boxlock
Produced in all gauges, with barrel lengths and choke combinations to the customer's specifications. They were available with any trigger option and automatic extractors or ejectors. The materials and workmanship were of the highest order, and values would be based on options. This model was produced with exposed hammers and Damascus barrels and would be worth approximately 50 percent less in that configuration. Small gauges would add approximately 50 percent.

Exc.	V.G.	Good	Fair	Poor
4000	3500	2500	1600	900

Sidelock
The quality is similar to that of the boxlock, with the added value of the sidelock action. This was also a made-to-order gun, and values cannot be accurately estimated without an individual appraisal. Hammerguns with Damascus barrels would bring approximately 50 percent less. Small gauges would add approximately 50 percent.

Exc.	V.G.	Good	Fair	Poor
9000	7500	5000	3250	1650

Rifles
Single Shot
Built on the Farquharson Falling Block action and was chambered for many calibers up to the .600 Nitro Express. This was also a custom-order gun, and the barrel length was optional. There are usually folding express sights; and the finish is usually blued with a select, hand-checkered walnut stock. These were high quality firearms; and the values would be determined, for the most part, by the options and embellishments on the particular specimen. Individual appraisal is definitely advised. The caliber in which a rifle is chambered will also have an effect on the value. Obsolete calibers bring less, and the larger express calibers bring more.

Exc.	V.G.	Good	Fair	Poor
4000	3250	2500	1750	900

Boxlock Double Rifle
A boxlock chambered for many different calibers. It can be found with either a top or underlever action and has folding express sights. The stock and forearm are select, handcheckered walnut; and the finish is usually blue. This was a custom-order proposition, and values can be affected by many variables — such as caliber, options, and embellishment. Damascus-barreled hammer guns are worth approximately 50 percent less.

Exc.	V.G.	Good	Fair	Poor
8000	6500	4500	3500	2500

Sidelock Double Rifle
Has detachable sidelocks and otherwise is comparable to the boxlock version. Individual appraisal is recommended.

Exc.	V.G.	Good	Fair	Poor
12500	10000	7500	5000	4000

JENISON, J. & CO.
Southbridge, Connecticut

Under Hammer Pistol
A .28 caliber single shot under hammer percussion pistol with a 4" half-octagonal barrel marked "J.Jenison & Co./Southbridge, Mass." Blued with a maple or oak grip. Manufactured during the 1950s.

Exc.	V.G.	Good	Fair	Poor
500	425	350	250	150

JENKS CARBINE
Springfield, Massachusetts
N. P. Ames Manufacturer

Jenks "Mule Ear Carbine"
A .54 caliber percussion side hammer carbine with a 24.5" round barrel and full length stock secured by two barrel bands. The lock case-hardened, the barrel browned and the furniture of brass. The lock marked "N.P.Ames/Springfield/Mass." The barrel stamped "Wm.Jenks/USN" followed by the inspector's initials. The buttstock carries an inspector's cartouche. Approximately 4,250 were made between 1841 and 1846. Some were marked "USR" for the "U.S. Revenue Cutter Service," and these would bring approximately an 80 percent premium over the values listed below. However, prospective purchasers should secure a qualified appraisal prior to acquisition.

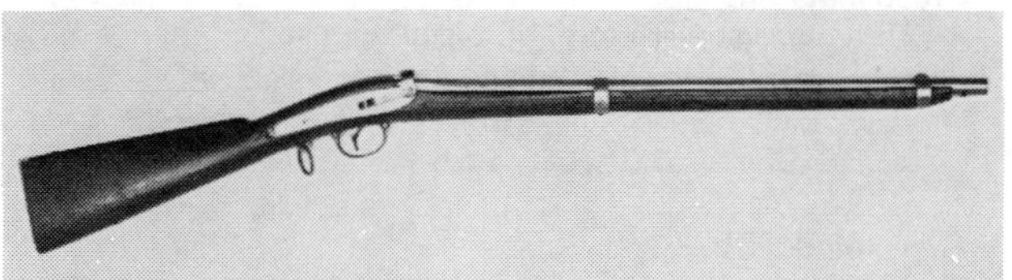
Courtesy Milwaukee Public Museum, Milwaukee, Wisconsin.

Exc.	V.G.	Good	Fair	Poor
1000	850	750	500	375

Jenks Navy Rifle

As above, with a 30" round barrel and full length stock secured by three barrel bands. Approximately 1,000 were made for the U.S. Navy in 1841.

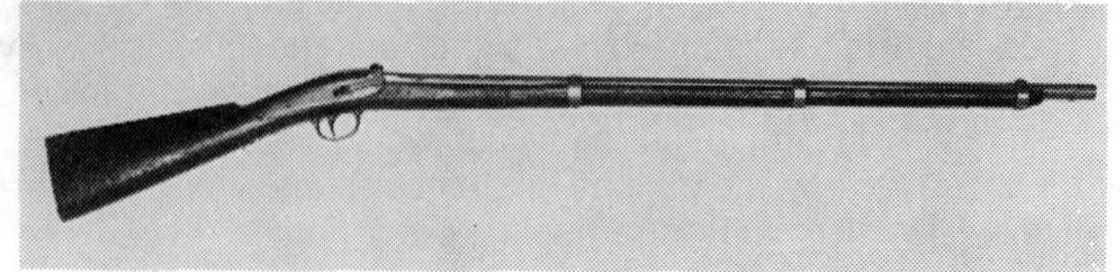

Courtesy Milwaukee Public Museum, Milwaukee, Wisconsin.

Exc.	V.G.	Good	Fair	Poor
1500	1250	950	700	400

JENKS-HERKIMER

New York
Manufacturer—E. Remington & Son

Jenks Carbine

Identical to the Jenks Carbine listed in the previous entry except that the barrel length is 24.25" and the lock is fitted with a Maynard tape primer. The lock marked "Remington's/Herkimer/N.Y." The barrel is marked "W. Jenks/USN/RC/P/Cast Steel." Approximately 1,000 of these carbines manufactured circa 1846.

Exc.	V.G.	Good	Fair	Poor
1250	1000	800	650	450

JENKS-MERRILL

Baltimore, Maryland

An alteration of the Jenks Carbine listed previously to a breech loading system developed by J.H. Merrill. The conventional sidelock marked "J. H. Merrill Balto./Pat. July 1858." The breech retains the mark "Wm.Jenks/USN." Approximately 300 were altered between 1858 and 1860.

Exc.	V.G.	Good	Fair	Poor
1850	1650	1400	900	650

JENNINGS

Windsor, Vermont
Manufacturer — Robbins & Lawrence
SEE—Winchester Repeating Arms

JENNINGS F. A., INC.

Carson City, Nevada

Distributors of arms manufactured by Calwestco in Chino, California, and Bryco Firearms in Carson City, Nevada.

J-22

A .22 caliber semi-automatic pistol with a 2.5" barrel and 6-shot magazine. Aluminum, finished in bright chrome, Teflon or satin nickle with plastic or wood grips.

Exc.	V.G.	Good	Fair	Poor
75	65	50	35	25

Bryco Model 25

A .25 caliber semi-automatic pistol with a 2.5" barrel and 6-shot magazine. Constructed and finished as above.

Exc.	V.G.	Good	Fair	Poor
90	75	65	50	35

Bryco Model 38

A .22, .32 or .380 semi-automatic pistol with a 2.8" barrel and 6-shot magazine. Constructed and finished as above.

Exc.	V.G.	Good	Fair	Poor
90	75	65	50	35

Bryco Model 48

Similar to the above, with a redesigned triggerguard with a squared forward section. Introduced in 1988.

Exc.	V.G.	Good	Fair	Poor
90	75	65	50	35

JERICHO

Harrisburg, Pennsylvania
Israeli Military Industries
Israel

Jericho

A 9mm or .41 Action Express double-action semi-automatic pistol with a 4.72" barrel, polygonal rifling, ambidextrous safety and fixed sights. Blued with plastic grips.

Exc.	V.G.	Good	Fair	Poor
450	400	350	300	200

JIEFFCO

Robar et Cie
Liege, Belgium

Pocket Pistol

A .25 or .32 caliber semi-automatic pistol with a 3" barrel and 6-shot magazine. Blued with composition grips. Manufactured prior to WWI.

Exc.	V.G.	Good	Fair	Poor
275	250	200	150	100

New Model Melior

A .25 caliber semi-automatic pistol with a 2" barrel and 6-shot magazine. Blued with composition grips. Manufactured during the 1920s and imported by Davis-Warner.

Exc.	V.G.	Good	Fair	Poor
250	225	175	125	90

JOHNSON AUTOMATIC RIFLE

Cranston Arms Co.
Providence, Rhode Island

Model 1941

A 7mm or .30-06 semi-automatic rifle with a 22" barrel and 10-shot rotary magazine. Parkerized with a walnut stock. Manufactured from 1941 to 1945. Rifles of this design were purchased by the United States Government, the Dutch Government and various South American governments.

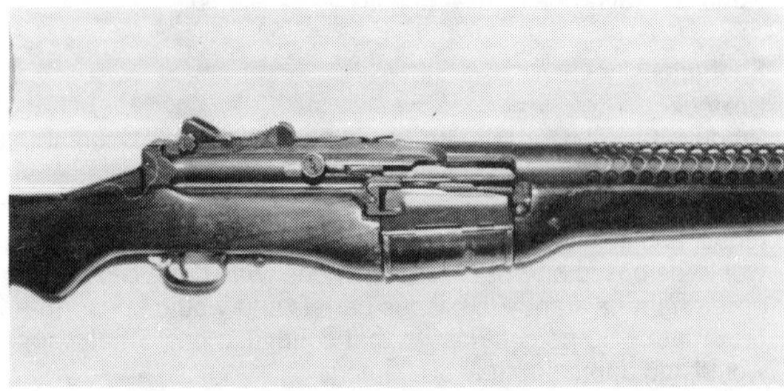

Exc.	V.G.	Good	Fair	Poor
2000	1500	1000	750	500

JOHNSON, BYE & CO.

Worcester, Massachusetts

Established in 1871 by Martin Bye and Iver Johnson. This company primarily manufactured inexpensive pistols. In 1883 Johnson assumed full control of the company and renamed it the Iver Johnson Arms Company.

Defender, Eagle, Encore, Eureka, Favorite, Lion, Smoker and Tycoon

A .22, .32, .38 or .44 caliber spur trigger revolver manufactured with various barrel lengths and normally nickle-plated. The barrel marked with one of the above tradenames.

Exc.	V.G.	Good	Fair	Poor
125	100	75	50	25

Eclipse

A .22 caliber spur trigger single shot pistol with a 1.5" barrel. Blued with walnut grips.

Exc.	V.G.	Good	Fair	Poor
125	100	75	50	25

American Bulldog

A .22, .32 or .38 caliber double-action revolver with a 3" barrel. Blued or nickle-plated with walnut or composition grips.

Exc.	V.G.	Good	Fair	Poor
125	100	75	50	25

JOSEF JESCHER

SEE—Austrian Military Firearms

JOSLYN

Milbury, Massachusetts
A. H. Waters—Manufacturer

Model 1855 Carbine

A .54 caliber breech loading single shot percussion carbine with a 22.5" barrel secured to the forend by one barrel band. Blued, case-hardened with brass mounts. The lock marked "A.H.Waters & Co./Milbury, Mass.", and the patent dates stamped on the breech lever. Approximately 1,000 manufactured in 1855 and 1856.

Exc.	V.G.	Good	Fair	Poor
2250	1950	1600	1200	950

Model 1855 Rifle

Similar to the above, in .58 caliber with a 38" barrel secured by three barrel bands. Several hundred were made in 1856.

Exc.	V.G.	Good	Fair	Poor
2500	2200	1800	1400	1100

JOSLYN FIREARMS COMPANY

Stonington, Connecticut

Model 1862 Carbine

A .52 rimfire breech loading single shot carbine with a 22" round barrel secured by one barrel band. Blued, case-hardened with brass mounts. The lock marked "Joslyn Firearms Co./Stonington/Conn.", and the patent date marked on the barrel. The triggerplate is 8" long, and the upper tang measures 4.5". Approximately 4,000 manufactured in 1862.

Courtesy Milwaukee Public Museum, Milwaukee, Wisconsin.

Exc.	V.G.	Good	Fair	Poor
1500	1250	1000	700	400

Model 1864 Carbine

As above, with case-hardened iron mounts, a 7" triggerplate and 2" upper tang. Approximately 12,000 were made in 1864 and 1865.

Courtesy Milwaukee Public Museum, Milwaukee, Wisconsin.

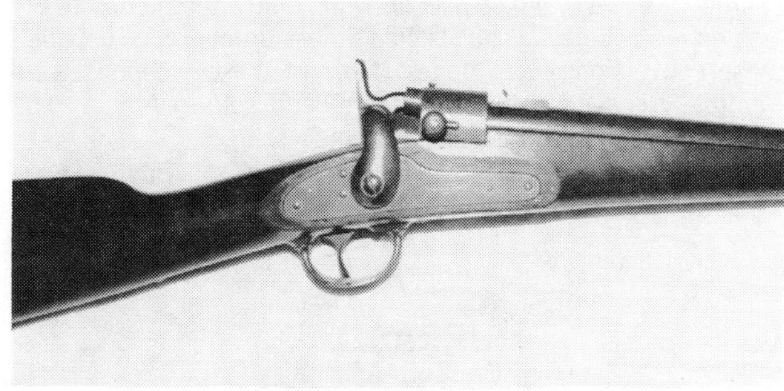

Exc.	V.G.	Good	Fair	Poor
1400	1150	900	800	500

Army Model Revolver

A .44 caliber side hammer percussion revolver with an 8" octagonal barrel and 5-shot cylinder. Blued, case-hardened with walnut grips. The barrel marked "B. F. Joslyn/ Patd. May 4, 1858." Martially marked examples are worth a premium of approximately 25% over the values listed below. The two models of this revolver are as follows:

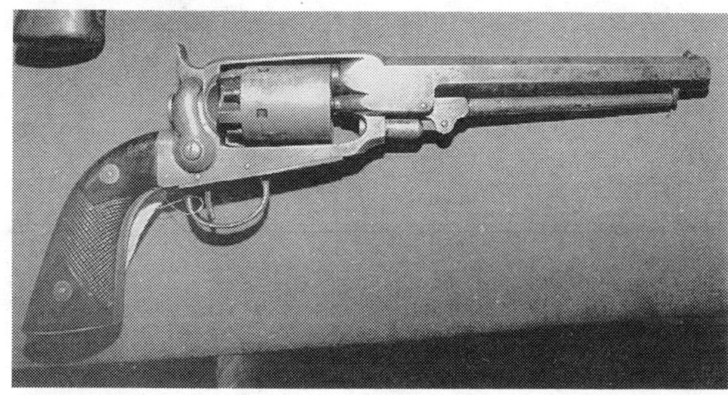

First Model

With a brass triggerguard and iron butt cap. Approximately 500 made in 1861.

Exc.	V.G.	Good	Fair	Poor
1750	1500	1200	800	550

Second Model

Fitted with an iron triggerguard and without a butt cap. Approximately 2,500 were made in 1861 and 1862.

Exc.	V.G.	Good	Fair	Poor
1500	1250	1000	700	400

JOSLYN

Springfield, Massachusetts
Manufacturer—Springfield Armory

Joslyn Breechloading Rifle

The first mass-produced, true breech loading cartridge firearm manufactured in a national armory. The actions were supplied by the Joslyn Firearms Company, and the rifles were chambered for the .56-50 rimfire cartridge. This rifle has a 35.5" round barrel and a full-length stock that is held on by three barrel bands. The lock is marked "U.S./Springfield" with "1864" at the back. The barrel is marked "B. F. Joslyn's Patent / Oct. 8th, 1861 / June 24th, 1862." There were approximately 3,000 of these manufactured circa 1865. They were probably issued to Union forces, but it is unknown if they saw action before the end of the Civil War.

Exc.	V.G.	Good	Fair	Poor
1500	1250	1000	700	500

.50-70 Alteration

Approximately 1,600 Joslyn rifles were re-chambered to fire the .50-70 centerfire cartridge. The conversion consisted of re-chambering and drilling a new firing pin hole after the rimfire pin was sealed. There was no specific serial-number range in which these conversions were done. Most of these weapons were eventually converted to smoothbores and sold in Africa. The original military specimens are extremely scarce.

Exc.	V.G.	Good	Fair	Poor
2000	1750	1400	1000	750

JURRAS, LEE

Prescott, Arizona

SEE—Auto-Mag

While Jurras is best known for manufacturing the last model of the Auto-Mag, he also produced the following pistol sold by J. & G. Sales in Prescott, Arizona.

Howdah Pistol

A .375, .416, .460, .475, .500, and the .577. caliber single shot pistol with a 12" barrel, adjustable sights and Nitex finish, built upon a Thompson Center Contender frame.

Exc.	V.G.	Good	Fair	Poor
1200	1000	800	650	500

JUSTICE, P. S.

Philadelphia, Pennsylvania

Percussion Rifle

A .58 caliber percussion rifle with a 35" round barrel secured by two barrel bands, browned barrel, polished lock and brass furniture. The lock marked "P.S.Justice/Philada." Approximately 2,500 were manufactured in 1861.

Courtesy Milwaukee Public Museum, Milwaukee, Wisconsin.

Exc.	V.G.	Good	Fair	Poor
1500	1250	1000	750	450

KBI, INC.
Harrisburg, Pennsylvania

PSP-25

A .25 caliber semi-automatic pistol with a 2" barrel manufactured in Charlottesville, Virginia under license from Fabrique Nationale. Introduced in 1989.

NIB	Exc.	V.G.	Good	Fair
225	200	175	150	100

KDF, INC.
Seguin, Texas
Kleinguenther Distinctive Firearms

The former importer of Voere and Mauser rifles into the U.S.

Condor

A 12 gauge boxlock Over/Under shotgun with 28" barrels with ventilated-ribs, single selective trigger and automatic ejectors. Blued with a walnut stock. Manufactured in Italy.

Exc.	V.G.	Good	Fair	Poor
650	600	525	375	275

Brescia

A 12 gauge boxlock double barrel shotgun with 28" barrels, double triggers and extractors. Blued with a walnut stock. Manufactured in Italy.

Exc.	V.G.	Good	Fair	Poor
350	325	300	200	125

K-14 Insta Fire Rifle

A bolt-action sporting rifle manufactured in a variety of calibers with 24" or 26" barrels furnished without sights. Blued with a Monte Carlo-style walnut stock.

Exc.	V.G.	Good	Fair	Poor
600	550	450	325	250

K-15

Similar to the above, with a 60 degree bolt angle and an accurized barrel guaranteed to fire a .5" group at 100 yards. Manufactured with a variety of optional features.

Exc.	V.G.	Good	Fair	Poor
1000	850	750	550	400

K-15 Pro-Hunter

As above, matte blued or electroless nickle-plated with a fiberglass stock.

Exc.	V.G.	Good	Fair	Poor
1400	1250	1000	700	500

K-15 Swat Rifle

A 7.62x54mm caliber bolt-action rifle with a 24" or 26" barrel furnished without sights, 4-shot magazine and parkerized finish. Walnut stock.

Exc.	V.G.	Good	Fair	Poor
1500	1300	1100	800	550

K-15 Dangerous Game

As above, in .411 KDF caliber.

Exc.	V.G.	Good	Fair	Poor
2000	1600	1300	1000	700

K-16

A bolt-action sporting rifle manufactured in a variety of calibers with a 24" or 26" barrel furnished without sights, single stage adjustable trigger, accurized barrel and Dupont Rynite stock. Produced with a variety of optional features.

Exc.	V.G.	Good	Fair	Poor
775	675	500	400	300

Titan Menor

A .222 or .223 caliber bolt-action rifle with a 24" or 26" barrel furnished without sights and Monte Carlo-style or standard Schnabel tipped walnut stock. Blued.

Exc.	V.G.	Good	Fair	Poor
650	600	550	400	300

Titan II Standard

As above, with a mid-sized action.

Exc.	V.G.	Good	Fair	Poor
900	800	700	500	400

Titan II Magnum

As above, with a long action. Discontinued in 1988.

Exc.	V.G.	Good	Fair	Poor
1000	850	750	550	450

Titan .411 KDF Mag.

As above, in .411 KDF with a 26" barrel having an integral muzzle brake. Blued or electroless nickle-plated with a walnut stock. Discontinued in 1988.

Exc.	V.G.	Good	Fair	Poor
1200	1050	850	650	550

K-22

A .22 caliber bolt-action rifle with a 21" free floating barrel furnished without sights, adjustable trigger and 5-shot magazine. Also known as the Mauser 201.

Exc.	V.G.	Good	Fair	Poor
300	275	250	175	125

K-22 Deluxe

Exc.	V.G.	Good	Fair	Poor
400	375	350	275	225

K-22 Deluxe Custom

Exc.	V.G.	Good	Fair	Poor
650	550	450	375	325

K-22 Deluxe Special Select

Exc.	V.G.	Good	Fair	Poor
1000	850	750	650	525

Model 2005

A .22 caliber semi-automatic rifle with a 19.5" barrel, open sights and 5-shot magazine. Blued with a walnut stock. Also available in a deluxe model. Imported in 1986.

NIB	Exc.	V.G.	Good	Fair	Poor
125	100	80	60	40	30

Model 2107

A .22 or .22 Magnum caliber bolt-action rifle with a 19.5" barrel, open sights and 5-shot magazine. Blued with a walnut stock.

Exc.	V.G.	Good	Fair	Poor
175	150	125	100	75

Model 2112

The deluxe version of the Model 2107.

Exc.	V.G.	Good	Fair	Poor
250	200	175	125	90

K.F.C.

Japan
Importer—LaPaloma Marketing
Tucson, Arizona

E-1 Trap or Skeet Over/Under

A 12 gauge boxlock double barrel shotgun with 26" or 30" barrels, competition rib, single selective trigger and automatic ejectors. Engraved, blued with a walnut stock. Manufactured until 1986.

Exc.	V.G.	Good	Fair	Poor
950	800	700	500	400

E-2 Trap or Skeet Over/Under

As above, but more finely finished.

Exc.	V.G.	Good	Fair	Poor
1400	1250	1000	750	500

Field Grade Over/Under

As above, with a narrow rib and 26" or 28" barrels. Discontinued in 1986.

Exc.	V.G.	Good	Fair	Poor
650	575	500	400	275

Model 250

A 12 gauge semi-automatic shotgun with 26", 28" or 30" barrels fitted for choke tubes. Matte blued with a walnut stock. Manufactured from 1980 to 1986.

Exc.	V.G.	Good	Fair	Poor
350	300	275	200	100

KASSNAR IMPORTS, INC.

Harrisburg, Pennsylvania

Currently the following firearms are imported by this company.

Omega Shotguns

Standard Over/Under

A 12, 20, 28 or .410 bore boxlock double-barrel shotgun with 26" or 28" barrels, ventilated-ribs, single trigger and extractors. Blued with a walnut stock.

NIB	Exc.	V.G.	Good	Fair	Poor
320	275	225	200	150	100

Deluxe Over/Under

As above, with a more finely figured stock.

NIB	Exc.	V.G.	Good	Fair	Poor
375	325	250	225	175	125

Standard Side x Side

A 20, 28 or .410 bore boxlock folding double-barrel shotgun with 26" barrels, double triggers and extractors. Blued with a walnut stock.

NIB	Exc.	V.G.	Good	Fair	Poor
225	200	175	150	100	75

Deluxe Side x Side

As above, in .410 bore only and with more finely figured wood.

NIB	Exc.	V.G.	Good	Fair	Poor
250	225	200	175	125	100

KEBERST INT.

Kendall International
Paris, Kentucky

Keberst Model 1A

A .338 Lapua Magnum, .338-416 Rigby, and the .338-06 caliber bolt-action rifle with a 24" barrel having an integral muzzle brake, and fitted with a 3-9 power Leupold telescope. Matte blued with a camouflaged composition stock. Manufactured in 1987 and 1988.

Exc.	V.G.	Good	Fair	Poor
3500	3000	2500	1800	1200

KENDALL, INTERNATIONAL

Paris, Kentucky
SEE—Keberst International

KENDALL, NICANOR

Windsor, Vermont

Under Hammer Pistol

A .31 to .41 caliber under hammer percussion pistol with 4" to 10" octagonal/round barrels marked "N.Kendall/Windsor,Vt." Browned or blued with brass mounts and maple grips. Manufactured in the 1850s.

Exc.	V.G.	Good	Fair	Poor
550	500	400	300	175

KENO

Unknown

Derringer

A .22 caliber single shot spur trigger pistol with a 2.5" barrel, brass frame and walnut grips. The barrel blued or nickle-plated and marked "Keno".

Exc.	V.G.	Good	Fair	Poor
300	250	200	150	100

KEPPLINGER, I. HANNES

Kufstein, Austria

3-S Rifle System

A short-action rifle chambered for all popular American and European cartridges. The major parts are constructed of a high-strength alloy, and it features a de-cocking lever that allows manual cocking and de-cocking of the firing-pin spring. The barrel is 23" in length, and the detachable magazine holds 3 rounds. This is essentially a custom-built gun and is rarely encountered on the market. The engraving varies with the customer's wishes; and the walnut stock, either full-length Mannlicher style or with a Schnabel forend, is made of the highest-grade wood available. This company does not have an importer at this time. We are not able to evaluate, as there are too few traded. It is listed for reference only.

KERR

London, England

Kerr Revolver

A .44 caliber double-action percussion revolver with a 5.5" barrel and 6-shot cylinder. Blued with walnut grips. The frame marked "Kerr's Patent 648"; and "London Armoury Bermondsey."

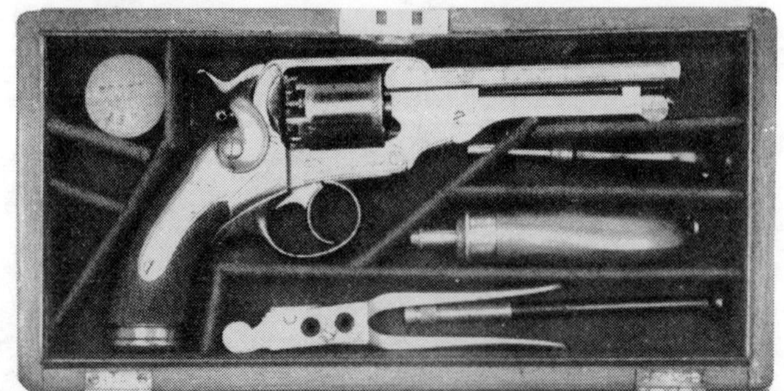

Courtesy Butterfield & Butterfield, San Francisco, California.

Exc.	V.G.	Good	Fair	Poor
1500	1250	1000	750	500

KERR
SEE—English Military Firearms

KESSLER ARMS CORPORATION
Silver Creek, New York

Bolt Action Shotgun

A 12, 16 or 20 gauge shotgun with 26" or 28" barrels. Blued with a walnut stock. Manufactured between 1951 and 1953.

Exc.	V.G.	Good	Fair	Poor
100	75	50	30	20

Levermatic Shotgun

A 12, 16 or 20 gauge lever action shotgun with a 26" or 28" barrel. Blued with a walnut stock. Manufactured between 1951 and 1953.

Exc.	V.G.	Good	Fair	Poor
125	100	75	50	25

KETTNER, EDWARD
Suhl, Germany

Drilling

This is a high quality three-barrelled firearm chambered for 12x12 gauge or 16x16 gauge over various metric rifle cartridges. The barrels are 25" in length and feature ejectors, selective triggers, and pop-up rifle sights that appear when the rifle barrel is selected. This gun is deep-relief engraved in the German style and has a high-grade checkered walnut stock. It was manufactured between 1922 and 1939.

Exc.	V.G.	Good	Fair	Poor
2250	2000	1750	1400	950

KIMBALL ARMS COMPANY
Detroit, Michigan

Semi-automatic Pistol

A .30 carbine caliber semi-automatic pistol with a 3.5" or 5" barrel. Blued with plastic grips. Also believed to have been made in .22 Hornet and .357 Magnum, though legitimate examples have been seen. Manufactured from 1955 to 1958. Approximately 238 were made.

Exc.	V.G.	Good	Fair	Poor
850	750	650	500	375

KIMBER OF OREGON, INC.
Clackamas, Oregon

Kimber of Oregon was established in April 1979 by Greg and Jack Warner. The company produced high quality rimfire and centerfire rifles until going out of business in early 1991. Kimber produced approximately 60,000 rifles during its operation. In April 1993, Greg Warner opened Kimber of America in Clackamas, Oregon. This new company presently manufactures the same high quality rifles built on an improved Model 82 Sporter action and stock but in rimfire only. At the present time there is no centerfire rifle production.

Model 82 Classic

A .22, .22 Magnum or .22 Hornet bolt-action rifle with a 22" barrel furnished without sights and 4 or 5-shot magazine. Blued with a walnut stock. Discontinued in 1988.

Exc.	V.G.	Good	Fair	Poor
700	600	550	450	350

Cascade Model

As above, with a Monte Carlo-style stock.

Exc.	V.G.	Good	Fair	Poor
750	650	600	500	400

Custom Classic Model

As above, in .218 Bee or .25-20.

Exc.	V.G.	Good	Fair	Poor
800	725	650	400	300

Mini Classic

The Model 82 with an 18" barrel. Manufactured in 1988.

Exc.	V.G.	Good	Fair	Poor
600	550	475	400	300

Deluxe Grade

Similar to the Custom Classic. Introduced in 1989.

NIB	Exc.	V.G.	Good	Fair	Poor
1000	850	650	550	450	350

Model 82A Government

A .22 caliber bolt-action rifle with a 25" heavy barrel fitted with telescope mounts. Matte blued with a walnut stock. Introduced in 1987.

NIB	Exc.	V.G.	Good	Fair	Poor
575	525	450	375	300	200

Continental

Similar to the Custom Classic with a 20" barrel, open sights and full length Mannlicher-style stock. Introduced in 1987.

NIB	Exc.	V.G.	Good	Fair	Poor
850	750	650	500	400	300

Super Continental

As above, but more finely finished. Discontinued in 1988.

Exc.	V.G.	Good	Fair	Poor
1200	1100	1000	750	600

Super America

The Model 82 but more finely finished. Discontinued in 1988.

Exc.	V.G.	Good	Fair	Poor
1200	950	850	650	500

Super Grade

As above, introduced in 1989.

NIB	Exc.	V.G.	Good	Fair	Poor
1200	1000	900	750	600	475

Centennial

A commemorative rifle moderately engraved including a special match barrel, skeleton buttplate, hand-selected walnut stock, and light engraving. Issued to commemorate the 100th anniversary of the 22 l.r. cartridge. 100 were manufactured in 1987.

NIB	Exc.	V.G.	Good	Fair	Poor
2500	2250	2000	1750	1500	1150

Brownell

In 1986, 500 commemorative rifles were produced in honor of the Leonard Brownell, featuring a high-grade, Mannlicher-style, full-length walnut stock.

NIB	Exc.	V.G.	Good	Fair	Poor
1500	1250	1000	800	600	500

Model 84 Series

A bolt-action rifle manufactured in a variety of smallbore calibers with a 22" or 24" barrel and 5-shot magazine. Blued with a walnut stock. Variations are as follows:

Classic Model

Exc.	V.G.	Good	Fair	Poor
700	650	600	400	250

Custom Classic Model

Exc.	V.G.	Good	Fair	Poor
950	800	700	500	350

Deluxe Grade Sporter

NIB	Exc.	V.G.	Good	Fair	Poor
1200	1000	850	750	500	400

Continental

NIB	Exc.	V.G.	Good	Fair	Poor
975	900	800	700	500	350

Super Continental

Exc.	V.G.	Good	Fair	Poor
1300	1100	850	700	575

Super America

Exc.	V.G.	Good	Fair	Poor
1000	925	825	600	450

Super Grade

NIB	Exc.	V.G.	Good	Fair	Poor
1250	1100	1000	850	650	450

Ultra Varmint

As above, with a 24" stainless-steel barrel and laminated birch wood stock. Introduced in 1989.

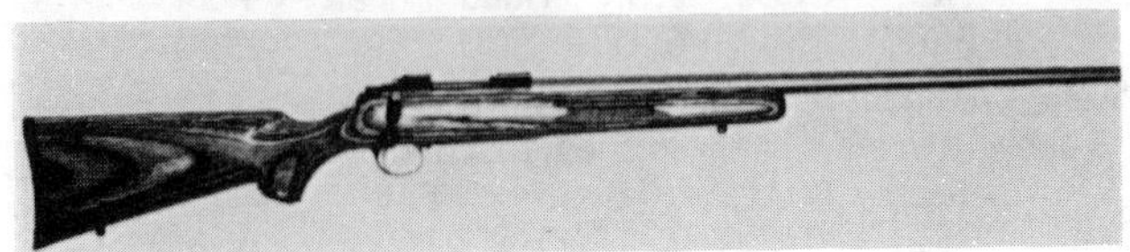

NIB	Exc.	V.G.	Good	Fair	Poor
1150	1000	900	750	550	400

Super Varmint

As above with a walnut stock. Introduced in 1989.

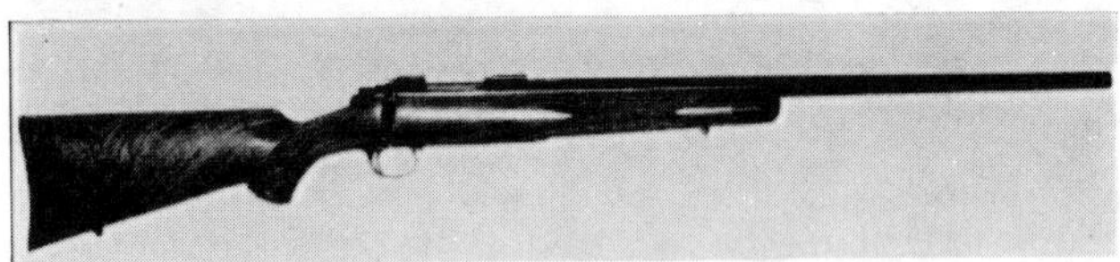

NIB	Exc.	V.G.	Good	Fair	Poor
1250	1100	1000	850	650	500

Model 89 Series

A bolt-action sporting rifle produced in .270 Winchester to .375 Holland & Holland caliber with a 22" or 24" barrel. Blued with a walnut stock. The variations of this model are as follows:

Classic Model

Exc.	V.G.	Good	Fair	Poor
800	650	550	400	300

Custom Classic Model

Exc.	V.G.	Good	Fair	Poor
1000	850	650	450	350

Deluxe Grade

NIB	Exc.	V.G.	Good	Fair	Poor
1400	1250	1000	750	650	500

Super America

Exc.	V.G.	Good	Fair	Poor
1100	900	700	500	400

Super Grade

NIB	Exc.	V.G.	Good	Fair	Poor
1500	1350	1100	800	700	600

Predator

A .221 Fireball, .223 Rem., 6mm TCU, 7mm TCU, or the 6x45mm caliber single shot bolt-action pistol based upon the Model 84 action with a 14.75" barrel adopted for a telescope. Blued with a walnut stock and available in two grades as follows. Manufactured in 1987 and 1988 only.

Hunter Grade

Exc.	V.G.	Good	Fair	Poor
800	650	575	400	300

Super Grade

Exc.	V.G.	Good	Fair	Poor
1000	850	675	500	400

KING PIN

Unknown

Derringer

A .22 caliber spur trigger brass constructed single shot pistol with a 2.5" barrel and walnut grips. Believed to have been made during the 1880s.

Exc.	V.G.	Good	Fair	Poor
300	250	200	150	90

KIRRIKALE, ENDUSTRISI

Ankara, Turkey

Kirrikale Pistol

A 7.65 or 9mm short caliber semi-automatic pistol with a 3.5" barrel and 6-shot magazine. Blued with plastic grips. The slide marked "MKE"; and "Kirrikale Tufek Fb Cal.---." Imported by Firearms Center in Victoria, Texas, and also by Mandall Shooting Supplies.

NIB	Exc.	V.G.	Good	Fair	Poor
400	350	275	225	150	100

KLIPZIG & COMPANY

San Francisco, California

Pocket Pistol

A .41 caliber single shot percussion pistol with a 2.5" barrel, German silver mounts and walnut stocks. Manufactured during the 1850s and early 1860s.

Exc.	V.G.	Good	Fair	Poor
1500	1000	400	300	200

KOHOUT & SPOLECNOST

Kdyne, Czechoslovakia

Mars

A 6.35 or 7.65mm caliber semi-automatic pistol, the larger caliber having a grip safety. Blued with plastic grips impressed with the word "Mars". The slide marked "Mars 7.65 (or 6.35) Kohout & Spol. Kdyne." Manufactured between 1928 and 1945.

Exc.	V.G.	Good	Fair	Poor
275	250	200	150	100

Niva, PZK

Similar to the above in 6.35mm caliber.

Exc.	V.G.	Good	Fair	Poor
275	250	200	150	100

KOLB, HENRY M.

Philadelphia, Pennsylvania

The revolvers listed below were manufactured by Henry Kolb and Charles Foehl until 1912 when R. F. Sedgely replaced Foehl. Manufacture continued until approximately 1930.

Baby Hammerless

A .22 caliber folding trigger double-action revolver with an enclosed hammer and 5-shot cylinder.

Exc.	V.G.	Good	Fair	Poor
250	225	200	150	100

New Baby Hammerless

Similar to the above, with a hinged barrel to facilitate loading.

Exc.	V.G.	Good	Fair	Poor
250	225	200	150	100

KOLIBRI

SEE—Grabner

KOMMER, THEODOR WAFFENFABRIK

Zella Mehlis, Germany

Model 1

A 6.35mm semi-automatic pistol with an 8-shot magazine. Blued with plastic grips. Manufactured during the 1920s.

Exc.	V.G.	Good	Fair	Poor
275	250	200	150	100

Model 2

As above, with straight grips and a 7-shot magazine.

Exc.	V.G.	Good	Fair	Poor
275	250	200	150	100

Model 3

Similar to the above, with an 8-shot magazine and marked with the Roman numeral III after the manufacturer's name.

Exc.	V.G.	Good	Fair	Poor
250	225	175	125	90

Model 4

A 7.65mm caliber semi-automatic pistol with a 7-shot magazine and without a grip safety. The slide marked "Waffenfabrik Kommer Zella Mehlis Kal. 7.65". Manufactured between 1936 and 1940.

Exc.	V.G.	Good	Fair	Poor
275	250	200	150	100

KORRIPHILIA

West Germany
Importer—Osborne's
Sheboygan, Michigan

HSP Type I

A 7.65mm Luger, .38 Special, 9mm Police, 9mm Luger, 9mm Steyr, 10mm ACP, and the .45 ACP caliber double-action semi-automatic pistol with a 4" barrel made of stainless-steel.

NIB	Exc.	V.G.	Good	Fair	Poor
2400	2050	1600	1000	850	700

HSP Type II

As above, with a 5" barrel.

NIB	Exc.	V.G.	Good	Fair	Poor
2600	2250	1750	1100	950	750

HSP Type III

As above, but single action.

NIB	Exc.	V.G.	Good	Fair	Poor
2800	2500	2000	1650	1250	775

KORTH

West Germany
Importer—Beeman Precision Arms
Santa Rosa, California

Semi-automatic Pistol

A 9mm caliber double-action semi-automatic pistol with a 4.5" barrel, adjustable sights and 13-shot magazine. Matte or polished blue with walnut grips. Introduced in 1985.

NIB	Exc.	V.G.	Good	Fair	Poor
3000	2750	2500	2000	1750	1400

Revolver

A .22 l.r., .22 Magnum, .357 Magnum, and 9mm caliber revolver with a 3", 4" or 6" barrel and 6-shot cylinder. The barrels and cylinders are interchangeable, matte or polished blue with walnut grips.

NIB	Exc.	V.G.	Good	Fair	Poor
2450	2100	1750	1500	1200	900

KRAG JORGENSEN

Springfield, Massachusetts

The first smallbore, bolt-action repeating rifle that used smokeless powder that was adopted by the U.S. Government as a service rifle. It was adopted as the Model 1892 and was very similar to the rifle being used by Denmark as a service rifle. All of the Krag-Jorgensens were manufactured at the Springfield Armory. There are 11 basic variations of Krag Rifles, and all except one are chambered for the .30-40 Govt. cartridge. They are bolt actions that hold 5 rounds in the unique side-mounted hinged magazine. All of the Krags have walnut stocks and handguards that are oil-finished. They all have dark gray case-hardened receivers and blued barrels. One should be aware that there have been many alterations based on the Krag rifle by many gunsmiths through the years, and the one consistency is that all of these conversions lowered the value of the rifle and rendered it uncollectible. Please be warned.

Model 1892

Approximately 24,500 of these rifles produced, dated 1894, 1895, and 1896. They have 30" barrels and are serial numbered from 1-24562. Nearly all were converted to the latter Model 1896, and the original 1st Type is extremely scarce.

1st Type

Serial numbered from 1-1500 and is dated 1894 only. It features a wide upper barrel band and an iron one-piece cleaning rod mounted under the barrel. There is no compartment in the butt, and the muzzle is not crowned and appears flat. The upper handguard does not extend over the receiver, and the buttplate is flat, without a compartment. One should be wary of fakes and secure expert appraisal if a transaction is contemplated. Unaltered specimens are extremely rare.

Exc.	V.G.	Good	Fair	Poor
4000	3750	3500	3000	2500

2nd Type

Similar to the 1st Type, with a front barrel band that is cut out in the center and does not appear solid. The serial range is 1500-24562, and the dates 1894 or 1895 are stamped on the receiver and the stock. Again—be wary of fakes. This is a very rare rifle.

Exc.	V.G.	Good	Fair	Poor
1800	1500	1000	750	600

Altered to 1896 Model

Encompassed very nearly the entire production run of the Model 1892 Krag rifle. They still bear the dates 1894, 1895, and 1896 on the receiver; but they do not have the cleaning rod, and the hole in the stock has been plugged. The front barrel band was changed, and the butt has a compartment for a cleaning kit. The top handguard covers the receiver, and the buttplate is curved at the bottom.

Exc.	V.G.	Good	Fair	Poor
300	250	200	150	100

Model 1896 Rifle

Similar to the altered Model 1892 and has a 30" barrel with the cleaning kit in the butt. The rear sight was improved, and the receiver is marked "U.S.Model 1896" and "Springfield Armory." The serial range runs from 35000-110000; and the stock is dated 1896, 1897, and 1898. There were many of these altered to the later stock configurations—in the field or at the Springfield Armory. These changes would lower the value, and one should secure expert appraisal on this Model.

Exc.	V.G.	Good	Fair	Poor
450	400	350	275	175

Model 1896 Carbine

Similar to the 1896 Rifle, with a 22" barrel and half-length stock held on by one barrel band. There were approximately 19,000 manufactured between 1896 and 1898, and the serial number range is 35000-90000. There were many rifles cut to carbine dimensions—be wary of these alterations!

Exc.	V.G.	Good	Fair	Poor
650	600	500	400	250

Model 1895 Carbine (Variation)

Marked "1895" and "1896" on the receiver—without the word Model. They were produced before the Model 1896 was officially adopted, and they are serial numbered from 25000-35000. They are similar to the Model 1896 Carbine, with a smaller safety and no oiler bottle in the butt.

Exc.	V.G.	Good	Fair	Poor
900	700	600	500	400

Model 1896 Cadet Rifle

A very rare variation produced for use by the Military Academy at West Point. The dimensions are the same as the 1896 Rifle with a one-piece cleaning rod under the barrel and the 1896-type front band. There were 400 manufactured, and most were altered to standard configuration when they were phased out in 1898.

Exc.	V.G.	Good	Fair	Poor
3000	2500	2200	1750	1250

Model 1898 Rifle

This model is similar to the Model 1896 in appearance except that the receiver is marked "U.S./Model 1898." The bolt handle was modified, and the sights and handguards were improved. There were 330,000 manufactured between 1898 and 1903, and the serial number range is 110000-480000.

Exc.	V.G.	Good	Fair	Poor
450	400	350	250	150

Model 1898 Carbine

Similar to the rifle, with a 22" barrel and a bar and ring on the left side of the receiver. There were approximately 5,000 manufactured in 1898 and 1899. The serial range is 125000-135000. Again, be aware that many of the rifles have been converted to carbine dimensions over the years. When in doubt secure an independent appraisal.

Exc.	V.G.	Good	Fair	Poor
1500	1250	1000	700	500

Model 1898 Carbine 26" Barrel

An attempt to satisfy both the infantry and the cavalry. There were 100 manufactured for trial, and the serial range is between 387000-389000. Be very wary of fakes.

Exc.	V.G.	Good	Fair	Poor
3000	2500	2200	1750	1250

Model 1898 Practice Rifle

The only Krag not chambered for the .30-40 cartridge. It is chambered for the .22 rimfire and was designed as a target-practice rifle. It has a 30" barrel and is identical in exterior appearance to the Model 1898 Rifle. The receiver is marked the same as the standard model—with "Cal.22" added. There were approximately 840 manufactured in 1906 and 1907.

Exc.	V.G.	Good	Fair	Poor
2000	1750	1500	1100	850

Model 1899 Carbine

The last of the Krags; and it is similar to the 1898, with the "Model 1899" stamped on the receiver and a 2" longer stock. There were approximately 36,000 manufactured between 1899 and 1902.

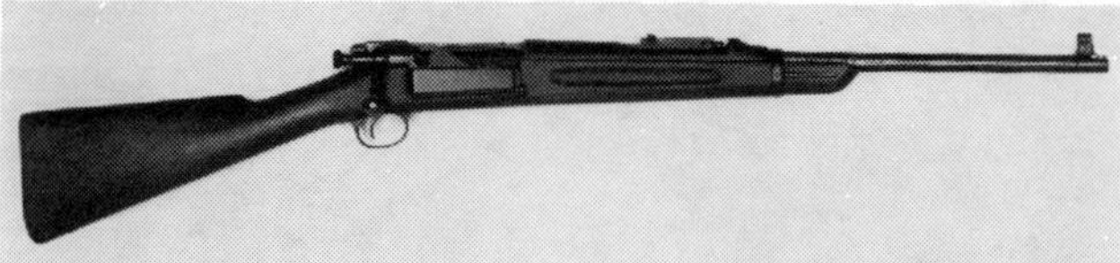

Courtesy Milwaukee Public Museum, Milwaukee, Wisconsin.

Exc.	V.G.	Good	Fair	Poor
650	550	500	400	275

Model 1899 Philippine Constabulary Carbine

Approximately 8,000 altered to accept the knife bayonet at the Springfield Armory and the Rock Island Arsenal. The Springfield pieces are marked "J.F.C." on the stock. This Model has a 22" barrel, with the full stock of the rifle held on with two barrel bands. One must exercise extreme care as many rifles were altered in a similar manner at later dates.

Exc.	V.G.	Good	Fair	Poor
1000	850	750	600	475

Benicia Arsenal Conversion

In the 1920s the Department of Civilian Marksmanship had a number of Krag rifles converted for their use. These are Model 1898 rifles shortened and fitted with Model 1899 Carbine stocks. These conversions are beginning to be regarded as legitimate variations by some collectors of Krag rifles.

Exc.	V.G.	Good	Fair	Poor
350	300	250	175	100

KRAUSER, ALFRED

Zella Mehlis, Germany

Helfricht or Helkra

A 6.35mm semi-automatic pistol with a 2" barrel. Produced in 4 models, the 4th having an enclosed barrel. Blued with composition grips. Manufactured from 1921 to 1929.

Exc.	V.G.	Good	Fair	Poor
450	400	350	250	150

KRICO

Stuttgart, West Germany
Importer—Beeman's Precision Arms
Santa Rosa, California

Sporting Rifle

A .22 Hornet or .222 caliber bolt-action rifle with 22", 24" or 26" barrels, single or double set trigger, adjustable sights and a 4-shot magazine. Blued with a walnut stock. Manufactured between 1956 and 1962.

Exc.	V.G.	Good	Fair	Poor
600	550	475	375	275

Sporting Carbine

As above, with a 20" barrel and full length stock.

Exc.	V.G.	Good	Fair	Poor
625	575	500	400	300

Varmint Special Rifle

The Sporting Rifle with a heavier barrel.

Exc.	V.G.	Good	Fair	Poor
600	550	475	375	275

Model 300

A .22 caliber bolt-action rifle with a 23.5" barrel, 5-shot magazine and grooved receiver. Blued with a walnut stock. Imported prior to 1989.

Exc.	V.G.	Good	Fair	Poor
675	600	550	400	300

Model 302 and 304

Variations of the above. Discontinued in 1986.

Exc.	V.G.	Good	Fair	Poor
675	600	550	400	300

Model 311 Smallbore

A .22 caliber bolt-action rifle with a 22" barrel, double set triggers, adjustable sights and a 5- or 10-shot magazine. Blued with walnut stock. Not imported after 1988.

Exc.	V.G.	Good	Fair	Poor
325	275	225	150	100

Model 320

As above, with a 19.5" barrel and full length stock. Discontinued in 1988.

Exc.	V.G.	Good	Fair	Poor
675	600	550	400	300

Model 340

A .22 caliber bolt-action rifle with a 21" heavy barrel furnished without sights, adjustable trigger and 5-shot magazine. Blued with a walnut stock. Not imported after 1988.

Exc.	V.G.	Good	Fair	Poor
700	625	575	425	325

Model 340 Mini-Sniper

As above, but matte finished, the barrel fitted with a muzzle brake and the stock with a raised cheekpiece as well as ventilated handguard.

Exc.	V.G.	Good	Fair	Poor
1000	850	750	500	400

Model 340 Kricotronic

The Model 340 fitted with an electronic trigger. Not imported after 1988.

Exc.	V.G.	Good	Fair	Poor
1250	1000	850	600	500

Model 400 Sporter

A .22 Hornet caliber bolt-action rifle with a 23.5" barrel, open sights and 5-shot magazine. Blued with a walnut stock. Not imported after 1988.

Exc.	V.G.	Good	Fair	Poor
700	625	550	425	325

Model 420

As above, with a 19.5" barrel, double set triggers and a full length stock. Discontinued in 1988.

Exc.	V.G.	Good	Fair	Poor
875	750	675	500	400

Model 440

Similar to the Model 340. Not imported after 1988.

Exc.	V.G.	Good	Fair	Poor
900	800	700	500	375

Model 600 Sporter

A .17 Remington to .308 Winchester caliber bolt-action rifle with a 23.5" barrel, open sights and 3-shot magazine. Blued with a walnut stock. Not imported after 1988.

Exc.	V.G.	Good	Fair	Poor
1100	950	875	700	575

Model 620

As above, with a 20.5" barrel, double set triggers and full length stock.

Exc.	V.G.	Good	Fair	Poor
1150	1000	900	750	600

Model 640 Varmint Rifle

Similar to the above, in .22-250, .222 or .223 caliber with a 23.5" heavy barrel. Not imported after 1988.

Exc.	V.G.	Good	Fair	Poor
1175	1025	925	775	625

Model 640 Sniper Rifle

As above, but matte finished. Discontinued in 1988.

Exc.	V.G.	Good	Fair	Poor
1300	1100	950	750	600

Model 640 Deluxe Sniper Rifle

As above, in .223 or .308 caliber with a 23" barrel, stippled stock and adjustable trigger. Not imported after 1988.

Exc.	V.G.	Good	Fair	Poor
1500	1250	1000	750	650

Model 700 Sporter

A .270 or .30-06 caliber bolt-action rifle with a 23.5" barrel, open sights, single set trigger and 3-shot magazine. Blued with a walnut stock. Discontinued in 1988.

Exc.	V.G.	Good	Fair	Poor
1000	850	750	600	500

Model 720

As above, with a 20.5" barrel, double set triggers and full length stock. Discontinued in 1988.

Exc.	V.G.	Good	Fair	Poor
1000	850	750	600	500

Model 720 Limited Edition

As above, in .270 caliber only with gold-plated furniture and gold highlighted engraving. Not imported after 1988.

Exc.	V.G.	Good	Fair	Poor
2250	2000	1750	1400	900

KRIDER, J. H.

Philadelphia, Pennsylvania

Pocket Pistol

A .41 caliber percussion pocket pistol with a 3" barrel, German silver furniture and walnut stock. The barrel marked "Krider Phila." Manufactured during the 1850s and 1860s.

Exc.	V.G.	Good	Fair	Poor
750	650	500	400	300

Militia Rifle

A .58 caliber percussion rifle with a 39" barrel and full length stock secured by two barrel bands. The barrel browned, the lock marked "Krider". Case-hardened and furniture of brass. Several hundred were manufactured in 1861.

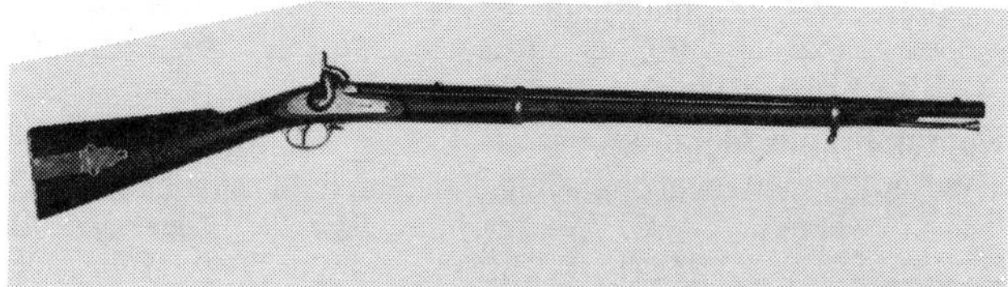

Courtesy Milwaukee Public Museum, Milwaukee, Wisconsin.

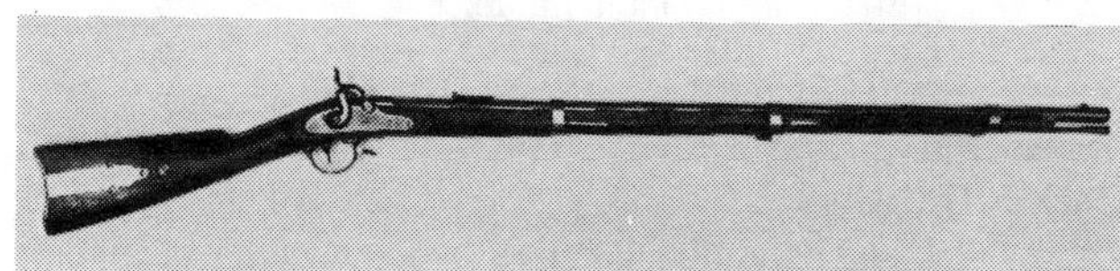

Courtesy Milwaukee Public Museum, Milwaukee, Wisconsin.

Exc.	V.G.	Good	Fair	Poor
1750	1500	1350	1000	750

KRIEGHOFF, HEINRICH, GUN CO.

Ulm, Germany

Importer—Krieghoff International

Ottisville, Pennsylvania

Krieghoff manufactured Lugers are listed in the Luger section.

Drillings and Combination Guns

Plus Model

A 3 barrel combination rifle/shotgun produced in a variety of gauges and calibers with 25" barrels, double triggers and automatic ejectors. Blued with a walnut stock. Introduced in 1988.

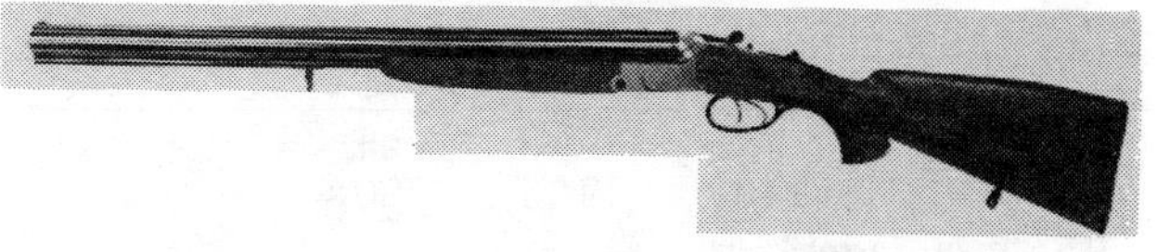

NIB	Exc.	V.G.	Good	Fair	Poor
3800	3500	3000	2500	1850	1250

Trumpf Model
A combination rifle/shotgun produced in a variety of calibers and gauges with 25" barrels and double triggers. Blued with a walnut stock.

Exc.	V.G.	Good	Fair	Poor
7000	6000	4750	3200	2400

Trumpf Dural
As above, with a Duraluminum frame.

Exc.	V.G.	Good	Fair	Poor
7000	6000	4750	3200	2400

Neptun Model
A combination Over/Under rifle/shotgun with sidelocks produced in a variety of gauges and calibers. Engraved, blued with a walnut stock.

Exc.	V.G.	Good	Fair	Poor
11750	10000	7750	5000	4000

Neptun Dural
As above, with a Duraluminum frame.

Exc.	V.G.	Good	Fair	Poor
11750	10000	7750	5000	4000

Neptun Primus Model
The Neptun with relief engraving and detachable sidelocks.

Exc.	V.G.	Good	Fair	Poor
15000	12500	9500	7000	5250

Neptun Primus Dural
As above, with a Duraluminum frame.

Exc.	V.G.	Good	Fair	Poor
15000	12500	9500	7000	5250

Double Rifles

Teck Over/Under
A boxlock Over/Under rifle manufactured in a variety of calibers with 25" barrels, double triggers, extractors and express sights. Blued with a walnut stock.

Exc.	V.G.	Good	Fair	Poor
7500	6500	5000	3750	3000

Ulm Model
As above, with sidelocks.

Exc.	V.G.	Good	Fair	Poor
12500	10000	8000	6750	5000

Ulm Primus
As above, with detachable sidelocks.

Exc.	V.G.	Good	Fair	Poor
15000	12500	10000	7500	6000

Model 32 Standard
A 12, 20, 28 or .410 bore boxlock Over/Under shotgun with 26.5" to 32" barrels, single selective trigger and automatic ejectors. Blued with a walnut stock. Discontinued in 1980.
28 Gauge or .410 Two-Barrel Set—Add 50%.

Exc.	V.G.	Good	Fair	Poor
2000	1750	1500	1000	750

Model 32 Single-Barrel Trap Gun
The Model 32 with a single 32" to 34" barrel.

Exc.	V.G.	Good	Fair	Poor
1750	1400	1100	750	600

KS-5 Single-Barrel Trap
This model is a box lock 12 gauge only Trap gun with 32" or 34" ventilated tapered rib barrel and case-hardened frame with a satin grey finish. The barrel features an adjustable point of impact and is offered with screw-in choke tubes. Weight is approximately 8.6 lbs.

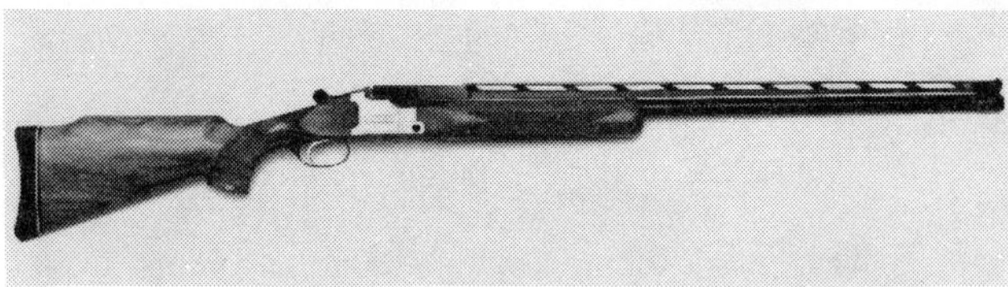

NIB	Exc.	V.G.	Good	Fair	Poor
2850	2250	1750	1500	1250	800

KS-5 Special
Same as above but furnished with adjustable rib and adjustable comb.

NIB	Exc.	V.G.	Good	Fair	Poor
3500	3000	2500	2000	1500	1000

KS-80 Trap
This is a boxlock 12 gauge shotgun built to Trap dimensions. This model is offered in a variety of variations. Available is Over/Under Trap with choice of 30" or 32" vent tapered step rib barrels. Also a single barrel is offered in 32" or 34" tapered step rib lengths. These single barrels are adjustable for point of impact. A top single barrel is available as well in 34" length. Trap Combos are offered also. All barrels are offered with or without choke tubes. The checkered walnut stock is offered in Monte Carlo or straight Trap dimensions. Trap guns weigh approximately 8.75 lbs. Prices below are for Standard Grade.

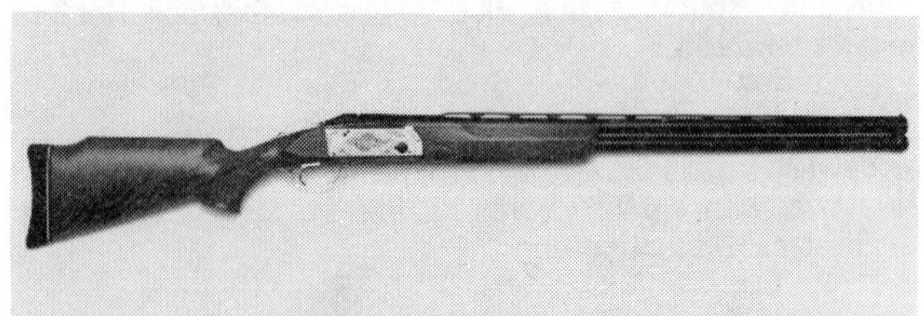

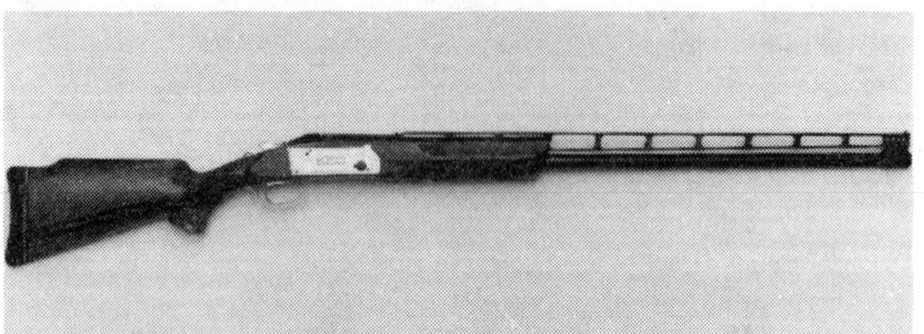

O/U Trap

NIB	Exc.	V.G.	Good	Fair	Poor
5400	4900	4000	3500	2000	1000

Unsingle Trap

NIB	Exc.	V.G.	Good	Fair	Poor
5800	5300	4500	4000	2250	1250

Top Single Trap

NIB	Exc.	V.G.	Good	Fair	Poor
7500	6500	5000	4000	3000	1500

Trap Combos

NIB	Exc.	V.G.	Good	Fair	Poor
8200	7000	6000	4000	3000	1500

Bavaria Grade add 70%.
Danube Grade add 100%.
Gold Target Grade add 200%.

K-80 Sporting Clays
The frame is the same as the Trap model with the addition of a lightweight alloy model and is available in 12 gauge only. Barrel lengths for standard weight model are 28", 30", or 32" with

tapered flat rib. The lightweight model is offered with 28" or 30" flat rib barrels. Select European walnut stock with hand checkering and supplied with a #3 Sporting stock with Schnabel forearm. The standard weight model weighs about 8.25 lbs. while the lightweight model weighs 7.75 lbs. Prices below are for the Standard Grade.

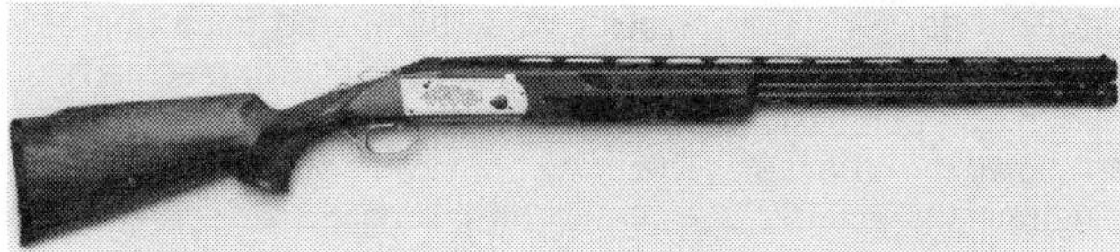

NIB	Exc.	V.G.	Good	Fair	Poor
5800	5250	4500	3000	2000	1000

Bavaria Grade add 70%.
Danube Grade add 100%.
Gold Target Grade add 200%.

K-80 Skeet

This model is offered in a number of variations. The standard weight skeet with 28" or 30" tapered or parallel ribs, lightweight skeet with 28" or 30" tapered or parallel ribs, International skeet with 28" parallel broadway rib, and the 4-barrel skeet set in 12, 20, and 28 gauge as well as .410 bore with 8mm rib. Stock is hand checkered select European walnut with a choice of several skeet dimensions. Prices below are for Standard Grade.

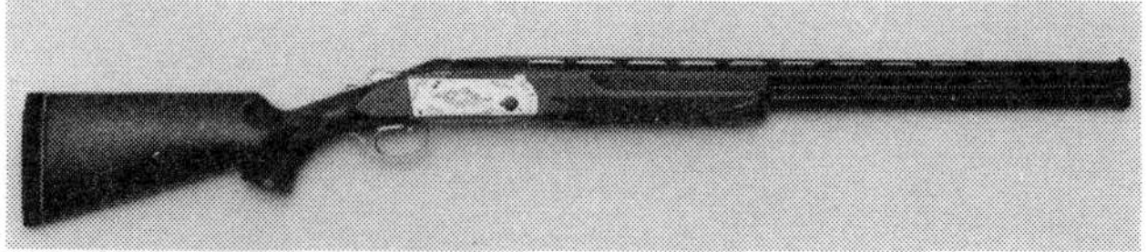

Standard Weight Skeet

NIB	Exc.	V.G.	Good	Fair	Poor
5000	4500	3500	2500	1750	1250

Lightweight Skeet

NIB	Exc.	V.G.	Good	Fair	Poor
5000	4500	3500	2500	1750	1250

International Skeet

NIB	Exc.	V.G.	Good	Fair	Poor
5500	5000	3750	2750	1950	1300

4-Barrel Set

NIB	Exc.	V.G.	Good	Fair	Poor
11250	8000	6000	4000	3000	2000

Bavaria Grade add 70%.
Danube Grade add 100%.
Gold Target Grade add 200%.

Optional Engravings available by special order on NIB or Exc. conditions guns add:
Pacours add $1500.
Parcours Special add $2800.
Super Scroll add $1100.
Gold Super Scroll add $2900.
Custom Bavaria $4700 over Bavaria Grade price.

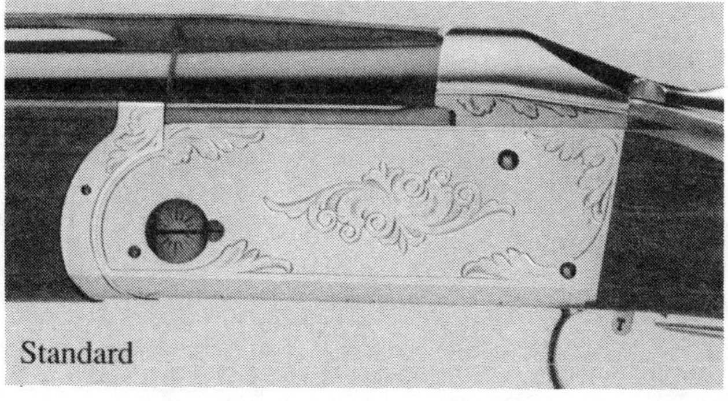
Standard

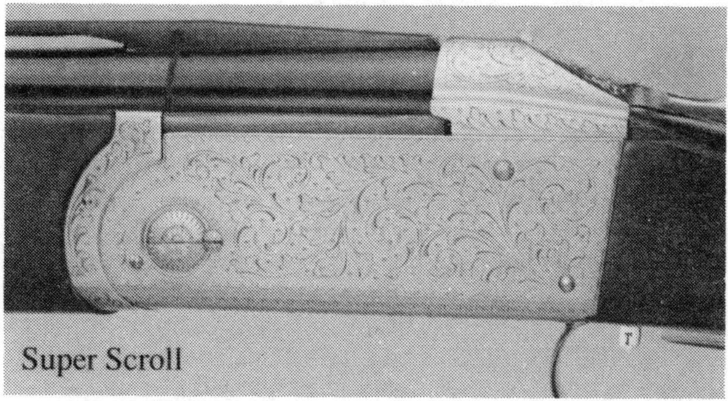
Super Scroll

Parcours

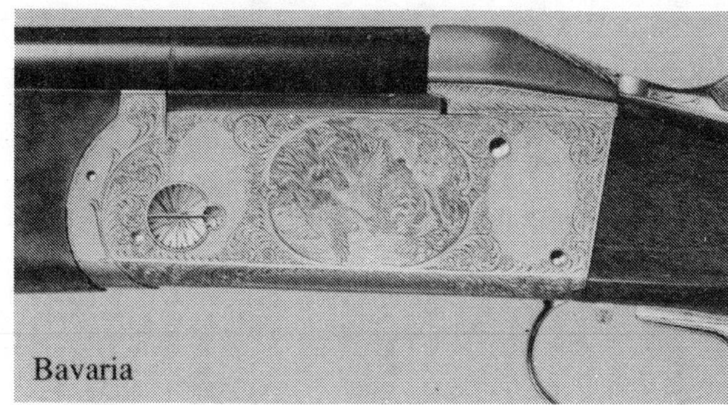
Bavaria

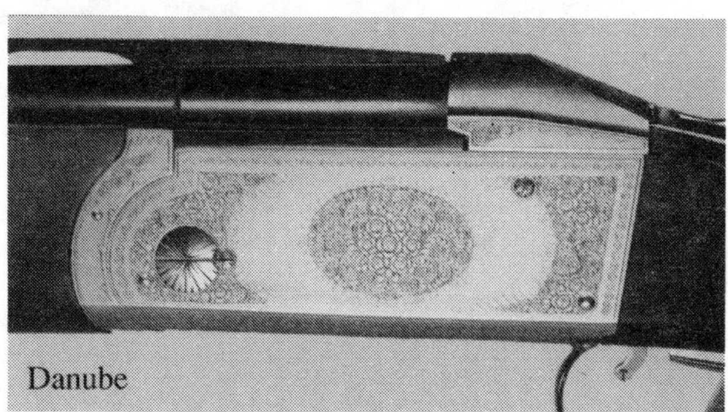
Danube

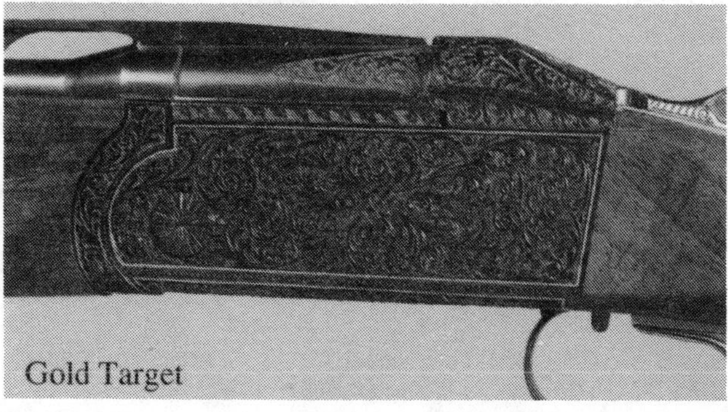
Gold Target

KRNKA, KAREL

Vienna, Austria

Karel Krnka was a very talented firearms inventor born in 1858. He began his career in firearms design as a member of the Austro-Hungarian army. He made many improvements to their service rifle design. After he left the military, he took the job of head engineer with the ill-fated and short-lived "Gatling Gun Co." This company ceased operations in 1890, and then Krnka went to work for the patent office and remained there for a few years. In 1898 he became foreman of the Roth Cartridge Co. and worked with Roth on firearms designs until the death of Roth in 1909. After this he became associated with the Hertenberger Cartridge Company; and finally in 1922 he moved to Czechoslovakia, where he became a firearms designer for the firm of C.Z. He remained at this post until his death in 1926. He recorded his first firearm patent in 1888 for a mechanical repeater with a ring trigger. His best known innovations are the internal butt magazine that is loaded by means of a stripper clip and the rotating locked bolt with internal firing pin. These designs were never actually turned into a mass-marketed pistol but were major contributions in the development of a practical semi-automatic pistol design.

Exc.	V.G.	Good	Fair	Poor
7000	6000	5000	3000	1500

KROPATSCHEK

Steyr-Werke
Steyr, Austria

Model 1878

An 11mm caliber bolt-action rifle with a 32" barrel, full length stock secured by three barrel bands and 7-shot magazine. Finished in the white with a walnut stock.

Exc.	V.G.	Good	Fair	Poor
250	225	200	125	75

KUFAHL, G. L.

Sommerda, Germany

Kufahl Needle-Fire Revolver

Designed and patented in Britain in 1852 by G. L. Kufahl, who tried unsuccessfully to interest a British company in producing it. He then went to the firm of Rheinmettal Dreyse, where a needle-fire gun was produced in 1838. This company manufactured his design. This revolver was chambered for a unique, totally consumed .30-caliber "cartridge." A lead projectile had the ignition percussion cap affixed to its base, with the propellant powder in the rear. The firing pin had to be long enough to penetrate the powder charge and hit the percussion cap. This does not sound efficient, but realize that these were the days before cartridges. This revolver has a 3.2" barrel and an unfluted cylinder that holds 6 shots. It is not bored all the way through but is loaded from the front. The finish is blued, with a modicum of simple engraving and checkered wood grips that protrude all the way over the trigger. The markings are "Fv.V. Dreyse Sommerda."

Exc.	V.G.	Good	Fair	Poor
1500	1250	950	600	450

KYNOCH GUN FACTORY

Birmingham, England

Established by George Kynoch in approximately 1886, this company ceased operation in 1890.

Early Double Trigger Revolver

A .45 caliber double trigger revolver with a 6" barrel, 6-shot cylinder and enclosed hammer. Blued with walnut grips. Manufactured in 1885.

Exc.	V.G.	Good	Fair	Poor
850	750	600	450	350

Late Double Trigger Revolver

Similar to the above, but in .32, .38 or .45 caliber with the cocking trigger enclosed within the triggerguard. Approximately 600 of these revolvers were made between 1896 and 1890.

Exc.	V.G.	Good	Fair	Poor
950	850	700	550	450

L

LAR MFG. CO.
West Jordan, Utah

Grizzly Mark I

A .357 Magnum or .45 Winchester Magnum semi-automatic pistol with a 6.5", 8" or 10" barrel, Millett sights, ambidextrous safety and 7-shot magazine. Parkerized or hard-chrome plated with rubber grips. Available with cartridge conversion units, telescope mounts or a compensator. Introduced in 1984.

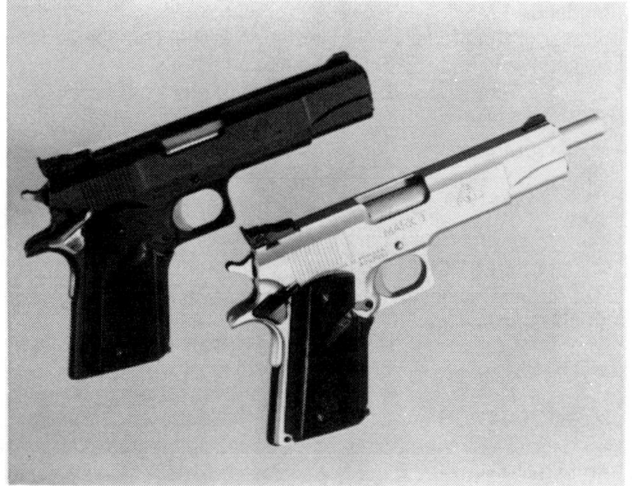

NIB	Exc.	V.G.	Good	Fair	Poor
800	725	650	550	450	300

Grizzly Mark II

As above, with fixed sights and without the ambidextrous safety. Manufactured in 1986.

Exc.	V.G.	Good	Fair	Poor
650	600	500	375	300

LES, INC.
Skokie, Illinois

Rogak P-18

A 9mm caliber double-action semi-automatic pistol with a 5.5" barrel and 18-shot magazine. Stainless steel. Discontinued.

Exc.	V.G.	Good	Fair	Poor
350	300	275	200	150

LABEAU-CORALLY
Liege, Belgium
Importer—Midwest Gun Sport
Zebulon, North Carolina

Shotguns Side x Side

Sologne Model

A 12, 16 or 20 gauge boxlock shotgun with 26" to 30" barrels, single trigger and automatic ejectors. Also available with false sideplates. Blued with a walnut stock.

Exc.	V.G.	Good	Fair	Poor
7500	6750	5000	4200	3750

Grand Russe Model

As above, but engraved and with a more finely figured stock.

Exc.	V.G.	Good	Fair	Poor
8500	7500	6500	4500	4000

Sidelock Ejector Grade

A 12, 16, 20, 28 or .410 bore sidelock double-barrel shotgun with 26" to 30" barrels, double triggers and automatic ejectors. Engraved, blued with a walnut stock.

28 Gauge and .410—Add 10%.

Exc.	V.G.	Good	Fair	Poor
20000	17500	12500	7500	6500

Over/Unders

Sidelock Over/Under

A 12 or 20 gauge sidelock Over/Under shotgun manufactured solely to a specific customer's requirements.

Exc.	V.G.	Good	Fair	Poor
20000	17500	12500	7500	6500

Boss Model

As above, but very finely engraved and with best quality walnut stock.

Exc.	V.G.	Good	Fair	Poor
30000	25000	20000	15000	11500

Double Rifles

Boxlock Ejector Grade

A 8x57JRS, 9.3x74R, .375 H&H, and the .458 Win. Mag. caliber boxlock double-barrel rifle with a 25" barrel, double triggers, automatic ejectors and express sights. Engraved, blued with a walnut stock. Imported prior to 1989.

Exc.	V.G.	Good	Fair	Poor
9000	8000	6000	4500	3500

Sidelock Ejector Grade

As above, but with sidelocks and first quality engraving as well as a finely figured walnut stock.

Exc.	V.G.	Good	Fair	Poor
22500	18500	15000	10000	7500

LAGRESE
Paris, France

Lagrese Revolver

A large ornate revolver chambered for the .43 rimfire cartridge. It has a 6.25" barrel and a 6-shot fluted cylinder. This revolver has no top strap; and the frame, as well as the grip straps, are cast in one piece with the barrel screwed into the frame. It is loaded through a gate and has double-action lockwork. The outstanding feature about this well-made revolver is its extremely ornate appearance. There are more sweeps and curves than could be imagined. It is engraved and blued, with well-figured curved walnut grips. It is marked "Lagrese Bte a Paris" and was manufactured in the late 1860s.

Exc.	V.G.	Good	Fair	Poor
2000	1750	1500	1150	800

LAHTI
Finland
SEE—Husqvarna

Lahti
Designed by Aimo Lahti and produced by Valtion, the Finnish State Arms Factory. It was also made by Husqvarna in Sweden, and this model is found in the Husqvarna section of this book. This pistol is a locked-breech semi-automatic that features a bolt accelerator which does much to make this a very reliable firearm. It is chambered for the 9mm Parabellum cartridge and has a 4.7" barrel. The detachable magazine holds 8 rounds; and the finish is blued, with checkered plastic grips. This pistol was designed to function in extreme cold and has a reputation for reliability. The Swedish version known as the M40 is a fine pistol but is not considered on a par with the Finnish version. It was introduced in 1935.

Exc.	V.G.	Good	Fair	Poor
1250	1000	800	550	450

LAMB, H. C. & CO.
Jamestown, North Carolina

Muzzle Loading Rifle
Chambered for .58 caliber and utilizes the percussion ignition system. It has a 33" barrel and a full-length oak stock held on by two barrel bands. There is a ramrod mounted under the barrel that is made of iron. All other trim is brass, and there is a bayonet lug at the muzzle. This rifle was made for the Confederacy; and the workmanship was crude, as it was on most CSA weapons. The stock is marked "H.C.Lamb & Co.,N.C." There were supposedly 10,000 rifles ordered, but actually there were approximately 250 manufactured between 1861 and 1863. The rarity of the guns of the Confederacy gives them a great deal of collector appeal. One should always be aware that there have been fraudulent examples noted, and a qualified independent appraisal is definitely advisable when dealing with weapons of this nature.

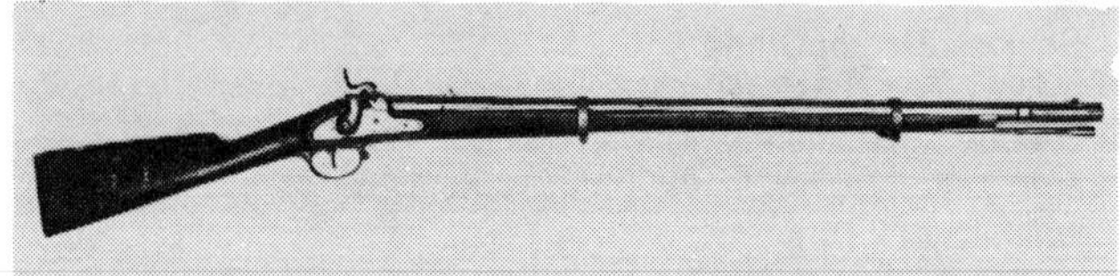

Courtesy Milwaukee Public Museum, Milwaukee, Wisconsin.

Exc.	V.G.	Good	Fair	Poor
6500	5500	4000	3250	2500

LAMES
Chiavari, Italy

Skeet or Trap Grade
An Over/Under shotgun chambered for 12 gauge with either 26" skeet-and-skeet barrels or 30" or 32" full-choked barrels. It has a competition-style wide vent-rib and automatic ejectors. The trigger is single selective, and the finish is blued. The trap gun has a Monte Carlo stock of checkered walnut. Both models feature recoil pads.

Exc.	V.G.	Good	Fair	Poor
600	525	450	350	275

California Trap Grade
This Over/Under is similar to the standard Trap model, with separated barrels. All other features are the same.

Exc.	V.G.	Good	Fair	Poor
700	600	550	450	325

Field Grade
Similar in design to the standard Trap model, with 3" chambers and barrel lengths of 26", 28", or 30" and a field dimensioned stock. It features various choke combinations and was also available with the separated barrels of the California Trap for an additional 20 percent in cost.

Exc.	V.G.	Good	Fair	Poor
400	350	300	225	150

LANBER ARMAS S.A.
Vizcaya, Spain
Lanber Arms of America
Adrian, Michigan

Model 844 ST
A 12-gauge Over/Under shotgun with 26" or 28" vent-rib barrels. The chokes vary, and the gun features a single-selective trigger, extractors, and an engraved receiver with a blued finish and a walnut stock. This gun was manufactured until 1986, when the entire line was no longer imported.

Exc.	V.G.	Good	Fair	Poor
400	350	300	250	175

Model 844 MST
Similar to the Model 844 ST except that it is chambered for 3" Magnum and has 30" full-and-modified barrels.

Exc.	V.G.	Good	Fair	Poor
400	350	300	250	175

Model 844 EST
Similar to the others, but it features automatic ejectors.

Exc.	V.G.	Good	Fair	Poor
450	400	350	300	200

Model 844 EST CHR
Has automatic ejectors and double triggers. All other features are the same as the EST.

Exc.	V.G.	Good	Fair	Poor
425	375	325	275	175

Model 2004 LCH
An Over/Under chambered for 12 gauge and features 28" vent-rib barrels with screw-in choke tubes. It has a single selective trigger, automatic ejectors, and an engraved boxlock action that is matte finished, with a hand-checkered walnut stock. This model was also discontinued in 1986.

Exc.	V.G.	Good	Fair	Poor
750	650	550	475	375

Model 2008 LCH and Model 2009 LCH
The Trap and Skeet versions of the series. The basic differences are in the barrel lengths and the stock dimensions.

Exc.	V.G.	Good	Fair	Poor
850	750	650	575	475

LANCASTER, CHARLES
London, England

4 Barrelled Pistol
A unique pistol for several reasons. It is chambered for the .476 rimfire cartridge and has four 6.25" barrels. The bore has a slightly twisted oval pattern that imparts a spin to the bullet. The barrels are hinged at the bottom and break downward for loading. It is a double-action type lockwork with a very long, difficult trigger pull. The pistol is well made; and the caliber, suitably heavy to insure stopping power. The primary goal was military; and it was successful, seeing action in the Sudan campaigns of 1882 and 1885. This powerful weapon was also popular with big game hunters as a backup sidearm. The finish is blued, with checkered walnut grips. It is marked "Charles Lancaster (Patent) 151 New Bond St. London." This model was introduced in 1881. There are smaller-caliber versions of this pistol with shorter barrels. They are not as well known as the large-caliber version, and the values would be similar as their rarity would be balanced by the desirability of the large-bore models.

Exc.	V.G.	Good	Fair	Poor
2500	2000	1600	1000	750

2 Barrelled Pistol

Similar to the 4-barrelled version, with only two superposed barrels chambered for the .476 rimfire cartridge. The advantage to the 2-barrelled pistol is that it is lighter and better balanced.

Exc.	V.G.	Good	Fair	Poor
2000	1750	1300	900	600

4 Barrelled Shotgun

This company also produced a shotgun in the 4-barrel configuration. It is chambered for 12 or 16 gauge and has 28" barrels. The gun is, as one would imagine, quite heavy and poorly balanced; and it was not a great success.

Exc.	V.G.	Good	Fair	Poor
2000	1750	1300	900	600

Bolt Action Rifle

A high-grade sporting rifle chambered for various different calibers. The barrel is 24" in length; and the finish is blued with a classic-styled, hand-checkered walnut stock. This rifle was discontinued in 1936.

Exc.	V.G.	Good	Fair	Poor
1250	1000	800	550	400

LANG, J.
London, England

Percussion Pistol

Chambered for .60-caliber percussion. It is a single-barrelled, muzzle-loading pistol with a 3.25" barrel. This is essentially a defensive weapon that was very well made, with Damascus barrels and an ornate engraved hammer and frame. The grips are finely checkered walnut, and there is a hinged ramrod under the barrel. There is a spring steel belt hook mounted to the left side of the frame. This pistol was manufactured circa 1836 and was marked "J.Lang."

Exc.	V.G.	Good	Fair	Poor
3000	2500	2000	1500	1000

Gas Seal Revolver

Chambered for the .42-caliber percussion and has a 4.75" barrel. The unfluted cylinder holds 6 shots and is spring-loaded to be forced into the barrel when cocked, in order to obtain the "Gas Seal" feature desired. This revolver was very well made and finished. It is lightly engraved, with a case-colored cylinder and a blued barrel and frame. The grips are finely checkered walnut, and the markings are "J.Lang 22 Cockspur St. London." This type of firearm was the forerunner of later designs such as the Russian Nagant. This revolver was manufactured in the 1850s.

Exc.	V.G.	Good	Fair	Poor
1750	1500	1250	900	550

LANGENHAN, FRIEDRICH
Zella Mehlis, Germany

Langenhan Army Model

A blowback-operated semi-automatic pistol chambered for the 7.65mm Auto Pistol cartridge. It has a 4" barrel and a detachable magazine that holds 8 rounds. The pistol was made with a separate breech block that is held into the slide by a screw. This feature doomed this pistol to eventual failure as when this screw became worn, it could loosen when firing and allow the breech block to pivot upwards—and the slide would then be propelled rearward and into the face of the shooter. This is not a comforting thought. This pistol was produced and used in WWI only and was never offered commercially. It is marked "F.L.Selbstlade DRGM." The finish is blued, and the grips are molded rubber, with "F.L." at the top.

Exc.	V.G.	Good	Fair	Poor
250	225	200	150	100

Model 2

A blowback-operated semi-automatic pistol chambered for the 6.35mm cartridge. It has a 3" barrel and an 8-round detachable magazine. The pistol fires by means of a concealed hammer, and the breechblock is separate from the rest of the slide and is held in place by a heavy crossbolt. The finish is blued, and the grips are molded checkered black plastic with the monogram "F.L." at the top. The slide is marked "Langenhan 6.35." This model was manufactured between 1921 and 1936.

Exc.	V.G.	Good	Fair	Poor
300	250	225	175	125

Model 3

Similar to the Model 2 except that it is somewhat smaller. The barrel is 2.25" in length, and the butt is only large enough to house a 5-round detachable magazine. The markings are the same with the addition of "Model III" on the slide. This model was also manufactured until 1936.

Exc.	V.G.	Good	Fair	Poor
325	275	250	200	150

LASALLE
France
Manufrance

Slide Action Shotgun

Chambered for 12 or 20 gauge and is offered with a 26", 28", or 30" barrel with improved-cylinder, modified, or full chokes. The receiver is alloy, anodized blue; and the vent-rib barrel is blued. The stock is checkered walnut.

Exc.	V.G.	Good	Fair	Poor
275	250	200	150	100

Semi-automatic Shotgun

A gas-operated semi-automatic shotgun chambered for 12 gauge only, with the same barrel length and choke combinations as are available on the Slide Action model. The receiver is also alloy, and the stock is checkered walnut.

Exc.	V.G.	Good	Fair	Poor
325	275	225	175	125

LAURONA
Eibar, Spain
Importer—Galaxy Imports
Victoria, Texas

Model 67G

An Over/Under chambered for 12 gauge, with double triggers and 28" vent-rib barrels with extractors. The boxlock action and barrels are blued, and the stock is checkered walnut.

Exc.	V.G.	Good	Fair	Poor
250	225	200	150	100

Model 82

Similar to the Model 67 except that it features a double-selective trigger system that would function either as a single or double triggers.

Exc.	V.G.	Good	Fair	Poor
550	500	400	300	225

Model 82 G Super Game

A higher-grade model that is chambered for 12 or 20 gauge and features 28" barrels with various chokes. The twin single triggers were offered, as well as automatic ejectors and a good deal of fine scroll engraving. The finish is black chrome-plated, and the stock is hand- checkered select walnut.

Exc.	V.G.	Good	Fair	Poor
1000	950	850	600	450

Model 83 Super Game

Similar to the Model 82 except that it features screw-in choke tubes.

Exc.	V.G.	Good	Fair	Poor
1000	800	650	400	300

Model 84 Super Game

Has a single selective trigger and 3" magnum chambers.

Exc.	V.G.	Good	Fair	Poor
1000	800	650	400	300

LAW ENFORCEMENT ORDNANCE CORP.

Ridgeway, Pennsylvania

Striker 12

A semi-automatic shotgun designed for self-defense. It is chambered for 12 gauge and has an 18.25" cylinder bored barrel. The unique feature about this gun is its 12-round drum magazine. The barrel is shrouded, and the stock folds. A fixed-stock model is also available. This gun was introduced primarily as a law enforcement tool, and the original models had 12" barrels and were legal for law enforcement agencies and Class 3 licensed individuals only. The 18.25" version is legal for private ownership and was introduced in 1986.

Exc.	V.G.	Good	Fair	Poor
750	650	525	450	350

LEBEL

French State

The Lebel system was invented by Nicolas Lebel in 1886. The French replaced the singleshot Gras Model 1874 rifle with this weapon. This was the first successful smallbore rifle and sent the rest of the European continent into a dash to emulate it. The Lebel system was used until it was made obsolete by the Berthier rifle in the 1890s.

Model 1886 "Lebel"

Chambered for the 8mm Lebel cartridge. It has a 31" barrel and holds 8 shots in a tubular magazine that runs beneath the barrel. This design is very long and heavy and was not in use for very long before being replaced by the more efficient box magazine weapons, such as those from Mauser. This rifle has a two-piece stock with no upper handguard. It is held on by two barrel bands, and a cruciform bayonet could be fixed under the muzzle. Although this rifle was made obsolete rather quickly, it did have the distinction of being the first successful smokeless-powder smallbore rifle; and there were shortened examples in use until the end of WWII.

Exc.	V.G.	Good	Fair	Poor
150	125	100	75	50

Revolver Model 1892

Chambered for an 8mm centerfire cartridge and has a 4.5" barrel with a 6-shot cylinder. It is referred to as a "Lebel," but there is no certainty that Nicolas Lebel had anything to do with its design or production. This revolver is a simple double-action, with a swing-out cylinder that swings to the right side for loading. The design of this weapon is similar to the Italian Model 1889. There is one redeeming feature on this revolver, and that is a hinged sideplate on the left side of the frame that could be swung away after unlocking so that repairs or cleaning of the lockwork could be performed with relative simplicity. The cartridge for which this weapon was chambered was woefully inadequate. This revolver remained in use from its introduction in 1893 until the end of WWII in 1945, mainly because the French never got around to designing a replacement.

Exc.	V.G.	Good	Fair	Poor
175	150	125	100	75

LEE FIREARMS CO.

Milwaukee, Wisconsin

Lee Single Shot Carbine

A very rare single-shot break-open carbine that pivots to the right side for loading. It is chambered for the .44 rimfire cartridge and has a 21.5" barrel with a hammer mounted in the center of the frame. The carbine has a walnut buttstock but no forearm and is marked "Lee's Firearms Co. Milwaukee, Wisc." There were approximately 450 manufactured between 1863 and 1865. There are very few surviving examples, and one should be wary of fakes.

Courtesy Milwaukee Public Museum, Milwaukee, Wisconsin.

Exc.	V.G.	Good	Fair	Poor
1500	1250	1000	750	500

Lee Sporting Rifle

Similar to the military carbine except that it has a longer octagonal barrel. The barrel length was varied, and there were more of these manufactured. The survival rate appears to have been better than for the Carbine model.

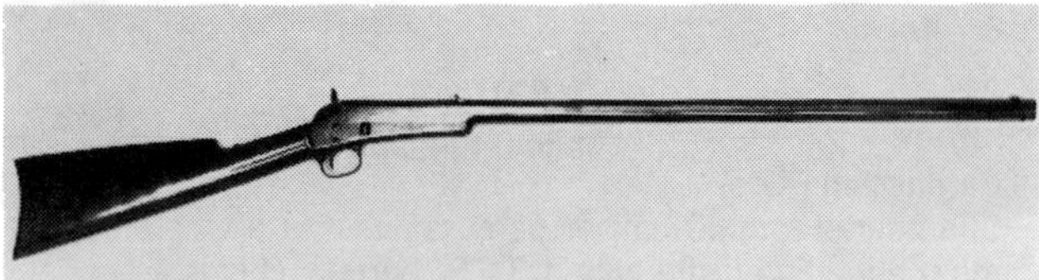

Courtesy Milwaukee Public Museum, Milwaukee, Wisconsin.

Exc.	V.G.	Good	Fair	Poor
650	550	450	300	175

LEE-ENFIELD

Middlesex, England

Royal Small Arms Factory

The British service rifle from 1895 through WWII. There are a number of minor variations, and it would behoove the potential collector to avail oneself of the material written on this weapon. We furnish descriptions and values of most of these variations.

Mark 1

Introduced on the 11th of November, 1895. Its outward appearance is similar to that of the Lee-Metford Mark 2* Rifle. The method of rifling is different, since smokeless powder had been developed. It is chambered for the .303 British cartridge and has a 30.2" barrel and a full-length stock held on by two barrel bands. There is a cleaning rod mounted under the barrel. It has military-type sights and a box magazine located in front of the triggerguard. The finish is blued, with a walnut stock with sling swivels and a stacking swivel.

Exc.	V.G.	Good	Fair	Poor
250	225	175	125	90

Mark 1*

Produced by fitting a .303 British barrel to a Mark 3 Martini-Henry action. It has a 30.2" barrel and features a stripper-clip guide on the receiver. It was introduced in 1899.

Exc.	V.G.	Good	Fair	Poor
250	225	175	125	90

Mark 1**

Similar to the Mark 1 except that the cleaning rod was removed. It was introduced in 1899.

Exc.	V.G.	Good	Fair	Poor
250	225	175	125	90

Short Magazine Mark 1 Rifle

A carbine-length version that is chambered for the .303 British cartridge and has a 25" barrel with a 10-round, detachable box magazine. Upon its introduction it was intended to be the perfect infantryman's rifle. At first, it was not accepted because its short length was deemed to be detrimental from an accuracy standpoint. It did, however, survive; and the "SMLE" earned the reputation of one of the finest bolt-action service rifles ever produced. The finish is blued, and it has a full-length walnut stock held on by two barrel bands. The stock extended very nearly to the muzzle, creating a snubnose effect with the protruding barrel. It was introduced in 1903.

Exc.	V.G.	Good	Fair	Poor
225	200	150	100	75

Mark 2

Similar to the SMLE Mark 1 except that it has a shorter, lighter barrel, improved sights, and a stripper-clip guide on the receiver. It was also introduced in 1903.

Exc.	V.G.	Good	Fair	Poor
225	200	150	100	75

Mark 3

Similar to the Mark 1, with the addition of improved sights. It was introduced in 1907.

Exc.	V.G.	Good	Fair	Poor
225	200	150	100	75

Mark 4

A Mark 2 rifle converted by adding the features of the Mark 3. It was introduced in 1907.

Exc.	V.G.	Good	Fair	Poor
200	175	150	100	75

No. 4 Mark 1

Features the addition of a hinged aperture rear sight. The nose cap was removed from the stock. It was introduced in 1942.

Exc.	V.G.	Good	Fair	Poor
200	175	150	100	75

No. 4 Mark 2

Similar to the No. 4 Mark 1, with an improved trigger mechanism. It was introduced in 1949.

Exc.	V.G.	Good	Fair	Poor
200	175	150	100	75

No. 5 Mark 1

Known as the "Jungle Carbine." It is chambered for the .303 British cartridge and has an 18.5" barrel with a flash-hider on the muzzle. It has a shortened stock, with a rear handguard held on by one barrel band. The stock has a rubber recoil pad. The finish is blued.

Although the weapon was light and compact for carrying, it had an excessive recoil and muzzle blast and was not popular with the soldiers who used it.

Exc.	V.G.	Good	Fair	Poor
300	250	200	150	100

LEE-METFORD
Great Britain

Mark 1

A bolt-action service rifle chambered for the .303 British cartridge. It was designed by James Lee and incorporated rifling developed by William Metford. This rifling was specifically designed to alleviate the problem of black powder fouling. It has a 30.2" barrel and a 10-round, detachable box magazine located in front of the triggerguard. It features military-type sights and a cleaning rod mounted underneath the barrel. The finish is blued, with a full-length walnut stock held on by two barrel bands. It was introduced in 1888.

Exc.	V.G.	Good	Fair	Poor
200	175	150	100	75

Mark 1*

Similar to the Mark 1 except that the safety catch was removed from the cocking piece and a brass disc was inletted into the buttstock for regimental markings. There were a number of internal improvements, as well as the fitting of a different, blade-type front sight. It was introduced in 1892.

Exc.	V.G.	Good	Fair	Poor
175	150	125	100	75

Mark 2

Has a modified magazine that holds 10 rounds in a double column. It was introduced in 1892.

Exc.	V.G.	Good	Fair	Poor
175	150	125	100	75

Mark 2*

Has a lengthened bolt, with the addition of a safety catch. It was introduced in 1895.

Exc.	V.G.	Good	Fair	Poor
200	175	150	100	75

Mark 1 Carbine

Has a 20.75" barrel, and the receiver was modified to accept a stripper-clip guide. It was introduced in 1894.

Exc.	V.G.	Good	Fair	Poor
200	175	150	100	75

LEECH & RIGDON
Greensboro, Georgia

Leech & Rigdon Revolver

This Confederate revolver was patterned after the 1851 Colt Navy. It is chambered for .36 caliber percussion and has a 6-shot unfluted cylinder. The 7.5" barrel is part-octagonal and has a loading lever beneath it. The frame is open-topped; and the finish is blued, with brass grip straps and walnut one-piece grips. The barrel is marked "Leech & Rigdon CSA." There were approximately 1,500 revolvers manufactured in 1863 and 1864. These were all contracted for by the Confederacy and are considered to be a prime acquisition for collectors. Be wary of fakes, and trust in qualified independent appraisals only.

Exc.	V.G.	Good	Fair	Poor
10000	8000	5000	3000	2500

LEFAUCHAUX, CASIMER & EUGENE
Paris, France

Pinfire Revolver

The pinfire ignition system was invented by Casimir Lefauchaux in 1828 but was not widely used until the 1850s. It consists of a smooth rimless case which contains the powder charge and a percussion cap. A pin protrudes from the side of this case at the rear and when struck by the hammer is driven into the cap, thereby igniting the charge and firing the weapon. The pistols for this cartridge are slotted at the end of the cylinder to allow the pins to protrude and be struck by the downward blow of the hammer. This particular revolver is chambered for .43 caliber and has a 5.25" barrel. The cylinder holds 6 shots; and the finish is blued, with checkered walnut grips. This revolver was manufactured after 1865 and was selected for service by the French military.

Exc.	V.G.	Good	Fair	Poor
375	300	275	200	125

LEFEVER ARMS CO.
Syracuse, New York

Founded by Dan Lefever, who was a pioneer in the field of breech-loading firearms. This company was founded in 1884, with Lefever as the president. He was referred to as "Uncle Dan" within the firearms industry. He was responsible for many improvements in the double-barrel shotgun design. He developed the automatic hammerless system in the late 1880s. He also developed a compensating action that allowed simple adjustments to compensate for action wear. In 1901 he was forced out of the company and organized another company—the D. M. Lefever, Sons & Company—also in Syracuse. Dan Lefever died in 1906, and his new company went out of business. The original company was acquired by Ithaca in 1916. They continued to produce Lefever guns until 1948.

Sidelock Shotgun
A double-barrel, side-by-side shotgun chambered for 10, 12, 16, or 20 gauge. It was offered with 26", 28", 30", or 32" barrels with various choke combinations. The barrels are either Damascus or fluid steel. Damascus guns have become very collectible and in better condition—very good to excellent—can bring nearly the same price as the fluid-steel guns. It features a full sidelock action. Double triggers are standard. The finish is blued, with a checkered walnut stock. There are a number of variations that differ in the amount of ornamentation and the quality of materials and workmanship utilized in their construction. Automatic ejectors are represented by the letter "E" after the respective grade designation. This shotgun was manufactured between 1885 and 1919. We strongly recommend that a qualified appraisal be secured if a transaction is contemplated.
20 Gauge—Add 25%.
Single Selective Trigger—Add 10%.

DS Grade

Exc.	V.G.	Good	Fair	Poor
1200	1050	800	600	400

DSE Grade

Exc.	V.G.	Good	Fair	Poor
1600	1450	1100	750	500

H Grade

Exc.	V.G.	Good	Fair	Poor
1400	1250	950	650	550

HE Grade

Exc.	V.G.	Good	Fair	Poor
1800	1650	1300	1000	750

G Grade

Exc.	V.G.	Good	Fair	Poor
1500	1300	1000	750	500

GE Grade

Exc.	V.G.	Good	Fair	Poor
2000	1800	1500	1200	850

F Grade

Exc.	V.G.	Good	Fair	Poor
1500	1000	800	650	475

FE Grade

Exc.	V.G.	Good	Fair	Poor
2250	2000	1750	1250	950

E Grade

Exc.	V.G.	Good	Fair	Poor
2000	1800	1550	1000	800

EE Grade

Exc.	V.G.	Good	Fair	Poor
2750	2450	1800	1300	1000

D Grade

Exc.	V.G.	Good	Fair	Poor
2500	2200	1650	1050	800

DE Grade

Exc.	V.G.	Good	Fair	Poor
3250	2800	2250	1500	1200

C Grade

Exc.	V.G.	Good	Fair	Poor
4000	3400	2850	2000	1500

CE Grade

Exc.	V.G.	Good	Fair	Poor
6000	5000	4000	3000	2250

B Grade

Exc.	V.G.	Good	Fair	Poor
6000	5000	4000	3000	2250

BE Grade

Exc.	V.G.	Good	Fair	Poor
10000	9000	6500	4500	3000

A Grade

Exc.	V.G.	Good	Fair	Poor
20000	16000	11000	7000	3500

AA Grade

Exc.	V.G.	Good	Fair	Poor
30000	22500	15000	8000	4500

There was also an Optimus Grade and a Thousand Dollar Grade offered. These are extremely high-grade, heavily ornamented firearms inlaid with precious metals. They are extremely rare, and evaluating them on a general basis is impossible.

Nitro Special
A side-by-side, double-barrel shotgun chambered for 12, 16, or 20 gauge, as well as .410. The barrels were offered in lengths of 26" to 32" with various choke combinations. It features a boxlock action with double triggers and extractors standard. The finish is blued, with a case-colored receiver and a checkered walnut stock. This model was manufactured between 1921 and 1948; and incredible as it may seem, its price at introduction was $29.
20 Gauge—Add 25%.
.410—Add 100%.
Single Selective Trigger—Add 20%.

Exc.	V.G.	Good	Fair	Poor
400	300	250	200	150

A Grade
A more deluxe version of the Nitro Special. It was manufactured between 1934 and 1942. The additional values for small gauges and single selective triggers would apply, as well as an optional automatic ejector which would add 30 percent to the value.

Exc.	V.G.	Good	Fair	Poor
900	775	550	450	375

A Grade Skeet
A higher-grade competition version with 26" skeet-bored barrels. It was offered standard with a single trigger, automatic ejectors, and a beavertail forearm. The additional values for the small-bore options would apply.

Exc.	V.G.	Good	Fair	Poor
1200	1000	850	725	600

Long Range Single Barrel
A field-grade single shot shotgun chambered for all gauges and offered with 26" through 32" barrel lengths. It has a boxlock action with an extractor. The finish is blued, with a checkered walnut stock. It was discontinued in 1942.

Exc.	V.G.	Good	Fair	Poor
350	300	250	175	125

Single Barrel Trap
A single shot, competition-grade gun chambered for 12 gauge with a 30" or 32" full-choke vent-rib barrel. It has a boxlock action and features an automatic ejector. The finish is blued, with a checkered walnut stock. It was discontinued in 1942.

Exc.	V.G.	Good	Fair	Poor
550	450	350	250	175

LEFEVER, D. M., SONS & COMPANY

Syracuse, New York

"Uncle Dan" Lefever founded the Lefever Arms Company in 1884. In 1901 he was forced out of his company and founded the D. M. Lefever, Sons & Company. He continued to produce high-grade, side-by-side, double-barrel shotguns until his death in 1906, when the company ceased operations. There were approximately 1,200 shotguns of all variations produced during this period, making them extremely rare and difficult to evaluate on a general basis. We list the models and average values but strongly suggest securing qualified appraisal if a transaction is contemplated.

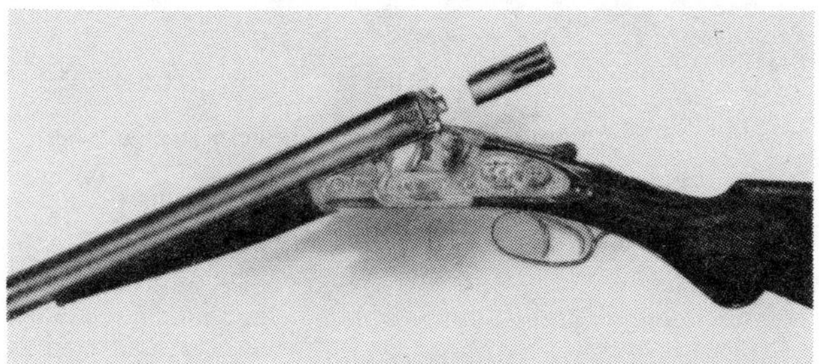

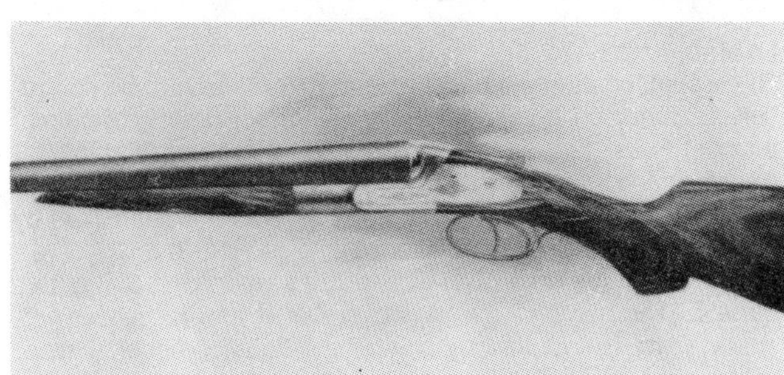

Lefever Double Barrel Shotgun

A side-by-side, double-barrel shotgun chambered for 12, 16, or 20 gauge. It was offered with various-length barrels and choke combinations that were made to order. It features double triggers and automatic ejectors. A single selective trigger was available as an option. The finish is blued, with a checkered walnut stock. The individual grades differ in the amount of ornamentation and the general quality of the materials and workmanship utilized in their construction. This model was discontinued in 1906.

Single Selective Trigger—Add 10%.

20 Gauge—Add 25%.

O Excelsior Grade—Extractors

Exc.	V.G.	Good	Fair	Poor
2400	2000	1650	950	700

Excelsior Grade—Auto Ejectors

Exc.	V.G.	Good	Fair	Poor
2700	2500	2000	1250	900

F Grade, No. 9

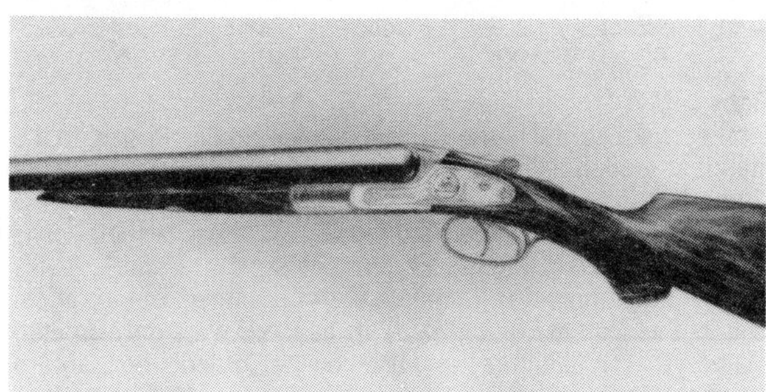

Exc.	V.G.	Good	Fair	Poor
3000	2750	2250	1500	1100

G Grade—10 Gauge, Damascus Barrels

Exc.	V.G.	Good	Fair	Poor
3500	3100	2600	2000	1350

E Grade, No. 8

Exc.	V.G.	Good	Fair	Poor
4000	3500	3000	2400	1700

D Grade, No. 7

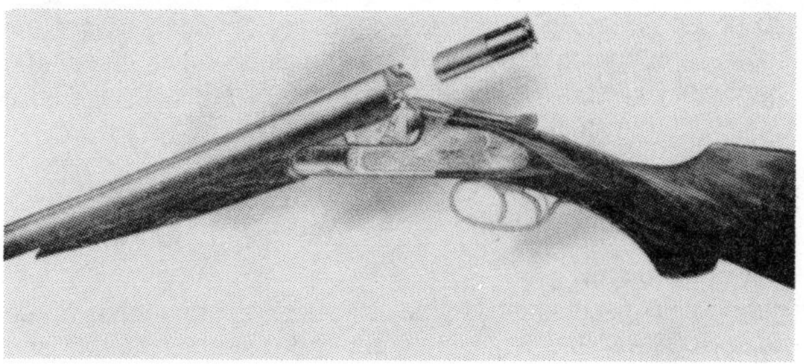

Exc.	V.G.	Good	Fair	Poor
4500	3900	3400	2750	2000

C Grade, No. 6

Exc.	V.G.	Good	Fair	Poor
5000	4500	3750	3000	2500

B Grade, No. 5

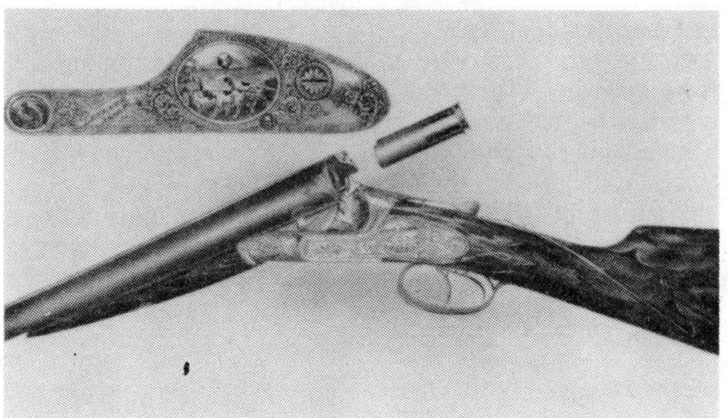

Exc.	V.G.	Good	Fair	Poor
6500	5750	4800	3500	3000

AA Grade, No. 4

Exc.	V.G.	Good	Fair	Poor
9000	7800	6500	4200	2750

There is an "Uncle Dan" grade, which is the top-of-the-line version, that features extremely high quality in materials and workmanship and a great deal of ornamentation. This firearm is extremely rare and seldom found in today's market. It is impossible to evaluate it on a general basis.

LE FORGERON

Liege, Belgium
Importer—Midwest Guns
Zebulon, North Carolina

Model 6020 Double Rifle

A boxlock-actioned side-by-side rifle that is chambered for the 9.3x74R cartridge. It has 25" barrels with double triggers and automatic ejectors. The finish is blued, and the pistol grip stock is checkered walnut.

Exc.	V.G.	Good	Fair	Poor
5000	4500	4000	3000	2500

Model 6040

Simply the Model 6020 with false sideplates. All other specifications are the same.

Exc.	V.G.	Good	Fair	Poor
5750	5200	4500	3500	3000

Model 6030

A double rifle that has a true sidelock action and is engraved. It has a deluxe French walnut stock.

Exc.	V.G.	Good	Fair	Poor
9000	8000	7250	5500	4200

Boxlock Shotgun

This is a side-by-side, double barrelled shotgun chambered for 20 or 28 gauge. The barrel lengths are optional, as are the choke combinations. This gun has a single selective trigger and automatic ejectors. It is engraved and blued, with a deluxe French walnut stock.

False Sideplates—Add 20%.

Exc.	V.G.	Good	Fair	Poor
4500	4000	3250	2250	1750

Sidelock Shotgun

Has similar specifications to the boxlock except that it has a true sidelock action and is generally more deluxe in materials and workmanship.

Exc.	V.G.	Good	Fair	Poor
11500	10500	8500	6500	5500

LE FRANCAIS

St. Etienne, France
Francais D'Armes et Cycles

Le Francais Model 28

A unique pistol chambered for the 9mm Browning cartridge. It is a large pistol, with a 5" barrel that was hinged with a tip-up breech. This is a blowback-operated semi-automatic pistol that has no extractor. The empty cases are blown out of the breech by gas pressure. The one feature about this pistol that is desirable is that it is possible to tip the barrel breech forward like a shotgun and load cartridges singly, while holding the contents of the magazine in reserve. This weapon has fixed sights and a blued finish, with checkered walnut grips. It was manufactured between 1928 and 1938.

Exc.	V.G.	Good	Fair	Poor
1250	1050	850	650	450

Police Model

A blowback-operated, double-action semi-automatic that is chambered for the .32 ACP cartridge. It has a 3.5" barrel and a 7-round magazine. It has the same hinged-barrel feature of the Model 28 and is blued, with fixed sights and molded rubber grips. This model was manufactured between 1914 and 1938.

Exc.	V.G.	Good	Fair	Poor
800	700	550	375	275

Officers Model

Also a blowback-operated semi-automatic chambered for the .25 ACP cartridge. It has a 2.5" barrel and a concealed hammer. It has fixed sights, and the finish is blued. The grips are molded rubber. This model was manufactured between 1914 and 1938.

Exc.	V.G.	Good	Fair	Poor
300	250	200	150	100

LEMAN, H. E.

Lancaster, Pennsylvania

Leman Militia Rifle

A .58 caliber percussion muzzleloader that has a 33" round barrel. The stock is full-length and is held on by two barrel bands. There is a ramrod mounted under the barrel. The trim is brass; and the barrel is browned, with a case-colored lock. The lock is marked "H.E.Leman/ Lancaster, Pa." There were approximately 500 manufactured between 1860 and 1864. They are believed to have been used by the Pennsylvania State Militia in the Civil War.

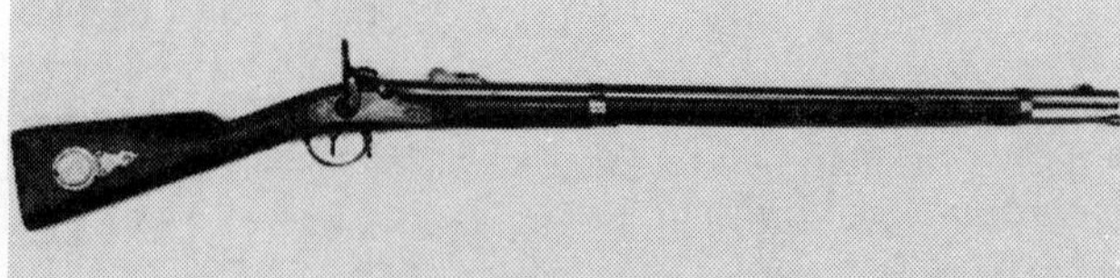

Courtesy Milwaukee Public Museum, Milwaukee, Wisconsin.

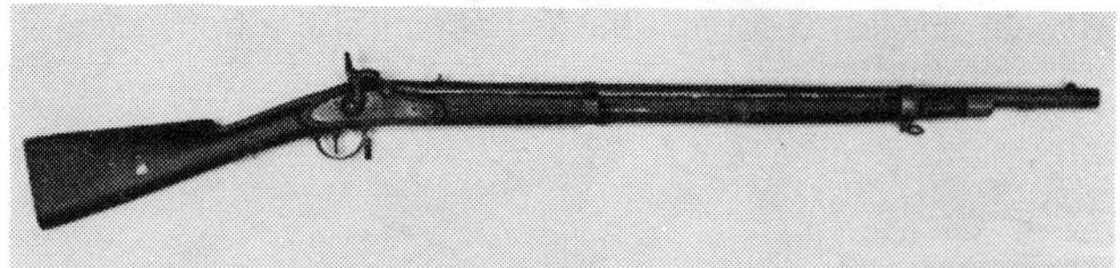

Courtesy Milwaukee Public Museum, Milwaukee, Wisconsin.

Exc.	V.G.	Good	Fair	Poor
2000	1800	1500	900	650

LE MAT

Paris, France

Le Mat

Has a somewhat unique background that makes it a bit controversial among collectors. It is a foreign-made firearm manufactured in Paris, France, as well as in Birmingham, England. It was designed and patented by an American, Jean Alexander LeMat of New Orleans, Louisiana; and it was purchased for use by the Confederate States of America and used in the Civil War. This is a curious firearm as it is a huge weapon that has two barrels. The top 6.5" barrel is chambered for .42 caliber percussion and is supplied by a 9-shot unfluted cylinder that revolves on a 5", .63-caliber, smoothbore barrel that doubles as the cylinder axis pin. These two barrels are held together by a front and a rear ring. The rear sight is a notch in the nose of the hammer, and there is an attached ramrod on the side of the top barrel. The weapon is marked "Lemat and Girards Patent, London." The finish is blued, with checkered walnut grips. There were fewer than 3,000 manufactured, of which approximately one half were purchased by the Confederate States of America. They were made between 1856 and 1865.

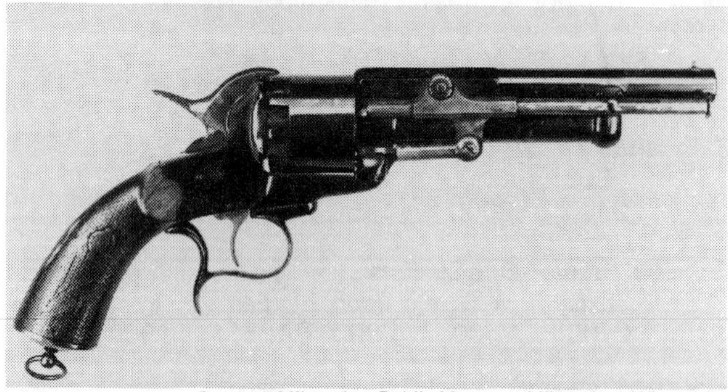

Courtesy Milwaukee Public Museum, Milwaukee, Wisconsin.

Exc.	V.G.	Good	Fair	Poor
5000	4000	3250	2400	1750

Baby LeMat

Similar in appearance (though a good deal smaller in size) to the standard model pistol. It is chambered for .32 caliber percussion and has a 4.25" top barrel and a .41-caliber smoothbore lower barrel. The cylinder is unfluted and holds 9 shots. The barrel is marked "Systeme Le Mat Bte s.g.d.g. Paris." It has British proofmarks and is blued, with checkered walnut grips. This is the scarcest model Le Mat, as there were only an estimated 100 manufactured and used by the Confederate States of America in the Civil War.

Exc.	V.G.	Good	Fair	Poor
6500	5500	4500	3250	2500

LEONARD, G.

Charlestown, Massachusetts

Pepperbox

A .31-caliber, four-barrelled pepperbox with a concealed hammer. The barrels are 3.25" in length. There is a ring trigger used to cock the weapon, while a smaller trigger located outside the ring is used to fire the weapon. The barrels on this pistol do not revolve. There is a revolving striker inside the frame that turns to fire each chamber. The barrels must be removed for loading and capping purposes. The frame is iron and blued, with engraving. The rounded grips are walnut. The barrel is stamped "G.Leonard Jr. Charlestown." There were fewer than 200 manufactured in 1849 and 1850.

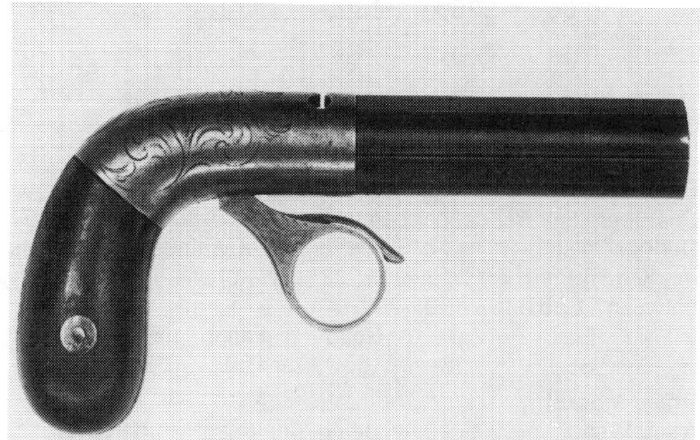

Exc.	V.G.	Good	Fair	Poor
1500	1000	650	450	300

LE PAGE SA.
Liege, Belgium

Pinfire Revolver

Was in the business of revolver manufacture in the 1850s, producing a .40-caliber pinfire revolver that was very similar to the Lefauchaux and other pinfires of the day. The barrel lengths vary, and the unfluted cylinder holds 6 shots. These pistols are double-action and sometimes are found with ornate but somewhat crude engraving. The finish is blued, with wood grips. The quality of these weapons is fair. They were serviceable; but the ammunition created somewhat of a problem, as it is rather fragile and difficult to handle with the protruding primer pin to contend with.

Exc.	V.G.	Good	Fair	Poor
350	300	250	200	125

Semi-Automatic Pistol

Was dormant for many years and was revived in 1925 to produce this blowback-operated semi-automatic with an open-topped slide and exposed barrel. It is chambered for the 7.65mm, 9mm Short, and the 9mm Browning Long cartridges. The barrel is 4" in length, and the grip is oversized, has finger grooves, and houses a 12-shot magazine. The pistol was not a commercial success, and there were not a great many manufactured.

Exc.	V.G.	Good	Fair	Poor
300	250	200	150	100

LIDDLE & KAEDING
San Francisco, California

Pocket Revolver

Manufactured by Forehand and Wadsworth and stamped with the above name. This company was a dealer in California and had nothing whatever to do with the production of this revolver. It is chambered for the .32 rimfire cartridge and has a 3.25" octagonal barrel and a 5-shot fluted cylinder. The frame is iron; and the finish is blued, with walnut grips. There were a few hundred manufactured between 1880 and 1886. The dealer's name is marked on the top strap.

Exc.	V.G.	Good	Fair	Poor
300	250	200	150	100

LIEGEOISE D ARMES
Liege, Belgium

Side x Side Boxlock Shotgun

This double-barrelled gun is chambered for 12 and 20 gauge. The barrels are 28" or 30" in length, and the choke combinations are varied. It has a single trigger and automatic ejectors. The action is moderately engraved; and the finish is blued, with a checkered walnut stock.

Exc.	V.G.	Good	Fair	Poor
750	675	600	450	350

LIGNOSE
Suhl, Germany

Einhand Model 2A

This unique design was based on the Chelewski. It allows the shooter to cock and fire this blowback-operated semi-automatic pistol with one hand (Einhand). It is chambered for the 6.35mm cartridge and has a 2" barrel. The magazine holds 6 shots; and the finish is blued, with molded rubber grips marked "Lignose." The triggerguard on this pistol has a reverse curve that fits the finger, and it moves backward to cock the slide. It was manufactured in 1917 by the Bergman Company, but the rights were then sold to Lignose where it was produced after 1921.

Exc.	V.G.	Good	Fair	Poor
250	225	200	150	100

Einhand Model 3A

Similar to the Model 2A, with a longer grip that houses a 9-shot magazine. All other specifications are the same as the Model 2A.

Courtesy Orville Reichert.

Exc.	V.G.	Good	Fair	Poor
250	225	200	150	100

Model 2

Similar to the Model 2A, with the extended grip and 9-shot capacity but no provision for one-hand cocking.

Exc.	V.G.	Good	Fair	Poor
200	175	150	100	75

LILLIPUT

SEE—Menz

LINDE A.

Memphis, Tennessee

Pocket Pistol

This company manufactured a small, concealable firearm patterned after the Henry Deringer Philadelphia-type pistol. It is chambered for .41-caliber percussion and has a 2.5" barrel, German silver mountings, and a walnut stock. It was manufactured in the 1850s.

Exc.	V.G.	Good	Fair	Poor
650	600	500	400	300

LINDSAY, JOHN P.

Naugatuck, Connecticut
Union Knife Company

The Union Knife Co. manufactured the Lindsay 2-shot pistols for the inventor, John P. Lindsay. There are three separate and distinct models as follows.

2 Shot Belt Pistol

Is an oddity. It is a single-barrelled, .41-caliber percussion pistol with a double chamber that contains two powder charges and projectiles that are simultaneously fired by two separate hammers. The hammers are released by a single trigger that allows them to fall in the proper sequence. The 5.5" octagonal barrel is contoured into a radical stepped-down shape, and there is a spur trigger. The frame is brass and has scroll engraving. The barrel is blued and is marked "Lindsay's Young America." There were estimated to be fewer than 100 manufactured between 1860 and 1862.

Exc.	V.G.	Good	Fair	Poor
2000	1750	1500	1150	900

2 Shot Pocket Pistol

A smaller version of the Belt Pistol. It is chambered for the same caliber but has a 4" barrel. There were approximately 200 manufactured between 1860 and 1862.

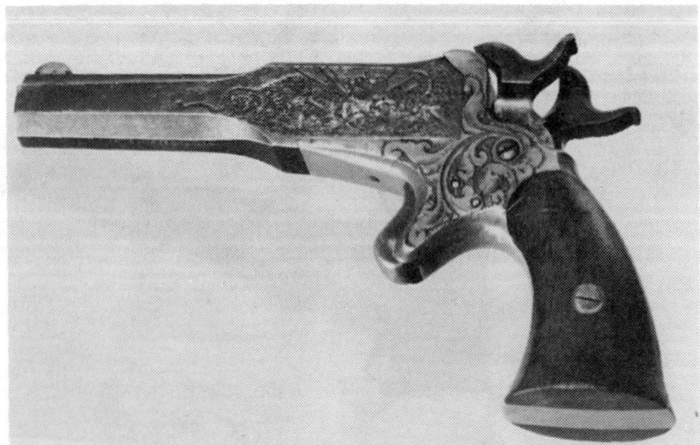

Courtesy W.P. Hallstein III and son Chip.

Exc.	V.G.	Good	Fair	Poor
1500	1250	1000	750	500

2 Shot Martial Pistol

A large version of the Lindsay design. It is chambered for .45-caliber smoothbore and has an 8.5" part-round/part-octagonal barrel. In other respects it is similar to the smaller models. The inventor tried to sell this pistol to the government but was unsuccessful. It was estimated that there were 100 manufactured between 1860 and 1862.

Exc.	V.G.	Good	Fair	Poor
2500	2250	1800	1450	1200

LINS, A. F.

Philadelphia, Pennsylvania

Pocket Pistol

Chambered for .41 caliber percussion and is a copy of the Henry Deringer pistol. It has a 3" barrel and a walnut stock and is marked "A.Fred. Lins. Philada." This pistol was manufactured between 1855 and 1860.

Exc.	V.G.	Good	Fair	Poor
850	750	650	450	350

Rifled Musket

A single shot, muzzleloading, percussion rifle chambered for .58 caliber. It has a 39" barrel and a full-length walnut stock held on by three barrel bands. There is an iron ramrod mounted under the barrel. The mountings are iron, and there is a bayonet lug combined with the front sight. The lock is marked "A. Fred. Lins/Philada." This is a rare weapon that was used by Union forces in the Civil War. There were approximately 200 manufactured in 1861 and 1862.

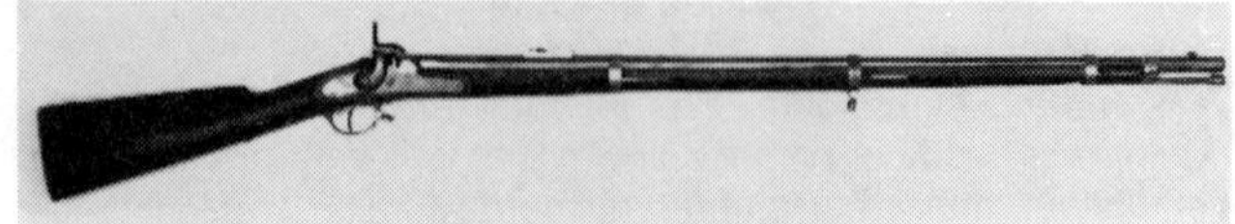

Courtesy Milwaukee Public Museum, Milwaukee, Wisconsin.

Exc.	V.G.	Good	Fair	Poor
2000	1750	1450	1100	750

LITTLE ALL RIGHT FIREARMS CO.

Lawrence, Massachusetts

Little All Right Palm Pistol

An unusual-appearing pocket-sized palm pistol. It is chambered for the .22 short rimfire cartridge and has a 1.75" barrel. The cylinder holds 5 shots. The trigger is mounted on the top of the barrel at the muzzle and is hinged and connected to a rod that cocks the concealed hammer, cycles the cylinder, and fires the weapon in double-action fashion. The grip was designed to be fit into the palm and not gripped as in a conventional pistol. The finish is nickle-plated, and the grips are pearl.

Exc.	V.G.	Good	Fair	Poor
500	400	350	275	175

LJUNGMAN

Eskilstuna, Sweden
Carl Gustav

Ljungman AG-42

Designed by Eril Eklund and was placed in service with the Swedish military in 1942—less than one year after it was designed. The rifle is a direct gas-operated design with no piston or rod. It is chambered for the 6.5mm cartridge and has a 24.5" barrel with a 10-round detachable magazine. This rifle has military-type sights and a full-length stock and handguard held on by barrel bands. There are provisions for a bayonet. There is also an Egyptian version of this rifle known as the "Hakim" and a Danish version that was manufactured by Madsen. Our AR-15 rifles use the same type of gas system.

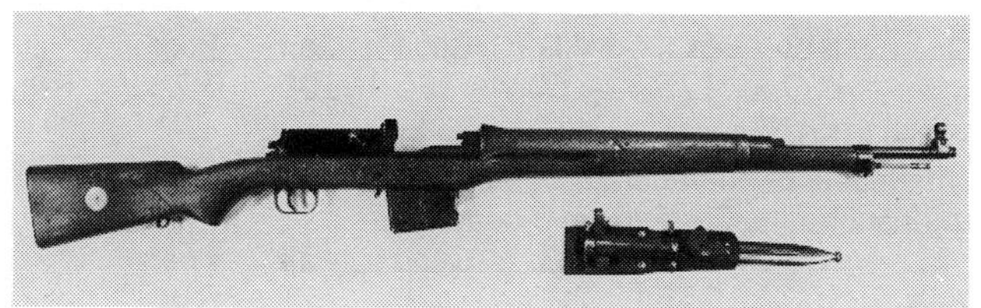

Exc.	V.G.	Good	Fair	Poor
750	675	500	400	275

Egyptian Hakim

Exc.	V.G.	Good	Fair	Poor
300	250	200	150	100

LJUTIC INDUSTRIES
Yakima, Washington

Bi-Matic Semi-Automatic

A custom-built, gas-operated, semi-automatic shotgun that is known for its low level of felt recoil. It is chambered for 12 gauge and has 26" to 32" barrels choked for either Skeet or Trap. The stock specifications are to the customer's order. There are options available that affect the value, so we recommend an individual appraisal.

Exc.	V.G.	Good	Fair	Poor
2000	1800	1500	1200	900

Dynatrap Single Barrel

A single shot trap gun chambered for 12 gauge. It has a 33" vent-rib full-choke barrel and features a pushbutton opener and a manual extractor. The stock is made to Trap specifications. There are many options that affect the value; independent appraisal is recommended.

Exc.	V.G.	Good	Fair	Poor
2000	1800	1500	1200	900

Model X-73 Single Barrel

Similar features to the Dynatrap, with a very high competition rib. Appraisal is recommended.

Exc.	V.G.	Good	Fair	Poor
2500	2250	1750	1400	1100

Mono Gun Single Barrel

Chambered for 12 gauge and has a 34" vent-rib barrel. It is essentially a custom-order proposition that is available with a standard, as well as a release, trigger. There are many value-affecting options available. Appraisal is recommended.

NIB	Exc.	V.G.	Good	Fair	Poor
3800	3500	3000	2500	2000	1750

LTX Model

A deluxe version of the Mono Gun with a 33" medium-height vent rib and a high-grade walnut stock with fine hand checkering. Options raise values drastically. Appraisal is recommended.

NIB	Exc.	V.G.	Good	Fair	Poor
5000	4500	4000	3500	2500	2000

Space Gun

A unique single barrel gun chambered for 12 gauge, with Trap choking. It has a stock and forearm that reminds one of a crutch in appearance but which allows the shooter to have in-line control with very little felt recoil. The barrel, forearm, and stock are all on one line. There is a recoil pad and a very high ventilated-rib.

NIB	Exc.	V.G.	Good	Fair	Poor
3750	3450	3050	2400	1750	1500

Bi-Gun O/U

An Over/Under double chambered for 12 gauge. It has 30" or 32" vent-ribbed barrels that are separated. The choking is to Trap specifications, and the stock is deluxe hand-checkered walnut.

NIB	Exc.	V.G.	Good	Fair	Poor
10000	8500	7000	6000	5000	4000

Bi Gun Combo

The Over/Under Bi Gun supplied with a high-ribbed single barrel in addition to the separated Over/Under barrels. It is furnished in a fitted case, and the walnut is of exhibition grade.

NIB	Exc.	V.G.	Good	Fair	Poor
17000	15000	11000	9000	7500	6500

LLAMA
Manufactured by
Gabilondo Y Cia
Vitoria, Spain
Importers—Stoeger Industries and SGS Importers

This is the same firm that was founded in 1904 and produced several inexpensive revolvers and pistols prior to 1931. In 1931 the company began to produce a semi-automatic pistol based on the Colt Model 1911. They were of high quality and have been sold around the world. After the Spanish Civil War the company moved its facilities to Vitoria, Spain where it continued to built handguns under the Llama trade name. In the 1980's the firm introduced a new line of pistols that were more up modern in design and function. The Llama pistol is still produced today. For Llama pistol built prior to 1936 the slide marking reads: **GABILONDO Y CIA ELOEIBAR(ESPANA) CAL 9MM/.380IN LLAMA.** For pistol built after 1936 the slide marking reads: **LLAMA GABILONDO Y CIA ELOEIBAR (ESPANA) CAL 9MM .380.** Current production Llama pistol will show a slide marking with either **LLAMA CAL...** or **GABILONDO Y CIA VITORIA (ESPANA)** and the Llama logo.

Llama Automatics

Model I-A

This is a 7.65mm blowback design introduced in 1933. Magazine capacity is 7 rounds. The barrel was 3.62", overall length 6.3", and weight about 19 oz.

Exc.	V.G.	Good	Fair	Poor
180	150	125	100	75

Model II

Chambered for the 9mm Short introduced in the same year. Identical to the Model I. Discontinued in 1936.

Exc.	V.G.	Good	Fair	Poor
200	175	150	125	100

Model III

An improved version of the Model II. Introduced in 1936 and discontinued in 1954.

Exc.	V.G.	Good	Fair	Poor
190	170	150	125	100

Model III-A

Similar to the Model III but with the addition of the Colt type grip safety. Introduced in 1955.

Exc.	V.G.	Good	Fair	Poor
200	175	150	125	100

Model IV

Chambered for the 9mm Largo or .380 ACP. Is not fitted with a grip safety. Introduced in 1931, it is the first of the Llama designs.

Exc.	V.G.	Good	Fair	Poor
180	150	125	100	75

Model V

The same as the Model V but was intended for export to the United States and is stamped "made in spain" on the slide.

Exc.	V.G.	Good	Fair	Poor
180	150	125	100	75

Model VI

Chambered for the 9mm Short and without a grip safety.

Exc.	V.G.	Good	Fair	Poor
180	150	125	100	75

Model VII
This model was introduced in 1932 and manufactured until 1954. It is chambered for the .38 Super Auto cartridge. It does not have a grip safety.

Exc.	V.G.	Good	Fair	Poor
225	200	150	125	100

Model VIII
This model was introduced in 1955 and is chambered for the .45 ACP, .38 Super, or 9mm Largo. It is fitted with a grip safety. Barrel length is 5", overall length is 8.5", and weight is about 38 oz. Magazine capacity is 7 rounds.

Exc.	V.G.	Good	Fair	Poor
250	200	150	125	100

Model IX
Chambered for the 7.65mm Para, 9mm Largo, or .45 ACP this model has a locked breech with no grip safety. Built from 1936 to 1954.

Exc.	V.G.	Good	Fair	Poor
275	225	150	125	100

Model IX-A
This version of the Model IX if fitted with a grip safety. Current production models are chambered for the .45 ACP only. Weighs about 30 ozs. with 5" barrel.

Exc.	V.G.	Good	Fair	Poor
275	225	150	125	100

Model IX-B
This is the current version of the Model IX series chambered in .45 ACP. It is fitted with an extended slide release, black plastic grips, and target type hammer. Offered in blue or satin chrome finish.

NIB	Exc.	V.G.	Good	Fair	Poor
300	275	225	150	125	100

Model X
First produced in 1935 this model is chambered for the 7.65mm cartridge. It has no grip safety.

Exc.	V.G.	Good	Fair	Poor
180	150	125	100	75

Model X-A
This version is similar to the Model X but with a grip safety. Produced from 1954 to the present.

Exc.	V.G.	Good	Fair	Poor
200	175	125	100	75

Model XI
Chambered for the 9mm Parabellum cartridge this model is different from previous models with a longer curved butt, ring hammer, and vertically grooved walnut grips. Magazine capacity is 9 rounds. Barrel length is 5". Discontinued in 1954.

Exc.	V.G.	Good	Fair	Poor
275	225	175	125	100

Model XI-B (Currently imported by Century International Arms Co.)
Similar to the Model XI but with a spur hammer and shorter barrel. Currently in production.

NIB	Exc.	V.G.	Good	Fair	Poor
200	175	150	125	100	75

Model XII-B
This model is chambered for the .40 S&W cartridge. It has a compact frame. Currently in production.

NIB	Exc.	V.G.	Good	Fair	Poor
300	275	225	175	125	100

Model XV
Chambered for the .22 Long Rifle this marked is marked "Especial". It is fitted with a grip safety and comes in several finishes and with different grip styles. The barrel length is 3.6:, the overall length is 6.5", and the weight is about 17 oz.

Exc.	V.G.	Good	Fair	Poor
225	175	150	125	100

Model XVI
This is a deluxe version of the Model XV with engraving, ventilated rib, and adjustable sights.

Exc.	V.G.	Good	Fair	Poor
300	225	175	150	100

Model XVII
This model is chambered for the .22 Short. It is small version of the Model XV with a finger shaped grip.

Exc.	V.G.	Good	Fair	Poor
275	225	175	125	100

Model 82
This is a large frame double action semi-automatic pistol. It features plastic grips, ambidextrous safety, 3-dot sights. The barrel length is 4.25" and overall length is 8". Weight is approximately 39 oz. Choice of blue or satin chrome finish.

NIB	Exc.	V.G.	Good	Fair	Poor
400	350	300	250	200	100

Mugica
Eibar gun dealer Jose Mugica sold Llama pistols under his private trade name. They are marked "mugica-ebir-spain" on the slide. These pistols do not seem to have any additional value over and above their respective Llama models. For the sake of clarification the Mugica models will be listed with their Llama counterparts:

Mugica Model 101	Llama Model X
Mugica Model 101-G	Llama Model X-A
Mugica Model 105	Llama Model III
Mugica Model 105-G	Llama Model III-A
Mugica Model 110	Llama Model VII
Mugica Model 110-G	Llama Model VIII
Mugica Model 120	Llama Model XI

Tauler
In an arrangement similar to Mugica a gun dealer in Madrid sold Llama pistols under his own brand name. Most of these pistols were sold in the early 1930's to police and other government officials. The most common Llama models were Models I to VIII. Slide inscriptions were in English and had the name Tauler in them. No additional value is attached to this private trade mark.

Revolvers

Ruby Extra Models
These revolvers were produced in the 1950's and were copies of Smith & Wessons. They were marked RUBY EXTRA on the left side of the frame. At the top of the grips was a RUBY medallion. The barrel address is stamped: gabilondo y cia elgoeibar espana. The Ruby Extra Models represent the company's attempts to produce and sell a low cost revolver.

Model XII
This model is chambered for the .38 Long cartridge and is fitted with a 5" barrel and a squared butt.

Exc.	V.G.	Good	Fair	Poor
175	150	125	100	75

Model XIII (Currently imported by Century International Arms Co.)

Chambered for the .38 Special this revolver has a round butt with 4" or 6" ventilated rib barrel. The 6" barreled gun was fitted with adjustable sights and target grips.

Exc.	V.G.	Good	Fair	Poor
175	150	125	100	75

Model XIV

Offered in .22 Long Rifle or .32 caliber this model was available in a wide choice of barrel lengths and sights.

Exc.	V.G.	Good	Fair	Poor
175	150	125	100	75

Model XXII Olimpico

This model was designed as a .38 Special target revolver. It features an adjustable anatomic grip, adjustable rear sight, ventilated rib barrel, and a web that joins the barrel to the ejector shroud.

Exc.	V.G.	Good	Fair	Poor
250	200	150	125	100

Model XXVI

Chambered for the .22 Long Rifle, it features traditional grips and shrouded ejector rod.

Exc.	V.G.	Good	Fair	Poor
175	150	125	100	75

Model XXVII

Similar to the model above but fitted with a 2" barrel and chambered for the .32 Long cartridge.

Exc.	V.G.	Good	Fair	Poor
175	150	125	100	75

Model XXVIII

This model is chambered for the .22 Long Rifle and is fitted with a 6" barrel. It has a ramp front sight and adjustable rear sight.

Exc.	V.G.	Good	Fair	Poor
200	175	150	100	75

Model XXIX Olimpico

This is the Model XXII chambered for the .22 Long Rifle.

Exc.	V.G.	Good	Fair	Poor
250	200	150	125	100

Model XXXII Olimpico

This model is a .32 target revolver with an unusual cylinder and frame design.

Exc.	V.G.	Good	Fair	Poor
275	225	150	125	100

Llama Omni

A .45 ACP and the 9mm caliber double-action semi-automatic pistol with a 4.25" barrel and a 7-shot detachable magazine (.45 caliber) and a 13-shot magazine (9mm), a double sear bar and three distinct safeties. Steel with a blued finish. Discontinued in 1986.

Exc.	V.G.	Good	Fair	Poor
275	250	200	150	100

Llama Small Frame Semi-Automatic

A .22, .32 ACP, and the .380 ACP caliber semi-automatic pistol with a 3-11/16" barrel and 7-shot detachable magazine. Either blued or satin chrome finished.

Satin Chrome Finish—Add $75.

NIB	Exc.	V.G.	Good	Fair	Poor
200	175	150	125	100	75

Llama Compact Frame Semi-Automatic

A 9mm or the .45 ACP caliber semi-automatic pistol with a 4.25" barrel and either a 7- or 9-shot detachable magazine. Blued. Introduced in 1986.

NIB	Exc.	V.G.	Good	Fair	Poor
250	225	175	125	100	75

Llama Large Frame Semi-Automatic

A 9mm, .38 Super or .45 ACP caliber semi-automatic pistol with a 5.25" barrel and either a 7- or 9-shot detachable magazine, depending on the caliber. Blued or satin chrome.

Satin Chrome Finish—Add $125.

NIB	Exc.	V.G.	Good	Fair	Poor
250	225	175	125	100	75

Llama Model 82

A 9mm Parabellum caliber double-action semi-automatic pistol with a 4.25" barrel, a three-dot sighting system, 15-shot detachable magazine, a loaded-chamber indicator, and an ambidextrous safety. Blued, with black plastic grips. Introduced in 1988.

NIB	Exc.	V.G.	Good	Fair	Poor
400	350	300	250	200	100

Llama Model 87 Competition

As above with a compensator special barrel bushing, a bevelled magazine well, a squared and checkered triggerguard, with an adjustable trigger. Blued. Introduced in 1989.

NIB	Exc.	V.G.	Good	Fair	Poor
850	700	500	300	200	100

Llama Martial

A .22 or the .38 Special caliber double-action semi-automatic pistol with a 6-round swingout cylinder, a 4" or 6" barrel and adjustable sights. Blued, with checkered hardwood grips. Manufactured between 1969 and 1976.

Exc.	V.G.	Good	Fair	Poor
225	175	150	110	85

Llama Comanche I

As above, in .22 caliber.

Exc.	V.G.	Good	Fair	Poor
250	200	175	125	100

Llama Comanche II

As above, in .38 Special caliber. Manufactured between 1977 and 1982.

Exc.	V.G.	Good	Fair	Poor
250	200	175	125	100

Llama Comanche III

As above, in .357 Magnum with a 4", 6", or 8.5" barrel and adjustable sights. Introduced in 1975.

Satin Chrome Finish—Add 20%.

NIB	Exc.	V.G.	Good	Fair	Poor
250	200	175	125	100	75

Llama Super Comanche

As above, in .44 Magnum with a 6" or 8.5" ventilated-rib barrel and adjustable sights. Blued, with walnut grips.

NIB	Exc.	V.G.	Good	Fair	Poor
275	225	175	125	100	75

LOEWE, LUDWIG & CO.

Berlin, Germany
SEE—Borchardt

During the 1870s and 1880s this firm manufactured a close copy of the Smith & Wesson Russian Model for the Russian Government. They are marked "Ludwig Loewe Berlin" on the top of the barrel.

Loewe Smith & Wesson Russian Revolver

Exc.	V.G.	Good	Fair	Poor
250	225	200	125	75

LOHNER, C.
Philadelphia, Pennsylvania

Pocket Pistol

A .44 caliber single shot percussion pistol with a 5" barrel, German silver mounts and walnut grip. The barrel marked "C.Lohner." Manufactured during the 1850s.

Exc.	V.G.	Good	Fair	Poor
850	750	650	450	350

LOMBARD, H. C. & CO.
Springfield, Massachusetts

Pocket Pistol

A .22 caliber single shot spur trigger pistol with a 3.5" octagonal barrel. The frame silver plated, barrel blued and grips of walnut. Barrel marked "H.C.Lombard & Co. Springfield, Mass."

Exc.	V.G.	Good	Fair	Poor
350	300	250	150	100

LONDON ARMORY CO.
SEE—English Military Firearms

LORCIN ENGINEERING CO., INC.
Riverside, California

Model L—25

A .25 caliber semi-automatic pistol with a 2.5" barrel and 7-shot magazine. Introduced in 1989.

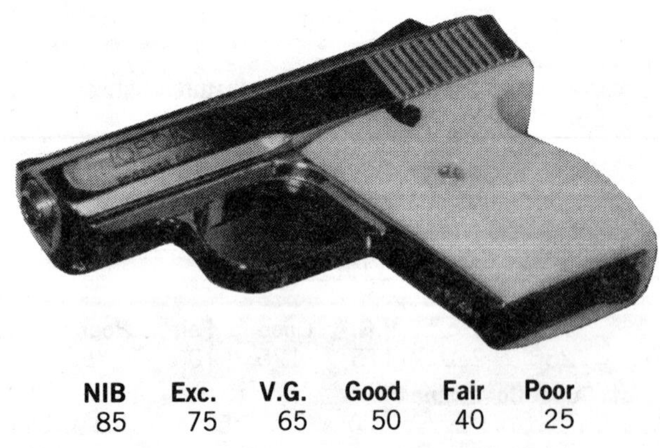

NIB	Exc.	V.G.	Good	Fair	Poor
85	75	65	50	40	25

LOWELL ARMS CO.
SEE—Rollin White Arms Co.

LOWER, J. P.
SEE—Slotter & Co.

LUGERS
Various Manufacturers

Just before the turn of the Twentieth Century, Georg Luger redesigned the Borchardt semi-automatic pistol so that its mainspring was housed in the rear of the grip. The resulting pistol was to prove extremely successful and his name has become synonymous with the pistol despite the fact his name never appeared on it.

The following companies manufactured Luger pattern pistols at various times.

1. DWM - Deutsch Waffen und Munitions - Karlsruhe, Germany
2. The Royal Arsenal of Erfurt Germany
3. Simson & Co. - Suhl,Germany
4. Mauser - Oberndorf, Germany
5. Vickers Ltd. - England
6. Waffenfabrik Bern - Bern, Switzerland
7. Heinrich Krieghoff - Suhl, Germany

Those interested in these pistols are advised to read the various books written about the marque which are listed in the bibliography at the close of this book.

Deutsch Waffen und Munitions

1899/1900 Swiss Test Model

4.75" barrel, 7.65mm caliber. The Swiss Cross in Sunburst is stamped over the chamber. The serial range runs to three digits. With less than 100 manufactured and only one known to exist, it is one of the rarest of the Lugers and the first true Luger that was produced. This model is far too rare to estimate an accurate value.

1900 Swiss Contract

4.75" barrel, 7.65mm caliber. The Swiss Cross in Sunburst is stamped over the chamber. The military serial number range is 2001-5000; the commercial range, 01-21250. There were approximately 2,000 commercial and 3,000 military models manufactured.

Wide Trigger—Add 20%.

Exc.	V.G.	Good	Fair	Poor
4500	3800	2000	1500	1000

1900 Commercial

4.75" barrel, 7.65mm caliber. The area above the chamber is blank. The serial range is 01-19000, and there were approximately 5,500 manufactured for commercial sale in Germany or other countries. Some have "Germany" stamped on the frame. These pistols were imported into the U.S., and some were even stamped after blueing.

Exc.	V.G.	Good	Fair	Poor
4250	3000	1500	1000	650

1900 American Eagle

a 4.75" barrel, 7.65mm caliber. The American Eagle Crest is stamped over the chamber. The serial range is between 2000-200000, and there were approximately 11,000-12,000 commercial models marked "Germany" and 1,000 military test models without the commercial import stamp. The serial numbers of this military lot have been estimated at between 6100-7100.

Exc.	V.G.	Good	Fair	Poor
3850	2800	1500	850	600

1900 Bulgarian Contract
An old model, 1900 Type, with no stock lug. It has a 4.75" barrel and is chambered for the 7.65mm cartridge. The Bulgarian crest is stamped over the chamber, and the safety is marked in Bulgarian letters. The serial range is 20000-21000, with 1,000 manufactured. This is a military test model and is quite rare as most were rebarreled to 9mm during the time they were used. Even with the 9mm versions, approximately 10 are known to exist. It was the only variation to feature a marked safety before 1904.

Exc.	V.G.	Good	Fair	Poor
10000	7500	4000	2500	1800

1900 Carbine
11.75" barrel, 7.65mm caliber. The carbines have a gracefully contoured and finely checkered walnut forearm and detachable shoulder stock. The rear sight on this extremely rare variation is a five-position sliding model located on the rear link. The area above the chamber is blank. The serial range is three digits or under, and this may have been a prototype as less than 100 were produced with only one known to exist today. This model is far too rare to estimate an accurate value.

1902 Prototype
6" barrel, 7.65mm caliber. The serial numbers are in the 10000 range with a capital B, and the chamber is blank. The 6" barrel is of a heavy contour, and there were less than 10 manufactured. The rarity of this variation precludes estimating value.

1902 Carbine
11.75" barrel, 7.65mm caliber. The sight has four positions and is silver-soldered to the barrel. A stock and forearm was sold with this weapon. The serial range was 21000-22100 and 23500-24900. There were approximately 2,500 manufactured for commercial sale in and out of Germany. Many were imported into the U.S., but none here have been noted with the "Germany" import stamp.
With Stock—Add 50%.

Exc.	V.G.	Good	Fair	Poor
12000	9000	5000	2500	1500

1902 Commercial
Thick 4" barrel, 7.65mm caliber. The area above the chamber is blank. It is chambered for the 9mm cartridge, and the serial numbers fall within the 22300-22400 and the 22900-23500 range. There were approximately 600 manufactured, and the greater part of those noted were marked "Germany" for export purposes.

Exc.	V.G.	Good	Fair	Poor
7500	5000	3500	1800	1100

1902 American Eagle
As above, with an American Eagle stamped over the chamber. It is chambered for the 9mm cartridge, and the serial numbers fall within the 22100-22300 and the 22450-22900 range. This model was solely intended for export sales in the U.S.A., and all are marked "Germany" on the frame. There were approximately 700 manufactured.

Exc.	V.G.	Good	Fair	Poor
7500	4600	3200	2000	1200

1902 American Eagle Cartridge Counter
As above, with a "Powell Indicating Device" added to the left grip. A slotted magazine with a numbered window that allows visual access to the number of cartridges remaining. There were 50 lugers altered in this way at the request of the U.S. Board of Ordnance, for U.S. Army evaluation. The serial numbers are 22401-22450. Be especially wary of fakes!

Exc.	V.G.	Good	Fair	Poor
23000	11000	11000	5000	3500

1902 Presentation Carbine
11.75" barrel, 7.65mm caliber. These carbines have the initials of the owner gold-inlaid above the chamber. They are furnished with a checkered walnut stock and forearm. Only four have been noted in the 9000C serial number range. They have the initials "GL" for Georg Luger on the back of the rear toggle. They are too rare to estimate value.

1902/06 Carbine (Transitional)
11.75" barrel, 7.65mm caliber. Assembled from Model 1902 parts with a new toggle assembly. They have the four-position sliding sight, silver-soldered to the barrel, and a checkered walnut stock and forearm. There were approximately 100 manufactured in the 23600 serial number range.
With Stock—Add 25%.

Exc.	V.G.	Good	Fair	Poor
12000	9000	7000	3750	2600

1903 Commercial
4" barrel, 7.65mm caliber. The chamber area is blank. There were approximately 50 manufactured for export to France, serial numbered 25000-25050. The extractor on this model is marked "CHARGE."

Exc.	V.G.	Good	Fair	Poor
10000	8500	5000	3200	2500

1904 Navy
6" thick barrel, 9mm caliber. The chamber area is blank, and the extractor is marked "Geladen." The safety is marked "Gesichert." There were approximately 1,500 manufactured in the one- to four-digit serial range, for military sales to the German Navy.

Exc.	V.G.	Good	Fair	Poor
35000	28000	16000	6000	4500

1906 Navy Commercial
This is a new model, 1906 Type, with stock lug. It has a 6" barrel and is chambered for the 9mm cartridge. The chamber is blank, and the extractor is marked "Geladin." The safety is marked "Gesichert," and some have the "Germany" export stamp. The proper magazine has a wood bottom with concentric circles on the sides. There were approximately 2,500 manufactured in the 25050-65000 serial range. They were produced for commercial sales in and outside of Germany.

Exc.	V.G.	Good	Fair	Poor
5000	3500	2500	1200	900

1906 Commercial
4" barrel, 9mm caliber. The extractor is marked "Geladin," and the area of the frame under the safety in its lower position is polished and not blued. The chamber is blank. There were approximately 4,000 manufactured for commercial sales. Some have the "Germany" export stamp. The serial range is 26500-68000.

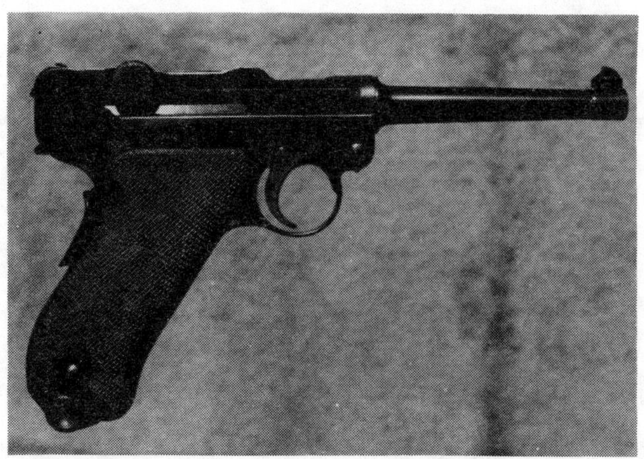

Courtesy Orville Reichert.

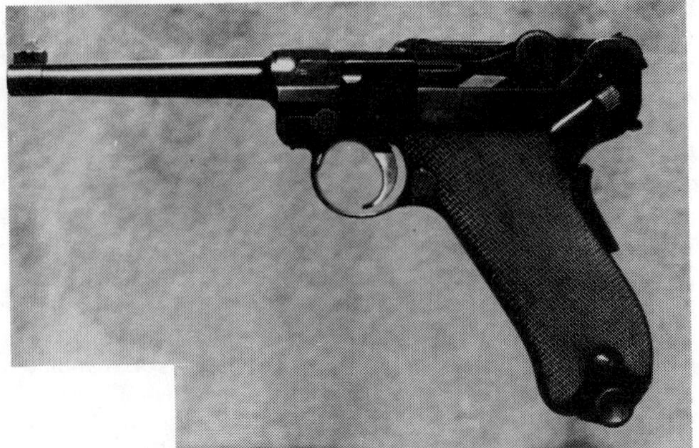
Courtesy Orville Reichert.

Exc.	V.G.	Good	Fair	Poor
3500	2500	1000	800	600

1906 Commercial (Marked Safety)
As above, with the area of the frame under the safety in its lowest position is marked "Gesichert" and the barrel is 4.75" in length and chambered for the 7.65mm cartridge. There were approximately 750 manufactured, serial numbered 25050-26800.

Exc.	V.G.	Good	Fair	Poor
3500	2500	1200	800	600

1906 American Eagle
4" barrel, 9mm caliber. The chamber area has the American Eagle stamped upon it. The extractor is marked "Loaded," and the frame under the safety at its lowest point is polished and not blued. This model has no stock lug. There were approximately 3,000 manufactured for commercial sale in the U.S.A. in the serial range 26500-69000.

Exc.	V.G.	Good	Fair	Poor
3000	2500	1200	700	500

1906 American Eagle (Marked Safety)
4.75" barrel, 7.65mm caliber. The frame under the safety at its lowest point is marked "Gesichert." There were approximately 750 manufactured in the 25100-26500 serial number range.

Exc.	V.G.	Good	Fair	Poor
3700	2700	1500	1200	800

1906 American Eagle 4.75" Barrel
As the Model 1906 with a marked safety. Approximately 8,000 manufactured in the 26500-69000 serial range.

Exc.	V.G.	Good	Fair	Poor
3000	1800	900	500	450

1906 U.S.Army Test Luger .45 Caliber
5" barrel, .45 ACP caliber. Sent to the U.S. for testing in 1907. The chamber is blank; the extractor is marked "Loaded," and the frame is polished under the safety lever. The trigger on this model has an odd hook at the bottom. Reportedly only two of these pistols were manufactured. Serial No. 1 has never been located, and it was rumored to have been destroyed after the tests were concluded. Serial No. 2 is in a collection in the U.S.A.
In any condition, Serial No. 1 would be priceless.

1906 Swiss Commercial
4.75" barrel, 7.65mm caliber. The Swiss Cross in Sunburst appears over the chamber. The extractor is marked "Geladen," and the frame under the safety is polished. There is no stock lug, and the proofmarks are commercial. There were approximately 1,000 manufactured in the 35000-55000 serial number range.

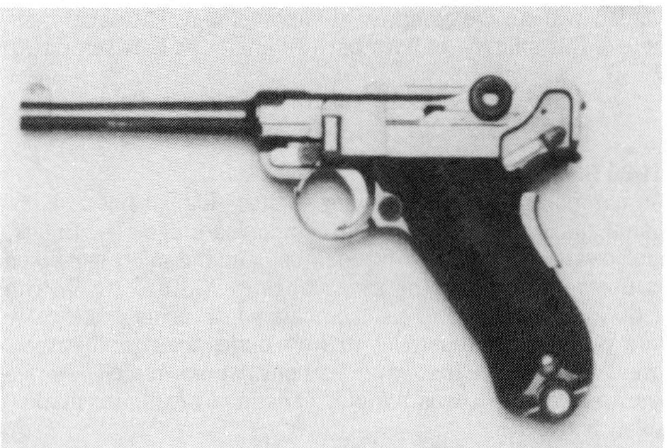
Courtesy Butterfield & Butterfield, San Francisco, California.

Exc.	V.G.	Good	Fair	Poor
3200	2600	2000	1400	800

1906 Commercial
4.75" barrel, 7.65mm caliber. It had no stock lug. The chamber area is blank, and the extractor is marked "Geladen." The frame under the safety is polished and unmarked. There were approximately 5,000 manufactured for commercial sales both in and outside of Germany. They will be found in the 26500-69000 serial-number range.

Exc.	V.G.	Good	Fair	Poor
2750	2000	1200	850	550

1906 Swiss Military
As the Swiss Commercial, with the Geneva Cross appearing on all major parts.

Exc.	V.G.	Good	Fair	Poor
3000	2500	1800	900	700

1906 Swiss Military Cross in Shield
As above, with a cross replacing the sunburst on the chamber marking. There were 10,215 of both models combined. They are in the 5000-15215 serial number range.

Exc.	V.G.	Good	Fair	Poor
3100	2500	1800	1000	700

1906 Dutch Contract
4" barrel, 9mm caliber. It has no stock lug, and the chamber is blank. The extractor is marked "Geladen" on both sides, and the safety is marked "RUST" with a curved upward pointing arrow. This pistol was manufactured for military sales to the Netherlands, and a date will be found on the barrel of most examples encountered. The Dutch refinished their pistols on a regular basis and marked the date on the barrels. There were approximately 4,000 manufactured, serial numbered between 1 and 4000.

Exc.	V.G.	Good	Fair	Poor
2800	2000	1100	800	600

1906 Royal Portuguese Navy
4" barrel, 9mm caliber, and has no stock lug. The Royal Portuguese Naval Crest, an anchor under a crown, is stamped above the chamber. The extractor is marked "CARREGADA" on the left side. The frame under the safety is polished. There were approximately 1,000 manufactured with one- to four-digit serial numbers.

Exc.	V.G.	Good	Fair	Poor
10000	8000	5500	4000	2500

1906 Royal Portuguese Army
4.75" barrel, 7.65mm caliber. It has no stock lug. The chamber area has the Royal Portuguese Crest stamped upon it. The extractor is marked "CARREGADA." There were approximately 5,000 manufactured, with one- to four-digit serial numbers.

Exc.	V.G.	Good	Fair	Poor
1400	1200	900	600	500

1906 Republic of Portugal Navy
4" barrel, 9mm caliber. It has no stock lug, and the extractor was marked "CARREGADA." This model was made after 1910,

when Portugal had become a republic. The anchor on the chamber is under the letters "R.P." There were approximately 1,000 manufactured, with one- to four-digit serial numbers.

Exc.	V.G.	Good	Fair	Poor
10000	8000	5500	3500	2500

1906 Brazilian Contract

4.75" barrel, 7.65mm caliber. It has no stock lug, and chamber area is blank. The extractor is marked "CARREGADA," and the frame under the safety is polished. There were approximately 5,000 manufactured for military sales to Brazil.

Exc.	V.G.	Good	Fair	Poor
2000	1600	1100	750	450

1906 Bulgarian Contract

4.75" barrel, 7.65mm caliber. It has no stock lug, and the extractor and safety are marked in cyrillic letters. The Bulgarian Crest is stamped above the chamber. Nearly all of the examples located have the barrels replaced with 4" 9mm units. This was done after the later 1908 model was adopted. Some were refurbished during the Nazi era, and these pistols bear Waffenamts and usually mismatched parts. There were approximately 1,500 manufactured, with serial numbers of one to four digits.

Exc.	V.G.	Good	Fair	Poor
8500	6500	4500	3000	1500

1906 Russian Contract

4" barrel, 9mm caliber. It has no stock lug, and the extractor and safety are marked with cyrillic letters. Crossed Nagant rifles are stamped over the chamber. There were approximately 1,000 manufactured, with one- to four-digit serial numbers; but very few survive. This is an extremely rare variation, and caution should be excercised if purchase is contemplated.

Exc.	V.G.	Good	Fair	Poor
10000	8000	6500	4000	2500

1906 Navy 1st Issue

6" barrel, 9mm caliber. The safety and extractor are both marked in German, and the chamber area is blank. There is a stock lug, and the unique two-position sliding Navy sight is mounted on the rear toggle link. There were approximately 12,000 manufactured for the German Navy, with serial numbers of one to five digits. The wooden magazine bottom features concentric rings.

Exc.	V.G.	Good	Fair	Poor
2850	2000	1500	1100	850

1906 Navy 2nd Issue

As above, with reversed safety positions. Approximately 11,000 2nd Issue Navies manufactured, with one- to five-digit serial numbers—some with an "a" suffix. They were produced for sale to the German Navy.

Exc.	V.G.	Good	Fair	Poor
2500	1850	1250	950	700

1908 Commercial

4" barrel, 9mm caliber. It has no stock lug, and the chamber area is blank. The extractor and the safety are both marked in German, and many examples are marked with the "Germany" export stamp. There were approximately 9,000 manufactured in the 39000-71500 serial number range.

Exc.	V.G.	Good	Fair	Poor
1250	1000	750	600	450

1908 Navy Commercial

6" barrel, 9mm caliber. It has a stock lug, no grip safety, and the characteristic two-position sliding sight mounted on the rear toggle link. The chamber area is blank, and the safety and extractor are both marked. The "Germany" export stamp appears on some examples. There were approximately 1,500 manufactured, in the 44000-50000 serial number range.

Exc.	V.G.	Good	Fair	Poor
4500	3500	2500	1750	1250

1908 Navy Military

As above, with the "Crown M" military proof. They may or may not have the concentric rings on the magazine bottom. There were approximately 40,000 manufactured, with one- to five-digit serial numbers with an "a" or "b" suffix. These Lugers are quite scarce as many were destroyed during and after WWI.

Exc.	V.G.	Good	Fair	Poor
2750	1900	1400	1000	750

1914 Navy

Similar to the above, but stamped with the dates from 1914-1918 above the chamber. Most noted are dated 1916-1918. There were approximately 40,000 manufactured, with one- to five-digit serial numbers with an "a" or "b" suffix. They are scarce as many were destroyed as a result of WWI.

Exc.	V.G.	Good	Fair	Poor
2500	1850	1250	950	700

1908 Military 1st Issue

4" barrel, 9mm caliber. It has no stock lug, and the extractor and safety are both marked in German. The chamber is blank. There were approximately 20,000 manufactured, with one- to five-digit serial numbers—some with an "a" suffix.

Exc.	V.G.	Good	Fair	Poor
950	750	600	500	350

1908 Military Dated Chamber

As above, with the date of manufacture stamped on the chamber.

Exc.	V.G.	Good	Fair	Poor
950	750	600	500	350

1914 Military

As above, with a stock lug.

Exc.	V.G.	Good	Fair	Poor
1000	800	650	500	350

1913 Commercial

As above, with a grip safety. Approximately 1,000 manufactured, with serial numbers 71000-72000; but very few have been noted, and it is considered to be quite rare.

Exc.	V.G.	Good	Fair	Poor
1250	1450	1100	850	600

1914 Artillery

8" barrel, 9mm caliber. It features a nine-position adjustable sight that has a base that is an integral part of the barrel. This model has a stock lug and was furnished with a military-style flat board stock and holster rig (see Accessories). The chamber is dated from 1914-1918, and the safety and extractor are both marked. This model was developed for artillery and machine gun crews; and many thousands were manufactured, with one- to five-digit serial numbers—some have letter suffixes. This model is quite desirable from a collector's standpoint and is rarer than its production figures would indicate. After the war many were destroyed as the allies deemed them more insidious than other models, for some reason.

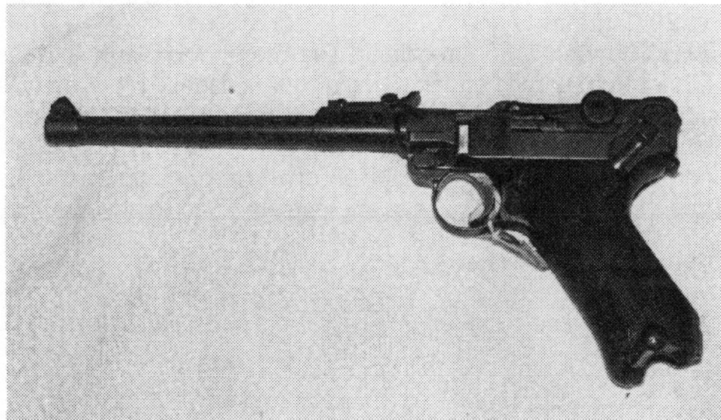

Exc.	V.G.	Good	Fair	Poor
1750	1350	1100	800	600

DWM Double Dated

4" barrel, 9mm cartridge. The date 1920 or 1921 is stamped over the original chamber date of 1910-1918, creating the double-date nomenclature. These are arsenal-reworked WWI military pistols and were then issued to the German army and/or police units within the provisions of the Treaty of Versailles. Many thousands of these Lugers were produced.

Exc.	V.G.	Good	Fair	Poor
900	700	550	400	300

1920 Police Rework

As above, except that the original manufacture date was removed before the rework date was stamped. There were many thousands of these produced.

Exc.	V.G.	Good	Fair	Poor
800	650	500	350	300

1920 Commercial

Similar to the above, with 3.5" to 6" barrels in 7.65mm or 9mm and marked "Germany" or "Made in Germany" for export. Others are unmarked and were produced for commercial sale inside Germany. Some of these pistols are military reworks with the markings and the proofmarks removed; others were newly manufactured. The extractors and safety are both marked, and the chamber is blank. The serial number range is one to five digits, and letter suffixes often appear.

Exc.	V.G.	Good	Fair	Poor
850	650	500	450	350

1920 Commercial Navy

6" barrel, 9mm caliber. Some have a stock lug; others have been noted without. The chamber area is generally blank, but some have been found with 1914-1918 dates stamped upon them. These were reworked by DWM from Military Navy Lugers after WWI for commercial sales. They are marked "Germany" or "Made in Germany" and were sold by Stoeger Arms, among others. The extractor and safety are both marked, and the unique Navy sight is on the rear toggle link. No one knows exactly how many were produced, but they are quite scarce.

Exc.	V.G.	Good	Fair	Poor
2800	2000	1600	1100	850

1920 Commercial Artillery

8" barrel, 9mm caliber. Erfurt-manufactured pistols, as well as DWM-manufactured pistols, were reworked in this manner. The export markings "Germany" or "Made in Germany" are found on most examples. The number produced is not known, but examples are quite scarce.

Exc.	V.G.	Good	Fair	Poor
2000	1800	1100	700	450

1920 Long Barrel Commercial

10" to 24" barrels, 7.65mm or 9mm caliber. The extractor and safety are both marked, and an artillery model rear sight is used. This model was often built to a customer's specifications. They are very rare, and the number manufactured is not known.

Exc.	V.G.	Good	Fair	Poor
2750	2000	1500	1000	800

1920 Carbine

11.75" barrel, 7.65mm caliber. The chamber is blank, and the extractor is marked either "Geladen" or "Loaded." The safety is not marked. The Carbine has a checkered walnut forearm and stock, and most have the "Germany" or "Made in Germany" export stamp. There were very few of these Carbines manufactured for commercial sales in and outside of Germany, and they are highly prized by collectors.

With Stock—Add 25%.

Exc.	V.G.	Good	Fair	Poor
6500	5000	4500	2500	1500

1920 Navy Carbine

Assembled from surplus Navy parts with the distinctive two-position, sliding navy sight on the rear toggle link. Most are marked with the export stamp and have the Naval Military proofmarks still in evidence. The safety and extractor are marked, and rarely one is found chambered for the 9mm cartridge. Very few were manufactured.

Exc.	V.G.	Good	Fair	Poor
3500	2800	2100	1400	900

1920 Swiss Commercial

3.5"-6" barrels, 7.65mm or 9mm caliber. The Swiss Cross in Sunburst is stamped over the chamber, and the extractor is marked "Geladen." The frame under the safety is polished. There were a few thousand produced, with serial numbers in the one- to five-digit range, sometimes with a letter suffix.

Exc.	V.G.	Good	Fair	Poor
2750	2200	1600	1000	800

1923 Stoeger Commercial

3.5" to 24" barrels, 7.65mm or 9mm caliber. There is a stock lug. The chamber area is either blank or has the American Eagle stamped on it. The export stamp and "A.F.Stoeger Inc. New York" is found on the right side of the receiver. The extractor and safety are marked in German or English. This was the model that Stoeger registered with the U.S. Patent office to secure the Luger name, and some examples will be so marked. There were less than 1,000 manufactured, with one- to five-digit serial numbers without a letter suffix. Individual appraisal must be secured on barrel lengths above 6". Be wary as fakes have been noted. The values given here are for the shorter-barrelled models.

Barrel Lengths Over 8"—Add 25%.

Exc.	V.G.	Good	Fair	Poor
3200	2500	1800	1000	700

Abercrombie & Fitch Commercial

100 Swiss Lugers were made for commercial sale in the U.S. by "Abercrombie & Fitch Co. New York. Made in Switzerland."—in either one or two lines—is stamped on the top of the barrel. The barrel is 4.75" in length, and there were 49 chambered for 9mm and 51 chambered for the 7.65mm cartridge. This pistol has a grip safety and no stock lug. The Swiss Cross in Sunburst is stamped over the chamber. The extractor is marked, but the safety area is polished. The serial range is four digits—some with a letter suffix. This is a very rare and desirable Luger. Be very careful of fakes on models of this type and rarity.

Exc.	V.G.	Good	Fair	Poor
6500	5000	4000	2800	1800

1923 Commercial

7½" barrel, 7.65mm caliber. It has a stock lug, and the chamber area is blank. The extractor and safety are both marked in German. These pistols were manufactured for commercial sales in and outside of Germany. There were approximately 18,000 produced, with serial numbers in the 73500-96000 range.

Exc.	V.G.	Good	Fair	Poor
950	800	650	450	350

1923 Commercial Safe & Loaded

As above, except that the extractor and safety are marked in English "Safe" & "Loaded." There were approximately 7,000 manufactured in the 73500-96000 serial number range.

Exc.	V.G.	Good	Fair	Poor
1700	1500	1000	800	500

1923 Dutch Commercial & Military

4" barrel, 9mm caliber. It has a stock lug, and the chamber area is blank. The extractor is marked in German, and the safety is marked "RUST" with a downward pointing arrow. This model was sold commercially and to the military in the Netherlands. There were approximately 1,000 manufactured in the one- to three-digit serial range, with no letter suffix.

Exc.	V.G.	Good	Fair	Poor
2500	1850	1000	850	550

Royal Dutch Air Force

4" barrel, 9mm caliber. Marked with the Mauser Oberndorf proofmark and serial numbered in the 10000 to 14000 range. The safety marked "RUST".

Exc.	V.G.	Good	Fair	Poor
2500	1800	950	800	550

Vickers Ltd.

1906 Vickers Dutch

4" barrel, 9mm caliber. There is no stock lug, and it uses a grip safety. The chamber is blank, and the extractor is marked "Geladen." "Vickers Ltd." is stamped on the front toggle link. The safety is marked "RUST" with an upward pointing arrow. Examples have been found with an additional date as late as 1933 stamped on the barrel. These dates indicate arsenal refinishing and in no way detract from the value of this variation. Arsenal reworks are matte-finished, and the originals are a higher-polished rust blue. There were approximately 10,000 manufactured in the 1-10100 serial-number range.

Exc.	V.G.	Good	Fair	Poor
3500	2800	1800	1200	750

Erfurt Royal Arsenal

1908 Erfurt

4" barrel, 9mm caliber. It has no stock lug; and the year of manufacture, from 1910-1913, is stamped above the chamber. The extractor and safety are both marked in German, and "ERFURT" under a crown is stamped on the front toggle link. There were many thousands produced as Germany was involved in WWI. They are found in the one- to five-digit serial range, sometimes with a letter suffix.

Exc.	V.G.	Good	Fair	Poor
850	700	600	400	350

1914 Erfurt Military

4" barrel, 9mm caliber. It has a stock lug and the date of manufacture over the chamber, 1914-1918. The extractor and safety are both marked in German, and the front link is marked "ERFURT" under a crown. The finish on this model is very rough; and as the war progressed in 1917 and 1918, the finish got worse. There were many thousands produced with one- to five-digit serial numbers, some with letter suffixes.

Exc.	V.G.	Good	Fair	Poor
850	700	600	400	350

1914 Erfurt Artillery

8" barrel, 9mm caliber. It has a stock lug and was issued with a flat board-type stock and other accessories which will be covered in the section of this book dealing with same. The sight is a nine-position adjustable model soldered to the barrel. The chamber is dated 1914-1918, and the extractor and safety are both marked in German. "ERFURT" under a crown is stamped on the front toggle link. There were a great many manufactured with one- to five-digit serial numbers, some with a letter suffix. This model is similar to the DWM Artillery except that the finish is not as fine.

Exc.	V.G.	Good	Fair	Poor
2500	1800	1100	800	600

Double Date Erfurt

4" barrel, 9mm caliber. The area above the chamber has two dates: the original 1910-1918, and the date of rework, 1920 or 1921. The extractor and safety are both marked in German, and this model can be found with or without a stock lug. "ERFURT" under a crown is stamped on the front toggle link. Police or military unit markings are found on the front of the grip straps more often than not. There were thousands of these produced by DWM as well as Erfurt.

Exc.	V.G.	Good	Fair	Poor
750	600	500	400	350

WAFFENFABRIK BERN

See separate section on Bern.

Simson & Co. Suhl, Germany

Simson & Co. Rework

4" barrels, 7.65 or 9mm caliber. The chamber is blank, but some examples are dated 1917 or 1918. The forward toggle link is stamped "SIMSON & CO. Suhl". The extractor and safety are marked in German. Most examples have stock lugs; some have been noted without them. The only difference between military models and commercial models is the proofmarks.

Exc.	V.G.	Good	Fair	Poor
1400	1100	850	600	500

Simson Grip Safety Rework

4" barrel, 9mm caliber and a grip safety was added. There is a stock lug. The chamber area is blank; the extractor is marked but the safety is not. There were only a few of these commercial reworks manufactured, and caution should be taken to avoid fakes.

Exc.	V.G.	Good	Fair	Poor
2800	2000	1500	850	550

Simson Dated Military

4" barrel, 9mm caliber. There is a stock lug, and the year of manufacture from 1925-1928 is stamped above the chamber. The extractor and the safety are both marked in German. The checkered walnut grips of Simson-made Lugers are noticeably thicker than others. This is an extremely rare variation. Approximately 2,000 were manufactured with one- to three-digit serial numbers, and very few seem to have survived.

Exc.	V.G.	Good	Fair	Poor
3000	2200	1800	900	650

Simson S Code

4" barrel, 9mm caliber. The forward toggle link is stamped with a gothic S. It has a stock lug, and the area above the chamber is blank. The extractor and the safety are both marked. The grips are also thicker. There were approximately 12,000 manufactured with one- to five-digit serial numbers—some with the letter "a" suffix. This pistol is quite rare on today's market.

Exc.	V.G.	Good	Fair	Poor
4000	3000	1500	1000	750

Early Nazi Era Reworks Mauser

Produced between 1930 and 1933, and normally marked with Waffenamt markings.

Deaths Head Rework

4" barrel, 9mm caliber. It has a stock lug; and a skull and crossbones are stamped, in addition to the date of manufacture, on the chamber area. This date was from 1914-1918. The extractor and safety are both marked. The Waffenamt proof is present. It is thought that this variation was produced for the 1930-1933 era "SS" division of the Nazi Party. Mixed serial numbers are encountered on this model and do not lower the value. This is a very rare Luger on today's market, and caution should be exercised if purchase is contemplated.

Exc.	V.G.	Good	Fair	Poor
1400	1100	950	600	450

Kadetten Institut Rework

4" barrel, 9mm caliber. It has a stock lug, and the chamber area is stamped "K.I." above the date 1933. This stood for Cadets Institute, an early "SA" and "SS" officers' training school. The extractor and safety are both marked, and the Waffenamt is present. There were only a few hundred reworked, and the variation is quite scarce. Be wary of fakes.

Exc.	V.G.	Good	Fair	Poor
2500	1850	1100	800	600

Mauser Unmarked Rework

4" barrel, 9mm caliber. The entire weapon is void of identifying markings. There is extensive refurbishing, removal of all markings, rebarrelling, etc. The stock lug is present, and the extractor and safety are marked. The Waffenamt proofmark is on the right side of the receiver. The number manufactured is not known.

Exc.	V.G.	Good	Fair	Poor
1450	1000	850	600	450

Mauser Manufactured Lugers 1930-1942

DWM - Mauser Oberndorf

4" barrel, 9mm caliber. It has a stock lug, blank chamber area and a marked extractor and safety. This is an early example of Mauser Luger, and the front toggle link is still marked DWM as leftover parts were intermixed with new Mauser parts in the production of this pistol. This is one of the first Lugers to be finished with the "Salt" blue process. There were approximately 500 manufactured with one- to four-digit serial numbers with the letter "v" suffix. This is a very rare variation.

Exc.	V.G.	Good	Fair	Poor
3500	2850	1850	1450	900

1934/06 Swiss Commercial Mauser

4.75" barrel, 7.65mm caliber. There is no stock lug, but it has a grip safety. The Swiss Cross in Sunburst is stamped above the chamber. The extractor and safety are marked in German. The front toggle link is marked with the Mauser banner. There were approximately 200 manufactured for commercial sale in Switzerland. This variation is very well finished, and the serial numbers are all four digits with a "v" suffix.

Exc.	V.G.	Good	Fair	Poor
6000	4850	3850	1500	1000

1935/06 Portuguese "GNR"

4.75" barrel, 7.65mm caliber. It has no stock lug but has a grip safety. The chamber is marked "GNR," representing the Republic National Guard. The extractor is marked "Carregada"; and the safety, "Seguranca." The Mauser banner is stamped on the front toggle link. There were exactly 564 manufactured according to the original contract records which the Portuguese government made public. They all have four-digit serial numbers with a "v" suffix.

Exc.	V.G.	Good	Fair	Poor
3000	2400	1600	900	750

1934 Mauser Commercial

4" barrel, 7.65mm or 9mm caliber. It has a stock lug, and the chamber area is blank. The extractor and the safety are marked. The Mauser banner is stamped on the front toggle link. The finish on this pistol was very good, and the grips are either checkered walnut or black plastic on the later models. There were a few thousand manufactured for commercial sales in and outside of Germany.

Exc.	V.G.	Good	Fair	Poor
3500	2800	1650	1100	700

S/42 K Date

4" barrel, 9mm caliber. It has a stock lug, and the extractor and safety are marked. This was the first Luger that utilized codes to represent maker and date of manufacture. The front toggle link is marked S/42 in either gothic or script; this was the code for Mauser. The chamber area is stamped with the letter "K," the code for 1934, the year of manufacture.

S/42 K Date

Approximately 10,500 were manufactured with one- to five-digit serial numbers—some with letter suffixes.

Exc.	V.G.	Good	Fair	Poor
3500	2850	1850	1000	800

S/42 G Date

As above, with the chamber stamped "G", the code for the year 1935. The gothic lettering was eliminated, and there were many thousands of this model produced.

Exc.	V.G.	Good	Fair	Poor
1250	900	650	500	350

Dated Chamber S/42

4" barrel, 9mm caliber. The chamber area is dated 1936-1940, and there is a stock lug. The extractor and safety are marked. In 1937 the rust blue process was eliminated entirely, and all subsequent pistols were salt blued. There were many thousands manufactured with one- to five-digit serial numbers—some with the letter suffix.

Exc.	V.G.	Good	Fair	Poor
1100	950	600	450	350

S/42 Commercial Contract

4" barrel, 9mm caliber. It has a stock lug, and the chamber area is dated. It has a marked extractor and safety. The unusual feature is that, although this was a commercial pistol, the front toggle link is stamped S/42, which was the military code for Mauser. There were only a few hundred manufactured, so perhaps the toggles were left over from previous military production runs. The serial number range is four digits with the letter "v."

Exc.	V.G.	Good	Fair	Poor
2500	1850	950	750	450

Code 42 Dated Chamber

4" barrel, 9mm caliber. The new German code for Mauser, the number 42, is stamped on the front toggle link. There is a stock lug. The chamber area is dated 1939 or 1940. Some are found with walnut grips; others, with black plastic. There were at least 50,000 manufactured with one- to five-digit serial numbers; some have letter suffixes.

Exc.	V.G.	Good	Fair	Poor
950	800	550	400	350

41/42 Code

As above, except that the date of manufacture is represented by the final two digits (e.g. 41 for 1941). There were approximately 20,000 manufactured with the one- to five-digit serial-number range.

Exc.	V.G.	Good	Fair	Poor
1500	1200	850	600	400

byf Code

As above, with the "byf" code stamp. The year of manufacture, either 41 or 42, is stamped on the chamber. This model was also made with black plastic, as well as walnut grips. There were many thousands produced with the one- to five-digit serial numbers—some with a letter suffix.

Exc.	V.G.	Good	Fair	Poor
950	750	650	450	350

Persian Contract 4"

4" barrel, 9mm caliber. It has a stock lug, and the Persian Crest is stamped over the chamber. All identifying markings on this variation—including extractor, safety and toggle—are marked in Farsi, the Persian alphabet. There were 1,000 manufactured. The serial numbers are also in Farsi.

Exc.	V.G.	Good	Fair	Poor
6500	5000	3500	2500	2000

Persian Contract Artillery

As above, with an 8" barrel and nine-position adjustable sight on the barrel. This model is supplied with a flat board stock. There were 1,000 manufactured and sold to Persia.

Exc.	V.G.	Good	Fair	Poor
3500	2850	1800	1300	1000

1934/06 Dated Commercial

4.75" barrel, 7.65mm caliber. It has a grip safety but no stock lug. The year of manufacture, from 1937-1942, is stamped above the chamber, and the Mauser banner is stamped on the front link. The extractor is marked, but the safety is not. There were approximately 1,000 manufactured with one- to three-digit serial numbers—some with the letter suffix.

Exc.	V.G.	Good	Fair	Poor
2500	1800	1250	800	450

1934 Mauser Dutch Contract

4" barrel, 9mm caliber. The year of manufacture, 1936-1940, is stamped above the chamber. The extractor is marked "Geladen," and the safety is marked "RUST" with a downward pointing arrow. The Mauser banner is stamped on the front toggle link. This was a military contract sale, and approximately 1,000 were manufactured with four-digit serial numbers with a letter "v" suffix.

Exc.	V.G.	Good	Fair	Poor
3000	2500	1800	950	700

1934 Mauser Swedish Contract

4.75" barrel, 9mm or 7.65mm caliber. The chamber is dated 1938 or 1939. The extractor and safety are both marked in German, and there is a stock lug. The front toggle link is stamped with the Mauser banner. There were only 275 dated 1938 and 25 dated 1939 in 9mm. There were only 30 chambered for 7.65mm dated 1939. The serial number range is four digits with the letter "v" suffix.

Exc.	V.G.	Good	Fair	Poor
2850	1950	1600	950	700

1934 Mauser Swedish Commercial

4" barrel, 7.65mm caliber. 1940 is stamped over the chamber; "Kal. 7.65" is stamped on the left side of the barrel. The extractor and safety are both marked, and the Mauser banner is stamped on the front toggle link. There is a stock lug. This model is very rare as there were only a few hundred manufactured with four digit serial numbers with the letter "w" suffix.

Exc.	V.G.	Good	Fair	Poor
2500	1800	1200	850	600

1934 Mauser German Contract

4" barrel, 9mm caliber. The chamber is dated 1939-1942, and the front toggle link is stamped with the Mauser banner. There is a stock lug, and the extractor and safety are both marked. The grips are either walnut or black plastic. There were several thousand manufactured with one- to five-digit serial numbers—some with letter suffixes. They were purchased for issue to police or paramilitary units.

Exc.	V.G.	Good	Fair	Poor
2500	1900	1200	800	550

Austrian Bundes Heer (Federal Army)

4" barrel, 9mm caliber. The chamber is blank, and there is a stock lug. The extractor and safety are marked in German, and the Austrian Federal Army Proof is stamped on the left side of the frame above the triggerguard. There were approximately 200 manufactured with four digit serial numbers and no letter suffix.

Exc.	V.G.	Good	Fair	Poor
2500	1850	1200	700	500

Mauser 2 Digit Date

4" barrel, 9mm caliber. The last two digits of the year of manufacture—41 or 42—are stamped over the chamber. There is a stock lug, and the Mauser banner is on the front toggle link. The extractor and safety are both marked, and the proofmarks were commercial. Grips are either walnut or black plastic. There were approximately 2,000 manufactured for sale to Nazi political groups. They have one- to five-digit serial numbers; some have the letter suffix.

Exc.	V.G.	Good	Fair	Poor
2500	1600	1000	700	450

Krieghoff Manufactured Lugers

1923 DWM Krieghoff Commercial

4" barrel, 7.65mm or 9mm caliber. The chamber is dated 1921 or left blank. There is a stock lug. The front toggle is marked DWM, as they manufactured this Luger to be sold by Krieghoff. "Krieghoff Suhl" is stamped on the back above the lanyard loop. The second "F" in Krieghoff was defective, and all specimens have this distinctive die strike. The safety and extractor are marked in German. There were only a few hundred manufactured with four-digit serial numbers with the letter "i" suffix.

Exc.	V.G.	Good	Fair	Poor
1800	1400	950	650	500

DWM/Krieghoff Commercial

As above, but marked "Heinrich Krieghoff Waffenfabrik Suhl" on the right side of the frame. Some examples have the "Germany" export stamp. There were several hundred manufactured with four-digit serial numbers with a letter suffix.

Exc.	V.G.	Good	Fair	Poor
3500	2850	2000	950	800

Krieghoff Commercial Inscribed Side Frame

4" or 6" barrel, 7.65mm or 9mm caliber. 1,000 were marked "Heinrich Krieghoff Waffenfabrik Suhl" on the right side of the frame, and 500 were devoid of this marking. All have the dagger and anchor trademark over "H.K. Krieghoff Suhl" on the front toggle link. The extractor and the safety are both marked. There is a stock lug, and the grips are of brown checkered plastic. There were approximately 1,500 manufactured with one- to four-digit serial numbers with a "P" prefix.

Exc.	V.G.	Good	Fair	Poor
4500	3600	2500	1800	1000

S Code Krieghoff

4" barrel, 9mm caliber. The Krieghoff trademark is stamped on the front toggle link, and the letter "S" is stamped over the chamber. There is a stock lug, and the extractor and safety are both marked. The grips are brown checkered plastic. There were approximately 4,500 manufactured for the Luftwaffe with one- to four-digit serial numbers.

Exc.	V.G.	Good	Fair	Poor
2850	2500	1800	950	750

Grip Safety Krieghoff

4" barrel, 9mm caliber. The chamber area is blank, and the front toggle link is stamped with the Krieghoff trademark. There is a stock lug and a grip safety. The extractor is marked "Geladen," and the safety is marked "FEUER" (fire) in the lower position. The grips are checkered brown plastic. This is a very rare Luger, and the number produced is not known.

Exc.	V.G.	Good	Fair	Poor
5000	3650	2500	1200	900

36 Date Krieghoff

4" barrel, 9mm caliber. It has a stock lug and the Kreighoff trademark on the front toggle link. The safety and extractor are marked, and the grips are brown plastic. The two-digit year of manufacture, 36, is stamped over the chamber. There were approximately 700 produced in the 3800-4500 serial number range.

Exc.	V.G.	Good	Fair	Poor
3500	2900	2000	1200	850

4 Digit Dated Kreighoff

As above, with the date of production, 1936-1940, stamped above the chamber. There were approximately 9,000 manufactured within the 4500-14000 serial number range.

Exc.	V.G.	Good	Fair	Poor
3000	2500	1850	950	750

2nd Series Krieghoff Commercial

4" barrel, 9mm caliber. There is a stock lug, and the Krieghoff trademark is stamped on the front link. The chamber area is blank, and the extractor and safety are marked. There were approximately 500 manufactured for commercial sales inside Germany. The date of manufacture is estimated at 1939-1940, as this variation has the dark finish that results from blueing without polishing the surface, which was done during these years. The grips are coarsely checkered black plastic. The serial number range is one to three digits with a "P" prefix.

Exc.	V.G.	Good	Fair	Poor
3300	2850	1950	1000	800

Postwar Krieghoff

4" barrel, 9mm caliber. There is a stock lug, and the chamber area is blank. The extractor and safety are marked, and the serial numbers in the one- to three-digit range are unusually large —about 3/16ths of an inch. There were 300 of these postwar Lugers produced for the occupation forces. They were assembled from leftover parts, and only 150 have the Krieghoff trademark on the front toggle link—the second 150 have blank links.

Exc.	V.G.	Good	Fair	Poor
3500	1500	1000	750	650

Kreighoff Postwar Commercial

As above, in 7.65mm caliber and the extractor not marked. Approximately 200 manufactured with standard-sized two- or three-digit serial numbers. They were supposedly sold to the occupation forces in the PX stores.

Exc.	V.G.	Good	Fair	Poor
2500	1650	1000	700	550

Luger Accessories

Detachable Carbine Stocks

Approximately 13" in length, with a sling swivel and horn buttplate.

Exc.	V.G.	Good	Fair	Poor
1500	1150	850	700	500

Artillery Stock with Holster
The artillery stock is of a flat board style approximately 13.75" in length. There is a holster and magazine pouches with straps attached. This is a very desirable addition to the Artillery Luger. A word of caution—one must check federal laws regarding detachable stocks and short-barrelled pistols; there are a number of restrictions that must be observed.

Exc.	V.G.	Good	Fair	Poor
500	450	400	300	200

Navy Stock
As above, but 12.75" in length with a brass disc inlaid on the left side.

Exc.	V.G.	Good	Fair	Poor
1000	850	750	400	300

Ideal Stock/Holster
A telescoping metal tube stock with an attached leather holster. It is used in conjunction with a metal-backed set of plain grips that correspond to the metal hooks on the stock and allow attachment. This Ideal Stock is U.S. patented and is so marked.

Exc.	V.G.	Good	Fair	Poor
1400	1100	850	700	450

Drum Magazine 1st Issue
A 32-round, snail-like affair that is used with the Artillery Luger. It is also used with an adapter in the German 9mm submachine gun. The 1st Issue has a telescoping tube that is used to wind the spring. There is a dust cover that protects the interior from dirt.

Exc.	V.G.	Good	Fair	Poor
800	600	450	350	300

Drum Magazine 2nd Issue
As above, with a folding spring winding lever.

Exc.	V.G.	Good	Fair	Poor
700	500	400	350	300

Drum Magazine Loading Tool
This tool is slipped over the magazine and allows the spring to be compressed so that cartridges could be inserted.

Exc.	V.G.	Good	Fair	Poor
600	450	350	300	200

Drum Magazine Unloading Tool
The origin of this tool is unknown and caution should be exercised prior to purchase.

Drum Carrying Case
The same caveat as above applies.

Exc.	V.G.	Good	Fair	Poor
250	200	125	100	50

Holsters
Produced in a wide variety of styles.

Exc.	V.G.	Good	Fair	Poor
200	150	100	50	40

Late Production Mauser Lugers
Manufactured during the 1970s.

P.08 Interarms
4" or 6" barrel, 7.65mm or 9mm caliber.

NIB	Exc.	V.G.	Good	Fair	Poor
800	650	500	400	350	300

Swiss Eagle Interarms
Swiss-style straight front grip strap and the American Eagle Crest over the chamber. It is chambered for 7.65mm or 9mm and is offered with a 4 or 6" barrel.

NIB	Exc.	V.G.	Good	Fair	Poor
700	550	450	350	325	300

Commemorative Bulgarian
The Bulgarian Crest is stamped over the chamber. There were only 100 produced.

NIB	Exc.	V.G.	Good	Fair	Poor
1900	1500	1200	950	650	450

Commemorative Russian
Crossed Nagant Rifles are stamped over the chamber. There were 100 produced.

NIB	Exc.	V.G.	Good	Fair	Poor
1900	1500	1200	950	650	450

Modern Production Carbine
This splendid reproduction was produced on a limited basis. The workmanship is excellent, and the carbine and stock are furnished in a case.

NIB	Exc.	V.G.	Good	Fair	Poor
6000	5000	4000	3200	2500	2000

John Martz Custom Lugers
Manufactured for a number of years.

Martz Luger Carbine
16" barrel. Approximately 60 were manufactured.

NIB	Exc.	V.G.	Good	Fair	Poor
5000	4000	2500	2250	1850	1250

.45 ACP
6" barrel, .45 ACP caliber. Assembled from two Luger pistols which were split and welded together. 40 manufactured.

NIB	Exc.	V.G.
4500	4000	3000

Baby Luger 9mm
A compact 9mm caliber pistol. Approximately 130 were produced.

NIB	Exc.	V.G.	Good
2500	2000	1500	1000

Baby Luger .380 ACP
As above, in .380 caliber. Approximately six were manufactured.

NIB	Exc.	V.G.
4500	4000	2500

LUNA

Zella-Mehlis, Germany

Model 200 Free Pistol
A .22 caliber Martini action single shot pistol with an 11" barrel, adjustable sights and walnut grips. Manufactured prior to WWII.

Exc.	V.G.	Good	Fair	Poor
1250	1000	800	600	500

Target Rifle
A .22 or .22 Hornet caliber Martini action single shot rifle with a 20" barrel, adjustable sights and walnut stock. Manufactured prior to WWII.

Exc.	V.G.	Good	Fair	Poor
1000	850	650	500	400

MAB
SEE—Bayonne

MAC
SEE—Ingram

MAS
St. Etienne, France
Manufacture d'Armes de St. Etienne

MAS 36
A 7.5mm caliber bolt-action rifle with a 22.6" barrel and 5-shot magazine. Blued with a walnut stock. The standard French service rifle from 1936 to 1949.

Exc.	V.G.	Good	Fair	Poor
200	175	150	100	75

MAS 36 CR39
As above, with an aluminum folding stock.

Exc.	V.G.	Good	Fair	Poor
225	200	175	125	90

Model 1917
An 8mm Lebel caliber semi-automatic rifle with a 31.4" barrel, 5-shot magazine and full length walnut stock.

Exc.	V.G.	Good	Fair	Poor
375	325	250	175	125

Model 1918
As above, with a 23.1" barrel.

Exc.	V.G.	Good	Fair	Poor
375	325	250	175	125

MAS 49
A 7.5mm semi-automatic rifle with a 22.6" barrel and full length walnut stock.

Exc.	V.G.	Good	Fair	Poor
325	275	225	150	100

MBA GYROJET
San Ramon, California

Established in 1960, by R. Maynard and Art Biehl, MBA manufactured a pistol as well as carbine which utilized a spin stabilized rocket. Initially, these arms were of 13mm caliber and later of 12mm.

Mark I Pistol

Exc.	V.G.	Good	Fair	Poor
700	600	500	400	300

Mark I Carbine
This model is similar to the pistol except that it has an 18" barrel and a buttstock with a pistol grip.

Exc.	V.G.	Good	Fair	Poor
1250	1050	850	600	500

MK ARMS, INC.
Irvine, California

K 760
A 9mm caliber semi-automatic carbine with a 16" shrouded barrel, fixed sights and 14-, 24- or 36-shot magazine. Parkerized with a folding stock. Introduced in 1983.

NIB	Exc.	V.G.	Good	Fair	Poor
500	450	375	300	250	200

MKE
Ankara, Turkey
Importer—Mandall Shooting Supplies
Scottsdale, Arizona

Kirrikale
A 7.65 or 9mm short semi-automatic pistol with a 4" barrel and 7-shot magazine. Blued with plastic grips.

NIB	Exc.	V.G.	Good	Fair	Poor
400	350	275	225	150	100

M.O.A. CORP.
Dayton, Ohio

Maximum
A single shot pistol manufactured in a variety of calibers with an 8.5", 10" or 14" barrel, adjustable sights, blued finish and walnut grip. Introduced in 1986.

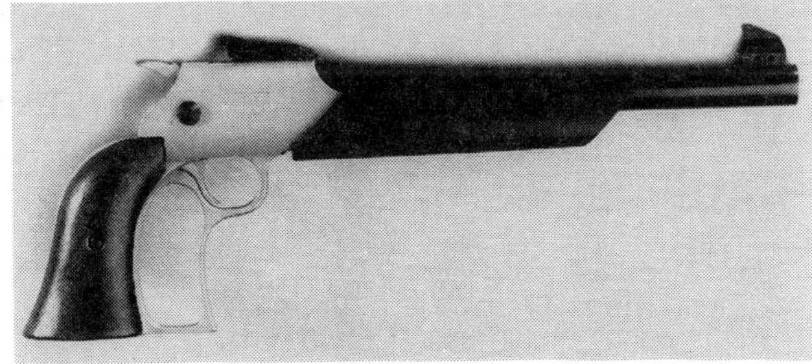

NIB	Exc.	V.G.	Good	Fair	Poor
500	425	375	300	250	200

Carbine
As above with an 18" barrel. Manufactured during 1986 and 1987.

NIB	Exc.	V.G.	Good	Fair	Poor
500	425	375	300	250	200

MAGNUM RESEARCH, INC.
SEE—Desert Eagle

MAKAROV
Former Soviet Union and Warsaw Pact Nations
Importer—Centruy International Arms Co.
St. Albans, Vermont

Makarov
This semi-automatic pistol is similar in appearance to the Wal-

ter PP pistol and is chambered for the 9mm Makarov (9x18mm) cartridge. It has a double-action trigger and is fitted with fixed sights. Barrel length is 3.6" and overall length is 6.4". Weight is approximately 25 ozs. Magazine capacity is 8 rounds.

Exc.	V.G.	Good	Fair	Poor
130	100	80	60	50

MALIN, F. E.

London, England
Importer—Cape Horn Outfitters
Charlotte, North Carolina

Boxlock and Sidelock Shotguns made by Malin were imported into the United States for a number of years. As these arms were all essentially built to specific customer's requirements, standard values cannot be provided. Prospective purchasers are advised to secure a qualified appraisal prior to acquisition.

Boxlock

Features an Anson & Deeley action and high-grade walnut. All other specification were on a custom-order basis. This gun should definitely be individually appraised as values will fluctuate greatly with options.

Basic Model Estimated Value Only

NIB	Exc.	V.G.	Good	Fair	Poor
4000	3500	3000	2500	1850	1450

Sidelock

Features a Holland & Holland-type detachable sidelock action, and all other features (as on the boxlock) were on a custom-order basis. This model should also be appraised individually.

Basic Model Estimated Value Only

NIB	Exc.	V.G.	Good	Fair	Poor
5500	5000	4250	3000	2500	1850

MALTBY, HENLEY AND CO.

New York, New York

Spencer Safety Hammerless Revolver

A .32 caliber double action revolver with a 3" barrel and 5-shot cylinder. The frame and barrel made of brass and the cylinder of steel. The barrel marked "Spencer Safety Hammerless Pat. Jan. 24, 1888 & Oct.29, 1889." Several thousand were manufactured during in the 1890's.

Courtesy Mike Stuckslager.

Exc.	V.G.	Good	Fair	Poor
250	225	175	125	75

MANHATTAN FIREARMS COMPANY

Norwich, Connecticut
Newark, New Jersey

Bar Hammer Pistol

A .31, .34, or .36 caliber single shot percussion pistol with a 2" or 4" barrel. The hammer marked "Manhattan F.A. Mfg. Co. New York." Blued with walnut grips. Approximately 1,500 were made during the 1850s.

Exc.	V.G.	Good	Fair	Poor
500	425	350	250	150

Shotgun Hammer Pistol

A .36 caliber bar hammer single shot percussion pistol with a 5.5" half octagonal barrel marked as above. Blued with walnut grips. Approximately 500 were made.

Exc.	V.G.	Good	Fair	Poor
550	450	375	225	175

Courtesy Milwaukee Public Museum, Milwaukee, Wisconsin.

Pepperbox

A .28 or .31 caliber double action percussion pepperbox with 3", 4" or 5" barrels and 5- or 6-shot barrel groups. Blued, case-hardened with walnut grips. Marked as above and also "Cast Steel". The major variations of this pistol are as follows:

Three-shot with 3" Barrel

Manually rotated barrels.

Exc.	V.G.	Good	Fair	Poor
750	675	600	450	350

Five-shot with 3", 4", 5" Barrel

Automatically rotated barrels.

Exc.	V.G.	Good	Fair	Poor
600	525	450	350	250

Six-shot with 3" or 4" Barrel

Automatic rotation.

Exc.	V.G.	Good	Fair	Poor
600	525	450	350	250

Six-shot W/5" Barrel
Automatic rotation.

Exc.	V.G.	Good	Fair	Poor
750	675	600	450	350

Pocket Revolver
A .31 caliber percussion revolver with a 4", 5" or 6" barrel and either 5-shot or 6-shot cylinder. Blued, case-hardened with walnut grips. The barrel marked, "Manhattan Firearms/Manufg. Co. New-York" on the 5-shot model, serial numbers from 1 to approximately 1,000, and "Manhattan Firearms Mf'g. Co. New York" on the 6-shot model. The frame marked "December 27, 1859".

Courtesy Milwaukee Public Museum, Milwaukee, Wisconsin.

First Model—5-Shot

Exc.	V.G.	Good	Fair	Poor
500	425	350	250	150

Second Model—6-Shot

Exc.	V.G.	Good	Fair	Poor
450	400	300	200	100

London Pistol Company
As above, but marked "London Pistol Company". Approximately 200 manufactured between 1859 and 1861.

Exc.	V.G.	Good	Fair	Poor
450	400	300	200	100

.36 Caliber Percussion Revolver
A .36 caliber percussion revolver with a 4", 5" or 6.5" octagonal barrel and 5- or 6-shot cylinder. Blued, case-hardened with walnut grips. Approximately 78,000 were made between 1859 and 1868. There were five variations—see below.

Courtesy Milwaukee Public Museum, Milwaukee, Wisconsin.

Model I
A 5-shot cylinder marked "Manhattan Firearms Mfg. Co. New York." The serial numbers from 1 through 4200. The 6"-barrelled version would be worth a 15 percent premium.

Exc.	V.G.	Good	Fair	Poor
750	675	600	450	350

Model II
As above with the 1859 patent date marked on the barrel. The serial range is 4200 to 14500.

Exc.	V.G.	Good	Fair	Poor
600	525	450	350	250

Model III
A 5-shot cylinder and marked, "Manhattan Firearms Co. Newark NJ," together with the 1859 patent date. The serial numbers are from 14500 to 45200.

Exc.	V.G.	Good	Fair	Poor
500	425	350	250	150

Model IV
As above, with a modified recoil shield and the patent date March 8, 1864 added to the barrel inscription. Serial numbers from 45200 to 69200.

Exc.	V.G.	Good	Fair	Poor
500	475	350	250	150

Model V
As above, with a 6-shot cylinder and numbered 1 to approximately 9000.

Exc.	V.G.	Good	Fair	Poor
600	525	450	350	250

.22 Caliber Pocket Revolver
A .22 caliber spur trigger revolver with a 3" barrel and 7-shot cylinder. Blued, silver plated with walnut or rosewood grips. Approximately 17,000 were made during the 1860s.

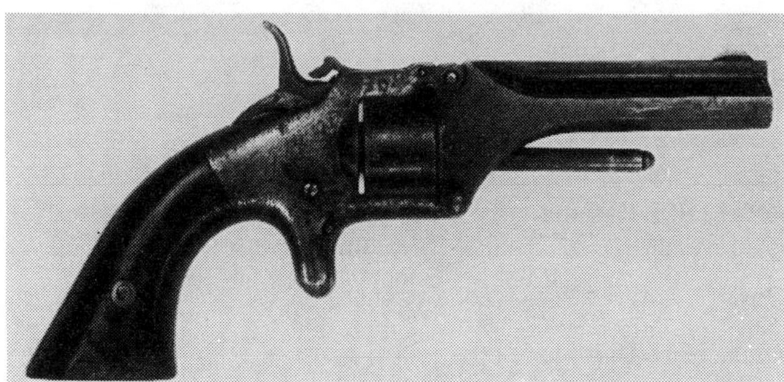
Courtesy Milwaukee Public Museum, Milwaukee, Wisconsin.

Exc.	V.G.	Good	Fair	Poor
450	400	300	200	100

Manhattan-American Standard Hero
A .34 caliber single shot percussion pistol with a 2" or 3" round barrel which unscrews for loading. Blued, brass frame with walnut grips. Marked "A.S.T. Co./HERO". Made by the American Standard Tool Company, Manhattan's successor. Approximately 30,000 manufactured between 1868 and 1873.

Manhattan Manufactured
Marked, "HERO/M.F.A.Co." Approximately 5,000 were produced.

Exc.	V.G.	Good	Fair	Poor
350	300	250	150	100

American Standard Manufactured
Approximately 25,000 were produced.

Exc.	V.G.	Good	Fair	Poor
300	250	200	100	75

MANN, FRITZ
Suhl, Germany

6.35mm Pocket Pistol
A 6.35mm caliber semi-automatic pistol with a 1.65" barrel and 5-shot magazine. Blued with plastic grips having the name "Mann" cast in them. This pistol which weighs only 9 ounces is

one of the smallest semi-automatic pistols ever manufactured. Made between 1920 and 1922.

Exc.	V.G.	Good	Fair	Poor
300	250	200	150	100

7.65mm Pocket Pistol

A 7.65mm or 9mm short semi-automatic pistol with a 2.35" barrel and 5-shot magazine. Blued with plastic grips having the name "Mann" cast in them. Manufactured between 1924 and 1929.

Exc.	V.G.	Good	Fair	Poor
350	300	250	200	125

MANNLICHER PISTOL

Steyr, Austria

SEE—Steyr

MANNLICHER SCHOENAUER

Steyr, Austria

Model 1903 Mountain Carbine

A 6.5x54mm caliber bolt-action rifle with a 17.7" barrel, 5-shot rotary magazine, folding rear sight, double set triggers and full length walnut stock.

Exc.	V.G.	Good	Fair	Poor
1250	1000	750	600	400

Model 1905 Carbine

As above, but in 9x56mm caliber.

Exc.	V.G.	Good	Fair	Poor
1150	1000	900	750	450

Model 1908 Carbine

As above, but in 7x57mm or 8x56mm caliber.

Exc.	V.G.	Good	Fair	Poor
1000	875	750	500	350

Model 1910 Carbine

As above, but in 9.5x57mm.

Exc.	V.G.	Good	Fair	Poor
1000	875	750	500	350

Model 1924 Carbine

As above, but in .30-06 caliber.

Exc.	V.G.	Good	Fair	Poor
1750	1500	1000	750	500

High Velocity Rifle

As above, but in 7x64mm Brenneke, .30-06, 8x60Smm Magnum, 9.3x62mm, and the 10.75x68mm caliber with a 23.5" barrel and folding-leaf sight. Half-length walnut stock.

Takedown Model—Add 75%.

Exc.	V.G.	Good	Fair	Poor
2250	2000	1750	1000	700

All of the above models were discontinued prior to WWII.

Model 1950

A .257 Roberts, .270 Winchester, and the .30-06 caliber bolt-action rifle with a 24" barrel and 5-shot rotary magazine. Blued with a half length walnut stock. Manufactured between 1950 and 1952.

Exc.	V.G.	Good	Fair	Poor
1000	850	700	500	400

Model 1950 Carbine

As above, with a 20" barrel and a full-length stock.

Exc.	V.G.	Good	Fair	Poor
1250	1000	850	650	500

Model 1950 6.5 Carbine

As above, in 6.5x54mm Mannlicher Schoenauer caliber with a 18.5" barrel and full-length stock.

Exc.	V.G.	Good	Fair	Poor
1350	1100	850	650	500

Model 1952

Similar to the above, with a turned back bold handle. Manufactured between 1952 and 1956.

Exc.	V.G.	Good	Fair	Poor
1000	850	750	500	400

Model 1952 Carbine

Similar to the Model 1950 carbine, but additionally in 7x57mm caliber. Manufactured between 1952 and 1956.

Exc.	V.G.	Good	Fair	Poor
1150	1000	850	600	500

Model 1952 6.5mm Carbine

As above, in 6.5x54mm Mannlicher Schoenauer caliber with an 18.5" barrel. Manufactured between 1952 and 1956.

Exc.	V.G.	Good	Fair	Poor
1350	1100	850	650	500

Model 1956 Rifle

A .243 or .30-06 caliber bolt-action rifle with a 22" barrel and Monte Carlo-style stock. Manufactured between 1956 and 1960.

Exc.	V.G.	Good	Fair	Poor
900	800	650	500	400

Model 1956 Carbine

As above, with a 20" barrel and full-length stock. Manufactured between 1956 and 1960.

Exc.	V.G.	Good	Fair	Poor
1000	900	750	600	450

Model 1961 MCA Rifle

As above, but modified for easier use with a telescopic sight.

Exc.	V.G.	Good	Fair	Poor
900	800	650	500	400

Model 1961 MCA Carbine

As above, with a 20" barrel and half length stock.

Exc.	V.G.	Good	Fair	Poor
1100	1000	850	650	500

Model M72 LM Rifle

As above, with a 23" fluted barrel, double set or single trigger and full-length stock. Manufactured between 1972 and 1980.

Exc.	V.G.	Good	Fair	Poor
900	800	650	500	400

MANUFRANCE

St. Etienne, France

SEE—Le Francais

Auto Stand

A .22 caliber semi-automatic pistol manufactured by Pyrenees and sold by Manufrance under the tradename Auto Stand.

Exc.	V.G.	Good	Fair	Poor
250	225	200	150	100

Buffalo Stand

A .22 caliber bolt-action pistol with a 12" barrel and adjustable sights. Blued with a walnut stock. Manufactured prior to 1914.

Exc.	V.G.	Good	Fair	Poor
250	225	200	150	100

Le Agent
An 8mm caliber double-action revolver with a 5" barrel. Blued with walnut grips.

Exc.	V.G.	Good	Fair	Poor
200	175	150	100	75

Le Colonial
As above, with an enclosed hammer.

Exc.	V.G.	Good	Fair	Poor
200	175	150	100	75

MANURHIN
Mulhouse, France

This company manufactured the Walther PP and PPK models under license and these are marked "Manufacture de Machines du Haut-Rhin" on the left front of the slide and "Lic Excl. Walther" on the left rear. These arms were imported into the U.S.A. in the early 1950s by Thalson Import Co. of San Francisco, California, and later by Interarms. The latter are marked "Mark II" and "Made in France."

New Production
Currently, the Matra Manurhin Defense Corp. is manufacturing handguns, and they are imported by Atlantic Business Organizations of New York.

Model 73 Defense Revolver
A .38 Special or .357 Magnum caliber double-action swing-out cylinder revolver with a 2.5", 3" or 4" barrel having fixed sights. Blued with walnut grips.

NIB	Exc.	V.G.	Good	Fair	Poor
1150	1000	850	750	500	350

Model 73 Gendarmerie
As above, with a 5.5", 6", or 8" long barrel and adjustable sights.

NIB	Exc.	V.G.	Good	Fair	Poor
1250	1100	900	800	550	400

Model 73 Sport
Similar to the above, with a shortened lock time and target style adjustable sights.

NIB	Exc.	V.G.	Good	Fair	Poor
1250	1100	900	800	550	400

Model 73 Convertible
As above, with interchangeable .22, .32 or .38 caliber barrels and cylinders.

NIB	Exc.	V.G.	Good	Fair	Poor
2250	1850	1600	1400	950	750

Model 73 Silhouette
Similar to the Model 73 Sport, but in .22 to .357 Magnum caliber with a 10" or 10.75" shrouded barrel and form fitting walnut grips.

NIB	Exc.	V.G.	Good	Fair	Poor
1200	1050	850	750	500	350

Model PP
Similar to the Walther Model PP, with a revised safety.

Exc.	V.G.	Good	Fair	Poor
400	350	300	225	150

Model PPK/S
Similar to the Walther Model PPK/S, with a revised safety.

Exc.	V.G.	Good	Fair	Poor
400	350	300	225	150

MARATHON PRODUCTS, INC.
Santa Barbara, California

.22 First Shot
A .22 caliber single shot bolt-action rifle with a 16.5" barrel and overall length of 31". Blued with a walnut stock. Manufactured between 1985 and 1987.

Exc.	V.G.	Good	Fair	Poor
65	55	45	30	25

.22 Super Shot
As above, with a 24" barrel. Manufactured between 1985 and 1987.

Exc.	V.G.	Good	Fair	Poor
65	55	45	30	25

.22 Hot Shot Pistol
A .22 caliber bolt-action pistol with a 14.5" barrel. Blued with a walnut stock. Manufactured in 1986 and 1987.

Exc.	V.G.	Good	Fair	Poor
65	55	45	30	25

Centerfire Rifle
A bolt-action sporting rifle manufactured in a variety of calibers with a 24" barrel, open sights, adjustable trigger and 5-shot magazine. Blued with a walnut stock. Manufactured in 1985 and 1986.

Exc.	V.G.	Good	Fair	Poor
300	250	200	150	125

MARBLES GAME GETTER
Gladstone, Michigan

Game Getter
A combination .22 caliber by 410 bore or .44-40 shot cartridge Over/Under shotgun/rifle with 12", 15" or 18" barrels and a folding stock. The 12" or 15" barrelled versions are subject to the 1968 Gun Control Act and may only be owned or sold by Class 3 License holders. The values listed below are for the 18" model.

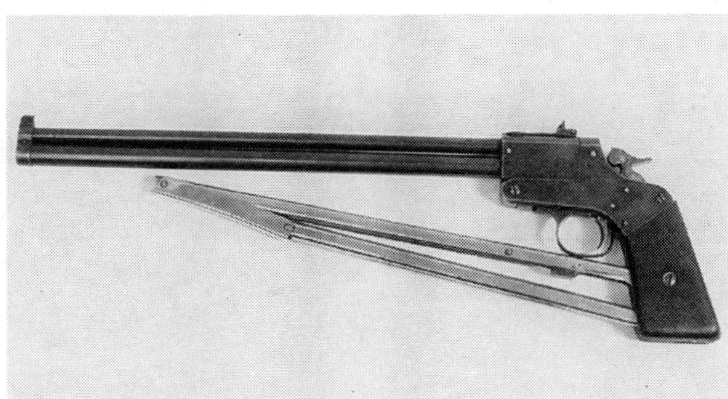

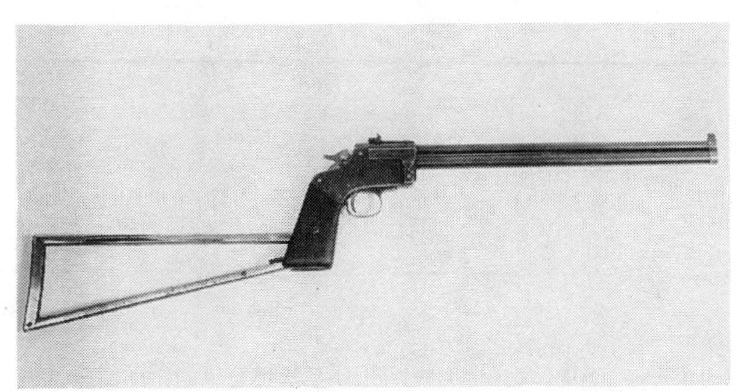

Exc.	V.G.	Good	Fair	Poor
800	700	650	500	400

MARGOLIN
Tula, Soviet State Arsenal

Courtesy Orville Reichert.

Model MTS-1
A .22 short semi-automatic pistol with a 7.5" barrel having an integral muzzle brake, adjustable walnut grips and a 6-shot magazine. Normally, accompanied by a case with cleaning accessories.

Exc.	V.G.	Good	Fair	Poor
800	700	600	450	350

Model MTS-2
As above, in .22 l.r. with a 6" barrel.

Exc.	V.G.	Good	Fair	Poor
800	700	600	450	350

MARIETTE BREVETTE
Liege, Belgium

A number of European manufacturers produced percussion pepperbox pistols based upon a patent issued to Mariette during the 1840s and 1850s. These pistols have detachable barrels which are loaded at the breech, double-action ring triggers and internally mounted hammers. They are normally blued and foliate engraved.

6 Barrel Pepperbox

Exc.	V.G.	Good	Fair	Poor
1850	1600	1250	900	650

4 Barrelled Pepperbox

Exc.	V.G.	Good	Fair	Poor
1600	1300	1000	750	500

MARLIN

MARLIN FIREARMS CO.
New Haven, Connecticut

Ballard Rifles

Established by John Mahlon Marlin in 1863. Marlin manufactured pistols until 1875 when he began production of Ballard rifles. In 1881 he made his first lever-action repeating rifle for which his company became famous.

The Marlin Firearms Company has the distinction of being the oldest family owned firearms company in the United States.

The Ballard single shot rifle was invented by C. H. Ballard of Worcester, Massachusetts. It was patented in 1861. The first of the Ballard rifles was manufactured by the Ball and Williams Co. of Worchester, Massachusetts. In 1866 Merwin and Bray purchased the firm, calling it Merrimack Arms Co., and operated until 1869, when they sold it to the Brown Manufacturing Co. of New York City. This venture took a decidedly negative turn, and in 1873 mortgage foreclosure forced the sale to Schoverling and Daly of New York City. These gentlemen were arms dealers, not manufacturers, so they entered into an agreement with John M. Marlin to produce the Ballard rifle. The rifles produced during this period are regarded as some of the finest single shots ever made, and the venture finally became successful. In 1881 the business became incorporated as the Marlin Firearms Co., and the Ballard was produced under this banner until it was discontinued around the year 1891. The popularity of the repeating rifle simply eroded the demand for the fine single shot until it was no longer a profitable venture.

Ball & Williams Ballards

First Model

This model was the first Ballard produced. It was introduced in 1861 and was offered with a 24" or 28" octagonal barrel. The frame is case-colored, and the barrel is blued. The walnut stock is varnished. The major identifying feature of this model is the inside extractor. This was the only Ballard that had this feature before Marlin began to manufacture the rifle in 1875. The barrel is stamped "Ball & Williams/Worchester, Mass." and "Ballards Patent/Nov. 5, 1861." There were approximately 100 manufactured and serial numbered from 1-100.

Exc.	V.G.	Good	Fair	Poor
1500	1300	1000	800	550

Military Rifle

There is not enough known about these rifles and probably never will be. They were chambered most frequently for the .44 and .54 rimfire cartridges and feature the outside tangs and extractors. They were offered with a 30" round barrel and full-length forearm. There are three barrel bands and sling swivels. The government ordered only 35 of these for use in the Civil War; and if one was to be definitely authenticated as a genuine martial specimen, it would be quite valuable. Many of these rifles were marked "Kentucky" on top of the receiver because the militia of that state armed its men with the Ballard rifles and carbines. This marking was a sales aid used by the company and does not indicate militia ownership. The amount manufactured is not known. Barrel markings are as on the First Model.

Exc.	V.G.	Good	Fair	Poor
900	750	650	500	350

Civil War Military Carbine

This model has a 22" part-round/part-octagonal barrel and is chambered for the .44 rimfire cartridge. It has the outside tang and extractor. The stock and forearm are walnut with a barrel-band sling swivel. The buttstock bears an oval cartouche surrounding the inspector's marks, "MM." These letters also appear stamped on major metal parts. There were 1,509 ordered by the government for use in the Civil War. The barrel was marked the same as the rifle.

Exc.	V.G.	Good	Fair	Poor
1500	1300	1000	800	550

Sporting Rifle

This model is chambered for the .32, .38, and .44 rimfire cartridges. The octagonal barrel is 24", 26", or 28" in length and is blued. The frame is case-colored. The stock and forearm are varnished walnut, and there is a knob that protrudes in front of the frame to operate the outside manual extractor. There is a crescent buttplate standard. There were approximately 6,500 manufactured, and barrel markings are the same as on the First Model.

Exc.	V.G.	Good	Fair	Poor
800	650	550	400	300

Sporting Carbine

This model is similar in appearance to the Sporting Rifle with a 22" part-round/part-octagon barrel. It is chambered for the .44 and .54 caliber cartridge, and the sling swivel is found on a barrel band in the front. The knob on the bottom activates the outside extractor. There have been some encountered with "Kentucky" stamped on the top, but this does not affect the value. The markings are the same as on the previous models. There are no production figures available, but some estimate approximately 2,000 were manufactured.

Exc.	V.G.	Good	Fair	Poor
900	750	650	500	350

Dual Ignition System

This system allows the use of the rimfire cartridge or percussion method by simply turning the striker on the hammer from one position to the other. This model features a percussion nipple mounted on the breechblock, and the hammer is marked "Patented Jan.5,1864." The patent was held by Merwin and Bray. This swivel system is usually found on the sporting models and would increase the value of the weapon by 20 percent.

Merrimack Arms Co. and Brown Manufacturing Co.

The values for the Ballard rifles manufactured by these two firms are the same, and the specifications are similar. The identifying difference is in the markings, "Merrimack Arms & Mfg. Co./Newburyport Mass." or "Brown Mfg.Co. Newburyport, Mass." Merrimack produced approximately 3,000 of these rifles between 1867 and 1869 serial numbered in the 18000-20000 range. Brown produced approximately 1,800 between 1869 and 1873 in the 20000-22000 serial number range.

Sporting Rifle

This model was produced in .22 (rare), .32, .38, .44, .46, and .52 caliber rimfire or percussion, as most encountered featured the dual ignition system and had the nipple in the breechblock. They have either a round or octagonal barrel in 24", 26", or 28" lengths. The appearance and finish is similar to the Ball & Williams rifles; and the major difference is the inside tang. The extractor was still outside mounted and manually activated. Exact production breakdown is unknown. There is no premium for the dual ignition system on these later guns.

Exc.	V.G.	Good	Fair	Poor
850	700	550	450	300

Sporting Carbine

This model is quite similar in appearance to the Sporting Rifle, with a 22" part-round/part-octagonal barrel.

Exc.	V.G.	Good	Fair	Poor
950	800	650	550	400

Military Rifle

The Military Rifle is similar to the sporting version except that it has a 30" round barrel and full-length forearm with three barrel bands. It is chambered for the .44 and .52 caliber rimfire or percussion with the dual ignition system.

Exc.	V.G.	Good	Fair	Poor
950	800	650	550	400

Shotgun

This model is similar to the Sporting Rifle in appearance but is chambered for 24 gauge, with a 30" round barrel. There is a groove milled in the top of the frame to use as a sight. The buttplate is shotgun-style instead of the usual crescent shape.

Exc.	V.G.	Good	Fair	Poor
650	550	450	350	250

Marlin-Ballard Rifles

Commencing in 1875 the Ballard single-shot rifle was made by John Marlin for Schoverling and Daly. In 1881 the business was incorporated and became the Marlin Firearms Co. All the Ballards made from then until 1891, when they were discontinued, were produced under this banner. The only real difference in the rifles manufactured during these periods was in the markings. The earlier rifles are stamped "J.M.Marlin New Haven. Conn. U.S.A./Ballards Patent. Nov.5,1861"; and the post-1881 models are stamped "Marlin Firearms Co. New Haven Ct. U.S.A./Patented Feb.9,1875/Ballards Patent Nov.5,1861." The major difference between Marlin-made Ballards and the earlier models is the inside tang and the internal extractor on the Marlin-made rifles. All of the Marlin-made Ballards have an octagonal frame top, and the Marlin Firearms Co. models have grooved receiver sides. The standard finish on all these later rifles is case-colored frames and blued octagonal or part-round/part-octagonal barrels. There are many variations in these rifles as to types of sights, stock, engraving, and other special-order features—such as barrel lengths, weights, and contours. These rifles must be considered individually and competently appraised. There is also the fact that many of these Ballards have been rebarrelled and rechambered over the years, as they were known for their shooting ability and were used quite extensively. This can seriously affect the value in a negative manner unless it can be authenticated that the work was done by the likes of Harry Pope or George Schoyen and other noted and respected gunsmiths of that era. This can add considerably to the value of the rifle. One must approach this model with caution and learn all that can be learned before purchasing.

Ballard Hunters Rifle

This model resembles the earlier Brown Mfg. Co. rifles, and it utilizes many leftover parts acquired by Marlin. It is chambered for the .32, .38, and .44 rimfire and centerfire and features John Marlin's unique reversible firing pin that allows the same gun to use both rimfire and centerfire ammunition simply by rotating the firing pin in the breechblock. This model still had the external ejector and bears the J. M. Marlin markings. There were approximately 500 manufactured in the 1 to 500 serial range. They were produced in 1875 and 1876.

Exc.	V.G.	Good	Fair	Poor
1500	1300	1000	800	550

Ballard No. 1 Hunters Rifle

This model bears the early J. M. Marlin marking only, as it was manufactured from 1876 until 1880 and was discontinued before the incorporation. It has a 26", 28", and 30" barrel and is chambered for the .44 rimfire or centerfire cartridge. It has the reversible firing pin and also the new internal extractor. Production figures are not available, but the serial number range is between 500 and 4000.

Exc.	V.G.	Good	Fair	Poor
900	750	650	500	375

Ballard No. 1-1/2 Hunters Rifle

This model is similar to the No. 1 except that it is chambered for the .45-70, .40-63, and the .40-65 cartridges and does not have the reversible firing pin. The barrel length is 30" and 32". It was manufactured between 1879 and 1883. This model is found with both early and later markings.

Exc.	V.G.	Good	Fair	Poor
1100	950	850	700	500

Ballard No. 1-3/4 "Far West" Hunters Rifle

This model was made by J. M. Marlin only and is similar to the 1-1/2, the difference being the addition of double-set triggers and a ring on the opening lever. It was manufactured in 1880 and 1881.

Exc.	V.G.	Good	Fair	Poor
1000	850	750	600	400

Ballard No. 2 Sporting Rifle

This model is chambered for the .32, .38 rimfire or centerfire cartridges, and the .44 centerfire. It has the reversible firing pin and was offered in 26", 28", and 30" barrel lengths. This model features "Rocky Mountain" sights and was manufactured between 1876 and 1891. It is found with both early and late markings.

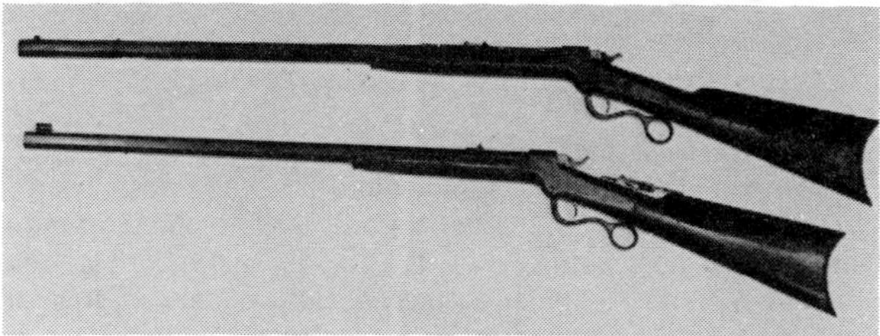

Courtesy Milwaukee Public Museum, Milwaukee, Wisconsin.

Exc.	V.G.	Good	Fair	Poor
850	750	600	450	300

Ballard No. 3 Gallery Rifle

This model is similar to the No. 2 rifle but is chambered for the .22 rimfire cartridge and has a manually operated external extractor. The sights are the same; and a 24" barrel was offered in addition to the 26", 28", and 30". This rifle was manufactured between 1876 and 1891.

Exc.	V.G.	Good	Fair	Poor
950	850	700	400	250

Ballard No. 3F Gallery Rifle

This is a deluxe version of the No. 3. It has a pistol grip stock, a nickle-plated Schutzen-style buttplate, and an opening lever like a repeating rifle. It features a 26" octagonal barrel and an oil-finished stock. It was manufactured in the late 1880s and is quite scarce in today's market.

Exc.	V.G.	Good	Fair	Poor
1300	1150	1000	850	650

Ballard No. 4 Perfection Rifle

This model is chambered for a number of centerfire calibers from .32-40 to .50-70. The barrel lengths are from 26" to 30", and the sights are of the "Rocky Mountain" type. This model was manufactured between 1876 and 1891.

Exc.	V.G.	Good	Fair	Poor
850	750	650	500	350

Ballard No. 3-1/2 Target Rifle

This model is similar to the No. 4 Perfection Rifle except that it has a checkered stock with a shotgun-style buttplate, a 30" barrel, and a tang peep sight with globe front sight. It was chambered for the .40-65 cartridge and was manufactured from 1880-1882.

Exc.	V.G.	Good	Fair	Poor
1200	1050	800	650	450

Ballard No. 4-1/2 Mid Range Rifle

This model is also a variation of the No. 4 Perfection model. It has a higher-grade checkered stock with a shotgun buttplate. It has a 30" part-round/part-octagonal barrel and is chambered for the .38-40, .40-65, and the .45-70 cartridges. It features a Vernier tang peep sight and a globe front sight. It was manufactured between 1878 and 1882.

Exc.	V.G.	Good	Fair	Poor
1500	1300	1150	950	675

Ballard No. 4-1/2 A-1 Mid Range Target Rifle

This is a deluxe version of the No. 4-1/2 rifle. It features scroll engraving on the frame—with "Ballard A-1" on the left and "Mid-Range" on the right. It is chambered for the .38-50 and the .40-65 cartridge and has a high-grade checkered stock with a horn forend tip. The sights are the highest-grade Vernier tang sight and a spirit lever front sight. The shotgun or rifle-style butt was optional. This model was manufactured between 1878 and 1880.

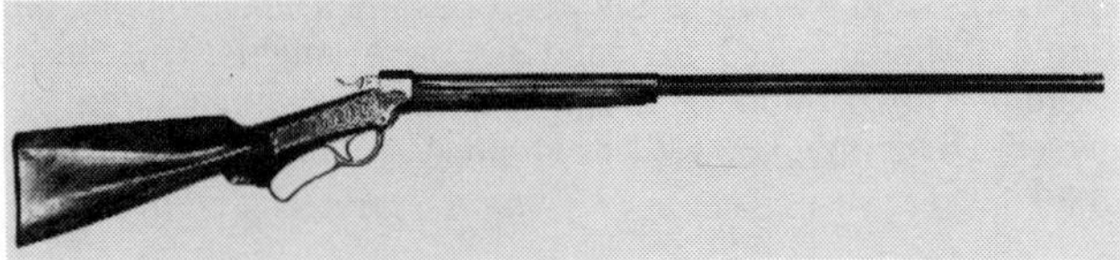

Courtesy Milwaukee Public Museum, Milwaukee, Wisconsin.

Exc.	V.G.	Good	Fair	Poor
2000	1800	1500	1150	850

Ballard No. 5 Pacific Rifle

This model has a 30" or 32" medium- to heavy-weight barrel, with a ramrod mounted underneath. It is chambered for many different calibers from .38-50 to .50-70. This model features "Rocky Mountain" sights, a crescent butt, double-set triggers, and a ring-style opening lever. It was manufactured between 1876 and 1891.

Courtesy Milwaukee Public Museum, Milwaukee, Wisconsin.

Exc.	V.G.	Good	Fair	Poor
1800	1650	1300	950	650

Ballard No. 5-1/2 Montana Rifle

This model is similar to the Pacific Rifle, with an extra heavy-weight barrel, and is chambered for the .45 Sharps cartridge only. It features a checkered steel shotgun-style buttplate. It was manufactured from 1882-1884 and has the late markings only.

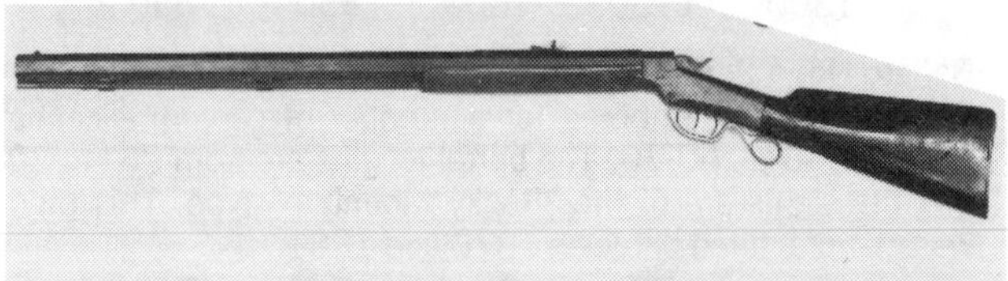

Courtesy Milwaukee Public Museum, Milwaukee, Wisconsin.

Exc.	V.G.	Good	Fair	Poor
2500	2250	1750	1300	1000

Ballard No. 6 Schuetzen Off Hand Rifle

This model has a 30" or 32" octagonal barrel and is chambered for the .40-65, .44-75, and the .38-50 cartridges. The stock is of select walnut in the high-combed Schuetzen style. The buttplate is nickle-plated, and the receiver is not engraved. The sights are Vernier tang type on the rear and a spirit lever front. The triggers are double set, and the opening lever has a ring and a spur. This model is marked J. M. Marlin only and was manufactured between 1876 and 1880.

Exc.	V.G.	Good	Fair	Poor
2200	2000	1750	1300	1100

Ballard No. 6 Schuetzen Rifle

This model is similar to the Off Hand model but was produced by the later Marlin Firearms Co. and was so marked. It is a more deluxe version with checkered stock, horn forend tip, and a fully engraved receiver. This model was chambered for the .32-40 and the .38-55 cartridges and was manufactured between 1881 and 1891.

Courtesy Milwaukee Public Museum, Milwaukee, Wisconsin.

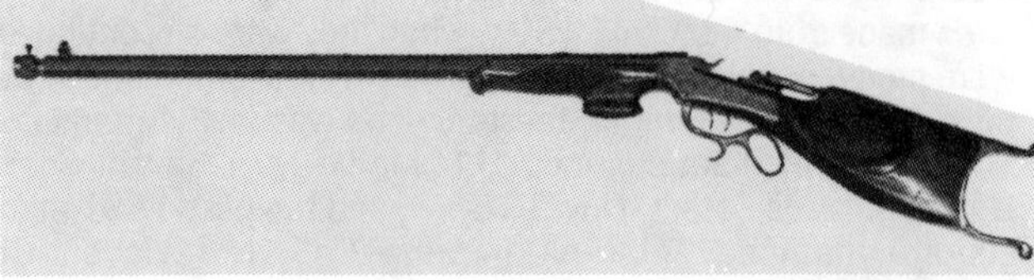

Courtesy Milwaukee Public Museum, Milwaukee, Wisconsin.

Exc.	V.G.	Good	Fair	Poor
2500	2250	1750	1300	1000

Ballard No. 6-1/2 Off Hand Mid Range Rifle

This model is chambered for the .40-54 Everlasting cartridge only. It has a 28" or 30" part-round/part-octagonal barrel, a Schuetzen-style stock, and a plain non-engraved receiver. It was manufactured between 1880 and 1882.

Exc.	V.G.	Good	Fair	Poor
2000	1800	1500	1150	850

Ballard No. 6-1/2 Rigby Off Hand Mid Range Rifle

This model is chambered for the .38-50 and the .40-65 cartridges. It features the Rigby ribbed-style barrel in 26" and 28" lengths, with Vernier rear and globe front sights and a high-grade, checkered walnut, Schuetzen-style stock with horn forend tip, and pistolgrip cap. The buttplate is nickle-plated, and the opening lever is of the ring type with a single trigger and extensively engraved receiver. This model was manufactured from 1880 to 1882.

Exc.	V.G.	Good	Fair	Poor
2500	2250	1750	1300	1000

Ballard No. 6-1/2 Off Hand Rifle

This model is chambered for the .32-40 and .38-55 cartridges and features barrel lengths of 28" and 30". It has a checkered, high-grade walnut, Schuetzen-style stock with nickle-plated buttplate. The forend tip and pistolgrip cap are of horn, and the receiver is engraved. This model has a single trigger, full-ring opening lever, Vernier tang rear sight, and spirit lever front sight. The 6-1/2 Off Hand was made by the Marlin Firearms Co. between 1883 and 1891 and is found with the later markings only.

Exc.	V.G.	Good	Fair	Poor
2250	1850	1550	1200	900

Ballard No. 7 "Creedmore A-1" Long Range Rifle

This model is commonly chambered for the .44-100 or the .45-100 cartridges. It has a 34" part-round/part-octagonal barrel and a high-grade checkered pistolgrip stock, with a horn forend tip and shotgun-style butt. The sights are a special 1300-yard Vernier tang rear and a spirit level front. There is another sight base on the heel of the stock for mounting the rear sight for ultra long-range shooting. The opening lever is similar to a repeating rifle, and a single trigger is featured. The receiver is engraved and marked "Ballard A-1" on the left and "Long Range" on the right. This model was manufactured between 1876 and 1886 and is found with both early and late markings.

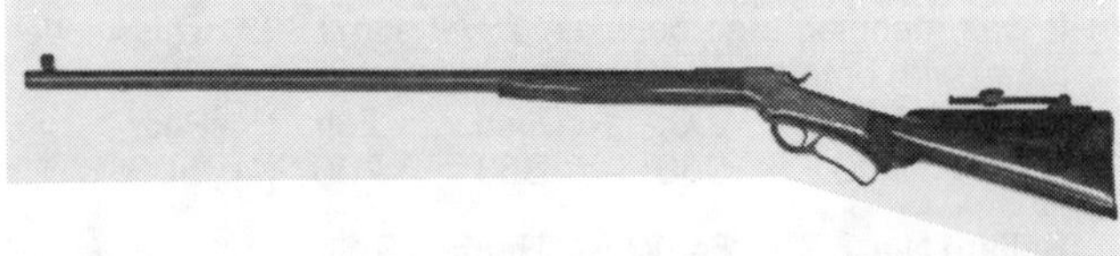

Courtesy Milwaukee Public Museum, Milwaukee, Wisconsin.

Exc.	V.G.	Good	Fair	Poor
3000	2750	2250	1500	1200

Ballard No. 7 Long Range Rifle

This model is similar to the "Creedmore A-1" but is slightly less deluxe. The engraving is less elaborate, and the lettering on the receiver is absent. This model was manufactured between 1883 and 1890 and is found with the later markings only.

Exc.	V.G.	Good	Fair	Poor
2750	2500	2000	1250	1000

Ballard No. 7A-1 Long Range Rifle

This model is a higher-grade version of the "Creedmore A-1," with fancier walnut and a checkered straight stock. Better sights and deluxe engraving are also featured. This model was manufactured between 1879 and 1883 and is found with both markings.

Exc.	V.G.	Good	Fair	Poor
3500	3250	2750	2000	1500

Ballard No. 7A-1 Extra Long Range Rifle

This is the highest-grade version of the No. 7 rifles. It features a 34" "Rigby"-type ribbed, round barrel. This was usually a special-order rifle with most features to customer specifications. The model was manufactured in very limited numbers between 1879 and 1883. It is found with both markings.

Exc.	V.G.	Good	Fair	Poor
4000	3500	3000	2250	1700

Ballard No. 8 Union Hill Rifle

This model has a 28" and 30" part-round/part-octagonal barrel and is chambered for the .32-40 and the .38-55 cartridges. It has a checkered pistolgrip stock with nickle-plated buttplate; and the opening lever is fully enclosed ring, as on the repeaters. There is a double-set trigger and a tang peep with globe front sight. The receiver is not engraved. This model was manufactured between 1884 and 1890 and is found only with the late markings. This was one of the most popular rifles in the Ballard line.

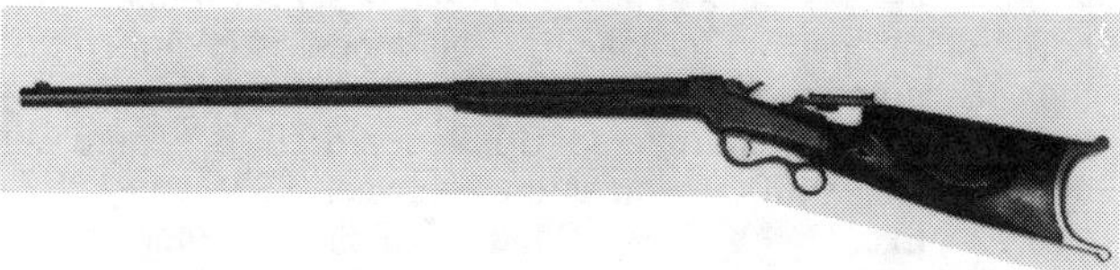

Courtesy Milwaukee Public Museum, Milwaukee, Wisconsin.

Exc.	V.G.	Good	Fair	Poor
1500	1250	1000	750	500

Ballard No. 9 Union Hill Rifle

This model is similar to the No. 8 except that it features a single trigger and better sights. It was manufactured between 1884 and 1891 and has the later markings only.

Courtesy Butterfield & Butterfield, San Francisco, California.

Exc.	V.G.	Good	Fair	Poor
1800	1600	1250	1000	700

Ballard No. 10 Schuetzen Junior Rifle

This model is simply a heavier-barrelled version of the No. 9. The barrel is 32" long, and the checkered pistolgrip stock is of the off-hand style. The rear sight is a Vernier Mid Range model, and the front sight is a spirit-level type. This was a popular model that was manufactured between 1885 and 1891. It is found with the later markings only.

Exc.	V.G.	Good	Fair	Poor
2000	1800	1500	1150	850

Marlin Handguns

The first firearm that was manufactured by John M. Marlin was actually a derringer-type single shot that was small enough to be hidden in the palm of the hand. From this beginning evolved the company that became known for its highly accurate and dependable rifles. The Marlin Company manufactured handguns up to the turn of the century, discontinuing their last and only double-action model in 1899.

1st Model Derringer

This was the first handgun produced by Marlin. The barrel is 2-1/16" long and pivots to the side for loading. There is a plunger under the frame that is depressed to free the barrel. This device is a Ballard patent. This pistol is chambered for the .22 rimfire cartridge, and there is no extractor. The frame is brass and usually nickle-plated. It has two grooves milled beneath the blued barrel. The grips are of rosewood. The barrel is stamped "J.M. Marlin, New Haven, Ct." There were approximately 2,000 manufactured between 1863 and 1867. They are quite scarce on today's market.

Exc.	V.G.	Good	Fair	Poor
500	425	350	250	175

O.K. Model Derringer

The O.K. Model is chambered for .22, .30, and .32 rimfire cartridges. The barrel is 2-1/8" or 3-1/8" on the .32. There is no extractor, and it functions as the 1st Model. The frame is plated brass with flat sides, and the barrel is found either blued or nickle-plated. The grips are rosewood. The markings are the same as on the 1st Model but are located on the right side of the barrel. The top of the barrel is marked "O.K." There were approximately 5,000 manufactured between 1863 and 1870.

Exc.	V.G.	Good	Fair	Poor
450	400	325	225	150

Victor Model Derringer

This model is similar in appearance to the "O.K." Model but is larger in size and is chambered for the .38-caliber rimfire cartridge. The barrel is 2-11/16" long; and there was, for the first time, an extractor. The finish and function were unchanged. The right side of the barrel is stamped "J.M. Marlin/New Haven, Ct./Pat. April 5.1870." "Victor" is stamped on the top of the barrel. There were approximately 4,000 manufactured between 1870 and 1881.

Exc.	V.G.	Good	Fair	Poor
500	425	350	250	175

Nevermiss Model Derringer

This model was made in three different sizes chambered for the .22, .32, and .41 rimfire cartridges. The barrel is 2.5" long and swings sideways for loading. The frame is plated brass, and the barrels are either blued or nickle-plated. The grips are rosewood. The frame is grooved under the barrels as on the 1st model. There is an extractor on this model. The barrel markings are the same as on the "Victor," with the top of the barrel marked "Nevermiss." There were approximately 5,000 manufactured between 1870 and 1881.

.22 and .32 Caliber Models

Exc.	V.G.	Good	Fair	Poor
300	250	200	150	100

.41 Caliber Model

Exc.	V.G.	Good	Fair	Poor
400	350	300	250	175

Stonewall Model Derringer

This model is identical to the .41-caliber "Nevermiss," but the top of the barrel is marked "Stonewall." It is very rarely encountered.

Exc.	V.G.	Good	Fair	Poor
500	450	400	350	225

O.K. Pocket Revolver

This is a solid-frame, spur-trigger, single action revolver chambered for the .22 rimfire short. The round barrel is 2.25", and the 7-shot cylinder is unfluted. The frame is nickle-plated brass with a blue or nickle-plated barrel, and the birdshead grips are rosewood. The cylinder pin is removable and is used to knock the empty cases out of the cylinder. The top of the barrel is marked "O.K." and "J.M.Marlin. New Haven, Conn. U.S.A." There were approximately 1,500 manufactured between 1870 and 1875.

Exc.	V.G.	Good	Fair	Poor
350	300	250	200	150

Little Joker Revolver

This model is similar in appearance to the "O.K." Model except that it features engraving and ivory or pearl grips. There were approximately 500 manufactured between 1871 and 1873.

Exc.	V.G.	Good	Fair	Poor
400	350	300	250	175

J. M. Marlin Standard Pocket Revolvers

In 1872 Marlin began production of its Smith & Wesson look-alike. The Manhattan Firearms Co. had developed a copy of the Model 1 S&W .22 cartridge revolver. In 1868 the company ceased business, and the revolvers were produced by the American Standard Tool Co. until their dissolution in 1873. In 1872 Marlin had entered into an agreement with this company to manufacture these revolvers which were no longer protected by the Rollin White patent after 1869. The Marlin revolvers are very similar to those made by American Standard, the only real difference being that Marlin grips are of the birdshead round configuration. A contoured grip frame and a patented pawl spring mechanism is utilized on the Marlin revolvers.

Marlin XXX Standard 1872 Pocket Revolver

This is the first in the series of four Standard model revolvers. It is chambered for the .30 caliber rimfire. The earlier model has an octagonal 3-1/8" barrel; and the later, a round 3" barrel. There are round and octagonal barrel variations (with unfluted cylinder) and round barrel variations (with short and long fluted cylinders). All of the barrels are ribbed and tip up for loading. They have plated brass frames, and the barrels are nickle-plated. The birdshead grips are of rosewood or hard rubber, bearing the monogram "M.F.A. Co." inside a star. There is a spur trigger. The markings "J.M. Marlin-New Haven Ct." appear on the earlier octagonal barrelled models. "U.S.A. Pat. July 1.1873" was added to the later round-barrelled models. All barrels are marked "XXX Standard 1872." There were approximately 5,000 of all types manufactured between 1872 and 1887.

Courtesy Milwaukee Public Museum, Milwaukee, Wisconsin.

Octagon Barrel—Early Variation

Exc.	V.G.	Good	Fair	Poor
400	350	300	250	175

Round Barrel—Non-Fluted Cylinder

Exc.	V.G.	Good	Fair	Poor
375	325	275	225	150

Round Barrel—Short Fluted Cylinder

Exc.	V.G.	Good	Fair	Poor
350	300	250	200	125

Round Barrel—Long Fluted Cylinder

Exc.	V.G.	Good	Fair	Poor
300	250	200	150	100

Marlin XX Standard 1873 Pocket Revolver

This model is similar in appearance to the XXX 1872 model except that it is chambered for the .22 long rimfire and is marked "XX Standard 1873." There are three basic variations—the early octagonal barrel model with non-fluted cylinder, the round-barrel model with non-fluted cylinder, and the round barrel with fluted cylinder. Function and features are the same as described for the "XXX Standard 1872" model. There were approximately 5,000 manufactured between 1873 and 1887.

Early Octagon Barrel Model

Exc.	V.G.	Good	Fair	Poor
350	300	250	200	150

Round Barrel—Non-Fluted Cylinder

Exc.	V.G.	Good	Fair	Poor
300	250	200	150	100

Round Barrel—Fluted Cylinder

Exc.	V.G.	Good	Fair	Poor
275	225	175	125	80

Marlin No. 32 Standard 1875 Pocket Revolver

This model is also similar in appearance to the "XXX Standard 1872" model except that it is chambered for the .32 rimfire cartridge. The 3" barrel is round with a rib, and the 5-shot cylinder is fluted and is in two different lengths to accommodate either the .32 short or long cartridge. The finish, function, and most markings are the same as on previous models with the exception of the barrel top marking "No.32 Standard 1875." There were approximately 8,000 manufactured between 1875 and 1887.

Exc.	V.G.	Good	Fair	Poor
275	225	175	125	80

Marlin 38 Standard 1878 Pocket Revolver

This model is different than its predecessors in that it features a steel frame and flat bottom butt, with hard rubber monogram grips. There was still a spur trigger, and the 3.25" ribbed round barrel still tipped up for loading. This model is chambered for the .38 centerfire cartridge. The finish is full nickle plate, and the top of the barrel is marked "38 Standard 1878." There were approximately 9,000 manufactured between 1878 and 1887.

Exc.	V.G.	Good	Fair	Poor
300	250	200	150	100

Marlin 1887 Double Action Revolver

This is the last handgun that Marlin produced and the only double action. It is chambered for the .32 or the .38 caliber centerfire cartridges and is of the break-open auto-ejector type. The fluted cylinder holds 6 shots in .32 and 5 shots in .38 caliber. The round ribbed barrel is 3.25" in length, and the frame is made of steel. The standard finish is nickle-plated with a blued triggerguard. Many full-blued examples have been noted. The round butt grips are hard rubber, and the top of the barrel is marked "Marlin Firearms Co. New Haven Conn. U.S.A./Patented Aug. 9 1887." There were approximately 15,000 manufactured between 1887 and 1899.

Exc.	V.G.	Good	Fair	Poor
325	275	225	150	100

Early Production Marlin Rifles

Model 1881 Lever Action Rifle

This was the first of the Marlin lever-action rifles and has always been regarded as a high quality rifle. It is capable of handling the large calibers and was well received by the shooting public. The rifle is chambered for the .32-40, .38-55, .40-60, .45-70, and the .45-85. The 24", 28" or 30" octagonal barrel is standard. Round barrels were offered and are scarce today. There is a tubular magazine beneath the barrel, and the rear sight is the buckhorn type with a blade on the front. This model ejects its empty cartridges from the top. The finish is blued, with a case-colored hammer, lever, and buttplate. The walnut stock is varnished. There were approximately 20,000 manufactured between 1881 and 1892; but this is not easy to ascertain, as the factory records on Marlin rifles are quite incomplete.

Early Model Produced in 1881 with a Removable Trigger Plate

Courtesy Butterfield & Butterfield, San Francisco, California.

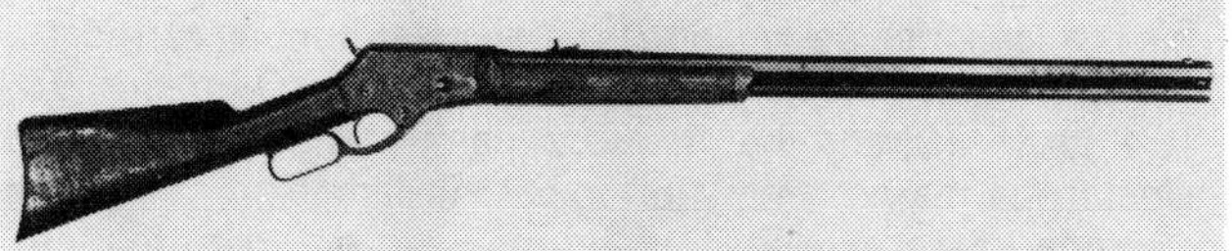

Courtesy Butterfield & Butterfield, San Francisco, California.

Exc.	V.G.	Good	Fair	Poor
4000	3500	3000	2250	1750

Standard Model Made 1882-1892—Trigger Plate Non-Removable

Exc.	V.G.	Good	Fair	Poor
2000	1750	1500	1000	700

Lightweight Model—Thinner Frame, Lever, and Barrel—.32-40 and .38-55 Caliber Only—24" and 28" Barrel

Exc.	V.G.	Good	Fair	Poor
2250	2000	1750	1250	900

Model 1888 Lever Action Rifle

This model is chambered for the .32-20, .38-40, and the .44-40 cartridges. This is a shorter action that was designed (chiefly by Lewis Hepburn) to handle the pistol cartridges for which it was chambered. The standard barrel was octagonal, but round barrels were available as special-order items. This is a top-ejecting action. It has a buckhorn rear and a blade front sight. The finish is blued with a case-colored hammer, lever, and buttplate. The walnut stock is varnished. There were approximately 4,800 manufactured in 1888 and 1889. As with most of these fine old rifles, many special-order options were available that affect today's market value. Individual appraisal would be necessary for these special models, to ascertain both value and authenticity.

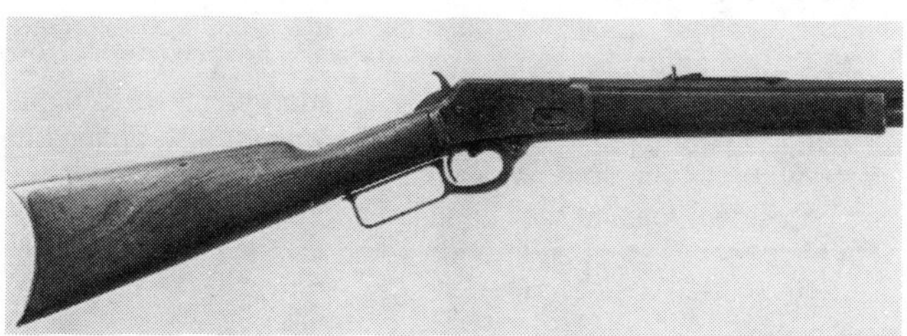

Exc.	V.G.	Good	Fair	Poor
2250	2000	1750	1250	900

Model 1889 Lever Action Rifle

This was Marlin's first side-eject, solid-top rifle. It is chambered for .25-20, .32-20, .38-40, and the .44-40 cartridges. It features either octagonal or round barrels in lengths from 24" to 32" with buckhorn rear and blade front sights. The finish is blued with a case-colored hammer, lever, and buttplate. The plain walnut stock is varnished. The barrel is stamped "Marlin Fire-Arms Co.New Haven Ct. U.S.A./Patented Oct.11 1887 April 2.1889." This model features a lever latch, and many options were offered. Again one must urge individual appraisal on such variations. Values fluctuate greatly due to some seemingly insignificant variation. There were approximately 55,000 manufactured between 1889 and 1899.

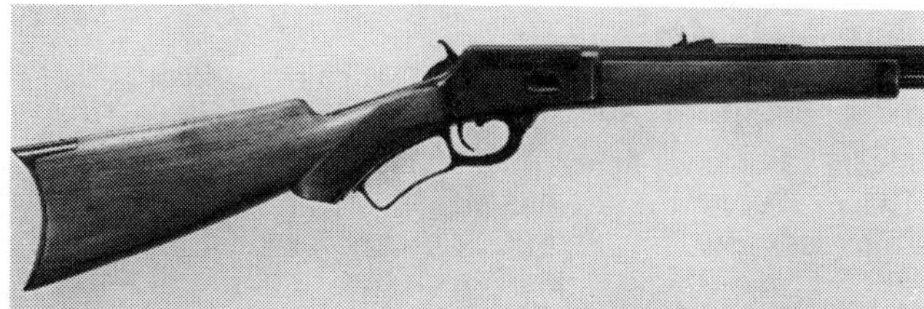

Production Model 24" Barrel

Exc.	V.G.	Good	Fair	Poor
800	700	550	400	250

Carbine 20" Barrel and Saddle Ring on Left Side of Receiver

Exc.	V.G.	Good	Fair	Poor
1500	1300	1000	750	500

Musket 30" Barrel with Full-length Stock—68 Made in .44-40

Exc.	V.G.	Good	Fair	Poor
3500	3250	2750	2250	1500

Model 1891 Lever Action Rifle

This was Marlin's first rifle designed to fire the .22 rimfire and the first repeating rifle to accept the .22 short, long, and long-rifle cartridges interchangeably. It was also chambered for the .32 rimfire and centerfire. The 24" octagonal barrel is standard, with a buckhorn rear and blade front sight. The finish is blued with a case-colored hammer, lever, and buttplate. The stock is plain walnut. The first variation is marked "Marlin Fire-Arms Co. New Haven, Ct. U.S.A./Pat'd Nov.19.1878.April 2.1889. Aug.12 1890" on the barrel, with the solid-topped frame marked "Marlin Safety." The second variation was marked the same with "March 1,1892" added. There were approximately 18,650 manufactured between 1891 and 1897.

1st Variation .22 Rimfire Only—Side Loading—Appr. 5,000

Exc.	V.G.	Good	Fair	Poor
1500	1250	1000	750	500

2nd Variation—.22 and .32 Rimfire, .32 Centerfire, Tube Loading, Model 1891 on Later Model Tangs

Exc.	V.G.	Good	Fair	Poor
750	650	500	400	275

Model 1892 Lever Action Rifle

This is basically an improved version of the Model 1891 and is similar to the second variation of the 1891. The only notable exceptions were the tang marking "Model 1892" and "Model 92" on later models. The .22 rimfire was scarce in the Model 1892. There were approximately 45,000 manufactured between 1895 and 1916. There were many options, and these special-order guns must be individually appraised to ascertain value and authenticity.

Antique (Pre-1898)—Add 20%.

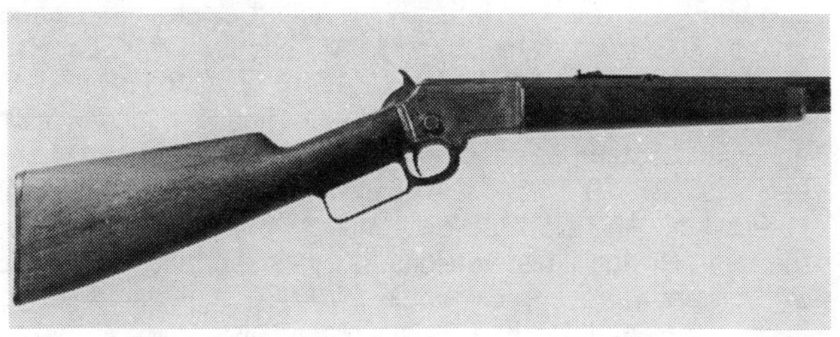

Exc.	V.G.	Good	Fair	Poor
1050	900	700	500	400

.32 Rimfire and Centerfire

Exc.	V.G.	Good	Fair	Poor
950	800	600	400	300

Model 1893 Lever Action Rifle

This model was the first rifle Marlin designed for the then new smokeless powder cartridges. It is chambered for the .25-36, .30-30, .32 Special, .32-40, and the .38-55. It was offered standard with either a round or octagonal barrel, in lengths of 24" to 32". Buckhorn rear and blade front sights were also standard. The receiver, lever, hammer, and buttplate are case-colored, and the rest is blued. The stock is varnished walnut.

As with all of these early Marlins, many options were offered and, when encountered, will drastically alter the value of the particular rifle. For this reason we supply the values for the basic model and urge securing competent appraisal on non-standard specimens. The barrel on earlier guns is marked "Marlin Fire-Arms Co. New Haven,Ct.U.S.A./ Patented Oct.11.1887.April 2.1889.Aug.1.1893." In 1919 the markings were changed to "The Marlin Firearms Corporation/ New Haven,Conn.U.S.A.-Patented." The rifles manufactured after 1904 are marked "Special Smokeless Steel" on the left side of the barrel. The upper tang is marked "Model 1893" on early guns; and "Model 93," on later specimens. There were approximately 900,000 manufactured between 1893 and 1935. Factory records are incomplete on the Model 1893.

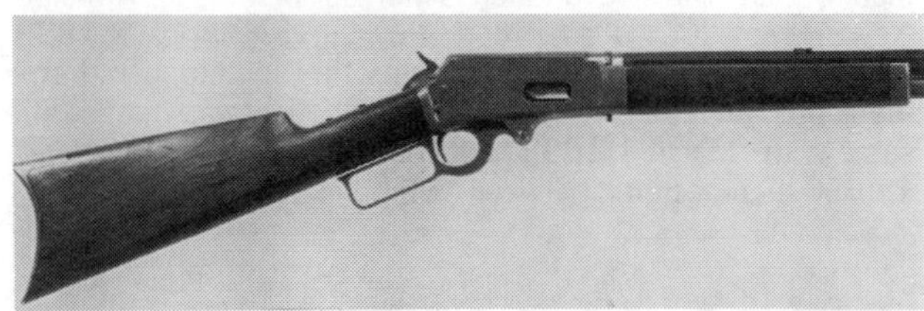

Antique Production Pre-1898

Courtesy Butterfield & Butterfield, San Francisco, California.

Exc.	V.G.	Good	Fair	Poor
1000	800	650	450	275

Modern Production 1899-1935

Exc.	V.G.	Good	Fair	Poor
800	600	450	350	225

Model 1894 Lever Action Rifle

This model is similar to the Model 1893, with a shorter action. It is chambered for the .25-20, .32-20, .38-40, and the .44-40. 24" to 32" round or octagonal barrels with full-length magazine tubes are standard, as are buckhorn rear and blade front sights. The finish is case-colored receiver, lever, hammer, and buttplate, with the rest blued. The walnut stock is varnished. The first versions were marked "Marlin Fire-Arms Co.,New Haven,Ct.U.S.A./Patented Oct.11,1887.April 2,1889." The top of the frame is marked "Marlin Safety," and the model designation is not stamped on the tang. These early rifles were chambered for .38-40 and .44-40 only. The later rifles added the patent date "Aug.1,1893"; and "Model 1894" was stamped on the tang. On the latest versions this was shortened to "Model 94." There were approximately 250,000 manufactured between 1894 and 1935. This model was also produced with a great many options. Individual appraisal should be secured when confronted with these features.

Antique Production (Pre-1898)

Exc.	V.G.	Good	Fair	Poor
1000	800	650	450	275

Modern Production (1899-1935)

Exc.	V.G.	Good	Fair	Poor
800	600	450	350	225

Model 1895 Lever Action Rifle

This is a large rifle designed to fire the larger hunting cartridges. It is chambered for the .33 W.C.F., .38-56, .40-65, .40-70, .40-83, .45-70, and the .45-90. It came standard with round or octagonal barrels from 26" to 32" in length. A bull-length magazine tube was also standard, as were buckhorn rear and blade front sights. The finish is case-colored receiver, lever, and hammer; the rest is blued with a varnished walnut stock. The barrel markings are the same as the Model 1894, and the top tang is marked "Model 1895." After 1896 "Special Smokeless Steel" was stamped on the barrel. There were also many options available for this model, and they have a big effect on the value. There were approximately 18,000 manufactured between 1895 and 1917.

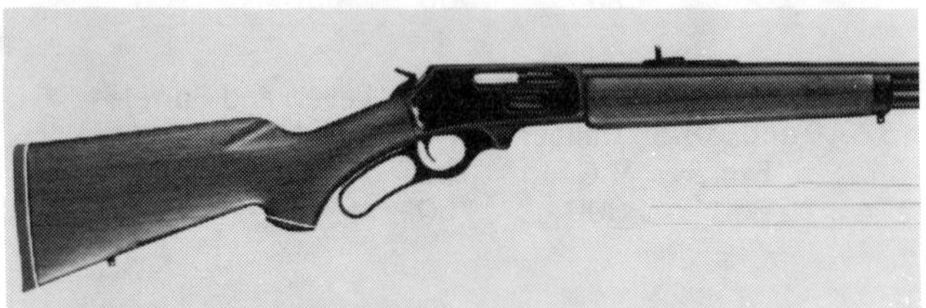

Antique Production (Pre-1898)

Exc.	V.G.	Good	Fair	Poor
1250	1100	850	550	400

Modern Production (1899-1917)

Exc.	V.G.	Good	Fair	Poor
1000	900	650	350	225

Model 1897 Lever Action Rifle

This model is an improved version of the Model 1892. It was chambered for the .22 rimfire only and came standard with a 24", 26", or 28" round, octagonal, or part-round/ part-octagonal barrel. The standard sights are buckhorn rear and blade front, and all were manufactured as takedown rifles. They have casecolored receiver, lever, and hammer. The rest is blued, and the walnut stock is varnished. There were approximately 125,000 manufactured between 1897 and 1917. In 1922 production was begun with the designation changed to Model 39 which is produced to this day. There were also options offered with this rifle that have great effect on the value; take this into consideration and seek qualified appraisal.

For First Year Production Antique—Add 40%.

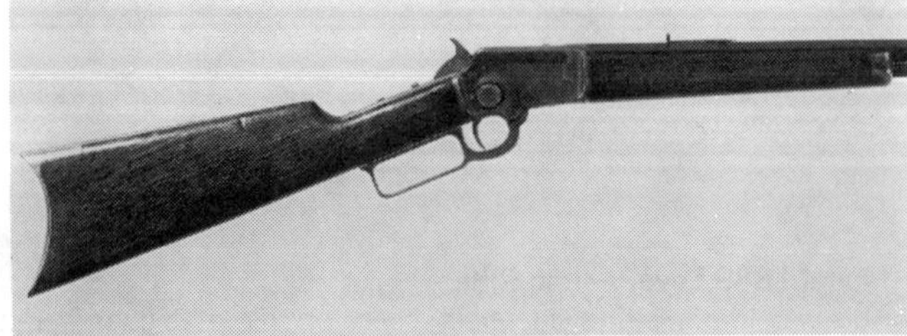

Standard Production Rifle

Exc.	V.G.	Good	Fair	Poor
2000	1800	1500	1150	850

Modern Production Marlin Rifles

Model 18 Slide Action Rifle

This model is chambered for the .22 rimfire cartridges. It was offered standard with a 20" round or octagonal barrel, open sights, and a straight walnut stock. It has an exposed hammer and blued finish with blued steel buttplate. There is a half-length tubular magazine, and the stock features a quick takedown screw on the top tang which was marked "Model 18." This rifle was manufactured between 1906 and 1909.

Exc.	V.G.	Good	Fair	Poor
350	300	250	150	100

Model 20 Slide Action Rifle

The Model 20 was chambered for the .22 rimfire cartridges and was offered standard with a 24" octagonal barrel and open sight, with an exposed hammer. This rifle was only made as a "Takedown" receiver model and is blued, with a straight walnut stock. It was manufactured between 1907 and 1909.

Exc.	V.G.	Good	Fair	Poor
350	300	250	150	100

Model 25 Slide Action Rifle

This model was chambered for the .22 short only and was not a commercial success. The 23" round or octagonal barrel is standard, as are open sights. It is called a takedown model, but only the stock is removable—the receiver does not separate. It has an exposed hammer, tubular magazine, and straight walnut stock. The finish is blued. This rifle was manufactured in 1910.

Exc.	V.G.	Good	Fair	Poor
375	325	275	175	125

Model 27 Slide Action Rifle

This is a centerfire rifle chambered for the .25-20 and .32-20 cartridges. It features a 24" octagonal barrel with 2/3-length magazine tube that holds 7 shots. It has open sights, a blued finish, and straight walnut stock with crescent buttplate. It was manufactured between 1910 and 1932.

Exc.	V.G.	Good	Fair	Poor
350	300	250	150	100

Model 27S Slide Action Rifle

The Model 17S is similar to the Model 27 but was offered with a round or octagonal 24" barrel. The .25 rimfire cartridge was added to those already available. This model was introduced in 1913 and was manufactured until 1932.

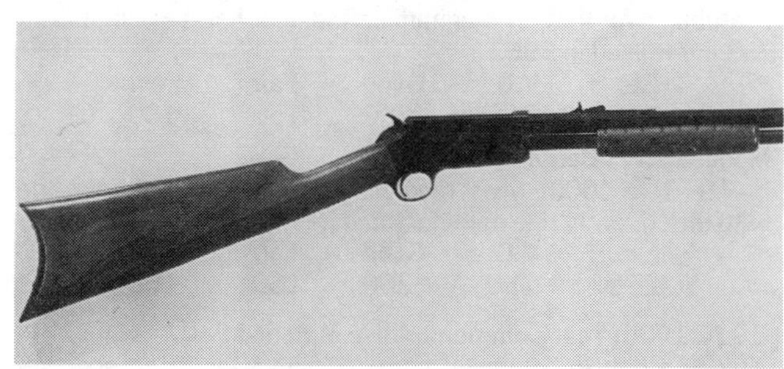

Exc.	V.G.	Good	Fair	Poor
350	300	250	150	100

Model 29 Slide Action Rifle

This model is identical to the Model 20 with a 23" round barrel and smooth walnut forend instead of a grooved one as found on the Model 20. It was manufactured between 1913 and 1916.

Exc.	V.G.	Good	Fair	Poor
350	300	250	150	100

Model 32 Slide Action Rifle

This model was the first of the hammerless slide-action rifles. It is chambered for the .22 rimfire and has a 24" octagonal barrel and half-length magazine tube. The Model 32 is a takedown rifle with adjustable sights and features "Ballard" rifling. It is blued, with a pistolgrip walnut stock. The advent of WWI and the need for Marlin to produce military arms cut short the production of this Model. It was manufactured in 1914 and 1915 only.

Exc.	V.G.	Good	Fair	Poor
350	300	250	150	100

Model 37 Slide Action Rifle

This model is the same as the Model 29 with a 24" round barrel and full-length magazine tube. It was manufactured between 1913 and 1916.

Exc.	V.G.	Good	Fair	Poor
350	300	250	150	100

Model 38 Slide Action Rifle

This was the hammerless model introduced after the end of WWI to replace the Model 32. It is similar in appearance but features a Rocky Mountain adjustable rear and an ivory bead front sight instead of the distinctive round Swebilius sight on the Model 32. The Model 38 was manufactured between 1920 and 1930.

Exc.	V.G.	Good	Fair	Poor
350	300	250	150	100

Model 40 Slide Action Rifle

This model is identical to the Model 27S centerfire rifle except that the barrel is marked "Marlin-Rockwell." The top tang is stamped "Marlin/Mod. 40." This is a very rare model, and not many marked in this manner have been noted.

Exc.	V.G.	Good	Fair	Poor
350	300	250	150	100

Model 47 Slide Action Rifle

This model is similar to the Model 20, with a 23" round barrel and an improved magazine tube. The Model 47 has a case-colored receiver and a checkered buttstock. This model was not offered for sale nor was it listed in Marlin's catalog but was offered free of charge to anyone purchasing four shares of Marlin stock for $100. One other fact about this model is that it was the first Marlin to be case-colored with the new cyanide method; this created a tiger-striped pattern that is peculiar to the Model 47 Rifle.

Exc.	V.G.	Good	Fair	Poor
350	300	250	150	100

Model 1936 Lever Action Carbine

This model is a direct descendant of the Model 1893. It is chambered for the .30-30 and the .32 Special cartridge. The stock is streamlined with a pistol grip added and a 20" round barrel. A barrel band and improved sights are utilized. It has a 7-shot tube magazine and a semi-beavertail forearm. The receiver, lever, and hammer are case-colored; and the rest is blued. This model was manufactured between 1936 and 1948. It was designated the Model 36 in 1937.

Exc.	V.G.	Good	Fair	Poor
300	250	200	150	100

Model 36 Lever Action Rifle

This model is similar to the Model 1936 Carbine, with a 24" barrel, 2/3-length magazine tube, and steel forend tip instead of the barrel band.

Exc.	V.G.	Good	Fair	Poor
325	275	225	175	125

Model 36A or Sporting Carbine

This model is similar to the 1936 Carbine, with a 24" barrel. It features a 2/3-length magazine tube and holds 6 shots instead of 7. The front sight is the "Huntsman" non-glare type with a silver bead.

Exc.	V.G.	Good	Fair	Poor
325	275	225	175	125

Model 36A-DL Lever Action Rifle

This model is similar to the Model 36A, with a deluxe checkered stock. It features slight swivels and is furnished with a leather sling.

Exc.	V.G.	Good	Fair	Poor
350	300	250	200	150

Model 336 Carbine

This model was introduced in 1948 and was an improved version of the Model 36. It features a new-type round bolt, chrome-plated with improved extractor and redesigned cartridge carrier that improved feeding. It is chambered for the .30-30 and the .32 Special cartridges and has a 20" tapered round barrel with Ballard-type rifling. The finish is blue, with the receiver top matted to reduce reflections. The pistolgrip stock and semi-beavertail forend are of American walnut. It features Rocky Mountain-style rear and bead front sights, and the hammer is lowered to facilitate scope mounting.

Exc.	V.G.	Good	Fair	Poor
250	200	175	125	100

Model 336C

The same as the Model 336 Carbine. In 1951 the catalog model designation was changed. In 1953 the .35 Remington cartridge was added to the line.

Exc.	V.G.	Good	Fair	Poor
250	200	175	125	100

Model 336A

This model is similar to the 336C, with a 24" barrel and steel forend tip instead of a barrel band. The magazine tube is 2/3-length and holds 6 shots. This model was introduced in 1948.

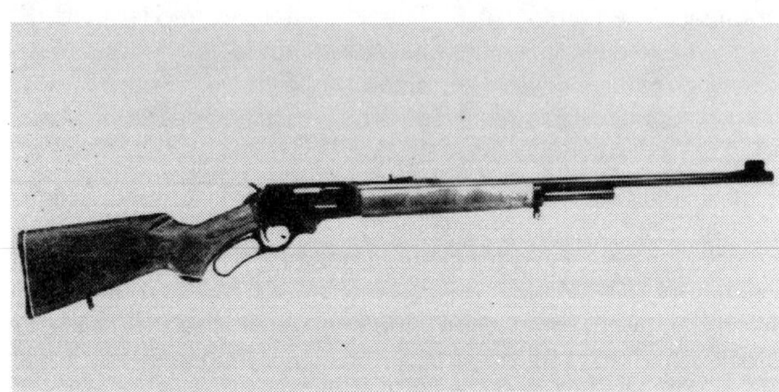

Exc.	V.G.	Good	Fair	Poor
250	200	175	125	100

Model 336 ADL

This model differs from the Model 336A by having a checkered stock and forend, swivels, and a sling.

Exc.	V.G.	Good	Fair	Poor
275	225	200	150	125

Model 336 SC

This is basically a 336A with forend tip and 2/3 magazine but has a 20" barrel instead of the 24" found on the 336A.

Exc.	V.G.	Good	Fair	Poor
225	200	175	150	100

Model 336 SD

This is the 336 SC in a deluxe checkered stock version, with swivels and supplied with a sling.

Exc.	V.G.	Good	Fair	Poor
300	250	225	175	125

Model 336 Zipper

This model was advertised as a fast-handling, lever-action carbine chambered for the .219 Zipper cartridge—a flat trajectory, varmint-type round. It has a 20" barrel, which was the feature that doomed it to failure as this was too short to coax the maximum performance and accuracy from the cartridge. The "Micro-Groove" rifling that was used did not yield long barrel life; and the model survived from 1955 through 1959, when it was discontinued. It is externally similar to the 336 SC.

Exc.	V.G.	Good	Fair	Poor
400	350	300	200	150

Model 336T (Texan)

This is a straight-stock version of the 336 C, chambered for the .30-30 cartridge, with an 18.5" barrel. It was manufactured from 1954-1983.

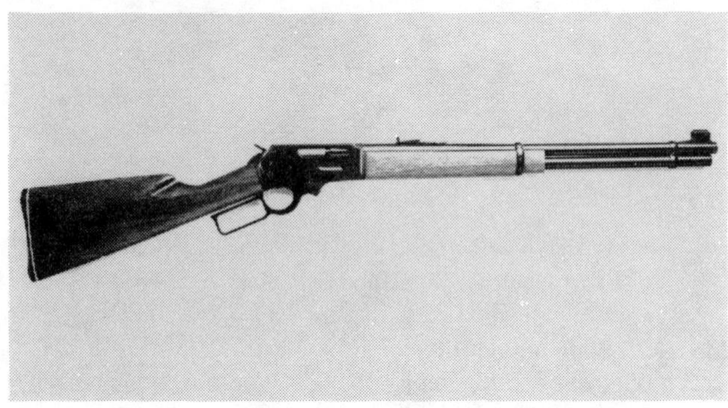

Exc.	V.G.	Good	Fair	Poor
250	200	175	125	100

Model 336 DT

A deluxe-stock version of the "Texan," with the map of Texas and a longhorn carved on the butt. It was manufactured between 1962 and 1964.

Exc.	V.G.	Good	Fair	Poor
300	250	225	175	125

Model 336 "Marauder"

This is simply a 336 T with a 16.25" barrel and a slimmer forend. It is chambered for either the .30-30 or .35 Remington cartridges, has a gold trigger, and is drilled and tapped for both scope mounts and receiver sights. It was manufactured in 1963 and 1964.

Exc.	V.G.	Good	Fair	Poor
275	250	200	150	100

Model 336 .44 Magnum

This is the 336 "Marauder" with a 20" Micro-Groove barrel chambered for the .44 Magnum cartridge. It holds 10 shots and was introduced in 1963.

Exc.	V.G.	Good	Fair	Poor
275	250	200	150	100

Model 336 T "Centennial"

In 1970 a 100th year medallion was embedded into the buttstock of every rifle manufactured.

Exc.	V.G.	Good	Fair	Poor
275	250	200	150	100

1970 100th Year Commemorative Matched Pair

This is a deluxe octagonal barrelled .30-30 with an engraved receiver and deluxe wood with an inlaid medallion, accompanied by a matching Model 339 .22 rimfire rifle. They are numbered the same and are furnished in a deluxe luggage case. There were 1,000 sets manufactured in 1970. These are commemoratives, and as such it should be noted that collectors usually will only show interest if they are new and uncocked in the original packaging. All accessories and brochures should be included for them to be worth top dollar. Once a commemorative has been used, it has no more value than as a shooter.

NIB	Exc.	V.G.	Good	Fair	Poor
1000	850	650	500	400	300

Model 336 "Zane Grey Century"

This model was introduced in 1972, the 100th anniversary of

the birth of Zane Grey, the famous Western author. This model has a 22" octagonal barrel chambered for the .30-30. The stock is high-grade walnut and features a brass buttplate and pistolgrip cap. A Zane Grey medallion is inlaid into the receiver. There were 10,000 manufactured in 1972. This is a commemorative rifle and must be new in the box to generate the top collector appeal.

NIB	Exc.	V.G.	Good	Fair	Poor
350	300	250	200	150	100

Model 336 Octagon

This model was introduced to utilize the octagonal barrel making equipment that was on hand from the manufacture of the commemoratives. It is essentially a 336T with a 22" tapered octagonal barrel chambered for .30-30 only. It features a full-length magazine tube, slim forend with steel cap, and a classic-style hard rubber buttplate. The walnut stock is straight, and the lever is square. The finish, including the trigger, is blued. This model was made in 1973 only.

Exc.	V.G.	Good	Fair	Poor
250	200	175	150	100

Model 336 ER (Extra Range)

This model was introduced in 1983 and was advertised as being chambered for the .307 Winchester and the .356 Winchester cartridges. The .307 was never produced. The .356 Winchester was supposed to add new capabilities to this classic rifle, but it never caught on with the shooting public and was discontinued in 1986 after only 2,441 Model ER's were manufactured. It has a 20" barrel and 5-shot tube magazine.

Exc.	V.G.	Good	Fair	Poor
400	350	300	250	150

Model 336 CS

This is the current carbine model of this line. It has a hammer-block safety and is chambered for the .30-30, .35 Remington, and until 1988 the .375 Winchester. The barrel is 20", and the magazine tube holds 6 shots. The pistolgrip stock and semi-beavertail forearm are American walnut. This model has been manufactured since 1984. The 1983 model was known as the 336 C and had no hammer-block safety.

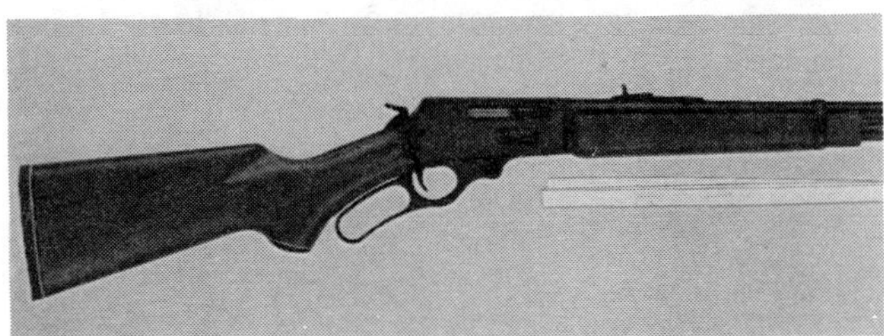

NIB	Exc.	V.G.	Good	Fair	Poor
275	225	200	175	150	100

Model 336 LTS

This is the latest version of the old "Marauder" carbine. It was dubbed the LTS or "Lightweight" model instead of the Marauder as it was feared that the latter designation would be inappropriate in today's society. The model features a 16.5" barrel with full-length tube magazine that holds 5 shots. The walnut stock has a straight grip, and there is a barrel band on the forearm. The butt has a rubber rifle pad. This model was introduced in 1988.

NIB	Exc.	V.G.	Good	Fair	Poor
350	300	250	200	150	100

Model 30 AS

This model is similar to the 336 CS, but the stock is made of walnut-finished hardwood instead of genuine American walnut. It is chambered for .30-30 only.

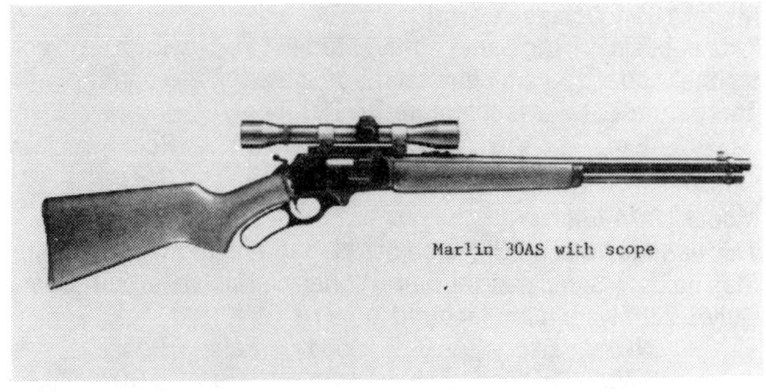
Marlin 30AS with scope

NIB	Exc.	V.G.	Good	Fair	Poor
285	250	200	175	125	100

Model 375 Lever Action

This model was introduced in 1980. It has a 20" Micro-Groove barrel and is chambered for the .375 Winchester cartridge. This should have been a popular rifle; but perhaps because of difficulty in obtaining ammunition, it was not a commercial success. Its appearance is much the same as the Model 336, with walnut pistolgrip stock and steel forend tip. This model was discontinued in 1983 after 16,315 were manufactured.

Exc.	V.G.	Good	Fair	Poor
250	225	175	125	100

Model 444 Lever Action

This model was introduced in 1965. It is chambered for the .444 Marlin, a large and powerful cartridge that has the capability of dropping any game in North America, theoretically speaking. The rifle is essentially a Model 336 action modified to accept the larger cartridge. It has a 24" round barrel that was cut back to 22" in 1971. It holds 5 shots total and, when introduced, featured a straight-gripped Monte Carlo stock and semi-beavertail forend with barrel band. Another band holds the 2/3-length magazine tube in place. In 1971 the stock was changed to a pistolgrip without the Monte Carlo comb.

Exc.	V.G.	Good	Fair	Poor
275	225	175	125	100

Model 444 S

This model was introduced in 1972 and is essentially the later 444 with a steel forend tip instead of the barrel bands.

Exc.	V.G.	Good	Fair	Poor
250	200	175	150	125

Model 444 SS

In 1984 the company added a crossbolt hammer-block safety to the 444 S and redesignated it the 444 SS. This Model is currently in production.

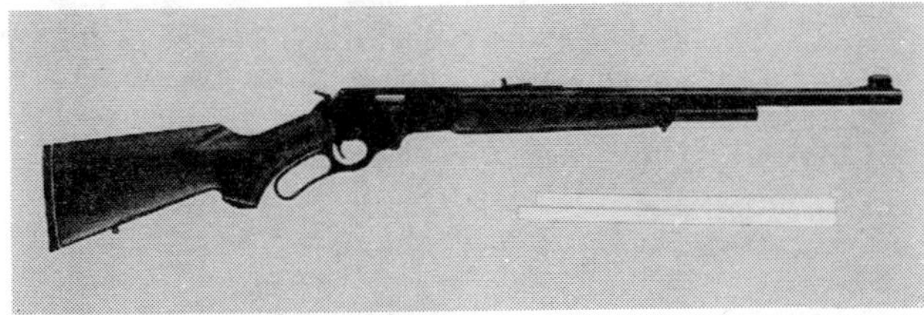

NIB	Exc.	V.G.	Good	Fair	Poor
300	250	225	175	150	125

Model 1894 Lever Action

The production of the Model 336 in .44 Magnum was a frustrating experience as the action was simply too long for a short-pistol case. In 1969 Marlin reintroduced the Model 1894 chambered for the .44 Magnum cartridge. The barrel is 20", and the full-length magazine tube holds 10 rounds. It features an adjustable rear and a ramp-type front sight. The finish is blued, with a matted receiver top. The walnut stock has a straight grip; and the forend, a barrel band. From 1969 to 1971 there was a brass saddle ring.

NIB	Exc.	V.G.	Good	Fair	Poor
300	275	225	175	125	100

Model 1894 Octagon Barrel
This is basically the same as the Model 1894, with a 20" octagonal barrel and a steel forend tip instead of the barrel band. There were 2,957 manufactured in 1973 only.

Exc.	V.G.	Good	Fair	Poor
275	225	175	125	100

Model 1894 Sporter
This variation has a 20" round barrel, half-length magazine tube that holds 6 shots, and a hard rubber classic-style butt plate. Only 1,398 were manufactured in 1973.

NIB	Exc.	V.G.	Good	Fair	Poor
375	325	275	225	150	100

Model 1894 C Lever Action
This model is chambered for the .38 Special and .357 Magnum cartridges. It features an 18.5 round barrel, with full-length magazine tube and two barrel bands. It holds 9 shots and has a walnut straight-grip stock. This model was manufactured between 1969 and 1984. In 1984 a hammer-block crossbolt safety was added, and the model number was changed to 1894 CS. All other specifications remained the same.

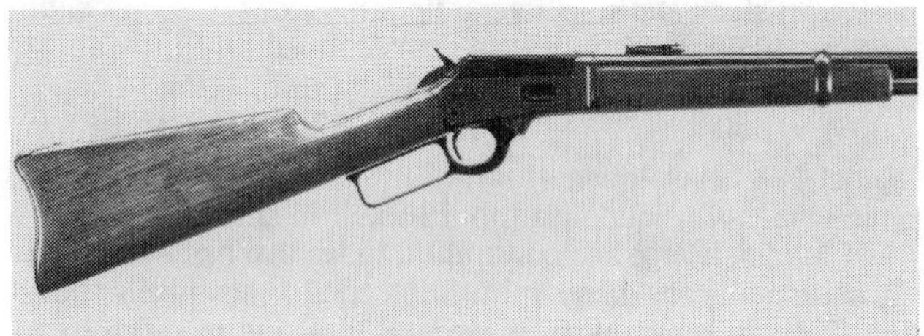

Exc.	V.G.	Good	Fair	Poor
275	225	175	125	100

Model 1894 M Lever Action Rifle
This model is similar to the other 1894 rifles except that it is chambered for the .22 Magnum cartridge and features an outside loading tube magazine that holds 11 shots. The barrel is 20" long, and there is a steel forend tip instead of a barrel band.

It is important to note that this model will not function properly with any cartridge except the .22 Magnum and that injury could result from attempting to chamber and fire the shorter .22 l.r. This model was manufactured between 1983 and 1988 and was only produced with the crossbolt safety.

Exc.	V.G.	Good	Fair	Poor
275	225	175	150	100

Model 1894 S Lever Action Rifle
This model was introduced in 1984. It is chambered for the .41 Magnum and the .44 Special/.44 Magnum cartridges. In 1988 the .45 Colt chambering was offered. This model has a 20" barrel and a straight-grip stock. The forend has a steel cap. This model is currently produced and features the hammer-block safety.

NIB	Exc.	V.G.	Good	Fair	Poor
350	325	250	200	175	125

Model 1894 CL (Classic) Lever Action Rifle
This model was introduced in 1988 and is the same basic rifle chambered for the old .25-20 and .32-20 cartridges. The barrel is 22", and the half-length magazine tube holds 6 shots. The walnut stock has no white spacers and has a black buttplate.

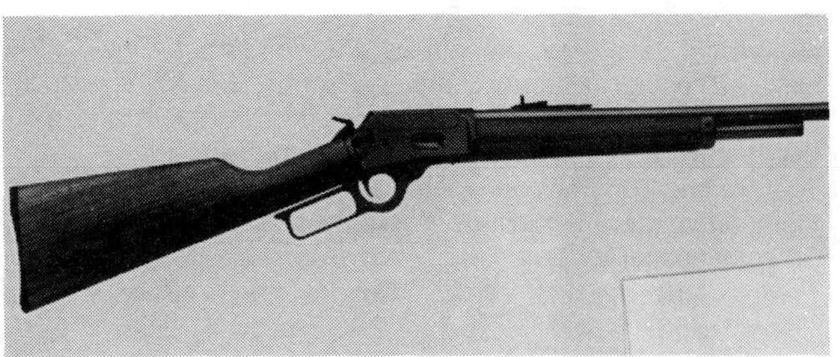

NIB	Exc.	V.G.	Good	Fair	Poor
300	275	225	200	175	125

Model 1895 Lever Action SS
The model 1895 was reintroduced on the Model 336 action that had been modified to handle the .45-70 cartridge. This was done to capitalize on the nostalgia wave that descended on the country in the early 1970s. This model features a 22" round barrel with a 2/3-length magazine tube that holds 4 shots. The walnut stock had a straight grip until the Model 1895 S was released in 1980, when a pistolgrip stock was used. In 1983 the Model 1895 SS with the crossbolt hammer-block safety was added; and it is currently produced in this configuration.

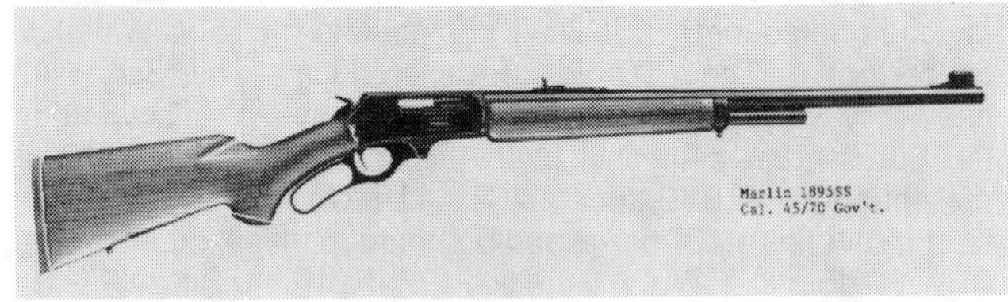

Exc.	V.G.	Good	Fair	Poor
350	275	225	150	100

Marlin Glenfield Lever Action Rifles
The Glenfield line of rifles was designed to be sold in large outlet chainstores and were simply cheaper versions that were to be sold for less money. The rifles functioned fine, but birch was used instead of walnut and pressed checkering instead of handcut. These rifles were manufactured under the Glenfield name between 1964 and 1983. There are five models of Lever Action Glenfields—the 36G, 30, 30A, 30 GT, and the 30 AS. They are chambered for the .30-30 cartridge, and the basic differences are slight and, in most cases, merely cosmetic. They are good, serviceable rifles but have little or no collector interest or investment potential.

NIB	Exc.	V.G.	Good	Fair	Poor
150	125	100	90	75	50

Model 39 Lever Action Rifle
This model originally evolved from the Model 1891 invented by L. L. Hepburn. The 1891 rifle became the 1892 and eventually developed into the takedown Model 1897. The latter two were produced until 1915, when they were discontinued in favor of machine gun production for WWI. In 1922, when the company was sold to John Moran and became the Marlin Firearms Corp., the .22 rimfire lever action was reintroduced as the Model 39. It has been in production in one form or another ever since.

Model 39
As it was introduced in 1922, the Model 39 was chambered for

the .22 rimfire and had a 22" octagonal barrel and a takedown receiver. It has a full-length magazine tube which holds 25 shorts, 20 longs, or 18 long-rifle cartridges. It has a solid top frame and side ejection, a Rocky Mountain rear, and ivory bead front sight. The receiver, lever, and hammer are case-colored; the barrel is blued. The pistolgrip stock and steel-capped forearm are varnished walnut. This model was manufactured in this form between 1922 and 1947 with a number of options that could affect value and would warrant individual appraisal.

Note: Model 39s made prior to 1932 which have either no prefix or the prefix S to the serial number should not be used with high-speed ammunition. The prefix HS indicates the improved bolt that is safe for this ammunition.

Exc.	V.G.	Good	Fair	Poor
800	650	500	350	175

Model 39A Lever Action Rifle

This is an improved version of the Model 39. It has a heavier, tapered round barrel and semi-beavertail forearm and a redesigned pistolgrip stock. The rubber buttplate was replaced by one of a synthetic fiber; otherwise, specifications were similar to the Model 39. This model was manufactured from 1938 to 1960.

Exc.	V.G.	Good	Fair	Poor
275	225	175	125	100

Model 39A Mountie

This is basically a carbine version of the Model 39A. It features a 20" tapered round barrel, straight-grip walnut stock, and slimmed-down forearm. It was manufactured between 1953 and 1960.

Exc.	V.G.	Good	Fair	Poor
275	225	175	125	100

Model 39A 1960 Presentation Model

Released in 1960, this was Marlin's 90th Anniversary model. It is similar to the 39A but has a chrome-plated barrel and receiver with a high-grade, checkered walnut stock and forend. There is a squirrel carved on the right side of the buttstock. There were 500 produced in 1960. This is a commemorative and as such will be desirable to collectors only if NIB with all boxes and papers with which it was originally sold. Once used, it becomes a shooter and is not easily sold.

NIB	Exc.	V.G.	Good	Fair	Poor
600	500	400	300	175	125

Model 39M Mountie 1960 Presentation Model

This is the carbine version of the 90th Anniversary model. This is the same as the 39A with a 20" barrel and straight-grip stock. There were 500 of this model manufactured in 1960.

NIB	Exc.	V.G.	Good	Fair	Poor
600	500	400	300	175	125

Model 39A-DL Lever Action Rifle

This model is the same as the 90th Anniversary issue except that it is blued instead of chrome-plated. There were 3,306 manufactured between 1960 and 1963.

Exc.	V.G.	Good	Fair	Poor
250	200	150	100	75

Golden 39A Lever Action Rifle

This model is similar to the 39A, with a gold-plated trigger and sling swivels. It was manufactured between 1960 and 1983.

Exc.	V.G.	Good	Fair	Poor
200	175	150	100	75

Model 39 Carbine

This is a slimmer, lighter version of the Model 39A. It features a slimmer forend and thinner barrel. There were 12,140 manufactured between 1963 and 1967.

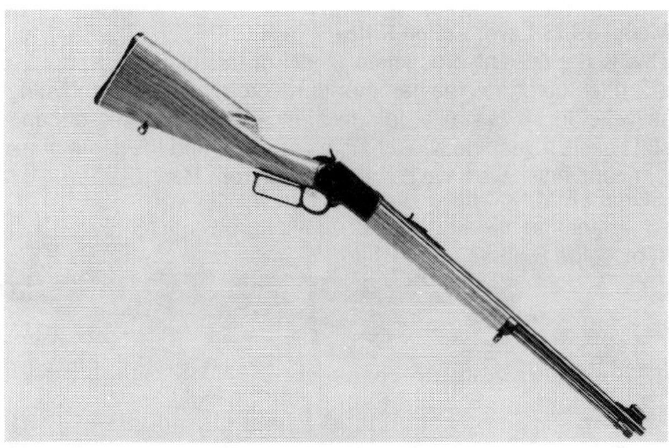

Exc.	V.G.	Good	Fair	Poor
175	150	125	90	60

Model 39 Century Limited

The introduction of this model marked the 100th Anniversary of the Marlin Company. This model features a 20" octagonal barrel with semi-buckhorn rear and brass blade front sight. The stock is fancy walnut, with a straight grip and a brass forend tip and buttplate. There is a medallion inlaid into the right side of the receiver and a brass plate on the stock. There were 34,197 manufactured in 1970. As a commemorative this model needs to be as it came from the factory to command collector interest.

NIB	Exc.	V.G.	Good	Fair	Poor
300	250	200	150	125	100

Model 39A Article II

This model commemorated the National Rifle Association's 100th Anniversary in 1971. It has a 24" octagonal barrel, high-grade walnut pistolgrip stock, and brass forend tip and buttplate. The right side of the receiver has the NRA's Second Amendment "Right to Keep and Bear Arms" medallion inlaid. There were 6,244 of these .22 rifles manufactured in 1971.

NIB	Exc.	V.G.	Good	Fair	Poor
300	250	200	150	125	100

Model 39M Article II

This model is the same as the Model 39A Article II except that it is a carbine version with a 20" octagonal barrel and a straight-grip stock. There were 3,824 manufactured in 1971. As commemoratives NIB condition is essential to collector interest.

NIB	Exc.	V.G.	Good	Fair	Poor
300	250	200	150	125	100

Model 39A Octagon

This model was produced because the company had the machinery and some leftover barrels from the two commemorative models produced in 1970 and 1971. This was a regular production run which was meant to be used and was not a special issue. It has a 24", tapered octagonal barrel and is chambered for the .22 rimfire cartridges. It has a pistolgrip walnut stock, with steel forend tip. There were 2,551 manufactured in 1972 and 1973. This was not a commercially successful model, and it was discontinued for that reason.

Exc.	V.G.	Good	Fair	Poor
200	175	150	100	75

Model 39M Octagon

This is the 20", octagonal-barrelled carbine version with a straight-grip stock. There were 2,140 manufactured in 1973.

Exc.	V.G.	Good	Fair	Poor
200	175	150	100	75

Model 39D Lever Action Rifle

This is essentially the Model 39M carbine, 20"-barrel version with a pistolgrip stock. It was manufactured between 1970 and 1974.

Exc.	V.G.	Good	Fair	Poor
175	150	125	75	50

Model 39AS Lever Action Rifle

This is the current production model of this extremely popular .22 rifle. It features the hammer-block crossbolt safety and sling swivel studs. It is similar in appearance to its predecessors and still boasts a genuine walnut pistolgrip stock and the same quality fit and finish we have come to expect from Marlin.

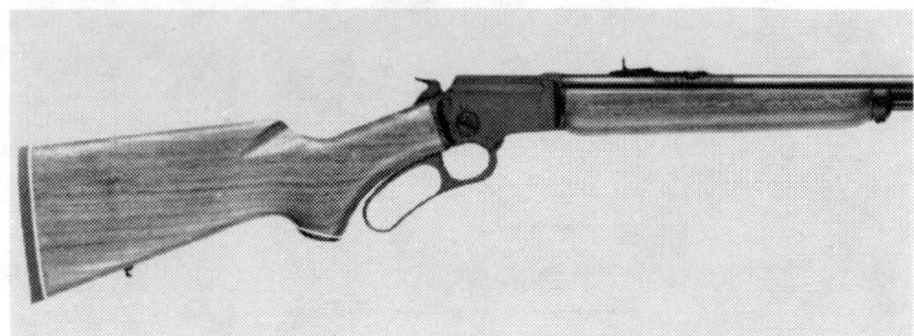

NIB	Exc.	V.G.	Good	Fair	Poor
340	275	225	200	150	100

Model 39TDS Lever Action Rifle

This is another current production model. It is similar to the Model 39AS, with a 20" carbine barrel and straight-grip stock. It replaced the Model 39M and was introduced in 1988.

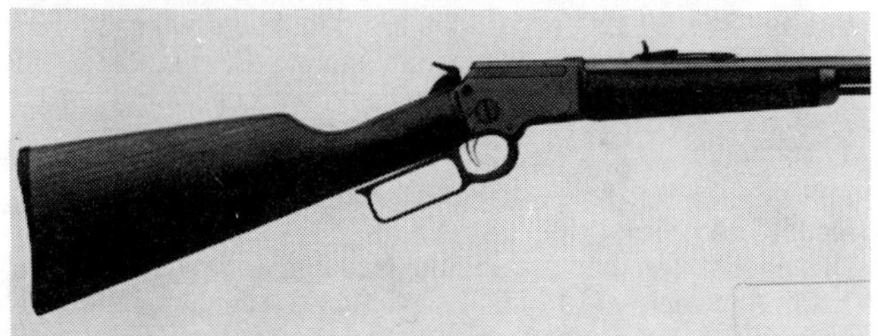

NIB	Exc.	V.G.	Good	Fair	Poor
375	325	250	225	150	100

Model 56 Levermatic Rifle

This is a streamlined version of the lever action. It features a very short lever throw and a one-piece walnut stock. The 22" barrel is round and is chambered for the .22 rimfire cartridges. There are a 7-shot detachable magazine, open sights, and a gold-plated trigger. The receiver on this model was made of aluminum after 1956. There were 31,523 manufactured between 1955 and 1964.

Exc.	V.G.	Good	Fair	Poor
150	125	100	75	50

Model 56 "Clipper King" Levermatic

This is the same as the Model 56 except that it is specially packaged and comes with a 4X .22 scope. The name "Clipper King" is stamped on the barrel, and the buttplate is red hard rubber. There were only 152 of these manufactured in 1959.

Exc.	V.G.	Good	Fair	Poor
175	150	125	100	75

Model 57 Levermatic Rifle

This model is similar to the Model 56, with a tube magazine and Monte Carlo stock. In 1960 Marlin went back to a steel receiver on this Model. There were 34,628 manufactured from 1959 to 1965.

Exc.	V.G.	Good	Fair	Poor
150	125	100	75	50

Model 57M Levermatic Rifle

This is the Model 57 chambered for the .22 Magnum cartridge. There were 66,889 manufactured between 1959 and 1969.

Exc.	V.G.	Good	Fair	Poor
175	150	125	100	75

Model 62 Levermatic Rifle

This model is similar in appearance to the Model 57 except that it is chambered for the centerfire .256 Magnum cartridge and has a 4-shot magazine. In 1966 the .30 carbine cartridge was added. This model has a 23" "Micro-Groove" barrel with open sights and a walnut one-piece stock. The first 4,000 Model 62s were shipped without serial numbers in violation of federal law. The company recalled the rifles for numbering; and, to this day, the owner of a centerfire Model 62 can return the rifle for numbering. There were 15,714 manufactured between 1963 and 1969.

Exc.	V.G.	Good	Fair	Poor
175	150	125	100	75

It is important to note that the year of manufacture of Marlin modern production rifles made between 1946 and 1968 can be ascertained by the letter prefix on the serial number. The prefixes are as follows:

1946 - C	1951 - H	1956 - N	1961 - U	1966 - AB
1947 - D	1952 - J	1957 - P	1962 - V	1967 - AC
1948 - E	1953 - K	1958 - R	1963 - W	1968 - AD
1949 - F	1954 - L	1959 - S	1964 - Y, Z	
1950 - G	1955 - M	1960 - T	1965 - AA	

The Marlin Firearms Company produced a great many bolt-action, rifles, both single shot and repeaters, starting in 1930 and continuing today. These rifles were low-priced and designed primarily as utility rifles. They also manufactured many autoloaders of the same type during these years. The Glenfield name will also be found on these models, as many were produced to be marketed by the large chain outlets. These rifles have no collectible value of which I am aware, and they sell for under $100 in today's market. This list is for reference purposes.

BOLT ACTIONS

Model 65 - SS- 1935-37
Model 65E - SS- 1935-37
Model 100 - SS- 1935-59
Model 80 - Rep-1935-59
Model 80E - Rep-1935-39
Model 100S- SS- 1937-38
Model 81 - Rep-1939
Model 81E - Rep-1939
Model 80B - Rep-1940
Model 80BE- Rep-1940
Model 81B- Rep-1940
Model 81BE- Rep-1940
Model 101- SS- 1941-77
Model 101DL- SS- 1941-45
Model 80C- Rep-1941-71
Model 80DL- Rep-1941-64
Model 80 CSB-Rep-1941
Model 100 SB-SS- 1941
Model 101- SS- 1959
Model 122- SS- 1962-65
Model 980- Rep-1966-71
Model 780- Rep-1971-88
Model 781- Rep-1971-88
Model 782- Rep-1971-88
Model 783- Rep-1971-88
Model 880- Rep-1988-
Model 881- Rep-1988-
Model 882- Rep-1988-
Model 883- Rep-1988-

AUTOLOADERS

Model 50 - 1931-34
Model 50E - 1931-34
Model A-1 - 1935-46
Model A-1E - 1935-46
Model A-1C - 1940-46
Model A-1DL - 1940-46
Model 88-C - 1947-56
Model 88-DL - 1953-56
Model 89-C - 1950-61
Model 89-DL - 1950-61
Model 98 - 1950-61
Model 99 - 1959-61
Model 99C - 1962-78
Model 99G - 1960-65
Model DL - 1960-65
Model 60 - 1960-Pres.
Model 49 - 1968-71
Model 49DL - 1971-78
Model 990 - 1979-87
Model 995 - 1979-Pres.

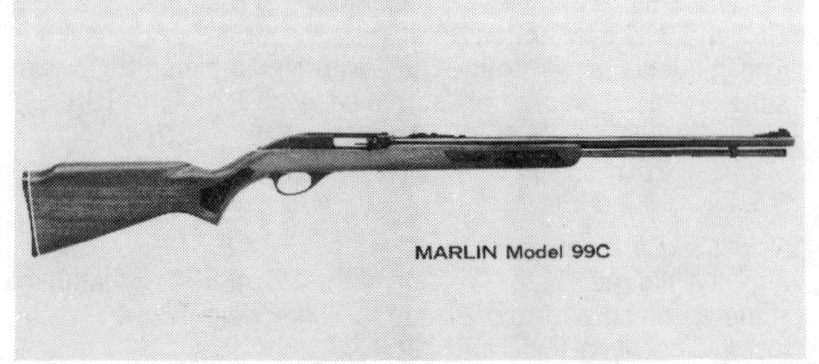

MARLIN Model 99C

Model 70P "Papoose"

This model is quite unique in that it is a total package concept. It is a semi-automatic takedown carbine chambered for the .22 rimfire family of cartridges. It has a 16.25" barrel and a 7-shot detachable magazine. It is supplied with 4X scope and bright red case that will float if dropped overboard. The stock is walnut-finished birch, with a pistol grip and rubber buttplate. It was introduced in 1986.

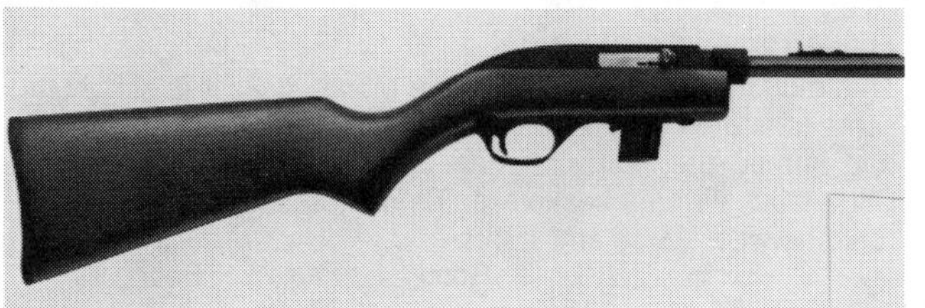

NIB	Exc.	V.G.	Good	Fair	Poor
160	140	110	85	75	50

Model 70HC

This is the Model 70 .22 rimfire that has been produced since 1983 with a high-capacity, 25-round "Banana" magazine.

Exc.	V.G.	Good	Fair	Poor
160	125	100	75	50

Model 9 Camp Carbine

This model has a 16.5 barrel and is chambered for the 9mm Parabellum pistol cartridge. It has a 12- or 20-shot detachable magazine, walnut-finished hardwood pistolgrip stock, and a sandblasted matte-blued finish. There are open sights, and the receiver is drilled and tapped for scope mounting. This model was introduced in 1985.

NIB	Exc.	V.G.	Good	Fair	Poor
310	275	225	175	125	100

Model 45 Carbine

This is the same as the 9mm version but is chambered for the .45 ACP cartridge and has a 7-shot detachable magazine.

NIB	Exc.	V.G.	Good	Fair	Poor
310	275	225	175	125	100

Model 922M

First offered in 1993 this model is a semi-automatic .22 Win. Magnum Rimfire rifle. It features a 7-shot clip, 20.5" Micro-Grove barrel. The receiver is sandblasted and drilled and tapped for scope mounting. Monte Carlo black walnut stock with rubber rifle butt pad. Adjustable rear sight and ramp front sight with hood. Rifle weighs 6.5 lbs.

NIB	Exc.	V.G.	Good	Fair	Poor
275	250	200	150	125	110

Model 995

Semi-automatic .22 Long Rifle only rifle features a 7-shot clip, 18" Micro-Grove barrel. Receiver is grooved for scope mount and receiver has a serrated non-glare top. Adjustable sights. Monte Carlo American black walnut stock with checkered pistol grip and forearm. White butt plate spacer is standard. Rifle weighs 5 lbs. Introduced in 1979 and still in production.

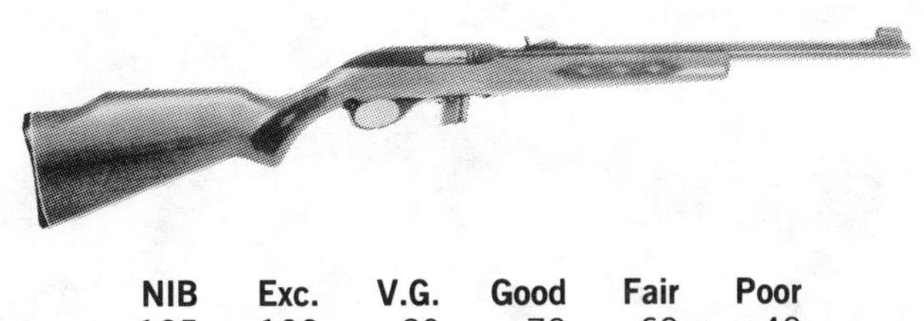

NIB	Exc.	V.G.	Good	Fair	Poor
125	100	80	70	60	40

Model 990L

This semi-automatic .22 Long Rifle Marlin features a tubular 14-round magazine with 22" Micro-Grove barrel. The trigger is gold plated. The receiver is grooved for a scope mount while the stock is a two-tone brown birch Monte Carlo. Rubber rifle butt pad is standard. Rifle weighs 5.75 lbs.

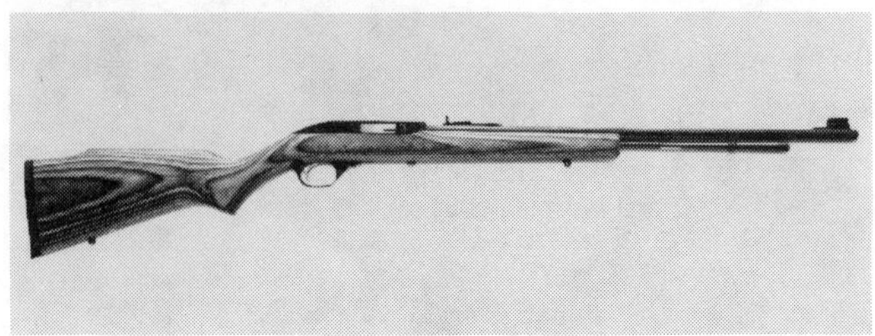

NIB	Exc.	V.G.	Good	Fair	Poor
140	120	100	80	65	50

Model 60

A Marlin promotional model. This semi-automatic 14-shot .22 caliber Long Rifle features a 22" Micro-Grove barrel with adjustable rear sight. Receiver is grooved for scope mount and stock is birch with Monte Carlo comb. Rifle weighs 5.5 lbs. Introduced in 1960 and still in current production.

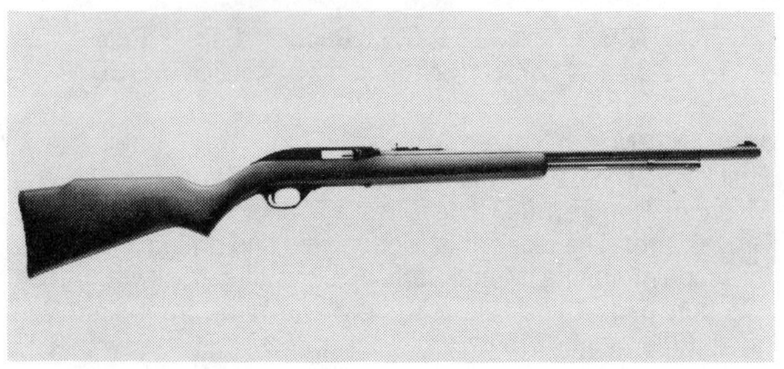

NIB	Exc.	V.G.	Good	Fair	Poor
100	85	70	60	50	40

Model 60 SS

Introduced in 1993 this model is similar to the Model 60 except that it features a stainless barrel, bolt, and magazine tube. All other metal parts are nickel plated. The stock is a two-tone black and gray laminated birch Monte Carlo.

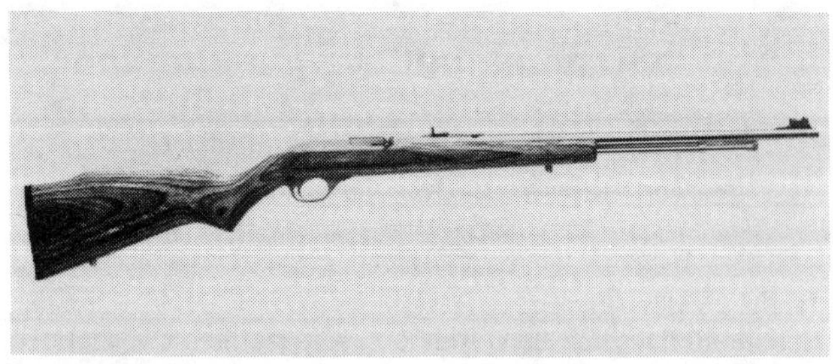

NIB	Exc.	V.G.	Good	Fair	Poor
160	135	100	80	60	50

Model 9N

Similar to the Model 9 mp Carbine but furnished with nickel plated metal parts.

NIB	Exc.	V.G.	Good	Fair	Poor
270	245	210	175	125	100

Model 322 Bolt Action Rifle

This model is chambered for the .222 cartridge and has a 24" medium-weight barrel with Micro-Groove rifling. It has a checkered walnut pistolgrip stock. The magazine holds 4 shots, and the adjustable trigger and sights are Sako products. The Sako receiver is fitted for Sako scopemounting bases. The Micro-Groove rifling in the barrel was not successful for this caliber, and accuracy fell off after as few as 500 shots—so this model was dropped and replaced. The serial numbers were Sako, and there were 5,859 manufactured between 1954 and 1959.

Exc.	V.G.	Good	Fair	Poor
375	325	250	175	125

Model 422 Bolt Action Rifle

This model is the successor to the Model 322. It is simply the same rifle fitted with a 24", featherweight, stainless steel barrel and named the "Varmint King." The stock features a Monte Carlo stock with a cheekpiece. There were only 354 manufactured between 1956 and 1958.

Exc.	V.G.	Good	Fair	Poor
375	325	275	175	125

Model 455 Bolt Action Rifle

This model is built on the Fabrique Nationale Belgian Mauser action. It is chambered for the .308 and the .30-06 cartridges. It has a stainless steel barrel made by Marlin and has a 5-shot magazine. It has a Bishop checkered walnut stock with detachable sling swivels and a leather sling. The rear sight is a Lyman 48, and the front is a ramp type with a detachable hood. The receiver is drilled and tapped for scope mounts. The trigger is an adjustable Sako unit. There were 1,079 manufactured in .30-06 and only 59 in .308 between 1955 and 1959.

Exc.	V.G.	Good	Fair	Poor
375	325	275	175	125

Model 2000

This is a bolt action singel shot target rifle chambered for the .22 Long Rifle. The barrel is a 22" long Micro-Groove design with match chamber and recessed muzzle. The rear sight is a fully adjustable target peep sight with a hooded front sight supplied with 10 aperture inserts. The stock is a Marlin blue fiberglass/Kelvar material with adjustable butt plate. There is an aluminum forearm rail with forearm stop and quick detachable swivel. Rifle weighs 8 lbs.

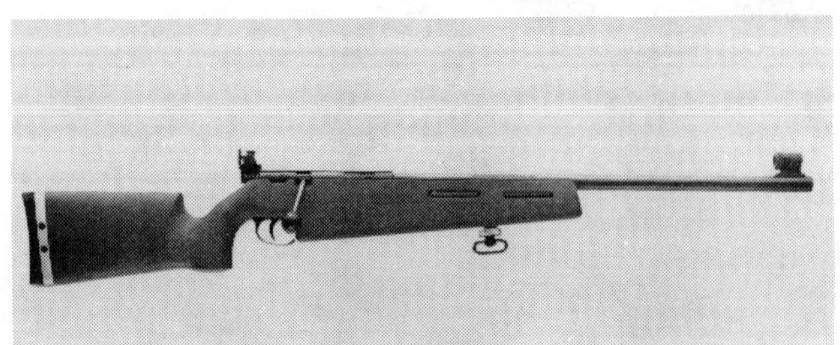

NIB	Exc.	V.G.	Good	Fair	Poor
350	300	250	200	150	125

Model 880

This is a bolt action clip fed rifle chambered for the .22 Long Rifle caliber. The clip is a 7-shot magazine. The Micro-Groove barrel is 22" and has adjustable folding rear sight and ramp front sight with hood. Rifle weighs 5.5 lbs. and was introduced in 1988 and is still in production.

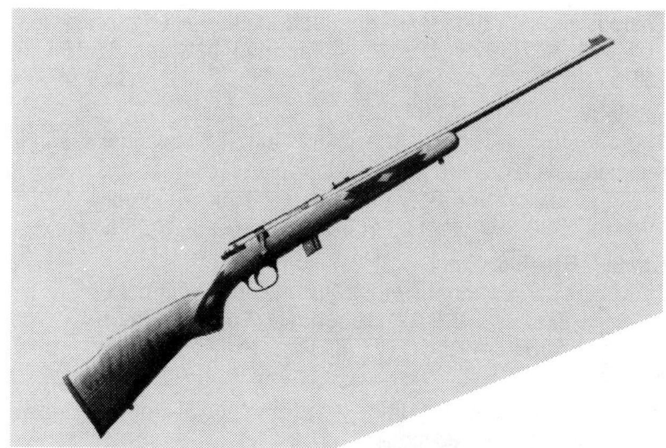

NIB	Exc.	V.G.	Good	Fair	Poor
160	135	110	90	75	50

Model 881

Bolt action .22 caliber rifle has a tubular magazine that holds 25 Shorts, 19 Longs, and 17 Long rifles. A 22" Micro-Groove barrel has adjustable folding rear sight and ramp front sight with hood. Stock is black walnut with Monte Carlo and a rubber rifle butt pad with sling swivels. Rifle weighs 6 lbs. First offered in 1988 and still in production.

NIB	Exc.	V.G.	Good	Fair	Poor
175	150	125	100	80	60

Model 25N

A Marlin promotional model. Bolt action rifle chambered for the .22 Long Rifle only. Seven-shot clip magazine with a 22" Micro-Groove barrel. Receiver grooved for scope mount. Walnut finished birch stock. Gun weighs 5.5 lbs.

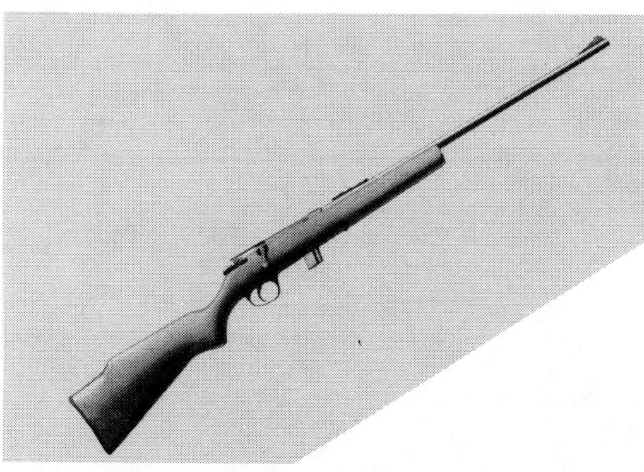

NIB	Exc.	V.G.	Good	Fair	Poor
100	90	80	70	60	40

Model 25 MN

Same as above but chambered for the .22 Win. Magnum Rimfire cartridge. Gun weighs 6 lbs.

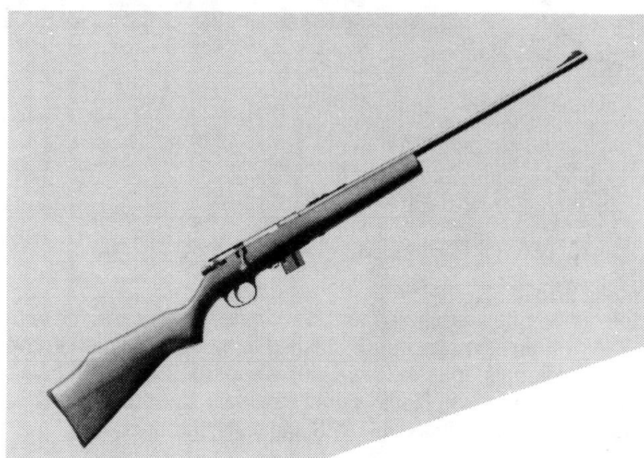

NIB	Exc.	V.G.	Good	Fair	Poor
120	100	85	75	65	50

Model 15YN

A Marlin promotional model referred to as the "Little Buckaroo". A bolt action .22 caliber single shot rifle for the beginner. Features a Micro-Groove 16.25" barrel adjustable rear sight and receiver grooved for scope mount. Birch stock. Rifle weighs 4.25 lbs.

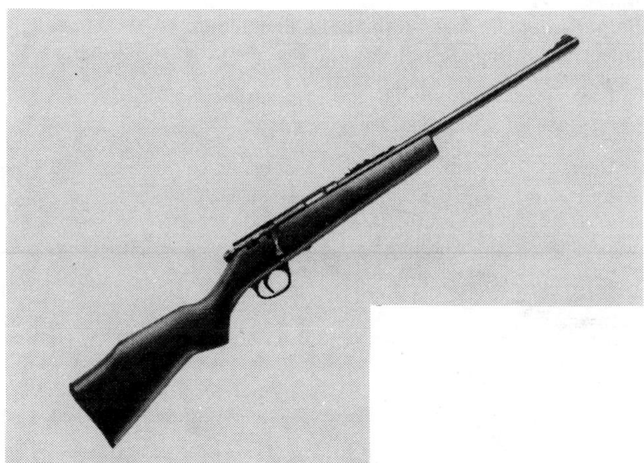

NIB	Exc.	V.G.	Good	Fair	Poor
90	80	70	60	50	40

Model 882

Bolt action rifle chambered for .22 Win. Magnum Rimfire cartridge. A 7-shot clip is standard. A Micro-Groove 22" barrel with adjustable rear sight and ramp front sight with hood. Receiver grooved for scope mount. Black walnut stock with Monte Carlo and rubber rifle butt. Rifle weighs 6 lbs. Introduced in 1988 and still in production.

NIB	Exc.	V.G.	Good	Fair	Poor
150	125	100	80	65	50

Model 882L

Same as above but furnished with a two-tone brown hardwood Monte Carlo stock. Rifle weighs 6.25 lbs.

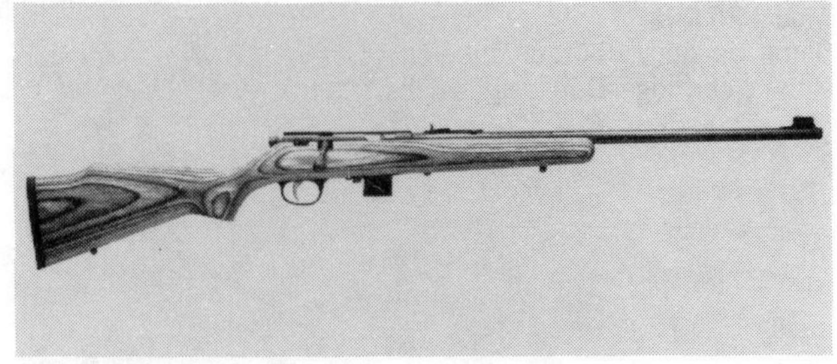

NIB	Exc.	V.G.	Good	Fair	Poor
180	155	130	100	80	60

Model 883

Bolt action rifle chambered for .22 Win. Magnum cartridge with 12-shot tubular magazine. Furnished with a 22" Micro-Groove barrel and adjustable rear sight with ramp front sight with hood. Checkered American black walnut stock with Monte Carlo. Rifle weighs 6 lbs. Introduced in 1988 and still in production.

NIB	Exc.	V.G.	Good	Fair	Poor
160	125	100	80	65	50

Model 883N

Same as above but furnished with stainless steel barrel, receiver, front breech bolt, and striker. All other metal parts, except for sights, are nickel plated.

NIB	Exc.	V.G.	Good	Fair	Poor
180	155	130	100	80	60

Model 883SS

Introduced in 1993 this model is similar to the Model 883 but with all metal parts in stainless steel or nickel and the stock is a two-tone brown birch Monte Carlo that is not checkered.

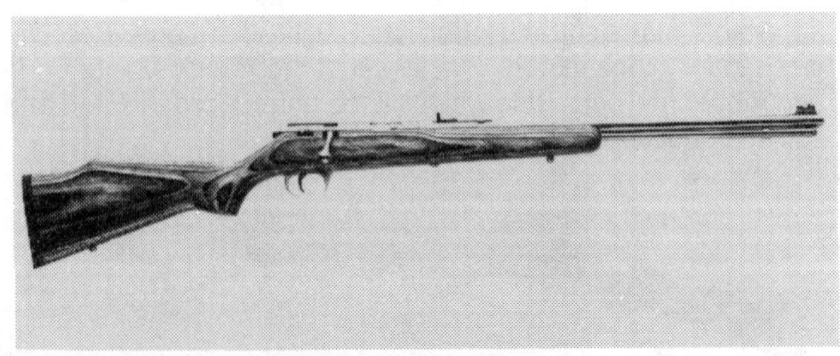

NIB	Exc.	V.G.	Good	Fair	Poor
170	150	125	100	80	60

Marlin Shotguns

Model 1898 Slide Action Shotgun

This model was made in 12 gauge, with an exposed hammer. It has a takedown receiver and walnut pistolgrip stock and forend. There is a 5-shot tube magazine, and the barrel lengths are from 26" and 32". They were manufactured between 1898 and 1905.

Grade A

This variation has a 38", 30", or 32" barrel, is full choke, and is the plainest grade.

Exc.	V.G.	Good	Fair	Poor
500	450	400	300	175

Grade A Brush or Riot

This is the same shotgun with a 26" cylinder-bore barrel.

Exc.	V.G.	Good	Fair	Poor
500	450	400	300	175

Grade B

This is the same as the Grade A with a special smokeless steel barrel and a checkered stock.

Exc.	V.G.	Good	Fair	Poor
600	550	500	400	275

Model 1898 Grade C

This is a more deluxe version with engraving and fancier wood.

Exc.	V.G.	Good	Fair	Poor
800	725	650	500	400

Grade D

This variation has a Damascus barrel and the greatest amount of engraving.

Exc.	V.G.	Good	Fair	Poor
1800	1600	1250	900	700

Model 16 Slide Action Shotgun

This model is exactly the same as the Model 1898 except that it is chambered for 16 gauge only. The four grades are the same also. They were manufactured between 1903 and 1910.

Grade A

Exc.	V.G.	Good	Fair	Poor
400	350	300	250	150

Grade B

Exc.	V.G.	Good	Fair	Poor
500	450	400	350	225

Grade C

Exc.	V.G.	Good	Fair	Poor
650	575	500	425	300

Grade D

Exc.	V.G.	Good	Fair	Poor
1400	1200	1000	700	550

Model 17 Slide Action Shotgun

This model is an exposed-hammer gun with a solid frame and a straight-grip stock. It is chambered for 12 gauge, with a 30" or 32" barrel. The Model 17 was manufactured between 1906 and 1908.

Exc.	V.G.	Good	Fair	Poor
450	400	350	275	175

Model 17 Brush Gun

This variation is similar to the standard Model 17, with a 26" cylinder-bore barrel.

Exc.	V.G.	Good	Fair	Poor
475	425	375	300	200

Model 17 Riot Gun

This variation has a 20" cylinder-bore barrel.

Exc.	V.G.	Good	Fair	Poor
400	350	300	225	125

Model 19 Slide Action Shotgun

This is a takedown gun, chambered for 12 gauge. It is basically an improved and lightened version of the Model 1898. It is available in the same four grades. It was manufactured in 1906 and 1907.

Grade A

Exc.	V.G.	Good	Fair	Poor
400	350	300	250	150

Grade B

Exc.	V.G.	Good	Fair	Poor
500	450	400	350	225

Grade C

Exc.	V.G.	Good	Fair	Poor
650	575	500	425	300

Grade D

Exc.	V.G.	Good	Fair	Poor
1400	1200	1000	700	550

Model 21 "Trap" Slide Action Shotgun

This model is basically the same as the Model 19 with a straight-grip stock. The 1907 catalog listed it as a Trap model. This model was manufactured in 1907 and 1908. The four grades are similar to the previous models.

Grade A

Exc.	V.G.	Good	Fair	Poor
400	350	300	250	150

Grade B

Exc.	V.G.	Good	Fair	Poor
500	450	400	350	225

Grade C

Exc.	V.G.	Good	Fair	Poor
650	575	500	425	300

Grade D

Exc.	V.G.	Good	Fair	Poor
1400	1200	1000	700	550

Model 24 Slide Action Shotgun

This model is actually an improved version of the Model 21. It has a pistolgrip stock and exposed hammer. It features an automatic recoil lock on the slide and a matte rib barrel. Otherwise, it is quite similar to its predecessor. It was manufactured between 1908 and 1917.

Grade A

Exc.	V.G.	Good	Fair	Poor
350	300	250	200	100

Grade B

Exc.	V.G.	Good	Fair	Poor
500	450	400	350	225

Grade C

Exc.	V.G.	Good	Fair	Poor
650	575	500	425	300

Grade D

Exc.	V.G.	Good	Fair	Poor
1400	1200	1000	700	550

Marlin "Trap Gun"

This model is unique in that it has no numerical designation and is simply known as the "Trap Gun." It is a takedown gun with interchangeable barrels from 16" to 32". It has a straight-grip buttstock and is quite similar in appearance to the Model 24. It was manufactured between 1909 and 1912.

Exc.	V.G.	Good	Fair	Poor
450	400	350	250	175

Model 26 Slide Action Shotgun

This model is similar to the Model 24 Grade A, with a solid frame. It has 30" or 32" barrels.

Exc.	V.G.	Good	Fair	Poor
275	225	175	125	100

Model 26 Brush Gun

This model has a 26" cylinder-bored barrel.

Exc.	V.G.	Good	Fair	Poor
300	250	200	150	125

Model 26 Riot Gun

This variation has a 20" cylinder-bored barrel.

Exc.	V.G.	Good	Fair	Poor
250	200	150	100	75

Model 28 Hammerless Slide Action Shotgun

This model was the first of the Marlin hammerless shotguns. It is a takedown 12 gauge, with barrels from 26" to 32" in length. The stock has a pistol grip, and it comes in four grades like its predecessors. The Model 28 was manufactured between 1913 and 1922.

Grade A

Exc.	V.G.	Good	Fair	Poor
400	350	300	250	150

Grade B

Exc.	V.G.	Good	Fair	Poor
500	450	400	350	225

Grade C

Exc.	V.G.	Good	Fair	Poor
650	575	500	425	300

Grade D

Exc.	V.G.	Good	Fair	Poor
1400	1200	1000	700	550

Model 28 TS Trap Gun

This variation is the same as the Model 28 with a 30" full-choke barrel with matted rib and a high-comb straightgrip stock. It was manufactured in 1915.

Exc.	V.G.	Good	Fair	Poor
425	375	300	225	175

Model 28T Trap Gun

This variation is the deluxe model, similar to the Model 28TS, with engraving, high-grade walnut, and hand checkering. It was manufactured in 1915.

Exc.	V.G.	Good	Fair	Poor
600	525	450	375	250

Model 30 Slide Action Shotgun

This model is an improved version of the Model 16, 16 gauge shotgun. Its features are similar, with the addition of the improved takedown system and the automatic recoil lock on the slide. This model was manufactured between 1910 and 1914.

Grade A

Exc.	V.G.	Good	Fair	Poor
400	350	300	250	150

Grade B

Exc.	V.G.	Good	Fair	Poor
500	450	400	350	225

Grade C

Exc.	V.G.	Good	Fair	Poor
650	575	500	425	300

Grade D

Exc.	V.G.	Good	Fair	Poor
1400	1200	1000	700	550

Model 30 Field Grade

This model is similar to the Model 30 Grade B, with a 25" modified-choke barrel and a straight-grip stock. It was manufactured in 1913 and 1914.

Exc.	V.G.	Good	Fair	Poor
400	350	300	225	150

Model 31 Slide Action Shotgun

This model is a smaller version of the Model 28 hammerless takedown shotgun, chambered for 16 and 20 gauge. It was produced with barrel lengths of 26" and 28" and was available in the usual four grades, with various different chokes. This model was manufactured between 1915 and 1922.

Grade A

Exc.	V.G.	Good	Fair	Poor
400	350	300	250	150

Grade B

Exc.	V.G.	Good	Fair	Poor
500	450	400	350	225

Grade C

Exc.	V.G.	Good	Fair	Poor
650	575	500	425	300

Grade D

Exc.	V.G.	Good	Fair	Poor
1400	1200	1000	700	550

Model 42/42A Slide Action Shotgun

This model was originally listed as the Model 42; but in the second year of production, the designation was changed to 42/A for no more apparent reason than standardization of models. This model is similar to the Model 24 except that the barrel markings are different. It is still an exposed hammer takedown gun chambered for 12 gauge. It was manufactured between 1922 and 1933.

Exc.	V.G.	Good	Fair	Poor
275	250	200	150	100

Model 43A Slide Action Shotgun

This hammerless model was quite similar to the Model 28, with different markings and less attention to finishing detail. It was manufactured between 1923 and 1930.

Exc.	V.G.	Good	Fair	Poor
350	300	250	200	150

Model 43T Slide Action Shotgun

This model is the same as the Model 43A takedown hammerless with a 30" or 32" matte-rib barrel. The straight-grip stock is of high-grade walnut, with a non-gloss oil finish and fitted recoil paid. This model was manufactured between 1922 and 1930.

Exc.	V.G.	Good	Fair	Poor
400	350	300	250	200

Model 43TS Slide Action Shotgun

This is a custom-order version of the Model 43T, the same in all respects except that the stock could be ordered to any specifications the shooter desired. It was manufactured between 1922 and 1930.

Exc.	V.G.	Good	Fair	Poor
600	550	500	350	275

Model 44A Slide Action Shotgun

This model is similar to the Model 31 and was advertised as its successor. It is a hammerless takedown chambered for the 20 gauge. It features an improved boltopening device located in the triggerguard area instead of at the top of the receiver and has a shorter 4-shot magazine tube. The model was manufactured from 1922 until 1933.

Exc.	V.G.	Good	Fair	Poor
375	325	275	225	175

Model 44S Slide Action Shotgun

This model is similar to the Model 44A, with a higher-grade walnut stock that featured hand-cut checkering.

Exc.	V.G.	Good	Fair	Poor
450	400	350	300	225

Model 49 Slide Action Shotgun

This model is a 12-gauge, exposed-hammer takedown that combines features of the Model 42 and the Model 24. It is basically a lower-priced model that was never listed in the Marlin catalog. This model was part of Frank Kenna's money-raising program—anyone who purchased four shares of stock for $25 per share was given one free of charge. This model was manufactured between 1925 and 1928.

Exc.	V.G.	Good	Fair	Poor
450	400	350	275	200

Model 53 Slide Action Shotgun

This model is a hammerless, takedown, 12 gauge that was not in production for very long. It is theorized that the Model 53 was produced to use up old parts on hand when the Model 43 was introduced. It was manufactured in 1929 and 1930.

Exc.	V.G.	Good	Fair	Poor
350	300	250	175	125

Model 63 Slide Action Shotgun

This was the last of the slide action shotguns produced by Marlin until the Model 120 in 1971. It is a hammerless, takedown 12 gauge and replaced the Model 43A in the Marlin catalog. This model had improvements over the earlier guns, but its introduction during the Depression did little to bolster sales. This model was also offered free of charge to anyone purchasing four shares of Marlin stock at $25 per share. It was manufactured between 1931 and 1933.

Exc.	V.G.	Good	Fair	Poor
350	300	250	175	125

Model 63T Slide Action Shotgun

This is the trap-grade version of the Model 63. It has a better-grade hand-checkered stock, with a fitted recoil pad and oil finish. It was manufactured between 1931 and 1933.

Exc.	V.G.	Good	Fair	Poor
375	325	275	200	150

Model 63TS Slide Action Shotgun

This variation is the same as the Model 63T except that the stock dimensions were custom-made to the customer's specifications. It was manufactured between 1931 and 1933.

Exc.	V.G.	Good	Fair	Poor
400	350	300	225	175

Model 60 Single Barrel Shotgun

This is a break-open, exposed-hammer, top lever-opening 12 gauge with either 30" or 32" full-choke barrel. It has a pistolgrip stock. There were approximately 60 manufactured in 1923.

Exc.	V.G.	Good	Fair	Poor
200	175	150	125	100

Model .410 Lever Action Shotgun

This was a unique venture for the Marlin Company—a lever-action shotgun based on the Model 1893 action with a longer loading port, modified tube magazine that held 5 shots, and a smoothbore barrel chambered for the .410 shot shell. The finish of this gun is blued, with a walnut pistolgrip stock and grooved beavertail forend. It has a hard rubber rifle-type buttplate. The model was available with either a 22" or 26" full-choke barrel. This gun was also part of the stock-purchase plan and was given free of charge to anyone purchasing four shares at $25 per share. It was also cataloged for sale and was manufactured between 1929 and 1932.

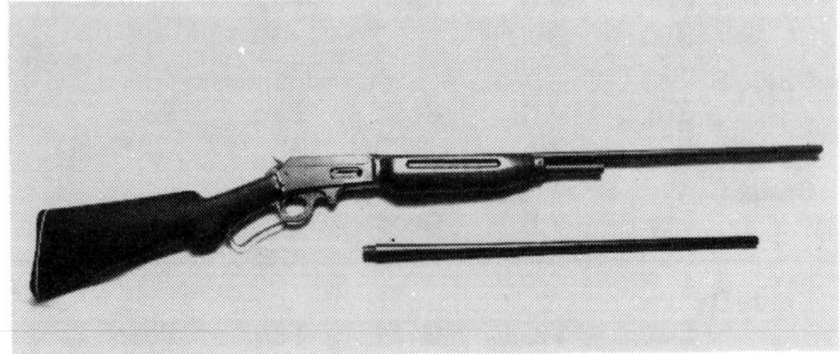

Courtesy Mike Stuckslager.

Exc.	V.G.	Good	Fair	Poor
600	500	400	300	250

Model .410 Deluxe

This variation was never cataloged and is essentially the same as the standard version with a hand-checkered stock. The forend does not have the grooves found on the standard model. Be wary of fakes!

Exc.	V.G.	Good	Fair	Poor
850	750	650	550	400

Model 90 Over/Under Shotgun

This gun was produced in response to a request from Sears Roebuck that Marlin should manufacture an Over/Under shotgun for Sears to market in their stores. The guns produced for Sears have the prefix 103 in their serial numbers and were marked "Ranger" before WWII and "J.C.Higgins" after the War. Prior to 1945 they were not marked Marlin; after that date Sears requested that the company stamp their name on the guns. They were also produced as the Marlin Model 90 during the same period and were chambered for 12, 16, and 20 gauge, as well as .410 bore. The barrels are either 26", 28", or 30", with various chokes. The action is a boxlock with extractors. Guns made prior to 1949 had a space between the barrels; after that date they were solid. They can be found with double or single triggers

and a checkered walnut stock. There were approximately 34,000 Model 90s manufactured between 1937 and 1963.
Single Trigger—Add 35%.

Exc.	V.G.	Good	Fair	Poor
500	425	350	275	200

Premier Mark I Slide Action Shotgun
This model was made by Manufrance and called the LaSalle. Marlin was able to purchase them without the barrels at a good enough price for them to barrel and market them under their own name. This model is 12 gauge only, with an alloy receiver and seven interchangeable barrels in 26"-30" lengths and various chokes. The plain stock is French walnut. The biggest problem with this gun is that the light weight (six pounds) produced very bad recoil, and it was less than enjoyable to shoot. This model was in production from 1959 through 1963, with approximately 13,700 sold.

Exc.	V.G.	Good	Fair	Poor
225	175	150	100	75

Premier Mark II
This model is similar to the Mark I, with light engraving and a checkered stock.

Exc.	V.G.	Good	Fair	Poor
250	200	175	125	100

Premier Mark IV
This model is similar to the Mark II, with more engraving on the receiver.

Exc.	V.G.	Good	Fair	Poor
300	250	200	150	125

Model 120 Slide Action Shotgun
This model was styled to resemble the Winchester Model 12 and was advertised as an all steel and walnut shotgun. It was offered with interchangeable barrels from 26"-40", and various chokes were available. The checkered stock is of walnut, with a fitted recoil pad. The tube magazine holds 5 shots, 4 in 3". There was a Trap Model available (1973-1975), as well as a slug gun (1974-1984). This model was manufactured between 1971 and 1985.

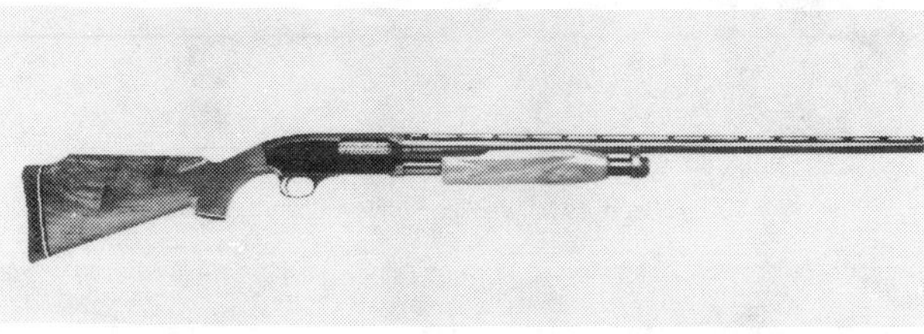

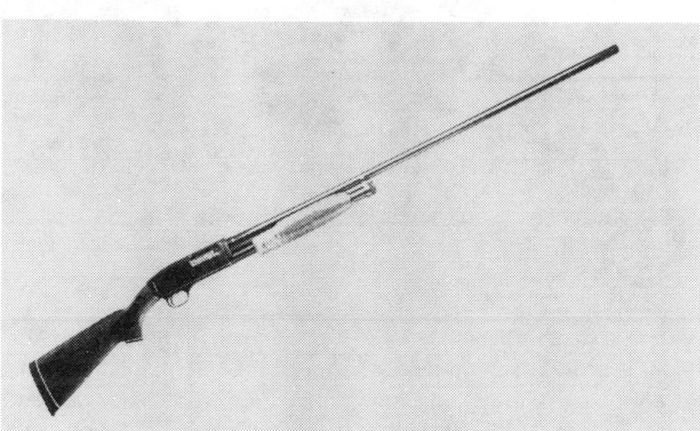

Exc.	V.G.	Good	Fair	Poor
300	250	200	150	125

Model 778 Slide Action Shotgun (Glenfield)
This model is similar to the Model 120, with a walnutfinished hardwood stock instead of walnut, and the Glenfield name stamped on it. It was manufactured between 1979 and 1984.

Exc.	V.G.	Good	Fair	Poor
225	175	150	125	100

Model 55 Bolt Action Shotgun
This model is chambered for 12, 16, and 20 gauge, with full or adjustable choke and barrels of 26" or 28". It is a bolt-action with 2-shot box magazine. The pistolgrip stock is plain. This model was manufactured between 1950 and 1965.

Exc.	V.G.	Good	Fair	Poor
100	75	50	35	25

Model 55 Swamp Gun
This is simply the Model 55 with a 3" Magnum, 20" barrel and an adjustable choke. It was manufactured between 1963 and 1965.

Exc.	V.G.	Good	Fair	Poor
110	80	65	45	25

Model 55 Goose Gun
This is the Model 55 with a 3" chambered, 36" fullchoke barrel and a recoil pad and sling. It was introduced in 1962 and is still manufactured.

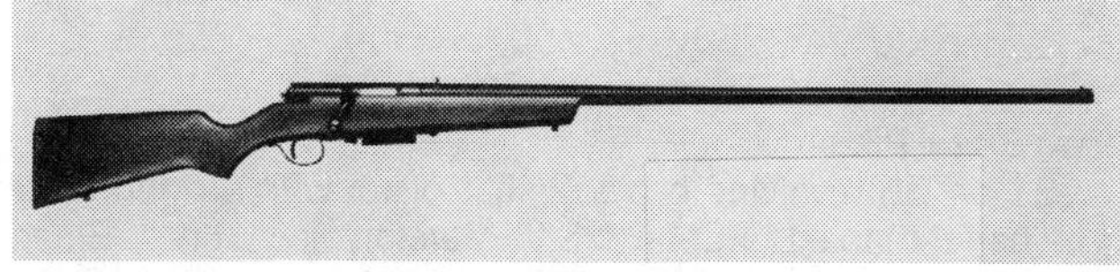

NIB	Exc.	V.G.	Good	Fair	Poor
230	175	140	125	100	75

Model 55S Slug Gun
This is the Model 55 with a 24" cylinder-bore barrel and rifle sights. It was manufactured between 1974 and 1983.

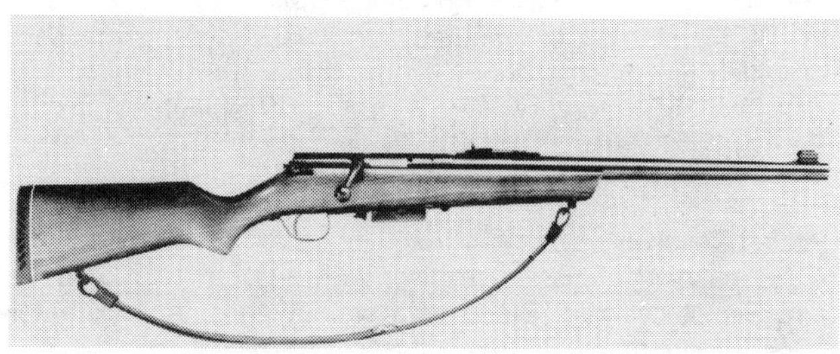

Exc.	V.G.	Good	Fair	Poor
150	125	100	75	50

Model 5510 Bolt Action Shotgun
This model is chambered for the 3.5" 10 gauge. It has a 34" full-choke barrel and a recoil pad and sling. It was manufactured between 1976 and 1985.

Exc.	V.G.	Good	Fair	Poor
200	150	125	100	75

MARROCHI, ARMI

Brescia, Italy
Importer—Sile Distributors Inc.
New York, New York

Model 2000
A 12 gauge Magnum single shot shotgun with a 28" barrel, exposed hammer and automatic ejector. Blued with a walnut stock.

Exc.	V.G.	Good	Fair	Poor
100	80	65	50	35

Field Master I
A 12 gauge Over/Under shotgun with 26" or 28" ventilated-rib barrels fitted for choke tubes, single trigger and automatic ejectors. Blued, French case-hardened with a walnut stock.

Exc.	V.G.	Good	Fair	Poor
400	350	300	200	150

Field Master II
As above, with a single selective trigger.

Exc.	V.G.	Good	Fair	Poor
425	375	325	225	175

MARS
SEE—Gabbet-Fairfax

MARSTON, S.W.
New York, New York

Double Action Pepperbox
A .31 caliber double-action percussion pepperbox with a 5" barrel group and ring trigger. Blued with walnut grips. Manufactured between 1850 and 1855.

Exc.	V.G.	Good	Fair	Poor
1000	850	750	500	350

Two Barrel Pistol
A .31 or .36 revolving barrel 2-shot pistol with a ring trigger. The barrel marked "J.Cohn & S.W.Marston-New York." Blued, brass frame with walnut grips. Manufactured during the 1850s.

Exc.	V.G.	Good	Fair	Poor
1250	1000	850	600	450

MARSTON, W. W. & CO.
New York, New York

W. W. Marston & Co. manufactured a variety of firearms some of which are marked only with the tradenames—Union Arms Co., Phoenix Armory, Western Arms Co., Washington Arms Co., Sprague and Marston, and Marston and Knox.

Pocket Revolver
A .31 caliber percussion revolver with a 3.25" to 7.5" barrel and 6-shot cylinder. Blued with walnut grips. Approximately 13,000 were manufactured between 1857 and 1862.

Exc.	V.G.	Good	Fair	Poor
550	450	400	300	200

Navy Revolver
A .36 caliber percussion revolver with a 7.5" or 8.5" octagonal barrel and 6-shot cylinder. Blued with walnut grips. Manufactured between 1857 and 1862.

Exc.	V.G.	Good	Fair	Poor
1150	1000	800	550	400

Double Action Single Shot Pistol
A .31 or .36 caliber bar hammer percussion pistol with a 2.5" or 5" half octagonal barrel. Blued with walnut grips. Manufactured during the 1850s.

Exc.	V.G.	Good	Fair	Poor
450	375	325	250	175

Single Action Pistol
A .31 or .36 caliber percussion pistol with a 4" or 6" barrel. Blued with walnut grips. Manufactured during the 1860s.

Exc.	V.G.	Good	Fair	Poor
500	400	350	275	200

Breech Loading Pistol
A .35 caliber breech loading percussion pistol with a 4" to 8.5" half octagonal barrel and either a brass or iron frame. Blued, case-hardened with walnut grips. Approximately 1,000 were manufactured in the 1850s.

Courtesy Milwaukee Public Museum, Milwaukee, Wisconsin.

Brass Frame

Exc.	V.G.	Good	Fair	Poor
2000	1800	1500	1200	800

Iron Frame

Exc.	V.G.	Good	Fair	Poor
2250	2000	1700	1400	1000

Double Action Pepperbox
A .31 caliber double-action 6-shot percussion pepperbox with 4" or 5" barrel groups and a bar hammer. Blued, case-hardened with walnut grips. Manufactured during the 1850s.

Courtesy Milwaukee Public Museum, Milwaukee, Wisconsin.

Courtesy Milwaukee Public Museum, Milwaukee, Wisconsin.

Exc.	V.G.	Good	Fair	Poor
650	550	450	350	200

3 Barreled Derringer
A .22 caliber 3 barrelled spur trigger pocket pistol with a sliding knife blade mounted on the left side of the 3" barrel group. Blued, silver-plated with walnut grips. The barrel marked "Wm.W. Marston/New York City." Approximately 1,500 were manufactured between 1858 and 1864.

Knife Bladed Model

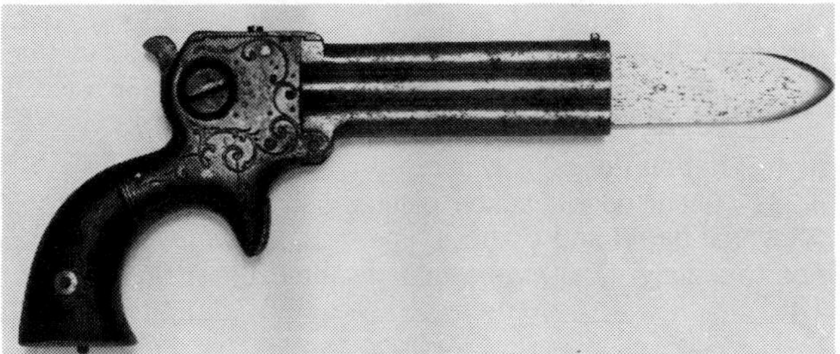

Courtesy Milwaukee Public Museum, Milwaukee, Wisconsin.

Exc.	V.G.	Good	Fair	Poor
1500	1000	650	450	350

Model Without Knife

Courtesy Milwaukee Public Museum, Milwaukee, Wisconsin.

Exc.	V.G.	Good	Fair	Poor
850	750	500	350	300

.32 Caliber 3 Barrel Derringer

Similar to the above, but in .32 caliber with either 3" or 4" barrels and not fitted with a knife blade. Approximately 3,000 were manufactured between 1864 and 1872.

Courtesy Milwaukee Public Museum, Milwaukee, Wisconsin.

Exc.	V.G.	Good	Fair	Poor
750	650	450	300	200

MASQUELIER S. A.

Liege, Belgium

Carpathe

A .243, .270, .7x57mm, 7x65Rmm, or .30-06 caliber single shot rifle with a 24" barrel, adjustable trigger and adjustable sights. Blued, with an engraved receiver and walnut stock. Imported until 1986.

Exc.	V.G.	Good	Fair	Poor
3500	3250	2750	2000	1500

Express

A .270, .30-06, 8x57JRSmm, or 9.3x74Rmm caliber Over/Under double barrel rifle with 24" barrels, single selective trigger and automatic ejectors. Blued, engraved with a walnut stock. Not imported after 1986.

Exc.	V.G.	Good	Fair	Poor
3500	3250	2750	2000	1500

Ardennes

As above, but made on custom order only. Discontinued in 1986.

Exc.	V.G.	Good	Fair	Poor
6500	5750	5000	4000	3250

Boxlock Side x Side Shotgun

A 12 gauge boxlock double barrel shotgun manufactured in a variety of barrel lengths with a single selective trigger and automatic ejectors. Blued with a walnut stock. Imported prior to 1987.

Exc.	V.G.	Good	Fair	Poor
4500	3750	3000	2500	2000

Sidelock Side x Side Shotgun

Similar to the above, but with detachable sidelocks and finely engraved. Imported prior to 1987.

Exc.	V.G.	Good	Fair	Poor
13000	11500	8500	5000	4000

MASSACHUSETTS ARMS CO.

Chicopee Falls, Massachusetts

Wesson & Leavitt Dragoon

A .40 caliber percussion revolver with a 7" round barrel, 6-shot cylinder and side mounted hammer. Blued, case-hardened with walnut grips. Approximately 800 were manufactured in 1850 and 1851.

Early Model with 6" Barrel—Approximately 30 Made

Exc.	V.G.	Good	Fair	Poor
2500	2000	1750	1300	1000

Fully Marked 7" Barrel Standard Model

Exc.	V.G.	Good	Fair	Poor
2250	1800	1500	1100	850

Wesson & Leavitt Belt Revolver

A .31 caliber percussion revolver with a 3" to 7" round barrel and 6-shot cylinder. Similar in appearance to the above. Approximately 1,000 were manufactured in 1850 and 1851.

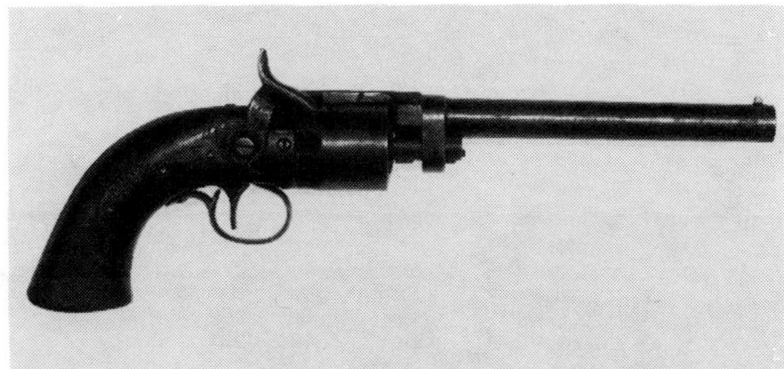

Courtesy Milwaukee Public Museum, Milwaukee, Wisconsin.

Exc.	V.G.	Good	Fair	Poor
1000	850	700	500	350

Maynard Primed Belt Revolver

Similar to the above, with a Maynard tape primer. Approximately 1,000 were manufactured between 1851 and 1857.

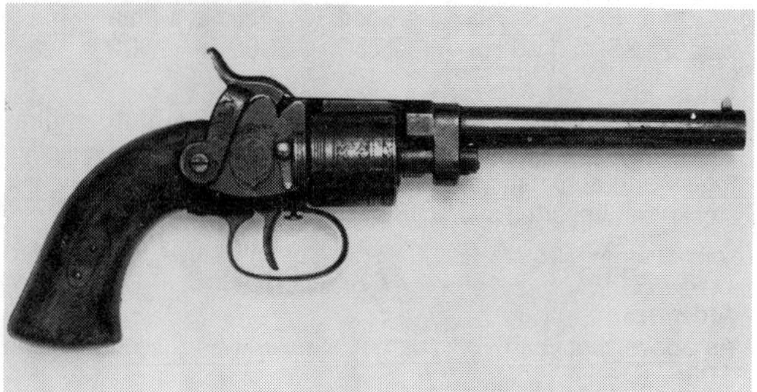

Courtesy Milwaukee Public Museum, Milwaukee, Wisconsin.

Exc.	V.G.	Good	Fair	Poor
1000	850	700	500	350

Maynard Primed Pocket Revolver

Similar to the above, but in .28 or .30 caliber with 2.5" to 3.5" octagonal or round barrels. Approximately 3,000 were made between 1851 and 1860.

Courtesy Milwaukee Public Museum, Milwaukee, Wisconsin.

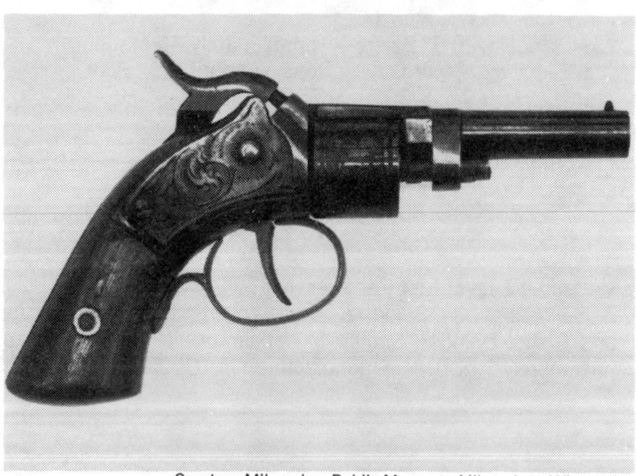

Courtesy Milwaukee Public Museum, Milwaukee, Wisconsin.

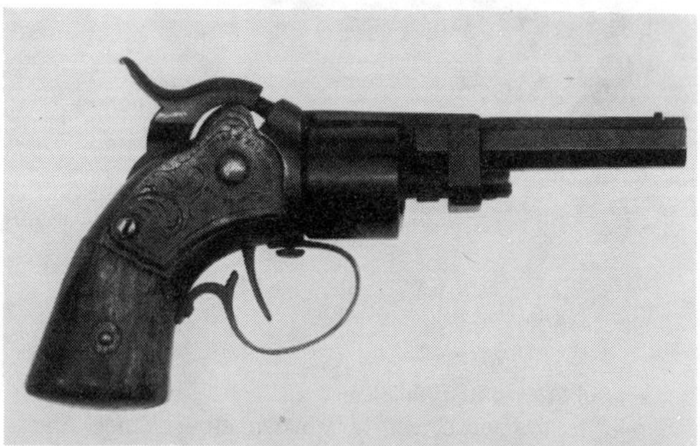

Courtesy Milwaukee Public Museum, Milwaukee, Wisconsin.

Early Model .28 Caliber Only—Manually Revolved

Exc.	V.G.	Good	Fair	Poor
850	750	600	400	300

Automatic Cylinder Model

Exc.	V.G.	Good	Fair	Poor
800	700	550	350	250

Adams Patent Pocket Revolver

A .31 caliber double-action percussion revolver with a 3.25" octagonal barrel and 5-shot cylinder. Blued with walnut grips. Approximately 4,500 were manufactured between 1857 and 1861.

Courtesy Milwaukee Public Museum, Milwaukee, Wisconsin.

Exc.	V.G.	Good	Fair	Poor
750	650	500	350	250

Adams Patent Navy Revolver

As above, in .36 caliber with a 6" octagonal barrel. Approximately 600 of the 1,000 made were purchased by the U.S. Government. Those bearing inspection marks will bring approximately a 20% premium over the values listed below.

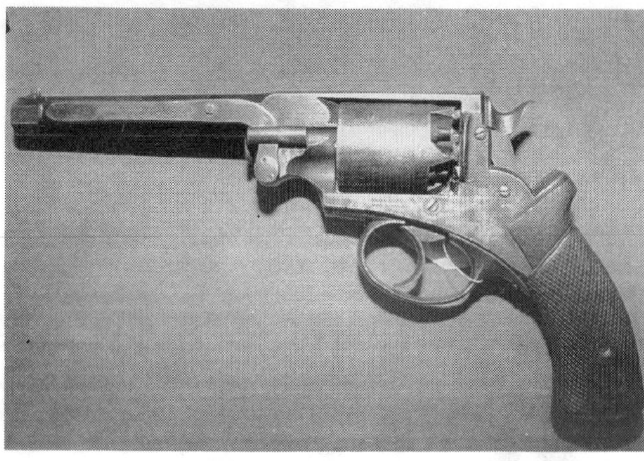

Exc.	V.G.	Good	Fair	Poor
1100	950	800	500	400

Single Shot Pocket Pistol

A .31 caliber single shot percussion pistol with a 2.5" to 3.5" half octagonal barrel and a Maynard tape primer. The barrel marked "Mass. Arms Co/Chicopee Falls" and the primer door "Maynard's Patent Sept. 22, 1845." Blued, case-hardened with walnut grips. Manufactured in the 1850s.

Exc.	V.G.	Good	Fair	Poor
750	650	500	350	250

Maynard Carbine

This is a single-shot breechloader chambered for .35 or .50 caliber percussion. The barrel is round and 20" in length. The triggerguard is the lever that pivots the barrel in break-open fashion when it is lowered. The finish is blued, with a case-colored frame. The buttstock is walnut, and there is no forend. This carbine was designed by the same Maynard who invented the tape primer system. There are two models—a 1st and a 2nd. They were made for both sporting use and as a U.S. Martial carbine. The 2nd Model was used considerably during the Civil War.

1st Model

This Model is marked "Maynard Patentee/May 27, 1851/June 17, 1856." It has an iron patchbox and a curved buttplate. It has a Maynard tape primer system and a tang sight. Later production was fitted with a sling swivel. There are approximately 400 of these carbines that are U.S. marked, but the total manufactured in the late 1850s is unknown.

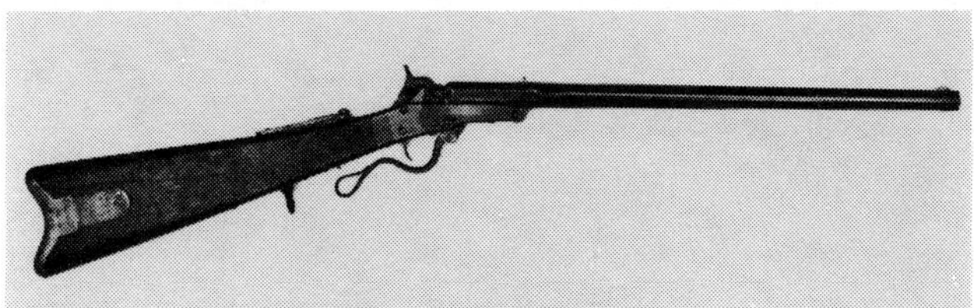

Courtesy Milwaukee Public Museum, Milwaukee, Wisconsin.

U.S.Martially Marked and AUTHENTICATED

Exc.	V.G.	Good	Fair	Poor
2000	1700	1500	1150	850

Commercial Model

Exc.	V.G.	Good	Fair	Poor
1100	950	750	600	450

2nd Model

This model is chambered for .50 caliber only and does not have the tape primer system or the tang sight. There is no patchbox, and the buttplate is not as curved as on the 1st Model. It is marked "Manufactured By/Mass. Arms Co./Chicopee Falls." There were approximately 20,000 manufactured between 1860 and 1865. This model was used by Union forces during the Civil War.

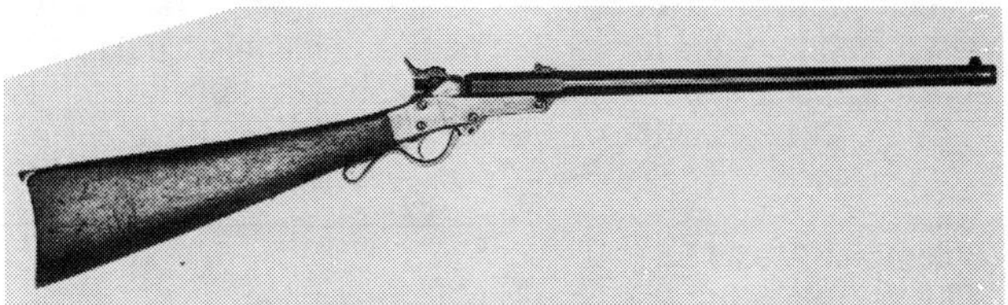

Courtesy Milwaukee Public Museum, Milwaukee, Wisconsin.

Exc.	V.G.	Good	Fair	Poor
950	850	750	550	350

Maynard Patent Sporting Rifles

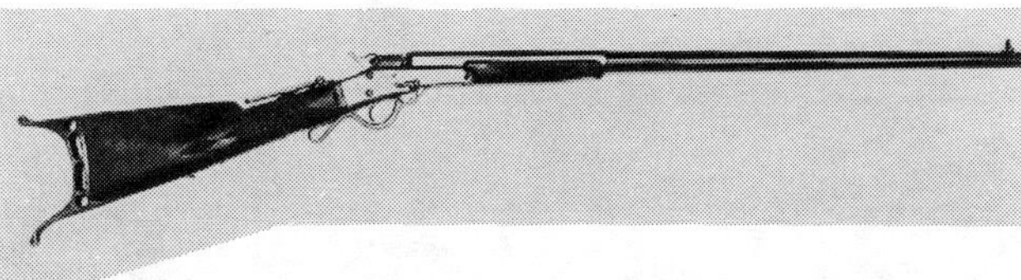

Courtesy Milwaukee Public Museum, Milwaukee, Wisconsin.

Courtesy Milwaukee Public Museum, Milwaukee, Wisconsin.

Sporting rifles bearing the designations Model 1865, 1873 and 1882 were manufactured in a wide variety of calibers, gauges, stock styles, finishes, and options. As these features effect the values of individual arms considerably, it is recommended that prospective purchasers are advised to secure a qualified appraisal prior to acquisition.

MATRA MANURHIN DEFENSE

Mulhouse, France
SEE—Manurhin

MAUSER WERKE

Oberndorf-am-Neckar, Germany

Established in 1869 by Peter and Wilhelm Mauser, this company came under the effective control of Ludwig Loewe and Company of Berlin in 1887. In 1896 the latter company was reorganized under the name Deutsches Waffen und Munition or as it is better known, DWM.

Model 1871

An 11mm caliber single shot bolt-action rifle with a 33.5" barrel with bayonet lug, full length stock secured by two barrel bands and a cleaning rod. The barrel marked "Mod. 71" together with the year of production and the manufacturer's name. Blued with a walnut stock.

Courtesy Milwaukee Public Museum, Milwaukee, Wisconsin.

Exc.	V.G.	Good	Fair	Poor
400	350	300	200	125

Model 1871 Jaeger Rifle

As above, with a 29.4" barrel.

Exc.	V.G.	Good	Fair	Poor
500	450	400	300	200

Model 1871 Carbine

As above, with a 20" barrel and no bayonet lug.

Exc.	V.G.	Good	Fair	Poor
500	450	400	300	200

Serbian Model 78/80

Identical to the Model 1871 except in 10.15mm caliber and with a 30.7" barrel. All markings in Cyrillic.

Exc.	V.G.	Good	Fair	Poor
350	300	250	150	100

Model 71/84 Rifle

The Model 71 modified by the addition of a tubular magazine. Barrel length 31.5".

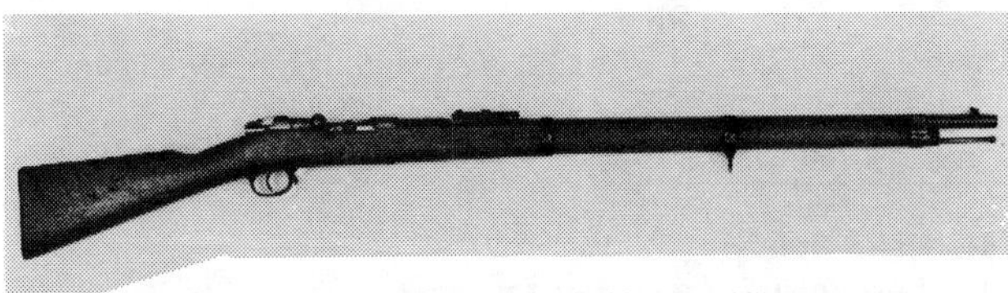

Courtesy Milwaukee Public Museum, Milwaukee, Wisconsin.

Exc.	V.G.	Good	Fair	Poor
400	350	300	200	125

Serbian Model 71/84

As above, in 10.15mm caliber with an 18.3" barrel. Marked in Cyrillic.

Exc.	V.G.	Good	Fair	Poor
350	300	250	150	100

Turkish Model 87 Rifle

Similar to the above, in 9.5mm caliber with a 30" barrel and 8-shot tubular magazine. Marked in Turkish script.

Exc.	V.G.	Good	Fair	Poor
300	250	200	125	80

Model 88 Commission Rifle
A 7.92mm caliber bolt-action rifle with a 29" barrel, 5-shot magazine, full length stock, bayonet lug and cleaning rod. Marked "GEW. 88" together with the year of manufacture and the maker's name.

Exc.	V.G.	Good	Fair	Poor
225	175	150	100	75

Belgian Model 1889 Rifle
A 7.65mm bolt-action rifle with a 30.6" barrel, 5-shot magazine, full length stock, cleaning rod and bayonet lug. Also made with a 21.65" barrel.

Exc.	V.G.	Good	Fair	Poor
225	175	150	100	75

Argentine Model 91 Rifle
A 7.65mm caliber bolt-action rifle with a 29" barrel, 5-shot magazine, full length stock, cleaning rod and bayonet lug. Also made with a 17.6" barrel without a bayonet lug. Approximately 180,000 rifles and 30,000 carbines were made in 1891. They all are stamped with the Argentinian code of arms.

Exc.	V.G.	Good	Fair	Poor
250	200	175	125	90

Spanish Model 91
As above, but with a Spanish code of arms.

Exc.	V.G.	Good	Fair	Poor
250	200	175	125	90

Spanish Model 93
A 7x57mm caliber bolt-action rifle with a 29" barrel and staggered column magazine. Adopted by the Spanish Government in 1893.

Exc.	V.G.	Good	Fair	Poor
250	200	175	125	90

Brazilian Model 94
Similar to the above, but with the Brazilian code of arms.

Exc.	V.G.	Good	Fair	Poor
250	200	175	125	90

Chilean Model 1895
As above, but marked "Mauser-Chileno Modelo 1895."

Exc.	V.G.	Good	Fair	Poor
200	150	125	100	80

Swedish Model 94 Carbine
A 6.5mm caliber bolt-action carbine with a 17.7" barrel, 5-shot magazine, full length stock and bayonet lug. Marked with the Swedish Royal Crown and the date of manufacture.

Exc.	V.G.	Good	Fair	Poor
200	150	125	100	80

Swedish Model 96 Rifle
As above, with a 29" barrel.

Exc.	V.G.	Good	Fair	Poor
200	150	125	100	80

Swedish Model 38 Rifle
As above, with a 23.6" barrel and without the Swedish crown marking.

Exc.	V.G.	Good	Fair	Poor
225	175	150	100	75

Model 98 Rifle
The best known of all Mauser rifles. A 7.92mm bolt-action rifle with a 29" barrel, 5-shot magazine, full length stock, hand guard, cleaning rod and bayonet lug. Marked "GEW. 98" together with the date of manufacture and maker's name.

Courtesy Buffalo Bill Historical Center, Cody, Wyoming.

Exc.	V.G.	Good	Fair	Poor
275	250	200	150	100

Model 98a Carbine
As above, with a 23.6" barrel and marked "KAR. 98".

Exc.	V.G.	Good	Fair	Poor
275	250	200	150	100

Model 98k Carbine
As above, with a laminated stock and marked "Mod. 98".

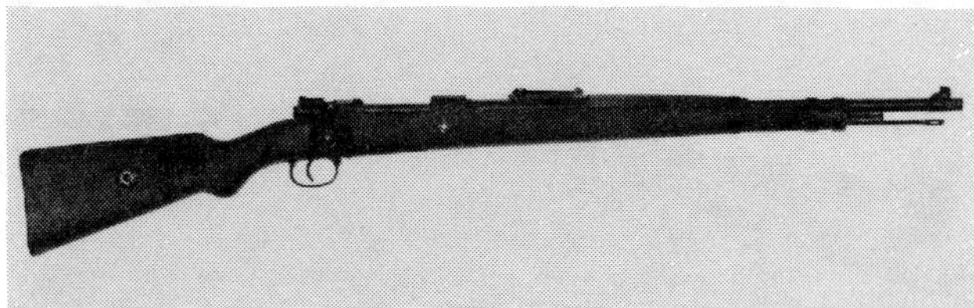

Courtesy Buffalo Bill Historical Center, Cody, Wyoming.

Exc.	V.G.	Good	Fair	Poor
300	250	225	175	125

Model 33/40 Carbine
As above, with a 19.2" barrel and marked "G. 33/40" together with the year of production and the maker's code.

Exc.	V.G.	Good	Fair	Poor
650	550	450	300	200

Czech Model 98 VZ24
Assembled from Model 98k parts and identifiable by the large stamped steel triggerguard and permanent magazine floorplate. The original markings removed and replaced by Czech markings.

Exc.	V.G.	Good	Fair	Poor
350	300	275	225	175

French Occupation Model
Assembled from the Model 98k parts and identifiable by a hexagonal extension with a stacking rod protruding from it.

Exc.	V.G.	Good	Fair	Poor
275	225	200	150	100

Colombian Model 98
A Model 98a with a 29" barrel in .30-06 caliber.

Exc.	V.G.	Good	Fair	Poor
275	225	200	150	100

Iranian Model 98
Similar to the above, in 7.92mm caliber and also made with an 18" barrel. All markings in Farsi.

Courtesy Orville Reichert.

Exc.	V.G.	Good	Fair	Poor
275	225	200	150	100

Peruvian Model 1935 Rifle
Similar to the above, with a 23" barrel and in .30-06 caliber. The receiver ring stamped with a Peruvian crest.

Exc.	V.G.	Good	Fair	Poor
250	200	175	125	90

Polish Model 29

A Model 98a marked "F.B. Radom" together with the date of production. Barrel length 23.6", caliber 7.92mm.

Exc.	V.G.	Good	Fair	Poor
375	325	300	250	200

Standard Mauser Banner Rifle

A 7mm, 7.65mm or 7.92mm caliber bolt-action rifle with a 23.6" barrel and full-length stock. The receiver ring stamped with the Mauser Banner trademark.

Exc.	V.G.	Good	Fair	Poor
550	500	400	250	200

Mexican Model 1936

Similar to a Model 98a, with a 23.2" barrel in 7x57mm caliber with a full-length stock and 5-shot magazine. The receiver ring stamped with the Mexican code of arms.

Exc.	V.G.	Good	Fair	Poor
250	200	175	125	90

Spanish Model 43

Similar to the above, with a 23.6" barrel in 7.92mm caliber. Manufactured by La Coruna Arsenal.

Exc.	V.G.	Good	Fair	Poor
225	175	150	100	75

Early Sporting Rifle

A wide variety of commercial Model 98 Sporting Rifles were made, most of which had 23.5" ribbed barrels, open sights, 5-shot magazines, single or double set triggers, and either full or semi-pistolgrip stocks. While the following values are representative, it is suggested that prospective purchasers secure a qualified appraisal prior to acquisition.

Type A—Short Action

Exc.	V.G.	Good	Fair	Poor
3500	3000	2500	1500	1000

Type A—Medium Action

Exc.	V.G.	Good	Fair	Poor
2250	1750	1500	1250	1000

Type A—Long Action

Exc.	V.G.	Good	Fair	Poor
4000	3500	3000	2500	2000

Type B

Exc.	V.G.	Good	Fair	Poor
2500	2000	1500	1250	1000

Type K—21.65" Barrel

Exc.	V.G.	Good	Fair	Poor
4000	3500	3000	2250	1000

Type M—Full-length Stock, Spoon Bolt Handle

Exc.	V.G.	Good	Fair	Poor
3500	3000	2500	1500	1000

Type S—Full-length Stock, No Forend Cap

Exc.	V.G.	Good	Fair	Poor
3500	3000	2500	1500	1000

Model 1896 "Broomhandle Mauser Pistol"

Manufactured from 1896 to 1939, the Model 1896 Pistol was produced in a wide variety of styles as listed below. It is recommended that those considering the purchase of any of the following models should consult Breathed & Schroeder's System Mauser (Chicago, 1967) as it provides detailed descriptions and photographs of the various models. A correct, matching stock/holster will add approximately 40 percent to value of each category.

NOTE: Collectors and shooters should be aware that within the past several years a large quantity of Model 96 pistols have been imported into the United States from China.

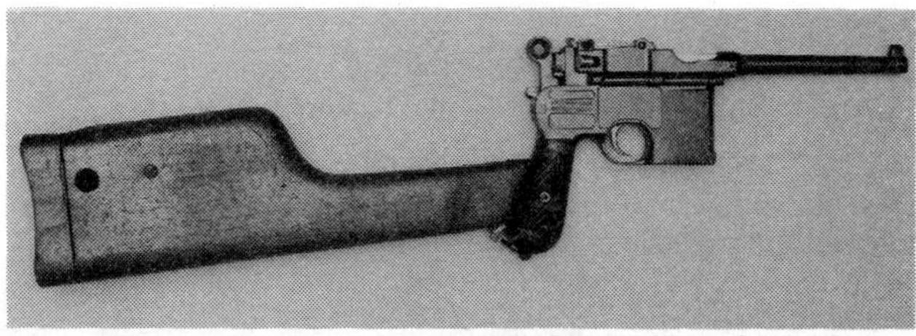

Courtesy Wallis & Wallis, Lewes, Sussex, England.

Six-Shot Step-Barrel Cone Hammer

A 7.63mm semi-automatic pistol with a 5.5" barrel, fixed rear sight and checkered walnut grips. Marked "Ruecklauf Pistole System Mauser, Oberndorf am/Neckar 1896." Fewer than 200 were manufactured. Too rare to price.

Twenty-Shot Step-Barrel Cone Hammer

As above, with a 20-shot extended magazine. Too rare to price.

System Mauser Cone Hammer

As above, with the upper sides of the hammer machined with concentric rings and the grips with 22 grooves. Magazine capacity 10 rounds.

Exc.	V.G.	Good	Fair	Poor
15000	12000	10000	8000	7000

Six-Shot Cone Hammer

Similar to the above, with a 4.75" barrel, fixed rear sight, 6-shot magazine and 21 groove grips. Marked "Waffenfabrik Mauser, Oberndorf A/N" over the chamber.

Exc.	V.G.	Good	Fair	Poor
11000	9000	6000	5000	3000

Twenty-Shot Cone Hammer

As above, with an extended magazine holding 20 cartridges.

Exc.	V.G.	Good	Fair	Poor
24000	20000	15000	10000	7000

Standard Cone Hammer

As above, with a 10-shot magazine and 23 groove grips.

Exc.	V.G.	Good	Fair	Poor
3200	2750	1800	1400	1000

Turkish Contract Cone Hammer

As above, but marked in Turkish script and bearing the crest of Sultan Abdul-Hamid II on the frame. Approximately 1,000 were made.

Exc.	V.G.	Good	Fair	Poor
7500	6500	5000	3000	2000

Early Transitional Large Ring Hammer

As above, but the upper section of the hammer pierced with a hole.

Exc.	V.G.	Good	Fair	Poor
3200	2400	1850	1150	800

Model 1899 Flat Side—Italian Contract

Similar to the above, with a 5.5" barrel, adjustable rear sight and the frame sides milled flat. Marked "Pistole Automatiche Modello 1899." Approximately 5,000 were manufactured in 1899.

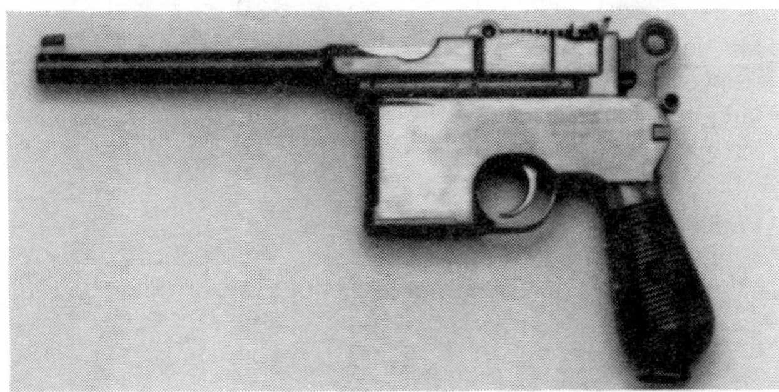

Courtesy Butterfield & Butterfield, San Francisco, California.

Exc.	V.G.	Good	Fair	Poor
3500	2750	1500	700	500

Early Flat Side

Similar to the above, but without the Italian markings.

Exc.	V.G.	Good	Fair	Poor
2750	2450	1500	1000	750

Late Flat Side

Similar to the above, with a different adjustable rear sight and often marked with dealer's names such as "Von Lengerke & Detmold, New York".

Exc.	V.G.	Good	Fair	Poor
2500	2000	1500	1000	750

Flat Side Bolo

Similar to the above, but with a 3.9" barrel, fixed sights and checkered walnut grips.

Exc.	V.G.	Good	Fair	Poor
2700	2250	1850	1300	1000

Early Large Ring Hammer Bolo

As above, with a milled frame, adjustable rear sight and hard rubber grips cast with a floral pattern. 10-shot magazine.

Exc.	V.G.	Good	Fair	Poor
3400	3000	1600	1000	650

Shallow-Milled Panel Model

Similar to the above, with a 5.5" barrel and either 23 groove walnut or checkered hard rubber grips.

Exc.	V.G.	Good	Fair	Poor
2400	1700	1000	750	500

Deep-Milled Panel Model

As above, with deeper milled panels on the sides of the receiver.

Exc.	V.G.	Good	Fair	Poor
2500	2000	1500	1000	750

Late Large Ring Hammer Bolo

Similar to the Early Large Ring Hammer Bolo, but with the late style adjustable rear sight.

Exc.	V.G.	Good	Fair	Poor
2500	2000	1500	1000	750

Early Small Hammer Model, Transitional

The Model 96 with the hammer having a small diameter hole in the hammer and a 5.5" barrel. The grips with 34 grooves.

Exc.	V.G.	Good	Fair	Poor
2000	1850	1000	750	500

Early Small Hammer Bolo Model

As above, with a 3.9" barrel and hard rubber grips cast with a floral pattern.

Exc.	V.G.	Good	Fair	Poor
2400	1750	1400	950	600

Six-Shot Small Hammer Model

As above, with 27 groove walnut grips.

Exc.	V.G.	Good	Fair	Poor
6750	5500	4000	2250	1600

Standard Prewar Commercial

A Model 96 with a 5.5" barrel, late style adjustable rear sight and either 34 groove walnut grips or checkered hard rubber grips. Often found with dealers markings such as "Von Lengerke & Detmold."

Exc.	V.G.	Good	Fair	Poor
1350	1000	750	450	300

Mauser Banner Model

As above, with the Mauser Banner trademark and 32 goove walnut grips. Approximately 10,000 were manufactured.

Exc.	V.G.	Good	Fair	Poor
3000	2800	1500	800	600

Persian Contract

As above, with Persian issuance marks. Prospective purchasers should secure a qualified appraisal prior to acquisition.

Exc.	V.G.	Good	Fair	Poor
3700	3000	2250	1400	1000

9mm Export Model

As above, in 9mm Mauser with 34 goove walnut grips.

Exc.	V.G.	Good	Fair	Poor
2500	2250	1500	1000	700

Standard Wartime Commercial

Identical to the Prewar Commercial Model 96, except that it has 30 groove walnut grips and the rear of the hammer is stamped "NS" for new safety.

Exc.	V.G.	Good	Fair	Poor
1200	850	600	500	350

9mm Parabellum Military Contract

As above, in 9mm Parabellum caliber with 24 groove grips, stamped with a large "9" filled with red paint.

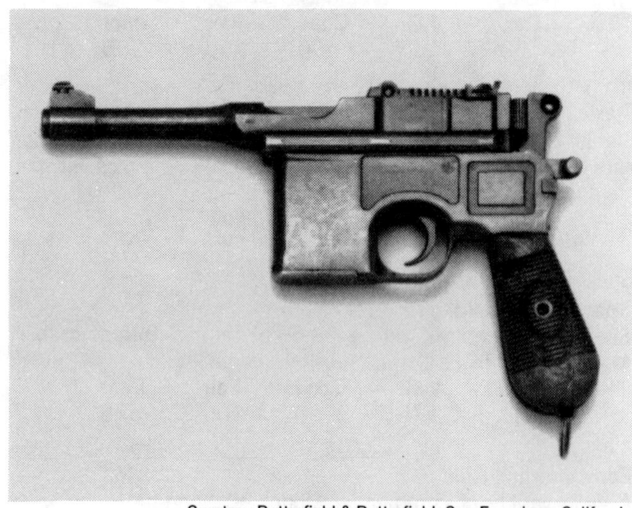

Courtesy Butterfield & Butterfield, San Francisco, California.

Exc.	V.G.	Good	Fair	Poor
1400	1100	1000	600	450

1920 Rework

A Model 96 modified to a barrel length of 3.9" and in 7.63mm Mauser or 9mm Parabellum caliber. Often encountered with police markings.

Exc.	V.G.	Good	Fair	Poor
1000	750	500	400	350

Luger Barrelled 1920 Rework

Similar to the above, but fitted with a Luger barrel of 4" in length. 23 groove walnut grips and of 9mm caliber.

Exc.	V.G.	Good	Fair	Poor
1250	1000	750	500	450

French Gendarme Model

A standard Model 96 fitted with a 3.9" barrel and checkered hard rubber grips. Although reputed to have been made under a French contract, no record of that has been found to date.

Exc.	V.G.	Good	Fair	Poor
2800	2100	1300	800	600

Early Postwar Bolo Model

A Model 96 in 7.63mm caliber with a 2.9" barrel, adjustable rear sight and 22 groove walnut grips.

Exc.	V.G.	Good	Fair	Poor
2000	1500	1200	650	400

Late Postwar Bolo Model

As above, with the Mauser Banner trademark stamped on the left rear panel.

Exc.	V.G.	Good	Fair	Poor
1750	1500	1000	750	500

Early Model 1930

A 7.63mm caliber Model 96 with a 5.2" stepped barrel, 12 groove walnut grips and late style safety.

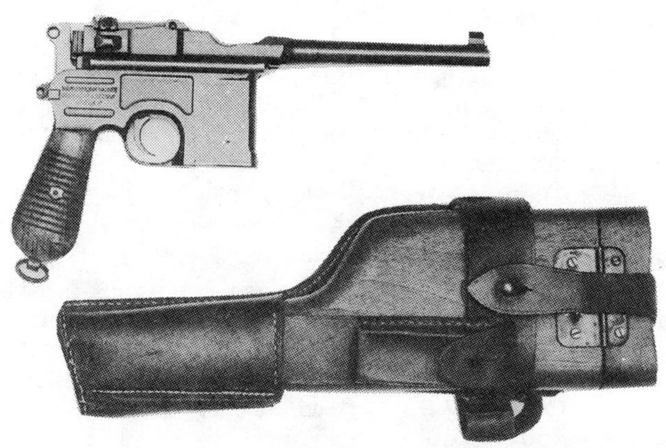

Courtesy Wallis & Wallis, Lewes, Sussex, England.

Exc.	V.G.	Good	Fair	Poor
2300	1800	1200	800	500

Late Model 1930

Identical to the above, except for solid receiver rails.

Exc.	V.G.	Good	Fair	Poor
2100	1600	1000	700	400

Model 1930 Removable Magazine

Similar to the above, but with a detachable magazine. Prospective purchasers should secure a qualified appraisal prior to acquisition. Too rare to price.

Cone Hammer Flat Side Carbine

A 7.63mm caliber carbine with an 11.75" barrel, early adjustable sight, flat frame and integral pistol grips/buttstock. Prospective purchasers should secure a qualified appraisal prior to acquisition. Too rare to price.

Large Ring Hammer Transitional Carbine

Similar to the above, with milled frame panels. Prospective purchasers should secure a qualified appraisal prior to acquisition.

Exc.	V.G.	Good	Fair	Poor
18500	16000	11000	5000	3000

Large Ring Hammer Carbine

Similar to the above, with a 14.5" barrel. Prospective purchasers should secure a qualified appraisal prior to acquisition.

Exc.	V.G.	Good	Fair	Poor
16000	13500	8500	4000	3000

Small Ring Hammer Carbine

Similar to the above, with the hammer having a smaller diameter hole at its tip. Prospective purchasers should secure a qualified appraisal prior to acquisition.

Exc.	V.G.	Good	Fair	Poor
18500	16000	11000	5000	3000

Within the past several years, a large quantity of Model 96 pistols exported to or made in China have been imported into the United States.

Chinese Marked, Handmade Copies

Very crude copies of the Model 96 and unsafe to fire.

Exc.	V.G.	Good	Fair	Poor
500	400	350	250	175

Taku-Naval Dockyard Model

Approximately 6,000 copies of the Model 96 were made at the Taku-Naval Dockyard. Values listed below include a correct shoulder stock/holder.

Exc.	V.G.	Good	Fair	Poor
1800	950	750	500	400

Shansei Arsenal Model

Approximately 8,000 Model 96 pistols were manufactured in .45 ACP caliber.

Exc.	V.G.	Good	Fair	Poor
5500	3000	2250	1500	1300

Copies of the Model 96 were made by Unceta (Astra) and Zulaica y Cia (Royal) and marketed by the firm of Beistegui Hermanos. These copies are covered in their own sections of this text.

Model 1910

A 6.35mm caliber semi-automatic pistol with a 3" barrel, 9-shot magazine and either checkered walnut or hard rubber grips. The slide marked "Waffenfabrik Mauser A.-G. Oberndorf A.N. Mauser's Patent." Manufactured between 1910 and 1934.

Exc.	V.G.	Good	Fair	Poor
350	275	225	150	100

Model 1914

A 7.65mm caliber semi-automatic pistol with a 3.5" barrel, fixed sights, and wrap-around walnut grips. The slide marked "Waffenfabrik Mauser A.G. Oberndorf A.N. Mauser's Patent" on the slide. The frame has the Mauser Banner stamped on its left side. Manufactured between 1914 and 1934.

Courtesy Butterfield & Butterfield, San Francisco, California.

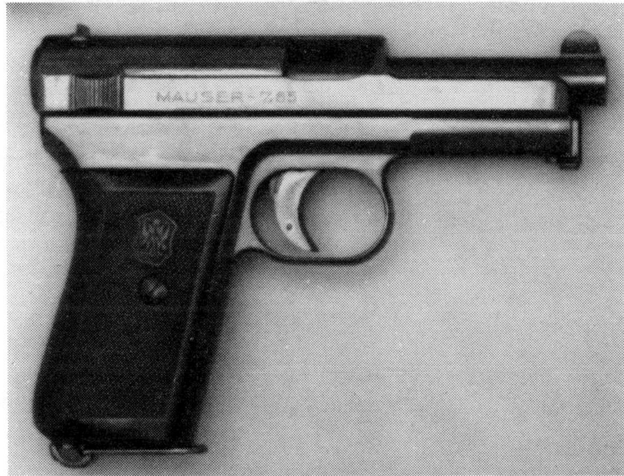

Courtesy Wallis & Wallis, Lewes, Sussex, England.

Exc.	V.G.	Good	Fair	Poor
400	275	225	150	100

WTP Model I Vest Pocket Pistol

A 6.35mm semi-automatic pistol with a 2.5" barrel, 6-shot magazine and either plastic or hard rubber grips bearing the Mauser Banner. The slide marked "Mauser-Werke A.G. Oberndorf A.N." Manufactured between 1922 and 1937.

Exc.	V.G.	Good	Fair	Poor
500	400	275	200	150

WTP Model II Vest Pocket Pistol

Similar to the above, with a 2" barrel. Manufactured between 1938 and 1940.

Exc.	V.G.	Good	Fair	Poor
525	425	300	225	150

Model 1934

Similar to the Model 1914, with the slide marked "Mauser-Werke A.G. Oberndorf A.N." It has the Mauser Banner stamped on the frame. The reverse side is marked with the caliber and "D.R.P. u A.P." Manufactured between 1934 and 1939. Those with Nazi Waffenamt markings are worth approximately 20 percent more than the values listed below. Those marked with an eagle over the letter "M" are worth approximately 100% more than the values listed below.

Courtesy Orville Reichert.

Courtesy Orville Reichert.

Exc.	V.G.	Good	Fair	Poor
400	275	225	150	100

Model HSC

A 7.65mm or 9mm short caliber double-action semi-automatic pistol with a 3.4" barrel, 7- or 8-shot magazine and fixed sights. Introduced in 1938 and produced in the variations listed below.

Courtesy Orville Reichert.

Low Grip Screw Model

As above, with screws which attach the grip located near the bottom of the grip. Highly-polished blue, checkered walnut grips and the early address without the lines and has the Eagle N proof. Some have been observed with Nazi Kreigsmarine markings. Approximately 2,000 were manufactured.

Exc.	V.G.	Good	Fair	Poor
2500	2000	1200	750	650

Early Commercial Model

A highly-polished blued finish, checkered walnut grips, the standard Mauser address on the slide, and the Eagle N proofmark. The floorplate of the magazine stamped with the Mauser Banner.

Exc.	V.G.	Good	Fair	Poor
450	400	350	175	125

Transition Model

As above, but not as highly finished.

Exc.	V.G.	Good	Fair	Poor
400	350	300	150	100

Early Nazi Army Model

Highly polished with Waffenamt No. 135 or 655 markings. Checkered walnut grips. Acceptance marks are located on the left side of the triggerguard.

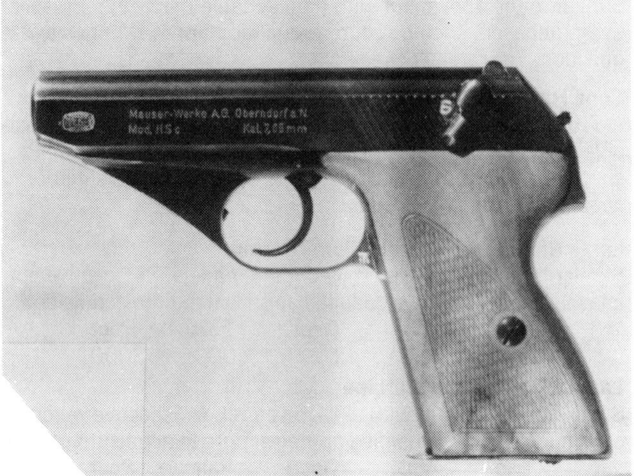

Courtesy Orville Reichert.

Exc.	V.G.	Good	Fair	Poor
425	350	300	200	125

Late Nazi Army Model

Blued or parkerized, with walnut or plastic grips, and the 135 acceptance mark only. It also has the Eagle N proof.

Exc.	V.G.	Good	Fair	Poor
375	300	250	150	100

Early Nazi Navy Model

Highly polished with checkered walnut grips and the eagle over "M" marking on the front grip strap.

Exc.	V.G.	Good	Fair	Poor
850	700	550	400	300

Wartime Nazi Navy Model

Similar to the above, with the navy acceptance mark on the side of the triggerguard. Blued, with either checkered walnut or plastic grips. It has the standard Mauser address and Banner and also the Eagle N proof.

Exc.	V.G.	Good	Fair	Poor
700	600	500	400	200

Early Nazi Police Model

Identical to the Early Commercial Model with an eagle over "L" mark on the left side of the triggerguard.

Courtesy Orville Reichert.

Exc.	V.G.	Good	Fair	Poor
450	400	350	250	175

Wartime Nazi Police Model
As above, with a 3 line Mauser address.

Exc.	V.G.	Good	Fair	Poor
450	400	350	250	175

Wartime Commercial Model
As above, without acceptance markings on the triggerguard.

Exc.	V.G.	Good	Fair	Poor
425	350	300	200	125

French Manufactured Model
Blued or parkerized with walnut or plastic grips and the triggerguard marked on the left side with the monogram "MR".

Exc.	V.G.	Good	Fair	Poor
325	275	225	150	100

Late Mauser Production Model
Manufactured from 1968 to 1981, this model was almost identical to the early Commercial Model.

Exc.	V.G.	Good	Fair	Poor
325	275	225	150	100

Interarms Import Models
As above, but made by Gamba in Italy and sold by Interarms of Alexandria, Virginia from 1983 to 1985.

Exc.	V.G.	Good	Fair	Poor
275	250	200	150	100

Mauser Lugers
P 08 semi-automatic pistols manufactured by Mauser are located in the Luger section of this text.

Mauser rifles are currently imported into the U.S.A. by the firm of KDF, Inc., in Seguin, Texas.

Model 2000
A .270, .308, or the .30-06 caliber bolt-action rifle with a 24" barrel, open sights and a 5-shot magazine. Blued, with a checkered walnut stock. Manufactured between 1969 and 1971.

Exc.	V.G.	Good	Fair	Poor
350	300	250	200	150

Model 3000
As above, with a 22" barrel, no sights and Monte Carlo-style stock. Manufactured from 1971 to 1974.

Exc.	V.G.	Good	Fair	Poor
450	400	350	300	250

Model 3000 Magnum
As above, in 7mm Rem. Mag., .300 Win. Mag. and the .375 H&H Mag. caliber with a 26" barrel and a 3-shot integral magazine. Blued, with a checkered walnut stock.

Exc.	V.G.	Good	Fair	Poor
500	450	400	350	300

Model 4000
Similar to the Model 3000, but in .222 or .223 caliber with folding open sights.

Exc.	V.G.	Good	Fair	Poor
400	350	300	250	200

Model 225
A .243 to .300 Weatherby Magnum caliber bolt-action rifle with a 24" or 26" barrel, no sights, adjustable trigger or 3- or 5-shot magazine. Blued with a walnut stock.

NIB	Exc.	V.G.	Good	Fair	Poor
1400	1250	1000	750	600	500

Model ES340
A .22 caliber single shot bolt-action rifle with a 25.5" barrel, open sights and walnut stock. Manufactured before WWII.

Exc.	V.G.	Good	Fair	Poor
300	250	225	175	125

Model DSM34
Similar to the above, with a 25" barrel and full-length walnut stock. Manufactured prior to WWII.

Exc.	V.G.	Good	Fair	Poor
325	275	250	200	150

Model MS420B
Similar to the above, with a 25" barrel and 5-shot magazine. Manufactured before WWII.

Exc.	V.G.	Good	Fair	Poor
375	325	300	275	200

Model ES350
A .22 caliber single shot bolt-action rifle with a 27.5" barrel and checkered pistol grip walnut stock. Manufactured before WWII.

Exc.	V.G.	Good	Fair	Poor
450	400	375	350	275

Model M410
Similar to the above, with a 23.5" barrel and 5-shot magazine. Manufactured before WWII.

Exc.	V.G.	Good	Fair	Poor
375	325	300	275	200

Model M420
As above, with a 25.5" barrel.

Exc.	V.G.	Good	Fair	Poor
375	325	300	275	200

Model EN310
A .22 caliber single shot bolt-action rifle with a 19.75" barrel, open sights and plain walnut stock. Manufactured before WWII.

Exc.	V.G.	Good	Fair	Poor
250	225	200	150	100

Model EL320
As above, with a 23.5" barrel and checkered walnut stock.

Exc.	V.G.	Good	Fair	Poor
275	250	225	175	125

Model KKW
A .22 caliber single shot bolt-action rifle with a 26" barrel, ladder rear sight and full-length walnut stock. Manufactured prior to WWII.

Exc.	V.G.	Good	Fair	Poor
400	350	300	225	150

Model MS350B
A .22 caliber bolt-action rifle with a 26.75" barrel, adjustable rear sight and 5-shot magazine. Blued with a walnut stock.

Exc.	V.G.	Good	Fair	Poor
475	400	350	275	200

Model ES340B

Similar to the above, but in single shot form.

Exc.	V.G.	Good	Fair	Poor
375	300	250	175	100

Model MM410BN

A .22 caliber bolt-action rifle with a 23.5" barrel, adjustable sights and 5-shot magazine. Blued with a walnut stock.

Exc.	V.G.	Good	Fair	Poor
400	350	300	200	125

Model MS420B

As above, with a 26.75" barrel and target style stock.

Exc.	V.G.	Good	Fair	Poor
400	350	300	200	125

CURRENTLY IMPORTED MAUSER RIFLES AND PISTOLS

Importer—Precision Imports
San Antonio, Texas

Model 107

This is a bolt action rifle chambered for the .22 Long Rifle. Barrel length is 21.6" and box magazine has a 5-shot capacity. The beechwood checkered Monte Carlo stock is full size with pistol grip, plastic butt plate. The rear sight is adjustable. Metal finish is blue. Weighs about 5 lbs.

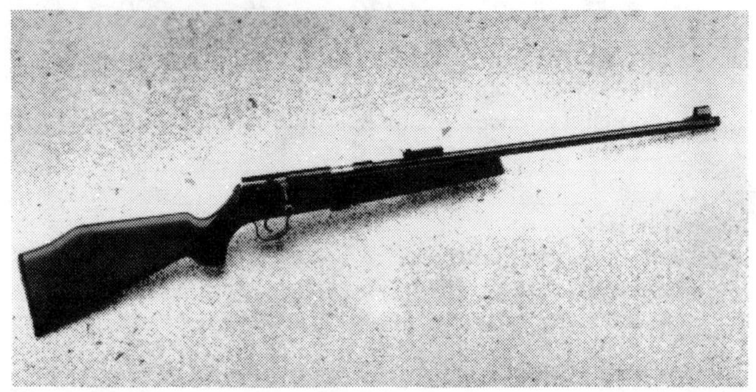

NIB	Exc.	V.G.	Good	Fair	Poor
265	225	180	150	125	100

Model 201 Standard

This model features a 21" medium heavy free-floating barrel. The receiver accepts all rail mounts and is also drilled and tapped for scope mount. Magazine capacity is 5-shot. Chambered for .22 Long Rifle or .22 WMR cartridge. The beechwood stock is hand checkered with plastic butt plate. The Monte Carlo stock is fitted with cheekpiece. Weighs about 6.5 lbs.

NIB	Exc.	V.G.	Good	Fair	Poor
390	370	325	275	225	175

Model 201 Luxus

Same as above but features a European walnut stock with rosewood forend, hand checkering, rubber butt pad, and 1" quick disconnect sling swivels. Available with or without sights.

NIB	Exc.	V.G.	Good	Fair	Poor
550	475	400	350	300	200

Model 66 Standard

This is a centerfire bolt action rifle fitted with a European Walnut hand checkered oil finish stock. Stock is half stock design. Rosewood firends and pistol grips caps are standard. Fitted with rubber recoil pad and 1" quick disconnect sling swivels. Barrel are interchangeable on this model. Barrels with standard calibers is 24" and approximate weight is 7.5 lbs. Standard calibers are: .243 Win., .270, .308, .30-06, 5.6x57, 6.5x57, 7.64, and 9.3x62.

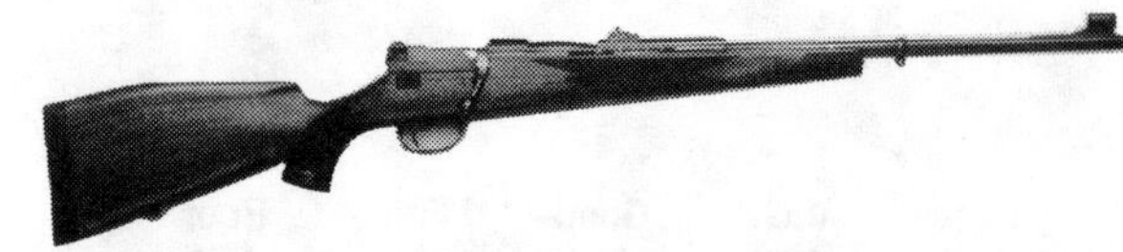

NIB	Exc.	V.G.	Good	Fair	Poor
1400	1150	850	700	550	350

Model 66 Magnum

Same as above but chambered for 7mm Re. Mag., .300 and .338 Win. Mag., 6.5x68, 8x86S, 9.3x64. Fitted with a 26" barrel and weighs about 7.9 lb.

NIB	Exc.	V.G.	Good	Fair	Poor
1500	1250	950	800	600	400

Model 66 Safari

Same as above but chambered for .375 H&H and .458 Win. Mag. Fitted with a 26" barrel and weighs about 9.3 lb.

NIB	Exc.	V.G.	Good	Fair	Poor
1650	1400	1100	850	650	400

Model 66 Stuzen

Same as the Standard Model 66 but fitted with a full stock. Barrel length is 21" and calibers are same as Standard. Weighs about 7.5 lb.

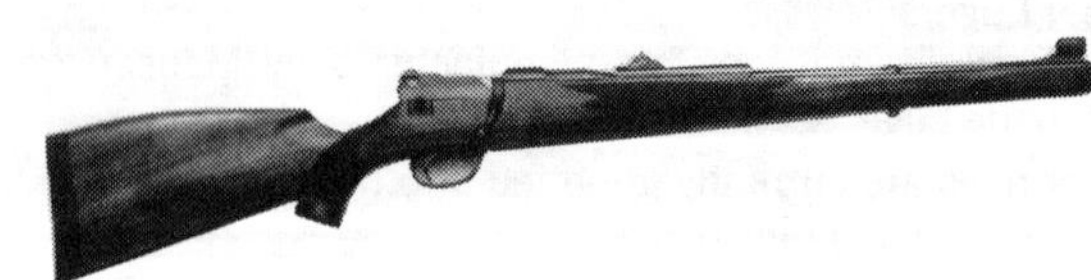

NIB	Exc.	V.G.	Good	Fair	Poor
1500	1250	950	800	600	400

Model 86 SR

Introduced in 1993 this bolt action .308 is sometimes referred to as the Specialty Rifle. Fitted with a laminated wood and special match thumb hole stock or fiberglass stock with adjustable cheekpiece. Stock has rail in forearm and an adjustable recoil pad. Magazine capacity is 9 rounds. Finish is a non-glare blue. The barrel length with muzzle brake is 28.8". Many special features are found on this rifle from adjustable trigger weight to silent safety. Mauser offers many options on this rifle as well that will effect the price. Weight is approximately 11 lb.

NIB	Exc.	V.G.	Good	Fair	Poor
3300	2950	2500	1750	1250	750

Model 99 Standard

This model is a bolt action centerfire sporting rifle. It is offered with two stock designs: a classic with straight oil finish stock or high luster with cheekpiece and schnabel forend and Monte Carlo with rosewood forend tip and pistol grip cap. Chambered for standard calibers: .243, .25-06, .270, .308, .30-06, 5.6x57, 6.5x57, 7x57, 7x64. Barrel length is 24". Weight about 8 lb.

NIB	Exc.	V.G.	Good	Fair	Poor
900	700	600	500	400	300

Model 99 Magnum

Same as above but chambered for magnum calibers: 7mm Rem. Mag., .257 Wby., .270 Wby., .300 Wby., .300 and .338 Win. Mag., 8x68S, and 9.3x64. Fitted with 26" barrel. Weighs about 8 lb.

NIB	Exc.	V.G.	Good	Fair	Poor
950	750	650	550	400	300

Model 80 SA

This single action semi-automatic pistol is based on the Browning HI-Power design. Chambered for the 9mm Para cartridge it has a barrel length of 4.66" and a magazine capacity of 14 rounds. Weighs approximately 35 oz.

NIB	Exc.	V.G.	Good	Fair	Poor
300	275	225	175	125	100

Model Compact DA

Same as above but double action trigger and shorter barrel: 4.13". Weighs approximately 33 oz.

NIB	Exc.	V.G.	Good	Fair	Poor
340	320	250	175	125	100

Model 90 DA

Similar to the Model 80 but with a double action trigger.

NIB	Exc.	V.G.	Good	Fair	Poor
310	285	235	175	125	100

MAVERICK ARMS, INC.

Eagle Pass, Texas

Model 88

A 12 gauge Magnum slide action shotgun with 28" or 30" barrels, annodized receiver and composition stock. Introduced in 1989.

NIB	Exc.	V.G.	Good	Fair	Poor
175	150	125	100	75	50

MAYNARD/PERRY

Keen, Walker & Co.
Danville, Virginia

Brass Framed Carbine

Overall length 40"; barrel length 22.5"; caliber .54. Browned, blued barrel, brass frame and walnut stock. Manufactured in 1861 and 1862. Prospective purchasers are advised to secure a qualified appraisal prior to acquisition.

Exc.	V.G.	Good	Fair	Poor
6500	5000	3500	1500	1000

MCMILLAN, G. & CO. INC.

Phoenix, Arizona

Competition Model

A custom order bolt-action rifle in .308, 7mm/08, and the .300 Winchester Magnum caliber with the barrel length, stock type, and dimensions to the customer's specifications. Introduced in 1988.

NIB	Exc.	V.G.	Good	Fair	Poor
1700	1500	1150	800	600	300

Model 86 Snipers Rifle

A custom order rifle in .308 Winchester or the .300 Winchester Magnum calibers with a synthetic stock and a choice of scope systems. Introduced in 1988.

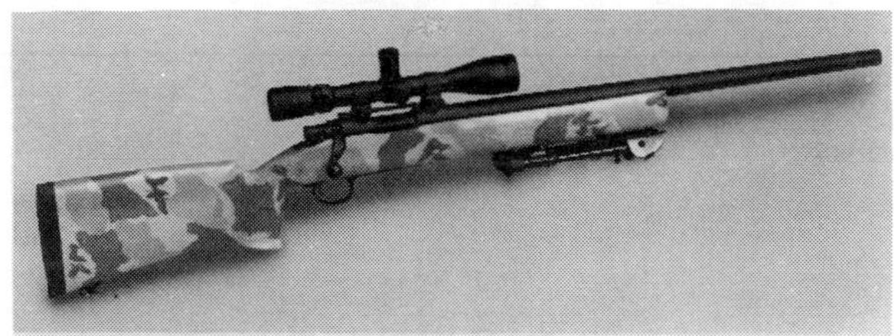

NIB	Exc.	V.G.	Good	Fair	Poor
1350	1100	900	600	400	200

Model 86 System

As above, with the Ultra scope, mounting system, bipod, and fitted case. Introduced in 1988.

NIB	Exc.	V.G.	Good	Fair	Poor
2150	1850	1500	1100	550	250

Model 87 Long Range Snipers Rifle

A large stainless steel, single shot bolt-action rifle in .50 BMG caliber with a 29" barrel having an integral muzzle brake. Camouflaged synthetic stock. Weight 21 lbs. Accurate to 1,500 meters. Introduced in 1988.

NIB	Exc.	V.G.	Good	Fair	Poor
2700	2200	1800	1200	600	250

Model 87 System

As above, with a bipod and a 20X Ultra scope, mounting system and a fitted case. Introduced in 1988.

NIB	Exc.	V.G.	Good	Fair	Poor
3350	2700	2100	1500	900	400

Signature Model

A bolt-action sporting rifle manufactrured in a variety of calibers up to .375 Holland & Holland with a 22" or 24" stainless barrel, composition stock and either 3- or 4-shot magazine. Introduced in 1988.

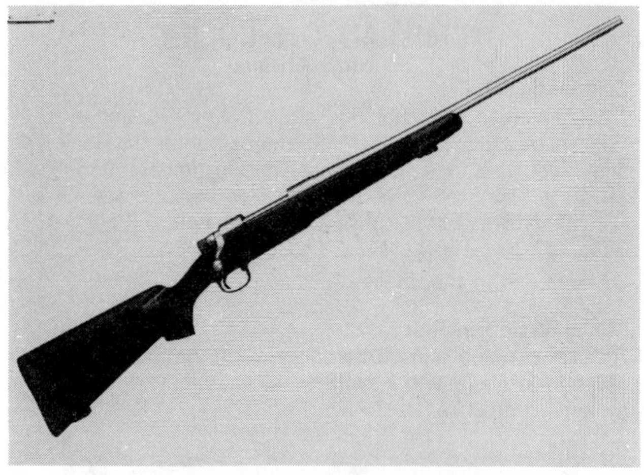

NIB	Exc.	V.G.	Good	Fair	Poor
2200	1750	1250	800	600	300

MEAD & ADRIANCE

St. Louis, Missouri

This company retailed a variety of single shot percussion pistols most of which were manufactured by Ethan Allen of Grafton, Massachusetts. In general, the value for pistols marked "Mead & Adriance" are as follows:

Exc.	V.G.	Good	Fair	Poor
700	600	500	400	300

MEIJA

SEE—Japan State

MENDENHALL, JONES & GARDNER

Greensboro, North Carolina

Muzzle Loading Rifle

A .58 caliber percussion rifle with a 33" barrel and full-length walnut stock secured by two barrel bands. Finished in the white with the lock marked "M.J.&G.,N.C." Prospective purchasers should secure a qualified appraisal prior to acquisition.

Exc.	V.G.	Good	Fair	Poor
7500	6000	5000	3500	2250

MENZ, AUGUST

Suhl, Germany

Established prior to WWI to manufacture Beholla pistols, this company was purchased by Lignose in 1937.

Menta

Identical to the Beholla which is listed separately.

Exc.	V.G.	Good	Fair	Poor
300	250	200	150	100

Liliput

A 4.25mm caliber semi-automatic pistol with a 2" barrel and 6-shot magazine. Overall length 3.5", weight 10 ounces. The slide marked "Liliput Kal. 4.25". Also manufactured in 6.35mm caliber. These pistols have an overall length of 4". Blued with composition grips.

Exc.	V.G.	Good	Fair	Poor
350	300	250	200	125

Menz Model II

As above in 7.65mm caliber.

Exc.	V.G.	Good	Fair	Poor
350	300	250	200	125

Menz VP Model

Similar to the Model 2, but in 6.35mm caliber with a 2.35" barrel, 6-shot magazine and fitted with a cocking indicator.

Exc.	V.G.	Good	Fair	Poor
350	300	250	200	125

Model III

A total redesign. It has a closed-top slide, and the quality is much better than the previous Menz pistols. It has a fixed barrel and is similar to the Model 1910 Browning with an exposed hammer. This model was produced until 1937.

Exc.	V.G.	Good	Fair	Poor
400	350	300	250	150

MERCURY

Liege, Belgium

Model 622 VP

A .22 caliber semi-automatic rifle with a 20" barrel, open sights and 7-shot magazine. Blued with a walnut stock. Manufactured by Robar & Son.

Exc.	V.G.	Good	Fair	Poor
300	275	250	200	125

MERCURY

Eibar, Spain

Double Barreled Shotgun

A 10, 12 or 20 gauge Magnum boxlock double-barrel shotgun with 28" or 32" barrels, double triggers and extractors. Blued with a walnut stock.

10 Gauge—Add 25%.

Exc.	V.G.	Good	Fair	Poor
325	250	225	175	125

MERKEL, GEBRUDER

Suhl, Germany
Importer—GSI
Trussville, Alabama

An Introduction to Merkel Brother's Guns
by Dan Sheil

Merkel Brothers shotgun and rifle makers began production around the turn of the century in Suhl, Germany. Merkel made a number of different models but the company was most well known for its Over/Under shotgun. It also made bolt action rifles, side by side double express rifles, falling block single shot rifles, side by side shotguns, drillings, and just about anything in the way of firearms its customer's desired.

Perhaps the company's greatest productive era fell between the end of World War I and the 1950's. During the 1930's most of the live pigeon shoots were won with Merkel shotguns. However, there seems to be a difference of opinion about when Merkel built its best quality guns. This is not an easy question to answer. Most shooters and collectors feel that pre-World War II guns are the best examples of Merkel craftsmanship. But, in my opinion, some of the finest Merkels I have seen were produced immediately after World War II. Outstanding examples of Merkel's quality continue to appear up to the construction of the Berlin Wall in 1961.

Another area of controversy is the high grade Merkel 300 series shotgun. Many have compared this gun to the Italian and British makers and believe it is a mass produced gun. This is not the case because all Merkel shotguns are handcrafted and as far as I know barrels will not interchange unless they are supplied with the gun from the factory. While the 100 and 200 series guns may be mass produced the 300 series is not, and that is easy to determine by looking at the serial number together with the date stamped on the barrel. Very few 300 series guns were produced in a given period.

In terms of durability, strength and reliability, there is not an over and under shotgun that is built as strong as the Merkel. It has two Kersten style locking lugs on the upper barrel which fit into the face of the receiver while the bottom has two under lugs which give the gun a rugged four position locking system. I don't think I have ever heard of a Merkel being sent back to the gunmaker or a gunsmith to have the frame tightened. It just is not necessary; the guns will not shoot loose.

With respect to value, the Merkel over and under guns have been sleepers in the gun industry for a number of years. Until recently they have not brought the price that they deserve. I am specifically talking about the 300 series; the 303 Luxus and the 304. Generally speaking all of the special order Merkel over and under shotguns have done well. I think the shooting public will begin to recognize the quality and craftsmanship built into every one of these fine guns.

One last comment regarding special order Merkel's and the company's reputation for building just about anything the customer wanted. It is impossible to cover all of the variations that the company produced in it's long history, but the buyer should be aware that he may encounter some different and uncataloged Merkels along the way.

As of August, 1993 Merkel Brothers declared bankruptcy. There may be a purchase of inventory and assets by another company in the future with the hope of rebuilding the company and producing these fine guns once again.

Editors Comment: The following Merkel gun prices are based on either one or two factors. First, they are no longer in production or second that the guns were built prior to the Berlin Wall which generally bring a premium.

Merkel Side by Side Shotguns

Model 117/117E

Offered in 12 and 16 gauge with various barrel lengths, this model featured a box lock action with double triggers and extractors. Ejectors were available under the "E" designation. The box lock action body was scrupled at the rear with fine line scroll engraving.

Exc.	V.G.	Good	Fair	Poor
3000	2500	1500	1000	500

Model 118/118E

Also offered in 12 and 16 gauge this model is similar to above model with slightly more engraving and better wood. This model also has some engraving coverage on the breech end of the barrels.

Exc.	V.G.	Good	Fair	Poor
3500	2750	1700	1200	650

Model 124/125

Similar to the above models but supplied with extractors for the Model 124 and ejectors for the Model 125. Both models have more engraving coverage with game scenes. Finer checkering and fancy wood is seen on this model.

Model 124

Exc.	V.G.	Good	Fair	Poor
3900	3500	2000	1500	700

Model 125

Exc.	V.G.	Good	Fair	Poor
4500	3750	3000	2000	1000

Model 170

This model was offered in 12 gauge only with automatic ejectors. The box lock action was engraved with fine full coverage scroll.

Exc.	V.G.	Good	Fair	Poor
5000	4000	3200	2500	1200

Model 130

This was one of Merkel's highest side by side shotguns. It featured a sidelock action, extra fancy wood, fine line checkering, and full coverage game scene engraving.

Exc.	V.G.	Good	Fair	Poor
15000	12000	7500	4500	2500

Model 126

Similar to the Model 130 but fitted with .

Exc.	V.G.	Good	Fair	Poor
15000	12000	7500	4500	2500

Model 127

This model was Merkel's highest and finest side by side shotgun. The sidelock action featured full coverage fine line scroll engraving of the best quality.

Exc.	V.G.	Good	Fair	Poor
21000	16000	12000	6000	4000

Merkel Side By Side Double Rifles

Model 128E

This side by side rifle is a droplock design with scroll and game scene engraving. The wood is Cirassisian walnut with fine line checkering. Offered in a variety of European calibers. Because of the rarity and uniqueness of each rifle a qualified appraisal should be sought prior to a sale.

Model 132E

Similar to the Model 128E but with full coverage scroll engraving and fancy wood. This model also should have an expert appraisal done prior to a sale.

Merkel Over and Under Shotguns

Model 102E

This was Merkel's standard over and under boxlock model. Offered in 12 gauge with 28" barrels or 16 gauge with 26" barrels. Both are fitted with double triggers, semi-pistol grip, and ejectors.

Exc.	V.G.	Good	Fair	Poor
1600	1200	1000	650	400

Model 103E

Similar to the standard but with more English scroll engraving coverage and better wood. This model was offered in 12, 16, and 20 gauge.

Exc.	V.G.	Good	Fair	Poor
2200	1500	1200	950	600

Model 204E

This model is essentially a Model 203E with finer engraving. This model was discontinued prior to 1939.

Exc.	V.G.	Good	Fair	Poor
6000	4500	3000	2200	1750

Model 301E

This is a boxlock model with scrupled action chambered for the 12, 16, 20, 24, 28, and 32 gauge. The engraving is an English scroll and the trigger guard is horn. Double triggers and pistol grip are standard. This model was produced prior to 1939.

Exc.	V.G.	Good	Fair	Poor
4500	4000	2500	2000	1850

Model 302E

Similar to the Model 301E but fitted with side plates. The full coverage engraving features game scenes. This model produced prior to World War II.

Exc.	V.G.	Good	Fair	Poor
12000	10000	7500	4000	2000

Model 303 Luxus

This over and under Merkel is custom built to the customer's specifications. Each gun is unique and should be appraised by a knowledgeable individual who is familiar with quality European shotguns.

Model 304E

This pre-war model was the highest grade in Merkel's over and under shotgun line. A side lock gun with full coverage scroll engraving of the highest quality. Fine line checkering and extra fancy wood make this gun difficult to appraise due to its rarity. A qualified appraisal before a sale is highly recommended.

Model 400E

A higher grade Over/Under fitted with Kersten crossbolt, finer engraving, and fancy wood. Merkel offered this grade in 12, 16, 20, 24, 28, and 32 gauge with choice of barrel lengths. This model was produced prior to 1939.

Exc.	V.G.	Good	Fair	Poor
1800	1300	1000	600	400

Model 401E

Similar to the model above but with full coverage game scene engraving.

Exc.	V.G.	Good	Fair	Poor
2500	1850	1200	800	600

Merkel Rifle/Shotgun Combinations

Model 410E

Merkel's base boxlock model with ejectors. Produced prior to World War II.

Exc.	V.G.	Good	Fair	Poor
2250	1800	1200	750	500

Model 411E

Similar to the above but with the addition of a small coverage of scroll engraving.

Exc.	V.G.	Good	Fair	Poor
2500	2000	1500	1000	600

Model 311E

This combination gun has additional English scroll engraving.

Exc.	V.G.	Good	Fair	Poor
7900	6500	5000	2250	1700

Model 312E

This model is fitted with sideplates and game scene engraving.

Exc.	V.G.	Good	Fair	Poor
9500	8150	6600	4000	2500

Model 313E

This model has sideplates with fine, full coverage scroll engraving. A expert appraisal is recommended due to this models rarity and unique features.

Model 314E

This sideplate model is also rare and unique. An expert appraisal is recommended prior to a sale. Extra barrels will frequently be seen with this model.

Single Shot and Bolt Action Rifles

Merkel built special single shot rifles and bolt action rifles. These guns were produced prior to World War II and are seldom seen in the United States. The buyer should exercise caution and seek expert assistance prior to a sale.

Model 180

This is a top lever single rifle with double under lugs built on a boxlock action. The stock is 3/4 with pistol grip. Commonly referred to as a stalking rifle. Offered in a variety of European calibers.

Exc.	V.G.	Good	Fair	Poor
3000	2100	1500	1000	500

Model 183

This top lever model features a Holland & Holland type sidelock action with the side lock on the left side and the removable side plate on the right side. Fitted with a straight grip stock and full length forearm with sling swivels, fine line checkering, and fancy wood.

Exc.	V.G.	Good	Fair	Poor
7500	5000	3500	2000	1200

Model 190

This is Merkel's version of a Sporting rifle built on a Mauser action. Offered in a variety of European calibers.

Exc.	V.G.	Good	Fair	Poor
3000	2200	1500	1000	650

CURRENTLY IMPORTED MODELS

Importer—GSI, Inc.
Trussvulle, Alabama

Side by Side Shotguns

Model 8

This model has a self-cocking Deeley boxlock action side by side with cocking indicators. The locking mechanism is a Greener cross-bolt with double barrel locking lug. Triggers are single selective or double. The safety is automatic and tang mounted. This model has an extractor. Offered in 12 and 16 gauge with 28: solid rib barrels or 20 gauge with 26.75" barrels. Available with straight or pistol grip oil finished walnut stock. Receiver is case colored with light scroll engraving. The 12 and 16 gauge guns weigh about 6.8 lb. while the 20 gauge weigh approximately 6 lb.

NIB	Exc.	V.G.	Good	Fair	Poor
1000	800	700	600	500	300

Model 47E

Same as above but fitted with ejectors.

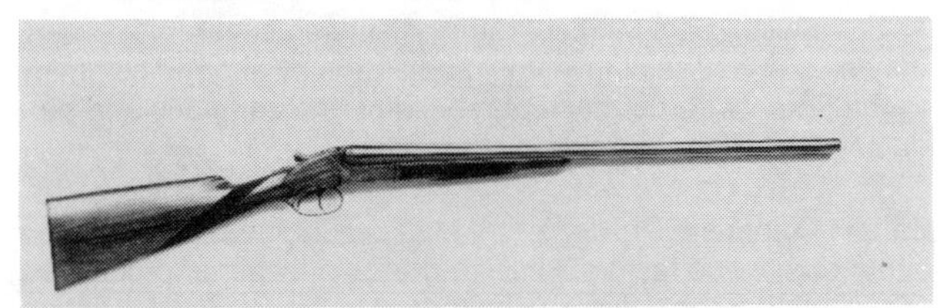

NIB	Exc.	V.G.	Good	Fair	Poor
1250	1000	800	700	500	300

Model 147

Same as Model 8 but with silver grayed receiver with fine engraved hunting scenes, engraved border, and screws.

NIB	Exc.	V.G.	Good	Fair	Poor
1500	1250	950	750	550	400

Model 147E

Same as above but fitted with ejectors.

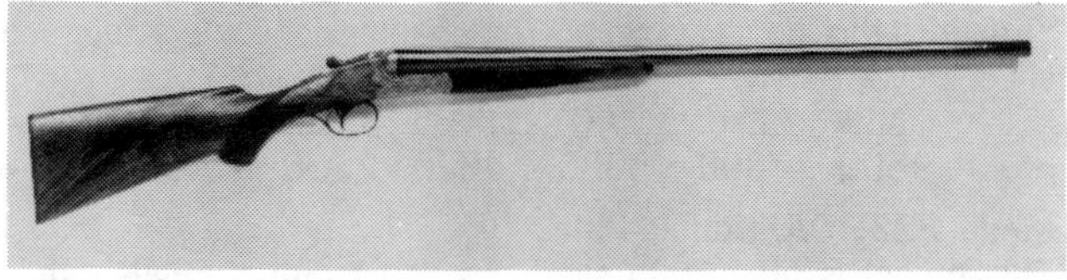

NIB	Exc.	V.G.	Good	Fair	Poor
1600	1350	1050	850	600	450

Model 122

This model features the same specifications as the above models but has false sideplates. This model is fitted with ejectors and the receiver is silver grayed with fine engraved hunting scenes on false sideplates, engraved border, and screws.

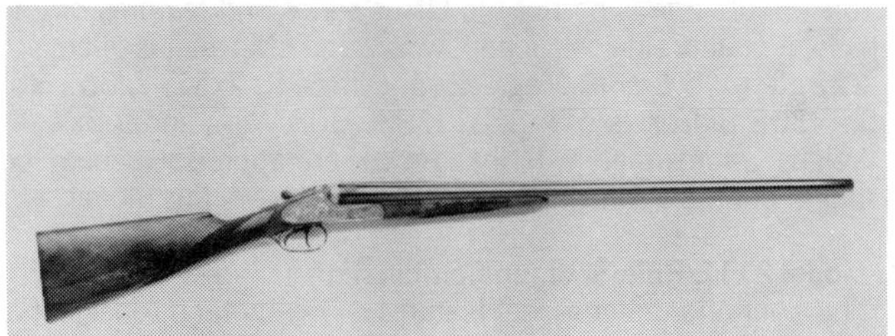

NIB	Exc.	V.G.	Good	Fair	Poor
2500	2000	1750	1200	750	600

Model 47S

Same as above but with scroll engraving in place of hunting scenes.

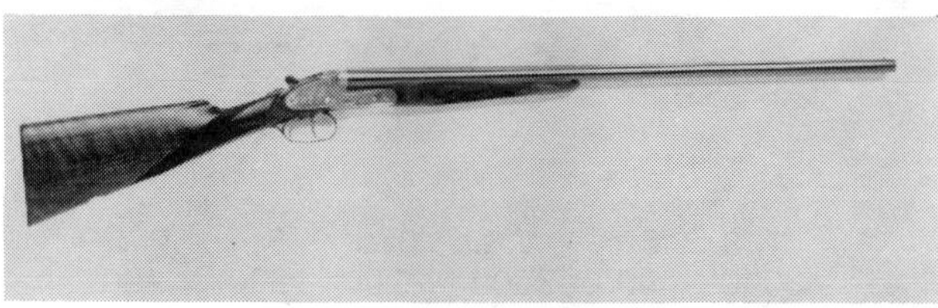

NIB	Exc.	V.G.	Good	Fair	Poor
3350	2750	2200	1750	1200	800

Model 147S

This model features true Holland and Holland style side locks with cocking indicators. Gauge and barrels lengths are as above. However, 20 gauge gun weighs 6.4 lb.

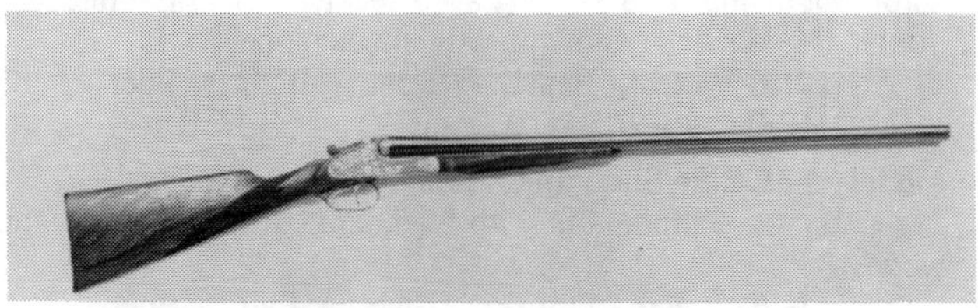

NIB	Exc.	V.G.	Good	Fair	Poor
4100	3700	3000	2000	1500	1000

Models 247S/347S/447S

These models are the same as the Model 147S with the exception of the types of engraving.

Model 247S-Large scroll engraving

NIB	Exc.	V.G.	Good	Fair	Poor
5500	4500	3500	2500	1750	1250

Model 347S-Medium scroll engraving

NIB	Exc.	V.G.	Good	Fair	Poor
6500	5500	4500	3500	2250	1500

Model 447S-Small scroll engraving

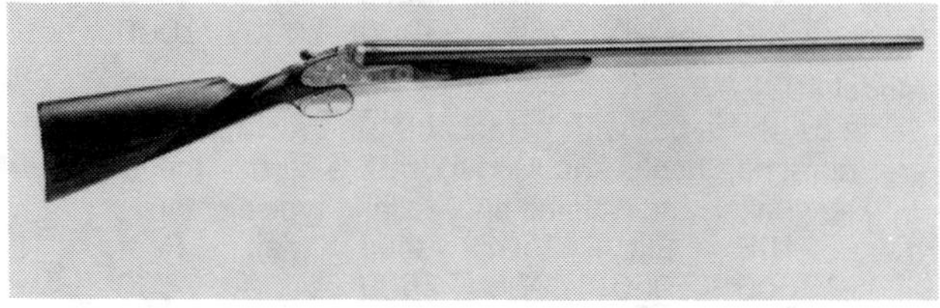

NIB	Exc.	V.G.	Good	Fair	Poor
7000	6000	5000	4000	2750	1750

Over and Under Shotguns

Model 200E

The action on this model is a self cocking Blitz where the hammers are attached to the trigger plates. The locking mechanism is a Kersten double cross bolt lock with release. Trigger may be either single selective or double. The manual safety is mounted on the tang. Fitted with coil spring ejectors. Offered in 12 and 16 gauge with 28: solid rib barrels or 20 gauge with 26.75" barrels. The oil finished stock is offered with straight or pistol grip. The receiver is case-colored with engraved border and screws. The 12 gauge weighs 7 lb., the 16 gauge 6.8 lb., and the 20 gauge 6.4 lb.

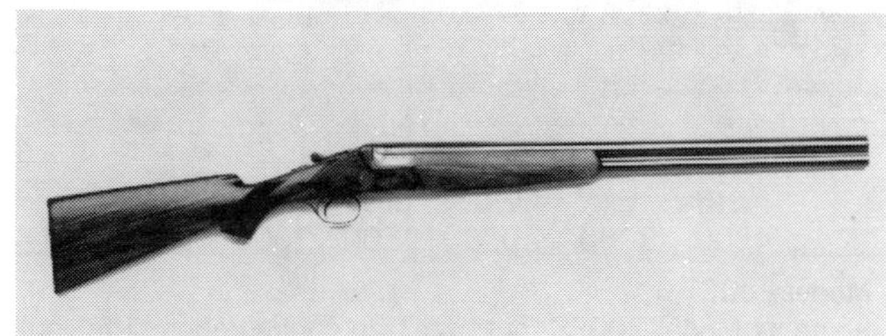

NIB	Exc.	V.G.	Good	Fair	Poor
2700	2000	1500	1000	800	500

Model 201E

Same as above but with silver grayed receiver with fine engraved hunting scenes, engraved border, and screws.

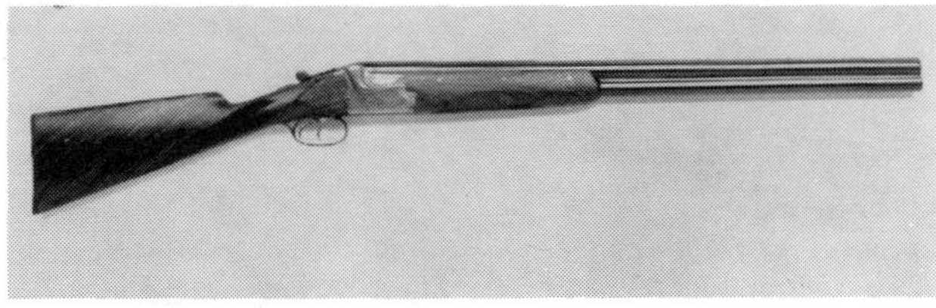

NIB	Exc.	V.G.	Good	Fair	Poor
3350	2850	2250	1500	1000	750

Model 202E

This model has the same basic specifications as the Model 201E but is fitted with false side plates with cocking indicators.

NIB	Exc.	V.G.	Good	Fair	Poor
6500	5000	3500	2500	1500	1000

Model 203E

This model has true Holland and Holland style side locks with cocking indicators. These sideplates are removable with cranked screw. The gauge selection and barrel are the same as those listed above. The silver grayed receiver as English style large scroll engraving.

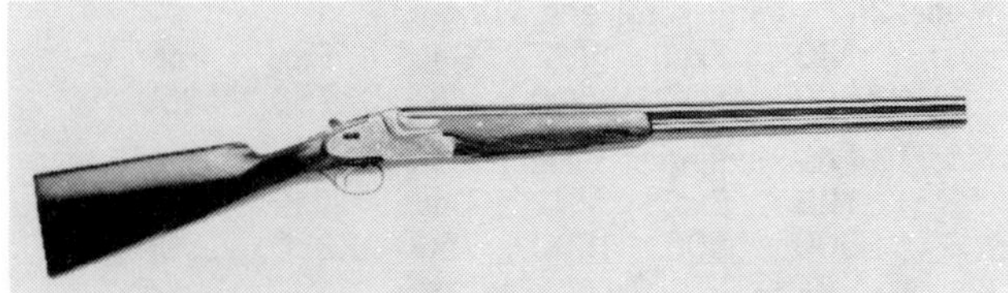

NIB	Exc.	V.G.	Good	Fair	Poor
7750	6000	4500	3000	2000	1000

Model 303E

Same as above but with detachable side lock plates with integral retracting hook. The Model 303E also has medium scroll work engraving and Holland and Holland type ejectors.

NIB	Exc.	V.G.	Good	Fair	Poor
17000	15000	12000	7500	5000	2500

Model 200ES

This model features a Blitz action with cocking indicators and Kersten double cross bolt lock with release. The trigger is single selective with tang mounted manual safety. Coil spring ejectors are standard. Offered in 12 gauge only with 26.75" or 28" ventilated rib barrel. The walnut stock has Skeet dimensions with pistol grip. Receiver is silver grayed with 1/2 coverage scroll engraving, engraved borders, and screws. Weighs approximately 7.3 lb.

NIB	Exc.	V.G.	Good	Fair	Poor
4000	3250	2500	2000	1500	1000

Model 201ES

Same as model above but with full coverage scroll engraving.

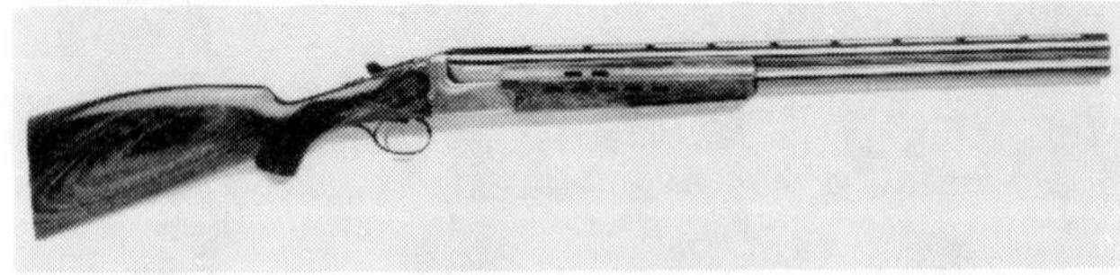

NIB	Exc.	V.G.	Good	Fair	Poor
4500	3750	3000	2500	2000	1000

Model 200ET

Same as Model 200ES, but in a Trap configuration. The ventilated rib barrel length offered is 30".

NIB	Exc.	V.G.	Good	Fair	Poor
4250	3500	2750	2250	1750	1000

Model 201ET

Same as Model 210ES but fitted with a 30" barrel and Trap stock dimensions.

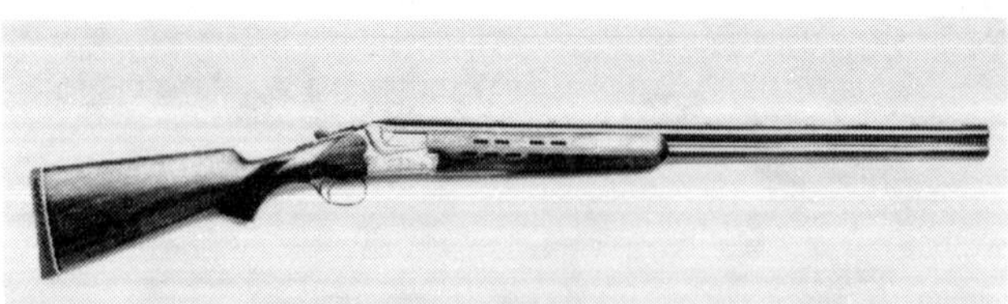

NIB	Exc.	V.G.	Good	Fair	Poor
4500	3750	3000	2500	2000	1000

MERKEL SHOTGUN CHOKE DESIGNATIONS

Choke ID	Description	Percentage
1/1	Full Choke	70 to 75
3/4	Imp. Modified	65 tp 70
1/2	Modified	60 to 65
1/4	Quarter Choke	55 to 60
VZ	Imp. Cylinder	45 to 50
S	Skeet Choke	70 to 75 (at 25 yrds)

DOUBLE RIFLES-COMBINATION GUNS-DRILLINGS

Model 220E O/U Double Rifle

This is a boxlock design with a Kersten double cross bolt, scroll engraved case hardened receiver, Blitz action, double triggers, and pistol grip stock with cheek piece.

NIB	Exc.	V.G.	Good	Fair	Poor
8500	6000	4500	3800	2000	950

Model 221E O/U Double Rifle

Similar to the model above but with game scene engraving on a silver greyed receiver.

NIB	Exc.	V.G.	Good	Fair	Poor
9500	7000	5000	4000	2250	1200

Model 223E O/U Double Rifle

This model is fitted with sidelocks and features English style arabesque engraving in large scrolls on silver grayed receiver.

NIB	Exc.	V.G.	Good	Fair	Poor
14500	12500	10000	6000	3500	1500

Model 323E O/U Double Rifle

Similar to the above model but with finer engraving.

NIB	Exc.	V.G.	Good	Fair	Poor
22500	17500	12500	7500	4500	2500

Model 160S Luxus Double Rifle

This double rifle is part of the Luxus series and features on the highest quality sidelock action, wood, and fittings. It is offered in .222 Rem., 5.6x50R Mag., .243, 6.5x57R, 7x57, 7x65, .30-06, .30R Blazer, 8x57IRS, 8x57RS, .308 Win., and 9.3x74R. Weighs approximately 8 lbs. An expert appraisal should be sought prior to a sale due to the unique nature of this model.

Model 211E Rifle/Shotgun Combination

This over and under model features a grey metal boxlock action with hunting scenes. The top barrel is available in 12, 16, or 20 gauge and the bottom barrel is offered in .22 Hornet, 5.6R Mag., 5.6R, .222Rem., .243 Win., 6.5x55, 6.5x57R, 7x57R, 7x65R, .30-06, 8x57IRS, 9.3x74R, and .375 H&H Mag. The barrel has a solid rib and the trigger is single selective. The select walnut stock is hand checkered. Weight is about 7 lb.

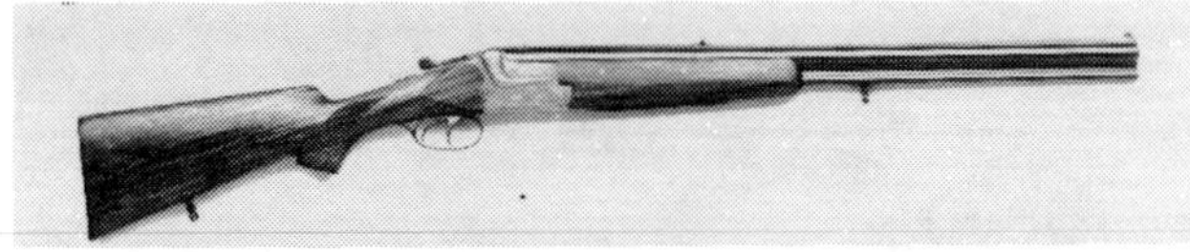

NIB	Exc.	V.G.	Good	Fair	Poor
6000	4500	3500	2250	1500	900

Model 210E Rifle/Shotgun Combination

Same as above model but features a scroll engraved case-hardened receiver.

NIB	Exc.	V.G.	Good	Fair	Poor
4750	3500	2500	1750	1200	700

Model 213E Rifle/Shotgun Combination

This combination gun features sidelocks with English style large scroll engraving on a silver grayed receiver. Also is fitted with double triggers and pistol grip with cheek piece.

NIB	Exc.	V.G.	Good	Fair	Poor
11500	9500	7500	5500	2500	1500

Model 313E Rifle/Shotgun Combination

Same as above model but with finer scroll engraving and fancy wood.

NIB	Exc.	V.G.	Good	Fair	Poor
17500	12500	7500	6500	4000	2500

Model 95K Drilling

This model is a three barrel shotgun/rifle combination. The top two barrels are chambered for 12, 16, or 20 gauge and the bottom barrel is available in rifle calibers from .22 Hornet to .375 H&H Mag. The action is a boxlock design with scroll engraving on borders and screws. The stock is select grade walnut with raised comb, pistol grip with cap, cheekpiece, and plastic butt plate. Weighs about 7.7 lb.

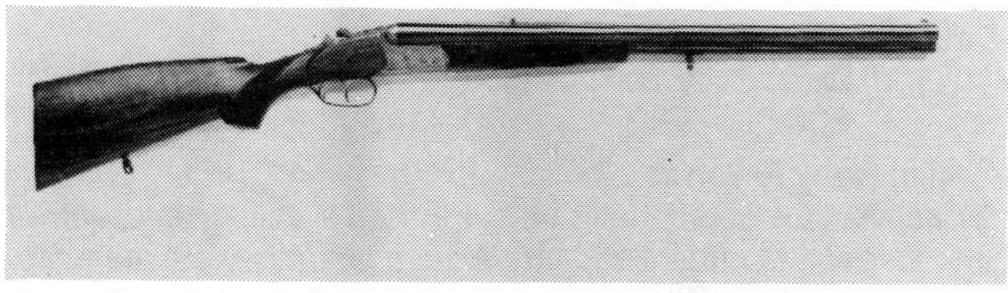

NIB	Exc.	V.G.	Good	Fair	Poor
6000	4500	3500	2500	1500	1000

MERIDEN FIREARMS CO.
Meriden, Connecticut

Pocket Pistol

A .32 or .38 caliber double-action revolver manufactured in a variety of barrel lengths and with either an exposed or enclosed hammer. Nickle-plated with rubber grips. The barrel marked "Meriden Firearms Co. Meriden, Conn. USA." Manufactured between 1895 and 1915.

Exc.	V.G.	Good	Fair	Poor
150	125	100	75	50

MERRILL
Fullerton, California

Sportsman

A single shot pistol manufactured in a variety of calibers with either a 9" or 12" octagonal barrel having a wide ventilated-rib, adjustable sights and integral telescope mounts. Blued with walnut grips.

Interchangeable Barrels—Add $75.

Wrist Support—Add $25.

Exc.	V.G.	Good	Fair	Poor
300	275	225	175	125

MERRILL, JAMES H.
Baltimore, Maryland

Merrill Rifle

A single-shot breechloading rifle that is chambered for .54 caliber and utilizes the percussion ignition system. The breech opens for loading by lifting and pulling back on a lever. The barrel is 33" in length, and there is a full-length walnut stock held on by two barrel bands. The mountings and patchbox are brass; and the lock is case-colored, with a browned barrel. The lock is marked "J.H.Merrill Balto./Pat. July 1858." There are military acceptance marks on the stock. There were approximately 775 of these rifles manufactured and purchased by the government for use during the Civil War. They were made in 1864 and 1865.

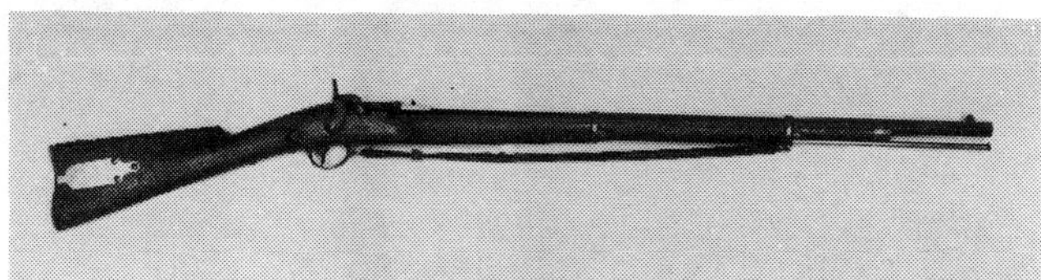

Courtesy Milwaukee Public Museum, Milwaukee, Wisconsin.

Exc.	V.G.	Good	Fair	Poor
2000	1750	1450	1000	750

Merrill Carbine

Similar in appearance to the rifle except that the barrel length is 22" and the stock is only half-length with one barrel band. There are some variations that are quite subtle in appearance but which have a considerable effect on values. We recommend that an independent appraisal be secured. The values given are for the standard 1st and 2nd Types. There were approximately 15,000 total manufactured, and most were used in the Civil War.

1st Type

No Eagle stamped on the lock, and the breech lever is flat.

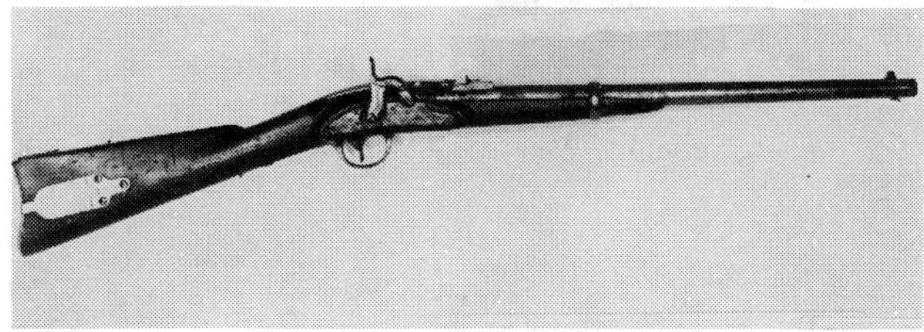

Courtesy Milwaukee Public Museum, Milwaukee, Wisconsin.

Exc.	V.G.	Good	Fair	Poor
1500	1250	1000	750	500

2nd Type

An Eagle stamped on the lock, and the stock has no patchbox. The breech lever has a round tip.

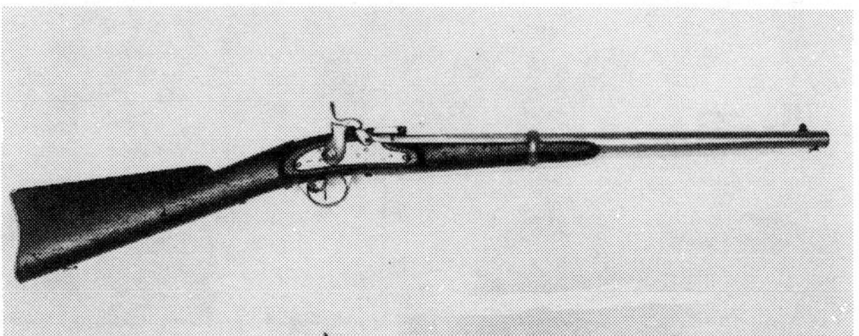

Courtesy Milwaukee Public Museum, Milwaukee, Wisconsin.

Exc.	V.G.	Good	Fair	Poor
1750	1500	1250	850	650

MERRILL, LATROBE & THOMAS
S. Remington—Maker
Ilion, New York

Carbine

A .58 caliber breech loading percussion carbine with an overall length of 38" and barrel length of 21". The lock marked "S.Remington/ Ilion, N.Y." and the barrel "Merrill, Latrobe & Thomas/Baltimore, Md./Patent Applied For." Approximately 170 were made in 1855. Prospective purchasers are advised to secure a qualified appraisal prior to acquisition.

Exc.	V.G.	Good	Fair	Poor
5500	4750	4000	3000	2000

MERRIMACK ARMS
SEE—Brown Manufacturing Co.

MERWIN & BRAY
Worcester, Massachusetts

This company marketed a number of firearms produced by various manufacturers under their own name.

Merwin & Bray Pocket Pistol

A .32 caliber spur trigger single shot pistol with a 3.5" barrel. Blued, silver-plated with walnut grips. The barrel marked "Merwin & Bray New York".

Exc.	V.G.	Good	Fair	Poor
300	250	200	150	100

MERWIN & HULBERT & CO.

New York, New York

The successor to Merwin & Bray Company. Primarily known as the sales agents for Hopkins & Allen as well as the Evans Rifle Company.

Army Revolver

A .44-40 or .44 M&H caliber single action revolver with a 7" barrel and 6-shot cylinder. The barrel rotates so that the cylinder and barrel unit can be pulled forward for cartridge ejection. Provided in a variety of finishes. The barrel marked with both "Merwin Hulbert & Co." and "Hopkins & Allen Manufacturing Co." A large quantity were manufactured between 1876 and 1885.

Courtesy Milwaukee Public Museum, Milwaukee, Wisconsin.

Courtesy Milwaukee Public Museum, Milwaukee, Wisconsin.

Open Top Frame with the Square Butt

Exc.	V.G.	Good	Fair	Poor
750	650	550	400	300

Open Top Frame with Birdshead Butt

Exc.	V.G.	Good	Fair	Poor
700	600	500	350	250

Square Butt with Topstrap

Exc.	V.G.	Good	Fair	Poor
700	600	500	350	250

Birdshead Grip with Topstrap

Exc.	V.G.	Good	Fair	Poor
600	500	400	300	200

Double Action Model

Exc.	V.G.	Good	Fair	Poor
600	500	400	300	200

Pocket Army Revolver

As above, but additionally in .44 Russian caliber and with a 3.5" barrel and birdshead butt. A large quantity were manufactured during the 1880s.

Courtesy Milwaukee Public Museum, Milwaukee, Wisconsin.

Exc.	V.G.	Good	Fair	Poor
600	500	400	300	200

Single Action Pocket Revolver

A .32 or .38 caliber spur trigger revolver with 3.5" to 5.5" barrels and either 5- or 6-shot cylinders. Nickle-plated with hard rubber grips. The barrel marked "Merwin & Hulbert & Co." with the patent dates. While the Hopkins & Allen name is marked on some examples, on others it is not present. Approximately 2,500 were made during the 1880s.

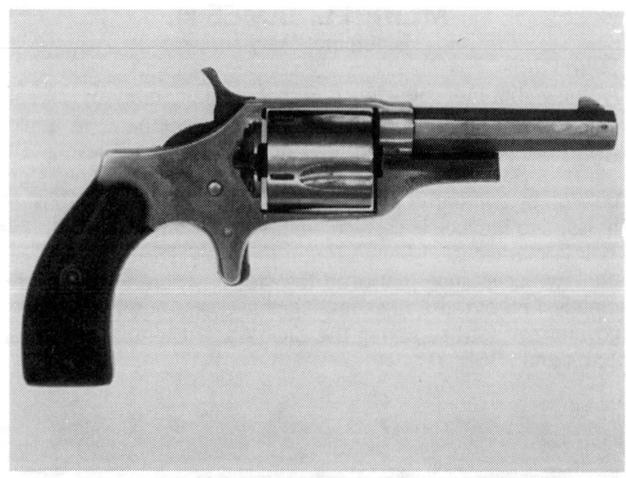

Courtesy Milwaukee Public Museum, Milwaukee, Wisconsin.

Exc.	V.G.	Good	Fair	Poor
350	300	250	200	100

Single Action .22 Revolver

Similar to the above in .22 caliber with a 3.5" barrel and 7-shot cylinder. The barrel marked "Merwin & Hulbert & Co." Nickle-plated with rubber grips. Manufactured during the 1880s.

Exc.	V.G.	Good	Fair	Poor
400	350	300	250	150

Double Action Pocket Revolver

A .32 or .38 double-action revolver with a 3.5" or 5.5" barrel and 5- or 7-shot cylinder. Nickle-plated with rubber grips. The barrel marked "Merwin & Hulbert". This model is also encountered with a folding hammer spur which commands a slight premium. Manufactured during the 1880s.

Courtesy Milwaukee Public Museum, Milwaukee, Wisconsin.

Exc.	V.G.	Good	Fair	Poor
300	250	200	150	100

METROPOLITAN ARMS CO.

New York, New York

Established in February of 1864, this company manufactured copies of the Colt Model 1851 and 1861 Navy Revolvers, as well as, copies of the Colt Model 1862 Police Revolver. Two of the firm's principle officers were Samuel and William Syms (formerly of Blunt & Syms) and it is believed that they were responsible for production. Curiously, although most Metropolitan pistols were produced during the 1864 to 1866 period, the company itself was not dissolved until 1920.

1851 Navy Revolver

A .36 caliber percussion revolver with a 7.5" octagonal barrel and 6-shot cylinder. Blued, case-hardened with walnut grips. The barrel marked "Metropolitan Arms Co. New York." Approximately 6,000 of these revolvers were made during the 1860s. Those bearing H.E. Dimick markings are worth considerably more than the standard marked examples.

H.E. Dimick Navy Model

Exc.	V.G.	Good	Fair	Poor
3500	3000	2850	2250	1400

Standard Navy Model

Exc.	V.G.	Good	Fair	Poor
1200	1000	800	600	400

1861 Navy Revolver

A .36 caliber percussion revolver with a 7.5" round barrel and 6-shot cylinder. The loading lever of the rack and pinion type. Blued, casehardened with walnut grips. The barrel marked "Metropolitan Arms Co. New York." Approximately 50 were made in 1864 and 1865.

Exc.	V.G.	Good	Fair	Poor
5000	4250	3500	2750	1800

Police Revolver

A .36 caliber percussion revolver with either 4.5", 5.5" or 6.5" round barrels and a fluted 5-shot cylinder. Blued, casehardened with walnut grips. The barrel normally marked Metropolitan Arms Co. New York," although examples have been noted without any markings. Approximately 2,750 were made between 1864 and 1866.

Exc.	V.G.	Good	Fair	Poor
1000	850	700	500	400

MIIDA

Japan

Marubena America Corp.

Model 612

A 12 gauge boxlock Over/Under shotgun with 26" or 28" ventilated-rib barrels, single selective trigger and automatic ejectors. Blued with a walnut stock. Imported between 1972 and 1974.

Exc.	V.G.	Good	Fair	Poor
900	800	750	600	450

Model 612 Skeet

As above, with 27" skeet choked barrels and some engraving. Imported between 1972 and 1974.

Exc.	V.G.	Good	Fair	Poor
1000	900	850	700	500

Model 2200 Trap or Skeet

As above, with either 30" trap or 27" skeet bored barrels and more finely engraved. Imported between 1972 and 1974.

Exc.	V.G.	Good	Fair	Poor
1100	1000	900	800	600

Model 2300 Trap or Skeet

A more finely finished Model 2200. Imported from 1972 until 1974.

Exc.	V.G.	Good	Fair	Poor
1350	1250	1100	1000	750

Model GRT Trap or GRS Skeet

A 12 gauge boxlock shotgun fitted with false sideplates, 27" skeet or 29" full choked barrels, single selective trigger and automatic ejector. Imported between 1972 and 1974.

Exc.	V.G.	Good	Fair	Poor
2250	1850	1650	1200	1000

MINNEAPOLIS F. A. CO.

Minneapolis, Minnesota

Palm Pistol

A .32 caliber radial cylinder pistol with a 1.75" barrel manufactured by the Ames Manufacturing Company (see the Ames entry). Nickle-plated with hard rubber grips. The sideplates marked "Minneapolis Firearms Co." and "The Protector." Several thousand were sold during the 1890s.

Exc.	V.G.	Good	Fair	Poor
850	750	550	400	300

MIROKU B. C.
Miroku Japan

Firearms produced by this manufacturer have been imported and marketed by a variety of companies such as Charles Daly, Browning, Winchester, and SKB.

MITCHELL ARMS, INC.
Santa Ana, California

An importer and distributor of foreign made firearms.

M-16

A .22rf copy of the Colt AR-15. Introduced in 1987.

NIB	Exc.	V.G.	Good	Fair	Poor
275	225	200	175	125	100

MAS

A .22 or .22 Magnum caliber copy of the French MAS Bullpup Service Rifle. Introduced in 1987.

NIB	Exc.	V.G.	Good	Fair	Poor
275	225	200	175	125	100

Galil

A .22 or .22 Magnum caliber copy of the Galio rifle. Introduced in 1987.

NIB	Exc.	V.G.	Good	Fair	Poor
275	225	200	175	125	100

AK-22

A .22 or .22 Magnum caliber copy of the AK47 rifle. Introduced in 1985.

NIB	Exc.	V.G.	Good	Fair	Poor
275	225	200	175	125	100

PPS-50

A .22 or .22 Magnum caliber copy of the PPSh Submachine gun.

NIB	Exc.	V.G.	Good	Fair	Poor
275	225	200	175	125	100

This company also imported Yugoslavian-manufactured semi-automatic AK-47 rifles in 7.62x39mm, as well as 7.62x54mm.

Skorpion

A .32 caliber semi-automatic pistol with a 4.75" barrel and either 20- or 30-shot magazine. Blued with plastic grips. Imported from Yugoslavia in 1987 and 1988 only.

Exc.	V.G.	Good	Fair	Poor
600	500	425	350	300

Spectre

A 9mm caliber semi-automatic pistol with an 8" shrouded barrel and either 30- or 50-shot magazine. Blued with plastic grips. Also produced with an 18" barrel and folding buttstock. Imported from Yugoslavia in 1987 and 1988.

Exc.	V.G.	Good	Fair	Poor
600	500	425	350	300

MODESTO SANTOS CIA.
Eibar, Spain

Action, Corrientes, and M.S.

A 6.35mm or 7.65mm caliber semi-automatic pistol of low quality marked on the slide "Pistolet Automatique Model 1920." Blued with composition grips having the monogram "M.S." cast in them. Manufactured between 1920 and 1935.

Exc.	V.G.	Good	Fair	Poor
150	125	100	75	50

MONDRAGON
Mexico City, Mexico

Firearms designed by Manuel Mondragon were produced on an experimental basis first at St. Chamond Arsenal in France and later at SIG in Neuhausen, Switzerland. The latter company was responsible for the manufacture of the two known production models; the Model 1890 and 1908.

The Model 1890 Mondragon semi-automatic rifle holds the distinction of being the first self-loading rifle to be issued to any armed forces.

MONTENEGRAN-GASSER
SEE—Gasser, Leopold

MOORE-ENFIELD
SEE—English Military Firearms

MOORES PATENT FIREARMS CO.
Brooklyn, New York

In 1866 this company became known as the National Arms Company.

No. 1 Derringer

A .41 caliber spur trigger all metal pistol with a 2.5" barrel. Blued or silver-plated. Approximately 10,000 were manufactured between 1860 and 1865. This model was also marketed as the No. 1 Derringer by the Colt Company after they purchased the National Arms Company in 1870.

Courtesy Milwaukee Public Museum, Milwaukee, Wisconsin.

1st Variation Marked "Patent Applied For"

Exc.	V.G.	Good	Fair	Poor
950	850	700	600	450

2nd Variation Marked "D.Moore Patented Feb. 19 1861"

Exc.	V.G.	Good	Fair	Poor
750	650	500	400	250

Standard Model Marked "Moore's Pat F.A.Co."

Exc.	V.G.	Good	Fair	Poor
550	475	400	250	150

National Arms Co. Production

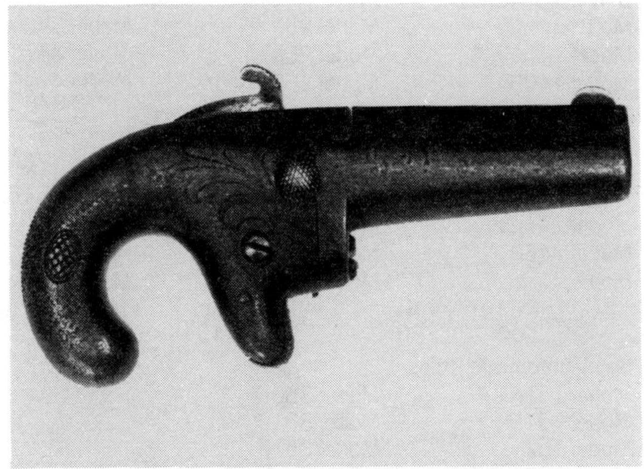

Courtesy Milwaukee Public Museum, Milwaukee, Wisconsin.

Exc.	V.G.	Good	Fair	Poor
550	475	400	250	150

Iron Model

Exc.	V.G.	Good	Fair	Poor
750	475	400	250	150

Pocket Revolver

A .32 teat fire caliber spur trigger revolver with a round 3.25" barrel and 6-shot cylinder. Blued or silver plated with walnut grips. Approximately 30,000 were manufactured between 1864 and 1870.

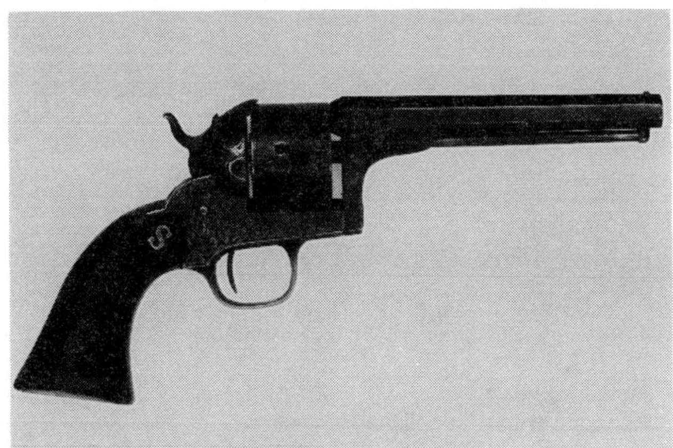

Courtesy Milwaukee Public Museum, Milwaukee, Wisconsin.

Exc.	V.G.	Good	Fair	Poor
500	400	325	250	150

Belt Revolver

A .32rf caliber revolver with a 4", 5" or 6" octagonal barrel and 7-shot cylinder. The barrel and cylinder blued, the brass frame sometimes silver-plated with walnut grips. The barrel marked "D.Moore Patent Sept. 18, 1860." Several thousand were manufactured between 1861 and 1863.

Exc.	V.G.	Good	Fair	Poor
500	400	325	250	150

MORGAN & CLAPP
New Haven, Connecticut

Single Shot Pocket Pistol

A .22 or .23 caliber spur trigger single shot pistol with a 3.5" octagonal barrel. Blued, silver-plated frame with walnut grips. The barrel marked "Morgan & Clapp New Haven". Active 1864 to 1867.

Exc.	V.G.	Good	Fair	Poor
300	250	200	150	100

MORINI
Italy
Importer—Osborne's
Cheboygan, Michigan

C-80 Standard

A .22 caliber single shot pistol with a free floating 10" barrel, match sights, adjustable frame and adjustable grips.

Exc.	V.G.	Good	Fair	Poor
1000	850	675	550	450

CM-80 Super Competition

As above, with a trigger adjustable from 5 to 120 grams pressure, Plexiglass front sight and a polished finish.

Exc.	V.G.	Good	Fair	Poor
1200	1000	850	750	600

MORRONE
Hope Valley, Rhode Island
SEE—Rhode Island Arms Company

MORSE
Greenville, South Carolina
State Armory

Morse Carbine

Overall length 40"; barrel length 21"; caliber .50 (other calibers are known to have been made on an experimental basis). The round barrel blued, the frame of brass and the stock of either walnut or beechwood. Approximately 1,000 were manufactured during the Civil War. Prospective purchasers are advised to secure a qualified appraisal prior to acquisition.

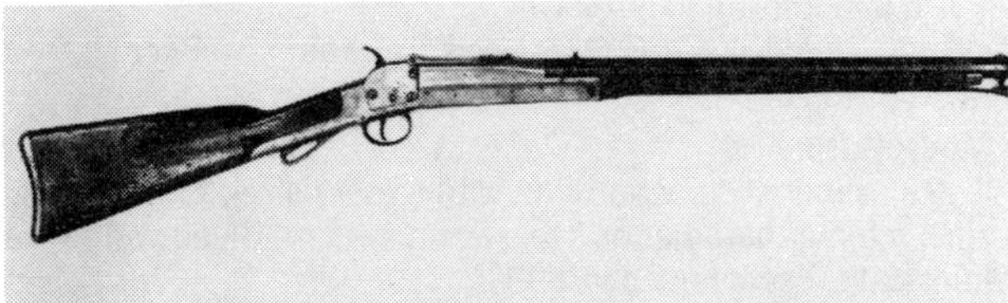

Courtesy Milwaukee Public Museum, Milwaukee, Wisconsin.

Courtesy Milwaukee Public Museum, Milwaukee, Wisconsin.

Exc.	V.G.	Good	Fair	Poor
4500	3750	2750	2000	1750

MOSIN-NAGANT
Russia

Model 1891

A 7.62mm caliber bolt-action rifle with a 28.75" barrel, 5-shot integral magazine, ladder rear sight and a full-length stock secured by two barrel bands. Blued with a walnut stock.

Exc.	V.G.	Good	Fair	Poor
175	150	125	100	75

Model 1910 Carbine

As above, with a 20" barrel and modified sights.

Exc.	V.G.	Good	Fair	Poor
175	150	125	100	75

Model 1930 Rifle

Similar to the Model 1891, but with a round receiver ring and improved sights.

Exc.	V.G.	Good	Fair	Poor
175	150	125	100	75

Model 1938 Carbine

As above, with a 20" barrel.

Exc.	V.G.	Good	Fair	Poor
175	150	125	100	75

Model 1944 Carbine

As above, but fitted with a folding bayonet at the barrel muzzle.

Exc.	V.G.	Good	Fair	Poor
150	125	100	75	50

Model 1895 "Gas Seal" Revolver

A 7.62mm caliber single (troopers) or double-action (officers) revolver with a 4.35" barrel and 7-shot cylinder. As the hammer is cocked, the cylinder is moved forward to engage the barrel breech. Blued with either walnut or plastic grips. Manufactured from 1895 to approximately 1933.

Exc.	V.G.	Good	Fair	Poor
300	250	200	150	100

MOSSBERG, O. F. & SONS, INC.
North Haven, Connecticut

Founded by Oscar F. Mossberg in 1892 at Fitchburg, Massachusetts, this company for a time was located at Chicopee Falls, Massachusetts, and since 1919 has been in North Haven, Connecticut.

Brownie

A .22 caliber 4 barrelled pocket pistol with a revolving firing pin. This pistol resembles a semi-automatic. Manufactured from 1906 to approximately 1940.

Exc.	V.G.	Good	Fair	Poor
350	325	300	225	150

Model K Rifle

A .22 caliber slide action rifle with a 22" barrel, tubular magazine, internal hammer and takedown system. Blued with a walnut stock. Discontinued in 1931.

Exc.	V.G.	Good	Fair	Poor
175	150	125	75	50

Model M Rifle

As above, with a 24" octagonal barrel. Manufactured from 1928 and 1931.

Exc.	V.G.	Good	Fair	Poor
175	150	125	75	50

Model L Rifle

A .22 caliber single shot takedown rifle with a 24" barrel. Manufactured from 1927 to 1932.

Exc.	V.G.	Good	Fair	Poor
300	250	200	150	100

Beginning in 1930, the Mossberg company manufactured a variety of utilitarian single shot and repeating bolt-action rifles. Later they introduced a similar line of semi-automatic rifles. As these arms were intended for extensive use and were low priced, the values for them may be categorized as follows:

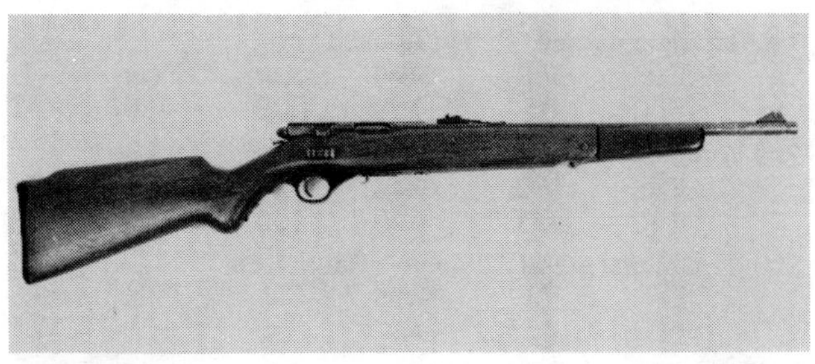

Bolt Action Rifles

Model 10, Model 14, Model 140B, Model 140K, Model 142A, Model 142K, Model 144, Model 144LS, Model 146B, Model 20, Model 25, Model 25A, Model 26B, Model 26C, Model 30, Model 320B, Model 320K, Model 321K, Model 340B, Model 340K, Model 340M, Model 341, Model 342K, Model 346B, Model 346K, Model 352K, Model 450, Model 432, Model 50, Model 51, Model 51M

Exc.	V.G.	Good	Fair	Poor
100	80	65	45	20

Semi-Automatic Rifles

Model 151K, Model 151M, Model 152, Model 152K, Model 350K, Model 351C, Model 351K

Exc.	V.G.	Good	Fair	Poor
125	100	80	60	40

Model 400 Palomino

A .22 caliber lever-action rifle with a 22" barrel, open sights and tubular magazine. Also made with an 18.5" barrel. Blued with a walnut stock. Manufactured from 1959 to 1964.

Exc.	V.G.	Good	Fair	Poor
150	125	100	75	50

Model 800

A bolt-action rifle manufactured in a variety of calibers with a 22" barrel and folding leaf rear sight. Blued with a walnut stock. Introduced in 1967.

Exc.	V.G.	Good	Fair	Poor
225	200	150	100	75

Model 800D

As above, with a comb stock, rosewood forend tip and pistol-grip cap. Manufactured from 1970 to 1973.

Exc.	V.G.	Good	Fair	Poor
300	250	200	150	100

Model 800V

As above, with a 24" heavy barrel not fitted with sights. Introduced in 1968.

Exc.	V.G.	Good	Fair	Poor
225	200	150	100	75

Model 800M

As above, with a Mannlicher-style stock.

Exc.	V.G.	Good	Fair	Poor
275	250	200	150	100

Model 800SM

As above, with a 4X scope.

Exc.	V.G.	Good	Fair	Poor
300	275	225	150	100

Model 810

A .270 to .338 Winchester Magnum caliber bolt-action rifle with a 22" or 24" barrel fitted with a folding rear sight. Blued with a Monte Carlo-style stock. Introduced in 1970.

Exc.	V.G.	Good	Fair	Poor
275	250	200	150	100

Model 472C

A .30-30 or .35 Remington Caliber lever-action rifle with a 20" barrel, open sights and tubular magazine. Blued with a walnut stock. Introduced in 1972.

Exc.	V.G.	Good	Fair	Poor
200	175	150	100	75

Model 472P

As above, with a pistol grip stock and not fitted with a saddle ring.

Exc.	V.G.	Good	Fair	Poor
200	175	150	100	75

Model 472 One In Five Thousand

As above, with an etched receiver, brass buttplate, saddle ring and barrel band. A total of 5,000 were made in 1974.

Exc.	V.G.	Good	Fair	Poor
400	350	300	200	150

Model 479 PCA

Similar to the Model 472C in .30-30 caliber with a 20" barrel. Blued with a walnut stock.

Exc.	V.G.	Good	Fair	Poor
200	175	150	100	75

Model 479 RR

As above, with a gold-plated trigger and barrel band as well as "Roy Rogers" signature. A total of 5,000 were made in 1983.

Exc.	V.G.	Good	Fair	Poor
300	250	200	150	100

Mossberg manufactured a variety of shotguns which were sold at low to moderate prices. The values for these arms are approximately all the same.

Bolt Action Shotguns

Model 173	Model 190D	Model 390K
Model 173Y	Model 190K	Model 390T
Model 183D	Model 195D	Model 395K
Model 183K	Model 195K	Model 395S
Model 183T	Model 385K	Model 395T
Model 185D	Model 385T	Model 73
Model 185K		

Exc.	V.G.	Good	Fair	Poor
75	65	50	40	25

Model 200K

A 12 gauge slide-action shotgun with a 28" barrel and Mossberg select choke. Blued with a composition slide handle and walnut stock. Manufactured from 1955 to 1959.

Exc.	V.G.	Good	Fair	Poor
150	125	100	75	50

Model 500 Series

A 12, 20 or .410 bore slide action shotgun manufactured in a variety of barrel lengths and styles, as follows:

Model 500 Regal

Exc.	V.G.	Good	Fair	Poor
250	200	150	100	75

Model 500 Field Grade

Exc.	V.G.	Good	Fair	Poor
250	200	150	100	75

Model 500 Steel Shot—Chrome Bore

Exc.	V.G.	Good	Fair	Poor
300	250	200	125	100

Model 500 Slugster—Iron Sights

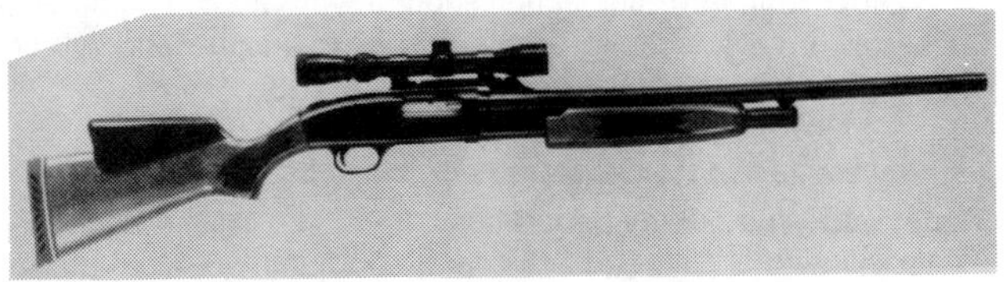

Exc.	V.G.	Good	Fair	Poor
275	250	200	150	100

Model 500 Camper—18.5" Barrel, Camo Case

Exc.	V.G.	Good	Fair	Poor
295	275	225	175	125

Model 500 Hi-Rib Trap

Exc.	V.G.	Good	Fair	Poor
275	250	200	150	100

Model 500 Super Grade

Exc.	V.G.	Good	Fair	Poor
200	175	150	100	75

Model 500 Pigeon Grade

Exc.	V.G.	Good	Fair	Poor
375	300	250	200	125

Model 500 Pigeon Grade Trap

Exc.	V.G.	Good	Fair	Poor
450	375	300	250	175

Model 500 Persuader—Riot Gun

NIB	Exc.	V.G.	Good	Fair	Poor
250	200	175	150	125	100

Model 500 Mariner—Marinecote Finish

NIB	Exc.	V.G.	Good	Fair	Poor
350	300	225	200	150	125

Model 500 Cruiser—Pistol Grip Only

NIB	Exc.	V.G.	Good	Fair	Poor
250	200	175	150	125	100

Model 500 Bullpup

A 12 gauge slide action Bullpup shotgun with an 18.5" or 20" shrouded barrel. Matte black finish with a composition stock. Introduced in 1986.

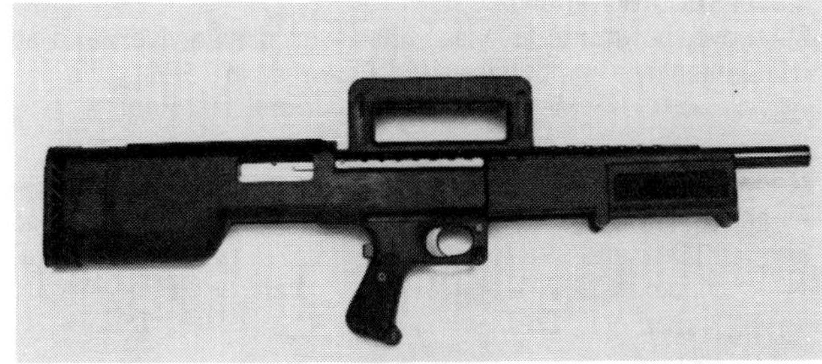

NIB	Exc.	V.G.	Good	Fair	Poor
400	325	250	200	150	100

Model 590

As above, with a 20" shrouded barrel, bayonet lug, parkerized or blued finish. Introduced in 1987.

NIB	Exc.	V.G.	Good	Fair	Poor
325	275	200	175	125	100

Model 590 Mariner—Marinecote Finish

NIB	Exc.	V.G.	Good	Fair	Poor
425	350	275	225	150	100

Model 590 Bullpup

The Model 500 with a 20" barrel and 9-shot magazine. Introduced in 1989.

NIB	Exc.	V.G.	Good	Fair	Poor
475	400	325	250	200	125

Model 835 Ulti-Mag

A 12 gauge Magnum slide action shotgun with a 28" ventilated-rib barrel fitted for choke tubes, 6-shot magazine and either composition or walnut stock. Introduced in 1988.

NIB	Exc.	V.G.	Good	Fair	Poor
425	350	275	225	150	100

Model 835 Wild Turkey Federation

As above, with a Wild Turkey Federation Medallion inlaid in the stock. Introduced in 1989.

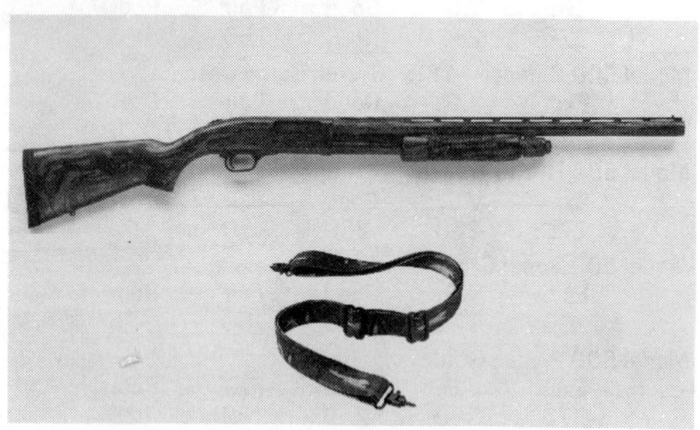

NIB	Exc.	V.G.	Good	Fair	Poor
475	400	325	250	200	125

Model 3000

A 12 or 20 gauge slide action shotgun manufactured in a variety of barrel lengths and styles. Blued with a walnut stock. Also known as the Smith & Wesson Model 3000.

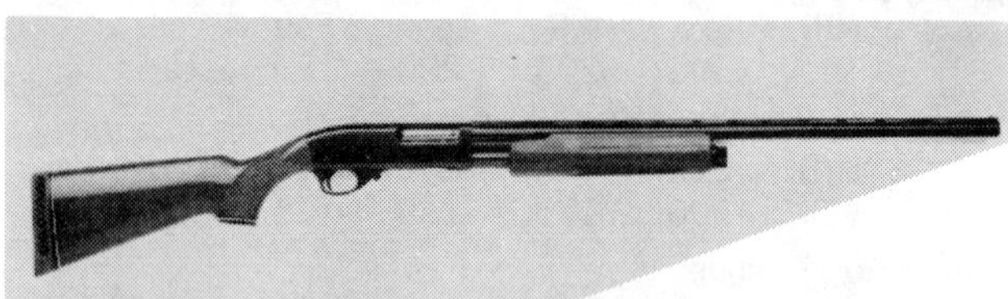

Exc.	V.G.	Good	Fair	Poor
325	250	175	125	75

Model 3000 Waterfowler

As above, but matte finished, fitted with sling swivels and accompanied by a camouflage sling. Produced in 1986.

Exc.	V.G.	Good	Fair	Poor
350	275	200	150	100

Model 3000 Law Enforcement

As above, with an 18.5" or 20" cylinder-bore barrel. Manufactured in 1986 and 1987.

Exc.	V.G.	Good	Fair	Poor
325	250	175	125	75

Model 1000

A 12 or 20 gauge semi-automatic shotgun manufactured in a variety of barrel lengths and styles, the receiver of an aluminum alloy and blued. Also known as the Smith & Wesson Model 1000. Offered in 1986 and 1987.

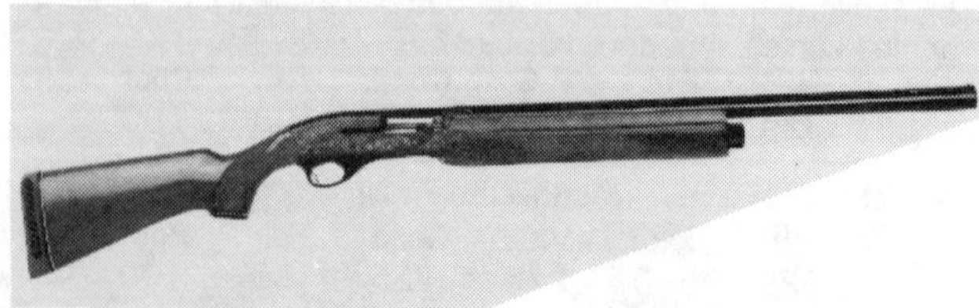

Exc.	V.G.	Good	Fair	Poor
400	325	250	200	125

Model 1000 Slug

As above, with a 22" barrel having rifle sights. Offered in 1986 and 1987.

Exc.	V.G.	Good	Fair	Poor
400	325	250	200	125

Model 1000 Super Series

As above, with a steel receiver and a self-regulating gas system which allows the use of either standard or Magnum shells.

Exc.	V.G.	Good	Fair	Poor
500	450	400	300	200

Model 1000 Super Waterfowler—Matte Finish

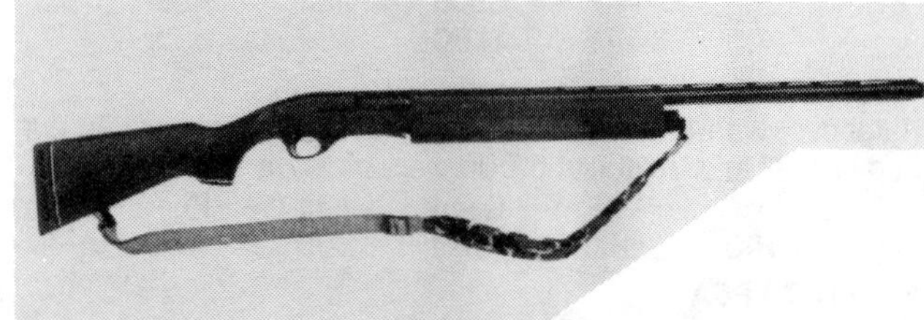

Exc.	V.G.	Good	Fair	Poor
500	450	400	300	200

Model 1000 Super Slug—Rifle Sights

Exc.	V.G.	Good	Fair	Poor
500	450	400	300	200

Model 1000 Super Trap—30" High Rib Barrel

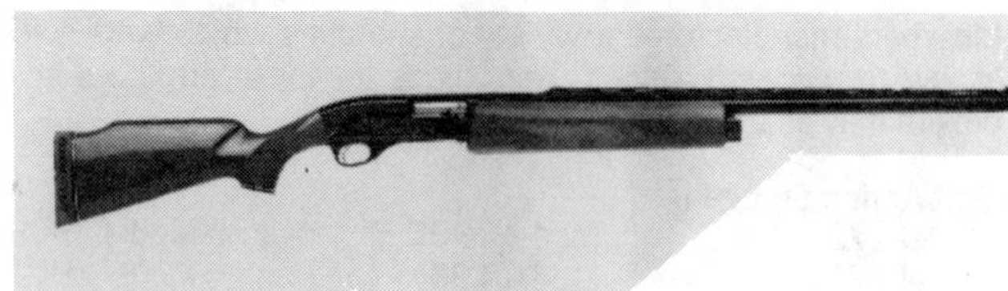

Exc.	V.G.	Good	Fair	Poor
475	425	350	250	175

Model 1000 Super Skeet—25" Barrel

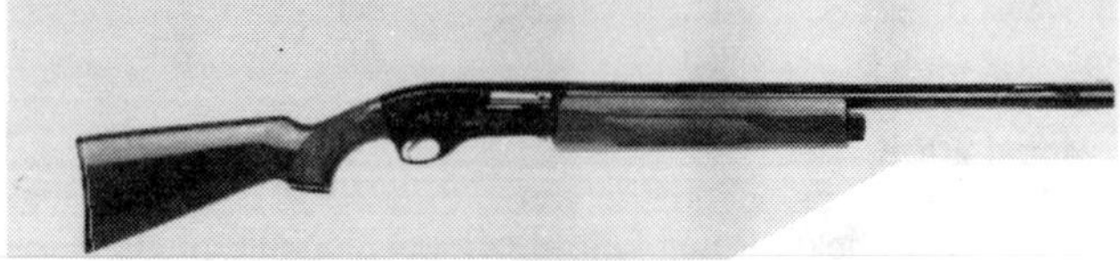

Exc.	V.G.	Good	Fair	Poor
575	525	450	350	225

Model 5500 MKII

A 12 gauge semi-automatic shotgun supplied with either a 26" barrel for 2.75" shells or a 28" barrel for 3" shells. Blued with a walnut stock. Introduced in 1989.

NIB	Exc.	V.G.	Good	Fair	Poor
435	375	275	225	175	125

Model 1500 Series

A .223 to .338 Winchester Magnum bolt-action rifle with a 22" or 24" barrel, 5- or 6-shot magazine and various sights. Blued with a hardwood or walnut stock. Manufactured by Howa in Japan and also known as the Smith & Wesson Model 1500. Offered in 1986 and 1987.

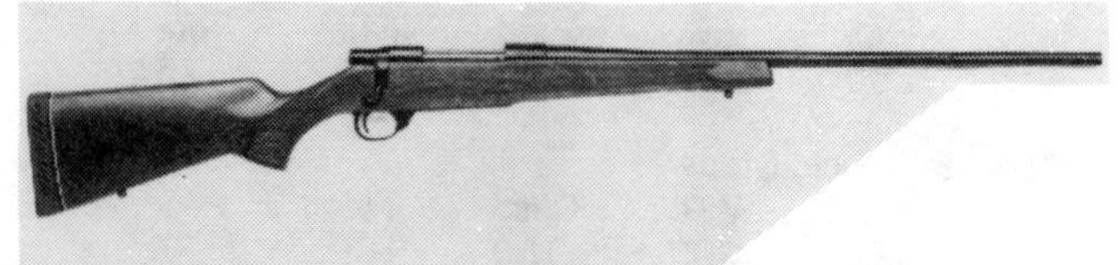

Model 1500 Mountaineer Grade I

Exc.	V.G.	Good	Fair	Poor
300	250	225	150	125

Model 1500 Mountaineer Grade II

Exc.	V.G.	Good	Fair	Poor
325	275	250	175	125

Model 1500 Varmint—24" Heavy Barrel

Exc.	V.G.	Good	Fair	Poor
350	300	275	200	150

Model 1550

As above, but in .243, .270 or .30-06 caliber. Offered in 1986 and 1987.

Exc.	V.G.	Good	Fair	Poor
325	275	250	175	125

Model 1700 LS

Similar to the above, and in the same calibers with a 22" barrel not fitted for sights, machine jeweled bolt and knurled bolt handle. Blued with a walnut stock having a schnabel forend. Offered in 1986 and 1987.

Exc.	V.G.	Good	Fair	Poor
400	350	275	200	150

MUGICA, JOSE

Eibar, Spain
SEE—Llama

A tradename found on Llama pistols that were manufactured by Gabilondo.

MURATA

SEE—Japan State

MURRAY, J. P.

Columbus, Georgia

Percussion Rifle

A .58 caliber percussion rifle with a 33" barrel, full stock and brass mounts. Also made with a 23.5" to 24" barrel as a carbine. The lock marked "J.P.Murray/Columbus Ga." Several hundred were manufactured between 1862 and 1864. Prospective purchasers are advised to secure a qualified appraisal prior to acquisition.

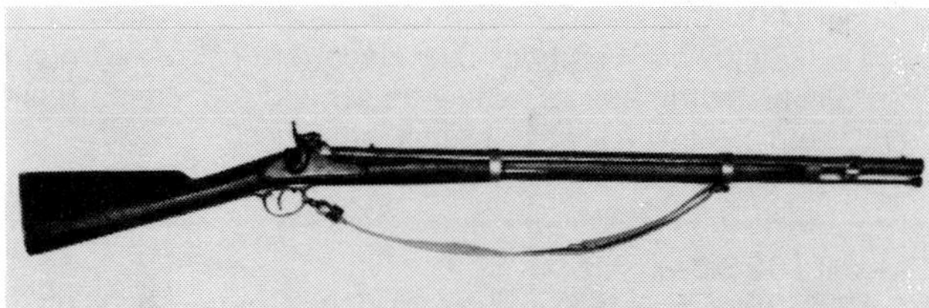

Courtesy Milwaukee Public Museum, Milwaukee, Wisconsin.

Exc.	V.G.	Good	Fair	Poor
4500	3750	3000	2500	1800

MURPHY & O'CONNEL

New York, New York

Pocket Pistol

A .41 caliber single shot percussion pocket pistol with a 3" barrel, German silver mounts and a walnut stock. Manufactured during the 1850s.

Exc.	V.G.	Good	Fair	Poor
650	575	450	350	250

MUSGRAVE

Republic of South Africa

RSA NR1 Single Shot Target Rifle

A .308 caliber single shot bolt-action rifle with a 26" barrel, match sights, adjustable trigger and target style stock. Made of walnut. Manufactured between 1971 and 1976.

Exc.	V.G.	Good	Fair	Poor
325	275	225	175	125

Valiant NR6

A .243, .270, .308, .30-06, and 7mm Remington Magnum caliber bolt-action sporting rifle with a 24" barrel, open sights and English style stock. Imported from 1971 to 1976.

Exc.	V.G.	Good	Fair	Poor
300	250	200	150	100

Premier NR5

As above, with a 26" barrel and pistol grip Monte Carlo-style stock. Discontinued in 1976.

Exc.	V.G.	Good	Fair	Poor
350	300	250	200	150

MUSKETEER RIFLES

Washington, D.C.
Importer—Firearms International

Sporter

A .243 to .300 Winchester Magnum caliber bolt-action rifle with a 24" barrel without sights, and Monte Carlo-style stock. Imported between 1963 and 1972.

Exc.	V.G.	Good	Fair	Poor
300	250	200	175	125

Deluxe Sporter

As above, with an adjustable trigger and more finely figured walnut stock.

Exc.	V.G.	Good	Fair	Poor
350	300	250	200	150

Carbine

The Sporter with a 20" barrel.

Exc.	V.G.	Good	Fair	Poor
325	275	225	175	125

NAGANT, EMILE & LEON

Liege, Belgium

SEE—Mosin-Nagant

Model 1878 Officers Revolver

A 9mm caliber double-action revolver with a 5" octagonal barrel and 6-shot cylinder. Blued with walnut grips. Also manufactured in 7.5mm caliber for the Swedish Government. Those purchased by Argentina, Brazil and Norway bear those country's acceptance marks.

Exc.	V.G.	Good	Fair	Poor
250	225	200	150	100

NAMBU

SEE—Japan State

NATIONAL ARMS CO.

Brooklyn, New York

SEE—Moore's Patent Firearms Co.

The successor to the Moore's Patent Firearms Company in 1865. Purchased by the Colt Company in 1870.

Large Frame Teat-Fire Revolver

A .45 Teat Fire caliber revolver with a 7.5" barrel and 6-shot cylinder. Blued or silver-plated with walnut grips. The barrel marked "National Arms Co.,Brooklyn". The exact number of these revolvers made is unknown, but it is estimated to be less than 30. Prospective purchasers are advised to secure a qualified appraisal prior to acquisition.

Exc.	V.G.	Good	Fair	Poor
5000	4000	2500	1500	1000

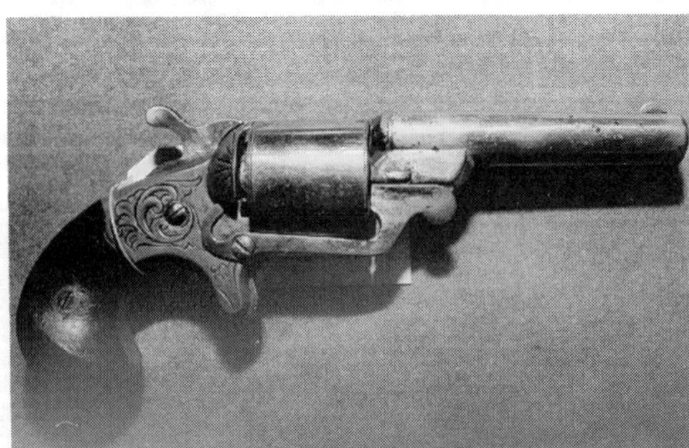

No. 2 Derringer

A .41 caliber spur trigger pocket pistol with a 2.5" barrel. Blued or silver-plated with walnut grips. Later manufactured by the Colt Company as their No. 2 Derringer.

Exc.	V.G.	Good	Fair	Poor
450	400	350	275	200

NAVY ARMS COMPANY

Ridgefield, New Jersey

Founded in 1957 by Val Forgett to enhance the shooting of black powder firearms without destroying the originals. The first replica was the Colt 1851 Navy. Thus, the name of the new company, "Navy Arms". In the early 1980's Navy Arms began importing surplus firearms from European countries. Navy Arms continues to offer both black powder replicas and foreign imports. For a short period of time the company imported double barrel shotguns. This was discontinued in 1990.

SHOTGUNS

The shotguns listed below were no longer imported by Navy Arms in 1990.

Model 83

A 12 or 20 gauge Magnum Over/Under shotgun manufactured in a variety of barrel lengths and styles with double triggers and extractors. Blued, engraved, with a walnut stock. Introduced in 1985.

NIB	Exc.	V.G.	Good	Fair	Poor
385	325	275	200	175	125

Model 93

As above, with automatic ejectors.

NIB	Exc.	V.G.	Good	Fair	Poor
450	400	325	275	225	175

Model 95

As above, with a single trigger and screw-in choke tubes.

NIB	Exc.	V.G.	Good	Fair	Poor
475	425	350	300	250	200

Model 96 Sportsman

As above, in 12 gauge only with a gold-plated receiver.

NIB	Exc.	V.G.	Good	Fair	Poor
575	525	450	400	350	300

Model 100

A 12, 20, 28 or .410 bore Over/Under boxlock shotgun with 26" ventilated-rib barrels, single trigger and extractors. Blued, chrome-plated, with a walnut stock. Introduced in 1989.

NIB	Exc.	V.G.	Good	Fair	Poor
300	250	225	200	150	100

Model 100 Side x Side

A 12 or 20 gauge Magnum boxlock double-barrel shotgun with 27.5" barrels, double triggers and extractors. Blued with a walnut stock. Imported between 1985 and 1987.

Exc.	V.G.	Good	Fair	Poor
375	325	275	200	125

Model 150

As above, with automatic ejectors.

Exc.	V.G.	Good	Fair	Poor
450	400	325	225	150

Model 105

A 12, 20, or .410 bore folding single barrel shotgun with a 26" or 28" barrel, chrome-plated engraved receiver, blued barrel and hardwood stock. Introduced in 1985.

NIB	Exc.	V.G.	Good	Fair	Poor
100	80	75	65	50	35

Model 105 Deluxe

As above, with vent-rib barrel and a checkered walnut stock.

NIB	Exc.	V.G.	Good	Fair	Poor
120	100	85	75	60	45

Replica Long Guns

Harpers Ferry Flint Rifle

This model is a copy of the 1803 rifle in the original .54 caliber. It features a rust blued 35" barrel. Weight is 8.5 lb.

NIB	Exc.	V.G.	Good	Fair	Poor
475	400	350	300	200	100

Brown Bess Musket

This replica is a copy of the second model used between 1760 and 1776. Bright finish on metal and one piece walnut stock with polished brass locks. Barrel is 42" and weight is 9.5 lb.

NIB	Exc.	V.G.	Good	Fair	Poor
500	450	400	300	250	100

Brown Bess Carbine

Same as above but fitted with a 30" barrel. Weighs 7.75 lb.

NIB	Exc.	V.G.	Good	Fair	Poor
550	500	450	325	250	100

1777 Charleville Musket

Copy of French flintlock in .69 caliber. Fittings are steel with brass front sight and brass flashpan. Barrel length is 44.625" and weighs about 8.75 lb.

NIB	Exc.	V.G.	Good	Fair	Poor
590	500	450	400	300	150

1777 Standard Charleville Musket

Same as above with polished steel barrel and select walnut stock.

NIB	Exc.	V.G.	Good	Fair	Poor
500	450	400	350	250	100

1816 M.T. Wickham Musket

Furnished in .69 caliber with steel ramrod with button head. Brass flashpan and walnut stock are standard.

NIB	Exc.	V.G.	Good	Fair	Poor
600	550	450	350	250	100

1808 Springfield Musket

This model is a U.S. copy of the 1763 Charleville musket with 1808 Springfield markings. Barrel length is 44" and weight is 8.75 lb.

NIB	Exc.	V.G.	Good	Fair	Poor
530	475	400	300	200	100

Pennsylvania Long Rifle

This model is offered in either percussion or flintlock ignition and is offered in a choice of .32 caliber or .45 caliber. It has an octagonal 40.5" rust blued barrel, polished lock, double set triggers, and brass furniture on a walnut stock. Weighs 7.5 lb.

Percussion

NIB	Exc.	V.G.	Good	Fair	Poor
335	290	250	200	150	100

Flintlock

NIB	Exc.	V.G.	Good	Fair	Poor
350	300	250	200	150	100

Kentucky Rifle

Offered in either percussion or flintlock ignition it has a blue steel barrel, case-colored lockplate, and a polished brass patch box inletted into a walnut stock. The barrel length is 35" and the rifle is available in .45 or .50 caliber. Weight is 6 lb., 14 oz.

Percussion

NIB	Exc.	V.G.	Good	Fair	Poor
280	250	200	150	100	75

Flintlock

NIB	Exc.	V.G.	Good	Fair	Poor
300	260	210	150	100	75

Mortimer Flintlock Rifle

Offered in .54 caliber with rust blued barrel, walnut stock with cheek piece and checkered straight grip. It also has a external safety and sling swivels. Barrel length is 36" and weight is 9 lb. Optional shotgun barrel.

NIB	Exc.	V.G.	Good	Fair	Poor
590	550	500	450	350	200

ADD: $240 for optional shotgun barrel.

Tryon Creedmoor Rifle

This .45 caliber model features a heavy blued 33" octagonal barrel, hooded front sight, adjustable tang sight, double set triggers, sling swivels, and a walnut stock. Weighs about 9.5 lb.

NIB	Exc.	V.G.	Good	Fair	Poor
580	525	450	400	300	200

Standard Tryon Rifle

Same as above but without target sights.

NIB	Exc.	V.G.	Good	Fair	Poor
400	350	300	250	200	100

Deluxe Tryon Rifle

Same as above but with polished and engraved lock and patch box.

NIB	Exc.	V.G.	Good	Fair	Poor
425	375	325	250	200	100

Parker-Hale Whitworth Rifle

This is a replica of a British sniper rifle, .451 caliber, used by the Confederates during the Civil War. Round barrel is 36" and features a globe front sight and ladder rear sight. The walnut stock is hand checkered. Weighs 9 lb., 10 oz.

NIB	Exc.	V.G.	Good	Fair	Poor
700	650	600	450	300	150

ADD: $150 for Limited Edition w/Telescope.

Parker-Hale Volunteer Rifle

A .451 caliber rifle with hand checkered walnut stock. Fitted with 32" barrel with globe front sight and ladder rear sight. Weighs 9.5 lb.

NIB	Exc.	V.G.	Good	Fair	Poor
640	600	550	400	300	200

Parker-Hale 3 Band Volunteer Rifle

Same basic specifications as Whitworth rifle but furnished with Alexander Henry rifling.

NIB	Exc.	V.G.	Good	Fair	Poor
700	650	600	400	250	150

Rigby Target Rifle

The 1880s replica is chambered for the .451 caliber. It is fitted with adjustable front sight and vernier tang sight. The lock, breech plug, trigger guard, butt plate, and escutcheons are case-colored. Barrel length is 32" and weighs 7 lb., 12 oz.

NIB	Exc.	V.G.	Good	Fair	Poor
550	500	450	300	200	100

1861 Springfield Rifle

This .58 caliber replica is fitted with a 1855 style hammer. Barrel length is 40" and weight is 10 lb., 4 oz.

NIB	Exc.	V.G.	Good	Fair	Poor
470	425	350	300	200	100

1862 C.S. Richmond Rifle

This Confederate rifle is .58 caliber and is a faithful reproduction of those produced at the Richmond Armory. Barrel length is 40". Weighs 10 lb., 4 oz.

NIB	Exc.	V.G.	Good	Fair	Poor
470	425	350	300	200	100

J.P. Murray Carbine

This Confederate cavalry .58 caliber carbine has a case-colored lock and brass furniture on a walnut stock. Barrel length is 23.5" and weighs 8 lb., 5 oz.

NIB	Exc.	V.G.	Good	Fair	Poor
325	275	250	200	150	100

1863 Springfield Rifle

An exact replica of the famous Springfield Musket. Barrel is 40" with 3 barrel bands. All metal parts are finished bright. Weighs 9.5 lb.

NIB	Exc.	V.G.	Good	Fair	Poor
470	425	350	300	200	100

1841 Mississippi Rifle
Also know as the "Yager" rifle it is offered in either .54 or .58 caliber. Barrel length is 33" and weighs 9.5 lb.

NIB	Exc.	V.G.	Good	Fair	Poor
380	325	250	200	150	100

Zouave Rifle
This Civil War replica is a .58 caliber with polished brass hardware and blued 33" barrel. Weighs 9 lb.

NIB	Exc.	V.G.	Good	Fair	Poor
380	325	250	200	150	100

Parker-Hale 1861 Musketoon
Made by Gibbs Rifle Co. using 130 year old gauges for reference this .577 caliber replica features a 24" barrel with folding ladder military sight. The stock is walnut and the lock is case-colored. All furniture is polished brass. Weighs 7.5 lb.

NIB	Exc.	V.G.	Good	Fair	Poor
380	325	250	200	150	100

Navy Arms Musketoon
Same as above but manufactured in Italy.

NIB	Exc.	V.G.	Good	Fair	Poor
315	275	225	200	150	100

Parker-Hale 1858 Two Band Musket
This .577 caliber model is based on the 1858 Enfield naval pattern.Fitted with a military sight graduated to 1100 yards. Case-colored lock and walnut stock with brass fittings. Barrel length is 33" and weighs 8.5 lb.

NIB	Exc.	V.G.	Good	Fair	Poor
470	425	350	300	200	100

Navy Arms 1858 Two Band Musket
Same as above but built in Italy.

NIB	Exc.	V.G.	Good	Fair	Poor
380	325	250	200	150	100

Parker-Hale Three Band Musket
This replica is based on the design produced between 1853 and 1863. The rear sight is based on a 1853 model graduated to 900 yards. Is fitted with a case-colored lock and walnut stock with brass furniture. Barrel is 39" and weighs 9 lb.

NIB	Exc.	V.G.	Good	Fair	Poor
500	450	400	300	200	100

Navy Arms Three Band Musket
Same as above but produced in Italy.

NIB	Exc.	V.G.	Good	Fair	Poor
400	350	300	250	200	100

Sharps Cavalry Carbine
A breech loading .54 caliber carbine with 22" blued barrel. Military style sights, walnut stocks, and saddle bar with ring are standard. Weighs 7 lb., 12 oz.

NIB	Exc.	V.G.	Good	Fair	Poor
600	550	500	400	300	150

Sharps Cavalry Carbine Cartridge Model
Same as above but chambered for the .45-70 Gov't cartridge.

NIB	Exc.	V.G.	Good	Fair	Poor
620	570	520	400	300	150

Sharps Plains Rifle
This model features a case-colored receiver, blued barrel, and checkered walnut stock. Offered in .44-70 or .54 caliber percussion. Barrel length is 28.5". Weight is 8 lb., 10 oz.

NIB	Exc.	V.G.	Good	Fair	Poor
600	550	500	400	300	150

1873 Winchester Rifle
This replica features a case-colored receiver, blued octagon 24" barrel, and walnut stocks. Offered in either .440-40 or .45 Long Colt. Weighs about 8lb., 4 oz.

NIB	Exc.	V.G.	Good	Fair	Poor
715	650	600	500	400	200

1873 Winchester Carbine
Same specifications as rifle above but fitted with a 19" round barrel, blued receiver, and saddle ring. Weighs 7 lb., 4 oz.

NIB	Exc.	V.G.	Good	Fair	Poor
700	635	595	500	400	200

1873 Winchester Sporting Rifle
This model features a 30" octagonal barrel, case-colored receiver, and checkered pistol grip. Offered in .44-40 or .45 Long Colt. Weighs about 8 lb., 14 oz. A 24" model is also offered.

NIB	Exc.	V.G.	Good	Fair	Poor
760	700	650	525	400	200

1866 "Yellowboy" Rifle
This model features a brass receiver, 24" octagon barrel, and walnut stocks. Weighs 8.5 lb.

NIB	Exc.	V.G.	Good	Fair	Poor
580	525	450	400	300	150

1866 "Yellowboy" Carbine
Same as above but fitted with a 19" round barrel and saddle ring. Weighs 7 lb., 4 oz.

NIB	Exc.	V.G.	Good	Fair	Poor
600	550	475	400	300	150

Iron Frame Henry
This is a replica of the famous and rare .44-40 Iron Frame Henry that features a case-colored frame. Barrel length is 24" and rifle weighs 9 lb.

NIB	Exc.	V.G.	Good	Fair	Poor
750	700	650	500	400	200

Blued Iron Frame Henry
Same as above but furnished with a highly polished blued receiver.

NIB	Exc.	V.G.	Good	Fair	Poor
750	700	650	500	400	200

Military Henry
Based on the brass frame military version of the Henry rifle this model is furnished with sling swivels mounted on the left side. The butt plate is fitted with a trap door. Caliber is .44-40 and barrel length is 24". Weighs 9 lb., 4 oz.

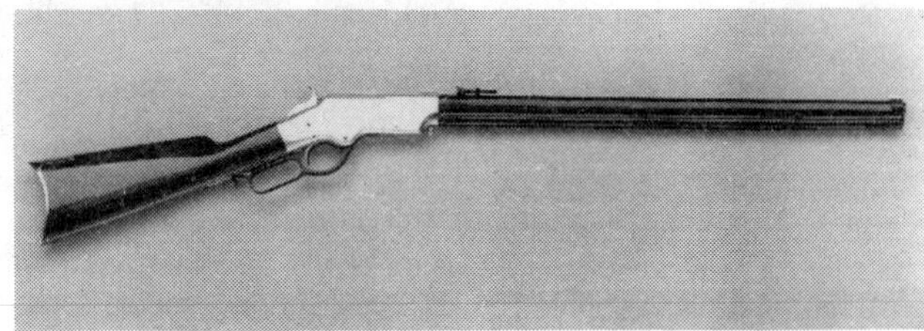

NIB	Exc.	V.G.	Good	Fair	Poor
750	700	650	500	400	200

Henry Carbine
This is the brass frame carbine version and features a 22" barrel. Chambered for the .44-40 cartridge. Weighs 8 lb., 12 oz.

NIB	Exc.	V.G.	Good	Fair	Poor
750	700	650	500	400	200

Henry Trapper
This replica is not based on an actual Henry. Fitted with a unique 16.5" barrel, this brass frame model weighs 7 lb., 7 oz. Chambered for the .44-40 cartridge.

NIB	Exc.	V.G.	Good	Fair	Poor
750	700	650	500	400	200

No.2 Creedmoor Target Rifle
This is a reproduction of the Remington No. 2 Creedmore. It features a case-colored receiver, tapered 30" octagonal barrel, hooded front sight, Creedmore tang sight, and walnut stock with checkered pistol grip. Furnished in .45-70 Gov't. Weighs 9 lb.

NIB	Exc.	V.G.	Good	Fair	Poor
595	550	500	400	300	150

Rolling Block Buffalo Rifle
This rifle is a replica of the Remington Buffalo rifle. It is fitted with a 26" or 30" octagonal or half octagonal barrel, case-colored receiver, blade front sight, notch rear sight, brass trigger

guard, with walnut stocks. Tang is drilled and tapped for tang sight.

NIB	Exc.	V.G.	Good	Fair	Poor
440	390	350	300	200	100

Half Octagon Barrel Model

NIB	Exc.	V.G.	Good	Fair	Poor
440	390	350	300	200	100

Ithaca/Navy Hawken Rifle

Offered in either .50 or .54 caliber percussion. Features a 31.5" rust blued octagon barrel. the percussion lockplate is case-colored, while the rest of the hardware is blued with the exception of the nose cap and escutcheons. Weighs about 9 lb., 13 oz.

NIB	Exc.	V.G.	Good	Fair	Poor
340	300	250	200	150	100

Hawken Rifle

This model features a case-colored lock, 28" blued octagon barrel, adjustable sights, double set triggers, and hooked breech. The polished brass furniture and patchbox are mounted on a walnut stock. Weighs about 8.5 lb.

NIB	Exc.	V.G.	Good	Fair	Poor
195	150	125	100	75	60

Hawken Hunter Rifle

Offered in .50, .54, or .58 caliber, this model features blued hardware, adjustable sights, case-colored lock, and hooked breech. The walnut stock is hand checkered with a cheek piece. Rubber recoil pad is standard. Barrel length is 28". Weighs approximately 7 lb., 12 oz.

NIB	Exc.	V.G.	Good	Fair	Poor
210	170	130	100	75	60

Hawken Hunter Carbine

Same as above but fitted with a 22.5" barrel. Weighs about 6 lb., 12 oz.

NIB	Exc.	V.G.	Good	Fair	Poor
210	170	130	100	75	60

Kodiak Double Rifle

Built in Europe this model features a walnut stock with cheek piece and hand checkering. Barrel length is 28.5" with adjustable sights. Engraved side plates are polished bright. Sling Swivels standard. Weighs 11 lb.

NIB	Exc.	V.G.	Good	Fair	Poor
575	500	450	300	200	100

Mortimer Flintlock Shotgun

Replica of 12 gauge English Mortimer this model features a waterproof pan, roller frizzen, external safety. All parts are case-colored. Barrel is 36" long. Weighs 7 lb.

NIB	Exc.	V.G.	Good	Fair	Poor
575	500	450	300	200	100

Fowler Shotgun

This 12 gauge model is a side by side with straight gripstock. The gun features a hooked breech and 28" blued barrels. The side plates are engraved and case-colored. Double triggers and checkered walnut stock are standard. weighs 7.25 lb.

NIB	Exc.	V.G.	Good	Fair	Poor
275	225	150	125	100	75

Navy Arms Steel Shot Magnum

Same as above but chambered for 10 gauge shells. Weighs 7 lb., 9 oz.

NIB	Exc.	V.G.	Good	Fair	Poor
440	400	350	300	200	100

T&T Shotgun

This Turkey and Trap model has a straight grip stock and 28" barrel choked full and full. Locks are case-colored and engraved. Walnut stock is checkered. Weighs 7.5 lb.

NIB	Exc.	V.G.	Good	Fair	Poor
400	350	300	250	200	100

Japanese Matchlock

This model is a .50 caliber with 41" barrels. Weighs 8.5 lb.

NIB	Exc.	V.G.	Good	Fair	Poor
420	350	300	200	100	75

HANDGUNS

Le Page Pistol

This .44 caliber percussion pistol has a 10.25" tapered octagon barrel, adjustable single set trigger. The lock, trigger guard, and butt cap are engraved. The walnut stocks are hand checkered. Weighs 36 oz.

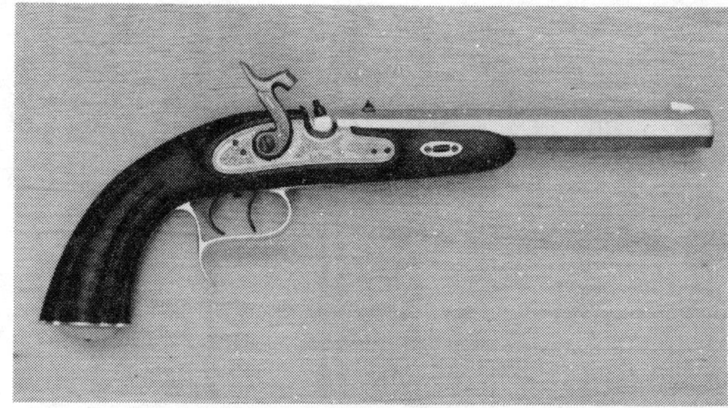

NIB	Exc.	V.G.	Good	Fair	Poor
400	350	300	250	200	100

Single Cased Set

NIB	Exc.	V.G.	Good	Fair	Poor
580	530	475	400	300	150

Double Cased Set

NIB	Exc.	V.G.	Good	Fair	Poor
995	875	750	600	400	200

Le Page Flintlock

Same as above but with flintlock ignition. Weighs 41 oz.

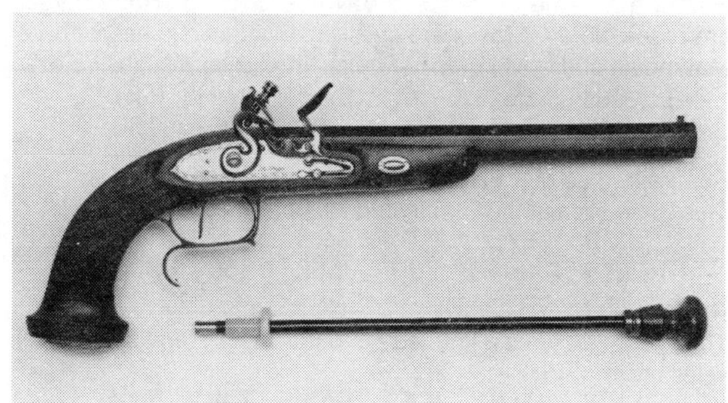

NIB	Exc.	V.G.	Good	Fair	Poor
470	425	350	250	150	100

Le Page Smoothbore Flintlock Pistol

Same as above but with a smooth bore.

NIB	Exc.	V.G.	Good	Fair	Poor
470	425	350	250	150	100

Single Cased Set

NIB	Exc.	V.G.	Good	Fair	Poor
650	600	500	400	300	150

Double Cased Set

NIB	Exc.	V.G.	Good	Fair	Poor
1200	995	750	600	400	200

Kentucky Pistol

A percussion replica of a pistol developed in the 1840s. It has a 10.125" blued barrel, case-colored lock, brass furniture and trigger guard with walnut stock. Weighs 32 oz.

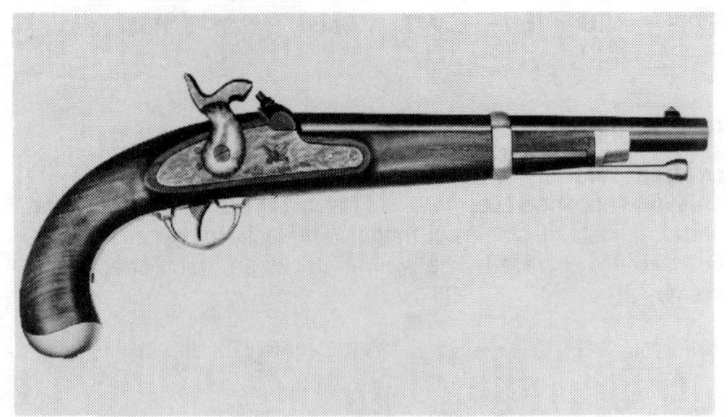

NIB	Exc.	V.G.	Good	Fair	Poor
165	150	125	100	85	60

Single Cased Set

NIB	Exc.	V.G.	Good	Fair	Poor
250	200	150	125	100	75

Double Cased Set

NIB	Exc.	V.G.	Good	Fair	Poor
420	350	300	250	150	100

Kentucky Flintlock Pistol

Same as above but with flintlock ignition.

NIB	Exc.	V.G.	Good	Fair	Poor
175	150	125	100	75	60

Single Cased Set

NIB	Exc.	V.G.	Good	Fair	Poor
250	200	150	125	100	75

Double Cased Set

NIB	Exc.	V.G.	Good	Fair	Poor
440	400	350	275	175	100

18th Georgia Le Mat Pistol

This 9-shot .44 caliber percussion revolver has a 7.625" blued barrel and engraved cylinder. An engraved banner on the left side of the frame reads "DEO VINDICE". Hammer and trigger are case-colored. Stocks are checkered walnut. Comes with Le Mat mould and velvet draped French fitted case. Weighs 55 oz.

NIB	Exc.	V.G.	Good	Fair	Poor
675	600	500	400	300	150

Beauregard Le Mat Pistol

This is a replica of the Cavalry model. Comes cased.

NIB	Exc.	V.G.	Good	Fair	Poor
850	800	700	550	350	200

Navy Le Mat

This model features a knurled pin barrel release and spur barrel selector.

NIB	Exc.	V.G.	Good	Fair	Poor
500	450	400	350	300	150

Army Le Mat

This model features a knurled pin barrel release and cross pin barrel selector.

NIB	Exc.	V.G.	Good	Fair	Poor
500	450	400	350	300	150

Cavalry Le Mat

This model features a lanyard ring, spur trigger, lever type barrel release, and cross pin barrel selector.

NIB	Exc.	V.G.	Good	Fair	Poor
500	450	400	350	300	150

1862 New Model Police

This replica is based on the Colt .36 caliber pocket pistol of the same name. It features a half fluted and re-dated cylinder, case-colored frame and loading gate, and a polished brass trigger guard and backstrap. Barrel length is 5.5" and pistol weigh 26 oz.

NIB	Exc.	V.G.	Good	Fair	Poor
240	200	175	150	100	75

1862 New Model Book Style Cased Set

NIB	Exc.	V.G.	Good	Fair	Poor
300	250	200	150	100	75

Paterson Revolver

This replica is the five shot. 36 caliber. The cylinder is scroll engraved with a stagecoach scene. The hidden trigger drops down when the hammer is cocked. Barrel is 9" and the pistol weighs 43 oz.

NIB	Exc.	V.G.	Good	Fair	Poor
275	225	200	150	125	100

1851 Navy

This Colt replica is offered in either .36 or .44 caliber. A naval battle scene is engraved in the cylinder. The octagon barrel length is 7.5". The trigger guard, backstrap are polished brass. The walnut grips are hand rubbed. Weighs 32 oz.

NIB	Exc.	V.G.	Good	Fair	Poor
125	100	75	60	50	40

Single Cased Set

NIB	Exc.	V.G.	Good	Fair	Poor
200	150	125	100	75	60

Double Cased Set

NIB	Exc.	V.G.	Good	Fair	Poor
350	300	250	200	150	75

ADD: $100 for optional shoulder stock.

Augusta 1851 Navy Pistol

Available with either 5" or 7.5" barrel. Engraved with "A" coverage.

NIB	Exc.	V.G.	Good	Fair	Poor
200	150	100	75	60	50

Reb Model 1860 Pistol

This is a replica of the Confederate Griswold and Gunnison revolver. It features a blued round 7.5" barrel, brass frame, trigger guard and backstrap. Offered in .36 or .44 caliber. Weighs 44 oz.

NIB	Exc.	V.G.	Good	Fair	Poor
100	80	70	60	50	35

Reb 1860 Sheriff's Model

Same as above but fitted with a 5" barrel. Weighs 40 oz.

NIB	Exc.	V.G.	Good	Fair	Poor
100	80	70	60	50	35

Engraved Paterson Revolver

This model features hand engraving with silver inlays.

NIB	Exc.	V.G.	Good	Fair	Poor
395	350	300	250	200	150

1847 Walker Dragoon

This is a replica of the very rare Colt .44 caliber revolver. The barrel and cylinder are blued while the frame and loading lever are case-colored. Barrel length is 9" and pistol weighs 75 oz.

NIB	Exc.	V.G.	Good	Fair	Poor
225	200	175	150	125	100

Single Cased Set

NIB	Exc.	V.G.	Good	Fair	Poor
325	300	275	250	200	100

Single Deluxe Cased Set

NIB	Exc.	V.G.	Good	Fair	Poor
430	400	350	300	200	100

1860 Army Pistol

This .44 caliber model features a case-colored frame and loading lever with blued barrel, cylinder, and backstrap.The trigger guard is brass. The cylinder is engraved with a battle scene. Barrel is 8" and pistol weighs 41 ozs.

NIB	Exc.	V.G.	Good	Fair	Poor
140	120	100	75	60	45

Single Cased Set

NIB	Exc.	V.G.	Good	Fair	Poor
225	200	175	150	100	75

Double Cased Set

NIB	Exc.	V.G.	Good	Fair	Poor
365	325	300	250	200	100

1858 New Model Remington Style Pistol

This replica has a solid frame as did the original. the frame and 8" barrel are blued while the trigger guard is brass. Walnut grips are standard. Weighs 40 oz.

NIB	Exc.	V.G.	Good	Fair	Poor
140	120	100	75	60	45

Single Cased Set

NIB	Exc.	V.G.	Good	Fair	Poor
220	180	150	125	100	75

Double Cased Set

NIB	Exc.	V.G.	Good	Fair	Poor
350	300	250	200	150	100

Stainless Steel 1858 New Model Army

Same as above but in stainless steel. Weighs 40 oz.

NIB	Exc.	V.G.	Good	Fair	Poor
220	180	150	125	100	80

Single Cased Set

NIB	Exc.	V.G.	Good	Fair	Poor
300	250	200	150	125	100

Double Cased Set

NIB	Exc.	V.G.	Good	Fair	Poor
525	475	400	300	200	150

Brass Framed 1858 New Model Army

This version features a highly polished brass frame. Barrel length is 7.75".

NIB	Exc.	V.G.	Good	Fair	Poor
100	80	70	60	50	35

Single Cased Set

NIB	Exc.	V.G.	Good	Fair	Poor
180	150	125	100	75	60

Double Cased Set

NIB	Exc.	V.G.	Good	Fair	Poor
275	250	200	150	100	75

1858 Target Model

Same as above but features a patridge front sight and an adjustable rear sight. Barrel length is 8".

NIB	Exc.	V.G.	Good	Fair	Poor
175	150	125	100	75	50

Deluxe 1858 New Model Army

This replica is built to the exact dimensions as the original. the Barrel is 8" with adjustable front sight. The trigger guard is silver plated. the action is tuned for competition. Weighs 46 oz.

NIB	Exc.	V.G.	Good	Fair	Poor
310	250	200	150	100	75

Spiller and Burr Pistol

This is a .36 caliber pistol with 7" blued octagon barrel. the frame is brass with walnut grips. Weighs 40 oz.

NIB	Exc.	V.G.	Good	Fair	Poor
115	100	80	65	50	40

Single Cased Set

NIB	Exc.	V.G.	Good	Fair	Poor
195	150	125	100	75	60

Double Cased Set

NIB	Exc.	V.G.	Good	Fair	Poor
315	250	200	150	125	100

Rogers and Spencer Pistol

This model features a 7.5" barrel with blued frame and barrel. Offered in .44 caliber. Walnut grips. Weighs 48 ozs.

NIB	Exc.	V.G.	Good	Fair	Poor
200	150	125	100	75	50

"London Gray" Rogers and Spencer Pistol

Same as above but with a burnished satin chrome finish.

NIB	Exc.	V.G.	Good	Fair	Poor
220	180	140	125	100	80

Rogers and Spencer Target Model

Same as standard model but fitted with adjustable target sights.

NIB	Exc.	V.G.	Good	Fair	Poor
220	180	140	125	100	80

1873 Colt-Style Single Action Army

This replica features a case-colored frame and hammer with blued round barrel in 3", 4.75", 5.5", or 7.5" lengths. Cylinder , trigger guard, and cylinder are blued. Offered in .44-40 or .45 Long Colt.

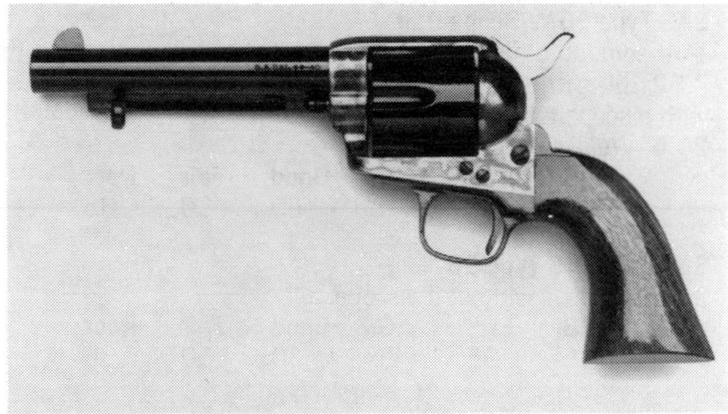

NIB	Exc.	V.G.	Good	Fair	Poor
315	275	200	150	125	100

Economy Model 1873 S.A.A.

Same as above but with brass trigger guard and backstrap.

NIB	Exc.	V.G.	Good	Fair	Poor
275	250	200	150	125	100

Nickel 1873 S.A.A.

NIB	Exc.	V.G.	Good	Fair	Poor
370	325	275	225	150	100

1873 U.S. Cavalry Model

This .45 Long Colt model features U.S. arsenal stampings, case-colored frame, and walnut grips. Barrel length is 7.5" and pistol weighs 45 oz.

NIB	Exc.	V.G.	Good	Fair	Poor
385	350	300	250	200	100

1895 U.S. Artillery Model

Same as Cavalry Model but fitted with a 5.5" barrel. Weighs 42 oz.

NIB	Exc.	V.G.	Good	Fair	Poor
385	350	300	250	200	100

1875 Remington-Style Revolver

The frame is case-colored while all other parts are blued except for brass trigger guard. Available in .44-40 or .45 Long Colt. Furnished with walnut grips. Barrel length is 7.5". Weighs 41 oz.

NIB	Exc.	V.G.	Good	Fair	Poor
310	275	225	175	150	100

1890 Remington-Style Revolver
This is a modified version of the 1875 model which is also offered in .44-40 or .45 Long Colt. The web under the barrel has been eliminated. It has blued 5.5" steel barrel and frame. Lanyard loop is on bottom of walnut grips. Weighs 39 oz.

NIB	Exc.	V.G.	Good	Fair	Poor
315	280	225	175	150	100

MILITARY SURPLUS ARMS

SKS Type 56 W/Scope Rail
This semi-automatic gas operated rifle is chambered for the 7.62x39 cartridge. It has a 10 round clip. This model is fitted with a scope rail on the left side of the receiver. Barrel length is 20.5" Weighs is 8 lb.

NIB	Exc.	V.G.	Good	Fair	Poor
120	100	75	60	50	35

Standard SKS Type 56
Same as above without the scope rail.

NIB	Exc.	V.G.	Good	Fair	Poor
115	95	75	60	50	35

SKS "Sharpshooter"
This model is fitted with a 2.75 power Type 89 scope an RPK style folding bipod.

NIB	Exc.	V.G.	Good	Fair	Poor
280	250	200	150	125	100

SKS "Cowboys Companion" Carbine
Barrel length on this version is 16.5". Weighs 7 lb., 8 oz.

NIB	Exc.	V.G.	Good	Fair	Poor
135	110	85	70	60	40

SKS "Para" Carbine
This is the military version of the "Cowboys Companion" fitted with a short cruciform folding bayonet.

NIB	Exc.	V.G.	Good	Fair	Poor
145	120	90	75	60	40

SKS "Hunter" Carbine
This model has a checkered composite Monte Carlo stock with full length pull. Comes with 5 round magazine.

NIB	Exc.	V.G.	Good	Fair	Poor
195	175	150	125	100	75

TT-Olympia Pistol
This is a reproduction of the Walther target pistol. Chambered for .22 LR. Barrel length is 4.625" and pistol weighs 27 oz.

NIB	Exc.	V.G.	Good	Fair	Poor
260	225	200	150	125	100

TU-90 Pistol
This model is based on the Tokagypt pistol. It features a wraparound grip with thumb rest. Barrel length is 4.5" and pistol weighs 30 oz.

NIB	Exc.	V.G.	Good	Fair	Poor
110	90	80	70	50	40

TU-KKW Training Rifle
Based on the 98 Mauser and chambered for the .22 Long Rifle cartridge it is fitted with military sights, bayonet lug, cleaning rod and take down disc. comes with detachable 5 round box magazine. Barrel length is 26" and weighs 8 lb.

NIB	Exc.	V.G.	Good	Fair	Poor
180	150	125	100	80	60

TU-KKW Sniper Trainer
Same as above but fitted with a 2.75 power Type 89 scope and quick detachable mounting system.

NIB	Exc.	V.G.	Good	Fair	Poor
240	200	175	150	125	90

TU-33/40 Carbine
This model is based on the WWII Mauser G 33/40 mountain carbine. Chambered for the .22 Long Rifle or 7.62x39 cartridge. Barrel length is 20.75" and weighs 7.5 lb.

NIB	Exc.	V.G.	Good	Fair	Poor
180	150	125	100	80	60

JW-15 Rifle
This model is a bolt action design based on the BRNO Model 5 action. Chambered for the .22 Long Rifle it features adjustable sights, sling swivels, an detachable 5 round magazine. The top of the receiver is dovetailed for easy scope mounting. Barrel is 24" long and rifle weighs 5 lb., 12 oz.

NIB	Exc.	V.G.	Good	Fair	Poor
100	80	70	60	50	35

Martini Target Rifle
A .444 or .45-70 caliber single shot Martini-action rifle with a 26" or 30" octagonal barrel, tang sight and walnut stock. Offered between 1972 and 1984.

Exc.	V.G.	Good	Fair	Poor
475	425	350	275	175

Parker-Hale Sniper Rifle
See Parker-Hale section of this text.

RPKS-74
A 5.56mm or 7.62x39mm caliber semi-automatic rifle with a 19" barrel patterned after the Russian AK series rifles.

Luger
A .22 caliber semi-automatic pistol with a 4", 6" or 8" barrel, fixed sights, and 10-shot magazine. Blued with walnut grips.

Manufactured in the U.S.A. in 1986 and 1987.

Exc.	V.G.	Good	Fair	Poor
175	150	125	100	75

Grand Prix Silhouette Pistol

A .30-30, .44 Magnum, 7mm Special, and .45-70 caliber single shot pistol with a 13.75" barrel, adjustable sights, and an aluminum, heat-disbursing rib. Matte-blued, walnut grips and forearm. Manufactured in 1985.

Exc.	V.G.	Good	Fair	Poor
325	275	225	175	125

NEAL, W.

Bangor, Maine

Under Hammer Pistol

A .31 caliber under hammer percussion pistol with 5" to 8" barrels, iron frame and walnut grip. The barrel marked " Wm. Neal/Bangor,Me."

Exc.	V.G.	Good	Fair	Poor
550	475	400	300	200

NEPPERHAN FIREARMS CO.

Yonkers, New York

Pocket Revolver

A .31 caliber percussion revolver with 3.5" to 6" barrels and a 5-shot cylinder. Blued, case-hardened with walnut grips. The barrel marked "Nepperhan/Fire Arms Co" and on some additionally "Yonkers New York". The latter are worth a slight premium over the values listed below. Approximately 5,000 were made during the 1860s.

Exc.	V.G.	Good	Fair	Poor
600	525	450	350	225

NEWBURY ARMS CO.

Catskill, New York
Albany, New York

Pocket Pistol

A .25 caliber spur trigger pocket pistol with a 4" octagonal barrel. Blued, silver-plated with walnut grips.

Exc.	V.G.	Good	Fair	Poor
550	475	400	300	200

Pocket Revolver

A .26 caliber double-action percussion revolver with a 5" barrel and C-shaped exposed trigger. Blued with an iron or brass frame and walnut grips. The barrel marked "Newbury Arms Co. Albany." Produced in very limited numbers between 1855 and 1860. Prospective purchasers are advised to secure a qualified appraisal prior to acquisition.

Exc.	V.G.	Good	Fair	Poor
2500	2000	1500	1000	750

NEW ENGLAND FIREARMS CO.

Gardner, Massachusetts

Model R22

A .22, .22 Magnum or .32 H&R Magnum double-action revolver with a 2.5", 4" or 6" barrel and either a 6- or 9-shot cylinder. Blued or nickle-plated with walnut grips. Introduced in 1988.

NIB	Exc.	V.G.	Good	Fair	Poor
110	95	80	70	60	40

Pardner

A 12, 16, 20 or .410 bore single shot shotgun with a 24", 26" or 28" barrel. Blued with a walnut stock. Introduced in 1987.

NIB	Exc.	V.G.	Good	Fair	Poor
100	85	75	65	50	35

Handi-Rifle

A .22 Hornet, .223, .30-30, or .45-70 caliber version of the above with a 22" barrel fitted with open sights. Blued, with a walnut stock. Introduced in 1989.

NIB	Exc.	V.G.	Good	Fair	Poor
150	125	100	75	65	40

Handi-Gun

As above, including an interchangeable shotgun barrel. Introduced in 1988.

NIB	Exc.	V.G.	Good	Fair	Poor
200	175	150	125	100	75

NEWCOMB, H. G.

Natchez, Mississippi

Pocket Pistol

A .41 caliber percussion pocket pistol with a 2.5" barrel, German silver mounts and a walnut stock. Manufactured in the 1850s.

Exc.	V.G.	Good	Fair	Poor
650	550	450	350	250

NEWTON ARMS CO.

Buffalo, New York

Also known as the Buffalo Newton Rifle Co. and the Charles Newton Rifle Company. In operation from 1913 to 1932.

Newton-Mauser Rifle

A .256 Newton caliber bolt-action rifle with a 24" barrel and double set triggers. Blued with a walnut stock. Manufactured circa 1914.

Exc.	V.G.	Good	Fair	Poor
750	675	550	400	275

Standard Rifle First Type

A .22, .256, .280., 30, .33, and .35 Newton as well as .30-06 caliber bolt-action rifle with a 24" barrel, open or aperture sights and double set triggers. Blued with a walnut stock. Manufactured between 1916 and 1918.

Exc.	V.G.	Good	Fair	Poor
1200	1000	750	550	400

Standard Rifle Second Model

A .256, .30, or .35 Newton as well as .30-06 caliber bolt-action rifle as above, but with an Enfield-style bolt handle. Manufactured after 1918.

Exc.	V.G.	Good	Fair	Poor
1000	800	650	400	350

Buffalo Newton Rifle

As above, but marked "Buffalo Newton Rifle Company".

Exc.	V.G.	Good	Fair	Poor
1000	800	650	400	350

NICHOLS & CHILDS

Conway, Massachusetts

Percussion Belt Revolver

A .34 caliber percussion revolver with a 6" round barrel and 6-shot cylinder. Blued or browned with walnut grips. It is estimated that less than 25 were made in 1838. Prospective purchasers are advised to secure a qualified appraisal prior to acquisition.

Exc.	V.G.	Good	Fair	Poor
7500	6500	5000	3250	2500

Revolving Percussion Rifle

A .36 or .40 caliber percussion rifle with a 22", 26" or 30" barrel and a 5-, 6-, 7- or 9-shot cylinder. Blued or browned with a walnut stock having a patchbox. Is believed that approximately 150 were made between 1838 and 1840. Prospective purchasers are advised to secure a qualified appraisal prior to acquisition.

Exc.	V.G.	Good	Fair	Poor
7500	6500	5000	3250	2500

NOBLE
Haydenville, Massachusetts

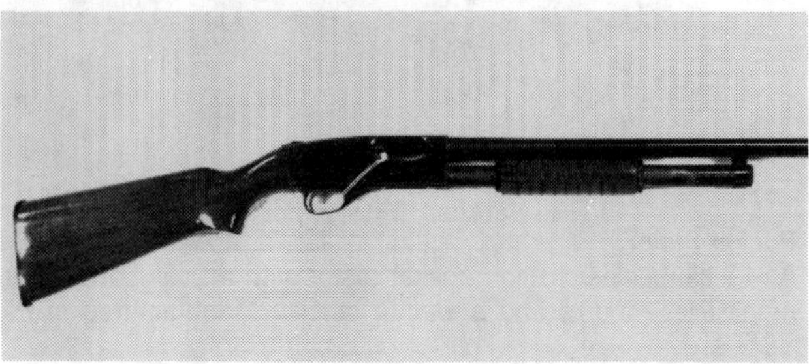

In business between 1950 and 1971, this company manufactured a variety of plain, utilitarian firearms. In general, these arms are all worth approximately the same, that is, less than $150.00 in excellent condition.

NORINCO
Peoples Republic of China
China North Industries Corp.

Imported by China Sports, as well as Interarms of Alexandria, Virginia.

ATD .22

A .22 caliber semi-automatic rifle with a 19.4" barrel and 11-shot magazine located in the butt. Blued with a hardwood stock. Importation began in 1987.

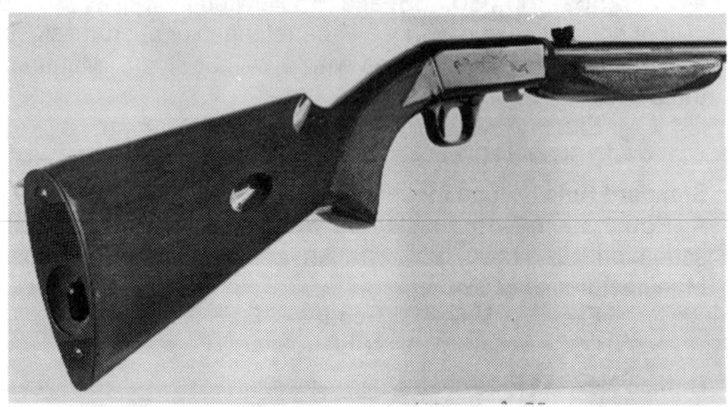

NIB	Exc.	V.G.	Good	Fair	Poor
180	150	125	100	75	50

EM-321

A .22 caliber slide action rifle with a 19.5" barrel and 10-shot tubular magazine. Blued with a hardwood stock. Introduced in 1989.

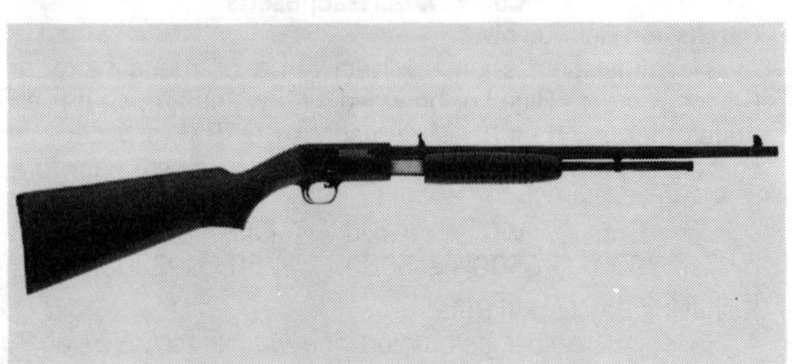

NIB	Exc.	V.G.	Good	Fair	Poor
125	100	85	75	65	50

Model HL-12-203 Shotgun

A 12 gauge boxlock Over/Under shotgun with 30" ventilated-rib barrels fitted for choke tubes, single trigger and automatic ejectors. Blued with a hardwood stock. Introduced in 1989.

NIB	Exc.	V.G.	Good	Fair	Poor
375	325	275	225	175	125

Model HL-12-102 Shotgun

A 12 gauge slide action shotgun with a 28" barrel and 3-shot magazine. Blued with a hardwood stock. Introduced in 1989.

NIB	Exc.	V.G.	Good	Fair	Poor
250	225	200	175	125	100

Model 213 Pistol

A copy of the Browning P-35 semi-automatic pistol. Sold in 1988 only.

Exc.	V.G.	Good	Fair	Poor
175	150	125	100	75

Type 54-1 Tokarev

A 7.62x25mm caliber semi-automatic pistol with a 4.6" barrel, fixed sights and 8-shot magazine. Blued with plastic grips. Imported in 1989.

Exc.	V.G.	Good	Fair	Poor
175	150	125	100	80

Type 59 Makarov

A .380 or 9mm Makarov caliber double-action semi-automatic pistol with a 3.5" barrel and 8-shot magazine. Blued with plastic grips.

Exc.	V.G.	Good	Fair	Poor
275	250	225	175	125

SKS Rifle
A 7.62x39mm caliber semi-automatic rifle with a 20.5" barrel, folding bayonet and either a 10-shot fixed magazine or 30-shot detachable magazine. Blued with a hardwood stock. Importation began in 1988.

Exc.	V.G.	Good	Fair	Poor
250	225	200	150	100

Type 84S AK
Similar to the AKS service rifle, in 5.56mm caliber with a 16" barrel and 30-shot magazine.

Type 84S-1
As above, with a underfolding metal stock.

Type 84S-3
As above, with a composition stock.

Type 84S-5
As above, with a stock which folds to the side and without a bayonet.

Type 81S
A semi-automatic copy of the AK47.

Type 81S-1
As above, with a folding stock.

NORTH AMERICAN ARMS CORP.
Toronto, Canada

Brigadier
A .45 NAACO caliber semi-automatic pistol with a 5" barrel, 8-shot magazine and alloy frame. Weight 4.5 lbs. Produced in very limited quantity between 1948 and 1951. Prospective purchasers are advised to secure a qualified appraisal prior to acquisition.

Exc.	V.G.	Good	Fair	Poor
1250	1000	800	600	500

NORTH AMERICAN ARMS
Spanish Fork, Utah

Mini-Revolver
A .22 or .22 Magnum caliber spur trigger revolver with a 1", 2" or 2.5" barrel and 5-shot cylinder. Stainless steel with plastic or laminated rosewood grips. Introduced in 1975 and made in the following styles:

Standard Rimfire Version

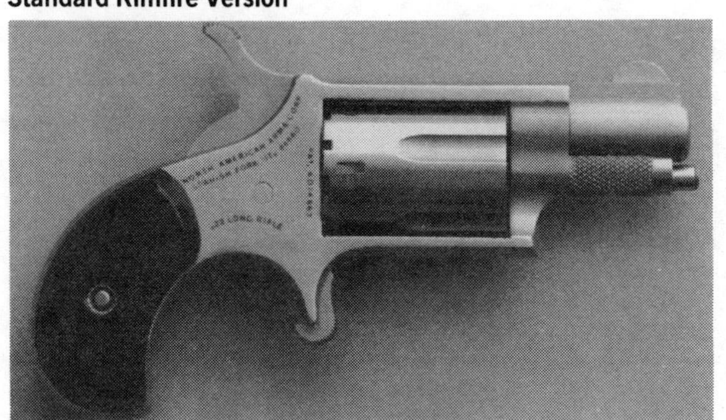

NIB	Exc.	V.G.	Fair	Poor
140	125	110	85	60

Magnum Version

NIB	Exc.	V.G.	Fair	Poor
160	145	125	100	75

2 Cylinder Magnum Convertible Version

NIB	Exc.	V.G.	Fair	Poor
185	165	150	125	100

Viper Belt Buckle Version

NIB	Exc.	V.G.	Fair	Poor
165	140	120	100	75

Standard 3 Gun Set

NIB	Exc.	V.G.	Fair	Poor
575	500	400	300	225

Deluxe 3 Gun Set

NIB	Exc.	V.G.	Fair	Poor
625	550	450	350	275

Cased .22 Magnum

NIB	Exc.	V.G.	Fair	Poor
285	250	200	150	125

Single Action Revolver
A polished stainless steel single action revolver chambered for the .45 Winchester Magnum and the .450 Magnum Express cartridge. It has a 7.5" barrel and a 5-shot cylinder. There is a transfer bar safety, and the grips are walnut. This model was discontinued in 1988.

Exc.	V.G.	Good	Fair	Poor
850	775	650	500	400

NORTH AMERICAN SAFARI EXPRESS
Liege, Belgium
SEE—Francotte

A tradename used by Francotte on their double rifles imported and distributed by Armes De Chasse of Chads Ford, Pennsylvania.

NORTH & COUCH
New York, New York

Animal Trap Gun
A .28 or .30 caliber percussion pepperbox with either a 1.75" or 2.12" barrel group and a hammer made with or without a spur. Marked "North & Couch, Middletown, Conn." or "North & Couch New York." Manufactured during the 1860s.

Disk Hammer Model

Exc.	V.G.	Good	Fair	Poor
750	650	550	400	300

Spur Hammer Model

Exc.	V.G.	Good	Fair	Poor
800	700	600	450	350

NORTON ARMS CO.

Mt. Clemens, Michigan

SEE—Budischowsky

This firm manufactured Budischowsky Model TP-70 semi-automatic pistols prior to 1979. After that date, these arms were made by the American Arms and Amunition Company. The values for both manufacturer's products are as follows:

Exc.	V.G.	Good	Fair	Poor
300	250	200	125	100

NORWICH PISTOL CO.

Norwich, Connecticut

Established in 1875 by the New York retailer Maltby, Curtis & Company, this firm manufactured a wide variety of inexpensive spur trigger revolvers which were sold under the tradenames listed below:

America, Bulldozer, Challenge, Chieftain, Crescent, Defiance, Hartford Arms, Maltby Henley, Metropolitan Police, Nonpariel, Norwich Arms, Parole, Patriot, Pinafore, Prairie King, Protector, Spy, True Blue, U.M.C. Winfield Arms

The Company ceased operations in 1881. The value for any of their arms is approximately as follows:

Exc.	V.G.	Good	Fair	Poor
150	125	100	75	50

O.D.I.
Midland Park, New Jersey

Viking
A .45 caliber double-action semi-automatic pistol with a 5" barrel and 7-shot magazine. Stainless steel with teak grips. Manufactured in 1981 and 1982.

Exc.	V.G.	Good	Fair	Poor
600	550	450	325	225

Viking Combat
As above, with a 4.24" barrel.

Exc.	V.G.	Good	Fair	Poor
600	550	450	325	225

O.K.
Unknown
SEE—Marlin

OBREGON
Mexico City, Mexico

This is a .45 caliber semi-automatic pistol with a 5" barrel. Similar to the Colt M1911A1 but with a combination side and safety latch on the left side of the frame. The breech is locked by rotating the barrel, instead of the Browning swinging link. This unusual locking system results in a tubular front end appearance to the pistol. Originally designed for the Mexican military it was not adopted as such and only about 1,000 pistols were produced and sold commercially. The pistol is 8.5" overall and weighs about 40 ozs. The magazine holds seven cartridges.

Exc.	V.G.	Good	Fair	Poor
650	600	500	400	300

O'CONNELL, DANIEL
New York, New York

Pocket Pistol
A .41 caliber percussion pocket pistol with a 2.5" barrel, German silver mounts and walnut stock. Manufactured during the 1850s.

Exc.	V.G.	Good	Fair	Poor
1500	1000	500	350	250

O'DELL, STEPHEN
Natchez, Mississippi

Pocket Pistol
A .34 to .44 caliber percussion pocket pistol with a 2" to 4" barrel, German silver mounts and walnut stock. Manufactured during the 1850s. Prospective purchasers are advised to secure a qualified appraisal prior to acquisition.

Exc.	V.G.	Good	Fair	Poor
2250	2000	1750	1400	1150

OJANGUREN Y VIDOSA
Eibar, Spain

This typical Eibar company produced mediocre firearms from the early 1920s and was forced out of business during the Spanish Civil War.

Apache
A typical Eibar Browning copy that is chambered for the 6.35mm cartridge. It is of the typical low quality associated with most Spanish arms of this era. The slide is marked "Pistole Browning Automatica Cal.6.35 Apache." The finish is blued, and the plastic grips have a head with a beret and the word "Apache" molded into them.

Exc.	V.G.	Good	Fair	Poor
175	150	125	75	50

Ojanguren
The tradename this company used to cover the line of revolvers they produced in the 1930s. They produced two in .32 caliber and two chambered for the .38 Special cartridge. They are similar in appearance and have barrel lengths of either 3" or 6". The finishes are blued, and they have plastic grips. One of the .38 caliber models—the "Legitimo Tanque"—is a reasonably well-made gun that was very popular with the Spanish target shooters. These guns have very little collector value and little practical value and are all valued alike.

Exc.	V.G.	Good	Fair	Poor
150	125	100	75	50

Tanque
A blowback-operated semi-automatic chambered for the 6.35mm cartridge. It has a 1.5" barrel and is actually an original design, which was rarely found on Eibar guns of this period. It has an oddly shaped slide, and the barrel is retained by means of a screw in the front of the frame. It has a 6-shot magazine, and the slide is marked "6.35 Tanque Patent." The plastic grips have a tank molded into them and the word "Tanque," as well as the letters "O&V."

Exc.	V.G.	Good	Fair	Poor
150	125	100	75	50

OLD WEST GUN CO.
Houston, Texas

An importer of reproduction firearms primarily manufactured by Aldo Uberti of Italy. In 1987 this company purchased the inventory of Allen Firearms and subsequently changed their name to Cimarron Arms.

OLYMPIC ARMS, INC.
Olympia, Washington

Black Widow
A .45 caliber semi-automatic pistol with a 3.9" barrel and 6-shot magazine. Nickle-plated with ivory Micarta grips having a spider engraved on them.

Exc.	V.G.	Good	Fair	Poor
575	500	450	350	300

Enforcer
A .45 caliber semi-automatic pistol with a 3.8" barrel and 6-

shot magazine. Parkerized, annodized or nickle-plated with rubber grips.

NIB	Exc.	V.G.	Good	Fair	Poor
630	575	500	425	350	300

Match Master

As above, with a 5" barrel and 7-shot magazine.

NIB	Exc.	V.G.	Good	Fair	Poor
650	600	525	450	375	300

SGW Ultra Match

A match grade copy of the AR-15 with a 20" or 24" barrel and not fitted with a carrying handle.

NIB	Exc.	V.G.	Good	Fair
1000	850	750	500	400

OMEGA

Harrisburg, Pennsylvania
Importer—Kassnar

Over/Under Shotgun

A 12, 20, 28 or .410 bore boxlock Over/Under shotgun with 26" or 28" ventilated-rib barrels, single trigger and extractors. Blued with a walnut stock.

Exc.	V.G.	Good	Fair	Poor
325	275	250	200	125

Side x Side Double Barreled Shotgun

A 20, 28 or .410 bore boxlock double-barrel shotgun with 26" barrels, double triggers and extractors. Blued with a hardwood stock.

Exc.	V.G.	Good	Fair	Poor
250	200	150	100	75

Single Barreled Shotgun

A 12, 20 or .410 bore single barrel shotgun manufactured in a variety of barrel lengths and fitted with an extractor. Blued with a hardwood stock.

Exc.	V.G.	Good	Fair	Poor
100	85	65	50	35

OMEGA

Eibar, Spain
SEE—Armero Especialistas

OMEGA

Geneseo, Illinois
Springfield Armory

Omega Pistol

A high-grade target-type pistol that is patterned after the Colt Model 1911 type pistol, with marked improvements. It is chambered for the .38 Super, 10mm, and the .45 ACP cartridges. The barrel is either 5" or 6" in length and has polygonal rifling. The barrels are furnished either ported or plain and feature a lockup system that eliminates the barrel link and bushing associated with the normal Browning design. This pistol has a dual extractor system, adjustable sights, and Pachmayr grips. It was introduced in 1987.

NIB	Exc.	V.G.	Good	Fair	Poor
850	775	675	575	400	300

OMEGA FIREARMS CO.

Flower Mound, Texas

Bolt Action Rifle

A .25-06 to .358 Norma Magnum bolt-action rifle with a 22" or 24" barrel, octagonal bolt, adjustable trigger and rotary magazine. Blued with a 2 piece walnut or laminated stock. Discontinued circa 1975.

Exc.	V.G.	Good	Fair	Poor
750	650	550	400	300

OPUS SPORTING ARMS, INC.

Long Beach, California

Opus One

A .243, .270 or .30-06 caliber bolt-action rifle with a 24" barrel, well figured walnut stock and an ebony pistol grip cap as well as forend tip. Built on a Model 70 Winchester action. Manufactured in 1987 and 1988.

Exc.	V.G.	Good	Fair	Poor
2400	2000	1750	1000	800

Opus Two

As above, in .7mm Remington Magnum and .300 Winchester Magnum.

Exc.	V.G.	Good	Fair	Poor
2400	2000	1750	1000	800

Opus Three

As above, in .375 Holland & Holland and .458 Winchester Magnum.

Exc.	V.G.	Good	Fair	Poor
2600	2250	1850	1150	850

ORBEA & CIA

Eibar, Spain

Pocket Pistol

A 6.35mm semi-automatic pistol with a 2.5" barrel. Blued with plastic grips. The slide marked "Orbea y Cia Eibar Espana Pistola Automatica Cal. 6.35." Manufactured from approximately 1918 to 1936.

Exc.	V.G.	Good	Fair	Poor
175	150	125	75	50

ORTGIES, HEINRICH & CO.

Erfurt, Germany

Ortgies Pistol

A 6.35mm or 7.65mm semi-automatic pistol with a 2.75" or 3.25" barrel. Blued with walnut grips. The slide marked "Ortgies & Co. Erfurt." After 1921, these pistols were manufactured by Deutsche Werke.

Exc.	V.G.	Good	Fair	Poor
275	225	175	125	85

ORVIS

Dallas, Texas

An importer and retailer of sporting goods including foreign manufactured firearms.

OSBORN, S.

Canton, Connecticut

Under Hammer Pistol

A .34 caliber under hammer percussion pistol with a 7" half octagonal barrel, brass mounts and a walnut grip. The barrel marked "S.Osborn/Canton, Conn."

Exc.	V.G.	Good	Fair	Poor
450	400	350	250	175

OSGOOD GUN WORKS
Norwich, Connecticut

Duplex Revolver

A .22 caliber spur trigger revolver with two super-impossed barrels, the upper most of .22 caliber and the lower a .32 caliber. The cylinder with 8 .22 chambers. The hammer fitted with a moveable firing pin so that the pistol can be used either as a revolver or as a single shot with a .32 caliber barrel. Blued or nickle-plated with hard rubber grips. The barrel marked "Osgood Gun Works-Norwich Conn." and "Duplex." An unknown quantity were manufactured during the 1880s.

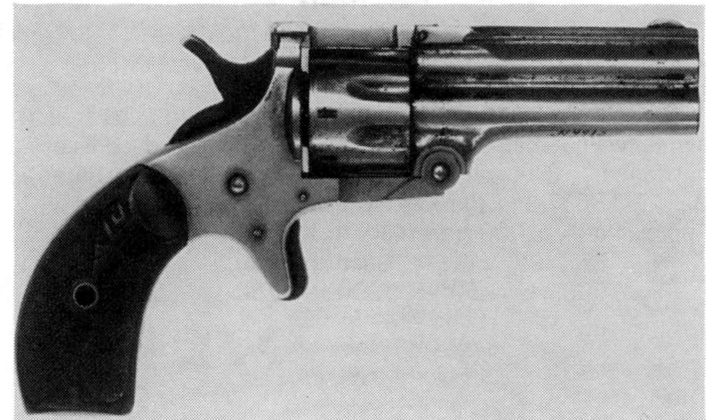

Courtesy Milwaukee Public Museum, Milwaukee, Wisconsin.

Exc.	V.G.	Good	Fair	Poor
1000	750	500	350	250

OWA
Vienna, Austria
Osterreiche Werke Anstalt

OWA Pocket Pistol

A 6.35mm semi-automatic pistol with a 2" barrel. Unmarked except for "OWA" logo cast in the grips. Blued with plastic grips. Manufactured between 1920 and 1925.

Courtesy Orville Reichert.

Courtesy Orville Reichert.

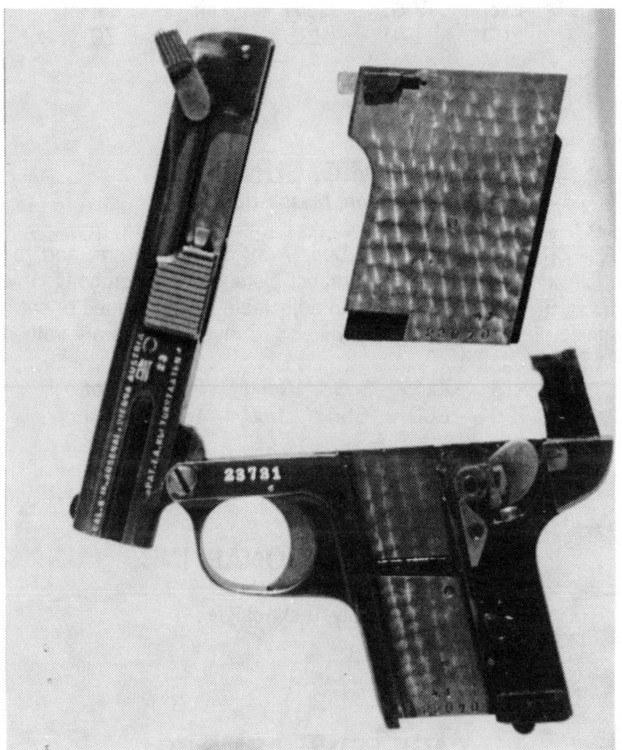

Courtesy Orville Reichert.

Exc.	V.G.	Good	Fair	Poor
250	200	175	100	75

P

P-38
SEE—German Military

P.A.F.
Pretoria, South Africa
Pretoria Small Arms Factory

P.A.F. Junior
A .22 or .25 caliber semi-automatic pistol with a 2" barrel and 6-shot magazine. Blued with plastic grips. Slide marked "Junior Verwaardig in Suid Afrika Made in South Africa". Manufactured during the 1950s.

Exc.	V.G.	Good	Fair	Poor
200	170	125	100	70

P.S.M.G. GUN CO.
Arlington, Massachusetts

Six In One Supreme
A .22 l.r., .30 Luger, .38 Super, .38 Special, 9mm, and the .45ACP caliber semi-automatic pistol with interchangeable 3.5", 5", or 7.5" barrels, and adjustable sights. Blued or satin nickle-plated. Introduced in 1988. Conversion kits are valued at $450 per unit.

NIB	Exc.	V.G.	Good	Fair	Poor
900	800	650	500	400	350

PTK INTERNATIONAL, INC.
Atlanta, Georgia
SEE—Poly-Technologies

PAGE-LEWIS ARMS CO.
Chicopee Falls, Massachusetts

Model A Target
A .22 caliber single shot lever-action rifle with a 20" barrel and open sights. Blued with a walnut stock. Manufactured from 1920 to 1926.

Exc.	V.G.	Good	Fair	Poor
250	225	175	125	100

Model B Sharpshooter
As above, with a 24" barrel and longer forend.

Exc.	V.G.	Good	Fair	Poor
250	225	175	125	100

Model C Olympic
As above, with a 24" barrel and improved sights.

Exc.	V.G.	Good	Fair	Poor
300	250	200	150	100

PALMER
Windsor, Vermont
E. G. Lamson & Co.

Palmer Bolt Action Carbine
A .50 caliber single shot bolt-action carbine with a 20" round barrel, walnut half stock and full sidelock. Blued and case-hardened. The receiver marked "Wm. Palmer/Patent/ Dec.22,1863" and the lock "G.Lamson & Co./ Windsor, Vt." Approximately 1,000 were made in 1865.

Exc.	V.G.	Good	Fair	Poor
1500	1250	1000	750	500

PARA-ORDNANCE MFG. INC.
Scarborough, Ontario, Canada

Model P14.45
Similar in appearance to the Colt Government model this .45 ACP semi-automatic pistol features a 5" barrel, flared ejection port, combat style hammer beveled magazine well and a 13 round magazine capacity. Over all length is 8.5" and weight is 38 oz. for steel and stainless steel version and 28 oz. for alloy frame model. Finish is black except for stainless steel model.

NIB	Exc.	V.G.	Good	Fair	Poor
650	600	550	475	400	300

NOTE: Add $50 for steel frame.

Model P12.45
Similar to the Model P14 but in a smaller package. Introduced in 1993. Has all the same features as the Model P14 but has a magazine capacity of 11 rounds. Also available in alloy, steel, or stainless steel this model weighs 24 oz. in alloy model and 33 oz. in steel models.

NIB	Exc.	V.G.	Good	Fair	Poor
650	600	550	475	400	300

NOTE: Add $50 for steel frame.

PARDINI
Italy
Importer—Fiocchi of America
Ozark, Missouri

Standard Target Pistol

A .22 caliber semi-automatic pistol with a 4.9" barrel, adjustable rear sight and adjustable trigger. Blued with two sizes of walnut grips one suitable for use by ladies. Introduced in 1986.

NIB	Exc.	V.G.	Good	Fair	Poor
950	875	700	600	500	375

Rapidfire Pistol

Similar to the above, in .22 short with an alloy bolt, 5.1" barrel and enclosed grip.

NIB	Exc.	V.G.	Good	Fair	Poor
950	875	700	600	500	375

Centerfire Pistol

Similar to the standard model, but in .32 Smith & Wesson caliber. Introduced in 1986.

NIB	Exc.	V.G.	Good	Fair	Poor
950	875	700	600	500	375

Free Pistol

A .22 caliber single shot pistol with a 9" barrel, adjustable sights and adjustable grip. Furnished with barrel weights.

NIB	Exc.	V.G.	Good	Fair	Poor
1100	950	800	700	600	450

PARKER
Springfield, Massachusetts

4-Shot Pistol

A .33 caliber percussion pistol with a 4" half-octagonal barrel and a 4-shot sliding chamber. Marked "Albert Parker/Patent Secured/Springfield, Mass." Original finish unknown with walnut grips. Prospective purchasers are advised to secure a qualified appraisal prior to acquisition.

Exc.	V.G.	Good	Fair	Poor
5500	4500	3500	2750	2000

PARKER BROS.
Meriden, Connecticut

Perhaps the best known of all American shotgun manufacturers. Established by Charles Parker shortly after the Civil War, this company has produced a wide variety of shotguns in a number of different styles over the years. In the early 1930s the company was purchased by Remington Arms Company.

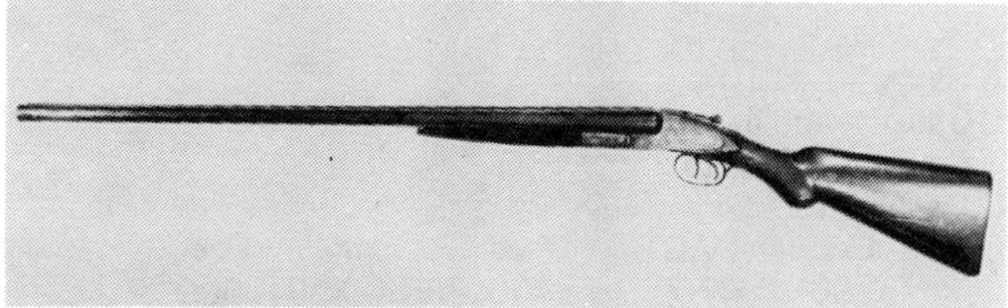

Parker shotguns are one of the most collectable of American made shotguns. Both the beginning and the veteran collector should be aware that originality and condition are absolutely critical in establishing such high values for these shotguns. There are numerous upgraded and refinished guns which are represented as original. Beware that such misrepresentations exist because refinished and upgraded Parker guns should sell for as much as 75 percent below the price of an original gun. Extreme caution should be exercised and we would recommend that an expert be consulted. Even the most advanced collectors may benefit from such consultations. Also, the prices indicated for guns in excellent condition may fluctuate drastically, especially in high grade or small bore guns, due to their extreme rarity. In addition, uncommon extras such as single triggers, ventilated ribs, beavertail forearms, straight grip stocks, and skeleton steel butt plates may add substantial value to an individual gun.

Trojan

A 12, 16 or 20 gauge boxlock double-barrel shotgun manufactured in a variety of barrel lengths with either single or double triggers and extractors. Blued, case-hardened receiver with a walnut stock. Approximately 48,000 were made.

20 Gauge—Add 40%.

Exc.	V.G.	Good	Fair	Poor
2400	1700	1300	700	500

VH

A 12, 16, 20, 28 or .410 bore boxlock double-barrel shotgun manufactured in a variety of barrel lengths with double triggers and extractors. Blued, casehardened receiver with a walnut stock. Approximately 60,000 were made.

Note: Also made with automatic ejectors and known as the Model VHE. The E suffix was used on all models to denote automatic ejectors.

VHE—Add 40%.
20 Gauge—Add 45%.
28 Gauge—Add 120%.
.410—Add 300%.

Exc.	V.G.	Good	Fair	Poor
2800	1900	1500	800	600

PH

Similar to the above, but not made in .410 bore. Approximately 8,500 were made.

PHE—Add 40%.
20 Gauge—Add 45%.
28 Gauge—Add 120%.

Exc.	V.G.	Good	Fair	Poor
3000	2200	1600	900	700

GH

Similar to the above, with a modest amount of engraving and the barrels marked "Parker Special Steel". Approximately 28,500 were made.

GHE—Add 35%.
16 Gauge—Add 15%.

20 Gauge—Add 40%.
28 Gauge—Add 100%.
.410—Add 300%.

Exc.	V.G.	Good	Fair	Poor
3500	2500	2000	1300	800

DH
As above, but more finely finished. Approximately 48,000 were made.
DHE—Add 35%.
16 Gauge—Add 10%.
20 Gauge—Add 40%.
28 Gauge—Add 125%.
.410—Add 400%.

Exc.	V.G.	Good	Fair	Poor
5500	4700	3400	1800	1000

CH
As above, with Acme steel barrels. Approximately 5,000 were made.
CHE—Add 35%.
16 Gauge—Add 10%.
20 Gauge—Add 40%.
28 Gauge—Add 200%.
.410—Add 700%.

Exc.	V.G.	Good	Fair	Poor
6500	5500	4000	2500	1200

BH
As above, but offered with 4 different styles of engraved decoration. Approximately 13,000 were made. Prospective purchasers are advised to secure a qualified appraisal prior to acquisition.
BHE—Add 35%.
16 Gauge—Add 10%.
20 Gauge—Add 40%.
28 Gauge—Add 200%.
.410—Add 800%.

Exc.	V.G.	Good	Fair	Poor
8500	7000	5000	3000	2000

AH
As above, but highly engraved with finely figured walnut stocks. Approximately 5,500 were made. Prospective purchasers are advised to secure a qualified appraisal prior to acquisition.
AHE—Add 30%.
16 Gauge—Add 15%.
20 Gauge—Add 50%.
28 Gauge—Add 200%.
.410—Add 500%.

Exc.	V.G.	Good	Fair	Poor
18000	14000	9000	6500	3500

AAH
As above, with either Whitworth or Peerless barrels and not made in .410 bore. The engraving is more extensive and of the first quality. Approximately 340 were made. Prospective purchasers are advised to secure a qualified appraisal prior to acquisition.
AAHE—Add 30%.
16 Gauge—Add 25%.
20 Gauge—Add 50%.
28 Gauge—Add 250%.

Exc.	V.G.	Good	Fair	Poor
30000	23000	16000	10000	7000

A-1 Special
As above, but made strictly on special order and not manufactured in .410 bore. Approximately 320 were made. Prospective purchasers are advised to secure a qualified appraisal prior to acquisition.
16 Gauge—Add 25%.
20 Gauge—Add 50%.
28 Gauge—Add 200%.

Exc.	V.G.	Good	Fair	Poor
50000	40000	33000	20000	13000

Single Barrel Trap
A 12 gauge single shot shotgun with a 30", 32" or 34" barrel, automatic ejector and walnut stock. Produced in a variety of grades as follows. Prospective purchasers are advised to secure a qualified appraisal prior to acquisition.

S.C. Grade

Exc.	V.G.	Good	Fair	Poor
3500	2100	1500	1000	700

S.B. Grade

Exc.	V.G.	Good	Fair	Poor
4000	3000	2500	2000	1300

S.A. Grade

Exc.	V.G.	Good	Fair	Poor
5500	4200	3000	2000	1300

S.A.A. Grade

Exc.	V.G.	Good	Fair	Poor
9000	7000	4000	2700	1800

S.A-1 Special Grade

Exc.	V.G.	Good	Fair	Poor
10000	7500	5000	3200	2000

Under Lifter Hammer Gun
A side hammer double barrel shotgun manufactured in a variety of gauges with the barrel release located in front of the trigger guards. Damascus barrels, case-hardened locks, blued furniture with walnut stocks. Manufactured during the 1870s and later.

Exc.	V.G.	Good	Fair	Poor
1000	850	750	500	400

PARKER FIELD & SONS
SEE—English Military Firearms

PARKER FIELD & SONS
London, England

Gas Seal Revolver
A .42 caliber percussion revolver with a 6" barrel and 6-shot cylinder. Blued, casehardened with walnut grips. Manufactured during the 1860s.

Exc.	V.G.	Good	Fair	Poor
1500	1250	950	650	450

PARKER HALE LTD.
Birmingham, England

S&W Victory Conversion
A .22 caliber double-action revolver with a 4" barrel and 6-shot cylinder. Blued with walnut grips. An alteration of the Smith & Wesson Victory model.

Exc.	V.G.	Good	Fair	Poor
250	200	150	100	75

Model 1200
A .22-250 to .300 Winchester Magnum bolt-action rifle with a 24" barrel and open sights. Blued, with walnut stock.

NIB	Exc.	V.G.	Good	Fair	Poor
700	600	450	400	350	300

Model 1100 Lightweight
As above, with a 22" barrel and 4-shot magazine. Introduced in 1985.

NIB	Exc.	V.G.	Good	Fair	Poor
600	500	400	350	300	250

Model 81 Classic
A .22-250 to 7mm Remington Magnum bolt-action rifle with a 24" barrel and open sights. Blued with a walnut stock. Introduced in 1985.

NIB	Exc.	V.G.	Good	Fair	Poor
875	750	600	500	400	350

Model 81 African

As above, but in .375 Holland & Holland caliber. Introduced in 1986.

NIB	Exc.	V.G.	Good	Fair	Poor
1200	950	800	700	600	500

Model 84 Target

Similar to the Model 81, but in .308 caliber with adjustable rear sights and an adjustable cheekpiece.

NIB	Exc.	V.G.	Good	Fair	Poor
1300	1000	900	750	650	550

Model 85 Sniper

As above, with a telescope and bipod.

Exc.	V.G.	Good	Fair	Poor
1700	1550	1050	800	700

Model 640E Shotgun

A 12, 16 or 20 gauge boxlock double-barrel shotgun manufactured in a variety of barrel lengths with double triggers and extractors. Blued, French casehardened with a walnut stock. Introduced in 1986.

NIB	Exc.	V.G.	Good	Fair	Poor
575	500	450	400	300	225

Model 640A

As above, with a pistol grip, beavertail forend and single trigger. Introduced in 1986.

NIB	Exc.	V.G.	Good	Fair	Poor
675	600	550	500	400	325

Model 645E

As above, but more finely finished and engraved.

NIB	Exc.	V.G.	Good	Fair	Poor
700	625	575	525	425	350

Model 670E

A sidelock double-barrel shotgun made on special order. Introduced in 1986.

NIB	Exc.	V.G.	Good	Fair	Poor
3000	2750	2250	1750	1250	950

Model 680E-XXV

As above, with case-hardened lockplates and 25" barrels.

NIB	Exc.	V.G.	Good	Fair	Poor
3000	2750	2250	1750	1250	950

PARKER REPRODUCTIONS

Japan

Importer—Regent Chemical & Research

Middlesex, New Jersey

This company had exact reproductions of Parker D, DHE, B and A-1 Special shotguns made in Japan. They are of the finest quality and workmanship. The styles of engraving and features of these shotguns correspond exactly to the original Parker Arms.

D-Grade

This side by side shotgun is offered in 12 gauge, 20 gauge, and 28 gauge. Barrel lengths are 26" or 28" with sold matte rib. Stocks are select walnut with choice of pistol or straight grip. Choice splinter or beavertail forearms are offered. Single or double triggers are available as well. The receiver is case-colored and scroll engraved with game scenes to match the original Parker DHE grade. Weight of 12 gauge is 6.75 lb, 20 gauge is 6.5 lb., and 28 gauge weighs 5.3 lb.

12 or 20 Gauge

NIB	Exc.	V.G.	Good	Fair	Poor
2750	2450	1750	1250	850	400

16/20 Combination

Introduced in 1993 and limited to 500 sets. Offered with 28" barrels only this set features a 16 gauge barrel on a 20 gauge frame. Weighs 6.25 lbs.

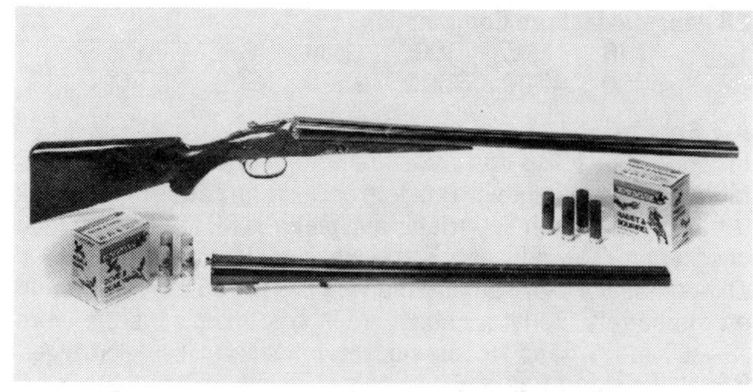

NIB	Exc.	V.G.	Good	Fair	Poor
4700	4400	3700	3000	1500	750

28 Gauge

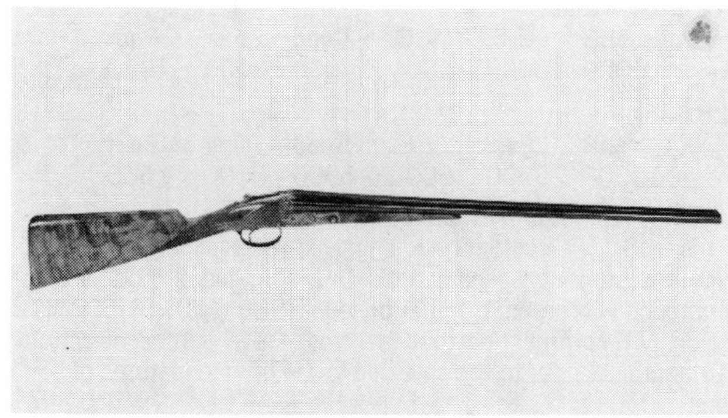

NIB	Exc.	V.G.	Good	Fair	Poor
2950	2600	1850	1300	850	400

28 gauge/.410 bore Combination

NIB	Exc.	V.G.	Good	Fair	Poor
5000	4500	3500	2500	1500	750

NOTE: Add $990 for an additional barrel and $170 for beavertail forearm. For the D Grade three barrels sets are offered in 16/20/20 combinations for an additional $2300.

DHE Grade Steel Shot Special

Offered in 12 gauge only with 28" barrels. Fitted with 3" chambers and special chrome lined barrels. Weighs 7 lb.

NIB	Exc.	V.G.	Good	Fair	Poor
3750	3000	2500	1500	800	400

B-Grade Limited Edition

This model features engraving similar to the original Parker BHE Grade. Fancy walnut stocks with fine line checkering was standard. It was offered in 12 gauge, 20 gauge, and 28 gauge. A 28 gauge/.410 bore combinations was also offered. Only 100 shotguns in this grade were produced in 1989.

NIB	Exc.	V.G.	Good	Fair	Poor
4000	3650	2900	1750	900	450

28 gauge/.410 bore Combination

NIB	Exc.	V.G.	Good	Fair	Poor
5000	4500	3500	2500	1500	750

A-1 Special

Introduced in 1988 this grade fine scroll engraving and presentation French walnut with custom checkering pattern. The stock is hand carved with fleur-de-lis and features 32 lines to the inch checkering. The grip cap is rosewood and gold or gold initial plate on straight grip guns. Gold wire is used on the breech end on the barrels. Serial numbers are in gold relief as is the word "SAFE" and "L" and "R" on models with selective single trigger. Barrels flats and frame water table is jeweled. This grade is offered in 12, 20, and 28 gauge with a few early guns sold with 28 gauge/.410 bore combinations. Furnished with English style Oak and Leather case with canvas and leather cover, engraved snap caps and engraved oil bottle.

12 or 20 Gauge

NIB	Exc.	V.G.	Good	Fair	Poor
10000	8000	5000	4000	2500	1000

28 Gauge

NIB	Exc.	V.G.	Good	Fair	Poor
12000	9500	6000	5000	3000	1000

A-1 Special Custom Engraved

This model is a custom hand engraved A-1 Special to each individual customer's specifications. Only a limited number of these shotguns will be built. Initial price in 1989 was $10,500. It is strongly recommended that the prospective purchaser acquire an appraisal prior to the sale due to the unique features of each gun.

PEABODY

Providence, Rhode Island
Providence Tool Company

Peabody Rifle and Carbine

A .43 Spanish, .443, .45 Peabody, .45-70, .50 or .50-70 caliber single shot rifle with a 33" or 20" (carbine) barrel and either a full length or half stock. The receiver marked "Peabody's Patent July 22, 1862/ Mann'f'd by Providence Tool Co. Prov. R.I." Blued, with a walnut stock. Produced in large quantities during the 1860s and 1870s.

Courtesy Milwaukee Public Museum, Milwaukee, Wisconsin.

Exc.	V.G.	Good	Fair	Poor
750	650	550	400	300

Sporting Rifle

As above, in a sporting configuration with either 26" or 28" barrels. The frame marked, "Peabody's Patent, July 22, 1862/Man'f'd by Providence Tool Co., Prov. R.I." Blued, case-hardened with a walnut stock. Manufactured from approximately 1866 to 1875.

Exc.	V.G.	Good	Fair	Poor
1000	850	750	500	400

Peabody-Martini Sporting Rifles

Creedmoor

A .40-90 or .44-100 caliber Martini-action single shot rifle with a 32" round/octagonal barrel, butt mounted vernier rear sight, combination wind gauge and spirit level front sight. The receiver marked, "Peabody & Martini Patents" and the barrel "Manufactured by the Providence Tool Co. Providence R.I. U.S.A." Blued, case hardened with a walnut stock.

Courtesy Milwaukee Public Museum, Milwaukee, Wisconsin.

Exc.	V.G.	Good	Fair	Poor
2500	2250	1850	1100	850

Creedmoor Mid-Range

Similar to the above, but in .40-70 or .40-90 caliber with a 28" round/octagonal barrel, vernier tang sight and wind gauge front sight. Blued, case-hardened with a walnut stock.

Exc.	V.G.	Good	Fair	Poor
1850	1650	1250	850	600

What Cheer

The Creedmoor without a pistol grip.

Exc.	V.G.	Good	Fair	Poor
2500	2250	1850	1100	850

What Cheer Mid-Range

The Mid-Range Creedmoor without a pistol grip.

Exc.	V.G.	Good	Fair	Poor
1850	1650	1250	850	600

Kill Deer

A .45-70 caliber single shot Martini-action rifle with 28" or 30" round/octagonal barrels, adjustable tang rear sight and globe front sights. Blued, case-hardened with a walnut stock.

Exc.	V.G.	Good	Fair	Poor
1750	1500	1000	750	500

PEAVY, A. J.

South Montville, Maine

Knife-Pistol

A .22 caliber single shot knife pistol constructed of steel and brass with a folding trigger. The side plates marked "A.J.Peavy-Pat.Sept.5,'65 & Mar.27,'66." Produced between 1866 and 1870.

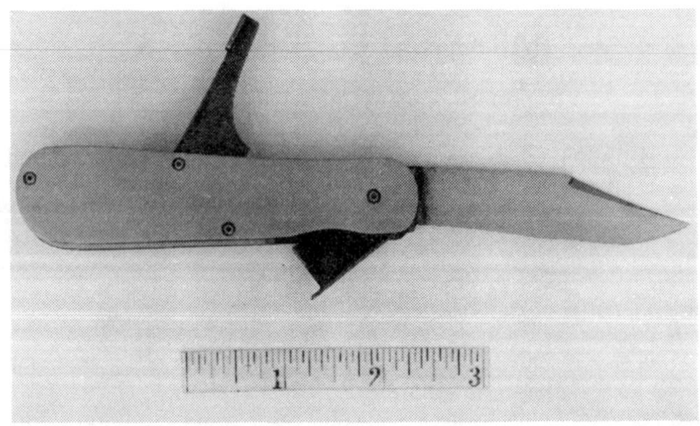

Exc.	V.G.	Good	Fair	Poor
1000	850	750	500	400

PECARE & SMITH

New York, New York

Pepperbox

A .28 or .31 caliber 5-shot percussion pepperbox with a folding trigger and 4" barrel group. The barrel group enclosed within an iron casing. Blued, silver-plated frame with walnut grips. The barrel casing marked "Pecare & Smith." Manufactured during the 1840s early 1850s.

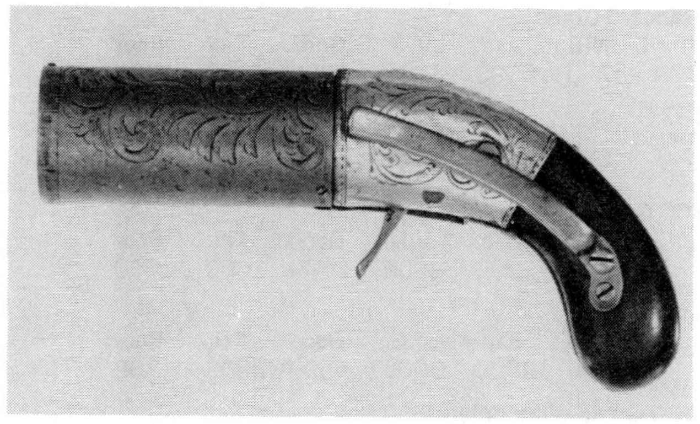

Exc.	V.G.	Good	Fair	Poor
2500	2000	1500	900	650

PEDERSEN CUSTOM GUNS

North Haven, Connecticut

A division of the O. F. Mossberg Company operated between 1973 and 1975.

Model 4000 Shotgun

The Mossberg Model 500 slide action shotgun in 12, 20 or .410 bore with 26", 28" or 30" ventilated-rib barrels. Blued, engraved with a walnut stock. Manufactured in 1975.

Exc.	V.G.	Good	Fair	Poor
450	375	300	250	200

Model 4500

As above, but with a reduced amount of engraving.

Exc.	V.G.	Good	Fair	Poor
400	350	275	225	175

Model 1500

A 12 gauge Magnum Over/Under shotgun with 26", 28" or 30" ventilated-rib barrels, single selective trigger and automatic ejectors. Blued with a walnut stock. Manufactured between 1973 and 1975.

Exc.	V.G.	Good	Fair	Poor
750	600	500	400	300

Model 1000

As above, but manufactured in two grades of decoration. Manufactured between 1973 and 1975.

Grade I

Exc.	V.G.	Good	Fair	Poor
2250	2000	1750	1450	1300

Grade II

Exc.	V.G.	Good	Fair	Poor
1850	1500	1350	1150	950

Model 200

A 12 or 20 gauge boxlock double-barrel shotgun with 26", 28" or 30" barrels, single selective trigger and automatic ejectors. Produced in two grades of decoration. Manufactured in 1973 and 1974.

Grade I

Exc.	V.G.	Good	Fair	Poor
2500	2000	1750	1250	1000

Grade II

Exc.	V.G.	Good	Fair	Poor
2250	1850	1500	1000	800

Model 2500

A 12 or 20 gauge boxlock double-barrel shotgun with 26" or 28" barrels, double triggers and automatic ejectors. Blued with a walnut stock.

Exc.	V.G.	Good	Fair	Poor
450	400	350	275	200

Model 3000

A Mossberg Model 810 bolt-action rifle manufactured in .270 to .338 Winchester Magnum caliber with a 22" or 24" barrel with open sights. Produced in three grades as follows:

Grade III Plain

Exc.	V.G.	Good	Fair	Poor
550	475	400	350	300

Grade II

Exc.	V.G.	Good	Fair	Poor
650	575	500	450	400

Grade I

Exc.	V.G.	Good	Fair	Poor
1000	800	650	550	475

Model 4700

The Mossberg Model 472 in .30-30 or .35 Remington caliber with a 24" barrel and 5-shot tubular magazine. Blued with a walnut stock.

Exc.	V.G.	Good	Fair	Poor
250	200	150	125	100

PERAZZI

Brescia, Italy
Importer—Perazzi USA, Inc.
Monrovia, California

This company was founded in 1963. During the 1960's and 1970's Winchester and Ithaca imported and sold Perazzi shotguns. Perazzi has now taken over its own importation and distribution in the United States with the creation of Perazzi USA, Inc. Many shooters consider the Perazzi to be the finest currently produced shotgun in the world.

Perazzi has an extensive variety of models to choose from. In addition, each model may be available in different grades. These grades are based on the type of finish, engraving, and wood quality. The vast majority of Perazzi shotguns that are sold in this country are Standard Grade guns. According to Perazzi USA, these Standard Grade guns account for approximately 98 percent of North American sales. Therefore, it is unlikely that the shooter or collector will encounter high grade Perazzi guns. It should be pointed out that in some models no Extra Grade or

PERAZZI GRADES

1. **Standard Grade:** Furnished with blued receiver and barrels with hand checkered select walnut stock and forend.

2. **SC3 Grade:** The receiver has a silver finish with scroll engraving and choice of game scenes. Barrel is blued and stocks are a higher grade of walnut.

3. **SCO Grade:** Silver receiver with choice of Continental or English scroll with choice of game scenes. Barrels are blued and fancy walnut stocks with fine line checkering are used.

4. **Gold Grade:** Customer has a choice of several different game scenes with gold inlays. Blued barrels with fancy walnut stock. Custom checkering.

5. **SCO Grade W/Sideplates:** Similar to the SCO Grade but with more coverage available due to addition of sideplates.

6. **Gold Grade W/ Sideplates:** Similar to Gold Grade but with more coverage on sideplates.

7. **Extra Grade:** This is Perazzi's finest grade. The customer has a choice of almost any pattern he desires done in a fine bank note engraving style. Only the finest walnut is used on this grade with very fine line checkering. This is a very rare and seldom seen Perazzi grade.

7. **Extra Gold Grade:** Similar to all of the refinement on the Extra Grade with the addition of the birds and animals are gold inlaid. Again, this is a seldom seen grade.

Extra Gold Grade shotguns have ever been sold in the United States.

For the benefit of the reader an approximate description of each grade is given on the previous page. It is a general description because the Perazzi customer may order practically any combination of finishes or engraving patterns he or she desires. Use this list as a general guide.

OUT OF PRODUCTION SHOTGUNS

COMP1-SB TRAP

This model is a single barrel trap gun in 12 gauge only with 32" or 34"vent rib barrel.

Standard Grade

NIB	Exc.	V.G.	Good	Fair	Poor
2750	2250	1500	1000	750	500

COMP1-TRAP

This is an O/U version of the above model.

Standard Grade

NIB	Exc.	V.G.	Good	Fair	Poor
4500	3750	2750	1750	900	500

Light Game Model

Offered in 12 gauge with a 27.5" vent rib barrel. Trigger group is not detachable. Produced between 1972 and 1974.

Standard Grade

NIB	Exc.	V.G.	Good	Fair	Poor
5000	4200	3500	2500	1200	700

MT-6 Model

This model was offered in 12 gauge with a tapered vent rib. The trigger group was not removable. Discontinued in 1983.

Standard Grade

NIB	Exc.	V.G.	Good	Fair	Poor
4750	4000	3250	2300	1200	700

MX3

This model was discontinued in 1988 and was available in 12 gauge only for single barrel Trap, O/U Trap, Combination Trap, Skeet, and Sporting configurations.

Standard Grade

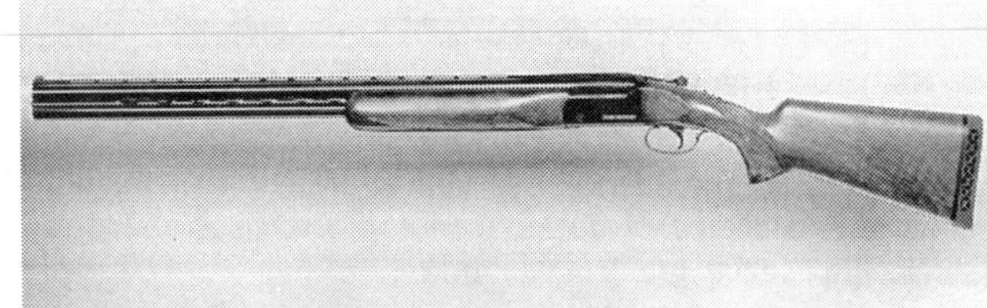

NIB	Exc.	V.G.	Good	Fair	Poor
6000	5250	4500	3500	2000	1000

SC3 Grade

NIB	Exc.	V.G.	Good	Fair	Poor
8500	6000	4700	3700	2200	1000

SCO Grade

NIB	Exc.	V.G.	Good	Fair	Poor
15000	11000	8500	4500	2500	1000

Gold Grade

NIB	Exc.	V.G.	Good	Fair	Poor
16500	12000	9000	5000	2700	1200

NOTE: Add 50% to above prices for Combination Trap Guns.

Grand American Special

This model was introduced in 1988 and features a high ramped rib similar to the MX3 model. The forend was grooved. Discontinued in 1991. It was offered in single barrel Trap, Combination Trap, and O/U Trap configurations.

Standard Grade

NIB	Exc.	V.G.	Good	Fair	Poor
5750	5000	4000	3000	1500	700

SC3 Grade

NIB	Exc.	V.G.	Good	Fair	Poor
9750	8500	5500	4000	1700	900

SCO Grade

NIB	Exc.	V.G.	Good	Fair	Poor
16500	12000	8500	5000	2000	1000

Gold Grade

NIB	Exc.	V.G.	Good	Fair	Poor
17500	13000	9000	5500	2500	1200

SCO Grade W/Sideplates

NIB	Exc.	V.G.	Good	Fair	Poor
25000	17500	11000	6000	3000	1500

Gold Grade W/Sideplates

NIB	Exc.	V.G.	Good	Fair	Poor
27500	19000	12500	6500	3200	1500

Extra Grade

NIB	Exc.	V.G.	Good	Fair	Poor
44000	35000	25000	12500	5000	2000

Extra Gold Grade

NIB	Exc.	V.G.	Good	Fair	Poor
48000	39000	26000	13000	5500	2000

SHO Model

This O/U sidelock model is available in 12 gauge only and features a silver finish with fine scroll engraving with game scenes to customer's specifications. Select walnut stock built to customer's dimensions with fine line checkering. A custom built shotgun. Special order only. An expert appraisal is recommended for this model due to its unique features.

DHO Model

This is a side by side shotgun offered in 12 gauge only. It has full sidelocks and a silver receiver finish with scroll and game scene engraving of the same quality as the SHO Model. Fancy walnut stock with fine line checkering. An expert appraisal is recommended for this model due to its unique features.

DHO Extra Gold

Available in any gauge and barrel length combination. Only the finest presentation walnut and checkering. A totally custom built shotgun. Special order only. An expert appraisal is recommended for this model due to its unique features.

CURRENT PRODUCTION SHOTGUNS

American Trap-Single Barrel Models

MX9

Introduced in 1993 this model features a removable inserts on rib to adjust point of impact and a walnut stock with adjustable comb. Offered in 12 gauge with 32" or 34" barrel with screw in chokes. The trigger group is removable. Available in several different grades of ormentation.

Standard Grade

NIB	Exc.	V.G.	Good	Fair	Poor
7350	6500	5000	4000	2000	1000

SC3 Grade

NIB	Exc.	V.G.	Good	Fair	Poor
11500	10000	8000	5000	3000	1500

SCO Grade

NIB	Exc.	V.G.	Good	Fair	Poor
18000	15000	10000	7500	3500	1500

Gold Grade

NIB	Exc.	V.G.	Good	Fair	Poor
20000	17500	12000	9500	5000	2000

SCO Grade W/Sideplates

NIB	Exc.	V.G.	Good	Fair	Poor
28500	22500	17500	11000	6000	2500

Gold Grade W/Sideplates

NIB	Exc.	V.G.	Good	Fair	Poor
31500	25000	20000	15000	7500	3000

MX10

This model was introduced in 1993. It features a different method of rib height and pattern adjustment. This model also has an adjustable stock. Available in 12 gauge with 32" or 34" barrels. Chokes are fixed. Trigger is removable.

Standard Grade

NIB	Exc.	V.G.	Good	Fair	Poor
7500	6570	5500	4500	3000	1200

SC3 Grade

NIB	Exc.	V.G.	Good	Fair	Poor
11700	10250	8250	5000	3000	1500

SCO Grade

NIB	Exc.	V.G.	Good	Fair	Poor
18500	15000	10000	7500	3500	1500

Gold Grade

NIB	Exc.	V.G.	Good	Fair	Poor
20300	1800	12500	9500	5000	2000

SCO Grade W/Sideplates

NIB	Exc.	V.G.	Good	Fair	Poor
28750	22750	17750	11000	6000	2500

Gold Grade W/ Sideplates

NIB	Exc.	V.G.	Good	Fair	Poor
31750	25250	20000	15000	7500	3000

TM1 Special

This basic single barrel Perazzi Trap model is offered in 12 gauge with 32" or 34" barrel. Trigger is adjustable.

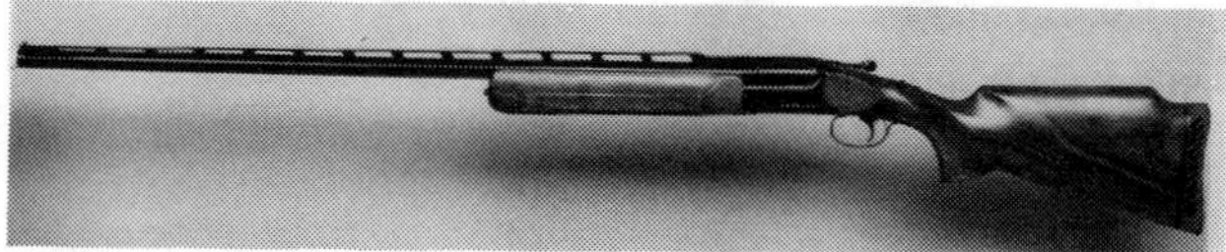

Standard Grade

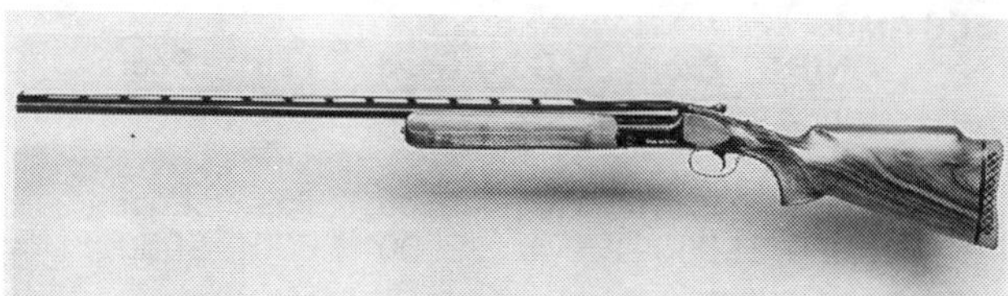

NIB	Exc.	V.G.	Good	Fair	Poor
4600	4000	3500	2750	2000	1000

SC3 Grade

(Not Offered)

SCO Grade

NIB	Exc.	V.G.	Good	Fair	Poor
13500	11000	7500	5000	2500	1200

Gold Grade

NIB	Exc.	V.G.	Good	Fair	Poor
15000	12000	8500	5500	2500	1200

TMX Special

Similar to TM1 Special with select walnut.

Standard Grade

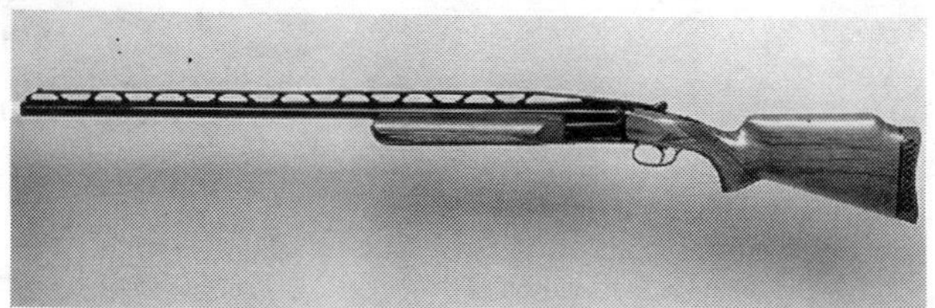

NIB	Exc.	V.G.	Good	Fair	Poor
4750	4200	3700	2750	2000	1000

SC3 Grade

(Not Offered)

SCO Grade

NIB	Exc.	V.G.	Good	Fair	Poor
13500	11000	7500	5000	2500	1200

Gold Grade

NIB	Exc.	V.G.	Good	Fair	Poor
15000	12000	8500	5500	2500	1200

MX8 Special

This model features a low contour vent rib, adjustable trigger, and grooved forend.

Standard Grade

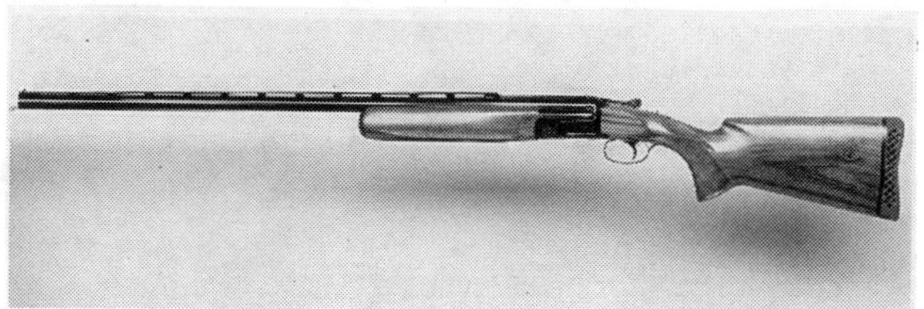

NIB	Exc.	V.G.	Good	Fair	Poor
5800	5000	4000	3000	2000	1000

SC3 Grade

NIB	Exc.	V.G.	Good	Fair	Poor
10000	8500	5000	4000	3000	1200

SCO Grade

NIB	Exc.	V.G.	Good	Fair	Poor
16500	13500	9500	6000	3000	1500

Gold Grade

NIB	Exc.	V.G.	Good	Fair	Poor
18500	14500	10000	6000	3000	1500

SCO Grade W/Sideplates

NIB	Exc.	V.G.	Good	Fair	Poor
26000	21000	15000	10000	5000	2000

Gold Grade W/Sideplates

NIB	Exc.	V.G.	Good	Fair	Poor
30000	24500	19000	12000	6000	3000

DB81 Special

This model features a very high ventilated rib.

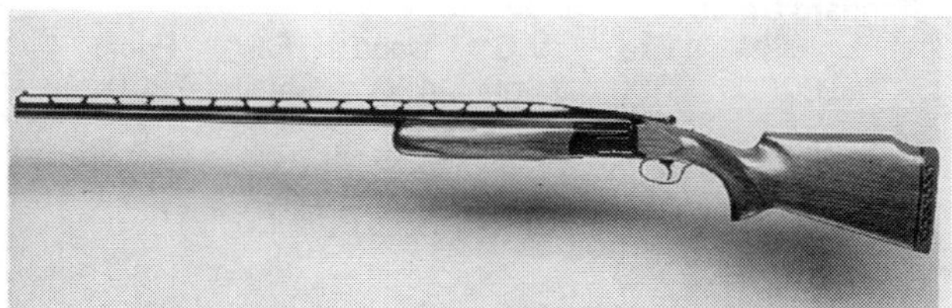

Standard Grade

NIB	Exc.	V.G.	Good	Fair	Poor
6000	5000	4000	3000	2000	1000

SC3 Grade

NIB	Exc.	V.G.	Good	Fair	Poor
10000	8500	5000	4000	3000	1200

SCO Grade

NIB	Exc.	V.G.	Good	Fair	Poor
17000	12500	8500	5000	3000	1200

Gold Grade

NIB	Exc.	V.G.	Good	Fair	Poor
18750	14750	10000	6000	3000	1500

SCO Grade W/Sideplates

NIB	Exc.	V.G.	Good	Fair	Poor
26200	21200	15200	10000	5000	2000

Gold Grade W/Sideplates

NIB	Exc.	V.G.	Good	Fair	Poor
30200	24700	19200	12000	6000	3000

American Trap-Combo Models

MX7

Introduced in 1993. This an over and under Trap model that is offered in 12 gauge with 29.5" or 31.5" O/U barrels with either 32" or 34" single barrel. This model has a non removeable trigger group feathering fixed coil spring trigger mechanism. The trigger is selective and works in conjunction with the safety catch. The vent rib is ramped on the Combo Trap model. The walnut is custom made to the customer's dimensions.

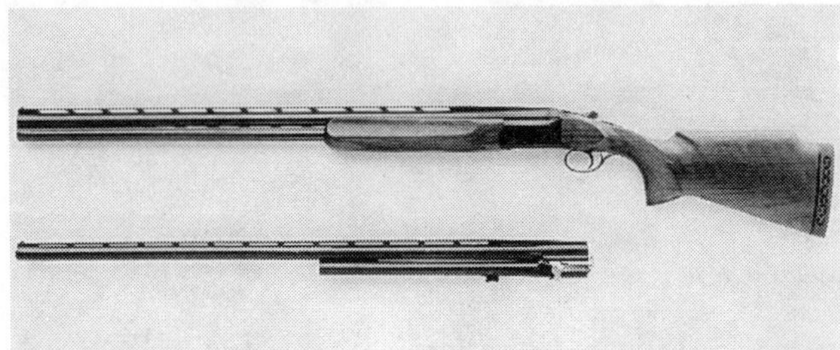

Standard Grade

NIB	Exc.	V.G.	Good	Fair	Poor
5400	4750	4000	3000	2000	1000

MX9

Offered in 12 gauge with 29.5" or 31.5" O/U barrels with 32" or 34" single barrel. All barrels are fitted with MX9 removable inserts to adjust point of impact. Walnut stock has adjustable comb. Comes with screw in chokes. Trigger group is removable.

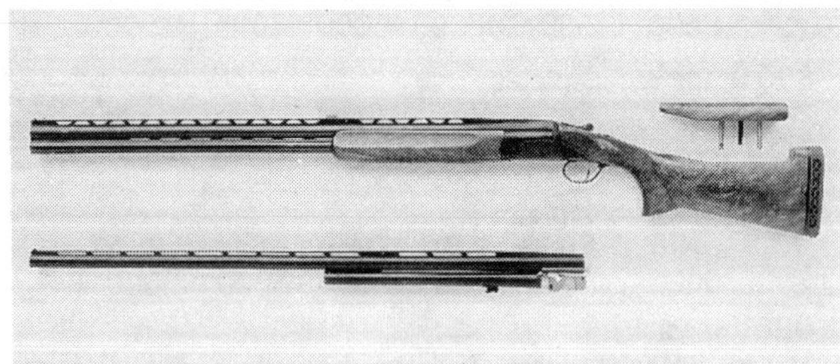

Standard Grade

NIB	Exc.	V.G.	Good	Fair	Poor
10200	9000	7000	4500	3500	1200

SC3 Grade

NIB	Exc.	V.G.	Good	Fair	Poor
15000	12500	9500	6500	3000	1500

SCO Grade

NIB	Exc.	V.G.	Good	Fair	Poor
22500	17000	14000	9000	4500	2000

Gold Grade

NIB	Exc.	V.G.	Good	Fair	Poor
25000	19000	15000	9000	4500	2000

SCO Grade W/Sideplates

NIB	Exc.	V.G.	Good	Fair	Poor
31750	25250	20000	15000	7500	3000

Gold Grade W/Sideplates

NIB	Exc.	V.G.	Good	Fair	Poor
35000	27500	22500	16000	8000	3000

MX10

Introduced in 1993 this model features a higher rib and different method of point of impact adjustment. Stock is adjustable for comb height. Offered in 12 gauge with 29.5" or 31.5" O/U barrels with 32" or 34" single barrel.

Standard Grade

NIB	Exc.	V.G.	Good	Fair	Poor
10500	9000	7000	5000	3000	1500

SC3 Grade

NIB	Exc.	V.G.	Good	Fair	Poor
15000	12500	9000	6000	3000	1500

SCO Grade

NIB	Exc.	V.G.	Good	Fair	Poor
23000	17500	14500	9000	4500	2000

Gold Grade

NIB	Exc.	V.G.	Good	Fair	Poor
25250	19250	15250	9000	4500	2000

SCO Grade W/Sideplates

NIB	Exc.	V.G.	Good	Fair	Poor
32000	25000	20000	15000	7500	3000

Gold Grade W/Sideplates

NIB	Exc.	V.G.	Good	Fair	Poor
36000	27000	22000	17000	8000	4000

247X8 Special

This model features a grooved forend, low contour ventilated rib, and adjustable trigger with internal selector. Same barrel combinations as above.

Standard Grade

NIB	Exc.	V.G.	Good	Fair	Poor
8200	7500	6000	4000	2000	1000

SC3 Grade

NIB	Exc.	V.G.	Good	Fair	Poor
13000	10000	7500	5000	2500	1200

SCO Grade

NIB	Exc.	V.G.	Good	Fair	Poor
20500	17500	12000	9500	5000	2000

Gold Grade

NIB	Exc.	V.G.	Good	Fair	Poor
23000	19000	12500	9500	5000	2000

SCO Grade W/Sideplates

NIB	Exc.	V.G.	Good	Fair	Poor
30000	25000	20000	15000	7500	3000

Gold Grade W/Sideplates

NIB	Exc.	V.G.	Good	Fair	Poor
33500	27500	22000	17000	8000	3000

DB81 Special

This model is similar to the above model but features a very high ramped ventilated rib. Trigger is adjustable with internal selector.

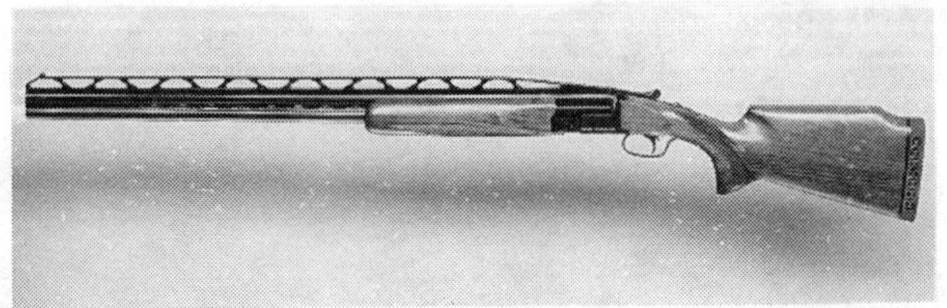

Standard Grade

NIB	Exc.	V.G.	Good	Fair	Poor
8700	7500	6000	4000	2000	1000

SC3 Grade

NIB	Exc.	V.G.	Good	Fair	Poor
13400	10500	8000	5500	2500	1200

SCO Grade

NIB	Exc.	V.G.	Good	Fair	Poor
21000	17500	12000	9500	5000	2000

Gold Grade

NIB	Exc.	V.G.	Good	Fair	Poor
23500	19000	13000	9500	5000	2000

SCO Grade W/Sideplates

NIB	Exc.	V.G.	Good	Fair	Poor
30000	24500	19000	14000	7000	3000

Gold Grade W/Sideplates

NIB	Exc.	V.G.	Good	Fair	Poor
34000	27000	20000	15000	8000	3000

COMPETITION MODELS

Competition versions are over and under shotguns in Trap, Skeet, Pigeon, and Sporting models. Stock dimensions are based on the particular model chosen. Trap models feature trap stock dimensions and forearm designed for that purpose. The other models also have their own particular specifications. However, prices are based on a common style referred to by Perazzi as Competition. Thus, all models within this group are priced the same regardless of specific type.

MX7C

Introduced in 1993 this model is offered in 12 gauge with a non-removable trigger group. It has a coil spring mechanism, fully selective in conjunction with the safety. Offered in 27.5", 29.5", or 31.5" flat vent rib barrels. Screw in chokes are standard. Walnut stock is custom made to customer's dimensions. The forend is beavertail.

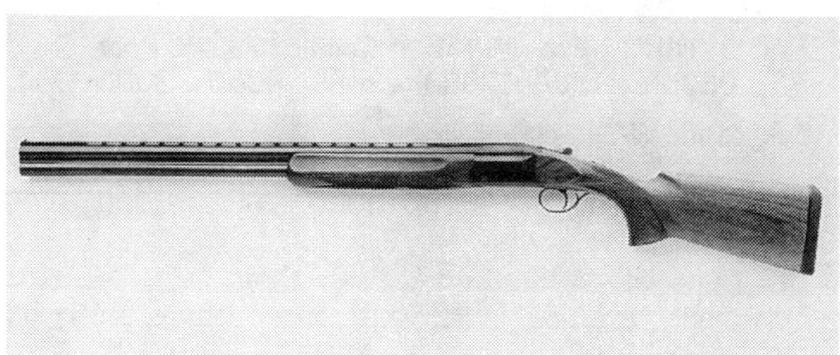

Standard Grade

NIB	Exc.	V.G.	Good	Fair	Poor
4900	4250	3500	2500	1250	750

MX9

This model was introduced in 1993 and features an adjustable Comb on the stock with unique vent rib inserts to correct for point of impact. Offered in 12 gauge with 29.5" or 31.5" barrels. Trigger group is removable. Comes standard with screw in chokes.

Standard Grade

NIB	Exc.	V.G.	Good	Fair	Poor
7600	6500	5000	4000	2000	1000

SC3 Grade

NIB	Exc.	V.G.	Good	Fair	Poor
11500	10000	8000	5000	3000	1500

SCO Grade

NIB	Exc.	V.G.	Good	Fair	Poor
18000	15000	10000	7500	3500	1500

Gold Grade

NIB	Exc.	V.G.	Good	Fair	Poor
20000	17500	12000	9500	5000	2000

SCO Grade W/Sideplates

NIB	Exc.	V.G.	Good	Fair	Poor
28000	22000	17000	11000	6000	2500

Gold Grade W/Sideplates

NIB	Exc.	V.G.	Good	Fair	Poor
32000	25000	20000	15000	7500	3000

MX10

This model was introduced in 1993 and is offered in 12 gauge and 20 gauge with choice of 29.5" or 31.5" barrel for 12 gauge and 29.5" barrel for 20 gauge. The ventilated rib height is adjustable as is the comb position on the stock. Chokes are fixed. Trigger group is removable with external selection.

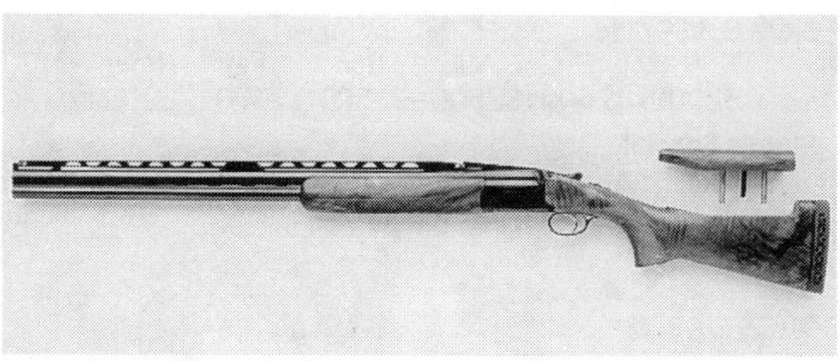

Standard Grade

NIB	Exc.	V.G.	Good	Fair	Poor
8000	7000	5000	4000	2000	1000

SC3 Grade

NIB	Exc.	V.G.	Good	Fair	Poor
12000	10500	8500	5000	3000	1500

SCO Grade

NIB	Exc.	V.G.	Good	Fair	Poor
19000	15000	10000	7500	3500	1500

Gold Grade

NIB	Exc.	V.G.	Good	Fair	Poor
21250	19500	13000	9500	5000	2000

SCO Grade W/Sideplates

NIB	Exc.	V.G.	Good	Fair	Poor
28000	22500	17500	11000	6000	2500

Gold Grade W/Sideplates

NIB	Exc.	V.G.	Good	Fair	Poor
32000	25000	20000	15000	7500	3000

MX8/20

This model was first introduced in 1993. It features a removable trigger group. Available in 20 gauge only with choice of 27.5", 28.375", 29.5" flat ventilated rib barrels. Choice of fixed or screw in chokes on Sporting model. Stock is custom made to customer's dimensions with beavertail forend.

Standard Grade

NIB	Exc.	V.G.	Good	Fair	Poor
5800	5000	4000	3000	2000	1000

SC3 Grade

NIB	Exc.	V.G.	Good	Fair	Poor
10000	9000	7500	4500	2500	1200

SCO Grade

NIB	Exc.	V.G.	Good	Fair	Poor
17000	14000	9000	6500	3500	1500

Gold Grade

NIB	Exc.	V.G.	Good	Fair	Poor
19000	15000	10000	7500	3500	1500

SCO Grade W/Sideplates

NIB	Exc.	V.G.	Good	Fair	Poor
26000	19000	13000	9000	4500	2000

Gold Grade W/Sideplates

NIB	Exc.	V.G.	Good	Fair	Poor
30000	25000	20000	15000	7500	3000

Extra Grade

NIB	Exc.	V.G.	Good	Fair	Poor
48500	40000	30000	20000	10000	5000

Extra Gold Grade

NIB	Exc.	V.G.	Good	Fair	Poor
52000	42500	32500	22500	12500	6000

Extra Model

Same as MX 8/20 but available in 12 gauge only with choice of barrel lengths to 31.5".

Extra Grade

NIB	Exc.	V.G.	Good	Fair	Poor
48500	40000	30000	20000	10000	5000

Extra Gold Grade

NIB	Exc.	V.G.	Good	Fair	Poor
52000	42500	32500	22500	12500	6000

Mirage Special

This model features a adjustable trigger and is available in 12 gauge with choice of 27.5", 28.375", 29.5", or 31.5" ventilated rib barrels.

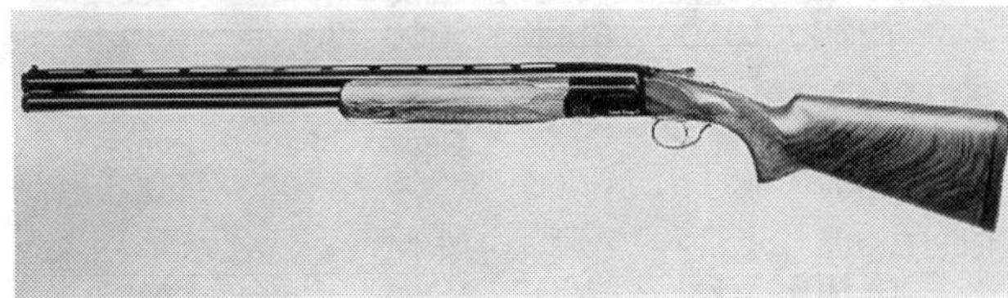

Standard Grade

NIB	Exc.	V.G.	Good	Fair	Poor
6100	5500	4500	3500	2500	1000

Mirage Special Sporting

Similar to the Mirage Special, listed above, but with external trigger selection and screw in chokes. Offered in 12 gauge only with choice of 27.5", 28.375", or 29.5" vent rib barrels.

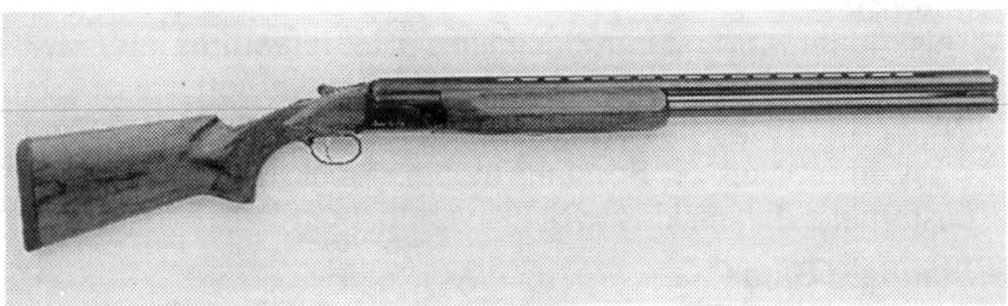

Standard Grade

NIB	Exc.	V.G.	Good	Fair	Poor
6400	5700	5000	4000	3000	1500

Mirage Special Sporting Classic

This model features the same basic specifications as the Mirage Special Sporting with the addition of a scroll border on the receiver and trigger guard. The wood is of slightly higher quality. Offered in 12 gauge only with 27.5", 28.375", or 29.5" vent rib barrels.

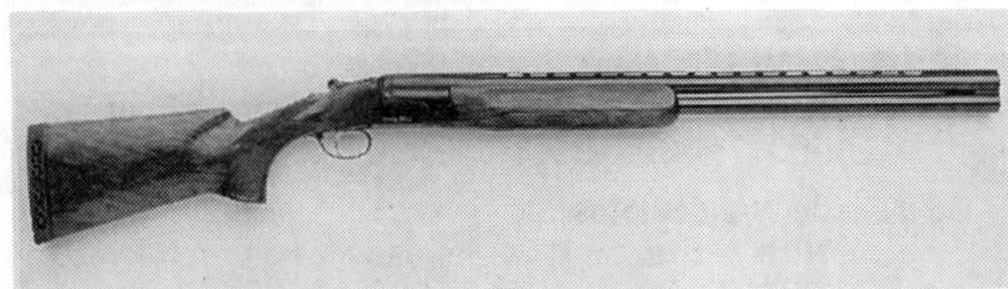

Standard Grade

NIB	Exc.	V.G.	Good	Fair	Poor
7300	6750	6000	5000	3500	1500

Mirage MX8

(Check on this model)

Standard Grade

NIB	Exc.	V.G.	Good	Fair	Poor
5800	5000	4000	3000	2000	1000

MX8 Special

This model features a four position adjustable trigger. It also has a low contour rib and a grooved forearm. Offered in 12 only with choice of 29.5" or 31.5" vent rib barrels.

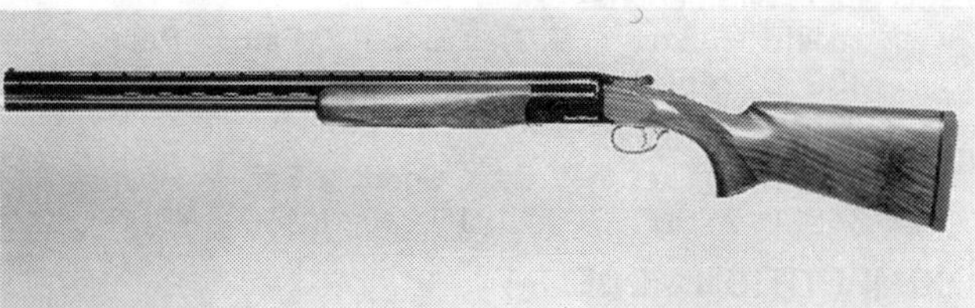

Standard Grade

NIB	Exc.	V.G.	Good	Fair	Poor
6100	5500	4500	3500	2500	1000

SCO Model

This model is similar to the MX8 but offered only in 12 gauge with barrel length from 27.5" to 31.5". The trigger is adjustable instead of removable.

SCO Grade

NIB	Exc.	V.G.	Good	Fair	Poor
17000	12500	8500	6000	3000	1500

Gold Grade

NIB	Exc.	V.G.	Good	Fair	Poor
19000	13500	9500	6500	3250	1500

SCO Grade W/Sideplates

NIB	Exc.	V.G.	Good	Fair	Poor
26000	21500	17000	12000	6000	3000

Gold Grade W/Sideplates

NIB	Exc.	V.G.	Good	Fair	Poor
30000	25000	19000	14000	7000	3000

DB81 Special

This model, available in 12 gauge only, features a very high ramped ventilated rib. Barrel length are 29.5" or 31.5". Adjustable trigger standard.

Standard Grade

NIB	Exc.	V.G.	Good	Fair	Poor
7000	6500	5750	4500	3000	1000

SC3 Grade

NIB	Exc.	V.G.	Good	Fair	Poor
10500	9500	8500	5000	3500	1200

SCO Grade

NIB	Exc.	V.G.	Good	Fair	Poor
17500	13500	8500	5000	3500	1200

Gold Grade

NIB	Exc.	V.G.	Good	Fair	Poor
19500	15000	10000	7500	3500	1200

SCO Grade W/Sideplates

NIB	Exc.	V.G.	Good	Fair	Poor
26500	21500	17000	11000	5500	2000

Gold Grade W/Sideplates

NIB	Exc.	V.G.	Good	Fair	Poor
30500	27000	19000	12000	6500	3000

Mirage Special 4-Gauge Set

Similar to the Mirage Special in appearance and specifications but fitted with four barrel sets in 12, 20, 28 gauge, and .410 bore.

Standard Grade

NIB	Exc.	V.G.	Good	Fair	Poor
14000	9500	8000	4000	3000	2000

SC3 Grade

NIB	Exc.	V.G.	Good	Fair	Poor
21000	15000	9500	4500	3500	2500

SCO Grade

NIB	Exc.	V.G.	Good	Fair	Poor
28000	22500	15000	8500	4200	2500

Gold Grade

NIB	Exc.	V.G.	Good	Fair	Poor
30000	24500	17000	9500	4500	2500

SCO Grade W/Sideplates

NIB	Exc.	V.G.	Good	Fair	Poor
40000	32500	25000	12500	6500	3000

Gold Grade W/Sideplates

NIB	Exc.	V.G.	Good	Fair	Poor
44000	35000	27000	13500	7000	3000

GAME GUN MODELS

MX12/12C

Offered in 12 gauge only with 26.75" or 27.5" vent rib barrels. The single selective trigger is non-removable. The walnut stock is fitted with a Schnabel forend and the receiver gas a light scroll engraved border. The MX12 is supplied with fixed chokes while the MX12C is fitted with 5 screw-in choke tubes. Add $400 to MX12 prices to get MX12C values.

Standard Grade

NIB	Exc.	V.G.	Good	Fair	Poor
5800	5200	4500	3000	2000	1000

SC3 Grade

NIB	Exc.	V.G.	Good	Fair	Poor
9900	9000	5500	4000	3000	1200

SCO Grade

NIB	Exc.	V.G.	Good	Fair	Poor
17000	14000	9500	4500	3200	1200

Gold Grade

NIB	Exc.	V.G.	Good	Fair	Poor
19000	16000	10000	5000	3500	1200

SCO Grade W/Sideplates

NIB	Exc.	V.G.	Good	Fair	Poor
26000	22500	17000	8500	4200	2000

Gold Grade W/Sideplates

NIB	Exc.	V.G.	Good	Fair	Poor
30000	26500	19000	10000	5000	2500

MX20/20C

This model is offered in 20 gauge. It features a non-removable trigger group. The frame is smaller than 12 gauge. Offered with 26" or 27.5" vent rib barrels. The MX20 has fixed chokes while the MX20C is supplied with 5 screw-in choke tubes. Add $400 to MX20 prices to get MX20C values.

Standard Grade

NIB	Exc.	V.G.	Good	Fair	Poor
6000	5500	4000	3000	2000	1000

SC3 Grade

NIB	Exc.	V.G.	Good	Fair	Poor
10500	9500	4500	3250	2000	1000

SCO Grade

NIB	Exc.	V.G.	Good	Fair	Poor
17000	14000	9500	4500	2500	1200

Gold Grade

NIB	Exc.	V.G.	Good	Fair	Poor
20000	17000	12000	6000	3000	1500

SCO Grade W/Sideplates

NIB	Exc.	V.G.	Good	Fair	Poor
28000	25000	17000	8500	4000	2000

Gold Grade W/Sideplates

NIB	Exc.	V.G.	Good	Fair	Poor
34000	31000	23000	12000	6000	3000

MX8/20-8/20C

Introduced in 1993 and offered in 20 gauge with 26" or 27.625" vent rib barrels. The Trigger group on this model is removable. The stock is a high grade walnut custom made to customer's own specifications. The forend is round. The MX8/20 is supplied with fixed chokes while the Mx8/20C has 5 screw-in choke tubes. Add $400 for MX8/20C values.

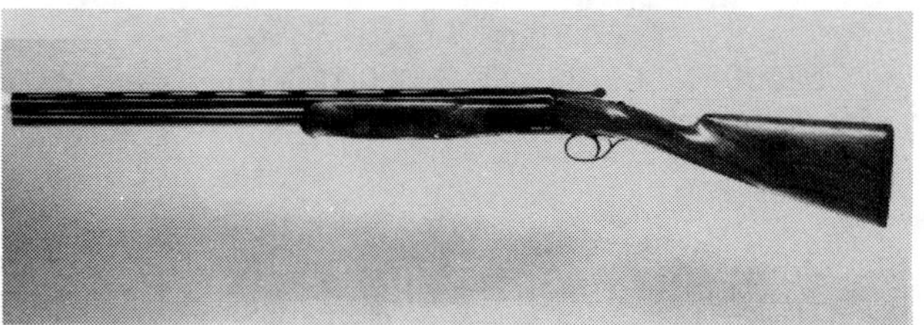

Standard Grade

NIB	Exc.	V.G.	Good	Fair	Poor
5800	5200	4500	3000	2000	1000

SC3 Grade

NIB	Exc.	V.G.	Good	Fair	Poor
9900	9000	5500	4000	3000	1200

SCO Grade

NIB	Exc.	V.G.	Good	Fair	Poor
17000	14000	9500	4500	3200	1200

Gold Grade

NIB	Exc.	V.G.	Good	Fair	Poor
19000	16000	10000	5000	3500	1200

SCO Grade W/Sideplates

NIB	Exc.	V.G.	Good	Fair	Poor
26000	22500	17000	8500	4200	2000

Gold Grade W/Sideplates

NIB	Exc.	V.G.	Good	Fair	Poor
30000	26500	19000	10000	5000	2500

MX28 and MX410

Introduced in 1993 these two models feature a non-removable trigger group and a special small frame for each. The MX28, .28 gauge, weighs about 5.5 lb while the MX410, .410 bore, weighs slightly less. Both a supplied with fixed chokes, flat ribs, custom made stocks, and round forends. Each model is offered with a choice of 26" or 27.5" barrels. Both the MX28 and MX410 are priced the same.

Standard Grade

NIB	Exc.	V.G.	Good	Fair	Poor
11500	10000	8000	5000	3000	1500

SC3 Grade

Not Available

SCO Grade

NIB	Exc.	V.G.	Good	Fair	Poor
22500	19000	13000	9000	4500	2000

Gold Grade

NIB	Exc.	V.G.	Good	Fair	Poor
25000	20000	15000	10000	5000	2500

SCO Grade W/Sideplates

NIB	Exc.	V.G.	Good	Fair	Poor
31500	25250	20000	15000	7500	3000

Gold Grade W/Sideplates

NIB	Exc.	V.G.	Good	Fair	Poor
36000	30000	23000	17500	8500	3000

Extra Grade Models

There are three different configurations offered for this model. In Extra Grade they are chambered for 12 gauge and 20 gauge with non-removable trigger group or 20 gauge with removable trigger group. In Extra Gold Grade they are offered in 12 gauge and 20 gauge with non-removable trigger group and in 20 gauge with removable group. 12 gauge guns are offered with 26.75" or 27.5" vent rib barrels while 20 gauge guns can be had with 26" or 27.5" vent rib barrels. The 20 gauge guns with removable trigger groups were first introduced in 1993.

Extra Grade

NIB	Exc.	V.G.	Good	Fair	Poor
48500	40000	30000	20000	10000	5000

Extra Gold Grade

NIB	Exc.	V.G.	Good	Fair	Poor
52000	42000	32000	20000	10000	5000

PERRY PATENT FIREARMS CO.

Newark, New Jersey

Perry Single Shot Pistol

A .52 caliber breech loading percussion pistol with a 6" round barrel. Blued with walnut grips. The barrel marked "Perry Patent Firearms Co./Newark, N.J." Approximately 200 were made between 1854 and 1856 in two styles.

1st Type—Long, Contoured Triggerguard,Opening Lever

Exc.	V.G.	Good	Fair	Poor
3500	2850	2000	1500	1000

2nd Type S Curved Shorter Triggerguard and an Automatic Primer Feed that Protrudes from the Butt

Exc.	V.G.	Good	Fair	Poor
3000	2500	1750	1250	850

Perry Carbine

A .54 caliber breech loading percussion carbine with a 20.75" barrel and half length walnut stock secured by one barrel band. Blued with a case-hardened lock. Approximately 200 were made. Prospective purchasers are advised to secure a qualified appraisal prior to acquisition.

Courtesy Milwaukee Public Museum, Milwaukee, Wisconsin.

Exc.	V.G.	Good	Fair	Poor
2000	1750	1500	1250	850

PERRY & GODDARD RENWICK ARMS CO.

New York, New York

Derringer

A .44 caliber single shot spur trigger pistol with a 2" octagonal barrel. Blued or silver-plated with walnut or gutta percha grips. The barrel may be swiveled so that either end can serve as the chamber and is marked "Double Header/ E.S.Renwick." Produced in very limited quantities during the 1860s. Prospective purchasers are advised to secure a qualified appraisal prior to acquisition.

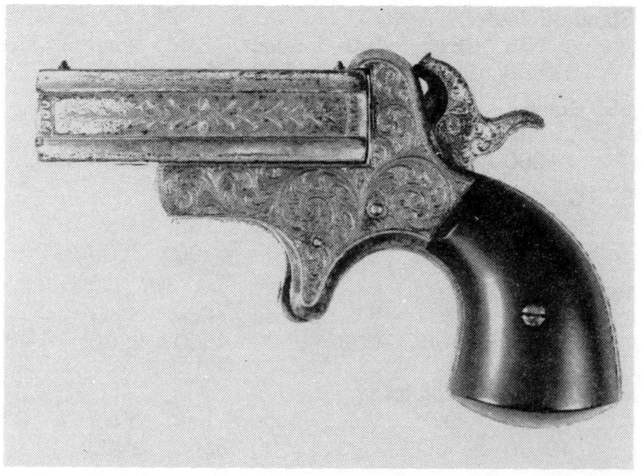

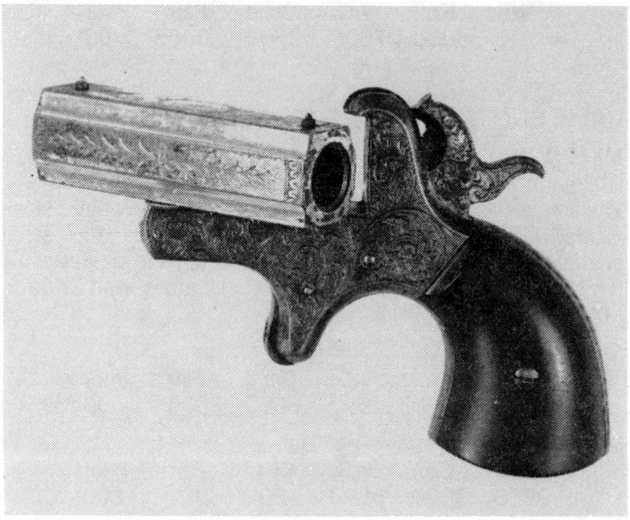

Exc.	V.G.	Good	Fair	Poor
6000	5000	3500	2250	1500

PERUGINI & VISINI

Brescia, Italy

Arms by this maker were imported by W. L. Moore of Westlake Village, California.

Liberty Model

A side-by-side 12, 20, 28 and .410 gauge shotgun having 28" barrels. Anson & Deeley action with a double Purdy lock. Blued overall with checkered walnut stock.

Exc.	V.G.	Good	Fair	Poor
5000	4250	3500	2750	2000

Classic Model

A 12 or 20 gauge double-barrel shotgun having a Holland & Holland style sidelock with a double Purdy lock. The barrels 28" in length. Single trigger and automatic ejectors. The sidelocks and mounts engraved and blued. Well figured and checkered walnut stock.

Exc.	V.G.	Good	Fair	Poor
11000	8500	7000	5500	4750

Bolt-Action Rifle

A Mauser type bolt-action rifle available in a variety of chamberings, with 24" or 26" barrels. Sights not furnished. Well figured checkered walnut stock.

Exc.	V.G.	Good	Fair	Poor
4000	3500	2750	2000	1500

Deluxe Bolt-Action Rifle

As above with first quality walnut stocks and a case.

Exc.	V.G.	Good	Fair	Poor
4500	3750	3000	2250	1750

Eagle Single Shot

An Anson & Deeley single shot rifle fitted with either 24" or 26" barrels, open sights, automatic ejector and adjustable trigger. Stock of checkered walnut.

Exc.	V.G.	Good	Fair	Poor
5000	4250	3500	2750	2000

Boxlock Express Rifle

An Anson & Deeley action double-barrel rifle chambered for .444 Marlin or 9.3x74R cartridges. The barrel length is 24" and is fitted with express sights. Double triggers and automatic ejectors. Receiver casehardened and the barrels as well as mounts blued. Checkered walnut stock.

Exc.	V.G.	Good	Fair	Poor
3250	2750	2200	1750	1450

Magnum O/U

An Anson & Deeley action Over/Under rifle available in .270, .375 Holland & Holland and .458 Winchester Magnum. The barrels 24" in length and fitted with express sights. Double triggers and automatic ejectors. Receiver and barrels blued, the stock of checkered walnut.

Exc.	V.G.	Good	Fair	Poor
5500	4750	3900	2750	2250

Super Express Rifle

A Holland & Holland-style sidelock double-barrel rifle. Having 24" barrels fitted with express sights. Available in a variety of chamberings. The receiver and sidelocks either casehardened or finished in the bright and fully engraved. Checkered walnut stock.

Exc.	V.G.	Good	Fair	Poor
9500	8500	6750	5500	4850

Victoria Side x Side Rifle

Similar to the Boxlock Express Rifle but chambered for .30-06, 7x65R or 9.3x74R cartridges. Either 24" or 26" barrels were available. Double triggers and automatic ejectors. Blued with minimal engraving. Stock of checkered walnut.

Exc.	V.G.	Good	Fair	Poor
6500	5750	4850	3900	2750

Selous Side x Side Rifle

First quality double-barrel express rifle with 24" or 26" barrels. Fully detachable Holland & Holland-style sidelocks, double triggers and automatic ejectors. Fully engraved with well figured checkered walnut stocks.

Exc.	V.G.	Good	Fair	Poor
20000	16500	13500	9000	6500

PETTINGILL C. S.

New Haven, Connecticut
Rogers, Spencer & Co.
Willowvale, New York

Pocket Revolver

A hammerless, double-action .31-caliber percussion revolver having a 4" octagonal barrel. The frame of brass or iron. Blued barrel, the grips of oil finished walnut. The First and Second Models are marked "Pettingill's Patent 1856" as well as "T.K.Austin." The Third Model is marked "Pettengill Patent 1856", and "Raymond and Robitaille Patented 1858." Approximately 400 were manufactured in the late 1850s and early 1860s.

1st Model with Brass Frame

Exc.	V.G.	Good	Fair	Poor
1400	1250	1000	800	600

2nd Model with Iron Frame

Exc.	V.G.	Good	Fair	Poor
1000	850	700	500	400

3rd Model, Iron Frame and Improved Action

Exc.	V.G.	Good	Fair	Poor
1000	850	700	500	400

Navy Revolver

As above but in .34-caliber with a 4.5" barrel and a 6-shot cylinder. The frame of iron, blued overall, and the grips of walnut. This model is marked "Pettengill's Patent 1856" and "Raymond & Robitaille Patented 1858." Approximately 900 were manufactured in the late 1850s and early 1860s.

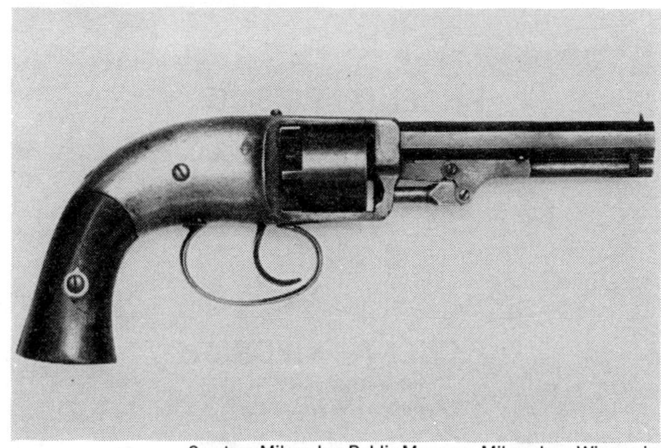

Courtesy Milwaukee Public Museum, Milwaukee, Wisconsin.

Exc.	V.G.	Good	Fair	Poor
1500	1250	1000	750	500

Army Model Revolver

As above but of .44 caliber and fitted with a 7.5" barrel. The frame of iron which is casehardened, the octagonal barrel blued, the grips of oil finished walnut. Early production models are marked as the Navy models, while later production examples are marked "Petingill's Patent 1856, pat'd July 22, 1856 and July 27, 1858." Some examples will be found with government inspector's marks and are worth approximately 25% more. It is believed that 3,400 were made in the 1860s.

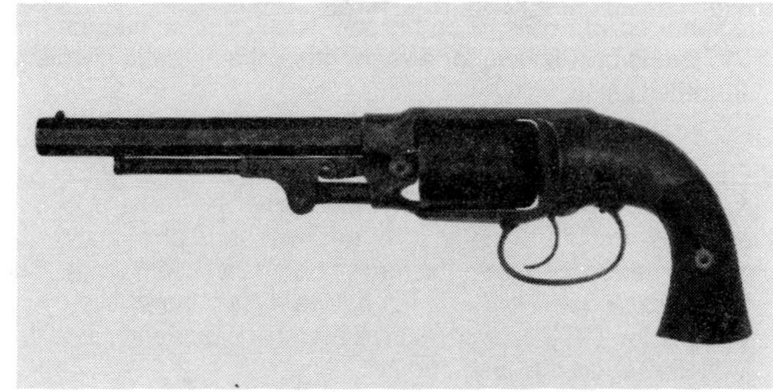

Courtesy Milwaukee Public Museum, Milwaukee, Wisconsin.

Exc.	V.G.	Good	Fair	Poor
1500	1250	1000	750	500

PFANNL, FRANCOIS

Krems, Austria

Erika

A 4.25mm semi-automatic pistol with a hinged barrel assembly. The barrel either 1.5" or 2.25" in length. The grips are marked "Erika". Approximately 3,500 made between 1912 and 1926.

Exc.	V.G.	Good	Fair	Poor
400	350	300	200	125

PHOENIX
Lowell, Massachusetts

Pocket Pistol
A rare .25 ACP semi-automatic pistol with a 2.25" barrel and 6-round magazine. Receiver and slide blued, the grips of hard rubber. Manufactured during the 1920s.

Exc.	V.G.	Good	Fair	Poor
500	450	400	300	200

PHOENIX ARMS CO.
Liege, Belgium
SEE—Robar et DeKerkhove

PICKERT, FRIEDRICH
Zella-Mehlis, Germany
Arminius Waffenfabrik

This firm produced revolvers bearing the tradename "Arminius". The revolvers manufactured by Pickert of the double-action type, with or without exposed hammers. Some models are fitted with ejectors, while others have removable cylinders. Calibers and barrel lengths vary. After World War II, the tradename was acquired by Hermann Wiehauch.

Exc.	V.G.	Good	Fair	Poor
175	150	125	100	75

PIEPER, HENRI & NICOLAS
Liege, Belgium

Originally founded by Henri Pieper in 1859, the company was reorganized in 1898 when his son, Nicolas, assumed control. The firm is best known for a series of semi-automatic pistols as described below.

Pieper
A 6.35 or 7.65mm semi-automatic pistol featuring a hinged barrel assembly 2.5" in length. Receiver and barrel blued, the grips of hard rubber with the firm's trademark cast in them. The Model 1907 variation does not have a hinged barrel assembly. The Model 1908 is also known as the "Basculant", and the Model 1918 as the "Demontant".

Courtesy Orville Reichert.

Courtesy Orville Reichert.

Exc.	V.G.	Good	Fair	Poor
175	150	125	100	75

Pieper Bayard Revolver
In competition with the Nagant gas seal revolver, Henri Pieper developed a superior design. Revolvers of this type have 5" barrels and are chambered for 8mm cartridges. The first model of this revolver had an automatic ejection system, while the second version utilized a swing-out cylinder. Standard finish is blued, with checkered hard rubber grips.

Exc.	V.G.	Good	Fair	Poor
275	250	200	150	100

Legia
This model was patterned after that of the Browning, and is chambered for the 6.35mm cartridge. The standard magazine holds 6 cartridges but a 10-round magazine was also available.

Exc.	V.G.	Good	Fair	Poor
175	150	125	100	75

Bayard
A 6.35, 7.65 or 9mm short semi-automatic pistol with a 2.5" barrel. Standard magazine capacity 6 rounds. The slide stamped "Anciens Etablissement Pieper Liege, Belgium".

Exc.	V.G.	Good	Fair	Poor
175	150	125	100	75

PILSEN, ZBROVKA
Pilsen, Czechoslovakia

Pocket Pistol
Essentially a Model 1910 Browning semi-automatic pistol without a grip safety, this pistol was of 7.65mm caliber and had a 3.5" barrel with a 6-round magazine. The slide is marked "Akciova Spolecnost drive Skodovny zavody Zbrovka Plzen." Standard finish is blued, the grips of hard rubber. Manufactured during the 1920s.

Exc.	V.G.	Good	Fair	Poor
225	200	150	125	100

PIOTTI
Brescia, Italy
Importer—W. L. Moore
Westlake Village, California

This Italian gunmaking firm is located in Gardone Val Trompia in the province of Brescia. Its shotguns are hand crafted and limited to a few each year. Each gun is made to individual specifications. Many consider them one of the best double shotguns made in the world today. Actions are either Anson & Deeley box lock or Holland & Holland side lock. Several features are offered on these shotguns at no additional cost: type of stock and forearm, barrel length and chokes, rib, action shape and finish.

Other features are considered extra cost options and will affect the value of the gun. There are: single triggers, detachable side locks, automatic safety, recoil pads, up-graded wood, engraving, and multi-gauge sets. With the exception of a few grades Piotti guns are available in 10, 12, 16, 20, and 28 gauge, as well as .410 bore. Depending on gauge barrel lengths are from 25" to 34".

Model Piuma (BSEE)

This model is the firm's standard box lock offering. Available in 12 gauge to .410 bore it features ejectors and a scolloped frame. Fine scroll and rosette engraving is standard.

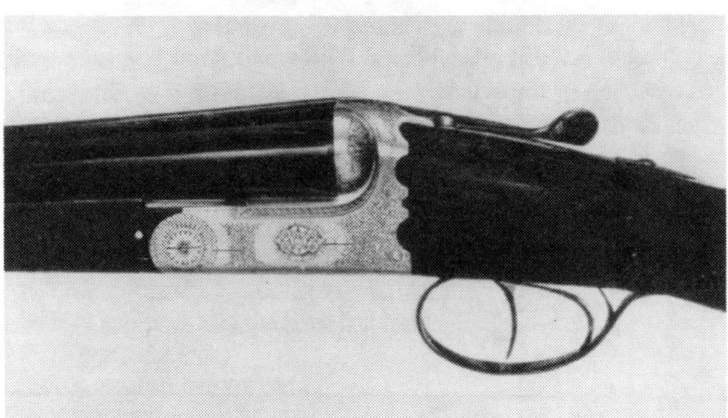

NIB	Exc.	V.G.	Good	Fair	Poor
12000	9500	6500	3000	2000	1000

Model King No. 1

This model features a side locks with either fine line scroll engraving with full coverage. A gold crown is inlaid on the top lever. Select walnut with hand checkering is standard. Chambered from 10 gauge to .410 bore.

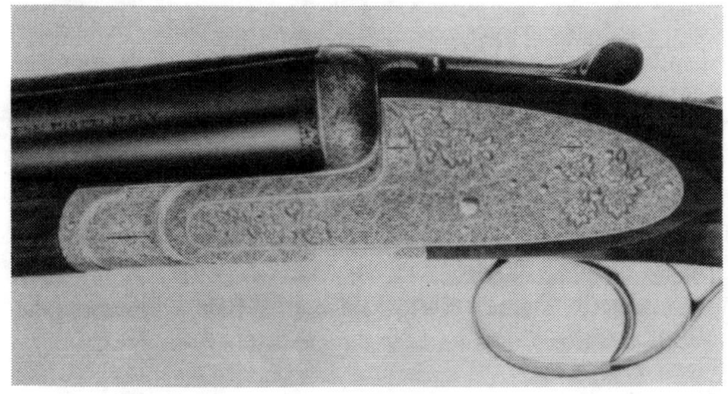

NIB	Exc.	V.G.	Good	Fair	Poor
20000	12500	8500	5000	3000	1500

Model Lunik

This model is fitted with Holland & Holland side locks. Engraving is Renaissance style relief cut scroll engraving. A gold crown is inlaid on the top lever. Offered in gauges from 10 to .410 bore.

NIB	Exc.	V.G.	Good	Fair	Poor
21500	16500	11500	8500	4000	2000

Model Monaco

This side lock model features all of the best that Piotte has to offer and extra attention is paid to hand work and fitting. Only the finest European hardwoods are used. Available in 10 gauge to .410 bore. Offered with three different types of engraving designated No. 1, No. 2, and No. 4.

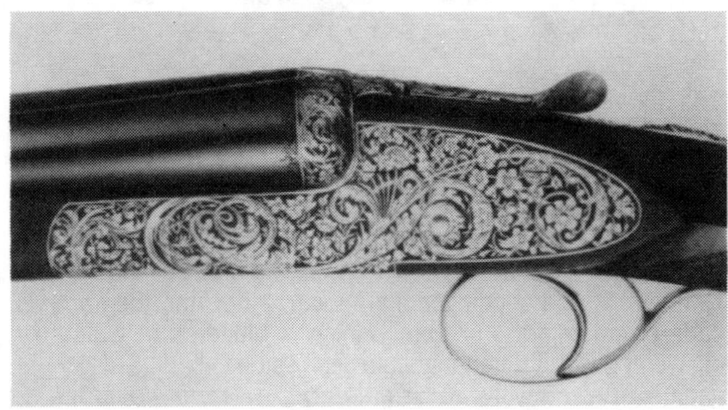

Monaco No. 1 or No. 2

NIB	Exc.	V.G.	Good	Fair	Poor
28500	22500	17000	11000	5000	2500

Monaco No. 4

NIB	Exc.	V.G.	Good	Fair	Poor
37000	31000	22000	14000	7000	3000

Model King Extra

This model is similar to the King No. 1 but with the addition of a number of engraving styles from English to game scenes with gold inlays. Because of the wide variety of engraving patterns offered on this model it is advisable to secure a qualified appraisal before purchase.

PIRKO

SEE—Austrian Military Firearms

PLAINFIELD MACHINE CO.

Dunellen, New Jersey

Super Enforcer

A cut-down version of the U.S.M1 Carbine with a 12" barrel and pistol grip. The finish is blued and stocks are walnut.

Exc.	V.G.	Good	Fair	Poor
225	200	175	125	100

M1 Carbine

A commercial reproduction of the U.S.M1 Carbine. The finish is blued. Walnut stock.

Exc.	V.G.	Good	Fair	Poor
200	175	150	100	75

M1 Paratrooper Carbine.

As above with a folding wire buttstock and walnut forend.

Exc.	V.G.	Good	Fair	Poor
225	200	175	125	100

PLAINFIELD ORDNANCE CO.

Middlesex, New Jersey

Model 71

A stainless-steel .22 caliber semi-automatic pistol with a 10-shot magazine and 1" barrel. Also available in .25 ACP and conversion kits were available.

Conversion Kit

Exc.	V.G.	Good	Fair	Poor
50	40	30	25	20

.22 or .25 Caliber Pistol

Exc.	V.G.	Good	Fair	Poor
150	125	100	75	50

Model 72

As above except with an alloy frame.

Exc.	V.G.	Good	Fair	Poor
150	125	100	75	50

PLANT'S MANUFACTURING CO.

New Haven, Connecticut

Army Model Revolver

A large single action revolver chambered for a .42caliber cup-primed cartridge which loads from the front of the cylinder. Barrel length 6" and of octagonal form with a rib. And the frame is made of either brass or iron. Finish is blued, with walnut or rosewood grips. Interchangeable percussion cylinders also were made for these revolvers. If present, the values would be increased approximately 30 percent. This revolver was marketed by Merwin & Bray, and there were approximately 1,500 of the 1st and 2nd Models manufactured and 10,000 of the 3rd Model in the 1860s.

1st Model Brass Frame

Marked "Plant's Mfg. Co. New Haven, Ct." on the barrel, "M & B" on the side of the frame, and "Patented July 12, 1859" on the cylinder. Approximately 100 manufactured.

Exc.	V.G.	Good	Fair	Poor
950	850	750	600	450

1st Model Iron Frame

As above with an iron frame. Approximately 500 made.

Exc.	V.G.	Good	Fair	Poor
850	750	650	500	350

2nd Model Rounded Brass Frame

This model is distinguished by the markings "Merwin & Bray, New York" on the frame and the patent date "July 21, 1863". Approximately 300 made.

Exc.	V.G.	Good	Fair	Poor
850	750	650	550	350

2nd Model Iron Frame

As above with an iron frame.

Exc.	V.G.	Good	Fair	Poor
750	650	550	450	275

3rd Model

As above with a flat brass frame.

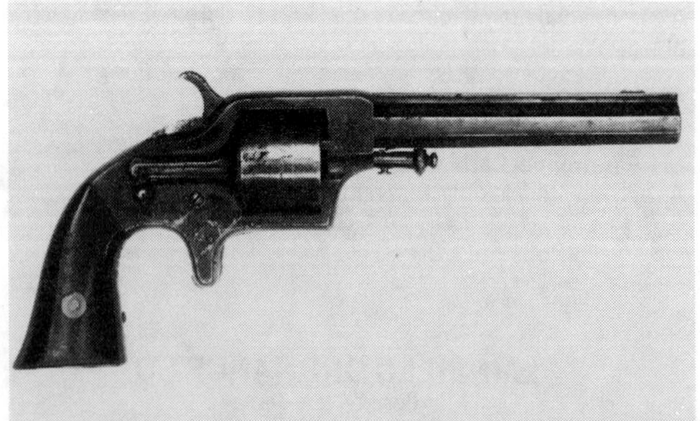

Courtesy Milwaukee Public Museum, Milwaukee, Wisconsin.

Exc.	V.G.	Good	Fair	Poor
600	500	400	300	200

Pocket Revolver

Similar to the Army model described above except chambered for .30 caliber cartridges. Barrel length 3.5", five-shot cylinder. The frame normally silver plated, barrel and cylinder blued and the grips of rosewood or walnut. This model is encountered with a variety of retailer's markings; Eagle Arms Co., New York," "Reynolds, Plant & Hotchkiss, New Haven, Ct.," and Merwin & Bray Firearms Co., N.Y." Approximately 20,000 were made.

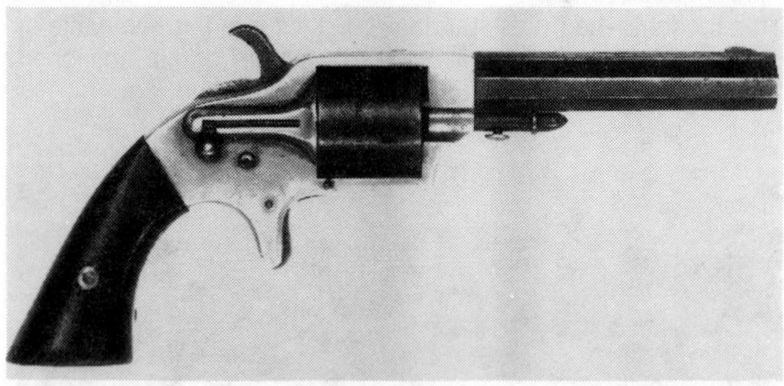

Courtesy Milwaukee Public Museum, Milwaukee, Wisconsin.

Exc.	V.G.	Good	Fair	Poor
500	400	350	275	200

POLY-TECHNOLOGIES, INC.

China
Importer—Keng's
Riverdale, Georgia
Distributor—PTK Int.
Atlanta, Georgia

SKS

A semi-automatic rifle chambered for the 7.62x39mm cartridge with a 20.5" barrel and 10-shot fixed magazine, based on the Soviet Siminov carbine. Finish is blued, and the stock and handguard are made of a Chinese hardwood.

NIB	Exc.	V.G.	Good	Fair	Poor
125	100	80	70	50	35

AKS-762

A semi-automatic version of the Chinese-type 56 Assault rifle chambered for the 7.62x39mm cartridge with a 16.5" barrel. Furnished with a 20-round magazine and a Chinese bayonet. The finish is blued, and the stock is hardwood.

NIB	Exc.	V.G.	Good	Fair	Poor
250	200	175	150	125	100

AK-47/S

As above with a Soviet style bayonet—Add $15.00.

M-14/S

A reproduction of the U.S.M14 rifle chambered for the 7.62mm cartridge with a 22" barrel and 20-round magazine. Finish is blued and the stock is of hardwood.

NIB	Exc.	V.G.	Good	Fair	Poor
350	300	250	200	150	100

POINTER

Hopkins & Allen
Norwich, Connecticut

Single Shot Derringer

An unmarked Hopkins & Allen single shot pistol stamped "Pointer" on the barrel. Barrel length 2.75", caliber .22, frame of nickle-plated brass. The barrel swings sideways for loading. Birdshead walnut grips. It is believed that about 2,500 were made between 1870 and 1890.

Exc.	V.G.	Good	Fair	Poor
300	250	200	150	100

POND, LUCIUS, W.

Worchester, Massachusetts

Pocket Revolver

A single action, spur trigger .32 caliber revolver with octagonal barrels of 4", 5", or 6" length. The barrel top strap and cylinder pivot upwards for loading. Made with either brass or iron frames. A screwdriver is fitted in the butt. As these revolvers were an infringement of Rollin White's patent, they were discontinued. Some revolvers are to be found with the inscription "Manuf'd. for Smith & Wesson Pat'd. April 5, 1855." These examples are worth approximately 20% more than the values listed below.

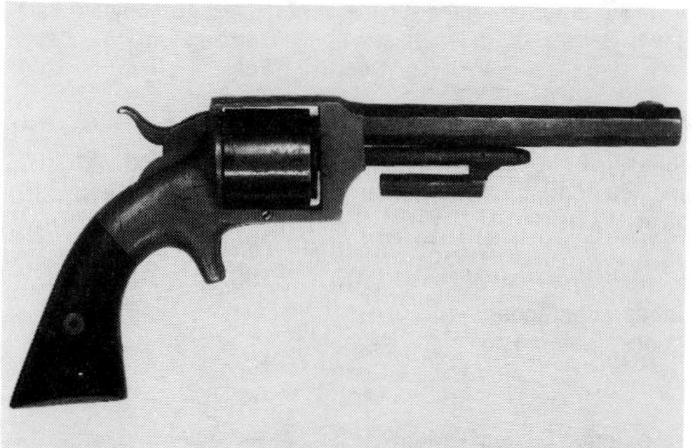

Courtesy Milwaukee Public Museum, Milwaukee, Wisconsin.

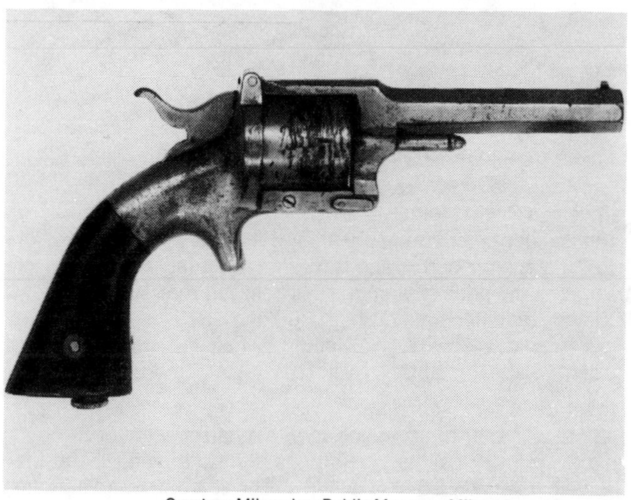

Courtesy Milwaukee Public Museum, Milwaukee, Wisconsin.

Brass Framed Revolver

Exc.	V.G.	Good	Fair	Poor
500	400	300	200	125

Iron Framed Revolver

Exc.	V.G.	Good	Fair	Poor
375	300	200	150	100

Separate Chamber Revolver

To avoid the Rollin White patent, this revolver is chambered for .22 or .32 caliber rimfire cartridges which fit into separate steel-chamber inserts that can be removed from the front of the cylinder for loading. The .22 caliber version has a 3.5" octagonal barrel with a 7-round unfluted cylinder; the .32 caliber version has a 4", 5", or 6" octagonal barrel and 6-shot unfluted cylinder. Frames are of silver-plated brass; and the barrels and cylinders are blued. Grips of walnut. Standard markings include "L.W. Pond, Worcester, Mass." and patent dates. Approximately 2,000 manufactured in .22 caliber and 5,000 in .32 caliber between 1863 and 1870.

.22 Caliber Version

Exc.	V.G.	Good	Fair	Poor
600	500	400	300	200

.32 Caliber Version

Exc.	V.G.	Good	Fair	Poor
450	400	300	250	150

PORTER, P. W.

New York, New York

Turret Revolver

An extremely rare 9-shot vertical cylinder .41 caliber percussion revolver with a 5.25" round barrel. The triggerguard is also a lever which turns the cylinder and cocks the hammer. An automatic primer system is also fitted to this revolver. Manufactured during the 1850s in an unknown quantity.

Exc.	V.G.	Good	Fair	Poor
8500	7500	6000	4000	3000

Turret Rifle

A 9-shot vertical cylinder .44 caliber rifle with either a 26" or 28" octagonal barrel. The only markings are "Address P.W. Porter/New York." Four variations of this rifle are known and the 22" barreled carbine would command a 25% premium. Approximately 1,250 were manufactured during the 1850s.

1st Model with Canister Magazine

Fitted with a 30-shot round canister magazine over the turret, this model was made in Tennessee and is extremely rare. Most often the canisters are not encountered and values reflect this. Approximately 25 were made.

Exc.	V.G.	Good	Fair	Poor
7500	6500	5500	4500	3500

2nd Model (New York)

Exc.	V.G.	Good	Fair	Poor
4500	3500	2750	2000	1500

3rd Model (New York)

This model has a screw-off cover over the magazine.

Exc.	V.G.	Good	Fair	Poor
4750	3750	3000	2250	1750

4th Model (New York)

As above but without an automatic primer magazine and the nipples are exposed.

Exc.	V.G.	Good	Fair	Poor
3500	3000	2500	1750	1250

POWELL, W. & SON LTD.

Birmingham, England
Importer—Jaqua's
Findlay, Ohio

Number 3 Boxlock

A custom order double-barrel shotgun available in all standard gauges, fitted with single trigger and automatic ejectors. A receiver engraved and blued. Stock of French walnut. Prospective purchasers should seek individual appraisals for these arms.

Exc.	V.G.	Good	Fair	Poor
7500	6500	5250	4000	3250

Number 1 Sidelock

A sidelock double-barrel shotgun of the first quality. Prospective purchasers should seek individual appraisals.

Exc.	V.G.	Good	Fair	Poor
17500	16000	12000	9000	7500

PRAGA, ZBROVKA

Prague, Czechoslovakia

Established in 1918 by A. Novotny, this company ceased operations in 1926.

Vz21

A 7.65mm semi-automatic pistol patterned after the Model

1910 Browning, but without a grip safety. Barrel length 3.5", magazine capacity 6 rounds, grips of wood. The slide is marked "Zbrojowka Praga Praha."

Exc.	V.G.	Good	Fair	Poor
300	250	200	150	100

Praga 1921

A 6.35mm semi-automatic pistol with a slide of stamped steel cut with a finger groove at the front. Folding trigger. The barrel 2" in length. The slide is marked "Zbrojowka Praga Praha Patent Cal 6.35." The grips of molded plastic, with the name "Praga" cast in them. A dangerous feature of this pistol is that it is striker-fired with no hammer and is intended to be carried fully loaded and cocked in the pocket with absolutely no safety of any kind. The folding trigger does not spring out until the slide is drawn back slightly by using the finger groove in the front of it.

Exc.	V.G.	Good	Fair	Poor
250	225	200	150	100

PRANDELLI & GASPARINI

Brescia, Italy
Importer—Richland Arms Co.
Blissfield, Michigan

Boxlock Side x Side Shotgun

A good quality double-barrel 12 or 20 gauge shotgun with 26" or 28" barrels. Single selective trigger, automatic ejectors and an Anson & Deeley action. Blued, stock of select walnut.

Exc.	V.G.	Good	Fair	Poor
1500	1250	1000	750	450

Sidelock Side x Side Shotgun

Similar to the above, but with full sidelocks.

Exc.	V.G.	Good	Fair	Poor
2500	2250	1750	1250	700

Boxlock Over/Under Shotgun

An Over/Under double-barrel 12 or 20 gauge shotgun with 26" or 28" barrels, single triggers and automatic ejectors. Blued, with select walnut stock.

Exc.	V.G.	Good	Fair	Poor
1750	1500	1250	900	650

Sidelock Over/Under Shotgun

As above with full sidelocks.

Exc.	V.G.	Good	Fair	Poor
3000	2500	2250	1800	1200

PRATT, GEORGE

Middletown, Connecticut

Trap Gun

A doubled-barrelled, stationary burglar alarm or animal trap gun that chambered for .38 caliber centerfire. The barrels 4" in length; and all of the components are made of cast of iron, with a galvanized finish. Barrels and action are mounted on a round base, which can turn 360 degrees. The patent date "Dec. 18, 1883" is marked on the gun. There were many manufactured between 1880 and the early 1890s.

Exc.	V.G.	Good	Fair	Poor
400	350	300	200	100

PRATT, H.

Roxbury, Massachusetts

Under Hammer Pistol

A .31 caliber percussion single shot pistol with an 8.5" octagonal barrel. The frame marked "H. Pratt's/ Patent." Manufactured during the 1850s.

Exc.	V.G.	Good	Fair	Poor
550	450	400	300	200

PREMIER

Italy and Spain

A tradename used by various retailers on shotguns manufactured in Italy and Spain which were imported during the late 1950s and early 1960s.

Regent Side x Side Shotgun

A double-barrel shotgun with 26" to 30" barrels available in all standard gauges. Receiver blued, stock of walnut. Normally found with a pistol grip and beavertail forend.

Exc.	V.G.	Good	Fair	Poor
300	275	225	175	100

Regent Magnum

As above but chambered for the 3.5" 10 gauge Magnum cartridge. Barrels 32" in length and choked full and full.

Exc.	V.G.	Good	Fair	Poor
350	300	250	200	150

Brush King

Identical to the Regent Model except that it is fitted with 22" modified and improved cylinder barrels and a straight grip English style stock.

Exc.	V.G.	Good	Fair	Poor
275	250	200	150	100

Ambassador Model

A more ornate version of the Regent Model.

Exc.	V.G.	Good	Fair	Poor
400	350	300	250	175

Presentation Custom Grade

A custom-order shotgun with gamescenes as well as gold and silver inlays.

Exc.	V.G.	Good	Fair	Poor
1000	750	600	500	400

PRESCOTT, E. A.

Worcester, Massachusetts

Percussion Pocket Revolver

A .31 caliber percussion spur trigger revolver with either 4" or 4.25" octagonal barrel and a 6-shot cylinder. The frame of brass, and the grips of walnut. It is believed that approximately 100 were manufactured during 1860 and 1861.

Exc.	V.G.	Good	Fair	Poor
800	650	550	450	300

Pocket Revolver

A .22 or .32 spur trigger revolver with a barrel of either 3" or 4" length. The .22 caliber version has a 7-shot cylinder and the .32 caliber version a 6-shot cylinder. The standard markings are "E.A. Prescott Worchester Mass. Pat. Oct. 2, 1860." Approximately 1,000 were manufactured between 1862 and 1867.

Exc.	V.G.	Good	Fair	Poor
650	550	450	350	225

Belt Revolver

Although similar in appearance to early Smith & Wesson revolvers, the Prescott has a solid frame. Available in either .22 or .32 caliber, the .22 caliber model has a 3" barrel and the .32 caliber a 5.75" barrel. Markings are identical found on the Pocket Revolver. Approximately 200 were manufactured between 1861 and 1863.

Exc.	V.G.	Good	Fair	Poor
650	550	450	350	225

Navy Revolver

A single action revolver fitted with a conventional trigger, chambered for .38-rimfire cartridges with a 7.25" octagonal barrel. The unfluted cylinder holds 6 shots. The frame is of either silver-plated brass or blued iron; and the barrel and the cylinder are blued, with walnut grips. The barrel marked "E.A.Prescott, Worcester, Mass. Pat. Oct. 2, 1860." It is believed that several hundred were manufactured between 1861 and 1863.

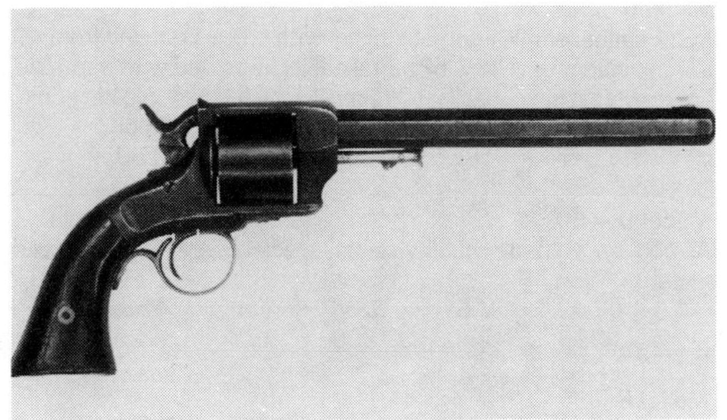

Courtesy Milwaukee Public Museum, Milwaukee, Wisconsin.

Exc.	V.G.	Good	Fair	Poor
650	550	450	350	225

PRETORIA
Pretoria, South Africa
SEE—PAF

PRINZ
Germany
Importer—Helmut Hofmann
Placitas, New Mexico

Grade 1 Bolt Action Rifle

A high quality bolt-action rifle chambered for the .243, .30-06, .308, .7mm Remington Magnum or the .300 Winchester Magnum cartridges. Barrel length 24", double-set triggers available. Finish is blued, stock of oil-finished select walnut. Introduced in 1989.

NIB	Exc.	V.G.	Good	Fair	Poor
500	450	400	350	300	225

Grade 2 Bolt Action Rifle

As above with a rosewood forend tip and pistol grip cap.

NIB	Exc.	V.G.	Good	Fair	Poor
550	500	450	400	350	250

Tip Up Rifle

A high quality single shot rifle available in a variety of American cartridges. Barrel length 24" and not furnished with sights. Finish blued, stock of select walnut.

NIB	Exc.	V.G.	Good	Fair	Poor
2200	1850	1500	1150	950	750

Model 85 "Princess"

A combination 12 gauge shotgun and rifle with 24" or 26" barrels, double triggers and automatic ejectors. Finish blued, stock of select walnut.

NIB	Exc.	V.G.	Good	Fair	Poor
1500	1250	1000	800	750	600

PRITCHETT, POTTS & HUNT
SEE—English Military Firearms

PROTECTION
Unknown

Protection Pocket Revolver

A .28 caliber percussion spur trigger revolver with a 3.25" octagonal barrel and 6-shot cylinder roll engraved with a police arrest scene. The frame of brass and grips of walnut. The cylinder is marked "Protection". Approximately 1,000 were manufactured during the late 1850s and early 1860s.

1st Model Roll Engraved Cylinder

Exc.	V.G.	Good	Fair	Poor
650	600	500	400	250

2nd Model Plain Cylinder Above Serial No. 650

Exc.	V.G.	Good	Fair	Poor
550	500	400	300	200

PURDEY, J. & SONS LTD.
London, England

Perhaps the finest manufacturer of shotguns, double-barrel and bolt-action rifles in the world. Virtually all their products are made on special order and it is impossible to establish general values for their products. Prospective purchasers are advised to seek qualified guidance prior to the acquisition of any arms made by this maker.

PYRENEES
Hendaye, France

Founded in 1923 and still in operation today, this company has produced a variety of models. The most popular of which was the "Unique" series. Prior to 1939, a variety of tradenames were marked on their products such as the following: Superior, Capitan, Cesar, Chantecler, Chimere Renoir, Colonial, Prima, Rapid-Maxima, Reina, Demon, Demon-marine, Ebac, Elite, Gallia, Ixor, Le Majestic, St. Hubert, Selecta, Sympathique, Touriste, Le Sanspariel, Le Tout Acier, Mars, Perfect, Triomphe Francais, Unis & Vindex. Following 1939 this company's products are simply stamped "Unique".

Model 10 Unique

A 6.35mm semi-automatic pistol similar to the Model 1906 Browning. The slide is marked "Le Veritable Pistolet Francais Unique." Introduced in 1923.

Exc.	V.G.	Good	Fair	Poor
200	175	150	100	75

Model 11

As above with a grip safety and loaded chamber indicator.

Exc.	V.G.	Good	Fair	Poor
250	200	175	125	100

Model 12

As above but without the loaded chamber indicator.

Exc.	V.G.	Good	Fair	Poor
225	185	165	110	90

Model 13

As above with a 7-shot magazine.

Exc.	V.G.	Good	Fair	Poor
225	185	165	110	90

Model 14

As above with a 9-shot magazine.

Exc.	V.G.	Good	Fair	Poor
225	185	165	110	90

Model 15

As above but in 7.65mm caliber. Introduced in 1923.

Exc.	V.G.	Good	Fair	Poor
250	175	150	100	75

Model 16

As above with a 7-shot magazine.

Exc.	V.G.	Good	Fair	Poor
250	175	150	100	75

Model 17

As above with a 9-shot magazine.

Exc.	V.G.	Good	Fair	Poor
300	250	200	150	100

Model 18

A 7.65mm caliber semi-automatic pistol patterned after the Model 1920 Browning but without a grip safety.

Exc.	V.G.	Good	Fair	Poor
250	175	150	100	75

Model 19

As above with a 7-shot magazine.

Exc.	V.G.	Good	Fair	Poor
250	175	150	100	75

Model 20

As above but with a 9-shot magazine.

Exc.	V.G.	Good	Fair	Poor
275	200	175	125	100

Model 21

As above except chambered for the 9mm short cartridge.

Exc.	V.G.	Good	Fair	Poor
275	200	175	125	100

During World War II production at this company was taken over by the Nazis. Consequently, the various models listed above will be found with German inspection marks. These arms are worth approximately 25% more than the values listed.

Postwar Unique

Model Bcf66

A 9mm short semi-automatic pistol with a 3.5" barrel, open top slide and external hammer. The slide marked "Armes Unique Hendaye BP France." Finish blued, grips of plastic.

Exc.	V.G.	Good	Fair	Poor
225	185	165	125	100

Model C

Virtually identical to the Model 17 listed above. The slide marked "7.65 Court 9 coups Unique." Finish blued, plastic grips with the trademark "PF" in a circle cast into them.

Exc.	V.G.	Good	Fair	Poor
200	150	125	100	75

Model D

A .22 caliber semi-automatic pistol with barrels ranging from 4" to 7.5" in length. The 7.5" barrelled version fitted with a muzzle brake. Magazine capacity 10 rounds. Finish blued, plastic grips.

Exc.	V.G.	Good	Fair	Poor
225	185	165	125	100

Model Des 69

As above with better quality sights, special trigger and improved grips.

Exc.	V.G.	Good	Fair	Poor
275	250	200	175	125

Model E

Identical to the Model D but chambered for .22 caliber short cartridges.

Exc.	V.G.	Good	Fair	Poor
225	185	165	125	100

Model F

Identical to the Model C except chambered for 9mm short cartridges. Magazine capacity 8 rounds.

Exc.	V.G.	Good	Fair	Poor
225	185	165	125	100

Model L

Similar to the Model D except chambered for .22, .32 ACP and 9mm short cartridges. Available with either a steel or alloy frame.

Exc.	V.G.	Good	Fair	Poor
250	225	200	150	125

QUACKENBUSH
Herkimer, New York

.22 Rifle
A single shot, takedown boy's rifle chambered for .22 rimfire cartridges. Barrel length 18". All metal parts nickle-plated. The breech swings to the side for loading. Stock of walnut. Manufactured in a wide variety of styles between 1870 and 1910.

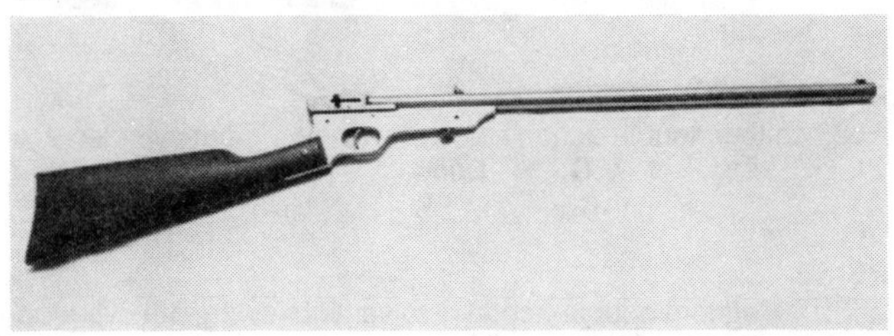

Courtesy Mike Stuckslager.

Exc.	V.G.	Good	Fair	Poor
500	400	200	150	100

QUINABAUG MFG. CO.
Southridge, Massachusetts

Under Hammer Pistol
A .31 caliber percussion under hammer pistol with barrels from 3" to 8" in length. Frame of blued iron, the grips of walnut or maple. The top of the frame is marked "Quinabaug Rifle M'g Co. Southbridge, Mass." The barrels are normally marked "E. Hutchings & Co. Agents". Manufactured during the 1850s.

Exc.	V.G.	Good	Fair	Poor
650	550	450	350	250

R.E.

Valencia, Spain

The initials "R.E." stand for "Republica Espana". This copy of the Spanish army Model 1921, also known as the Astra 400, was produced between 1936 and 1939 during the Spanish Civil War by the Republican forces. This variation can be identified by the "RE" monogram on the butt and the absence of any manufacturer's stampings.

Exc.	V.G.	Good	Fair	Poor
300	250	200	150	100

R. G. INDUSTRIES

Miami, Florida
Rohm Gmbh
Sontheim/Brenz, Germany

An importer of inexpensive handguns which ceased operations in 1986.

RG-25

A .25 caliber semi-automatic pistol available with either a blued or chrome-plated finish.

Exc.	V.G.	Good	Fair	Poor
75	65	50	35	25

RG-16

A double barrel .22 caliber chrome-plated derringer.

Exc.	V.G.	Good	Fair	Poor
75	65	50	35	25

RG-17

As above except chambered for .38 special cartridge.

Exc.	V.G.	Good	Fair	Poor
90	80	70	50	25

RG-14

A .22 caliber double-action revolver with a 4" barrel and 6-shot cylinder. Blued finish, plastic grips.

Exc.	V.G.	Good	Fair	Poor
90	80	70	50	25

RG-30

A .22 L.R. or Magnum double-action revolver. Blued finish, plastic grips.

Exc.	V.G.	Good	Fair	Poor
75	65	50	35	25

RG-40

A .38 special double-action revolver with swing-out cylinder. Blued finish, plastic grips.

Exc.	V.G.	Good	Fair	Poor
90	80	70	50	25

RG-57

A .357 or .44 Magnum double-action revolver with 6-shot cylinder. Blued finish, checkered wood grips.

Exc.	V.G.	Good	Fair	Poor
125	100	80	65	50

RG-63

A .22 caliber double-action revolver resembling a Colt Model 1873.

Exc.	V.G.	Good	Fair	Poor
60	50	40	35	25

RG-66

A .22 or .22 Magnum single action revolver patterned after the Colt Model 1873.

Exc.	V.G.	Good	Fair	Poor
60	50	40	35	25

RG-66T

As above with adjustable sights.

Exc.	V.G.	Good	Fair	Poor
65	55	45	35	25

RG-74

A .22 caliber double-action revolver with swing-out cylinder.

Exc.	V.G.	Good	Fair	Poor
75	65	55	45	35

RG-88

A .357 Magnum double-action revolver with swing-out cylinder.

Exc.	V.G.	Good	Fair	Poor
90	80	70	60	40

RWS

Nurenberg, Germany
Dynamit Nobel

Model 820 S

A .22 caliber target rifle with 24" heavy barrel and adjustable aperture sights. The trigger fully adjustable, three position adjustable match stock with stippled pistol grip and forend. Discontinued in 1986.

Exc.	V.G.	Good	Fair	Poor
800	700	550	450	350

Model 820 SF

As above with a heavier barrel. Discontinued in 1986.

Exc.	V.G.	Good	Fair	Poor
825	725	575	475	375

Model 820 K

Offhand "Running Boar" Model of the above with a lighter barrel. Furnished without sights. Discontinued in 1986.

Exc.	V.G.	Good	Fair	Poor
775	675	525	425	325

RADOM

Radom, Poland
Fabryka Broni w Radomu

This company was established after World War I and produced military arms for Poland. During World War II the Radom factory was operated by the Nazis. Production was not recommenced after the war.

Ng 30

A copy of the Russian Nagant revolver chambered for the 7.62mm Russian cartridge. Approximately 20,000 were manufactured during 1930 and 1936.

Exc.	V.G.	Good	Fair	Poor
300	250	200	150	100

VIS-35

A 9mm semi-automatic pistol with a 4.5" barrel, fixed sights and an 8-shot magazine. On the first model there is no manual safety, however, a decocking lever is installed which allows the hammer to be safely lowered on a loaded chamber. Versions made prior to World War II are engraved with a Polish eagle on the slide and "FB" and "VIS" are molded into the grips. German production pistols were made without the decocking lever and subsequently without the stripping catch. These pistols were stamped "P-35" and bear the Waffenamt inspector's mark "WaA77."

Polish Eagle Model-1936 through 1939

Exc.	V.G.	Good	Fair	Poor
800	650	500	350	200

Nazi Captured Polish Eagle—Waffenamt Marked

Exc.	V.G.	Good	Fair	Poor
950	750	600	450	300

Nazi Production Model

Exc.	V.G.	Good	Fair	Poor
450	350	250	200	175

Nazi Production Model-"bnz" code

This is a late Nazi production with no other slide markings other than "bnz". A very rare variation.

Exc.	V.G.	Good	Fair	Poor
1000	850	750	650	500

RANDALL FIREARMS CO.

Sun Valley, California

By Rick 'KK' Kennerknecht & Steve Comus

Stainless steel semi-auto handguns are now common, but this fact of life in the '90s would never have come to be had it not been for a small, now defunct company which dared to show the rest of the firearms industry the pathway to the future. Randall Firearms Company of Sun Valley, California, made it all happen with a line of high-quality Model 1911 derivatives.

Although Randall pistols were only manufactured from June 7, 1983 to May 15, 1985, they ushered in an entirely new era for handguns, thus carving for themselves a place in the history of firearms around the world. This historic niche, coupled with the fact that Randall pistols are exemplary specimens of their genre, has made Randall pistols collectible.

There were 24 different models with 12 variations in three different calibers. Among Randall's innovations were two significant breakthroughs in the 1911 field. One of these breakthroughs came when Randall made the very first production pistol if its kind in stainless steel. The second was the introduction of a true mirror image of the 1911 in a left-hand configuration. This had never been done before on a production basis.

It began with a small company called KEN-AIR, Inc., which had been in the aircraft instrument repair business in the San Fernando Valley area of Los Angeles County in California since the mid-1950s. Then, in 1981, the company entered into a diversification program which ultimately led to the Randall pistol.

The "KEN" in KEN-AIR stands for Ken Lau, founder and chairman of the company. Lau and World War II Air Force hero, Brigadier General Russell Randall, met while working together as advisors to China Airlines.

In 1981, Lau and his KEN-AIR company received a contract from the government of South Korea to build a .45 ACP handgun. By the time production facilities at the Sun Valley manufacturing plant were established, the Korean government changed its mind and canceled the contract.

This left Lau's firm with the facilities to produce Model 1911 handguns, but no customer. By then, Lau had done more than just set up another firearms production line. He had relied on his long experience in the manufacture of parts for the aerospace industry when formulating exactly how the line would operate, and even used his knowledge of materials seen in the aerospace business as a basis for a series of decisions which helped make the Randall pistol unique.

In addition to the manufacturing hardware and engineering, Lau also assembled a team of management experts from throughout the firearms industry, people who held responsible posts at other companies such as Colt, Smith & Wesson, Remington, Winchester, Vega, Detonics and Thomas.

Not only were Lau and Gen. Randall friends, but they were also business associates, which included Randall as a member of the board of directors of the company when it incorporated in January 1981. In addition to Randall's association with Lau in China Airlines and KEN-AIR, the general also was an advisor with Litton Industries.

Trading on the general's worldwide name identification, the new gun company was named after him: Randall Firearms Company. When the Korean government contract fell through, Lau decided to continue with the project and court the civilian markets instead. By November 1982, everything was set, and Randall announced the introduction of its first handgun — the all-stainless-steel auto.

Except for some minor changes necessitated in manufacturing, Randall pistols were much unchanged from the traditional Browning design. However, because every part except for the grips was made of aircraft quality stainless steel, this really was a new gun and quickly became known as "the only stainless steel auto fit for duty."

Although some prototype pistols were made as early as 1982, the first production Randalls came off the line on June 7, 1983. They were examples of the Service Model A111, which was a standard 1911A1. It featured the typical round-top slide with fixed sights and a five-inch, 10-groove barrel. The A111 pistols were produced throughout the life of the company and, in all, there were 3,431 produced in a serial number range of RF02000C through RF09208C. All A111 Randalls were chambered in .45 ACP.

Next came the Model A121 on Sept. 14, 1983. Initially, the A121 was also called a Service Model, but since there was some confusion with the designation, the marketing folks at Randall decided to make a change. In 1984 it became known as the Combat Model, and at that time those guns were roll-marked "Combat" just under the ejection port. The only other changes in that model at that time were cosmetic: the hammer was rounded, and Pachmayr grips were supplied as standard. Although catalogs of the era stated that it would be supplied with a flat mainspring housing, no such guns were ever actually produced.

The only other distinguishing factor between the A111 and the A121 was the A121 had a flat-top slide rather than the rounded top on the slide of the A111. Both models had fixed sights and were in .45 ACP only. Model A121 pistols were in the Randall line through June 11, 1984. In all, 1,067 of these pistols were made in a serial number range of RF02211C through RF08620C.

By Sept. 28, 1983, Randall was ready to offer a third variation in its line of .45s; this was the Service Model A131. The only difference between the A121 and A131 pistols was that the latter model sported a Millett Model 100 Gold Cup-type adjustable rear sight, which fit into a milled slot atop the rear of the slide. This model also stayed in the Randall line throughout the life of the company. In all, 2,083 of these pistols were made in a serial-number range of RF02135C through RF09201C. The last model A131 pistol was built on Oct. 22, 1984.

Collectors should note that more than 322 Service Models were made from parts outside the factory after the company closed. These pistols are not as highly collectible.

SERVICE MODEL 9MM PISTOLS

Introduced on Jan. 11, 1984 was the first Service Model A112 in 9mm Parabellum. Essentially, this was the same gun as the A111 except for caliber. In fact, the slides for the A112 pistols were made from the same 17-4 stainless steel investment casting as were the slides for the A111 in .45 ACP. This model remained in the line until July 23, 1984. In all, 301 of these 9mm pistols were produced in a serial number range of RV04666C through RF07599C.

Although there were relatively few Randall A112 pistols ever made, a change in production early on resulted in what was essentially two separate sub-models. The first Model A112 pistols employed stainless steel, six-groove standard Colt-type barrels and barrel bushings. The outside diameter of the muzzle of those barrels was 0.495 inch.

By 1984, it became apparent that the company could facilitate production by using a fatter barrel which would allow the standardization of barrel bushings. These later production Model A112 pistols featured barrels that had the same outside diameter as the standard .45 ACP. There was more of a change than simply the outside diameter of the barrel in these latter-day Model A112 handguns. Randall, at that time, went from six-groove rifling to its hallmark 10-groove configuration in these 9mm fat barrel units. The rifling was changed to enhance accuracy, and it also made the number of grooves standard throughout the Randall line as the .45s always had 10-groove barrels.

Production of the Combat Model A122 began on July 23, 1984, and ended Dec. 13, 1984. It was essentially nothing more than the Model A121 (.45 ACP) in 9mm. This meant that it differed from the Model A112 9mm in that it had a slide with a flat top and fixed rear sight, a round hammer and Pachmayr grips. Only 18 Model A122 pistols were ever made, making it the rarest of the right-handed, full-size service pistols Randall ever produced. Of the total production of 9mm Randalls, nearly 75 percent were exported to the European countries of England, Germany, Austria, Switzerland and France. Only 35 percent of those 9mm Randalls had the fat barrels. Of Randall's total production of full-size, right-handed service models, the 9mm pistols represented 3.2 percent.

"COMMANDER"-SIZE .45 ACP PISTOLS

By August 1983, Randall expanded its line of pistols to include the Service Model-C configuration. The "C" stood for compact. Initially, these handguns were roll-marked "Service Model-C." However, in the beginning of 1984, the company decided to give the guns a new identity, and dubbed this configuration as the "Raider," named for General Randall's unit, which had been known as Randall's Raiders.

Introduced Aug. 31, 1983, the first in the Service Model-C series was the A211, which featured a round-top slide and fixed sights. Barrel length was 4.25 inches, making the overall length .75 of an inch less than the standard A111. Magazine capacity (seven) and height remained the same. Weight of the A211 was 36 ounces compared to 38 ounces for the full-sized Model A111. After 992 of the Model A211 pistols were made, production of that model ceased on Sept. 6, 1984. The serial number range went from RF02001C through RF05808C.

Next came the Model A231, which differed from the A211 in that it had a flat-top slide and Millet Model 100 Gold Cup-type adjustable rear sight. The Model A231 was introduced on Nov. 7, 1983. Only 574 of these pistols were manufactured, with a serial-number range of RF02009C through RF03814C. The last of this model was manufactured on Oct. 6, 1984.

"COMMANDER"-SIZE 9MM PISTOLS

The Model A212 was introduced on Feb. 1, 1984. Like its .45 ACP counterparts, it also went through a name change in 1984, becoming another in the "Raider" family. Primarily, the biggest difference between the A212 and the A211 (.45 ACP) was the caliber. However, the A212 also was made in two different barrel widths — the latter are rarer, being the fat barrel guns. In all, there were only 76 of the A212 pistols manufactured, of which a mere 25 had fat barrels. The serial number range was RF02359C through RF03815C. The last A212 was manufactured on Dec. 13, 1984.

Randall Model A232 came on-line on Oct. 11, 1984, and differed from the A212 in that it had a flat-top slide with the Millett Model 100 adjustable rear sight. In all, only five Model A232 pistols were ever produced, and it is believed that they all were exported to Europe since none have surfaced since in the United States. The serial number range was from RF02473C through RF03777C. The last of this model was made on Nov. 12, 1984.

This completes all of the right-handed Service Model-C and Raider pistols produced by Randall, accounting for 16.5 percent of total pistol production during the life of the company.

THE CURTIS E. LeMAY 4-STAR PISTOLS

In 1984, Randall expanded its line with the introduction of a true compact .45 auto which was designed by Air Force Gen. Curtis E. LeMay. Among his many accomplishments, LeMay had been responsible for establishing the Air Force's Marksmanship Training Unit.

When LeMay created his pistol design, he intended it to be used by members of the Strategic Air Force Command. The general initially tried to have the diminutive .45 produced by Colt, but that never occurred.

As it happened, Art Hanke, who was the head of manufacturing and engineering for Randall, was a personal friend of Gen. LeMay. It was through this liaison that Randall Firearms Company came to produce the LeMay model line of pistols.

Right- and left-hand Randall LeMay and letters of authenticity. (Photo by Larry Gray)

First of the LeMay pistols was the A311. It sported a 4.25-inch, 10-groove barrel. The slide had a round top and a fixed rear sight. The handle and magazine were shortened by a half inch, limiting the magazine to six rounds. Overall weight was 35 ounces. Exclusive to the LeMay models were factory-squared triggerguards.

In all, 361 of the Model A311 pistols were made in a serial-number range of RF0211C through RF02011C. The first A311 was made on March 1, 1984, and production of that model ended on Oct. 25, 1984. Next came the A331, which featured a flat-top slide and Millett Low-Profile adjustable rear sight. The top of the slide was milled deeply so the rear sight would sit low enough to preclude its catching on clothing when drawn. There were 293 of this model produced in a serial number range of RF02010C through RF03169C. The first LeMay A311 was made on March 1, 1984, and the last one was completed on Oct. 23rd of that same year.

Among the rarest of the Randall pistols was the Model A312 which was introduced March 1, 1984, but which was never a production gun because only two sample pistols were ever made. The company intended to market this model in Europe, and had Randall Firearms Company survived, it no doubt would have made regular production runs. The company failed before any orders were taken. This pistol has a round-top slide and fixed rear sight. The only difference between the single Model A312 and the production A311 is the caliber. The A311 is a .45 ACP, and the A312 is in 9mm. Serial numbers were RF02012C and RF02031C respectively.

Also quite rare is the 9mm Model A332. It differed from the A312 in that it had a flat-top slide with Millett Low Profile adjustable rear sight. Only nine were ever made, and production of this model was limited to the period between March 1, 1984 and Dec. 13, 1984.

Of all the pistols produced by Randall, 6.7 percent were in the right-handed LeMay family. The LeMay is also one of the most highly collectible of all Randall pistols. Randall LeMay models were shipped from the factory with a dog-leg magazine, featuring a finger extension on the bottom. For every two of the dog leg magazines, however, Randall produced one without an extension. All LeMay magazines are rare and command premiums, even more so for the LeMay magazines without the dog leg. Also, most of the LeMay pistols were shipped in a pistol rug rather than in a factory box. Add 15 percent in price for LeMay pistols with a factory box.

Collectors should note that more than 225 LeMay pistols were assembled from parts outside the factory after the company closed. These pistols are not as highly collectible and do not command such high prices. A list of these guns is available from the Randall Historian.

LEFT-HANDED RANDALL PISTOLS

Randall shocked the firearms industry during the week of May 17, 1984 when it introduced the first of 10 left-handed models. These pistols were entire mirror-images of their right-hand counterparts, including the reversal of twist-in rifling from the left-to-right in the right-handed guns to right-to-left in the left-handed guns.

What the Randall company did was to make the entire breadth of its line available to southpaws in left-hand configuration. All left-handed Randalls are considered to be desirable and highly collectible, due to the fact that only 7.4 percent of total production was in the form of left-handed guns.

In order to make this a truly left-handed handgun, it was necessary to retool for 17 major parts changes. This meant that special left-handed magazines needed to be produced.

First among the lefties was the Service Model B111, which was a full-size government model with a five-inch, 10-groove barrel and round-top slide with fixed sights. There were 297 pistols of this model made, with a serial number range of RF02100C to RF03092C. The first Model B111 was made on May 17, 1984, and the last came off the line Sept. 7 of that same year.

Next was the B121, which sported a flat-top slide and fixed sights. Otherwise, it was the same as the B111, and differed from the right-handed A121 in that Pachmayr did not make left-handed grips, so it lacked the rubber grips of the right-handed counterpart. Randall produced 110 B121 pistols with a serial number range of RF02132C to RF03078C. The B131 was essentially the same as the B121, except that it was furnished with a Millett Model 100 adjustable rear sight. There were 225 of the B131 pistols produced in a serial number range of RF02110C through RF03092C. The first B121 was made on May 17, 1984, and the last one was completed Aug. 28, 1984. The first B131 was made on May 24, 1984, and the last one was completed Aug. 28, 1984.

Also among the most collectible of the Randall pistols were the Models B122 and B123. These left-handers were made in 9mm and .38 Super, respectively, and were otherwise counterparts to the B121. There were only two each made of these models, and those were special-order guns when they were produced. All of the full-size, left-handed pistols represented only 6.4 percent of Randall's entire production.

There were also three different production variations of the left-handed LeMay profile pistol. These were the B311, B312 and B331. The B311 was a LeMay with round-top slide and fixed rear sight in .45 ACP, and there were 52 manufactured in serial number range of RF02100C through RF02207C. The first B311 and B331 were made on July 13, 1984, and the last ones went off the line slightly more than a month later on Aug. 29, 1984.

The B312 was a left-handed LeMay in 9mm with a round-top and fixed rear sight. Only nine were manufactured. The B331 was the LeMay in .45 ACP, with a flat top and Millett Low Profile adjustable rear sight. There were 45 of these manufactured in a serial number range of RF02100C through RF02207C. All B213 pistols were made on or about Aug. 23, 1984.

The left-handed LeMay series constituted only one percent of the Randall factory's production.

FACTORY RARITIES AND VARIATIONS

Starting in 1984, Randall produced and experimented with a number of model variations. They are, by model:

1. B2/321 - Only one of these was produced, and it was made on special custom order for Texas-based collector Robert F. Mueschke, who has the largest collection of left-handed Randall pistols in the world. This variation was built on a left-hand Raider receiver and a left-hand LeMay (B321) slide. Its serial-number is RF03069C.

2. B312 with a .45 ACP Factory Conversion unit. There was only one of these produced. It was a 9mm left-handed LeMay with a .45 ACP conversion unit. Its serial number is RF02164C.

3. A131/SO - A right-handed Service Model with a flat-top slide and adjustable sight, chambered in .451 Detonics Magnum. Only one was made with serial number RF00451C.

4. B131/SO - A left-handed Service Model with a custom low profile Millett model 100 rear sight, custom squared triggerguard, scrimshawed ivory handles, custom metal checkering cover 40 percent of the gun's surface, and a special slide conversion stamped with both .38 Super and 9mm with respective barrels and ejectors.

5. A111/B111 Matched Sets - There were four such sets manufactured. These were standard government configuration pistols, and the right-hand and left-hand in each set shared a common serial number. Those serial-numbers were RF00000C, RF00001C, RF00010C and RF00024C. Interestingly, the RF00010 pair was originally made for the television series "Magnum P.I." However, those two guns were never delivered

to the television production and have since found their way into a private collection in the state of Arizona.

6. C211 - A lightweight Raider in .45 ACP with a round-top and fixed rear sights. There were five manufactured for law enforcement evaluation as off-duty carry weapons.

7. B321 Set - This set was based on the left-handed LeMay, and it was the only set to have all three slide variations fitted to a single receiver. The receiver and all three slides were identically engraved in a high relief pattern. The set was mirror-polished and was fitted with ivory grips bearing scrimshawed Randall logo on each side. The set was delivered in a custom-fitted walnut presentation case. It has the serial number of REK 1.

8. AUSTRIAN RANDALLS - Five Randall A111 pistols were sent to the Austrian government for law enforcement evaluation. Upon entering that country, the guns were processed through the Austrian proof house, where they received proofmarks on the barrels, receivers and slides. When the Austrian government learned that Randall had gone out of business, the guns were returned to Randall's San Francisco-based exporter. Since then, all five have been acquired by a central California-based investor.

PROTOTYPES

All Randall prototype serialization begins with the letter "T" followed by a two-digit number. In all, there were 43 prototype pistols made in 15 different model designations. Prototypes included many factory variations that never saw production, such as guns with an all-black oxide finish, black oxide and silver finish, and a pink and purple LeMay.

Generally, prototypes are valued at about 150 percent of the same production model.

SERIALIZATION VARIATIONS

Production serial numbers on Randall pistols generally began at 02000 for right-handed models and 02100 for left-handed models. However, by special order there were 78 pistols with custom serial-numbers under 02000. All but about the first 200 serial-numbers started with the letters "RF" and ended with a B, C, or W. A few mismarks are in circulation. Most Randalls had serial-number prefixes like the following: RF, RFO, RFOOO, 2RFO or 2RFOOO. The breakdown of Randall serial-numbers to satisfy the U.S. Bureau of Alcohol, Tobacco and Firearms is simple. The RF signified Randall Firearms, and the last letter in the serial number designated the vendor who machined the receiver. In the case of letter "B," the vendor was Bellmore-Johnson of Vermont. In the case of the letter "C," the vendor was Caspian Arms of Hardwick, Vermont. In the case of the letter "W," the vendor was Ward Machine Company of Santa Ana, California. It is believed there could have been a factory error in which the serializing machine malfunctioned, resulting in serial number suffixes of "D," "E" and "F". These would be extremely rare.

Randall matched set, serial-number RFOOO10C. Made for the TV series "Magnum PI." (Photo by Steve Comus)

HOW TO IDENTIFY THE VARIOUS MODELS

Randall models are designated by a single letter prefix, followed by a three-digit number. Prefixes are A, B or C. Prefix A designates a right-handed pistol. Prefix B denotes a left-handed configuration, and prefix C represented a right-handed, featherweight model.

In a logical sequence, the first numerical digit reflects the frame type, the second digit is for the slide configuration and the third number denotes caliber.

The first numerical digit is 1, 2 or 3. If the first number is 1, it means Service Model. A number 2 refers to Service Model-C or Raider, and a 3 denotes the LeMay Model.

The second digit is 1, 2 or 3. A 1 refers to round-top, fixed sight slide. A 2 stands for flat-top, fixed-sight slide, and 3 is for flat-top, adjustable-sight slide.

The third digit is 1, 2 or 3. A 1 refers to .45 ACP, a 2 is for 9mm Parabellum and a 3 is for .38 Super.

A marketing upgrade affected most Randall pistols made from late November 1983 through the end of production. All Randalls sold had slide stops and grip safeties upgraded to "extended" and "beavertail" types, respectively. Long triggers were installed. This was not retroactive to pistols already sold. All Randalls were shipped with extended safety locks.

Having pioneered stainless steel construction and left-handed configurations, Randall carved for itself a unique place in the history of semi-auto handguns. In two years of production, Randall cranked out an astounding 24 models in 12 variations and three different calibers.

The Randall Firearms Company officially stopped production on Dec. 15, 1984, and closed its doors on May 15, 1985. There were many reasons why Randall did not survive. To a number of industry observers, it appeared as though the fledgling firm may have attempted to accomplish too much, too quickly. The company's agenda was packed with so many innovative approaches and ideas that the production output could not keep up with the voracious R&D appetite.

Note: Randall prototypes can be identified by a "T" prefix. Add 50 percent to the price for this variety.

Model A111

Caliber is .45 Auto, barrel length 5", round-slide top, right-hand with fixed sights. Total production: 3,431.

NIB	Exc.	V.G.	Good	Fair	Poor
700	615	525	450	400	350

Model A121

Caliber is .45 Auto, barrel length 5", flat-slide top, right-hand with fixed sights. Total production: 1,067.

NIB	Exc.	V.G.	Good	Fair	Poor
745	650	550	475	425	375

Model A131

Caliber is .45 Auto, barrel length 5", flat-slide top, right-hand with Millett sights. Total production: 2,083.

Randall A131/SO in. 451 Detonics Magnum with Randall memorabilia. (Photo by Larry Gray)

NIB	Exc.	V.G.	Good	Fair	Poor
750	665	575	500	450	400

Model A112
Caliber is 9mm, barrel length 5", round-slide top, right-hand with fixed sights. Total production: 301.

NIB	Exc.	V.G.	Good	Fair	Poor
895	790	700	625	550	475

Model A122
Caliber 9mm. barrel length 5", flat-slide top, right-hand with fixed sights. Total production: 18.

NIB	Exc.	V.G.	Good	Fair	Poor
1400	1250	1000	900	800	700

Model A211
Caliber .45 Auto, barrel length 4¼", round-slide top, right-hand with fixed sights. Total production: 922.

NIB	Exc.	V.G.	Good	Fair	Poor
750	660	575	500	450	400

Model A231
Caliber .45 Auto, barrel length 4¼", flat-slide top, right-hand with Millett sights. Total production: 574.

NIB	Exc.	V.G.	Good	Fair	Poor
850	750	675	600	525	450

Model A212
Caliber 9mm, barrel length 4¼", round-slide top, right-hand with fixed sights. Total production: 76.

NIB	Exc.	V.G.	Good	Fair	Poor
1000	885	725	650	575	500

Model A232
Caliber 9mm. barrel length 4¼", flat-slide top, right-hand with Millett sights. Total production: 5.

NIB	Exc.	V.G.
1500	925	750

Model A311
Caliber .45 Auto, barrel length 4¼", round-slide top, right-hand with fixed sights. Total production: 361.

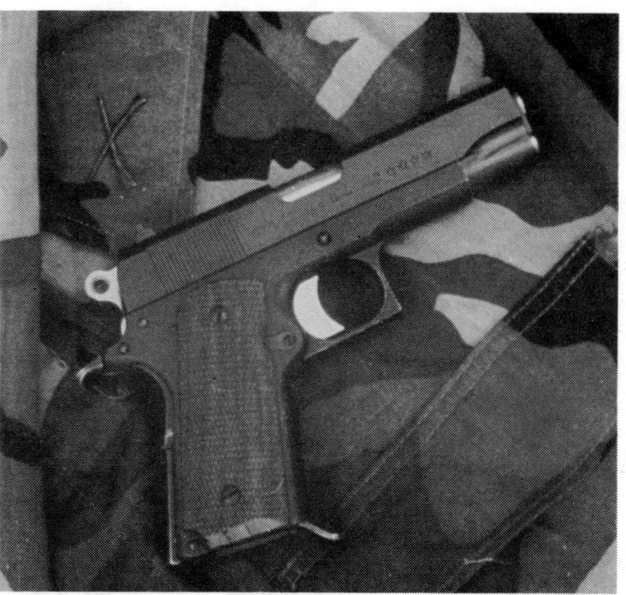

A311B black oxide LeMay special order by *Soldier of Fortune* magazine for field testing in El Salvador. (Photo by Steve Comus)

NIB	Exc.	V.G.	Good	Fair	Poor
1050	900	825	750	675	575

Model A331
Caliber .45 Auto, barrel length 4¼", flat-slide top, right-hand with Millett sights. Total production: 293.

NIB	Exc.	V.G.	Good	Fair	Poor
1325	1175	975	875	800	700

Model A312
Caliber 9mm. barrel length 4¼", round-slide top, right-hand with fixed sights. Total production: 2.

NIB
3000

Model A332
Caliber 9mm. barrel length 4¼", flat-slide top, right-hand with Millett sights. Total production: 9.

NIB	Exc.	V.G.	Good	Fair	Poor
1450	1275	1000	850	750	700

Model B111
Caliber .45 Auto, barrel length 5", round-slide top, left-hand with fixed sights. Total production: 297.

NIB	Exc.	V.G.	Good	Fair	Poor
1350	1200	975	900	900	700

Model B121
Caliber .45 Auto, barrel length 5", flat-slide top, left-hand with fixed sights. Total production: 110.

NIB	Exc.	V.G.	Good	Fair	Poor
1750	1550	1100	975	875	775

Model B122
Caliber .9mm. barrel length 5", flat-slide top, left-hand with fixed sights. Total production: 2.

NIB
3250

Model B123
Caliber .38 Super, barrel length 5", flat-slide top, left-hand with fixed sights. Total production: 2

NIB
3250

Model B131
Caliber .45 Auto, barrel length 5", flat-slide top, left-hand with Millet sights. Total production: 225.

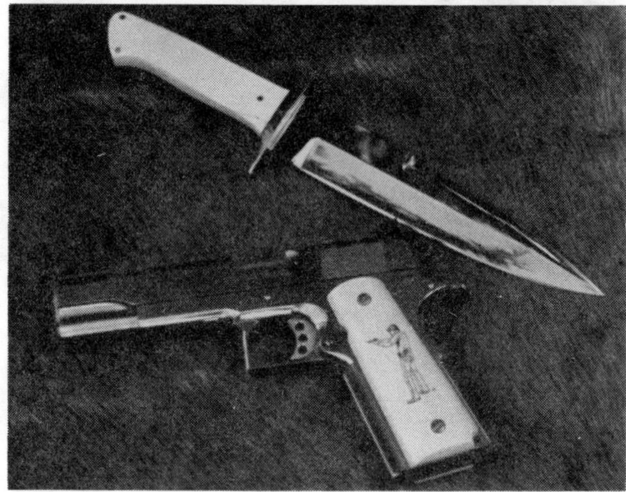

B131/SO left-hand service model with custom Chuck Stapel knife. (Photo by Steve Comus)

NIB	Exc.	V.G.	Good	Fair	Poor
1650	1450	1150	975	875	775

Model B311

Caliber .45 Auto, barrel length 4¼", round-slide top, left-hand with fixed sights. Total production: 52.

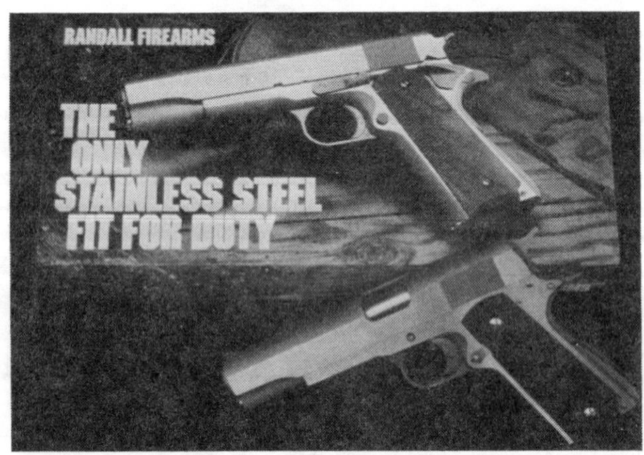

Randall left-hand B311 with original box. Very few left-hand Randalls were shipped in boxes. Most were shipped in Randall pistol rugs. (Photo by Steve Comus)

NIB	Exc.	V.G.	Good	Fair	Poor
1700	1500	1250	1050	950	800

Model B312

Caliber 9mm. barrel length 4¼", round-slide top, left-hand with fixed sights. Total production: 9.

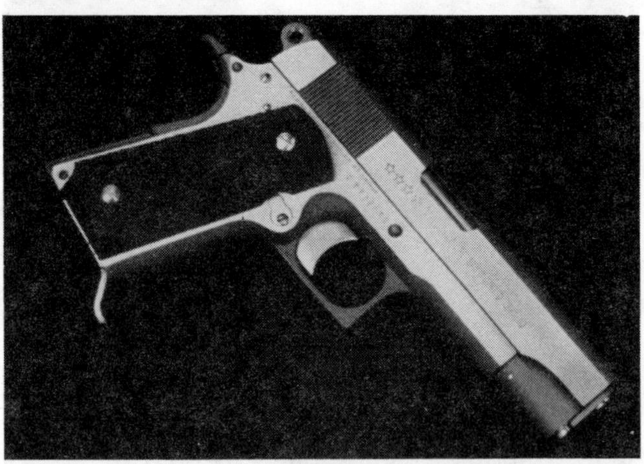

Randall B312 left-hand 9mm LeMay, one of the most sought after of the B-series guns. Only nine were manufactured. (Photo by Steve Comus)

Randall B312 with factory 45ACP conversion Unit. Only one of these factory units were made. (Photo by Steve Comus)

NIB	Exc.	V.G.	Good	Fair	Poor
2750	2450	1750	1500	1250	1000

Note: For pistol with .45 ACP conversion in NIB 3500. Total production of this conversion is 1 pistol.

Model B331

Caliber .45 Auto, barrel length 4¼", flat-slide top, left-hand with Millett sights. Total production: 45.

NIB	Exc.	V.G.	Good	Fair	Poor
1800	1585	1200	975	875	800

Model C311

Caliber .45 Auto, barrel length 4¼", round-slide top, right-hand with fixed sights. Total production: 1.

NIB
3000

Model C332
Caliber 9mm. barrel length 4¼", flat-slide top, right-hand with Millett sights. Total production: 4.

NIB	Exc.	V.G.	Good	Fair	Poor
1375	1175	1000	900	850	800

Model B321 SET
Serial Number REK 1

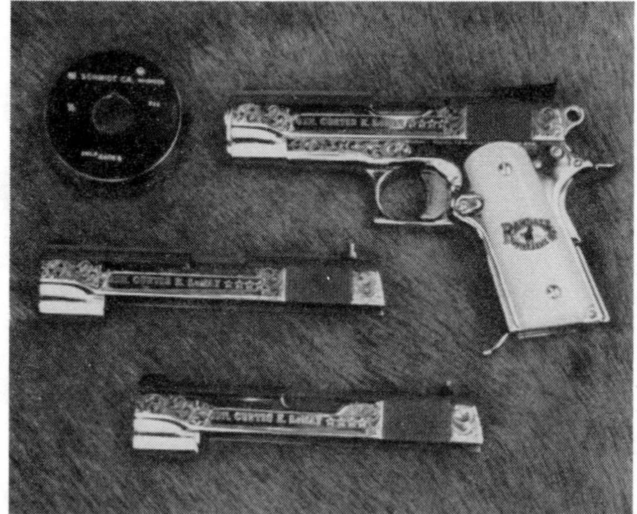

B321 set with gold-plated LeMay roll mark die. (Photo by Steve Comus)

Randall B321 of the B321 set, serial-number REK1. (Photo by Steve Comus)

NIB
20,000

Model A111/B111 Matched Set
Serial Numbers RF00000C, RF00001C, RF00010C, RF00024C.

NIB
8500

Austrian Randall
Total production: of 5

Four of the five Austrian Randalls. Each of these A111s bear cartouches from an Austrian proof house. These Randalls were proofed for the Austrian government for law enforcement evaluation. (Photo by Christopher Todd)

NIB
3000

Close-up view of Austrian proof marks. (Photo by Christopher Todd)

RANGER ARMS, INC.
Gainesville, Texas

Statesman
A bolt-action rifle produced in various calibers with a 22" barrel, no sights and a checkered walnut stock. Standard finish blued. Manufactured in the early 1970s.

Exc.	V.G.	Good	Fair	Poor
325	300	250	200	125

Statesman Magnum
As above, but chambered for magnum calibers and with a 24" barrel.

Exc.	V.G.	Good	Fair	Poor
350	325	300	250	150

Senator
As above with a better finish.

Exc.	V.G.	Good	Fair	Poor
400	350	325	275	175

Senator Magnum
As above chambered for magnum cartridges.

Exc.	V.G.	Good	Fair	Poor
425	375	350	300	200

Governor
As above with better walnut and finer lined checkering.

Exc.	V.G.	Good	Fair	Poor
450	400	375	325	225

Governor Magnum
As above chambered for magnum cartridges.

Exc.	V.G.	Good	Fair	Poor
475	425	400	350	250

RASHID
Egypt

Rashid Carbine
A gas operated 7.62x39mm caliber semi-automatic carbine with a 20.5" barrel and 10-round integral magazine. Fitted with a folded bayonet similar to that found on the Russian SKS. Blued finish and hardwood stock. This rifle is based upon the Swedish Ljungman.

Exc.	V.G.	Good	Fair	Poor
350	300	200	150	100

RAST & GASSER
SEE—Gasser

RAVELL
Barcelona, Spain

Maxim Double Rifle
A Holland & Holland-styled sidelock double-barrel rifle available in either .375 Holland & Holland or 9.3x74R with 23" barrels having express sights. Double triggers and automatic ejectors. The sidelocks and mounts engraved, stock of well figured walnut normally fitted with a recoil pad.

Exc.	V.G.	Good	Fair	Poor
4500	4000	3500	2750	2000

RAVEN ARMS
Industry, California

P-25
A .25 caliber semi-automatic pistol with a 2.75" barrel and 6-round magazine. Available with a blued, chrome or nickle-plated finish and walnut grips. Manufacture ceased in 1984.

Exc.	V.G.	Good	Fair	Poor
75	65	50	35	25

MP-25
As above with a die-cast frame and imitation ivory grips.

NIB	Exc.	V.G.	Good	Fair	Poor
75	65	55	45	35	25

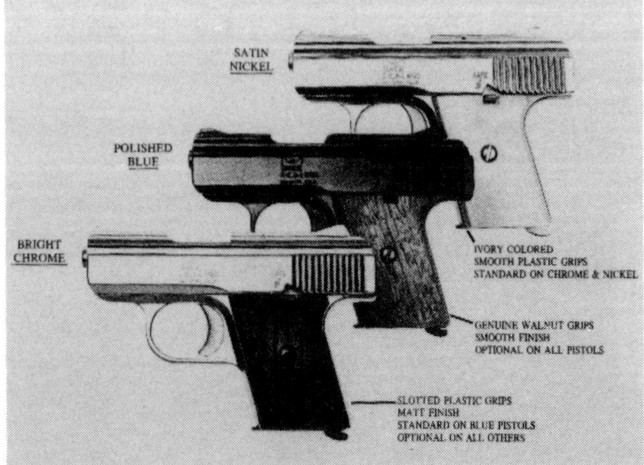

RECORD-MATCH ANSCHUTZ
Zella-Mehlis, Germany

Model 210 Free Pistol
A single shot .22 caliber target pistol using a Martini falling block action. Barrel length 11", set trigger, and adjustable sights. Blued finish with checkered walnut grips and forend. Manufactured during the 1930s.

Exc.	V.G.	Good	Fair	Poor
1250	1000	850	750	600

Model 210A
As above with a lightweight alloy frame.

Exc.	V.G.	Good	Fair	Poor
1200	950	800	700	550

Model 200 Free Pistol
As above without a set trigger.

Exc.	V.G.	Good	Fair	Poor
950	850	750	550	400

REFORM
Suhl, Germany
August Schuler

Reform Pistol
A 6mm four barrelled double-action pistol constructed so that the barrel unit rises upward when the trigger is pulled. It superficially resembles a semi-automatic pistol. Blued with hard rubber grips. Manufactured between 1900 and 1905.

Exc.	V.G.	Good	Fair	Poor
550	500	400	300	225

REICHSREVOLVER
Germany

There are two basic versions of the German Standard Service Revolver designed by the Small Arms Commission of the Prussian Army in the 1870s. Revolvers of this type were produced by the Erfurt Royal Arsenal, F. Dreyse of Sommerda, Sauer & Sohn, Spangenberg & Sauer, and C. H. Haenel of Suhl. Normally, the maker's initials are to be found on an oval above the triggerguard.

Model 1879
A 10.55mm caliber revolver with a 7.2" barrel, 6-shot cylinder and fixed sights. Standard finish blued with walnut grips having a lanyard ring at the base. These revolvers are fitted with a safety catch.

Exc.	V.G.	Good	Fair	Poor
450	400	350	250	175

Model 1883

As above with a 5" barrel and round bottom grips.

Exc.	V.G.	Good	Fair	Poor
400	350	300	225	150

REID, JAMES

New York, New York

Model 1 Revolver

A spur trigger .22 caliber revolver with a 3.5" octagonal barrel and 7-shot unfluted cylinder. Blued with walnut grips. The barrel marked "J. Reid, New York." Approximately 500 were manufactured between 1862 and 1865.

Exc.	V.G.	Good	Fair	Poor
1000	750	350	250	150

Model 2 Revolver

As above but in .32 caliber, the barrel marked "Address W.P. Irving, 20 Cliff Street. N.Y." or "James P. Fitch. N.Y." Approximately 1,300 were manufactured between 1862 and 1865.

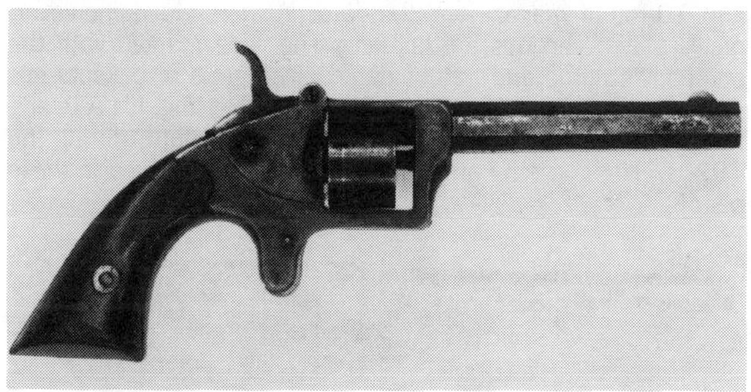

Exc.	V.G.	Good	Fair	Poor
900	500	350	250	150

Model 3 Revolver

Similar to the above, but with the grip angle sharpened. Chambered for the .32 rimfire cartridge with a 4.75" barrel. The cylinder chambers are threaded so that percussion nipples can be inserted. The barrel is marked "J. Reid N.Y. City". Approximately 50 were made between 1862 and 1865.

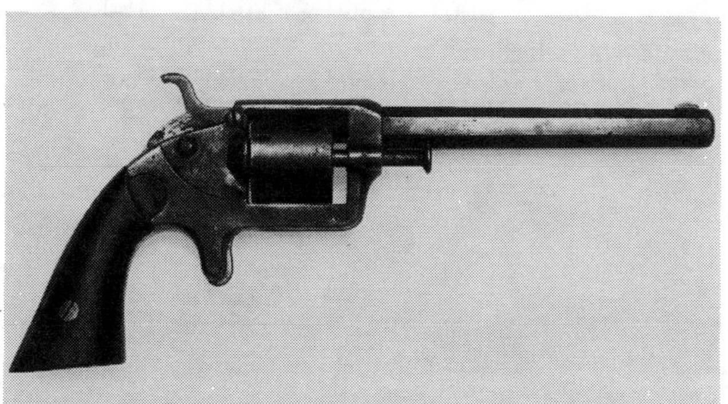

Exc.	V.G.	Good	Fair	Poor
1200	1000	600	450	300

Model 4 Revolver

As above with barrel lengths varying from 3.75" to 8". Approximately 1,600 were manufactured between 1862 and 1865.

Exc.	V.G.	Good	Fair	Poor
450	375	325	225	125

"My Friend" Knuckle Duster

A 7-shot .22 caliber revolver constructed entirely of metal and without a barrel. The frame of silver-plated brass or blued iron and marked "My Friend Patd. Dec. 26, 1865." The grip is formed with a finger hole so that the pistol can be used as a set of brass knuckles.

Courtesy W.P. Hallstein III and son Chip.

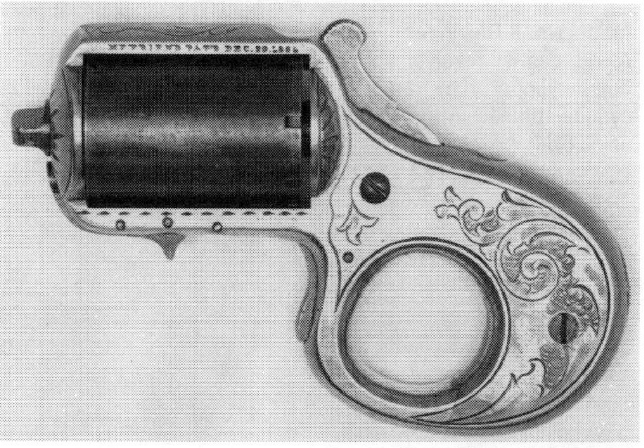

Courtesy W.P. Hallstein III and son Chip.

Brass Frame

Exc.	V.G.	Good	Fair	Poor
900	500	450	350	250

Iron Frame

Exc.	V.G.	Good	Fair	Poor
1200	650	550	450	350

.32 Caliber Knuckle Duster
As above but .32 caliber. Approximately 3,400 were manufactured between 1869 and 1884.

Brass Frame

Exc.	V.G.	Good	Fair	Poor
850	550	500	400	300

Iron Frame

Exc.	V.G.	Good	Fair	Poor
1200	700	600	500	400

.41 Caliber Knuckle Duster
As above but .41 caliber and marked "J.Reid's Derringer." Approximately 300 were manufactured between 1875 and 1878.

Exc.	V.G.	Good	Fair	Poor
3500	2500	1500	1250	950

Model No. 1 Knuckle Duster
As above with a 3" barrel. Approximately 350 were made between 1875 and 1880.

Courtesy W.P. Hallstein III and son Chip.

Exc.	V.G.	Good	Fair	Poor
1400	850	750	600	450

Model No. 2 Knuckle Duster
As above with a 1.75" barrel. Approximately 150 were made between 1875 and 1880.

Exc.	V.G.	Good	Fair	Poor
1500	950	850	700	500

Model No. 3 Derringer
A .41 caliber revolver with a 3" octagonal barrel and 5-shot fluted cylinder. The frame silver-plated and the barrel as well as cylinder blued. Approximately 75 were made between 1880 and 1884.

Exc.	V.G.	Good	Fair	Poor
2500	1800	1000	800	600

Model No. 4 Derringer
As above but with a brass frame and walnut grips and marked "Reid's Extra." Approximately 200 were made during 1883 and 1884.

Exc.	V.G.	Good	Fair	Poor
1750	1100	800	600	450

New Model Knuckle Duster
Similar to the Model 2 with a 2" barrel and 5-shot cylinder. The barrel marked "Reid's New Model .32 My Friend." Approximately 150 were made in 1884.

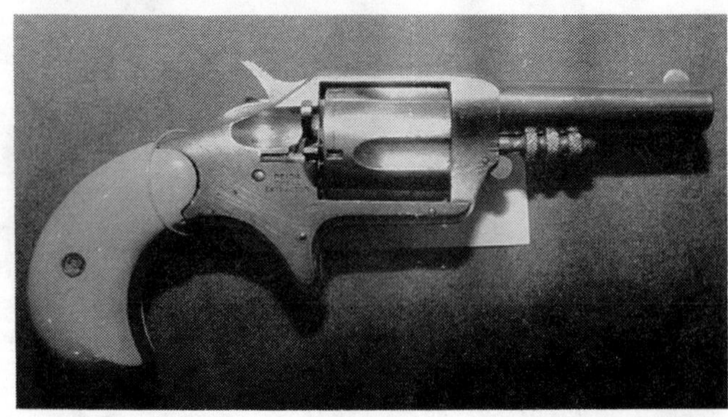

Exc.	V.G.	Good	Fair	Poor
1200	900	550	450	350

REISING ARMS CO.
Hartford, Connecticut

Standard Model
A .22 caliber semi-automatic pistol with a hinged 6.5" barrel and 10-round magazine. Standard finish is blued, however, nickle-plated versions are known. The slide marked with the company's name and patent dates. The grips of bakelite impressed with a bear's head and the motto "Reising, It's A Bear". Manufactured in both New York City and Hartford, during the 1920s. High velocity ammunition should not be used in these pistols.

New York Manufacture

Exc.	V.G.	Good	Fair	Poor
600	400	300	200	150

Hartford Manufacture

Exc.	V.G.	Good	Fair	Poor
550	400	275	175	125

REMINGTON

REMINGTON ARMS COMPANY, INC.

Bridgeport, Connecticut

Founded in 1816 by Eliphalet Remington, this company has the distinction of being the oldest firearms manufacturing firm in the United States. Since 1856 it has been known by four different names: between 1856 and 1888—E. Remington & Sons; 1888-1910—Remington Arms Co.; 1910-1925—Remington Arms U.M.C. Co. (Union Metallic Cartridge Company); and 1925 to the present—Remington Arms Co.

1st Model Remington-Beals Revolver

A .31 caliber 5-shot percussion revolver with a 3" octagonal barrel. The cylinder turning mechanism is mounted on the left outside frame. Blued, case-hardened, silver-plated, brass triggerguard and gutta percha grips. The barrel marked, "F. Beal's Patent, June 24, '56 & May 26, '57" and the frame, "Remington's Ilion, N.Y." Approximately 5,000 were manufactured in 1857 and 1858.

Courtesy Milwaukee Public Museum, Milwaukee, Wisconsin.

Exc.	V.G.	Good	Fair	Poor
900	750	550	400	300

2nd Model Remington-Beals Revolver

A spur trigger .31 caliber 5-shot percussion revolver with a 3" octagonal barrel. Blued, case-hardened with a squared gutta percha grip. The barrel marked, "Beals Patent 1856 & 57, Manufactured by Remingtons Ilion, N.Y." Approximately 1,000 were manufactured between 1858 and 1860.

Exc.	V.G.	Good	Fair	Poor
4500	3750	2500	1850	1500

3rd Model Remington-Beals Revolver

A .31 caliber 5-shot percussion revolver with a 4" octagonal barrel. A loading lever mounted beneath the barrel. Blued, case-hardened with gutta percha grips. The barrel marked, "Beals Pat. 1856, 57, 58" and also "Manufactured by Remingtons, Ilion, N.Y." Approximately 1,500 were manufactured in 1859 and 1860.

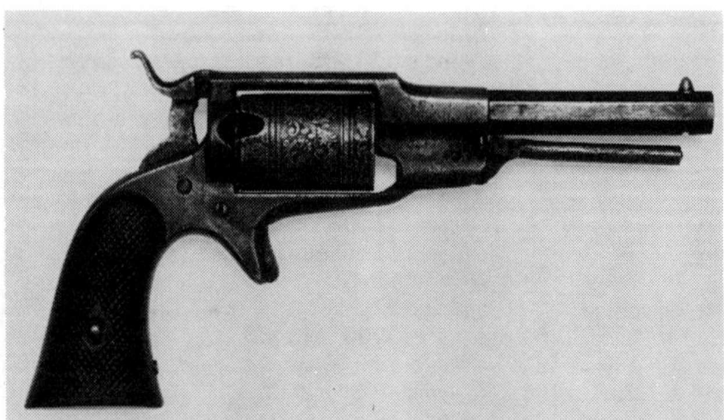

Courtesy Milwaukee Public Museum, Milwaukee, Wisconsin.

Exc.	V.G.	Good	Fair	Poor
1200	1000	750	600	475

Remington-Rider Revolver

A double-action .31 caliber percussion revolver with a 3" barrel and 5-shot cylinder. Blued, or nickle-plated, casehardened with gutta percha grips. This model is also encountered altered to .32 rimfire. The barrel marked, "Manufactured by Remingtons, Ilion, N.Y., Riders Pt. Aug. 17, 1858 May 3, 1859." Approximately 20,000 were manufactured between 1860 and 1873. The cartridge variation is worth approximately 10 percent more than the percussion original version.

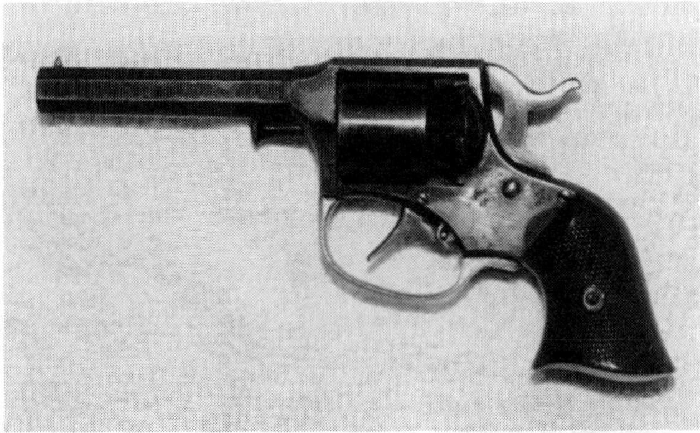

Exc.	V.G.	Good	Fair	Poor
700	550	425	300	225

Remington-Beals Army Revolver

A .44 caliber percussion revolver with an 8" barrel and 6-shot cylinder. Blued, case-hardened with walnut grips. The barrel marked "Beals Patent Sept. 14, 1858 Manufactured by Remington's Ilion, New York." Approximately 2,500 were manufactured between 1860 and 1862. A martially marked example is extremely rare and would be worth approximately 35 percent additional.

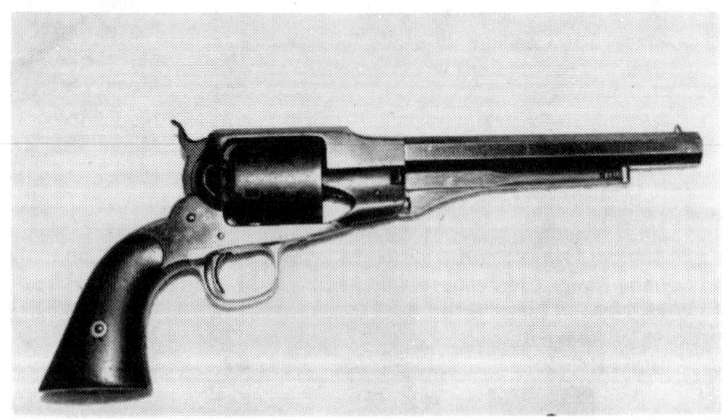

Exc.	V.G.	Good	Fair	Poor
3250	2750	1850	1100	800

Remington-Beals Navy Revolver

Similar in appearance to Remington-Beals Army Revolver, but in .36 caliber with a 7.5" octagonal barrel. The first examples of this model were fitted with a loading lever that would not allow the cylinder pin to be completely removed. These examples are worth approximately 80% more than the standard model. Approximately 1,000 of these revolvers were purchased by the United States Government and marshally marked examples are worth approximately 40% more than the values listed below. Manufactured from 1860 to 1862 with a total production of approximately 15,000.

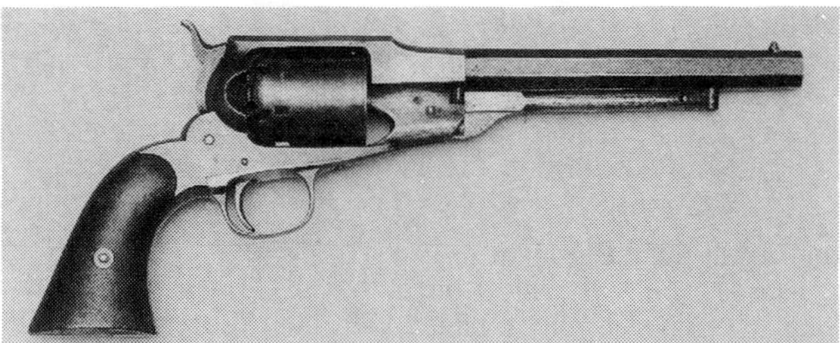
Courtesy Wallis & Wallis, Lewes, Sussex, England.

Exc.	V.G.	Good	Fair	Poor
1100	900	750	575	425

1861 Army Revolver

A .44 caliber percussion revolver with an 8" octagonal barrel and 6-shot cylinder. The loading lever is cut with a slot so that the cylinder pin can be drawn forward without the lever being lowered. Blued, case-hardened with walnut grips. The barrel marked "Patented Dec. 17, 1861 Manufactured by Remington's, Ilion, N.Y." Some examples were converted to .46 caliber rimfire cartridge, and would be worth approximately 20 percent less than the original, martially marked, standard percussion model. Approximately 12,000 were manufactured in 1862. This model is also known as the "Old Army Model."

Exc.	V.G.	Good	Fair	Poor
1750	1500	1050	650	450

1861 Navy Revolver

As above, but .36 caliber with a 7.25" octagonal barrel. Blued, casehardened with walnut grips. This model is also found altered to .38 metalic cartridge. Cartridge examples are worth approximately 35% less than the percussion versions. Approximately 8,000 were manufactured in 1862.

Exc.	V.G.	Good	Fair	Poor
1750	1500	1050	650	450

New Model Army Revolver

A .44 caliber 6-shot percussion revolver with an 8" octagonal barrel. Blued, case-hardened with walnut grips. The barrel marked "Patented Sept. 14, 1858 E. Remington & Sons, Ilion, New York, U.S.A. New Model." Approximately 132,000 were made between 1863 and 1873.

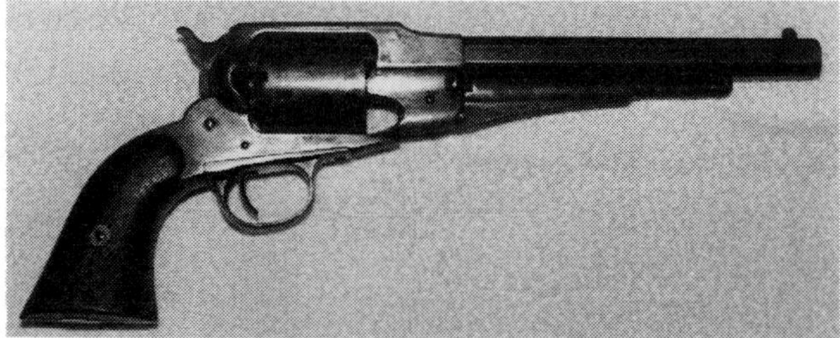

Standard Model—Military Version

Exc.	V.G.	Good	Fair	Poor
1400	1150	800	550	350

Civilian Model—No Government Inspector's Markings

Exc.	V.G.	Good	Fair	Poor
1400	1150	800	500	350

.44 or .46 Cartridge Conversion

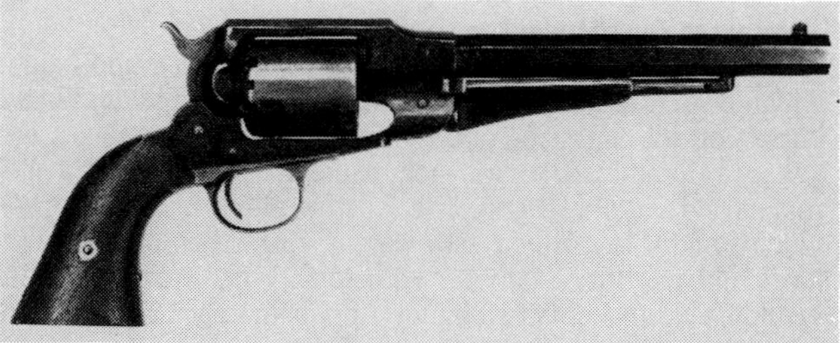
Courtesy Milwaukee Public Museum, Milwaukee, Wisconsin.

Exc.	V.G.	Good	Fair	Poor
1250	1000	700	500	300

New Model Navy Revolver

As above, but .36 caliber with a 7.23" octagonal barrel. Approximately 22,000 were made between 1863 and 1875.

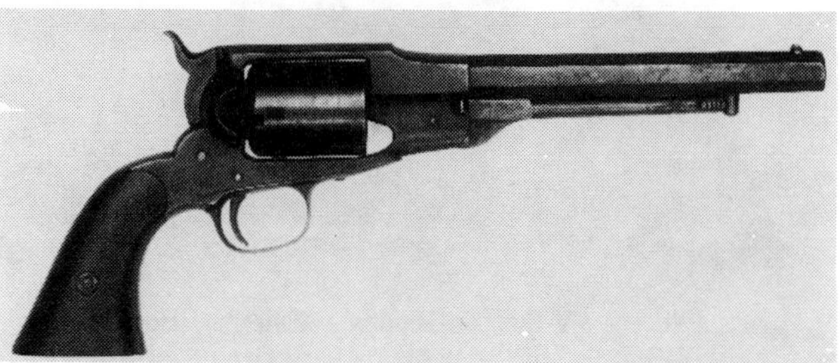
Courtesy Milwaukee Public Museum, Milwaukee, Wisconsin.

Military Version

Exc.	V.G.	Good	Fair	Poor
1850	1600	1250	900	650

Civilian Version

Exc.	V.G.	Good	Fair	Poor
1200	950	650	450	300

.38 Cartridge Conversion—1873 to 1888

Exc.	V.G.	Good	Fair	Poor
1000	750	500	400	250

New Model Belt Revolver

As above, but with a 6.5" barrel. Blued or nickle-plated, casehardened with walnut grips. This model is sometimes encountered altered to .38 cartridge. Cartridge examples are worth approximately 25% less than the values listed below. Approximately 3,000 were made between 1863 and 1873.

Exc.	V.G.	Good	Fair	Poor
1150	900	600	400	275

Remington-Rider Double Action Belt Revolver

A double-action .36 caliber percussion revolver with a 6.5" octagonal barrel marked, "Manufactured by Remington's, Ilion, N.Y. Rider's Pt. Aug. 17, 1858, May 3, 1859." Blued or nickle-plated, casehardened with walnut grips. This model is also found altered to cartridge and such examples would be worth approximately 20% less than the values listed below. Several hundred of this model were made with fluted cylinders and are worth a considerable premium. Approximately 5,000 were made between 1863 and 1873.

Courtesy Milwaukee Public Museum, Milwaukee, Wisconsin.

Exc.	V.G.	Good	Fair	Poor
1250	1000	700	500	350

New Model Police Revolver

A .36 caliber percussion revolver with octagonal barrels ranging from 3.5" to 6.5" and with a 5-shot cylinder. Blued or nickle-plated, case-hardened with walnut grips. This model is also found altered to cartridge and such examples would be worth approximately 20% less than the values listed below. Approximately 18,000 were manufactured between 1863 and 1873.

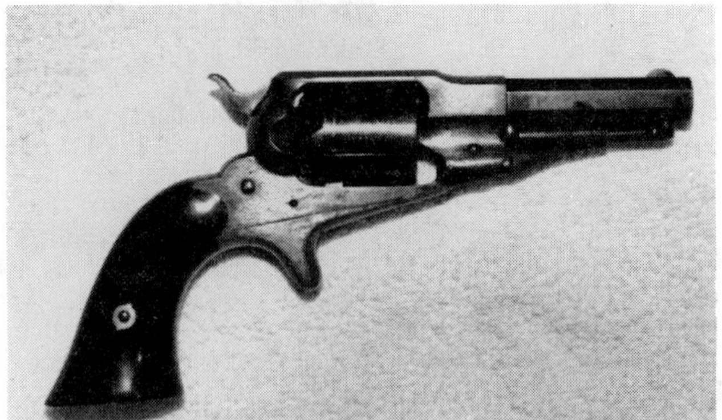

Exc.	V.G.	Good	Fair	Poor
1000	750	600	450	300

New Model Pocket Revolver

A .31 caliber spur trigger percussion revolver with octagonal barrels ranging from 3" to 4.5" in length and a 5-shot cylinder. Blued or nickle-plated, case-hardened with walnut grips. The barrel marked, "Patented Sept. 14, 1858, March 17, 1863 E. Remington & Sons, Ilion, New York U.S.A. New Model." Approximately 25,000 were manufactured between 1863 and 1873.

1st Version—Brass Frame and Trigger

Exc.	V.G.	Good	Fair	Poor
2500	1850	1500	1150	850

2nd Version—Iron Frame, Brass Trigger

Exc.	V.G.	Good	Fair	Poor
1250	1000	750	525	375

3rd Version—Iron Frame, Iron Trigger

Exc.	V.G.	Good	Fair	Poor
1000	750	600	450	300

.32 Cartridge Conversion

Exc.	V.G.	Good	Fair	Poor
850	700	550	400	275

Remington-Rider Derringer

A small, silver-plated brass single shot .17 caliber percussion pistol with a 3" round barrel. The barrel marked, "Rider's Pt. Sept 13, 1859." Approximately 1,000 were manufactured between 1860 and 1863. Prospective purchasers are advised to secure a qualified appraisal prior to acquisition.

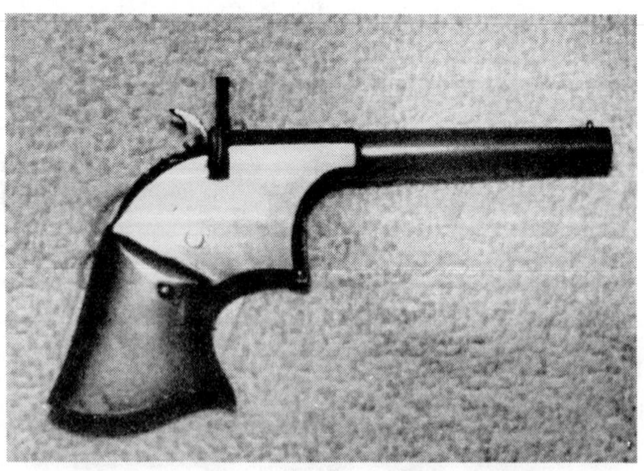

Exc.	V.G.	Good	Fair	Poor
5500	4750	4000	3000	2000

Zig-Zag Derringer

A 6-shot .22 caliber revolving barrel pocket pistol with barrels 3.25" in length. The barrels are cut with zigzag groves which are part of the revolving mechanism. The trigger is formed as a ring which when moved forward and rearward turns the barrels and cocks the internal hammer. The barrel group marked "Elliot's Patent Aug. 17, 1858 May 29, 1860" as well as "Manufactured by Remington's Ilion, N.Y." Approximately 1,000 were manufactured in 1861 and 1862.

Exc.	V.G.	Good	Fair	Poor
3000	2500	1850	1100	750

Remington-Elliot Derringer

A 5-shot .22 or .32 caliber pepperbox pistol with a revolving firing pin. Blued or nickle-plated with hard rubber grips. The barrel group marked "Manufactured by E. Remington & Sons, Ilion, N.Y. Elliot's Patents May 19, 1860 - Oct.1, 1861." Approximately 25,000 were manufactured between 1863 and 1888.

Courtesy W.P. Hallstein III and son Chip.

Exc.	V.G.	Good	Fair	Poor
1200	950	750	475	300

Vest Pocket Pistol

A .22 caliber single shot pistol with a 3.25" barrel. Blued or nickle-plated with walnut grips. The barrel marked "Remington's Ilion, N.Y. Patent Oct. 1, 1861." Early examples have been noted without any barrel markings. Approximately 25,000 were manufactured from 1865 to 1888.

Exc.	V.G.	Good	Fair	Poor
775	600	500	350	225

Large-Bore Vest Pocket Pistol

As above, but in .30, .32 or .41 caliber with barrel lengths of either 3.5" or 4". Blued or nickle-plated with walnut or rosewood grips. The barrel markings as above except for the addition of the patent date, November 15, 1864. The smaller caliber versions are worth approximately 20% more than the .41 caliber. Approximately 10,000 were made from 1865 to 1888.

Exc.	V.G.	Good	Fair	Poor
1100	850	650	500	375

Remington-Elliot Derringer

A .41 caliber single shot pistol with a 2.5" round barrel. Blued or nickle-plated with walnut, ivory or pearl grips. The barrel marked "Remingtons, Ilion, N.Y. Elliot Pat. Aug. 27, 1867." Approximately 10,000 were manufactured between 1867 and 1888.

Exc.	V.G.	Good	Fair	Poor
1500	1250	950	700	500

Remington Over/Under Derringer

A double barrel .41 caliber pocket pistol with 3" round barrels which pivot upward for loading. There is a lock bar to release the barrels on the right side of the frame. The firing pin raises and lowers automatically to fire each respective barrel. It has a spur trigger and birdshead grip. The finish is either blued or nickel-plated; and it is featured with walnut, rosewood, or checkered hard rubber grips. Examples with factory pearl or ivory grips would be worth a small premium. Approximately 150,000 were manufactured between 1866 and 1935.

Early Type I

Manufactured without an extractor, this type is marked "E. Remington & Sons, Ilion, N.Y." on one side and "Elliot's Patent Dec. 12, 1865" on the other side of the barrel rib. Only a few hundred were manufactured in 1866.

Exc.	V.G.	Good	Fair	Poor
1500	1250	800	650	400

Type I Mid-Production

As above, but fitted with an extractor. Manufactured in the late 1860s.

Exc.	V.G.	Good	Fair	Poor
1750	1400	1000	800	550

Type I Late Production

Fitted with an automatic extractor and marked on the top of the barrel rib. Manufactured from the late 1860s to 1888.

Exc.	V.G.	Good	Fair	Poor
750	600	500	400	300

Type II

Marked "Remington Arms Co., Ilion, N.Y." on the barrel rib. Manufactured between 1888 and 1911.

Exc.	V.G.	Good	Fair	Poor
600	475	375	300	225

Type III

Marked "Remington Arms - U.M.C. Co., Ilion, N.Y." on the barrel rib. Manufactured between 1912 and 1935.

Exc.	V.G.	Good	Fair	Poor
600	475	375	300	225

Model 1865 Navy Rolling Block Pistol

A spur trigger single shot rolling block .50 caliber rimfire cartridge pistol with an 8.5" round barrel. Blued, case-hardened with walnut grips and forend. The barrel marked "Remingtons, Ilion N.Y. U.S.A. Pat. May 3d Nov. 15th, 1864 April 17th, 1866." Examples bearing military inspection marks are worth approximately 25% more than the values listed below. Examples are also to be found altered to centerfire cartridge and these are worth approximately 10% less than the values listed below. Approximately 6,500 were manufactured between 1866 and 1870.

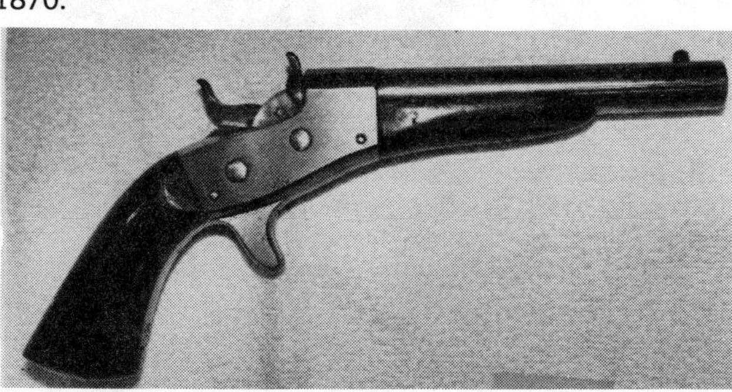

Exc.	V.G.	Good	Fair	Poor
2400	2000	1650	1000	750

Model 1867 Navy Rolling Block Pistol

A .50 caliber single shot rolling block pistol with a 7" round barrel. Blued, case-hardened with walnut grips and forend. The majority of these pistols were purchased by the United States Government and civilian examples without inspection marks are worth approximately 30% more than the values listed below.

Exc.	V.G.	Good	Fair	Poor
2000	1750	1450	850	600

Remington-Rider Magazine Pistol

A 5-shot .32 caliber magazine pistol with a spur trigger and 3" octagonal barrel. The magazine is located beneath the barrel and can be loaded from the front. Blued, nickle-plated or case-hardened with walnut, pearl or ivory grips. The barrel marked "E. Remington & Sons, Ilion, N.Y. Riders Pat. Aug. 15, 1871." Approximately 10,000 were manufactured between 1871 and 1888.

Exc.	V.G.	Good	Fair	Poor
750	600	450	350	225

Model 1871 Army Rolling Block Pistol

A .50 caliber rolling block single shot pistol with an 8" round barrel. Blued, case-hardened with walnut grips and forend. The distinguishing feature of this model is that it has a rearward extension at the top of the grip and a squared butt. Approximately 6,000 were made between 1872 and 1888. Engraved ivory-stocked versions, as pictured below, will bring considerable premiums.

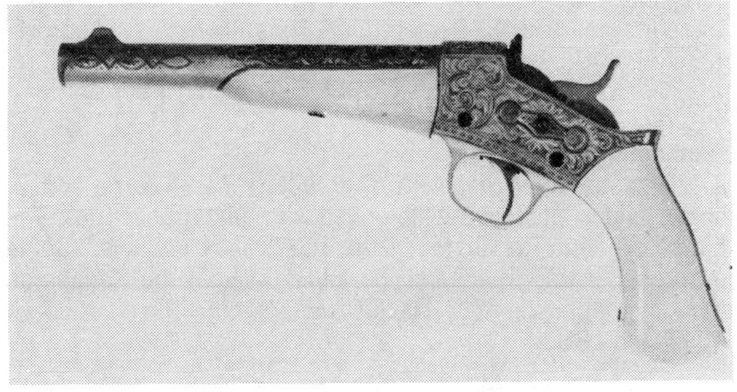

Exc.	V.G.	Good	Fair	Poor
1750	1500	1250	750	500

Remington-Smoot No. 1 Revolver

A .30 caliber spur trigger revolver with a 2.75" octagonal barrel and 5-shot fluted cylinder. Blued or nickel plated with walnut or hard rubber grips. The barrel rib is marked, "E. Remington & Sons, Ilion, N.Y. Pat. W. S. Smoot Oct. 21, 1873." Examples dating from the beginning of production are found with a revolving recoil shield. Such examples would command approximately a 300% premium over the values listed below.

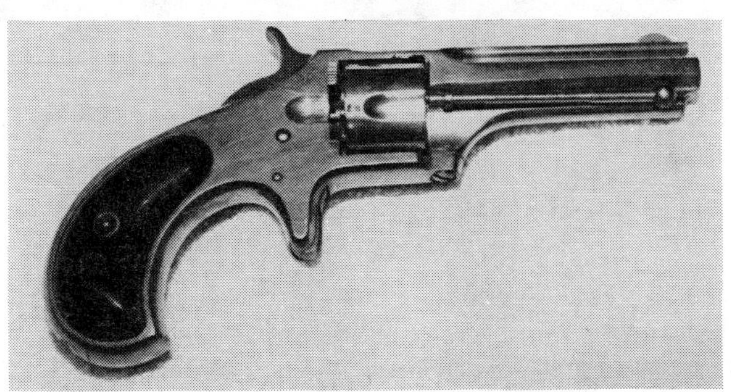

Exc.	V.G.	Good	Fair	Poor
400	300	250	175	125

Remington-Smoot No. 2 Revolver

As above, except in .32 caliber approximately 20,000 were made between 1878 and 1888.

Exc.	V.G.	Good	Fair	Poor
375	275	225	150	100

Remington-Smoot No. 3 Revolver

Two variations of this spur trigger .38 caliber revolver exist. One with a rounded grip and no barrel rib, the other with a squared back, squared butt grip with a barrel rib. Centerfire versions are also known and they are worth approximately 10% more than the values listed below. Blued or nickle-plated with hard rubber grips. Approximately 25,000 were made between 1878 and 1888.

Exc.	V.G.	Good	Fair	Poor
500	400	325	250	175

No. 4 Revolver

A .38 or .41 caliber spur trigger revolver with a .25" barrel and no ejector rod. Blued or nickle-plated with hard rubber grips. The barrel marked "E. Remington & Sons, Ilion, N.Y." Approximately 10,000 were manufactured between 1877 and 1888.

Exc.	V.G.	Good	Fair	Poor
375	275	225	150	100

Remington Iroquois Revolver

A .22 caliber spur trigger revolver with a 2.25" barrel and 7-shot cylinder. Blued or nickle-plated with hard rubber grips. The barrel marked "Remington, Ilion, N.Y." and "Iroquois." Some examples of this model will be found without the Remington markings. Approximately 10,000 were manufactured betweeen 1878 and 1888.

Exc.	V.G.	Good	Fair	Poor
400	300	250	175	125

Model 1875 Single Action Army

A .44 Remington or .44-40 or .45 caliber single action revolver with a 7.5" barrel. Blued or nickle-plated, case-hardened with walnut grips. Some examples are to be found fitted with a lanyard ring at the butt. The barrel marked "E. Remington & Sons Ilion, N.Y. U.S.A." Approximately 25,000 were manufactured between 1875 and 1889.

Blued Version—Add 40%.

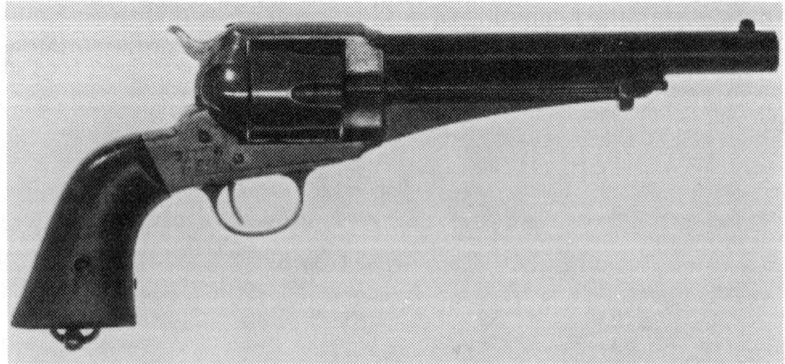

Courtesy Milwaukee Public Museum, Milwaukee, Wisconsin.

Exc.	V.G.	Good	Fair	Poor
4000	3000	2000	1250	600

Model 1890 Single Action Army

A .44-40 caliber single action revolver with a 5.5" or 7.5" barrel and 6-shot cylinder. Blued or nickle-plated with hard rubber grips bearing the monogram "RA" at the top. The barrel marked "Remington Arms Co., Ilion, N.Y." Approximately 2,000 were made between 1891 and 1894. Prospective purchasers are advised to secure a qualified appraisal prior to acquisition.

Blued Version—Add 40%.

Exc.	V.G.	Good	Fair	Poor
4500	3500	2500	1750	1000

Model 1891 Target Rolling Block Pistol

A .22, .25 Stevens or .32 S&W caliber single shot rolling block pistol with a 10" half octagonal barrel fitted with target sights. Blued, case-hardened with walnut grips and forend. The barrel marked "Remington Arms Co. Ilion, N.Y.," and the frame "Remingtons Ilion N.Y. U.S.A. Pat. May 3 Nov. 15, 1864 April 17, 1866 P S." This is an extremely rare pistol, with slightly over 100 manufactured between 1892 and 1898. Prospective purchasers are advised to secure a qualified appraisal prior to acquisition.

Exc.	V.G.	Good	Fair	Poor
2000	1800	1250	775	575

Model 1901 Target Rolling Block

As above, with the exception that the bridge block thumb piece has been moved out of the line of sight and the rear sight is mounted on the frame instead of the barrel. Approximately 735 were made between 1901 and 1909. Prospective purchasers are advised to secure a qualified appraisal prior to acquisition.

Exc.	V.G.	Good	Fair	Poor
2000	1800	1250	775	575

Mark III Signal Pistol

A 10 gauge spur trigger flare pistol with a 9" round barrel. The frame of brass and the barrel of iron finished matte black with walnut grips. The barrel marked "The Remington Arms - Union Metallic Cartridge Co., Inc. Mark III, Remington Bridgeport Works Bridgeport, Connecticut U.S.A." Approximately 25,000 were manufactured between 1915 and 1918.

Exc.	V.G.	Good	Fair	Poor
350	275	200	125	75

Remington 1911 and 1911A1

See the Colt section of this book for pistols of this type.

Model 51

A .32 or .380 caliber semi-automatic pistol with a 3.5" barrel and magazines capable of holding either 7 or 8 cartridges depending on the caliber. Blued with hard rubber grips having the legend "Remington UMC" in a circle at the top. The slide marked "The Remington Arms - Union Metallic Cartridge Co., Inc. Remington Ilion Wks. Ilion, N.Y. U.S.A. Pedersen's Patents Pending." Later versions carried a 1920 and a 1921 patent date. The early examples have nine grooves on the slide; later models have 15 grooves with the frame marked "Remington Trademark." Early variations are worth approximately 10 percent more than the values listed below and .32 caliber examples are worth approximately 25 percent additional. Approximately 65,000 were manufactured between 1918 and 1934.

Courtesy Orville Reichert.

Exc.	V.G.	Good	Fair	Poor
400	350	275	200	125

Model 1841 "Mississippi Rifle"

A .54 caliber percussion rifle with a 33" barrel and full stock secured by two barrel bands. The lock (marked Remington's Herkimer N.Y.) case-hardened, the barrel browned and the furniture of brass. The stock is fitted with a brass patchbox on the right side. Approximately 20,000 were made between 1846 and 1855.

Exc.	V.G.	Good	Fair	Poor
1500	1250	950	675	450

Model 1861 U.S. Rifle Musket

A .58 caliber percussion rifle with a 40" barrel and full length stock secured by three barrel bands. The lock marked "Remington's Ilion, N.Y." Finished in the white with a walnut stock. Approximately 40,000 were made between 1864 and 1866.

Exc.	V.G.	Good	Fair	Poor
1250	1000	750	500	400

Model 1863 Zouave Rifle

A .58 caliber percussion rifle with a 33" barrel and full length stock secured by two barrel bands. The lock case-hardened and marked "Remington's Ilion N.Y.", the barrel blued and the furniture of brass. Approximately 12,500 were manufactured between 1862 and 1865.

Exc.	V.G.	Good	Fair	Poor
1500	1250	950	675	450

Breech-Loading Carbine

A .46 or .50 rimfire single shot rolling block carbine with a 20" barrel. Blued, case-hardened with a walnut stock. The tang marked "Remington's Ilion, N.Y. Pat. Dec. 23, 1863 May 3 & Nov. 16, 1864." The .50 caliber version is worth approximately 15 percent more than the .46 caliber. Approximately 15,000 .50-caliber variations were made, most of which were sold to France. Approximately 5,000 carbines were made in .46 caliber. Manufactured from 1864 to 1866.

Exc.	V.G.	Good	Fair	Poor
1500	1250	950	675	450

Revolving Rifle

A .36 or .44 caliber revolving rifle with either 24" or 28" octagonal barrels with a 6-shot cylinder. The trigger guard formed with a scrolled finger extension at the rear. Blued, case-hardened with a walnut stock. These rifles are also encountered altered to cartridge and would be worth approximately 20% less than the percussion values listed below. The barrel marked "Patented Sept. 14, 1858 E. Remington & Sons, Ilion, New York, U.S.A. New Model." Approximately 1,000 were manufactured between 1866 and 1879.

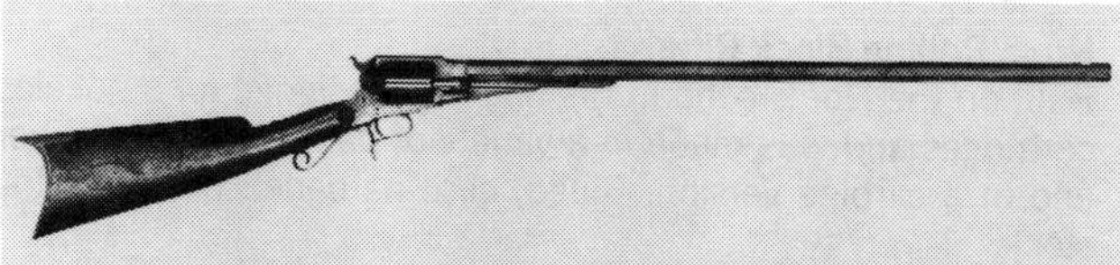

Courtesy Milwaukee Public Museum, Milwaukee, Wisconsin.

Courtesy Buffalo Bill Historical Center, Cody, Wyoming.

Exc.	V.G.	Good	Fair	Poor
4000	3250	2500	1800	1250

Remington-Beals Rifle

A .32 or .38 caliber sliding barrel single shot rifle with octagonal barrels of 24", 26" or 28" length. The barrel can be moved forward by lowering the triggerguard/lever. This model is to be found with either frames made of brass or iron. The latter being worth approximately 20% more than the values listed below. Walnut stock. The barrel marked "Beals Patent June 28, 1864 Jan. 30, 1866 E. Remington & Sons, Ilion, New York." Approximately 800 were manufactured between 1866 and 1888. A few examples are known to have been factory engraved. Prospective purchasers are advised to secure a qualified appraisal prior to acquisition.

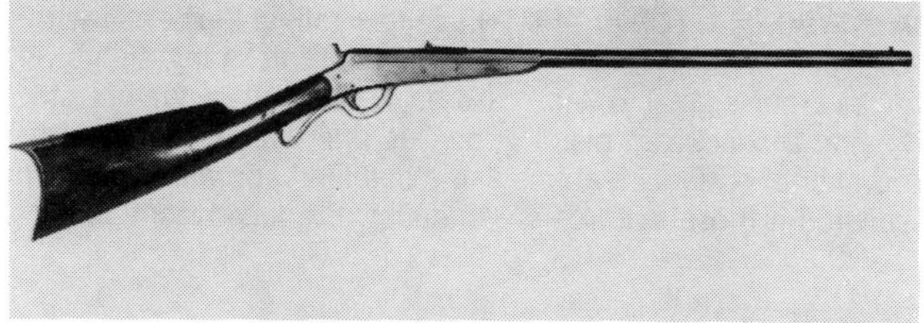

Courtesy Milwaukee Public Museum, Milwaukee, Wisconsin.

Exc.	V.G.	Good	Fair	Poor
700	550	425	350	225

U.S. Navy Rolling Block Carbine

A .50-70 caliber single shot rolling block carbine with a 23.25" round barrel. A sling ring is normally fitted to the left side of the frame and sling swivels are mounted on the barrel band and the bottom of the butt. Inspector's markings are to be found on the right side of the frame as well as the stock. Blued, case-hardened with a walnut stock. The barrel marked "Remington's Ilion, N.Y. U.S.A." along with the patent dates. Approximately 5,000 were manufactured in 1868 and 1869.

Exc.	V.G.	Good	Fair	Poor
1500	1250	950	675	450

Model 1867 Navy Cadet Rifle

A .50-45 caliber single shot rolling block rifle with a 32.5" barrel and full length forend secured by two barrel bands. Markings identical to the above with the exception that "U.S." is stamped on the buttplate tang. Blued, case-hardened with a walnut stock. Approximately 500 were made in 1868.

Exc.	V.G.	Good	Fair	Poor
1750	1450	1100	750	525

Rolling Block Military Rifles

Between 1867 and 1902 over 1,000,000 rolling block military rifles and carbines were manufactured by the Remington Company. Offered in a variety of calibers and barrel lengths, the values listed below are for full length rifles. Carbines are worth approximately 40% more.

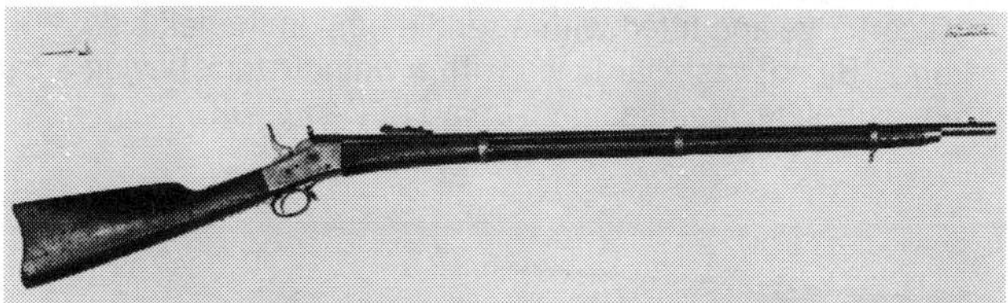

Courtesy Milwaukee Public Museum, Milwaukee, Wisconsin.

Exc.	V.G.	Good	Fair	Poor
500	400	300	175	100

No. 1 Rolling Block Sporting Rifle

Standard No. 1 Sporting Rifle

A single shot rolling block rifle produced in a variety of calibers from .40-50 to .50-70 centerfire as well as .44 and .46 rimfire. Standard barrel lengths were either 28" or 30" and of octagonal form.

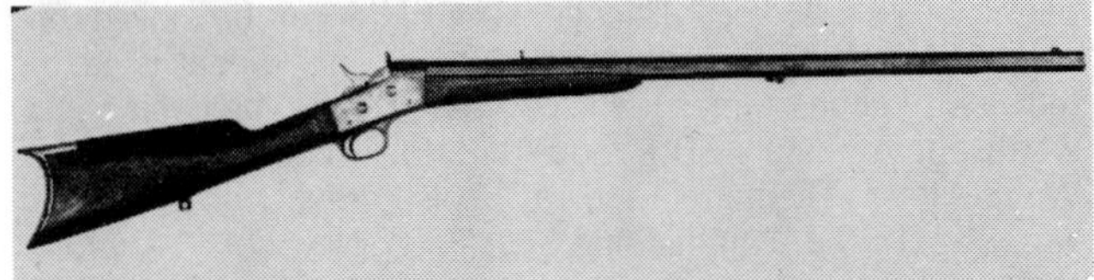

Courtesy Milwaukee Public Museum, Milwaukee, Wisconsin.

Exc.	V.G.	Good	Fair	Poor
950	800	600	375	200

Long-Range Creedmoor Rifle

A .44-90, .44-100 or .44-105 caliber rolling block rifle with a 34" half octagonal barrel, long range vernier tang sights and globe front sights. Blued, case-hardened with a walnut stock having a checkered pistol grip. This rifle was available with a number of optional features and a qualified appraisal should be secured if those features are in doubt. Produced from 1873 to 1890.

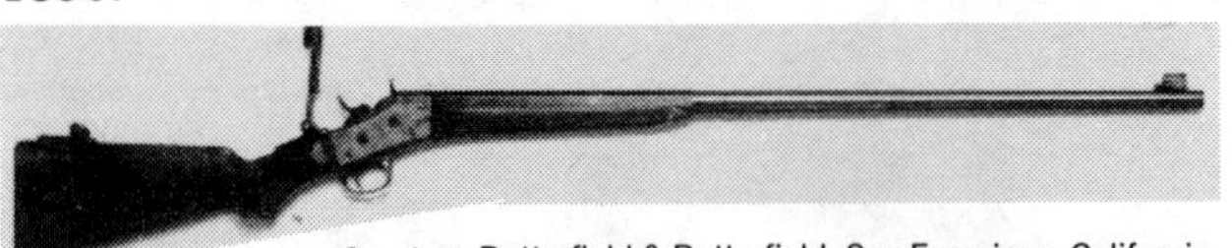

Courtesy Butterfield & Butterfield, San Francisco, California.

Exc.	V.G.	Good	Fair	Poor
3500	2750	2000	1150	600

Mid-Range Target Rifle

As above, except chambered for .40-70, .44-77, .45-70 or .50-70 caliber with 28" or 30" half octagonal barrels. Produced from 1875 to 1890.

Exc.	V.G.	Good	Fair	Poor
3000	2250	1750	950	500

Short-Range Rifle

As above, chambered for cartridges between .38 and .44 caliber with 26" or 30" round or octagonal barrels. Open rear sight with beach front sight. The walnut stock checkered. Produced from 1875 to 1890.

Exc.	V.G.	Good	Fair	Poor
2500	1800	1250	800	450

Black Hills Rifle

As above, in .45-60 caliber with a 28" round barrel fitted with open sights and a plain straight grip stock. Produced from 1877 to 1882.

Exc.	V.G.	Good	Fair	Poor
2200	1600	1050	650	400

Shotgun

As above, in 16 gauge with either a 30" or 32" Damascus or fluid steel barrels. Produced from 1870 to 1892.

Exc.	V.G.	Good	Fair	Poor
700	600	450	325	200

Baby Carbine

As above, with a 20" thin round barrel chambered for the .44-40 cartridge and fitted with a saddle ring on the left side of the frame. Blued, case-hardened with a walnut stock having a carbine buttplate. Manufactured from 1892 to 1902.

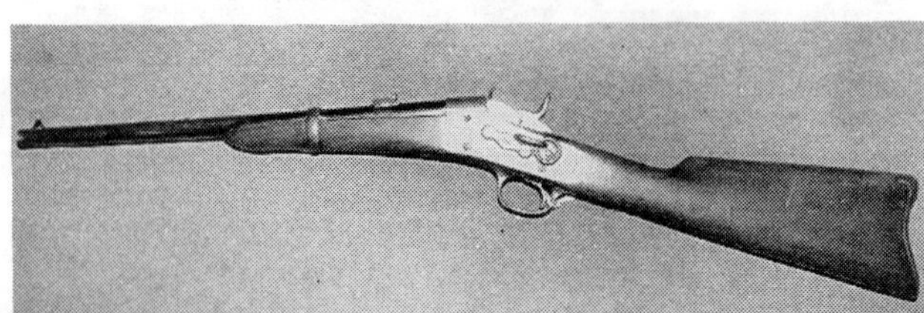

Exc.	V.G.	Good	Fair	Poor
3000	2250	1750	950	500

Model 1-1/2 Sporting Rifle

A lightweight variation of the above using a 1.25" wide, No. 1 rolling block action. Chambered for rimfire cartridges from .22 to the .38 extra long, as well as centerfire cartridges from .32-20 to the .44-40. Medium weight octagonal barrels from 24" to 28" in length, with open rear and a blade-type front sight. Blued, case-hardened with a walnut stock. There were several thousand manufactured between 1888 and 1897.

Exc.	V.G.	Good	Fair	Poor
800	650	500	375	225

Model 2 Sporting Rifle

As above, using a No. 2 action and chambered for various cartridges from .22 to .38 caliber with 24" or 26" octagonal barrels. Blued, case-hardened with a walnut stock. This model was produced with a number of optional features which affect its value. Prospective purchasers are advised to secure a qualified appraisal prior to acquisition. Manufactured from 1873 to 1910.

Exc.	V.G.	Good	Fair	Poor
800	650	500	375	225

No. 4 Rolling Block Rifle

Built on the lightweight No. 4 action, this rifle was available in .22, .25 Stevens or .32 caliber, with either a 22.5" or 24" octagonal barrel. Blued, case-hardened with a walnut stock. A takedown version was also made and these are worth approximately 10% more than the values listed below. Approximately 50,000 were made between 1890 and 1933.

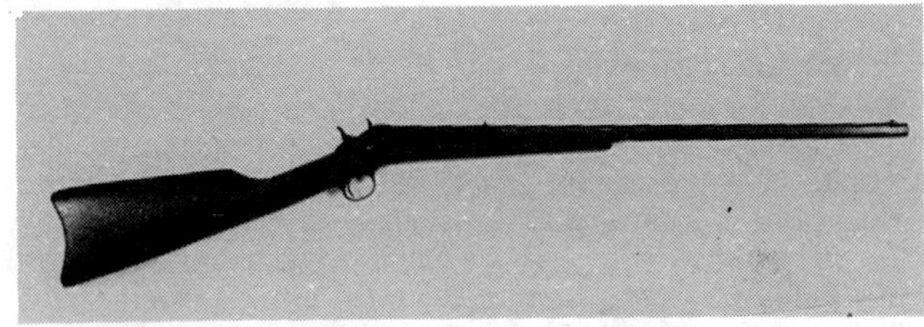

Exc.	V.G.	Good	Fair	Poor
500	400	300	200	125

Model No. 4 S Military Rifle

At the request of the United States Boy Scouts in 1913, the Remington Company designed a military style rifle having a 28" barrel and full length forend secured by one barrel band. A short upper hand guard was also fitted and a bayonet stud is to be found at the muzzle. In 1915 the designation of this model was changed from "Boy Scout" to "Military Model." Approximately 15,000 were made between 1913 and 1923.

Exc.	V.G.	Good	Fair	Poor
850	650	500	400	275

No. 5 Rolling Block Rifle

Built on the No. 5 action, this rifle was designed for smokeless cartridges and was made in a variety of barrel lengths, calibers and in a carbine version. Blued, case-hardened with a walnut stock.

Sporting or Target Rifle

Chambered for the .30-30, .303 British, 7mm, .30 U.S., .32-40, .32 U.S., and the .38-55 cartridges. This rifle was offered with 28" or 30" round barrels and features a plain, straight-grip stock with a half-length forend. It has open rear sights and was available with double-set triggers that would add approximately 10 percent to the value. It was manufactured between 1898 and 1905.

Exc.	V.G.	Good	Fair	Poor
850	650	500	400	275

Model 1897

A 7x57mm and .30 U.S. caliber full stock rolling block rifle. The Model 1902 is of identical form except that it was fitted with an automatic ejector. Manufactured from 1897 to 1902.

Exc.	V.G.	Good	Fair	Poor
550	450	300	200	125

Carbine

As above, fitted with a 20" round barrel and a half-length forend secured by one barrel band.

Exc.	V.G.	Good	Fair	Poor
850	700	500	400	300

No. 6 Rolling Block Rifle

A very lightweight, small rifle designed expressly to be used by young boys. It is chambered for the .22 rimfire cartridge, as well as the .32 short or long. It was also produced with a smoothbore barrel to be used with shot cartridges. The round barrel is 20" in length. It has a takedown action with a barrel held on by a knurled knob underneath the frame. It is a very lightweight rolling block, with a thin operating knob on the breech. The finish is blued overall. Very early models featured a case-colored frame, and these versions would be worth approximately 10 percent additional. It has a straight-grip walnut stock with a small forearm. Over 250,000 manufactured between 1902 and 1903.

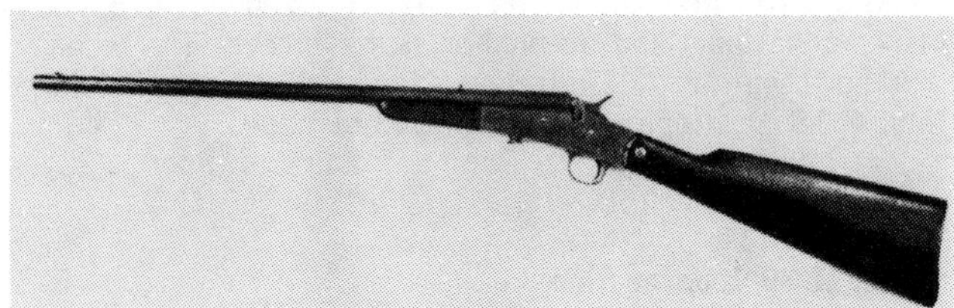

Exc.	V.G.	Good	Fair	Poor
350	300	225	125	75

No. 7 Rolling Block Rifle

Readily identifiable by its accentuated checked pistol grip, this model was available in .22 or .25-10 Stevens caliber with 24", 26" or 28" half octagonal barrels. Fitted with a tang mounted aperture rear sight. Blued, case-hardened with a walnut stock. Approximately 1,000 were made between 1903 and 1911.

Exc.	V.G.	Good	Fair	Poor
2750	2250	1750	1250	850

Remington-Hepburn No. 3 Rifle

A lever activated falling block single shot rifle designed by Lewis Hepburn available in a variety of calibers from .22 Winchester centerfire to .50-90 Sharps with octagonal or round barrels of 26", 28" or 30" length. Blued, case-hardened with a walnut stock. This model was available with a variety of optional features which affect the value considerably. Prospective purchasers are advised to secure a qualified appraisal prior to acquisition. Approximately 10,000 were made between 1883 and 1907.

Exc.	V.G.	Good	Fair	Poor
1500	1250	1000	700	450

No. 3 Match Rifle

As above, but fitted with a high comb buttstock and a nickle-plated Schuetzen buttplate. Manufactured in various calibers from .25-20 Stevens to .40-65 with 30" half octagonal barrels. This model was made in two versions: "A Quality" with a plain stock, tang mounted rear sight and a Beach front sight, and; "B Quality" with a checkered walnut stock having a cheekrest, checkered forend, vernier rear sight and a combination wind gauge and spirit level front sight. Double set triggers were also available and these would add approximately 10% to the values listed below. Approximately 1,000 were made between 1883 and 1907.

A Quality

Exc.	V.G.	Good	Fair	Poor
1750	1500	1250	900	650

B Quality

Exc.	V.G.	Good	Fair	Poor
2000	1750	1500	1100	850

No. 3 Long-Range Creedmoor Rifle

As above, in .44 caliber with a 32" or 34" half octagonal barrel, long range vernier rear sight, combination wind gauge and spirit level front sight, with a deluxe checkered walnut stock having a rubber shotgun buttplate. Produced with a number of optional features which affect the value. Prospective purchasers are advised to secure a qualified appraisal prior to acquisition. Manufactured from 1880 to 1907.

Exc.	V.G.	Good	Fair	Poor
2500	2200	1750	1200	800

No. 3 Mid-Range Creedmoor Rifle

As above, but chambered for the .40-65 cartridge and fitted with a 28" barrel.

Exc.	V.G.	Good	Fair	Poor
2250	2000	1500	1000	650

No. 3 Long-Range Military Rifle

This is a very rare variation that is chambered for the .44-75-520 Remington cartridge. It has a round 34" barrel and a full-length forearm held on by two barrel bands. The finish is blued and case-colored, and the stock is walnut. There are two basic versions. The plain grade has an uncheckered, straight-grip stock with military-type sights. There is also a fancy grade that features a high-grade, checkered, pistolgrip stock with a full-length, checkered forend, Vernier tang sight, and wind gauge, spirit lever front sight. There were very few manufactured in the 1880s.

Plain Grade

Exc.	V.G.	Good	Fair	Poor
3500	2800	2000	1400	900

Fancy Grade

Exc.	V.G.	Good	Fair	Poor
4250	3500	2750	1850	1250

No. 3 Schuetzen Match Rifle

As above, with the exception that instead of the side lever, the action is raised or lowered by means of the lever on the triggerguard. Chambered for various popular cartridges and offered with a 30" or 32" part-octagonal, heavy barrel. It features a Vernier tang sight with a hooded front sight. It was standard with double-set triggers and a palmrest. The finish is blued and case-colored, with a very high grade checkered walnut stock and forend. It has an ornate, Swiss-type Schuetzen buttplate and is also known as the "Walker-Hepburn Rifle." There were two versions available—one, a standard breechloader with the Remington Walker-marked barrel; and the other, a muzzleloading variation that was fitted with a removable false muzzle. This version was supplied with a brass bullet starter and other accessories. Prospective purchasers are advised to secure a qualified appraisal prior to acquisition.

Breechloading Version

Exc.	V.G.	Good	Fair	Poor
5000	4250	3250	2250	1750

Muzzleloading Version

Exc.	V.G.	Good	Fair	Poor
6000	5250	4250	3250	2750

No. 3 High-Power Rifle

The Model No. 3 was also made available in a variety of smokeless cartridges; .30-30, .30-40, .32 Special, .32-40 and .38-

55. Standard barrel lengths were 26", 28" or 30". Produced from 1900 to 1907.

Exc.	V.G.	Good	Fair	Poor
1500	1250	1000	700	500

Remington-Keene Magazine Rifle

A bolt-action rifle chambered for the .40, .43, and .45-70 centerfire cartridges with 22", 24.5", 29.25", or 32.5" barrels. It is readily identifiable by the exposed hammer at the end of the bolt. Blued, case-hardened hammer and furniture, with a walnut stock. The receiver marked "E. Remington & Sons, Ilion, N.Y." together with the patent dates 1874, 1876, and 1877. The magazine on this rifle was located beneath the barrel and the receiver is fitted with a cut-off so that the rifle could be used as a single shot. Approximately 5,000 rifles were made between 1880 and 1888 in the following variations:

Sporting Rifle—24.5" Barrel

Exc.	V.G.	Good	Fair	Poor
1050	850	650	450	325

Army Rifle

Barrel length 32.5" with a full-length stock secured by two barrel bands.

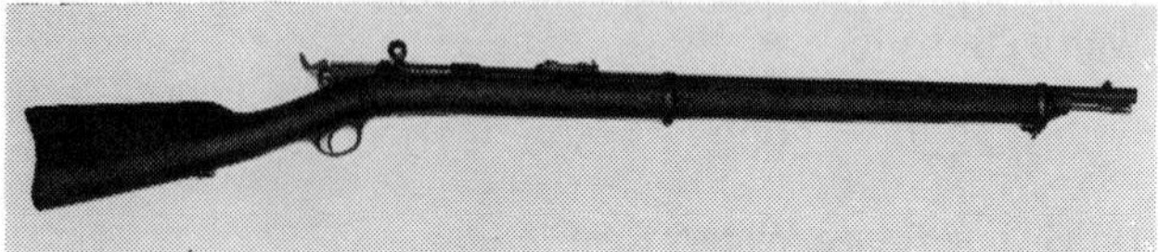

Courtesy Milwaukee Public Museum, Milwaukee, Wisconsin.

Exc.	V.G.	Good	Fair	Poor
1150	950	750	500	425

Navy Rifle

As above, with a 29.25" barrel.

Exc.	V.G.	Good	Fair	Poor
1150	950	750	550	425

Carbine

As above, with a 22" barrel and a half-length forend secured by one barrel band.

Courtesy Milwaukee Public Museum, Milwaukee, Wisconsin.

Exc.	V.G.	Good	Fair	Poor
1150	950	750	550	425

Frontier Model

As above, with a 24" barrel and half-length forend secured by one barrel band. Those purchased by the United States Department of the Interior for arming the Indian Police are marked "U.S.I.D." on the receiver.

Exc.	V.G.	Good	Fair	Poor
1500	1250	900	750	450

Remington-Lee Magazine Rifle

Designed by James Paris Lee, rifles of this type were originally manufactured by the Sharps Rifle Company in 1880. The Remington Company began production of this model in 1881 after the Sharps Company ceased operations. Approximately 100,000 Lee magazine rifles were made between 1880 and 1907. Their variations are as follows:

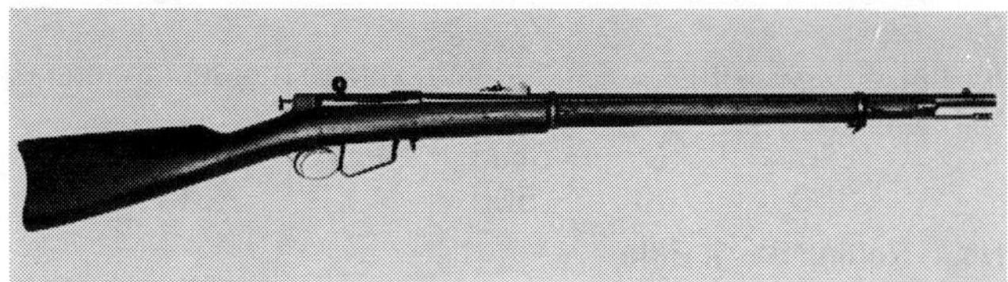

Courtesy Milwaukee Public Museum, Milwaukee, Wisconsin.

Model 1879—Sharps Mfg.

Barrel length 28" with a full-length stock secured by two barrel bands. The barrel marked "Sharps Rifle Co. Bridgeport, Conn." and "Old Reliable" in a rectangular cartouche. Approximately 300 were made prior to 1881.

Exc.	V.G.	Good	Fair	Poor
3000	2400	1850	1250	700

Model 1879 U.S. Navy Model

Barrel length 28", .45-70 caliber with a full-length stock secured by two barrel bands. The barrel is marked with U.S. Navy Inspector's Marks and an anchor at the breech. The receiver marked "Lee Arms Co. Bridgeport, Conn. U.S.A." and "Patented Nov. 4, 1879." Approximately 1300 were made.

Exc.	V.G.	Good	Fair	Poor
1500	1250	950	650	450

Model 1879 Sporting Rifle

Barrel length 28" or 30", .45-70 or .45-90 caliber, checkered pistol grip stock with a sporting style forend. Markings on the receiver as above. Approximately 450 made.

Exc.	V.G.	Good	Fair	Poor
1800	1550	1250	850	600

Model 1879 Military Rifle

Identical to the Navy model, except chambered for the .43 Spanish cartridge. A limited number were also produced in .45-70 caliber. The Spanish versions are worth approximately 25% less than the values listed below. Approximately 1,000 were made.

Exc.	V.G.	Good	Fair	Poor
1250	1000	750	500	350

Model 1882 Army Contract

This model is identifiable by the two grooves pressed into the side of the magazine. The receiver is marked "Lee Arms Co. Bridgeport Conn., U.S.A." and on some examples it is also marked "E. Remington & Sons, Ilion, N.Y. U.S.A. Sole Manufactured & Agents." Barrel length 32", caliber .45-70, full-length stock secured by two barrel bands. U.S. Inspector's marks are stamped on the barrel breech and the stock. Approximately 750 were made.

Exc.	V.G.	Good	Fair	Poor
1750	1400	1100	800	650

Model 1885 Navy Contract

As above, with the inspection markings (including an anchor) on the receiver ring and the left side of the stock. Approximately 1,500 were made.

Exc.	V.G.	Good	Fair	Poor
1500	1250	950	650	450

Model 1882 & 1885 Military Rifles

Barrel length 32", full-length stock secured by two barrel bands, chambered for .42 Russian, .43 Spanish, .45 Gardner or .45-70 cartridges. The values for those rifles not in .45-70 caliber would be approximately 25% less than those shown below. Approximately 10,000 Model 1882 rifles were made and 60,000 Model 1885 rifles. The two models can be differenciated by the fact that the cocking piece on the bolt of the Model 1885 is larger.

Exc.	V.G.	Good	Fair	Poor
1000	800	600	450	325

Model 1882 & 1885 Sporting Rifle
As above, chambered for .45-70 and .45-90 caliber with 26" or 30" octagonal barrels and walnut sporting stocks. Approximately 200 were made.

Exc.	V.G.	Good	Fair	Poor
950	750	600	400	300

Model 1882 & 1885 Carbine
As above, with a 24" barrel and a half-length forend secured by one barrel band. Prospective purchasers are advised to secure a qualified appraisal prior to acquisition.

Exc.	V.G.	Good	Fair	Poor
1500	1250	950	650	450

Model 1899
Designed for use with smokeless and rimless cartridges, this model is marked on the receiver "Remington Arms Co. Ilion, N.Y. Patented Aug. 26th 1884 Sep't 9th 1884 March 17th 1885 Jan 18th 1887." Produced from 1889 to 1907 in the following variations:

Military Rifle
Barrel length 29", 6mm USN, .30-40, .303, 7x57mm or 7.65mm caliber with a full-length stock secured by two barrel bands.

Exc.	V.G.	Good	Fair	Poor
900	700	550	425	300

Military Carbine
As above, with a 20" barrel and a 3/4 length carbine stock secured by one barrel band.

Exc.	V.G.	Good	Fair	Poor
1000	750	600	475	350

Sporting Rifle
As above, with a 24", 26" or 28" round or octagonal barrel and a half-length sporting stock with a checkered pistol grip. Approximately 7,000 were manufactured.

Exc.	V.G.	Good	Fair	Poor
1000	750	600	475	350

Remington Lebel Bolt-Action Rifle
Produced for the French Government, this rifle has a 31.5" barrel of 8mm Lebel caliber and a full-length stock secured by two barrel bands. The barrel marked "RAC 190715" and the left side of the receiver marked "Remington M'LE 1907-15." Several thousand were manufactured between 1907 and 1915.

Exc.	V.G.	Good	Fair	Poor
375	300	225	150	100

Remington Mosin-Nagant Bolt-Action Rifle
Produced for the Imperial Russian Government, this rifle has a 32" barrel of 7.62mm caliber with a full-length stock secured by two barrel bands. The barrel is marked "Remington Armory" with the date of manufacture and the receiver ring is stamped with the Russian coat-of-arms. Approximately 500,000 were made between 1916 and 1918.

Exc.	V.G.	Good	Fair	Poor
300	250	175	125	75

U.S. Model 1917 Magazine Rifle
Produced for the United States Government, this rifle has a 26" barrel of .30-06 caliber and a full length stock secured by two barrel bands. Those sold to the British Government during World War II are often found with a 2" wide red painted stripe around their butt which was intended to show that they were chambered for the .30-06 cartridge instead of the .303 British cartridge. Total production unknown.

Exc.	V.G.	Good	Fair	Poor
350	275	200	150	100

Remington-Whitmore Model 1874
A sidelock double barrel shotgun, combination shotgun rifle or double barrel rifle with 28" or 30" fluid steel barrels. Also available with Damascus barrels. The barrels released by pushing forward the top lever. Blued, case-hardened with a straight or semi-pistol grip walnut stock. The barrels marked "A. E. Whitmore's Patent Aug. 8, 1871, April 16, 1872." The rib between the barrels is marked "E. Remington & Sons, Ilion, N.Y." Several thousand were manufactured between 1874 and 1882.

Shotgun

Exc.	V.G.	Good	Fair	Poor
800	650	500	400	275

Combination Gun

Exc.	V.G.	Good	Fair	Poor
2000	1750	1250	900	650

Double Rifle
Prospective purchasers are advised to secure a qualified appraisal prior to acquisition.

Exc.	V.G.	Good	Fair	Poor
5000	4000	2750	1850	1000

Model 1882 Shotgun
A sidelock double barrel 10 or 12 gauge shotgun with 28" or 30" fluid steel or Damascus barrels. Blued, case-hardened with a checkered pistol grip stock and hard rubber buttplate. The barrels marked "E. Remington & Sons, Ilion, N.Y." and the lock is marked "Remington Arms Co." This model has a conventional top lever which moves to the side. Offered with optional engraving, and such models should be individually appraised. Approximately 7,500 were manufactured between 1882 and 1889.

Exc.	V.G.	Good	Fair	Poor
800	650	500	400	275

Model 1883 through 1889 Shotgun
A sidelock 10, 12, or 16 gauge double barrel shotgun with fluid steel or Damascus barrels 28" to 32" in length. The models 1883, 1885, 1887 and 1889 are all somewhat alike, varying only in the form of their hammers and internal mechanisms. Blued, case-hardened, checkered pistol grip stock with a grip cap. Available in a variety of styles including highly engraved models which should be individually appraised. Approximately 30,000 were made between 1883 and 1909.

Exc.	V.G.	Good	Fair	Poor
800	650	500	400	275

Hammerless Shotgun Model 1894
A boxlock 10, 12, or 16 gauge double shotgun with fluid steel or Damascus barrels 26" to 32" in length. Blued, case-hardened with a pistol grip stock. Available in a variety of styles and it is advised that highly engraved examples should be individually appraised.

Exc.	V.G.	Good	Fair	Poor
800	650	500	400	275

Model 1900 Shotgun
As above, in 12 and 16 gauge only. The same cautions apply to highly engraved examples.

Exc.	V.G.	Good	Fair	Poor
800	650	500	400	275

Model 8
A .25, .30, .32 or .35 Remington semi-automatic rifle with a 22" barrel having open sights. The barrel is covered by a full length tube which encloses the recoil spring. Blued with walnut stock. Approximately 60,000 were made between 1906 and 1936 in the following styles.

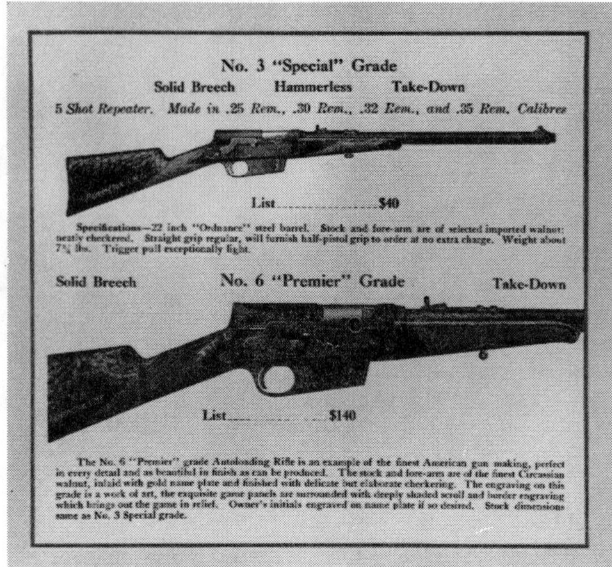

No. 3 "Special" Grade

Solid Breech Hammerless Take-Down

5 Shot Repeater. Made in .25 Rem., .30 Rem., .32 Rem., and .35 Rem. Calibres

List $40

Specifications—22 inch "Ordnance" steel barrel. Stock and fore-arm are of selected imported walnut; neatly checkered. Straight grip regular, will furnish half-pistol grip to order at no extra charge. Weight about 7¾ lbs. Trigger pull exceptionally light.

Solid Breech No. 6 "Premier" Grade Take-Down

List $140

The No. 6 "Premier" grade Autoloading Rifle is an example of the finest American gun making, perfect in every detail and as beautiful in finish as can be produced. The stock and fore-arm are of the finest Circassian walnut, inlaid with gold name plate and finished with delicate but elaborate checkering. The engraving on this grade is a work of art, the exquisite game panels are surrounded with deeply shaded scroll and border engraving which brings out the game in relief. Owner's initials engraved on name plate if so desired. Stock dimensions same as No. 3 Special grade.

Standard Grade

Exc.	V.G.	Good	Fair	Poor
400	325	250	175	125

Model 8A—Checkered Stock

Exc.	V.G.	Good	Fair	Poor
450	375	300	225	150

Model 8C

Exc.	V.G.	Good	Fair	Poor
525	450	375	300	200

Model 8D Peerless—Light Engraving

Exc.	V.G.	Good	Fair	Poor
1000	750	500	400	300

Model 8E Expert

Exc.	V.G.	Good	Fair	Poor
1200	1100	850	600	450

Model 8F Premier—Heavily Engraved

Exc.	V.G.	Good	Fair	Poor
1500	1275	900	750	550

Model 81 Woodsmaster

An improved variation of the Model 8, chambered for the same calibers as well as the .300 Savage cartridge. Produced from 1936 to 1950 in the following styles.

Standard Model

Exc.	V.G.	Good	Fair	Poor
400	325	250	175	125

Model 81A—Takedown

Exc.	V.G.	Good	Fair	Poor
450	375	300	225	150

Model 81D Peerless—Engraved

Exc.	V.G.	Good	Fair	Poor
1000	750	500	400	300

Model 81F Premier—Heavily Engraved

Exc.	V.G.	Good	Fair	Poor
1500	1275	900	750	550

Model 12 or 12 A

A .22 caliber slide action rifle with a 22" round or octagonal barrel having open sights. Blued with a walnut stock. Manufactured from 1909 to 1936 in the following styles.

Model 12A

Exc.	V.G.	Good	Fair	Poor
450	375	300	225	150

Model 12B—.22 Short, Gallery Model

Exc.	V.G.	Good	Fair	Poor
450	375	300	225	150

Model 12C—24" Octagon Barrel

Exc.	V.G.	Good	Fair	Poor
500	425	350	250	175

Model 12CS—.22 Remington Special

Exc.	V.G.	Good	Fair	Poor
475	400	325	250	175

Model 12D Peerless—Light Engraving

Exc.	V.G.	Good	Fair	Poor
550	475	400	300	225

Model 12E Expert

Exc.	V.G.	Good	Fair	Poor
1200	1000	750	600	450

Model 12F Premier—Heavily Engraved

Exc.	V.G.	Good	Fair	Poor
1500	1250	900	750	550

Model 121 and/or 121A

A .22 caliber slide action rifle with a 24" round barrel. Blued with a walnut stock. Manufactured from 1936 to 1954 in the following styles.

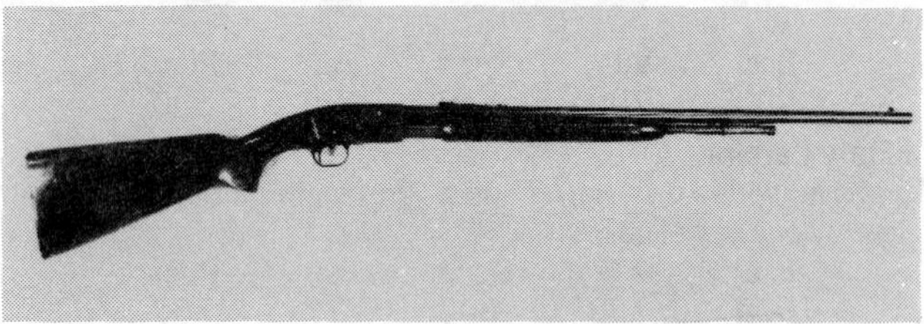

Standard Grade

Exc.	V.G.	Good	Fair	Poor
375	300	250	175	100

Model 121D Peerless—Engraved

Exc.	V.G.	Good	Fair	Poor
500	400	350	250	175

Model 121F Premier—Heavily Engraved

Exc.	V.G.	Good	Fair	Poor
1200	1000	750	600	450

Model 121S—.22 WRF

Exc.	V.G.	Good	Fair	Poor
450	375	300	200	125

Model 121SB—Smooth Bore

Exc.	V.G.	Good	Fair	Poor
450	375	300	200	125

Model 14 or 14A

A .25, .30, .32 or .35 Remington caliber slide action rifle with a 22" round barrel having open sights. Blued, plain walnut stock. Manufactured from 1912 to 1936.

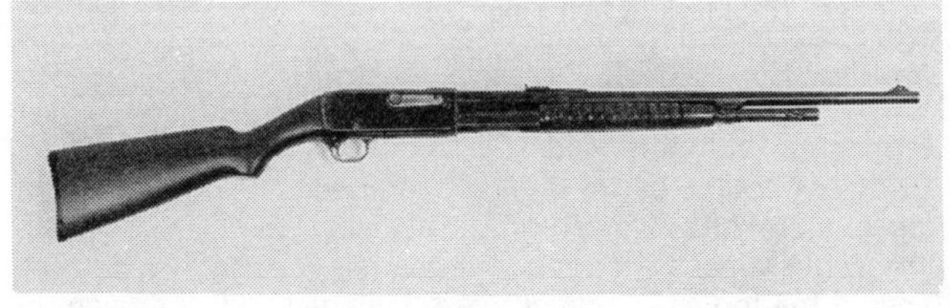

Exc.	V.G.	Good	Fair	Poor
350	275	225	150	100

Model 14R

As above, with an 18.5" barrel.

Exc.	V.G.	Good	Fair	Poor
400	325	275	200	125

Model 14-1/2

As above, except chambered for the .38-40 or .44-40 cartridge with a 22.5" barrel. A carbine with an 18.5" barrel known as the Model 14-1/2R, would be worth approximately 10% more than the values listed below. Manufactured from 1912 to 1922.

Exc.	V.G.	Good	Fair	Poor
450	375	300	200	125

Model 141

A .30, .32 or .35 Remington caliber slide action rifle with a 24" barrel having open sights. Blued with a plain walnut stock. Later production versions of this rifle were known as the Model 141A. Manufactured from 1936 to 1950.

Exc.	V.G.	Good	Fair	Poor
400	325	275	200	125

Model 25

A .25-30 or .32-30 caliber slide action rifle with a 24" barrel having open sights. Blued with a walnut stock. Later production examples were known as the Model 25A and a carbine version with an 18" barrel as the Model 25R. Manufactured from 1923 to 1936.

Exc.	V.G.	Good	Fair	Poor
350	275	225	150	100

Model 16

A .22 caliber semi-automatic rifle with a 22" barrel having open sights. Blued with a walnut stock. Later production examples were known as the Model 16A. Manufactured from 1914 to 1928.

Exc.	V.G.	Good	Fair	Poor
300	225	175	125	75

Model 24

Designed by John M. Browning, this semi-automatic rifle is of .22 caliber with a 19" barrel having open sights. Blued with a walnut pistol grip stock. Later production versions were known as the Model 24A. Produced from 1922 to 1935.

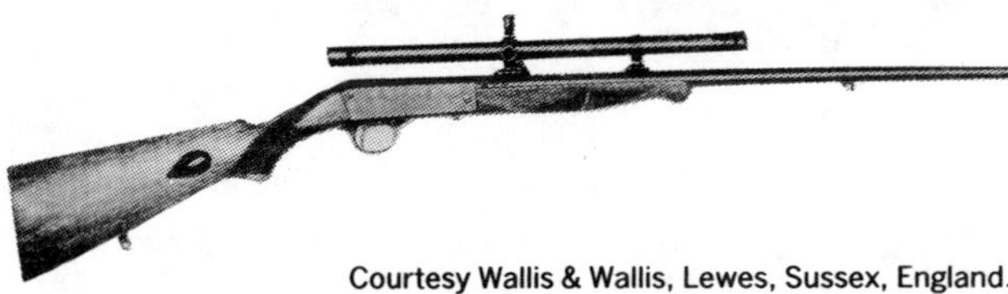

Courtesy Wallis & Wallis, Lewes, Sussex, England.

Exc.	V.G.	Good	Fair	Poor
325	250	200	150	100

Model 241 Speedmaster

A .22 caliber takedown semi-automatic rifle with a 24" barrel having open sights. Blued with a walnut stock. Later production versions were known as the Model 241A. Approximately 56,000 were made between 1935 and 1949 in the following styles:

Model 241

Exc.	V.G.	Good	Fair	Poor
375	300	250	200	150

Model 241D Peerless—Engraved

Exc.	V.G.	Good	Fair	Poor
450	375	325	275	200

Model 241E Expert

Exc.	V.G.	Good	Fair	Poor
850	775	650	450	350

Model 241F Premier—Heavily Engraved

Exc.	V.G.	Good	Fair	Poor
1000	800	600	500	425

Model 550A

A .22 short, long, or long rifle caliber semi-automatic rifle with a 24" barrel and open sights. Blued with a walnut pistol grip stock. Approximately 220,000 were made between 1941 and 1971.

Exc.	V.G.	Good	Fair	Poor
200	175	150	100	75

Model 550P

As above, with an aperture rear sight.

Exc.	V.G.	Good	Fair	Poor
225	200	175	125	100

Model 55-2G

As above, except fitted with a shell deflector and a screw eye for securing it to a shooting gallery counter.

Exc.	V.G.	Good	Fair	Poor
200	175	150	100	75

Model 30A

A sporting rifle using the U.S. Model 1917 Enfield bolt action chambered for various Remington cartridges as well as the 7x57mm and .30-06 cartridges. Barrel length 22". Checkered walnut stock. A carbine model fitted with a 20" barrel was known as the Model 30R. Manufactured from 1921 to 1940.

Exc.	V.G.	Good	Fair	Poor
375	325	250	175	100

Model 30S

As above, chambered for the .257 Roberts, 7x57, and the .30-06 cartridges and with 24" barrel with a Lyman receiver sight. Select checkered walnut stock. Manufactured from 1930 to 1940.

Exc.	V.G.	Good	Fair	Poor
450	375	300	225	150

From 1930 to 1970 the Remington Company produced a variety of single shot and repeating .22 caliber rifles. The values for these are much the same so consequently we list them for reference only.

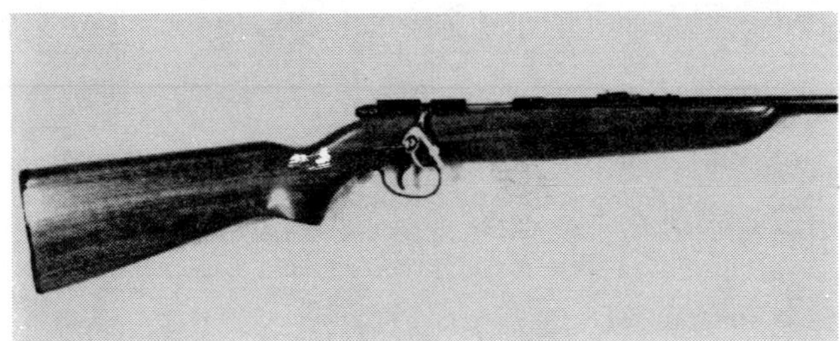

Model 33
Model 33 NRA
Model 34
Model 34 NRA
Model 341 A
Model 341 P
Model 341 SB
Model 510 A
Model 510 P
Model 510 SB
Model 510 X
Model 511 A
Model 511 P
Model 511 X
Model 512 A
Model 512 P
Model 512 X
Model 514
Model 514 P
Model 514 BC

Smooth-Bore Models—Add 20%.

Exc.	V.G.	Good	Fair	Poor
125	100	75	50	25

Model 37

A .22 caliber bolt-action magazine target rifle with a heavy 28" barrel having target sights and telescope bases. Blued with a walnut target style stock. Manufactured from 1937 to 1940.

Exc.	V.G.	Good	Fair	Poor
400	325	250	175	100

Model 37-1940

As above, with an improved lock, trigger pull and redesigned stock. Manufactured from 1940 to 1954.

Exc.	V.G.	Good	Fair	Poor
450	375	300	200	125

Model 511 Scoremaster

A .22 caliber bolt-action magazine sporting rifle with a 22" barrel. Blued with a walnut stock.

Exc.	V.G.	Good	Fair	Poor
250	200	175	125	75

Model 513 TR

A .22 caliber bolt-action magazine target rifle with a heavy 27" barrel and Redfield aperture rear sight. Blued with a target style walnut stock. Manufactured from 1940 to 1969.

Exc.	V.G.	Good	Fair	Poor
300	250	200	150	100

Model 513 S

As above, with Marble sights and a checkered walnut sporting style stock. Manufactured from 1941 to 1956.

Exc.	V.G.	Good	Fair	Poor
375	300	250	200	150

Model 521 TL Jr.

A .22 caliber bolt-action magazine target rifle with a heavy 25" barrel and Lyman sights. Blued with a targetstyle walnut stock. Manufactured from 1947 to 1969.

Exc.	V.G.	Good	Fair	Poor
250	200	175	125	75

Model 760

A slide-action sporting rifle chambered for various popular centerfire cartridges from the .222 up to the .35 Remington cartridge, with a 22" round barrel having open sights. It features a detachable box magazine. Blued with a checkered, walnut, pistol grip stock. Manufactured between 1952 and 1982. Examples of this rifle chambered for the .222, .223, .244, and the .257 Roberts are worth a premium over other calibers. Prospective purchasers are advised to secure a qualified appraisal prior to acquisition. This model was produced in the following styles.

Standard Model

Exc.	V.G.	Good	Fair	Poor
250	200	175	125	100

Model 760 Carbine—18.5" Barrel

Exc.	V.G.	Good	Fair	Poor
275	225	200	150	125

Model 760D Peerless—Engraved

Exc.	V.G.	Good	Fair	Poor
1000	850	650	550	450

Model 760F Premier—Gamescene Engraved

Exc.	V.G.	Good	Fair	Poor
2500	2000	1500	1200	1000

Model 760F Gold Inlaid

Exc.	V.G.	Good	Fair	Poor
5000	4000	3000	2200	1750

Model 760 Bicentennial—1976 Only

Exc.	V.G.	Good	Fair	Poor
350	300	250	175	100

Model 760 ADL

Exc.	V.G.	Good	Fair	Poor
275	225	175	125	75

Model 760 BDL—Basketweave Checkering

Exc.	V.G.	Good	Fair	Poor
300	250	200	150	100

Model 552A Speedmaster

A .22 caliber semi-automatic rifle with a 23" barrel having open sights. Blued with a pistol grip walnut stock. Manufactured from 1959 to 1988.

Exc.	V.G.	Good	Fair	Poor
150	125	100	75	50

Model 552 BDL

As above, with a more fully figured stock and impressed checkering. Introduced in 1966.

NIB	Exc.	V.G.	Good	Fair	Poor
200	175	150	125	100	75

Model 572 Fieldmaster

A .22 caliber slide-action rifle with a 21" barrel having open sights. Blued with a walnut stock. Manufactured from 1955 to 1988.

Exc.	V.G.	Good	Fair	Poor
150	125	100	75	50

Model 572 BDL

As above, but with a more fully figured walnut stock with impressed checkering. Introduced in 1966.

NIB	Exc.	V.G.	Good	Fair	Poor
210	185	165	145	110	85

Model 580

A .22 caliber single shot bolt-action rifle with a 24" barrel having open sights and a Monte Carlo-style stock. Blued. The Model 580BR has a 1" shorter stock and would be worth approximately 10% more than the values listed below. Manufactured from 1968 to 1978.

Exc.	V.G.	Good	Fair	Poor
100	80	60	50	25

Model 581

A .22 caliber bolt-action magazine rifle, blued with a 24" barrel and walnut stock. Manufactured from 1967 to 1983.

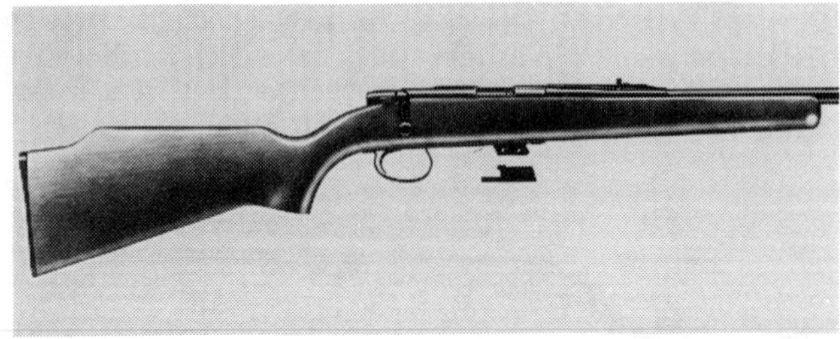

Exc.	V.G.	Good	Fair	Poor
150	125	100	75	50

Model 582

As above, fitted with a tubular magazine in place of the detachable box magazine. Manufactured from 1967 to 1983.

Exc.	V.G.	Good	Fair	Poor
150	125	100	75	50

Model 581-S

As above, fitted with a 5-round detachable magazine. Introduced in 1986.

Exc.	V.G.	Good	Fair	Poor
185	165	145	110	85

Model 591

A 5mm rimfire Magnum bolt-action rifle with a 24" barrel and Monte Carlo-style stock. Approximately 20,000 were made between 1970 and 1973.

Exc.	V.G.	Good	Fair	Poor
175	150	125	100	75

Model 592

As above, with a tubular magazine. Approximately 7,000 were made.

Exc.	V.G.	Good	Fair	Poor
300	250	200	150	100

Model 740

A .308 or .30-06 semi-automatic rifle with a 22" barrel and detachable box magazine. Blued with a plain walnut stock. Also available with an 18.5" barrel which would be worth approximately 10% more than the values listed below. Manufactured from 1955 to 1960.

Exc.	V.G.	Good	Fair	Poor
250	225	200	150	100

Model 740 ADL

As above, with a checkered walnut stock with a pistol grip.

Exc.	V.G.	Good	Fair	Poor
275	250	225	150	100

Model 740 BDL

As above, with a more finely figured walnut stock.

Exc.	V.G.	Good	Fair	Poor
300	275	250	150	100

Model 742

A 6mm Remington, .243, .280, .30-06 or .308 caliber semi-automatic rifle with a 22" barrel and 4-shot magazine. Also available with an 18" barrel in calibers .308 and .30-06 which are worth approximately 10% more than the values listed below. Blued with a checkered walnut stock. Manufactured from 1960 to 1980.

Exc.	V.G.	Good	Fair	Poor
300	275	250	150	100

Model 742 BDL

As above, with a Monte Carlo-style stock having basketweave checkering.

Standard Grade

Exc.	V.G.	Good	Fair	Poor
325	275	225	175	125

Model 742D Peerless—Engraved

Exc.	V.G.	Good	Fair	Poor
2100	1750	1500	1150	800

Model 742F Premier—Gamescene Engraved

Exc.	V.G.	Good	Fair	Poor
4000	3500	2750	1850	1300

Model 742F Premier—Gold Inlaid

Exc.	V.G.	Good	Fair	Poor
6500	5500	4000	3000	2250

Model 742 Bicentennial—Mfg. 1976 Only

Exc.	V.G.	Good	Fair	Poor
340	300	250	175	125

Model 76 Sportsman

A .30-06 slide action rifle with a 22" barrel and 4-shot magazine. Blued with walnut stock. Manufactured from 1985 to 1987.

Exc.	V.G.	Good	Fair	Poor
250	225	175	125	75

Model 7600

A variation of the above, chambered for a variety of cartridges from 6mm Remington to .35 Whelen with a 22" barrel and a detachable magazine. Also available with an 18.5" barrel. Blued with a checkered walnut stock.

Standard Grade

NIB	Exc.	V.G.	Good	Fair	Poor
350	300	250	200	150	100

Model 7600D Peerless—Engraved

NIB	Exc.	V.G.	Good	Fair	Poor
2250	1800	1400	1200	950	750

Model 7600F Premier—Gamescene Engraved

NIB	Exc.	V.G.	Good	Fair	Poor
4750	4000	3500	2750	1850	1250

Model 7600 Premier—Gold Inlaid

NIB	Exc.	V.G.	Good	Fair	Poor
7000	6250	5000	4000	2750	1850

Model 7600 Special Purpose

The same configuration as the standard Model 7600 but equipped with a special finish on both the wood and metal that is non-reflective. First offered in 1993.

NIB	Exc.	V.G.	Good	Fair	Poor
350	300	250	200	150	100

Model Six

A centerfire slide-action rifle with a 22" barrel and a 4-shot detachable magazine. Blued with a walnut stock. Manufactured from 1981 to 1987.

Exc.	V.G.	Good	Fair	Poor
400	350	275	200	125

Model 74 Sportsman

A .30-06 caliber semi-automatic rifle with a 22" barrel and a 4-shot detachable magazine. Blued with a walnut stock. Manufactured from 1985 to 1987.

Exc.	V.G.	Good	Fair	Poor
300	250	175	125	75

Model Four

As above, with a select Monte Carlo-style stock. Manufactured from 1982 to 1987.

Exc.	V.G.	Good	Fair	Poor
450	400	350	275	175

Model 7400

As above, with either an 18.5" or 22" barrel. Blued with a checkered walnut stock. Introduced in 1982.

NIB	Exc.	V.G.	Good	Fair	Poor
400	350	300	250	200	100

Model 7400 Special Purpose

The same configuration as the standard Model 7400 but equipped with a special finish on both the wood and metal that is non-reflective. First offered in 1993.

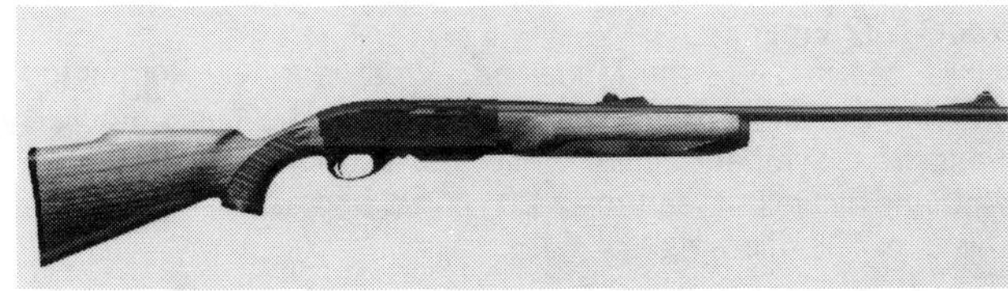

NIB	Exc.	V.G.	Good	Fair	Poor
400	350	300	250	200	100

Model 11

A .22 caliber bolt-action magazine rifle with a 20" barrel. Blued with a nylon stock. Manufactured from 1962 to 1964.

Exc.	V.G.	Good	Fair	Poor
150	125	100	75	50

Model 12

As above, fitted with a tubular magazine. Manufactured from 1962 to 1964.

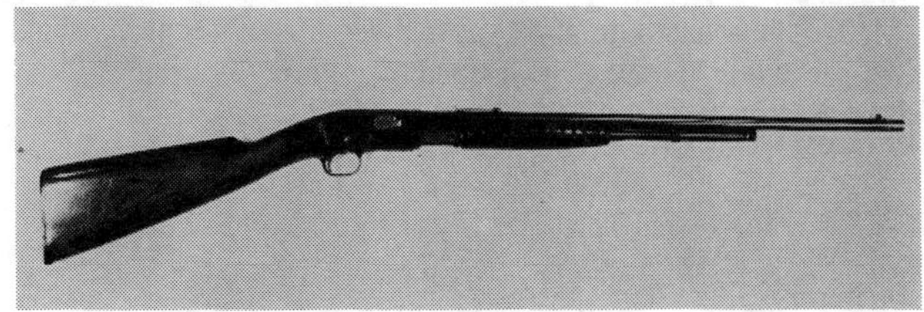

Exc.	V.G.	Good	Fair	Poor
175	150	125	100	75

Model 10

A bolt-action .22 caliber single shot rifle with a nylon stock. Manufactured from 1962 to 1964.

Exc.	V.G.	Good	Fair	Poor
125	100	75	50	25

Model 66

A .22 caliber semi-automatic rifle with a 20" barrel and tubular magazine in the butt. Black or chrome-plated finish with a black, brown or green checkered nylon stock. Manufactured from 1959 to 1988.

Note: Apache Black models are worth 15% more than the values listed below and the Seneca Green model is worth an additional 25%.

Exc.	V.G.	Good	Fair	Poor
150	125	100	75	50

Model 66 Bicentennial Commemorative

As above, but with a 1976 commemorative inscription on the barrel. Manufactured in 1976.

Exc.	V.G.	Good	Fair	Poor
125	100	85	70	55

Model 77

As above, with a 5-round detachable box magazine. Manufactured during 1970 and 1971.

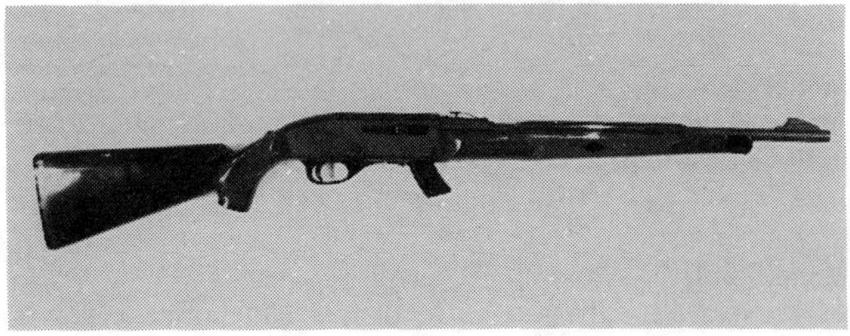

Exc.	V.G.	Good	Fair	Poor
150	125	100	75	50

Model 76

A .22 caliber lever action magazine rifle with a nylon stock. Manufactured from 1962 to 1964.

Exc.	V.G.	Good	Fair	Poor
175	150	125	100	75

Model 522 Viper

Introduced in 1993 the Model 522 Viper is a new Remington .22 rimfire caliber semi-automatic design. The black stock is made from synthetic resin, while the receiver is made from a synthetic as well. It features a 20" barrel and a 10-shot detachable clip. The rifle weighs 4.6 lbs.

NIB	Exc.	V.G.	Good	Fair	Poor
140	120	100	80	60	40

Model 541S Custom

A .22 caliber bolt-action magazine rifle with a 24" barrel. Blued with a scroll engraved receiver, and checkered walnut stock having a rosewood pistol grip cap and forend tip. Manufactured from 1972 to 1984.

Exc.	V.G.	Good	Fair	Poor
400	325	275	200	125

Model 541T

As above, drilled and tapped for telescopic sights. Introduced in 1986.

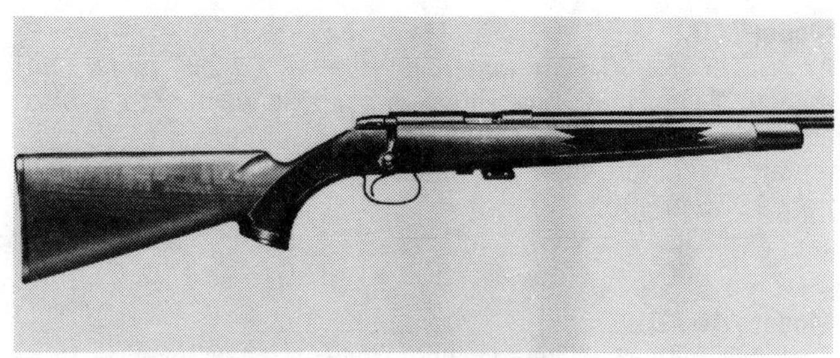

NIB	Exc.	V.G.	Good	Fair	Poor
335	275	200	175	125	75

Model 541T Heavy Barrel

This model is the same as the standard 541-T with the exception of a 24" heavy barrel. First introduced in 1993.

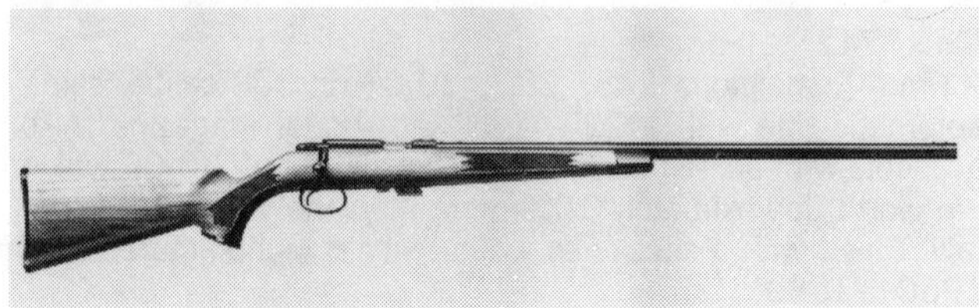

NIB	Exc.	V.G.	Good	Fair	Poor
400	350	300	250	200	125

Model 40X

A .22 caliber single shot bolt-action rifle with a heavy 28" barrel fitted with Redfield Olympic sights or telescopic sight bases. Blued with a walnut target style stock having a hard rubber buttplate. Manufactured from1955 to 1964.

Exc.	V.G.	Good	Fair	Poor
500	400	325	250	150

Model 40X Sporter

As above, with a 24" barrel, 5-shot magazine and a walnut sporting style stock. Less than 700 were made between 1969 and 1980.

Exc.	V.G.	Good	Fair	Poor
1500	1250	950	750	550

Model 40X Centerfire

As above, chambered for .22, .22 Magnum, .308 or .30-06 centerfire cartridges. Manufactured from 1961 to 1964.

Exc.	V.G.	Good	Fair	Poor
550	450	350	300	200

Model 720A

A .257 Roberts, .270 or .30-06 bolt-action sporting rifle with a 22" barrel and a 5-shot integral magazine. Blued with a checkered walnut stock. Approximately 2,500 were manufactured in 1941.

Exc.	V.G.	Good	Fair	Poor
1250	1000	800	600	475

Model 721

A .264 Magnum, .270 or .30-06 bolt-action rifle with a 24" barrel and a 4-shot magazine. Blued with a plain walnut stock. Manufactured from 1948 to 1962.

Standard Version

Exc.	V.G.	Good	Fair	Poor
300	250	200	150	100

Model 721 ADL

Exc.	V.G.	Good	Fair	Poor
350	300	250	200	125

Model 721 BDL—Select Stock

Exc.	V.G.	Good	Fair	Poor
400	350	300	250	150

Model 721A Magnum—.300 H&H

Exc.	V.G.	Good	Fair	Poor
450	400	350	275	150

Model 722

As above, with a shorter action chambered for .257 Roberts, .300 Savage or .308 cartridges. Manufactured from 1948 to 1962.

Exc.	V.G.	Good	Fair	Poor
300	250	200	150	100

Model 725 ADL

A centerfire bolt-action sporting rifle with a 22" barrel, 4-shot magazine and Monte Carlo-style stock. The .222 caliber version was produced in very limited quantities and should be individually appraised. Manufactured from 1958 to 1961.

Exc.	V.G.	Good	Fair	Poor
375	325	275	225	150

Model 725 Kodiak

A .375 Holland & Holland Magnum or .458 Winchester Magnum, bolt-action sporting rifle with a 26" barrel having a muzzle brake and open sights, and 3-shot magazine. Blued with a checkered walnut stock. Manufactured in 1961.

Exc.	V.G.	Good	Fair	Poor
800	700	550	400	300

Model 600

A centerfire bolt-action sporting rifle with an 18.5" ventilated-rib barrel and a checkered walnut stock. Manufactured from 1964 to 1967.

Exc.	V.G.	Good	Fair	Poor
400	325	250	175	125

Model 600 Mohawk

As above, but with a plain barrel and chambered only for the .222 Remington, .243 Winchester or .308 Winchester cartridges. Manufactured from 1971 to 1979.

Exc.	V.G.	Good	Fair	Poor
275	250	200	175	150

Model 660 Magnum

As above, chambered for the 6.5mm Remington Magnum and .350 Remington Magnum cartridges. Stock of laminated walnut and beech wood. Manufactured from 1965 to 1967.

Exc.	V.G.	Good	Fair	Poor
575	500	425	350	275

Model 660 (Improved)

An improved version of the Model 600. Manufactured from 1968 to 1971.

Exc.	V.G.	Good	Fair	Poor
500	425	350	250	200

Model 660 Magnum (Improved)

As above, but chambered for either the 6.5mm Remington Magnum or .350 Remington Magnum cartridges and fitted with a laminated stock.

Exc.	V.G.	Good	Fair	Poor
600	500	450	350	275

Model 78 Sportsman

A centerfire bolt-action sporting rifle with a 22" barrel and 4-shot magazine. Blued with a walnut stock. Introduced in 1985.

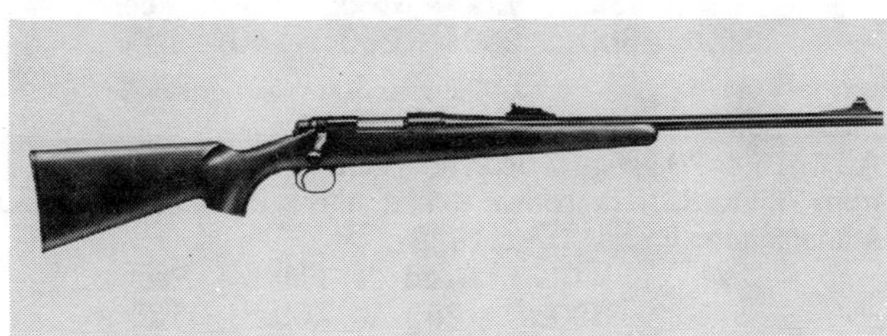

NIB	Exc.	V.G.	Good	Fair	Poor
335	275	225	200	150	100

Model 700 ADL

A centerfire bolt-action sporting rifle with either a 22" or 24" barrel having open sights and a 4-shot magazine. Blued with a checkered Monte Carlo-style walnut stock. Introduced in 1962.

NIB	Exc.	V.G.	Good	Fair	Poor
450	375	300	250	200	125

Model 700 BDL

As above, with a hinged floorplate, hand cut checkering, black forend tip and pistol grip cap.

NIB	Exc.	V.G.	Good	Fair	Poor
465	400	325	275	225	150

Model 700 Mountain Rifle

As above, with a tapered 22" lightweight barrel, blued with checkered walnut stock. Introduced in 1986.

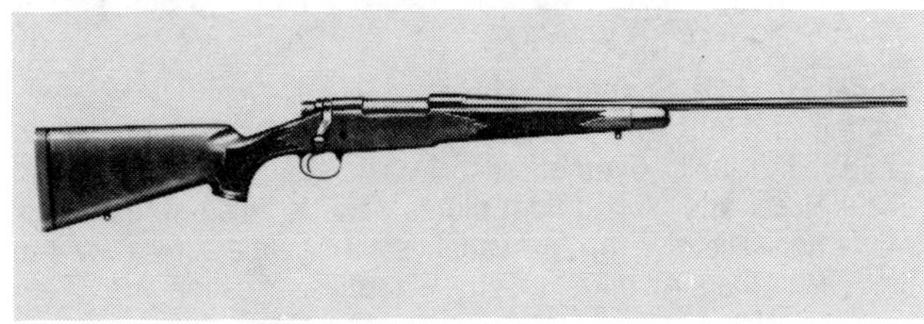

NIB	Exc.	V.G.	Good	Fair	Poor
470	425	350	300	250	175

Model 700KS Mountain Rifle

As above, with a lightweight Kevlar stock. Introduced in 1986.

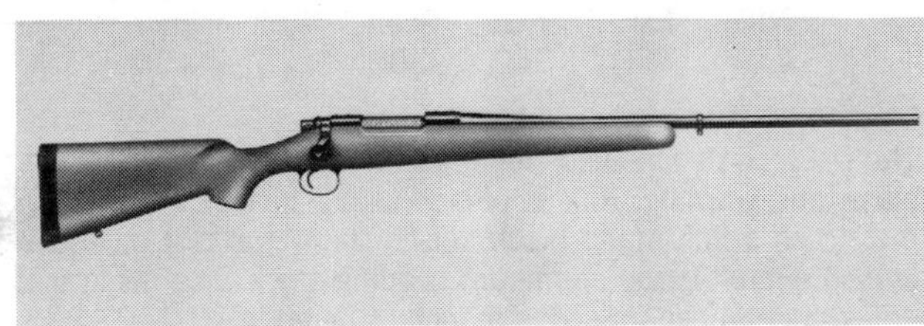

NIB	Exc.	V.G.	Good	Fair	Poor
750	700	600	500	400	300

Model 700 Safari Grade

As the Model 700BDL chambered for 8mm Remington Magnum, .375 Holland & Holland, .416 Remington Magnum or .458 Winchester Magnum cartridges, 24" barrel and 3-shot magazine. Blued with a finely figured walnut checkered stock. The Model KS Safari Grade was fitted with a Kevlar stock and would be worth approximately 20% more than the values listed below. Introduced in 1962.

NIB	Exc.	V.G.	Good	Fair	Poor
875	750	600	500	400	300

Model 700 RS

As above, chambered for the .270 Winchester, .280 Remington, or .30-06 cartridges, 22" barrel and 4-shot magazine.

Blued with a DuPont Rynite stock. Manufactured during 1987 and 1988.

Exc.	V.G.	Good	Fair	Poor
500	425	350	250	150

Model 700 FS

As above, with a Kevlar stock.

Exc.	V.G.	Good	Fair	Poor
550	475	400	300	200

Model 700 BDL European

Available for the first time in 1993, this new model features an oil finish stock with Monte Carlo comb and raised cheekpiece. The checkering is fine line. In addition the rifle is standard with hinged floorplate, sling swivel studs, hooded ramp front sight, and adjustable rear sight. Offered in the following calibers: .243, .207, .280, 7MM-08, 7MM Mag. 30-.06, and .308.

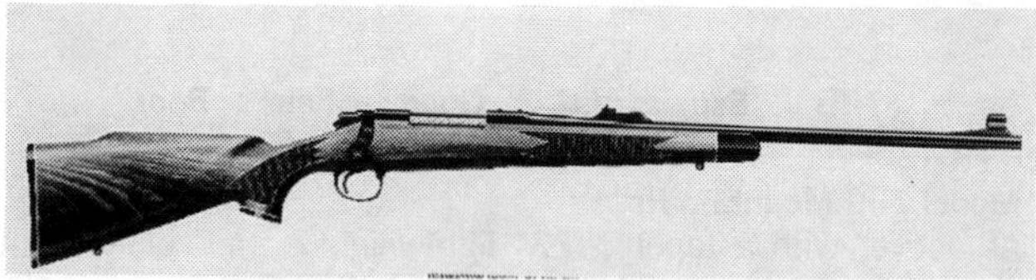

NIB	Exc.	V.G.	Good	Fair	Poor
400	350	300	250	200	125

Model 700 BDL Stainless Synthetic

Offered in 1993 this model features a stainless steel receiver, barrel, and bolt. Synthetic stock has straight comb, raised cheekpiece, and hinged floor plate. Metal is finished in a black matte non reflective finish. Available in 14 calibers from .223 to .338 Win. Mag. All barrel lengths regardless of caliber are 24".

NIB	Exc.	V.G.	Good	Fair	Poor
450	400	350	300	225	150

Model 700 Mountain Rifle Stainless Synthetic

This model is the same as the Mountain rifle but with stainless steel receiver, bolt, and barrel. Offered in 25-.06 Rem., .270, .280, and 30-06. All calibers are supplied with a 22" barrel.

NIB	Exc.	V.G.	Good	Fair	Poor
450	400	350	300	225	150

Model 700 Varmint Special Synthetic

The stock on this model is reinforced with DuPont Kevlar, fiberglass, and graphite. Rifle is offered with a heavy barrel and all metal has a fine matte black finish. The barrel rest on a machined aircraft-grade aluminum bedding stock. The receiver is drilled and tapped for scope mounts. Offered in 22-250, .223, and .308 calibers. In 1993 the .220 Swift was added to the line.

NIB	Exc.	V.G.	Good	Fair	Poor
500	450	400	350	300	200

Model 700 Varmint Special Wood

Same as above but furnished with walnut stock and offered in the following calibers: .222, .22-250, .223, 6MM, .243, 7MM-08, and .308.

NIB	Exc.	V.G.	Good	Fair	Poor
450	400	350	300	250	150

Model 700 Classic

This model is furnished with a straight comb, satin finished walnut stock, sling swivel studs, and hinged magazine floor plate.

NIB	Exc.	V.G.	Good	Fair	Poor
450	400	350	300	250	150

Model 700 Custom

A special order rifle available in either American, English, or California walnut. Stock can be fitted to customer's own dimensions. Engraving is available as is a large selection of calibers. Model 700 Custom rifles should be priced individually and an appraisal should be obtained.

Model 700 Safari KS Stainless

A new addition to the Remington line in 1993, the Safari KS Stainless has a special reinforced Kevlar stock in a non-reflective gray finish. Checkering is 18 lines to the inch. Offered in the following calibers: .375 H&H Mag., .416 Rem. Mag., and the .458 Win. Mag.

NIB	Exc.	V.G.	Good	Fair	Poor
500	450	400	350	300	150

Model 788

A centerfire bolt-action sporting rifle with either a 22" or 24" barrel and a plain walnut stock. An 18" barrel carbine was also manufactured and is worth approximately 10% more than the values listed below. Manufactured from 1967 to 1984.

Exc.	V.G.	Good	Fair	Poor
325	275	225	150	100

Model Seven

A centerfire bolt-action sporting rifle with an 18.5" barrel and 4- or 5-shot magazine. Blued with a checkered walnut stock. Introduced in 1982.

NIB	Exc.	V.G.	Good	Fair	Poor
450	400	325	275	200	100

Model Seven FS

As above with a Kevlar stock. Introduced in 1987.

NIB	Exc.	V.G.	Good	Fair	Poor
600	525	450	375	275	150

Model Seven MS

First introduced in 1993 and available through the Remington Custom Shop. This rifle features a 20" barrel with Mannlicher stock made from select grain wood and laminated for strength. Available in calibers for .270 Rem. to .308.

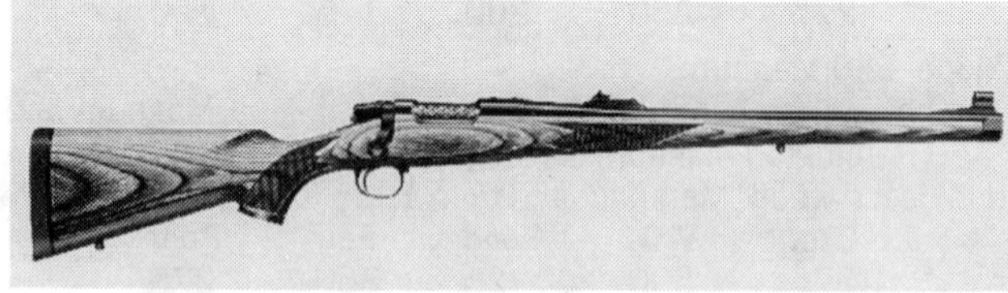

NIB	Exc.	V.G.	Good	Fair	Poor
800	700	550	350	250	150

Model Seven Youth

First offered in 1993 this variation is a youth version of the standard Model Seven. The butt stock is 1" shorter than standard. Available in 6MM, .243, and 7MM-08.

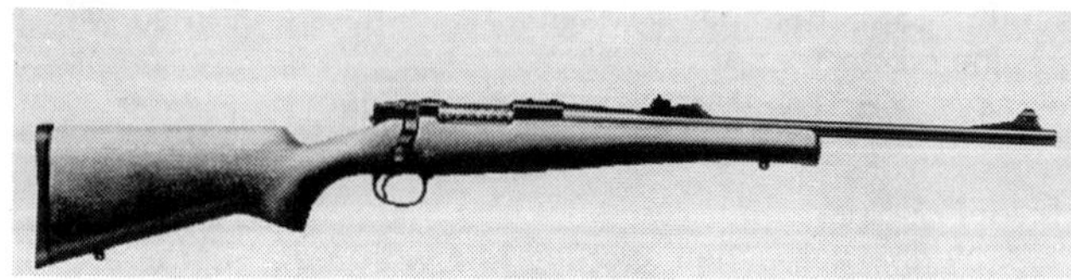

NIB	Exc.	V.G.	Good	Fair	Poor
350	300	250	200	150	100

Model 10A

A 12, 16 or 20 gauge slide action shotgun with barrels ranging from 26" to 32". Takedown, blued with a plain walnut stock. Manufactured from 1907 to 1929.

Exc.	V.G.	Good	Fair	Poor
375	300	250	200	125

Model 11

A 12, 16, or 20 gauge semi-automatic shotgun with barrels ranging in length from 26" to 32". Designed by John M. Browning and produced under license from Fabrique Nationale. Blued with a checkered walnut stock. Approximately 300,000 were made from 1911 to 1948.

Solid Rib or Vent-Rib—Add 30%.

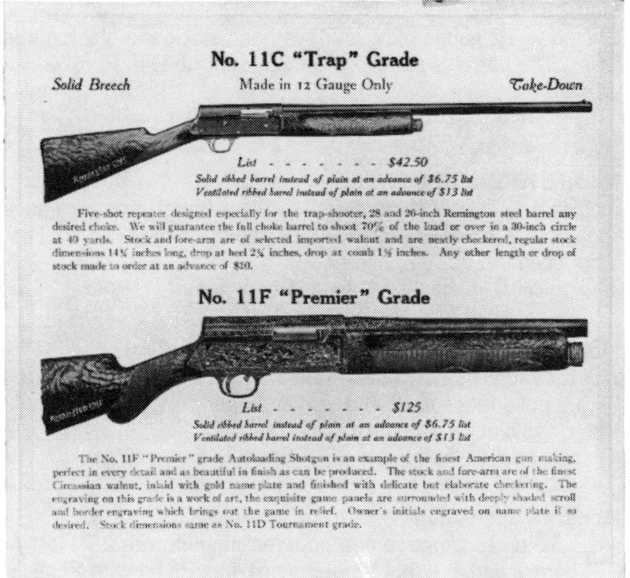

No. 11C "Trap" Grade

Solid Breech Made in 12 Gauge Only *Take-Down*

List - - - - - - - - $42.50

Solid ribbed barrel instead of plain at an advance of $6.75 list

Ventilated ribbed barrel instead of plain at an advance of $13 list

Five-shot repeater designed especially for the trap-shooter, 28 and 26-inch Remington steel barrel any desired choke. We will guarantee the full choke barrel to shoot 70% of the load or over in a 30-inch circle at 40 yards. Stock and fore-arm are of selected imported walnut and are neatly checkered, regular stock dimensions 14¼ inches long, drop at heel 2¾ inches, drop at comb 1⅜ inches. Any other length or drop of stock made to order at an advance of $10.

No. 11F "Premier" Grade

List - - - - - - - - $125

Solid ribbed barrel instead of plain at an advance of $6.75 list

Ventilated ribbed barrel instead of plain at an advance of $13 list

The No. 11F "Premier" grade Autoloading Shotgun is an example of the finest American gun making, perfect in every detail and as beautiful in finish as can be produced. The stock and fore-arm are of the finest Circassian walnut, inlaid with gold name plate and finished with delicate but elaborate checkering. The engraving on this grade is a work of art, the exquisite game panels are surrounded with deeply shaded scroll and border engraving which brings out the game in relief. Owner's initials engraved on name plate if so desired. Stock dimensions same as No. 11D Tournament grade.

Exc.	V.G.	Good	Fair	Poor
300	250	200	150	100

Model 11B Special—Engraved

Exc.	V.G.	Good	Fair	Poor
550	475	375	275	175

Model 11D Tournament

Exc.	V.G.	Good	Fair	Poor
1000	800	650	450	300

Model 11E Expert—Engraved

Exc.	V.G.	Good	Fair	Poor
1500	1250	1000	650	450

Model 11F Premier—Heavily Engraved

Exc.	V.G.	Good	Fair	Poor
2750	2250	1850	1250	850

Model 11R—20" Barrel Riot Gun

Exc.	V.G.	Good	Fair	Poor
350	300	250	175	100

Model 17

A 20 gauge slide-action shotgun with barrels ranging in length from 26" to 32". Takedown, blued with a plain walnut stock. Approximately 48,000 were made from 1917 to 1933.

Vent-Rib—Add 25%.

Exc.	V.G.	Good	Fair	Poor
350	300	250	175	100

Model 29

As above, chambered for 12 gauge cartridges. Approximately 24,000 manufactured from 1929 to 1933.

Ventilated-Rib—Add 25%.

Exc.	V.G.	Good	Fair	Poor
300	250	200	125	75

Model 31

A 12, 16 or 20 gauge slide-action shotgun with barrels ranging in length from 26" to 32" and a magazine capacity of either 2 or 4 rounds. Takedown, blued with a walnut stock. Approximately 160,000 were made from 1931 to 1949.

Solid Rib or Vent-Rib—Add 25%.

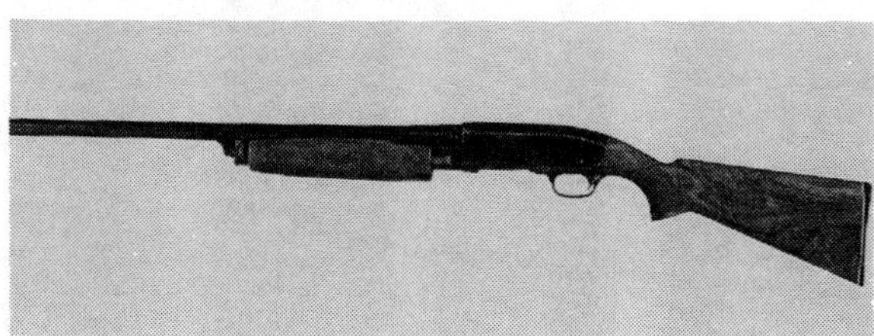

Exc.	V.G.	Good	Fair	Poor
400	325	275	200	125

Model 870 Wingmaster

A 12, 16 or 20 gauge slide action shotgun with 26", 28" or 30" barrels and a 5-shot tubular magazine. Blued with a plain walnut stock. Manufactured from 1950 to 1963.

Vent-Rib—Add 10%.

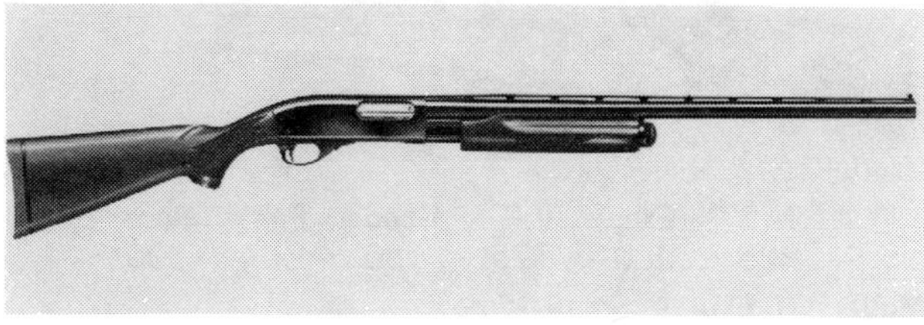

Exc.	V.G.	Good	Fair	Poor
250	225	200	150	100

Model 870 Field Wingmaster

As above, with a checkered walnut stock and screw-in choke tubes. Introduced in 1964.

NIB	Exc.	V.G.	Good	Fair	Poor
440	325	275	225	150	100

Model 870 Magnum

As above, chambered for 12 or 20 gauge 3" Magnum cartridges. Introduced in 1964. Choke tubes introduced in 1987.

NIB	Exc.	V.G.	Good	Fair	Poor
440	325	275	225	150	100

Model 870 Express

As above, for 3", 12 gauge cartridges with a 28" ventilated-rib and one choke tube. Parkerized with a matte finished stock. Introduced in 1987.

NIB	Exc.	V.G.	Good	Fair	Poor
235	200	175	150	100	75

Model 870TA Trap

As above, with a competition ventilated-rib and checkered stock. Produced in 12 gauge only. Discontinued in 1986.

Exc.	V.G.	Good	Fair	Poor
375	300	250	175	125

Model 870TB Trap

As above, with a 28" or 30" full choke, ventilated-rib barrel and a trap style walnut stock. Manufactured from 1950 to 1981.

Exc.	V.G.	Good	Fair	Poor
400	325	275	200	125

Model 870TC Trap

As above, with a finely figured walnut stock and screw-in choke tubes.

NIB	Exc.	V.G.	Good	Fair	Poor
575	475	400	350	250	150

Model 870 Special Field

This Remington pump action shotgun is available in either 12 or 20 gauge and features an English style straight grip stock, 21" vent rib barrel and slim shortened slide handle. In 12 gauge the gun weighs 7 lbs. and in 20 gauge it weighs 6.25 lbs. Comes with a set of Rem. choke tubes.

NIB	Exc.	V.G.	Good	Fair	Poor
350	300	250	200	150	100

Model 870 Brushmaster Deer Gun

This 12 gauge slide action shotgun is fitted with a 20" Rem. choke plain barrel and Monte Carlo stock. Available for either left hand or right hand shooters.

NIB	Exc.	V.G.	Good	Fair	Poor
350	300	250	200	150	100

Model 870 Express Turkey

Furnished in 12 gauge with 21" vent rib barrel with Extra-full Rem. choke Turkey tube.

NIB	Exc.	V.G.	Good	Fair	Poor
225	200	175	150	125	100

Model 870 Express Deer Gun

This model is fitted with a 20" fully rifled barrel, iron sights, and

Monte Carlo stock. Also offered with a 20" IC rifle sighted barrel. Available in 12 gauge only.

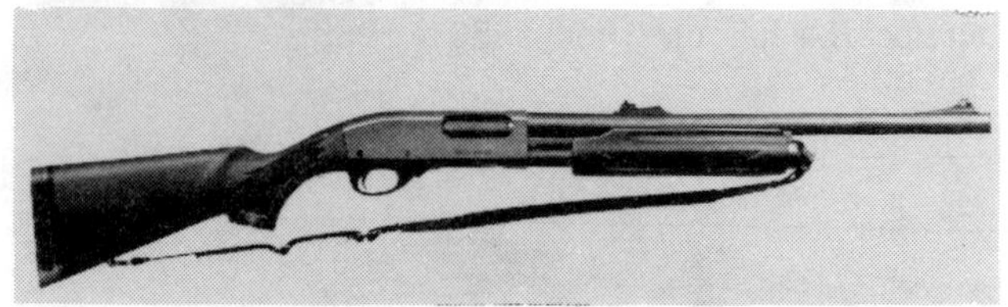

NIB	Exc.	V.G.	Good	Fair	Poor
225	200	175	150	125	100

Model 870 Express Small Game

Offered in 20 gauge or .410, this model has a non-reflective metal and wood finish. The .410 bore is furnished with a 25" vent rib full choke barrel, while the 20 gauge is available with a 26" or 28" vent rib barrel with Mod. Rem. tube choke.

NIB	Exc.	V.G.	Good	Fair	Poor
225	200	175	150	125	100

Model 870 Youth Gun

Available in 20 gauge only this shotgun is built for children. It has a 13" length of pull, a 21" vent rib barrel, and is sold with a Modified Rem. choke tube.

NIB	Exc.	V.G.	Good	Fair	Poor
225	200	175	150	125	100

Model 870 Security

Offered in 12 gauge only this personal protection shotgun has a 18.5 cylinder choked plain barrel with front bead sight.

NIB	Exc.	V.G.	Good	Fair	Poor
225	200	175	150	125	100

Model 870 SPS-Camo

Offered in 12 gauge only and a choice of 26" or 28" vent rib barrel with Rem. choke tubes. The wood and metal are finished in a brown camo color.

NIB	Exc.	V.G.	Good	Fair	Poor
325	275	225	175	125	100

Model 870 SPS-BG Camo

Available for the first time in 1993 this model features a 12 gauge 20" plain barrel with IC and Turkey Super Full Rem. choke tubes. The wood and metal are finished in a brown camo color.

NIB	Exc.	V.G.	Good	Fair	Poor
325	275	225	175	125	100

Model 870 SPS-T Camo

Same as above with the exception of a 21" vent rib barrel with IC and Turkey Super Full Rem. choke tubes. Both wood and metal are finished in a green camo color.

NIB	Exc.	V.G.	Good	Fair	Poor
325	275	225	175	125	100

Model 870 Marine Magnum

This 12 gauge shotgun has a nickel finish now the receiver and barrel both inside and outside. Synthetic stock is checkered. The 18" barrel is bored cylinder and is fitted with a 7-round magazine. Sling swivel studs are standard.

NIB	Exc.	V.G.	Good	Fair	Poor
325	275	225	175	125	100

Model 870 SPS

Offered in 12 gauge only with synthetic stock and black matte finish. The barrel is either 26" or 28" vent rib with Rem. choke tubes.

NIB	Exc.	V.G.	Good	Fair	Poor
325	275	225	175	125	100

Model 870 SPS-Deer

Available with a 20" rifle wighted plain barrel, this 12 gauge shotgun has a black synthetic stock and black matte finish. First introduced in 1993.

NIB	Exc.	V.G.	Good	Fair	Poor
300	250	225	175	125	100

Model 870 SPS-T

This 12 gauge model comes standard with a 21" vent rib barrel, Rem. choke tubes in IC and Turkey Super Full, black synthetic stock, and black matte finish.

NIB	Exc.	V.G.	Good	Fair	Poor
300	250	225	175	125	100

Model 48 Sportsman

A 12, 16 or 20 gauge semi-automatic shotgun with 26", 28" or 32" barrels and a 3-shot tubular magazine. Blued with a checkered walnut stock. Approximately 275,000 were made from 1949 to 1959.

Vent-Rib—Add 20%.

Exc.	V.G.	Good	Fair	Poor
325	300	250	175	100

Model 11-48

As above, with the addition of 28 gauge and .410 bore. Approximately 425,000 were made from 1949 to 1968.

Exc.	V.G.	Good	Fair	Poor
300	250	200	150	75

Model 58 Sportsman

A 12, 16, or 20 gauge semi-automatic shotgun with 26", 28" or 30" barrels and a 3-shot tubular magazine. The receiver scroll engraved and blued, checkered walnut stock. Approximately 270,000 were made from 1956 to 1963.

Exc.	V.G.	Good	Fair	Poor
300	250	200	150	75

Model 878 Automaster

As above, in 12 gauge only. Approximately 60,000 were made from 1959 to 1962.

Exc.	V.G.	Good	Fair	Poor
275	225	175	125	75

Model 1100

A 12, 16, 20 or 28 gauge or .410 bore semi-automatic shotgun with barrels ranging in length from 26" to 30" fitted with choke tubes after 1987. The smaller bore versions are worth approximately 20% more than the values listed below. Blued with a checkered walnut stock. Manufactured from 1963 to 1988.

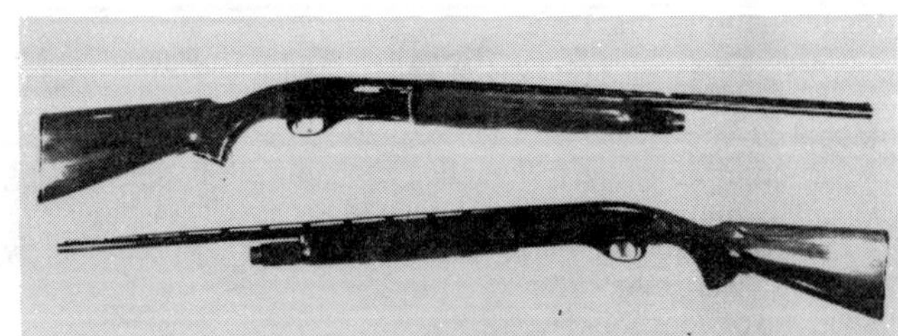

Exc.	V.G.	Good	Fair	Poor
375	300	250	200	100

Model 1100 Youth Gun

Offered in 20 gauge only with a 21" vent rib 2 3/4" barrel. The stock has a special 13" length of pull. Gun is supplied with a set of Rem. choke tubes.

NIB	Exc.	V.G.	Good	Fair	Poor
425	400	350	300	200	150

Model 1100 Small Game

Available in 20, 28 gauge or .410 bore fitted with 25" vent rib barrels. The 28 gauge and .410 have fixed chokes while the 20 gauge has Rem. choke tubes.

NIB	Exc.	V.G.	Good	Fair	Poor
500	450	400	350	250	150

Model 1100 Tournament Skeet

Offered in 20, 28 guage, and .410 bore. The 28 gauge and .410 come with 25" Skeet choked vent rib barrels while the 20 gauge is supplied with a 26" Skeet choked vent rib barrel.

NIB	Exc.	V.G.	Good	Fair	Poor
550	490	425	350	250	150

Model 11-87 Premier

A 3", 12 gauge semi-automatic shotgun with 26" to 32" ventilated-rib barrels having screw-in choke tubes. Blued with a checkered walnut stock. Introduced in 1987.

NIB	Exc.	V.G.	Good	Fair	Poor
560	475	425	350	275	175

Model 11-87 Premier Cantilever Scope Mount Deer Gun

This semi-automatic model has a Monte Carlo stock and the option of a barrel mounted scope (not included). Optional with a fully rifled barrel 21" long with a 1 in 35" twist. Also available in a 21" non-rifled barrel with Rifled and IC Rem. choke tubes. Available in 12 gauge only. Sling swivel studs and camo are standard.

NIB	Exc.	V.G.	Good	Fair	Poor
500	450	400	300	200	150

Model 11-87 Premier Trap

Available in either right or left hand models. Is available with either a straight or Monte Carlo comb, 2.75" chamber, 30" vent rib overbored barrel and special Rem. Trap choke tubes. This model is set up to handle 12 gauge target loads only.

NIB	Exc.	V.G.	Good	Fair	Poor
525	475	425	300	200	150

Model 11-87 Premier Sporting Clays

This model features a special target stock with a 3.16" length of pull longer than standard and 1/4" higher at the heel. The butt pad is radiused at the heel and rounded at the toe. The receiver top, barrel, and rib have a fine matte finish on the bluing. The vent rib is a medium wide 8MM with stainless steel mid bead and a Bradely style front bead sight. Gun is supplied new with the following Rem. choke tubes: Skeet, Improved Skeet, Imp. Cyl., Modl., and Full. Supplied from the factory with a two-barrel custom fitted hard case.

NIB	Exc.	V.G.	Good	Fair	Poor
575	525	450	300	200	150

Model 11-87 SPS-BG Camo

This 12 gauge model is fitted with a rifle sighted 21" barrel with a brown camo finish on the stock and metal parts. Introduced in 1993.

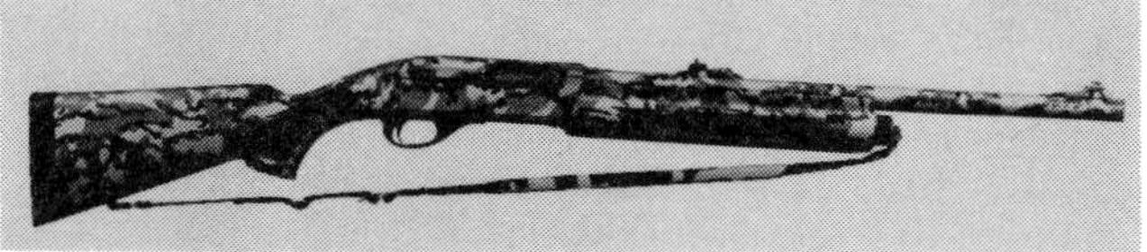

NIB	Exc.	V.G.	Good	Fair	Poor
525	475	425	300	200	150

Model 11-87 SPS-T Camo

Same as above but supplied with a 21" vent rib barrel with IC and Turket Super full Rem. choke tubes. Camo finish is green. Introduced in 1993.

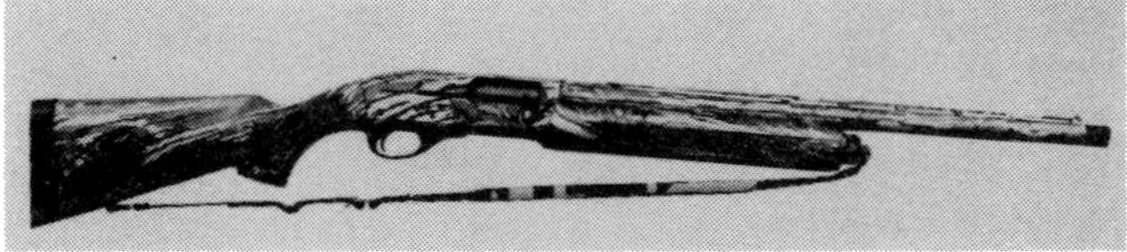

NIB	Exc.	V.G.	Good	Fair	Poor
525	475	425	300	200	150

Model 11-87 SPS

This 12 gauge model is furnished with a 26" or 28" vent rib barrel with IC, Mod., and Full Rem. choke tubes. The stock is a black synthetic material and the metal is finished in a black matte.

NIB	Exc.	V.G.	Good	Fair	Poor
450	400	300	250	200	150

Model 11-87 SPS-Deer

The same as above but fitted with a 21" rifle sighted barrel. First introduced in 1993.

NIB	Exc.	V.G.	Good	Fair	Poor
525	475	425	300	200	150

Model 11-87 SPS-T

Same as above but fitted with a 21" vent rib barrel with IC and Turkey Super Full Rem. choke tubes.

NIB	Exc.	V.G.	Good	Fair	Poor
525	475	425	300	200	150

Model SP-10

A 3.5", 10 gauge semi-automatic shotgun with 26" or 30" ventilated-rib barrels having screw-in choke tubes. Matte blued with a checkered walnut stock.

NIB	Exc.	V.G.	Good	Fair	Poor
1275	1000	800	650	550	400

Model SP-10 Magnum Camo

A new model introduced in 1993, this 10 gauge semi-automatic is designed for the Turkey or deer hunter. Available with either 26" or 30" vent rib barrel or a 26" vent rib barrel with a 22" deer barrel. An additional barrel option is a 23" vent rib barrel with a camo finish. All barrels are fitted with Remington choke tubes.

NIB	Exc.	V.G.	Good	Fair	Poor
875	800	700	500	350	200

Model 32
A 12 gauge Over/Under shotgun with 26", 28" or 30" separated barrels and a single selective trigger. Approximately 15,000 were made from 1932 to 1942.

Standard Grade
Solid or Vent-Rib—Add 10%.

Exc.	V.G.	Good	Fair	Poor
2400	1900	1600	1250	1000

Model 32 Skeet

Exc.	V.G.	Good	Fair	Poor
2750	2250	1950	1500	1250

Model 32 TC

Exc.	V.G.	Good	Fair	Poor
3000	2500	2250	1750	1450

Model 32D

Exc.	V.G.	Good	Fair	Poor
3500	3000	2500	2000	1650

Model 32E Expert

Exc.	V.G.	Good	Fair	Poor
4500	3500	3000	2500	2000

Model 32F Premier

Exc.	V.G.	Good	Fair	Poor
7000	5500	4000	3250	2500

Model 3200
A 12 gauge Over/Under shotgun with 26", 28" or 30" separated ventilated-rib barrels, single selective trigger and automatic ejector. Blued with a checkered walnut stock. Manufactured from 1972 to 1984.

Field Grade

Exc.	V.G.	Good	Fair	Poor
800	725	600	450	300

Model 3200 Magnum—3" Chambers

Exc.	V.G.	Good	Fair	Poor
1000	850	750	550	450

Model 3200 Skeet

Exc.	V.G.	Good	Fair	Poor
800	725	600	450	300

Model 3200 4-Gauge Set

Exc.	V.G.	Good	Fair	Poor
4500	3750	3000	2250	1500

Model 3200 Trap

Exc.	V.G.	Good	Fair	Poor
850	775	650	500	350

Model 3200 Special Trap—Deluxe Wood

Exc.	V.G.	Good	Fair	Poor
1000	850	750	550	450

Model 3200 Competition Trap—Engraved

Exc.	V.G.	Good	Fair	Poor
1250	1000	850	650	550

Model 3200 Premier—Heavily Engraved

Exc.	V.G.	Good	Fair	Poor
2250	2000	1750	1500	1000

Model 3200 "One of One Thousand"—1,000 Produced

Exc.	V.G.	Good	Fair	Poor
2500	2000	1500	1100	500

Remington Peerless
Introduced in 1993 this new Remington Over/Under shotgun is offered in 12 gauge only. Available in 26", 28", and 30" vent rib barrel lengths and fitted with Remington choke tubes (IC, M, F). The side plates are removable and the stock is American walnut.

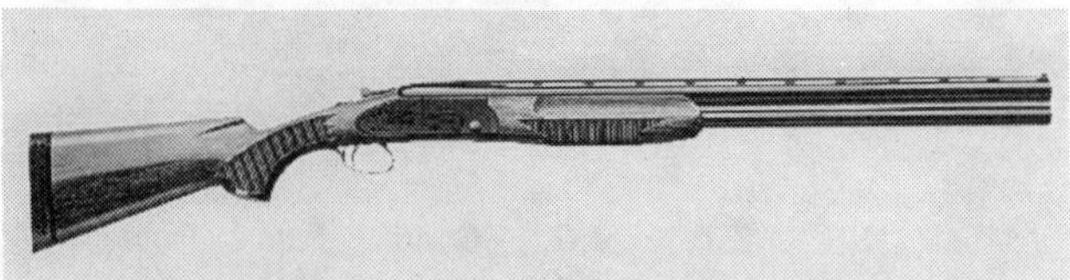

NIB	Exc.	V.G.	Good	Fair	Poor
1000	900	750	600	400	300

Model 90-T Single Barrel Trap
Offered in 12 gauge only, this single barrel Trap shotgun is fitted with either a 32" or 34" overbored full choke barrel.

NIB	Exc.	V.G.	Good	Fair	Poor
2500	1800	1300	900	600	300

Model 90-T Single Barrel Trap (High Rib)
The same shotgun as described above with the exception of an adjustable high rib for shooters who prefer a more open target picture and higher head position.

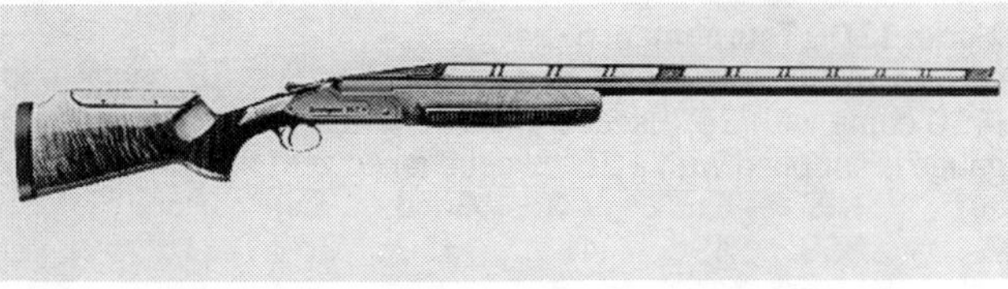

NIB	Exc.	V.G.	Good	Fair	Poor
2500	2200	1650	1200	750	400

Model XP-100
A .221 Remington Fireball or .223 Remington caliber bolt-action single shot pistol with a 14.5" ventilated-rib barrel and adjustable sights. Blued with a nylon stock. Introduced in 1963.

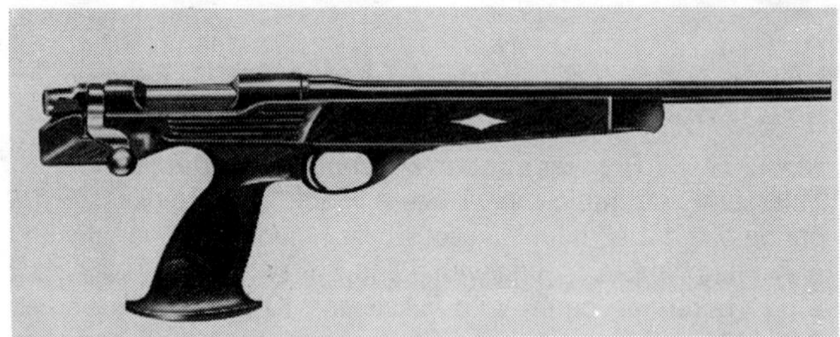

NIB	Exc.	V.G.	Good	Fair	Poor
375	325	275	225	175	100

Model XP-Silhouette
As above, chambered for either the 7mm Remington or .35 Remington cartridges and fitted with a 15" barrel drilled and tapped for a telescope.

NIB	Exc.	V.G.	Good	Fair	Poor
500	400	300	225	175	100

Model XP-100 Custom
A custom made version of the above with a 15" barrel and either a nylon or walnut stock. Available in .223 Remington, .250 Savage, 6mm Benchrest, 7mm Benchrest, 7mm-08 or .35 Remington calibers. Introduced in 1986.

NIB	Exc.	V.G.	Good	Fair	Poor
900	800	650	550	425	300

Model XP-100 Hunter

This model features a laminated wood stock, 14.5 drilled and tapped barrel, and no sights. It is offered in the following calibers: .223 Rem., 7MM BR Rem., 7MM-08 Rem., and .35 Rem.

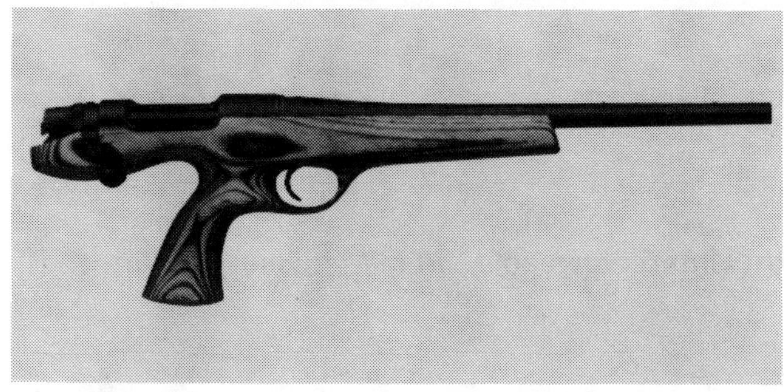

NIB	Exc.	V.G.	Good	Fair	Poor
500	400	300	225	175	100

Remington Model 11-87 SP deer gun autoloading action with 3'' chamber (21'' barrel with rifle sights).

Remington Model 11-87 Police 12-gauge autoloading shotgun (21'' barrel with 3'' chamber & rifle sights).

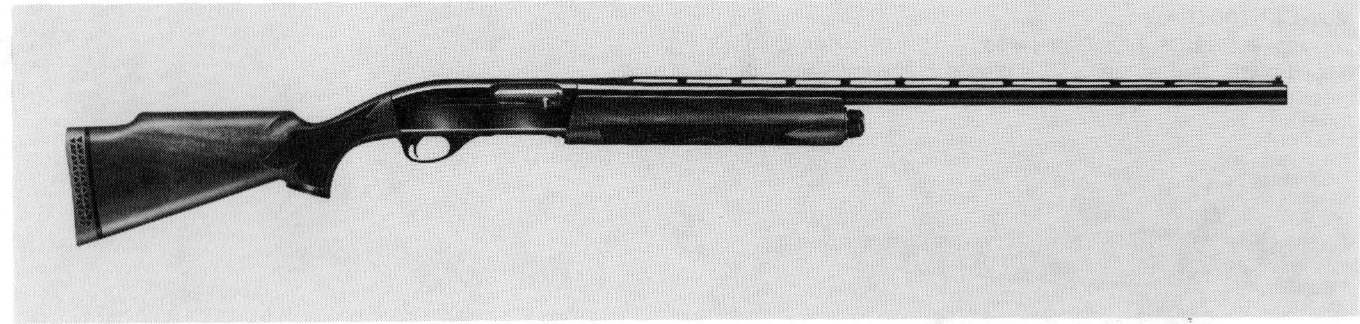

Remington Model 11-87 "Premier" autoloading trap gun with 3 interchangeable "REM" chokes (shown with Monte Carlo stock).

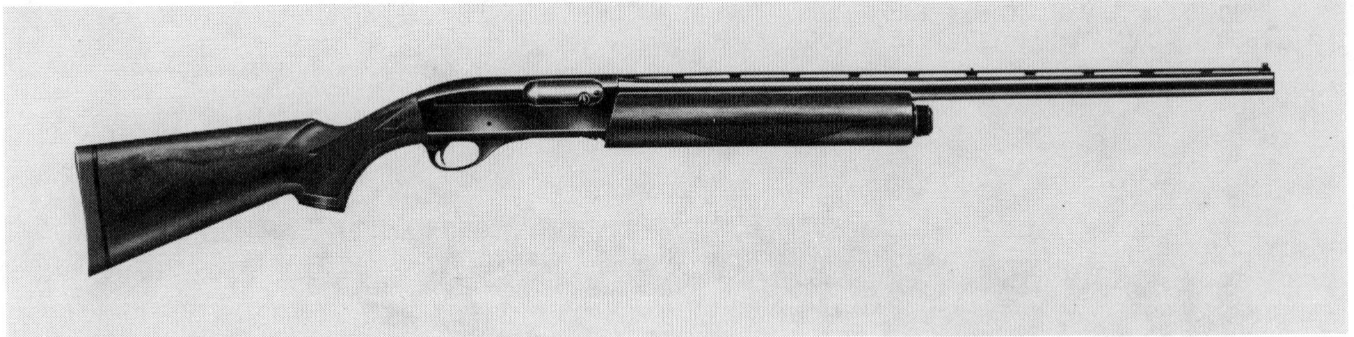

Remington Model 11-87 "Premier" 12-gauge autoloading shotgun with interchangeable "REM" chokes (handles all 2¾" & 3" magnum shells).

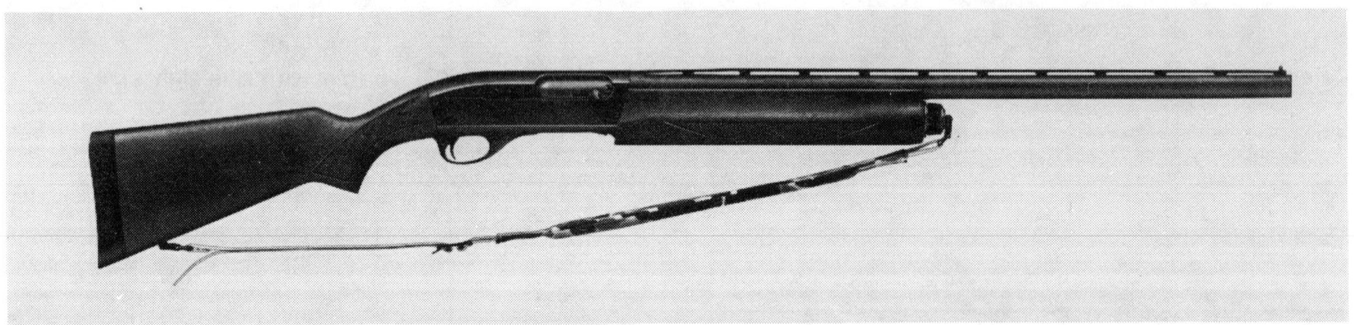

Remington Model 11-87 SP Magnum autoloading shotgun with interchangeable "REM" chokes (handles all 2¾" & 3" magnum shells).

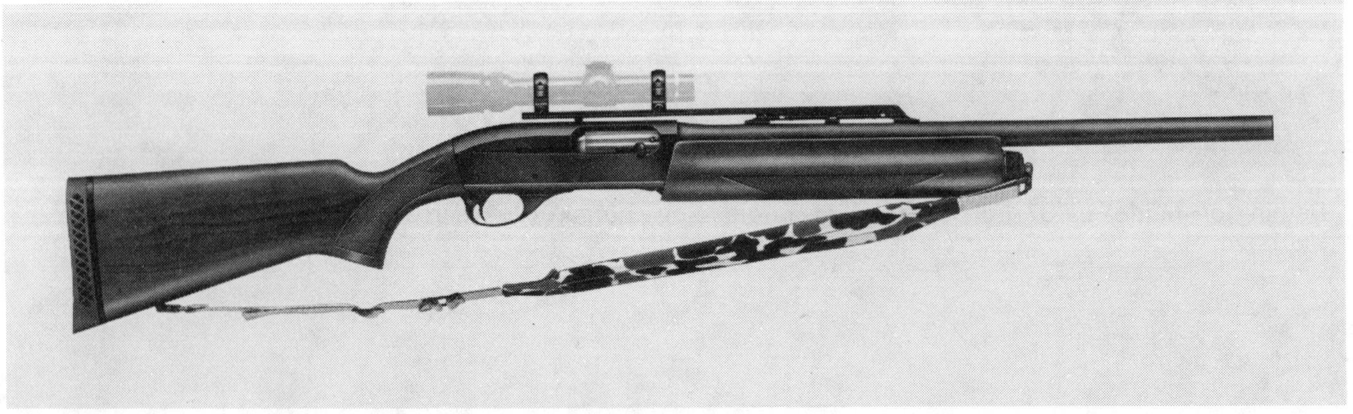

Remington Model 11-87 SP deer gun autoloading shotgun with 3" chamber, cantilever scope mount and interchangeable rifled and improved cylinder "REM" chokes.

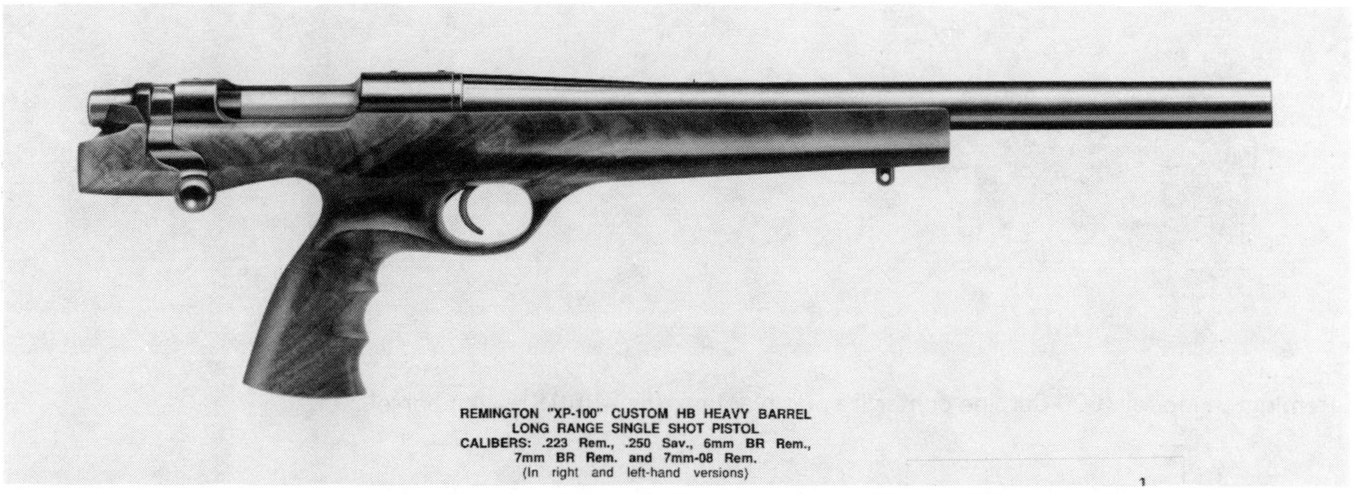

Remington "XP-100" Custom HB heavy barrel long range single shot pistol; Calibers: .223 Rem., .250 Sav., 6mm BR Rem., 7mm Br Rem. and 7mm-08 Rem. (In right and left-hand versions)

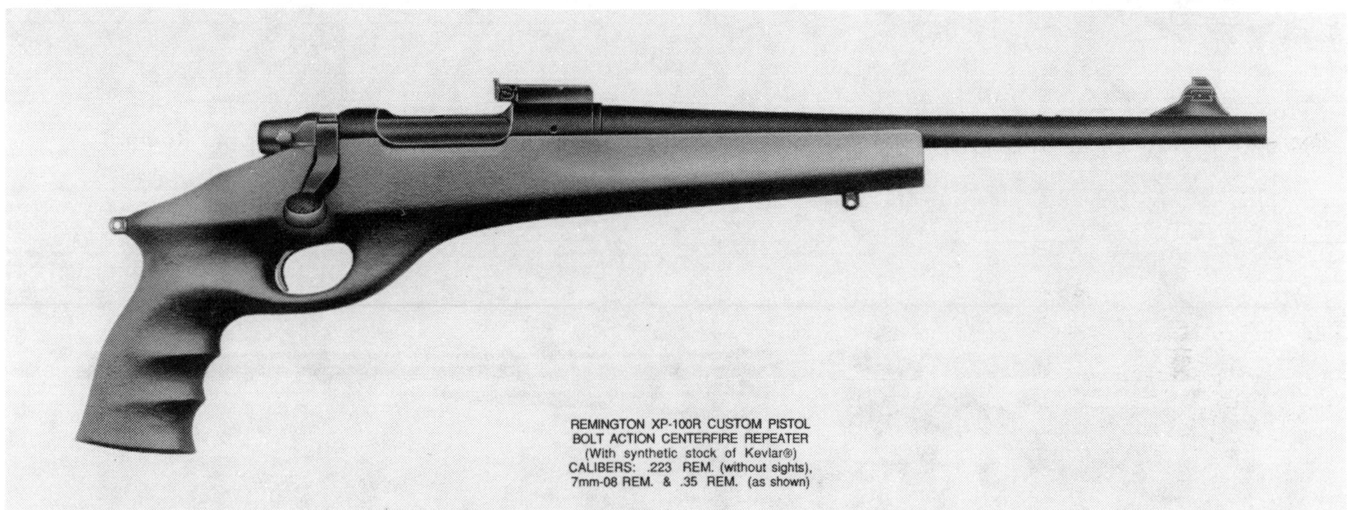

Remington XP-100R custom pistol bolt action centerfire repeater (with synthetic stock of "Kevlar" ®); Calibers: .223 Rem. (without sights), 7mm-08 Rem. & .35 Rem. (as shown).

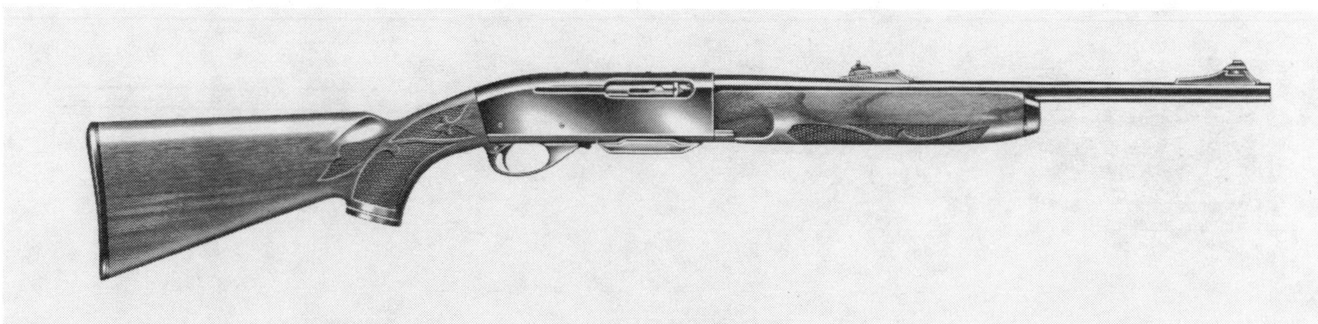

Remington Model 7400 Carbine autoloading centerfire rifle with 18½-inch barrel.

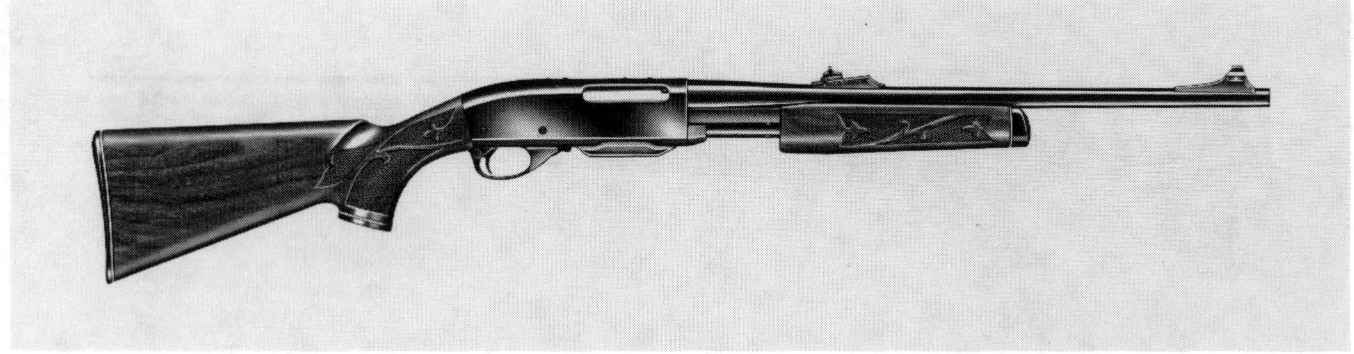

Remington Model 7600 Carbine centerfire pump action rifle with 18½-inch barrel.

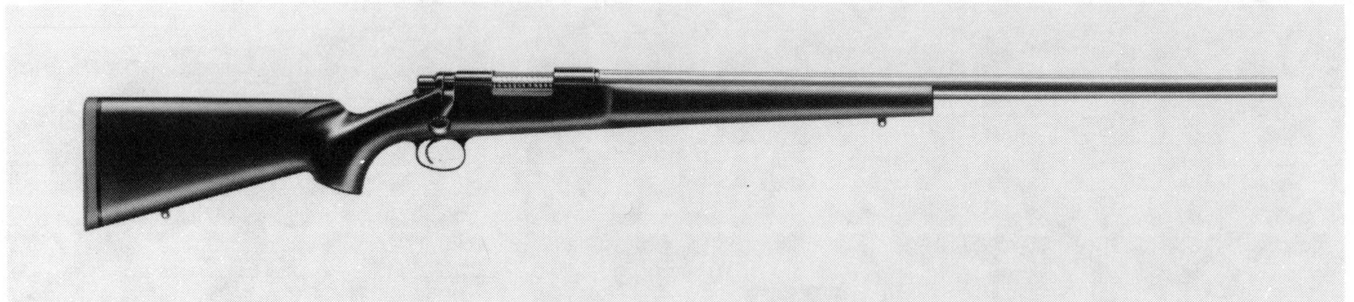

Remington Model 40-XB "Varmint Special" bolt action centerfire rifle with synthetic stock of "Kevlar." ®

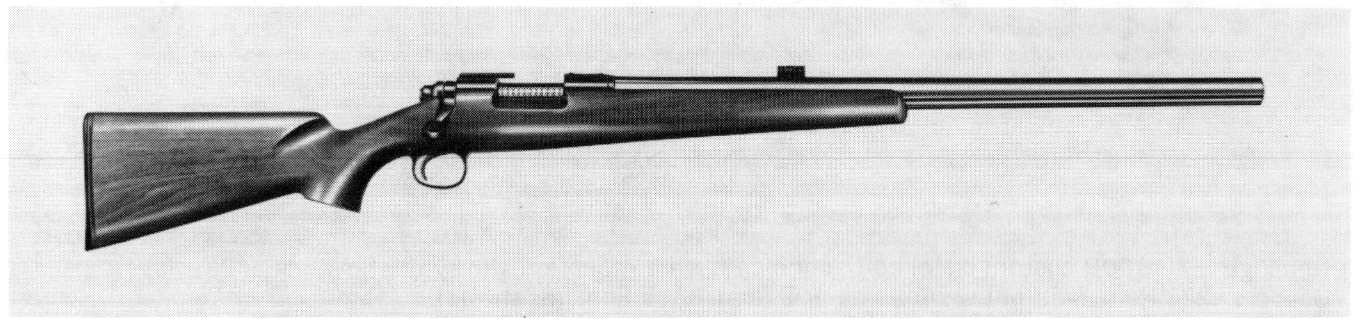

Remington Model 40-XBBR bench rest bolt action center fire rifle.

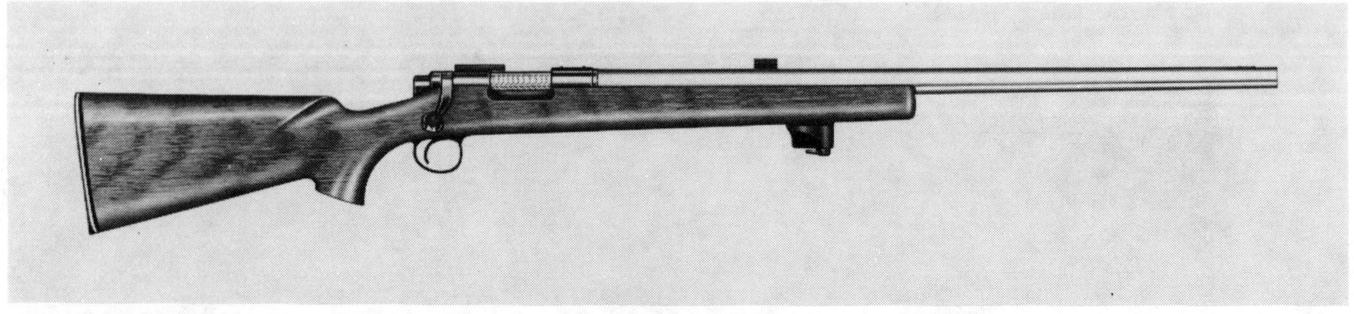

Remington Model 40-XB "Rangemaster" bolt action center fire target rifle.

Remington Model Seven custom "KS" lighweight centerfire rifle, synthetic stock of "Kevlar" ® aramid fiber; calibers: .223 Rem., 7mm BR Rem., 7mm-08 Rem., .35 Rem. and .350 Rem. Mag.

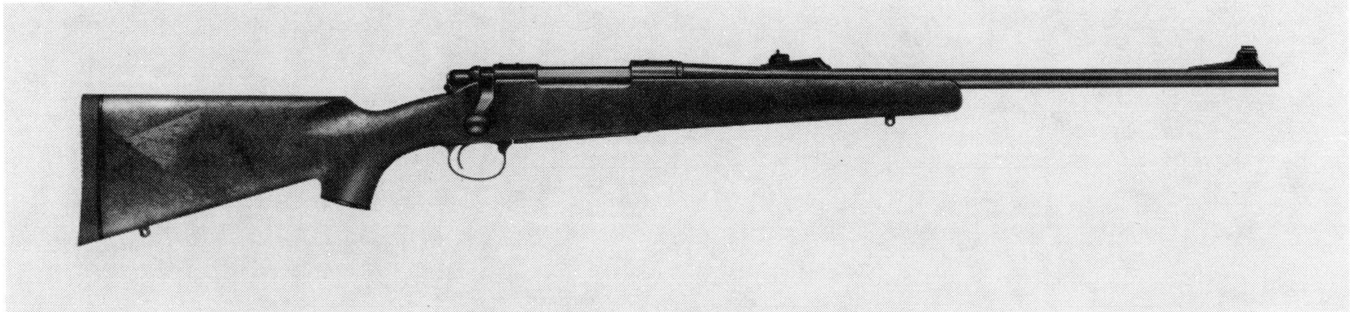

Remington Model 700 "AS" bolt action centerfire rifle with synthetic stock.

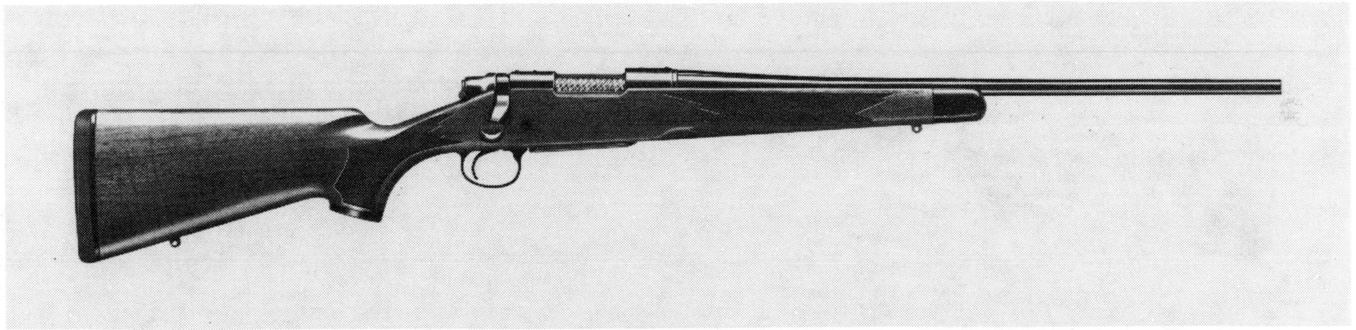

Remington Model 700 mountain rifle, short action version; Calibers: 243 win., 7mm-08 Rem., & 308 Win.

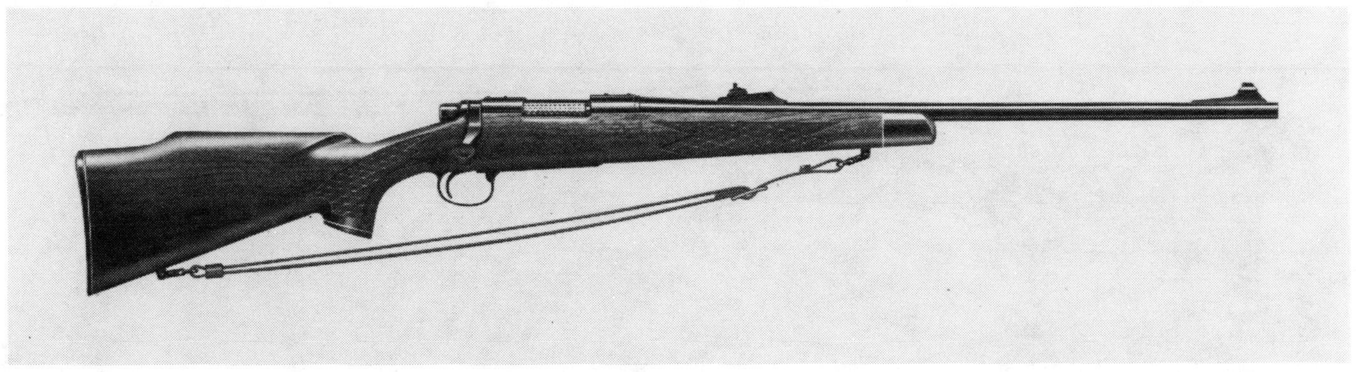

Remington Model 700 BDL, bolt action centerfire rifle (short action with 24-inch barrel).

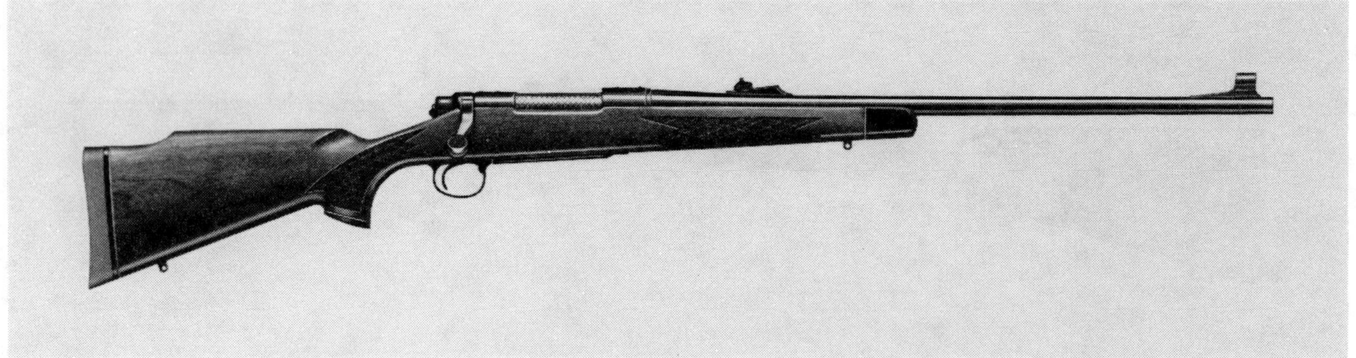

Remington Model 700 BDL Magnum; calibers: 7mm Rem. Mag., .300 Win. Mag., .338 Win. Mag. & .35 Whelen.

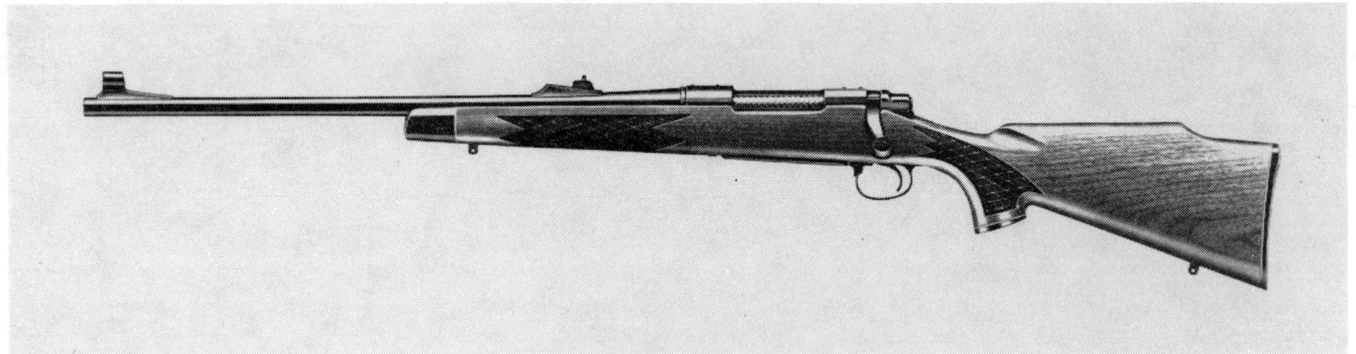

Remington Model 700 BDL left-hand bolt action centerfire rifle.

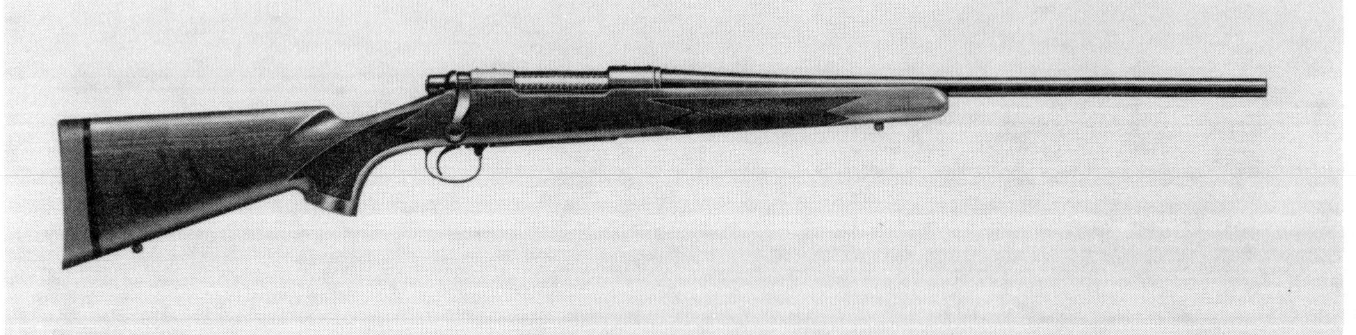

Remington Model 700 Classic bolt action centerfire rifle, Magnum caliber version.

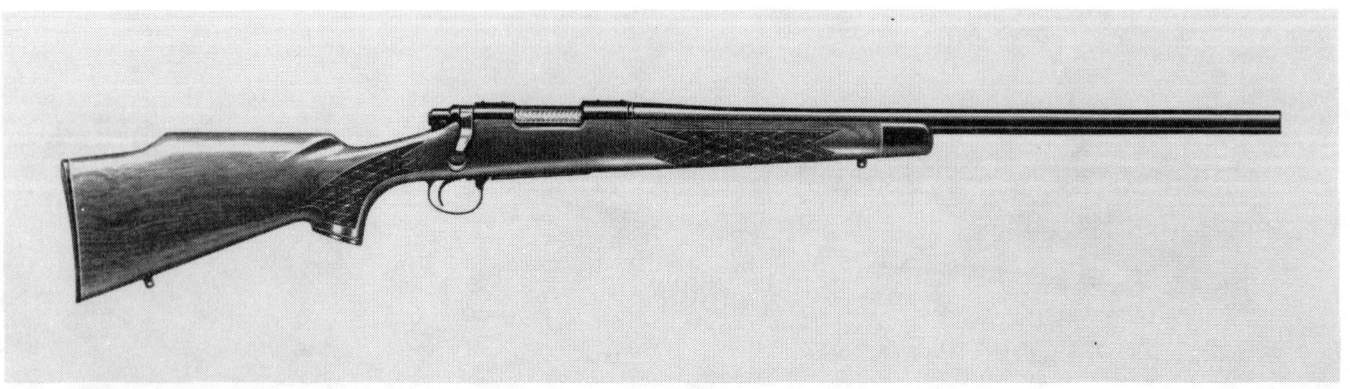

Remington Model 700 BDL "Varmint Special" bolt action centerfire rifle.

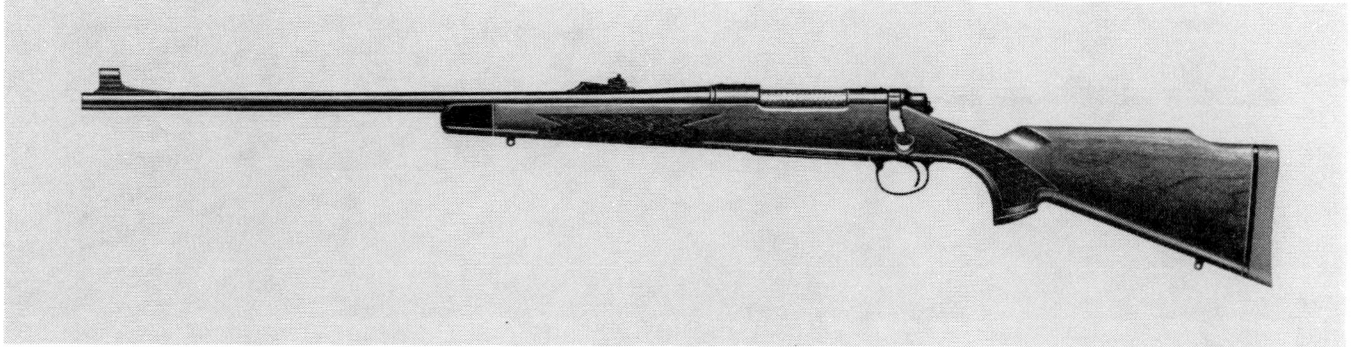

Remington Model 700 BDL magnum, left-hand action; calibers: 7mm Rem. Mag. & .338 Win. Mag.

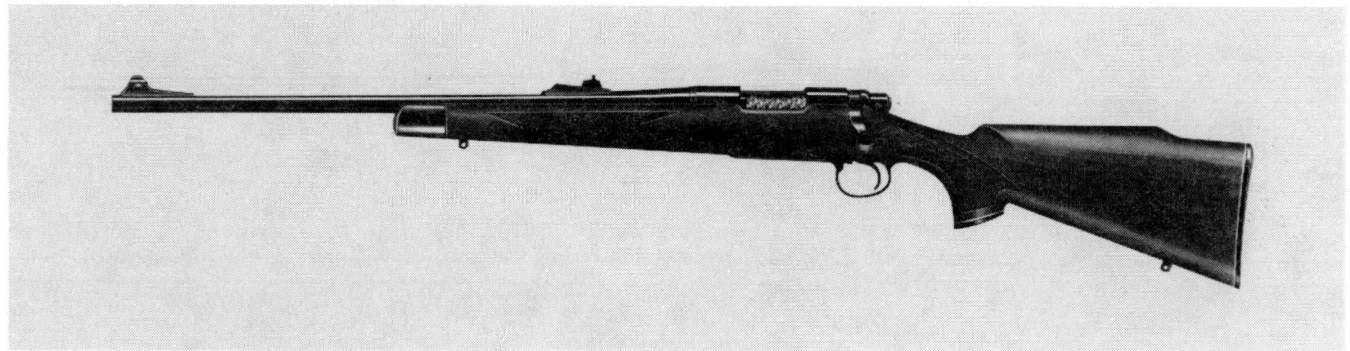

Remington Model 700 BDL left-hand bolt action (short) centerfire rifle; calibers: .22-250 Rem., .243 Win. & .308 Win.

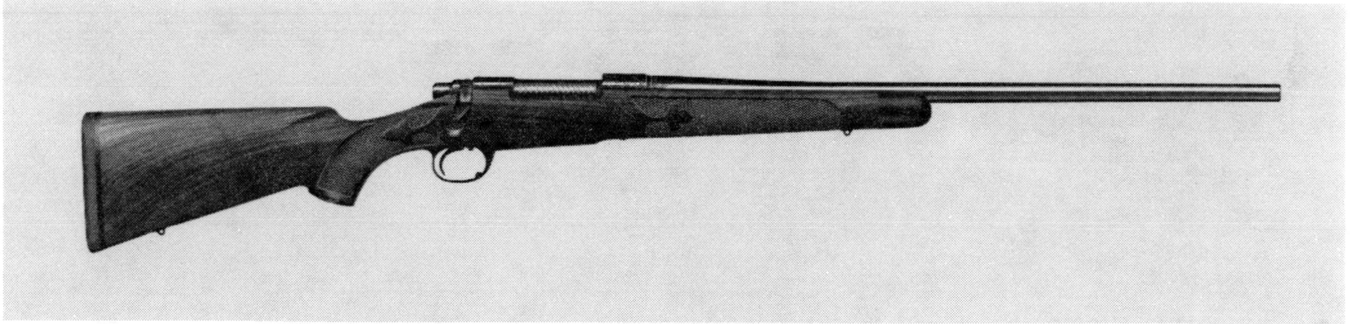

Remington Model 700 Custom bolt action centerfire rifle, Grade IV.

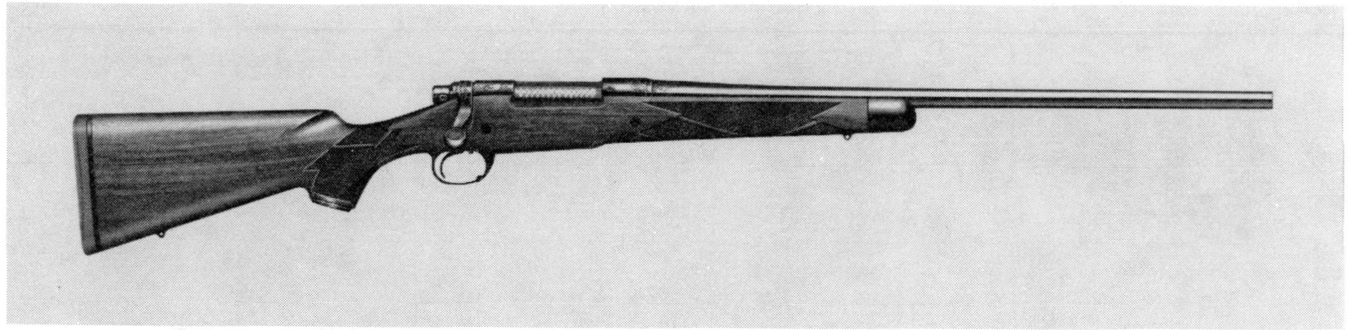

Remington Model 700 Custom bolt action centerfire rifle, Grade III.

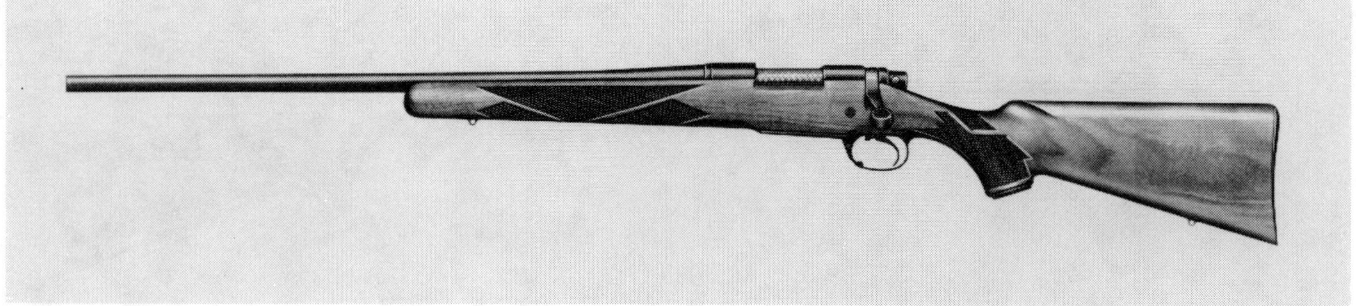

Remington Model 700 Custom Grade II, left hand short action centerfire rifle, available in Grades I to IV.

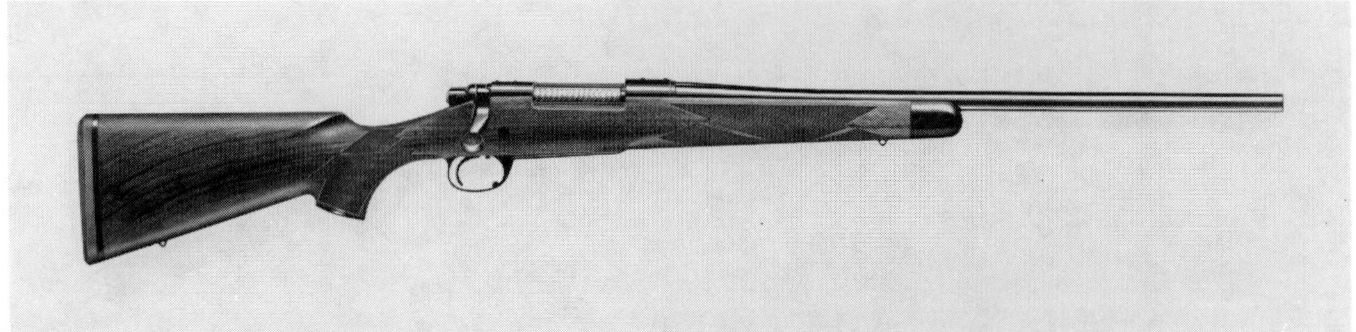

Remington Model 700 Custom bolt action centerfire rifle, Grade II.

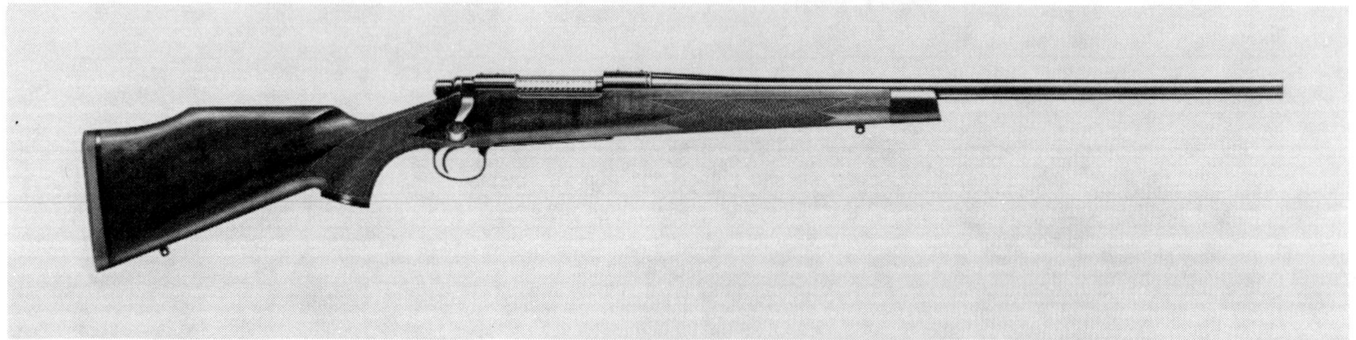

Remington Model 700 Custom bolt action centerfire rifle, Grade I.

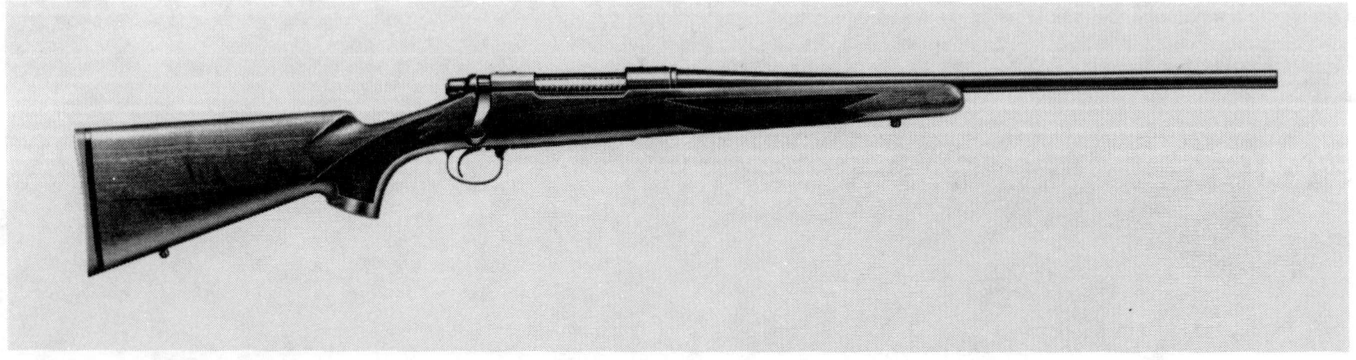

Remington Model 700 "Classic" bolt action centerfire rifle, limited edition - .25-06 Rem.

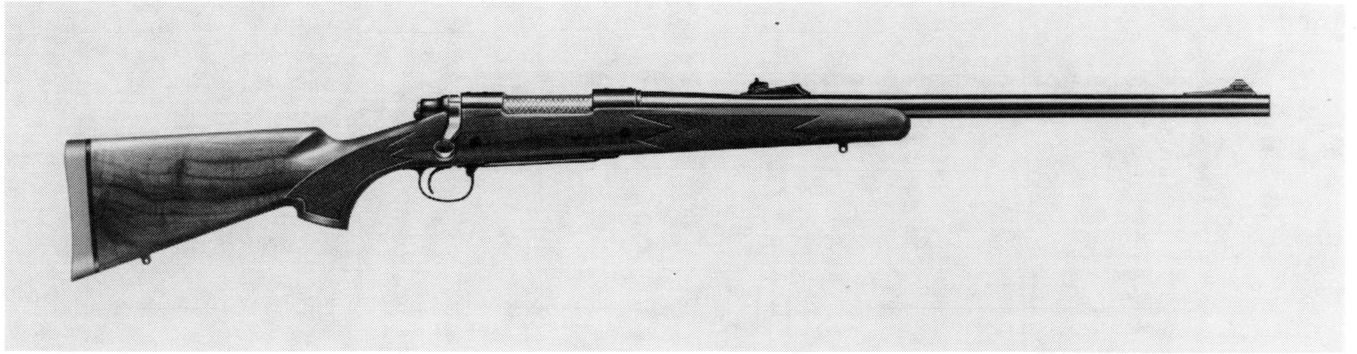

Remington Model 700 Safari Classic without sights: 8mm Rem. Mag. and .375 H&H Mag.; With sights: .416 Rem. Mag.* and .458 Win Mag.
** Heavy barrel.

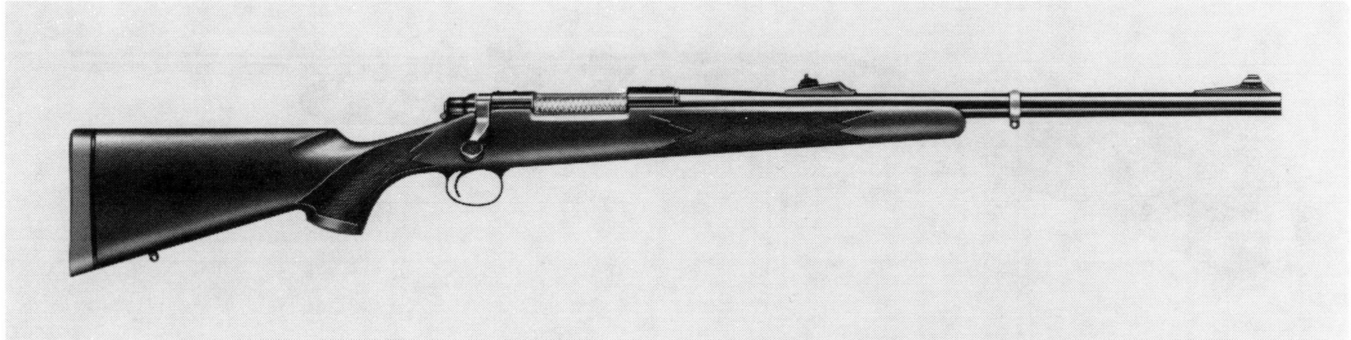

Remington Model 700 Safari KS, Synthetic stock of "Kevlar" aramid fiber; Calibers: 8mm Rem. Mag., .375 H&H Mag. 416 Rem. mag & .458 Win. Mag.

Remington Model 700 ADL "LS" bolt action centerfire rifle with laminated stock; Calibers: .243 Win., .270 Win., 30-06 & 7mm Rem. Magnum.

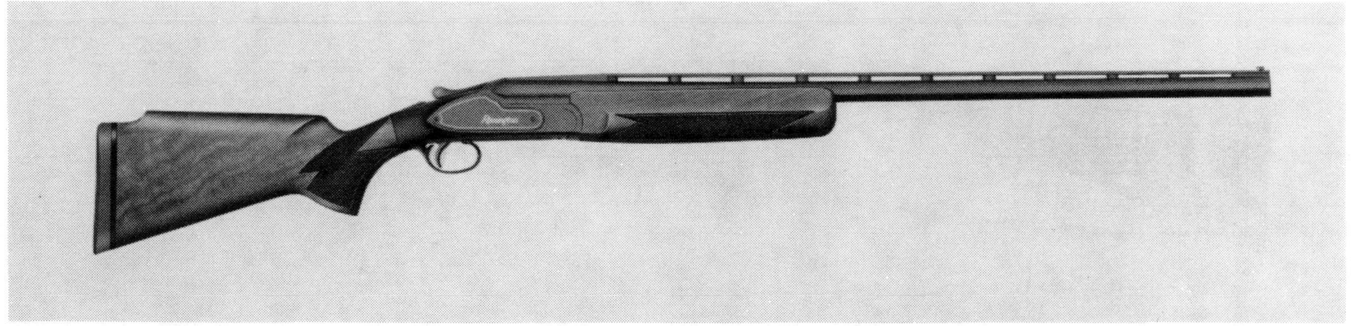

Remington Model 90-T super single trap gun, barrel lengths: 30", 32" & 34".

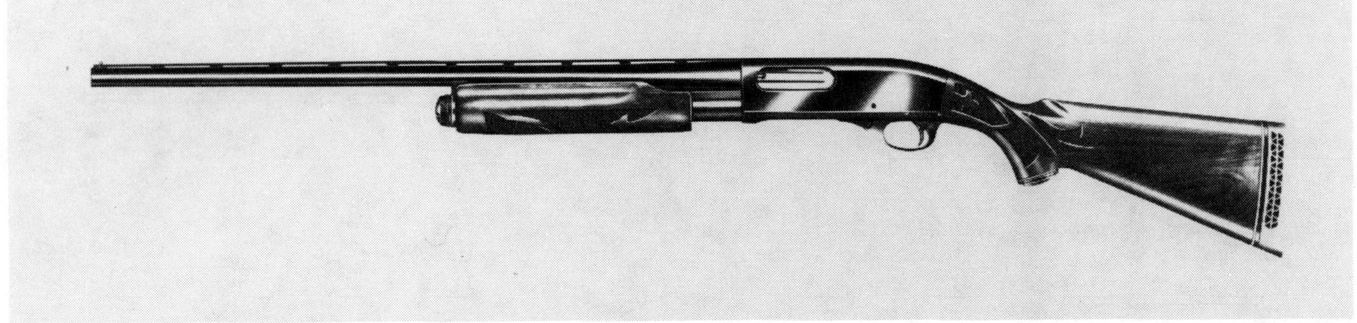

Remington Model 870 "Wingmaster" left-hand field grade pump action shotgun; 12- and 20-gauges (shown with ventilated rib).

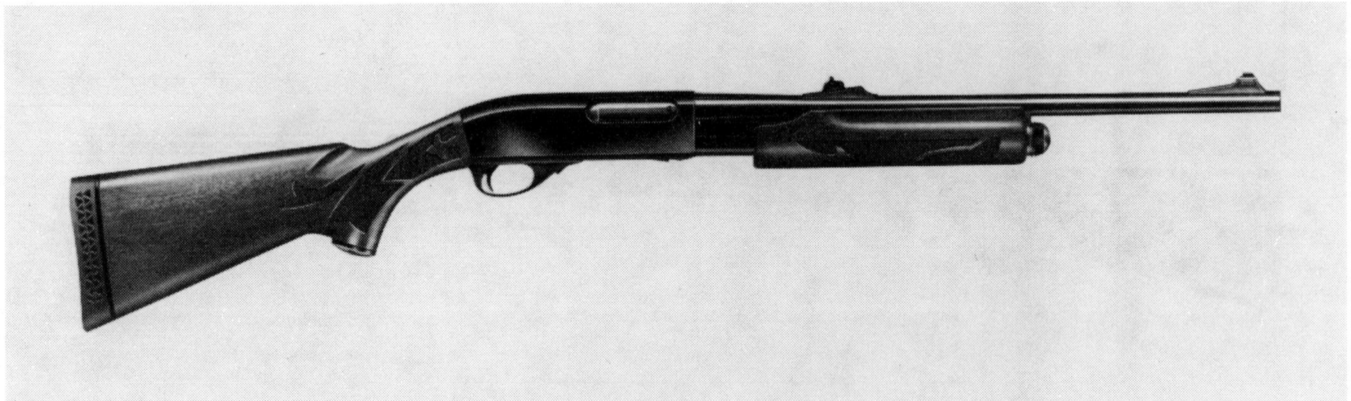

Remington Model 870 pump action 20 gauge "lightweight" deer gun.

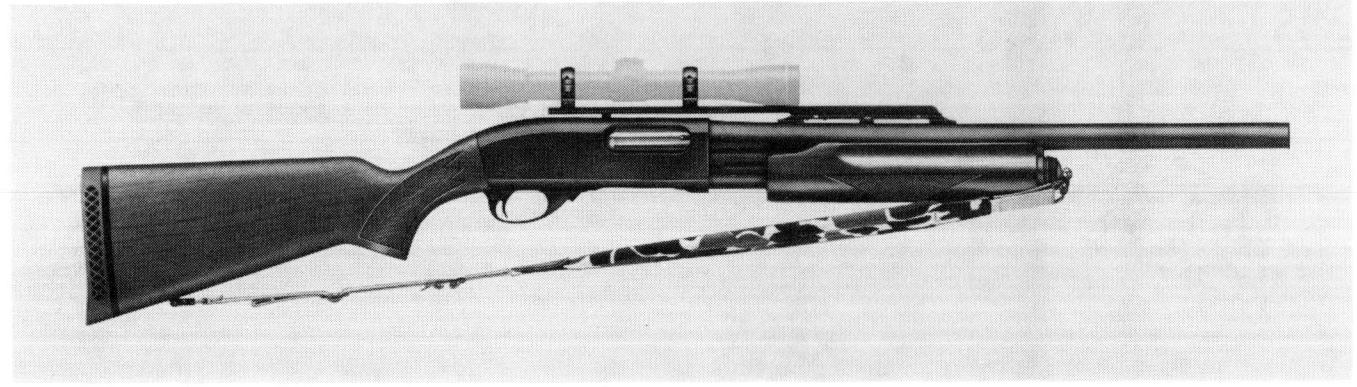

Remington Model 870 SP deer gun, pump action shotgun with 3" chamber, cantilever scope mount and interchangeable rifled and improved cylinder "REM" chokes.

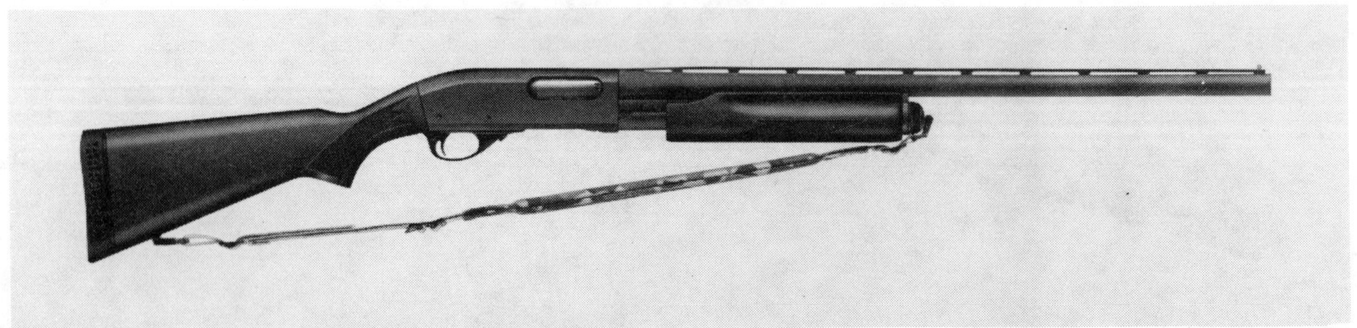

Remington Model 870 SP Magnum pump action shotgun, 3 inch chamber (shown with 26-inch barrel).

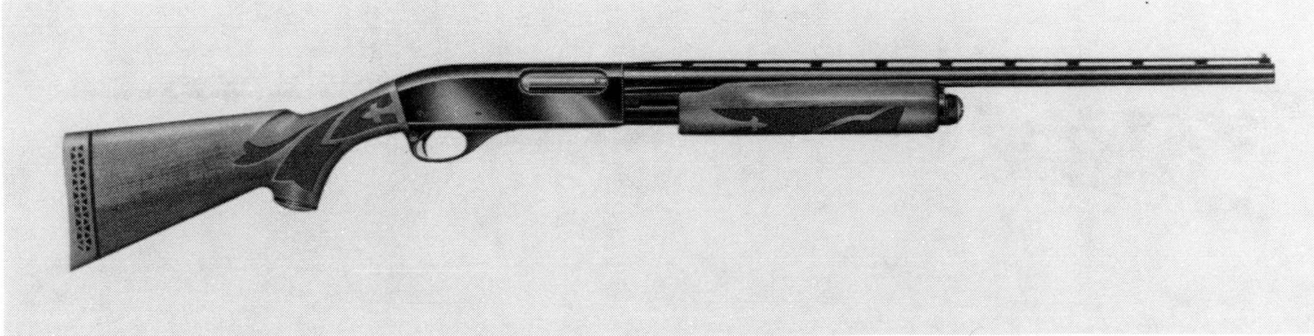

Remington Model 870 youth gun, 20-gauge lightweight pump action shotgun with interchangeable "REM" chokes. Stock: shortened 1½ inches. Barrel: 21 inches.

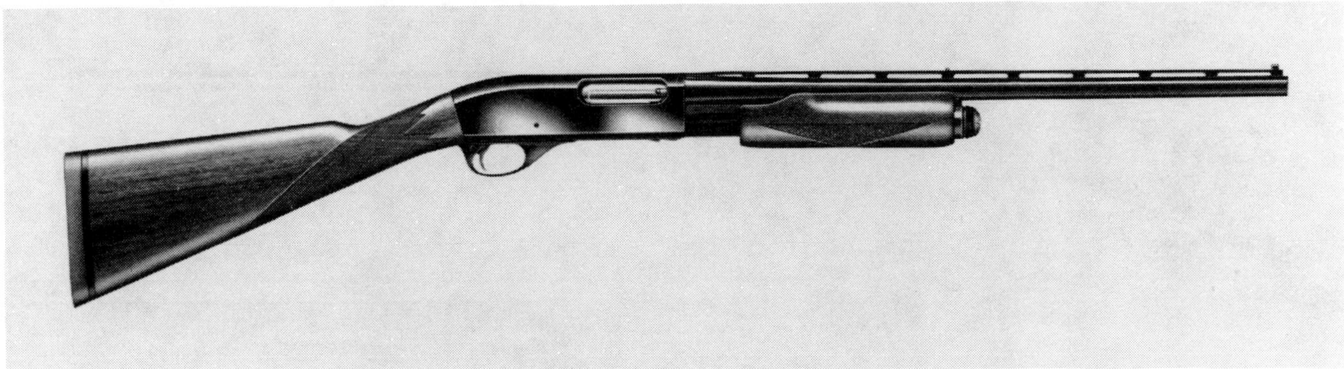

Remington Model 870 "Special Field" pump action shotgun with 21-inch vent rib barrel (20 gauge light-weight version).

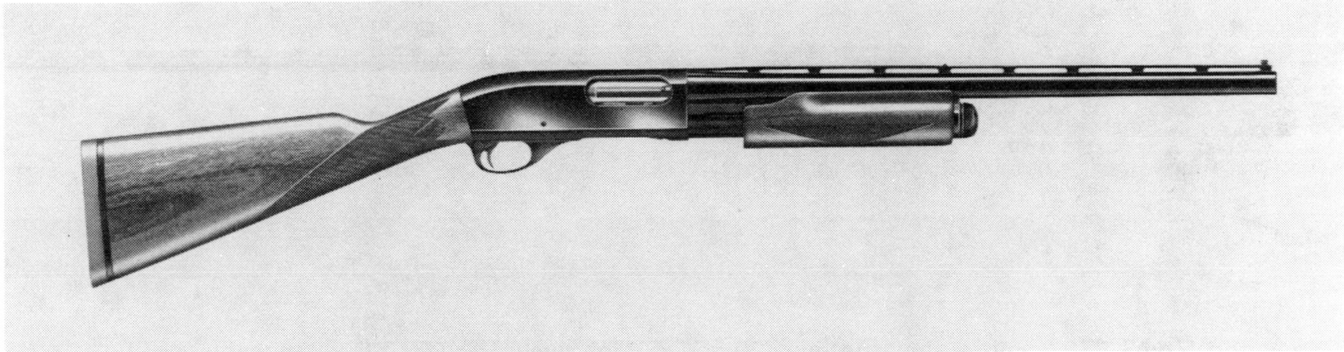

Remington Model 870 "Special Field" pump action shotgun with 21-inch vent rib barrel.

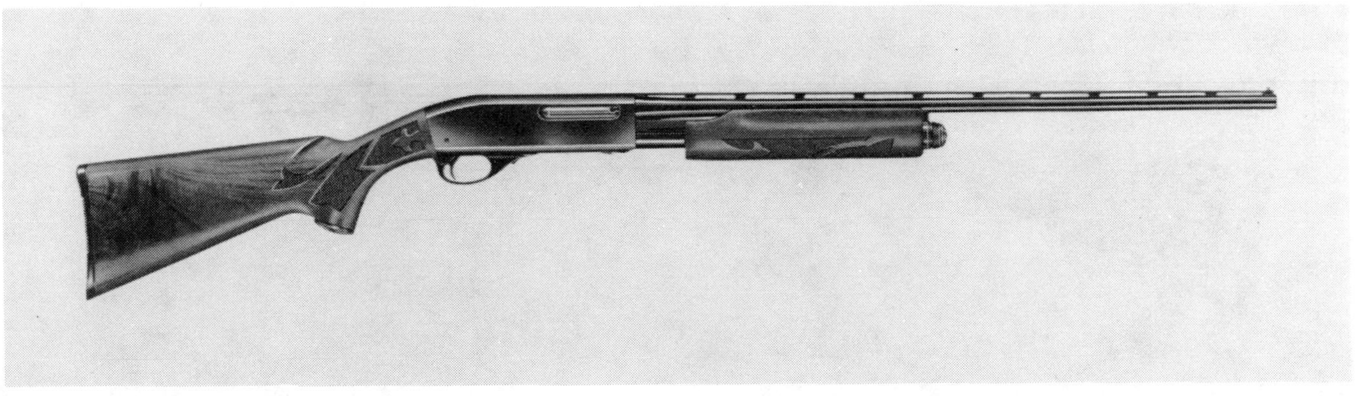

Remington Model 870 pump action shotgun, field grade small bore: 28-gauge & .410.

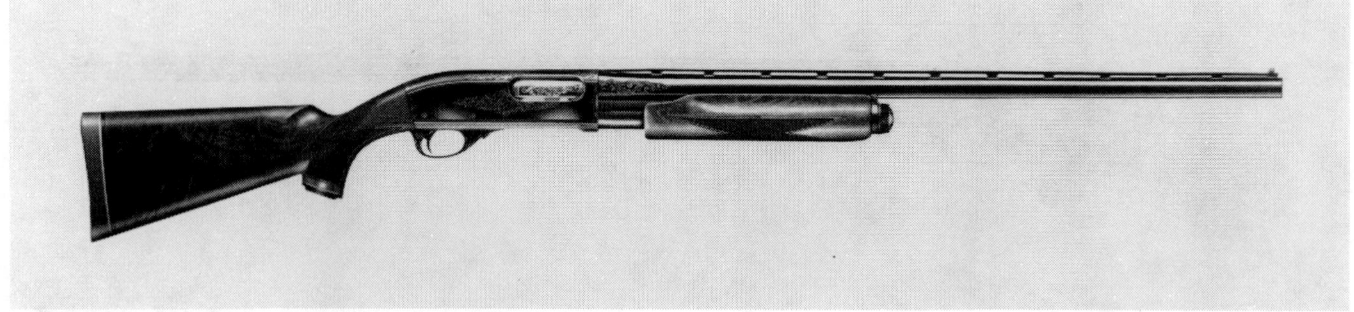

Remington Model 870 D tournament grade pump action shotgun.

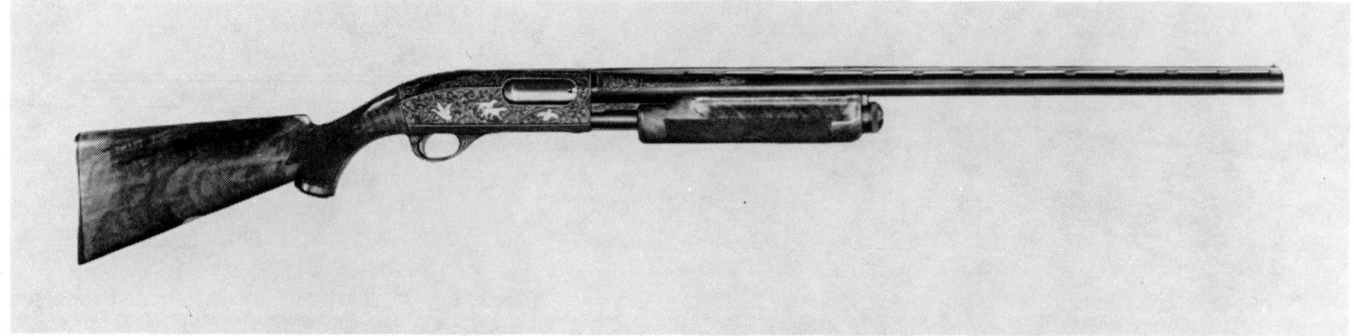

Remington Model 870 F pump action shotgun, premier grade with gold inlay.

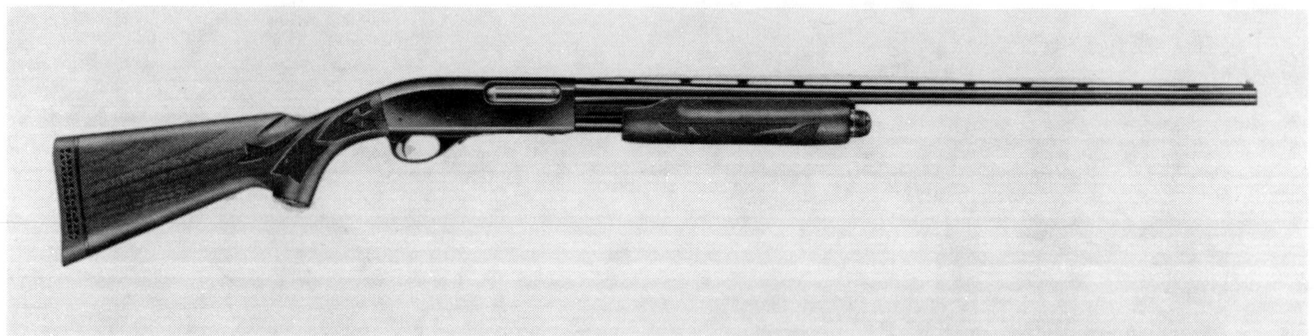

Remington Model 870 pump action shotgun, 20-gauge "lightweight" with interchangeable "REM" chokes.

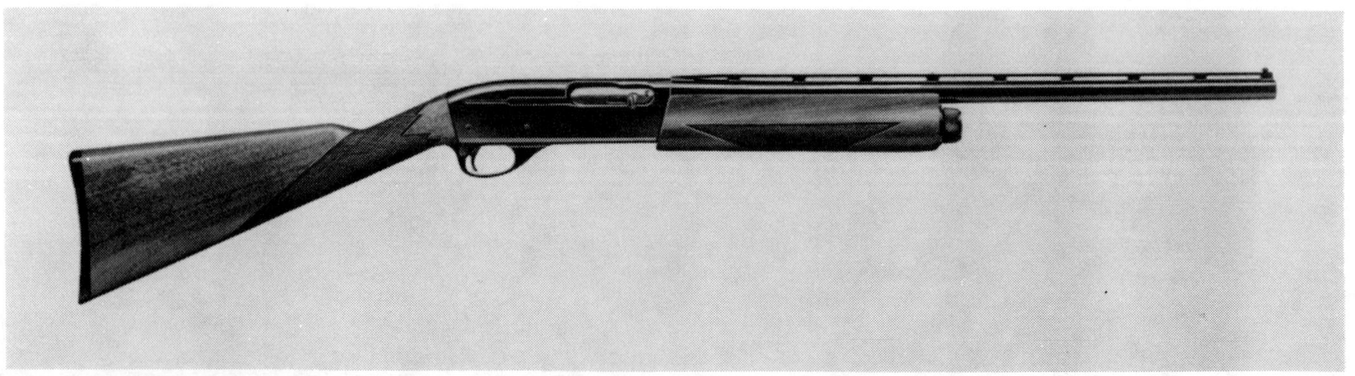

Remington Model 110 LT-20 "Special Field" 20-gauge autoloading shotgun with 21-inch vent rib barrel.

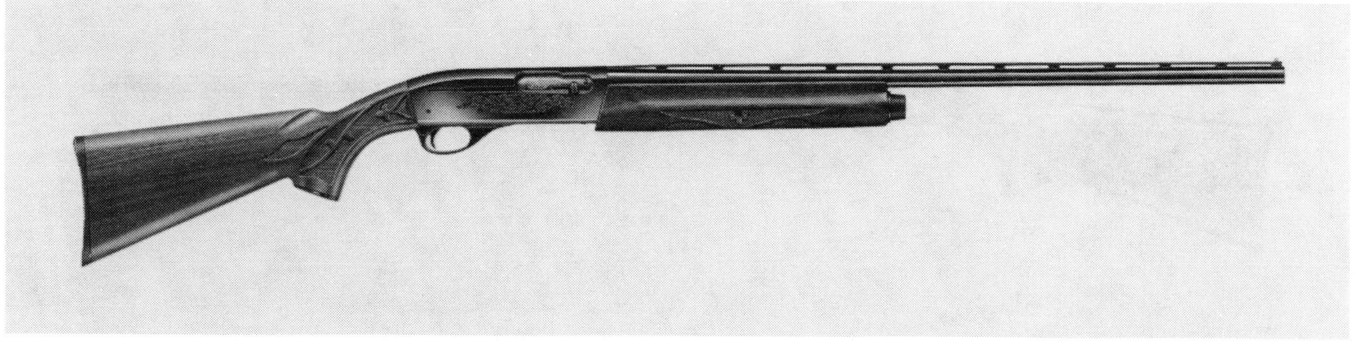

Remington Model 110 LT-20 autoloader, 20-gauge lightweight shotgun with interchangeable "REM" chokes.

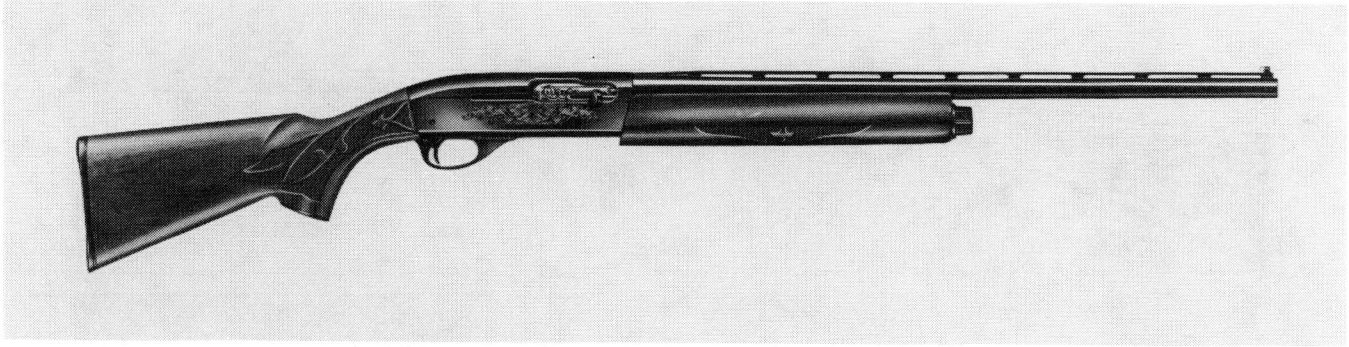

Remington Model 110 LT-20 youth gun, 20-gauge lightweight autoloading shotgun with interchangeable "REM" chokes. Stock: shortened 1½ inches. Barrel: 21 inches.

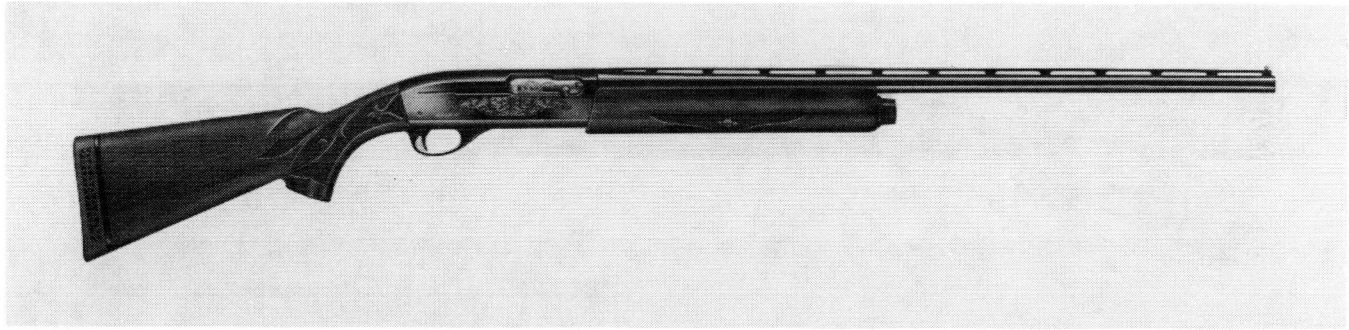

Remington Model 1100 LT-20 magnum 20-gauge lightweight autoloader with interchangeable "REM" chokes.

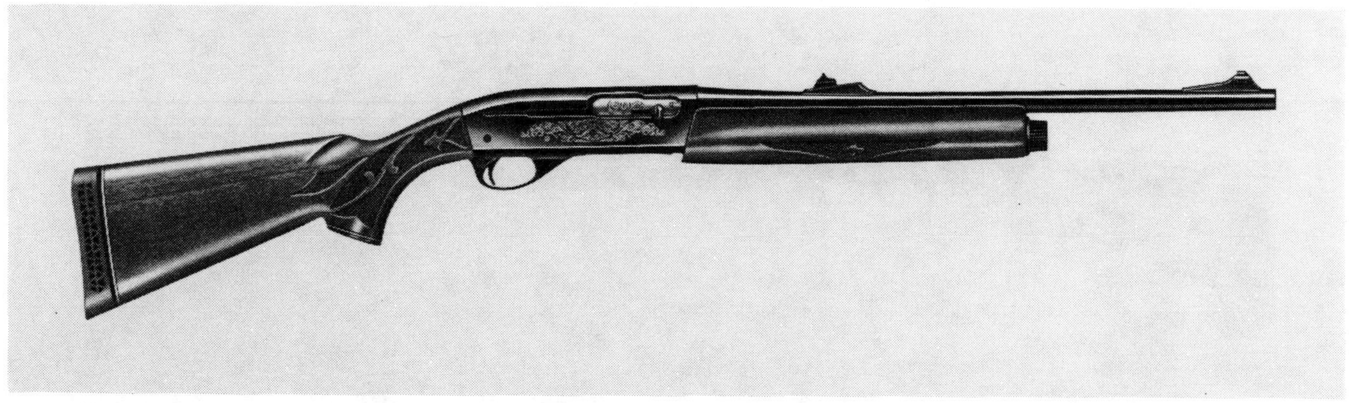

Remington Model 1100 LT-20 20-gauge lightweight autoloading deer gun.

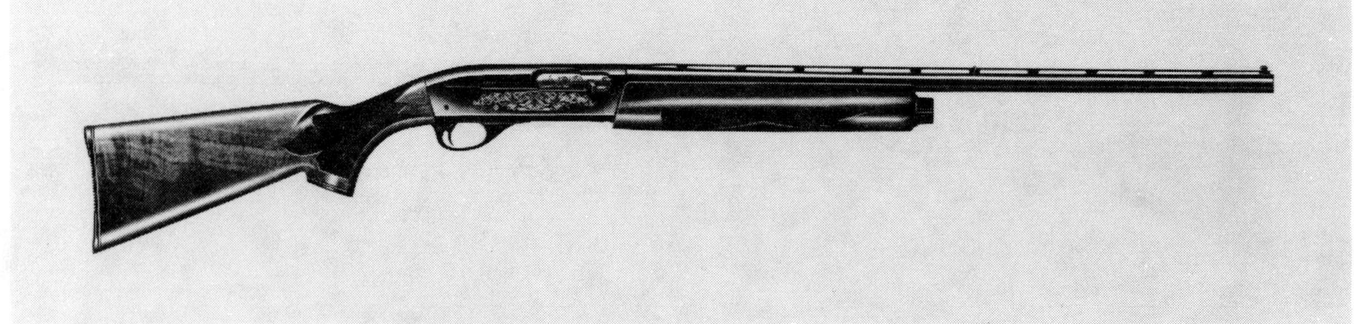

Remington Model 1100 LT-20 tournament skeet 20-gauge autoloading shotgun.

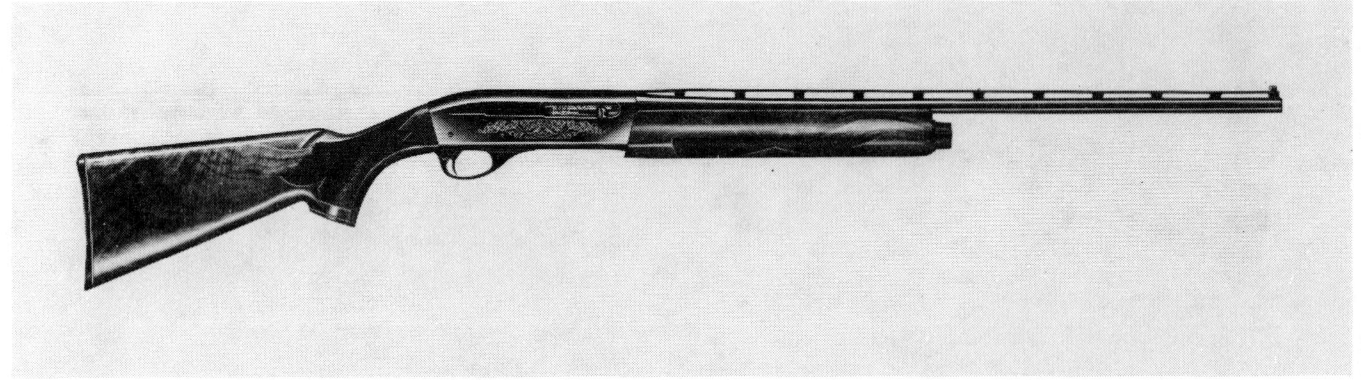

Remington Model 1100 tournament skeet autoloading shotgun, small bore version: 410 & 28 gauges.

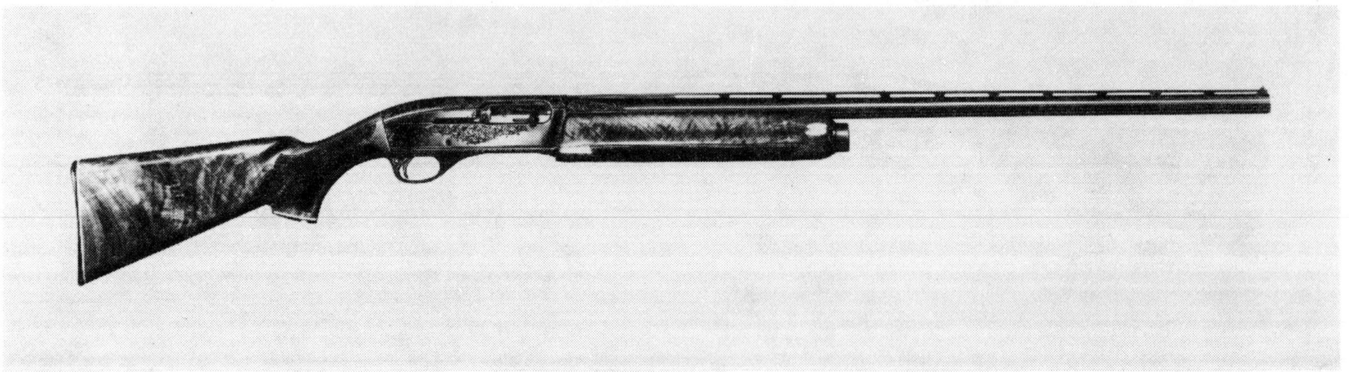

Remington Model 1100D tournament grade 12-gauge, 5 shot.

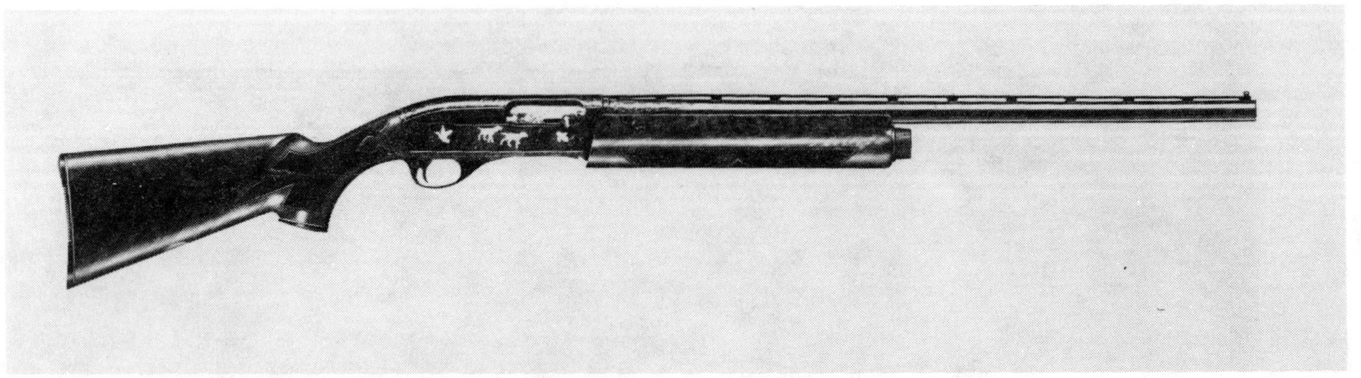

Remington Model 1100 F autoloading shotgun, premier grade with gold inlay.

RENETTE, GASTINE
Paris, France

Model 105
An Anson & Deeley action 12 or 20 gauge double barrel shotgun available in a variety of barrel lengths, with double triggers and automatic ejectors. Blued, case-hardened with a checkered walnut stock.

Exc.	V.G.	Good	Fair	Poor
1750	1600	1250	900	750

Model 98
As above, except more finely finished.

Exc.	V.G.	Good	Fair	Poor
2500	2250	1750	1400	1100

Model 202
A 12 or 20 gauge sidelock double barrel shotgun made only on custom order. French case-hardened and blued with a checkered walnut stock.

Exc.	V.G.	Good	Fair	Poor
3500	3000	2500	1750	1250

Model 353
A custom manufactured double barrel shotgun with detachable sidelocks. Highly finished.

Exc.	V.G.	Good	Fair	Poor
9000	7500	5000	4250	3000

Type G Rifle
A .30-06, 9.3x74R or .375 Holland & Holland double barrel rifle with 24" barrels, express sights, double triggers and automatic ejectors. Engraved, blued with a checkered walnut stock.

Exc.	V.G.	Good	Fair	Poor
2250	1850	1500	1150	950

Type R Deluxe
As above, engraved with hunting scenes and with a more finely figured walnut stock.

Exc.	V.G.	Good	Fair	Poor
2500	2250	1750	1450	1150

Type PT President
As above, inlaid in gold with extremely well figured walnut stock.

Exc.	V.G.	Good	Fair	Poor
3200	2750	2000	1750	1250

RENWICK ARMS CO.
SEE—Perry & Goddard

RETOLAZA HERMANOS
Eibar, Spain

Brompetier
A folding trigger 6.35mm or 7.65mm caliber double action revolver with a 2.5" barrel and a safety mounted on the left side of the frame. Manufactured until 1915.

Exc.	V.G.	Good	Fair	Poor
135	110	90	70	45

Gallus or Titan
A 6.35mm semi-automatic pistol normally marked "Gallus" or "Titan". Blued with plastic grips.

Exc.	V.G.	Good	Fair	Poor
150	125	100	75	50

Liberty, Military, Retolaza or Paramount
A 6.35mm or 7.65mm semi-automatic pistol with a 3" barrel and 8-shot magazine. The slide marked with any of the tradenames listed above.

Exc.	V.G.	Good	Fair	Poor
150	125	100	75	50

Puppy
A folding trigger .22 caliber double action revolver with a 5-shot cylinder. The tradename "Puppy" stamped on the barrel.

Exc.	V.G.	Good	Fair	Poor
125	100	75	50	25

Stosel
A 6.35mm semi-automatic pistol marked on the slide "Automatic Pistol Stosel No. 1 Patent". Blued with plastic grips.

Exc.	V.G.	Good	Fair	Poor
150	125	100	75	50

Titanic
A 6.35mm semi-automatic pistol with a 2.5" barrel, the slide marked "1913 Model Automatic Pistol Titanic Eibar". Blued with plastic grips.

Exc.	V.G.	Good	Fair	Poor
150	125	100	75	50

REUNIES
Liege, Belgium

Dictator
A 6.35mm semi-automatic pistol with a 1.5" barrel, 5-shot magazine and the name "Dictator" together with the company's details stamped on the slide. This pistol features a bolt of tubular form the front end of which is hollow and encloses the barrel breech. Manufactured from 1909 to approximately 1925.

Exc.	V.G.	Good	Fair	Poor
175	150	125	100	75

Texas Ranger or Cowboy Ranger
Patterned after the Colt Model 1873 revolver. This pistol is of .38 Special caliber and has a 5.5" barrel. The barrel marked with the company's details and either the legend "Cowboy Ranger" or "Texas Ranger". Manufactured from 1922 to 1931.

Exc.	V.G.	Good	Fair	Poor
150	125	100	75	50

REUTH, F.
Hartford, Connecticut

Animal Trap Gun
A cast iron .28 to .50 caliber percussion trap gun with either single or double barrels 3.5" or 5" in length. This firearm fires a barbed arrow and is triggered by a cord attached to an animal trap or bait. The barrels marked "F. Reuth's Patent, May 12, 1857." Several hundred were made between 1858 and 1862. The double-barrel model is more common than the single barrel and is worth approximately 20 percent less.

Exc.	V.G.	Good	Fair	Poor
450	400	350	250	200

RHEINMETALL
Sommerda, Germany

Dreyse 6.35mm
A 6.35mm semi-automatic pistol with a 2" barrel, manual safety and 6-shot magazine. The slide marked "Dreyse". Blued with plastic grips having the trademark "RFM" cast in them. The patent for this design was issued in 1909 to Louis Scmeisser.

Exc.	V.G.	Good	Fair	Poor
300	250	200	150	100

Dreyse 7.65mm
As above, but chambered for the 7.65mm cartridge, with a 3.6" barrel and a 7-shot magazine. The slide marked "Dreyse Rheinmetall Abt. Sommerda." Blued with plastic grips.

Exc.	V.G.	Good	Fair	Poor
275	225	175	125	90

Dreyse 9mm

As above, but chambered for the 9mm cartridge with a 5" barrel and an 8-shot magazine. The slide marked "Rheinische Mettell-waaren Und Maschinenfabrik, Sommerda." Blued with plastic grips.

Exc.	V.G.	Good	Fair	Poor
750	650	500	400	300

Rheinmetall

A 7.65mm semi-automatic pistol with a 3.65" barrel and an 8-shot magazine. The slide marked "Rheinmetell ABT. Sommerda." Blued with walnut grips.

Exc.	V.G.	Good	Fair	Poor
275	225	175	125	90

RHODE ISLAND ARMS CO.

Hope Valley, Rhode Island

Morrone

A 12 or 20 gauge Over/Under boxlock shotgun with 26" or 28" barrels, single trigger and automatic ejectors. Blued with either a straight or pistol grip walnut checkered stock. 450 were made in 12 gauge and 50 in 20 gauge. Manufactured from 1949 to 1953.

Exc.	V.G.	Good	Fair	Poor
1250	1000	750	600	450

RICHLAND ARMS CO.

Blissfield, Michigan

This company, which ceased operation in 1986, imported a variety of Spanish made shotguns.

Model 41 Ultra O/U

A 20, 28, or .410 bore double barrel shotgun with 26" or 28" ventilated-rib barrels, single non-selective trigger and automatic ejectors. French case-hardened, receiver and checkered walnut stock.

Exc.	V.G.	Good	Fair	Poor
275	250	200	150	100

Model 747 O/U

As above, in 20 gauge only with a single selective trigger.

Exc.	V.G.	Good	Fair	Poor
425	350	300	250	175

Model 757 O/U

A Greener style boxlock 12 gauge double barrel shotgun with 26" or 28" ventilated-rib barrels, double triggers and automatic ejectors. Finished as above.

Exc.	V.G.	Good	Fair	Poor
300	250	200	175	125

Model 787 O/U

As above, fitted with screw-in choke tubes.

Exc.	V.G.	Good	Fair	Poor
450	375	325	275	200

Model 808 O/U

A 12 gauge double barrel shotgun with 26", 28" or 30" ventilated-rib barrels, single trigger and automatic ejectors. Blued with checkered walnut stock. Manufactured in Italy from 1963 to 1968.

Exc.	V.G.	Good	Fair	Poor
425	350	300	250	175

Model 80 LS

A 12, 20 or .410 bore single barrel shotgun with 26" or 28" barrels. Blued with checkered walnut stock.

Exc.	V.G.	Good	Fair	Poor
150	125	100	80	60

Model 200

An Anson & Deeley style 12, 16, 20, 28 or .410 bore double barrel shotgun with 22", 26" or 28" barrels, double triggers and automatic ejectors. Blued with a checkered walnut stock.

Exc.	V.G.	Good	Fair	Poor
325	300	250	200	125

Model 202

As above, with an extra set of interchangeable barrels. Imported from 1963 to 1985.

Exc.	V.G.	Good	Fair	Poor
300	275	225	175	100

Model 711 Magnum

As above, chambered for 3" shells and fitted with 30" or 32" barrels.

Exc.	V.G.	Good	Fair	Poor
350	300	250	200	150

Model 707 Deluxe

As above, more finely finished and fitted with well figured walnut stocks.

Exc.	V.G.	Good	Fair	Poor
350	300	250	200	150

RICHMOND ARMORY

Richmond, Virginia

Carbine

This weapon was manufactured for use by the Confederate States of America and is extremely collectible. We recommend qualified individual appraisal if a transaction is contemplated. This muzzle-loading carbine is chambered for .58 caliber percussion and has a 25" round barrel and a full-length stock that is held on by two barrel bands. It was manufactured from parts that were captured at the Harper's Ferry Armory in 1861. The locks are marked "Richmond, VA" and dated from 1861 to 1865. There are sling swivels in front of the trigger guard and on the front barrel band; a third swivel is on the underside of the buttstock. The quantity manufactured is not known. They were made between 1861 and 1865.

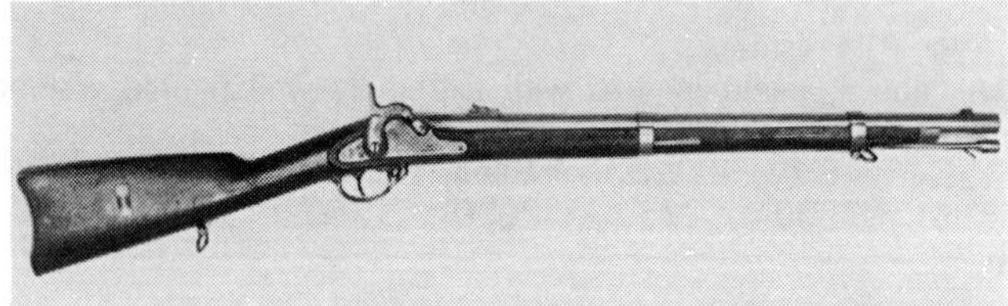

Courtesy Milwaukee Public Museum, Milwaukee, Wisconsin.

Exc.	V.G.	Good	Fair	Poor
5000	4000	2500	1750	1000

Musketoon

This weapon is very similar to the carbine except that the barrel is 30" in length and the front sight is also the bayonet lug. There is no sling swivel on the buttstock. This weapon was also manufactured between 1861 and 1865.

Exc.	V.G.	Good	Fair	Poor
6000	5000	3250	2250	1500

Rifled Musket

This model is also similar to the Carbine, with a 40" barrel and a full-length stock held on by three barrel bands. The front sling swivel is on the middle barrel band instead of on the front band. The Rifled Musket was also manufactured between 1861 and 1865.

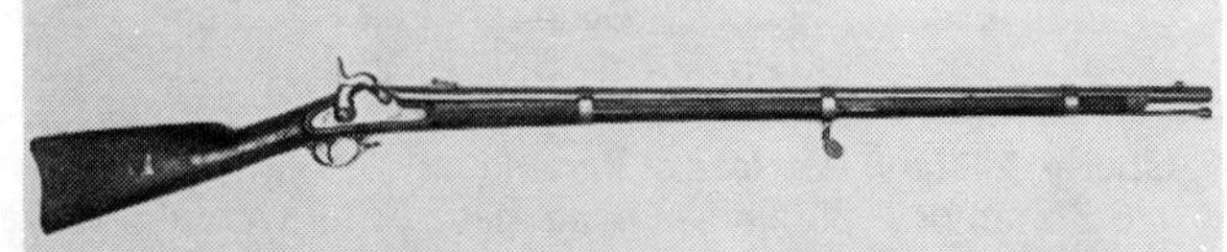

Courtesy Milwaukee Public Museum, Milwaukee, Wisconsin.

Exc.	V.G.	Good	Fair	Poor
4000	3000	2000	1500	900

RIEDL RIFLE CO.
Westminster, California

Single Shot Rifle
This company produced custom order dropping block single shot rifles in a variety of calibers and barrel lengths. Rifles were normally fitted only with telescopic or target sight bases. Blued with a checkered walnut stock.

Exc.	V.G.	Good	Fair	Poor
500	450	400	300	225

RIGBY, JOHN & CO., LTD.
London, England

This company was established in the early 19th Century and has produced a variety of shotguns and rifles over the years. Many of the arms produced by this company were custom ordered and prospective purchasers are advised to secure individual appraisals prior to the acquisition of such pieces.

Boxlock Shotgun
A boxlock shotgun manufactured in any gauge with double triggers, automatic ejectors and a hand fitted checkered walnut stock.
20 Gauge—Add 25%.
28 Gauge—Add 45%.
.410—Add 70%.

Chatsworth Grade

Exc.	V.G.	Good	Fair	Poor
4000	3000	2500	1750	1250

Sackville Grade

Exc.	V.G.	Good	Fair	Poor
5500	4500	3750	2750	2000

Boxlock Game Gun

NIB	Exc.	V.G.	Good	Fair	Poor
7500	6000	5000	4500	3000	2500

Sidelock Shotgun
A custom made double barrel shotgun fitted with detachable sidelocks.
20 Gauge—Add 25%.
28 Gauge—Add 45%.
.410—Add 70%.

Sandringham Grade

Exc.	V.G.	Good	Fair	Poor
9000	8000	6500	4000	2750

Regal Grade

Exc.	V.G.	Good	Fair	Poor
12500	10000	7500	6500	5000

Sidelock Game Gun

NIB	Exc.	V.G.	Good	Fair	Poor
20000	17000	13500	10000	8000	6500

Magazine Rifle
Utilizing a Mauser action, this rifle is available in a number of calibers, barrel lengths and with either a 3- or 5-shot magazine. Blued checkered walnut stock.

NIB	Exc.	V.G.	Good	Fair	Poor
4500	3750	2750	2250	1750	1200

Large Bore Magazine Rifle
Utilizing a Bruno square bridge Mauser action, this rifle is chambered for .375 Holland & Holland, .404 Gibbs, .416 Rigby, .458 Winchester Magnum and .505 Gibbs cartridges. Barrel lengths vary from 21" to 24" and a 4-shot magazine is standard.

NIB	Exc.	V.G.	Good	Fair	Poor
4750	4000	3000	2500	2000	1500

Single Shot Rifle
Utilizing a Farquharson dropping block action, this rifle is chambered for a variety of cartridges and has a 24" barrel. The receiver finely engraved and blued. Stock of well figured walnut.

Exc.	V.G.	Good	Fair	Poor
4000	3500	2750	2000	1500

Third Quality Boxlock Double Rifle
A double barrel rifle chambered for cartridges from .275 Magnum to .577 Nitro Express with a 24" to 28" barrel fitted with express sights. Double triggers and automatic ejectors. Blued with light engraving and a checkered walnut stock.

Exc.	V.G.	Good	Fair	Poor
12500	10500	8500	7000	5000

Second Quality Boxlock Double Rifle
As above, but more finely engraved and with better quality walnut stocks.

Exc.	V.G.	Good	Fair	Poor
16000	14000	10500	8000	6000

Best Quality Sidelock Double Rifle
As above, but fitted with full sidelocks, with best bouquet engraving and finely figured walnut stocks.

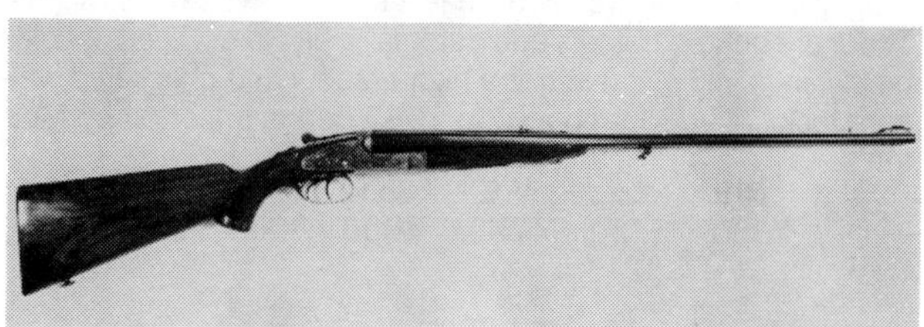

NIB	Exc.	V.G.	Good	Fair	Poor
35000	30000	25000	20000	15000	12000

RIGDON, ANSLEY & CO.
Augusta, Georgia

1851 Colt Navy Type
A .36 caliber percussion revolver with a 7.5" barrel and 6-shot cylinder. Blued with walnut grips. Initial production examples marked "Augusta, GA. C.S.A." and later models "C.S.A." Approximately 1,000 were manufactured in 1864 and 1865.

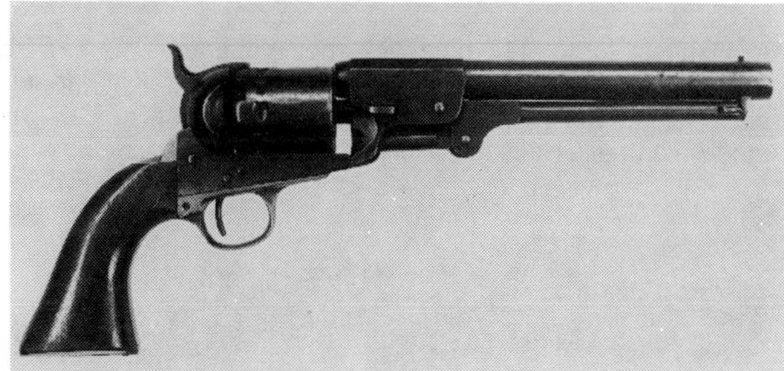

Courtesy Milwaukee Public Museum, Milwaukee, Wisconsin.

Early Production Model

Exc.	V.G.	Good	Fair	Poor
10000	8000	5000	3500	2000

Standard Production Model

Exc.	V.G.	Good	Fair	Poor
9500	7500	4000	2750	1750

RIPOMANTI, GUY
St. Etienne, France
Importer—Wes Gilpin
Dallas, Texas
Morton's Ltd.
Lexington, Kentucky

Side x Side Shotgun
A very high-grade shotgun offered on a strictly made-to-order basis. There is a boxlock model that begins at $8,500 and a sidelock that is priced from $22,500. These prices rise depending on the options and embellishments desired. These guns are

rarely seen on the used-gun market; but if a transaction is contemplated, we strongly urge competent individual appraisal. The shotguns are imported by Gilpin's.

Side x Side Double Rifles
Extremely high-grade and basically made to order. They are very rarely encountered on today's market. They have been imported since 1988. They range in price from $11,000 up. If a transaction is contemplated, we strongly urge competent individual appraisal. These guns are imported by Morton's.

Over/Under Double Rifle
A boxlock action Over/Under chambered for the 9.3x74R cartridge. The barrels are 23.5" in length and have express sights. There are double triggers and automatic ejectors. This model is highly engraved and features a high-grade, hand-checkered walnut stock. It was introduced in 1989 and is imported by Morton's.

NIB	Exc.	V.G.	Good	Fair	Poor
7000	5750	4750	4000	3000	2250

RIZZINI

Brescia, Italy
Importer—W.L.Moore & Co.
West Lake Village, California

This Italian gun company builds about 24 shotguns a year. Each gun is highly individualized for the customer. It is therefore advisable to secure a qualified appraisal before purchase. The company only produces two models. These are listed below to give the reader some idea of the value of one of these models. None of these models includes the cost of engraving and multi barrel set and multi gauge sets are extra.

Model R-1
Available in 12 to .410 bore with choice of barrels from 25" to 30". Choice of single or double trigger, pistol or straight grip, rib, barrel length and chokes are standard items on this model. This model features a Holland & Holland side lock action.

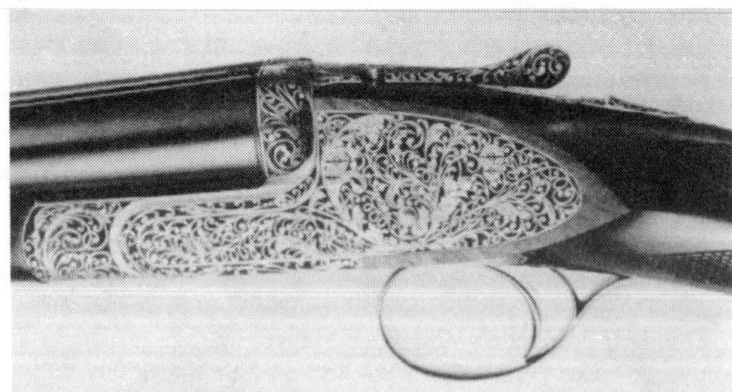

12, 16, or 20 gauge

NIB	Exc.	V.G.	Good	Fair	Poor
40,000	30000	19000	10000	6000	2000

.28 gauge or .410 bore

NIB	Exc.	V.G.	Good	Fair	Poor
46000	34500	22000	12000	7500	2500

Model R-2 This model has a box lock action and a removable inspection plate on the bottom of the frame. The stock and forearm is fitted with Turkish Circassian walnut. Offered in 12 gauge to .410 bore.

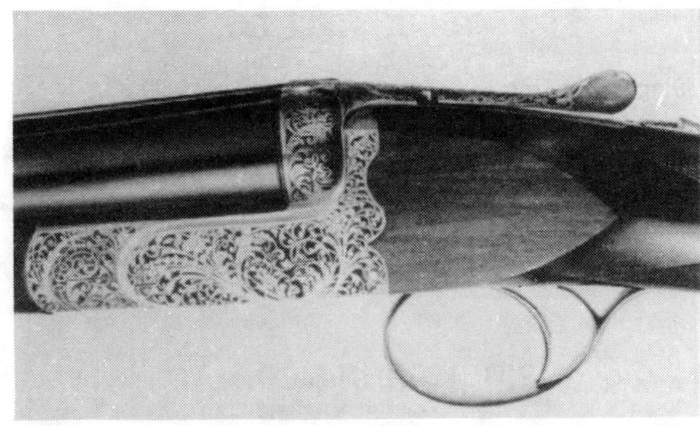

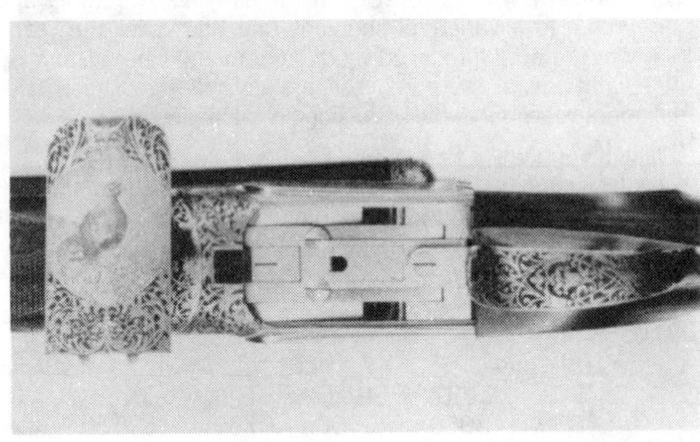

NIB	Exc.	V.G.	Good	Fair	Poor
15,000	11250	8500	6000	3000	1500

NOTE: Engraving extras for above models will add $8700 for English scroll pattern and $22,000 for Fracassi style engraving. Other types of engraving are offered and it is advisable to secure a qualified appraisal of an engraved Rizzini before purchase.

Extra set of barrels in same gauge add $12,500.

ROBAR ET CIE

Liege, Belgium

Jieffeco
A 6.35mm or 7.65mm caliber semi-automatic pistol with a 3" barrel. The slide is marked "Pistolet Automatique Jieffeco Depose Brevete SGDG." Blued with plastic grips. Manufactured from 1910 to 1914.

Exc.	V.G.	Good	Fair	Poor
175	150	125	100	75

Melior
As above, with a 2.5" barrel and the slide marked "Melior Brevete SGDG." Manufactured from 1910 to 1914.

Exc.	V.G.	Good	Fair	Poor
175	150	125	100	75

New Model Melior
A .22, 6.35mm, 7.65mm or 9mm short caliber semi-automatic pistol resembling the Browning Model 1910 with a 2" barrel. The barrel marked "Melior Brevets-Liege, Belgium." Blued, with plastic grips. Manufactured prior to 1958.

Exc.	V.G.	Good	Fair	Poor
175	150	125	100	75

Mercury
As above, in .22 caliber and imported by Tradewinds of Tacoma, Washington. The slide marked "Mercury Made in Belgium." Blue or nickle-plated. Manufactured from 1946 to 1958.

Exc.	V.G.	Good	Fair	Poor
175	150	125	100	75

ROBBINS & LAWRENCE
Windsor, Vermont

Pepperbox

A .28 or .31 caliber percussion 5 barrel pistol with the barrel groups measuring 3.5" or 4.5" in length. Ring trigger, blued iron frame with simple scroll engraving and browned barrels which are marked "Robbins & Lawrence Co. Windsor, VT. Patent. 1849." The barrel groups for this pistol were made in two types: fluted in both calibers, and ribbed in .31 caliber only. Approximately 7,000 were made between 1851 and 1854.

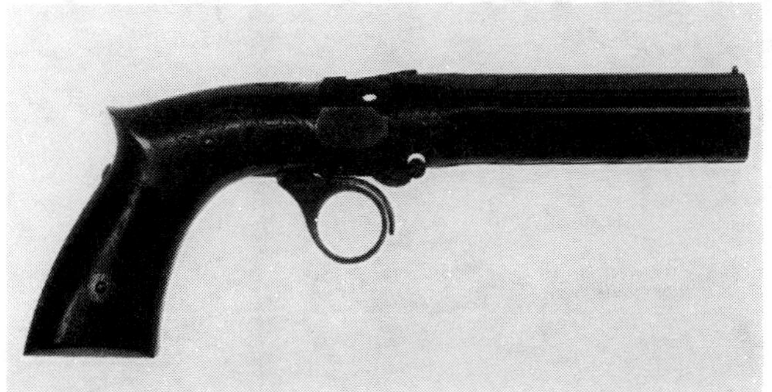

Exc.	V.G.	Good	Fair	Poor
750	650	600	450	300

ROBERTSON
Philadelphia, Pennsylvania

Pocket Pistol

A .41 caliber single shot percussion derringer with barrels ranging in length from 3" to 4.5". The barrel marked "Robertson, Phila."

Exc.	V.G.	Good	Fair	Poor
750	650	500	400	300

ROBINSON, ORVIL
SEE—Adirondack Arms Company

ROGERS & SPENCER
Utica, New York

Army Revolver

A .44 caliber 6-shot percussion revolver with a 7.5" octagonal barrel. The barrel marked "Rogers & Spencer/Utica, N.Y." Blued, case-hardened hammer with walnut grips bearing the inspector's mark "RPB". Approximately 5,800 were made between 1863 and 1865.

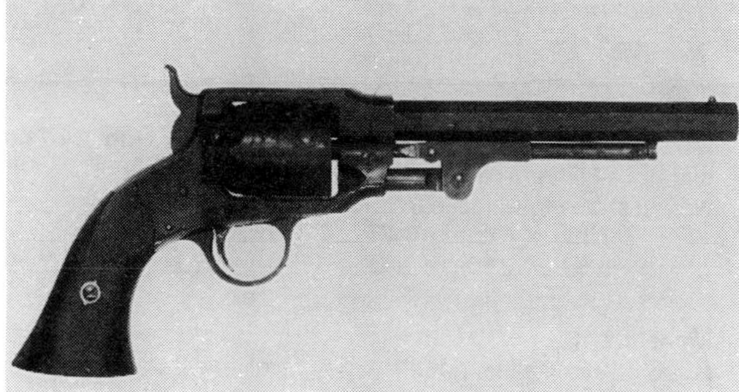

Courtesy Milwaukee Public Museum, Milwaukee, Wisconsin.

Exc.	V.G.	Good	Fair	Poor
975	850	750	600	450

ROHM GMBH
Sonthein/Brenz, Germany

This firm produced a variety of revolvers marked with various tradenames which were imported into the United States prior to 1968. Essentially, they are of three types: 1) solid-frame, gate-loading models; 2) solid-frame swingout-cylinder revolvers; and 3) solid-frame, swingout-cylinder revolvers. They are of low quality and little collector interest.

ROMERWERKE
Suhl, Germany

Romer

A .22 caliber semi-automatic pistol with a 2.5" or 6.5" barrel and 7-shot magazine. The barrels are interchangeable and marked "Kal. .22 Long Rifle," the slide marked "Romerwerke Suhl." Blued, with plastic grips. Manufactured between 1924 and 1926.

Exc.	V.G.	Good	Fair	Poor
500	450	400	300	225

RONGE, J. B.
Liege, Belgium

Bulldog

A .32, .380 or .45 caliber double-action revolver with a 3" barrel. Unmarked except for the monogram "RF" on the grips. Various tradenames have been noted on these revolvers and are believed to have been applied by retailers. Manufactured from 1880 to 1910.

Exc.	V.G.	Good	Fair	Poor
150	125	100	75	50

ROSS RIFLE CO.
Quebec, Canada

Designed in 1896 by Sir Charles Ross, this straight pole rifle was manufactured in a variety of styles. Due to problems with the bolt design, it never proved popular and was discontinued in 1915.

Mark I

Barrel length 28", .303 caliber with a "Harris Controlled Platform Magazine" which can be depressed by an external lever to facilitate loading.

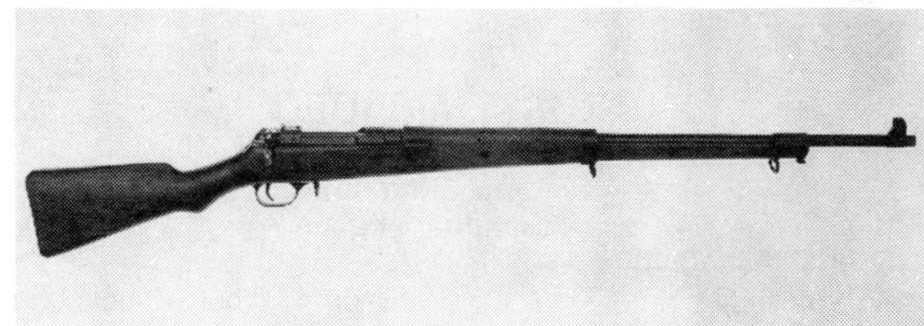

Courtesy Buffalo Bill Historical Center, Cody, Wyoming.

Exc.	V.G.	Good	Fair	Poor
300	250	200	150	100

Mark I Carbine

As above, with a 22" barrel.

Exc.	V.G.	Good	Fair	Poor
350	300	250	200	150

Mark 2

As above, with a modified rear sight.

Exc.	V.G.	Good	Fair	Poor
300	250	200	150	100

Mark 3

Introduced in 1910 with improved lockwork and stripper clip guides.

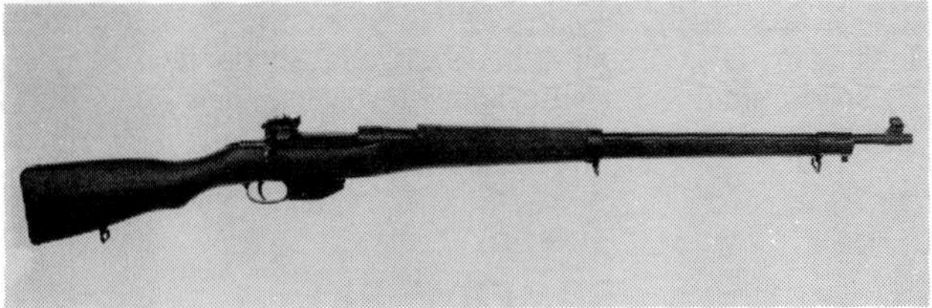

Courtesy Buffalo Bill Historical Center, Cody, Wyoming.

Exc.	V.G.	Good	Fair	Poor
325	275	225	175	125

Mark 3B

As above, with a magazine cut-off.

Exc.	V.G.	Good	Fair	Poor
350	300	250	200	150

Sporting Rifle

A .280 Ross or .303 caliber straight pole sporting rifle with a 24" barrel having open sights. Blued with a checkered walnut stock.

Courtesy Buffalo Bill Historical Center, Cody, Wyoming.

Courtesy Buffalo Bill Historical Center, Cody, Wyoming.

Exc.	V.G.	Good	Fair	Poor
275	225	200	150	125

ROSSI, AMADEO

Leopoldo, Brazil
Importer—Interarms
Alexandria, Virginia

Overland Shotgun

An exposed hammer sidelock 12, 20 or .410 bore double barrel shotgun with 26" or 28" barrels and double triggers. Manual extractors. Blued with a walnut stock. Discontinued in 1988.

Exc.	V.G.	Good	Fair	Poor
250	225	200	150	100

Squire Shotgun

A 12, 20 or .410 bore double barrel shotgun with 20", 26" or 28" barrels, double triggers and manual ejectors. Blued with a walnut stock.

NIB	Exc.	V.G.	Good	Fair	Poor
350	300	250	200	150	100

Model 92

A copy of the Winchester Model 1892, chambered for .357 Magnum, .44 Magnum or .44-40 with either a 16" or 20" barrel. Blued with a walnut stock. The engraved version of this model is worth approximately 20% more than the values listed below.

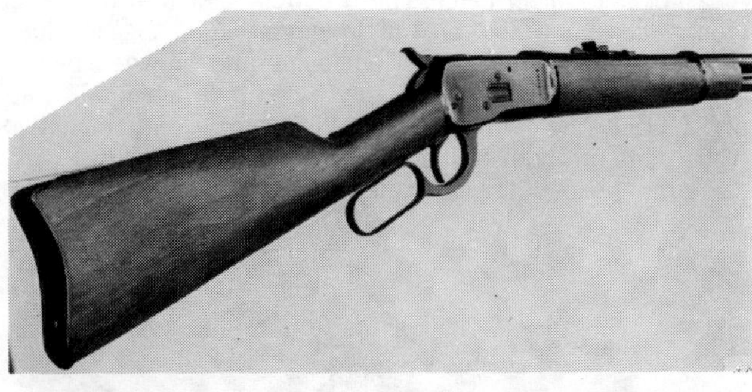

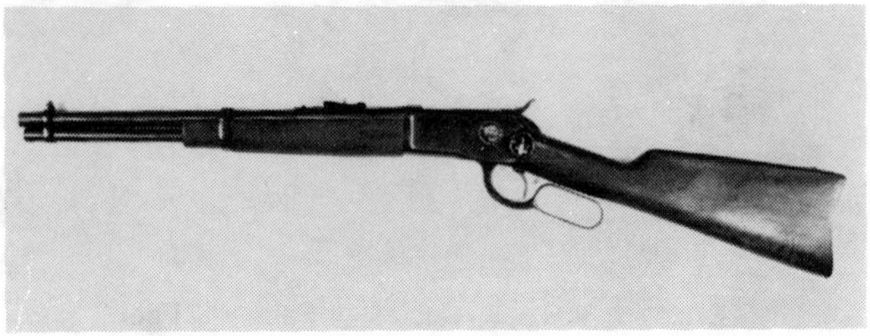

NIB	Exc.	V.G.	Good	Fair	Poor
285	225	175	150	100	75

Model 62

A copy of the Winchester Model 1890 rifle with either 16.5" or 23" round or octagonal barrels. Blued or stainless steel with a walnut stock.

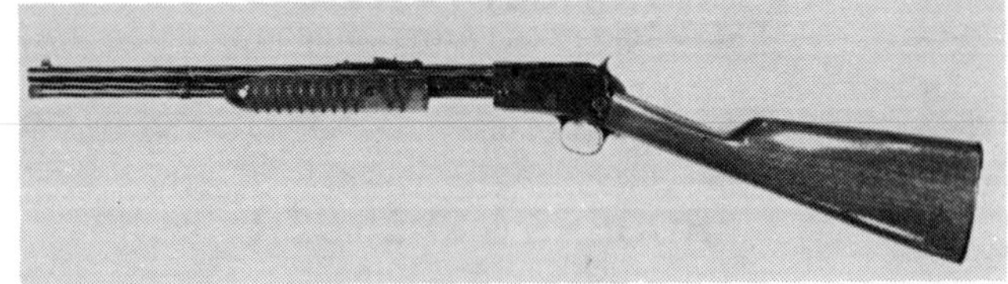

NIB	Exc.	V.G.	Good	Fair	Poor
200	175	150	125	100	75

Model 59

As above, in .22 Magnum caliber.

NIB	Exc.	V.G.	Good	Fair	Poor
210	175	150	125	100	75

Model 65

Similar to the Model 92, but chambered for either the .44 Special or .44 Magnum cartridge. Barrel length 20". Blued with a walnut stock. Introduced in 1989.

NIB	Exc.	V.G.	Good	Fair	Poor
300	250	200	175	150	125

Model 31

A .38 Special caliber double-action revolver with a 4" barrel and 5-shot cylinder. Blued or nickle-plated with walnut grips. Imported prior to 1986.

Exc.	V.G.	Good	Fair	Poor
125	100	75	50	40

Model 51

A .22 caliber double-action revolver with a 6" barrel, adjustable sights and a 6-shot cylinder. Blued with walnut grips. Imported prior to 1986.

Exc.	V.G.	Good	Fair	Poor
125	100	75	50	40

Model 511 Sportsman

As above, with a 4" barrel and made of stainless steel with walnut grips. Introduced in 1986.

NIB	Exc.	V.G.	Good	Fair	Poor
225	200	150	125	100	75

Model 68

A .38 Special double-action revolver with a 2" or 3" barrel and 5-shot cylinder. Blued or nickle-plated with walnut grips.

NIB	Exc.	V.G.	Good	Fair	Poor
185	150	125	100	75	50

Model 68S

This new version was introduced in 1993 and features a shrouded ejector rod and fixed sights. Chambered for the .38 Special cartridge it is offered with either 2" or 3" barrel. Grips or wood or rubber. Finish is blue or nickel. Weighs about 23 ozs.

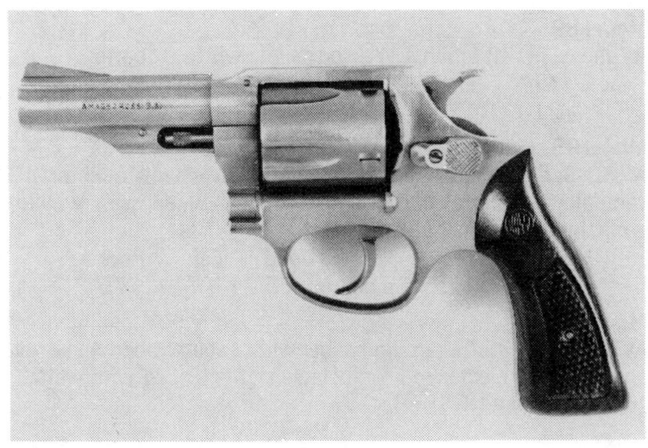

NIB	Exc.	V.G.	Good	Fair	Poor
175	150	125	100	75	60

Model 69

As above, in .32 Smith & Wesson caliber with a 3" barrel and 6-shot cylinder. Imported prior to 1986.

Exc.	V.G.	Good	Fair	Poor
125	100	75	50	40

Model 70

As above, in .22 caliber with a 3" barrel and 6-shot cylinder. Imported prior to 1986.

Exc.	V.G.	Good	Fair	Poor
125	100	75	50	40

Model 84

A stainless steel, .38 Special caliber double-action revolver with a ribbed 3" or 4" barrel. Blued with walnut grips. Imported in 1985 and 1986.

Exc.	V.G.	Good	Fair	Poor
175	150	125	100	75

Model 851

As above, with either a 3" or 4" ventilated-rib barrel and adjustable sights.

NIB	Exc.	V.G.	Good	Fair	Poor
210	175	150	125	100	75

Model 88S

Introduced in 1993 this improved model has the same features of the Model 68 with the addition of a stainless finish. It is chambered for the .38 Special cartridge and is fitted with either a 2" or 3" barrel. Available with either wood or rubber grips. Cylinder holds 5 cartridges. Weighs approximately 22 ozs.

NIB	Exc.	V.G.	Good	Fair	Poor
195	175	150	125	100	75

Model 89

As above, in .32 Smith & Wesson caliber with a 3" barrel.

NIB	Exc.	V.G.	Good	Fair	Poor
210	175	150	125	100	75

Model 951

A .38 Special caliber double-action revolver with a 3" or 4" ventilated-rib barrel and 6-shot cylinder. Blued with walnut grips. Introduced in 1985.

NIB	Exc.	V.G.	Good	Fair	Poor
200	175	150	125	100	75

Model 971

As above, in .357 Magnum caliber with a solid ribbed 4" barrel and enclosed ejector rod. Adjustable sights. Blued with walnut grips. Introduced in 1988.

NIB	Exc.	V.G.	Good	Fair	Poor
210	175	150	125	100	75

Model 971 Comp

Introduced in 1993. Similar to the Model 971 with the addition of a compensator on a 3.25" barrel. Overall length is 9" and weight is 32 ozs. Chambered for .357 Magnum cartridge.

NIB	Exc.	V.G.	Good	Fair	Poor
210	175	150	125	100	75

Model 971 Stainless

As above, but constructed of stainless steel with checkered black rubber grips. Introduced in 1989.

NIB	Exc.	V.G.	Good	Fair	Poor
225	200	150	125	100	75

Model 720

This double action revolver is chambered for the .44 Special and features a 5-round cylinder and 3" barrel. Overall length is 8" and weight is about 27.5 ozs. Finish is stainless steel.

NIB	Exc.	V.G.	Good	Fair	Poor
250	200	175	150	125	100

ROTH-SAUER

SEE—J. P. Sauer & Son

ROTH-STEYR

Austria-Hungary

Model 1907

An 8mm caliber semi-automatic pistol with a 5" barrel. Blued with ribbed walnut grips. This pistol is an unusual design in that the front of the bolt is hollow and encloses the barrel breech. When fired, the barrel recoils and rotates 90 degrees before the bolt is released to move rearward.

Exc.	V.G.	Good	Fair	Poor
400	350	300	200	125

TH. ROTTME

SEE—Austrian Military Firearms

ROTTWIEL

Rotwiel, West Germany

Importer—Dynamit Nobel of America Northvale, New Jersey

Model 650

A 12 gauge Over/Under shotgun with 28" ventilated-rib barrels having screw-in choke tubes, single selective trigger and automatic ejectors. The receiver engraved and in French casehardened, checkered stock of well figured walnut. Imported prior to 1987.

Exc.	V.G.	Good	Fair	Poor
700	600	500	400	375

Model 72

A 12 gauge Over/Under shotgun with 28" ventilated-rib barrels having screw-in choke tubes, single selective trigger and automatic ejectors. Blued with a well figured checkered walnut stock. Imported prior to 1988.

Exc.	V.G.	Good	Fair	Poor
1750	1650	1500	1000	750

Model 72 American Skeet

As above, with a 26.75" ventilated-rib barrel, single selective trigger and automatic ejectors. The receiver is also engraved. Imported prior to 1988.

Exc.	V.G.	Good	Fair	Poor
1750	1650	1500	1000	750

Model 72 Adjustable American Trap

As above, with a 34" ventilated-rib barrel, adjustable to point of impact. Imported prior to 1987.

Exc.	V.G.	Good	Fair	Poor
1500	1400	1200	900	650

Model 72 American Trap

As above, without the barrel being adjustable to the point of impact.

Exc.	V.G.	Good	Fair	Poor
1750	1650	1500	1000	950

Model 72 International Skeet

As above, with 26.75" ventilated-rib barrels having skeet chokes. Imported prior to 1988.

Exc.	V.G.	Good	Fair	Poor
1750	1650	1500	1000	950

Model 72 International Trap

As above, with 30" high ventilated-rib barrels which are improved-modified and full choked. Imported prior to 1988.

Exc.	V.G.	Good	Fair	Poor
1750	1650	1500	1000	950

ROYAL AMERICAN SHOTGUNS

Woodland Hills, California

Importer—Royal Arms International

Model 100

A 12 or 20 gauge Over/Under shotgun with 26", 28" or 30" ventilated-rib barrels, double triggers and extractors. Blued with a walnut stock. Imported from 1985 to 1987.

Exc.	V.G.	Good	Fair	Poor
350	300	250	175	150

Model 100AE

As above, with a single trigger and automatic ejectors.

Exc.	V.G.	Good	Fair	Poor
375	325	275	200	175

Model 600

A 12, 20, 28 or .410 bore double-barrel shotgun with 25", 26", 28" or 30" ventilated-rib barrels, double triggers and extractors. Blued with a walnut stock. Imported from 1985 to 1987.

Exc.	V.G.	Good	Fair	Poor
375	325	275	200	175

Model 800

A 12, 20, 28 or .410 bore detachable sidelock double-barrel shotgun with 24", 26" or 28" barrels, double triggers and automatic ejectors. Blued, French case-hardened with an English style walnut stock. Imported from 1985 to 1987.

Exc.	V.G.	Good	Fair	Poor
750	650	600	475	400

RUBY ARMS COMPANY

Guernica, Spain

Ruby

A 6.35mm or 7.35mm caliber semi-automatic pistol with a 3.5" barrel and 6-shot magazine. The slide marked "Ruby." Blued with plastic grips.

Exc.	V.G.	Good	Fair	Poor
175	150	100	75	50

RUGER

SEE—Sturm, Ruger Co.

RUPERTUS, JACOB

Philadelphia, Pennsylvania

Army Revolver

This is an extremely rare revolver chambered for .44 caliber percussion. It has a 7.25" octagon barrel with an integral loading lever that pivots to the side instead of downward. The hammer is mounted on the side, and there is a pellet priming device located on the backstrap. There is only one nipple on the breach that lines up with the top of the cylinder. The cylinder is unfluted and holds 6 shots. The finish is blued, with walnut grips; and the frame is marked "Patented April 19, 1859." There were less than 12 manufactured in 1859. It would behoove one to secure a qualified independent appraisal if a transaction were contemplated.

Exc.	V.G.	Good	Fair	Poor
6000	5000	3750	2750	2000

Navy Revolver

This model is equally as rare as the Army model. It is chambered for .36 caliber percussion. Otherwise it is quite similar in appearance to the Army model. There were approximately 12 manufactured in 1859. Both of these revolvers were manufactured for test purposes and were not well-received by the military, so further production was not accomplished.

Exc.	V.G.	Good	Fair	Poor
6000	5000	3750	2750	2000

Pocket Model Revolver

This is a smaller version of the Army and Navy model, chambered for .25 caliber percussion. It has no loading lever and has a 3-1/8" octagonal barrel. There were approximately 12 manufactured in 1859.

Exc.	V.G.	Good	Fair	Poor
4000	3250	2500	1850	1500

Single Shot Pocket Pistol

A .22, .32, .38, or .41 rimfire single shot pistol with half-octagonal barrels, ranging in length from 3" to 5". The barrel marked "Rupertus Pat'd. Pistol Mfg. Co. Philadelphia." Blued with walnut grips. Approximately 3,000 were made from 1870 to 1885. The .41 caliber variety is worth approximately 25% more than the values listed below.

Exc.	V.G.	Good	Fair	Poor
300	250	225	175	125

Double Barrel Pocket Pistol

A .22 caliber double-barrel pistol with 3" round barrels and a spur trigger. The hammer fitted with a sliding firing pin. Blued with walnut grips.

Exc.	V.G.	Good	Fair	Poor
750	650	500	400	300

Spur Trigger Revolver

A .22 caliber spur trigger revolver with a 2.75" round barrel and unfluted cylinder. The top strap marked "Empire Pat. Nov. 21, 71." Blued or nickle-plated with walnut grips. A .41 caliber spur trigger revolver with a 2 7/8" round barrel and a 5-shot fluted cylinder. Blued or nickle-plated with walnut grips. The top strap marked "Empire 41" and the barrel "J. Rupertus Phila. Pa." The .41 caliber variety is worth approximately 20% more than the values listed below. Manufactured during the 1870s and 1880s.

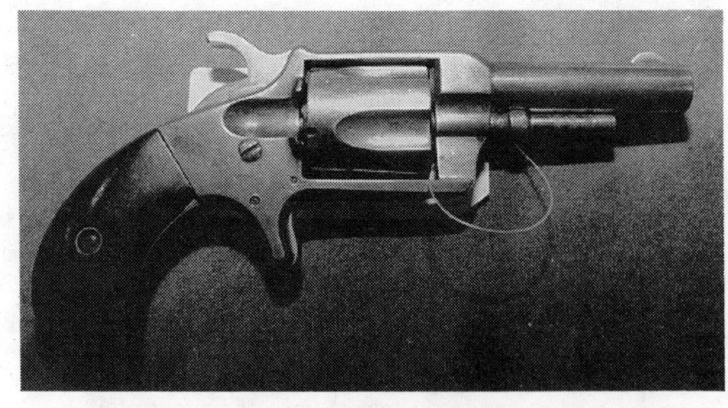

Exc.	V.G.	Good	Fair	Poor
300	250	225	175	125

S

S.A.C.M.
SEE—French State

S.A.E.
Eibar, Spain
Importer—Spain America Enterprises, Inc. Miami, Florida

Model 210S
A 12, 20, or .410 bore double-barrel shotgun with 26" or 28" barrels, double triggers and manual extractors. Blued, French casehardened with a checkered walnut stock. Imported in 1988.

Exc.	V.G.	Good	Fair	Poor
425	375	300	225	175

Model 340X
A Holland & Holland-style sidelock 10 or 20 gauge double-barrel shotgun with 26" barrels, double triggers and automatic ejectors. Blued, case-hardened with a checkered English style walnut stock. Imported in 1988.

Exc.	V.G.	Good	Fair	Poor
700	600	500	400	300

Model 209E
As above, with the exception that it was also chambered for .410 bore cartridges, and was more finely engraved. Imported in 1988.

Exc.	V.G.	Good	Fair	Poor
900	800	700	550	400

Model 70
A 12 or 20 gauge Over/Under shotgun with 26" ventilated-rib barrels having screw-in choke tubes, single trigger and automatic ejectors. The modestly engraved receiver either blued or French casehardened. Stock of finely figured walnut. Imported in 1988.

Exc.	V.G.	Good	Fair	Poor
400	300	250	200	150

Model 66C
A 12 gauge Over/Under shotgun with 26" or 30" ventilated-rib barrels choked for skeet or trap, single trigger and automatic ejectors. The boxlock action fitted with false sideplates which are engraved and gold inlaid. Blued with a checkered Monte Carlo-style stock and a beavertail forearm. Imported in 1988.

Exc.	V.G.	Good	Fair	Poor
900	800	700	575	450

S.E.A.M.
Eibar, Spain

This retailer sold a number of pistols produced by the firm of Urizar prior to 1935.

Praga
A 7.65 caliber semi-automatic pistol marked "Praga Cal 7.65" on the slide. Blued with plastic grips impressed with the trademark S.E.A.M.

Exc.	V.G.	Good	Fair	Poor
175	150	125	90	65

S.E.A.M.
A 6.35mm semi-automatic pistol with a 2" barrel. The slide marked "Fabrica de Armas SEAM." Blued with black plastic grips, having the trademark "SEAM" cast into them.

Exc.	V.G.	Good	Fair	Poor
175	150	125	90	65

Silesia
As above, but of 7.65mm caliber with a 3" barrel and having the word "Silesia" stamped on the slide.

Exc.	V.G.	Good	Fair	Poor
175	150	125	90	65

SKB ARMS COMPANY
Tokyo, Japan
Importer—SKB Company USA
Manhein, Pennsylvania

Model 100
A boxlock 12 or 20 gauge double-barrel shotgun with 25" to 30" barrels, single selective trigger and automatic ejectors. Blued with a walnut stock. Imported prior to 1981.

Exc.	V.G.	Good	Fair	Poor
475	425	375	300	250

Model 150
As above, with some engraving, a beavertail forearm and a figured walnut stock. Imported from 1972 to 1974.

Exc.	V.G.	Good	Fair	Poor
525	475	425	350	300

Model 200
As above, with a French case-hardened and scalloped receiver.

Exc.	V.G.	Good	Fair	Poor
550	500	450	375	325

Model 200E
As above, with an English style stock. Imported prior to 1989.

Exc.	V.G.	Good	Fair	Poor
750	675	600	475	375

Model 300
As above, with more engraving and a figured walnut stock.

Exc.	V.G.	Good	Fair	Poor
750	675	600	475	375

Model 400E
As above, with engraved false sideplates and an English style stock. Imported prior to 1990.

Exc.	V.G.	Good	Fair	Poor
975	875	750	600	500

Model 480E
As above, with a French case-hardened receiver and more finely figured walnut stocks.

Exc.	V.G.	Good	Fair	Poor
1200	1000	850	650	550

Model 500
A 12, 20, 28 or .410 Over/Under shotgun with 26", 28" or 30" ventilated-rib barrels. Blued with a walnut stock. Imported from 1966 to 1979.

Exc.	V.G.	Good	Fair	Poor
500	450	375	300	250

Model 600
As above, with a silver-plated receiver and better quality wood.

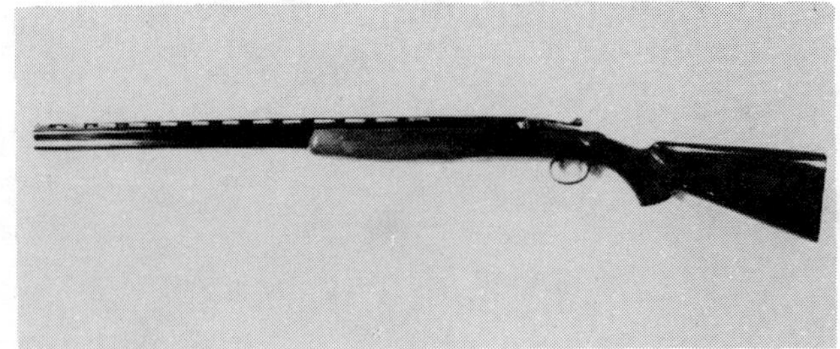

Exc.	V.G.	Good	Fair	Poor
700	625	550	450	325

Model 600 Magnum

As above, chambered for 3", 12 gauge cartridges. Imported from 1969 to 1972.

Exc.	V.G.	Good	Fair	Poor
725	650	575	475	350

Model 600 Trap Gun

As above, with 30" or 32" barrels trap choked, with a high comb walnut stock.

Exc.	V.G.	Good	Fair	Poor
675	600	525	425	300

Model 600 Skeet Gun

As above, chambered for 12, 20, 28 or .410 bore cartridges with 26" or 28" barrels which are skeet choked.

Exc.	V.G.	Good	Fair	Poor
700	625	550	450	325

Model 600 Skeet Combo Set

As above, with an extra set of interchangeable barrels. Furnished with a carrying case.

Exc.	V.G.	Good	Fair	Poor
700	625	550	450	325

Model 680E

Similar to the Model 600, with an engraved receiver and English style stock. Imported from 1973 to 1976.

Exc.	V.G.	Good	Fair	Poor
725	650	575	475	350

Model 700 Trap Gun

Similar to the Model 600 Trap, with a wider rib, additional engraving and a figured walnut stock. Imported from 1969 to 1975.

Exc.	V.G.	Good	Fair	Poor
825	750	675	575	450

Model 700 Skeet Gun

As above, with skeet chokes.

Exc.	V.G.	Good	Fair	Poor
850	775	700	600	475

Model 800 Trap Gun

As above, but with trap chokes and more engraving. Imported from 1969 to 1975.

Exc.	V.G.	Good	Fair	Poor
1200	1000	850	650	550

Model 800 Skeet Gun

As above, in 12 or 20 gauge with 26" or 28" skeet choked barrels. Imported from 1969 to 1975.

Exc.	V.G.	Good	Fair	Poor
1200	1000	850	650	550

Model 880 Crown Grade

A false sidelock 12, 20, 28 or .410 bore boxlock double-barrel shotgun with a single selective trigger and automatic ejectors. The engraved sideplates and receiver French case-hardened, and the figured walnut stock checkered. Imported prior to 1981.

Exc.	V.G.	Good	Fair	Poor
1700	1500	1250	1100	900

Model 505

A 12 or 20 gauge Over/Under shotgun with screw-in choke tubes, single selective trigger and automatic ejectors. Blued, checkered walnut stock.

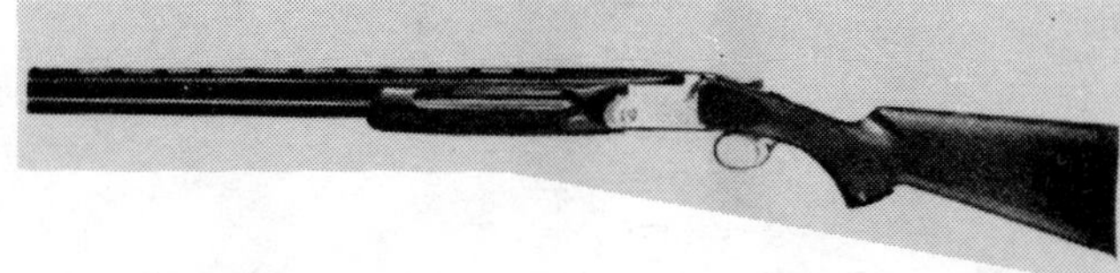

NIB	Exc.	V.G.	Good	Fair	Poor
750	675	600	500	450	375

The 505 Series is also produced in trap and skeet configurations, which are valued at approximately 5 percent additional.

Model 505 3-Gauge Skeet Set

As above, with 3 sets of barrels.

NIB	Exc.	V.G.	Good	Fair	Poor
1850	1650	1400	1100	900	750

Model 605

As above, with an engraved and French case-hardened receiver.

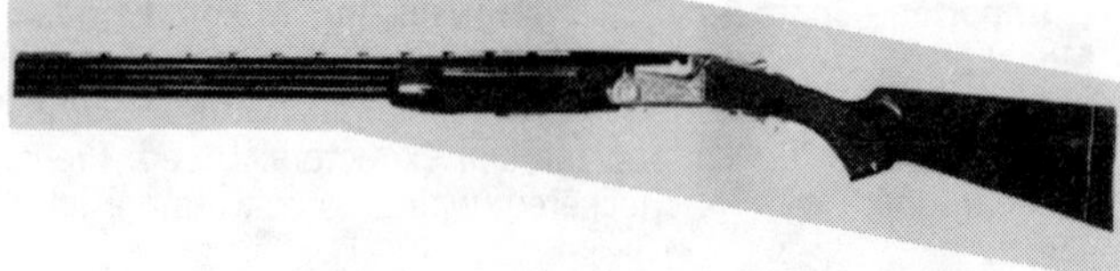

NIB	Exc.	V.G.	Good	Fair	Poor
900	750	650	550	400	350

The 605 Series is also available in trap or skeet configurations. The values are similar.

Model 605 3-Gauge Skeet Set

As above, with 3 extra sets of barrels.

NIB	Exc.	V.G.	Good	Fair	Poor
2000	1800	1550	1250	1000	850

Model 885

A false sidelock 12, 20, 28 or .410 bore boxlock shotgun. Similar to the model 800.

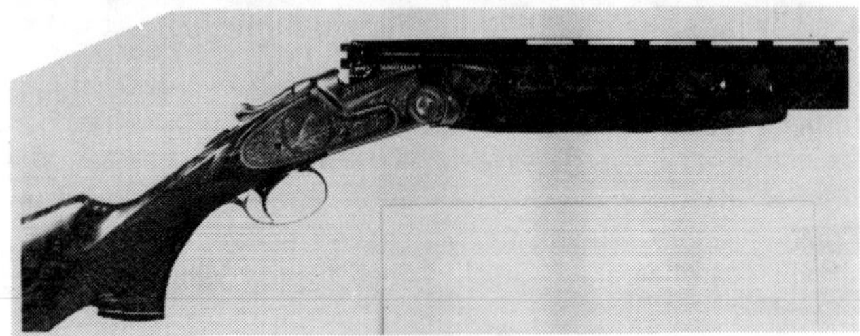

Exc.	V.G.	Good	Fair	Poor
1250	1050	900	700	600

Model 7300

A 12 or 20 gauge slide action shotgun. Blued with a walnut stock. Imported prior to 1981.

Exc.	V.G.	Good	Fair	Poor
300	250	200	150	100

Model 7900

As above, but skeet choked.

Exc.	V.G.	Good	Fair	Poor
350	300	250	200	150

Model 300

A 12 or 20 gauge semi-automatic shotgun with 26", 28" or 30" barrels. Blued with a walnut stock. Imported from 1968 to 1972.

Ventilated-Rib Barrel—Add 20%.

Exc.	V.G.	Good	Fair	Poor
300	250	200	150	100

Model 1300

A redesigned version of the Model 300 with a ventilated-rib barrel and screw-in choke tubes. Imported since 1988.

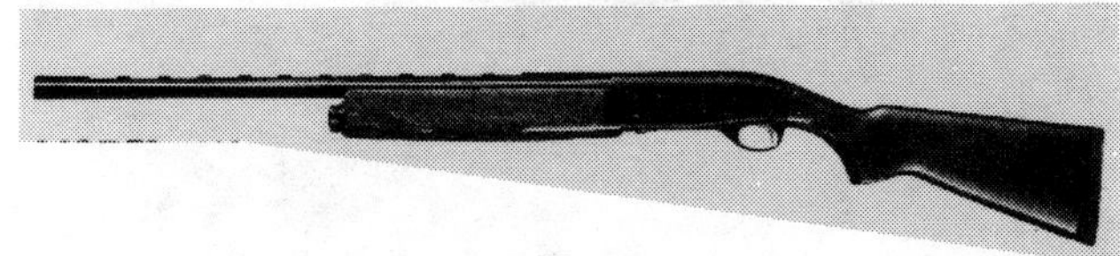

NIB	Exc.	V.G.	Good	Fair	Poor
450	400	350	300	200	150

Model XL 900 MR

A 12 gauge, semi-automatic shotgun with 26" to 30" ventilated-rib barrels, and etched alloy receiver and checkered walnut stock. Imported prior to 1981.

Exc.	V.G.	Good	Fair	Poor
325	275	225	175	125

Model 1900

As above, but also chambered for 20 gauge cartridges and available with 22", 26" or 28" ventilated-rib barrels having screw-in choke tubes. Blued with a walnut stock.

NIB	Exc.	V.G.	Good	Fair	Poor
500	425	375	300	250	175

Model 3000

Similar to the above, with a modified receiver design. Imported prior to 1990.

Exc.	V.G.	Good	Fair	Poor
475	400	350	250	150

SKS
Former Communist Bloc
Importer—Century International Arms

SKS

A 7.62x39mm semi-automatic rifle with a 20.5" barrel and 10-shot fixed magazine. Blued with oil finished stock. This rifle was a standard service arm for most Eastern Bloc countries prior to the adoption of the AK47.

Exc.	V.G.	Good	Fair	Poor
250	200	150	100	75

SSK INDUSTRIES
Bloomingdale, Ohio

SSK-Contender

A custom made pistol available in 74 different calibers from .17Bee to .588JDJ built on a Thompson Center action.

NIB	Exc.	V.G.	Good	Fair	Poor
575	500	475	425	350	275

SSK-XP100

A custom made pistol utilizing a Remington XP100 action. Available in a variety of calibers and sight configurations.

NIB	Exc.	V.G.	Good	Fair	Poor
650	600	550	500	400	300

.50 Caliber XP100

As above, with an integral muzzle brake and reinforced composition stock.

NIB	Exc.	V.G.	Good	Fair	Poor
1750	1500	1250	1000	750	500

S.W.D., INC.
Atlanta, Georgia

Cobray M-11

A 9mm semi-automatic pistol with a 32-round magazine. Parkerized finish.

Exc.	V.G.	Good	Fair	Poor
225	200	175	125	100

M-11 Carbine

As above, with a 16.25" barrel enclosed in a shroud and fitted with a telescoping wire stock.

Exc.	V.G.	Good	Fair	Poor
250	225	200	150	125

Terminator

A 12 or 20 gauge single shot shotgun with an 18" cylinder bored barrel. Parkerized finish.

Exc.	V.G.	Good	Fair	Poor
100	80	70	60	50

SABATTI
SEE—European American Armory

SACKET, D. D.
Westfield, Massachusetts

Under Hammer Pistol

A .34 or .36 single shot percussion pistol with a half octagonal 3" or 4" barrel marked "D. D. Sacket/Westfield/Cast Steel." Manufactured during the 1850s.

Exc.	V.G.	Good	Fair	Poor
500	400	350	250	175

SAFARI ARMS
Phoenix, Arizona

In operation from 1978 to 1987, this company was purchased by Olympic Arms of Olympia, Washington in 1987 and the models listed below are currently produced by that company under different tradenames.

Enforcer

A .45 caliber semi-automatic pistol with a 3.9" barrel and 5-shot magazine. Patterned after the Colt Model 1911. Blued, Armaloy, electroless nickle-plate or Parkerized finish with checkered walnut or neoprene grips.

Exc.	V.G.	Good	Fair	Poor
700	600	500	400	350

Match Master

As above, with a 5" barrel.

Exc.	V.G.	Good	Fair	Poor
700	600	500	400	350

Black Widow

As above, with ivory Micarta grips etched with a Black Widow.

Exc.	V.G.	Good	Fair	Poor
700	600	500	400	350

SSK Ruger Redhawk conversions.

SSK Custom Ruger Redhawk ''Beast.''

SSK Custom Ruger #1 .577 Nitro Express.

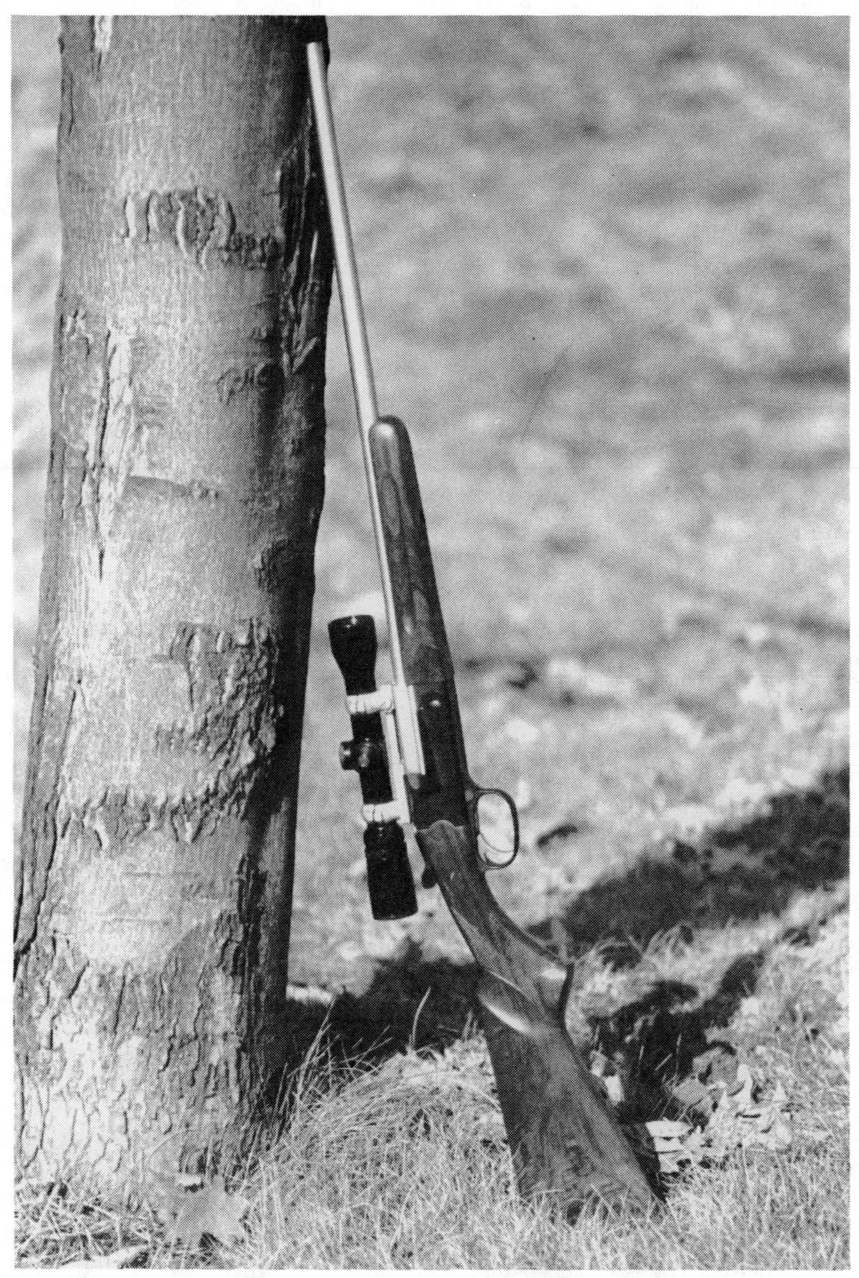

SSK Custom TCR Rifle available from .17 Rem.

Model 81

As above, without the grip etching and also offered in .38 caliber.

Exc.	V.G.	Good	Fair	Poor
800	700	600	500	400

Model 81L

As above, with a 6" barrel.

Exc.	V.G.	Good	Fair	Poor
850	750	650	550	450

Ultimate Unlimited

A bolt-action single shot pistol with a 15" barrel chambered for a variety of cartridges. Blued with a laminated stock.

Exc.	V.G.	Good	Fair	Poor
850	750	650	550	450

Survivor I Conversion Unit

A conversion unit fitted to the Model 1911 frame which alters that pistol to a bolt-action carbine. Barrel length 16.25", caliber .223, folding stock.

Exc.	V.G.	Good	Fair	Poor
300	275	250	200	150

Counter Sniper Rifle

A .308 caliber bolt-action target rifle with a heavy 26" barrel and 20-round detachable magazine. Matte blued with a colored composite stock.

Exc.	V.G.	Good	Fair	Poor
1200	1050	850	650	450

SAKO

Riihimaki, Finland
Importer—Stoeger
South Hackensack, New Jersey

Arms produced by this company prior to 1972 are worth approximately 25% more than arms of the same type produced thereafter.

Standard Sporter

A bolt-action magazine rifle produced in a wide variety of calibers with varying barrel lengths, etc. Blued with checkered walnut stocks.

Exc.	V.G.	Good	Fair	Poor
600	550	450	300	150

Deluxe Model

As above, with an engraved floorplate and checkered Monte Carlo-style stock having a rosewood pistol grip cap and forend tip.

Exc.	V.G.	Good	Fair	Poor
700	600	500	300	150

Finnbear

As above, with a long-action available in a variety of large bore calibers fitted with a 20" or 23.5" barrel. Blued with a checkered stock. .458 Winchester Magnum, 20 Produced, Values Doubled.

Exc.	V.G.	Good	Fair	Poor
700	600	500	300	150

Forester

As above, with a shorter-action suitable for use with intermediate cartridges.

Exc.	V.G.	Good	Fair	Poor
700	600	500	300	150

Vixen

As above, with a short-action.

Exc.	V.G.	Good	Fair	Poor
700	600	500	300	150

FN Action

Manufactured from 1950 to 1957, this model utilized a Fabrique Nationale manufactured receiver and was chambered for .270 Winchester and .30-06 cartridges. Otherwise, as above.

Exc.	V.G.	Good	Fair	Poor
600	550	450	250	125

FN Magnum Action

As above, with a long-action for .300 and .375 Holland & Holland.

Exc.	V.G.	Good	Fair	Poor
600	550	450	250	125

Finnwolf

A 4-shot lever action rifle produced in a variety of calibers. Blued, checkered walnut stock. Manufactured from 1962 to 1974.

Exc.	V.G.	Good	Fair	Poor
600	550	450	250	150

Anniversary Model

A 7mm Remington Magnum bolt-action rifle with a 24" barrel. Blued, checkered walnut stock. A total of 1,000 were manufactured. As with any commemorative firearm, this model should be NIB to realize its full resale potential.

NIB	Exc.	V.G.	Good	Fair	Poor
1200	700	550	450	250	200

Hunter

This model is offered in three action lengths; short, medium, and long. In the short action the calibers available are .17 Rem., .222, .223 in 21.25" barrel. In medium action the calibers are: .22-250, .243, .308, and 7MM-08 in 21.75" barrel. The long action calibers are: .25-06, .270 Win., .280 Rem., .30-06 in 22" barrel length. In 24" barrel the long action calibers are: 7MM Rem. Mag., .300 Win. and .300 Wby. Mag., .338 and .375 Win. Mag., and .416 Rem. Mag. Available in left handed version for all but short action calibers. Adjustable trigger is standard. Checkered European walnut stock. Weight for short action is 6.25 lbs., for medium action 6.5 lbs., and long action calibers 7.75 to 8.25 depending on caliber.

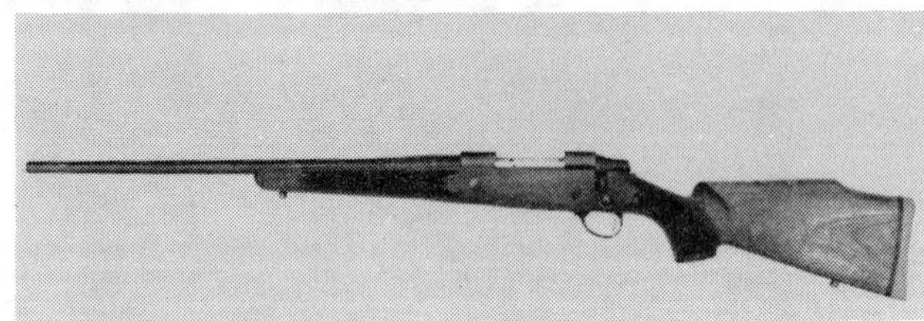

Medium Action

NIB	Exc.	V.G.	Good	Fair	Poor
795	600	500	400	300	200

Short Action

Add 10% for .222 Rem. and .223 Rem. For .17 Rem. add 20% to above prices.

Long Action

NIB	Exc.	V.G.	Good	Fair	Poor
795	600	500	400	300	200

NOTE: For long action calibers in .300 and .338 Win. Mag. add 10%. For .375 H&H Mag. add 20%. For .416 Rem. Mag. add 25%.

Carbine

As above, with an 18.5" barrel. Produced with either a medium or long-length action.

NIB	Exc.	V.G.	Good	Fair	Poor
795	600	500	400	300	200

FiberClass
This model features a black plain fiberglass stock. Offered in long action calibers only. The .25-06, .270, .280, and .30-06 are fitted with 22" barrels and weighs 7.25 lbs. The 7MM Rem. Mag., .300 Win. Mag., .338 Win. Mag., and .375 H&H are fitted with 24" barrel and weighs 7.25 lbs. The .416 Rem. Mag. has a 24" barrel and weighs 8 lbs.

NIB	Exc.	V.G.	Good	Fair	Poor
1050	800	600	500	300	200

NOTE: For long action calibers in .300 and .338 Win. Mag. add 10%. For .375 H&H Mag. add 20%. For .416 Rem. Mag. add 25%.

FiberClass Carbine
As above, with a fiberglass stock.

NIB	Exc.	V.G.	Good	Fair	Poor
1050	800	600	500	300	200

Carbine
This model features a Mannlicher-style stock with a two piece forearm. It has a checkered walnut stock with oil finish. It is offered in both medium and short actions, all with 18.5" barrels. In medium action the .243 and .308 are available and weighs 6 lbs. The long action calibers are: .270, and .30-06 weighing 7.25 lbs.; and the .338 Win. Mag. and .375 H&H weighing 7.75 lbs.

Medium Action

NIB	Exc.	V.G.	Good	Fair	Poor
900	700	500	400	300	200

Long Action

NIB	Exc.	V.G.	Good	Fair	Poor
900	700	500	400	300	200

NOTE: For long action calibers in .338 Win. Mag. add 10%. For .375 H&H Mag. add 20%.

Laminated Model
This model features a laminated checkered hardwood stock made up of 36 layers. Solid recoil pad is standard as are quick detachable sling swivels. Available in both medium and long action calibers. Medium action calibers are: .22-250, .243, .308, and 7MM-08 with 21.75" barrel and weighs 6.5 lbs. Long action aclibers are: .25-06, .270, .280, .30-06 with 22" barrel weighing 7.75 lbs. Offered with 24" barrels are: 7MM Rem. Mag., .300 and .338 Win. Mag., and .375 H&H which weighs 7.75 lbs.

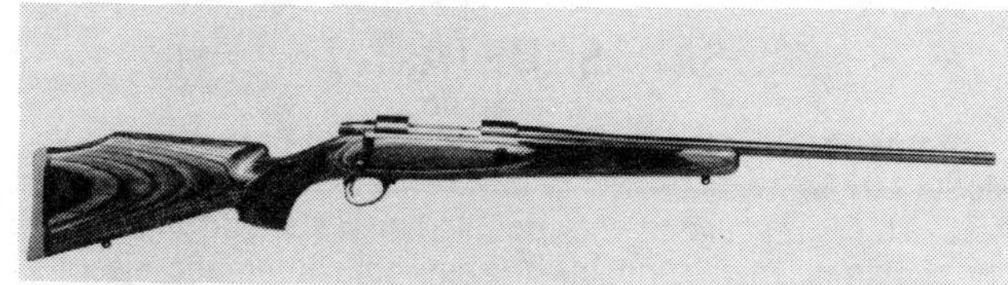

Medium Action

NIB	Exc.	V.G.	Good	Fair	Poor
950	750	600	500	300	200

Long Action

NIB	Exc.	V.G.	Good	Fair	Poor
950	750	600	500	300	200

NOTE: For long action calibers in .300 and .338 Win. Mag. add 10%. For .375 H&H Mag. add 20%. For .416 Rem. Mag. add 25%.

Varmint-Heavy Barrel
The checkered walnut stock on this model features an extra wide beavertail forearm with oil finish. Offered in both short and medium action all are fitted with a 23" heavy barrel weighing 8.5 lbs. Short action calibers are .17 Rem., .222, and .223. Medium action calibers are: .22-250, .243, 308, and 7MM-08.

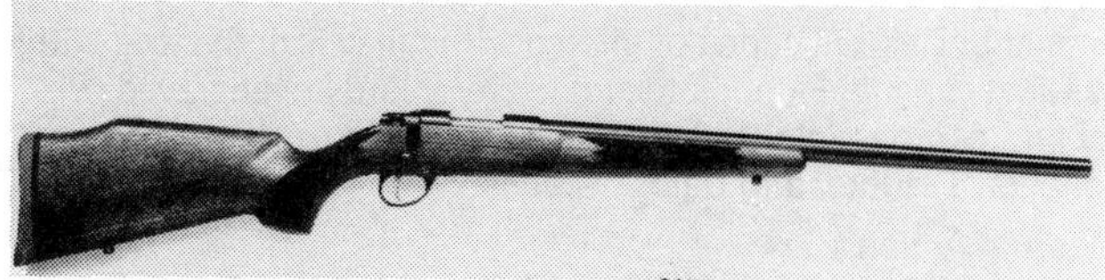

Short Action

NIB	Exc.	V.G.	Good	Fair	Poor
875	700	500	400	300	200

NOTE: Add 10% for .222 and .223 Rem. Add 20% for .15 Rem. to above prices.

Medium Action

NIB	Exc.	V.G.	Good	Fair	Poor
875	700	500	400	300	200

PPC Benchrest/Varmint
Similar to the Varmint but single shot. Fitted with 23.75" barrel and weighs 8.75 lbs. Available in short action special calibers .22PPC and 6mm PPC.

NIB	Exc.	V.G.	Good	Fair	Poor
1050	800	600	400	300	200

Classic Grade
Hand checkered select grade walnut stock with matte lacquer finish are featured on this grade. Offered in medium and long action. Long action rifles are offered in left hand model. The medium action caliber is .243 Win. with a 21.75" barrel weighing 6 lbs. The long action calibers are: .270, .30-06, and 7MM Rem. Mag. with 24" barrels. Long action calibers weighs about 7.5 lbs.

NIB	Exc.	V.G.	Good	Fair	Poor
795	600	500	400	300	200

Deluxe Grade
This grade features a high grade European walnut stock with hand cut basket weave checkering. The forend tip and grip are fitted with rosewood. English style recoil pad is standard. Long action models are offered in left hand configuration. As with the Hunter model short, medium, and long action are available in the same calibers, barrel lengths and weights as the Hunter.

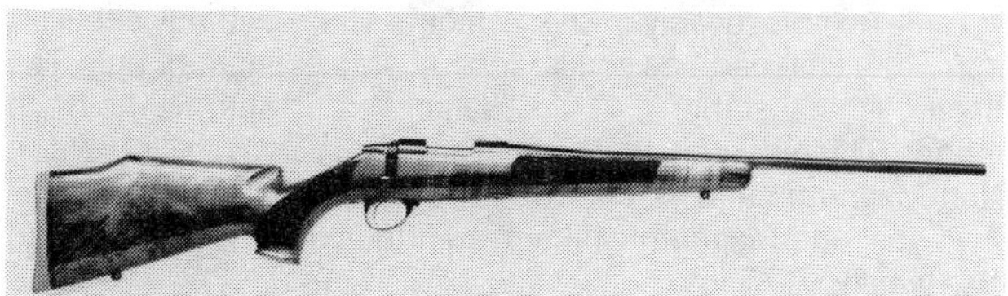

Medium Action

NIB	Exc.	V.G.	Good	Fair	Poor
1050	800	600	500	300	200

Short Action
Add 10% for .222 and .223 Rem. Add 20% for .17 Rem. to above prices.

Long Action

NIB	Exc.	V.G.	Good	Fair	Poor
1050	800	600	500	300	200

NOTE: For long action calibers in .300 and .338 Win. Mag. add 10%. For .375 H&H Mag. add 20%. For .416 Rem. Mag. add 25%.

Super Grade

Similar to Deluxe Grade but offered with fancy walnut stock with oak-leaf carving. Floor plate and trigger guard are engraved. Pistol grip cap has inlaid silver plate. Offered in same actions and calibers as Hunter and Deluxe Grades.

Medium Action

NIB	Exc.	V.G.	Good	Fair	Poor
2250	1500	900	600	400	200

Short Action

Add 10% for .222 and .223 Rem. Add 20% for .17 Rem. to above prices.

Long Action

NIB	Exc.	V.G.	Good	Fair	Poor
2250	1500	900	600	400	200

NOTE: For long action calibers in .300 and .338 Win. Mag. add 10%. For .375 H&H Mag. add 20%. For .416 Rem. Mag. add 25%.

Safari Grade

As above, chambered for .300 Winchester Magnum, .338 Winchester Magnum or .375 Holland & Holland cartridges.

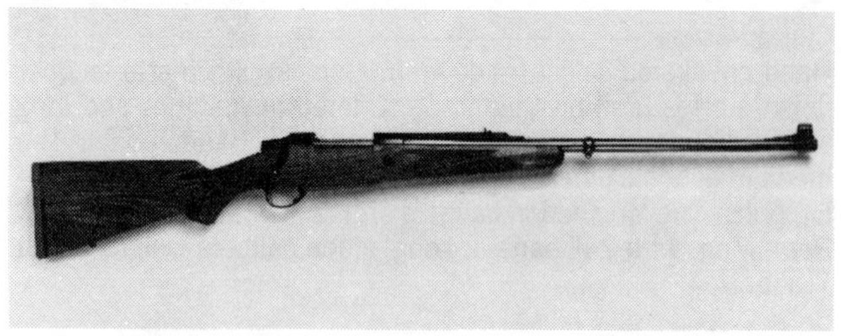

NIB	Exc.	V.G.	Good	Fair	Poor
2250	1500	900	600	400	200

Model 78

A .22 or .22 Hornet bolt-action rifle with a 22" barrel. Blued with a checkered walnut stock. Discontinued in 1986.

Exc.	V.G.	Good	Fair	Poor
500	450	400	300	200

Model 2700

A .270 to .300 Winchester Magnum bolt-action rifle with a 22" barrel. Blued, checkered walnut stock. Discontinued in 1985.

Exc.	V.G.	Good	Fair	Poor
600	500	400	300	200

TRG-S

This model features a unique cold forged receiver. The stock is a special reinforced polyurethane Monte Carlo without checkering. The recoil pad has spacer for adjustable length of pull. The trigger is adjustable and the detachable magazine holds 5 rounds. Offered in a variety of calibers from .243 to .375H&H. Non Magnum calibers are fitted with a 22" barrel and weighs 7.75 lbs. and Magnum calibers are fitted with a 24" barrel and also weighs 7.75 lbs.

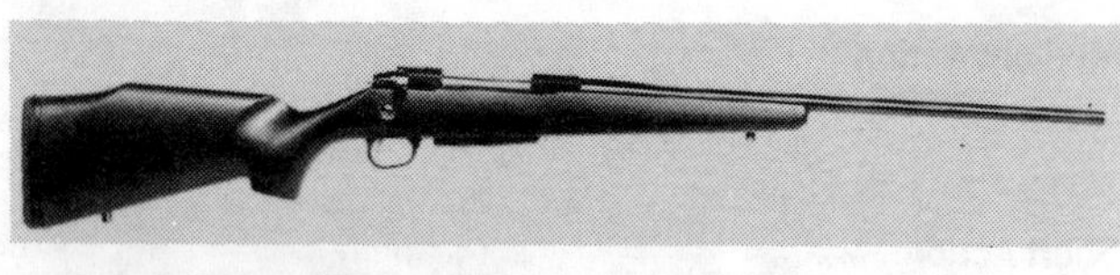

NIB	Exc.	V.G.	Good	Fair	Poor
595	500	400	300	200	100

TRG-21

The receiver is similar to the TRG-S but the polyurethane stock features a unique design. The trigger is adjustable for length and two-stage pull and also for horizontal or vertical pitch. This model also has several options that would affect the price; muzzle brake, one-piece scope mount, bipod, quick detachable sling swivels, and military nylon sling. The rifle is offered in .308 Win. only. It is fitted with a 25.75" barrel and weighs 10.5 lbs.

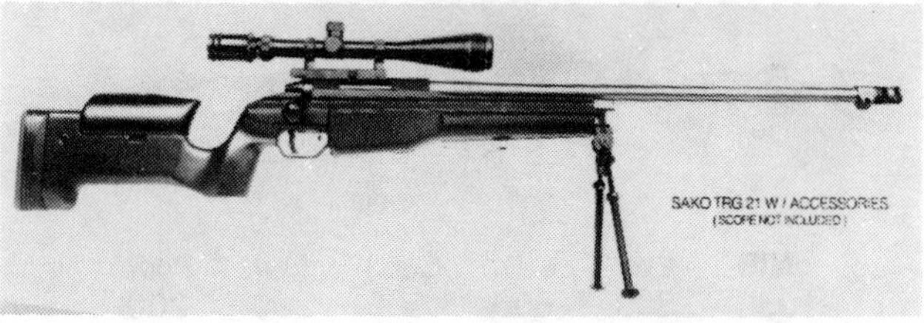

NIB	Exc.	V.G.	Good	Fair	Poor
3050	2400	1750	1000	700	400

SAM, INC.

Reston, Virginia

Special Service Arms Mfg., Inc.

Model 88 Crossfire

A semi-automatic combination 12 gauge—.308 caliber shotgun/rifle, with a 7-shot shotgun magazine and 20-shot rifle magazine. Barrel length 20", matte black finished with a composition stock. This weapon can be fired in either mode by means of a selector switch mounted on the receiver.

SAMCO GLOBAL ARMS, INC.

Miami, Florida

This firm imports a variety of military surplus firearms which under current law are marked with the importer's name.

SARASQUETA, FELIX

Eibar, Spain

Importer—SAE, Inc.Miami, Florida

Merke

A 12 gauge Over/Under double-barrel shotgun with 22" or 27" ribbed and separated barrels, non-selective trigger and manual extractors. Blued, checkered walnut stock. Imported in 1986 only.

Exc.	V.G.	Good	Fair	Poor
275	250	225	150	100

SARASQUETA, J. J.

Eibar, Spain

Importer—American Arms, Inc.Overland Park, Kansas

Model 107E

A 12, 16 or 20 gauge boxlock double-barrel shotgun with a variety of barrel lengths, double triggers and automatic ejectors. Blued with a checkered walnut stock. Discontinued in 1984.

Exc.	V.G.	Good	Fair	Poor
375	300	275	225	175

Model 119E

As above, with a more finely figured walnut stock.

Exc.	V.G.	Good	Fair	Poor
475	400	375	325	275

Model 130E

As above, but engraved.

Exc.	V.G.	Good	Fair	Poor
800	700	600	450	350

Model 131E

As above, with considerably more engraving.

Exc.	V.G.	Good	Fair	Poor
1100	900	800	650	500

Model 1882 E LUXE

As above, with a single selective trigger and gold inlays. A silver inlaid version is sold for approximately 10% less.

Exc.	V.G.	Good	Fair	Poor
800	700	600	450	350

SARASQUETA, VICTOR
Eibar, Spain

Model 3

A 12, 16 or 20 gauge boxlock or sidelock double-barrel shotgun available in a variety of barrel lengths, with double triggers and automatic ejectors. Blued with a checkered straight stock. The sidelock version is worth approximately 20% more than the values listed below. The basic Model 3 was offered in a variety of grades featuring different amounts of engraving and better quality wood. These shotguns are listed under the model designations of 4 to 12E below.

Exc.	V.G.	Good	Fair	Poor
600	500	450	350	300

Model 4

Exc.	V.G.	Good	Fair	Poor
600	550	475	400	300

Model 4E (Auto-ejectors)

Exc.	V.G.	Good	Fair	Poor
675	625	550	450	350

Model 203

Exc.	V.G.	Good	Fair	Poor
650	600	525	425	325

Model 203E

Exc.	V.G.	Good	Fair	Poor
700	650	575	475	375

Model 6E

Exc.	V.G.	Good	Fair	Poor
800	750	625	525	425

Model 7E

Exc.	V.G.	Good	Fair	Poor
850	800	675	575	475

Model 10E

Exc.	V.G.	Good	Fair	Poor
1750	1500	1250	950	750

Model 11E

Exc.	V.G.	Good	Fair	Poor
1850	1600	1350	1150	850

Model 12E

Exc.	V.G.	Good	Fair	Poor
2200	1850	1500	1300	1000

SARDIUS
Israel
Importer—Armscorp of America, Inc.

SD-9

A 9mm double-action semi-automatic pistol with a 3" barrel and 6-shot magazine. Matte black finish with composition grips. Imported since 1988.

NIB	Exc.	V.G.	Good	Fair	Poor
350	300	250	200	150	100

SAUER, J. P. & SON
Suhl, Germany

Bolt Action Rifle

A Mauser action sporting rifle chambered for a variety of cartridges with either a 22" or 24" barrel having a raised rib. Double set triggers, express sights, blued with a checkered walnut stock. Manufactured prior to World War II.

Ex.	V.G.	Good	Fair	Poor
700	600	500	400	300

Model 200

A bolt-action rifle chambered for a variety of cartridges with short or medium length actions, 24" barrels, set trigger, 4-round magazine. Blued, checkered walnut stock. Discontinued 1987. Extra barrels—Add $235.

Exc.	V.G.	Good	Fair	Poor
650	550	500	425	350

Model 200 Lightweight

As above, with an alloy receiver. Discontinued in 1987.

Exc.	V.G.	Good	Fair	Poor
600	500	400	325	250

Model 200 Lux

As above, with a finely figured walnut stock, rosewood pistol grip cap and forend tip, gold plated trigger and a machine jewelled bolt. Imported prior to 1988.

Exc.	V.G.	Good	Fair	Poor
700	600	550	475	400

Model 200 Carbon Fiber

The Model 200 fitted with a carbon composition stock. Imported in 1987 and 1988.

Exc.	V.G.	Good	Fair	Poor
800	750	650	500	400

Model 90

A bolt-action rifle produced in a number of calibers in all action lengths with 23" or 26" barrels, with a detachable magazine. Blued with a checkered walnut stock. Discontinued in 1989.

Exc.	V.G.	Good	Fair	Poor
800	700	600	450	400

Model 90 Stutzen

As above, with a full-length Mannlicher-style stock. Imported prior to 1990.

Exc.	V.G.	Good	Fair	Poor
825	725	625	475	425

Model 90 Safari

The Model 90 made for use with the .458 Winchester Magnum cartridge and fitted with a 24" barrel. Imported from 1986 to 1988.

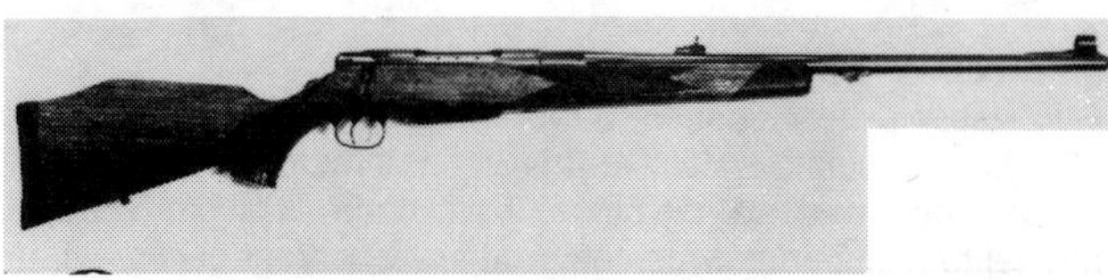

Exc.	V.G.	Good	Fair	Poor
1250	1100	950	750	600

The Model 90 Series of bolt-action rifles was available in a deluxe version that differed with the grade of workmanship and materials utilized. This deluxe series would be worth approximately 60 percent additional. There were optional engraved models; these should be individually appraised.

Model 90 Supreme

Similar to the above, with a gold-plated trigger, machine jewelled bolt and finely figured checkered walnut stock. Introduced in 1987.

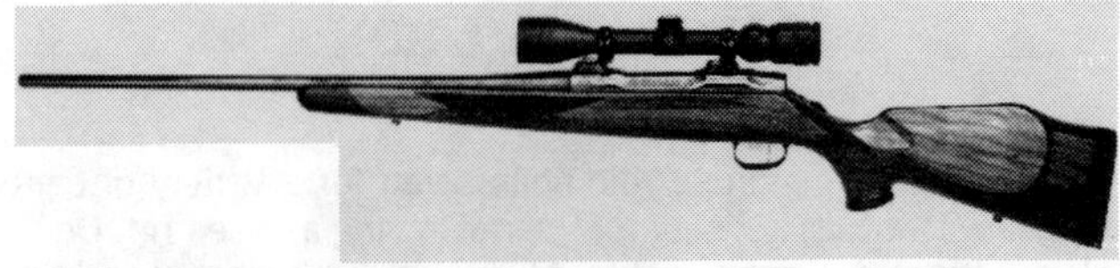

NIB	Exc.	V.G.	Good	Fair	Poor
1500	1250	1100	950	750	650

Luftwaffe Survival Drilling

A double barrel 12 gauge by 9.3x74R combination shotgun/rifle with 28" barrels. Blued with a checkered walnut stock and marked with Nazi inspection stampings on the stock and barrel breech. Normally, furnished with an aluminum case.

Exc.	V.G.	Good	Fair	Poor
5000	4000	3500	2500	2000

Model 3000 Drilling

This model was chambered for a variety of gauges and calibers and is built upon a boxlock action having a Greener crossbolt. The action lightly engraved. Blued, checkered walnut stock.

NIB	Exc.	V.G.	Good	Fair	Poor
3400	2900	2500	2000	1500	1250

Model 54 Combo

A combination rifle/shotgun chambered for a variety of gauges and calibers with an action as above. Discontinued in 1986.

Exc.	V.G.	Good	Fair	Poor
2200	2000	1750	1400	1200

Model 60

A 12, 16 or 20 gauge double-barrel boxlock shotgun produced in a variety of barrel lengths with double triggers and manual extractors. Blued with checkered walnut stock. Produced prior to World War II.

Exc.	V.G.	Good	Fair	Poor
700	625	550	400	300

Royal Model

A 12 or 20 gauge boxlock double-barrel shotgun with 26", 28" or 30" barrels, single selective triggers with automatic ejectors. The frame is scalloped, blued with a checkered walnut stock. Manufactured from 1955 to 1977.

Exc.	V.G.	Good	Fair	Poor
1500	1250	1000	750	500

Grade I Artemis

A 12 gauge sidelock double-barrel shotgun with 28" barrels, single selective trigger and automatic ejector. Engraved, blued with checkered walnut stock. Manufactured from 1966 to 1977.

Exc.	V.G.	Good	Fair	Poor
5000	4250	3500	2500	2000

Grade II Artemis

As above, but more finely finished.

Exc.	V.G.	Good	Fair	Poor
6500	5750	4750	3500	3000

Model 66

A 12 gauge sidelock double-barrel shotgun having a 26", 28" or 30" barrel, single selective trigger and automatic ejectors. Blued, checkered walnut stock. This model was produced in three different grades which have different degrees of engraving. Produced from 1966 to 1975.

Grade I

Exc.	V.G.	Good	Fair	Poor
2000	1800	1500	1150	800

Grade II

Exc.	V.G.	Good	Fair	Poor
3000	2800	2500	2150	1800

Grade III

Exc.	V.G.	Good	Fair	Poor
3750	3500	2850	2500	2000

Roth-Sauer

A 7.65mm locked breech semi-automatic pistol with a 4.5" barrel. The frame is marked "Patent Roth". Blued with composition grips bearing the figure of a bearded man (Sauer's Trademark).

Exc.	V.G.	Good	Fair	Poor
950	800	650	450	300

Model 1913

A 6.35mm or 7.65mm semi-automatic pistol with either a 2.5" or 3" barrel and 7-shot magazine. Blued with black composition grips impressed "Sauer" across the top. Manufactured from 1913 to 1930.

Exc.	V.G.	Good	Fair	Poor
300	250	200	150	100

.25 WTM

A 6.35mm semi-automatic pistol with a 2.5" barrel. Marked on the slide "JP Sauer & Sohn Suhl". Blued with black composition grips, marked as above. Introduced in 1924.

Exc.	V.G.	Good	Fair	Poor
300	250	200	150	100

Model 28

As above, with the grip marked "Cal.6.35 28". Manufactured from 1928 to 1939.

Exc.	V.G.	Good	Fair	Poor
275	225	175	125	90

Behorden Model

A 7.65mm semi-automatic pistol with a 3" barrel. Very similar in design to the Model 1913. Blued with black composition grips. Manufactured from 1930 to 1937.

Exc.	V.G.	Good	Fair	Poor
300	250	200	150	100

Model 38H

A 7.65mm semi-automatic pistol with a 3.25" barrel and double-action trigger. Early production varieties of this pistol have a safety catch at the rear of the slide. This catch was omitted on later production arms. The slide marked "JP Sauer & Sohn Cal. 7.65". Blued with black composition grips bearing the monogram "SuS". Manufactured from 1939 to 1945.

Courtesy Orville Reichert.

Courtesy Orville Reichert.

Exc.	V.G.	Good	Fair	Poor
350	300	275	200	150

SAVAGE ARMS CORPORATION
Utica, New York
Westfield, Massachusetts

Established in 1894 by Arthur W. Savage, this company has manufactured a wide variety of firearms of which their Model 99 is the best known.

Model 1895

A .303 Savage caliber lever action rifle with a 22", 26" or 30" barrel and 5-shot magazine. Identifiable by the hole in the bolt. The barrel marked "Savage Repeating Arms Co. Utica, N.Y. U.S.A. Pat. Feb. 7, 1893." Blued with a walnut stock. Approximately 6,000 were manufactured between 1895 and 1899.

22" or 30" Barrel—Add 10%.

Exc.	V.G.	Good	Fair	Poor
1500	1250	1000	750	500

Model 1899

A .25-35, .30-30, .303 Savage, .32-40 or .38-55 caliber lever action rifle with a 20", 22" or 26" barrel marked "Savage Arms Company, Utica, N.Y. Pat. Feb. 7, 1893." Approximately 75,000 were manufactured between 1899 and 1917. Also available in takedown form. Blued with a walnut stock. This model does not have a hole in the bolt.

Exc.	V.G.	Good	Fair	Poor
650	600	500	400	275

Model 99A

As above, but in .30-30, .250-3000, .300 Savage or .303 Savage caliber with a 24" round barrel. Manufactured between 1920 and 1936.

Exc.	V.G.	Good	Fair	Poor
550	500	400	300	200

Model 99B

As above, but in takedown form. Manufactured between 1920 and 1936.

Exc.	V.G.	Good	Fair	Poor
900	750	500	400	250

Model 99E

As above, but also chambered for .22 Hi Power and with a 22" barrel. Manufactured between 1920 and 1936.

Exc.	V.G.	Good	Fair	Poor
900	750	500	400	250

Model 99F

As above, but in takedown form. Manufactured between 1920 and 1942.

Exc.	V.G.	Good	Fair	Poor
500	400	300	200	150

Model 99G

As above, with a checkered stock. Manufactured between 1920 and 1942.

Exc.	V.G.	Good	Fair	Poor
650	500	400	300	250

Model 99R

As above, with a pistol grip stock and semi-beavertail forend. Manufactured between 1936 and 1942.

Exc.	V.G.	Good	Fair	Poor
500	400	300	200	150

Model 99RS

As above, with a Lyman aperture rear sight. Manufactured between 1936 and 1942.

Exc.	V.G.	Good	Fair	Poor
600	500	400	300	200

Model 99T

The Model 99R in solid frame form. Manufactured between 1936 and 1942.

Exc.	V.G.	Good	Fair	Poor
450	350	300	200	150

Model 99K

The Model 99E/F with an engraved receiver. Manufactured between 1931 and 1942.

Exc.	V.G.	Good	Fair	Poor
2000	1750	1500	1200	850

Model 99EG

The Model 99E produced additionally in .243, .308 and .358 caliber. Manufactured between 1946 and 1960.

Exc.	V.G.	Good	Fair	Poor
350	300	250	200	175

Model 99R

As above, with a 24" barrel and chambered for additional calibers. Manufactured between 1946 and 1960.

Exc.	V.G.	Good	Fair	Poor
350	300	250	200	175

Model 99RS

As above, with a Redfield rear sight. Manufactured between 1946 and 1958.

Exc.	V.G.	Good	Fair	Poor
350	300	250	200	175

Model 99A

A variation of the original Model 99A with a 20" or 22" barrel. Manufactured between 1971 and 1981.

Exc.	V.G.	Good	Fair	Poor
350	300	250	200	175

Model 99DL

As above, in .243 or .308 caliber with a Monte Carlo-style stock. Manufactured between 1960 and 1973.

Exc.	V.G.	Good	Fair	Poor
350	300	250	200	175

Model 99DE Citation

As above, with an engraved receiver and impressed checkering. Manufactured between 1968 and 1970.

Exc.	V.G.	Good	Fair	Poor
850	750	500	400	300

Model 99PE

Similar to the above, with an engraved and gold-plated receiver as well as a hand checkered walnut stock. Manufactured between 1966 and 1970.

Exc.	V.G.	Good	Fair	Poor
1250	1000	750	500	300

Model 99C

The current production model in .243, .284 Winchester, 7mm-08, or .308 caliber with a 22" barrel having open sights. Blued with a walnut stock. Introduced in 1965.

NIB	Exc.	V.G.	Good	Fair	Poor
525	450	375	300	225	175

Model 1895 Anniversary Edition

A .308 caliber reproduction of the Model 1895 with a 24" octagonal barrel, engraved receiver and walnut stock having a Schnabel forend. There were 9,999 manufactured in 1970.

NIB	Exc.	V.G.	Good	Fair	Poor
400	350	300	250	200	150

Model 1903

A .22 caliber slide action rifle with a 24" barrel having open sights. Blued with a walnut stock. Manufactured between 1903 and 1921.

Exc.	V.G.	Good	Fair	Poor
250	200	150	100	75

Model 1909

As above, with a 20" barrel. Manufactured between 1909 and 1915.

Exc.	V.G.	Good	Fair	Poor
250	200	150	100	75

Model 1914

As above, with a 24" octagonal barrel. Manufactured between 1914 and 1924.

Exc.	V.G.	Good	Fair	Poor
275	225	175	125	100

Model 25

A .22 caliber slide action rifle with a 24" octagonal barrel, open sights and tubular magazine. Blued with a walnut stock. Manufactured between 1925 and 1929.

Exc.	V.G.	Good	Fair	Poor
350	300	250	200	150

Model 29

As above, with a 22" octagonal barrel later changed to round and a checkered walnut stock, later changed to plain. Manufactured between 1929 and 1967.

Exc.	V.G.	Good	Fair	Poor
275	225	175	125	100

Model 170

A .30-30 or .35 Remington caliber slide action rifle with a 22" barrel and 3-shot tubular magazine. Blued with a walnut stock. Manufactured between 1970 and 1981.

Exc.	V.G.	Good	Fair	Poor
200	175	125	100	75

Model 1904

A .22 caliber single shot bolt-action rifle with an 18" barrel and walnut stock. Manufactured between 1904 and 1917.

Exc.	V.G.	Good	Fair	Poor
150	125	100	75	50

Model 1905

As above, with a 24" barrel. Manufactured between 1905 and 1919.

Exc.	V.G.	Good	Fair	Poor
150	125	100	75	50

Model 19 NRA

A .22 caliber bolt-action rifle with a 25" barrel, detachable magazine and full length military style stock. Approximately 50,000 were manufactured total between 1919 and 1937.

Exc.	V.G.	Good	Fair	Poor
225	175	150	100	75

Model 19L

As above, with a Lyman receiver sight. Manufactured between 1933 and 1942.

Exc.	V.G.	Good	Fair	Poor
350	300	250	200	150

Model 19M

As above, with a 28" barrel fitted with telescope sight bases. Manufactured between 1933 and 1942.

Exc.	V.G.	Good	Fair	Poor
350	300	250	200	150

Model 19H

The Model 19 chambered for .22 Hornet. Manufactured between 1933 and 1942.

Exc.	V.G.	Good	Fair	Poor
500	450	350	300	200

Model 10 Target

A .22 caliber bolt-action rifle with a 25" barrel, adjustable rear sight and speed lock action. Blued with a walnut stock. Manufactured between 1933 and 1946.

Exc.	V.G.	Good	Fair	Poor
250	200	150	100	75

Model 3

A .22 caliber single shot bolt-action rifle with a 24" barrel, open sights and walnut stock. Manufactured between 1933 and 1952.

Exc.	V.G.	Good	Fair	Poor
100	80	60	50	35

Model 4

Similar to the above, with a 24" barrel and 5-shot magazine.

Exc.	V.G.	Good	Fair	Poor
125	100	80	60	50

Model 4M

As above, in .22 Magnum.

Exc.	V.G.	Good	Fair	Poor
125	100	80	60	50

Model 5

The Model 4 with a tubular magazine. Manufactured between 1936 and 1961.

Exc.	V.G.	Good	Fair	Poor
125	100	80	60	50

Model 1920

A .250-3000 or .300 Savage caliber bolt-action rifle with a 22" or 24" barrel, open sights and 5-shot magazine. Blued, with a walnut stock having a Schnabel forend. Manufactured between 1920 and 1926.

Exc.	V.G.	Good	Fair	Poor
350	300	250	175	125

Model 23A

This bolt-action .22 L.R. rifle was introduced in 1923 and features a 5-round detachable box magazine and 23" barrel with open sights. The large loading port on the left side of the receiver permitted easy single shot loading. The stock was plain with pistol grip and a Schnabel forearm. A varnish wood finish was applied to this model. Production stopped in 1933.

Exc.	V.G.	Good	Fair	Poor
250	200	150	125	100

Model 23AA

This was an improved version of the Model 23A introduced in 1933. It features an better speed lock, redesigned stock with oil finish. The receiver was tapped for No. 15 Savage extension peep sight. The rifle weighs approximately 6 lbs. Production ceased in 1942.

Exc.	V.G.	Good	Fair	Poor
290	250	200	150	125

Model 23B

Similar to the Model 23A except chambered for the .25-20 cartridge. Barrel length was 25" and forearm was a full 1.5" wide beavertail. Receiver was tapped for peep sight and magazine capacity was 4 rounds. Production on the Model 23B was from 1923 to 1942.

Exc.	V.G.	Good	Fair	Poor
250	200	150	125	100

Model 23C

The same configuration as the Model 23B with the exception of the caliber; .32-20.

Exc.	V.G.	Good	Fair	Poor
250	200	150	125	100

Model 23D

The same configuration as the Model 23B but chambered for the .22 Hornet cartridge.

Exc.	V.G.	Good	Fair	Poor
325	300	250	200	150

Model 40

Similar to the above but in .250-3000, .300 Savage, .30-30, and .30-06 caliber. Manufactured between 1928 and 1940.

Exc.	V.G.	Good	Fair	Poor
350	300	250	175	125

Model 45 Super

As above, with a Lyman receiver sight and checkered walnut stock. Manufactured between 1928 and 1940.

Exc.	V.G.	Good	Fair	Poor
400	350	300	200	150

Model 35

A .22 caliber bolt-action rifle with a 22" barrel, open sights and 5-shot magazine. Blued with a Monte Carlo-style hardwood stock.

Exc.	V.G.	Good	Fair	Poor
100	80	70	50	35

Model 46

As above with a tubular magazine. Manufactured between 1969 and 1973.

Exc.	V.G.	Good	Fair	Poor
100	80	70	50	35

Model 340

A .22 Hornet, .222 Remington, .223, or .30-30 caliber bolt-action rifle with a 22" or 24" barrel, open sights and 4- or 5-shot magazine. Blued, with a plain walnut stock. Manufactured between 1950 and 1985.

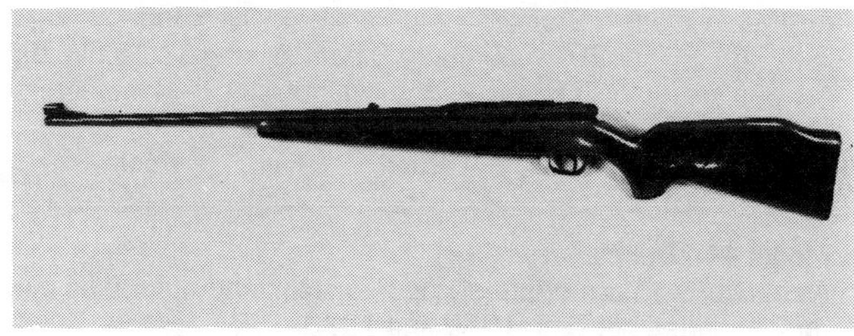

Exc.	V.G.	Good	Fair	Poor
250	200	175	125	90

Model 342

As above, but in .22 Hornet caliber. Manufactured between 1950 and 1955.

Exc.	V.G.	Good	Fair	Poor
250	200	175	125	90

Model 110 Sporter

A bolt-action rifle manufactured in a variety of calibers with a 22" barrel, open sights and 4-shot magazine. Blued with a walnut stock. Manufactured between 1958 and 1963.

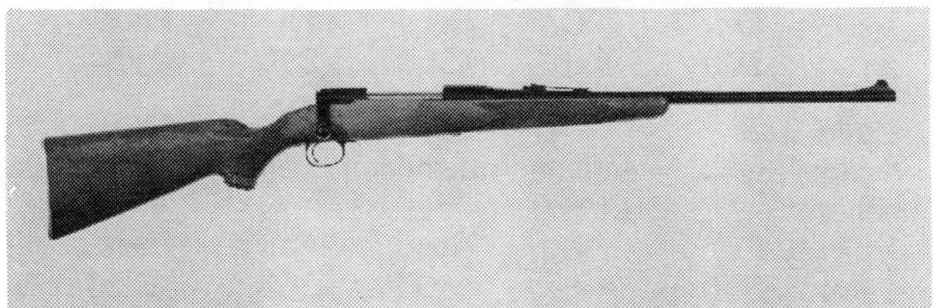

Exc.	V.G.	Good	Fair	Poor
200	150	125	100	75

Model 110-M

Similar to the above, in 7mm Magnum to .338 Winchester Magnum. Manufactured between 1963 and 1969.

Exc.	V.G.	Good	Fair	Poor
275	225	200	150	100

Model 110-D

Similar to the Model 110 in .22-250 to .338 Winchester Magnum caliber with a detachable magazine. Manufactured between 1966 and 1988.

Exc.	V.G.	Good	Fair	Poor
350	300	250	200	150

Model 110-P Premier Grade

As above, with a finely figured walnut stock, rosewood forend tip and pistol grip cap. Manufactured between 1964 and 1970.

Exc.	V.G.	Good	Fair	Poor
450	375	325	250	200

Model 110-PE

As above, with an engraved receiver, magazine floorplate and triggerguard. Manufactured between 1968 and 1970.

Exc.	V.G.	Good	Fair	Poor
650	575	500	400	300

Current production Model 110-F are made in the following styles:

Model 110-F—DuPont Rynite Stock and Sights

NIB	Exc.	V.G.	Good	Fair	Poor
450	400	350	300	250	200

Model 110-FX—Without Sights

NIB	Exc.	V.G.	Good	Fair	Poor
400	350	300	250	200	150

Model 110-G—Checkered Hardwood Stock and Sights

NIB	Exc.	V.G.	Good	Fair	Poor
375	325	275	225	175	125

Model 110-GX—Without Sights

NIB	Exc.	V.G.	Good	Fair	Poor
350	300	250	200	150	100

Model 1912

A .22 caliber semi-automatic rifle with a 20" barrel, open sights and in takedown form. Blued with a walnut stock. Manufactured between 1912 and 1916.

Exc.	V.G.	Good	Fair	Poor
350	300	200	125	90

Model 6

Similar to the above, with a 24" barrel and tubular magazine. The walnut stock checkered prior to 1941 and plain after 1945.

Exc.	V.G.	Good	Fair	Poor
150	125	100	75	50

Model 7

As above, with a detachable magazine. Manufactured between 1939 and 1951.

Exc.	V.G.	Good	Fair	Poor
150	125	100	75	50

Model 60

A .22 caliber semi-automatic rifle with a 20" barrel,open sights and tubular magazine. Blued with a Monte Carlo-style walnut stock. Manufactured between 1969 and 1972.

Exc.	V.G.	Good	Fair	Poor
100	80	70	50	35

Model 88

As above, with a hardwood stock. Manufactured between 1969 and 1972.

Exc.	V.G.	Good	Fair	Poor
100	80	70	50	35

Model 90 Carbine

As above, with a 16.5" barrel and carbine style stock having the forend secured to the barrel by a barrel band.

Exc.	V.G.	Good	Fair	Poor
100	80	70	50	35

Model 24

An external hammer combination rifle/shotgun with 24" barrels. Blued with a walnut stock. Manufactured from 1950 to 1965 in a variety of styles. The standard chambering was .22 by .410.

Exc.	V.G.	Good	Fair	Poor
150	125	100	75	50

Model 24S—20 Gauge

Exc.	V.G.	Good	Fair	Poor
160	140	125	100	75

Model 24MS—22 Rimfire Magnum

Exc.	V.G.	Good	Fair	Poor
150	125	100	75	50

Model 24DL—Satin Chrome With Checkered Stock

Exc.	V.G.	Good	Fair	Poor
150	125	100	75	50

Model 24 Field—Lightweight Version

Exc.	V.G.	Good	Fair	Poor
175	150	125	100	75

Model 24C—Nickle Finish

Exc.	V.G.	Good	Fair	Poor
200	175	150	125	100

Model 24VS—.357 Magnum/20 Gauge, Nickle Finish

Exc.	V.G.	Good	Fair	Poor
250	200	175	150	125

Model 24F—DuPont Rynite Stock

NIB	Exc.	V.G.	Good	Fair	Poor
350	300	250	200	150	100

Model 420

A 12, 16 or 20 gauge boxlock Over/Under shotgun with 26", 28" or 30" barrels, double triggers and extractors. Manufactured between 1938 and 1942.

Exc.	V.G.	Good	Fair	Poor
400	325	275	200	150

Model 430

As above, with a checkered walnut stock and solid barrel rib.

Exc.	V.G.	Good	Fair	Poor
450	375	325	225	175

Model 220

A 12, 16, 20 or .410 bore boxlock single barrel shotgun with 26" to 32" barrels. Blued with a walnut stock. Manufactured between 1938 and 1965.

Exc.	V.G.	Good	Fair	Poor
100	80	70	50	35

Model 720

A 12 or 16 gauge semi-automatic shotgun with 26" to 32" barrels. Blued with a walnut stock. Manufactured between 1930 and 1949.

Exc.	V.G.	Good	Fair	Poor
300	250	200	150	100

Model 726 Upland Sporter

As above, with a 2-shot magazine. Manufactured between 1931 and 1949.

Exc.	V.G.	Good	Fair	Poor
300	250	200	150	100

Model 740C Skeet

The Model 726 with a 24.5" barrel having a Cutts Compensator and skeet-style stock. Manufactured between 1936 and 1949.

Exc.	V.G.	Good	Fair	Poor
300	250	200	150	100

Model 745

The Model 720 in 12 gauge with an alloy receiver and 28" barrel. Manufactured between 1940 and 1949.

Exc.	V.G.	Good	Fair	Poor
275	225	175	125	75

Model 755

A 12 or 16 gauge semi-automatic shotgun with 26" to 30" barrels. Blued with a walnut stock. Also available with Savage Super Choke. Manufactured between 1949 and 1958.

Exc.	V.G.	Good	Fair	Poor
275	225	175	125	75

Model 775

As above, with an alloy receiver. Manufactured between 1950 and 1966.

Exc.	V.G.	Good	Fair	Poor
275	225	175	125	75

Model 750

A 12 gauge semi-automatic shotgun with a 26" or 28" barrel. The Model 750SC fitted with the Savage Super Choke and the Model 750AC with a Poly Choke. Blued with a walnut stock. Manufactured between 1960 and 1967.

Exc.	V.G.	Good	Fair	Poor
275	225	175	125	75

Model 30

A 12, 16, 20 or .410 bore slide action shotgun with 26" to 30" ventilated-rib barrels. Blued with a walnut stock. Manufactured between 1958 and 1970.

Exc.	V.G.	Good	Fair	Poor
225	175	150	100	75

Model 242

A .410 bore boxlock double-barrel shotgun with 26" barrels, single trigger, extractors and exposed hammers. Manufactured between 1977 and 1981.

Exc.	V.G.	Good	Fair	Poor
150	125	100	75	50

Model 550

A 12 or 20 gauge boxlock double-barrel shotgun with 26", 28" or 30" barrels, single triggers and automatic ejectors. Blued with a hardwood stock. Manufactured between 1971 and 1973.

Exc.	V.G.	Good	Fair	Poor
275	225	175	125	75

Model 440

An Italian made 12 or 20 gauge boxlock Over/Under shotgun with 26", 28" or 30" ventilated-rib barrels, single selective trigger and extractors. Blued with a walnut stock. Manufactured between 1968 and 1972.

Exc.	V.G.	Good	Fair	Poor
500	425	350	250	175

Model 444 Deluxe

As above, with a more finely figured stock and automatic ejectors. Imported between 1969 and 1972.

Exc.	V.G.	Good	Fair	Poor
550	475	400	300	225

Model 440T

A 12 gauge Model 440 with 30" barrels and a trap style stock. Imported between 1969 and 1972.

Exc.	V.G.	Good	Fair	Poor
550	475	400	300	225

Model 330

A Valmet manufactured 12 or 20 gauge Over/Under shotgun with 26", 28" or 30" barrels, single selective trigger and extractors. Blued with a walnut stock. Imported between 1969 and 1980.

Exc.	V.G.	Good	Fair	Poor
500	425	350	250	175

Model 333

As above, with a ventilated-rib and automatic ejectors. Imported between 1973 and 1980.

Exc.	V.G.	Good	Fair	Poor
550	475	400	300	225

Model 333T

As above, with a 30" barrel and trap style stock. Imported between 1972 and 1980.

Exc.	V.G.	Good	Fair	Poor
550	475	400	300	225

Model 2400

A combination 12 gauge by .222 or .308 caliber Over/Under rifle/shotgun with 23.5" barrels and a Monte Carlo-style stock. Made by Valmet and imported between 1975 and 1980.

Exc.	V.G.	Good	Fair	Poor
600	525	450	350	275

Pistols

Model 1907

A .32 or .380 semi-automatic pistol with a 3.75" or 4.25" barrel depending upon caliber and a 9- or 10-shot magazine. Blued with hard rubber grips. The .380 caliber model is worth approximately 20 percent more than the values listed below.

Courtesy Orville Reichert.

Exc.	V.G.	Good	Fair	Poor
300	250	200	125	75

Model 1915

Similar to the above, except fitted with a grip safety and having an internal hammer. Manufactured between 1915 and 1917.

Exc.	V.G.	Good	Fair	Poor
350	300	250	150	100

Model 1917

As above, with an external hammer and without the grip safety. The form of the grip frame widened. Manufactured between 1917 and 1928.

Exc.	V.G.	Good	Fair	Poor
275	225	175	100	75

U.S. Army Test Trial

A .45 caliber semi-automatic pistol resembling the above models which was made for trial by the U.S. Army Ordnance Department. Approximately 300 were manufactured. Prospective purchasers are advised to secure a qualified appraisal prior to acquisition.

Exc.	V.G.	Good	Fair	Poor
5000	4000	3000	2250	1750

Model 101

A .22 caliber single shot pistol resembling a revolver with a 5.5" barrel. Blued with hardwood grips. Manufactured between 1960 and 1968.

Exc.	V.G.	Good	Fair	Poor
175	150	125	90	75

SAVAGE & NORTH

Middletown, Connecticut

Figure 8 Revolver

A .36 caliber percussion revolver with a 7" octagonal barrel and 6-shot cylinder. The barrel marked "E. Savage, Middletown. CT./H.S. North. Patented June 17, 1856." The four models of this revolver are as follows: (1) With a rounded brass frame, and the mouths of the chamber fitting into the end of the barrel breech; (2) with a rounded iron frame and a modified loading lever which is marked "H.S. North, Patented April 6, 1858"; (3) with a flat-sided brass frame having a round recoil shield; (4) with an iron frame. Approximately 400 of these revolvers were manufactured between 1856 and 1859.

First Model

Exc.	V.G.	Good	Fair	Poor
5000	4000	3500	2500	2000

Second Model

Exc.	V.G.	Good	Fair	Poor
3500	3000	2500	1800	1500

Third Model

Exc.	V.G.	Good	Fair	Poor
3750	3250	2750	2000	1750

Fourth Model

Exc.	V.G.	Good	Fair	Poor
4000	3500	3000	2250	1800

SAVAGE REVOLVING FIREARMS CO.

Middletown, Connecticut

Navy Revolver

A .36 caliber double-action percussion revolver with a 7" octagonal barrel and 6-shot cylinder. The frame marked "Savage R.F.A. Co./H.S. North Patented June 17, 1856/Jan. 18, 1859, May 15, 1860." Approximately 20,000 were manufactured between 1861 and 1865, of which about 12,000 were purchased by the U.S. Government.

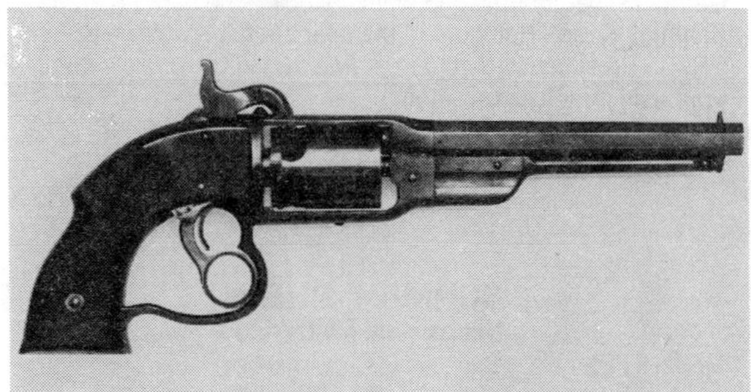

Courtesy Milwaukee Public Museum, Milwaukee, Wisconsin.

Exc.	V.G.	Good	Fair	Poor
1750	1500	1250	850	500

SCHALK, G. S.
Pottsville, Pennsylvania

Rifle Musket

A .58 caliber percussion rifle with a 40" round barrel and full-length stock secured by three barrel bands. The barrel marked "G. Schalk Pottsville 1861." Finished in white with a walnut stock. Approximately 100 were manufactured.

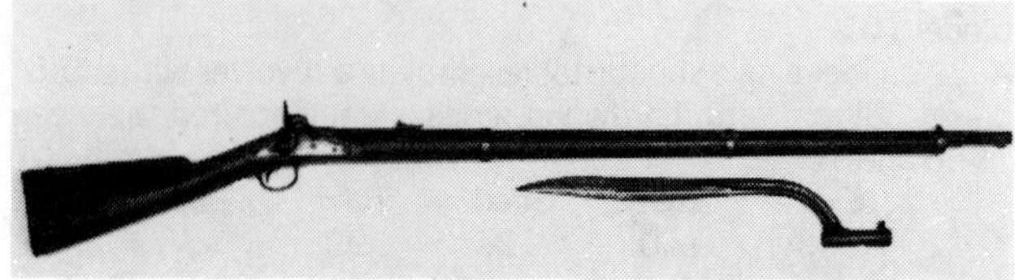

Courtesy Milwaukee Public Museum, Milwaukee, Wisconsin.

Exc.	V.G.	Good	Fair	Poor
2000	1750	1500	1200	750

SCHALL
Hartford, Connecticut

Target Pistol

A .22 caliber pistol with a 5" barrel and 10-shot magazine. Blued with walnut grips.

Exc.	V.G.	Good	Fair	Poor
450	400	350	250	175

SCHMIDT, HERBERT
Ostheim, West Germany

Model 11, Liberty 11, and Eig Model E-8

A .22 caliber double-action revolver with a 2.5" barrel and 6-shot cylinder. Blued with plastic grips.

Exc.	V.G.	Good	Fair	Poor
75	65	50	40	25

Model 11 Target

As above, with a 5.5" barrel and adjustable sights.

Exc.	V.G.	Good	Fair	Poor
80	70	55	45	30

Frontier Model or Texas Scout

A .22 caliber revolver with a 5" barrel and 6-shot cylinder. Blued with plastic grips.

Exc.	V.G.	Good	Fair	Poor
75	65	50	40	25

SCHMIDT, E. & COMPANY
Houston, Texas

Pocket Pistol

A .45 caliber percussion single shot pistol with a 2.5" barrel, German silver mounts and walnut stock. The barrel marked "E. Schmidt & Co. Houston." Manufactured between 1866 and 1870. Prospective purchasers are advised to secure a qualified appraisal prior to acquisition.

Exc.	V.G.	Good	Fair	Poor
2500	2250	1750	1250	1000

SCHMIDT-RUBIN
Neuhausen, Switzerland

Model 1889

A 7.5mm straight pull bolt-action rifle with a 30.75" barrel and 12-shot magazine. Blued with a full-length walnut stock secured by two barrel bands. Approximately 212,000 were manufactured.

Exc.	V.G.	Good	Fair	Poor
250	200	175	125	90

Model 1896

As above, with a shortened action. There were approximately 137,000 made.

Exc.	V.G.	Good	Fair	Poor
275	225	200	150	125

Model 1897 Cadet Rifle

Similar to the above, with a shortened stock and reduced weight. Approximately 7,000 were manufactured.

Exc.	V.G.	Good	Fair	Poor
300	250	200	150	100

Model 1900

A shortened version of the Model 1896, with a 6-shot magazine. Approximately 18,750 were manufactured between 1900 and 1904.

Exc.	V.G.	Good	Fair	Poor
400	350	300	200	150

Model 1905 Carbine

Similar to the above, without a bayonet. Approximately 7,900 were manufactured.

Exc.	V.G.	Good	Fair	Poor
350	300	250	200	150

Model 1911

A redesigned Model 1896 with a 6-shot magazine and pistol grip stock. Approximately 133,000 were manufactured.

Exc.	V.G.	Good	Fair	Poor
150	125	100	80	60

Model 1911 Carbine

As above, with a 23.30" barrel. Approximately 185,000 were manufactured.

Exc.	V.G.	Good	Fair	Poor
175	150	125	100	75

Model 1931

Similar to the above, with a redesigned block work, 25.7" barrel and 6-shot magazine. Approximately 528,180 were manufactured.

Exc.	V.G.	Good	Fair	Poor
175	150	125	100	75

SCHNEIDER & CO.
Memphis, Tennessee

Pocket Pistol

A .41 caliber single shot percussion pocket pistol with a 3.5" octagonal barrel, iron or German silver mounts and a walnut stock. The lock marked "Schneider & Co./Memphis, Tenn." Manufactured 1859 and 1860.

Exc.	V.G.	Good	Fair	Poor
2500	2000	1500	800	650

SCHNEIDER & GLASSICK
Memphis, Tennessee

Pocket Pistol

A .41 caliber percussion pocket pistol with a 2.5" barrel, German silver mounts and walnut stock. The barrel marked "Schneider & Glassick, Memphis, Tenn." Manufactured 1860 to 1862.

Exc.	V.G.	Good	Fair	Poor
2500	2000	1500	1000	800

SCHULER, AUGUST
Suhl, Germany

Reform

A 6.35mm caliber four-barrelled pocket pistol with 2.5" barrels. The barrel unit rises as the trigger is pulled. Blued with walnut or hard rubber grips. Manufactured between 1907 and 1914.

Exc.	V.G.	Good	Fair	Poor
850	750	650	450	300

SCHULTZ & LARSEN
Otterup, Denmark

Model 47 Match Rifle

A .22 caliber single shot bolt-action rifle with a 28" barrel, adjustable sights and adjustable trigger. Blued with an ISU style stock.

Exc.	V.G.	Good	Fair	Poor
700	650	550	400	350

Model 61 Match Rifle

As above, but fitted with a palm rest.

Exc.	V.G.	Good	Fair	Poor
900	850	750	600	500

Model 62 Match Rifle

Similar to the above, but manufactured for centerfire cartridges.

Exc.	V.G.	Good	Fair	Poor
1000	900	750	650	550

Model 54 Free Rifle

Similar to the above, with a 27" barrel and ISU stock.

Exc.	V.G.	Good	Fair	Poor
850	800	700	550	450

Model 68 DL

A .22-250 to .458 Winchester Magnum bolt-action rifle with a 24" barrel, adjustable trigger and well figured walnut stock.

Exc.	V.G.	Good	Fair	Poor
750	700	600	450	400

SCHWARZLOSE, ANDREAS
W.Berlin, Germany

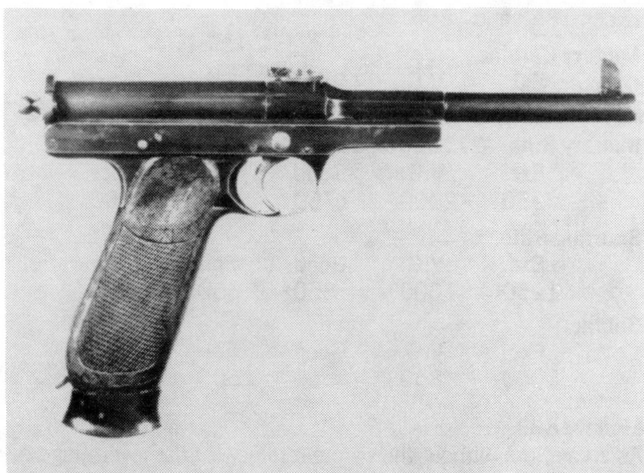

Military Model 96

A 7.63 Mauser caliber semi-automatic pistol with a 6.5" barrel, 7-shot magazine and adjustable rear sight. Blued with walnut grips.

Exc.	V.G.	Good	Fair	Poor
5000	3000	2250	1500	700

Model 08

A 7.65mm semi-automatic pistol with a 4" barrel and 7-shot magazine. The right side of the frame stamped "Schwarzlose" over a machine gun. Blued with plastic grips.

Exc.	V.G.	Good	Fair	Poor
475	400	350	300	200

SCOTT, W. C., LTD.
Birmingham, England

Currently offered by Holland & Holland of London.

Kinmount

A 12, 16, 20 or 28 gauge boxlock double-barrel shotgun manufactured in a variety of barrel lengths with a single non-selective trigger and automatic ejectors. Blued with a walnut stock.

NIB	Exc.	V.G.	Good	Fair	Poor
5700	5000	4000	3000	2500	2000

Bowood

As above, with a modest amount of engraving.

NIB	Exc.	V.G.	Good	Fair	Poor
6500	5750	4750	3500	2750	2250

Chatsworth

As above, but engraved in "best bouquet" style.

NIB	Exc.	V.G.	Good	Fair	Poor
8500	7500	6000	5000	3750	2750

SEAVER, E. R.
New York, New York

Pocket Pistol

A .41 caliber percussion pocket pistols with a 2.5" barrel, German silver mounts and a walnut stock.

Exc.	V.G.	Good	Fair	Poor
1500	1100	750	400	300

SECURITY INDUSTRIES
Little Ferry, New Jersey

Model PSS

A .38 Special double-action revolver with a 2" barrel, fixed sights and 5-shot cylinder. Stainless steel with walnut grips. Manufactured between 1973 and 1978.

Exc.	V.G.	Good	Fair	Poor
200	150	125	100	75

Model PM357

As above, with a 2.5" barrel and in .357 Magnum caliber. Manufactured between 1975 and 1978.

Exc.	V.G.	Good	Fair	Poor
250	200	175	150	100

Model PPM357

As above, with a 2" barrel and a hammer without a finger spur. Manufactured between 1975 and 1978.

Exc.	V.G.	Good	Fair	Poor
250	200	175	150	100

SEDCO INDUSTRIES, INC.
Lake Elsinore, California

Model SP22

A .22 caliber semi-automatic pistol with a 2.5" barrel. Blackened or nickle-plated with plastic grips. Introduced in 1989.

NIB	Exc.	V.G.	Good	Fair	Poor
75	65	55	50	35	25

TH. SEDERE
SEE—Austrian Military Firearms

SEDGELY, R. F., INC.
Philadelphia, Pennsylvania

R. F. Sedgely produced specialized bolt-action rifles using the Model 1903 Springfield action. As these arms were for the most part custom order pieces, it is impossible to provide standardized values. It should be noted that his prime engraver was Rudolph J. Kornbrath.

SEECAMP, L. W. CO., INC.
Milford, Connecticut

LWS .25 ACP Model

A .25 caliber semi-automatic pistol with a 2" barrel, fixed sights and 7-shot magazine. Stainless steel with plastic grips. Approximately 5,000 were manufactured between 1982 and 1985.

Exc.	V.G.	Good	Fair	Poor
400	350	300	200	150

LWS .32 ACP Model

A .32 caliber double-action semi-automatic pistol with a 2" barrel and 6-shot magazine. Matte or polished stainless steel with plastic grips.

NIB	Exc.	V.G.	Good	Fair	Poor
550	500	450	400	200	125

Matched Pair

A matched set of the above, with identical serial numbers. A total of 200 sets were made prior to 1968.

Exc.	V.G.	Good	Fair	Poor
900	800	700	500	350

SEMMERLING
Waco, Texas

SEE—American Derringer Corporation

SHARPS RIFLE MANUFACTURING COMPANY
Hartford, Connecticut

The first Sharps rifles to be manufactured were made by A. S. Nippes of Mill Creek, Pennsylvania. Later they were made by Robbins & Lawrence of Windsor, Vermont. It was not until 1855 that Sharps established his own factory in Hartford, Connecticut. After his death in 1874, the company was reorganized as the Sharps Rifle Company and remained in Hartford until 1876 when it moved to Bridgeport, Connecticut. It effectively ceased operations in 1880.

Sharps rifles and carbines were produced in an almost endless variety. Collectors should note that particular features and calibers can drastically affect the value of any given Sharps. They are, therefore, strongly advised to read Frank Sellers, Sharps Firearms (North Hollywood, California: 1978).

The following descriptions are just a brief guide and are by no means exhaustive.

Model 1849

A breechloading .44 caliber percussion rifle with a 30" barrel having a wooden cleaning rod mounted beneath it. The breech is activated by the triggerguard lever, and there is an automatic disk-type capping device on the right side of the receiver. The finish is blued and casecolored. The stock is walnut with a brass patchbox, buttplate, and forend cap. It is marked "Sharps Patent 1848." There were approximately 200 manufactured in 1849 and 1850 by the A. S. Nippes Company.

Exc.	V.G.	Good	Fair	Poor
6000	4500	4000	3000	2500

Model 1850

As above, with a Maynard priming mechanism mounted on the breech. Marked "Sharps Patent 1848" on the breech and the barrel "Manufactured by A. S. Nippes Mill Creek, Pa." The priming device marked "Maynard Patent 1845." There were approximately 200 manufactured in 1850. This Model is also known as the 2nd Model Sharps.

Exc.	V.G.	Good	Fair	Poor
5000	4000	3500	2500	2000

Model 1851 Carbine

A single shot breechloading percussion rifle in .36, .44 or .52 caliber with a 21.75" barrel and Maynard tape priming device. Blued and case-hardened with a walnut stock and forearm held on by a single barrel band. The buttplate and barrel band are brass, and the military versions feature a brass patchbox. The tang marked "C. Sharps Patent 1848," the barrel "Robbins & Lawrence," and the priming device "Edward Maynard Patentee 1845." Approximately 1,800 carbines and 180 rifles were manufactured by Robbins & Lawrence in Windsor, Vermont, in 1851. Those bearing U.S. inspection marks are worth approximately 75 percent more than the values listed below.

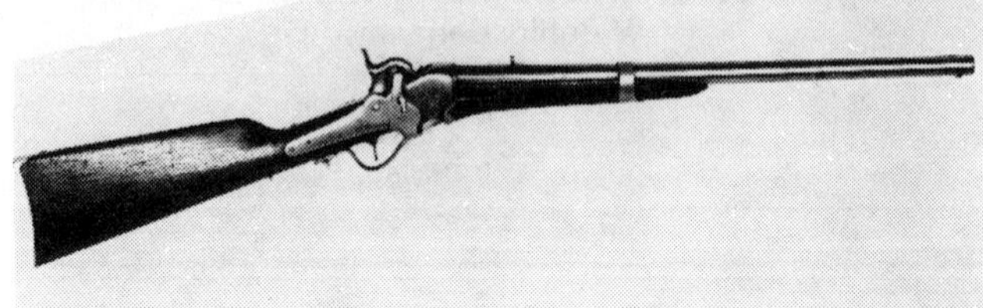

Courtesy Milwaukee Public Museum, Milwaukee, Wisconsin.

Exc.	V.G.	Good	Fair	Poor
4500	3500	3000	2000	1500

Model 1852

Similar to the above, but with Sharps' Patent Pellet Primer. The barrel marked "Sharps Rifle Manufg. Co. Hartford, Conn." Blued, case-hardened, brass furniture and a walnut stock. Manufactured in carbine, rifle, sporting rifle and shotgun form. Approximately 4,600 carbines and 600 rifles were made between 1853 and 1855.

Military Carbine

Exc.	V.G.	Good	Fair	Poor
1500	1250	1000	800	500

Military Rifle—27" Barrel, Bayonet Lug

Exc.	V.G.	Good	Fair	Poor
2250	2000	1750	1250	850

Sporting Rifle

Exc.	V.G.	Good	Fair	Poor
1250	1000	850	650	400

Shotgun

Exc.	V.G.	Good	Fair	Poor
1000	850	650	500	400

Model 1853

As above, but without the spring retainer for the lever hinge being mounted in the forestock. Approximately 10,500 carbines and 3,000 rifles were made between 1854 and 1858.

Military Carbine

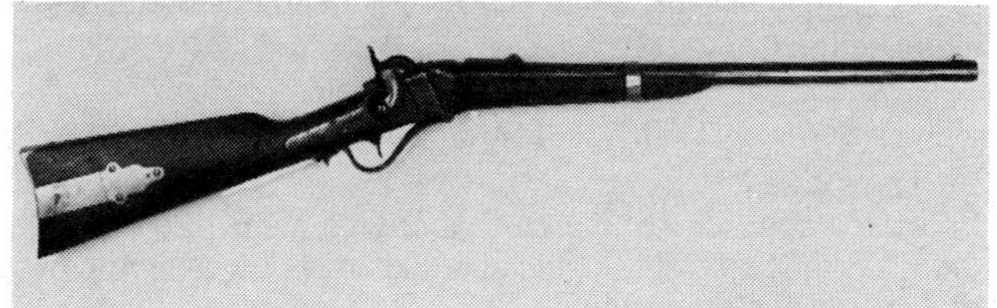

Courtesy Milwaukee Public Museum, Milwaukee, Wisconsin.

Exc.	V.G.	Good	Fair	Poor
4500	3000	1500	700	350

Military Rifle

Exc.	V.G.	Good	Fair	Poor
5000	3500	1700	1000	800

Sporting Rifle

Exc.	V.G.	Good	Fair	Poor
4500	3000	1500	700	350

Shotgun

Exc.	V.G.	Good	Fair	Poor
900	750	550	400	300

Model 1855

As above, in .52 caliber and fitted with a Maynard tape primer which is marked "Edward Maynard Patentee 1845." Approximately 700 were made between 1855 and 1856.

Exc.	V.G.	Good	Fair	Poor
2000	1750	1500	1000	750

Model 1855 U.S. Navy Rifle

As above, with a 28" barrel, full-length stock and bearing U.S. Navy inspection marks. Approximately 260 were made in 1855.

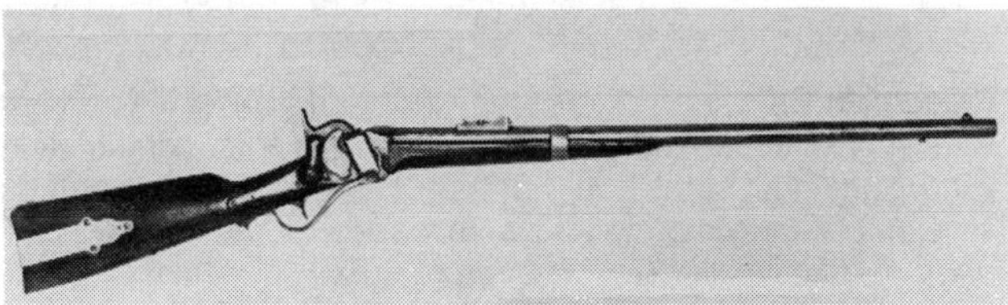

Courtesy Milwaukee Public Museum, Milwaukee, Wisconsin.

Exc.	V.G.	Good	Fair	Poor
2500	2000	1750	1250	1000

Model 1855 British Carbine

The Model 1855 with British inspection marks. Approximately 6,800 were made between 1855 and 1857.

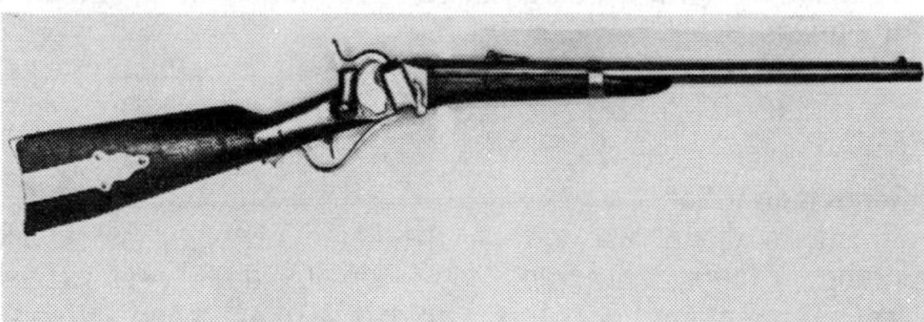

Courtesy Milwaukee Public Museum, Milwaukee, Wisconsin.

Exc.	V.G.	Good	Fair	Poor
1750	1300	1000	750	600

Sharps Straight Breech Models

Similar to the above models, but with the breech opening cut on an almost vertical angle.

Model 1859 Carbine—22" Barrel, Brass Mountings

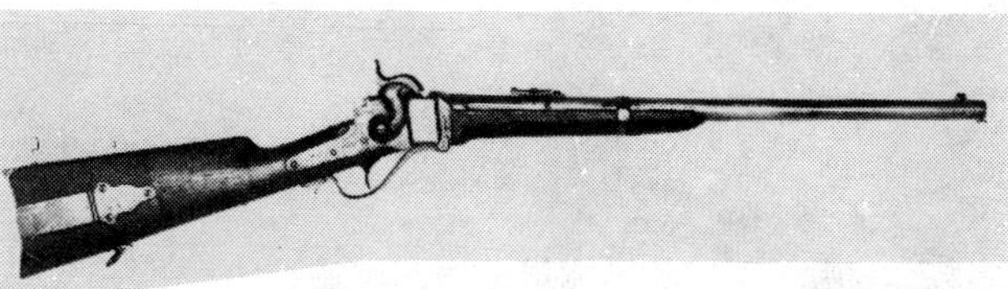

Courtesy Milwaukee Public Museum, Milwaukee, Wisconsin.

Exc.	V.G.	Good	Fair	Poor
2750	1700	850	650	500

Model 1859 Carbine—Iron Mountings

Courtesy Milwaukee Public Museum, Milwaukee, Wisconsin.

Exc.	V.G.	Good	Fair	Poor
2200	1400	650	500	400

Model 1863 Carbine

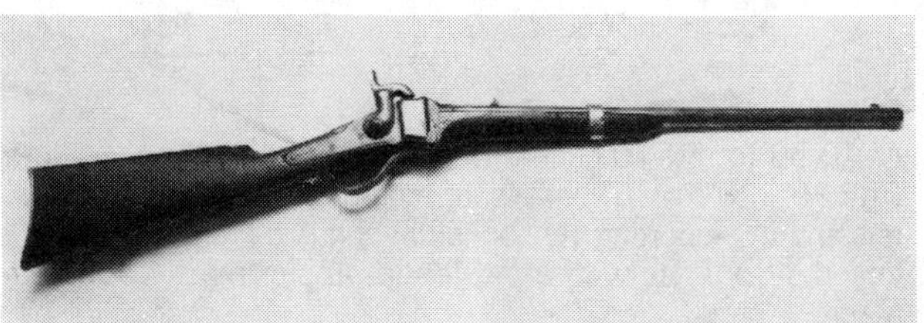

Courtesy Mike Stuckslager.

Exc.	V.G.	Good	Fair	Poor
1000	800	650	500	400

Model 1865 Carbine

Exc.	V.G.	Good	Fair	Poor
1250	1000	850	650	500

Model 1859 Rifle—30" Barrel

Exc.	V.G.	Good	Fair	Poor
1250	1000	850	650	500

Model 1859 Rifle—36" Barrel

Exc.	V.G.	Good	Fair	Poor
1500	1250	1000	750	600

Model 1863 Rifle—Without Bayonet Lug

Exc.	V.G.	Good	Fair	Poor
1250	1000	850	650	500

Model 1865 Rifle—Without Bayonet Lug

Exc.	V.G.	Good	Fair	Poor
1750	1500	1250	1000	750

Sporting Rifle

As above, with octagonal barrels, set triggers and finely figured walnut stocks.

Exc.	V.G.	Good	Fair	Poor
3000	2500	2000	1500	1000

Coffee-Mill Model

Some Sharps' carbines were fitted with coffee-mill style grinding devices set into their buttstocks. These arms are exceptionally rare and extreme caution should be exercised prior to purchase.

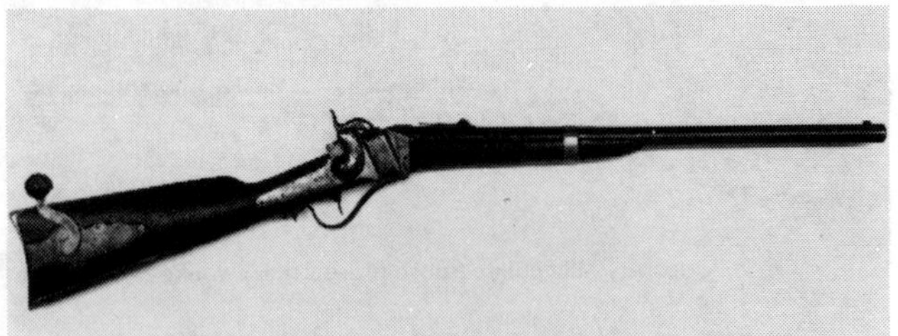

Courtesy Milwaukee Public Museum, Milwaukee, Wisconsin.

Exc.	V.G.	Good	Fair	Poor
10000	7500	6500	4500	3000

Metallic Cartridge Conversions

In 1867 approximately 32,000 Model 1859, 1863 and 1865 Sharps were altered to .52-70 rimfire and centerfire caliber.

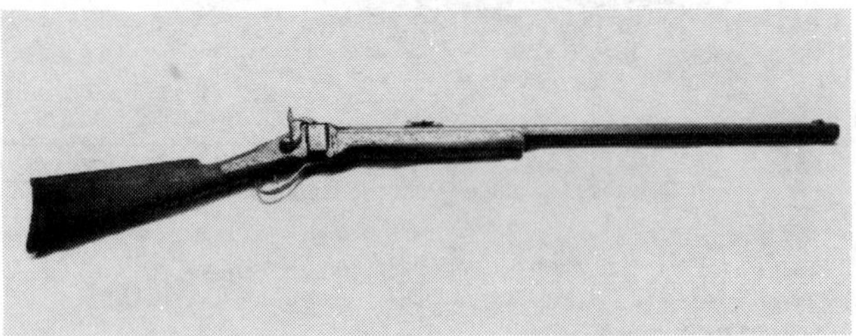

Courtesy Mike Stuckslager.

Exc.	V.G.	Good	Fair	Poor
1750	1000	700	500	400

Model 1869

A .40-50 to .50-70 caliber model produced in a military form with 26", 28" or 30" barrels; as a carbine with 21" or 24" barrels and in a sporting version with various barrel lengths and a forend stock fitted with a pewter tip. Approximately 650 were made.

Carbine—.50-70, Saddle Ring on Frame

Exc.	V.G.	Good	Fair	Poor
1250	1000	800	600	500

Military Rifle—.50-70, 30" Barrel With Three Barrel Bands

Exc.	V.G.	Good	Fair	Poor
3000	2500	2000	1500	1000

Sporting Rifle—26" Barrel, .44-77 and .50-70

Exc.	V.G.	Good	Fair	Poor
2500	2000	1500	1000	750

Model 1874

This model was manufactured in a variety of calibers, barrel lengths, and stock styles. The barrel markings are of three forms: initally, "Sharps Rifle Manufg. Co. Hartford, Conn."; then, "Sharps Rifle Co. Hartford, Conn."; and finally "Sharps Rifle Co. Bridgeport, Conn." As of 1876 "Old Reliable" was stamped on the barrels. This marking is usually found on Bridgeport-marked rifles only. The major styles of this model are as follows:

Military Carbine—.50-70, 21" Barrel (ca. 460 made)

Exc.	V.G.	Good	Fair	Poor
7500	5000	2250	1250	950

Military Rifle

In .45-70 and .50-70 centerfire caliber with a 30" barrel and full-length forend secured by three barrel bands. Approximately 1,800 made.

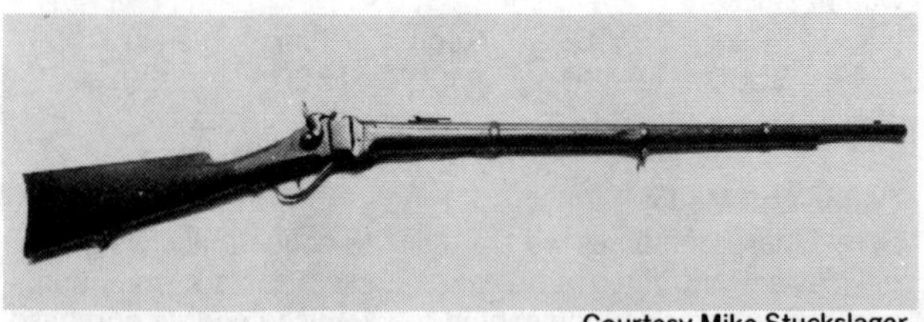

Courtesy Mike Stuckslager.

Exc.	V.G.	Good	Fair	Poor
3500	2500	2000	1000	800

Hunter's Rifle

In .40, .44, .45-70, and .50-70 caliber with 26", 28", or 30" round barrels having open sights. Approximately 600 were manufactured.

Exc.	V.G.	Good	Fair	Poor
3500	2500	2000	1000	800

Business Rifle

In .40-70 and .45-75 Sharps caliber with a 26", 28", or 30" round barrel, adjustable sights and double-set triggers. Approximately 1,600 manufactured.

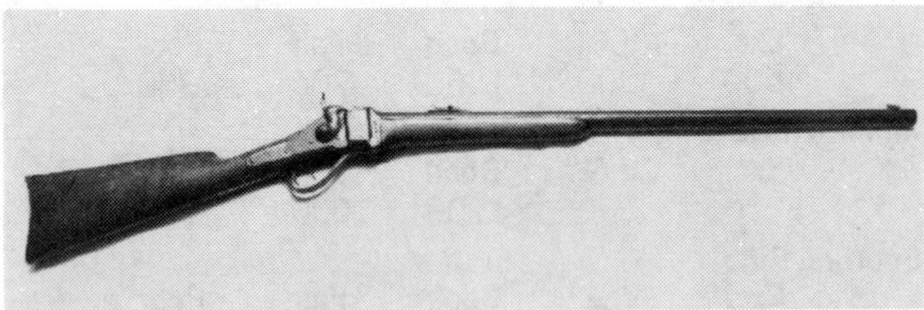

Courtesy Mike Stuckslager.

Exc.	V.G.	Good	Fair	Poor
4000	3000	1500	900	750

Sporting Rifle

Offered in a variety of calibers, barrel lengths, barrel weights, barrel styles and stock styles. Approximately 6,000 were manufactured.

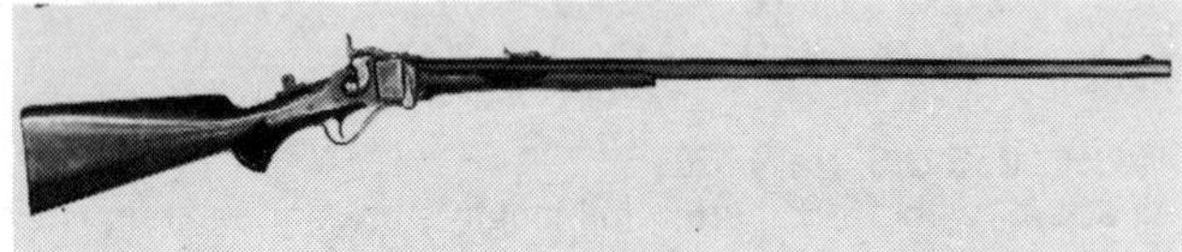

Courtesy Milwaukee Public Museum, Milwaukee, Wisconsin.

Exc.	V.G.	Good	Fair	Poor
5000	4500	3750	2000	1000

Creedmoor Rifle

With a checkered pistolgrip stock, vernier sights, combination wind gauge and spirit level front sight, set trigger and shotgun style butt. Approximately 150 were made.

Exc.	V.G.	Good	Fair	Poor
7500	6000	3000	2000	1000

Mid-Range Rifle

Similar to the above, with a crescent buttplate. Approximately 180 were made.

Exc.	V.G.	Good	Fair	Poor
6000	5500	4000	3000	1500

Long-Range Rifle

As above with a 34" octagonal barrel. Approximately 425 were manufactured.

Exc.	V.G.	Good	Fair	Poor
9000	5500	4000	3000	1500

Schuetzen Rifle

Similar to the above, with a checkered pistolgrip stock and forend, a large Schuetzen style buttplate, double-set triggers and a vernier tang sight. Approximately 70 were manufactured.

Exc.	V.G.	Good	Fair	Poor
9000	5500	4000	3000	1000

Model 1877

Similar to the Model 1874, and in .45-70 caliber with a 34" or 36" barrel which is marked "Sharps Rifle Co. Bridgeport, Conn. Old Reliable." Approximately 100 were manufactured in 1877 and 1878.

Exc.	V.G.	Good	Fair	Poor
9500	6500	5000	3500	1500

Model 1878 Sharps-Borchardt
An internal hammer breechloading rifle manufactured from 1878 to approximately 1880. The frame marked "Borchardt Patent Sharps Rifle Co. Bridgeport Conn. U.S.A."

Carbine
Approximately 385 were made in .45-70 caliber with a 24" barrel. The forend is secured by one barrel band.

Courtesy Milwaukee Public Museum, Milwaukee, Wisconsin.

Exc.	V.G.	Good	Fair	Poor
3500	2000	1250	1000	750

Military Rifle
Approximately 12,000 were made in .45-70 caliber with 32.25" barrels and full stocks secured by two barrel bands.

Exc.	V.G.	Good	Fair	Poor
3250	1900	900	600	500

Sporting Rifle
Approximately 1,600 were made in .45-70 caliber with 30" round or octagonal barrels.

Exc.	V.G.	Good	Fair	Poor
3500	2000	1250	800	650

Hunter's Rifle
Approximately 60 were made in .40 caliber with 26" barrels and plain walnut stocks.

Exc.	V.G.	Good	Fair	Poor
3250	2000	900	700	550

Business Rifle
Approximately 90 were made with 28" barrels in .40 caliber.

Exc.	V.G.	Good	Fair	Poor
3500	2000	1200	700	550

Officer's Rifle
Approximately 50 were made in .45-70 caliber with 32" barrels and checkered walnut stocks.

Exc.	V.G.	Good	Fair	Poor
3750	2500	1400	1250	900

Express Rifle
Approximately 30 were made in .45-70 caliber with 26" barrels, set triggers and checkered walnut stocks.

Exc.	V.G.	Good	Fair	Poor
4000	2850	1500	1350	1000

Short-Range Rifle
Approximately 155 were made in .40 caliber with 26" barrels, vernier rear sights, wind gauge front sight and a checkered walnut stock.

Exc.	V.G.	Good	Fair	Poor
4000	2850	1500	1350	1000

Mid-Range Rifle
Similar to the above, with a 30" barrel. Approximately 250 were manufactured.

Exc.	V.G.	Good	Fair	Poor
5000	3750	2500	1500	1000

Long-Range Rifle
Similar to the above, with different sights. Approximately 230 were manufactured.

Exc.	V.G.	Good	Fair	Poor
7000	5500	3750	1750	1000

C. Sharps & Company and Sharps & Hankins Company

Breech-Loading, Single-Shot Pistol
A .31, .34 or .36 caliber breechloading percussion pistol with 5" or 6.5" round barrels. Blued, casehardened with walnut grips. The barrel marked "Sharps Patent Arms Mf Fairmount Phila. Pa." Approximately 500 were manufactured between 1854 and 1857.

Courtesy Buffalo Bill Historical Center, Cody, Wyoming.

Exc.	V.G.	Good	Fair	Poor
2500	1900	1500	1000	750

Pistol-Grip Rifle
A .31 or .38 caliber breechloading percussion rifle resembling the above. Manufactured in a variety of barrel lengths. Blued, casehardened with a walnut stock having German silver mounts.

Exc.	V.G.	Good	Fair	Poor
2600	2000	1500	1000	750

Percussion Revolver
A .25 caliber percussion revolver with a 3" octagonal barrel and 6-shot cylinder. Blued with walnut grips. The barrel marked "C. Sharps & Co., Phila. Pa." Approximately 2,000 were manufactured between 1857 and 1858.

Exc.	V.G.	Good	Fair	Poor
1500	1000	750	500	400

4-Shot Pepperbox Pistols
Between 1859 and 1874, these companies manufactured 4 barrel cartridge pocket pistols in a variety of calibers, barrel lengths and finishes. The barrels slide forward for loading. The major models are as follows:

Courtesy Buffalo Bill Historical Center, Cody, Wyoming.

Model 1
Manufactured by C. Sharps & Co. and in .22 rimfire caliber.

Exc.	V.G.	Good	Fair	Poor
500	450	350	200	150

Model 2
As above, in .30 rimfire caliber.

Exc.	V.G.	Good	Fair	Poor
500	450	350	200	150

Model 3
Manufactured by Sharps & Hankins and marked "Address Sharps & Hankins Philadelphia Penn." on the frame. Caliber .32 short rimfire.

Exc.	V.G.	Good	Fair	Poor
450	375	300	175	100

Model 4

Similar to the above, in .32 long rimfire and having a rounded birdshead grip.

Exc.	V.G.	Good	Fair	Poor
500	450	350	200	150

Model 1861 Navy Rifle

A .54 Sharps and Hankins caliber breechloading single shot rifle with a 32.75" barrel and full stock secured by three barrel bands. Blued, case-hardened with a walnut stock. Approximately 700 were made in 1861 and 1862.

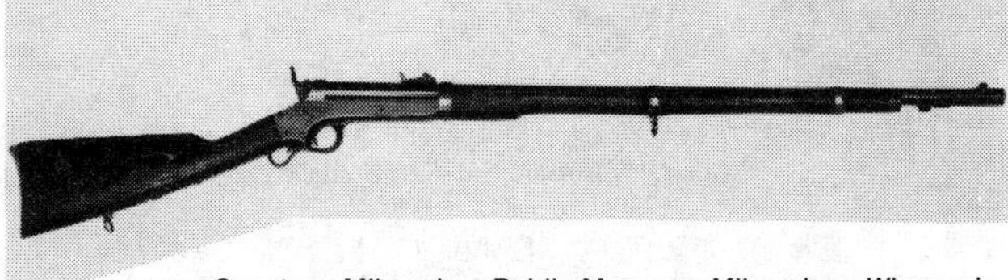

Courtesy Milwaukee Public Museum, Milwaukee, Wisconsin.

Exc.	V.G.	Good	Fair	Poor
1500	1200	950	700	500

Model 1862 Navy Carbine

A .54 caliber breechloading carbine with a 24" leather covered barrel. Case-hardened with a walnut stock. The frame marked "Sharps & Hankins Philada." Approximately 8,000 were manufactured between 1861 and 1862.

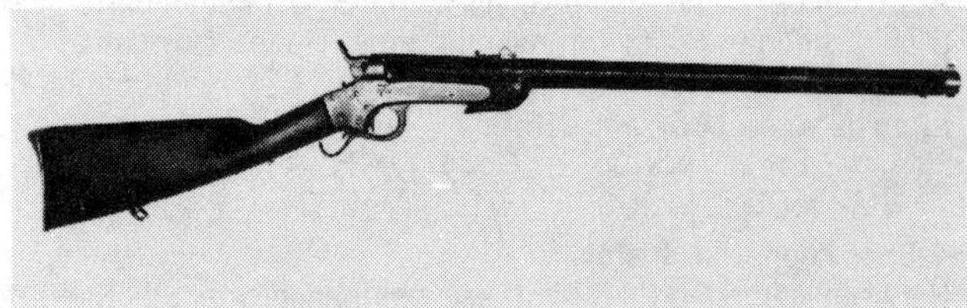

Courtesy Milwaukee Public Museum, Milwaukee, Wisconsin.

Exc.	V.G.	Good	Fair	Poor
1250	1000	750	500	400

Short Cavalry Carbine

Similar to the above, with a 19" blued barrel. Approximately 500 were manufactured.

Exc.	V.G.	Good	Fair	Poor
1400	1100	900	700	500

Army Model

Similar to the above, with a 24" barrel which does not have a leather covering. Approximately 500 were purchased by the Army.

Exc.	V.G.	Good	Fair	Poor
1250	1000	800	600	450

SHATTUCK, C. S.
Hatfield, Massachusetts

Boom

A .22 caliber spur trigger revolver with a 2" octagonal barrel and 6-shot cylinder. Nickle-plated with rosewood or walnut grips. The barrel marked "Boom" and "Pat. Nov. 4. 1879". Manufactured during the 1880s.

Exc.	V.G.	Good	Fair	Poor
250	200	150	100	75

Pocket Revolver

A .32 caliber spur trigger revolver with a 3.5" octagonal barrel and 5-shot cylinder. Nickle-plated with hard rubber grips. The barrel marked "C. S. Shattuck Hatfield, Mass. Pat. Nov. 4, 1879." Manufactured during the 1880s.

Exc.	V.G.	Good	Fair	Poor
300	250	200	150	100

SHAW & LEDOYT
Stafford, Connecticut

Under Hammer Pistol

A .31 caliber under hammer percussion pistol with a 2.5" to 3.5" half-octagonal barrel. Blued with a brass mounted walnut grip. The frame marked "Shaw & LeDoyt/Stafford. Conn." Manufactured during the 1850s.

Exc.	V.G.	Good	Fair	Poor
500	400	300	200	150

SHAWK & MCLANAHAN
St. Louis, Missouri

Navy Revolver

A .36 caliber percussion revolver with an 8" round barrel and 6-shot cylinder. Blued with a brass frame and walnut grips. Marked "Shawk & McLanahan, St. Louis, Carondelet, Mo." Produced in very limited quantities prior to 1860. Prospective purchasers are advised to secure a qualified appraisal prior to acquisition.

Exc.	V.G.	Good	Fair	Poor
7500	6000	5000	3000	2000

SHERIDEN PRODUCTS, INC.
Racine, Wisconsin

Knockabout

A .22 caliber single shot pistol with a 5" barrel having fixed sights. Blued with plastic grips. Manufactured between 1953 and 1960.

Exc.	V.G.	Good	Fair	Poor
125	100	90	75	50

SHILEN RIFLES, INC.
Ennis, Texas

Model DGA Sporter

A .17 Remington to .258 Winchester caliber bolt-action sporting rifle with a 24" barrel furnished without sights. Blued with a walnut stock.

Exc.	V.G.	Good	Fair	Poor
600	550	450	400	350

Model DGA Varminter

As above, in varmint calibers with a 25" barrel.

Exc.	V.G.	Good	Fair	Poor
600	550	450	400	350

Model DGA Silhouette Rifle

As above, in .308 Winchester only.

Exc.	V.G.	Good	Fair	Poor
600	550	450	400	350

Model DGA Benchrest Rifle

A centerfire single shot bolt-action rifle with a 26" barrel and either fiberglass or walnut stock.

Exc.	V.G.	Good	Fair	Poor
700	650	550	500	450

SHILOH RIFLE MFG. CO., INC.
Big Timber, Montana

Established in Farmingdale, New York in 1976, this company moved to Big Timber, Montana in 1983. Those interested in the Sharps reproduction rifles manufactured by this company are advised to contact them in Big Timber.

Model 1863 Military Rifle

A .54 caliber percussion rifle with a 30" barrel, single or double set triggers and full-length walnut stock secured by three barrel bands.

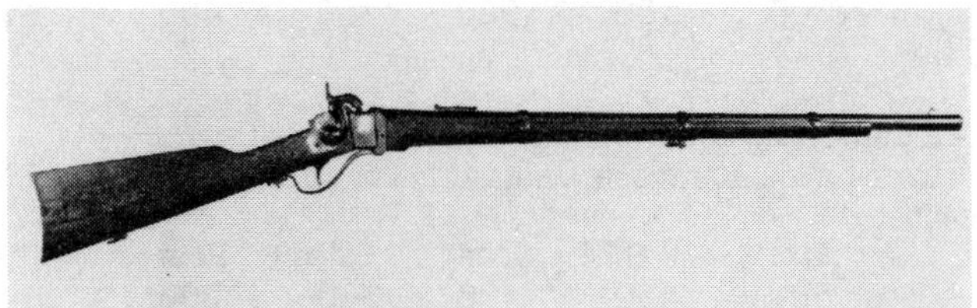

NIB	Exc.	V.G.	Good	Fair	Poor
850	800	700	600	500	400

Model 1863 Sporting Rifle
As above, with a 30" octagonal barrel, sporting sights and a half-length stock.

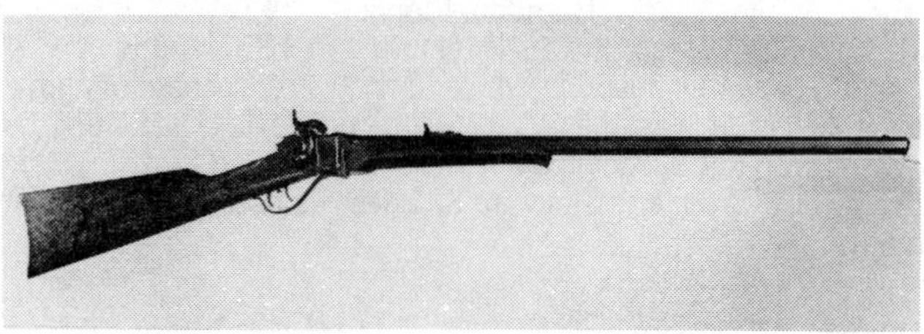

NIB	Exc.	V.G.	Good	Fair	Poor
750	700	600	500	400	350

Model 1863 Military Carbine
The Model 1863 with a 22" round barrel and carbine stock secured by one barrel band.

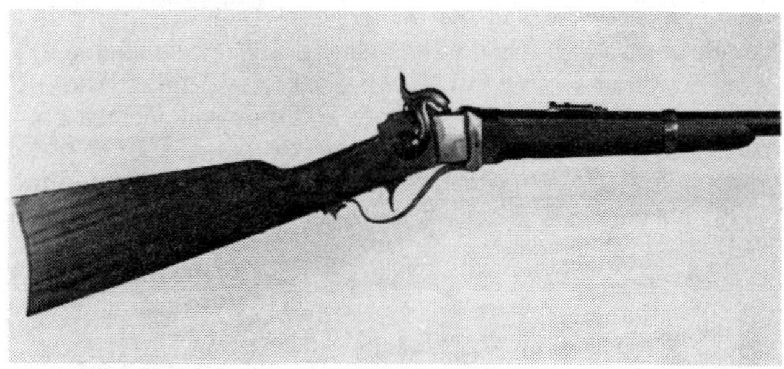

NIB	Exc.	V.G.	Good	Fair	Poor
750	700	600	500	400	350

Model 1862 Confederate Robinson
As above, with a 21.5" barrel, brass buttplate and barrel band.

NIB	Exc.	V.G.	Good	Fair	Poor
800	750	650	550	450	400

Model 1874 Express Rifle
Manufactured in a variety of calibers with a 34" octagonal barrel, double set triggers, verner rear sight and globe front sight.

NIB	Exc.	V.G.	Good	Fair	Poor
850	800	700	600	500	400

Montana Roughrider Rifle
As above, with either octagonal or half-octagonal barrels ranging in lengths from 24" to 34".

NIB	Exc.	V.G.	Good	Fair	Poor
750	700	600	500	400	350

No. 1 Deluxe Rifle
Similar to the above, with a 30" octagonal barrel.

NIB	Exc.	V.G.	Good	Fair	Poor
800	750	650	550	450	400

No. 3 Standard Sporter
As above, with a military-style stock.

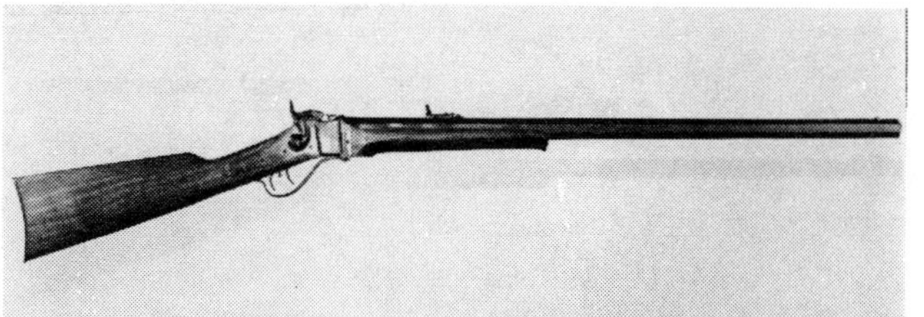

NIB	Exc.	V.G.	Good	Fair	Poor
750	700	600	500	400	350

The Business Rifle
As above, with a heavy 28" barrel.

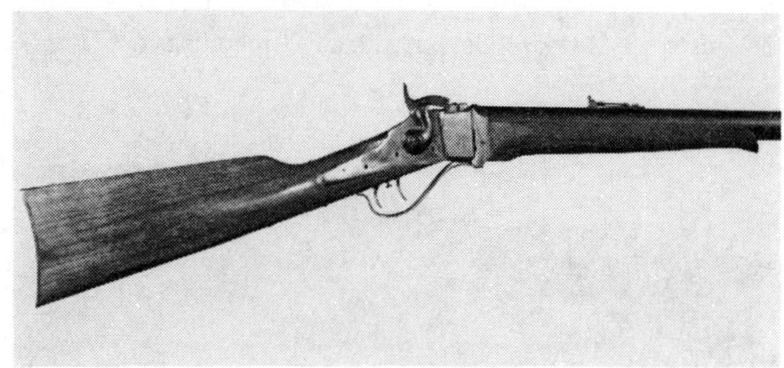

NIB	Exc.	V.G.	Good	Fair	Poor
750	700	600	500	400	350

The Saddle Rifle
As above, with a 26" barrel and shotgun butt.

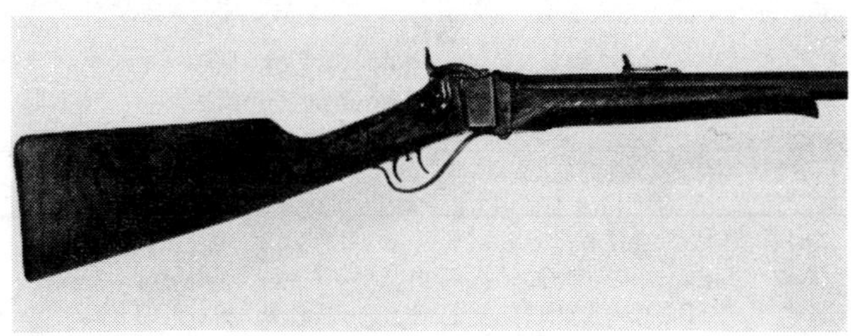

NIB	Exc.	V.G.	Good	Fair	Poor
800	750	650	550	450	400

Model 1874 Military Rifle
The Model 1874 with a 30" round barrel, military sights and full-length stocks secured by three barrel bands.

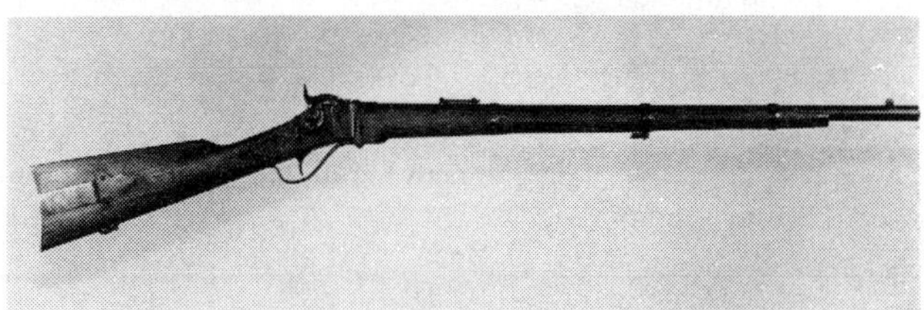

NIB	Exc.	V.G.	Good	Fair	Poor
850	800	700	600	500	400

Model 1874 Carbine
Similar to the above, with a 24" round barrel.

NIB	Exc.	V.G.	Good	Fair	Poor
750	700	600	500	400	350

The Jaeger
The Model 1874 with a 26" half-octagonal barrel, open sights and pistolgrips stock having a shotgun butt.

NIB	Exc.	V.G.	Good	Fair	Poor
800	750	650	550	450	400

Hartford Model
A reproduction of the Sharps Hartford Model.

NIB	Exc.	V.G.	Good	Fair	Poor
1400	1250	1000	850	650	500

Model 1874 Military Carbine
Similar to the Military Rifle, but with a 22" round barrel.

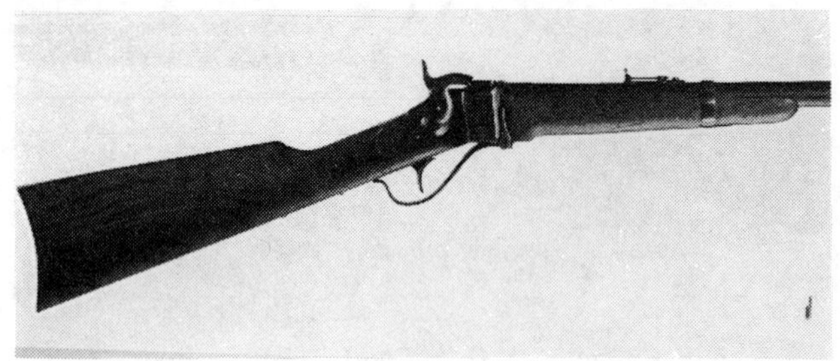

NIB	Exc.	V.G.	Good	Fair	Poor
750	700	600	500	400	350

SIG
Neuhausen, Switzerland
Importer—Mandall Shooting Supplies
Scottsdale, Arizona

P 210
A 7.65mm or 9mm semi-automatic pistol with a 4.75" barrel and 8-shot magazine. Blued with plastic grips.

Exc.	V.G.	Good	Fair	Poor
1500	1300	1100	800	300

P 210-1
As above, with an adjustable rear sight, polished finish and walnut grips. Imported prior to 1987.

Exc.	V.G.	Good	Fair	Poor
1700	1500	1150	800	400

P 210-2
As above, with a matte finish, fixed sights and plastic grips. Imported prior to 1988.

NIB	Exc.	V.G.	Good	Fair	Poor
2000	1750	1350	1000	750	300

P 210-5
As above, with an extended length barrel, adjustable rear sight and walnut grips.

Exc.	V.G.	Good	Fair	Poor
1850	1650	1000	800	400

P 210-6
As above, with a 4.75" barrel.

NIB	Exc.	V.G.	Good	Fair	Poor
2750	2250	1500	1150	800	400

SIG-HAMMERLI
Lenzburg, Switzerland

Model P240 Target Pistol
A .32 Smith & Wesson Long Wadcutter or .38 Midrange caliber semi-automatic pistol with a 5.9" barrel, adjustable rear sight, adjustable trigger and 5-shot magazine. Blued, with adjustable walnut grips. Imported prior 1987.

Exc.	V.G.	Good	Fair	Poor
1300	1150	950	750	600

.22 Conversion Unit
A barrel, slide and magazine used to convert the above to .22 caliber.

Exc.	V.G.	Good	Fair	Poor
500	450	400	300	200

SIG-ARMS
Eckernforde, West Germany
Importer—Sigarms
Herndon, Virginia

This old-line Swiss firm was established in 1853 and is now a broadly based engineering consortium. It first successful commercial design was the SP 47/8 introduced in 1948. Sig, a Swiss company, associated itself with the German firm of Sauer in 1970. SIG-Sauer pistols are SIG designs assembled in Germany.

P 220
This is a high-quality, double-action semi-automatic pistol chambered for .38 Super, .45 ACP, and 9mm Parabellum. It has a 4.41" barrel and fixed sights and features the de-cocking lever that was found originally on the Sauer Model 38H. There are two versions of this pistol--one with a bottom magazine release(commonly referred to as the European model) and the other with the release on the side(commonly referred to as the American model) as on the Model 1911 Colt. The frame is a lightweight alloy that is matte-finished and is available in either blue, nickel, or K-Kote finish with black plastic grips. The .45 ACP magazine capacity is 7 rounds and the pistol weighs 25.7 ozs.; the .38 Super magazine capacity is 9 rounds and the pistol weighs 26.5 ozs.; the 9MM magazine holds 9 rounds and the overall weight is 26.5 ozs.. This model was manufactured from 1976 and is still in production.

NIB	Exc.	V.G.	Good	Fair	Poor
550	500	400	300	200	150

P 225
This is similar to the Model P 220 except that it is chambered for 9mm cartridge. It is a more compact pistol, with a 3.86" barrel. It has an 8-shot detachable magazine and adjustable sights. The finish is matte blued. K-Kote, or electrolysis nickel plate with black plastic grips. The pistol weighs 26.1 ozs..

NIB	Exc.	V.G.	Good	Fair	Poor
625	575	500	400	200	150

P 226

This model is a full size, high-capacity pistol with a 4.41" barrel chambered for the 9MM cartridge. It is available with a 15- or 20-round detachable magazine and high-contrast sights. It is either blued, electrolysis nickel plated, or has a polymer finish known as K-Kote. The pistol weighs 26.5 ozs.. This model was introduced in 1983.

NIB	Exc.	V.G.	Good	Fair	Poor
650	600	550	450	300	200

JP 226 Jubilee Pistol

This variation is a special limited edition of the P 226. Each gun carries a special serial number prefixed JP. The grips are hand-carved select European walnut. The slide and frame are covered with solid gold wire inlays, while the trigger, hammer, decocking lever, slide catch lever, and magazine catch are all gold plated. Each pistol comes in a custom fitted hard case of full leather. This pistol is no longer imported into the U.S.. Fewer than 250 were imported between 1991 and 1992.

NIB	Exc.	V.G.	Good	Fair	Poor
1800	1500	1000	750	450	300

P 228

This model is a compact version of the P 226 fitted with a 3.86" barrel and chambered for the 9MM cartridge. Like the P 226 it is available in blue, K-Kote, of nickel finish with black grips. Pistol weighs 26.1 ozs..

NIB	Exc.	V.G.	Good	Fair	Poor
650	600	550	450	350	250

P 229

This model is similar to the P 228 except that it is chambered for the .40 S&W cartridge. The slide is slightly larger to accommodate the more powerful cartridge. Introduced in 1992. The pistol weighs 27.54 ozs. and has a magazine capacity of 12 rounds.

NIB	Exc.	V.G.	Good	Fair	Poor
650	600	550	450	350	250

NOTE: All of the above SIG pistols form the P 220 to the P 229 are available with "SIGLITE" night sights. Add $80 for these optional sights.

P 230

This is a semi-automatic, compact, pocket-type pistol chambered for .22 l.r., .32 ACP, .380 ACP, and 9mm Ultra. It has a 3.62" barrel and either a 10, 8, or 7 round magazine, depending on the caliber chambered. The pistol weighs between 16.2 ozs. and 20.8 ozs. The finish is blued or stainless, with black plastic grips; and it was manufactured from 1976. The .32 ACP and the .380 ACP versions are the only ones currently available.

NIB	Exc.	V.G.	Good	Fair	Poor
400	350	300	250	200	150

SSG 2000

This is a high-grade, bolt-action, sniping-type rifle chambered for .223, 7.5mm Swiss, .300 Weatherby Magnum, and .308 Winchester. It has a 24" barrel and was furnished without sights. It has a 4-round box magazine. The finish is matte blued with a thumbhole-style stippled walnut stock with an adjustable cheekpiece. This model was discontinued in 1986.

NIB	Exc.	V.G.	Good	Fair	Poor
2500	2250	1750	1250	900	450

SIMPLEX
Liege, Belgium

Simplex
An 8mm Simplex caliber semi-automatic pistol with a 2.75" barrel and a front mounted 8-shot magazine. Blued with hard rubber grips having the tradename "Simplex" cast in them. Manufactured from approximately 1901 to 1906.

Exc.	V.G.	Good	Fair	Poor
1500	950	500	400	200

SIMPSON, R. J.
New York, New York

Pocket Pistol
A .41 caliber single shot percussion pocket pistol with a 2.5" barrel, German silver mounts and walnut stock. Manufactured during the 1850s and 1860s.

Exc.	V.G.	Good	Fair	Poor
750	650	500	400	300

SIMSON & COMPANY
Suhl, Germany
SEE—Luger

Model 1922
A 6.35mm semi-automatic pistol with a 2" barrel and 6-shot magazine. The slide marked "Selbstlade Pistole Simson DRP" and "Waffenfabrik Simson & Co Suhl." Blued, with black plastic grips.

Exc.	V.G.	Good	Fair	Poor
500	450	400	300	200

Model 1927
Similar to the above, with a slimmer frame stamped with the trademark of three overlapping triangles having the letter "S" enclosed.

Exc.	V.G.	Good	Fair	Poor
500	450	400	300	200

SIRKIS INDUSTRIES, LTD.
Ramat-Gan, Israel
Importer—Armscorp of America
Baltimore, Maryland

SD 9
A 9mm double-action semi-automatic pistol with a 3" barrel, fixed sights and 7-shot magazine. Blued with plastic grips. Also known as the Sardius.

Exc.	V.G.	Good	Fair	Poor
325	275	225	175	125

Model 35 Match Rifle
A .22 caliber single shot bolt-action rifle with a 26" free floating barrel, adjustable rear sight and adjustable trigger. Blued with a walnut stock.

Exc.	V.G.	Good	Fair	Poor
600	550	500	400	300

Model 36 Sniper's Rifle
A 7.62x54mm caliber semi-automatic rifle with a 22" barrel. Matte blued with a composition stock.

Exc.	V.G.	Good	Fair	Poor
675	600	550	450	350

SLOTTER & CO.
Philadelphia, Pennsylvania

Pocket Pistol
A .41 caliber percussion pocket pistol with a 2.5" to 3.5" barrel, German silver mounts and walnut stock. Marked "Slotter/& Co. Phila." Manufactured during 1860s.

Exc.	V.G.	Good	Fair	Poor
950	850	750	600	450

SMITH AMERICAN ARMS COMPANY
Springfield, Massachusetts

Smith Carbine
A .50 caliber breechloading percussion carbine with a 21.75" round barrel having an octagonal breech. Blued, case-hardened with a walnut stock. The barrel marked "Address/Poultney & Trimble/Baltimore, USA" and the frame "Smith's Patent/June 23 1857" as well as "American Arms Co./Chicopee Falls." Approximately 30,000 were manufactured, most of which were purchased by the United States Government. The sales agents were Poultney & Trimble of Baltimore, Maryland.

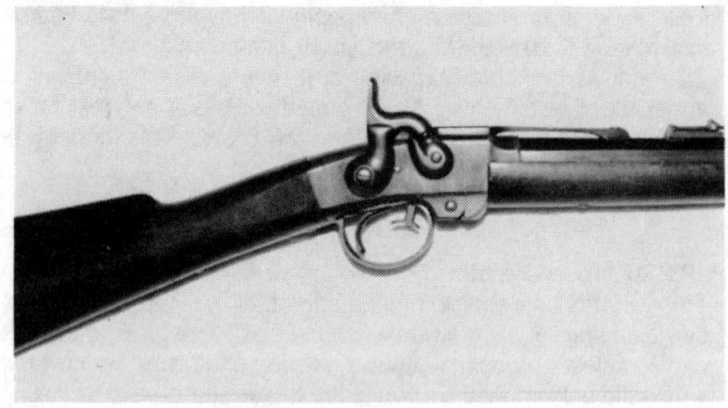

Exc.	V.G.	Good	Fair	Poor
1500	1250	1000	750	500

SMITH, L. C.
Syracuse, New York
Hunter Arms Company
Fulton, New York

One of the finest American-made double- barrel shotguns and is very collectible in today's market. It was manufactured between 1880 and 1888 in Syracuse, New York; and between 1890 and 1945, in Fulton, New York, by the Hunter Arms Company. In 1945 Marlin Firearms Company acquired Hunter Arms, and the L. C. Smith was made until 1951. In 1968 the L. C. Smith was resurrected for five years, and production ceased totally in 1973. The values given are approximate for standard production models; and we strongly feel that competent, individual appraisals should be secured, especially on the rarer and higher-grade models, if a transaction is contemplated.

The values given are for fluid steel, hammerless guns only. Damascus-barrelled guns have become very collectible if they are in very good or better condition, and values are approximately the same as for the fluid steel models. Damascus guns in less than good condition are worth considerably less.

Early Hammerless Shotguns
The following models were manufactured between 1890 and 1913. They are chambered for 10, 12, 16, and 20 gauge and were produced with various barrel lengths and choke combinations. They feature full sidelock actions. The difference in the models and their values is based on the degree of ornamentation and the quality of materials and workmanship utilized in their

construction. The general values furnished are for 10-, 12-, or 16-gauge guns only.
20 Gauge—Add 50%.
Single-Selective Trigger—Add $250.
Automatic Ejectors—Add 30%.

00 Grade—60,000 Manufactured

Exc.	V.G.	Good	Fair	Poor
1500	1250	1000	650	400

0 Grade—30,000 Manufactured

Exc.	V.G.	Good	Fair	Poor
1600	1350	1050	700	450

No. 1 Grade—10,000 Manufactured

Exc.	V.G.	Good	Fair	Poor
2500	2000	1500	800	550

No. 2 Grade—13,000 Manufactured

Exc.	V.G.	Good	Fair	Poor
3000	2250	1750	900	700

No. 3 Grade—4,000 Manufactured

Exc.	V.G.	Good	Fair	Poor
3500	2750	1800	1000	750

Pigeon Grade—1,200 Manufactured

Exc.	V.G.	Good	Fair	Poor
3500	2750	1800	1000	750

No. 4 Grade—500 Manufactured

Exc.	V.G.	Good	Fair	Poor
10000	7500	5000	3000	2000

A-1 Grade—700 Manufactured, All Damascus, No 20-Gauge

Exc.	V.G.	Good	Fair	Poor
5000	3500	2500	1750	1000

No. 5 Grade—500 Manufactured

Exc.	V.G.	Good	Fair	Poor
8500	7000	5000	2750	2000

Monogram Grade—100 Manufactured

Exc.	V.G.	Good	Fair	Poor
11000	8500	6000	3750	2500

A-2 Grade—200 Manufactured

Exc.	V.G.	Good	Fair	Poor
15000	10000	7500	4500	3750

A-3 Grade—20 Manufactured
This is too rare to generalize a value.

Later Production Hammerless Shotguns
These were manufactured at Fulton, New York, between 1914 and 1951. They are side-by-side double-barrel shotguns chambered for 12, 16, and 20 gauge, as well as the .410. They are offered with various barrel lengths and choke combinations. They feature a full sidelock action and are available with double or single triggers, extractors, and automatic ejectors. The finishes are blued and case-colored, with checkered walnut stocks that are of either straight, semi-pistolgrip, or pistolgrip configurations. The various models differ as to the degree of ornamentation and the quality of materials and workmanship utilized in their construction. These are very collectible American shotguns, and we strongly recommend securing a qualified, individual appraisal if a transaction is contemplated. The values supplied are for 12- and 16-gauge models only.
20 Gauge—Add 35%.
.410—Add 500%.
Single-Selective Trigger—Add $250.
Automatic Ejectors—Add 30%.

Courtesy Milwaukee Public Museum, Milwaukee, Wisconsin.

Field Grade

Exc.	V.G.	Good	Fair	Poor
1250	1000	750	500	350

Ideal Grade

Exc.	V.G.	Good	Fair	Poor
1500	1200	900	600	450

Trap Grade

Exc.	V.G.	Good	Fair	Poor
1600	1300	1000	700	500

Specialty Grade

Exc.	V.G.	Good	Fair	Poor
3000	2500	1750	1000	600

Eagle Grade

Exc.	V.G.	Good	Fair	Poor
5000	4000	3000	1750	1250

Skeet Special Grade

Exc.	V.G.	Good	Fair	Poor
3000	2500	1750	1000	600

Premier Skeet Grade

Exc.	V.G.	Good	Fair	Poor
3000	2500	1750	1000	600

Crown Grade
With this grade, automatic ejectors became standard equipment. The .410 is extremely rare in this model and non-existent in higher grades; there were only six manufactured, and they cannot be generally evaluated.

Exc.	V.G.	Good	Fair	Poor
6000	4500	3750	2750	2000

Monogram Grade
This version is offered standard with automatic ejectors and a single selective trigger.

Exc.	V.G.	Good	Fair	Poor
12500	10000	7500	5000	3750

There were two higher grades offered—the Premier Grade and the Deluxe Grade. They are extremely rare, and there have not been enough transactions to generally evaluate them.

Fulton Model
A utility, side-by-side double-barrel shotgun chambered for 12, 16, or 20 gauge. It is offered with various barrel lengths and choke combinations. It has double triggers and extractors. Although this is technically not an L. C. Smith, it was manufactured by Hunter Arms Company.

Exc.	V.G.	Good	Fair	Poor
650	550	450	300	200

Fulton Special
A slightly higher-grade version of the utility Fulton gun.

Exc.	V.G.	Good	Fair	Poor
750	650	500	350	250

Hunter Special

A similar utility-grade gun that features the rotary locking-bolt system found on the L. C. Smith shotguns.

Exc.	V.G.	Good	Fair	Poor
600	500	400	250	175

Single Barrel Trap Guns

High-grade, break-open, single-shot trap guns chambered for 12 gauge only. They feature 32" or 34" vent-rib barrels that are full-choked. They have boxlock actions and are standard with automatic ejectors. The finish is blued and case-colored, and they have a checkered walnut stock with a recoil pad. The various models differ in the amount of ornamentation and the quality of the materials and workmanship utilized in their construction. There was a total of approximately 2,650 manufactured between 1917 and 1951. Although these firearms are actually rarer and just as high a quality as their side-by-side counterparts, they are simply not as collectible as the side-by-side variations. It would still behoove the astute firearms investor to secure a qualified, individual appraisal if a transaction is contemplated.

Olympic Grade

Exc.	V.G.	Good	Fair	Poor
1500	1250	950	700	600

Specialty Grade

Exc.	V.G.	Good	Fair	Poor
2000	1750	1300	1000	800

Crown Grade

Exc.	V.G.	Good	Fair	Poor
3500	3000	2250	1500	1250

Monogram Grade

Exc.	V.G.	Good	Fair	Poor
6000	5000	3500	2500	1750

Premier Grade

Exc.	V.G.	Good	Fair	Poor
10000	8500	5500	4000	2750

Deluxe Grade

Exc.	V.G.	Good	Fair	Poor
14000	12500	9500	7500	4500

1968 Model

A side-by-side double-barrel shotgun chambered for 12 gauge with a 28" vent-rib barrel, choked full-and-modified. It features a sidelock action with double triggers and extractors. The finish is blued and casecolored, with a checkered walnut stock. This shotgun was manufactured by Marlin between 1968 and 1973.

Exc.	V.G.	Good	Fair	Poor
700	600	550	450	300

1968 Deluxe Model

Similar to the 1968 Model but features a Simmons floating rib and a beavertail-type forearm. It was manufactured by Marlin between 1971 and 1973.

Exc.	V.G.	Good	Fair	Poor
1000	850	750	600	400

SMITH, OTIS

Rockfall, Connecticut

This company manufactured a line of single-action, spur-trigger revolvers that are chambered for .22, .32, .38, and .41 rimfire cartridges. The pistols have varying barrel lengths. The cylinder access pin is retained by a button on the left side of the frame. The cylinder usually holds five shots. The finishes are either blued or nickle-plated, with birdshead grips. The quality was considered to be mediocre.

Model 1883 Shell-Ejector

A single-action, break-open, self ejecting revolver with a ribbed 3.5" barrel chambered for .32 centerfire. It has a 5-shot fluted cylinder and a spur trigger. It was quite well made. The finish is nickle-plated, with black plastic grips.

Exc.	V.G.	Good	Fair	Poor
250	200	150	100	75

Model 1892

A double-action, concealed-hammer revolver chambered for the .38 centerfire cartridge. It has a 4" barrel and, for the first time, a conventional trigger and triggerguard. It is gateloaded and has a solid frame. It is nickle-plated with black plastic grips and also appeared under the Maltby, Henley & Company banner marked "Spencer Safety Hammerless" or "Parker Safety hammerless." The Otis Smith Company ceased operations in 1898.

Exc.	V.G.	Good	Fair	Poor
250	200	150	100	75

SMITH & WESSON

SMITH & WESSON

Springfield, Massachusetts
By Roy G. Jinks
of Smith & Wesson

Smith & Wesson was founded by two men who shared the dream of developing a new type of firearm ... one capable of being fired repeatedly without the annoyance of having to reload it using loose powder, balls and a primer. Their idea was to direct the firearms makers out of the era of muzzleloading which had dominated the firearms industry since the invention of hand cannons in the 14th century.

Their dream became a reality when Horace Smith and Daniel B. Wesson formed their first partnership in 1852 to manufacture a lever action pistol incorporating a tubular magazine and firing a fully self-contained cartridge. This new repeating pistol could be fired as rapidly as an individual could operate the lever which loaded the pistol and cocked the hammer, making it ready to be fired. The firing power of this lever action pistol was so impressive that, in 1854 when the gun was reviewed by Scientific America, it was nicknamed the Volcanic since to the reviewer the rapid fire sequence appeared to have the force of an erupting volcano.

The original site of the Smith & Wesson Arms Company was in Norwich, Connecticut, and the company operated in those facilities until it ran into financial difficulties in 1854. In the reorganization of the company during that year, a new investor, Oliver Winchester, provided the additional financial support to continue the manufacture of this particular type of pistol. The factory was moved to New Haven, Connecticut, the site of some of Winchester's holdings, and at this time the name was changed to Volcanic Repeating Arms Company and Smith & Wesson sold the majority of their interests. It is interesting to note that this early company continued to develop using the original Smith & Wesson patents and emerged in 1866 as the Winchester Repeating Arms Company.

Horace Smith and D. B. Wesson moved from Connecticut to Springfield, Massachusetts, and in 1856 established their company for the purpose of manufacturing a revolving pistol which would fire a small .22 caliber rimfire cartridge, patented by the partners in 1854. This new rimfire cartridge was the beginning of one of the most famous cartridges developed in the world. It was originally called the "Number One Cartridge" but is today more commonly known as the .22 rimfire. The new revolver was called the Model 1 and it gained immediate popularity because of the advantages offered by the new cartridge. In 1859, finding that demand could no longer be met in the small twenty-five-man shop, Smith & Wesson built a new factory located on Stockbridge Street, close to the United States Armory in the center of springfield, Massachusetts. The factory continued in a progressive manner, improving on the Model 1, and introducing a larger frame gun more suitable to military and law enforcement use. This revolver was called the Model 2 and used a .32 rimfire cartridge.

The demand for the Smith & Wesson product was greatly accelerated in 1861 with the advent of the Civil War. In fact, by mid-1862, the demand for Smith & Wesson products had grown so great that it exceeded factory capacity and it was necessary to close the order books and only supply products against its heavy backlog. Wartime production helped firmly establish Smith & Wesson as one of the leading firearm manufacturers in the United States. However, in the postwar depression Smith & Wesson, like many other businesses, suffered severe business curtailments and sales dropped to only a few guns per month.

By 1867, the partners realized that a new approach was necessary. They had been experimenting with a new design but had lacked the necessary market. For this reason, in April 1867, they authorized Henry W. Hallott to negotiate contracts and establish a market in Europe, and sales agencies in England, France and Germany. One of Hallott's first functions was to organize a display of Smith & Wesson arms at a major exposition being held in Paris. The display included the total product line as well as some of their highly engraved works of art to further illustrate the quality craftsmen employed by the firm.

The Smith & Wesson arms exhibit was extremely popular and many nations expressed interest in its products. One of the most important persons to view their product line was the Russian Grand Duke Alexis. He was so impressed with Smith & Wesson's revolvers that he purchased several small pistols for himself and his aides. This marketing approach proved highly successful and European orders helped to relieve the effects of the domestic depression. With this new marketplace and the increase in sales, Smith & Wesson introduced their first large caliber 44 revolver called the Model 3.

The Model 3 was a totally new design known as a "top break" revolver which incorporated a fully automatic ejection system allowing rapid unloading and reloading of cartridges.

One of the first customers to receive the Model 3 was the Russian military attaché, General Gorloff. He promptly sent this sample to Russia for evaluation, and it was so well received that in May 1871 the Russian government signed a contract for 20,000 Model 3s, paying Smith & Wesson in advance with gold. This contract proved to be one of many signed with the Russian government but, more significantly, it influenced the total market and soon orders poured into the factory far exceeding its ability to supply handguns. The Model 3 became extremely popular throughout the world and on our own western frontier. One of the most interesting notes on the Model 3 appeared in an editorial in the Army/Navy Journal shortly after the Custer Massacre. This article noted that if Custer and his men had been armed with Schofield's variation of the Smith & Wesson Model 3, rather than the slower loading Colt Single Action revolver, they might have possibly survived the Indian attack.

Smith & Wesson continued to grow and in 1880 expanded their line by introducing the first group of "double action" revolver, the result of more than four years of extensive research.

In 1899, Smith & Wesson developed one of its most famous revolvers, the .38 Military & Police which was the predecessor of the Model 10. This revolver was designed to fire another first, the .38 Smith & Wesson Special.

In the summer of 1914 at the request of the British government, Smith & Wesson began development of its first side swing revolvers in .45 caliber. As World War I was engulfing the European continent, England needed a supply of service revolvers. Smith & Wesson responded by producing more than 75,000 revolvers chambered for the .455 Mark II British Service cartridge in slightly more than one year, thus helping to provide the British Army with the finest revolver available in the world.

During the 1930s, Smith & Wesson introduced two more famous revolvers, the K-22 Outdoorsman for the competitive shooter and the .357 Magnum for the law enforcement officers who needed a powerful handgun to continue their fight against crime. The .357 Magnum also was significant as it was the beginning of the era of Magnum handguns; an important first in the growth of handgunning in the world.

As it had done in World War I, Smith & Wesson answered the needs of World War II's fighting forces and by 1941 its total plant production was geared to supplying arms for the United States and all her allies. By March 1945 when World War II production was ended, Smith & Wesson had supplied 568, 204, .38 military and police revolvers to its close ally Great Britain. These revolvers were produced in the British Service caliber of .38/200.

At the close of World War II, Smith & Wesson continued its progressive leadership under the management of Mr. C. R. Hellstrom, who became president in 1946 and the first person outside the Wesson family to serve in this capacity. In 1949, the company moved to a totally new facility in Springfield, Massachusetts where it has continued to expand. It introduced the first American-made 9MM double action pistol called the Model 39, followed by the introduction of a gun which has become a legend with sportsmen and gun enthusiasts throughout the world, the Model 29, .44 Magnum, the most powerful handgun.

In 1964 Smith & Wesson entered into a completely new era as the independently owned company was purchased by Bangor Panta Corporation. Bangor Panta, recognizing an even greater potential for this giant of the firearms field, encouranged the president, W. G. Gunn, to further diversify the company. William Gunn succeeded C. R. Hellstrom as president in 1963 following the death of Mr. Hellstrom at the age of 68.

Gunn soon purchased other companies to augment Smith & Wesson's line of handgun and handcuff products to further meet the needs of the law enforcement and sporting markets. By the 1970s Smith & Wesson had increased its products to law enforcement by selling riot control equipment, police Identi-Kit identification equipment, night vision, breath testing equipment and leather products. The sporting dealers were now able to purchase not only Smith & Wesson handguns but ammunition, holsters and long guns, thus allowing them to sell a complete line of Smith & Wesson products.

Even with the expansion of Smith & Wesson's product line in other areas, the management in Springfield continued to concentrate on the development of new handguns. In 1965 the firm introduced the first stainless steel revolver, thus changing again the course of firearms history. The 1970s saw the continued development of stainless models and a new fifteen shot 9mm auto-loading pistol called the Model 59 to meet the requirement of many law enforcement agencies. Smith & Wesson opened the market of police commemorative handguns, allowing departments to purchase specially designed handguns to commemorate department history. These commemoratives helped further establish Smith & Wessons's position with law enforcement by providing the departments with a memento of their history on a fine quality Smith & Wesson handgun.

The 1970s saw many significant improvements in Smith & Wesson; the further modernization of its manufacturing facilities in Springfield, the development of the stainless steel Model 629, .44 Magnum, the Model 547, 9mm revolver using a special patented extractor system. But most important was the development of the Smith & Wesson L frame line producing the Models 581, 586, 681 and 686 which had a significant impact on both the law enforcement and sporting markets to become the most popular new revolver introduced.

With the new L frame models and the 1980s, Smith & Wesson began to consolidate its widely diversified product line by concentrating on those lines which were most profitable and beneficial to the company., Development was begun on a 9mm auto-loading pistol to meet the needs of the United States military and a new .45 auto-loading pistol called the Model 645.

In January 1984, Lear Siegler Corporation of Santa Monica, California, purchased Bangor Panta, thus acquiring Smith & Wesson. Lear Siegler, in their evaluation of Smith & Wesson, recognized the fact that Smith & Wesson's total strength laid in the manufacture and sales of handguns, handcuffs and police Identi-Kits. Under Lear's direction, Smith & Wesson divested itself of all other unrelated lines to concentrate on the product for which they were famous, thus further strengthening their position in the handgun market by concentrating Smith & Wesson's efforts in providing the highest quality, most innovative designs available to handgun users of the world.

In December 1986, Lear Siegler Corporation was purchased by Forstmann Little & Company in an agreed-upon friendly takeover. However, Forstmann Little had no interest in Smith & Wesson. Their primary interest was only in Lear Siegler holdings in the automotive and air space industry. Therefore, they offered Smith & Wesson for sale to help finance the takeover of Lear Siegler. For the first time since 1964, Smith & Wesson was going to be offered for sale on its own merits as one of the finest handgun manufacturers in the United States.

The successful bidder for Smith & Wesson was the F. H. Tomkins p.l.c. of London, England. Tomkins brings to Smith & Wesson a new strong leadership and a renewed dedication to quality and development of the finest handguns in the world.

SMITH & WESSON ANTIQUE HANDGUNS

Courtesy Mike Stuckslager.

Model 1, 1st Issue Revolver

This was the first metallic cartridge arm produced by S&W. It is a small revolver that weighs approximately 10 ounces and is chambered for the .22 short rimfire cartridge. The octagonal barrel is 3.25" long. It holds 7 cartridges. The barrel and non-fluted cylinder pivot upward upon release of the protruding bayonet- type catch under the frame. This model has a square butt with rosewood grips. The oval brass frame is silver-plated. The barrel and cylinder are blued. The barrel is stamped with the company name and address; the patent dates also appear. The edges of the frame are rounded on the 1st Issue, and the sideplate is round. Smith & Wesson manufactured approximately 11,000 of these revolvers between 1857 and 1860. Since this was the first of its kind, it is not difficult to understand the need for the number of variations within this model designation. Many small improvements were made on the way to the next model. These variations are as follows:

1st Type

Serial range 1 to low 200s, revolving recoil shield, bayonet type catch on frame.

Exc.	V.G.	Good	Fair	Poor
5000	4000	3000	2000	1000

2nd Type

Serial range low 200s to 1130, improved recoil plate.

Exc.	V.G.	Good	Fair	Poor
3000	2250	1750	900	500

3rd Type

Serial range 1130 to low 3000s, bayonet catch dropped for spring-loaded side catch.

Exc.	V.G.	Good	Fair	Poor
2250	1750	1400	850	450

4th Type

Serial range low 3000s to low 4200s, recoil shield made much smaller.

Exc.	V.G.	Good	Fair	Poor
2250	1750	1400	850	450

5th Type

Serial range low 4200s to low 5500s, has 5-groove rifling instead of 3.

Exc.	V.G.	Good	Fair	Poor
2250	1750	1400	850	450

6th Type

Serial range low 5500s to end of production 11670. A cylinder ratchet replaced the revolving recoil shield.

Exc.	V.G.	Good	Fair	Poor
2000	1500	1250	750	400

Model 1 2nd Issue

Very similar in appearance to the 1st Issue this 2nd Issue variation has several notable differences that make identification rather simple. The sides of the frame on the 2nd Issue are flat-not rounded as on the 1st Issue. The sideplate is irregular in shape-not round like on the 1st Issue. The barrel was 3 3/16" in length. The barrel is stamped "Smith & Wesson" while the cylinder is marked with the three patent dates: April 3, 1858, July 5, 1859, and December 18, 1860. There have been 2nd Issues noted with full silver or nickle-plating. Smith & Wesson manufactured approximately 115,000 of these revolvers between 1860 and 1868. The serial numbers started around 11000 where the 1st Issue left off and continued to 126400. There were approximately 4,400 revolvers marked "2D Quality" on the barrels. These revolvers were slightly defective and were sold at a lesser price. They will bring an approximate 100% premium on today's market.

Exc.	V.G.	Good	Fair	Poor
550	425	350	275	125

Model 1 3rd Issue

This is a redesigned version of its forerunners. Another .22 short rimfire, 7-shot revolver, this model has a fluted cylinder and a round barrel with a raised rib. This variation was manufactured totally from wrought iron. The three patent dates are stamped on top of the ribbed barrel as is "Smith & Wesson". It features birdshead type grips of rosewood and is either fully blued, nickle-plated, or two-toned with the frame nickle and the barrel and cylinder blued. There are two barrel lengths offered-3.25" and 2-11/16" inches. The shorter barrel was introduced in 1872. Serial numbering began with #1 and continued to 131163. They were manufactured between 1868 and 1882. The Model 1 3rd Issue was the last of the tip-up style produced by Smith & Wesson.

Courtesy Mike Stuckslager.

Shorter Barrelled Version

Exc.	V.G.	Good	Fair	Poor
750	675	500	300	150

Longer Barrelled Version

Exc.	V.G.	Good	Fair	Poor
800	450	350	275	125

Model 1-1/2 1st Issue

This model was the first of the .32-caliber Rim Fire Short revolvers that S&W produced. It is a larger version of the Model 1 but is physically similar in appearance. The Model 1-1/2 was offered with a 3.5" octagonal barrel and has a 5-shot non-fluted cylinder and a square butt with rosewood grips. In 1866 a 4" barrel version was produced for a very short time. It is estimated that about 200 were sold. The finish is blued or nickle-plated. The serial numbering on this model ran from serial number 1 to 26300; and, interestingly to note, S&W had most of the parts for this revolver manufactured on contract by King & Smith of Middletown, Connecticut. Smith & Wesson merely assembled and finished them. They were produced between 1865 and 1868.

Note: Add a 50 percent premium for the 4" barrel variation.

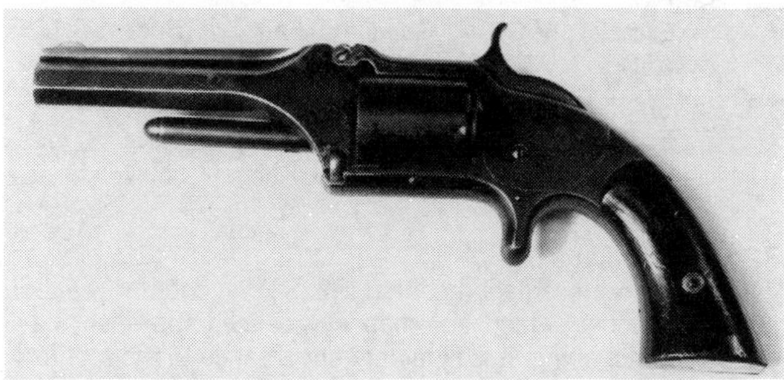

Courtesy Mike Stuckslager.

Exc.	V.G.	Good	Fair	Poor
500	400	350	275	125

Model 1-1/2 2nd Issue

The factory referred to this model as the New Model 1 1/2 and it is an improved version of the 1st Issue. It is somewhat similar in appearance with a few notable exceptions. The barrel is 2.5" or 3.5" in length, round with a raised rib. The grip is of the birdshead configuration, and the 5-shot cylinder is fluted and chambered for the .32 rimfire long cartridge. The cylinder stop is located in the top frame instead of the bottom. The finish and grip material are the same as the 1st Issue. There were approximately 100,700 manufactured between 1868 and 1875.

Courtesy W.P. Hallstein III and son Chip.

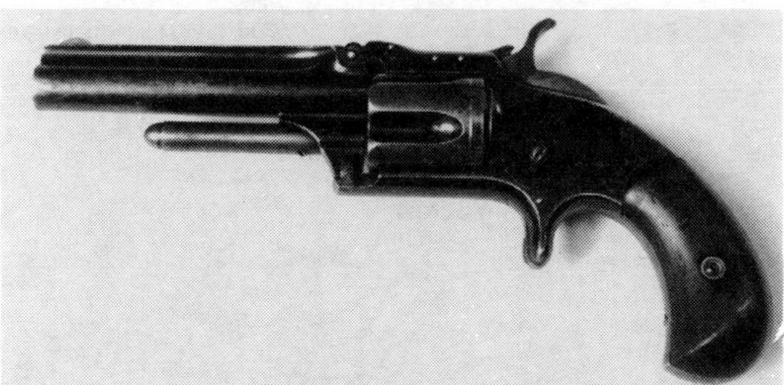

Courtesy Mike Stuckslager.

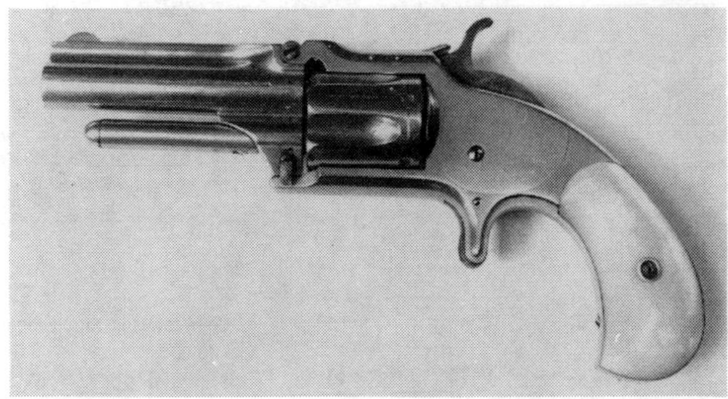

Courtesy Mike Stuckslager.

Transitional Model

Approximately 650 of these were produced by fitting 1st Issue cylinders and barrels to 2nd Issue frames. These revolvers fall into the serial number range 27200-28800.

Exc.	V.G.	Good	Fair	Poor
1500	1100	800	650	400

3.5" Barrel

Exc.	V.G.	Good	Fair	Poor
650	450	300	250	100

2.5" Barrel

Exc.	V.G.	Good	Fair	Poor
750	500	350	300	150

.32 Single Action

This model represented the first .32 S&W centerfire caliber topbreak revolver which automatically ejected the spent cartridges upon opening. It is similar in appearance to the Model 1 1/2 2nd Issue. This model has a 5-shot fluted cylinder and a birdshead grip of wood or checkered hard rubber and was offered with barrel lengths of 3", 3.5", 6", 8", and 10". The 8" and 10" barrel are rare and were not offered until 1887. This model pivots downward on opening and features a rebounding hammer which made the weapon much safer to fully load. There were approximately 97,599 manufactured between 1878 and 1892.

Early Model Without Strain Screw-Under #6500

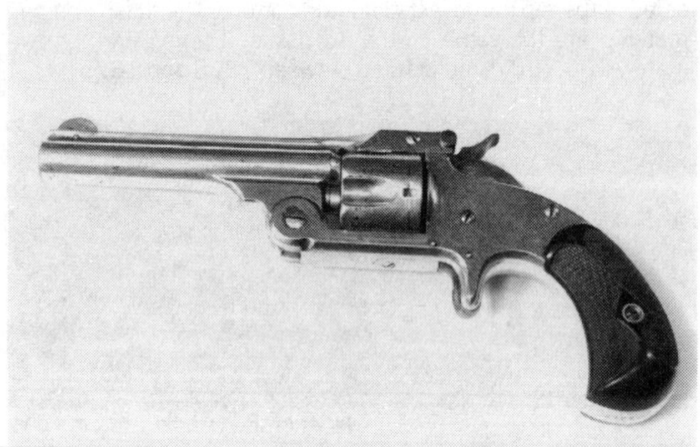

Courtesy Mike Stuckslager.

Exc.	V.G.	Good	Fair	Poor
500	400	350	200	125

Later Model With Strain Screw

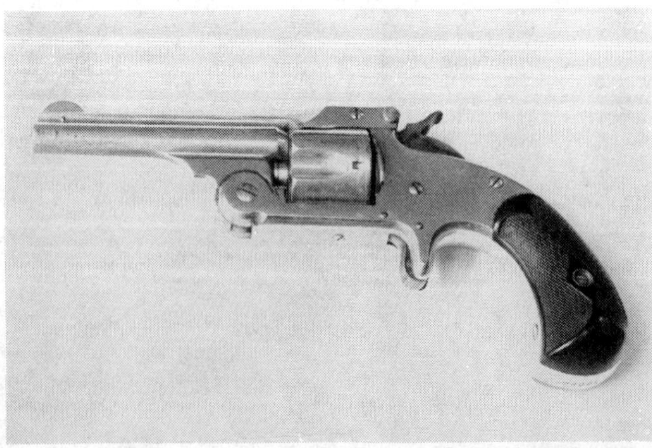

Courtesy Mike Stuckslager.

Exc.	V.G.	Good	Fair	Poor
450	400	350	200	125

8" or 10" Barrel Model

Exc.	V.G.	Good	Fair	Poor
1000	750	500	400	250

Model 2 Army or Old Model

Similar in appearance to the Model 1 2nd Issue, this revolver was extremely successful from a commercial standpoint. It was released just in time for the commencement of hostilities in the Civil War. Smith & Wesson had, in this revolver, the only weapon able to fire self-contained cartridges and be easily carried as a backup by soldiers going off to war. This resulted in a backlog of more than three years before the company finally stopped taking orders. This model is chambered for .32 rimfire long and has a 6-shot non-fluted cylinder and 4", 5", or 6" barrel lengths. It has a square butt with rosewood grips and is either blued or nickle-plated. There were approximately 77,155 manufactured between 1861 and 1874.

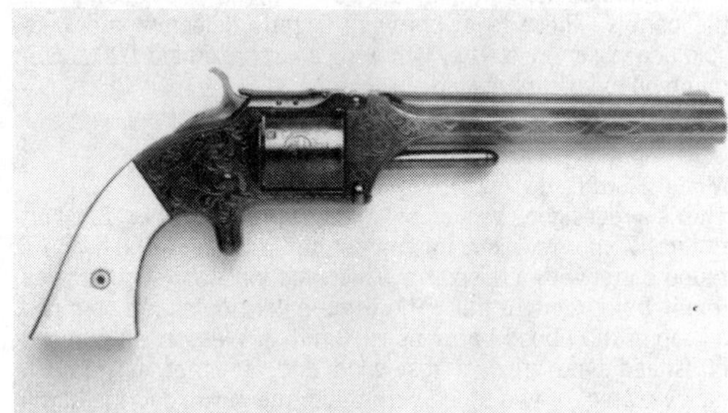

Courtesy Chester Krause.

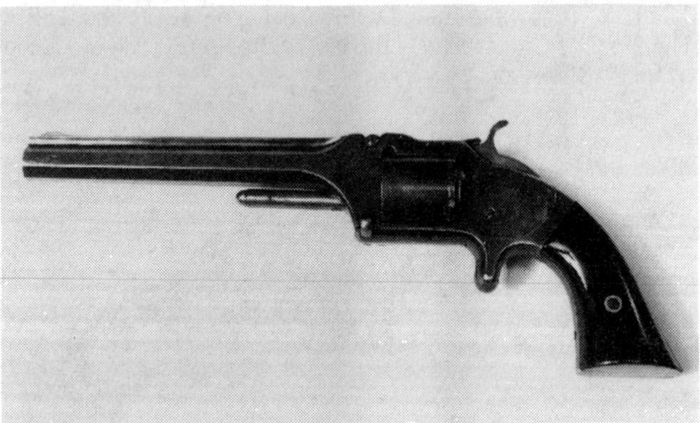

Courtesy Mike Stuckslager.

5" or 6" Barrel

Exc.	V.G.	Good	Fair	Poor
900	750	500	300	200

4" Barrel-Rare! Use Caution

Exc.	V.G.	Good	Fair	Poor
1300	900	700	500	300

.38 Single Action 1st Model (Baby Russian)

This model is sometimes called the "Baby Russian." It is a topbreak, automatic-ejecting revolver chambered for the .38 S&W center fire cartridge. It is offered with either a 3.25" or 4" round barrel with a raised rib, has a 5- shot fluted cylinder, and is finished in blue or nickle plating. A 5" barrel was added as an option a short time later. The butt is rounded, with wood or checkered hard rubber grips inlaid with the S&W medallion. It has a spur trigger. There were approximately 25,548 manufactured in 1876 and 1877 of which 16,046 were nickle and 6,502 were blued.

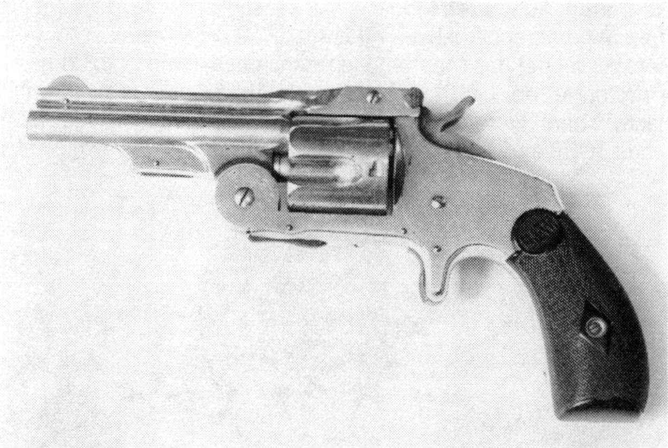
Courtesy Mike Stuckslager.

Exc.	V.G.	Good	Fair	Poor
475	350	300	200	150

.38 Single Action 2nd Model

With the exception of an improved and shortened extractor assembly and the availability of additional barrel lengths of 3.25", 4", 5", 6", 8", and 10" with the 8" and 10" barrel lengths being the most rare, this model is quite similar in appearance to the 1st Model. There were approximately 108,225 manufactured between 1877 and 1891.

Courtesy Mike Stuckslager.

8" and 10" Barrel

Exc.	V.G.	Good	Fair	Poor
900	675	550	400	300

3.25", 4", 5", and 6" Barrel Lengths.

Exc.	V.G.	Good	Fair	Poor
425	300	250	125	100

.38 Single Action 3rd Model

This model differs from the first two models because it is fitted with a triggerguard. It is chambered for the .38 S&W centerfire cartridge, has a 5-shot fluted cylinder, and is a topbreak design with automatic ejection upon opening. The barrel lengths are 3.25", 4", and 6". The finish is blued or nickle-plated. The butt is rounded, with checkered hard rubber grips featuring S&W medallions. There were approximately 26,850 manufactured between 1891 and 1911.

Courtesy Mike Stuckslager.

Exc.	V.G.	Good	Fair	Poor
600	550	450	300	175

.38 Single Action Mexican Model

This extremely rare model is quite similar in appearance to the 3rd Model Single Action. The notable differences are the flat hammer sides with no outward flaring of the spur. The spur trigger assembly was not made integrally with the frame but is a separate part added to it. One must exercise extreme caution as S&W offered a kit that would convert the triggerguard assembly of the Third Model to the spur trigger of the Mexican Model. This, coupled with the fact that both models fall within the same serial range, can present a real identification problem. Another feature of the Mexican Model is the absence of a half cock. The exact number of Mexican Models manufactured between 1891 and 1911 is unknown but it is estimated that the number is very small.

Exc.	V.G.	Good	Fair	Poor
1500	1250	900	650	450

.320 Revolving Rifle Model

This model is very rare and unique—a prize to a S&W collector. The Revolving Rifle is chambered for the .320 S&W Revolving Rifle cartridge, has a 6-shot fluted cylinder and is offered with a 16", 18", and 20" barrel. Only 76 of the rifles are nickle-plated, and the remainder of the production is blued. The butt is rounded, with red hard rubber checkered grips and a forearm of the same material. There is a detachable shoulder stock with a black hard rubber buttplate featuring the S&W logo. The rifle was furnished in a leather carrying case with accessories. As fine a firearm as this was, it was a commercial failure for S&W; and they finally came to the realization that the public did not want a revolving rifle. They manufactured only 977 of them between 1879 and 1887.

Values Are for Complete Unit.
Deduct 40 Percent Without Stock.

Courtesy Buffalo Bill Historical Center, Cody, Wyoming.

Courtesy Buffalo Bill Historical Center, Cody, Wyoming.

Exc.	V.G.	Good	Fair	Poor
6500	5500	3500	2000	1500

.32 Double Action 1st Model

This is one of the rarest of all S&W revolvers. There were only 30 manufactured. It also has a straight-sided sideplate which weakened the revolver frame. Perhaps this was the reason that so few were made. This model was the first break-open, double-action, automatic-ejecting .32 that S&W produced. It features a 3" round barrel with raised rib, a 5-shot fluted cylinder, and round butt with plain, uncheckered, black hard rubber grips. The finish is blued or nickle-plated. All 30 of these revolvers were manufactured in 1880.

Exc.	V.G.	Good	Fair	Poor
4000	2800	2000	1500	950

.32 Double Action 2nd Model

This revolver is chambered for the .32 S&W cartridge and has a 3" round barrel with a raised rib. The 5-shot cylinder is fluted, and the finish is blued or nickle-plated. It is a topbreak design with a round butt. The grips are either checkered or floral- embossed hard rubber with the S&W monogram. This model has an oval sideplate, eliminating the weakness of the 1st Model. There were approximately 22,142 manufactured between 1880 and 1882.

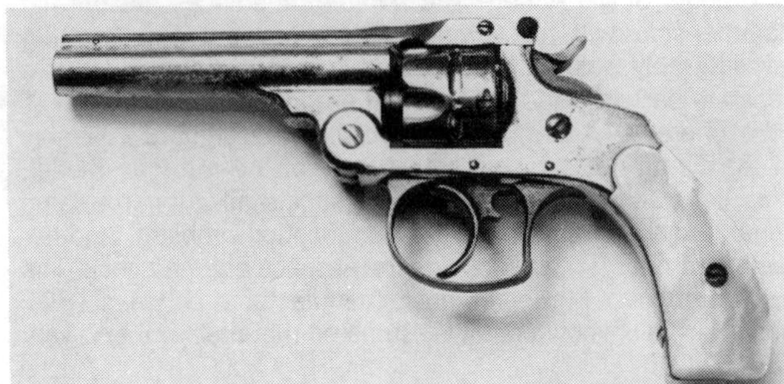

Courtesy Mike Stuckslager.

Exc.	V.G.	Good	Fair	Poor
375	250	200	125	100

.32 Double Action 3rd Model

This model incorporates internal improvements that are not evident in appearance. The most notable identifiable difference between this model and its predecessors is in the surface of the cylinder. The flutes are longer; there is only one set of stops instead of two; and the free groove is no longer present. There were approximately 21,232 manufactured in 1882 and 1883.

Courtesy Mike Stuckslager.

Exc.	V.G.	Good	Fair	Poor
300	250	200	125	100

.32 Double Action 4th Model

This model is quite similar in appearance to the 3rd Model except that the triggerguard is oval in shape instead of the squared back of the previous models. There were also internal improvements. There were approximately 239,600 manufactured between 1883 and 1909.

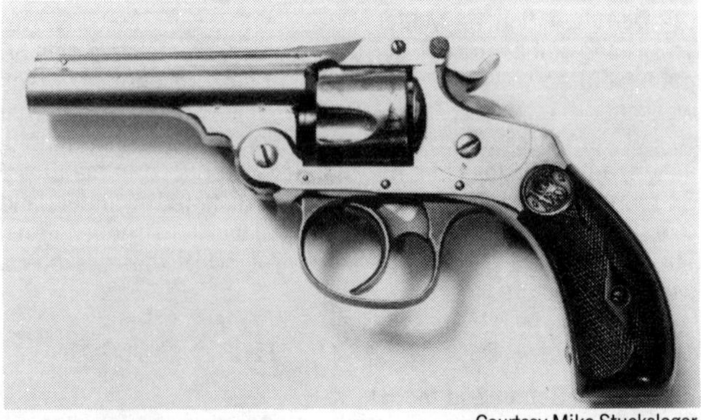

Courtesy Mike Stuckslager.

Exc.	V.G.	Good	Fair	Poor
325	275	225	150	100

.32 Double Action 5th Model

The only difference between this model and its predecessors is that this model has the front sight machined as an integral part of the barrel rib. On the other models, the sight was pinned in place. There were approximately 44,641 manufactured between 1909 and 1919.

Courtesy Mike Stuckslager.

Exc.	V.G.	Good	Fair	Poor
300	250	200	125	100

.38 Double Action 1st Model

This Model is similar in appearance to the .32 1st Model, having a straight cut side plate, but is chambered for the .38 S&W cartridge. The grips are checkered, and there were 4,000 manufactured in 1880.

Exc.	V.G.	Good	Fair	Poor
2500	1250	750	600	300

.38 Double Action 2nd Model

This is similar in appearance to the .32 2nd Model but is chambered for the .38 S&W cartridge. There were approximately 115,000 manufactured between 1880 and 1884.

Courtesy Mike Stuckslager.

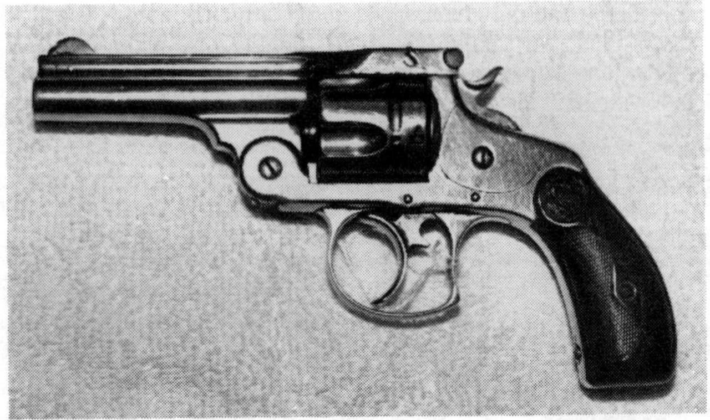

Exc.	V.G.	Good	Fair	Poor
375	250	200	125	100

.38 Double Action 3rd Model
Essentially the same in appearance as the .32 Model but chambered for the .38 S&W cartridge, it is also offered with a 3.25", 4", 5", 6", 8", and 10" barrel. There were numerous internal changes in this model similar to the .32 Double Action 3rd Model. There were approximately 203,700 manufactured between 1884 and 1895.

Courtesy Mike Stuckslager.

8" and 10" Barrel

Exc.	V.G.	Good	Fair	Poor
1300	900	700	500	400

Standard Barrel

Exc.	V.G.	Good	Fair	Poor
350	250	200	125	100

.38 Double Action 4th Model
This is the .38 S&W version of the 4th Model and is identical in outward appearance to the 3rd Model. The relocation of the sear was the main design change in this model. There were approximately 216,300 manufactured between 1895 and 1909.

Exc.	V.G.	Good	Fair	Poor
350	250	200	125	100

.38 Double Action 5th Model
This model is the same as the .32 except that it is chambered for the .38 S&W cartridge. There were approximately 15,000 manufactured between 1909 and 1911.

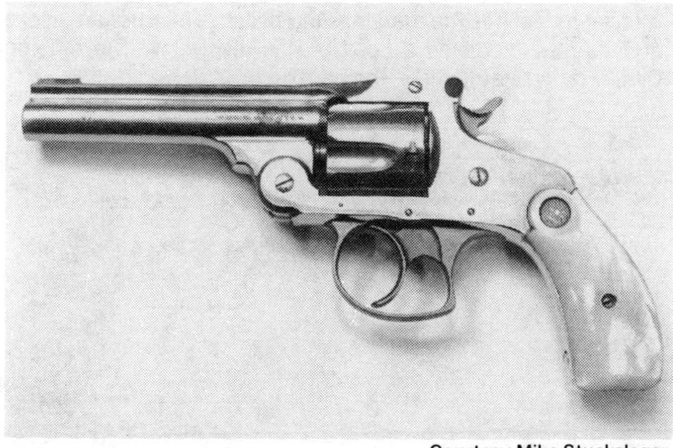

Courtesy Mike Stuckslager.

Exc.	V.G.	Good	Fair	Poor
400	300	250	150	125

Model 3 American 1st Model
This model represented a number of firsts for the Smith & Wesson Company. It was the first of the topbreak, automatic ejection revolvers. It was also the first Smith & Wesson in a large caliber (it is chambered for the .44 S&W American cartridge as well as the .44 Henry rimfire on rare occasions). It was also known as the 1st Model American. This large revolver is offered with an 8" round barrel with a raised rib as standard. Barrel lengths of 6" and 7" were also available. It has a 6-shot fluted cylinder and a square butt with walnut grips. It is blued or nickle-plated. It is interesting to note that this model appeared three years before Colt's Single Action Army and perhaps, more than any other model, was associated with the historic American West. There were only 8,000 manufactured between 1870 and 1872.

Standard Production Model

Exc.	V.G.	Good	Fair	Poor
2500	2250	1850	950	650

Transition Model—Serial Number Range 6466-6744
Shorter cylinder (1.423"), improved barrel catch.

Exc.	V.G.	Good	Fair	Poor
3000	2500	2000	1150	700

U.S. Army Order—Serial Number Range 125-2199
1000 produced with "U.S." stamped on top of barrel; "OWA," on left grip.

Exc.	V.G.	Good	Fair	Poor
3500	3000	2500	1500	800

.44 Rimfire Henry Model
Only 200 produced throughout serial range.

Exc.	V.G.	Good	Fair	Poor
4000	3500	3000	1750	1200

Model 3 American 2nd Model
An improved version of the 1st Model. The most notable difference is the larger diameter trigger pivot pin and the frame protrusions above the trigger to accommodate it. The front sight blade on this model is made of steel instead of nickle silver. Several internal improvements were also incorporated into this model. This model is commonly known as the American 2nd Model. The 8" barrel length was standard on this model. There were approximately 20,735 manufactured, including 3,014 chambered for .44 rimfire Henry, between 1872 and 1874.

Note: There have been 5.5", 6", 6.5", and 7" barrels noted; but they are extremely scarce and would bring a 40 percent premium over the standard 8" model. Use caution when purchasing these short barrel revolvers.

Courtesy Buffalo Bill Historical Center, Cody, Wyoming.

.44 Rimfire Henry

Exc.	V.G.	Good	Fair	Poor
3250	2750	2000	1250	750

Standard 8" Model

Exc.	V.G.	Good	Fair	Poor
2500	2000	1500	950	550

Model 3 Russian 1st Model
This model is quite similar in appearance to the American 1st and 2nd Model revolvers. S&W made several internal changes to this model to satisfy the Russian government. The markings on this revolver are distinct; and the caliber for which it is chambered, .44 S&W Russian, is different. There were approximately 20,000 Russian-Contract revolvers. The serial number range is 1-20000. They are marked in Russian Cyrillic letters. The Russian double-headed eagle is stamped on the rear portion of the barrel with inspector's marks underneath it. All of the contract

guns have 8" barrels and lanyard swivels on the butt. These are rarely encountered, as most were shipped to Russia. The commercial run of this model numbered approximately 4,655. The barrels are stamped in English and include the words "Russian Model." Some are found with 6" and 7" barrels, as well as the standard 8". There were also 500 revolvers that were rejected from the Russian contract series and sold on the commercial market. Some of these are marked in English; some, Cyrillic. Some have the Cyrillic markings ground off and the English restamped. This model was manufactured from 1871 to 1874.

Russian Contract Model

Exc.	V.G.	Good	Fair	Poor
3000	2500	1750	850	550

Commercial Model

Exc.	V.G.	Good	Fair	Poor
2000	1500	1250	750	450

Rejected Russian Contract Model

Exc.	V.G.	Good	Fair	Poor
2000	1500	1250	750	450

Model 3 Russian 2nd Model

This revolver was known as the "Old Model Russian." This is a complicated model to understand as there are many variations within the model designation. The serial numbering is quite complex as well, and values vary greatly due to relatively minor model differences. Before purchasing this model, it would be advisable to secure competent appraisal as well as to read reference materials solely devoted to this firearm. This model is chambered for the .44 S&W Russian, as well as the .44 rimfire Henry cartridge. It has a 7" barrel and a round butt featuring a projection on the frame that fits into the thumb web. The grips are walnut, and the finish is blue or nickle-plated. The triggerguard has a reverse curved spur on the bottom. There were approximately 85,200 manufactured between 1873 and 1878.

Commercial Model

6,200 made, .44 S&W Russian, English markings.

Exc.	V.G.	Good	Fair	Poor
1750	1250	950	600	400

.44 Rim Fire Henry Model

500 made.

Exc.	V.G.	Good	Fair	Poor
2500	1750	1300	850	600

Russian Contract Model

70,000 made; rare, as most were shipped to Russia. Cyrillic markings; lanyard swivel on butt.

Exc.	V.G.	Good	Fair	Poor
1750	1500	1250	800	550

1st Model Turkish Contract

.44 rimfire Henry, special rimfire frames, serial-numbered in own serial number range 1-1000.

Exc.	V.G.	Good	Fair	Poor
3000	2500	1750	850	550

2nd Model Turkish Contract

Made from altered centerfire frames from the regular commercial serial number range. 1,000 made. Use caution with this model.

Exc.	V.G.	Good	Fair	Poor
2750	2250	1500	750	500

Japanese Govt. Contract

5,000 made between the 1-9000 serial number range. The Japanese naval insignia, an anchor over two wavy lines, found on the butt. The barrel is Japanese proofed, and the words "Jan.19, 75 REISSUE July 25, 1871" are stamped on the barrel, as well.

Exc.	V.G.	Good	Fair	Poor
1500	1250	950	600	400

Model 3 Russian 3rd Model

This revolver is also known as the "New Model Russian." The factory referred to this model as the Model of 1874 or the Cavalry Model. It is chambered for the .44 S&W Russian and the .44 Henry rimfire cartridge. The barrel is 6.5", and the round butt is the same humped-back affair as the 2nd Model. The grips are walnut; and the finish, blue or nickle-plated. The most notable differences in appearance between this model and the 2nd Model are the shorter extractor housing under the barrel and the integral front sight blade instead of the pinned-on one found on the previous models. This is another model that bears careful research before attempting to evaluate. Minor variances can greatly affect values. Secure detailed reference materials and qualified appraisal. There were approximately 60,638 manufactured between 1874 and 1878.

Commercial Model

.44 S&W Russian, marked "Russian Model" in English, 13,500 made.

Exc.	V.G.	Good	Fair	Poor
1250	1000	800	500	300

.44 Rimfire Henry Model

Exc.	V.G.	Good	Fair	Poor
2000	1750	1250	750	550

Turkish Model

5,000 made of altered centerfire frames, made to fire .44 rimfire Henry. "W" inspector's mark on butt. Fakes have been noted; be aware.

Exc.	V.G.	Good	Fair	Poor
1750	1500	1250	800	400

Japanese Contract Model

1,000 made; has the Japanese naval insignia, an anchor over two wavy lines, stamped on the butt.

Exc.	V.G.	Good	Fair	Poor
1250	1000	800	500	250

Russian Contract Model

Barrel markings are in Russian Cyrillic. Approximately 41,100 were produced.

Exc.	V.G.	Good	Fair	Poor
2000	1750	1250	750	375

Model 3 Russian 3rd Model

The German firm of Ludwig Loewe produced a copy of this model that is nearly identical to the S&W. This German revolver was made under Russian contract, as well as for commercial sales. The contract model has different Cyrillic markings than the S&W and the letters "HK" as inspector's marks. The commercial model has the markings in English. The Russian arsenal at Tula also produced a copy of this revolver with a different Cyrillic dated stamping on the barrel.

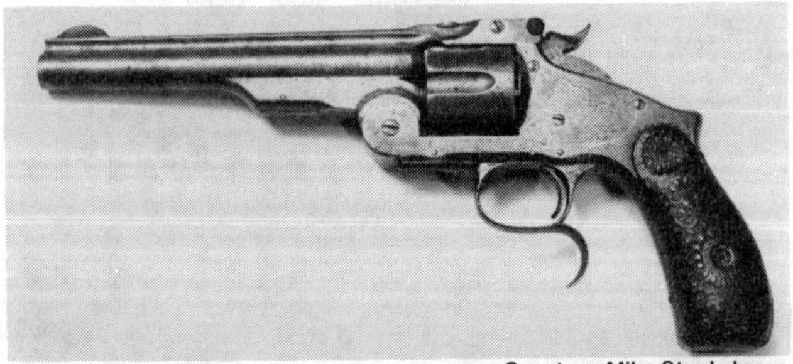

Courtesy Mike Stuckslager.

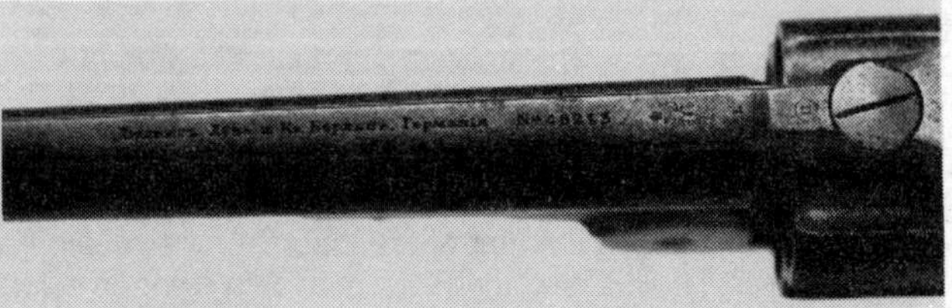

Courtesy Mike Stuckslager.

German and Russian copies

Exc.	V.G.	Good	Fair	Poor
1500	1250	950	600	300

Model 3 Schofield

In 1870 Major George W. Schofield heard about the new S&W Model 3 revolver and wrote to the company expressing a desire to be an exclusive sales representative for them. At that time S&W was earnestly attempting to interest the government in this revolver and obviously felt that the Major could be of help in this endeavor, perhaps because his brother, General John Schofield, was president of the Small Arms Board. Major Schofield was sent one Model 3 revolver and 500 rounds of ammunition free of charge. After testing the revolver, Schofield felt that it needed a few changes to make it the ideal cavalry sidearm. With the company's approval, Schofield made these changes, secured patents, and proceeded to sell them. The company eventually began production of what became known as the Model 3 Schofield 1st Model. The Major was paid a 50-cents royalty per revolver. The eventual production of this model ran to a total of 8,969, with the last one sold in 1878. What was hoped to be the adopted government-issue sidearm never materialized—for a number of reasons. First, the Colt Single Action Army being used by the cavalry had a longer chamber than the S&W and could fire the Schofield ammunition. The Schofield could not fire the longer Colt .45 cartridges. This resulted in disastrous mix-ups on more than one occasion, when Colt ammunition was issued to troops armed with the Schofields. It was eventually decided to drop the S&W as an issue weapon. At this time the company was not happy about paying the 50-cents royalty to Major Schofield. Sales of their other models were high; and they simply did not care about this model, so they eventually ceased its production. It was a very popular model on the American frontier and is quite historically significant.

Model 3 Schofield 1st Model

The modifications that made this model differ from the other Model 3 revolvers were quite extensive. The Schofield is chambered for the .45 S&W Schofield cartridge. The topbreak latch was moved from the barrel assembly to the frame. It was modified so that the action could be opened by simply pulling back on the latch with the thumb. This made it much easier to reload on horseback, as the reins would not have to be released. A groove was milled in the top of the raised barrel rib to improve the sighting plain. The extractor was changed to a cam-operated rather than rack-and-gear system. The removal of the cylinder was simplified. There were 3,000 contract Schofields and 35 commercial models. The contract revolvers were delivered to the Springfield Armory in July of 1875. These guns are stamped "US" on the butt and have the initials "L," "P," or "W" marking various other parts. The grips have an inspector's cartouche with the initials "CW," "JRJr," or "JFEC." There were 35 1st Models made for and sold to the civilian market; these revolvers do not have the "US" markings. The Schofield has a 7" barrel, 6-shot fluted cylinder, and walnut grips. The 1st Model is blued, with a nickle-plated original finish gun being extremely rare.

Courtesy Mike Stuckslager.

"US" Contract—3,000 Issued

Exc.	V.G.	Good	Fair	Poor
2500	2000	1500	950	650

Civilian Model, No "US" markings—35 Made

Exc.	V.G.	Good	Fair	Poor
3500	3000	2250	1250	800

Model 3 Schofield 2nd Model

The difference between the 1st and 2nd Model Schofield revolvers is in the barrel latch system. The 2nd Model latch is rounded and knurled to afford an easier and more positive grip when opening the revolver. A group of 3,000 of these revolvers was delivered to the Springfield Armory in October of 1876, and another 1,000 were delivered in April of 1877. These 2nd Model contract revolvers were all blued. There were an additional 649 civilian guns sold, as well. The civilian models were not "US" marked and were offered either blued or nickle-plated. A total of 8,969 Model 3 Schofield 2nd Models were manufactured. The last sale was recorded in 1878.

"US" Contract—4,000 Issued

Exc.	V.G.	Good	Fair	Poor
2800	2250	1750	1100	750

Civilian Model—646 Made

Exc.	V.G.	Good	Fair	Poor
2250	1800	1500	850	600

Model 3 Schofield-Surplus Models

After the government dropped the Schofield as an issue cavalry sidearm, the remaining U.S. inventory of these revolvers was sold off as military surplus. Many were sold to National Guard units; and the remainder were sold either to Bannerman's or to Schuyler, Hartley & Graham, two large gun dealers who then resold the guns to supply the growing need for guns on the Western frontier. Schuyler, Hartley & Graham sold a number of guns to the Wells Fargo Express Co. These weapons were nickle-plated and had the barrels shortened to 5", as were many others sold during this period. Beware of fakes when contemplating purchase of the Wells Fargo revolvers.

Wells Fargo & Co. Model

Exc.	V.G.	Good	Fair	Poor
2250	1800	1500	850	400

New Model No. 3 Single Action

Always interested in perfecting the Model 3 revolver D.B. Wesson redesigned and improved the old Model 3 in the hopes of attracting more sales. The Russian contracts were almost filled so the company decided to devote the effort necessary to improve on this design. In 1877 this project was undertaken. The extractor housing was shortened; the cylinder retention system was improved; and the shape of the grip was changed to a more streamlined and attractive configuration. This New Model has a 3.5", 4", 5", 6", 6.5", 7", 7.5", or 8" barrel length with a 6-shot fluted cylinder. The 6.5" barrel and .44 S&W Russian chambering is the most often encountered variation of this model, but the factory considered the 3-1/2" and 8" barrels as standard and these were kept in stock as well. The New Model No. 3 was also chambered for .32 S&W, .32-44 S&W, .320 S&W Rev. Rifle, .38 S&W, .38- 40, .38-44 S&W, .41 S&W, .44 Henry rimfire, .44 S&W American, .44-40, .45 S&W Schofield, .450 Rev., .45 Webley, .455 MkI and .455 MkII. They are either blued or nickle-plated and have checkered hard rubber grips with the S&W logo molded into them, or walnut grips. There are many sub-variations within this model designation, and the potential collector should secure detailed reference material that deals with this model. There were approximately 35,796 of these revolvers manufactured between 1878 and 1912. Nearly 40 percent were exported to fill contracts with Japan, Australia, Argentina, England, Spain, and Cuba. There were some sent to Asia, as well. The proofmarks of these countries will establish their provenance but will not add appreciably to standard values.

Standard Model

6.5" barrel, .44-S&W Russian.

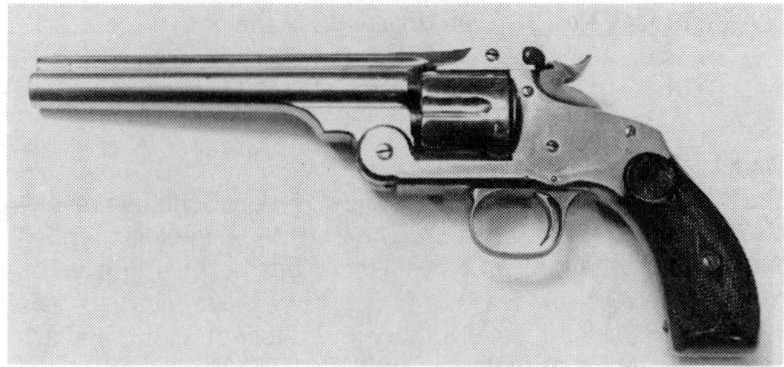

Courtesy Mike Stuckslager.

Exc.	V.G.	Good	Fair	Poor
1750	1300	950	600	300

Calibers other than .44 S&W Russian and barrel lengths other than 6.5" will bring premiums depending on rarity of the combination. It is suggested that collectors obtain an independent appraisal before purchase of a New Model No. 3 other than in standard configuration.

Japanese Naval Contract

This was the largest foreign purchaser of this model. There were over 1,500 produced with the anchor insignia stamped on the frame.

Courtesy Mike Stuckslager.

Courtesy Mike Stuckslager.

Exc.	V.G.	Good	Fair	Poor
1900	1250	800	650	300

Japanese Artillery Contract

This variation is numbered in the 25,000 serial range. They are blued, with a 7" barrel and a lanyard swivel on the butt. Japanese characters are stamped on the extractor housing.

Exc.	V.G.	Good	Fair	Poor
2200	1800	1000	800	400

Maryland Militia Model

This variation is nickle-plated, has a 6.5" barrel, and is chambered for the .44 S&W Russian cartridge. The butt is stamped "U.S.," and the inspector's marks "HN" and "DAL" under the date 1878 appear on the revolver. There were 280 manufactured between serial-numbers 7126 and 7405.

Exc.	V.G.	Good	Fair	Poor
4000	3200	2500	1500	1000

Australian Contract

This variation is nickle-plated, is chambered for the .44 S&W Russian cartridge, and is marked with the Australian Colonial Police Broad Arrow on the butt. There were 250 manufactured with 7" barrels and detachable shoulder stocks. The stock has the Broad Arrow stamped on the lower tang. There were also 30 manufactured with 6.5" barrels without the stocks. They all are numbered in the 12,000-13,000 serial range.

Courtesy Mike Stuckslager.

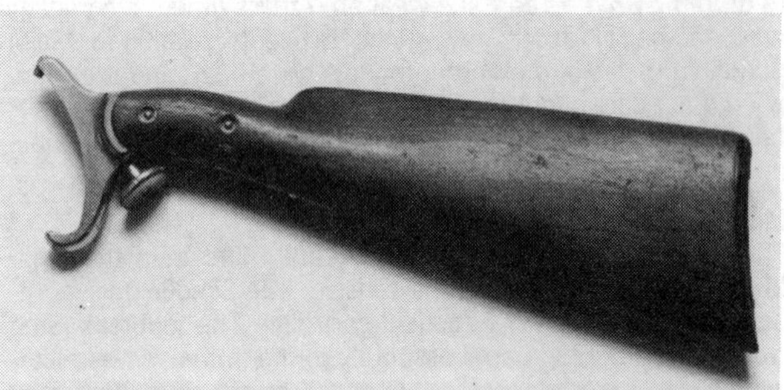

Courtesy Mike Stuckslager.

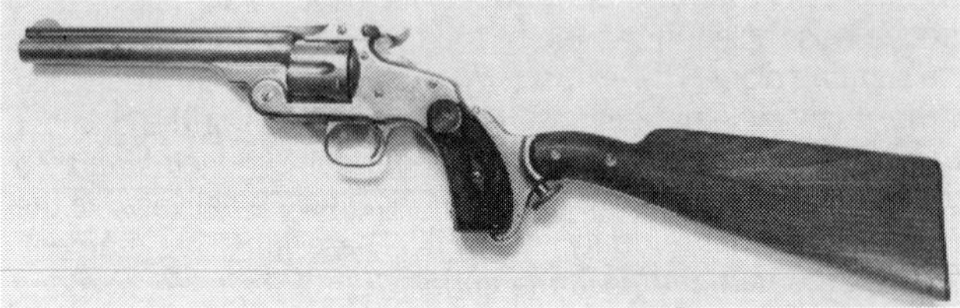

Courtesy Mike Stuckslager.

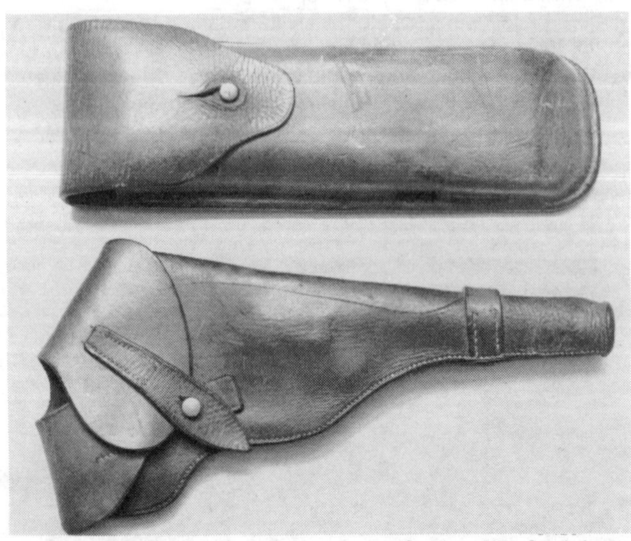

Courtesy Mike Stuckslager.

Revolver Only

Exc.	V.G.	Good	Fair	Poor
2100	1500	1000	800	400

Stock Only

Exc.	V.G.	Good	Fair	Poor
500	400	350	250	200

Argentine Model

This was essentially not a factory contract but a sale through Schuyler, Hartley and Graham. They are stamped "Ejercito/Argentino" in front of the triggerguard. The order amounted to some 2,000 revolvers between the serial numbers 50 and 3400.

Exc.	V.G.	Good	Fair	Poor
2250	1700	950	700	400

Turkish Model

This is essentially the New Model No. 3 chambered for the .44 rimfire Henry cartridge. It is stamped with the letters "P," "U" and "AFC" on various parts of the revolver. The barrels are all 6.5"; the finish, blued with walnut grips. Lanyard swivels are found on the butt. There were 5,461 manufactured and serial-numbered in their own range, starting at #1 through #5,461 between 1879 and 1883.

Courtesy Mike Stuckslager.

Exc.	V.G.	Good	Fair	Poor
2300	1750	1450	850	450

New Model No. 3 Target Single Action

This revolver is very similar in appearance to the standard New Model No. 3, but was the company's first production target model. It has a 6.5" round barrel with a raised rib and 6-shot fluted cylinder and is finished in blue or nickle-plated. The grips are either walnut or checkered hard rubber with the S&W logo molded into them. This model is chambered in either .32 S&W or .38 S&W. The company referred to these models as either the .32-44 Target or the .38-44 Target depending on the caliber. The designation of -44 referred to the frame size, i.e. a .32 caliber built on a 44 caliber frame. This model was offered with a detachable shoulder stock as an option. These stocks are extremely scarce on today's market. There were approximately 4,333 manufactured between 1887 and 1910.

Shoulder Stock—Add 50%.

Courtesy Mike Stuckslager.

Exc.	V.G.	Good	Fair	Poor
1500	1100	850	600	300

New Model No. 3 Frontier Single Action

This is another model very similar in appearance to the standard New Model No. 3. It has a 4", 5", or 6.5" barrel and is chambered for the .44-40 Winchester Centerfire cartridge. Because the original New Model No. 3 cylinder was 1-7/16" in length this would not accommodate the longer .44-40 cartridge. The cylinder on the No. 3 Frontier was changed to 1-9/16" in length. Later the company converted 786 revolvers to .44 S&W Russian and sold them to Japan. This model is either blued or nickle-plated and has checkered grips of walnut or hard rubber. They are serial numbered in their own range from #1 through #2072 and were manufactured from 1885 until 1908. This model was designed to compete with the Colt Single Action Army but was not successful.

Courtesy Mike Stuckslager.

.44-40 Commercial Model

Exc.	V.G.	Good	Fair	Poor
2000	1750	1500	1000	750

Japanese Purchase Converted to .44 S&W Russian

Exc.	V.G.	Good	Fair	Poor
2000	1750	1500	1000	750

New Model No. 3 .38 Winchester

This variation was the last of the New Model No.3s to be introduced. It was offered in .38-40 Winchester as a separate model from 1900 until 1907. The finish is blue or nickle-plate, and the grips are checkered hard rubber or walnut. Barrel lengths of 4" or 6.5" were offered. This model was not at all popular, as only 74 were manufactured in their own serial range #1 through #74. Todays collectors are extremely interested in this extremely rare model.

Courtesy Mike Stuckslager.

Exc.	V.G.	Good	Fair	Poor
2800	2000	1500	1000	750

.44 Double Action 1st Model

This model is a topbreak revolver that automatically ejects the spent cartridge cases upon opening. The barrel latch is located at the top and rear of the cylinder; the pivot, in front and at the bottom. This model was also known as "The D.A. Frontier" or "The New Model Navy." The revolver is chambered for the .44 S&W Russian and was built on a modified Model 3 frame. It is also found on rare occasions chambered for the .38-40 and the .44-40 Winchester. The barrel lengths are 4", 5", 6", and 6.5", round with a raised rib. A 3 1/2" barrel was produced on this model by special request. Collectors should be aware that the barrel for this model and the New Model No. 3 were interchangeable and the factory did in fact use barrels from either model. The serial number on the rear of the barrel should match the number on the butt, cylinder and barrel latch. The cylinder holds 6 shots and is fluted. It has double sets of stop notches and long free grooves between the stops. It is serial numbered in its own range, beginning at #1. There were approximately 54,000 manufactured between 1881 and 1913.

Standard .44 S&W Russian

Courtesy Mike Stuckslager.

Exc.	V.G.	Good	Fair	Poor
1000	800	600	400	250

Model .44 Double Action Wesson Favorite

The Favorite is basically a lightened version of the 1st Model D.A. .44. The barrel is thinner and is offered in 5" length only. There are lightening cuts in the frame between the triggerguard and the cylinder; the cylinder diameter was smaller, and there is a groove milled along the barrel rib. The Favorite is chambered for the .44 S&W Russian cartridge and has a 6-shot fluted cylinder with the same double-cylinder stop notches and free grooves as the 1st Model Double Action .44. The company name and address, as well as the patent dates, are stamped into the edge of the cylinder instead of on the barrel rib. It is serial-numbered in the same range, between #9000 and 10100. The revolver was most often nickle-plated but was also offered blued. The grips are walnut or checkered hard rubber with the S&W logo molded in. There were approximately 1,000 manufactured in 1882 and 1883.

Use Caution when purchasing a blued model—Add 25% for blued finish.

Courtesy Butterfield & Butterfield, San Francisco, California.

Nickle Plated

Exc.	V.G.	Good	Fair	Poor
3000	2500	2000	1250	800

Safety Hammerless Double Action 1st Model

This model was a departure from what was commonly being produced at this time. Some attribute the Safety Hammerless design to D. B. Wesson's hearing that a child had been injured by cocking and firing one of the company's pistols. This story has never been proven. Nevertheless, the concealed hammer and grip safety make this an ideal pocket pistol for those needing concealability in a handgun. This is a small revolver chambered for .32 S&W and .38 S&W cartridges. It has a 5-shot fluted cylinder and is offered with a 2", 3", and 3.5" round barrel with a raised rib. The butt is rounded and has checkered hard rubber grips with the S&W logo. The finish is blue or nickle-plated. The revolver is a topbreak, automatic-ejecting design; and the 1st Model has the latch for opening located in the rear center of the topstrap instead of at the sides. The latch is checkered for a positive grip. This model is commonly referred to as the "Lemon Squeezer" because the grip safety must be squeezed as it is fired. There were approximately 5,125 manufactured in .38 S&W in 1887 and 91,417 in .32 between 1888 and 1902.

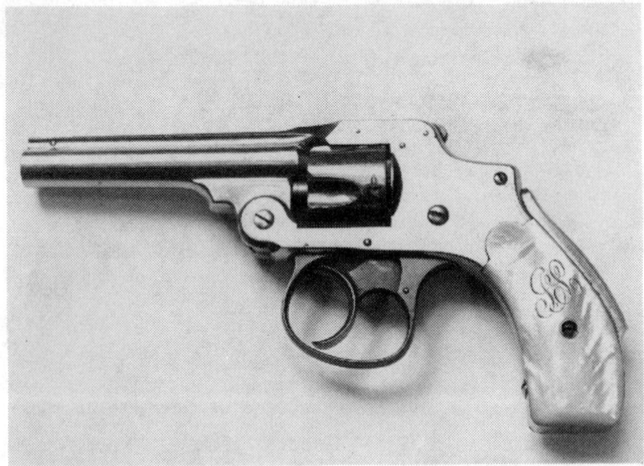

Courtesy Mike Stuckslager.

.38 S&W Model

Also offered with a 6" barrel. RARE! Add 50 percent.

Exc.	V.G.	Good	Fair	Poor
550	450	400	250	150

.32 S&W Model

Courtesy Mike Stuckslager.

Exc.	V.G.	Good	Fair	Poor
400	350	300	200	100

Safety Hammerless Double Action 2nd Model

This model is quite similar in appearance to the 1st Model. The only major difference is in the latch. This model, also called "The Lemon Squeezer," has a catch made up of two checkered buttons on the sides of the frame. A 6" barrelled version was also offered in the .32 S&W version. There were 37,350 manufactured in .38 S&W between 1887 and 1890; serial number range 5251 to 42483. 78,500 were made in .32 S&W between 1902 and 1909; serial number range 91418 to 169999.

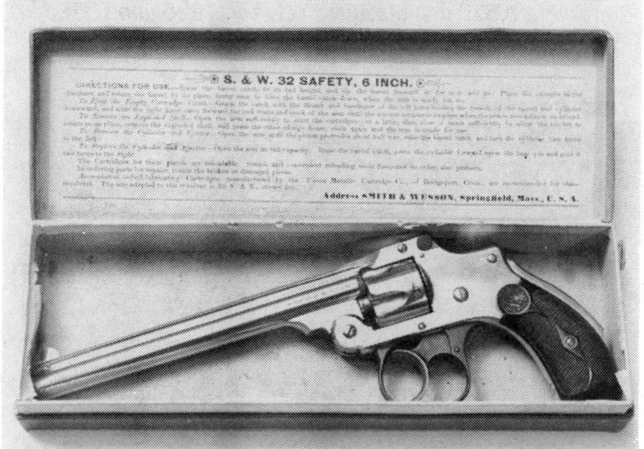

Courtesy Mike Stuckslager.

.38 S&W

Exc.	V.G.	Good	Fair	Poor
400	350	300	200	100

Courtesy Mike Stuckslager.

.32 S&W

2" barrel "Bicycle Revolver"—Add 50 percent.

Exc.	V.G.	Good	Fair	Poor
400	350	300	200	100

Safety Hammerless Double Action 3rd Model

With the exception of minor internal changes, there are virtually no differences in this and the 2nd Model "Lemon Squeezer." There were 73,500 made in .38 S&W between 1890 and 1898; serial number range 42484 to 116002. There were approximately 73,000 in .32 S&W manufactured between 1909 and 1937; serial-number range 170000 to 242981.

Courtesy Mike Stuckslager.

.38 S&W

Exc.	V.G.	Good	Fair	Poor
375	325	275	175	100

.32 S&W

2" barrel, Bicycle Model—Add 50 percent.

Exc.	V.G.	Good	Fair	Poor
300	275	200	150	100

Safety Hammerless Double Action 4th Model

This model was produced in .38 S&W only, and the only difference in the 4th Model and the 3rd Model is the adoption of the standard two-button type of barrel latch as found on most of the topbreak revolvers. ".38 S&W Cartridge" was also added to the left side of the barrel. There were approximately 104,000 manufactured between 1898 and 1907; serial-number range 116003 to 220000.

Courtesy Mike Stuckslager.

Exc.	V.G.	Good	Fair	Poor
300	275	200	150	100

Safety Hammerless 5th Model Double Action

This is the last of the "Lemon Squeezers," and the only appreciable difference between this model and the 4th Model is that the front sight blade on the 5th Model is an integral part of the barrel and not a separate blade pinned onto the barrel. There were approximately 41,500 manufactured between 1907 and 1940; serial number range 220001 to 261493.

2" Barrel Version—Add 50%.

Courtesy Mike Stuckslager.

Exc.	V.G.	Good	Fair	Poor
300	275	200	150	100

1st Model Single Shot

This unusual pistol combines the frame of the .38 Single Action 3rd Model with a single shot barrel. This model is a topbreak and functions exactly as the revolver models do. The barrel length is 6", 8", or 10"; and the pistol is chambered for .22 Long Rifle, .32 S&W, and .38 S&W. The finish is blue or nickle-plated, with a square butt. The grips are checkered hard rubber extension types for a proper target hold. This pistol is considered quite rare on today's market, as only 1,251 were manufactured between 1893 and 1905.

.22 L.R.

Exc.	V.G.	Good	Fair	Poor
800	650	450	250	150

.32 S&W

Exc.	V.G.	Good	Fair	Poor
950	700	500	300	200

.38 S&W

Exc.	V.G.	Good	Fair	Poor
1100	800	600	400	300

2nd Model Single Shot

The 2nd Model Single Shot has a frame with the recoil shield removed, is chambered for the .22 l.r. only, and is offered with the 10" barrel. The finish is blue or nickle-plated, and the grips are checkered hard rubber extension types. There were approximately 4,617 manufactured between 1905 and 1909.

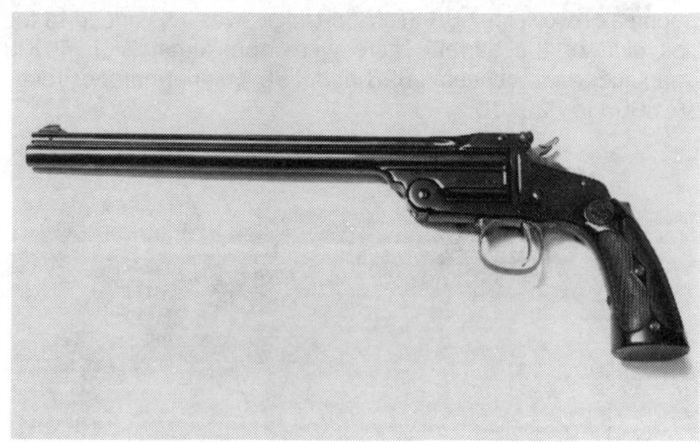

Courtesy Mike Stuckslager.

Exc.	V.G.	Good	Fair	Poor
700	500	350	200	150

3rd Model Single Shot

The basic difference between this model and the 2nd Model is that this pistol could be fired double-action as well as single-action, and the frame came from the double-action perfected model. There were 6,949 manufactured between 1909 and 1923.

Courtesy Mike Stuckslager.

Exc.	V.G.	Good	Fair	Poor
600	500	350	200	150

Straight Line Single Shot

This is a unique pistol that very much resembles a semi-automatic. The barrel is 10" in length and pivots to the left for loading. It is chambered for .22 Long Rifle cartridge and is finished in blue, with walnut grips inlaid with the S&W medallions. The hammer is straight-line in function and does not pivot. There were 1,870 manufactured between 1925 and 1936.

Courtesy Butterfield & Butterfield, San Francisco, California.

Exc.	V.G.	Good	Fair	Poor
2250	1600	1000	500	300

.32 Hand Ejector Model of 1896 or .32 Hand Ejector 1st Model

This model was the first time S&W made a revolver with a swing-out cylinder. Interestingly, there is no cylinder latch; but the action opens by pulling forward on the exposed portion of the cylinder pin. This frees the spring tension and allows the cylinder to swing free. Another novel feature of this model is the cylinder stop location which is located in the top of the frame over the cylinder. This model is chambered for the .32 S&W Long cartridge, has a 6-shot fluted cylinder, and is offered with 3.25", 4.25", and 6" long barrels. It is available with either a round or square butt, has checkered hard rubber grips, and is blued or nickle-plated. Factory installed target sights were available by special order. The company name, address, and patent dates are stamped on the cylinder instead of on the barrel. There were approximately 19,712 manufactured between 1896 and 1903.

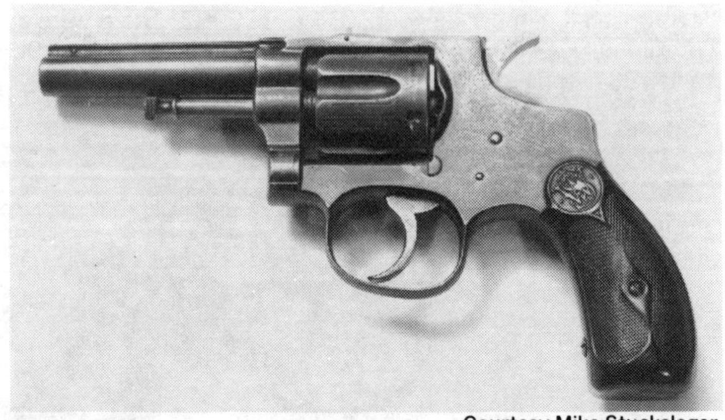

Courtesy Mike Stuckslager.

Exc.	V.G.	Good	Fair	Poor
450	400	350	250	175

Hand Ejector Model of 1903

This model is quite different from its predecessor. The cylinder locks front and back; the cylinder stop is located in the bottom of the frame, and the familiar sliding cylinder latch is found on the left side of the frame. The barrel lengths are 3.25", 4.25", and 6". The 6-shot cylinder is fluted, and the revolver is chambered for .32 S&W Long. It is offered either blued or nickle-plated, and the round butt grips are checkered hard rubber. There were approximately 19,425 manufactured in 1903 and 1904; serial-number range 1 to 19425.

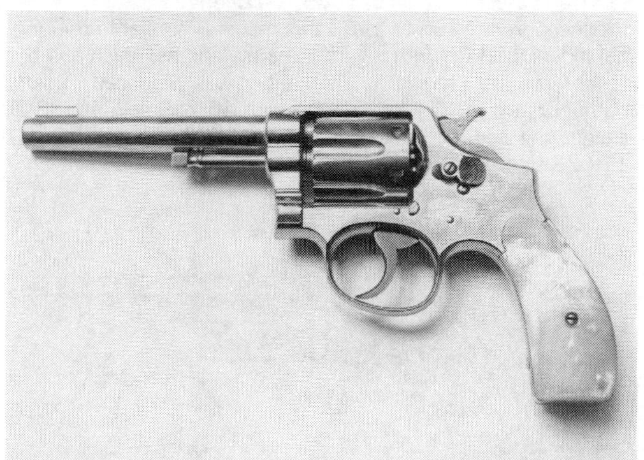

Courtesy Mike Stuckslager.

Exc.	V.G.	Good	Fair	Poor
300	250	200	150	100

.32 Hand Ejector Model of 1903 1st Change

This model differs from the model of 1903 internally, and the serial number range 19426 to 51126 is really the only way to differentiate the two. There were approximately 31,700 manufactured between 1904 and 1906.

Exc.	V.G.	Good	Fair	Poor
300	250	200	150	100

.32 Hand Ejector Model of 1903 2nd Change

Produced from 1906 to 1909 in serial number range 51127 to 95500. A total of 44,373 manufactured.

.32 Hand Ejector Model of 1903 3rd Change

Produced from 1909 to 1910 in serial number range 95501 to 96125. A total of 624 manufactured.

.32 Hand Ejector Model of 1903 4th Change

Produced in 1910 in serial number range 96126 to 102500. A total of 6,374 manufactured.

.32 Hand Ejector Model of 1903 5th Change

Produced from 1910 to 1917 in serial number range 102500 to 263000. A total of 160,500 manufactured.

.32 Hand Ejector Third Model

Produced from 1911 to 1942 in serial number range 263001 to 536684. A total of 273,683 were manufactured.

Exc.	V.G.	Good	Fair	Poor
300	250	200	150	100

.22 Ladysmith 1st Model

This model was designed primarily as a defensive weapon for women. Its small size and caliber made it ideal for that purpose. The 1st Model Ladysmith is chambered for .22 Long cartridge and has a 7-shot fluted cylinder and 3" and 3.5" barrel lengths. This little revolver weighed 9-5/8 ounces. It is either blued or nickle-plated and has a round butt with checkered hard rubber grips. The 1st Model has a checkered cylinder-latch button on the left side of the frame. There were approximately 4,575 manufactured between 1902 and 1906.

Exc.	V.G.	Good	Fair	Poor
1750	1200	850	650	450

.22 Ladysmith 2nd Model

This is essentially quite similar in appearance to the 1st Model, the difference being in the pull-forward cylinder latch located under the barrel, replacing the button on the left side of the frame. The new method allowed lockup front and back for greater action strength. The 2.25" barrel length was dropped; caliber and finishes are the same. There were approximately 9,374 manufactured between 1906 and 1910; serial number range 4576 to 13950.

Courtesy Mike Stuckslager.

Exc.	V.G.	Good	Fair	Poor
1550	900	800	600	400

.22 Ladysmith 3rd Model

This model is quite different in appearance to the 2nd Model, as it features a square butt and smooth walnut grips with inlaid S&W medallions. The barrel lengths remained the same, with the addition of a 2.25" and 6" variation. The under-barrel cylinder lockup was not changed, nor were the caliber and finishes. There were approximately 12,200 manufactured between 1910 and 1921; serial-number range 13951 to 26154.

Note: Add a 50 percent premium for 2.25" and 6" barrel lengths.

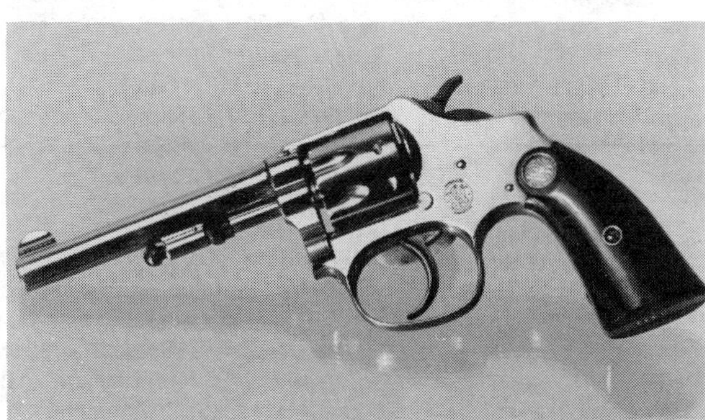

Courtesy W.P. Hallstein III and son Chip.

Exc.	V.G.	Good	Fair	Poor
1350	1000	800	600	400

.38 Hand Ejector Military & Police 1st Model or Model of 1899

This was an early swing-out cylinder revolver, and it has no front lockup for the action. The release is on the left side of the frame. This model is chambered for .38 S&W Special cartridge and the .32 Winchester centerfire cartridge (.32/20), has a 6-shot fluted cylinder, and was offered with a 4", 5", 6", 6.5", or 8" barrel in .38 caliber and 4", 5", and 6-1/2" in .32/20 caliber. The finish is blued or nickle-plated; the grips, checkered walnut or hard rubber. There were approximately 20,975 manufactured between 1899 and 1902 in .38 caliber; serial number range 1 to 20,975. In the .32/20 caliber 5,311 were sold between 1899 and 1902; serial-number range 1 to 5311.

Courtesy Mike Stuckslager.

Commercial Model

Exc.	V.G.	Good	Fair	Poor
750	650	600	450	350

U.S. Navy Model

1,000 produced in 1900, .38 S&W, 6" barrel, blued with checkered walnut grips, "U.S.N." stamped on butt, serial number range 5000 to 6000.

Exc.	V.G.	Good	Fair	Poor
700	600	550	400	300

U.S. Army Model

1,000 produced in 1901, same as Navy Model except that it is marked "U.S.Army/Model 1899" on butt, "K.S.M." and "J.T.T." on grips, serial-number range 13001 to 14000.

Exc.	V.G.	Good	Fair	Poor
850	600	550	400	300

.38 Hand Ejector M&P 2nd Model or Model of 1902

The 2nd Model is very similar in appearance to the 1st Model. The major difference is the addition of the front lockup under the barrel, and the ejector rod was increased in diameter. Barrel lengths for the .38 S&W were 4", 5", 6", or 6-1/2" while the .32/20 was available in 4", 5", or 6 1/2" barrel lengths. Both calibers were offered in round butt only configuration. There were approximately 12,827 manufactured in .38 S&W in 1902 and 1903; serial number range 20,976 to 33,803. In the .32/20 caliber 4,499 were produced; serial-number range 5312 to 9811.

Exc.	V.G.	Good	Fair	Poor
500	350	300	250	100

.38 Hand Ejector M&P 2nd Model, 1st Change.

Built between 1903 and 1905 this variation represents the change to the square butt which made for better shooting control and standardized frame shape. Both the .38 S&W and the .32/20 were available in 4", 5", or 6-1/2" barrel lengths. The company manufactured 28,645 .38 calibers; serial number range 33,804 to 62,449 and produced 8,313 .32/20s; serial-number 9812 to 18125.

Exc.	V.G.	Good	Fair	Poor
500	350	300	250	100

.38 Hand Ejector Model of 1905

This model was a continuation of the .38 M&P Hand Ejector series. Built from 1905 to 1906 it was available in 4", 5", 6", and 6-1/2" barrels for both the .38 and .32/20 calibers. Finished in either blue or nickle with round or square butt the .38 caliber model serial number range was from 62450 to 73250 or about 10,800 produced. The .32/20 caliber serial number range spans 18126 to 22426 or 4,300 produced.

Exc.	V.G.	Good	Fair	Poor
600	425	300	250	150

.38 Hand Ejector Model of 1905, 1st Change

Produced from 1906 to 1908 this model is similar to the original model of 1905 with regard to barrel lengths, finish and butt styles. The 1st change in .38 caliber was produced in serial number range 73251 to 120000 with 46,749 sold. In .32/20 caliber the serial-number range was 22427 to 33500 with 11,073 sold.

.38 Hand Ejector Model of 1905, 2nd Change

Produced from 1908 to 1909 only internal changes were made to this model. The best approach to differentiate this model is by serial number. The .38 caliber serial number range was from 120001 to 146899 with 26,898 produced. In the .32/20 caliber the serial-number range is between 33501 and 45200 with 11,699 produced.

.38 Hand Ejector Model of 1905, 3rd Change

Courtesy Mike Stuckslager.

Produced from 1909 to 1915 the 3rd Change variation was available in only 4" or 6" barrel lengths for both the .38 and .32/20 models. The .38 caliber serial number range was between 146900 to 241703 with 94,803 sold.

.38 Hand Ejector Model of 1905, 4th Change

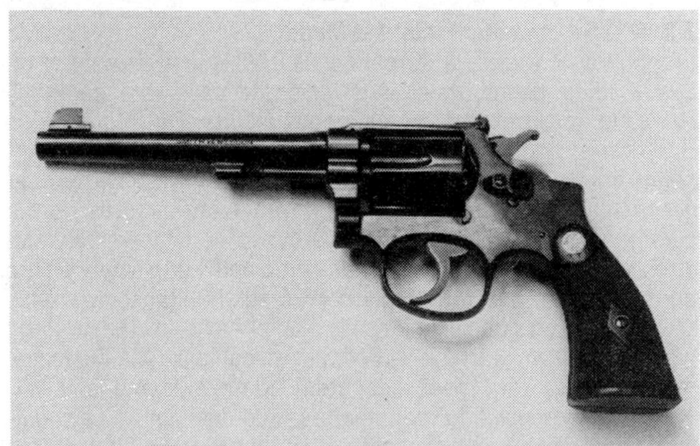

Courtesy Mike Stuckslager.

This last variation was also the longest production run. Produced from 1915 to 1942 the .38 caliber model was available in 2", 4", 5", or 6", barrel lengths while the .32/20 caliber was offered in 4", 5", or 6" barrel lengths. The .38 caliber serial number range was from 241704 to 1000000. The .32/20 caliber model was produced from 1915 to 1940 in serial number range from 65701 to 144684.

.22/32 Hand Ejector

This is a very interesting model from the collector's point of view. Phillip B. Bekeart, a San Francisco firearms dealer requested that S&W manufacture a .22 caliber target-grade revolver on the heavier .32 frame. He believed in his idea so passionately that he immediately ordered 1,000 of the guns for himself. This initial order is found within the serial number range 1 to 3000 and are known to collectors as the authentic Bekearts. The remainder of the extensive production run are simply .22/.32 Hand Ejectors. This model is chambered for .22 Long Rifle cartridge and has a 6-shot fluted cylinder with 6" barrel. The finish is blue, with square butt and checkered extension-type walnut grips. There were only 292 revolvers of his initial order delivered to Mr. Bekeart, but the first 1,000 pistols are considered to be True Bekearts. The production number of each respective pistol is stamped into the base of the extended wooden grips. S&W went on to manufacture several hundred thousand of these revolvers between 1911 and 1953.

Courtesy Mike Stuckslager.

"The True Bekeart"

Serial number range 138226 to 139275 in the .32 Hand Ejector series, production number stamped on butt. Professional appraisal should be secured.

Exc.	V.G.	Good	Fair	Poor
750	500	400	300	250

Standard Model

Exc.	V.G.	Good	Fair	Poor
500	300	250	200	125

.44 Hand Ejector 1st Model

This model is also known by collectors as the ".44 Triple lock" or "The New Century." The Triple Lock nickname came from a separate locking device located on the extractor rod shroud that is used in addition to the usual two locks. This model is chambered for the .44 S&W Special cartridge or the .44 S&W Russian. On a limited basis it is also chambered in .44-40, .45 Colt, and .38-40. The fluted cylinder holds 6 shots, and the barrel was offered in standard lengths of 5"or 6.5". A limited quantity of 4" barrel was produced. The finish is blued or nickle-plated; and the grips are checkered walnut, with the gold S&W medallion on later models. There were approximately 15,375 manufactured between 1908 and 1915.

Courtesy Mike Stuckslager.

Courtesy Mike Stuckslager.

.44 S&W Special and .44 S&W Russian

Exc.	V.G.	Good	Fair	Poor
800	600	500	350	200

Other Calibers (Rare)

Exc.	V.G.	Good	Fair	Poor
1100	800	600	450	300

.44 Hand Ejector 2nd Model

This model is quite similar in appearance to the 1st Model. The major difference is the elimination of the third or triple lock device and the heavy ejector rod shroud. Other changes are internal and not readily apparent. This model is also standard in .44 S&W Special chambering but was offered rarely in .38-40, .44-40, and .45 Colt. Specimens have been noted with adjustable sights in 6-1/2" barrel lengths. Standard barrel lengths were 4", 5", and 6-1/2". There were approximately 17,510 manufactured between 1915 and 1937 in serial number range 15376 to 60000.

Courtesy Mike Stuckslager.

.44 S&W Special

Exc.	V.G.	Good	Fair	Poor
650	600	500	350	200

.38-40, .44-40 or .45 Colt

Exc.	V.G.	Good	Fair	Poor
750	650	550	400	250

.44 Hand Ejector 3rd Model or Model of 1926

This model is similar in appearance to the 2nd Model but brought back the heavy ejector rod shroud of the 1st Model without the triple lock device. Barrel lengths were 4", 5", and 6-1/2". The .44 Hand Ejector Model was manufactured between 1926 and 1949.

Courtesy Mike Stuckslager.

.44 S&W Special

Exc.	V.G.	Good	Fair	Poor
650	450	350	275	150

.44-40 or .45 Colt

Exc.	V.G.	Good	Fair	Poor
800	550	400	300	150

.44 Hand Ejector 4th Model (Target Model)

The 4th Model featured a ribbed barrel, micrometer adjustable sight, and short throw hammer. Never a popular seller this model had only 5,050 pistol produced between 1950 and 1966.

Exc.	V.G.	Good	Fair	Poor
1500	1250	900	750	500

S & W .35 Automatic Pistol 1st Model

Production of the 35 Automatic was S&W's first attempt at an auto-loading pistol. As was always the case, the company strived for maximum safety and dependability. This model has a 3.5" barrel and a 7-shot detachable magazine and is chambered in .35 S&W Automatic, a one-time-only cartridge that eventually proved to be the major downfall of this pistol from a commercial standpoint. There were two separate safety devices—a revolving cam on the backstrap and a grip safety on the front strap that had to be fully depressed simultaneously while squeezing the trigger. The finish is blue or nickel-plated; and the grips are walnut, with the S&W inlaid medallions. The magazine release on the 1st Model slides from side to side and is checkered, very expensive to manufacture, and destined to be modified. There were approximately 3,000 1st Models manufactured in 1913 and 1914.

Exc.	V.G.	Good	Fair	Poor
500	350	250	200	150

S&W .35 Automatic Pistol 2nd Model

The only notable difference between the 1st and 2nd Models is the magazine release catch. On the 2nd Model the catch slides front and back and is serrated. This change seems irrelevant but resulted in a considerable savings in machining costs. Production of this model started and stopped a number of times for revolver production for England and then again in 1918 for WWI. Production was ceased finally in 1921 after a total of 8,350 1st and 2nd Models were manufactured.

Exc.	V.G.	Good	Fair	Poor
400	250	225	200	150

S&W .32 Automatic Pistol

In 1921 it became apparent to the powers that controlled S&W that the .35-caliber automatic was never going to be a commercial success. Harold Wesson, the new president, began to redesign the pistol to accept the .32 ACP, a commercially accepted cartridge, and to streamline the appearance to be more competitive with the other pistols on the market, notably Colt's. This new pistol used as many parts from the older model as possible for economy's sake. The pivoting barrel was discontinued, as was the cam-type safety in the rear grip strap. A magazine disconnector and a reduced-strength recoil spring to ease cocking were employed. The barrel length was kept at 3.5", and the 7-shot magazine was retained. The finish is blued only, and the grips are smooth walnut. There were only 957 of these manufactured between 1924 and 1936. They are eagerly sought by collectors.

Exc.	V.G.	Good	Fair	Poor
1650	1000	750	600	300

.45 Hand Ejector U.S. Service Model of 1917

WWI was on the horizon, and it seemed certain that the U.S. would become involved. The S&W people began to work with the Springfield Armory to develop a hand-ejector model that would fire the .45-caliber Government cartridge. This was accomplished in 1916 by the use of half-moon clips. The new revolver is quite similar to the .44 Hand Ejector in appearance. It has a 5.5" barrel, blued finish with smooth walnut grips, and a lanyard ring on the butt. The designation "U.S.Army Model 1917" is stamped on the butt. After the War broke out, the Government was not satisfied with S&W's production and actually took control of the company for the duration of the War. This was the very first time that the company was not controlled by a Wesson. The factory records indicate that there were 163,476 Model 1917s manufactured between 1917 and 1919, the WWI years. After the War, the sale of these revolvers continued on a commercial and contract basis until 1949, when this Model was finally dropped from the S&W product line.

Military Model

Exc.	V.G.	Good	Fair	Poor
500	350	300	200	150

Brazilian Contract

25,000 produced for the Brazilian government in 1938. The Brazilian crest is stamped on the sideplate.

Exc.	V.G.	Good	Fair	Poor
300	250	200	150	100

Commercial Model

Courtesy Mike Stuckslager.

High gloss blue and checkered walnut grips.

Exc.	V.G.	Good	Fair	Poor
600	450	350	275	200

SMITH & WESSON MODERN HANDGUNS

With the development of the Hand Ejector Models and the swingout cylinders, Smith & Wesson opened the door to a number of new advancements in the revolver field. This new system allowed for a solid frame, making the weapon much stronger than the old top-break design. The company also developed different basic frame sizes and gave them letter designations . The I frame, which later developed into the slightly larger J frame, was used for the .22/.32 and the small, concealable .38 revolvers. The medium K frame was used for .38 duty- and target-type weapons. The N frame was the heavy-duty frame used for the larger .357 and .44 and .45 caliber revolvers. The hand ejector went through many evolutionary changes over the years. We strongly recommend that the collector secure a detailed volume that deals exclusively with Smith & Wesson (see the bibliography), and learn all that is available on this fascinating firearm. Models are catalogued the by their numerical designations, brief description are given, and current values offered. It is important to note that the S&W revolver that we see marketed by the company today has undergone many changes in reaching its present configuration. The early models featured five screws in their construction, not counting the grip screw. There were four screws fastening the sideplate and another through the front of the triggerguard that retained the cylinder stop plunger. The first change involved the elimination of the top sideplate screw, and the five-screw Smith & Wesson became the four-screw. Later the frame was changed to eliminate the cylinder stop plunger screw, and the three-screw was created. Some models were offered with a flat cylinder latch that was serrated instead of the familiar checkering. Recently in 1978, the method of attaching the barrel to the frame was changed; and the familiar pin was eliminated. At the same time, the recessed cylinder commonly found on magnum models was also eliminated. All of these factors have a definite effect on the value and collectiblity of a particular S&W handgun.

IMPORTANT PRICING INFORMATION

Values reflected below will be affected by the following factors:

Five Screw Models will add an additional 40 to 50 percent.
Four Screw Models will add an additional 30 percent.
Models with flat latches add an additional 20 percent.
Models not pinned or recessed deduct 10 percent.

Model 10

This Model has been in production in one configuration or another since 1899. It was always the mainstay of the S&W line and was originally known as the .38 Military and Police Model. The Model 10 is built on the K, or medium frame, and was always meant as a duty gun. It was offered with a 2", 3", 4", 5", or 6" barrel. Currently only the 4" and 6" are available. A round or square butt is offered. It is chambered for the .38 Special and is offered in blue or nickle-plate, with checkered walnut grips. The Model designation is stamped on the yoke on June 12, 1957 on all S&W revolvers. This model, with many other modern S&W pistols, underwent several engineering changes. These changes may effect the value of the pistol and an expert should be consulted.

NIB	Exc.	V.G.	Good	Fair	Poor
325	250	200	150	125	90

Victory Model

Manufactured during WWII, this is a Model 10 with a sandblasted and parkerized finish, a lanyard swivel, and smooth walnut grips. The serial number has a V prefix. This model was available in only 2 inch and 4 inch barrel lengths. The Victory Model was discontinued on April 27, 1945 with serial number VS811,119.

Exc.	V.G.	Good	Fair	Poor
275	200	150	100	75

Model 11

First produced in 1947 S&W received many contracts for this service pistol. Nicknamed the .38/200 British Service Revolver, the company sold many of these models throughout the 1950s and 1960s. There are several rare variations of this model which will greatly affect its value. Consult an expert if special markings and barrel lengths are encountered.

Exc.	V.G.	Good	Fair	Poor
250	200	150	100	75

Model 12

The Model 12 was introduced in 1952, starting serial number C223,999, and is merely a Model 10 with a lightweight alloy frame and cylinder. In 1954 the alloy cylinder was replaced with one of steel which added an additional 4 ounces in weight.
Aluminum Cylinder Model—Add 40%.

Exc.	V.G.	Good	Fair	Poor
275	200	150	125	100

Model 13 "Air Force"

In 1953 the Air Force purchased a large quantity of Model 12's with alloy frames and cylinders. They were intended for use by flight crews as survival weapons in emergencies. This model was not officially designated "13" by S&W, but the Air Force stamped "M13" on the top strap. This model was rejected by the Air Force in 1954 because of trouble with the alloy cylinder.

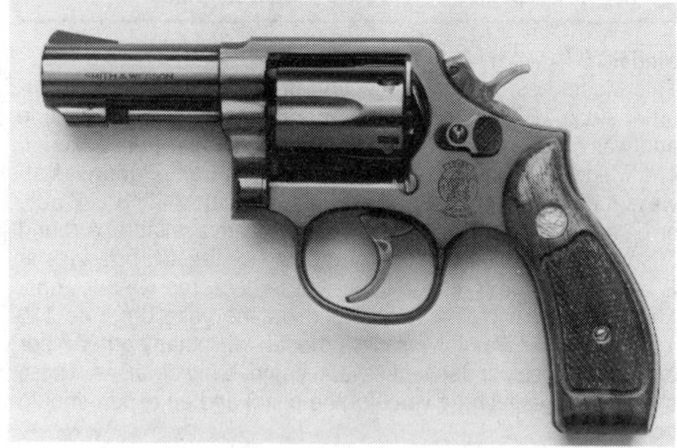

Exc.	V.G.	Good	Fair	Poor
800	750	600	450	250

Model 13 M&P

This is simply the Model 10 M&P chambered for the .357 Magnum and fitted with a heavy barrel. It was introduced in 1974.

Exc.	V.G.	Good	Fair	Poor
275	250	200	175	125

Model 14

This model is also known as the "K-38." In 1957 "Model 14" was stamped on the yoke. This model is offered in a 6" barrel with adjustable sights. In 1961 a single-action version with faster lock time was offered. This would be worth a small premium. This model was discontinued in 1981.
Single Action Model—Add 20%.

Courtesy Mike Stuckslager.

Exc.	V.G.	Good	Fair	Poor
275	250	200	175	125

Model 15

Also known as the "Combat Masterpiece" this model was produced at the request of law enforcement officers who wanted the "K-38" fitted with a 4" barrel. The model went into production in 1950 and was discontinued in 1987.

Exc.	V.G.	Good	Fair	Poor
300	250	200	175	125

Model 16

Also known as the "K-32" until 1957, this model is identical in appearance to the Model 14 except that it is chambered for .32 S&W. The Model 16 did not enjoy the commercial popularity of the Model 14 and was dropped from the line in 1973. Only 3,630 K-32s/Model 16s were sold between 1947 and 1973.

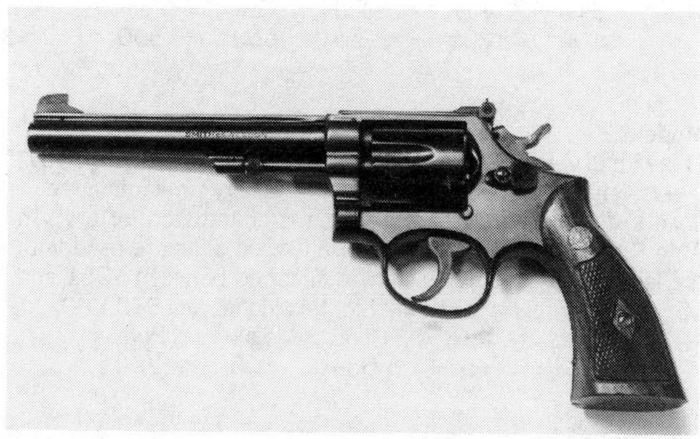

Courtesy Mike Stuckslager.

Exc.	V.G.	Good	Fair	Poor
1000	700	450	300	250

K-32 Combat Masterpiece

S&W produced a limited number of 4" barrelled K-32 revolvers. They were never given a number designation, as they were discontinued before 1957 when the numbering system began.

Exc.	V.G.	Good	Fair	Poor
1100	800	500	350	300

Model 17

This is the numerical designation that S&W placed on the "K-22" in 1957. This target model .22 rimfire revolver has always been very popular since its introduction in 1946. It is offered in 4", 6" and 8-3/8" barrel lengths, with all target options. The 8-3/8" barrel was dropped from the product line in 1993. The finish is blued, and it has checkered walnut grips.

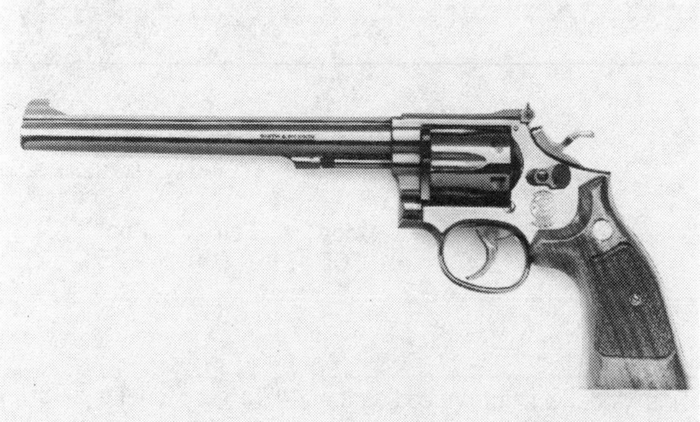

Courtesy Mike Stuckslager.

NIB	Exc.	V.G.	Good	Fair	Poor
275	225	200	150	125	100

Model 617

Identical to the Model 17 but furnished with stainless steel frame and cylinder.

NIB	Exc.	V.G.	Good	Fair	Poor
300	275	250	200	150	100

Model 648

Identical to the Model 617 but chambered for the .22 Magnum rim fire cartridge.

NIB	Exc.	V.G.	Good	Fair	Poor
300	275	250	200	150	100

Model 18

This is the model designation for the 4"-barrelled "Combat Masterpiece" chambered for the .22 rimfire.

Exc.	V.G.	Good	Fair	Poor
300	275	250	200	125

Note On "K-Frame" Target Models:

1.The factory eliminated the upper corner screw from the side plate in 1955. The 5-screw became a 4-screw. This change occurred around serial number K260,000.

2. Model number designations were stamped on the yoke in 1957.

3. Changed from right hand to left hand thread on extractor rod. Identified by -1 after serial number.

4. Cylinder stop changed eliminating screw in front of trigger guard in 1961. Identified by -2 after serial number.

5. Rear sight leaf screw relocated in 1967. Identified by -3 after serial number.

Model 19

Introduced in 1954 at the urging of Bill Jordan, a competition shooter with the U.S. Border Patrol, who went on to become a respected gun writer, this model is one of Smith and Wesson's most popular pistols. It was built on the "K-Frame" and was the first medium frame revolver chambered for the powerful .357 Magnum cartridge. Since its inception the Model 19 has been one of S&W's most popular revolvers. It was the first revolver to be introduced as a three-screw model. Originally it was offered with a 4" heavy barrel with extractor shroud; the 6" became available in 1963. The finish is blued or nickle-plated, and the grips are checkered walnut. The Goncalo Alves target stocks first appeared in 1959. In 1968 a 2.5" round-butt version was introduced. The Model 19 has been the basis for two commemoratives—the Texas Ranger/with Bowie Knife and the Oregon State Police/ with Belt Buckle.

NIB	Exc.	V.G.	Good	Fair	Poor
275	250	225	200	150	100

Texas Ranger Cased with Knife

NIB
700

Oregon State Police Cased with Buckle

NIB
900

Model 20

Known as the "38/44 Heavy Duty" before the change to numerical designations this model was brought out in 1930 in response to requests from law enforcement personnel for a more powerful sidearm. This Model, along with the .38/44 S&W Special cartridge, was an attempt to solve the problem. The revolver was manufactured with a standard 5" long barrel but has been noted rarely as short as 3 1/2" and as long as 8-3/8". It was built on the large N Frame and is blued or nickel-plated, with checkered walnut grips. Eventually the popularity of the .357 Magnum made the Model 20 superfluous, and it was discontinued in 1966. Post-war production for this model was about 20,000 revolvers.

Prewar .44 Special—Add 50%.

Courtesy Mike Stuckslager.

Exc.	V.G.	Good	Fair	Poor
475	350	250	200	150

Model 21

This Model was known as the "1950 Military" and the "4th Model .44 Hand Ejector" before the Model 21 designation was applied in 1957. The Model 21 was chambered for the .44 Special cartridge and as equipped with fixed sights. The Model 21 was built on the N Frame and is quite rare, as only 1,200 were manufactured in 16 years of production. It was discontinued in 1966.

Exc.	V.G.	Good	Fair	Poor
1500	1200	950	650	500

Model 22

This Model was known as the "1950 .45 Military" before 1957. It was actually introduced in 1951 and is very similar in appearance to the Model 21 except that it is chambered for the .45 Auto Rim or .45 ACP cartridge. Half-moon clips are used with the latter. There were 3,976 manufactured between 1951 and 1966. Beginning serial number for this model was S85,000.

Exc.	V.G.	Good	Fair	Poor
750	650	550	300	200

Model 23

The .38/44 Outdoorsman was the model name of this N- Frame revolver before the 1957 designation change. This is simply the Model 20 with adjustable sights. It was introduced in 1931 as a heavy-duty sporting handgun with hunters in mind. S&W produced 4,761 of these pre-war revolvers. It features a 6.5" barrel and blued finish and was the first S&W to have the new checkered walnut "Magna" grips. After 1949 this revolver was thoroughly modernized and had the later ribbed barrel. There were a total of 8,365 manufactured before the Model was discontinued in 1966. 6,039 were of the modernized configuration.

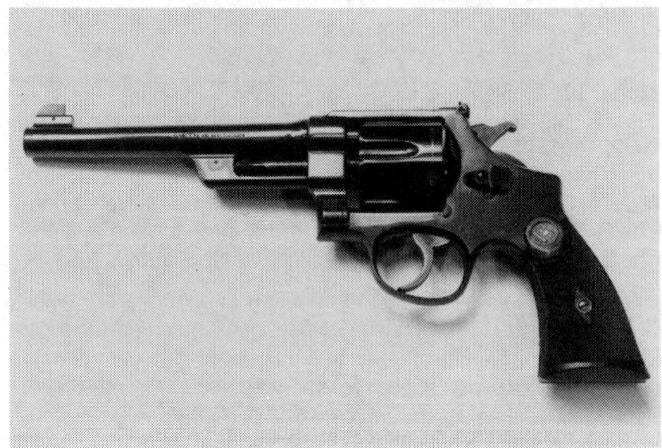

Courtesy Mike Stuckslager.

Exc.	V.G.	Good	Fair	Poor
550	400	300	200	125

Model 24

This Model was introduced as the .44 Target Model of 1950. It is simply the N-Frame Model 21 with adjustable target sights. This revolver was quite popular with the long-range handgunning devotees and their leader, Elmer Keith. The introduction of the .44 Magnum in 1956 began the death nell of the Model 24, and it was finally discontinued in 1966. S&W produced a total of 5,050 Model 24s. It was re-introduced in 1983 and 1984—and then was dropped again.

Exc.	V.G.	Good	Fair	Poor
550	400	300	250	200

Model 25

Prior to the model designation change in 1957 this model was also known as the .45 Target Model of 1955, this was an improved version of the 1950 Target .45. The Model 25 features a heavier barrel 4", 6.5" or 8" in length with blued or nickel-plated finish. All target options were offered. The Model 25 is chambered for the .45 ACP or .45 Auto-rim cartridges. This Model is still available chambered for .45 Colt as the Model 25-5.

Exc.	V.G.	Good	Fair	Poor
350	325	300	250	200

Model 25-3 125th Anniversary with Case

NIB
425

Model 25-2

This is the discontinued modern version of the Model 25 chambered in .45 ACP. The 6.5" barrel is shortened to 6" and is available in a presentation case.

Exc.	V.G.	Good	Fair	Poor
375	350	300	250	200

Model 625-2

This is the Stainless-steel version of the Model 25-2. It is fitted with a 5 inch barrel and has Pachmaayr SK/GR Gripper stocks as standard. Designed for pin shooting.

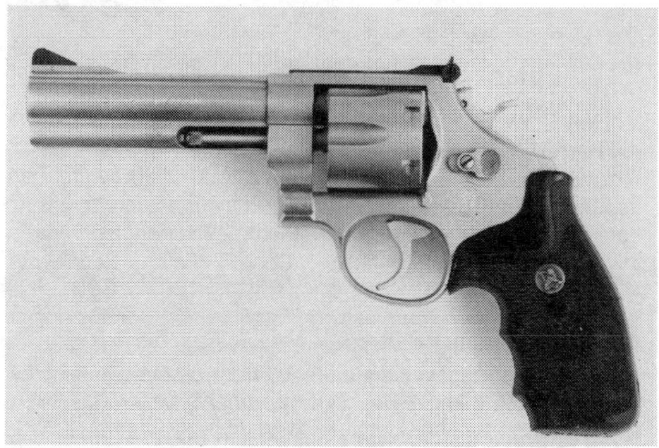

NIB	Exc.	V.G.	Good	Fair	Poor
425	350	300	250	200	150

Model 26

This is the numerical designation of the 1950 .45 Target Model. This large N-Frame revolver is basically the same as the Model 25 but has a lighter, thinner barrel. This caused its unpopularity among competitive shooters who wanted a heavier revolver. This brought about the Model 25 and the demise of the Model 26 in 1961 after only 2,768 were manufactured. The Model 26 also has two additional variations and are marked 26-1 and 26-2.

Exc.	V.G.	Good	Fair	Poor
750	650	500	400	250

Factory Registered .357 Magnum

In the early 1930's, a gun writer named Phillip B. Sharpe became interested in the development of high performance loads to be used in the then popular .38/44 S&W Revolvers. He repeatedly urged the company to produce a revolver especially made to handle these high pressure loads. In 1934 S&W asked Winchester to produce a new cartridge that would create the ballistics that Sharpe was seeking. This new cartridge was made longer than the standard .38 Special case so that it could not inadvertently be fired in an older gun. The company never felt that this would be a commercially popular venture and from the onset visualized the ".357 Magnum" as a strictly deluxe handbuilt item. They were to be individually numbered, in addition to the serial number, and registered to the new owner. The new Magnum was to be the most expensive revolver in the line. The gun went on the market in 1935, and the first one was presented to FBI Director J. Edgar Hoover. The gun was to become a tremendous success. S&W could only produce 120 per month, and this did not come close to filling orders. In 1938 the practice of numbering and registering each revolver was discontinued after 5,500 were produced. The ".357 Magnum," as it was designated, continued as one of the company's most popular items.

The Factory Registered Model was built on the N Frame. It could be custom ordered with any barrel length from 3.5" up to 8-3/8". The finish is blue, and the grips are checkered walnut. This Model was virtually hand built and test targeted. A certificate of registration was furnished with each revolver. The registration number was stamped on the yoke of the revolver with the prefix "Reg." This practice ceased in 1938 after 5,500 were produced.

Courtesy Mike Stuckslager.

Exc.	V.G.	Good	Fair	Poor
1800	1200	800	550	400

Pre-War .357 Magnum

This is the same as the Factory Registered Model without the certificate and the individual numbering. Approximately 1,150 were manufactured between 1938 and 1941. Production ceased for WWII weapons production.

Exc.	V.G.	Good	Fair	Poor
750	550	450	300	250

.357 Magnum - Model 27

In 1948 after the end of WWII, production of this revolver commenced. The new rebound slide operated hammer block and short throw hammer were utilized, and the barrel lengths offered were 3.5", 5", 6", 6-1/2", and 8-3/8". In 1957 the model designation was changed to Model 27; and in 1975 the target trigger, hammer and Goncalo Alves target grips were made standard. This revolver is still available from S&W and has been in production longer than any other N frame pistol. Some additional variations may be of interest to the collector. Around serial number S171,584 the 3 screw side plate model was first produced. In 1960 the model designation -1 was added to the model to indicate the change to a left hand thread to the extractor rod. In 1962 the cylinder stop was changed which disposed of the need for a plunger spring hole in front of the triggerguard. This change was indicated by a -2 behind the model number.

NIB	Exc.	V.G.	Good	Fair	Poor
350	325	300	250	200	150

Model 627

This is a current Stainless-steel version of the Model 27 and is offered with a 5-1/2 inch barrel

NIB	Exc.	V.G.	Good	Fair	Poor
450	375	350	300	250	200

Model 28

The Model 27 revolver was extremely popular among law enforcement officers, and many police agencies were interested in purchasing such a weapon—except for the cost. In 1954 S&W produced a new model called, at the time, the "Highway Patrolman." This model had all the desirable performance features of the deluxe Model 27 but lacked the cosmetic features that drove up the price. The finish is a matte blue; the rib is sandblasted instead of checkered or serrated, and the grips are the standard checkered walnut. Barrel lengths are 4" and 6.5". On late models the 6.5" barrel was reduced to 6", as on all S&W's. The model designation was changed to Model 28 in 1957. S&W discontinued the Model 28 in 1986.

Exc.	V.G.	Good	Fair	Poor
250	225	200	150	100

Model 29

In the early 1950's, handgun writers, under the leadership of Elmer Keith, were in the habit of loading the .44 Special cartridge to high performance levels and firing them in the existing .44 Hand Ejectors. They urged S&W to produce a revolver strong enough to consistently fire these heavy loads. In 1954 Remington, at the request of S&W produced the .44 Magnum cartridge. As was the case with the .357 Magnum, the cases were longer so that they would not fit in the chambers of the older guns. The first .44 Magnum became available for sale in early 1956. The first 500 were made with the 6.5" barrel; the 4" became available later that year. In 1957 the model designation was changed to 29, and the 8-3/8" barrel was introduced. The Model 29 is available in blue or nickle-plate. It came standard with all target options and was offered in a fitted wood case. The Model 29 is considered by many knowledgeable people to be the finest revolver S&W has ever produced. The older Model 29 revolvers are in a different collector category than most modern S&W revolvers. The early four-screw models can be worth a 50 percent premium in excellent condition. These early models were produced from 1956 to 1958 and approximately 6,500 were sold. One must regard these revolvers on a separate basis and have individually appraised for proper valuation. In 1993 the 4" barrel was dropped from production.

NIB	Exc.	V.G.	Good	Fair	Poor
400	350	300	250	200	150

5" Barrel Model 29

This is the rarest of the Model 29's. A total of 500 were manufactured in 1958. Collectors are cautioned to exercise care before purchasing one of these rare Model 29 variations.

NIB	Exc.	V.G.	Good	Fair	Poor
1250	1000	750	650	450	300

Note on N Frame Revolvers

1. N Frame models were changed from 5-screw to 4-screw between 1956 and 1958. Serial number S175,000.

2. Triggerguard screw was eliminated in 1961.

3. The pinned barrel and recessed cylinder were discontinued in 1978.

Model 629

This revolver is simply a stainless steel version of the Model 29 chambered for the .44 Magnum.

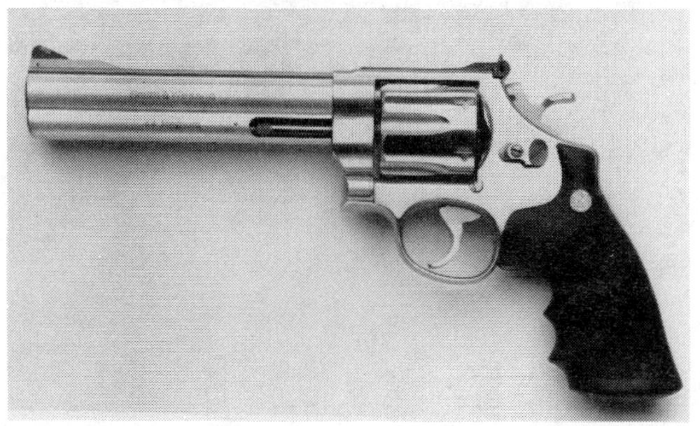

NIB	Exc.	V.G.	Good	Fair	Poor
375	325	300	250	225	200

Model 629 Mountain Gun

This limited edition 6-shot revolver, introduced in 1993, features a 4" barrel chambered for the .44 Magnum. Built on the large N frame this pistol is made from stainless steel and is drilled and tapped for scope mounts. It is equipped with a Hogue round butt rubber monogrip. Standard sights are a pinned black ramp front sight and an adjustable black rear blade.

NIB	Exc.	V.G.	Good	Fair	Poor
500	450	400	350	300	150

Model 629 Classic

This model has additional features that the standard Model 629 does not have such as: Chamfered cylinder, full lug barrel, interchangeable front sights, Hogue combat grips, and a drilled and tapped frame to accept scope mounts.

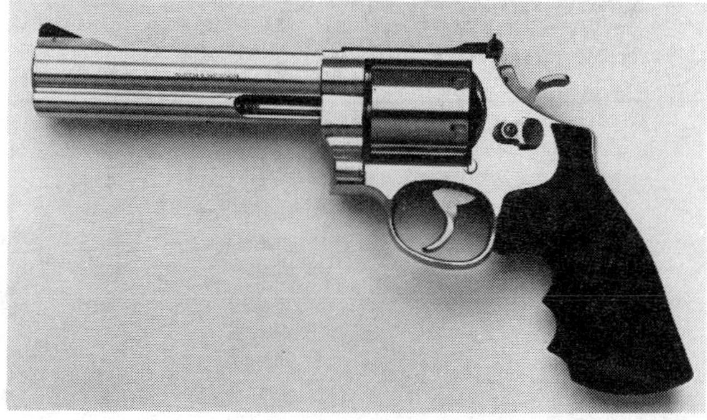

NIB	Exc.	V.G.	Good	Fair	Poor
400	375	325	250	225	200

Model 629 Classic DX

Has all of the features of the Model 629 Classic plus two sets of grips and five interchangeable front sights. This model was dropped from production in 1993.

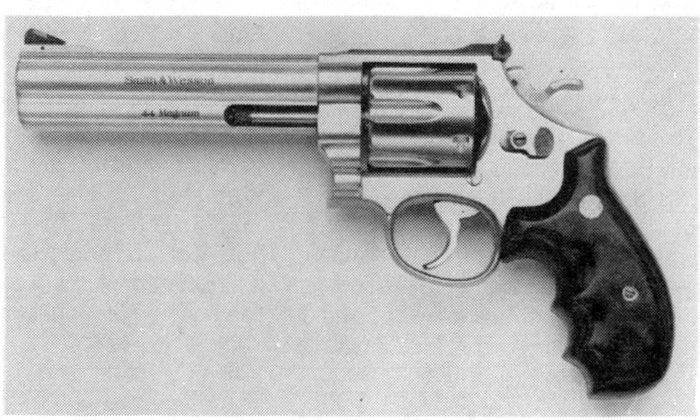

NIB	Exc.	V.G.	Good	Fair	Poor
650	500	450	350	300	150

Model 30

This Model was built on the small I frame and based on the .32 Hand Ejector Model of 1903. This older model was dropped from production in 1942. It was re-introduced in 1949 in a more modern version but still referred to as the .32 Hand Ejector. In 1957 the model designation was changed to Model 30. In 1960 this frame size was dropped, and the J frame, which had been in use since 1950, became standard for the Model 30. S&W stamped -1 behind the model number to designate this important change in frame size. The Model 30 is chambered for the .32 S&W long cartridge. It has a 6-shot cylinder and 2", 3", 4", and 6" barrel lengths. It has fixed sights and is either blued or nickle-plated. The butt is round, with checkered walnut grips. It was discontinued in 1976.

Courtesy W.P. Hallstein III and son Chip.

Exc.	V.G.	Good	Fair	Poor
350	250	200	150	100

Model 31

This Model is the same as the Model 30 with a square butt. It was known as the .32 Regulation Police before 1957. It is now discontinued.

Exc.	V.G.	Good	Fair	Poor
275	250	200	150	100

.32 Regulation Police Target

The Target model of the Regulation Police is very rare. Only 196 of these special variations were produced in 1957. All specifications are the same as the Model 31 except for the addition of adjustable sights.

Exc.	V.G.	Good	Fair	Poor
425	350	250	200	150

Model 32

This Model, known as the Terrier prior to 1957, was introduced in 1936. It is essentially a .38 Regulation Police chambered for .38 Special and having a 2" barrel and round butt. Like the Model 30 and 31 this revolver was originally built on the J frame which was changed to the I frame in 1960. The -1 behind the model number signifies this change. It is offered in blue or nickle-plate and has a 5-shot cylinder, fixed sights, and checkered walnut grips. This Model was discontinued in 1974.

Exc.	V.G.	Good	Fair	Poor
325	225	200	150	100

Model 33

This Model is simply the .38 Regulation Police with a square butt and 4" barrel chambered for the .38 Special. The factory referred to this model as the .38/.32 revolver. It too was built on the small I frame and later changed to the J frame in 1960. The Model 33 was discontinued in 1974.

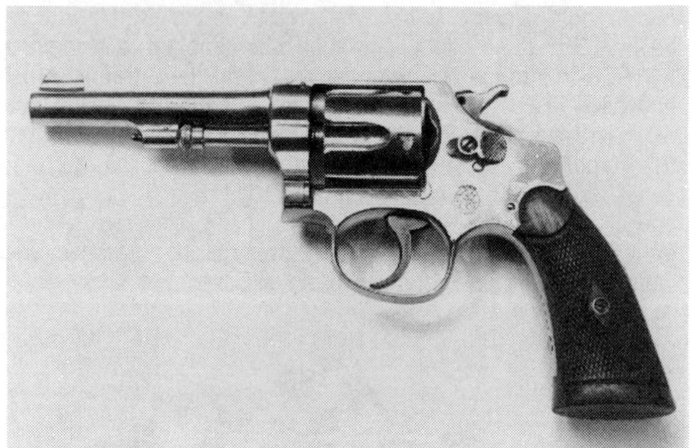

Courtesy Mike Stuckslager.

Exc.	V.G.	Good	Fair	Poor
325	250	200	150	100

Model 34

Introduced in 1936 as the .22/32 Kit Gun, it has a 2" or 4" barrel, either round or square butt, and adjustable sights. This model underwent several modifications before it reached its present form. S&W modernized this revolver in 1953 with the addition of a coil mainspring and micro-click sights. The Model 34 is built on this improved version. The revolver is a .32 Hand Ejector chambered for the .22 rimfire. It is built on the I frame until 1960 when the change over to the improved J frame occurred. The -1 behind the model number indicates this variation. The Model 34 is offered blued or nickle-plate and is currently in production.

Courtesy Mike Stuckslager.

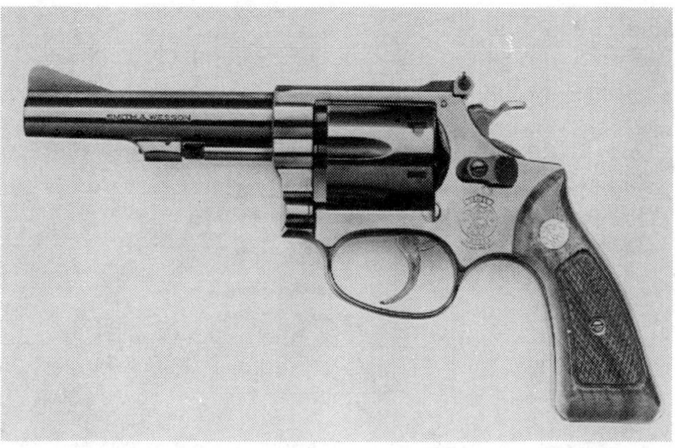

NIB	Exc.	V.G.	Good	Fair	Poor
325	275	250	225	175	125

Model 35

This is a square-butt, 6"-barreled version of the .22/.32 Hand Ejector. It was known prior to 1957 as the .22/32 Target. It underwent the same changes as the Model 34 but was discontinued in 1973.

Courtesy Mike Stuckslager.

Exc.	V.G.	Good	Fair	Poor
400	350	300	250	200

Model 36

This Model, known as the Chief's Special, was introduced in 1950. It was built on the J frame and is chambered for the .38 Special cartridge. It holds 5 shots, has a 2" or 3" barrel, and was initially offered in a round butt. In 1952 a square-butt version was released. It is finished in blue or nickle-plate and has checkered walnut grips. A 3" heavy barrel was first produced in 1967 and became standard in 1975. The 2" barrel was dropped from production in 1993.

NIB	Exc.	V.G.	Good	Fair	Poor
275	225	200	175	125	100

Model 36LS

This Model is similar to the Model 36 with the exception that it is only offered with a 2" barrel, comes with rosewood grips and a soft carrying case. Weighs 20 ozs.

NIB	Exc.	V.G.	Good	Fair	Poor
290	235	200	175	125	100

Chief's Special Target

Since 1955 a very limited number of Chief's Specials with adjustable sights have been manufactured. They have been offered with 2" or 3" barrels, round or square butts, and either blue or nickle-plated. Between 1957 and 1965, these target models were stamped Model 36 on the yoke. The revolvers manufactured between 1965 and the model discontinuance in 1975 were marked Model 50. This is a very collectible revolver. A total of 2313 of these special target models were sold in various model designations. Some are more rare than others.

Courtesy W.P. Hallstein III and son Chip.

Exc.	V.G.	Good	Fair	Poor
400	350	300	250	200

Model 37

Introduced in 1952 as the Chief's Special Airweight, this revolver initially had an alloy frame and cylinder. In 1954, following many complaints regarding damaged revolvers, the cylinders were made of steel. Barrel lengths, finishes, and grip options on the Airweight are the same as on the standard Chief Special. In 1957 the Model 37 designation was adopted. These early alloy frame and cylinder revolvers were designed to shoot only standard velocity .38 Special cartridges. The use of high velocity ammunition was not recommended by the factory.

NIB	Exc.	V.G.	Good	Fair	Poor
350	300	275	225	175	125

Model 38 - Airweight Bodyguard

This Model was introduced in 1955 as the Airweight Bodyguard. This was a departure from S&W's usual procedure in that the alloy-framed version came first. The Model 38 is chambered for .38 Special and is available with a 2" barrel standard. Although a 3" barrel was offered, it is rarely encountered. The frame of the Bodyguard is extended to conceal and shroud the hammer but at the same time allow the hammer to be cocked by the thumb. This makes this Model an ideal pocket revolver, as it can be drawn without catching on clothing. It is available either blue or nickle-plated, with checkered walnut grips.

NIB	Exc.	V.G.	Good	Fair	Poor
325	250	225	175	125	100

Bodyguard - Model 49

This Model was introduced in 1959 and is identical in configuration to the Model 38 except that the frame is made of steel.

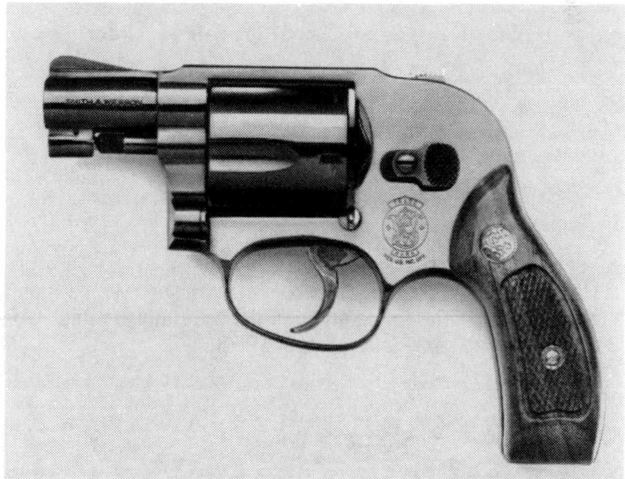

NIB	Exc.	V.G.	Good	Fair	Poor
325	250	225	200	150	100

Model 649

This stainless-steel version of the Model 49 was introduced in 1986.

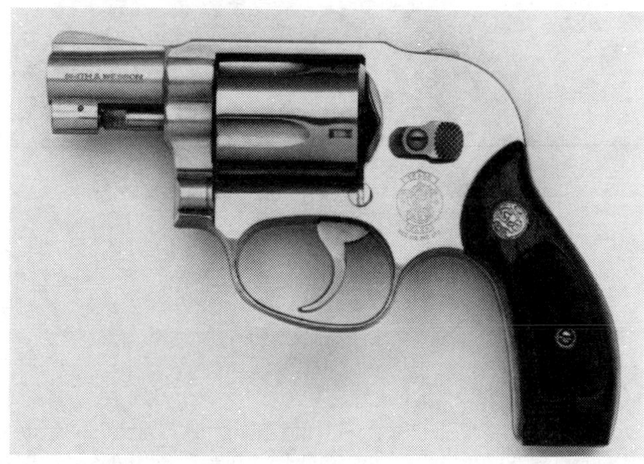

NIB	Exc.	V.G.	Good	Fair	Poor
275	250	225	200	175	125

Model 40 Centennial

This Model was introduced in 1952 as Smith & Wesson's 100th anniversary and appropriately called the "Centennial Model". It is of the Safety Hammerless design. This Model was built on the J frame and features a fully concealed hammer and a grip safety. The Model 40 is chambered for the .38 Special cartridge. It is offered with a 2" barrel in either blue or nickle-plate. The grips are checkered walnut. The Centennial was discontinued in 1974.

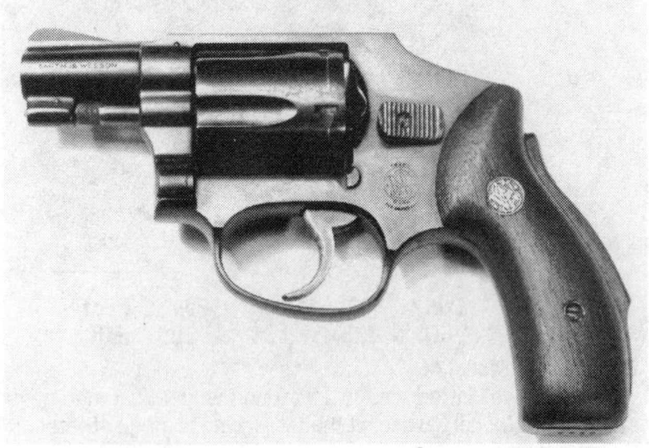

Courtesy Mike Stuckslager.

Exc.	V.G.	Good	Fair	Poor
475	350	300	250	200

Model 640 Centennial

A stainless steel version of the Model 40 furnished with a 2 or 3 inch barrel. Both the frame and cylinder are stainless steel. The 3" barrel was no longer offered as of 1993.

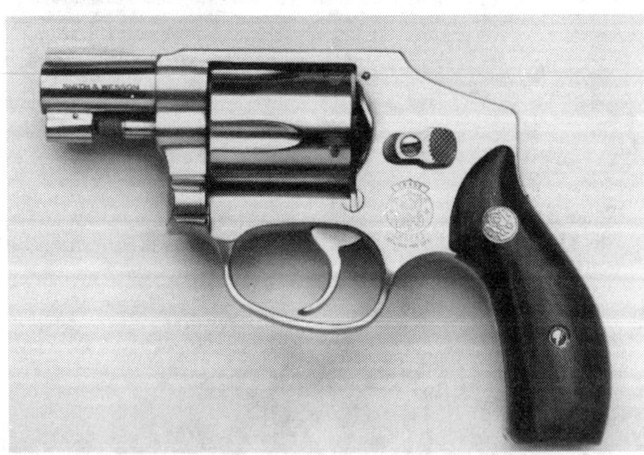

NIB	Exc.	V.G.	Good	Fair	Poor
375	300	225	175	125	100

Model 642 Centennial

Identical to the Model 640 with the exception of a stainless steel cylinder and aluminum alloy frame. Furnished with a 2 inch barrel. Discontinued in 1992. Replaced by the Model 442 introduced in 1993.

NIB	Exc.	V.G.	Good	Fair	Poor
325	275	225	175	125	100

Model 940

Styled like the other Centennial models, this model is chambered for the 9MM Parabellum cartridge. It has a stainless steel cylinder and frame and is furnished with a 2 or 3 inch barrel. The 3" barrel version was dropped from production in 1993.

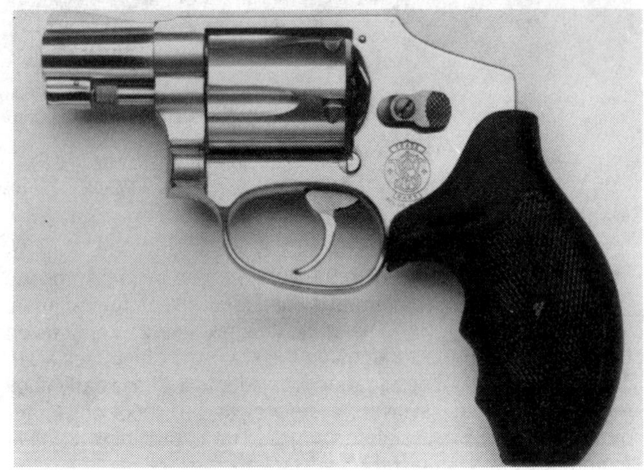

NIB	Exc.	V.G.	Good	Fair	Poor
325	275	225	175	125	100

Model 632 Centennial

This model is similar to the other Centennial models but is chambered for the .32 H&R Magnum cartridge. It comes standard with a 2 inch barrel, stainless steel cylinder and aluminum alloy frame. Dropped from the product line in 1993.

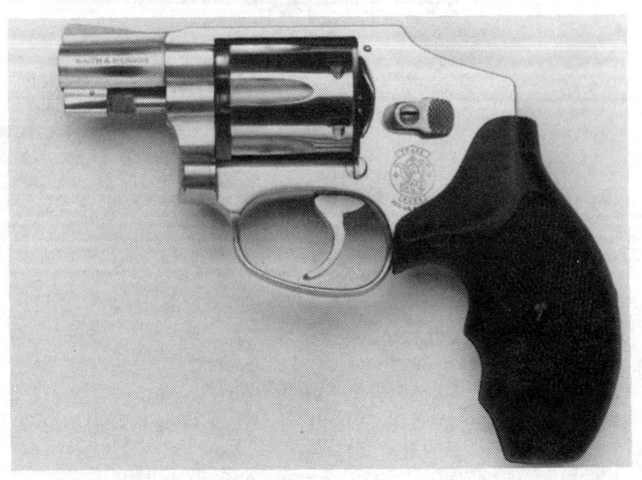

NIB	Exc.	V.G.	Good	Fair	Poor
325	275	225	175	125	100

Model 42 - Airweight Centennial

This Model is identical in configuration to the Model 40 except that it was furnished with an aluminum alloy frame. It was also discontinued in 1974.

Editors Note: The first 37 Model 42s were manufactured with aluminum alloy cylinders. They weigh 11-1/4 ounces compared to 13 ounces for the standard model. The balance of Model 42 production was with steel cylinders. Add 300% for this extremely rare variation.

Exc.	V.G.	Good	Fair	Poor
250	225	200	150	100

Model 442 Centennial Lightweight

This 5-shot revolver is chambered for the .38 Special and is equipped with a 2" barrel, aluminum alloy frame, and carbon steel cylinder. It has a fully concealed hammer and weighs 15.8 ozs. The front ramp sight is serrated and the rear sight is a fixed square notch. Rubber combat grips from Michael's of Oregon are standard. Finish is either blue or satin nickel. Introduced in 1993.

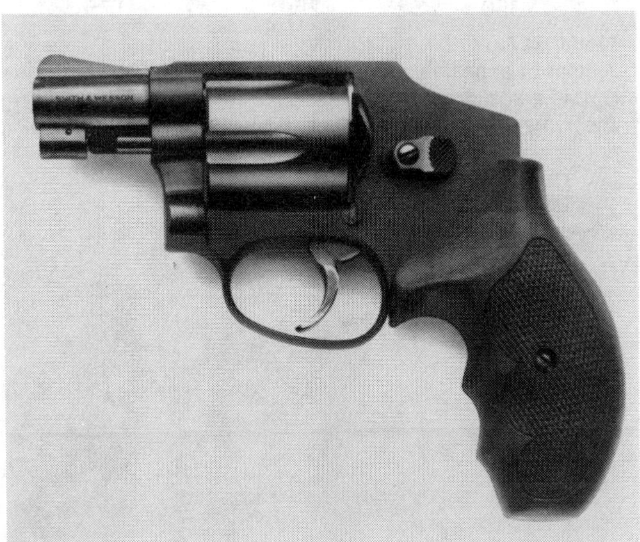

NIB	Exc.	V.G.	Good	Fair	Poor
325	300	250	200	150	100

Model 43

This Model was built on the J frame, is chambered for .22 rimfire, has a 4" barrel, and is offered in a round or square butt, with checkered walnut grips. It has adjustable sights and is either blued or nickle-plated. The frame is made of aluminum alloy. Except for this, it is identical to the Model 34 or .22/.32Kit Gun. The Model 43 was introduced in 1954 and was discontinued in 1974.

Courtesy Mike Stuckslager.

Exc.	V.G.	Good	Fair	Poor
350	300	250	200	150

Model 51

This Model is simply the Model 34 chambered for the .22 Winchester Magnum rimfire. It was first introduced in 1960 beginning with serial number 52,637. Available in both round and square butt with the round butt variation having a total production of only 600. The Model 51 was discontinued in 1974

Exc.	V.G.	Good	Fair	Poor
325	275	250	200	125

Model 651

This stainless-steel version of the Model 51 .22 Magnum Kit Gun was manufactured between 1983 and 1987.

Exc.	V.G.	Good	Fair	Poor
325	275	225	175	125

Note on J Frame Revolvers:

1. In 1953 the cylinder stop plunger screw was eliminated.
2. In 1955 the top corner sideplate screw was eliminated.
3. In 1957 the numerical model designation was stamped on the yoke.
4. In 1966 the flat latch was changed to the present contoured cylinder release.

Model 45

This Model is a special purpose K-Frame Military & Police Model chambered for the .22 rimfire. It was designed as a training revolver for police departments and the U.S. Postal Service. This Model was manufactured in limited quantities between 1948 and 1957. In 1963 production abruptly began and ended again. There were 500 of these revolvers released on a commercial basis, but they are rarely encountered.

NIB	V.G.	Good	Fair	Poor
750	650	550	350	250

Model 48

This Model is identical to the Model 17, K-22, except that it is chambered for the .22 Winchester Magnum rimfire. It was available with the same options as the Model 17, barrel lengths of 4", 6", and 8-3/8", and was built on the K Frame. The only finish offered was in blue. It was introduced in 1959 and was discontinued in 1986.

Exc.	V.G.	Good	Fair	Poor
325	300	250	200	150

Model 53

Introduced in 1961, the Model 53 was chambered for a totally new cartridge developed by Remington Arms Co.called the .22 Jet. The cartridge was based on the .357 Magnum necked down to .22 caliber, firing a 40-grain projectile at approximately 2,460 ft/sec. from the 8-3/8" barrel. This cartridge was brought out in response to the "Wildcatters" who were converting their Model 17's. The revolver that S&W brought out to chamber this new true .22 Magnum was based on the Model 19 K Frame. It was offered with a 4", 6", and 8-3/8" barrel. The finish is blue, with checkered walnut grips. The sights are adjustable, and the revolver could be furnished with cylinder inserts that would convert the Model 53 to fire .22 rimfire cartridges. The frame has two firing pins—one for centerfire and the other for rimfire. The hammer has a selective striker. The new high velocity cartridge created functioning problems, and the Model was discontinued in 1974 after approximately 15,000 were manufactured.

Courtesy Mike Stuckslager.

Exc.	V.G.	Good	Fair	Poor
800	650	450	350	300

Model 56

In 1962, in response to an order from the Air Force for a 2" heavy-barrelled K frame with adjustable sights, S&W brought out the Model 56. This revolver has a slightly heavier frame to accommodate the barrel and a longer rear sight that overlaps the barrel and is chambered for .38 Special. This model is similar in appearance to the Model 15 upon which frame the Model 56 was based and is part of the Combat Masterpiece series. It was produced until 1964, and there were approximately 15,200 manufactured. The Model was replaced by the Model 15 that was now offered with a 2" heavy barrel.

Exc.	V.G.	Good	Fair	Poor
550	450	375	300	200

Model 57

This Model was introduced in 1963. It is, for all intents and purposes, identical to the Model 29, chambered for the .41 Magnum cartridge. Available in 4", 6", and 8-3/8" barrels it was intended to fill a gap and to be the ultimate law enforcement cartridge. The Model 57 was available in both blue and nickle finish. The Model 57 has not realized that potential.

NIB	Exc.	V.G.	Good	Fair	Poor
325	300	275	225	200	150

Model 657

This is the stainless steel version of the Model 57. The 8-3/8" barrel was dropped from the product line in 1992.

NIB	Exc.	V.G.	Good	Fair	Poor
375	325	275	225	150	100

Model 58

This is a fixed sight, 4" barrel Military & Police Model, chambered for the .41 Magnum cartridge. It is available blued or nickle-plated, with the checkered walnut Magna grips. It was manufactured between 1964 and 1968.

Exc.	V.G.	Good	Fair	Poor
350	325	250	225	175

Model 547

Similar in appearance to the Model 58 but chambered for the 9MM Parabellum cartridge. Available in either 3 or 4 inch barrel the frame and cylinder are blued. Discontinued in 1986.

NIB	Exc.	V.G.	Good	Fair	Poor
375	275	250	200	150	100

Model 60

This was the pioneer effort in the stainless steel handgun market. Released in 1965 this revolver is essentially a Model 36 with a stainless steel J frame. It is offered with either a 2" or 3" barrel. From serial number 410,754 to 480,000 the stainless steel had a bright finish. After serial number 490,000 the finish was changed to a satin stainless. The barrel length also determines other features on the revolver. The 2" barrel version is supplied with checkered walnut grips, fixed sights and smooth trigger. The 3" barrel model is equipped with full underlug, adjustable sights, serrated trigger, and combat style rubber grips. The 2" version weighs about 20 ozs. while the 3" version weighs 25 ozs.

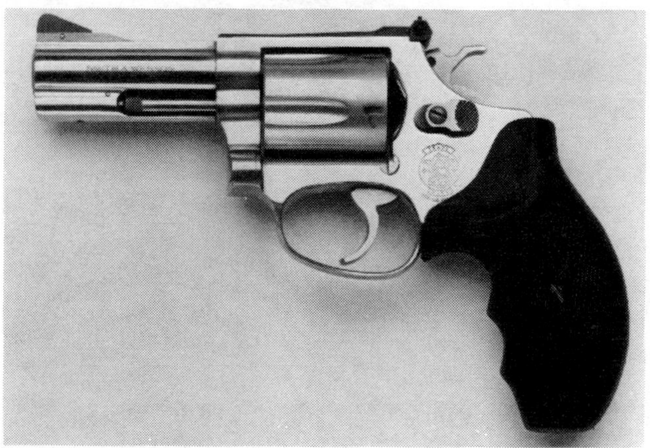

2" Barrel

NIB	Exc.	V.G.	Good	Fair	Poor
290	235	200	175	125	100

3" Barrel

NIB	Exc.	V.G.	Good	Fair	Poor
325	275	225	175	125	100

Model 60 LadySmith

Chambered for the .38 Special with 2 inch barrel and stainless steel frame and cylinder. This slightly smaller version of the Model 60 is made for small hands.

NIB	Exc.	V.G.	Good	Fair	Poor
300	275	250	200	150	100

Model 63

This model is simply the Model 34 made of stainless steel.

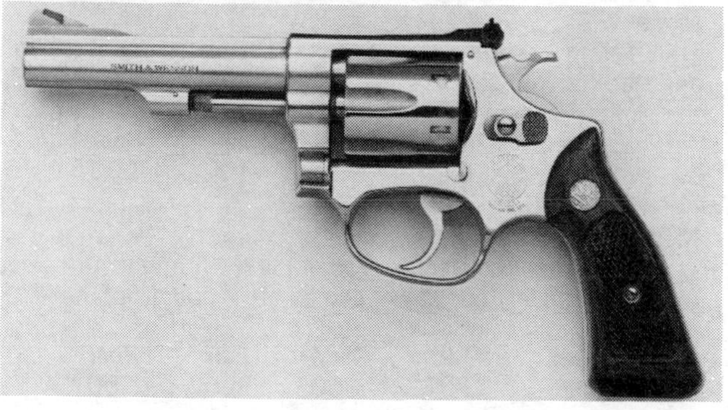

NIB	Exc.	V.G.	Good	Fair	Poor
300	275	250	225	200	150

Model 64

This model is the stainless steel version of the Model 10 M&P. It was introduced in 1970. The Model 64-1 variation was introduced in 1972 and is the heavy barrel version.

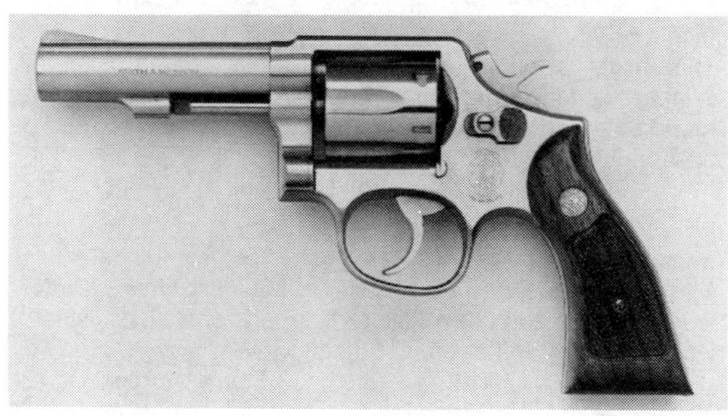

NIB	Exc.	V.G.	Good	Fair	Poor
350	300	275	225	175	125

Model 65

This is the stainless steel version of the Model 13 M&P .357 Magnum. It was introduced in 1974.

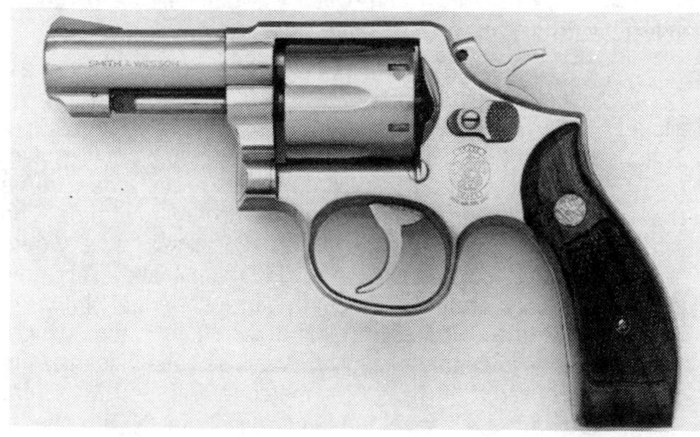

NIB	Exc.	V.G.	Good	Fair	Poor
350	300	275	225	175	125

Model 66

Released in 1971, this is the stainless steel version of the Model 19 or Combat Magnum. It is chambered for the .357 Magnum, has adjustable sights, a square butt with checkered walnut grips, and was initially offered with a 4" barrel. In 1974 a 2.5"-barrel, round-butt version was made available. It was available in a 6" barrel, as well as all target options until discontinued in 1993.

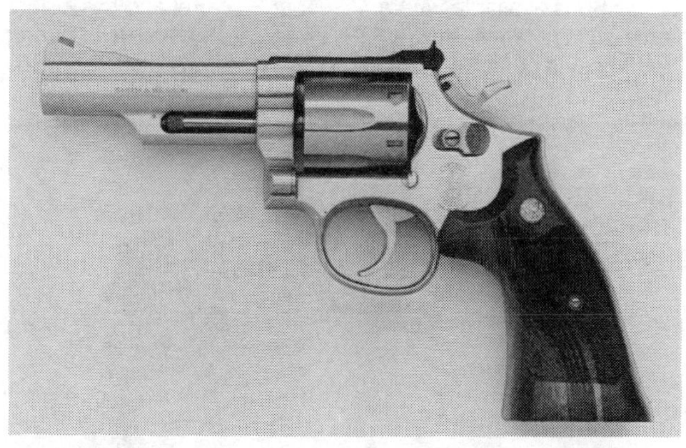

NIB	Exc.	V.G.	Good	Fair	Poor
325	300	250	200	150	125

Model 67

This is the 4"-barrelled stainless steel version of the Model 15 Combat Masterpiece. It was first produced in 1972. In appearance it is similar to the Model 66 except that it is chambered for the .38 Special. This Model was discontinued in 1988.

Exc.	V.G.	Good	Fair	Poor
300	250	200	150	125

Model 650

This model is the J-Frame, stainless steel version of the .22 Winchester Magnum rimfire Kit Gun, with a 3" heavy barrel, round butt, and fixed sights. This model was manufactured between 1983 and 1987.

Exc.	V.G.	Good	Fair	Poor
275	225	175	125	100

Model 651

This is the Model 51 .22 Winchester Magnum rimfire revolver, with 4" barrel and adjustable sights made of stainless steel. It was manufactured between 1983 and 1987.

Exc.	V.G.	Good	Fair	Poor
275	225	200	150	125

Model 520

This revolver was built on the N Frame, is chambered for the .357 Magnum cartridge, and has a 4" barrel. It is a M&P model with fixed sights, blued finish, and checkered walnut Magna grips. There were 1,000 manufactured to fill an order by the New York State Police. " N.Y.S.P." is stamped on the frame. The state of New York never completed the purchase, and the revolvers were sold through commercial outlets.

Exc.	V.G.	Good	Fair	Poor
325	275	225	175	125

Model 581

The Model 581 represented the first total redesign on a revolver for S&W in many years. It is built on the L Frame, a new frame that is between the smaller K frame and the larger N frame. The reasoning behind this change is that the larger frame would stand up better to a steady diet of Magnum loads. This new design also incorporates a full-length barrel underlug, similar to that found on the Colt Python. This heavier barrel adds weight and a better balance to the revolver. The 581 version is the Military & Police fixed sight-type. Chambered for the .357 Magnum, it is offered with a 4" barrel in blue or nickle finish with checkered walnut grips. It is also known as the "Distinguished Service Magnum." It was introduced in 1985.

NIB	Exc.	V.G.	Good	Fair	Poor
350	300	275	225	175	125

Model 681

Identical in configuration to the 581, this model is made of stainless steel.

NIB	Exc.	V.G.	Good	Fair	Poor
275	225	200	150	100	80

Model 586

This revolver is the target version of S&W's new L Frame series. The 586 is available with a 4", 6", or 8" barrel and has adjustable sights, target stocks, and all target options. It is offered either blued or nickle-plated. The 586 was introduced in 1986.

NIB	Exc.	V.G.	Good	Fair	Poor
375	275	250	225	200	100

Model 686

Known as "The Distinguished Combat Magnum", this is the stainless-steel version of the 586. It was introduced in 1986.

NIB	Exc.	V.G.	Good	Fair	Poor
400	300	250	225	200	150

Model 39

This was the first double action semi-automatic pistol produced in the U.S. It was released for sale in 1955. The Model 39 came standard with a lightweight alloy frame. It is chambered for the 9mm Parabellum cartridge. The barrel is 4" in length; and the finish, blued or nickle-plated. with checkered walnut grips. The sights are adjustable for windage only, and the detachable magazine holds 8 shots. The Model 39 was discontinued in 1982.

Exc.	V.G.	Good	Fair	Poor
300	275	250	200	150

Model 39 Steel Frame

S&W forged 1,000 Model 39 frames of steel early in the production run. These frames were not used except for some military test guns. Eventually the company decided to use these frames and produced 927 steel-framed pistols before 1966. These pistols were sold through normal distribution channels and today represent a find for the S&W collector.

Exc.	V.G.	Good	Fair	Poor
1000	800	650	500	400

Model 59

This Model is quite similar to the Model 39. The exception is the large grip that is needed to house the double-column 14-shot detachable magazine. This pistol was developed in 1971 in response to a military order and was produced with black checkered plastic grips. It has the same specifications as the Model 39 with these two exceptions. The Model was discontinued in 1981.

Exc.	V.G.	Good	Fair	Poor
350	325	300	225	175

Model 439

This is simply an improved version of the Model 39. It has fully adjustable sights. It offers all the same features and finishes as the Model 39 and was discontinued in 1988.

Exc.	V.G.	Good	Fair	Poor
400	350	325	250	200

Model 639

This is the stainless steel version of the 439 9mm pistol. It features an ambidextrous safety and all other options of the Model 439.

Exc.	V.G.	Good	Fair	Poor
325	300	250	200	150

Model 459

This improved-sight version of the 15-shot Model 59 9mm pistol was discontinued in 1988.

Exc.	V.G.	Good	Fair	Poor
400	350	300	250	200

Model 659

This stainless steel version of the Model 459 9mm pistol features an ambidextrous safety and all other options of the Model 459.

Exc.	V.G.	Good	Fair	Poor
450	400	350	300	250

Model 539

This is yet another version of the Model 439 9mm pistol. It incorporates all the features of the Model 439 with a steel frame instead of aluminum alloy. This Model was discontinued in 1983.

Exc.	V.G.	Good	Fair	Poor
400	350	300	250	200

Model 559

This variation of the Model 459 9mm pistol has a steel frame instead of aluminum alloy. It is identical in all other respects.

Exc.	V.G.	Good	Fair	Poor
450	400	350	300	250

Model 469

The Model 469 was brought out in answer to the need for a more concealable high-capacity pistol. It is essentially a "Mini" version of the Model 459. It is chambered for the 9mm Parabellum and has a 12-round detachable magazine with a finger-grip extension and a shortened frame. The barrel is 3.5" long; the hammer is bobbed and does not protrude; the safety is ambidextrous. The finish is matte blue, with black plastic grips. The Model 469 was discontinued in 1988.

Exc.	V.G.	Good	Fair	Poor
350	325	275	200	150

Model 681

Identical in configuration to the 581, this Model is made of stainless steel. Discontinued in 1993.

NIB	Exc.	V.G.	Good	Fair	Poor
275	225	200	150	125	100

Model 669

This is a stainless steel version of the Model 469 9mm pistol. All of the features of the 469 are incorporated. The Model 669 was manufactured from 1986 to 1988.

Exc.	V.G.	Good	Fair	Poor
375	350	300	250	200

Model 645

The Model 645 is a large-framed, stainless steel double-action pistol chambered for the .45 ACP cartridge. It has a 5" barrel, adjustable sights, and a detachable 8- shot magazine. It is offered with fixed or adjustable sights and an ambidextrous safety. The grips are molded black nylon. S&W manufactured this pistol between 1986 and 1988.

Exc.	V.G.	Good	Fair	Poor
450	400	350	300	250

Model 745 - IPSC

This Model is similar in outward appearance to the Model 645 but is quite a different pistol. The Model 745 is a single-action semi-auto chambered for the .45 ACP cartridge. The frame is made of stainless steel; and the slide, of blued carbon steel. The barrel is 5", and the detachable magazine holds 8 rounds. The sights are fully adjustable target types. The grips are checkered walnut.

Exc.	V.G.	Good	Fair	Poor
600	550	500	450	350

Model 41

The Model 41 was introduced to the shooting public in 1957. It is a very high quality .22-rimfire target pistol. It has an alloy frame, steel slide, and either a 5.5" or 7-3/8" barrel. It has a detachable 10-shot magazine, adjustable target sights, and checkered walnut target grips. The finish is blue.

Discontinued Barrels:
5" With Extended Sight— Add $100.
5.5" Heavy With Extended Sight—Add $100.
7.5" With Muzzle Brake— Add $75.

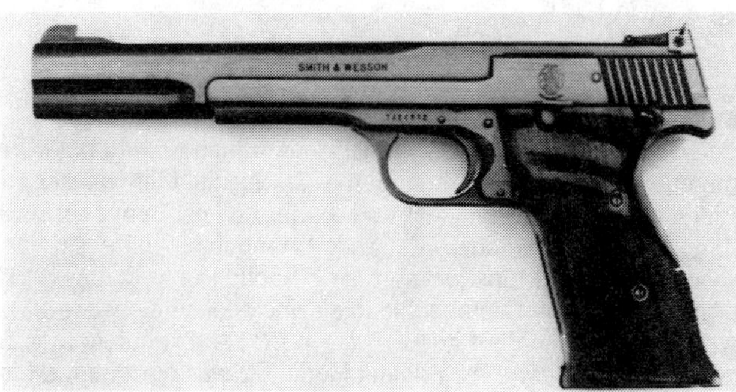

NIB	Exc.	V.G.	Good	Fair	Poor
750	500	350	300	225	150

Model 41-1

This Model was introduced in 1960 and is chambered for the .22 short rimfire only. It was developed for the International Rapid Fire competition. In appearance it is quite similar to the Model 41 except that the slide is made of aluminum alloy, as well as the frame, in order to lighten it to function with the .22 short cartridge. This Model was not a commercial success like the Model 41, so it was discontinued after fewer than 1,000 were manufactured.

Exc.	V.G.	Good	Fair	Poor
900	725	500	375	225

Model 46

This was a lower-cost version of the Model 41. It was developed for the Air Force in 1959. Its appearance was essentially the same as the Model 41 with a 7" barrel. Later a 5" barrel was introduced, and finally in 1964 a heavy 5.5" barrel was produced. This economy target pistol never had the popularity that the more expensive Model 41 had, and it was discontinued in 1968 after approximately 4,000 pistols were manufactured.

Courtesy Mike Stuckslager.

Exc.	V.G.	Good	Fair	Poor
800	625	475	400	250

Model 61 Escort

In 1970 the Model 61 was offered for sale. It was actually the only true pocket automatic that S&W produced. This pistol is chambered for the .22 long rifle cartridge, and has a 5 shot detachable magazine and 2.5" barrel. It is finished in blue or nickel-plated, with checkered plastic grips. The quality of this pistol never measured up to S&W's standards, and it was dropped in 1974.

Exc.	V.G.	Good	Fair	Poor
250	175	150	120	100

Model 52

This Model was introduced in 1961 as a high quality big-bore target pistol. It is chambered for the .38 Special Mid-Range cartridge and functions only with wadcutter bullets. In appearance it resembles the Model 39; and its action is quite similar, though locked to function as a single-action only. It has a 5" barrel and a 5-shot detachable magazine and is finished in blue with checkered walnut grips. There were approximately 3,500 manufactured before the original Model 52 was discontinued in 1963.

Exc.	V.G.	Good	Fair	Poor
750	550	450	350	250

Model 52-1

In 1963 the action was changed from a locked-out double action to a true single action. The new model designation was adopted, and they were produced in this configuration until 1971. This Model is similar to the original Model 52 in all other aspects.

Exc.	V.G.	Good	Fair	Poor
650	450	350	300	225

Model 52-2

In 1971 a new, more efficient extractor was added to the Model 52 design; and the designation was again changed. It has remained in this configuration since and is still offered by S&W.

NIB	Exc.	V.G.	Good	Fair	Poor
600	550	500	450	350	300

Model 52-A

In 1961 S&W produced 87 special pistols for the Army Marksmanship Training Unit. They are chambered for the .38 AMU cartridge, an experimental semi-rimless .38 Special round. The Army, after testing a few of these pistols, decided that they were not interested in them. In 1964 S&W, after stamping the letter A after the 52 designation, released the 87 pistols through normal distribution channels. They represent one of the ultimate finds for a S&W collector today.

Exc.	V.G.	Good	Fair	Poor
2500	2000	1500	1000	750

Model 2214

A light compact .22 Long Rifle rim fire semi-auto pistol designed for plinking. The barrel is 3 inches in length with a magazine capacity of 8 rounds. It has a blue carbon steel slide and alloy frame.

NIB	Exc.	V.G.	Good	Fair	Poor
200	175	150	125	100	60

Model 2206

This .22 Long Rifle rim fire pistol is offered in either a 4 1/2 inch or 6 inch barrel. Magazine capacity is 12 rounds. This model is designed for target shooting. It has a stainless steel slide and frame.

NIB	Exc.	V.G.	Good	Fair	Poor
200	175	150	125	100	60

Model 422 Field

This .22 rimfire pistol was introduced in 1987. It has a 4.5" or 6" barrel, an alloy frame and steel slide, and a 10-shot detachable magazine. The Field model has fixed sights and black plastic grips and is matte blued.

NIB	Exc.	V.G.	Good	Fair	Poor
200	175	150	125	100	75

Model 422 Target

This is similar to the Field model, with adjustable sights and checkered walnut grips.

NIB	Exc.	V.G.	Good	Fair	Poor
250	200	175	150	125	100

Model 622 Field

This is a stainless steel version of the Model 422 Field.

NIB	Exc.	V.G.	Good	Fair	Poor
225	200	175	150	125	100

Model 622 Target

This is the stainless steel version of the Model 422 Target.

NIB	Exc.	V.G.	Good	Fair	Poor
275	225	200	175	150	125

Model 3904

In 1989 S&W redesigned the entire line of 9mm semi-automatic handguns. The 3904 is chambered for the 9mm Parabellum and has an 8-shot detachable magazine and 4" barrel with a fixed bushing. The frame is alloy, and the triggerguard is squared for two-hand hold. The magazine well is beveled, and the grips are one-piece wrap-around made of delrin. The three-dot sighting system is employed. This model has been discontinued.

NIB	Exc.	V.G.	Good	Fair	Poor
400	350	325	300	275	225

Model 3906

This is the stainless steel version of the Model 3904. The features are the same. It was introduced in 1989. This model has been discontinued.

NIB	Exc.	V.G.	Good	Fair	Poor
400	350	325	300	275	225

Model 3914

Offered as a slightly smaller alternative to the Model 3904, this 9MM pistol has a 3-1/2 inch barrel, 8-round magazine, and blue carbon steel slide and alloy frame.

NIB	Exc.	V.G.	Good	Fair	Poor
475	450	400	350	300	250

Model 3913

This version is similar to the Model 3914 but features a stainless steel slide and alloy frame.

NIB	Exc.	V.G.	Good	Fair	Poor
475	450	400	350	300	250

Model 3914LS

Smith & Wesson redesigned the Model 3914 to give a more modern look. The result is a LadySmith 9MM pistol that has a slightly different style. All other features are the same as the Model 3914 including the blue carbon slide and alloy frame.

NIB	Exc.	V.G.	Good	Fair	Poor
475	450	400	350	300	250

Model 3913LS

Identical to the Model 3914LS with the exception of a stainless steel slide and alloy frame.

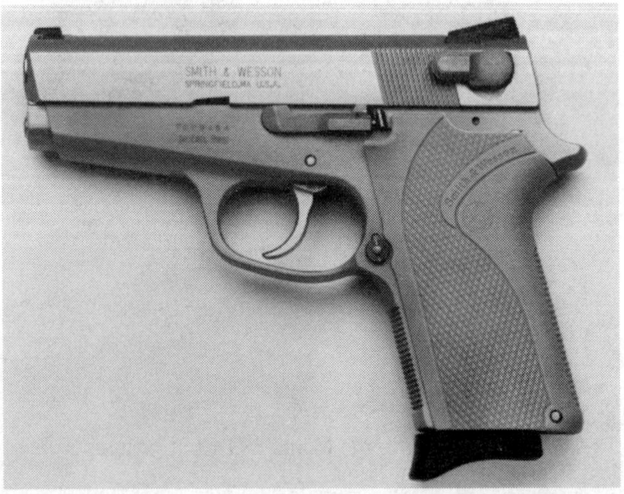

NIB	Exc.	V.G.	Good	Fair	Poor
475	450	400	350	300	250

Model 3954

This model is similar to Model 3914 but is offered in a double action only configuration. Discontinued 1993.

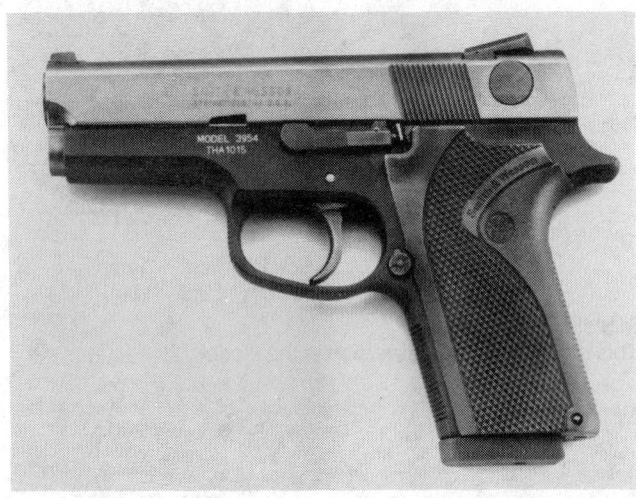

NIB	Exc.	V.G.	Good	Fair	Poor
475	425	375	300	250	150

Model 915

Introduced in 1993 this 9mm Parabellum features a 4" barrel, matte blue finish, fixed rear sight, and wrap around rubber grips. Overall length is 7.5" and weight is about 28 ozs.

NIB	Exc.	V.G.	Good	Fair	Poor
350	300	250	200	150	100

Model 5904

This full size high-capacity, 15-shot version of the Model 3904 was introduced in 1989. It features a slide-mounted decocking lever and a 4-inch barrel. This version has a blue carbon steel slide and alloy frame.

NIB	Exc.	V.G.	Good	Fair	Poor
475	425	375	325	275	225

Model 5906

This is the stainless steel version of the Model 5904. Both the slide and frame are stainless steel.

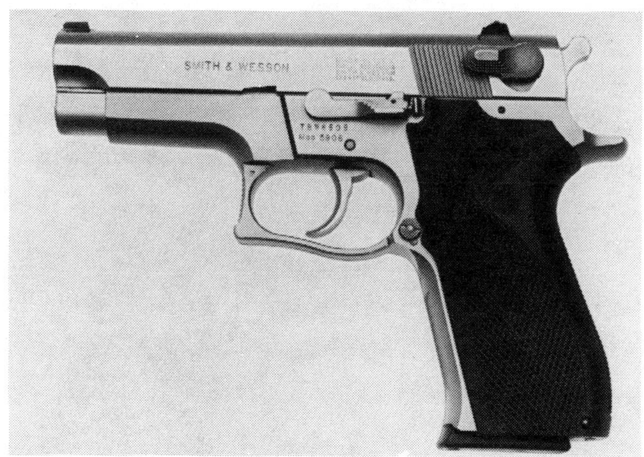

NIB	Exc.	V.G.	Good	Fair	Poor
475	425	375	325	275	225

Model 5906 Special Edition

A double action semi-automatic pistol chambered for the 9MM with a 15-round magazine. The frame and slide have a special machine finish while the grips are one-piece wraparound Xenoy. The front sight is a white dot post and the rear sight is a Novak L-Mount Carry with two white dots. This model has a manual safety/decocking lever and firing pin safety. Introduced in 1993.

NIB	Exc.	V.G.	Good	Fair	Poor
475	425	350	300	250	150

Model 5903

The same caliber and features as the Model 5904 and Model 5906, but furnished with a stainless steel slide and alloy frame.

NIB	Exc.	V.G.	Good	Fair	Poor
475	425	400	350	300	250

Model 5926

S&W offers a 9MM pistol similar to the 5906 but with a frame mounted decocking lever. Both the slide and frame are stainless steel. Discontinued in 1993.

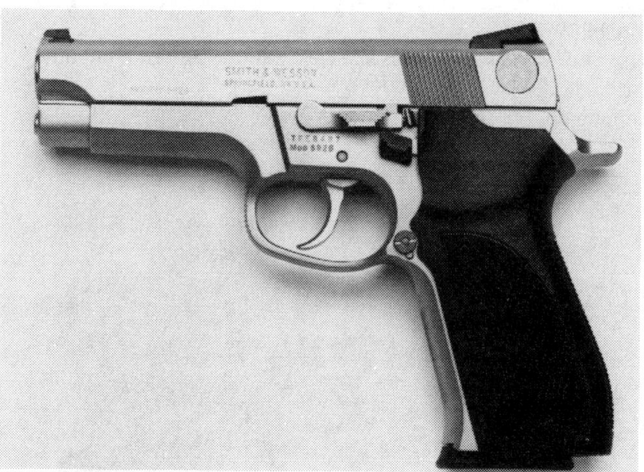

NIB	Exc.	V.G.	Good	Fair	Poor
475	425	375	300	250	150

Model 5946

This 9MM pistol offers the same features as the Model 5926, but in a double action only mode. The hammer configuration on this model is semi-bobbed instead of serrated.

NIB	Exc.	V.G.	Good	Fair	Poor
475	450	400	350	300	250

Model 6904

This is the concealable, shortened version of the Model 5904. It has a 12-shot magazine, fixed sights, bobbed hammer, and a 3.5" barrel.

NIB	Exc.	V.G.	Good	Fair	Poor
475	450	400	350	300	250

Model 6906
This version has a stainless steel slide and alloy frame but otherwise it is similar to the Model 6904.

NIB	Exc.	V.G.	Good	Fair	Poor
475	450	400	350	300	250

Model 6946
The Model 6946 is a double action only version of the Model 6906.

NIB	Exc.	V.G.	Good	Fair	Poor
475	450	400	350	300	250

Model 4003
Smith & Wesson offers this .40 S&W caliber pistol with a 4-inch barrel, 11-round magazine, serrated hammer with a stainless steel slide and alloy frame.

NIB	Exc.	V.G.	Good	Fair	Poor
475	450	400	350	300	250

Model 4004
Identical to the Model 4003 except for a blue carbon steel slide and alloy frame. No longer offered in the S&W product line for 1993.

NIB	Exc.	V.G.	Good	Fair	Poor
475	425	375	300	250	175

Model 4006
Identical to the Model 4003 except for weight. This model has a stainless steel slide and frame. The result is a pistol 8 oz. heavier than the Model 4003.

NIB	Exc.	V.G.	Good	Fair	Poor
475	450	400	350	300	250

Model 4026
Similar to the Model 4006 this version has a frame mounted decocking lever.

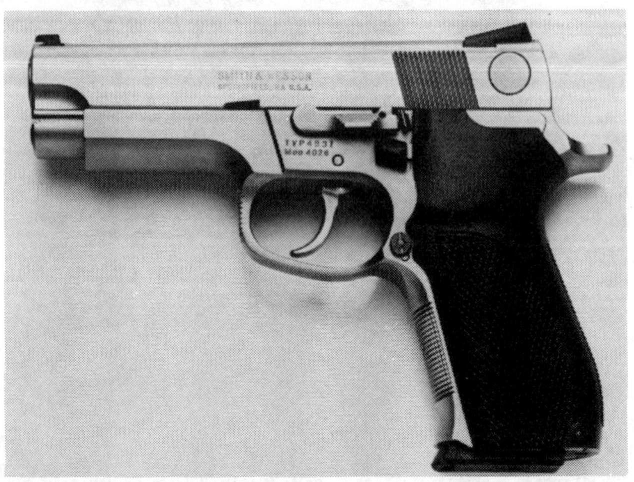

NIB	Exc.	V.G.	Good	Fair	Poor
475	450	400	350	300	250

Model 4046
Similar to the Model 4006 but with a double action only configuration.

NIB	Exc.	V.G.	Good	Fair	Poor
475	450	400	350	300	250

Model 4013
A compact version of the 4000 series, this .40 caliber model features a 3-1/2 inch barrel, 8-round magazine, and stainless steel slide and alloy frame.

NIB	Exc.	V.G.	Good	Fair	Poor
475	450	400	350	300	250

Model 4014
Identical to the Model 4013 except for a blue carbon steel slide and alloy frame.

NIB	Exc.	V.G.	Good	Fair	Poor
475	450	400	350	300	250

Model 4053
Identical to the Model 4013, stainless steel slide and alloy frame, except offered in a double action only configuration.

NIB	Exc.	V.G.	Good	Fair	Poor
475	450	400	350	300	250

Model 4054
This model is the same as the Model 4053 except for a blue carbon steel slide and alloy frame. Dropped from S&W product line in 1992.

NIB	Exc.	V.G.	Good	Fair	Poor
475	425	375	300	250	175

Model 411
This model was introduced in 1993 and features an alloy frame, 4" barrel, matte blue finish, fixed sights, and wrap around rubber grips. Chambered for .40 S&W cartridge with 11-round magazine capacity. Overall length is 7.5" and weight is approximately 29 ozs.

NIB	Exc.	V.G.	Good	Fair	Poor
400	350	300	250	200	150

Model 1006

A full size 10MM pistol with 5-inch barrel, 9-round magazine, and choice of fixed or adjustable sights. The slide and frame are stainless-steel.

NIB	Exc.	V.G.	Good	Fair	Poor
475	450	400	350	300	250

Model 1066

A slightly smaller version of the Model 1006 furnished with a 4-1/4 inch barrel. Discontinued in 1993.

NIB	Exc.	V.G.	Good	Fair	Poor
475	425	375	300	250	150

Model 1076

Identical to the Model 1066 with the exception of a frame mounted decocking lever.

NIB	Exc.	V.G.	Good	Fair	Poor
475	450	400	350	300	250

Model 1086

Similar to the Model 1066 but offered in double action only. This model was discontinued in 1993.

NIB	Exc.	V.G.	Good	Fair	Poor
475	425	375	300	250	175

Model 1026

Similar to the Model 1006 with a 5-inch barrel this model has a frame mounted decocking lever.

NIB	Exc.	V.G.	Good	Fair	Poor
475	450	400	350	300	250

Model 4506

This is the newly designed double action .45 ACP pistol. It is all stainless steel and has a 5" barrel, 8-shot detachable magazine, and wrap-around black delrin grips.

NIB	Exc.	V.G.	Good	Fair	Poor
475	450	400	350	300	250

Model 4505

This version is identical to the Model 4506 with the exception of a blued slide and frame.

NIB	Exc.	V.G.	Good	Fair	Poor
475	450	400	350	300	250

Model 4516

Offered in a .45 caliber this 4500 series is a compact version of the full size .45 calibers S & W autos. Furnished with a 3-3/4 inch barrel and a 7-round magazine this model has a stainless slide and frame. Discontinued in 1991.

NIB	Exc.	V.G.	Good	Fair	Poor
525	475	425	375	350	325

Model 4536

A compact version and similar to the Model 4616 this pistol is offered with a decock lever on the frame.

NIB	Exc.	V.G.	Good	Fair	Poor
475	450	400	350	300	250

Model 4546

A full size version of the Model 4506 but offered in double action only.

NIB	Exc.	V.G.	Good	Fair	Good
475	450	400	350	300	250

SMITH & WESSON PERFORMANCE CENTER HANDGUNS

The role of Smith & Wesson's Performance Center has changed since it was established in 1990. What was once a specialized tune-up and competition one-off production department has now become a separate facility in providing specialized and limited handguns to the public often with distributors participation. This change came about around 1991, when the Performance Center initiated its own limited edition designs. These editions are generally limited to between 300 and 600 pistols for each model. The Performance Center, in fact, has its own distinct product line. Performance Center pistols are made in its own shop using its own designers. One of these distributors that has played a major role in offering these special guns to the public is the Lew Horton Distribution Company. The Center still continues to offer action jobs and accurazing work but no longer executes one of a kind customizing. The Performance Center has built about eight to twelve different models in the last two years. Plans call for more of these unique handguns to be built in the future. Pistols that are available from a certain distributor or the Performance Center will be noted in the description of each pistol.

AUCTION
Lew Horton
DISTRIBUTING CO., INC.

Limited Edition Pistols and Revolvers of 1990

One of the first limited special series of Performance Center handguns was this offering which consisted of custom engraved S&W handguns limited to 15 units on any current (1990) production pistol or revolver. This Limited Edition featured: 24 karat gold and sterling inlays, special bright mirror finish, decorated in light scroll pattern, specially assigned serial number beginning with the prefix "PEC", tuned action, solid walnut presentation case inlaid with blue or burgundy leather insert, embossed with gold with performance center logo. Interior of case is custom fitted with a matching colored velvet. Each handgun is hand numbered and signed certificate of authenticity. Because of the unique nature of the Limited Edition offering it is strongly recommended to secure a professional appraisal.

.40 S&W Tactical

A limited edition semi-automatic handgun offered exclusively by Lew Horton through the Performance Center. This special pistol is fitted with a 5" match-grade barrel, hand fit spherical barrel bushing, custom tuned action, special trigger job, oversized frame and slide rails, wraparound straight backstrap grip. Replaceable front and Novak rear sights. Special serial numbers. Offered in 1992 and limited to 200 units.

Suggested Retail
Introductory Price: $1500

.40 S&W Compensated

Similar to the .40 S&W Tactical but furnished with a 4.625" barrel and single chamber compensator. This is also a Lew Horton/Performance pistol. A production of 250 units. Offered in 1992.

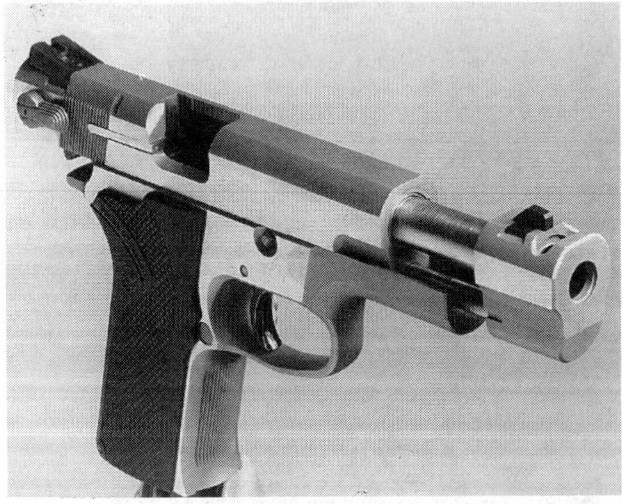

Suggested Retail
Introductory Price: $1700

.40 S&W Performance Action Pistol

Offered in limited quantities in 1990, this Performance Center .40 S&W semi-action pistol was used by the Smith & Wesson shooting Team. The frame and barrel are stainless steel with blue carbon steel slide, two port compensator, two fitted and numbered 13-round magazines, 5.25" match grade barrel extended frame beavertail, square combat trigger guard, oversize magazine release button, spherical barrel bushing, wraparound straight backstrap grip, extended magazine funnel, and Bo-mar adjustable rear sight. The action is tuned for accuracy and precision.

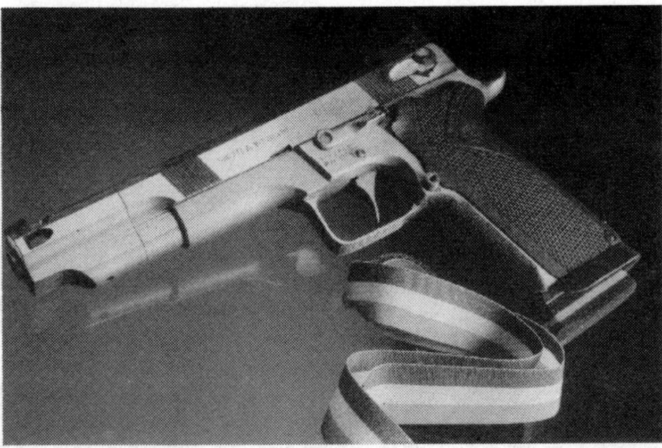

Suggested Retail
Introductory Price: N/A

Model 686 Competitor

Introduced by Lew Horton and the Performance Center for 1993 this limited edition revolver features a match grade barrel and unique under-barrel weight system. The action has been custom tuned and the receiver is drilled and tapped for scope mounts. Charge holes are chambered, ejector rod housing is enclosed, and the grip is an extended competition type. Special serial numbers.

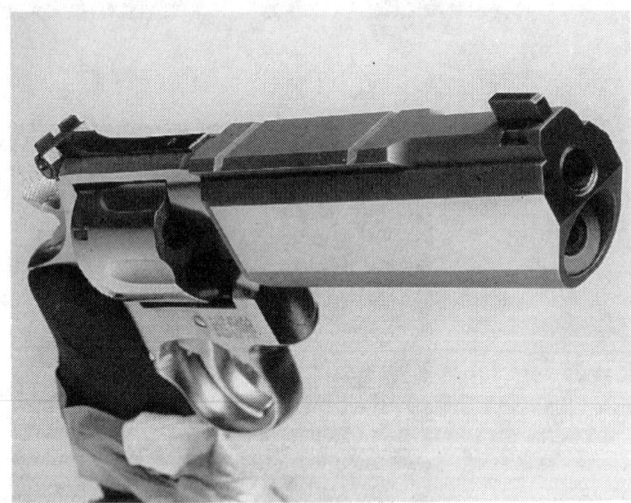

Suggested Retail
Introductory Price: $1100

Model 686 Hunter

Similar to the Model 686 Competitot. This is also a limited edition Lew Horton revolver chambered for the .357 Magnum and features the under-barrel weight system, internal scope mount, and custom tuned action. Special serial numbers.

Suggested Retail
Introductory Price: $1154

Model 686 Carry Comp 4"

Offered in limited quantities by Lew Horton and the Performance Center in 1992 this new design features the unique single chamber integral barrel compensator. Front is windage adjustable and the action is custom tuned. Chambered for the .357 Magnum cartridge. Special serial numbers.

Suggested Retail
Introductory Price: $1000

Model 686 Carry Comp 3"

The 1993 Lew Horton limited edition version of the Model 686 Carry Comp 4" model with a 3" barrel. The same features apply to both models.

Suggested Retail
Introductory Price: $1000

Model 629 Hunter

Introduced in 1992 by Lew Horton and the Performance Center this limited edition revolver features a new design that utilizes an 6" under-barrel weight system, special integral barrel compensator. The action has been custom tuned and the receiver has an integral scope mount. Chambered for the .44 Magnum. Special finger groove grips are standard. Special serial numbers.

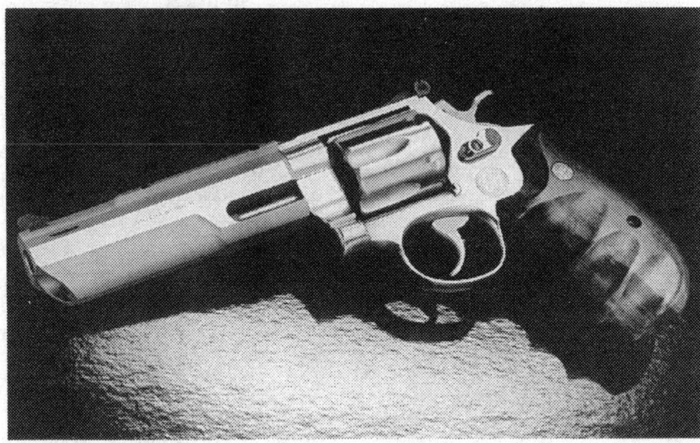

Suggested Retail
Introductory Price: $1234

Model 629 Hunter II

Another Lew Horton/Performance Center limited edition revolver that features 2x Nikon scope with steel see through rings. The barrel is Mag-na-ported and incorporates the Performance Center's under-barrel weight arrangement. The action is custom tuned and the revolver is supplied with a ballistic nylon range carry bag. Special serial numbers.

Suggested Retail
Introductory Price: $1234

Model 629 Carry Comp

Introduced in 1992 by Lew Horton and the Performance Center this limited edition revolver is chambered for the .44 magnum cartridge. It features a integral ported 3" barrel, fluted cylinder, radiused charge holes, dove tail front and fixed groove rear sight. Fitted with a rubber combat grip. The action is custom by the Performance Center. Special serial numbers.

Suggested Retail
Introductory Price: $1000

Model 629 Carry Comp II

A limited edition 1993 offering by Lew Horton and the Performance Center similar to the 1992 Model 629 Carry Comp with the exception that this 1993 model has a special unfluted cylinder and fully adjustable rear sight. Special serial numbers.

Suggested Retail
Introductory Price: $1000

Model 640 Carry Comp

Introduced in 1991 by Lew Horton and the Performance Center this revolver is chambered for the .38 S&W Special, but with a strengthened action to handle +P+ loads. Fitted with a heavy 2.625" barrel with unique integral barrel compensator. The front is replaceable and adjustable for windage. The rear sight is a fixed groove. custom trigger job and custom tuned action are also part of the package. Special serial numbers.

Suggested Retail
Introductory Price: $750

"Shorty-Forty" .40 S&W

Introduced in 1992 and available exclusively from Lew Horton, this limited edition Performance Center pistol features a light alloy frame, oversize slide rails, and spherical barrel bushing. A match grade barrel is joined to a custom tuned action. Special serial numbers.

Suggested Retail
Introductory Price: $950

Shorty .356 TSW

This new cartridge is also available in another Lew Horton/Performance Center limited edition pistol with a 4" barrel. It features a steel frame and handfitted slide, with spherical barrel bushing. The double action is custom tuned by the Performance Center. Magazine holds 12 rounds. Similar in appearance to the "Shorty-Forty". Offered in 1993. Special serial numbers.

Suggested Retail
Introductory Price: $1000

Model .356 TSW "Limited" Series

This is a Lew Horton gun. This model is chambered for the new .356 TSW caliber (TSW stands for Team Smith & Wesson). This is a new caliber, actually a 9MM X 21.5MM cartridge, with ballistics of around 1,235 fps. with a 147 grain bullet. Designer as a low end .,357 competition pistol. Built for the competitive shooter (IPSC) it features a 15-round magazine and distinctive profile and markings. The single action trigger is adjustable for reach while the slide, frame and barrel are custom fitted. The gun comes with a spherical barrel bushing and adjustable Bomar sights. The frame grip is checked 20 line to the inch, the magazine well is extended as is the magazine release. The magazine is fitted with a pad.

Suggested Retail
Introductory Price: $1350

Model 66 .357 Magnum F-Comp

A Performance Center revolver designed as a carry gun. Furnished with a 3" ported barrel and full underlug. The thumbpiece has been cut down to accommodate all speed loaders, the charge holes are counter sunk, and the pistol comes standard with a stainless steel finish. The K-frame action has been custom tuned and the rear sight is a fully adjustable black blade while the front sight features a tritium dot night sight. Furnished with a round butt combat style rubber grip. This is a Lew Horton special limited edition, 300 units, revolver.

Suggested Retail
Introductory Price: $800

Model 657 Classic

Offered in limited quantities of 350 units this Lew Horton/Performance Center revolver features an unfluted cylinder and 6.5" barrel on a drilled and tapped N-frame. Chambered for the .41 Magnum cartridge this handgun is fitted with adjustable rear sight. Special serial numbers.

Suggested Retail
Introductory Price: $550

Model 60 Carry Comp

Introduced in the summer of 1993 this J-frame revolver is fitted with a 3" full underlug barrel with integral compensator. The charge holes are radiused for quick loading and the action is tuned by the Performance Center. The pistol is rated for +P ammunition. The grips are fancy wood contoured for speed loaders. This Lew Horton revolver is limited to 300 guns and has special serial numbers.

Suggested Retail
Introductory Price: $795

Paxton Quigley Model 640

This is a Performance Center offering restricted to 300 revolvers. Built around the Model 640 this limited edition handgun has a 2" compensated barrel, windage adjustable front sight, specially tuned action, and a tapestry soft gun case. Each gun has a distinct serial number range.

Suggested Retail
Price: $720

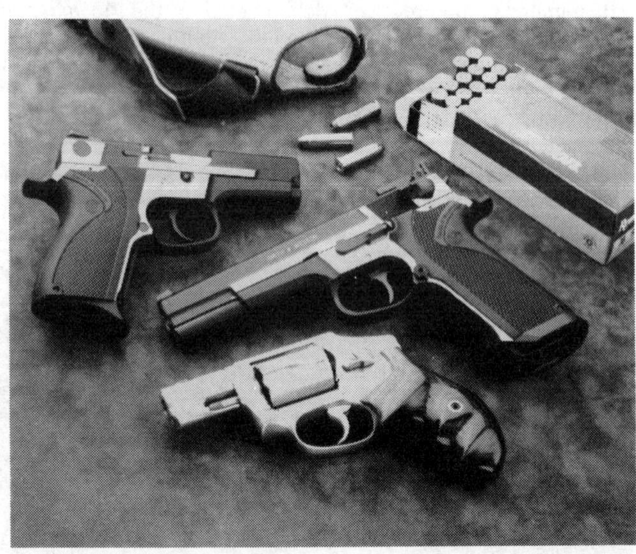

Model 940 Centennial .356

Offered exclusively from Lew Horton this J frame revolver is chambered for the new .356 cartridge and has a 2" compensated barrel. It will also fire the 9mm cartridge. This gun features a tuned action, radius hammer and trigger and special serial numbers.

Suggested Retail
Price: $760

SMITH & WESSON LONG ARMS

Model A Rifle

A bolt-action with 23.75" barrel, chambered for .22-250, .243, .270, .308, .30-06, 7mm Magnum, and .300 Winchester Magnum. It has a folding rear sight and a checkered Monte Carlo stock with contrasting rosewood forend tip and pistolgrip cap. It was manufactured for S&W by Husqvarna of Sweden.

Exc.	V.G.	Good	Fair	Poor
375	325	275	200	150

Model B

As above, with a Schnabel forend and 20.75" barrel.

Exc.	V.G.	Good	Fair	Poor
400	350	300	250	200

Model C

As above, with a cheekpiece.

Exc.	V.G.	Good	Fair	Poor
425	375	325	275	225

Model D

As above, with a Mannlicher-style stock.

Exc.	V.G.	Good	Fair	Poor
550	500	400	350	250

Model E

As above, without a cheekpiece.

Exc.	V.G.	Good	Fair	Poor
500	450	400	350	250

Model 1500 Deluxe

Made for S&W by Howa Machine in Japan. It is chambered for .222 through .300 Winchester Magnum. It has a 22" barrel and a walnut Monte Carlo stock with skipline checkering.

Exc.	V.G.	Good	Fair	Poor
350	300	250	200	150

Model 1500 Deluxe Varmint

As above with a 24" heavy barrel. Chambered for a variety of small bore calibers.

Exc.	V.G.	Good	Fair	Poor
350	300	250	200	150

Model 1500 Mountaineer

As above, but lighter in weight.

Exc.	V.G.	Good	Fair	Poor
325	275	225	175	125

Model 1700 Classic Hunter

This is a bolt-action rifle with 22" barrel, no sights, and a removable 5-round magazine. It has a nicely checkered walnut stock with schnabel forend. It was imported from Howa of Japan.

Exc.	V.G.	Good	Fair	Poor
400	350	300	250	200

S&W discontinued the importation of the Howa line in 1984.

Model 916 Slide Action Shotgun

This is offered in 12, 16, and 20 gauge and has barrel lengths of 20"-30" with various chokes. It has a plain stock and barrel. It was imported from Howa of Japan.

Exc.	V.G.	Good	Fair	Poor
175	150	125	100	75

Model 916T

As above, with interchangeable barrel capability.

Exc.	V.G.	Good	Fair	Poor
200	175	150	125	100

Model 3000 Slide Action

This is offered in 12 and 20 gauge. It has 3" chambers and 22"-30" barrel lengths and features a checkered walnut stock and forend.

Exc.	V.G.	Good	Fair	Poor
300	275	200	150	125

Model 3000 Police

As above with 18" or 20" barrels, a matte blue or parkerized finish, and a combat-style finish on the stock.

Exc.	V.G.	Good	Fair	Poor
325	300	250	200	150

Model 1000 Autoloader

Made by Howa Machine, this gas-operated shotgun has an alloy receiver with engraving. It was offered in 12 or 20 gauge with barrel lengths from 22"-30" and various chokes. The walnut stock is checkered, and the barrel features a vent-rib.

Exc.	V.G.	Good	Fair	Poor
375	325	275	225	150

Model 1000 Super 12

As above, with the capability of operating with different pressure cartridges.

Exc.	V.G.	Good	Fair	Poor
500	400	300	250	175

Courtesy Butterfield & Butterfield, San Francisco, California.

This rare Smith and Wesson revolving rifle with shoulder stock is chambered for .32 caliber. It is fitted with a 16-inch barrel and has hard red rubber grips and forearm. The stock is walnut and features a factory tang sight. Serial number 902.

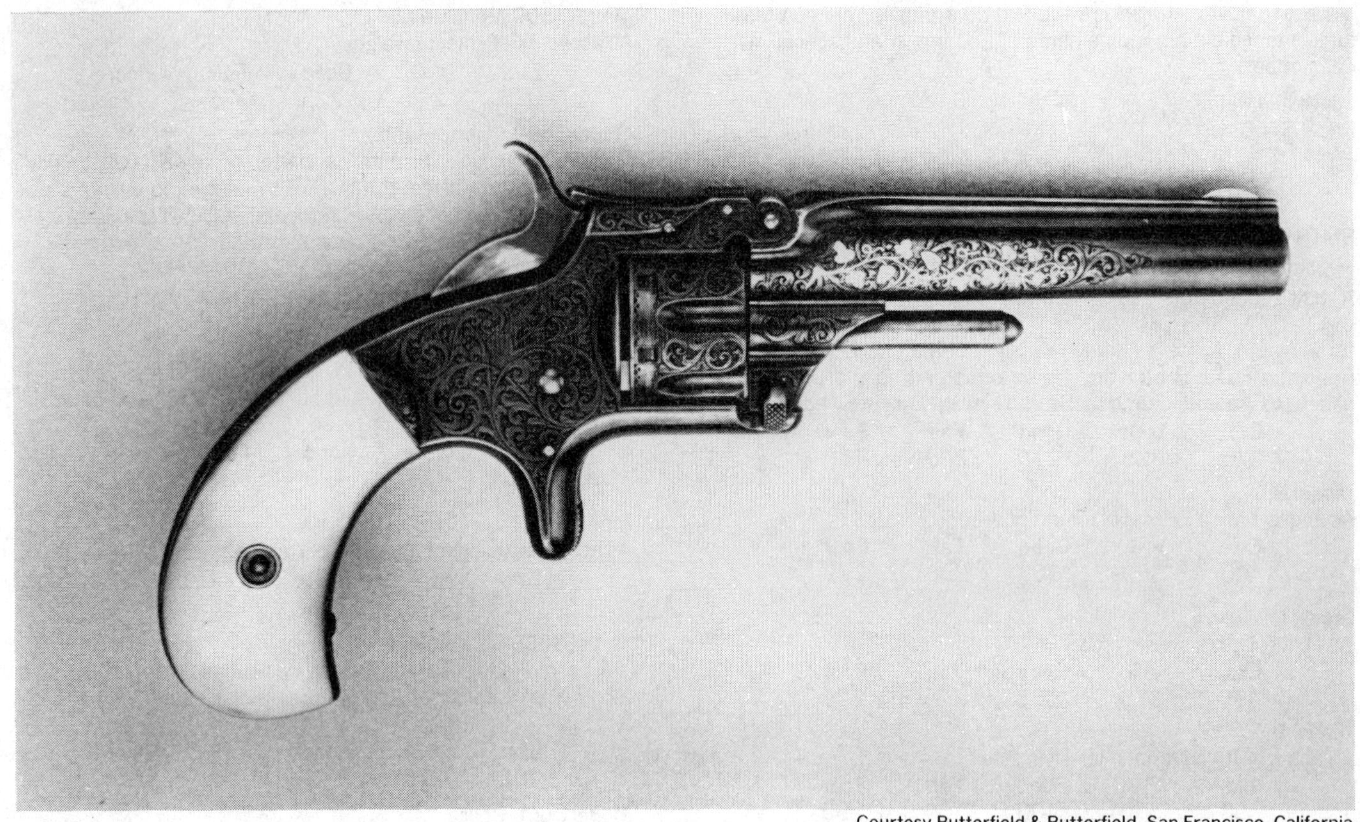

Courtesy Butterfield & Butterfield, San Francisco, California.

This First Model Third Issue Smith and Wesson revolver is chambered for .22 caliber and is engraved with gold inlays by Gustave Young with mother-of-pearl grips. Its condition is excellent. Serial number 1851

SNAKE CHARMER

Little Field, Texas
Sporting Arms Manufacturing, Inc.

Snake Charmer

A .410 bore single shot shotgun with an 18.5" barrel. Stainless steel with a composition stock.

NIB	Exc.	V.G.	Good	Fair	Poor
150	125	100	75	50	25

SNEIDER, CHARLES E.

Baltimore, Maryland

2-Cylinder Revolver

A .22 caliber spur trigger revolver with a 2.75" octagonal barrel and twin 7-shot cylinders which can be pivoted. The barrel marked "E. Sneider Pat. March 1862." Produced in very limited quantities during the 1860s. Prospective purchasers are advised to secure a qualified appraisal prior to acquisition.

Exc.	V.G.	Good	Fair	Poor
5000	4000	3000	2500	2000

SODIA, FRANZ

Ferlach, Austria

A wide variety of double-barrel shotguns, drillings, and combination shotgun/rifles are made by this maker. As these arms are essentially custom order pieces, it is advised that perspective purchasers secure individual appraisals.

SOKOLOVSKY CORP. SPORT ARMS

Sunnyvale, California

.45 Automaster

A .45 caliber stainless-steel semi-automatic pistol with a 6" barrel fitted with Millet adjustable sights and 6-shot magazine. Approximately 50 of these pistols have been made since 1984.

NIB	Exc.	V.G.	Good	Fair	Poor
3250	2750	2250	1750	1250	800

SPALDING & FISHER

Worcester, Massachusetts

Double Barreled Pistol

A .36 caliber percussion double-barrel pocket pistol with 5.5" barrels, blued iron frame and walnut grips. The top of the barrels marked "Spalding & Fisher." Produced during the 1850s.

Exc.	V.G.	Good	Fair	Poor
500	400	350	250	175

SPANG & WALLACE

Philadelphia, Pennsylvania

Pocket Pistol

A .36 caliber percussion pocket pistol with a 2.5 to 6" barrel, German silver furniture and checkered walnut stock. The barrel marked "Spang & Wallace/Phila." Manufactured during late 1840s and early 1850s.

Exc.	V.G.	Good	Fair	Poor
1250	1000	750	400	300

SPENCER
Boston, Massachusetts

Spencer Carbine
This was one of the most popular firearms used by Union forces during the Civil War. It is chambered for a metallic rimfire cartridge known as the "No. 56." It is actually a .52 caliber and was made with a copper case. The barrel is 22" in length. The finish is blued, with a carbine-length walnut stock held on by one barrel band. There is a sling swivel at the butt. There were approximately 50,000 manufactured between 1863 and 1865.

Courtesy Butterfield & Butterfield, San Francisco, California.

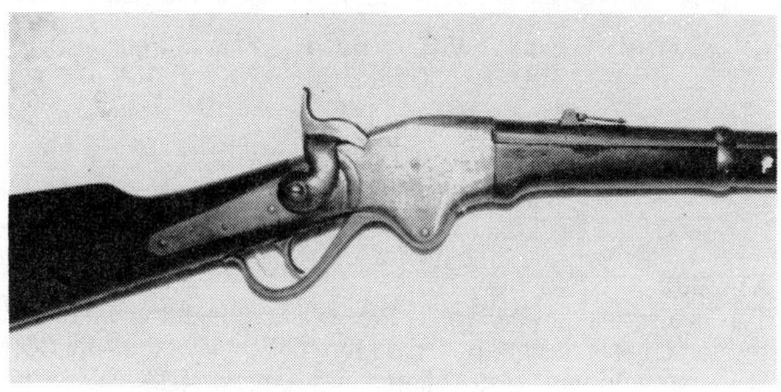

Exc.	V.G.	Good	Fair	Poor
1500	1250	950	750	450

Military Rifle—Navy Model
This model is similar to the carbine, with a 30" round barrel and a full-length walnut stock held on by three barrel bands. It features an iron forend tip and sling swivels. The Civil War production consisted of two models. A Navy model was manufactured between 1862 and 1864 (there were approximately 1,000 of these so marked).

Exc.	V.G.	Good	Fair	Poor
1750	1500	1250	900	600

Military Rifle—Army Model
There were approximately 11,450 produced for the Army during the Civil War. They are similar to the Navy model except that the front sight doubles as a bayonet lug. They were manufactured in 1863 and 1864.

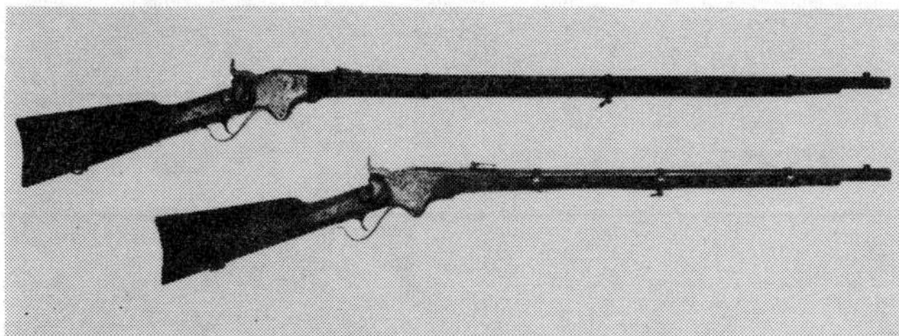

Courtesy Milwaukee Public Museum, Milwaukee, Wisconsin.

Exc.	V.G.	Good	Fair	Poor
1650	1400	1100	800	500

Springfield Armory Postwar Alteration
After the conclusion of the Civil War, approximately 11,000 carbines were refurbished and rechambered for .50 caliber rimfire. The barrels were sleeved, and a device known as the "Stabler cut-off" was added to convert the arm to single shot function. Often they were refinished and restocked. The inspector's marks "ESA" will be found in an oval cartouche on the left side of the stock. These alterations took place in 1867 and 1868.

Exc.	V.G.	Good	Fair	Poor
1250	1000	800	650	400

Model 1865 Contract
This model was manufactured by the Burnside Rifle Company in 1865. They are similar to the Civil War-type carbine and are marked "By Burnside Rifle Co./Model 1865." There were approximately 34,000 manufactured. Old records show that 30,500 were purchased by the United States Government, and 19,000 of these had the Stabler cut-off device.

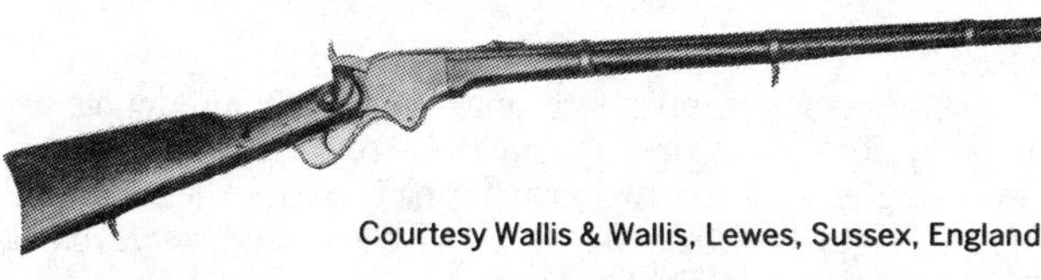

Courtesy Wallis & Wallis, Lewes, Sussex, England.

Exc.	V.G.	Good	Fair	Poor
1200	950	750	600	350

There were a number of other variations in the Spencer line. It would behoove anyone interested in collecting this fine Civil War firearm to educate oneself on these variances and to secure individual appraisal if transactions are contemplated. A book of this nature cannot possibly get into the idiosyncrasies and complicated model variations of every manufacturer. Space will simply not permit it.

SPENCER ARMS CO.
Windsor, Connecticut

From 1882 to 1889 they manuractured the first successful slide action repeating shotgun. Designed by Christopher M. Spencer who also designed the Civil War era Spencer military carbines. The shotgun came in both solid and takedown models in both 12 and 10 gauge. In 1890 Francis Bannerman & Sons of New York bought the patents and machinery and moved the operation to Brooklyn, NY. They produced what is known as the Spencer Bannerman models from 1890 to 1907. The takedown model is worth 20% premium and 10 gauge models are worth a 10% premium. The later Bannerman models are worth 20% less than the Spencer models.

Exc.	V.G.	Good	Fair	Poor
400	350	300	200	125

SPENCER REVOLVER
Maltby, Henley & Company
New York, New York

Safety Hammerless Revolver
A .32 caliber hammerless double-action revolver with a 3" barrel. The frame and barrel made of brass, the cylinder of steel and the grips are of walnut. The barrel is marked "Spencer Safety Hammerless Pat. Jan. 24, 1888 & Oct. 29, 1889." Manufactured by the Norwich Pistol Company circa 1890.

Exc.	V.G.	Good	Fair	Poor
300	250	200	150	100

SPHINX
Sphinx Engineering SA
Porrentru, Switzerland
Imported by
Sile Distributors Inc.

This Swiss based company was founded in 1876 and produced the first automatic turning machine. The company made small drills, tungsten carbine tools, and tool coatings. after World War

II Sphinx developed more exotic machines and drills. In 1990 Sphinx Engineering SA was established for the development and production of pistols. In 1991 the AT .380 was introduced to the market. the following year the AT 2000 was placed on the market. Sphinx purchased the rights to its current line of pistols from ITM AG, a Swiss firm that experienced financial problems with the development of its pistol line, in 1989. The AT series is essentially a copy of the famous Czech CZ 75 semi-automatic pistol.

AT-380

This semi-automatic pistol is a small .380 caliber in double action only. The magazine capacity is 11 rounds. It is offered in Stainless steel, blue, or two-tone finish. The barrel is 3.27" and overall length is 6.03". Sights are fixed and grips are black checkered plastic. Weight is 25 oz.

NIB	Exc.	V.G.	Good	Fair	Poor
450	400	350	300	200	100

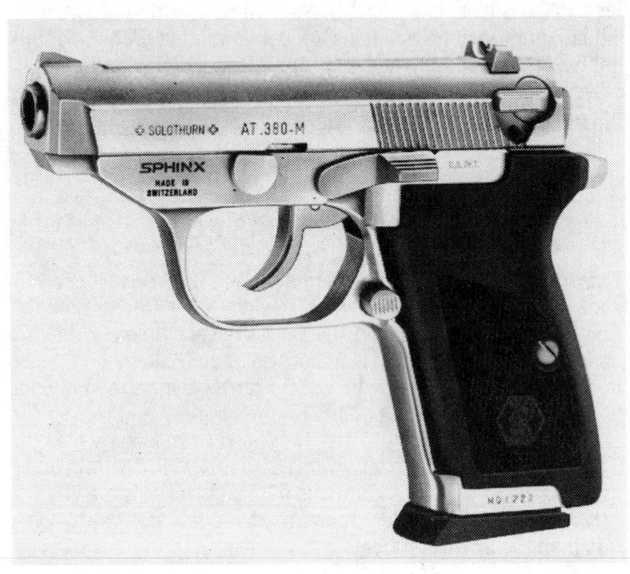

AT-2000

This is a series number applied to several different variations of the same basic design. Based on the CZ-75 pistol the AT-2000 is a semi-automatic pistol offered in 9mm and .40 S&W. Barrel lengths are different depending on variation, but the AT-2000 can be converted from double action to double only in just a matter of minutes.

AT-2000S/SDA

This model is chambered for the 9mm or .40S&W cartridge. The barrel length is 4.53" and overall length is 8.12". Magazine capacity is 15 rounds for 9mm and 13 rounds for .40S&W. Available in double action(S) or double action only(SDA). Offered with two-tone or all blue finish. Weighs 35 oz.

NIB	Exc.	V.G.	Good	Fair	Poor
675	600	500	400	300	200

AT-2000P/PDA
This is a slightly smaller of the AT-2000S. Magazine capacity is 13 rounds for 9mm and 11 rounds for .40S&W. The features are the same except that the barrel length is 3.66", overall length 7.25", and weight is 31 oz.

NIB	Exc.	V.G.	Good	Fair	Poor
650	600	500	400	300	200

AT-2000PS
This version, sometimes referred to as the Police Special, features the shorter barrel of the AT-2000P model on the larger AT-2000S frame. Barrel length is 3.66" and magazine capacity is 15 rounds for 9mm and 13 rounds for the .40S&W.

NIB	Exc.	V.G.	Good	Fair	Poor
650	600	500	400	300	200

AT-2000H/HDA
This is the smallest version of the AT-2000 series. Magazine capacity is 10 rounds for 9mm and 8 rounds for .40S&W. The barrel length is 3.34" and overall length is 6.78". Weight is 26 oz.

NIB	Exc.	V.G.	Good	Fair	Poor
650	600	500	400	300	200

AT-2000C
This is the competitor model. It features a competition slide, dual port compensator, match barrel, and Sphinx scope mount. Offered in double action/single action. available in 9mm, 9x21, and .40S&W.

NIB	Exc.	V.G.	Good	Fair	Poor
1600	1200	800	600	400	200

AT-2000CS

Same as above model but fitted with Bo-Mar adjustable sights.

NIB	Exc.	V.G.	Good	Fair	Poor
1400	1000	600	400	300	200

AT-2000GM

The Grand Master model. Features are similar to the AT-2000C but offered in single action only.

NIB	Exc.	V.G.	Good	Fair	Poor
2100	1750	1250	600	300	200

AT-2000GMS

Same as above but fitted with Bo-Mar adjustable sights.

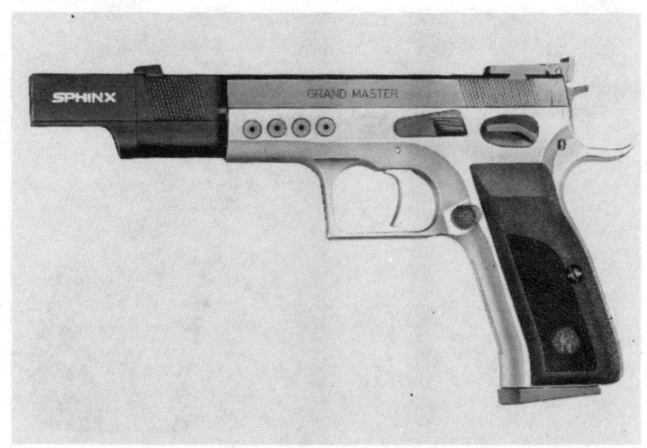

NIB	Exc.	V.G.	Good	Fair	Poor
2000	1650	1200	600	300	200

SPIES, A. W.

New York, New York

Pocket Pistol

A .41 caliber percussion pocket pistol with a 2.5" barrel, German silver furniture and a checkered walnut stock. Produced during the 1850s.

Exc.	V.G.	Good	Fair	Poor
1500	1000	750	400	300

SPILLER & BURR

Atlanta, Georgia

Navy Revolver

A .36 caliber percussion revolver with a 6" or 6.5" octagonal barrel and 6-shot cylinder. The barrel and cylinder blued, the frame of brass with walnut grips. Some pistols are marked "Spiller & Burr" while others are simply marked "C.S." Approximately 1,450 were made between 1862 and 1865. Prospective purchasers are advised to secure a qualified appraisal prior to acquisition.

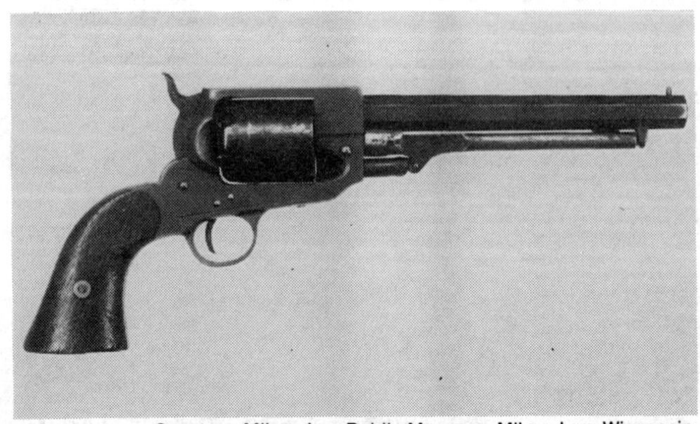

Courtesy Milwaukee Public Museum, Milwaukee, Wisconsin.

Exc.	V.G.	Good	Fair	Poor
5000	4250	3500	2750	1750

SPIRLET, A.

Leige, Belgium

Spirlet was erroneously credited with inventing the top-hinged tip-up revolver. This weapon was around well before Spirlet's time. Actually, the patent that he held covers lockwork and an ejection system that was used on tip-up revolvers. Although he manufactured some of these tip-up revolvers himself, there were never enough of them to establish him as little more than a small custom gunmaker. Revolvers that he manufactured bear his name and address on the breech end of the barrel. Many other makers utilized his developments.

SPITFIRE

JSL(Hereford) Ltd.
Hereford, England
Importer—Specialty Shooters
Ft. Lauderdale, FL

This semi-automatic pistol is a design based on the CZ 75. This is a hand built pistol designed by John Slough and built from a solid block of steel. The Stainless steel frame and slide are cut with spark erosion and diamond grinding. Barrels are built and bored in the same factory. This is primarily a competition pistol.

Spitfire Standard Model (G1)

Chambered for the 9x21, 9mm Parabellum, or .40 S&W cartridges this pistol uses the locked breech concept. The trigger system is single and double action and it is fitted with an ambidextrous safety. The barrel is 3.7" and the overall length is 7.1". Magazine capacity of the 9mm is 15 rounds. Sights are fixed. Empty weight is 35 oz. Finish is stainless steel. Comes supplied with presentation box, 2 magazines, and allen key.

NIB	Exc.	V.G.	Good	Fair	Poor
1300	900	700	500	300	200

Spitfire Sterling Model (G2)

This model is chambered for the 9x21, 9mm Parabellum, or .40 S&W cartridges. Its features are the same as the Standard Model with the exception that it has adjustable sights.

NIB	Exc.	V.G.	Good	Fair	Poor
1400	1000	800	600	300	200

Spitfire Super Sterling (G7)

Also chambered for the 9x21, 9mm Para., and .40 S&W this model features a single port compensator, 4.3" barrel, and overall length of 8.25". Weight is approximately 36 oz.

NIB	Exc.	V.G.	Good	Fair	Poor
1600	1200	900	700	350	200

Spitfire Competition Model (G3)

Chambered for 9x21, 9mm Parabellum, or .40 S&W cartridge this model features a tapered slide rib, adjustable rear sight, dual port compensator, match hammer, adjustable trigger stop with presentation box. Barrel is 5.27" with compensator and weight is 40 oz.

NIB	Exc.	V.G.	Good	Fair	Poor
1800	1400	1000	800	400	200

Spitfire Master Model

This is similar to the Standard Model but without sights. It is fitted with a stainless steel bridge mount to take an Aimpoint sight. Also has a dual port compensator. Supplied with presentation box and 2 magazines.

NIB	Exc.	V.G.	Good	Fair	Poor
2100	1750	1250	800	400	200

Spitfire Squadron Model

This model has a Standard Model frame, adjustable rear sight slide, adjustable rear sight slide with compensator, Master Model slide and barrel with stainless steel bridge mount and Aimpoint sight, 4 magazines, screwdriver, allen key, oil bottle, spare springs, cleaning kit, and fitted leather case.

NIB	Exc.	V.G.	Good	Fair	Poor
6000	4800	2100	900	450	200

Spitfire Battle of Britain Commemorative

This is a limited edition of 1,056 Spitfires in 9mm Parabellum. Each one represents one of the Spitfire aircraft. The stainless steel slide has the inscription "Battle of Britain-50th Anniversary", the grips are checkered walnut, log book of history of that particular aircraft, and a wooden presentation box with engraved plaque.

Retail Price: $1,900

Westlake Britarms

This is a .22 Long Rifle Match pistol. Barrel length is 5.77", sight base is 8.42", magazine capacity is 5 rounds. Weight is approximately 47 oz. Trigger is adjustable for length, front and rear trigger stops, adjustable palm rest on contoured wood grips, take-down barrel design with removable weight. Limited importation.

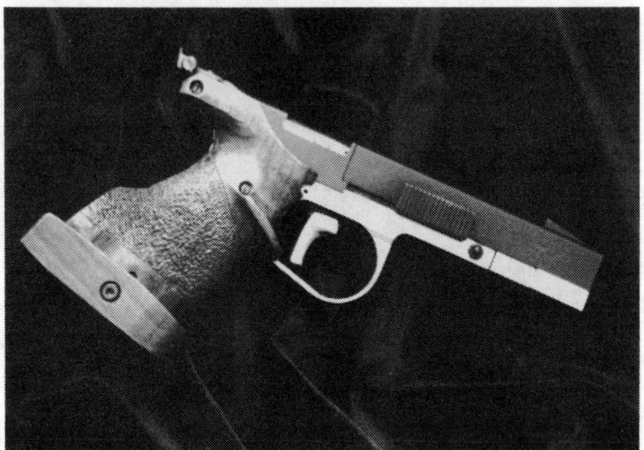

NIB	Exc.	V.G.	Good	Fair	Poor
1850	1400	1000	800	400	200

SPRINGFIELD ARMORY (MODERN)

SEE—Springfield Inc.

SPRINGFIELD INC.

Colona, Illinois

M1 Garand Rifle

A .270 (discontinued), .308 or .30-06 caliber semi-automatic rifle with a 24" barrel and 8-shot magazine. Patterned directly after the USM1 Rifle.

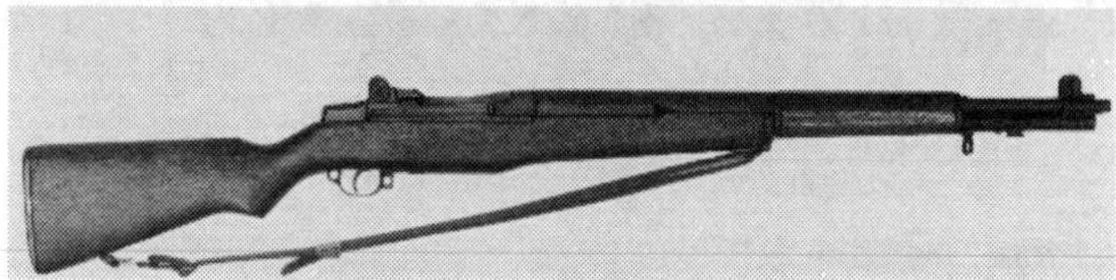

Courtesy Milwaukee Public Museum, Milwaukee, Wisconsin.

Exc.	V.G.	Good	Fair	Poor
775	650	550	400	300

As of January 1993 Springfield Inc. purchased the inventory, name, patents, trademarks, and logo of the Springfield Armory Inc. and intends to carry on the tradition of quality products and service in the future. Products, services, and distribution patterns remain unchanged. The Springfield Custom Shop, producing "Raceguns" will continue as before.

M1A Basic Rifle

Chambered for .308 Win. and fitted with a painted black fiberglass stock. Barrel length is 22" without flash suppresser. Front sights are military square post and rear military aperture(battle sights). Magazine capacity is 5,10, or 20 box. Rifle weighs 9 lbs.

NIB	Exc.	V.G.	Good	Fair	Poor
750	700	600	500	250	200

M1A Standard Rifle

This model is chambered for the .308 Win., .243, or 7mmx08 cartridges. Also fitted with a 22" barrel but with adjustable rear sight. Fitted with a walnut stock with fiberglass handguard, it comes equipped with a 20 round box magazine. Weighs 9 lbs.

NIB	Exc.	V.G.	Good	Fair	Poor
875	800	700	600	300	200

M1A-A1 Bush Rifle

Chambered for .308, .243, or 7mmx08 cartridge with choice of walnut stock or folding stock. Fitted with 18.25" barrel. Rifle weighs 8.75 lbs.

NIB	Exc.	V.G.	Good	Fair	Poor
875	800	700	600	300	200

NOTE: Add $150 for folding stock.

M1A National Match

Chambered for .308 as standard with choice of .243 or .7mmx08 cartridge. Fitted with a medium weight National Match 22" glass bedded barrel and walnut stock. Special rear sight adjustable to half minute-of angle clicks. Weighs 10.06 lbs.

NIB	Exc.	V.G.	Good	Fair	Poor
1050	900	750	600	300	200

M1A Super Match

This is Springfield's best match grade rifle. Chambered for .308 as standard and also .243 or 7mmx08 cartridge. Fitted with special oversize heavy walnut stock, heavy Douglas match glass bedded barrel, and special rear lugged receiver. Special rear adjustable sight. Weighs 10.125 lbs.

NIB	Exc.	V.G.	Good	Fair	Poor
1300	1050	850	700	350	200

M21 Law Enforcement Rifle

Similar to the Super Match with the addition of a special stock with rubber recoil pad and height adjustable cheek piece. Available as a special order only. Weighs 11.875 lbs.

NIB	Exc.	V.G.	Good	Fair	Poor
1450	1150	900	700	350	200

M6 Scout

A .22, .22 Magnum or .22 Hornet and .410 bore Over/Under combination shotgun rifle with an 18" barrel. Black anodized finish with a synthetic stock.

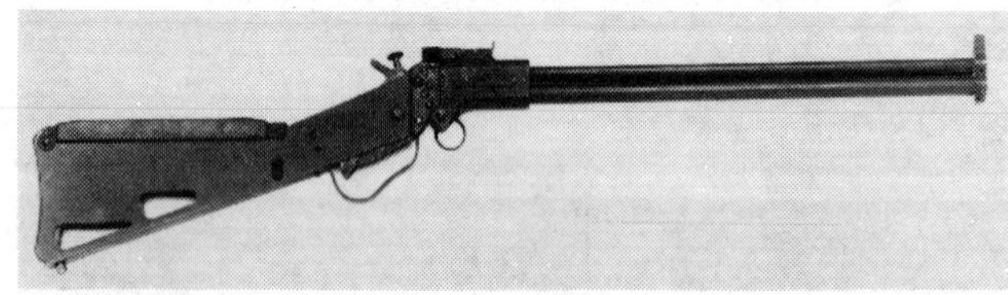

Exc.	V.G.	Good	Fair	Poor
125	100	80	60	40

Model 1911-A1

A 9mm, .38 Super or .45 caliber copy of the Colt Model 1911A1 semi-automatic pistol. Blued or parkerized. Introduced in 1985.

NIB	Exc.	V.G.	Good	Fair	Poor
425	375	350	300	250	200

Combat Commander

A copy of the Colt Model 1911 A1 Combat Commander chambered for .45 ACP only. Introduced in 1988.

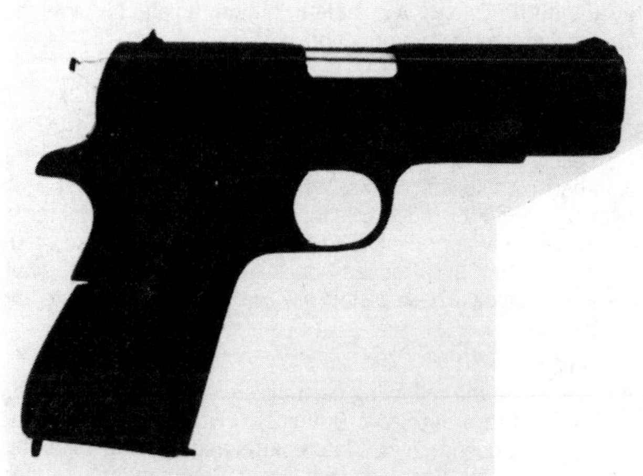

NIB	Exc.	V.G.	Good	Fair	Poor
475	425	400	350	300	250

Model 1911-A2 S.A.S.S.

This is a single shot pistol built on the Model 1911 frame. Available in two barrel lengths; 10.75" and 14.9". Offered in .22 Long Rifle, .223, .308, and .44 Magnum calibers. This conversion kit is available for those wishing to use it on their own Model 1911 pistol frames.

NIB	Exc.	V.G.	Good	Fair	Poor
225	200	175	150	100	50

Model 1911-A1 Stainless

Similar to the standard Model 1911 but chambered for the .45 ACP cartridge and offered in stainless steel. Equipped with 3-dot sights, beveled magazine well, and checkered walnut grips. Weighs about 39.2 oz.

NIB	Exc.	V.G.	Good	Fair	Poor
375	325	300	250	200	100

Model 1911-A1 Factory Comp.

Chambered for the .45 ACP or the .38 Super this pistol is fitted with a three chamber compensator. The rear sight is adjustable, an extended thumb safety and Videcki speed trigger are standard features. Also checkered walnut grips, beveled magazine well and Commander hammer are standard. Weighs 40 oz.

NIB	Exc.	V.G.	Good	Fair	Poor
600	500	400	300	200	100

Model 1911-A1 Defender

Chambered for the .45 ACP cartridge this pistol is fitted with a tapered cone dual port compensator. It also is fitted with reversed recoil plug, full length recoil spring guide, fully adjustable rear sight, serrated front strap, rubberized grips, and Commander style hammer. Eight round magazine capacity. The finish is bitone. Weighs 40.16 oz.

NIB	Exc.	V.G.	Good	Fair	Poor
675	575	450	350	200	100

Model 1911-A1 Compact

Available in blue or bi-tone this .45 ACP is fitted with a 4.5" barrel and compact compensator. It is equipped with Commander style hammer and three dot sights. Walnut grips are standard. Comes with 7 round magazine. Weighs 37.2 oz.

NIB	Exc.	V.G.	Good	Fair	Poor
575	500	400	300	200	100

Model 1911-A1 Champion

This .45 ACP pistol has a shortened slide, barrel, and reduced size frame.. The Champion is fitted withe 4" barrel, 8 round magazine, Commander hammer, checkered walnut grips, and special 3-dot sights. Weighs 33.4 oz.

NIB	Exc.	V.G.	Good	Fair	Poor
350	300	250	200	150	100

Champion Compact

Includes same features as Champion but with a shortened grip frame length and a 7 round magazine. Weighs 32 oz.

NIB	Exc.	V.G.	Good	Fair	Poor
350	300	250	200	150	100

Model 1911-A1 High Capacity

This model is chambered in .45 ACP(10 round magazine) or 9x21 caliber(16 round magazine). Standard features include Commander hammer, walnut grips, and beveled magazine well. Blue finish. Wights 42 oz.

NIB	Exc.	V.G.	Good	Fair	Poor
575	500	400	300	200	100

The Springfield P9 Pistol

This is a double action 9mm, 45. ACP, or .40 S&W pistol based on the Czech CZ-75 design. It incorporates several design features including: stainless steel trigger, sear safety mechanism, extended sear safety lever, redesigned back strap, lengthened beavertail grip area, and a new high strength slide stop. This model discontinued in 1993.

Model P9 Standard

This is the standard pistol fitted with a 4.7" barrel, low profile target sights, and a ribbed slide. The 9mm has a 16 round magazine, the .45 ACP has a 10 round magazine, and the .40 S&W holds 12 rounds. Offered in either blue or stainless finish. Weighs about 35 oz.

NIB	Exc.	V.G.	Good	Fair	Poor
375	325	300	250	200	100

Model P9 Factory Comp.

This is a competition pistol fitted withe triple port compensator, extended magazine release, adjustable rear sight, slim competition wood grips, and bi-tone finish. Weighs 34 oz. Dropped form the Springfield product in 1993.

NIB	Exc.	V.G.	Good	Fair	Poor
500	450	400	300	200	100

Model P9 Ultra (IPSC Approved)

This competition pistol features a longer slide and barrel, 5". Special target sights, rubberized competition grips. Pistol is engraved with IPSC logo. Available in bi-tone finish only. Weighs 34.5 oz. Dropped from production in 1993.

NIB	Exc.	V.G.	Good	Fair	Poor
450	400	350	300	200	100

SPRINGFIELD CUSTOM SHOP

This speciality shop was formed to build custom pistols to the customers own specifications. When these one-of-a-kind pistols are encountered it is advisable for the shooter or collector to get an independent appraisal. The Springfield Custom also offers standard custom and Racegun packages that are readily available and in stock. These pistols are commercially available and priced below.

Custom Carry

Chambered for the following cartridges: .45 ACP, 9mm Para., .38 Super, 10mm, .40S&W, 9mmx21. Pistol is fitted with fixed 3-dot sights, speed trigger, Match barrel and bushing, extended thumb safety, beveled magazine well, Commander hammer, polished feed ramp and throated barrel, tuned extractor, lowered and flared ejection port, fitted slide to frame, full length spring guide rod, and walnut grips. Supplied with 2 march magazines and plastic carrying case.

NIB	Exc.	V.G.	Good	Fair	Poor
1000	800	600	500	400	200

Bullseye Wadcutter

Chambered for .45 ACP, .38 Super, 10mm, and .40S&W. Slide is fitted with BoMar rib. Standard features include full length recoil spring guide rod, speed trigger, Commander hammer, lowered and flared ejection port, tuned extractor, fitted slide to frame, beveled magazine well, checkered front strap, checkered main spring housing, removable grip cope mount, match barrel and bushing, polished feed ramp and throated barrel, walnut grips, and two magazines with slam pads.

NIB	Exc.	V.G.	Good	Fair	Poor
1400	950	700	600	400	200

Trophy Master Expert Limited

Chambered for .45 ACP, .38 Super, and 9mmx21. Adjustable BoMAr rear sight, match barrel, polished ramp and throated barrel, extended ambidextrous thumb safety, beveled and polished magazine well, full length recoil spring guide, match trigger, Commander hammer, lowered and flared ejection port, tuned extractor, fitted slide to frame, extended slide release, flat mainspring housing, Pachmayr wraparound grips, 2 magazines with slam pads and plastic carrying case.

NIB	Exc.	V.G.	Good	Fair	Poor
1400	950	700	600	400	200

Springfield Formula "Squirtgun"
Chambered for .45 ACP, .38 Super, 9mmx19, 9mmx21, and 9mmx23. Fitted with a high capacity 20 round frame, customer specifications sights, hard chrome frame and slide, triple chambered tapered cone compensator, full recoil spring guide and reverse plug, shok buff, lowered and flared ejection port, fitted trigger, Commander hammer, polished feed ramp and throated barrel, flat checkered mainspring housing, extended ambidextrous thumb safety, tuned extractor, checkered front strap, bottom of trigger guard checkered, rear of slide serrated, cocking sensations on front of slide, built in beveled magazine well, and checkered wood grips.

NIB	Exc.	V.G.	Good	Fair	Poor
2900	2250	1250	950	400	200

Trophy Master Distinguished Pistol
This model is chambered for the following cartridges: .45 ACP, .38 Super, 10mm, .40S&W, 9mmx21. Special BoMar adjustable rear sight with hidden rear leaf, triple port compensator on match barrel, full length recoil spring guide rod and recoil spring retainer, shok buff, lowered and flared ejection port, fitted speed trigger, Commander hammer, polished feed ramp and throated barrel, flat checkered magazine well and mainspring housing matched to beveled magazine well, extended ambidextrous thumb safety, tuned extractor, checkered front strap, flattened and checkered trigger guard, serrated slide top and compensator, cocking sensations on front of slide, checkered walnut grips, 2 magazines with slam pads, and carrying case.

NIB	Exc.	V.G.	Good	Fair	Poor
2200	1700	1100	800	400	200

CMC Formula "Squirtgun"
Chambered for .45 ACP, .38 Super, 9mmx19, 9mmx21, 9mmx23. This pistol has a 20 round magazine and a modular frame. All other features the same as the Trophy Master.

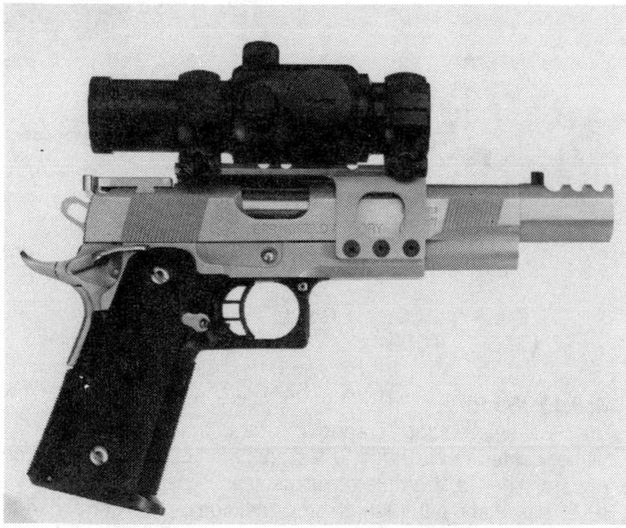

NIB	Exc.	V.G.	Good	Fair	Poor
2750	2000	1200	800	400	200

National Match Model
As above, with a National Match barrel and bushing, adjustable sights and checkered walnut grips. Introduced in 1988.

NIB	Exc.	V.G.	Good	Fair	Poor
850	750	650	550	450	350

Competition Grade
As above, hand-tuned, Match Grade trigger, low-profile combat sights, an ambidextrous safety, and a Commander-type hammer. Furnished with Pachmayr grips. Introduced in 1988.

NIB	Exc.	V.G.	Good	Fair	Poor
1050	950	850	700	600	500

A Model Master Grade Competition Pistol
Similar to the Custom Carry Gun, with a National Match barrel and bushing. Introduced in 1988.

NIB	Exc.	V.G.	Good	Fair	Poor
1700	1500	1250	950	800	700

Model B-1 Master Grade Competition Pistol
Specially designed for USPSA/IPSC competition. Introduced in 1988.

NIB	Exc.	V.G.	Good	Fair	Poor
2000	1750	1250	950	850	750

Omega
A .38 Super, 10mm Norma or .45 caliber semi-automatic pistol with a 5" or 6" polygon rifled barrel, ported or unported, adjustable sights and Pachmayr grips. Patterned somewhat after the Colt Model 1911. Introduced in 1987.
Caliber Conversion Units—Add $675.

NIB	Exc.	V.G.	Good	Fair	Poor
550	450	350	250	200	125

SPRINGFIELD ARMORY

Springfield, Massachusetts

This was America's first federal armory. They began producing military weapons in 1795. They have supplied military weapons to the United States throughout its glorious history.

Model 1841 Cadet Musket

This is a single shot, muzzle-loading rifle chambered for .57-caliber percussion. It has a 40" round barrel with a full-length stock held on by three barrel bands. This rifle features no rear sight. It is browned and case-colored, with iron mountings. There is a steel ramrod mounted under the barrel. The lockplate is marked "Springfield" with the date of manufacture and "US" over an eagle motif. There were approximately 450 produced between 1844 and 1845.

Exc.	V.G.	Good	Fair	Poor
5000	4000	3000	2500	1850

Model 1842 Musket

This is a single shot muzzleloader chambered for .69 caliber percussion. It has a 42" round barrel and a full-length stock held on by three barrel bands. The finish is white with iron mountings and a steel ramrod mounted beneath the barrel. There were a total of approximately 275,000 manufactured between 1844 and 1855 by both the Springfield Armory and the Harper's Ferry Armory. They are so marked.

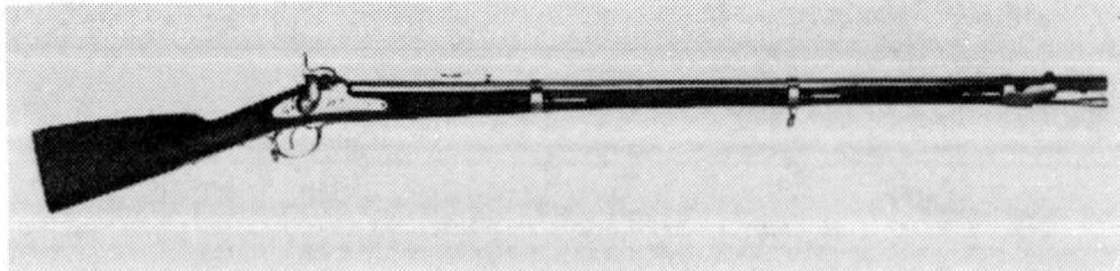

Courtesy Milwaukee Public Museum, Milwaukee, Wisconsin.

Exc.	V.G.	Good	Fair	Poor
1250	1000	750	450	350

Model 1847 Musketoon

This is a single shot muzzleloader chambered for .69 caliber percussion. It has a 26" round smooth-bore barrel. The finish is white, with a full-length walnut stock held on by two barrel bands. The lock is marked "Springfield." There were approximately 3,350 manufactured between 1848 and 1859.

Exc.	V.G.	Good	Fair	Poor
1750	1500	1000	850	600

Model 1855 Musket

This is a single shot muzzleloader chambered for .58 caliber percussion. It has a 40" round barrel with a full-length stock held on by three barrel bands. It has iron mountings and a ramrod mounted under the barrel. The front sight acts as a bayonet lug. The finish is white with a walnut stock. The lock is marked "U.S. Springfield." There was also a Harper's Ferry-manufactured version that is so marked. There were approximately 59,000 manufactured between 1857 and 1861.

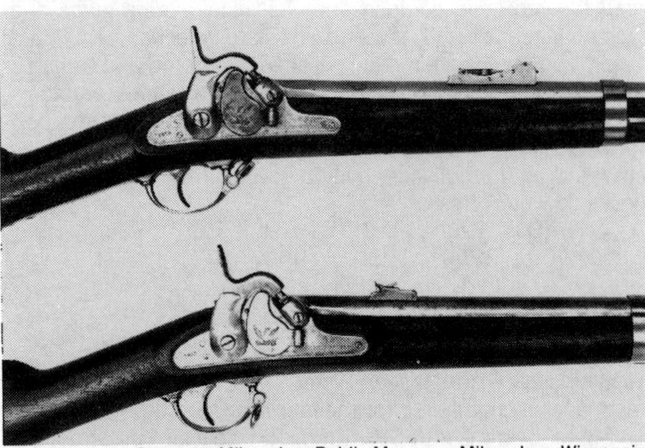

Courtesy Milwaukee Public Museum, Milwaukee, Wisconsin.

Exc.	V.G.	Good	Fair	Poor
1500	1250	1000	750	550

Model 1855 Rifled Carbine

This is a single shot muzzleloader chambered for .54 caliber percussion. It has a 22" round barrel with a 3/4-length stock held on by one barrel band. The finish is white with iron mountings and a ramrod mounted under the barrel. The lock is marked "Springfield" and dated. There were approximately 1,000 manufactured between 1855 and 1856.

Exc.	V.G.	Good	Fair	Poor
3500	3000	2500	1750	1250

Model 1863 Rifled Musket

This is a single shot muzzleloader chambered for .58 caliber percussion. It has a 40" round barrel and a full-length stock held on by three barrel bands. The finish is white with iron mountings, and the lock is marked "U.S. Springfield" and dated 1863. There were approximately 275,000 manufactured in 1863.

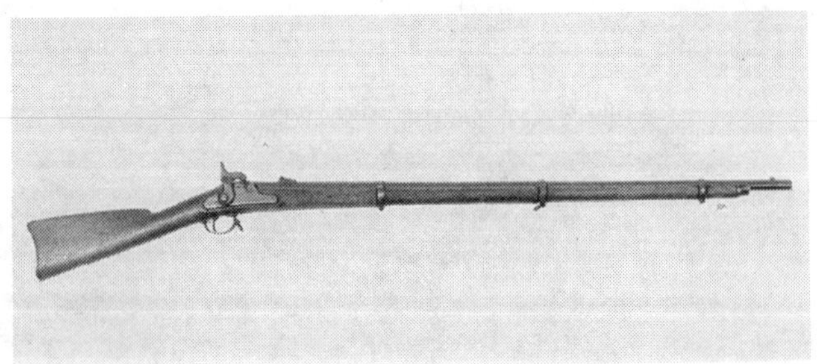

Exc.	V.G.	Good	Fair	Poor
1250	1000	750	600	400

Model 1868 Rifle

This is a single shot "Trapdoor" rifle chambered for the .50-caliber centerfire cartridge. It features a breechblock that pivots forward when a thumblatch at its rear is depressed. It has a 32.5" barrel and a full-length stock held on by two barrel bands. It has iron mountings and a cleaning rod mounted under the barrel. It features an oil-finished walnut stock. The lock is marked "US Springfield." It is dated either 1863 or 1864. The breechblock features either the date 1869 or 1870. There were approximately 51,000 manufactured between 1868 and 1872.

Exc.	V.G.	Good	Fair	Poor
800	675	500	400	250

Model 1869 Cadet Rifle

This is a single shot "Trapdoor" rifle chambered for .50 caliber centerfire. It is similar to the Model 1868 with a 29.5" barrel. There were approximately 3,500 manufactured between 1869 and 1876.

Exc.	V.G.	Good	Fair	Poor
1000	850	650	500	450

Model 1870

There are two versions of this "Trapdoor" breechloader—a rifle with a 32.5" barrel and a carbine that features a 22" barrel and a half-stock held on by one barrel band. They are both chambered for .50 caliber centerfire and feature the standard Springfield lock markings and a breechblock marked "1870" or "Model 1870." There were a total of 11,500 manufactured between 1870 and 1873. Only 340 are carbines; they are extremely rare.

Rifle

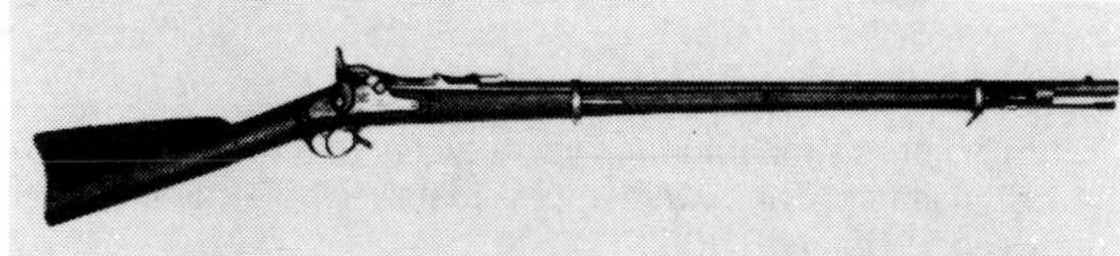

Courtesy Milwaukee Public Museum, Milwaukee, Wisconsin.

Exc.	V.G.	Good	Fair	Poor
1250	1000	750	600	500

Carbine

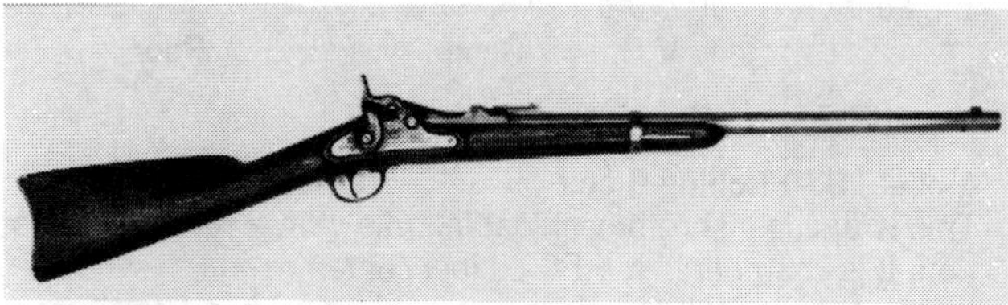

Exc.	V.G.	Good	Fair	Poor
3250	2750	2000	1500	1000

Model 1873

This is a "Trapdoor" breechloading rifle chambered for the .45-70 cartridge. The rifle version has a 32.5" barrel with a full-length stock held on by two barrel bands. The carbine features a 22" barrel with a half-stock held on by a single barrel band, and the cadet rifle features a 29.5" barrel with a full-length stock and two barrel bands. The finish of all three variations is blued and case-colored, with a walnut stock. The lock is marked "US Springfield 1873." The breechblock is either marked "Model 1873" or "US Model 1873." There were approximately 73,000 total manufactured between 1873 and 1877.

Rifle—50,000 Manufactured

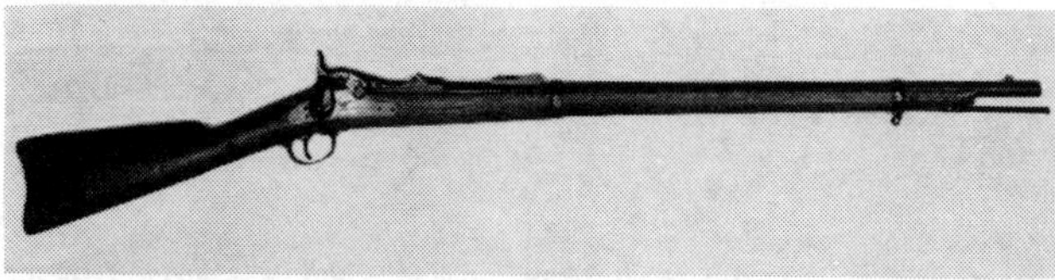

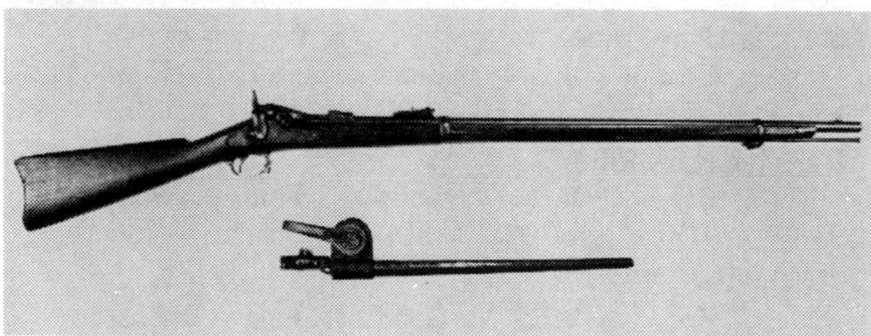

Courtesy Milwaukee Public Museum, Milwaukee, Wisconsin.

Exc.	V.G.	Good	Fair	Poor
1250	1000	600	300	200

Carbine—20,000 Manufactured

Exc.	V.G.	Good	Fair	Poor
2500	2000	1500	1000	750

Cadet Rifle—3,000 Manufactured

Exc.	V.G.	Good	Fair	Poor
1250	1000	750	600	500

Model 1875 Officer's Rifle

This is a high-grade "Trapdoor" breechloader chambered for the .45-70 cartridge. It has a 26" barrel and a half-stock fastened by one barrel band. It is blued and case-colored, with a scroll-engraved lock. It has a checkered walnut pistolgrip stock with a pewter forend tip. There is a cleaning rod mounted beneath the barrel. This rifle was not issued but was sold to army officers for personal sporting purposes. There were only 477 manufactured between 1875 and 1885.

Exc.	V.G.	Good	Fair	Poor
7500	6500	5000	3500	3000

Model 1877

This is a "Trapdoor" breechloading rifle chambered for the .45-70 cartridge. It was issued as a rifle with a 32" barrel and a full-length stock held on by two barrel bands, a cadet rifle with a 29.5" barrel, and a carbine with a 22" barrel, half-stock, and single barrel band. This version is similar to the Model 1873. In fact, the breechblock retained the Model 1873 marking. The basic differences are that the stock is thicker at the wrist and the breechblock was thickened and lowered. This is basically a mechanically improved version. There were approximately 12,000 manufactured in 1877 and 1878.

Rifle—3,900 Manufactured

Exc.	V.G.	Good	Fair	Poor
1400	1200	850	700	550

Cadet Rifle—1,000 Manufactured

Exc.	V.G.	Good	Fair	Poor
1500	1300	1000	850	650

Carbine—2,950 Manufactured

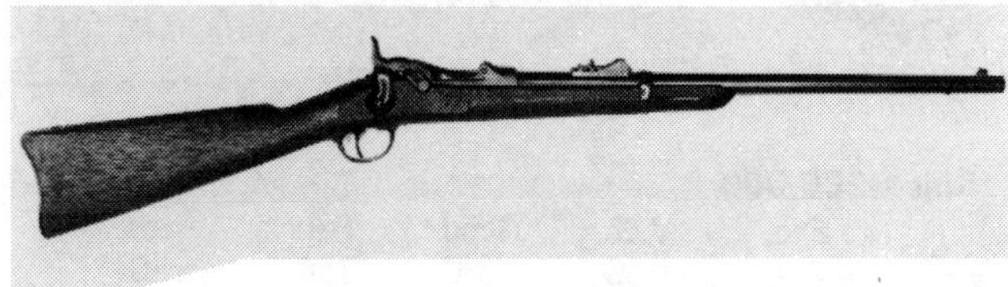

Courtesy Milwaukee Public Museum, Milwaukee, Wisconsin.

Exc.	V.G.	Good	Fair	Poor
3000	2500	1800	1250	850

Model 1880

This version features a sliding combination cleaning rod/bayonet that is fitted in the forearm under the barrel. It retained the 1873 breechblock markings. There were approximately 1,000 manufactured for trial purposes in 1880.

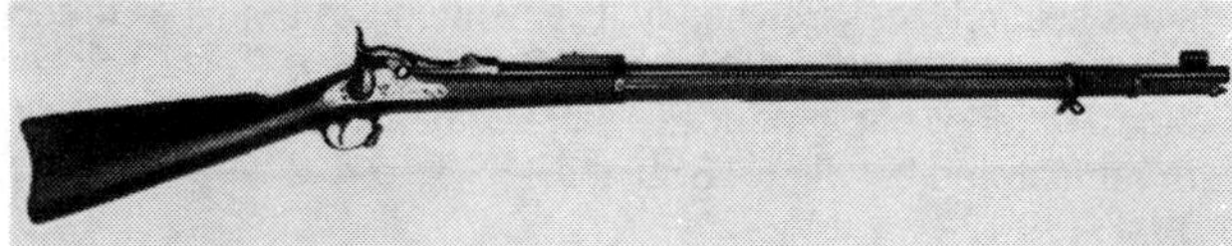

Courtesy Milwaukee Public Museum, Milwaukee, Wisconsin.

Exc.	V.G.	Good	Fair	Poor
1500	1300	1000	850	650

Model 1881 Marksman Rifle

This is an extremely high-grade Trapdoor breechloading rifle chambered for the .45-70 cartridge. It has a 28" round barrel and is similar to the Model 1875 Officer's Rifle in appearance. It features a full-length, highgrade, checkered walnut stock held on by one barrel band. It has a horn Schnabel forend tip. The metal parts are engraved, blued, and case-colored. It has a Vernier aperture sight as well as a buckhorn rear sight on the barrel and a globe front sight with a spirit level. There were only 11 manufactured to be awarded as prizes at shooting matches. This is perhaps the supreme rarity among the Trapdoor Springfields, and one should be extremely cognizant of fakes.

Exc.	V.G.	Good	Fair	Poor
35000	27500	22500	15000	10000

Model 1881 Shotgun

This version has a 26" round smooth-bore barrel that is chambered for 20 gauge. It was used by hunters and scouts at Western forts. There were approximately 1,376 manufactured between 1881 and 1885. This version is particularly susceptible to fakery. We advise a qualified appraisal.

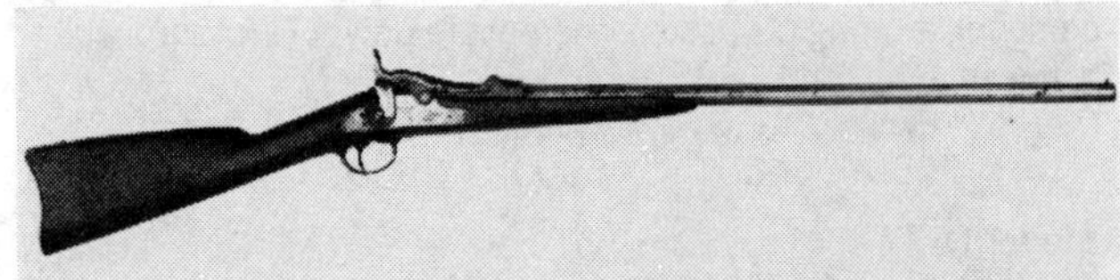

Courtesy Milwaukee Public Museum, Milwaukee, Wisconsin.

Exc.	V.G.	Good	Fair	Poor
1750	1500	1200	850	700

Model 1884

This is also a breechloading Trapdoor single shot rifle chambered for the .45-70 cartridge. It was issued as a standard rifle with a 32.75" barrel, a cadet rifle with a 29.5" barrel, and a military carbine with a 22" barrel. The finish is blued and case-colored. This model features the improved Buffington rear sight. It features the socket bayonet and a walnut stock. There were approximately 232,000 manufactured between 1885 and 1890.

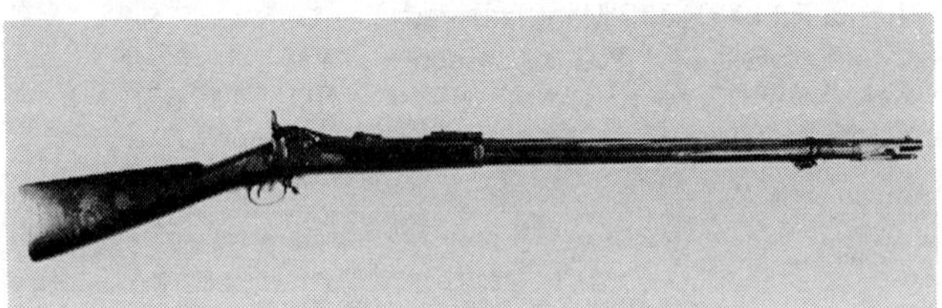

Rifle—200,000

Exc.	V.G.	Good	Fair	Poor
750	650	500	350	250

Cadet Rifle—12,000

Exc.	V.G.	Good	Fair	Poor
850	750	600	400	300

Carbine—20,000

Exc.	V.G.	Good	Fair	Poor
1000	850	700	500	400

Model 1888

This version is similar to its predecessors except that it features a sliding, ramrod-type bayonet that was improved so that it stays securely locked when in its extended position. The breechblock was still marked "Model 1884." This was the last Springfield Trapdoor rifle produced. There were approximately 65,000 manufactured between 1889 and 1893.

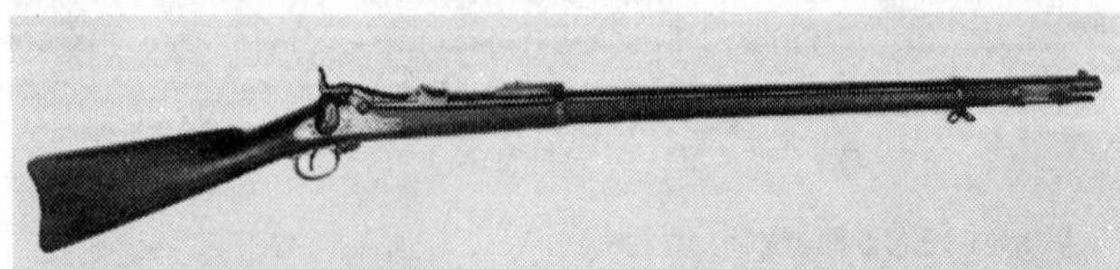

Courtesy Milwaukee Public Museum, Milwaukee, Wisconsin.

Exc.	V.G.	Good	Fair	Poor
750	650	500	350	250

Trapdoor Fencing Musket

This is a non-gun that was used by the Army in teaching bayonet drills. They had no desire to damage serviceable rifles during practice, so they produced this version to fill the bill. There were basically four types produced.

Type I

This version is similar to the Model 1873 rifle without a breech or lock. The finish is rough, and it is unmarked. It was designed to accept a socket bayonet. One should secure a qualified appraisal if a transaction is contemplated. There were 170 manufactured in 1876 and 1877.

Exc.	V.G.	Good	Fair	Poor
800	650	500	400	300

Type II

This version is basically a Model 1884 with the hammer removed and the front sight blade ground off. It accepted a socket bayonet that was covered with leather and had a pad on its point.

Exc.	V.G.	Good	Fair	Poor
500	400	300	250	200

Type III

This version is similar to the Type II except that it is shortened to 43.5" in length. There were approximately 1,500 manufactured between 1905 and 1906.

Exc.	V.G.	Good	Fair	Poor
750	650	450	350	300

Type IV

This version is similar to the Type III except that the barrel was filled with lead. There were approximately 11,000 manufactured between 1907 and 1916.

Exc.	V.G.	Good	Fair	Poor
500	400	300	250	200

Model 1870 Rolling Block

This is a single shot breechloading rifle with a rolling-block action. It is chambered for .50-caliber centerfire and has a 32.75" barrel. It has a full-length forend held on by two barrel bands. The finish is blued and case-colored, with a cleaning rod mounted under the barrel. The stock and forend are walnut. The frame is marked "USN Springfield 1870." There is an anchor motif marked on the top of the barrel. It also features Government inspector's marks on the frame. This rifle was manufactured by Springfield Armory under license from Remington Arms Company for the United States Navy. The first 10,000 produced were rejected by our Navy and were sent to France and used in the Franco-Prussian War. For that reason, this variation is quite scarce and would bring a 20 percent premium. There was also a group of approximately 100 rifles that were converted to the .22 rimfire cartridge and used for target practice aboard ships. This version is extremely rare. There were approximately 22,000 manufactured in 1870 and 1871.

Courtesy Milwaukee Public Museum, Milwaukee, Wisconsin.

Standard Navy Rifle

Exc.	V.G.	Good	Fair	Poor
800	700	600	400	300

Rejected Navy Rifle

Exc.	V.G.	Good	Fair	Poor
700	600	500	350	250

.22 Caliber

Exc.	V.G.	Good	Fair	Poor
2000	1750	1250	900	750

U.S. Krag Jorgensen Rifle

This firearm will be found listed in its own section of this text.

Model 1903

This rifle was a successor to the Krag Jorgensen and was also produced by the Rock Island Arsenal. It was initially chambered for the .30-03 cartridge and very shortly changed to the .30-06 cartridge. Its original chambering consisted of a 220-grain, round-nosed bullet. The German army introduced its spitzer bullet so our Government quickly followed suit with a 150-grain, pointed bullet designated the .30-06. This model has a 24" barrel and was built on what was basically a modified Mauser action. It features a 5-round integral box magazine. The finish is blued, with a full-length, straight-grip walnut stock with full handguards held on by two barrel bands. The initial version was issued with a rod-type bayonet that was quickly discontinued when President Theodore Roosevelt personally disapproved it. There were approximately 74,000 produced with this rod-bayonet; and if in an unaltered condition, these would be worth a great deal more than the standard variation. It is important to note that the early models with serial numbers under 800000 were not heat treated sufficiently to be safe to fire with modern ammunition. There were a great many produced between 1903 and 1930. The values represented reflect original specimens; WWII alterations would be worth approximately 15 percent less.

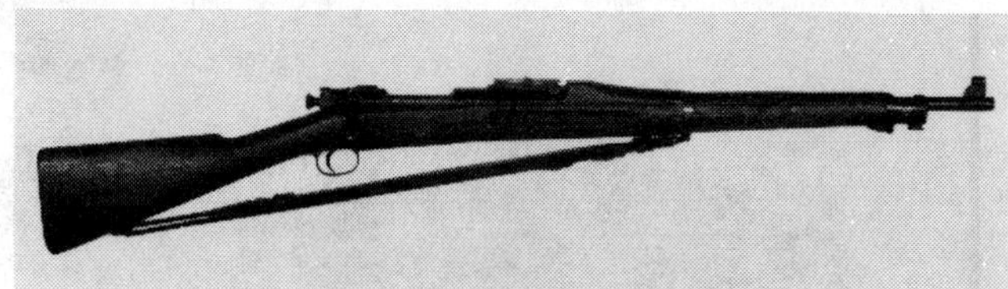

Courtesy Milwaukee Public Museum, Milwaukee, Wisconsin.

Rod Bayonet Version (Unaltered)

Exc.	V.G.	Good	Fair	Poor
4500	3750	3250	2500	2000

Standard Model 1903

Exc.	V.G.	Good	Fair	Poor
500	450	350	275	150

Model 1903 Mark I

This version is similar to the original except that it was cut to accept the Pedersen device. This device allows the use of a semi-auto bolt insert that utilizes pistol cartridges. The rifle has a slot milled into the receiver that acts as an ejection port. The device was not successful and was scrapped. There were approximately 102,000 rifles that were produced with this mill-cut between 1918 and 1920. The values given are for the rifle alone-not for the device.

Exc.	V.G.	Good	Fair	Poor
450	400	350	275	150

Model 1903 A1

This version is a standard Model 1903 rifle that was fitted with a Type C, semi-pistolgrip stock. All other specifications were the same.

Exc.	V.G.	Good	Fair	Poor
400	350	300	250	200

Model 1903 A3

This version was introduced in May of 1942 for use in WWII. It basically consisted of improvements to simplify mass production. It features an aperture sight and various small parts that were fabricated from stampings; this includes the triggerguard, floorplate, and barrel band. The finish is parkerized. This model was manufactured by Remington and Smith Corona.

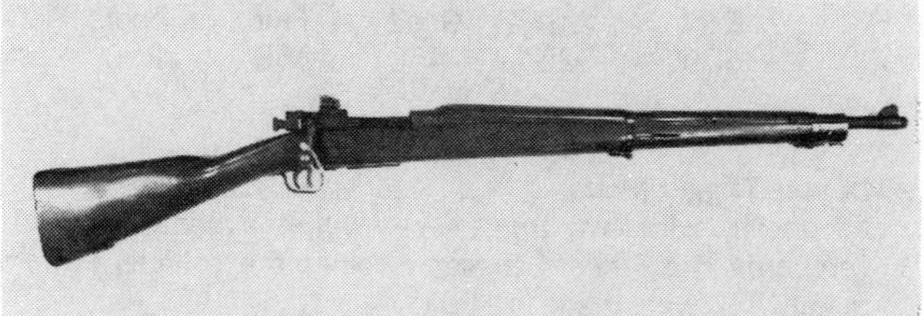

Exc.	V.G.	Good	Fair	Poor
400	350	300	200	100

Model 1903 A4

This is a sniper-rifle version of the Model 1903. It is fitted with permanently mounted scope locks and furnished with a telescopic sight known as the M73B1. This scope was manufactured by Weaver in El Paso, Texas, and was commercially known as the Model 330C. The rifle has no conventional iron sights mounted.

Exc.	V.G.	Good	Fair	Poor
1150	1000	800	550	350

Model 1903 NRA National Match

This version was based on a standard 1903 service rifle that was selected for having excellent shooting qualities. The parts were then hand-fit, and a special rifled barrel was added which was checked for tolerance with a star gauge. The muzzle of this barrel was marked with a special star with six or eight rays radiating from it. These NRA rifles were drilled and tapped to accept a Lyman No. 48 rear sight. They are marked with the letters "NRA" and have a flaming bomb proofmark on the triggerguard. There were approximately 18,000 manufactured between 1921 and 1928.

Exc.	V.G.	Good	Fair	Poor
1200	1100	900	700	400

Model 1903 NRA Sporter

This version is similar to the National Match rifle but features a half-length, Sporter-type stock with one barrel band. It also features the Lyman No. 48 receiver sight. This version was produced for commercial sales. There were approximately 6,500 manufactured between 1924 and 1933.

Exc.	V.G.	Good	Fair	Poor
1300	1150	900	700	400

Model 1917

In 1917 when the United States entered WWI, there was a distinct rifle shortage. There were production facilities set up for the British-pattern 1914 rifle. This "Enfield" rifle was re-designed to accept the .30-06 cartridge and was pressed into service as the U.S. rifle Model 1917. This rifle appears similar to the British-pattern 1914 rifle. In fact, they are so similar that in WWII, when over a million were sold to Britain for use by their Home Guard, it was necessary to paint a 2" stripe around the butt so that the caliber was immediately known. The barrel length is 26", and it has a 5-round integral box magazine. The finish is matte-blued, with a walnut stock. The breech is marked "U.S. Model 1917." This was a very robust and heavy-duty rifle, and many are used in the manufacture of large-bore custom rifles to this day. There were approximately 2,200,000 manufactured by Remington and Winchester between 1917 and 1918. The majority were produced at Eddystone, Pennsylvania.

Exc.	V.G.	Good	Fair	Poor
300	250	200	150	100

Model 1922

This is a bolt-action training rifle chambered for the .22 rimfire cartridge. It appears similar to the Model 1903 but has a 24.5" barrel and a half-length stock without hand guards, held on by a single barrel band. It has a 5-round detachable box magazine. The finish is blued, with a walnut stock. The receiver is marked "U.S. Springfield Armory Model of 1922 Cal. 22." It also has the flaming bomb ordnance mark. There were three basic types of the Model 1922: the standard issue type, the NRA commercial type, and the models that were altered to M1 or M2. There were a total of approximately 2,000 manufactured between 1922 and 1924. The survival rate of the original-issue types is not very large as most were converted.

Issue Type

Exc.	V.G.	Good	Fair	Poor
800	650	450	250	200

Altered Type

Exc.	V.G.	Good	Fair	Poor
450	350	250	200	150

NRA Type—Drilled and Tapped for Scope

Exc.	V.G.	Good	Fair	Poor
700	550	400	200	150

Model 1922 M1

This version is quite similar to the Model 1922, with a single firing pin that hits the top of the cartridge and a detachable box magazine that does not protrude from the bottom of the stock. The finish is parkerized; and the stock, of walnut. There were approximately 20,000 manufactured between 1924 and 1933.

Unaltered Type

Exc.	V.G.	Good	Fair	Poor
750	650	550	300	200

Altered to M2

Exc.	V.G.	Good	Fair	Poor
450	350	250	200	150

Unaltered NRA Type

Exc.	V.G.	Good	Fair	Poor
650	550	450	300	250

NRA Type Altered to M2

Exc.	V.G.	Good	Fair	Poor
550	500	400	300	250

Model M2

This is an improved version of the Model 1922 M1 that features an altered firing mechanism with a faster lock time. It has a knurled cocking knob added to the bolt and a flush-fitting detachable magazine with improved feeding. There were approximately 12,000 manufactured.

Exc.	V.G.	Good	Fair	Poor
600	500	400	300	200

U.S. Rifle M1 (Garand)

Springfield Armory was one of the manufacturers of this WWII service rifle. It is listed in the Garand section of this text.

SPRINGFIELD ARMS COMPANY

Springfield, Massachusetts

Dragoon

A .40 caliber percussion revolver with either a 6" or 7.5" round barrel, some fitted with loading levers, others without. The top strap marked "Springfield Arms Company." Blued with walnut grips. Approximately 110 revolvers were manufactured in 1851.

Exc.	V.G.	Good	Fair	Poor
4500	4000	3000	2000	1500

Navy Model

A .36 caliber percussion revolver with a 6" round barrel, centrally mounted hammer, and 6-shot etched cylinder. The top strap marked "Springfield Arms Company." Blued, case-hardened with walnut grips. This model was manufactured in two variations, one with a single trigger and the other with a double trigger, the forward one of which locks the cylinder. Both variations had loading levers. Approximately 250 of these pistols were made in 1851.

Exc.	V.G.	Good	Fair	Poor
1500	1250	1000	800	600

Belt Model

A .31 caliber percussion revolver with 4", 5" or 6" round barrels, centrally mounted hammer, and an etched 6-shot cylinder. Made with or without a loading lever. Early production versions of this revolver are marked "Jaquith's Patent 1838" on the frame and later production were marked "Springfield Arms" on the top strap. Approximately 150 were made.

Exc.	V.G.	Good	Fair	Poor
850	750	650	450	375

Warner Model

As above, but is marked "Warner's Patent/Jan. 1851." Approximately 150 of these were made.

Exc.	V.G.	Good	Fair	Poor
1250	1000	800	600	450

Double Trigger Model

As above, with 2 triggers, one of which locks the cylinder. Approximately 100 were made in 1851.

Exc.	V.G.	Good	Fair	Poor
850	750	650	450	375

Pocket Model Revolver

A .28 caliber percussion revolver with 2.5" round barrel, centrally mounted hammer, no loading lever and etched 6-shot cylinder. Marked "Warner's Patent Jan. 1851" and "Springfield Arms Company." Blued, case-hardened with walnut grips. Early production examples of this revolver do not have a groove on the cylinder and have a rounded frame. Approximately 525 were made in 1851.

Courtesy Milwaukee Public Museum, Milwaukee, Wisconsin.

Exc.	V.G.	Good	Fair	Poor
550	475	400	300	200

Ring Trigger Model

As above, but fitted with a ring trigger which revolved the cylinder. Approximately 150 were made in 1851.

Courtesy Milwaukee Public Museum, Milwaukee, Wisconsin.

Exc.	V.G.	Good	Fair	Poor
600	525	450	350	250

Double Trigger Model

As above, with two triggers set within a conventional triggerguard. The forward trigger revolves the cylinder. Approximately 350 were made in 1851.

Courtesy Milwaukee Public Museum, Milwaukee, Wisconsin.

Exc.	V.G.	Good	Fair	Poor
550	475	400	300	200

Late Model Revolver

As above, except that the cylinder is automatically turned when the hammer is cocked. The top strap marked "Warner's Patent/James Warner, Springfield, Mass." Approximately 500 were made in 1851.

Exc.	V.G.	Good	Fair	Poor
500	425	350	250	175

SQUIBBMAN

SEE—Squires, Bingham Mfg. Co., Inc.
Rizal, Philippine Islands

SQUIRES BINGHAM MFG. CO., INC.

Rizal, Philippine Islands

Firearms produced by this company are marketed under the trademark Squibman.

Model 100D

A .38 Special caliber double-action swingout cylinder revolver with a 3", 4" or 6" ventilated-rib barrel, adjustable sights, matte black finish and walnut grips.

Exc.	V.G.	Good	Fair	Poor
125	100	80	60	40

Model 100DC

As above, without the ventilated-rib.

Exc.	V.G.	Good	Fair	Poor
125	100	80	60	40

Model 100

As above, with a tapered barrel and uncheckered walnut grips.

Exc.	V.G.	Good	Fair	Poor
125	100	80	60	40

Thunder Chief

As above, but in .22 or .22 Magnum caliber with a heavier ventilated-rib barrel, shrouded ejector and ebony grips.

Exc.	V.G.	Good	Fair	Poor
150	125	100	80	60

STAFFORD, T. J.

New Haven, Connecticut

Pocket Pistol

A .22 caliber single shot spur trigger pistol with a 3.5" octagonal barrel marked "T.J. Stafford New Haven Ct.," silver-plated brass frame and walnut or rosewood grips.

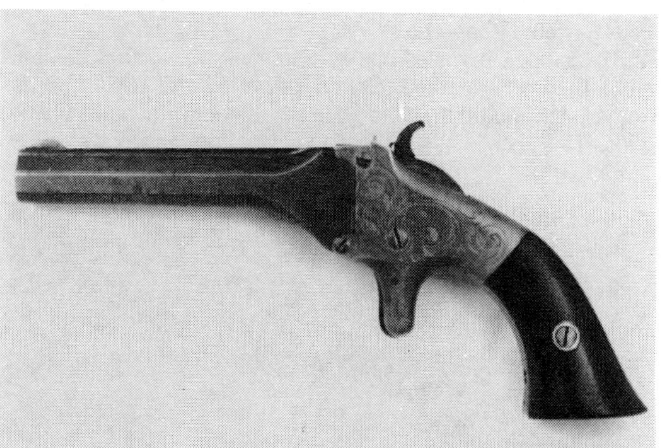

Courtesy W.P. Hallstein III and son Chip.

Exc.	V.G.	Good	Fair	Poor
700	500	200	150	100

Large Frame Model

As above, but in .38 rimfire caliber with a 6" barrel.

Exc.	V.G.	Good	Fair	Poor
850	600	300	250	200

STANDARD ARMS CO.

Wilmington, Delaware

Model G

Chambered for .25-35, .30-30, .25 Remington, .30 Remington, and .35 Remington, with a 22" barrel, and open sights. Integral box magazine and closeable gas port which allowed the rifle to be used as a slide action. Blued with a walnut stock. Produced in very limited quantities, circa 1910.

Exc.	V.G.	Good	Fair	Poor
450	400	350	250	150

STAR, BONIFACIO ECHEVERRIA

Eibar, Spain
SEE—Echeverria

STARR, EBAN T.

New York, New York

Single Shot Deringer

A .41 caliber single shot pistol with a pivoted 2.75" round barrel. The hammer mounted on the right side of the frame and the trigger formed in the shape of a button located at the front of the frame. The frame marked "Starr's Pat's May 10, 1864." The brass frame silver-plated, the barrel blued or silver-plated with checkered walnut grips. Manufactured from 1864 to 1869.

Courtesy Milwaukee Public Museum, Milwaukee, Wisconsin.

Exc.	V.G.	Good	Fair	Poor
500	400	300	200	100

Four Barreled Pepperbox
A .32 caliber 4 barrelled pocket pistol with 2.75" to 3.25" barrels. The frame marked "Starr's Pat's May 10, 1864." Brass frames, silver-plated. The barrel is blued with plain walnut grips. This pistol was produced in 6 variations as follows:

Courtesy Milwaukee Public Museum, Milwaukee, Wisconsin.

First Model
Fluted breech and a barrel release mounted on the right side of the frame.

Exc.	V.G.	Good	Fair	Poor
750	650	550	400	300

Second Model
Flat breech.

Exc.	V.G.	Good	Fair	Poor
650	550	450	300	200

Third Model
Rounded breech with a visible firing-pin retaining spring.

Exc.	V.G.	Good	Fair	Poor
450	350	250	200	150

Fourth Model
Rounded breech without visible springs.

Exc.	V.G.	Good	Fair	Poor
450	350	250	200	150

Fifth Model
A larger, more angular grip.

Exc.	V.G.	Good	Fair	Poor
400	300	200	150	100

Sixth Model
The frame length of this variation is of increased size.

Exc.	V.G.	Good	Fair	Poor
700	600	500	350	300

STARR ARMS COMPANY
New York, New York

1858 Navy Revolver
A .36 caliber double-action percussion revolver with a 6" barrel and 6-shot cylinder. Blued, case-hardened with walnut grips. The frame marked "Starr Arms Co. New York." Approximately 3,000 were made between 1858 and 1860.

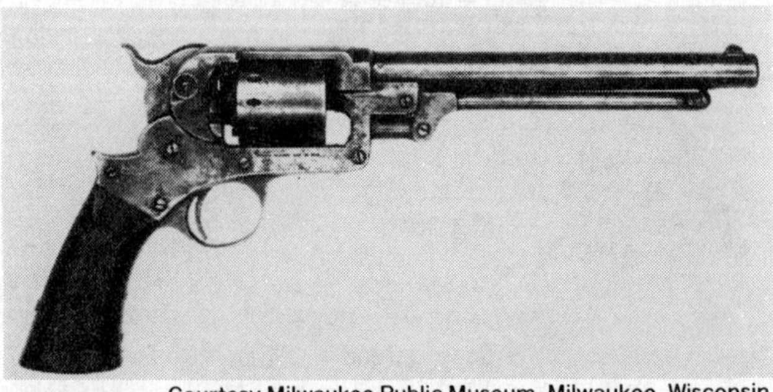
Courtesy Milwaukee Public Museum, Milwaukee, Wisconsin.

Standard Model

Exc.	V.G.	Good	Fair	Poor
750	675	550	400	300

Martially Marked (JT)

Exc.	V.G.	Good	Fair	Poor
1000	850	750	550	400

1858 Army Revolver
A .44 caliber double-action percussion revolver with a 6" barrel and 6-shot cylinder. Blued, case-hardened with walnut grips. The frame marked "Starr Arms Co. New York." Approximately 23,000 were manufactured.

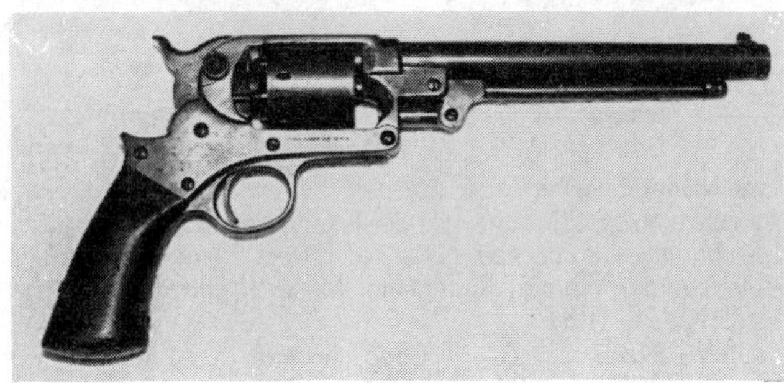

Exc.	V.G.	Good	Fair	Poor
650	575	500	350	250

1863 Army Revolver
Similar to the above, but double-action and with an 8" barrel. Approximately 32,000 were manufactured between 1863 and 1865.

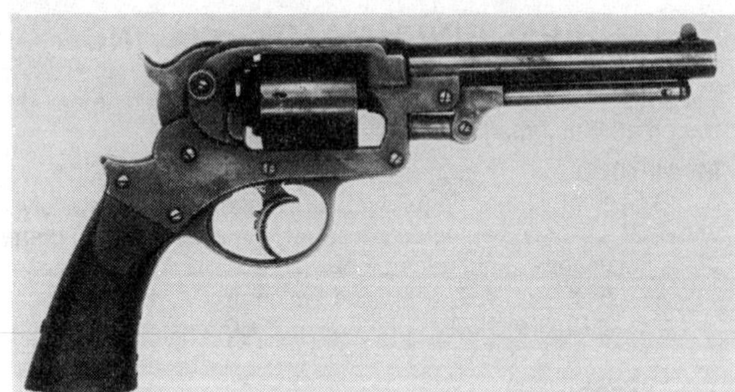
Courtesy Milwaukee Public Museum, Milwaukee, Wisconsin.

Exc.	V.G.	Good	Fair	Poor
650	575	500	350	250

Percussion Carbine
A .54 caliber breechloading percussion carbine with a 21" round barrel secured by one barrel band. Blued, case-hardened with a walnut stock. The lock marked "Starr Arms Co./Yonkers, N.Y."

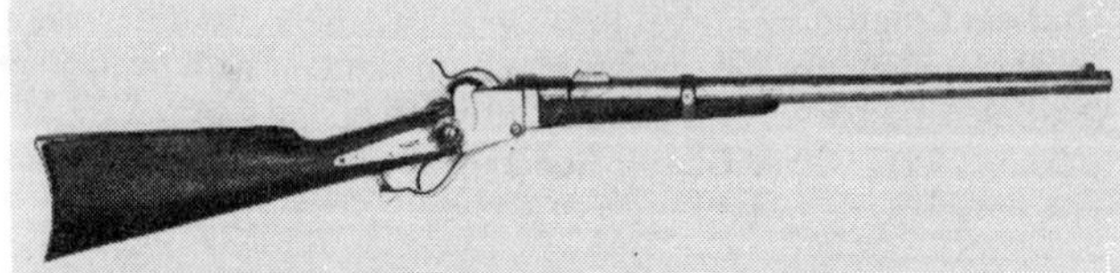
Courtesy Milwaukee Public Museum, Milwaukee, Wisconsin.

Exc.	V.G.	Good	Fair	Poor
900	800	700	500	400

Cartridge Carbine
Similar to the above, but in .52 rimfire caliber. Approximately 5,000 were manufactured.

Courtesy Milwaukee Public Museum, Milwaukee, Wisconsin.

Exc.	V.G.	Good	Fair	Poor
1000	900	800	600	500

STEEL CITY ARMS, INC.
Pittsburgh, Pennsylvania

Double Deuce
A .22 caliber stainless steel double-action semi-automatic pistol with a 2.5" barrel, 7-shot magazine and plain rosewood grips. Introduced in 1984.

Exc.	V.G.	Good	Fair	Poor
300	250	200	150	100

STENDA WAFFENFABRIK
Suhl, Germany

Pocket Pistol
A 7.65mm semi-automatic pistol very similar to the "Beholla," the "Leonhardt," and the "Menta." Stenda took over the production of the Beholla pistol design at the close of WWI. The only major difference in the Stenda design was the elimination of the Beholla's worst feature, the pin that went through the slide and retained the barrel. It was replaced by a sliding catch that anchored it in place and unlocked the slide so that the barrel could be removed without the need of a vise and drift pin. The Stenda pistol can be identified by the fact that there are no holes through the slide and there is a catch on the frame above the trigger. The finish blued, with plastic grips; and the slide is marked "Waffenfabrik Stendawerke Suhl." Approximately 25,000 manufactured before production ceased in 1926.

Exc.	V.G.	Good	Fair	Poor
250	225	200	150	100

STERLING ARMAMENT LTD.
London, England
Importer—Cassi, Inc.
Colorado Springs, Colorado

Parapistol MK 7 C4
A 9mm semi-automatic pistol with a 4" barrel, and detachable magazines of 10 — 68 round capacity. Black wrinkled paint finish with plastic grips.

Parapistol MK 7 C8
As above, with a 7.8" barrel.

Sterling MK 6
A semi-automatic copy of the Sterling Submachine gun with a 16.1" barrel, folding metal stock and side mounted magazine. Finished as above.

Sterling AR 180
A copy of the Armalite Model AR18, 5.56mm rifle. Finished with either black wrinkled paint or, more rarely, blued.

STEVENS, J. ARMS CO.
Chicopee Falls, Massachusetts

In 1864 this firm began doing business as J. Stevens & Company. In 1888 it was incorporated as the J. Stevens Arms & Tool Company. It operated as such until 1920, when it was taken over by the Savage Arms Company. It has operated as an independent division in this organization since. This Company produced a great many firearms—most that were of an affordable nature. They are widely collected, and one interested in them should take advantage of the literature available on the subject.

Vest Pocket Pistol
This is a single shot pocket pistol chambered for the .22 and the .30 rimfire cartridges. The .22 caliber version is rarely encountered and would be worth approximately 10 percent more than the values illustrated. It has a 2.75" part-octagonal barrel that pivots upward for loading. It has an external hammer and a spur-type trigger. The frame is nickle-plated or blued, with a blued barrel. The odd shaped flared grips are made of rosewood. The first models were marked "Vest Pocket Pistol" only. Later models have the barrels marked "J. Stevens & Co. Chicopee Falls, Mass." There were approximately 1,000 manufactured between 1864 and 1876.

Exc.	V.G.	Good	Fair	Poor
800	700	600	500	375

Pocket Pistol
This is a more conventional-appearing, single shot pocket pistol chambered for either the .22 or the .30 rimfire cartridges. It has a 3.5" part-octagonal barrel that pivots upward for loading. It features a plated brass frame with either a blued or nickle-plated barrel and rosewood, two-piece grips. The barrel is marked "J. Stevens & Co. Chicopee Falls, Mass." There were approximately 15,000 manufactured between 1864 and 1886.

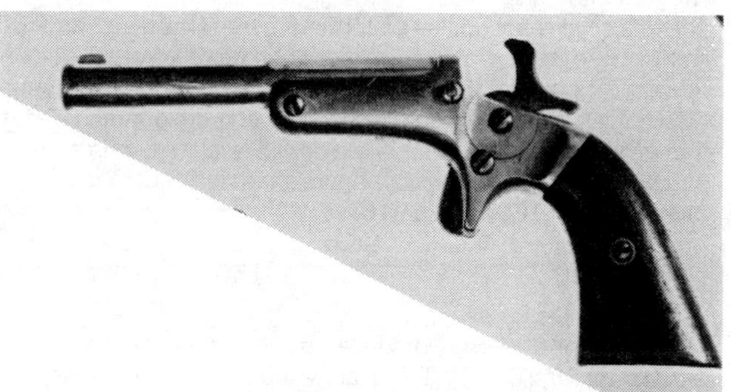

Courtesy Milwaukee Public Museum, Milwaukee, Wisconsin.

Exc.	V.G.	Good	Fair	Poor
350	275	200	100	75

Gem Pocket Pistol
This is a single shot, derringer-type pocket pistol chambered for either the .22 or .30 rimfire cartridges. It has a 3" part-octagonal barrel that pivots to the side for loading. It has a nickle-plated brass frame with either a blued or plated barrel. It has birdshead grips made of walnut or rosewood. The barrel is marked "Gem," and the Stevens name or address does not appear on this firearm. There were approximately 4,000 manufactured between 1872 and 1890.

Exc.	V.G.	Good	Fair	Poor
400	350	300	200	150

.41 Caliber Derringer
This is a single shot pocket pistol chambered for the .41 rimfire cartridge. It has a 4" part-octagonal barrel that pivots upward for loading. It has a spur trigger and an external hammer. The frame is plated brass with a blued barrel. It has walnut birdshead grips. This firearm is completely unmarked except for a serial number. There were approximately 100 manufactured in 1875.

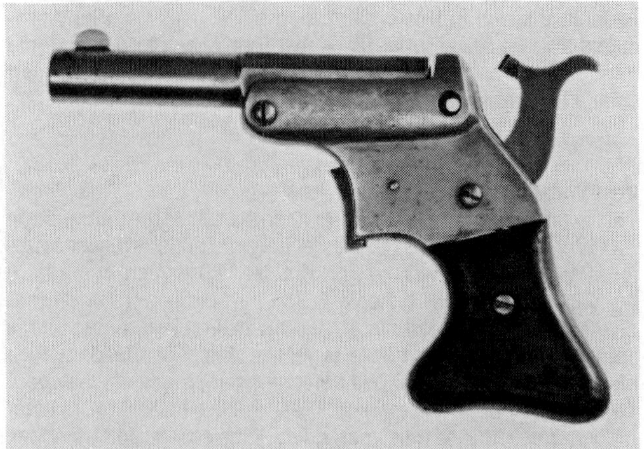

Courtesy Milwaukee Public Museum, Milwaukee, Wisconsin.

Exc.	V.G.	Good	Fair	Poor
850	700	600	500	400

Single Shot Pistol

This is a single shot pistol chambered for the .22 or .30 rimfire cartridges. It has a 3.5" part-octagonal barrel that pivots upward for loading. It is quite similar in appearance to the original pocket pistol. It has a plated brass frame and either a blued or nickle-plated barrel with walnut, square-butt grips. The barrel is marked "J. Stevens A&T Co." There were approximately 10,000 manufactured between 1886 and 1896.

Exc.	V.G.	Good	Fair	Poor
400	250	200	150	100

No. 41 Pistol

This is a single shot pocket pistol chambered for the .22 and .30 short cartridges. It has a 3.5" part-octagonal barrel that pivots upward for loading. It features an external hammer and a spur-type trigger. It has an iron frame with the firing pin mounted in the recoil shield. It is either blued or nickle-plated, with square-butt walnut grips. There were approximately 90,000 manufactured between 1896 and 1916.

Exc.	V.G.	Good	Fair	Poor
300	250	200	150	100

Stevens Tip Up Rifles

This series of rifles was produced by Stevens beginning in the 1870's through 1895. There are a number of variations, but they are all quite similar in appearance. They feature a distinctive sloped frame made of iron and nickle-plated. Most frames are similar in size, but there is a slightly lighter frame used on the "Ladies Model" rifles. These Tip Up rifles are chambered for various calibers from the .22 rimfire to the .44 centerfire cartridges. They are offered with barrel lengths of 24", 26", 28", or 30". The actions are nickle-plated, as well as the triggerguards and the buttplates. The barrels are blued, and the two-piece stocks are of walnut. They are offered with various buttplates and sights. A shotgun version is also offered. There are a number of variations that differ only slightly, and the model numbers are not marked on the rifles. We suggest securing a qualified appraisal if in doubt. The major variations and their values are as follows:

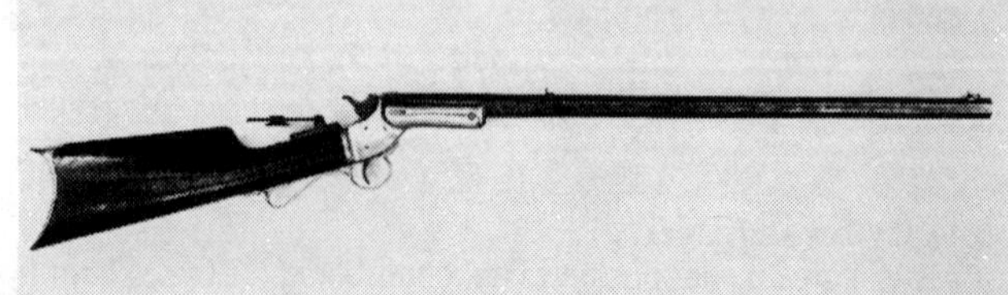

Courtesy Milwaukee Public Museum, Milwaukee, Wisconsin.

Ladies Model—.22 or .25 Rimfire Only, 24" or 26" Barrel

Exc.	V.G.	Good	Fair	Poor
800	750	650	550	450

Tip Up Rifle—Without Forend

Exc.	V.G.	Good	Fair	Poor
500	400	300	200	150

Tip Up Rifle—With Forend, Swiss-Type Buttplate

Exc.	V.G.	Good	Fair	Poor
550	450	350	250	175

Tip Up Shotgun—All Gauges, 30" or 32" Barrel

Exc.	V.G.	Good	Fair	Poor
350	300	200	150	100

Ideal Single Shot Rifle

This excellent rifle was manufactured by Stevens between 1896 and 1933. It is a single-shot, falling-block type action that is activated by a triggerguard-action lever. It was produced in many popular calibers from .22 rimfire up to .30-40. It was also manufactured in a number of special Stevens calibers. It was offered with various length barrels in many different grades, from plain Spartan starter rifles up to some extremely high-grade Schuetzen-type target rifles with all available options. In 1901 Harry Pope of Hartford, Connecticut, went to work for Stevens and brought his highly respected barrel to the Stevens Company. He remained an employee for only two years, and the firearms produced during this period have the name "Stevens-Pope" stamped on the top of the barrel in addition to the other factory markings. Rifles marked in this manner and authenticated would be worth an approximate 50 percent premium if they are in very good to excellent condition. Due to numerous variations and options offered, we strongly recommend securing a qualified appraisal, especially on the higher-grade Ideal series rifles, if a transaction is contemplated.

No. 44

This version is chambered for various calibers and is offered with a 24" or 26" barrel. It has an open rear sight with a Rocky Mountain-type front sight. The finish is blued and case-colored, with a walnut stock. There were approximately 100,000 manufactured between 1896 and 1933.

Exc.	V.G.	Good	Fair	Poor
450	400	350	250	150

No. 44-1/2

This rifle is similar in appearance to the No. 44 but features an improved action. It has barrel lengths up to 34" and will be found with the Stevens-Pope barrel. It was manufactured between 1903 and 1916.

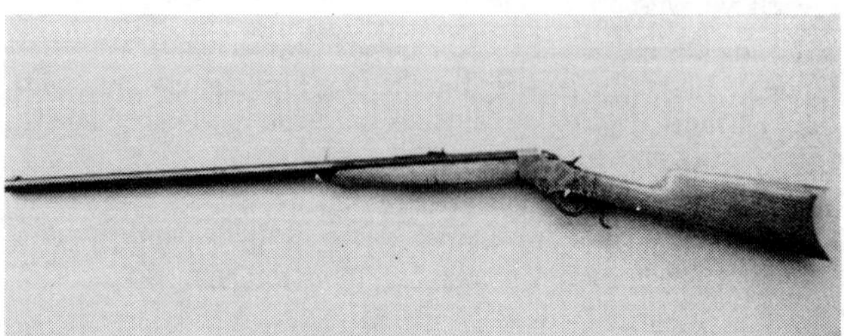

Courtesy J.B. Barnes.

Exc.	V.G.	Good	Fair	Poor
500	450	400	300	200

No. 044-1/2

This version is also known as the English Model rifle and is similar to the No. 44-1/2 except that it has a shotgun butt and a tapered barrel. There were a number of options offered which would affect the value. It was manufactured between 1903 and 1916.

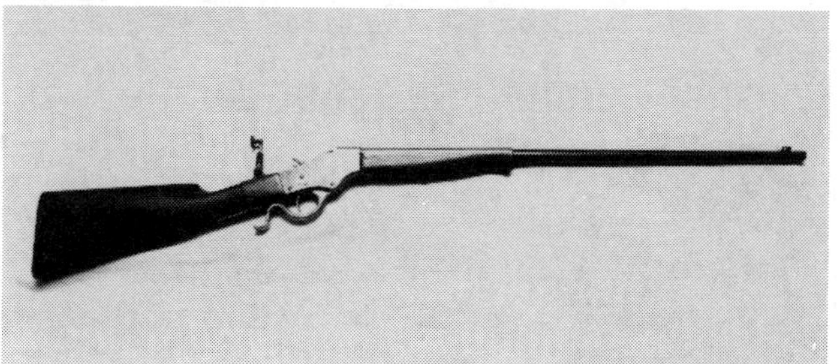

Courtesy Mike Stuckslager.

Exc.	V.G.	Good	Fair	Poor
750	600	450	250	150

No. 45

This version is also known as the Range Rifle. It is chambered for various calibers from the .22 rimfire to .44-40. Its identifying features are the Beach sights with an additional Vernier tang sight and a Swiss-type buttstock. It is offered with a 26" or 28" part-octagonal barrel. It was manufactured between 1896 and 1916. Values for a standard version are as follows:

Exc.	V.G.	Good	Fair	Poor
700	600	550	450	350

No. 47

This version is similar to the No. 45, with a pistolgrip buttstock.

Exc.	V.G.	Good	Fair	Poor
900	725	600	400	200

No. 49

This model is also known as the "Walnut Hill Rifle." It is a high-grade target rifle chambered for many calibers between the .22 rimfire and the .44-40. It is offered with a 28" or 30" part-octagonal barrel that is medium- or heavy-weight. It was furnished with a globe front sight and a Vernier tang sight. It is blued with a casecolored frame and has a high-grade, checkered, varnished walnut stock that has a high comb and features a pistol grip, cheekpiece, Swiss-type buttplate, and a loop-type triggerguard lever that resembles that of a lever-action rifle. The receiver is engraved, and there were a number of options available that would increase the value when present. We recommend an appraisal when in doubt. This rifle was manufactured between 1896 and 1932.

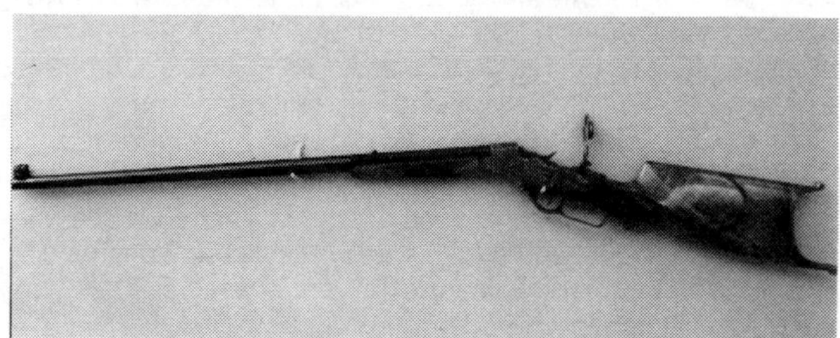

Courtesy J.B. Barnes.

Exc.	V.G.	Good	Fair	Poor
1650	1300	1000	800	550

Model 50

This version is identical to the Model 49 but was offered with a higher-grade walnut stock.

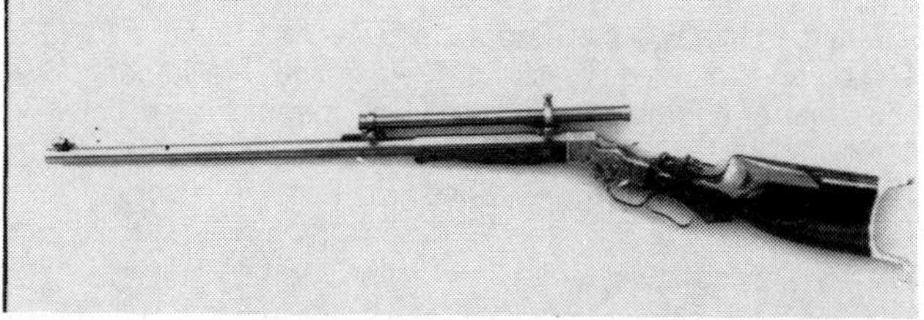

Courtesy J.B. Barnes.

Exc.	V.G.	Good	Fair	Poor
1900	1500	1250	800	400

Model 51

This version is known as the "Schuetzen Rifle" and is quite similar to the No. 49 except that it features double-set triggers, a higher-grade walnut stock, a wooden insert in the triggerguard action lever, and a heavy, Schuetzen-type buttplate. There were many options available on this model, and we recommend securing an appraisal when in doubt. It was manufactured between 1896 and 1916.

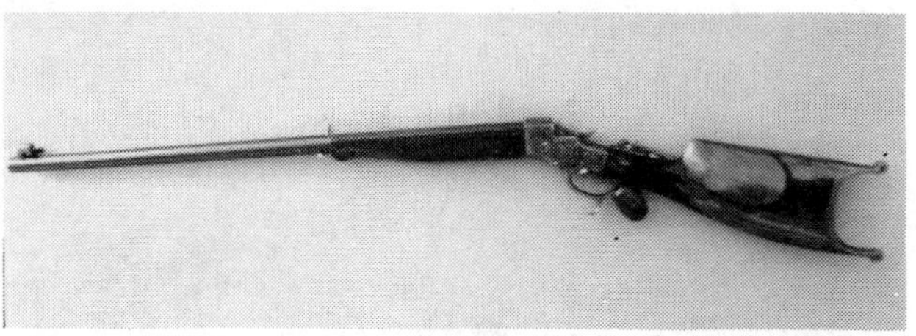

Courtesy J.B. Barnes.

Exc.	V.G.	Good	Fair	Poor
2300	1800	1400	800	500

No. 52

This version is also known as the "Schuetzen Junior." It is similar to the No. 51 except that it features more engraving and a higher-grade walnut stock. It was manufactured between 1897 and 1916.

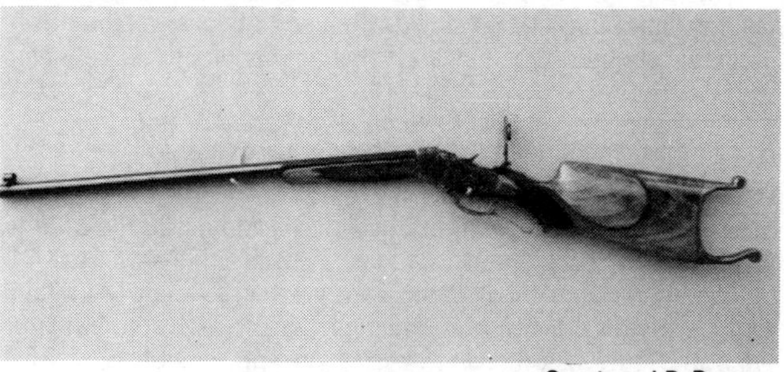

Courtesy J.B. Barnes.

Exc.	V.G.	Good	Fair	Poor
2400	2000	1600	1100	750

No. 54

This is similar to the No. 52 except that it has double-set triggers and a palmrest, as well as a very heavy, Swiss-style buttplate. It is offered with a 30" or 32" part-octagonal heavy barrel. This was Stevens' top-of-the-line rifle. It was offered with many options, and an appraisal should be secured if in doubt. It was manufactured between 1897 and 1916.

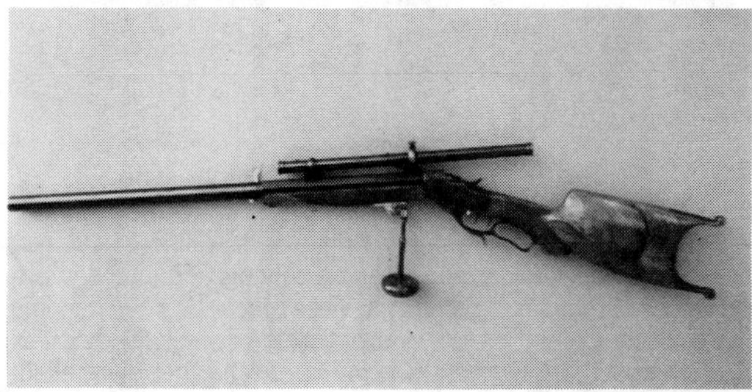

Courtesy J.B. Barnes.

Exc.	V.G.	Good	Fair	Poor
2800	2300	1800	1200	750

No. 55

This version is one of the Stevens' Ideal Ladies Models. It is chambered for the smaller rimfire calibers between .22 short and .32 long rimfire. It features a 24" or 26" part-octagonal barrel with a Vernier tang sight. The finish is blued and case-colored, with a checkered pistolgrip walnut stock that features a Swiss-type buttplate. This is a lighterweight rifle that was manufactured between 1897 and 1916.

Exc.	V.G.	Good	Fair	Poor
1250	1000	800	600	400

No. 56

This Ladies' Model rifle is similar to the No. 55 except that it is chambered for centerfire cartridges and has a higher-grade walnut stock. It was made on the improved No. 44-1/2 action. It was manufactured between 1906 and 1916.

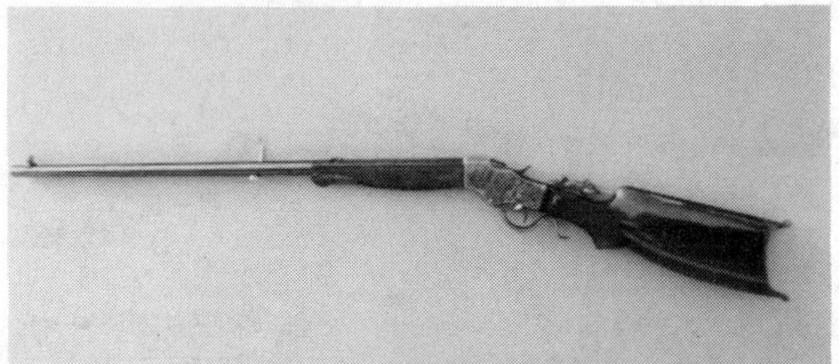

Courtesy J.B. Barnes.

Exc.	V.G.	Good	Fair	Poor
1250	1000	800	600	400

No. 404

This version is chambered for the .22 rimfire cartridge only. It features a 28" round barrel with a globe front sight and a Lyman No. 42 receiver sight. The finish is blued and case-colored. It has a walnut straight-grip stock with a semi-beavertail forend. It features a shotgun-type buttplate. It was manufactured between 1910 and 1916.

Exc.	V.G.	Good	Fair	Poor
750	650	550	400	300

No. 414

This version is also known as the Armory Model and is chambered for the .22 l.r. cartridge only. It was built on a No. 44 action and features a 26" round barrel. It has a Rocky Mountain front sight with a Lyman receiver sight at the rear. The finish is blued and case-colored, with a straight-grip walnut stock and forend held on by a single barrel band. It was manufactured between 1912 and 1932.

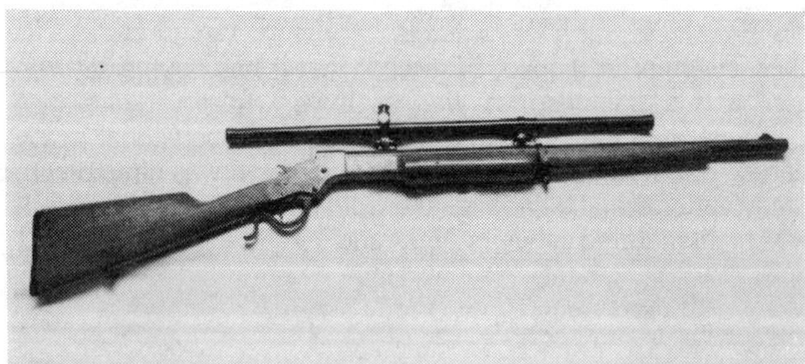

Courtesy Mike Stuckslager.

Exc.	V.G.	Good	Fair	Poor
700	550	450	300	150

Boys Rifles

The Stevens Company produced an extensive line of smaller, single shot rifles chambered for small calibers and intended primarily for use by young shooters. These firearms have become quite collectible and are considered a field of speciality by many modern collectors. There are many variations that were available with a number of options that would affect their value. We supply information and values for the major variations but would recommend securing a qualified appraisal if in doubt.

"Favorite" Rifles

This series of rifles is chambered for the .22, .25, and .32 rimfire. It has a 22" part-octagonal barrel and is blued, with a case-colored frame. It has a takedown-type action with an interchangeable barrel feature. It was available with optional sights, as well as buttplates. There were approximately 1,000,000 manufactured between 1893 and 1939. The variations are as follows:

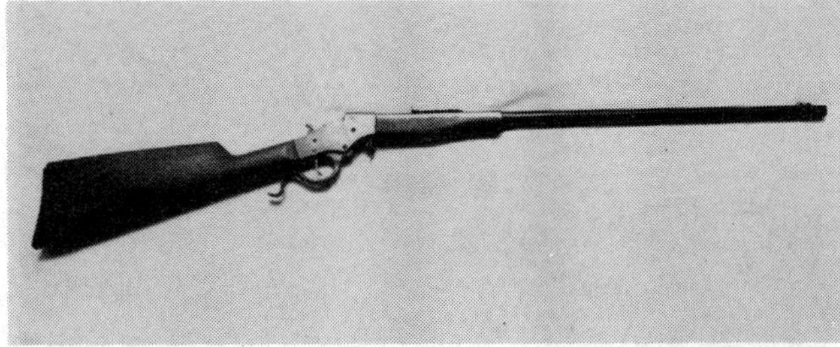

Courtesy Mike Stuckslager.

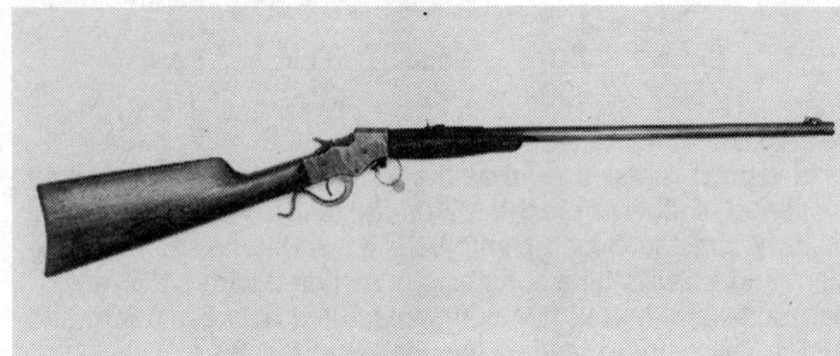

Courtesy Buffalo Bill Historical Center, Cody, Wyoming.

1st Model Favorite

This version is chambered for the .22 or .25 rimfire cartridge. It has a removable sideplate on the right side of the receiver not found on any other variation. There were approximately 1,000 manufactured between 1893 and 1894.

Exc.	V.G.	Good	Fair	Poor
850	750	650	500	350

No. 17

This is the standard, plain version with open sights.

Exc.	V.G.	Good	Fair	Poor
350	300	250	175	125

No. 20

This version is chambered for the .22 or .32 rimfire shot cartridges and has a smoothbore barrel and no rear sight.

Exc.	V.G.	Good	Fair	Poor
350	300	250	175	125

No. 21

This version is known as the Bicycle rifle and features a 20" barrel with open sights standard. It was furnished with a canvas carrying case that would be worth approximately a 10 percent premium. It was manufactured between 1898 and 1903.

Exc.	V.G.	Good	Fair	Poor
450	300	200	150	100

No. 21 Ladies Model

This version bears the same model number as the Bicycle rifle but has a 24" barrel and a high grade, checkered walnut stock with a Swiss buttplate. It features a Vernier tang sight. It was manufactured between 1910 and 1916.

Exc.	V.G.	Good	Fair	Poor
650	500	400	300	175

No. 16

This version is known as the "Crack Shot." It is chambered for .22 or .32 rimfire cartridges with a 20" round barrel. It has a rolling-block-type action with a thumb lever on the side. It is a utility-type rifle with open sights, a blued and case-colored finish, and a plain two-piece walnut stock with a rubber buttplate. The barrel is marked "Crack Shot" along with the standard Stevens' barrel address markings. It was manufactured between 1900 and 1913.

Exc.	V.G.	Good	Fair	Poor
300	250	200	150	100

No. 16-1/2

This version is similar to the No. 16 except that it is chambered for the .32 rimfire shot cartridge with a smooth-bore barrel. It was manufactured between 1900 and 1913.

Exc.	V.G.	Good	Fair	Poor
325	275	225	175	125

No. 23

This version is chambered for the .22 rimfire cartridge. It has a 20" round barrel that pivots to the right for loading. There is a barrel release on the frame. This version is blued and case-colored, with a plain walnut buttstock and no forend. It was manufactured between 1894 and 1897.

Exc.	V.G.	Good	Fair	Poor
350	300	250	200	150

No. 15

This version is also known as the "Maynard Junior." It is chambered for the .22 rimfire cartridge and has an 18" part-octagonal barrel. The action is similar to the Civil War Maynard rifle with a triggerguard-activating lever. The finish is all blued, with a bored-type buttstock and no forearm. The barrel is marked "Stevens Maynard, J. R." in addition to the standard Stevens' barrel address. It was manufactured between 1902 and 1912.

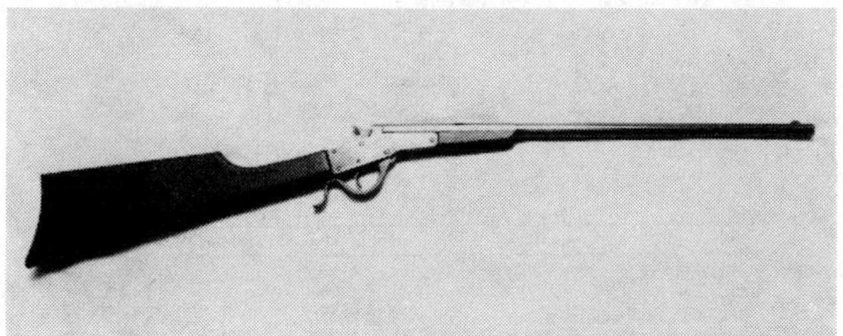

Courtesy Mike Stuckslager.

Exc.	V.G.	Good	Fair	Poor
250	225	200	150	100

No. 15-1/2

This is a smooth-bore version of the No. 15.

Exc.	V.G.	Good	Fair	Poor
325	250	225	175	125

No. 14

This version is also known as the "Little Scout." It is a utility, takedown rifle that is blued, with a one-piece bored-type stock. It features a rolling-block-type action and was manufactured between 1906 and 1910.

Exc.	V.G.	Good	Fair	Poor
300	250	200	150	125

No. 14-1/2

This version is similar to the No. 14 except that it has a two-piece stock. It is also marked "Little Scout." It was manufactured between 1911 and 1941.

Exc.	V.G.	Good	Fair	Poor
275	250	225	175	125

No. 65

This version is known as the "Little Krag." It is a single shot bolt-action rifle chambered for the .22 rimfire cartridge. It has a one-piece stock and a 20" round barrel that was marked "Little Krag." This version is quite scarce. It was manufactured between 1903 and 1910.

Exc.	V.G.	Good	Fair	Poor
275	250	225	175	125

No. 12

This version is also known as the "Marksman." It is chambered for the .22, .25, and the .32 rimfire cartridges. It has a 22" barrel that pivots upward for loading. It is activated by an S-shaped triggerguard lever. It was manufactured between 1911 and 1930.

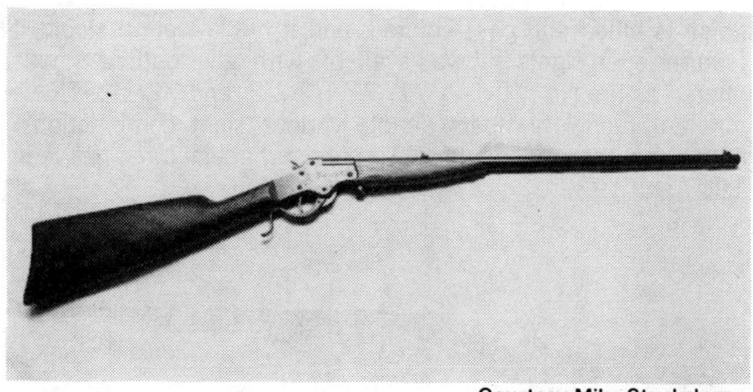

Courtesy Mike Stuckslager.

Exc.	V.G.	Good	Fair	Poor
275	250	225	175	125

No. 26

This version is also known as the "Crack Shot." It has a rolling-block-type action and is chambered for .22 or the .32 rimfire cartridges. It is offered with an 18" or 20" round barrel. It is blued and has a two-piece stock. It was manufactured between 1912 and 1939.

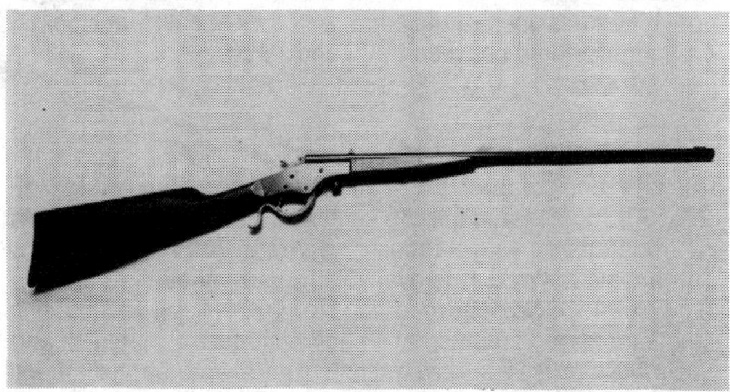

Courtesy Mike Stuckslager.

Exc.	V.G.	Good	Fair	Poor
275	250	225	175	125

No. 26-1/2

This is the smoothbore version of the No. 26.

Exc.	V.G.	Good	Fair	Poor
300	250	200	150	125

No. 11

This is a single shot, rolling-block rifle chambered for the .22 rimfire cartridge. It has a 20" barrel, is blued, and has a bore-type stock without a buttplate. This was the last model offered in the Boys Rifle series. It was manufactured between 1924 and 1931.

Exc.	V.G.	Good	Fair	Poor
250	200	150	100	75

Model 71

This was a re-introduced version of the "Stevens Favorite." It is chambered for the .22 l.r. cartridge and has a 22" octagonal barrel. The finish is blued and case-colored, with a plain walnut stock that has an inlaid medallion and a crescent buttplate. There were 10,000 manufactured in 1971.

Exc.	V.G.	Good	Fair	Poor
200	175	150	100	75

Model 72

This is a re-introduced version of the "Crack Shot" that features a single-shot, falling-block action. It is chambered for the .22 rimfire cartridge and has a 22" octagon barrel with open sights. It is blued and casecolored, with a straight walnut stock. It was introduced in 1972.

Exc.	V.G.	Good	Fair	Poor
175	150	125	100	75

Model 70

This is a slide-action rifle chambered for the .22 rimfire cartridge. It is also known as the "Visible Loading Rifle." It features a 20" round barrel with a 3/4-length, tubular magazine. The finish is blued and case-colored, and it has a walnut stock. It features open sights but was available with other options. It was offered as the No. 70-1/2, 71, 71-1/2, 72, and 72-1/2. These different model numbers denote various sight combinations. Otherwise, they are identical. They were manufactured between 1907 and 1932.

Exc.	V.G.	Good	Fair	Poor
275	250	200	150	100

No. 80

This is a slide-action repeating rifle chambered for the .22 rimfire cartridge. It has a 24" round barrel with a tubular magazine. It features open sights and is blued, with a walnut stock. It was manufactured between 1906 and 1910.

Exc.	V.G.	Good	Fair	Poor
300	275	225	175	125

High Power Rifle

This is a series of lever-action hunting rifles chambered for the .25, .30-30, .32, and the .35 centerfire cartridges. It features a 22" round barrel with a tubular magazine. The finish is blued, with a walnut stock. It is available in four variations—the No. 425, No. 430, No. 435, and the No. 440. These designations denote increased ornamentation and high quality materials and workmanship used in construction. There were approximately 26,000 manufactured between 1910 and 1917.

No. 425

Exc.	V.G.	Good	Fair	Poor
500	450	400	300	200

No. 430

Exc.	V.G.	Good	Fair	Poor
650	600	500	400	300

No. 435

Exc.	V.G.	Good	Fair	Poor
1000	800	700	600	400

No. 440

Exc.	V.G.	Good	Fair	Poor
2250	2000	1750	1250	850

Model 89

This is a single shot, Martini-type, falling-block rifle chambered for the .22 l.r. cartridge. It has an 18.5" barrel and a triggerguard loop-lever activator. The finish is blued, with a straight walnut stock. It was introduced in 1976 and is no longer manufactured.

Exc.	V.G.	Good	Fair	Poor
100	80	70	60	40

Model 987

This is a blowback-operated semi-automatic rifle chambered for the .22 l.r. cartridge. It has a 20" barrel with a 15-round tubular magazine. The finish is blued, with a hardwood stock.

Exc.	V.G.	Good	Fair	Poor
120	100	90	80	60

Beginning in 1869 the Stevens Company produced a series of single-shot, break-open target and sporting pistols that pivot upward for loading. They are chambered for the .22 and the .25 rimfire cartridges, as well as various centerfire cartridges from the .32 short Colt to the .44 Russian. These pistols were made with various barrel lengths and have either a spur trigger or conventional trigger with a guard. They are all single-actions with exposed hammers. The finishes are nickle-plated frames with blued barrels and walnut grips. These variations and their values are as follows:

Six-Inch Pocket Rifle

This version is chambered for the .22 rimfire cartridge and has a 6" part-octagonal barrel with open sights. The barrel is marked "J. Stevens & Co. Chicopee Falls, Mass." There were approximately 1,000 manufactured between 1869 and 1886.

Exc.	V.G.	Good	Fair	Poor
400	350	300	200	125

No. 36

This version is known as the Stevens-Lord pistol. It is chambered for various rimfire and centerfire calibers up to .44 Russian. It is offered with a 10" or 12" part-octagonal barrel and features a firing pin in the frame with a bushing. It has a conventional trigger with a spurred triggerguard. It features the standard Stevens' barrel address. It was named after Frank Lord, a target shooter well-known at this time. There were approximately 3,500 manufactured from 1880 to 1911.

Courtesy J.B. Barnes.

Exc.	V.G.	Good	Fair	Poor
650	500	400	300	200

First Issue Stevens-Conlin

This version is chambered for the .22 or .32 rimfire cartridges. It has a 10" or 12" part-octagonal barrel. It features a plated brass frame with a blued barrel and checkered walnut grips with a weighted butt cap. This version has a spur trigger either with or without a triggerguard. It was named after James Conlin, the owner of a shooting gallery located in New York City. There were approximately 500 manufactured between 1880 and 1884.

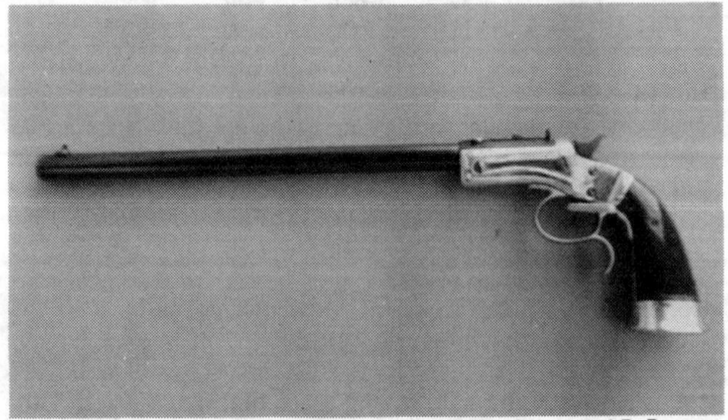

Courtesy J.B. Barnes.

Exc.	V.G.	Good	Fair	Poor
900	800	650	400	200

Second Issue Stevens-Conlin No. 38

This version is similar to the First Issue, with a conventional trigger and spurred triggerguard, as well as a fully adjustable rear sight. There were approximately 6,000 manufactured between 1884 and 1903.

Exc.	V.G.	Good	Fair	Poor
800	600	450	350	200

No. 37

This version is also known as the Stevens-Gould and was named after a nineteenth century firearms writer. It resembles the No. 38 without the spur on the triggerguard. There were approximately 1,000 manufactured between 1889 and 1903.

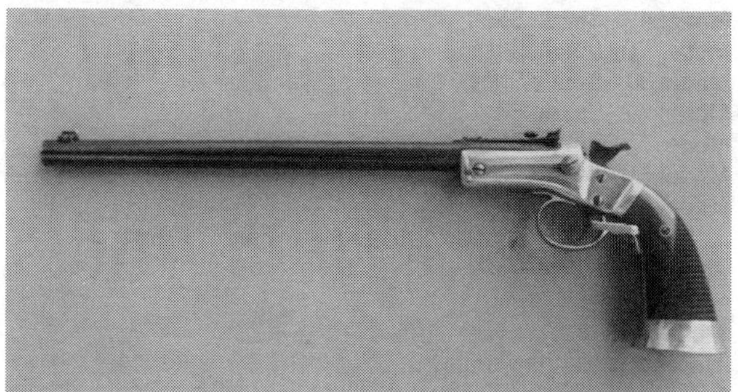

Courtesy J.B. Barnes.

Exc.	V.G.	Good	Fair	Poor
950	800	650	400	200

No. 35

This version is chambered for the .22 rimfire, the .22 Stevens-Pope, and the .25 Stevens cartridges. It is offered with a 6", 8", or 10" part-octagonal barrel. The firing pin has no bushing. It features an iron frame that is either blued or plated with a blued barrel. It has plain walnut grips with a weighted buttcap. It featured open sights. There were approximately 43,000 manufactured between 1923 and 1942.

Exc.	V.G.	Good	Fair	Poor
350	275	200	150	100

No. 35 Target

This version is similar to the No. 35 but has a better quality triggerguard and sights. There were approximately 35,000 manufactured between 1907 and 1916.

Exc.	V.G.	Good	Fair	Poor
400	325	275	175	100

No. 43

This version is also called the Diamond and was produced in two distinct variations—called the First Issue and the Second Issue. The First Issue has a brass frame; and the Second Issue, an iron frame and no firing pin bushing. Otherwise they are quite similar and would be valued the same. They are chambered for the .22 rimfire cartridge and are offered with either a 6" or 10" part-octagonal barrel. The frames are either nickle-plated or blued with blued barrels and square-butt walnut grips. There were approximately 95,000 manufactured between 1886 and 1916.

Exc.	V.G.	Good	Fair	Poor
375	300	250	150	75

No. 10 Target Pistol

This version was a departure from its predecessors. It very much resembles a semi-automatic pistol but is, in reality, a single-shot. It is chambered for the .22 rimfire cartridge and has an 8" round barrel that pivots upward for loading. It has a steel frame and is blued, with checkered rubber grips. Instead of the usual exposed hammer, this version has a knurled cocking piece that extends through the rear of the frame. There were approximately 7,000 manufactured between 1919 and 1933.

Exc.	V.G.	Good	Fair	Poor
500	400	350	250	150

Pocket Rifles

This series of pistols is similar to the target and sporting pistols except that these were produced with detachable shoulder stocks that bear the same serial number as the pistol with which they were sold. They are sometimes referred to as Bicycle rifles. The collector interest in these weapons is quite high; but it would behoove one to be familiar with the provisions of the Gun Control Act of 1968 when dealing in or collecting this variation—as when the stock is attached, they can fall into the category of a short-barrelled rifle. Some are considered to be curios and relics, and others have been totally declassified; but some models may still be restricted. We strongly recommend securing a qualified, individual appraisal on these highly collectible firearms if a transaction is contemplated. The values we supply include the matching shoulder stock. If the stock number does not match the pistol, the values would be approximately 25 percent less; and with no stock at all, 50 percent should be deducted.

Old Model Pocket Rifle

This version is chambered for the .22 rimfire cartridge and has an 8" or 10" part-octagonal barrel. It has a spur trigger and an external hammer on which the firing pin is mounted. The extractor is spring-loaded. It has a plated brass frame, blued barrel, and either walnut or rosewood grips. The shoulder stock is either nickle-plated or black. The barrel is marked "J. Stevens & Co. Chicopee Falls, Mass." There were approximately 4,000 manufactured between 1869 and 1886.

Exc.	V.G.	Good	Fair	Poor
775	575	475	300	175

Reliable Pocket Rifle

This version is chambered for the .22 rimfire cartridge and in appearance is quite similar to the Old Model. The basic difference is that the extractor operates as a part of the pivoting barrel mechanism instead of being spring-loaded. The barrel is marked "J. Stevens A&T Co." There were approximately 4,000 manufactured between 1886 and 1896.

Exc.	V.G.	Good	Fair	Poor
650	575	475	350	250

No. 42 Reliable Pocket Rifle

This version is similar to the first-issue Reliable except that it has an iron frame with the firing pin mounted in it without a bushing. The shoulder stock is shaped differently. There were approximately 8,000 manufactured between 1896 and 1916.

Exc.	V.G.	Good	Fair	Poor
650	575	475	350	250

First Issue New Model Pocket Rifle

This version is the first of the medium-frame models with a frame width of 1". All of its predecessors have a 5/8" wide frame. This model is chambered for the .22 and .32 rimfire cartridges and is offered with barrel lengths of 10", 12", 15", or 18" that are part-octagonal in configuration. The external hammer has the firing pin mounted on it. It has a plated brass frame, blued barrel, and either walnut or rosewood grips. The shoulder stock is nickle-plated and fitted differently than the small-frame models in that there is a dovetail in the butt and the top leg is secured by a knurled screw. The barrel is marked "J. Stevens & Co. Chicopee Falls, Mass." There were approximately 8,000 manufactured between 1872 and 1875.

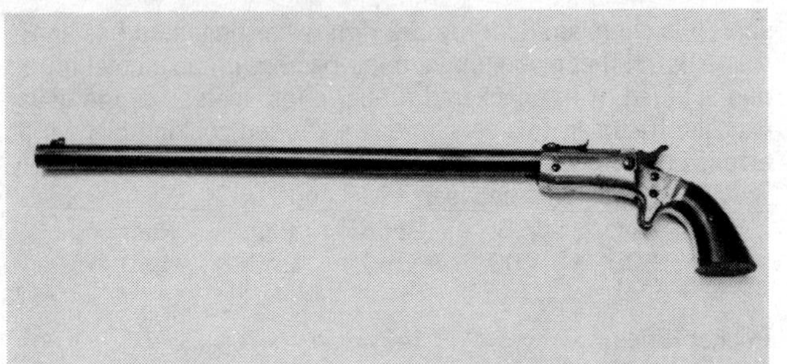

Courtesy Mike Stuckslager.

Exc.	V.G.	Good	Fair	Poor
700	600	500	400	300

Second Issue New Model Pocket Rifle

This version is similar to the First Issue except that the firing pin is mounted in the frame with a bushing. There were approximately 15,000 manufactured between 1875 and 1896.

Exc.	V.G.	Good	Fair	Poor
700	600	500	400	300

Vernier Model

This version is similar to the Second Issue except that it features a Vernier tang sight located on the backstrap. There were approximately 1,500 manufactured between 1884 and 1896.

Exc.	V.G.	Good	Fair	Poor
850	650	550	450	200

No. 40

This version is similar to its medium-frame predecessors except that it has a longer grip frame and a conventional trigger with triggerguard. There were approximately 15,000 manufactured between 1896 and 1916.

Exc.	V.G.	Good	Fair	Poor
500	450	375	300	200

No. 40-1/2

This version is similar to the No. 40, with a Vernier tang sight mounted on the backstrap. There were approximately 2,500 manufactured between 1896 and 1915.

Exc.	V.G.	Good	Fair	Poor
750	650	550	450	350

No. 34

This is the first of the heavy-frame pocket rifles that featured a 1.25" wide frame. This version is also known as the "Hunter's Pet". It is chambered for many popular cartridges from the .22 rimfire to the .44-40 centerfire. It is offered with a part-octagonal 18", 20", 22", or 24" barrel. It has a nickle-plated iron frame and blued barrel. The detachable stock is nickle-plated, and the grips are walnut. There were very few produced with a brass frame; and if located, these would be worth twice the value indicated. The firing pin is mounted in the frame with the bushing, and it features a spur trigger. There were approximately 4,000 manufactured between 1872 and 1900.

Exc.	V.G.	Good	Fair	Poor
650	575	475	350	250

No. 34-1/2

This version is similar to the No. 34 except that it features a Vernier tang sight mounted on the backstrap. There were approximately 1,200 manufactured between 1884 and 1900.

Exc.	V.G.	Good	Fair	Poor
750	650	550	450	350

The Stevens Company produced a number of inexpensive, utilitarian, bolt-action rifles. These were both single-shot and repeaters. They have been very popular over the years as starter rifles for young shooters. Their values are quite similar, and we list them for reference purposes only.

Model 053--Single Shot
Model 056--5-Shot Magazine
Model 066--Tube Magazine
Model 083--Single Shot
Model 084--5-Shot Magazine
Model 086--Tube Magazine
Model 15--Single Shot
Model 15Y--Single Shot
Model 419--Single Shot
Model 48--Single Shot
Model 49--Single Shot
Model 50--Single Shot
Model 51--Single Shot
Model 52--Single Shot
Model 53--Single Shot
Model 56--5-Shot Magazine
Model 66--Tube Magazine

Exc.	V.G.	Good	Fair	Poor
150	80	70	50	25

Model 416

This is a target rifle chambered for the .22 l.r. cartridge. It has a 24" heavy barrel with aperture sights. It features a 5-round detachable magazine and is blued, with a target-type walnut stock.

Exc.	V.G.	Good	Fair	Poor
200	175	150	100	75

Model 322

This is a bolt-action sporting rifle chambered for the .22 Hornet cartridge. It has a 20" barrel with open sights and a detachable box magazine. The finish is blued, with a plain walnut stock.

Exc.	V.G.	Good	Fair	Poor
150	125	100	75	50

Model 322-S

This version features an aperture rear sight.

Exc.	V.G.	Good	Fair	Poor
200	125	100	75	50

This company manufactured a number of single-barrel, break-open, single-shot shotguns. They were produced chambered for various gauges with various-length barrels and chokes. They are quite similar in appearance and were designed as inexpensive, utility-grade weapons. There is little or no collector interest in them at this time, and their values are similar. We list them for reference purposes only.

Model 100
Model 102
Model 104
Model 105
Model 106
Model 107
Model 108
Model 110
Model 120
Model 125
Model 140
Model 160
Model 165
Model 170
Model 180
Model 89
Model 90
Model 93
Model 94
Model 944
Model 94A
Model 94C
Model 95
Model 958
Model 97
Model 970

Exc.	V.G.	Good	Fair	Poor
120	80	75	50	25

Model 182

This is a single shot, break-open shotgun chambered for 12 gauge. It is offered with a 30" or 32" trap choked barrels and features a hammerless action with an automatic ejector and a lightly engraved receiver. The finish is blued, with a checkered trap-grade stock.

Exc.	V.G.	Good	Fair	Poor
125	100	75	50	25

Model 185

This version features a half-octagonal barrel with an automatic ejector and a checkered walnut stock.

Damascus Barrel—Deduct 25%.

Exc.	V.G.	Good	Fair	Poor
150	125	100	75	50

Model 190

This is a 12-gauge hammerless gun with an automatic ejector. It is lightly engraved with a half-octagonal barrel.

Damascus Barrel—Deduct 25%.

Exc.	V.G.	Good	Fair	Poor
150	125	100	75	50

Model 195

This is another deluxe version that features engraving, a half-octagonal barrel, and a high-grade, checkered walnut stock.

Damascus Barrel—Deduct 25%.

Exc.	V.G.	Good	Fair	Poor
275	250	200	150	100

The firm of J. Stevens produced a number of utility-grade, side-by-side double-barrel shotguns. These were excellent quality guns, with many of them still in use today. There is a modicum of collector interest, but values for most models are quite similar. They are chambered for 12, 16, or 20 gauge and have various length barrels and choke combinations. They feature double triggers except where noted and extractors. They are as follows:

Model 315
Model 215--External Hammers
Model 235--External Hammers
Model 250--External Hammers
Model 255--External Hammers
Model 260--External Hammers, Damascus
Model 265--External Hammers
Model 270--External Hammers
Model 311--Hammerless
Model 3151--Hammerless
Model 330--Hammerless
Model 335--Hammerless
Model 345--Hammerless
Model 355--Hammerless
Model 365--Hammerless
Model 515--Hammerless
Model 5151--Hammerless
Model 530--Hammerless
Model 53M--Hammerless, Plastic Stock

Exc.	V.G.	Good	Fair	Poor
200	175	150	100	75

Model 311-R

This version is chambered for 12 or 20 gauge and has 18.5" cylinder-bored barrels. It was designed as a riot gun to be used by prison guards.

Exc.	V.G.	Good	Fair	Poor
300	250	200	150	100

Model 311-ST

This version has a single selective trigger.

Exc.	V.G.	Good	Fair	Poor
200	175	150	100	75

Model 375

This version is chambered for 12 or 16 gauge and features a lightly engraved boxlock receiver and a fancy, checkered walnut stock.

Exc.	V.G.	Good	Fair	Poor
200	175	150	100	75

Model 385

This is a more deluxe version that features a higher degree of engraving.

Exc.	V.G.	Good	Fair	Poor
250	200	175	150	100

The Stevens Company produced a number of bolt-action shotguns that are either single shot or repeaters. They are chambered for the 20 gauge or .410 and are blued, with walnut stocks. The values for these utility-grade shotguns are similar.

Model 237--Single Shot
Model 258--Clip Fed
Model 37--Single Shot
Model 38--Clip Fed
Model 39--Tube Magazine
Model 58--Clip Fed
Model 59--Tube Magazine

Exc.	V.G.	Good	Fair	Poor
75	65	50	35	25

The J. Stevens Arms Company also produced a series of utility-grade slide-action shotguns. They are chambered for various gauges with various barrel lengths and chokes. The finishes are blued, with walnut stocks. The values are similar, and we list them for reference purposes as follows:

Model 520
Model 522
Model 620
Model 621
Model 67
Model 67-VR
Model 77
Model 77S C
Model 77-AC
Model 77-M
Model 820

Exc.	V.G.	Good	Fair	Poor
150	125	100	75	50

Model 124

This is a recoil-operated semi-automatic shotgun chambered for 12 gauge. It has a 28" barrel with various chokes, is blued, and has a brown plastic stock.

Exc.	V.G.	Good	Fair	Poor
125	100	75	65	50

Model 67

This is a slide-action shotgun chambered for 12 and 20 gauge, as well as .410. It has 3" chambers. It is offered with various-length barrels and choke tubes with a 5-shot tube magazine. It features a steel receiver and is blued, with a walnut stock. It was discontinued in 1989.

Exc.	V.G.	Good	Fair	Poor
200	175	150	100	75

Model 675

This is a slide-action shotgun chambered for 12 gauge with a 24" vent-rib barrel with iron sights. The finish is blued, with a hardwood stock and recoil pad. It was manufactured in 1987 and 1988.

Exc.	V.G.	Good	Fair	Poor
275	250	200	150	100

Model 69-RXL

This is a matte-finished riot version of the Model 67 series slide-action shotgun. It has an 18.25" cylinder-bore barrel and is furnished with a recoil pad. It was discontinued in 1989.

Exc.	V.G.	Good	Fair	Poor
200	175	150	100	75

Stevens-Fox Model B

This is a side-by-side double-barrel shotgun chambered for 12 or 20 gauge, as well as .410. It is offered with 26", 28", or 30" vent-rib barrels with double triggers and extractors. The BDE model features automatic ejectors and would be worth approximately 25 percent additional. The finish is blued, with a walnut stock.

Exc.	V.G.	Good	Fair	Poor
300	275	225	175	100

Stevens-Fox Model B-SE

This is a deluxe version with single trigger and automatic ejectors. It features a select walnut stock.

NIB	Exc.	V.G.	Good	Fair	Poor
525	450	325	250	200	150

Model 311

This is a side-by-side double-barrel shotgun chambered for 12 or 20 gauge, as well as .410. It has 3" chambers. It has 28" or 30" vent-rib barrels with various chokes, double triggers, and extractors. The finish is blued, with a walnut stock.

Exc.	V.G.	Good	Fair	Poor
300	275	225	175	125

Model 311-R

This is an 18.25", cylinder-bore, law enforcement version of the Model 311.

Exc.	V.G.	Good	Fair	Poor
300	275	225	175	125

STEYR
Steyr, Austria

Schonberger

A 8mm semi-automatic pistol with a 6" barrel and a magazine located in front of the trigger. Blued with checkered walnut grips. It is believed that approximately 36 examples of this pistol were made in 1892 and 1893.

Exc.	V.G.	Good	Fair	Poor
2750	2500	2000	1500	1250

Steyr Mannlicher Model 1894

A 7.65mm Mannlicher semi-automatic pistol with a 5.5" barrel. Marked "Model 1894" or "Model 1895". Blued with checkered walnut grips.

Exc.	V.G.	Good	Fair	Poor
2000	1750	1500	1000	800

Model 1900/01

A 7.63mm semi-automatic pistol with a 6" barrel and grip safety. Blued with checkered walnut grips. Adopted for use by the Argentine Army in 1905.

Exc.	V.G.	Good	Fair	Poor
750	700	600	500	400

Roth-Steyr Model 1907

This is listed under its own section in this text.

Model 1911 Steyr-Hahn (Currently imported by Century International Arms Co.)

A 9mm Steyr caliber, semi-automatic pistol with a 5" barrel and fixed magazine. After 1938, many of these pistols were rebarrelled for use with the 9mm Parabellum cartridge and these are marked "08". Blued with checkered walnut grips, the slide marked "Osterreichische Waffenfabrik Steyr M1911 9mm." Austrian military issue examples are marked "Steyr" and the date of manufacture on the slide. Those pistols sold to Chile and Romania are marked with those country's crests.

Courtesy Orville Reichert.

Exc.	V.G.	Good	Fair	Poor
450	400	300	200	150

Model 1909 Pocket Pistol

Although marked "Oesterr Waffenfabrik Ges Steyr", this pistol was actually made by Nicolas Pieper (see first entry for Nicolas Pieper). Manufactured prior to 1914 and from 1921 to 1939.

Exc.	V.G.	Good	Fair	Poor
300	250	200	150	100

Model P18

A 9mm caliber semi-automatic pistol with a 5" barrel and 18 shot magazine. Briefly manufactured in 1974 by L.E.S. of Morton Grove, Illinois under license. This pistol is also known as the "Rogak".

Exc.	V.G.	Good	Fair	Poor
400	350	300	250	200

Model GB

A 9mm caliber double action semi-automatic pistol with a 5.25" polygon rifled barrel, 18-shot magazine and black plastic grips. Blued. Imported prior to 1989.

Exc.	V.G.	Good	Fair	Poor
450	400	350	275	200

Steyr Mannlicher Model 1950

A .257 Roberts, .270 Winchester or .30-06 caliber bolt-action sporting rifle with a 24" barrel and 5-shot rotary magazine. Blued with a checkered walnut stock having an ebony pistol grip cap and forend tip. Manufactured from 1950 to 1952.

Exc.	V.G.	Good	Fair	Poor
1000	850	700	550	400

Model 1950 Carbine

As above, with a 20" barrel and Mannlicher-style stock. Fitted with a steel forend cap. Manufactured in 1950 to 1952.

Exc.	V.G.	Good	Fair	Poor
1150	1000	850	650	500

Model 1952

Similar to the above, with a swept back bolt handle. Manufactured from 1952 to 1956.

Exc.	V.G.	Good	Fair	Poor
1000	850	750	650	500

Model 1952 Carbine

As above, with a 20" barrel and Mannlicher-style stock.

Exc.	V.G.	Good	Fair	Poor
1150	1000	850	650	500

Model 1956 Rifle

Similar to the above, in .243 and .30-06 caliber with a 22" barrel and high comb stock. Manufactured from 1956 to 1960.

Exc.	V.G.	Good	Fair	Poor
900	800	650	500	400

Model 1956 Carbine

As above, with a 20" barrel and Mannlicher-style stock. Manufactured from 1956 to 1960.

Exc.	V.G.	Good	Fair	Poor
1000	900	750	600	500

Model 1961 MCA Rifle

As above, with a Monte Carlo-style stock.

Exc.	V.G.	Good	Fair	Poor
900	800	650	500	400

Model 1961 MCA Carbine

As above, with a Mannlicher-style Monte Carlo stock.

Exc.	V.G.	Good	Fair	Poor
1100	1000	850	650	500

SPORTER SERIES

This series includes rifles that are lightweight and have a reduced overall length. All Sporter models have an interchangeable 5-round rotary magazine. The stock is oil finish walnut in either the Mannlicher full stock design or the half stock version. In both stock configurations an oval European cheekpiece is standard. These rifles are offered in four different action lengths: **SL** (super light), **L** (light), **M** (medium), or **S** (magnum). They are also available with either single trigger or double set triggers.

Model M72 L/M

A .243, .270, 7x57mm, 7x64mm, .308 or .30-06 caliber bolt-action rifle with a 23" fluted barrel, and single or double set triggers. Blued, checkered walnut stock. Manufactured from 1972 to 1980.

Exc.	V.G.	Good	Fair	Poor
900	800	650	500	400

Model SL

This model features the super light action and is offered with 20" barrel in full stock version or 23.6" barrel in half stock version. A rubber butt pad is standard. This model does not have a forend tip on its half stock variation. Offered in the following calibers: .222 Rem., .222 Rem. Mag., .223, and 5.6x50 Mag. Weighs approximately 6.2 lbs. with full stock and 6.3 lbs. with half stock.

NIB	Exc.	V.G.	Good	Fair	Poor
1850	1650	1000	750	500	400

Model SL Carbine

As above, with a 20" fluted barrel and Mannlicher-style stock.

NIB	Exc.	V.G.	Good	Fair	Poor
1950	1750	1050	800	550	450

Varmint Model

This model features a heavy 26" barrel chambered for the .222 Rem., .223, 5.6x57, .243 Win., .308 Win., and .22-250. The forend of the stock is ventilated. The grip is enlarged and textured. Choice of single or double set triggers. Recoil pad is standard. Weighs about 8 lbs.

NIB	Exc.	V.G.	Good	Fair	Poor
1950	1750	1050	800	550	450

Model L

This rifle has the light action and is offered in the same stock configuration and barrel lengths as the Model SL. The calibers are: 5.6x57, .243 Win., .308, .22-250, and 6mm Rem. Weighs about 6.3 lbs. with full stock and 6.4 lbs. with half stock.

NIB	Exc.	V.G.	Good	Fair	Poor
1850	1650	1000	750	500	400

Luxus Series

This luxury model offers a choice of full or half stock variations in select walnut with fine line checkering. The pistol grip is steeply angled. The Luxus rifles are fitted with a swept back European cheekpiece. A single set trigger is standard. The box magazine holds 3 rounds. Optional engraving and stock carving may be encounter on these modes that will dramatically affect price. The Luxus rifles are available with light, medium, or magnum length actions.

Luxus Model L

Same dimensions and barrel lengths as the Sporter version. The calibers are: 5.6x57, .243 Win., .308, .22-250, and 6mm Rem.

NIB	Exc.	V.G.	Good	Fair	Poor
2400	2000	1100	800	600	550

Luxus Model M

Same dimensions and barrel lengths as the Sporter Model M. Available in the following calibers: 6.5x57, .270 Win., 7x64, .30-06, 9.3x626.5x55, 7.5 Swiss, 7x57, and 8x57JS.

NIB	Exc.	V.G.	Good	Fair	Poor
2400	2000	1100	800	600	550

Luxus Model S

Same as the Sporter Model S. Offered in the following calibers: 6.5x68, 7mm Rem. Mag., .300 Win. Mag., and 8x685.

NIB	Exc.	V.G.	Good	Fair	Poor
2400	2000	1100	800	600	550

Model M

This model features the medium action and has the same barrel and stock configurations as the other two models listed above with the exception that is has no butt pad and it does have a forend tip on its half stock variation. Available in the following calibers: 6.5x57, .270 Win., 7x64, .30-06, 9.3x62, 6.5x55, 7.5 Swiss, 7x57, and 8x57JS. Weighs approximately 6.8 lbs. with full stock and 7 lbs. with half stock.

NIB	Exc.	V.G.	Good	Fair	Poor
2500	2100	1200	900	600	500

Professional Model M

This model is fitted with a medium weight action and features a black synthetic checkered stock. Comes fitted with a ventilated rubber recoil pad. Offered with 20" or 23.6" barrel it is available with single or double set trigger. Available in the following calibers: 6.5x57, .270 Win., 7x64, .30-06, 9.3x626.5x55, 7.5 Swiss, 7x57, and 8x57JS. Weighs approximately 7.25 lbs.

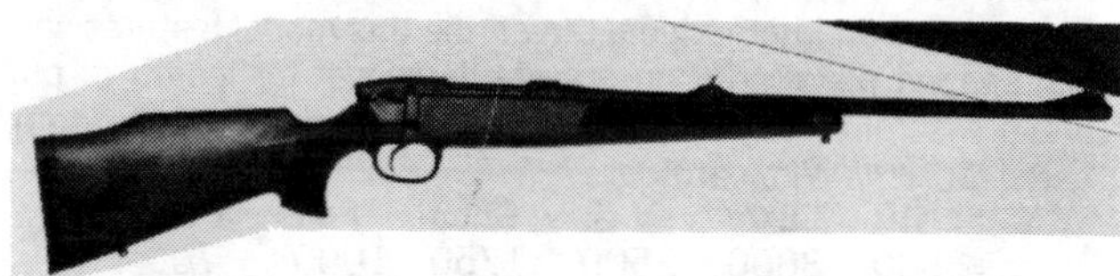

NIB	Exc.	V.G.	Good	Fair	Poor
1500	1400	950	700	600	500

Model S

This rifle is offered with half stock only and is fitted with a 26" barrel. The action is magnum length and is offered in the following calibers: 6.5x68, 7mm Rem. Mag., .300 Win. Mag., and 8x685. Rifle weighs about 8.4 lbs.

NIB	Exc.	V.G.	Good	Fair	Poor
1950	1750	1150	900	700	600

Model S/T

Similar to the model above but in a heavy barreled version. Offered in the following calibers: 9.3x64, .375 H&H, and .458 Win. Mag. An optional butt stock magazine is available. Weighs about 9 lbs.

NIB	Exc.	V.G.	Good	Fair	Poor
1950	1750	1150	900	700	600

Tropical Rifle

As above, with a 26" heavy barrel chambered for .375 Holland & Holland and .458 Winchester Magnum. Not imported after 1985.

Exc.	V.G.	Good	Fair	Poor
2000	1750	1000	600	500

Model SSG

This model features a black synthetic stock originally designed as a military sniper rifle. Fitted with a cocking indicator, single or double set trigger, 5-round rotary magazine, or 10-round magazine. Receiver is milled to NATO specifications for Steyr ring mounts. Barrel length is 26". Rifle weighs about 8.5 lbs. Offered in .243 Win. or .308 Win.

NIB	Exc.	V.G.	Good	Fair	Poor
1750	1500	900	600	500	400

PII Sniper Rifle

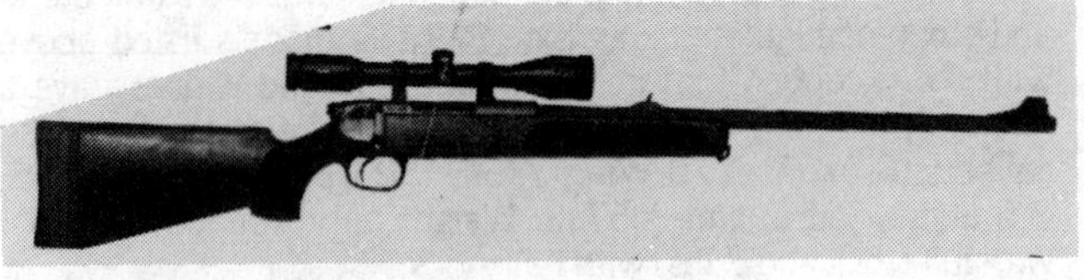

NIB	Exc.	V.G.	Good	Fair	Poor
1700	1350	900	700	600	500

Match

NIB	Exc.	V.G.	Good	Fair	Poor
3000	2500	2000	1500	800	650

Match UIT

Designed as an international target rifle this model features special shaped pistol grip, an adjustable trigger for length or pull and pressure. Enlarged bolt handle and non-glare barrel. Chambered for .308 Win. cartridge.

NIB	Exc.	V.G.	Good	Fair	Poor
3500	3000	2500	1750	1000	700

Steyr AUG

A 5.56mm semi-automatic, Bullpup semi-automatic rifle with a 20" barrel incorporating a Swarovski telescopic sight. Carbon composite stock. Recommend independent, local appraisals.

Steyr Zepher

This model is a .22 caliber rimfire bolt action carbine. It has a 5-round detachable magazine, dove-tailed receiver for scope rings. It is fitted with a full stock. Made from 1953 to 1968.

Exc.	V.G.	Good	Fair	Poor
1150	1000	750	500	350

Model SPP

Introduced in 1993 this is a 9mm semi-automatic pistol. It is made from synthetic materials and operates on a delayed blowback, rotating barrel system. The magazine capacity is either 15 or 30 rounds. The barrel is 5.9" in length overall length is 12.75" and weight is about 42 ozs. Due to its appearance and design this pistol was banned for importation into the U.S. shortly after its introduction. Because of this circumstance the price of this pistol may fluctuate widely.

NIB	Exc.	V.G.	Good	Fair	Poor
895	800	650	550	400	250

STEYR HAHN

SEE—Steyr

STEYR MANNLICHER

SEE—Steyr

STOCK, FRANZ

Berlin, Germany

Stock

A .22, 6.35mm or 7.65mm semi-automatic pistol with an open topped slide. The frame marked "Franz Stock Berlin". Blued with black composition grips impressed with the name "Stock" at the top. Manufactured from 1918 to the early 1930's.

Exc.	V.G.	Good	Fair	Poor
300	275	250	150	100

STOCKING & CO.

Worcester, Massachusetts

Pepperbox

A .28 or .31 6 barrelled percussion pepperbox revolver with barrel lengths from 4" to 6" in length. The hammer is fitted with a very long cocking piece at the rear and the triggerguard may or may not be made with a spur at the rear. Blued with walnut grips. The barrel group marked "Stocking & Co., Worcester." Manufactured between 1846 and 1854.

Courtesy Wallis & Wallis, Lewes, Sussex, England.

Exc.	V.G.	Good	Fair	Poor
500	400	350	250	150

Single Shot Pistol
A .36 caliber single shot percussion pistol of the same pattern as the pepperbox with a 4" half octagonal barrel. Marked as above. Manufactured from 1849 to 1852.

Exc.	V.G.	Good	Fair	Poor
375	325	250	175	125

STOEGER, A. F.
South Hackensack, New Jersey

.22 Luger
A .22 caliber simplified copy of the German Model P.08 semi-automatic pistol with a 4.5" or 5.5" barrel and an aluminum frame. The word "Luger" is roll engraved on the right side of the frame. Blued with checkered brown plastic grips.

Exc.	V.G.	Good	Fair	Poor
300	250	200	150	100

Target Luger
As above, with adjustable target sights.

Exc.	V.G.	Good	Fair	Poor
325	275	225	175	125

Luger Carbine
As above, with an 11" barrel, walnut forend and checkered walnut grips. Furnished with a red velvet lined black leatherette case. Manufactured during the 1970s.

Exc.	V.G.	Good	Fair	Poor
450	400	350	250	175

STREET SWEEPER
Atlanta, Georgia

Street Sweeper
A 12 gauge semi-automatic double-action shotgun with an 18" barrel and 12-shot rotary, drum magazine. Matte black finish. Introduced in 1989.

NIB	Exc.	V.G.	Good	Fair	Poor
600	500	400	350	250	200

STURM, RUGER & CO.
Southport, Connecticut

In 1946 W. B. Ruger applied for his first patent on a blowback-operated, semi-automatic, .22 caliber pistol. In 1949 Mr. Ruger and Alexander Sturm released this pistol for sale, and the Ruger dynasty began. This pistol was as perfect for the American marketplace as could be. It was accurate, reliable, and inexpensive and insured the new company's success. In 1951 Alexander Sturm passed away, but Mr. Ruger continued forward. At this time the fledgling television industry was popularizing the early American West, and Colt had not re-introduced the Single Action Army after WWII. Ruger decided that a Western-style six shooter would be a successful venture, and the Single Six was born. This was not a Colt copy but a new design based on the Western look. Again Ruger scored in the marketplace, and this has been pretty much the rule ever since. With few exceptions this company has shown itself to be very accurate in gauging what the gun-buying public wants. They have expanded their line to include double-action revolvers, single shots, semi-auto and bolt-action rifles, percussion revolvers, and even a semi-auto wonder nine. They have stayed ahead of the legal profession as much as possible by introducing safety devices and comprehensive instruction manuals and generally insured their future success. For such a relatively new company, collector interest in certain models is quite keen. There are a number of factors that govern Ruger collector values. All models made in 1976 were designated "200th Year of Liberty" models and if in NIB condition will bring up to a 25 percent premium if a market is found. The newer models that have a safety warning stamped on the barrel are generally purchased only by shooters and have no collector appeal whatsoever. The astute individual must be aware of these nuances when dealing in Rugers. There are some excellent works written on the Ruger (not as many as there are on the Colt or the Smith & Wesson), but the new collector can educate himself if he so desires. We list this company's models in chronological order.

Standard Model "Red Eagle Grips"
This is a blowback semi-automatic with a fixed, exposed, 4.75" barrel. The receiver is tubular, with a round bolt. There is a 9-shot detachable magazine, and the sights are fixed. The finish is blued, and the black hard rubber grips on this first model have the trademark Ruger Eagle inlaid in red. There were approximately 25,600 manufactured before Alexander Sturm's death in 1951, but this model may be seen as high as the 35000 serial-number range. Because variations of this model exist an expert opinion should be sought before a final price is established.

Exc.	V.G.	Good	Fair	Poor
550	500	380	350	225

Note: Factory plated pistols will bring between $2,500 and $5,000 depending on condition. For pistols in factory original wood "cod box" shipping carton add $1,000 to $1,500. For pistols in original hinged cardboard box add 20 percent.

Standard Model
This model is identical to the Red Eagle except that after Sturm's death the grip medallions were changed from red to black and have remained so ever since. This pistol was produced from 1952-1982 in 4-3/4" and 6" barrels. There are a great many variations of this pistol, but a book dealing with this pistol alone should be consulted as the differences in variations are very subtle and valuation of these variations is definitely a matter for individual appraisal.

Exc.	V.G.	Good	Fair	Poor
150	135	125	100	85

Standard Model—Marked "Hecho en Mexico"
These pistols were assembled and sold in Mexico. Approximately 200 were built with 4-3/4" barrels and about 50 were

produced with 6" barrels. Only about 12 of these pistols have been accounted for and for this reason an expert should be consulted.

Exc.	V.G.	Good	Fair	Poor
1500	1200	850	600	400

Mark I Target Model

The success of the Ruger Standard Model led quite naturally to a demand for a more accurate target model. In 1951 a pistol that utilized the same frame and receiver with a 6-7/8", target-type barrel and adjustable sights was introduced. Early target models number 15000 to 16999 and 25000 to 25300 have Red Eagle grips. In 1952 a 5-1/4" tapered barrel model was introduced, but was soon discontinued. In 1963 the popular 5-1/2" bull barrel model was introduced. These models enjoyed well-deserved success and were manufactured from 1951-1982.
With Factory Installed Muzzle Brake—Add $100.

Red Eagle 6-7/8" barrel.

Exc.	V.G.	Good	Fair	Poor
450	325	250	175	125

For other Mark I Target models under serial number 72500 in the original hinged box add 50 percent.

Add 25 percent to prices if in original hinged box.

The 5-1/4" tapered barrel model

Exc.	V.G.	Good	Fair	Poor
450	325	250	175	125

Add 250 percent if in original hinged box.

The 5-1/2" bull barrel model.

Exc.	V.G.	Good	Fair	Poor
200	175	150	125	95

Mark I Target Model—Rollmarked with U.S. on top of frame.

These pistols will have either 1/16" or 1/8" high serial numbers.

Exc.	V.G.	Good	Fair	Poor
300	250	200	175	150

Add 75 percent to price if pistol has 1/8" high serial numbers.

Stainless-Steel 1 of 5,000

This model is a special commemorative version of the first standard with the "Red Eagle" grips. It is made of stainless steel and had Bill Ruger's signature on it. The pistol is encased in a wood "salt cod" case.

NIB	Exc.	V.G.	Good	Fair	Poor
425	375	300	225	175	125

Mark II Standard Model

This is a generally improved version of the first Ruger pistol. There is a hold-open device, and the magazine holds 10 rounds. This model was introduced in 1982.

NIB	Exc.	V.G.	Good	Fair	Poor
210	175	150	125	100	75

Stainless-Steel Mark II Standard Model

This model is the same as the Mark II Standard except that it is made of stainless steel.

NIB	Exc.	V.G.	Good	Fair	Poor
275	250	200	150	125	100

Mark II Target Model

This model incorporates the same improvements as the Mark II Standard but is offered with 5.5" tapered, 5.5" bull, 6-7/8" tapered and 10" heavy barrel. It has adjustable target sights and was introduced in 1982.

NIB	Exc.	V.G.	Good	Fair	Poor
250	225	200	150	125	100

Stainless-Steel Mark II Target Model

This model is the same as the blued version but is made of stainless steel.

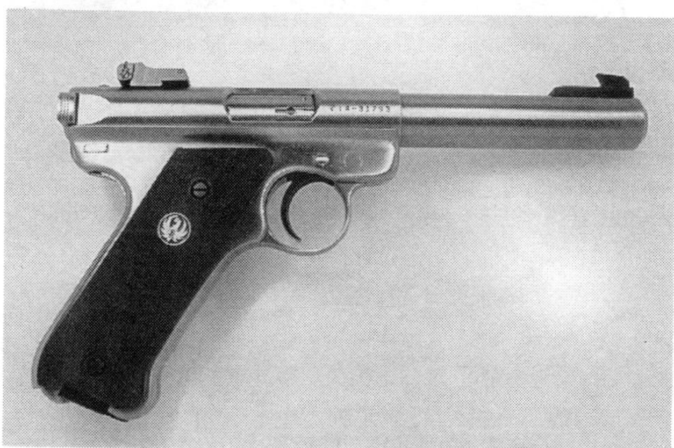

NIB	Exc.	V.G.	Good	Fair	Poor
325	300	250	200	175	125

Government Model

This model is similar to the blue Mark II Target, with a 6-7/8" bull barrel. It is the civilian version of a training pistol that the military is purchasing from Ruger. The only difference is that this model does not have the U.S. markings.

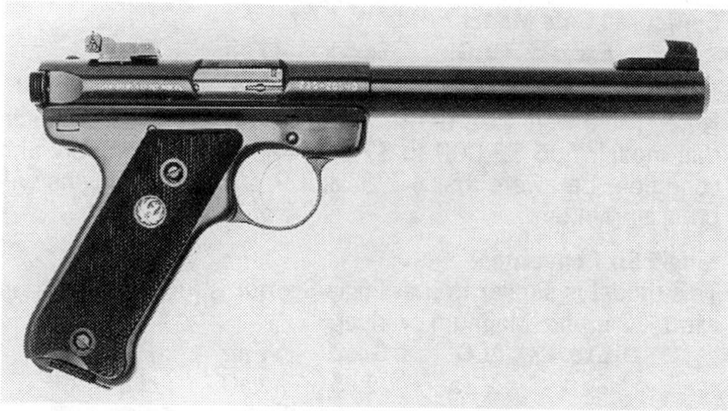

NIB	Exc.	V.G.	Good	Fair	Poor
300	275	225	200	150	100

Single Six Revolver

This is a .22 rimfire, 6-shot, single-action revolver. It was first offered with a 5-1/2", barrel length and a fixed sight. In 1959 additional barrel lengths were offered for this model in 4-5/8", 6-1/2", and 9-1/2". It is based in appearance on the Colt Single Action Army, but internally it is a new design that features coil springs instead of the old-style, flat leaf springs. It also features a floating firing pin and is generally a stronger action than what was previously available. The early model had a flat loading gate and was made this way from 1953-1957, when the contoured gate became standard. Early models had checkered hard rubber grips—changed to smooth walnut on later models.Black eagle grip medallions were used from the beginning of production to 1971 when a silver eagle grip medallion replaced it. No "Red Eagle" single-sixes were ever produced. This model was manufactured from 1953-1972.

Flat Gate Model

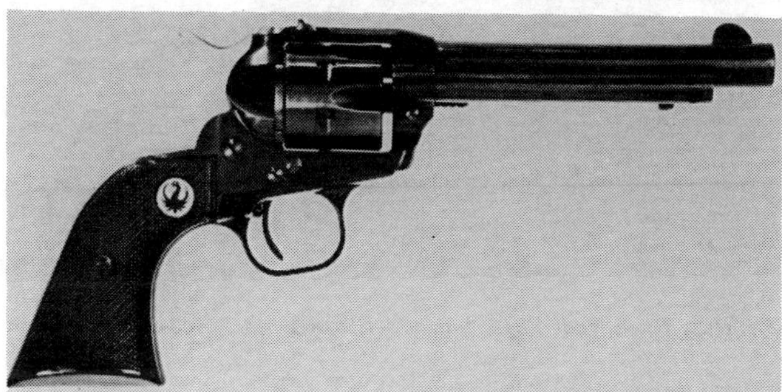

Courtesy John C. Dougan.

Courtesy *Know Your Ruger Single Action Revolvers 1953-63.* Blacksmith Corp.

Exc.	V.G.	Good	Fair	Poor
350	250	200	165	150

Note: Be aware that revolvers serial numbered under 2000 with unserrated front sights bring a premium of 25% to 125% depending on condition, low serial number, and color of cylinder frame-bright reddish purple the most desirable.

Contoured Gate Model

Exc.	V.G.	Good	Fair	Poor
295	225	175	150	125

Note: There were 258 5-1/2" barrel factory engraved pistols in this model. Add $2,000 to $7,000 depending on variety and condition. Be aware that 4-5/8" and 9-1/2" barrel lengths will bring a premium.

Single Six Convertible

This model is similar to the Single Six but is furnished with an extra .22 rimfire Magnum cylinder.

Exc.	V.G.	Good	Fair	Poor
275	225	175	150	125

Barrel lengths in 4-5/8" and 9-1/2" will bring a premium.

Single Six .22 Magnum Model

This model is similar to the Single Six except that it is chambered for the .22 rimfire Magnum and the frame was so marked. It was offered in the 6.5" barrel length only and was manufactured for three years. An extra long rifle cylinder was added later in production. The serial numbers are in the 300000-340000 range.

Exc.	V.G.	Good	Fair	Poor
300	250	200	175	150

Lightweight Single Six

This model is similar to the Single Six, with an aluminum alloy frame and 4-5/8" barrel. This variation was produced between 1956 and 1958 and was in the 200000-212000 serial number range. Approximately the first 6,500 were produced with alloy cylinders with steel chamber inserts.

Courtesy *Know Your Ruger Single Action Revolvers 1953-63.* Blacksmith Corp.

Courtesy *Know Your Ruger Single Action Revolvers 1953-63.* Blacksmith Corp.

Silver Anodized with Aluminum Cylinder Model

Exc.	V.G.	Good	Fair	Poor
400	350	250	225	195

Black Anodized with Aluminum Cylinder Model

Exc.	V.G.	Good	Fair	Poor
450	400	350	300	250

Black Anodized with Steel Cylinder Model

Exc.	V.G.	Good	Fair	Poor
400	350	250	225	195

Silver Anodized with Steel Cylinder Model

Only a few hundred pistols in this variation were produced by the factory.

Exc.	V.G.	Good	Fair	Poor
1000	800	600	400	200

NOTE: Prices may be as much as $200 higher if an "S" suffix is stamped on the serial number or the bottom of the frame. Varieties of "S" marked lightweights do exist. Individual appraisal is recommended.

NOTE: For original Lightweight Single-Six boxes add 25% to 40%.

Super Single Six

Introduced in 1964, this is the Single Six with adjustable sights. Prices given below are for pistols with 5-1/2" and 6-1/2" barrels.

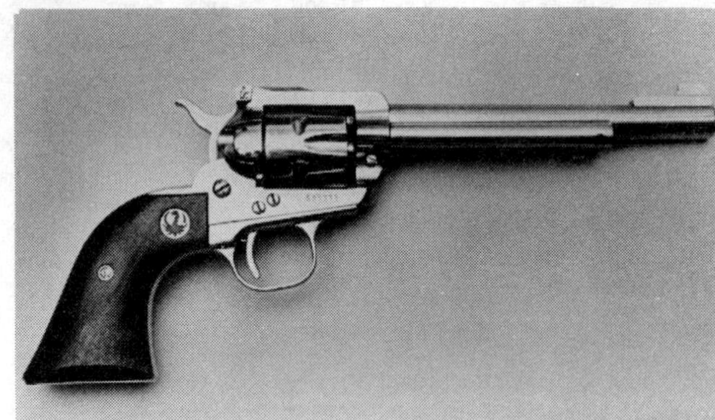

Courtesy *Know Your Ruger Single Actions: The Second Decade.* Blacksmith Corp.

Exc.	V.G.	Good	Fair	Poor
240	200	150	125	100

Super Single Six with 4-5/8" Barrel (200 built)

Exc.	V.G.	Good	Poor
1200	900	750	400

Super Single Six—Nickle-Plated Model (Approximately 100 built)

Exc.	V.G.	Good
2,500	2,250	2,000

Bearcat

This is a scaled-down version of the single action. It is chambered for .22 rimfire and has a 4" barrel and an unfluted, roll-engraved cylinder. The frame is alloy, and it has a brass colored anodized alloy triggerguard. The finish is blue, and the grips are walnut with eagle inlays. This model was manufactured from 1958-1970.

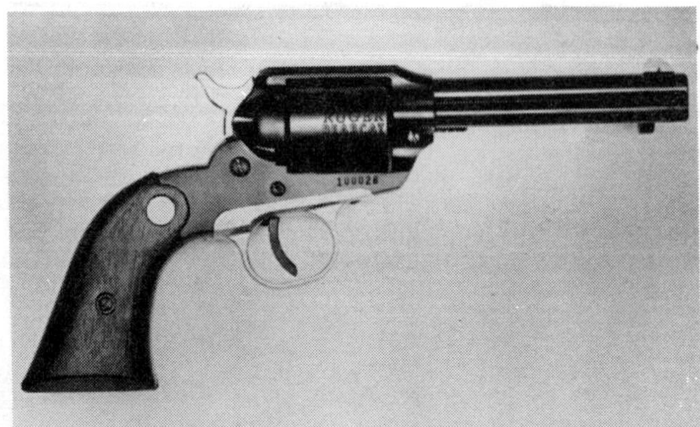

Courtesy *Know Your Ruger Single Actions: The Second Decade.* Blacksmith Corp.

Exc.	V.G.	Good	Fair	Poor
275	225	200	175	140

Alphabet Model

Exc.	V.G.	Good	Fair	Poor
350	325	300	275	225

Black Anodized Triggerguard Model (109 built)

Exc.	V.G.	Good	Fair	Poor
1,000	950	900	850	750

Alphabet Model-3-digit Serial Number with no Alpha

Exc.	V.G.	Good	Fair	Poor
400	375	350	325	275

Super Bearcat

This model is similar to the Bearcat, with a steel frame and, on later models, a blued steel triggerguard and grip frame. The early examples still used brass. This model was manufactured form 1971 to 1974.

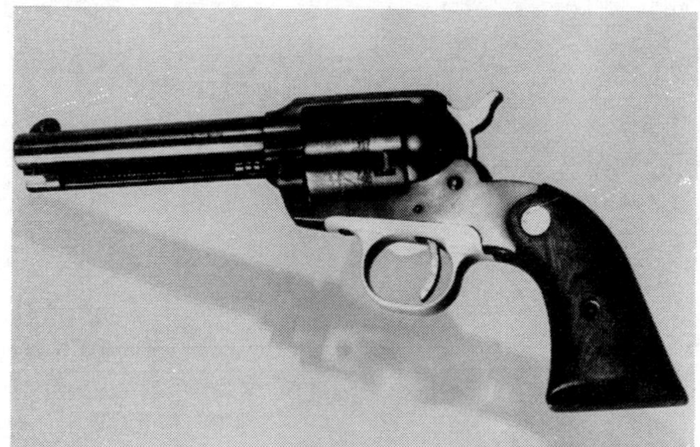

Courtesy W.P. Hallstein III and son Chip.

Exc.	V.G.	Good	Fair	Poor
275	225	200	175	125

Blackhawk Flattop—.357 Magnum

The success of the Single Six led to the production of a larger version chambered for the .357 Magnum cartridge. This model is a single action, with a 6-shot fluted cylinder and a flat top strap with adjustable "Micro sight." The barrel length is 4-5/8", 6.5", and 10". The finish is blue with checkered hard rubber grips on the early examples and smooth walnut on later ones. There were approximately 42,600 manufactured between 1955 and 1962.

6.5" Barrel—Add 50% for pistols with 6 grooves of barrel rifling.
10" Barrel— Add 100% regardless of barrel rifling.
Add 15% for 10" model in original box.
10" Barrel—Add 150% for 6-groove rifling and 300% for 8 groove rifling.

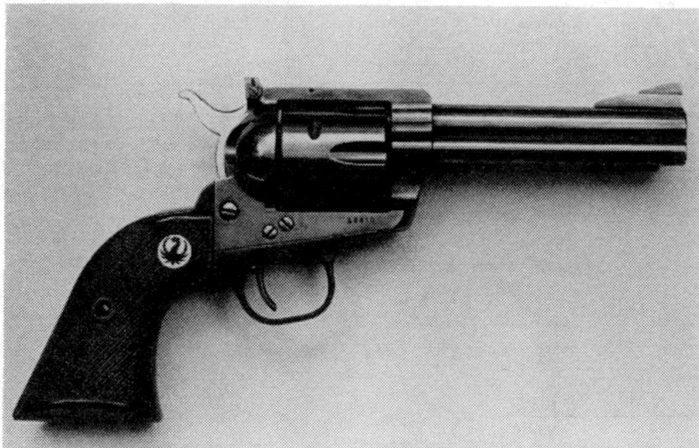

Courtesy *Know Your Ruger Single Action Revolvers 1953-63.* Blacksmith Corp.

Courtesy *Know Your Ruger Single Action Revolvers 1953-63.* Blacksmith Corp.

Exc.	V.G.	Good	Fair	Poor
400	350	300	225	200

Blackhawk Flattop .44 Magnum

In 1956 the .44 Magnum was introduced, and Ruger jumped on the bandwagon. This is very similar in appearance to the .357 but has a slightly heavier frame and a larger cylinder. It was available in a 6.5", 7.5", and 10" barrel. It was manufactured from 1956-1963. There were approximately 28,000 manufactured.

7.5" Barrel—Add 50%. With original box add 100%.
10" Barrel— Add 65%. With original box add 100%.

Courtesy *Know Your Ruger Single Action Revolvers 1953-63.* Blacksmith Corp.

Courtesy *Know Your Ruger Single Action Revolvers 1953-63.* Blacksmith Corp.

Exc.	V.G.	Good	Fair	Poor
600	550	475	350	225

Blackhawk

This model is similar to the "Flattop," but the rear sight is protected by two raised protrusions—one on each side. It was available chambered for the .357 Magnum, .41 Magnum, or the .45 Colt cartridge. Barrel lengths are 4-5/8" or 6.5". The finish is blue, and the grips are walnut with Ruger medallions. This model was produced from 1962 to 1972.

Courtesy *Know Your Ruger Single Action Revolvers 1953-63.* Blacksmith Corp.

Exc.	V.G.	Good	Fair	Poor
250	200	150	120	90

NOTE: Blackhawk models chambered for the rare .41 Magnum will bring a premium of $650 to $1200 depending on condition. Original factory brass grip frame will add at least $150 to above prices. It was available chambered for the .357 Magnum or .41 Magnum (4-5/8" or 6-1/2" barrel), .30 Carbine (7-1/2" barrel), or .45 Long Colt (4-5/8" or 7-1/2" barrel).

NOTE: Original factory brass grip frame will add at least $150 to above prices. The .41 Magnum with factory installed brass frame will bring $1200 to $650 depending on condition.

Blackhawk Convertible

This model is the same as the Blackhawk with an extra cylinder to change or convert calibers. The .357 Magnum has a 9mm cylinder, and the .45 Colt has a .45 ACP cylinder.

.357/9mm

Exc.	V.G.	Good	Fair	Poor
325	275	225	150	135

.45 L.C./.45ACP

Exc.	V.G.	Good	Fair	Poor
375	325	275	175	150

The 4-5/8" barrel will bring a slight premium.

NOTE: Non-prefix serial numbered .357/9mm Blackhawks will bring at least a 20% premium.

Super Blackhawk

The formidable recoil of the .44 Magnum cartridge was difficult to handle in a revolver with a small grip such as found on the Blackhawk, so it was decided to produce a larger-framed revolver with increased size in the grip. The rear of the triggerguard was squared off, and the cylinder was left unfluted to increase mass. This model was offered with a 7.5" barrel; 600 6.5" barrel Super Blackhawks were produced by factory error and are worth approximately 100 percent more. This model is blued and has smooth walnut grips with medallions. The very first of these revolvers were offered in a fitted wood case and are very rare today. The Super Blackhawk was made from 1959-1972.

Exc.	V.G.	Good	Fair	Poor
350	300	250	200	125

Early Model in Wood Presentation Case

Exc.	V.G.	Good	Fair	Poor
800	600	450	350	250

In Fitted White Cardboard Case

Exc.	V.G.	Good	Fair	Poor
1200	1000	950	850	

With Long Grip Frame in Wood Case (300 guns built)

Exc.	V.G.	Good	Fair	Poor
1250	1150	1050	800	675

NOTE: For pistols with factory installed brass grip frame add $200 to above prices.

NOTE: For pistols with factory installed brass grip frame add 100% to 300%. Each example should be appraised.

Hawkeye Single Shot

The shooting public wanted a small-caliber, high-velocity handgun. The Smith & Wesson Model 53, chambered for the .22 Jet, appeared in 1961; and the cartridge created extraction problems for a revolver. Ruger solved the problem with the introduction of the Hawkeye—a single shot that looked like a six shooter. In place of the cylinder was a breech block that cammed to the side for loading. This pistol was excellent from an engineering and performance standpoint but was not a commercial success. The Hawkeye is chambered for the .256 Magnum, a bottleneck cartridge, and has an 8.5" barrel and adjustable sights. The finish is blued with walnut, medallion grips. The barrel is tapped for a 1" scope base. This pistol is quite rare as only 3,300 were produced in 1963 and 1964.

Courtesy John C. Dougan.

Exc.	V.G.	Good	Fair	Poor
1000	800	700	600	500

Editors Comment: All of the above single action Ruger pistols that were fitted with factory optional grips will bring a premium regardless of model. This premium applies to pistols manufactured from 1954 to 1962 only. For the following optional grips the premium is: Ivory $500, Stag $225, and Pearl $500.

The Ruger firm has always demonstrated keen perception and in 1973 completely modified their single-action lockwork to accommodate a hammer block. This hammer block prevented accidental discharge should a revolver be dropped. In doing so, the company circumvented a great deal of potential legal problems and made collectibles out of the previous models. There are many individuals who simply do not care for the "New Models," as they are called, and will not purchase them; but judging from the continued success and growth of the Ruger company, those individuals must be the exception, not the rule.

Super Single Six Convertible (New Model)

This model is similar in appearance to the old model but has the new hammer block safety system. The frame has two pins instead of three screws, and opening the loading gate frees the cylinder stop for loading. Barrel lengths are 4-5/8", 5.5", 6.5", and 9.5". The sights are adjustable; the finish is blued. The grips are walnut with a medallion, and an interchangeable .22 Magnum cylinder is supplied. This model was introduced in 1973 and is currently in production.

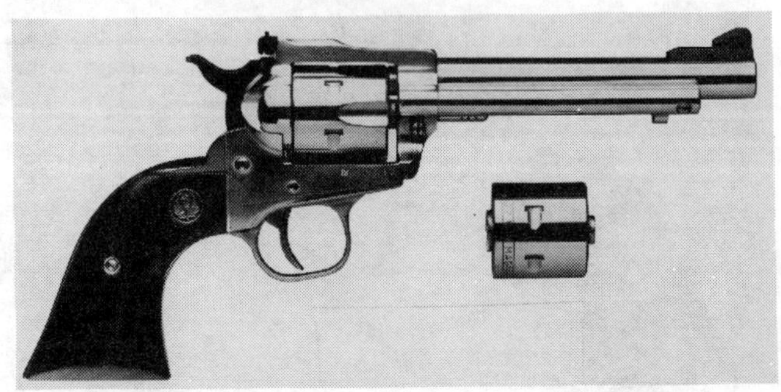

NIB	Exc.	V.G.	Good	Fair	Poor
250	200	150	125	100	80

Stainless-Steel Single Six Convertible
The same as the standard blued model but made from stainless steel. Offered with a 4-5/8", 6.5", and 9-1/2" barrel.

NIB	Exc.	V.G.	Good	Fair	Poor
325	250	200	175	125	100

Note: Pistols with 4-5/8" or 9-1/2" barrel will bring an additional 40 percent premium. Pistols with 4-5/8" barrels with "made in the 200th year of American Liberty" rollmark on the barrel will bring at least 300% premium to the NIB prices.

New Model Single-Six (Long Rifle only) "Star" Model
This model was produced in blue and stainless for one year only in 4-5/8", 5-1/2", 6-1/2", and 9-1/2" barrel lengths.

Blue Variation

NIB	Exc.	V.G.	Good	Fair	Poor
250	200	175	150	125	100

Stainless Variation

NIB	Exc.	V.G.	Good	Fair	Poor
350	300	200	150	125	100

Pistols with 4-5/8" or 9-1/2" barrels will bring a premium of 25 to 40% to NIB prices.

Colorado Centennial Single Six
This model had a stainless-steel grip frame, and the balance is blued. It has walnut grips with medallion insert. The barrel is 6.5", and the revolver is furnished with a walnut case with a centennial medal insert. There were 15,000 manufactured in 1975.

NIB	Exc.	V.G.
300	250	200

Model SSM Single Six
This is the Single Six chambered for the .32 H&R Magnum cartridge. The first 800 pistols were marked with "SSM" on the cylinder frame and will bring a slight premium.

NIB	Exc.	V.G.	Good	Fair	Poor
260	205	175	150	125	100

Blackhawk (New Model)
This model is similar in appearance to the old model Blackhawk, offered in the same calibers and barrel lengths. It has the hammer block safety device. It was introduced in 1973 and is currently in production.

NIB	Exc.	V.G.	Good	Fair	Poor
300	250	200	175	150	125

Stainless-Steel Blackhawk (New Model)
This is simply the New Model Blackhawk made from stainless steel. To date it has been offered in .357, .44, and .45 L.C.. calibers.

NIB	Exc.	V.G.	Good	Fair	Poor
375	325	275	225	175	150

Blackhawk Convertible (New Model)
This model is the same as the Blackhawk with interchangeable conversion cylinders—.357 Magnum/9mm and .45 Colt/.45 ACP. This model was discontinued in 1985. Prices below are given for blued model.

NIB	Exc.	V.G.	Good	Fair	Poor
315	280	225	175	150	125

Stainless Model (300 guns built) .357/9mm.

Exc.	V.G.	Good	Fair	Poor
650	550	450	375	250

Model SRM Blackhawk
This is the New Model Blackhawk with a 7.5" or 10.5" barrel. It was chambered for the .357 Maximum and was intended for silhouette shooting. This model experienced problems with gas cutting on the top strap and was removed from production in 1984 after approximately 11,000 were manufactured.

Exc.	V.G.	Good	Fair	Poor
450	375	350	275	250

Super Blackhawk (New Model)
This model is similar in appearance to the old model but has the hammer block safety device. It was manufactured from 1973 to the present and commenced at serial number 81-00001.

NIB	Exc.	V.G.	Good	Fair	Poor
350	300	275	225	175	125

Super Blackhawk Stainless-Steel
This model is the same as the blued version but is made of stainless-steel.

NIB	Exc.	V.G.	Good	Fair	Poor
375	325	300	250	200	150

Bisley Model
This model has the modified features found on the famous old Colt Bisley Target model—the flattop frame, fixed or adjustable sights, and the longer grip frame that has become the Bisley trademark. The Bisley is available chambered for .22 l.r., .32 H&R Magnum, .357 Magnum, .41 Magnum, .44 Magnum, and .45 Long Colt. The barrel lengths are 6.5" and 7.5"; cylinders are either fluted or unfluted and roll engraved. The finish is a satin blue, and the grips are smooth goncalo alves with medallions. The Bisley was introduced in 1986.

.22 LR and .32 H&R Magnum

NIB	Exc.	V.G.	Good	Fair	Poor
300	275	225	200	150	125

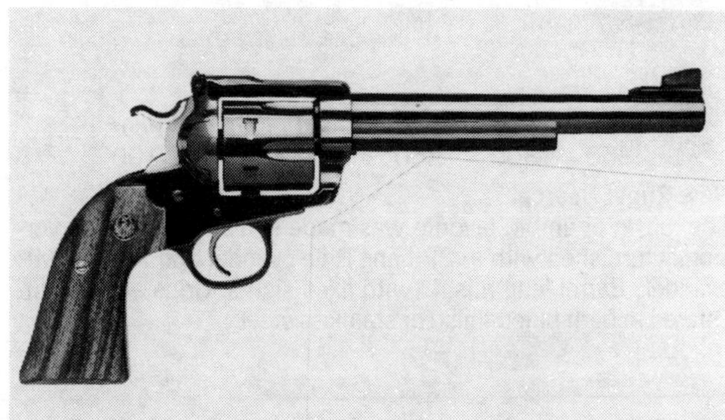

.357 Magnum, .41 Magnum .44 Magnum, and .45 Long Colt

NIB	Exc.	V.G.	Good	Fair	Poor
350	325	275	250	200	175

Old Army Percussion Revolver
This model is a .44 caliber percussion revolver with a 7.5" barrel. It has a 6-shot cylinder, with a blued finish and walnut grips.

NIB	Exc.	V.G.	Good	Fair	Poor
300	275	225	175	125	100

NOTE: For pistols with original factory installed brass grip frame add $150 to above prices.

Old Army Stainless Steel
This model is the same as the blued version except that it is made of stainless steel.

NIB	Exc.	V.G.	Good	Fair	Poor
375	300	250	200	150	125

Ruger Vaquero
This single action pistol was introduced in 1993 and was voted handgun of the year by the Shooting Industry. It is a fixed sight version of the New Model Blackhawk. It is available in stainless steel or blued with case-colored frame. Offered in three different barrel lengths: 4.62, 5.5", and 7.5". Chambered for the .45 Long Colt. Capacity is 6 rounds. Weighs between 39 and 41 ozs. depending on barrel length.

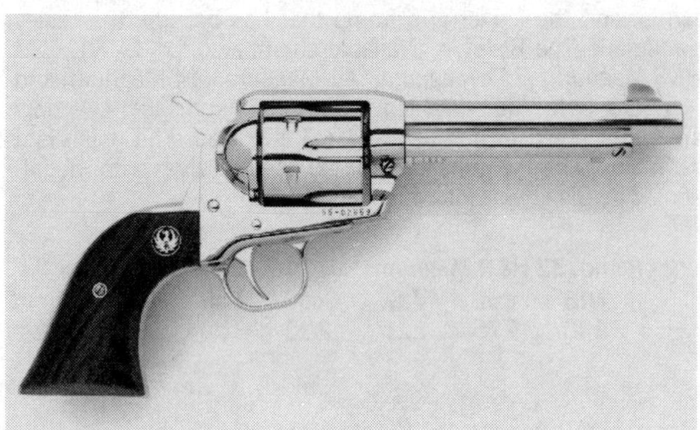

NIB	Exc.	V.G.	Good	Fair	Poor
350	300	250	200	150	100

New Ruger Bearcat

The return of an old favorite was made in 1993. This new version is furnished with a .22 Long Rifle cylinder and a .22 WMR cylinder. Barrel length is 4" with fixed sights. Grips are walnut. Offered in both blued finish or stainless steel.

NIB	Exc.	V.G.	Good	Fair	Poor
225	200	175	150	100	80

Double Action Revolvers

Security Six

This revolver, also known as the Model 117, is chambered for the .357 Magnum cartridge and has a 2.75", 4", or 6" barrel. It features adjustable sights and a square butt, with checkered walnut grips. It was manufactured between 1970 and 1985. Early guns with fixed sights and square butt were also marked "Security-Six". The model was later termed "Service-Six" and was so marked. The prices listed below are only for the adjustable sight and square butt "Security-Six" models. Round butt Security-Sixes with adjustable are worth a premium.

Exc.	V.G.	Good	Fair	Poor
250	225	200	150	100

NOTE: Fixed sight guns marked Security-Six and round butt Security-Sixes with adjustable sights are worth a premium.

Stainless Steel Model 717

This model is the Security-Six made from stainless steel.

Exc.	V.G.	Good	Fair	Poor
275	250	225	175	125

Speed Six

This model is known as the Model 207, chambered for .357 Magnum; Model 208, chambered for .38 Special; and Model 209, chambered for 9mm. It has a 2.75" or 4" barrel, fixed sights, and a round butt with checkered walnut grips and was blued. There are some with factory bobbed hammers. This model was introduced in 1973.

Exc.	V.G.	Good	Fair	Poor
250	225	200	150	100

Models 737, 738, 739

These are the designations for the stainless steel versions of the Speed-Six. They are the same revolver except for the material used in the manufacture.

Exc.	V.G.	Good	Fair	Poor
275	250	225	175	125

Police Service-Six

This model is also known as the Model 107, chambered for .357 Magnum; the Model 108, chambered for the .38 Special; and the 109, chambered for the 9mm. The barrel is 2.75" or 4". A few 6" barrel Service-Sixes were also produced and these are worth a premium. It has fixed sights and a square butt, with checkered walnut grips. The finish is blued. The 9mm was discontinued in 1984; the other two calibers, in 1988.

Exc.	V.G.	Good	Fair	Poor
250	225	200	150	100

Model 707 and 708

This is the designation for the stainless versions of the Police Service-Six. It was not produced in 9mm, and only the 4" barrel was offered. This model was discontinued in 1988.

Exc.	V.G.	Good	Fair	Poor
275	250	225	175	125

GP-100

This model is chambered for the .357 Magnum/.38 Special. It is available with fixed or adjustable sights in barrel lengths of 3", 4" or 6" barrel and has a frame designed for constant use of heavy magnum loads. The rear sight has a white outline, and the front sight features interchangeable colored inserts. The finish is blued, and the grips are a new design made of rubber with smooth goncalo alves inserts. This model was introduced in 1986.

NIB	Exc.	V.G.	Good	Fair	Poor
350	325	275	225	175	125

GP-100 Stainless

This model is the same as the GP-100 except that the material used is stainless steel.

NIB	Exc.	V.G.	Good	Fair	Poor
375	350	300	250	200	150

SP-101

This model is similar in appearance to the GP-100 but has a smaller frame and is chambered for the .22 l.r. (6-shot), .22 Magnum (6-shot), 38 Special (5-shot), .357 Magnum (5-shot), and 9mm (5-shot). The grips are all black synthetic, and the sights are adjustable for windage. Barrel lengths are 2" or 3", and construction is of stainless steel. This model was introduced in 1989. 6" barrel is available for .22 caliber.

NIB	Exc.	V.G.	Good	Fair	Poor
375	350	300	250	200	150

SP-101 Spurless-hammer

This model was introduced in 1993 and features a SP-101 without an exposed hammer spur. Available in two calibers: .38 Special and .357 Magnum with 2-1/4" barrel. This double action revolver has fixed sights, holds 5 rounds and weighs about 26 ozs.

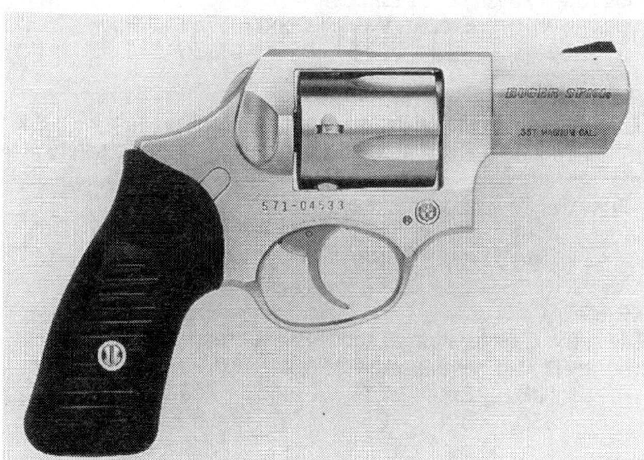

NIB	Exc.	V.G.	Good	Fair	Poor
290	250	200	150	100	80

Redhawk

This model is a large-frame, double-action revolver which was chambered for the .41 Magnum until 1992, and currently for the .44 Magnum cartridges. The barrel lengths are 5.5" and 7.5". The finish is blue, and the grips are smooth walnut. The Redhawk was introduced in 1986.

NIB	Exc.	V.G.	Good	Fair	Poor
395	325	275	225	175	125

Redhawk Stainless Steel

The same as the blued version except constructed of stainless steel. It was chambered for .357 Magnum until 1985, the .41 Magnum until 1992 , and currently for the .44 Magnum.

NIB	Exc.	V.G.	Good	Fair	Poor
375	350	300	250	200	150

Super Redhawk

This is a more massive version of the Redhawk. It weighs 53 ounces and is offered with a 7.5" or 9.5" barrel. It is made of stainless steel, and the barrel rib is milled to accept the Ruger scope-ring system. The grips are the combination rubber and Goncalo Alves-type found on the GP-100. This revolver was introduced in 1987.

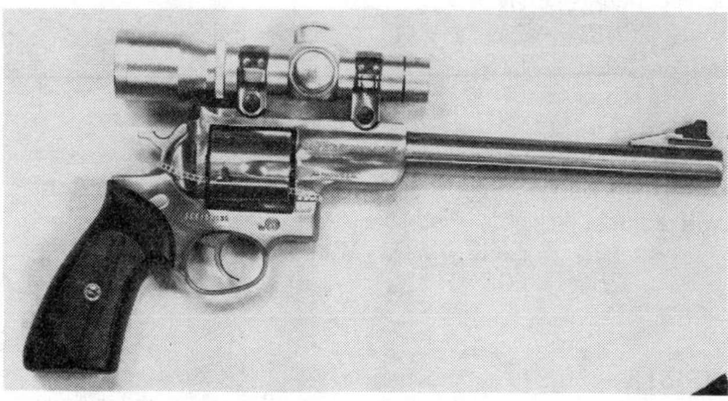

NIB	Exc.	V.G.	Good	Fair	Poor
500	450	400	350	300	225

Semi-Automatic Handguns (New Models)

Mark II Standard Model

This is a generally improved version of the first Ruger pistol. There is a hold-open device, and the magazine holds 10 rounds. This model was introduced in 1982.

NIB	Exc.	V.G.	Good	Fair	Poor
210	175	150	125	100	75

Stainless Steel Mark II Standard Model

This model is the same as the Mark II Standard except that it is made of stainless steel.

NIB	Exc.	V.G.	Good	Fair	Poor
275	250	200	150	125	100

Mark II .22 caliber pistol specifications: Supplied in .22 Long ifle with various barrel weights and lengths. Magazine capacity is 10 rounds. Trigger is grooved with curved finger surface. High speed hammer provides fast lock time. Grips are Delrin material with black gloss with diamond checkering. Stainless steel model have a brushed satin finish. Each model, except the MK-10 and the KMK-10 come from the factory with a hard plastic lockable case.

Mark II Bull Barrel Model

This variation of the Mark II is available in five different configurations. Three of these are furnished with 5.5" barrels and either blue or stainless steel finish. The front sight is a Partridge type with click adjustments for windage and elevation. These 5.5" barrel models weigh between 35 and 42 ozs. Two additional variations are offered that are furnished with 10" barrels in either blue or stainless steel. This model weighs around 51 ozs.

NIB	Exc.	V.G.	Good	Fair	Poor
225	190	165	125	100	80

Mark II Competition

The Competition model features a stainless steel frame with checkered laminated hardwood thumb rest grips, heavy 6.7/8" bull barrel factory drilled and tapped for scope mount, Partridge type front sight undercut to prevent glare and an adjustable rear sight. Pistol weighs 45 ozs.

NIB	Exc.	V.G.	Good	Fair	Poor
350	300	250	200	125	100

Ruger 22/45: This .22 Long Rifle caliber pistol has the same grip angel and magazine latch as the Model 1911 .45 ACP. The semi-automatic action is stainless steel and the grip frame is made from Zytel, a fiberglass reinforced lightweight composite material. Front sight is Partridge type. This model is available in three different configurations.

KP-4

This model features a 4.75" standard weight barrel with fixed sights. Pistol weighs 28 ozs.

NIB	Exc.	V.G.	Good	Fair	Poor
200	175	150	125	100	75

KP-514

Furnished with a target tapered barrel 5.25" in length. Comes with adjustable sights. Pistol weighs 38 ozs.

NIB	Exc.	V.G.	Good	Fair	Poor
250	200	175	150	100	75

KP-512

This model is equipped with a 5.5" bull barrel with adjustable sights. Weighs 42 ozs.

NIB	Exc.	V.G.	Good	Fair	Poor
250	200	175	150	100	75

P-85 or P-89

This model represents Ruger's entry into the wonder nine market. The P-85 is a double-action, high-capacity (15-shot detachable magazine) semi-automatic, with an alloy frame and steel slide. It has a 4.5" barrel, ambidextrous safety, and three-dot sighting system. It has a matte black finish and black synthetic grips. The latest option for this model is a decocking device to replace the standard safety. There is also an optional molded locking case and extra magazine with loading tool available. It is more reasonably priced than many of its competitors. This pistol was introduced in 1987 and was sold at large premium for some time due to limited supply and great demand. As of this writing, Ruger is producing this pistol in a new plant in Prescott, Arizona; and the premium situation no longer exists This model is also produced in a 9x21 cartridge for non-Nato countries.

NIB	Exc.	V.G.	Good	Fair	Poor
325	300	275	250	200	150

P-85 Stainless Steel

This model is the same as the matte black version except that the slide is made of stainless steel.

NIB	Exc.	V.G.	Good	Fair	Poor
355	335	300	275	225	175

KP-88X

Introduced in 1993 this pistol features a stainless steel convertible safety model which comes with both 9mm and .30 Luger barrels. The barrels are interchangeable without the use of tools. Magazine capacity is 15 rounds.

NIB	Exc.	V.G.	Good	Fair	Poor
375	325	275	200	150	100

P-89

This semi-automatic pistol is chambered for the 9mm cartridge. It has a blued finish and a 15-round magazine. The safety is a manual ambidextrous lever type. The barrel is 4.5" and the empty weight is approximately 36 ozs.

NIB	Exc.	V.G.	Good	Fair	Poor
300	250	200	150	100	80

KP-89

The same configuration as the P-89 but furnished with a stainless steel finish. Introduced in 1990.

NIB	Exc.	V.G.	Good	Fair	Poor
350	300	250	200	150	100

P-89DC

This model features a blued finish and is chambered for the 9mm Para cartridge but is fitted with a Decock-only lever (no manual safety). After decocking the gun can be fired by a double action pull of the trigger.

NIB	Exc.	V.G.	Good	Fair	Poor
300	250	200	150	100	80

KP-89DC

This is the stainless steel version of the P-89DC.

NIB	Exc.	V.G.	Good	Fair	Poor
350	300	250	200	150	100

KP-89DAO

Chambered for the 9mm cartridge this model is the stainless steel double action only version of the above model.

NIB	Exc.	V.G.	Good	Fair	Poor
350	300	250	200	150	100

KP-90

Chambered for the .45 ACP cartridge, this model stainless steel and holds 7 rounds in the magazine. It is fitted with a manual safety. Introduced in 1991.

NIB	Exc.	V.G.	Good	Fair	Poor
375	325	275	200	150	100

KP-90DC

This stainless steel version of the KP-90 has a decock-only system. Chambered for the .45 ACP cartridge.

NIB	Exc.	V.G.	Good	Fair	Poor
375	325	275	200	150	100

KP-91DC

This model features a stainless steel finish and is chambered for the .40 S&W cartridge. Magazine capacity is 11 rounds. It has a decock-only system. Introduced in 1992.

NIB	Exc.	V.G.	Good	Fair	Poor
375	325	275	200	150	100

KP-91DOA

Chambered for the .40 S&W with stainless steel finish it features a double action only system.

NIB	Exc.	V.G.	Good	Fair	Poor
375	325	275	200	150	100

KP-93DC

Introduced in 1993 this pistol is a new addition to the P series as a compact model. Stainless steel and chambered for the 9mm cartridge it has a magazine capacity of 15 rounds. Available in decock-only configuration. Barrel length is 3.9" and the weight is about 24 ozs. empty.

NIB	Exc.	V.G.	Good	Fair	Poor
350	300	250	200	150	100

KP-93DOA

The double action only version of the KP-93 compact series.

NIB	Exc.	V.G.	Good	Fair	Poor
350	300	250	200	150	100

Semi-Automatic Rifles

10/22 Standard Carbine With Walnut Stock

This model has an 18.5" barrel and is chambered for the .22 l.r. It has a 10-shot, detachable rotary magazine and a folding rear sight. The stock is smooth walnut, with a barrel band and carbine-style buttplate. This rifle enjoys a fine reputation for accuracy and dependability and is considered an excellent value. It was introduced in 1964.

Birch Stock—Deduct $20.

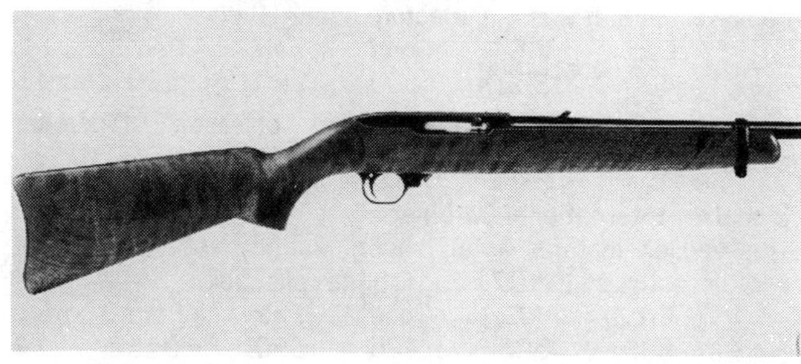

NIB	Exc.	V.G.	Good	Fair	Poor
185	165	125	100	75	50

10/22 Sporter

This model is similar to the Standard Carbine except that it has a Monte Carlo stock, finger-groove forend, and no barrel band. It was manufactured between 1966 and 1971.

Exc.	V.G.	Good	Fair	Poor
165	125	100	75	50

Add 300 percent for factory hand checkering.

10/22 Deluxe Sporter

The same as the Sporter with a checkered stock and better buttplate. This model was introduced in 1971.

NIB	Exc.	V.G.	Good	Fair	Poor
200	165	125	100	75	50

10/22 International Carbine

This model is similar to the Standard Carbine, with a full-length, Mannlicher-style stock. It was manufactured between 1966 and 1971 and is fairly rare on today's market.

Exc.	V.G.	Good	Fair	Poor
350	300	250	175	125

Add 50 percent for factory hand checkering.

10/22 Canadian Centennial

In 1966 and 1967 approximately 4,500 10/22 Sporters were built for the Canadian Centennial. The first 2,000 were sold with a Remington Model 742 in .308 caliber with matching serial numbers. The Ruger Sporter may be checkered or unchecked. The two gun set was either boxed separately or together.

NIB for two gun set
800

NIB for 10/22 only
400

Model 44 Carbine

This model is a short, 18.5" barrelled, gas-operated carbine chambered for the .44 Magnum cartridge. It has a 4-shot, non-detachable magazine, a folding rear sight, and a plain walnut stock. This is a very handy deer hunting carbine manufactured between 1961 and 1985.

Exc.	V.G.	Good	Fair	Poor
400	350	300	200	150

Deerstalker Model

The same as the Model 44 Carbine with "Deerstalker" stamped on it. This model was manufactured in 1961 and 1962 only.

Exc.	V.G.	Good	Fair	Poor
450	400	350	300	200

Model 44RS

This is the Model 44 with sling swivels and an aperture sight.

Exc.	V.G.	Good	Fair	Poor
350	300	250	200	150

NOTE: "Liberty" marked 44RS carbines are extremely rare and will bring at least a 300 percent premium. An individual appraisal is recommended.

Model 44 Sporter

This version has a Monte Carlo stock, finger groove forend, and no barrel band. It was manufactured until 1971.

Exc.	V.G.	Good	Fair	Poor
400	350	300	250	200

Factory hand checkered models will bring at least a 100 percent premium.

Model 44 International Carbine

This version features a full-length, Mannlicher-style stock. It was discontinued in 1971 and is quite collectible.

Exc.	V.G.	Good	Fair	Poor
600	500	425	350	275

Factory hand checkered models will bring at least a 75 percent premium.

Model 44 25th Anniversary Model

This version is lightly engraved, has a medallion in the stock and was only made in 1985, the last year of production.

NIB	Exc.	V.G.	Good	Fair	Poor
450	400	350	300	250	200

Mini-14

This is a para-military style carbine chambered for the .223 Remington and on a limited basis for the .222 cartridge. It has an 18.5" barrel and is gas-operated. The detachable magazines originally offered held 5, 10, or 20 rounds. The high-capacity magazines are now discontinued, and prices of them are what the market will bear. The Mini-14 has a military-style stock and aperture sight. It was introduced in 1975.

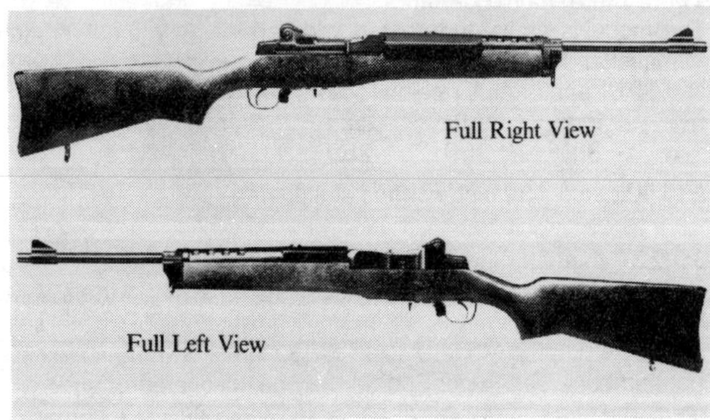

NIB	Exc.	V.G.	Good	Fair	Poor
425	375	325	275	225	150

NOTE: 10 and 20-round magazines are still offered but to law enforcement only.

Mini-14 Stainless Steel

The same as the Mini-14 except constructed of stainless steel.

NIB	Exc.	V.G.	Good	Fair	Poor
450	400	350	300	250	175

Mini-14 Ranch Rifle

This model is similar to the standard Mini-14, with a folding rear sight and the receiver milled to accept the Ruger scope-ring system. The rings are supplied with the rifle.

NIB	Exc.	V.G.	Good	Fair	Poor
450	400	350	300	250	175

Stainless Steel Mini-14 Ranch Rifle

This model is the same as the blued version except that it is made of stainless steel.

NIB	Exc.	V.G.	Good	Fair	Poor
500	450	400	350	300	225

GB Model

This model has a factory-installed folding stock, flash suppressor, and bayonet lug. It was designed and sold by Ruger to law enforcement agencies. A number have come on the civilian market through surplus sales and police trade-ins. With the assault-rifle hysteria, prices of this model have fluctuated wildly in some areas. Now that Ruger has discontinued the folding stock and the high capacity magazines, this could become even less predictable. It would behoove anyone contemplating purchase of this model to check their local ordinances and the current market in their area. Note that this is a semi-automatic and totally different than the full-auto version of this weapon available only through Class 3 dealers.

Mini-30

This model was brought out by Ruger in 1987 in answer to the influx of weapons imported from China that were chambered for this cartridge—the 7.62mm x 39 Russian. This cartridge is touted as a fine hunting cartridge for deer-sized game; and by adding this chambering, the very handy Mini-14 becomes a legitimate hunting gun—and a new market opened. This model is similar in appearance to the standard Mini-14 and is supplied with Ruger scope rings.

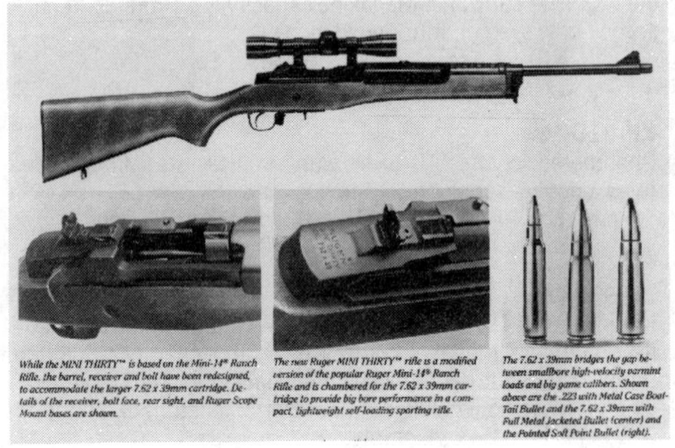

While the MINI THIRTY™ is based on the Mini-14® Ranch Rifle, the barrel, receiver and bolt have been redesigned, to accommodate the larger 7.62 x 39mm cartridge. Details of the receiver, bolt face, rear sight, and Ruger Scope Mount bases are shown.

The new Ruger MINI THIRTY™ rifle is a modified version of the popular Ruger Mini-14® Ranch Rifle and is chambered for the 7.62 x 39mm cartridge to provide big bore performance in a compact, lightweight self-loading sporting rifle.

The 7.62 x 39mm bridges the gap between smallbore high-velocity varmint loads and big game calibers. Shown above are the .223 with Metal Case Boat-Tail Bullet and the 7.62 x 39mm with Full Metal Jacketed Bullet (center) and the Pointed Soft Point Bullet (right).

NIB	Exc.	V.G.	Good	Fair	Poor
375	350	300	250	200	150

Mini-30 Stainless

NIB	Exc.	V.G.	Good	Fair	Poor
400	375	325	275	200	150

SINGLE SHOT RIFLES

All Ruger single shot rifles feature a sliding shotgun-type safety, that engage both the sear and the hammer, all metal parts are polished and blued, each receiver and stock is hand fitted, and the stock is American walnut with a satin finish. The pistol grip and forearm are hand checkered with 20 lines to the inch. Those No. 1 rifles offered with open sights are fitted with an adjustable folding leaf rear sight set into a quarter rib on the barrel and a dovetail-type gold bead front sight. All quarter ribs are machined to accommodate Ruger steel scope rings.

NOTE: There are many rare non-prefixed No. 1 rifles. Unique examples should be individually appraised. "Writers Club" 1 of 21 rifles that are engraved will bring $3000 to $5000 depending on the amount of engraving and gold inlay, caliber, and the person that it was presented to.

Ruger No. 1 Light Sporter (1-A)

This model features open sights, barrel band on lightweight barrel, and Alexander Henry style forearm. Offered with a 22" barrel in 4 calibers. Rifle weighs 7.25 lbs.

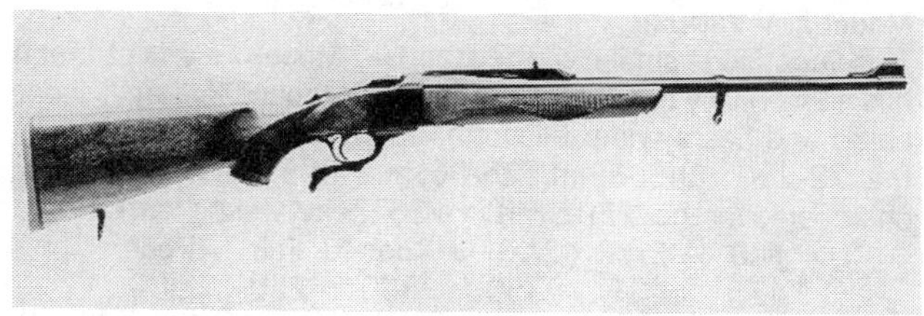

NIB	Exc.	V.G.	Good	Fair	Poor
475	425	350	300	250	200

Ruger No. 1 Standard (1-B)
This model is furnished with no sights, medium barrel, semi-beavertail forearm, and quarter rib with 1" Ruger scope rings. Weighs 8 lbs.

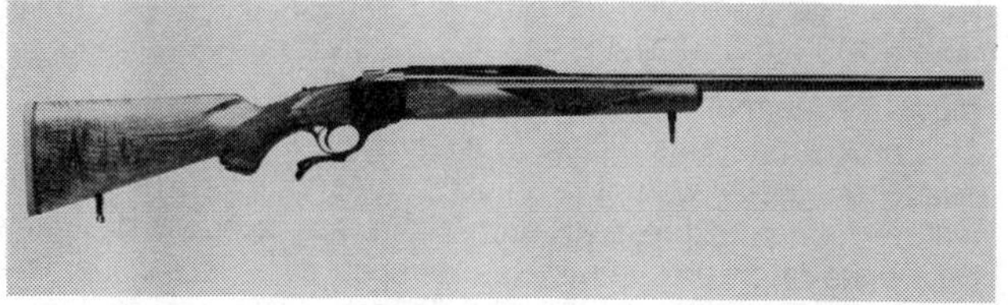

NIB	Exc.	V.G.	Good	Fair	Poor
475	425	350	300	250	200

Ruger No. 1 Tropical (1-H)
Fitted with open sights this model has a barrel band on a heavy barrel with Alexander Henry style forearm. Rifle weighs 9 lbs.

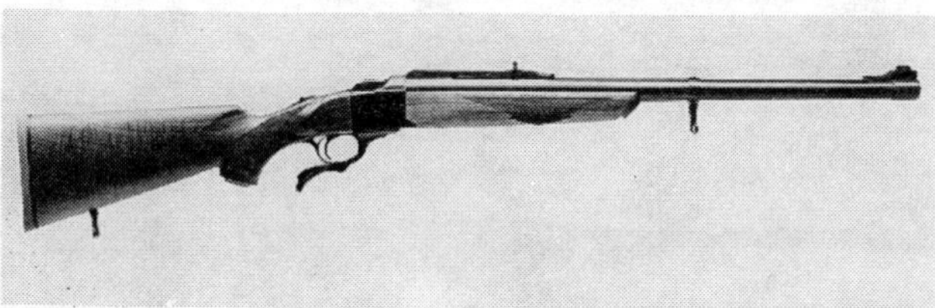

NIB	Exc.	V.G.	Good	Fair	Poor
475	425	350	300	250	200

NOTE: A very few 24" heavy barrel 1-H rifles were chambered for the .45-70 Gov't cartridge up to 1976. These bring a substantial premium of $2000 to $4000 and should be appraised individually.

Ruger No. 1 International (1-RSI)
This No. 1 rifle features a lightweight barrel with full length forearm, open sights. Rifle weighs 7.25 lbs.

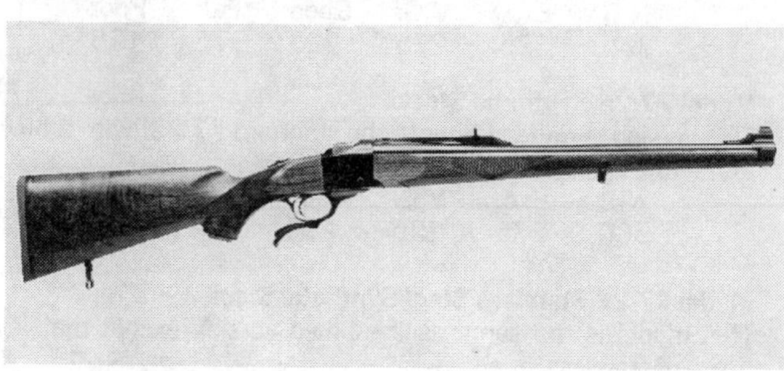

NIB	Exc.	V.G.	Good	Fair	Poor
525	475	400	300	200	150

Ruger No. 1 Medium Sporter (1-S)
The Medium Sporter is equipped with open sights, a barrel band on a medium weight barrel, and Alexander Henry style forearm. Rifle weighs 8 lbs.

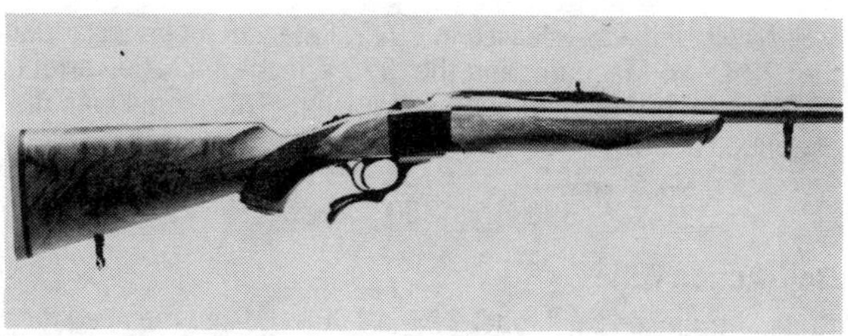

NIB	Exc.	V.G.	Good	Fair	Poor
475	425	350	300	250	200

Ruger No. 1 Special Varminter (1-V)
This model is furnished with no sights, a heavy barrel, target scope blocks with 1" Ruger scope rings, and semi-beavertail forearm. Rifle weighs about 9 lbs.

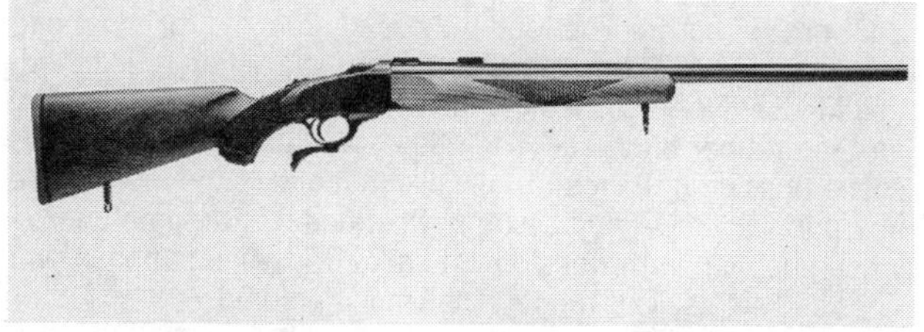

NIB	Exc.	V.G.	Good	Fair	Poor
475	425	350	300	250	200

RUGER NO. 1 SINGLE-SHOT RIFLES
Caliber, catalog number, and availability by barrel length.

Caliber	1-A	1-B	1-H	1-RSI	1-S	1-V
.218 Bee	—	26"	—	—	26"	—
.22 Hornet	—	26"	—	—	—	—
.223	—	26"	—	—	—	24"
.22 PPC	—	—	—	—	—	24"
.22-250	—	26"	—	—	—	24"
6mm Rem.	—	26"	—	—	—	24"
6mm PPC	—	—	—	—	—	24"
.243 Win.	22"	26"	—	20"	—	—
.257 Roberts	—	26"	—	—	—	—
.25-06	—	26"	—	—	—	24"
.270 Win.	22"	26"	—	20"	—	—
.270 Wby. Mag.	—	26"	—	—	—	—
7x57mm	22"	—	—	20"	—	—
.280	—	26"	—	—	—	—
7MM Rem. Mag.	—	26"	—	—	26"	—
.30-06	22"	26"	—	20"	—	—
.300 Win. Mag.	—	26"	—	—	26"	—
.300 Wby. Mag.	—	26"	—	—	—	—
.338 Win. Mag.	—	26"	—	—	26"	—
.375 H&H Mag.	—	—	24"	—	—	—
.404 Jeffery	—	—	24"	—	—	—
.416 Rigby	—	—	24"	—	—	—
.45-70	—	—	—	—	22"	—
.458 Win. Mag.	—	—	24"	—	—	—

Number 3 Carbine
This model is a less elaborate, inexpensive version of the Number 1. The action is the same except that the lever is less ornate in appearance and lacks the locking bar. The uncheckered stock is of a military carbine style with a barrel band. It is similar in appearance to the Model 44 and the 10/22. This serviceable rifle was chambered for the .22 Hornet, .30-40 Krag, and the

.45-70 when it was released in 1972. Later chamberings added the .223, .44 Magnum, and the .375 Winchester. The barrel is 22" long, and there is a folding rear sight. This model was discontinued in 1987.

Exc.	V.G.	Good	Fair	Poor
375	325	250	200	125

Bolt-Action Rifles

Ruger introduced the Model 77R in 1968. It filled the need for a good quality, reasonably priced, bolt-action hunting rifle. It has been a commercial success. There are certain variations of this rifle that collectors actively seek. One should avail oneself of the specialized literature on this model and secure individual appraisals on the rare variations as the differences are slight and beyond the scope of this book.

Model 77

This model was introduced in 1968. It is offered with a 22", 24", or 26" barrel. The Model 77 is chambered for most calibers from .22-250 through .35 Whelen. The action is of a modified Mauser type, finished in blue with a checkered walnut stock and red rubber buttplate. The rifle is available milled for Ruger scope rings or in the round-top style that allows the mounting of any popular scope ring system. This model is designated 77R when supplied with rings only; and 77RS, when supplied with rings and sights. This model is still manufactured.

NIB	Exc.	V.G.	Good	Fair	Poor
475	425	350	300	250	200

Model 77 Flat Bolt

This is an example of the slight variations that make this model collectible. This is essentially the same rifle with the knob on the bolt handle flattened. They were only produced in the configuration until 1972. Watch for fakes, and read specialized material.

Exc.	V.G.	Good	Fair	Poor
525	450	400	350	275

NOTE: Non-prefixed rifles exists in calibers and configurations other than those advertised by Ruger. These should be individually appraised.

Model 77 RL & RLS

This variation is similar to the standard model except that it features an ultra light 20" barrel and black forearm tip. This model is also available in an 18.5" carbine version with sights designated the RLS. They are chambered for the .257 Roberts, .270, and .30-06. Weight is only 6 pounds.

NIB	Exc.	V.G.	Good	Fair	Poor
500	450	375	325	275	225

Model 77 RSI

This version of the Model 77 has a full-length, Mannlicher-style stock and is chambered for the .250-3000, .270, and the .30-06.

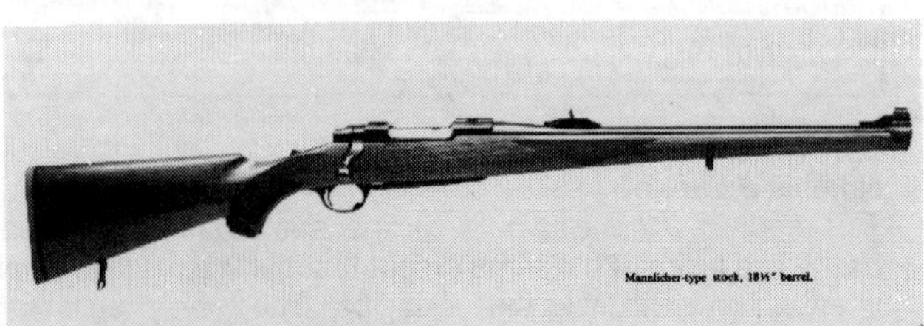

NIB	Exc.	V.G.	Good	Fair	Poor
550	475	400	350	300	250

Model 77V Varmint

This variation is similar to the standard Model 77 except that it has a 24" heavy barrel that is drilled and tapped for target scope bases and has a wider beavertail forearm. It is chambered for the .22-250, .243, 6mm,. 25-06, and .308. This model is also chambered for the .220 Swift in a 26" heavyweight barrel.

NIB	Exc.	V.G.	Good	Fair	Poor
475	425	350	300	250	200

Model 77 RS African

This is a heavier-barrelled version, with a steel triggerguard and floorplate. Earlier versions were stocked with fine quality Circassian walnut. This rifle is chambered for the .458 Winchester Magnum.

NIB	Exc.	V.G.	Good	Fair	Poor
625	550	500	425	350	250

NOTE: Less than 50 or these rifles chambered for the .416 Taylor cartridge were produced up to 1976. Selling prices range from $3000 to $5000 and should be individually appraised.

Model 77 Magnum

This new variation is deluxe in every way. It is stocked in fine quality Circassian walnut, with black forearm tip and rifle pad. It features a new express rib with sights and a newly designed floor-plate latch that eliminates dumped cartridges under the heavy recoil of these magnum calibers. This model is chambered for the .375 H&H Magnum and the .416 Rigby. These are heavy rifles, at approximately 10 pounds. At this time, price has not been established. Estimated NIB $1,550.

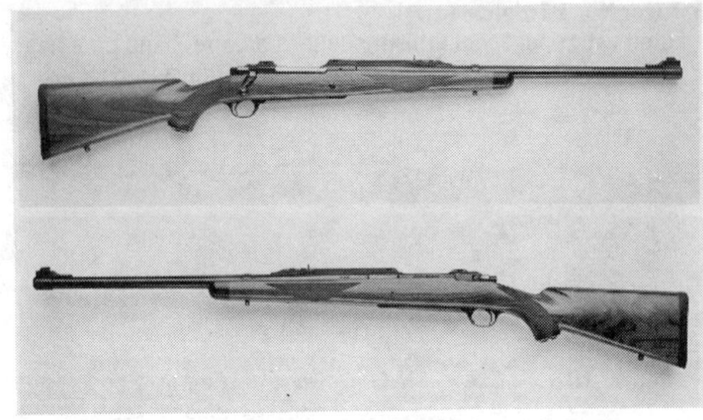

NIB	Exc.	V.G.	Good	Fair	Poor
1500	1200	900	650	450	300

Model 77/22

This is a high quality, .22 rimfire rifle designed for the serious shooter. This model has a 20" barrel and a 10-shot, detachable rotary magazine. It is made of steel and stocked with checkered walnut. It is available with sights, scope rings, or both as an extra cost ($20) option. This model was introduced in 1984.

NIB	Exc.	V.G.	Good	Fair	Poor
365	325	275	225	175	125

Model 77/22 Synthetic Stock

This version is quite similar to the standard 77/22, with a black matte finished synthetic stock.

NIB	Exc.	V.G.	Good	Fair	Poor
300	275	225	200	150	100

Model 77/22 Stainless Steel/Synthetic Stock

This model is the same as the blued version except that it is made of stainless steel.

NIB	Exc.	V.G.	Good	Fair	Poor
350	300	250	200	150	100

Model 77/22 Varmint

Introduced in 1993 this model features a stainless steel finish, laminated wood stock, heavy 20" varmint barrel with no sights. Scope rings are included as standard. Chambered for the .22 Win. Mag. Rimfire.

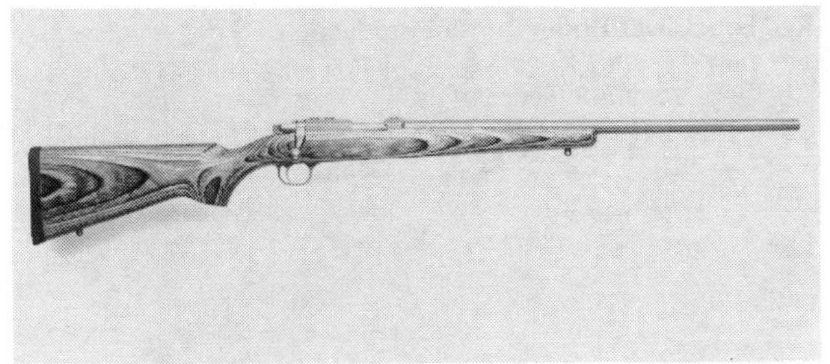

NIB	Exc.	V.G.	Good	Fair	Poor
350	300	250	200	150	100

Model 77/22M

This model is simply the 77/22 chambered for the .22 Magnum cartridge. The finish is blue, and the magazine capacity is 9 rounds.

NIB	Exc.	V.G.	Good	Fair	Poor
370	325	275	225	175	125

Model 77/22M Stainless Steel

This is the same as the blued 77/22M constructed of stainless-steel.

NIB	Exc.	V.G.	Good	Fair	Poor
350	300	250	200	150	100

Ruger Model 77: Mark I vs. Mark II

This Ruger bolt action was produced in the Mark I version until November, 1991 when it was dropped from the product line. In December of 1991 Ruger began producing a new bolt action Model 77 design referred to as the Mark II. There are several noticeable and important differences between the two versions. The Model 77 Mark I features a sliding tang safety while the Mark II has a new 3 position wing safety. The Mark I designed Model 77 holds 5 rounds while the newer Mark II holds 4 rounds. The Mark I incorporates and chromemoly bolt and the Mark II has a stainless steel bolt. The Mark I has a spring loaded ejector while the Mark II has a fixed pin design. The Mark I has an adjustable trigger as opposed to the newer Mark II's non-adjustable trigger. The Mark I bolt face does not incorporate a central feed system while the Mark II does have a central feed. The Mark II design also features a slimer action that the older Mark I design.

Model 77R MKII

Introduced in 1992 this model is the basic Model 77 rifle. Features blued metal parts and no sights. Available in 14 different calibers from .223 to .338 Win. Mag. in barrel lengths from 22" to 24" depending on caliber. Comes from factory with scope bases and rings. Rifle weighs approximately 7 lbs.

NIB	Exc.	V.G.	Good	Fair	Poor
390	350	300	250	200	150

Model 77RP MKII

This model was also introduced in 1992 and differs from the Model 77R with the addition of stainless steel barrel and receiver and synthetic stock. Available in 9 calibers.

NIB	Exc.	V.G.	Good	Fair	Poor
390	350	300	250	200	150

Model 77RS MKII

This is a blued version of the basic rifle with the addition of open sights. Available in 8 calibers from .243 Win. to .338 Win. Mag.

NIB	Exc.	V.G.	Good	Fair	Poor
450	400	350	300	250	175

Model 77RSP MKII

The stainless version of the basic rifle with the addition of a synthetic stock and open sights. Available in 6 calibers: .243, .270, 7MM Rem. Mag., .30-06, .330 Win. Mag., .338 Win. Mag. Introduced in 1993.

NIB	Exc.	V.G.	Good	Fair	Poor
450	400	350	300	250	175

Model 77RSI MKII

Also introduced in 1993 this model features a blued barrel and walnut stock. Offered in 4 calibers all with 18" barrel. The calibers are: .243, .270, .30-06, and .308.

NIB	Exc.	V.G.	Good	Fair	Poor
450	400	350	300	250	175

Model 77RL MKII

This model features a short action in 6 caliber from .223 to .308, all with 20" barrel. Rifle weighs about 6 lbs. Introduced in 1992.

NIB	Exc.	V.G.	Good	Fair	Poor
400	350	300	250	200	150

Model 77LR MKII

This model is a left-handed rifle furnished in long action calibers: .270, 7MM Rem. Mag., .30-06, .330 Win. Mag. Introduced in 1992.

NIB	Exc.	V.G.	Good	Fair	Poor
390	350	300	250	200	150

Model 77VT MKII

This rifle was introduced in 1993 and is a target rifle. Furnished with no sights, heavy laminated wood stock with beavertail forend, and adjustable trigger. Barrel, bolt, and action are stainless steel. Weighs approximately 9.75 lbs.

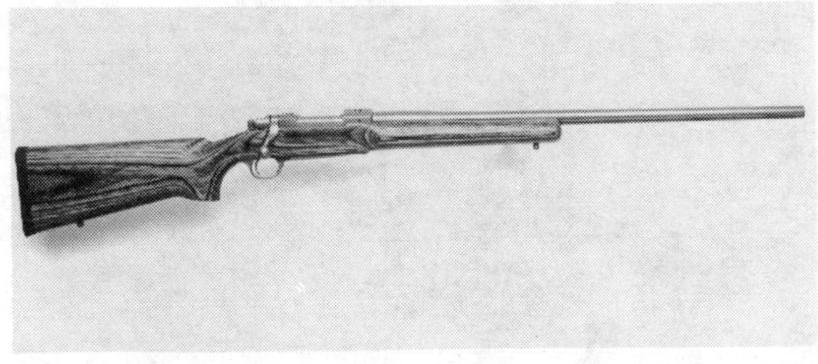

NIB	Exc.	V.G.	Good	Fair	Poor
475	425	350	300	250	175

Model 77 Express MKII

Introduced in 1992 the Ruger Express Mark II rifle features a select walnut straight comb checkered stock. The checkering is 22 lines to the inch and the butt stock is fitted with a rubber recoil pad. The pistol grip is fitted with a metal grip cap. The barrel length is 22" and features a blade front sight, V-notch rear express sights, and the receiver is machined for scope mounts which are included. Available in the following calibers: .270, .30-06, 7MM Rem. Mag., .300 Win. Mag., .338 Win. Mag. Rifle weighs about 7.5 lbs.

NIB	Exc.	V.G.	Good	Fair	Poor
1100	850	650	550	400	200

Model 77 Magnum MKII

Similar in all respects to the Model 77 Express MKII except offered in the following calibers: .375 H&H, .404 Jeffery, .416 Rigby, and .458 Win. Mag. The .375 and .404 rifles weigh about 9.25 lbs. while the .416 and .458 weigh about 10.25 lbs.

NIB	Exc.	V.G.	Good	Fair	Poor
1100	850	650	550	400	200

Shotguns

Red Label Over/Under Early Production

Ruger introduced the Red Label in 20 gauge in 1977; the 12 gauge followed shortly afterwards. This high quality shotgun is offered with 3" chambers in 26" or 28" barrel lengths. Various chokes are available. They are boxlocks with automatic ejectors. The stock is of checkered walnut. The finish is blue on the earlier guns.

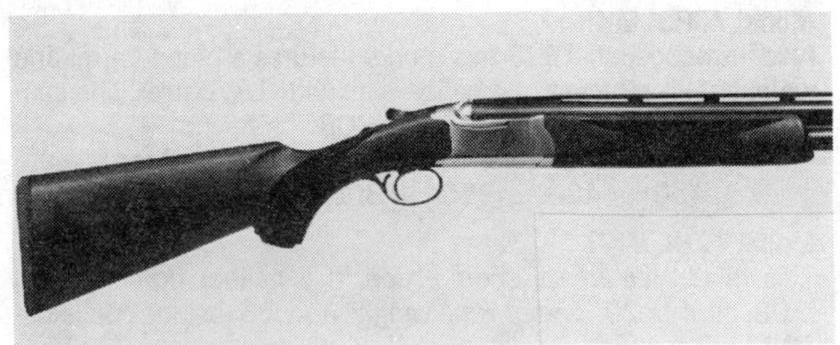

NIB	Exc.	V.G.	Good	Fair	Poor
700	575	500	400	300	250

Red Label Over/Under Current Production

The new 12 and 20 gauge Red Label shotgun has a stainless steel receiver and blued barrels. They are offered with screw-in choke tubes. Otherwise they are similar to the earlier models.

NIB	Exc.	V.G.	Good	Fair	Poor
900	800	600	475	400	300

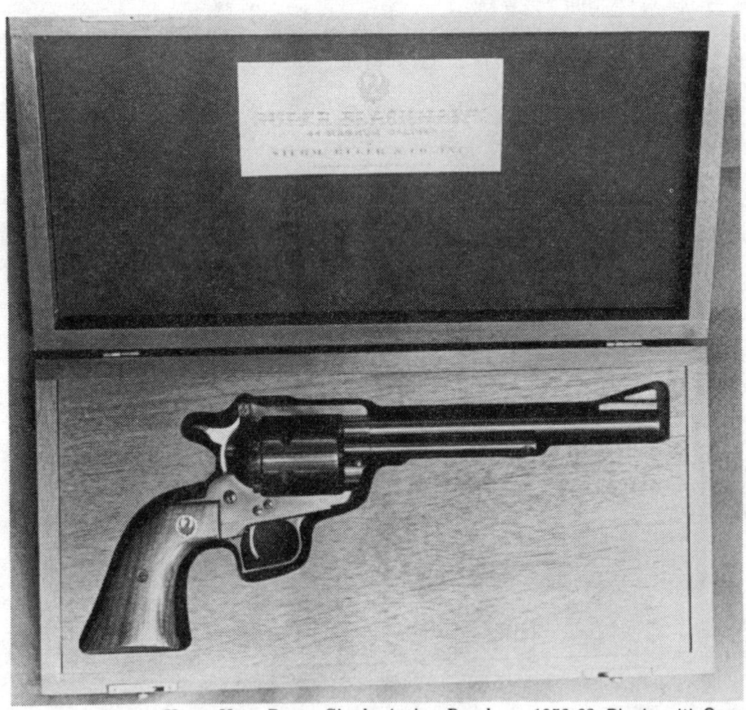

Courtesy *Know Your Ruger Single Action Revolvers 1953-63.* Blacksmith Corp.

Super Blackhawk in scarce mahogany case, serial numbers 1-8500.

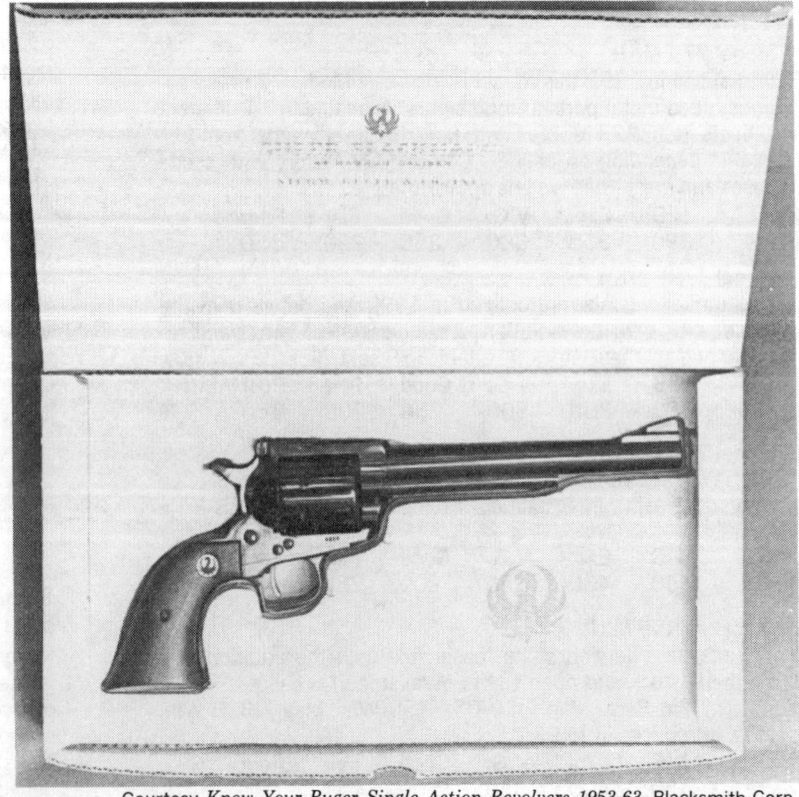

Courtesy *Know Your Ruger Single Action Revolvers 1953-63.* Blacksmith Corp.

Super Blackhawk in rare white cardboard case, serial numbers 3500-10500.

Courtesy compliments of Bill Ruger, John C. Dougan.

Full view of a Ruger Single Six engraved by Charles H. Jerred in 1954-1958. This gun was one of 238 such guns engraved by Jerred in this time span.

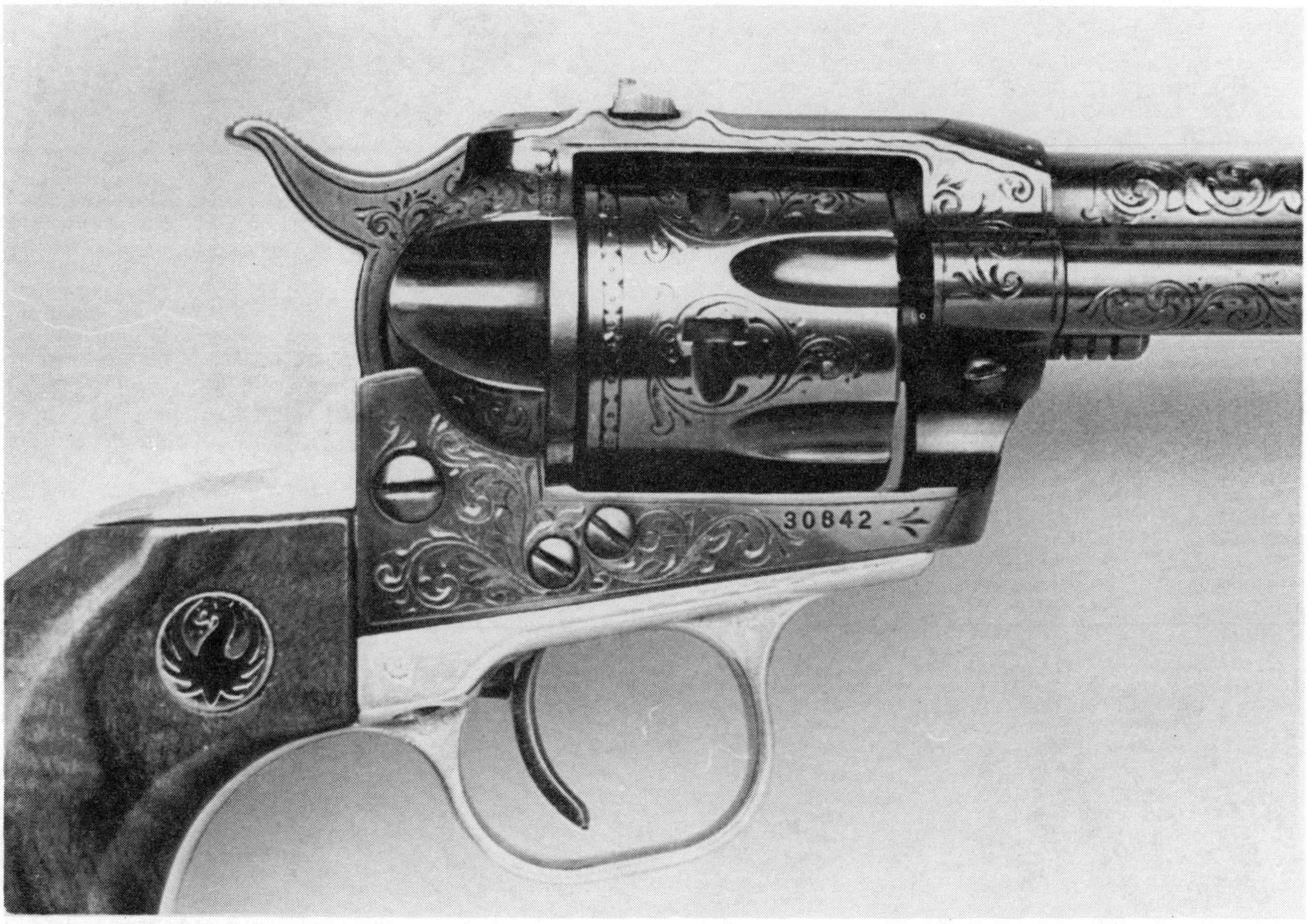

Courtesy compliments of Bill Ruger, John C. Dougan.

Ruger Single Six engraved by Charles H. Jerred in 1954-1958.

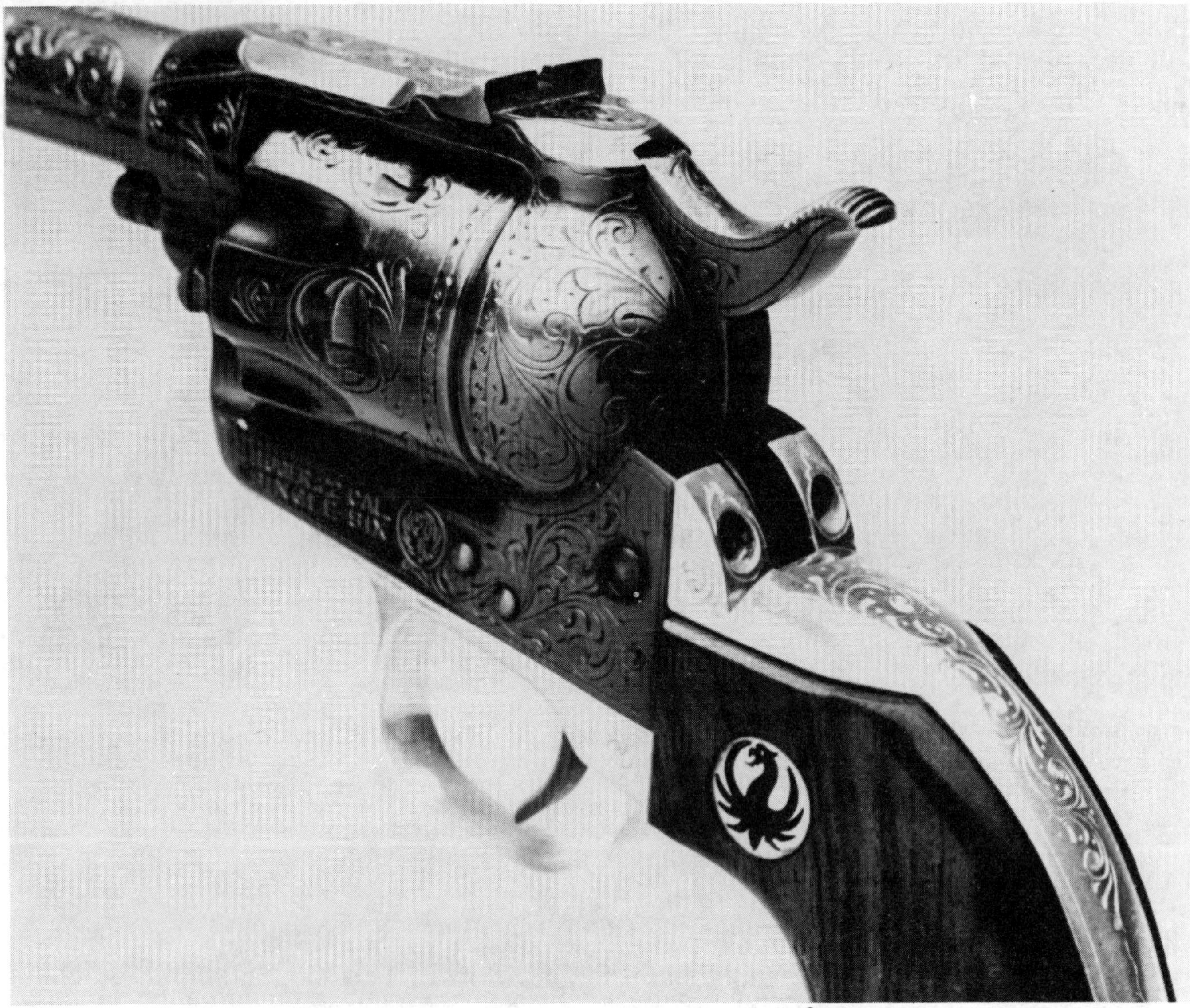

Courtesy compliments of Bill Ruger, John C. Dougan.

Another view of the Ruger Single Six engraved by Charles H. Jerred in 1954-1958.

Courtesy compliments of Bill Ruger, John C. Dougan.

Factory-engraved Ruger Single Six, one of 22 such guns engraved for Ruger in Spain in 1954.

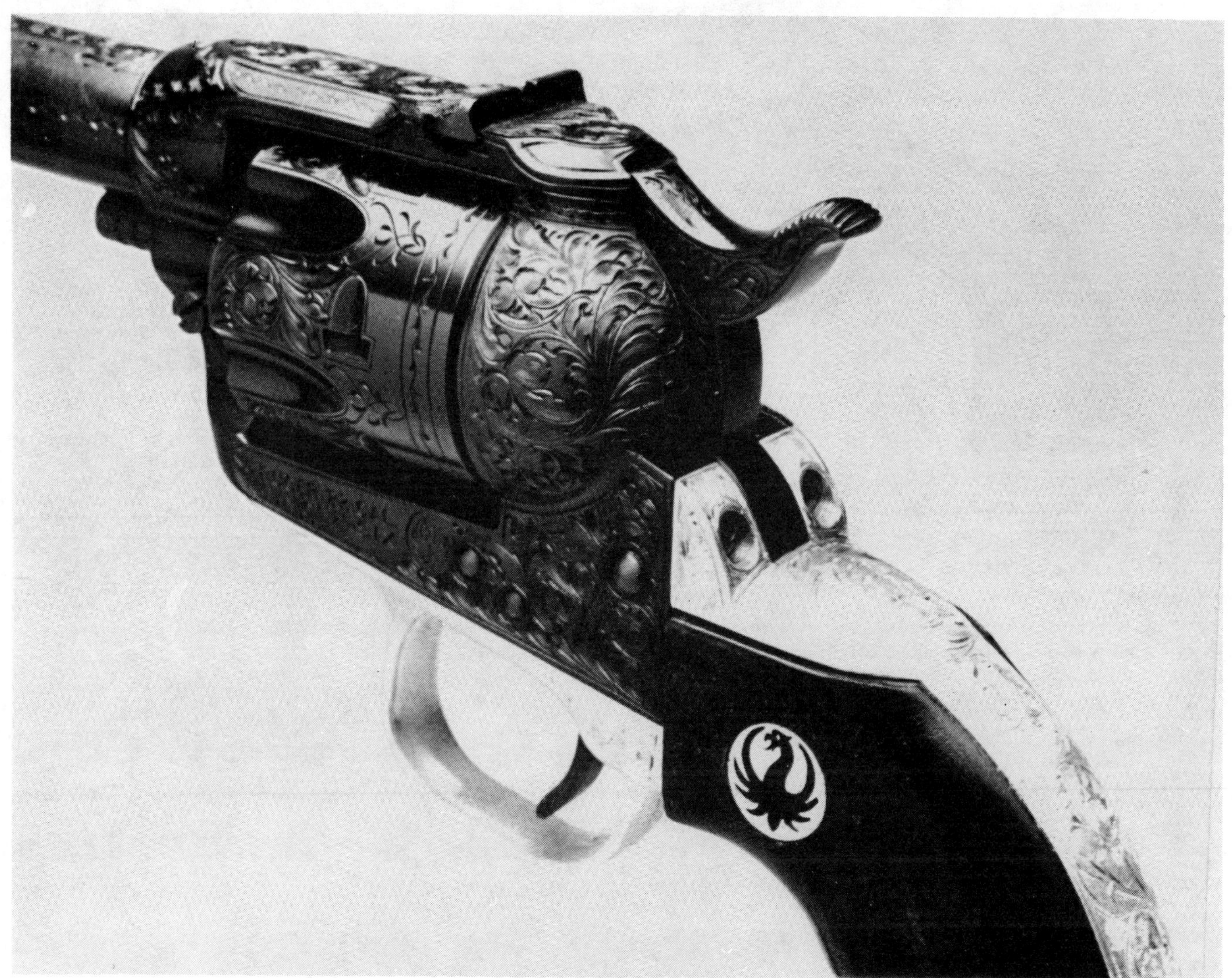

Courtesy compliments of Bill Ruger, John C. Dougan.

Another view of the Ruger Single Six engraved in Spain in 1954.

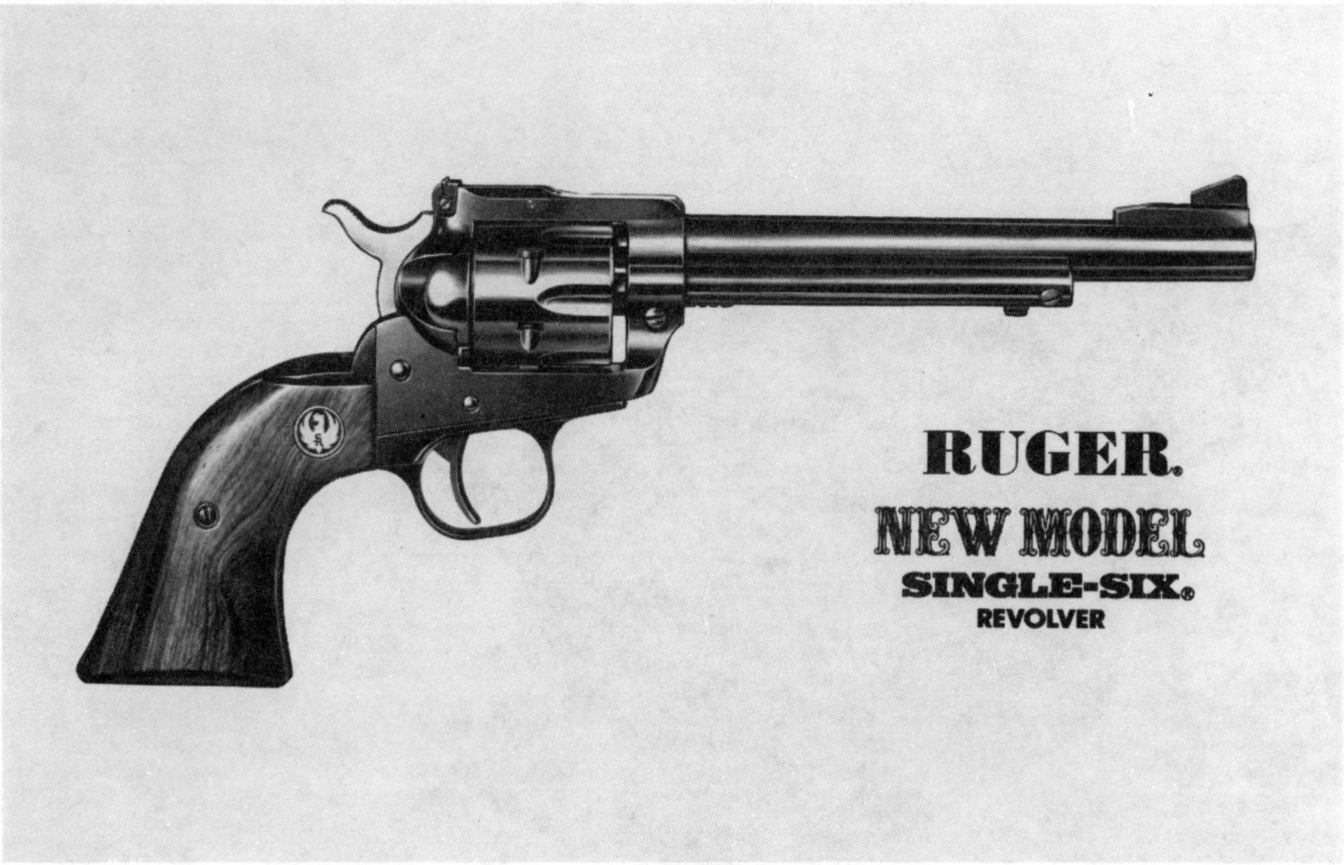

RUGER®
NEW MODEL
SINGLE-SIX®
REVOLVER

Ruger's New model single-six revolver.

Ruger's New model single-six revolver.

NEW MODEL BLACKHAWK®
.44 Magnum Caliber

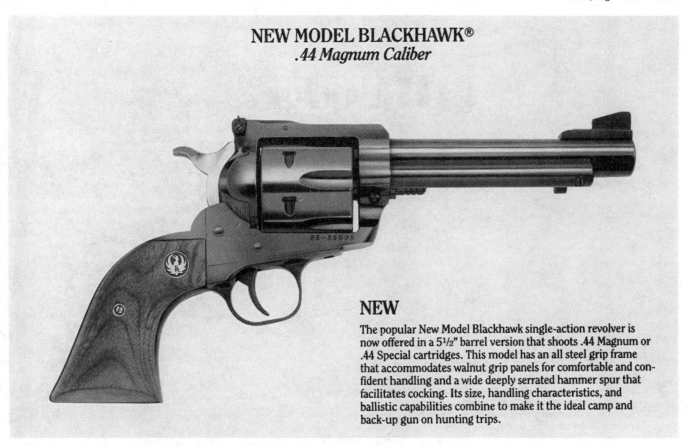

NEW
The popular New Model Blackhawk single-action revolver is now offered in a 5½" barrel version that shoots .44 Magnum or .44 Special cartridges. This model has an all steel grip frame that accommodates walnut grip panels for comfortable and confident handling and a wide deeply serrated hammer spur that facilitates cocking. Its size, handling characteristics, and ballistic capabilities combine to make it the ideal camp and back-up gun on hunting trips.

Ruger New Model Blackhawk; .44 magnum caliber.

RUGER®
New Super Blackhawk

.44 Magnum Stainless Steel
Single Action Revolver
Untapered Bull Barrel

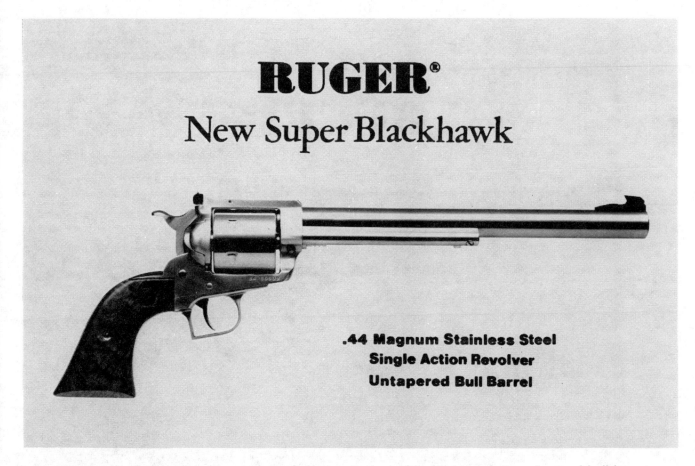

Ruger New Super Blackhawk; .44 magnum, stainless steel, single action revolver; untapered bull barrel.

RUGER®
New roll engraved cylinder.
NEW BISLEY
Large frame Ruger new model single-action Bisley revolvers are now also available with fluted cylinders that are roll engraved in a motif reminiscent of the turn-of-the century Bisley era. Earlier models have fluted cylinders without roll engraving. All models are satin polished and blued. Calibers: .357 Magnum, .41 Magnum, .44 Magnum and .45 Long Colt.

RUGER®
New roll engraved cylinder.
NEW BISLEY
Small frame Ruger new model single-action Bisley revolvers are now also available with fluted cylinders that are roll engraved in a classic styling reminiscent of the turn-of-the century Bisley era. Earlier models have fluted cylinders without roll engraving. All models are satin polished and blued. Calibers: .22 Long Rifle and .32 H&R Magnum.

.22 LR Caliber; 6 Shot

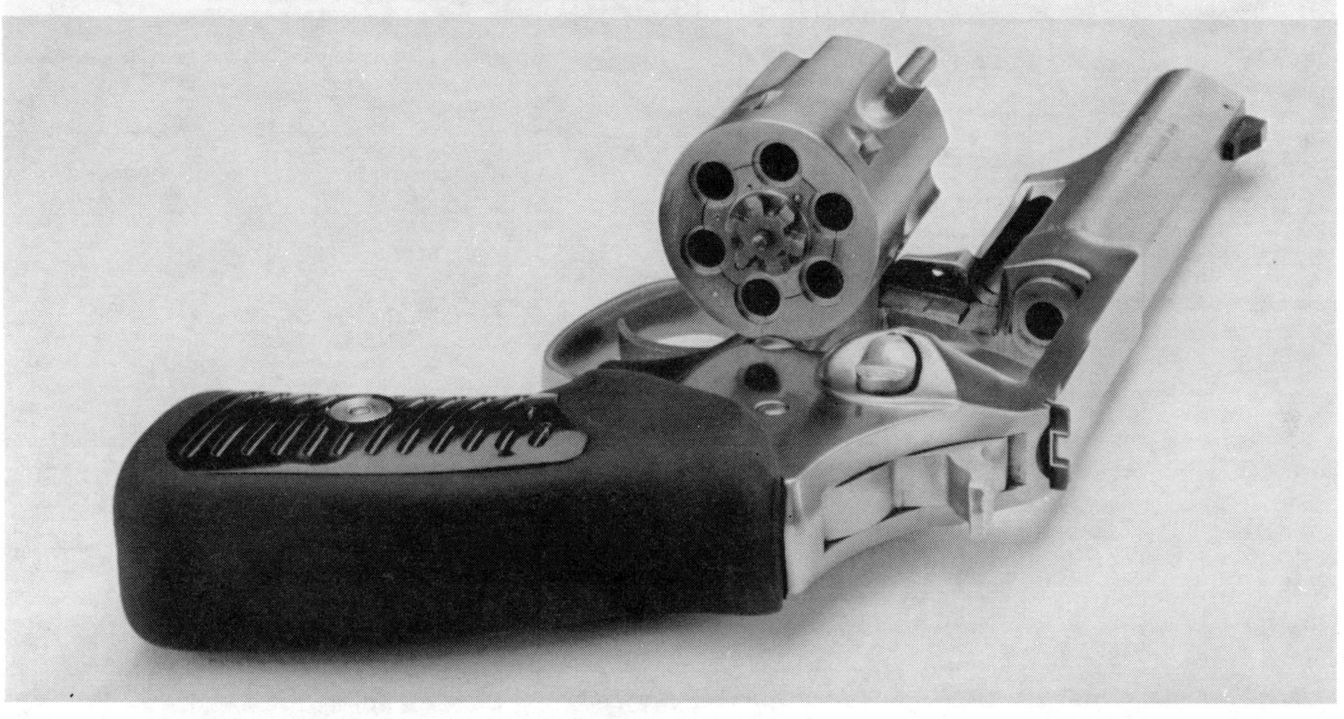

Ruger SP101 .22 LR caliber; 6 shot. The same attention to strength and secure cylinder lock-up found in the large-caliber Ruger double-action revolvers is evident in the SP101 .22 caliber.

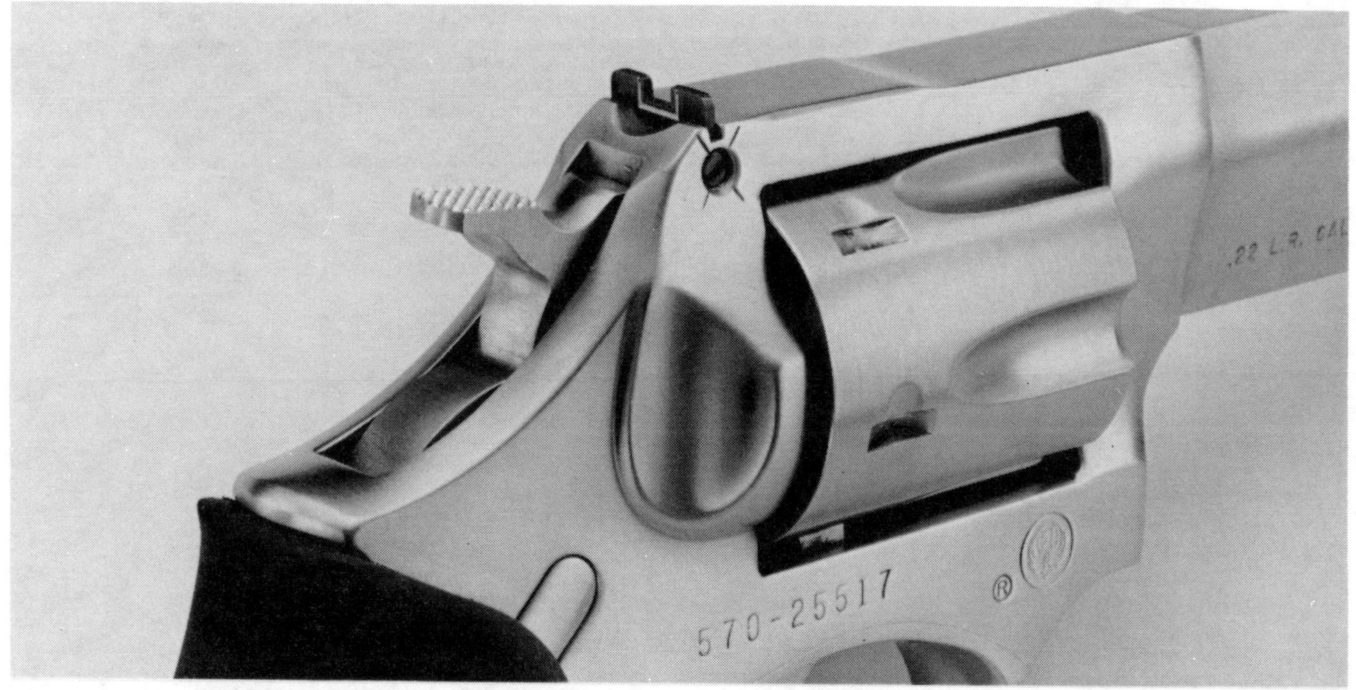

The white-outlined, square-notch rear sight on the .22 caliber SP101 is adjustable for windage.

.22 LR Caliber; 6 Shot

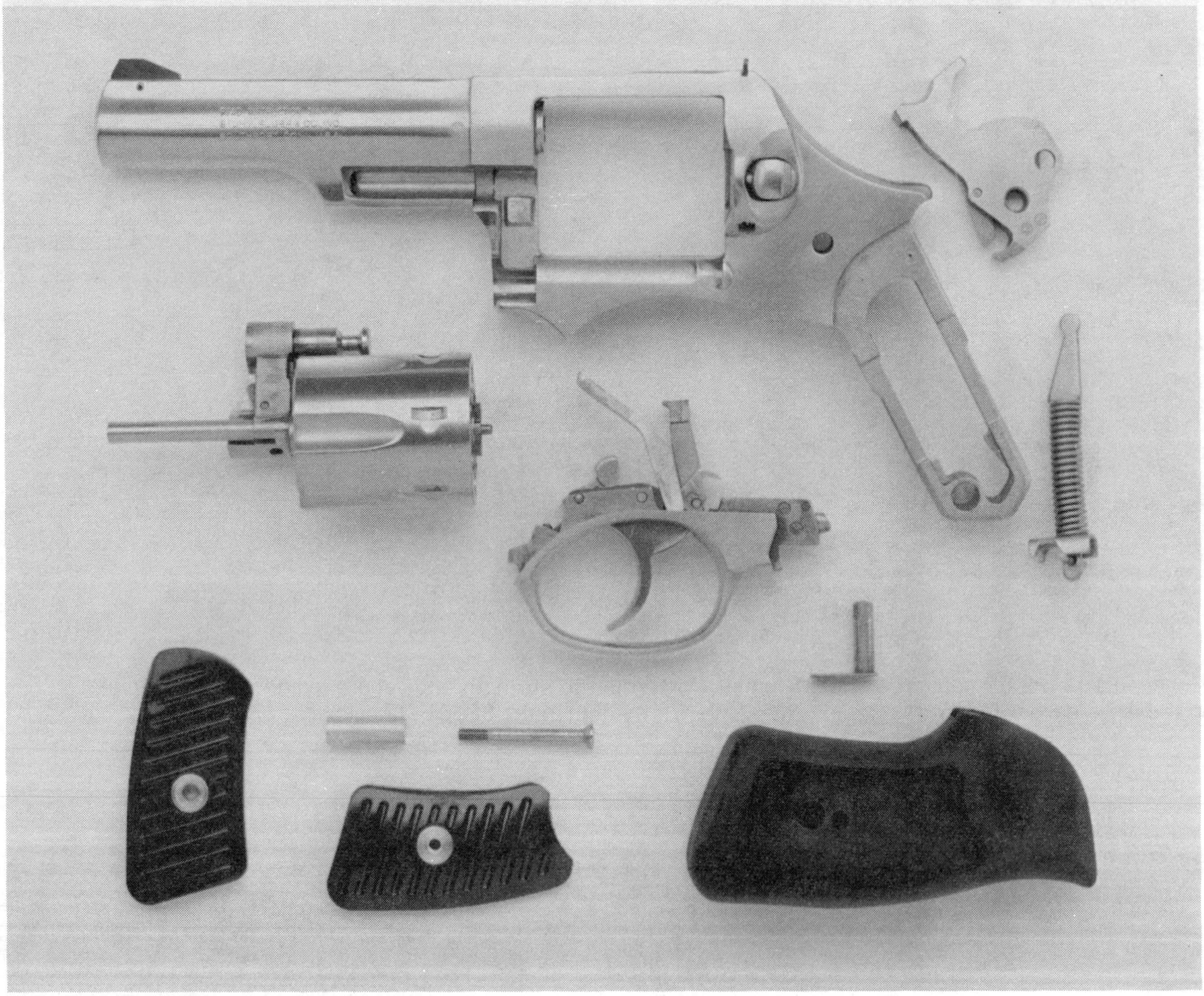

Ruger SP101 .22 LR caliber; 6 shot can be fieldstripped in a matter of seconds without special tools.

.357 Magnum, Double Action Revolver

Ruger's GP100 Is Available in a Fixed Sight, Compact Grip Version

Ruger GP100 .357 magnum, double action revolver. Ruger's GP100 is available in a fixed sight, compact grip version, 3'' barrel.

SUPER REDHAWK™
.44 Magnum Caliber

The new Super Redhawk™ has been expressly designed for the powerful .44 Magnum cartridge, and is seen as the ultimate development in a heavy-frame, double-action revolver of unusual appeal for today's outdoorsmen, hunters, and metallic silhouette shooters. (Model shown has 9½" barrel.)

SUPER REDHAWK™
.44 Magnum Caliber

The massive new Ruger Super Redhawk™ double-action revolver incorporates the exclusive Ruger Integral Scope Mounting System. The integral scope bases on the wide top strap offer a stronger mounting with no stress on the barrel. The Ruger Cushioned Grip System (patents pending) is another important feature of the Super Redhawk revolver. (Model shown has a 9½" barrel.)

Ruger Mark II standard model, full left view.

RUGER®
MARK II STANDARD MODEL
Caliber .22 Long Rifle

NEW!
STAINLESS STEEL

Ruger Mark II standard model, caliber .22 long rifle. Stainless steel.

Ruger Redhawk double-action revolver.

Redhawk revolver — KRH-44R with Ruger integral scope mounting system.

RUGER

MARK II BULL BARREL MODEL PISTOL

Caliber .22 Long Rifle

Ruger Mark II bull barrel model pistol, caliber .22 long rifle. Stainless steel.

Ruger Mark II target model pistol, full left view.

Ruger Decocker model P85, 9mm, parabellum, 15 shot. Ruger's new Decocker P85, preferred by many police departments, allows the shooter to decock the pistol without manipulating the trigger.

Ruger P85 9mm automatic pistol.

RUGER P85®

9mm Automatic Pistol

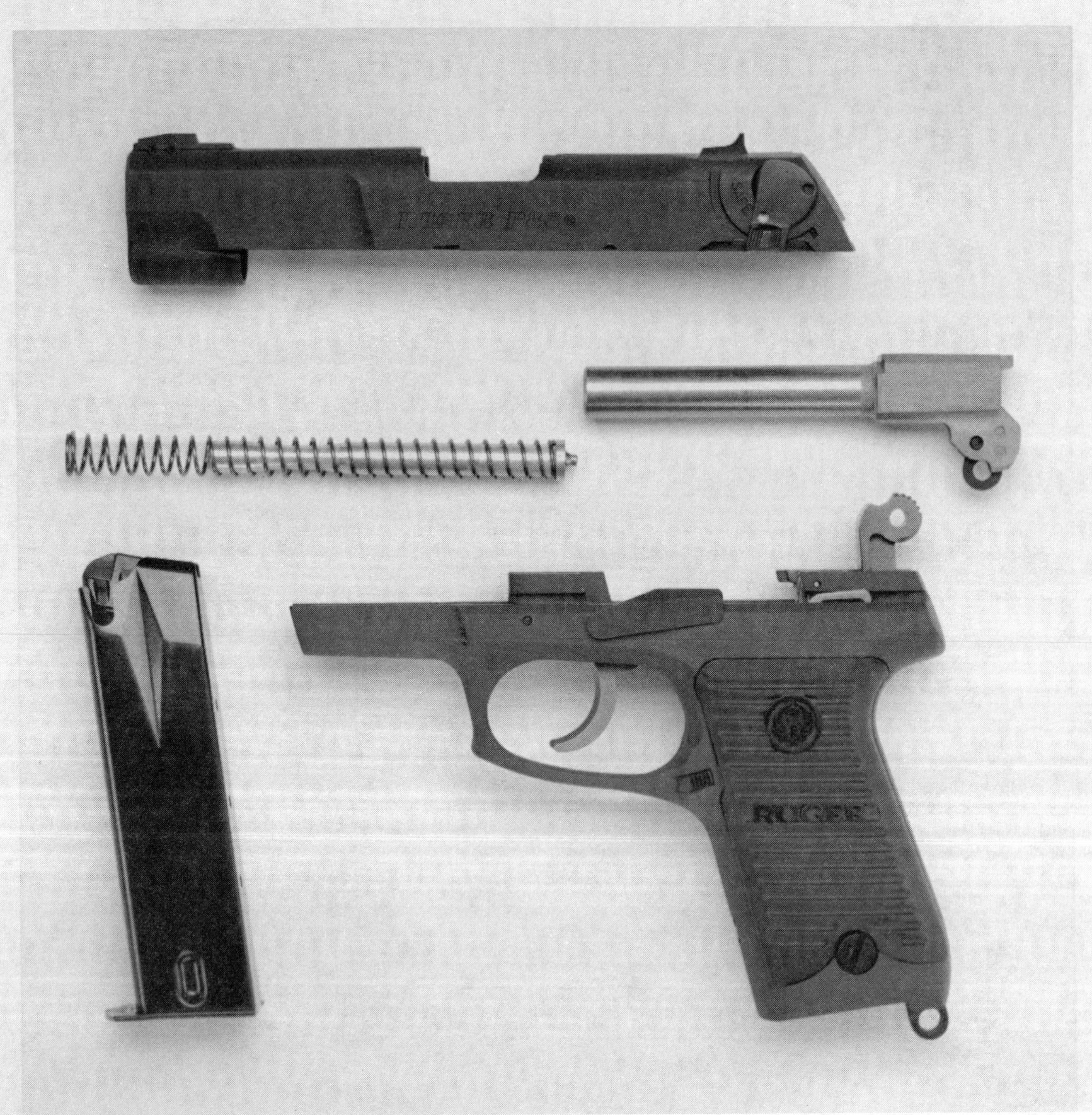

Ruger P85 9mm automoatic pistol.

RUGER STAINLESS STEEL P85

9mm, 15 Shot

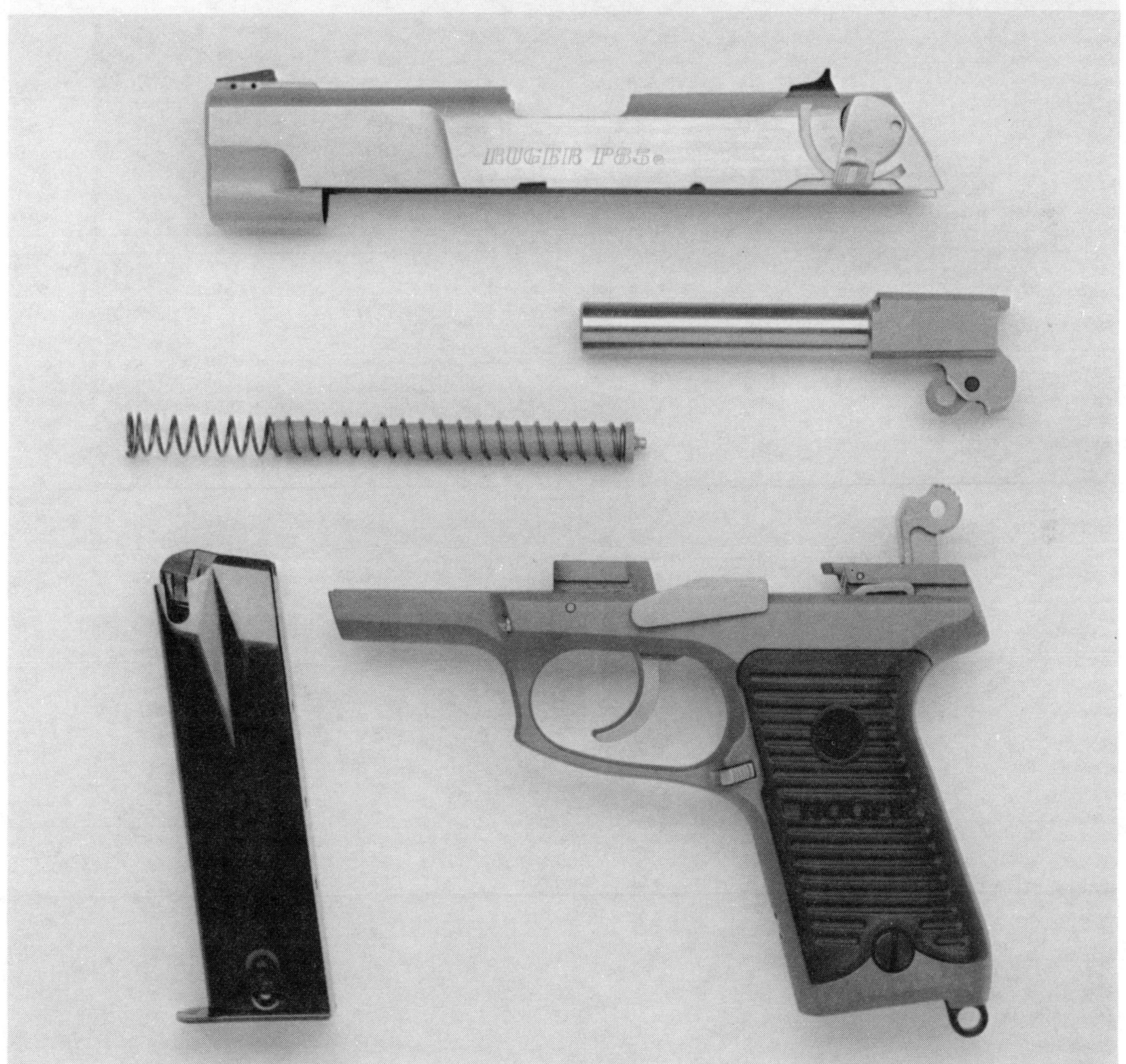

Ruger P85 9mm 15 shot. Basic fieldstripping of the stainless steel P85 is done quickly in the field without the use of tools.

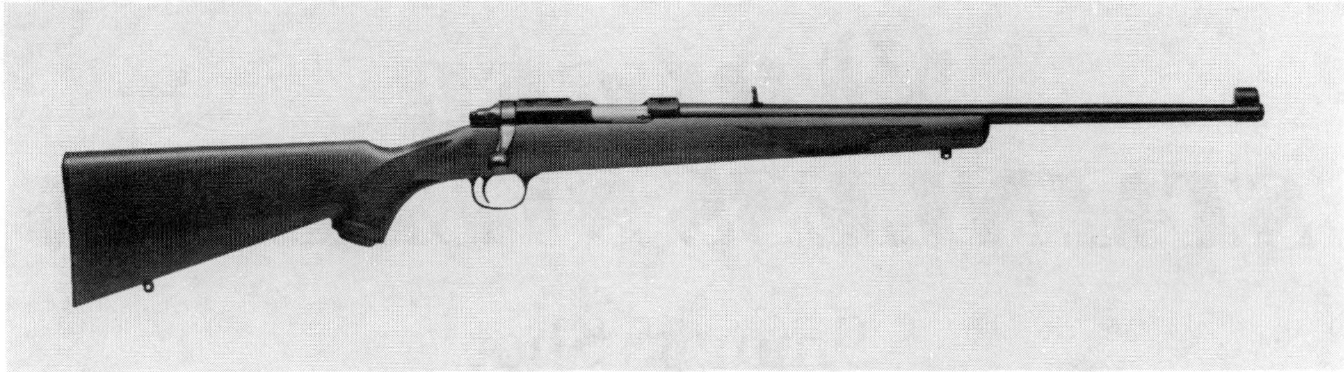

Ruger .22 rimfire bolt-action rifle.

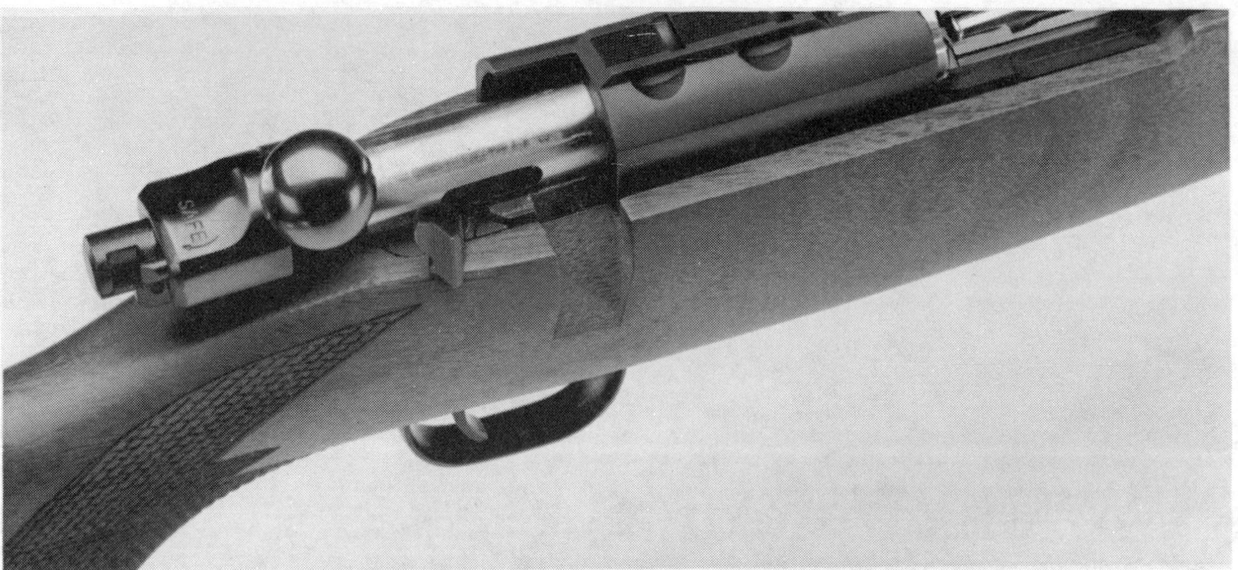

Bolt Open

Ruger 77.22 magnum .22 rimfire bolt-action rifle; 9-shot rotary clip.

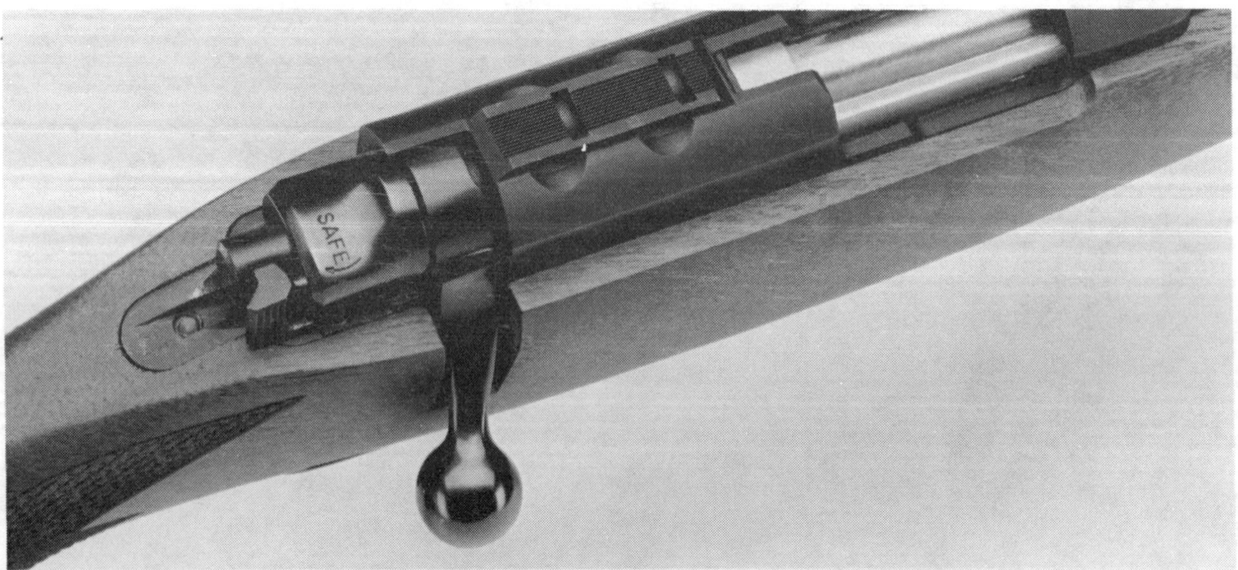

Bolt Closed

Ruger's magnum rimfire rifle is equipped with a readily accessible three-position safety that allows the shooter to unload the rifle with the safety on.

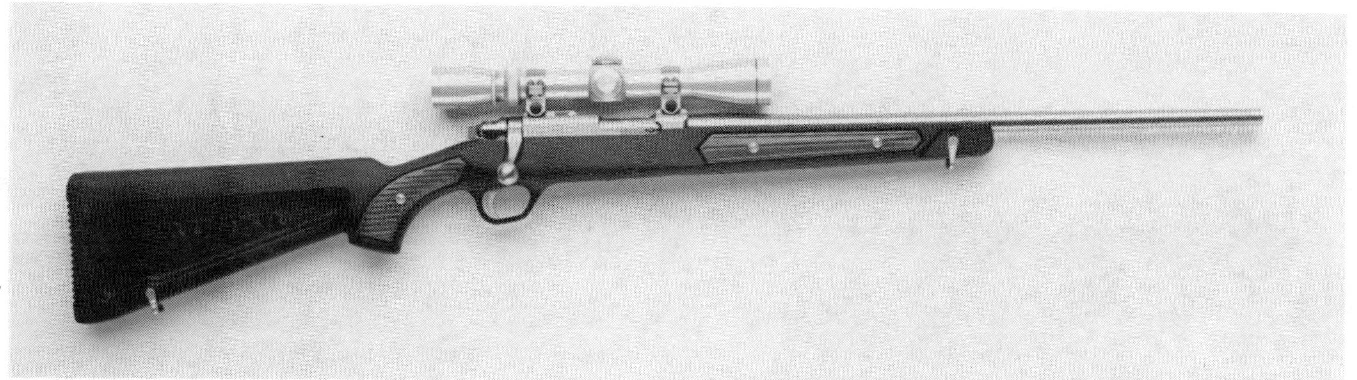

Ruger 77/22 .22 caliber rifle. The only all stainless steel, bolt-action rifle incorporating an impervious all-weather injection-moulded stock.

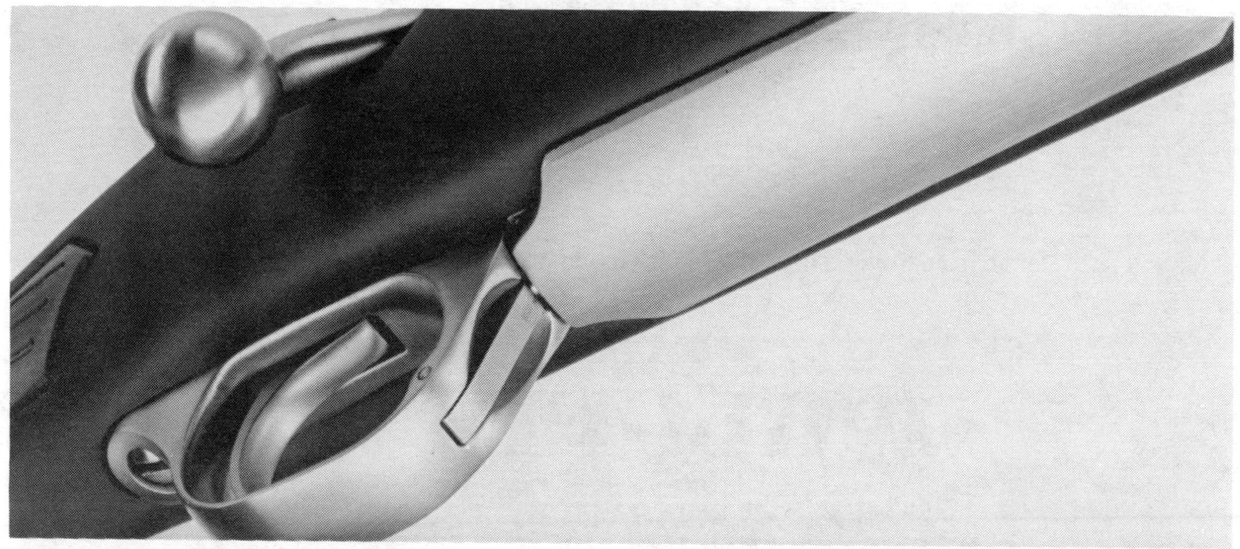

Ruger M77 Mark II stainless steel bolt-action rifle with all-weather stock. The redesigned, patented floorplate latch (flush with the contours of the trigger guard) securely holds the floorplate and prevents accidental dumping of the cartridges. The readily accessible three-position safety allows the shooter to unload the rifle with safety on for optimum convenience and security.

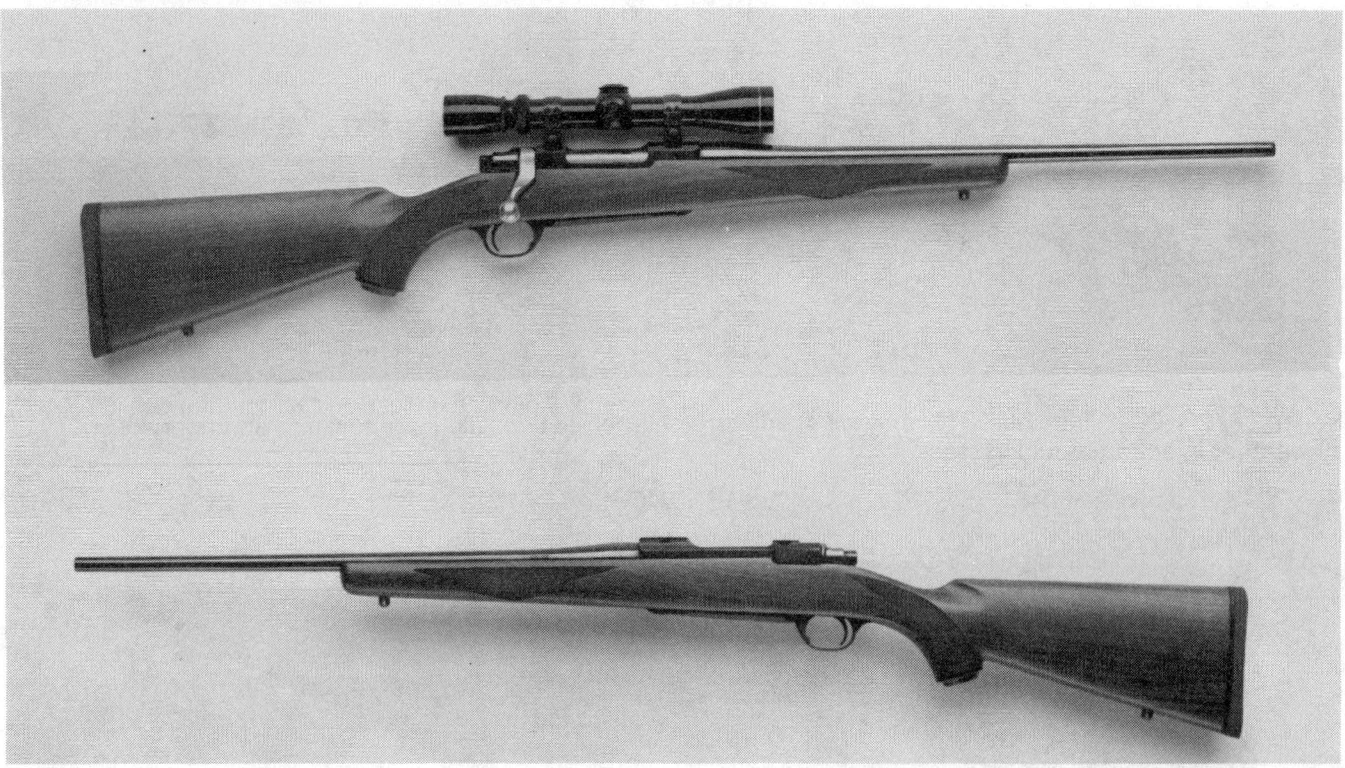

Ruger M-77 Mark II .223 Remington. Ruger's new M-77 Mark II bolt action is the slender, ideal hunter.

RUGER®

MODEL-77® ULTRA LIGHT
BOLT-ACTION CARBINE

Scope not included.

Ruger Model-77 ultra light bolt-action carbine.

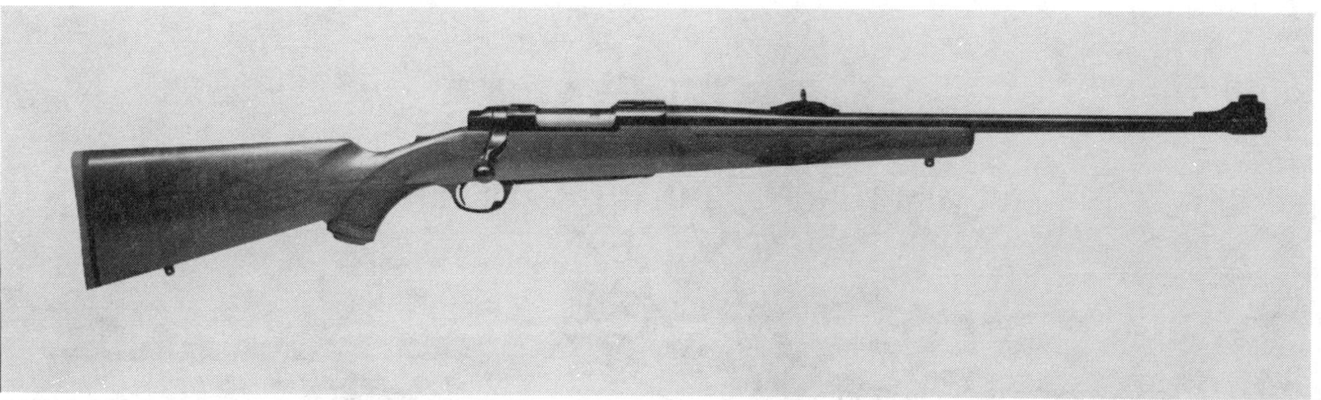

Ruger M-77RS bolt-action rifle.

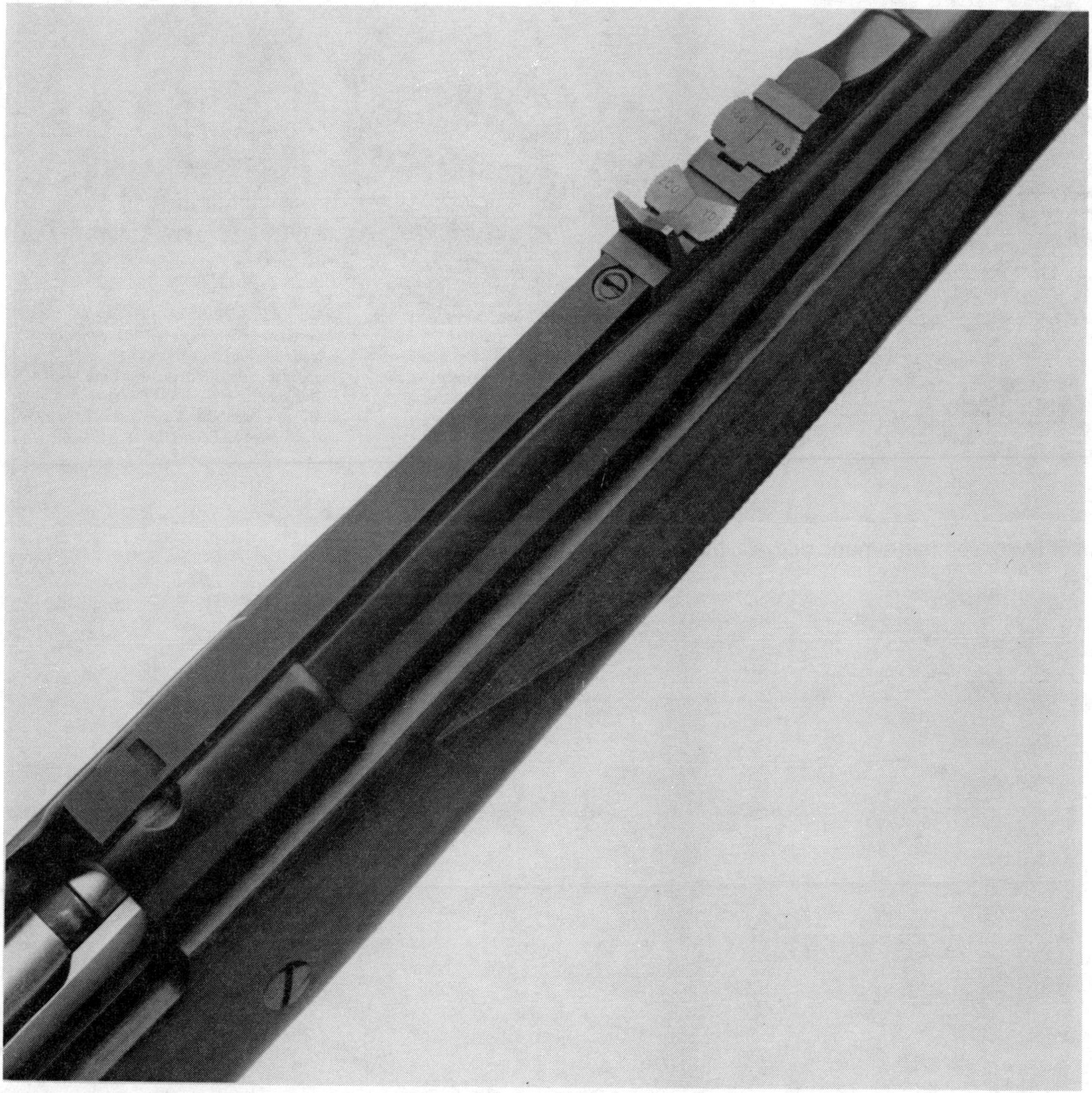

Ruger magnum rifle. The Ruger magnum barrel and sighting rib, with cross serrations is machined from a single bar of steel. This feature has customarily been available only on the most expensive custom built big game rifles traditionally associated with the British, Bond Street African safari rifles.

MINI THIRTY™ SEMI-AUTOMATIC RIFLE

Caliber 7.62 x 39mm

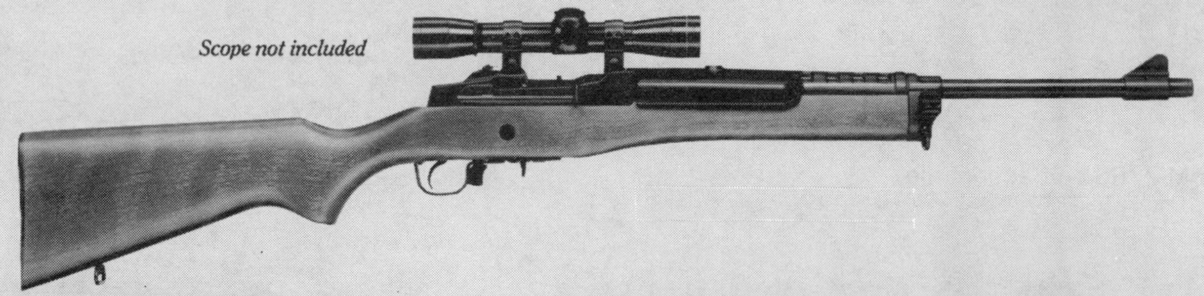

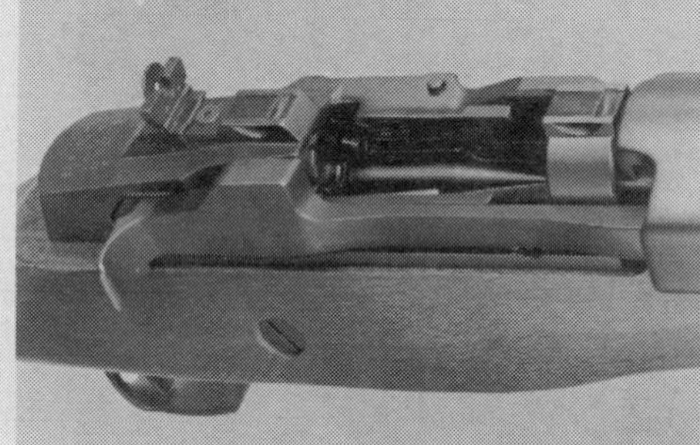

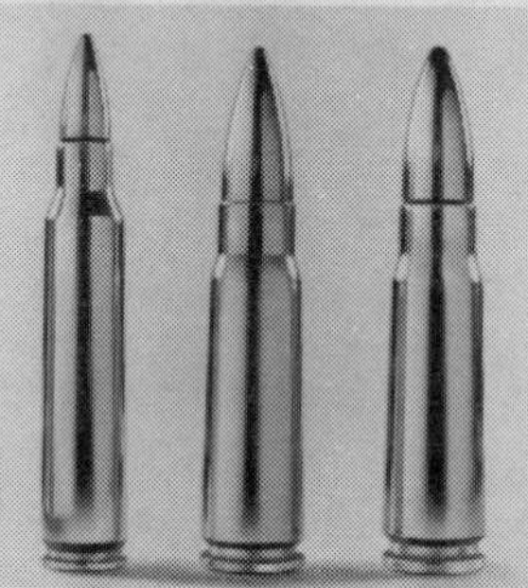

While the MINI THIRTY™ is based on the Mini-14® Ranch Rifle, the barrel, receiver and bolt have been redesigned, to accommodate the larger 7.62 x 39mm cartridge. Details of the receiver, bolt face, rear sight, and Ruger Scope Mount bases are shown.

The new Ruger MINI THIRTY™ rifle is a modified version of the popular Ruger Mini-14® Ranch Rifle and is chambered for the 7.62 x 39mm cartridge to provide big bore performance in a compact, lightweight self-loading sporting rifle.

The 7.62 x 39mm bridges the gap between smallbore high-velocity varmint loads and big game calibers. Shown above are the .223 with Metal Case Boat-Tail Bullet and the 7.62 x 39mm with Full Metal Jacketed Bullet (center) and the Pointed Soft Point Bullet (right).

Ruger Mini Thirty semi-automatic rifle. Caliber 7.62 x 39mm.

RUGER®

Screw-In Choke Inserts

for the 12 Gauge "Red Label" Over & Under Shotgun with the Stainless Steel Receiver

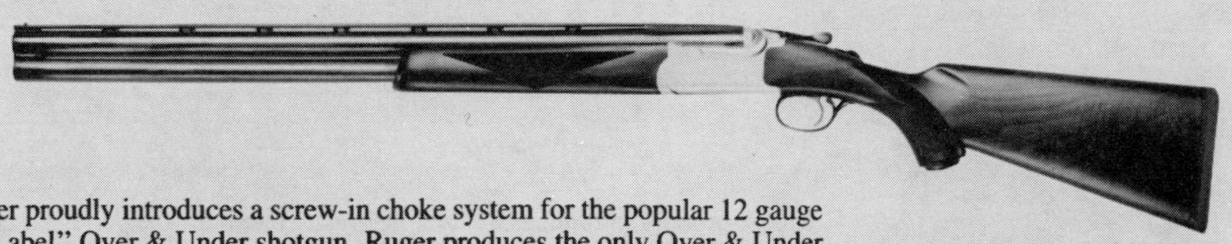

Ruger proudly introduces a screw-in choke system for the popular 12 gauge "Red Label" Over & Under shotgun. Ruger produces the only Over & Under shotgun that is made in America. Initial shipments are now being made. This new model will be offered with either 26″ or 28″ barrels and 3″ chambers.

This new system was designed for the upland game and waterfowl hunter as well as clay target shooters. Additionally, it is ideally suited for the game of sporting clays.

Ruger's screw-in chokes are easily installed with a key wrench packaged with each shotgun. The chokes fit flush to the muzzle with no visible distraction. Every shotgun is equipped with a Full, Modified, Improved Cylinder and two Skeet screw-in chokes. The muzzle edge of the chokes have been slotted for quick identification in or out of the barrels. The Full choke has 3 slots, Modified — 2 slots, Improved Cylinder — 1 slot, Skeet — no slots.

The Ruger Over & Under shotguns that are equipped with the screw-in chokes have a slightly different barrel configuration from the fixed choke models. Due to dimensional variations the screw-in chokes cannot be retrofitted into existing barrels.

Ruger screw-in choke inserts for the 12 gauge "Red Label" over and under shotgun with the stainless steel receiver.

RUGER®

Screw-In Choke Inserts

for the 12 Gauge "Red Label" Over & Under Shotgun with the Stainless Steel Receiver

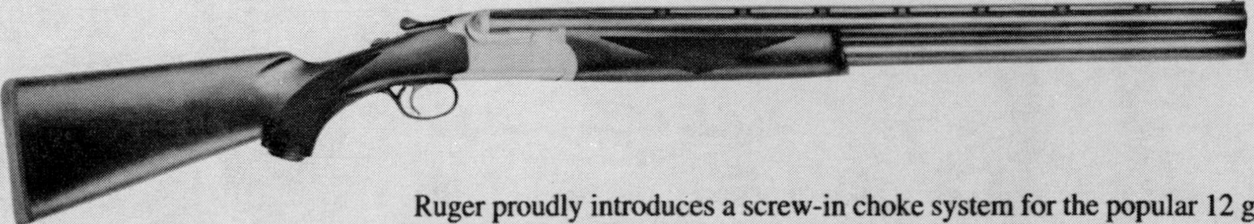

Ruger proudly introduces a screw-in choke system for the popular 12 gauge "Red Label" Over & Under shotgun. Ruger produces the only Over & Under shotgun that is made in America. Initial shipments are now being made. This new model will be offered with either 26″ or 28″ barrels and 3″ chambers.

This new system was designed for the upland game and waterfowl hunter as well as clay target shooters. Additionally, it is ideally suited for the game of sporting clays.

The muzzle edge of the chokes have been slotted for quick and easy identification in or out of the barrels.

CHOKE	NO. OF SLOTS
Full	3
Modified	2
Improved Cylinder	1
Skeet	None

The Ruger Over & Under shotguns that are equipped with the screw-in chokes have a slightly different barrel configuration from the fixed choke models. Due to dimensional variations the screw-in chokes cannot be retrofitted into existing barrels.

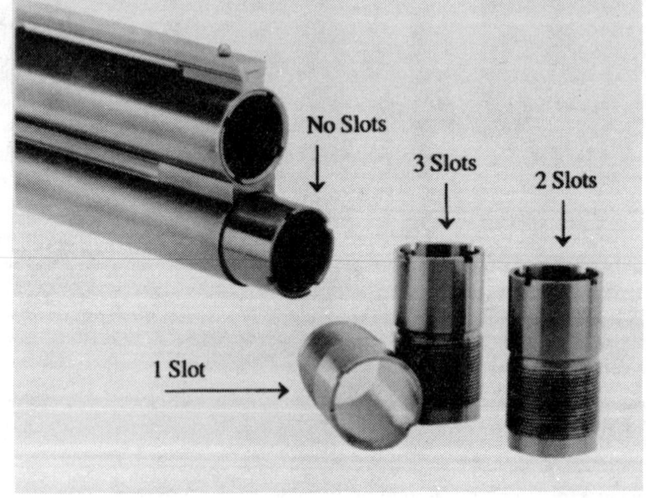

Ruger screw-in choke inserts for the 12 gauge "Red Label" over and under shotgun with the stainless steel receiver.

SUNDANCE INDUSTRIES, INC.
North Hollywood, California

Model D-22M

A .22 or .22 Magnum caliber double-barrel Over/Under pocket pistol with 2.5" barrels and an aluminum alloy frame. Blackened finish or chrome-plated with either simulated pearl or black grips. Introduced in 1989.

Exc.	V.G.	Good	Fair	Poor
225	200	150	100	80

SUTHERLAND, S.
Richmond, Virginia

Pocket Pistol

A .41 caliber percussion single shot pistol with round barrels of 2.5" to 4" in length, German silver mounts and a walnut stock. The lock normally marked "S. Sutherland" or "S. Sutherland/Richmond". Manufactured during the 1850s.

Exc.	V.G.	Good	Fair	Poor
1500	1000	750	400	300

SYMS, J. G.
New York, New York

Pocket Pistol

A .41 caliber single shot percussion pistol with 1.5" to 3.5" barrels, German silver mounts and a walnut stock. The lock normally marked "Syms/New York". Manufactured during the 1850s.

Exc.	V.G.	Good	Fair	Poor
1500	1000	750	400	300

T

TALLASSEE
Tallassee, Alabama

Carbine

A .58 caliber single shot percussion carbine with a 25" round barrel and full-length stock secured by two barrel bands. Fitted with sling swivels. Barrel and lock finished in the bright, brass furniture and walnut stock. The lock marked "C.S./Tallassee/ Ala." Approximately 500 of these carbines were manufactured in 1864. Perspective purchasers are advised to secure a qualified appraisal prior to acquisition.

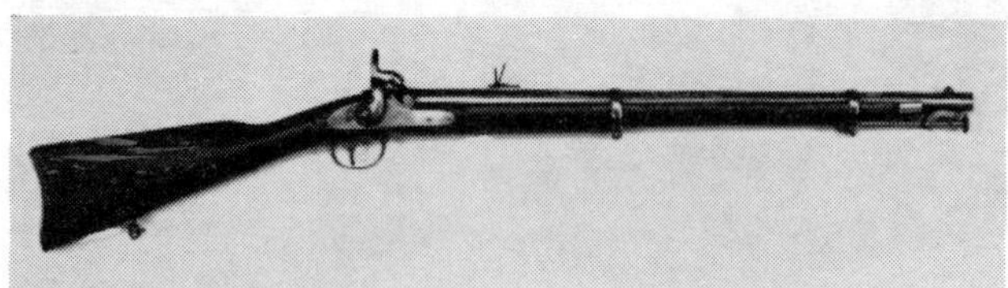

Courtesy Milwaukee Public Museum, Milwaukee, Wisconsin.

Exc.	V.G.	Good	Fair	Poor
6500	5500	4500	3000	2000

TANFOGLIO
Valtrompia, Italy

The products of this company which was established in the late 1940s, have been imported into the United States by various companies including Eig Corporation, F.I.E. of Hialeah, Florida and Excam.

Sata

A .22 or 6.35mm caliber semi-automatic pistol with a 3" barrel. The slide marked "Pistola SATA Made in Italy" and the grips "SATA". Blued with black plastic grips.

Exc.	V.G.	Good	Fair	Poor
175	150	125	90	75

Titan

A 6.35mm caliber semi-automatic pistol with a 2.5" barrel and external hammer. The slide marked "Titan 6.35" and on U.S. imported examples, "EIG". Blued with plastic grips.

Exc.	V.G.	Good	Fair	Poor
100	75	50	40	30

TA 90 or TZ-75

A 9mm caliber semi-automatic pistol with a 4.75" barrel and 15-shot magazine. Blued or chrome-plated with walnut or rubber grips. Those imported by Excam were known as the Model TA 90, while those imported by F.I.E. are known as the Model TZ-75.

NIB	Exc.	V.G.	Good	Fair	Poor
450	400	350	300	250	200

TA 90B

As above, with a 3.5" barrel, 12-shot magazine and Neoprene grips. Introduced in 1986.

NIB	Exc.	V.G.	Good	Fair	Poor
500	450	400	350	300	250

TA 90 SS

As above, with a ported 5" barrel, adjustable sights and two-tone finish. Introduced in 1989.

NIB	Exc.	V.G.	Good	Fair	Poor
650	600	500	450	400	300

TA 41

As above, in .41 Action Express caliber. Introduced in 1989.

NIB	Exc.	V.G.	Good	Fair	Poor
500	450	400	350	300	250

TA 41 SS

As above, with a ported 5" barrel, adjustable sights and two-tone finish. Introduced in 1989.

NIB	Exc.	V.G.	Good	Fair	Poor
650	600	500	450	400	300

TA 76

A .22 caliber single action revolver with a 4.75" barrel and 6-shot cylinder. Blued or chrome-plated with a brass backstrap and triggerguard. Walnut grips.

NIB	Exc.	V.G.	Good	Fair	Poor
100	90	80	65	50	25

TA 76M Combo

As above, with a 6" or 9" barrel and an interchangeable .22 Magnum caliber cylinder.

NIB	Exc.	V.G.	Good	Fair	Poor
110	100	90	75	60	35

TA 38SB

A .38 Special caliber Over/Under double barrel pocket pistol with 3" barrels and a hammerblock safety. Blued with checkered nylon grips. Discontinued in 1985.

Exc.	V.G.	Good	Fair	Poor
100	90	80	60	40

TANNER, ANDRE
Switzerland

Model 300 Free Rifle

A 7.5mm Swiss or .308 caliber single shot rifle with varying length barrels having adjustable target sights, adustable trigger, and a walnut stock fitted with a palm rest and adjustable cheekpiece. Blued. Imported prior to 1989.

Exc.	V.G.	Good	Fair	Poor
3500	2750	2250	1750	1400

Model 300S

As above, with a 10-shot magazine and not fitted with a palm rest. Discontinued in 1988.

Exc.	V.G.	Good	Fair	Poor
3000	2500	2000	1500	1300

Model 50F

As above, in .22 caliber with a thumbhole stock. Discontinued in 1988.

Exc.	V.G.	Good	Fair	Poor
2500	2000	1750	1400	1200

TARPLEY J. & F. AND E. T. GARRETT & CO.
Greensboro, North Carolina

Carbine

A .52 caliber breechloading single shot percussion carbine with a 22" round barrel and a plain walnut buttstock. Blued with a case-hardened frame. The tang marked "J H Tarpley's./Pat Feb 14./1863." Over 400 of these carbines were manufactured. It is advised that prospective purchasers should seek a qualified appraisal prior to acquisition.

Exc.	V.G.	Good	Fair	Poor
9000	7500	6000	4000	3000

TAURUS INTERNATIONAL MFG. CO.

Porto Alegre, Brazil
Importer—Taurus, Inc.
Miami, Florida

PT-92AF

A 9mm caliber double-action semi-automatic pistol with a 4.92" barrel, exposed hammer and 15-shot magazine. Blued or nickle-plated with plain walnut grips.

NIB	Exc.	V.G.	Good	Fair	Poor
425	375	325	300	200	150

PT-92C

This 9mm model is a large capacity semi-automatic pistol with a 4.25" barrel. Drift adjustable 3-dot combat rear sight. Magazine holds 13 rounds in a double column. Choice of blue, stain nickel, or stainless steel finish. Brazilian hardwood grips are standard. Weighs 31 ozs.

NIB	Exc.	V.G.	Good	Fair	Poor
375	325	275	220	160	100

PT-92

A slightly larger and heavier version of the PT-92C. This model has a 5" barrel with drift adjustable 3-dot combat rear sight. Magazine capacity is 15 rounds. This model is 1" longer overall than the above model and weighs 34 ozs. Also available in blue, nickel, and stainless steel.

NIB	Exc.	V.G.	Good	Fair	Poor
375	325	275	220	160	100

PT-99

Similar in appearance and specifications to the PT-92, this version has the additional feature of fully adjustable 3-dot rear sight.

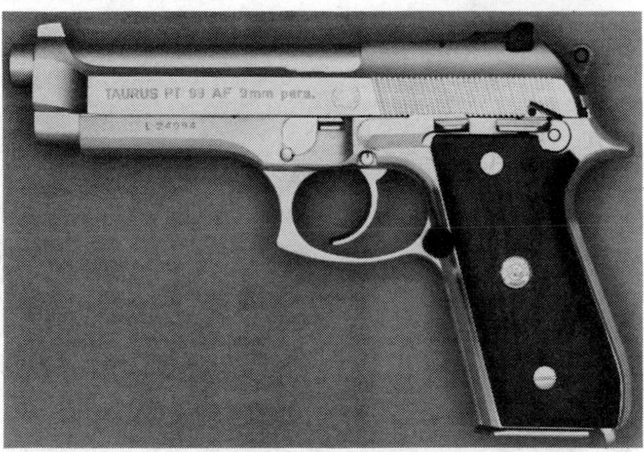

NIB	Exc.	V.G.	Good	Fair	Poor
400	350	300	250	160	100

PT-100

This model is similar to the other full size Taurus semi-autos except that it is chambered for the .40 S&W cartridge. Supplied with a 5" barrel, with drift adjustable rear sight, it has a magazine capacity of 11 rounds. Also available in blue, nickel, or stainless steel. Weighs 34 ozs.

NIB	Exc.	V.G.	Good	Fair	Poor
385	340	300	250	160	100

PT-101

Same as the model above but furnished with fully adjustable

rear 3-dot combat sight.

NIB	Exc.	V.G.	Good	Fair	Poor
415	375	325	260	170	100

PT-908

A semi-automatic double action pistol chambered for the 9mm Parabellum cartridge. It is fitted with a 3.8" barrel, with drift adjustable rear 3-dot combat sight. Magazine capacity is 8 rounds in a single column. Available in blue, satin nickel, or stainless steel. Stocks are black rubber. Pistol weighs 30 ozs. Introduced in 1993.

NIB	Exc.	V.G.	Good	Fair	Poor
380	325	275	220	160	100

Deluxe Shooter's Pak

Offered by Taurus as a special package it consists of the pistol, with extra magazine, in a fitted custom hard case. Available for the following models: PT-92, PT-99, PT-100, and PT-101.

NOTE: Add approximately 10 percent to the above prices of these models for this special feature.

PT-58

This model was introduced in 1988. Chambered for the .380 ACP cartridge it is fitted with a 4" barrel with drift adjustable rear sight. It is a conventional double action design. Available in blue, satin nickel, or stainless steel. It is fitted with Brazilian hardwood grips. Pistol weighs 30 ozs.

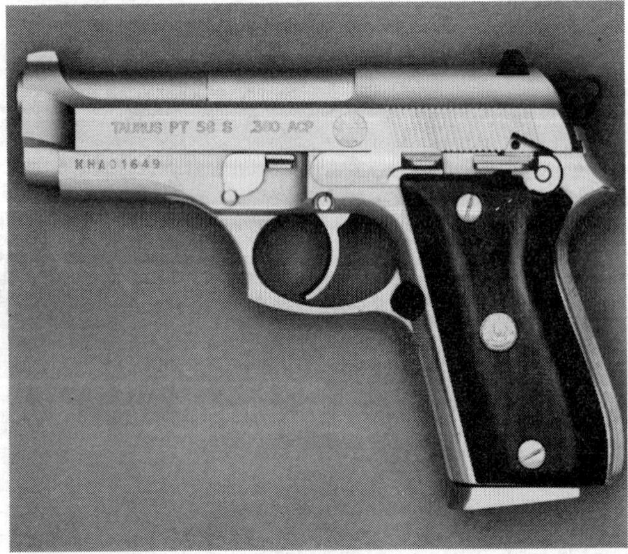

NIB	Exc.	V.G.	Good	Fair	Poor
340	300	250	200	150	100

PT-22

This is a semi-automatic double action only pistol that features a 2.75" barrel with fixed sights and a manual safety. It is chambered for the .22 Long Rifle cartridge and has a magazine capacity of 9 rounds. The stocks are Brazilian hardwood. Pistol weighs 12.3 ozs.

NIB	Exc.	V.G.	Good	Fair	Poor
150	125	100	75	60	50

PT-25

Similar in appearance to the PT-22, this model is chambered for the .25 ACP cartridge and has a magazine capacity of 8 rounds. This model is also fitted with a 2.75" barrel.

NIB	Exc.	V.G.	Good	Fair	Poor
150	125	100	75	60	50

Model 73

A .32 Smith & Wesson Long double-action swing-out cylinder revolver, with a 3" barrel and 6-shot cylinder. Blued or nickle-plated with walnut grips.

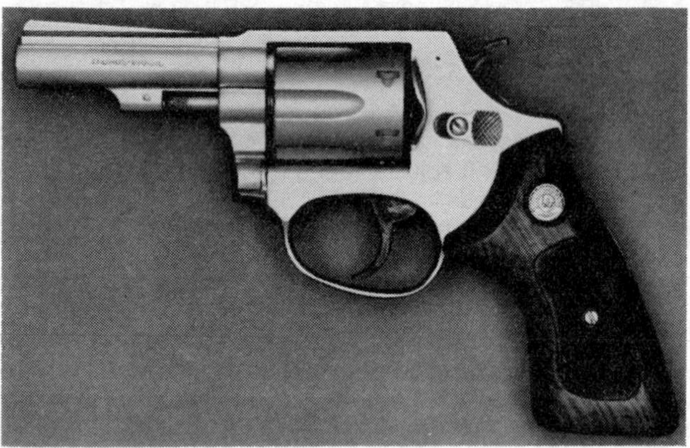

NIB	Exc.	V.G.	Good	Fair	Poor
200	175	150	125	100	75

Model 80

A full size 6-round .38 Special with 3" or 4" heavy tapered barrel. Supplied with fixed sights and offered with blue or stainless steel (S.S. offered new in 1993) finish. Brazilian hardwood grips are standard. Weighs 30 ozs.

NOTE: Add $40 for stainless steel.

NIB	Exc.	V.G.	Good	Fair	Poor
190	175	135	110	85	70

Model 82
Nearly identical with the Model 80, the Model 82 has a 3" or 4" heavy, solid rib barrel in place of the heavy tapered barrel. Pistol weighs 34 ozs.

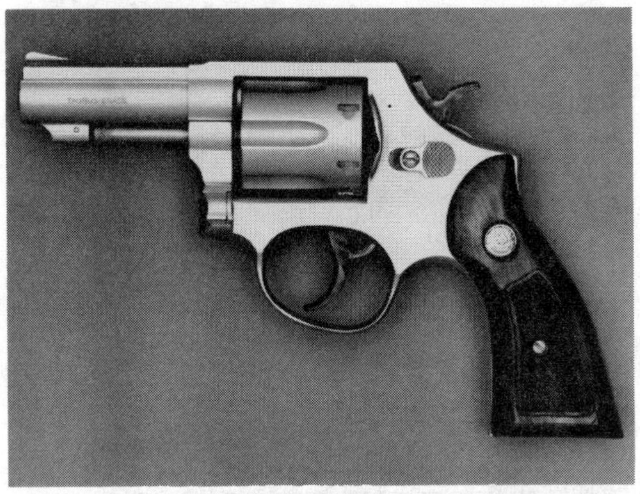

NIB	Exc.	V.G.	Good	Fair	Poor
190	175	135	110	85	70

NOTE: Add $40 for stainless steel.

Model 83
Similar to the Model 82 except for a fully adjustable rear sight and Parteidge type front sight. Offered with 4" barrel only with blue or stainless steel (S.S. finish new for 1993). Pistol weighs 34 ozs.

NIB	Exc.	V.G.	Good	Fair	Poor
200	175	150	125	100	75

Model 85
A double action revolver chambered for the .38 Special. This model is available in either a 2" or 3" heavy, solid rib barrel fitted with ejector shroud. Sights are fixed. Blue finish and stainless steel (new for 1993) are offered with Brazilian hardwood grips. Pistol weighs 21 ozs. with 2" barrel.

NIB	Exc.	V.G.	Good	Fair	Poor
200	175	150	125	100	75

Model 85 Stainless
As above, in stainless steel.

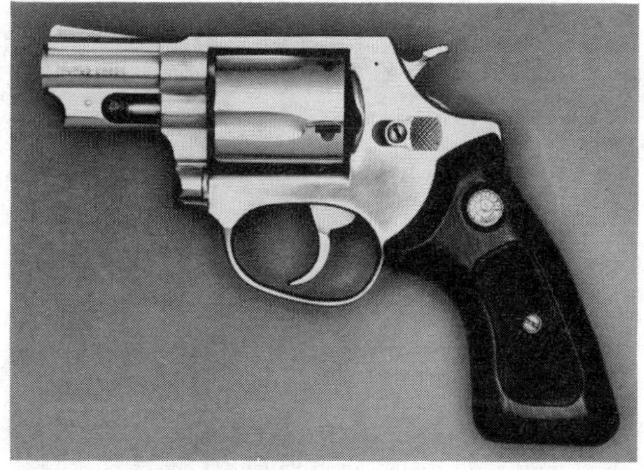

NIB	Exc.	V.G.	Good	Fair	Poor
220	190	175	150	125	100

Model 85CH
Same as above but offered in 2" barrel only, with shrouded hammer. Double action only.

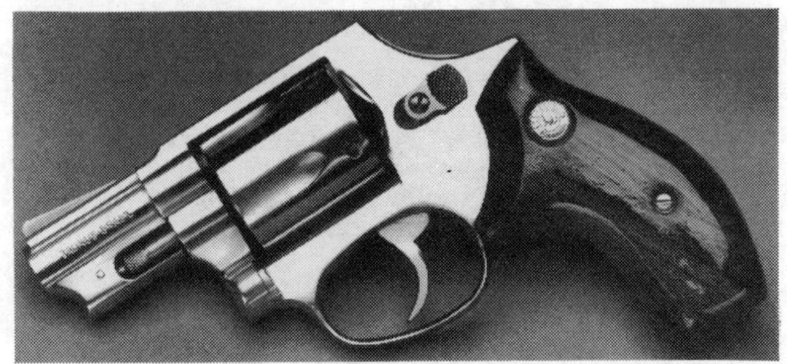

NIB	Exc.	V.G.	Good	Fair	Poor
200	175	150	125	100	75

Model 86
Similar to the Model 83 with the exception of a 6" barrel, target hammer, adjustable trigger, and blue only finish. Weighs 34 ozs.

NIB	Exc.	V.G.	Good	Fair	Poor
250	225	200	150	125	100

Model 94
This double action revolver is chambered for the .22 Long Rifle cartridge. The swing out holds 9 rounds and it is available with either a heavy, solid rib, 3" or 4" barrel. Ramp front sight with fully adjustable rear sight. Offered in blue or stainless steel with Brazilian hardwood grips. Pistol weighs 25 ozs. with 4" barrel.

NIB	Exc.	V.G.	Good	Fair	Poor
200	175	150	125	100	75

Model 941
Similar in appearance to the Model 94 this version is chambered for the .22 WMR. Available with a choice of 3" or 4" heavy, solid rib barrel. This model holds 8 rounds. Ramp front sight with fully adjustable rear sight. Available in blue or stainless steel with Brazilian hardwood grips. Pistol weighs 27.5 ozs.

NIB	Exc.	V.G.	Good	Fair	Poor
225	200	175	125	100	75

Model 96
A full size .22 caliber Long Rifle revolver with 6" heavy, solid rib barrel. Fully adjustable rear sight with target hammer and adjustable target trigger. Cylinder holds 6 rounds. Available in blue only with Brazilian hardwood grips. Pistol weighs 34 ozs.

NIB	Exc.	V.G.	Good	Fair	Poor
250	225	175	125	100	75

Model 741
This double action revolver is chambered for the .32 H&R Mag. cartridge. It features a 3" or 4" heavy, solid rib barrel with fully adjustable rear sight. Swing out cylinder holds 6 rounds. Available in either blue or stainless steel (Stainless steel model introduced in 1993) with Brazilian hardwood grips. Pistol weighs 30 ozs.

NIB	Exc.	V.G.	Good	Fair	Poor
200	175	150	125	100	75

NOTE: Add $40 for stainless steel.

Model 761
Similar to the Model 741 this version has a 6" barrel, target hammer, adjustable target trigger, and is available in blue only. Weighs 34 ozs.

NIB	Exc.	V.G.	Good	Fair	Poor
250	225	175	150	125	100

Model 65
This double action revolver is chambered for the .357 Magnum cartridge. It is offered with 2.5" or 4" heavy, solid rib barrel with ejector shroud. Fitted with fixed sights and Brazilian hardwood grips it is available in blue or stainless steel. The 2.5" barrel is a new addition to the Model 65 for 1993. Pistol weighs 34 ozs. with 4" barrel.

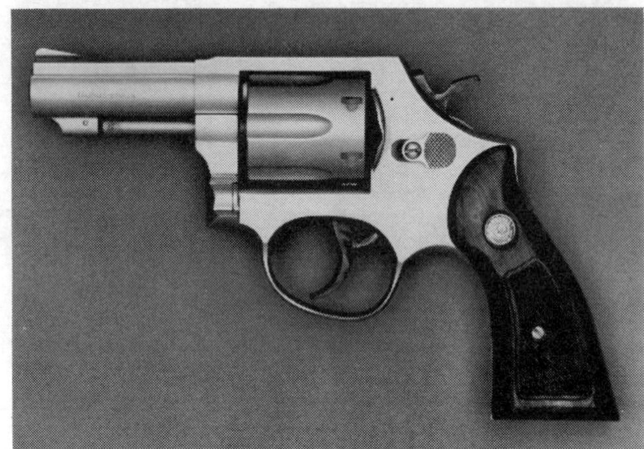

NIB	Exc.	V.G.	Good	Fair	Poor
200	175	150	125	100	75

Model 66
Similar to the Model 65 but offered with a choice of 2.5", 4", or 6" barrel with fully adjustable rear sight. Offered with either blue or stainless steel. Weighs 35 ozs. with 4" barrel. The 2.5" barrel was introduced in 1993.

NIB	Exc.	V.G.	Good	Fair	Poor
225	200	175	150	125	100

Model 66CP

This model is similar to the Model 66 but features a compensated heavy, solid rib 4" or 6" ejector shroud barrel. Introduced in 1993. Pistol weighs 35 ozs.

NIB	Exc.	V.G.	Good	Fair	Poor
250	225	200	150	125	100

Model 669

This model is chambered for the .357 Magnum cartridge and features a 4" or 6" heavy, solid rib barrel with full shroud. It has fully adjustable rear sight and is available with blue or stainless steel finish. Brazilian hardwood grips are standard. Pistol weighs 37 ozs. with 4" barrel.

NIB	Exc.	V.G.	Good	Fair	Poor
250	225	200	150	125	100

NOTE: Add $60 for stainless steel.

Model 669CP

This variation of the Model 699 was introduced in 1993 and features a 4" or 6" compensated barrel. Fully adjustable rear sights are standard and it is offered with either blue or stainless steel finish. Weighs 37 ozs.

NIB	Exc.	V.G.	Good	Fair	Poor
250	225	200	150	125	100

NOTE: Add $60 for stainless steel.

Model 689

This model is chambered for the .357 Magnum cartridge and features a heavy, vent rib barrel in either 4" or 6" lengths. Fully adjustable rear sight is standard. Offered in blue or stainless steel. Pistol weighs 37 ozs.

NIB	Exc.	V.G.	Good	Fair	Poor
250	225	200	150	125	100

NOTE: Add $60 for stainless steel.

Model 431

Chambered for the .44 Special cartridge this double action revolver is furnished with a 3" or 4" heavy, solid rib barrel with ejector shroud. Cylinder capacity is 5 rounds. Fixed sights are standard. Choice of blue or stainless steel finish. Pistol weighs 35 ozs.

NIB	Exc.	V.G.	Good	Fair	Poor
225	200	175	150	125	100

NOTE: Add $60 for stainless steel.

Model 441

Similar to the Model 431 but furnished with an additional choice of a 6" barrel as well as a 3" or 4". Comes standard with fully adjustable rear sight. Cylinder capacity is 5 rounds. Blue or stainless steel finish. Pistol weighs 40.25 ozs. with 6" barrel.

NIB	Exc.	V.G.	Good	Fair	Poor
250	225	200	175	125	100

NOTE: Add $60 for stainless steel.

TAYLOR, L. B.

Chicopee, Massachusetts

Pocket Pistol

A .32 caliber spur trigger single shot pocket pistol with a 3.5" octagonal barrel marked "L. B. Taylor & Co. Chicopee Mass." Silver-plated brass frame, blued barrel and walnut grips. Manufactured during the late 1860s and early 1870s.

Exc.	V.G.	Good	Fair	Poor
300	250	200	150	100

TERRIER ONE

Importer—Southern Gun Distributors
Miami, Florida

Terrier One

A .32 caliber double-action swing-out cylinder revolver with a 2.25" barrel and 5-shot cylinder. Nickle-plated with checkered walnut grips. Manufactured from 1984 to 1987.

Exc.	V.G.	Good	Fair	Poor
75	65	50	30	25

TERRY, J. C.

New York City

Pocket Pistol

A .22 caliber spur trigger single shot pocket pistol with a 3.75" round barrel. The backstrap marked "J.C. Terry/Patent Pending." Silver-plated brass frame, blued barrel and rosewood or walnut grips. Manufactured in the late 1860s.

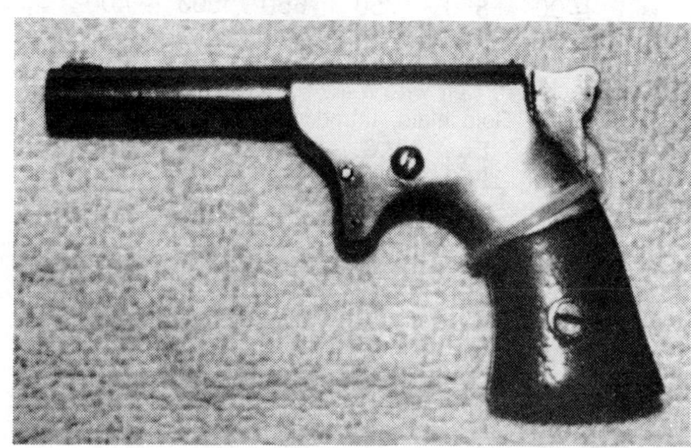

Exc.	V.G.	Good	Fair	Poor
600	400	350	250	200

TEXAS GUNFIGHTERS

Ponte Zanano, Italy
Importer—Texas Gunfighters
Irving, Texas

Shootist Single Action

A .45 Long Colt caliber single action revolver with a 4.75" barrel. Nickle-plated with one-piece walnut grips. This model is made by Aldo Uberti. Introduced in 1988.

NIB	Exc.	V.G.	Good	Fair	Poor
650	550	500	400	350	250

1 of 100 Edition

As above, with one-piece mother-of-pearl grips fitted in a case with an additional set of walnut grips. 100 were made in 1988.

NIB	Exc.	V.G.	Good	Fair	Poor
1400	1100	850	750	600	400

TEXAS LONGHORN ARMS, INC.
Richmond, Texas

Jezebel

A .22 or .22 Magnum single shot pistol with a 6" barrel. Stainless steel with a walnut stock and forend. Introduced in 1987.

NIB	Exc.	V.G.	Good	Fair	Poor
200	175	150	125	100	75

Texas Border Special

A .44 Special or .45 Colt caliber single action revolver with a 3.5" barrel having Pope style rifling. Blued, case-hardened with one-piece walnut grips.

NIB	Exc.	V.G.	Good	Fair	Poor
1500	1250	1000	800	600	500

South Texas Army

As above, but with a 4.75" barrel also chambered for the .357 Magnum cartridge and fitted with conventional one-piece walnut grips.

NIB	Exc.	V.G.	Good	Fair	Poor
1500	1250	1000	800	600	500

West Texas Target

As above, with a 7.5" barrel, flat top frame and in .32-20 caliber in addition to the calibers noted above.

NIB	Exc.	V.G.	Good	Fair	Poor
1500	1250	1000	800	600	500

Grover's Improved Number Five

Similar to the above, in .44 Magnum with a 5.5" barrel. Serial Numbered K1 to K1200. Introduced in 1988.

NIB	Exc.	V.G.	Good	Fair	Poor
1000	850	750	650	500	400

Mason Commemorative

As above, in .45 Colt with a 4.75" barrel and having the Mason's insignia. Gold inlaid. Introduced in 1987.

NIB	Exc.	V.G.	Good	Fair	Poor
1500	1250	1000	800	600	500

Texas Sesquicentennial Commemorative

As above, engraved in the style of Louis D. Nimschke with one-piece ivory grips and a fitted case.

NIB	Exc.	V.G.	Good	Fair	Poor
2500	2000	1750	1500	1000	750

THAMES ARMS CO.
Norwich, Connecticut

A .22, .32 or .38 caliber double-action top break revolver with varying length barrels normally marked "Automatic Revolver" which refers to the cartridge ejector. Nickle-plated with walnut grips.

Exc.	V.G.	Good	Fair	Poor
150	125	100	75	50

THIEME & EDELER
Eibar, Spain

Pocket Pistol

A 7.65mm caliber semi-automatic pistol with a 3" barrel marked "T E". Blued with black plastic grips. Manufactured prior to 1936.

Exc.	V.G.	Good	Fair	Poor
175	150	100	75	50

THOMPSON
SEE—Auto Ordnance

THOMPSON/CENTER ARMS
Rochester, New Hampshire

Contender

Introduced in 1967 this model is the basis for all past and present variations. The standard version is offered with a 10" octagon barrel and is available in 10" Bull barrel, 10" vent rib barrel, 14" Super models, 14" Super with vent rib, 16" Super models, and 16" Super models with vent rib. A stainless steel finish is available on all models except the 10" octagon barrel. The action on these handguns is a single shot, break open design. Unless otherwise stated the barrels are blued. The Competitor grip is walnut with rubber insert mounted on back of grip. A finger groove grip is also available made from walnut with finger notching and thumb rest. Forend is American black walnut in various length and designs depending on barrel size. Stainless steel models have rubber grips with finger grooves. Standard sights are standard Patridge rear with ramp front. An adjustable rear sight is offered as an option. Barrels with vent ribs are furnished with fixed rear sight and bead front sight. Due to the numerous variations of the Contender several breakdowns will be listed to help the reader find the closest possible handgun he may be looking for.

NOTE: Early frames with no engraving, called flatsides, and those with eagle engraving bring between $2,000 and $2,500 on the collector market.

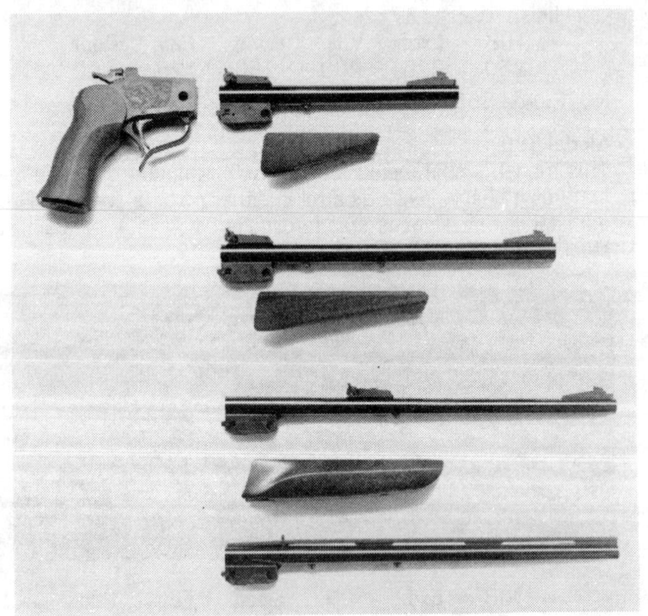

10" Octagon Barrel Model

This was the first Contender design and is offered in .22 Long Rifle only. It is supplied with adjustable rear sight and mounting holes for scope. Grips are Competitor or rubber. Weighs about 44 ozs.

NIB	Exc.	V.G.	Good	Fair	Poor
360	300	250	200	150	100

10" Bull Barrel Model

Comes standard with adjustable rear sight, mounting holes for scope mounts, and Competitor grips for blued models and rubber grips or stainless models. Available in blue or stainless steel. Offered in the following calibers as complete pistols: .22 Long Rifle, .22 LR Match, .22 Win. Mag. (blue only), .22 Hornet, .223, 7mm T.C.U. (blue only), .30-30, .32/20 (blue only), .357 Mag., .357 Rem. Max (blue only), .44 Mag., .45 Colt, .410 bore. Weighs 50 ozs.

NIB	Exc.	V.G.	Good	Fair	Poor
350	300	250	200	150	100

10" Vent Rib Model

This features a raised vent rib and is chambered for the .45 Long Colt/.410 bore. The rear sight is fixed and the front sight is a bead. A detachable choke screws into the muzzle for use with the .410 shell. Furnished with Competitor grips or rubber grips.

NIB	Exc.	V.G.	Good	Fair	Poor
370	320	270	220	150	100

Super 14" Model

This model features a 14" bull barrel. Furnished with adjustable rear sight and ramp front sight. Drilled and tapped for scope mounts. Competitor or rubber grips are offered. Available in blue or stainless steel finish. Furnished in the following calibers in a complete pistol only: .22 Long Rifle, .22 LR Match, .17 Rem. (blue only), .22 Hornet, .222 Rem. (blue only), .223 Rem., 7mm T.C.U. (blue only), 7-30 Waters, .30-30, .357 Rem. Max (blue only), .35 Rem., .375 Win. (blue only), .44 Mag. (blue only). Weighs approximately 56 ozs.

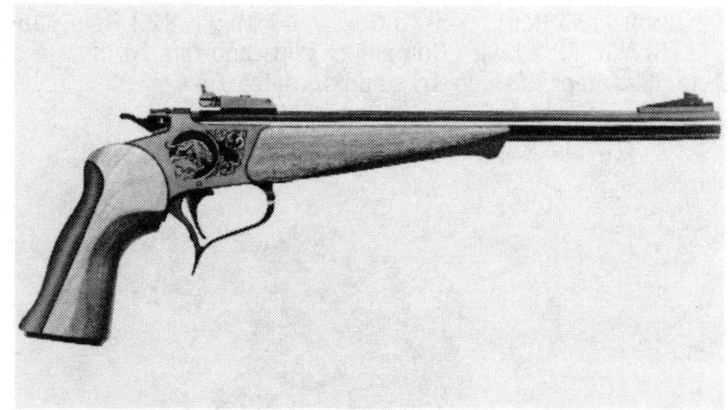

NIB	Exc.	V.G.	Good	Fair	Poor
360	300	250	200	150	100

Super 14" Vent Rib Model

Similar to the 10" Vent Rib Model chambered for the .45 Long Colt/.410 bore but furnished with a 14" vent rib barrel.

NIB	Exc.	V.G.	Good	Fair	Poor
385	325	275	215	150	100

Super 16" Model

Fitted with a 16.25" tapered barrel, two position adjustable rear sight. Drilled and tapped for scope mount. Furnished with Competitor grips or rubber grips and choice of blue or stainless steel finish. Available in the following calibers as complete pistols only: .22 Long Rifle, .22 Hornet, .223 Rem., 7-30 Waters, .30-30, .35 Rem., .45-70 Gov't. Weighs approximately 56 ozs.

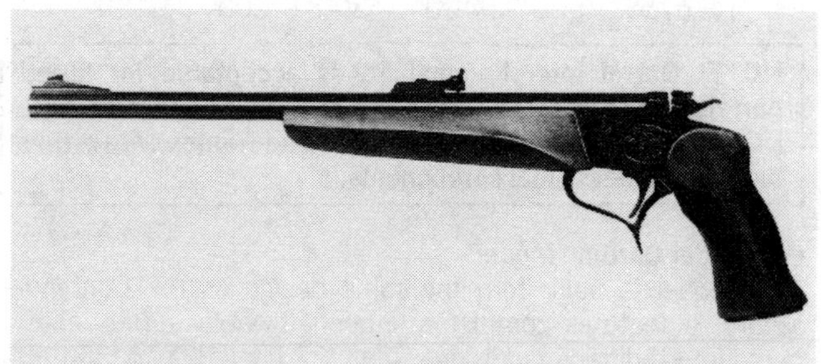

NIB	Exc.	V.G.	Good	Fair	Poor
370	320	275	215	150	100

Super 16" Vent Rib Model

Chambered for .45 Long Colt/.410 bore this model was offered for the first time in 1993. All other features are the same as the other Contender .45/.410 bore pistols.

NIB	Exc.	V.G.	Good	Fair	Poor
390	350	300	250	175	125

Contender Hunter Model

This model is designed for handgun hunting and is offered in two barrel lengths: 12" and 14". The barrels are fitted with a compensator and a 2.5 power scope. There are no iron sights fitted. A nylon carrying sling and soft leather carrying case are standard. Offered in the following calibers: 7-30 Waters, .30-

30 Win., .35 Rem., .45-70 Gov't., .44 Mag., .223 Rem., and .375 Win. Fitted with Competitor grips and offered in blue or stainless steel finish. Weighs approximately 64 ozs.

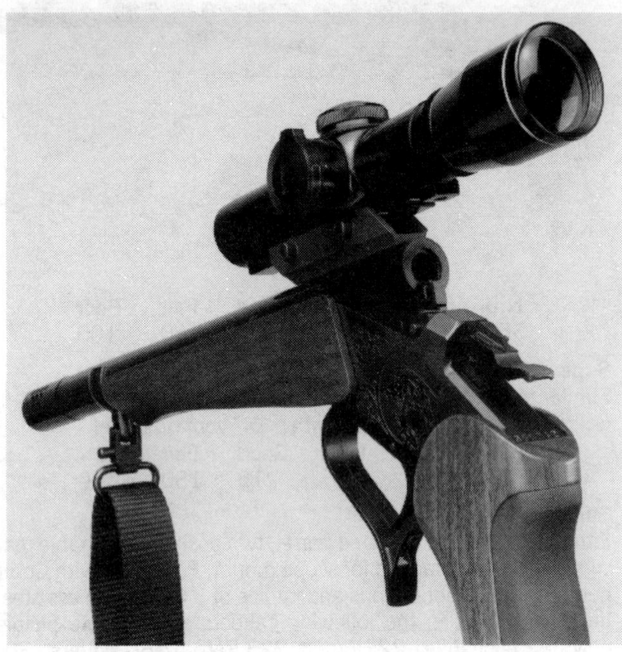

NIB	Exc.	V.G.	Good	Fair	Poor
575	500	400	300	200	100

NOTE: Barrel interchangeability is acceptable for blued barrels and frames with stainless steel barrels and frames. DO NOT interchange Alloy II barrels and frames with either blue or stainless steel components.

Contender Carbine Model

This model is built from the same design as the Contender Model. It features completely interchangeable barrels chambered for 12 different cartridges from .22 Long Rifle to .35 Rem. A .410 bore shotgun barrel is also offered. The standard model has a 21" barrel stocked with walnut. For stainless steel models a composite stock in fitted walnut is also available. All are drilled and tapped for scope mounts. Available in blue or stainless steel.

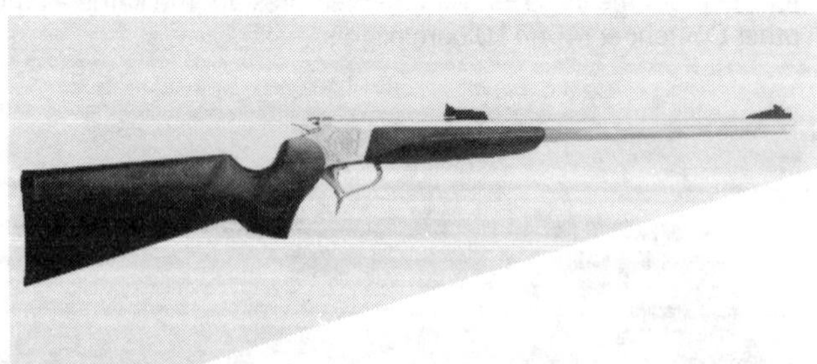

Standard 21" Carbine Model

This model is fitted with a 21" plain barrel and walnut stocks. Offered in the following calibers as a complete gun only: .22 Long Rifle, .22 LR Match (blue only), .17 Rem. (blue only), .22 Hornet, .223 Rem., 7-30 Waters, .30-30, .35 Rem. (blue only), .375 Win. (blue only). Weighs 5 lbs. 3 ozs.

NIB	Exc.	V.G.	Good	Fair	Poor
400	350	300	250	200	100

21" Carbine .410 Bore

Same as above but fitted with a vent rib barrel and screw in choke.

NIB	Exc.	V.G.	Good	Fair	Poor
410	360	300	250	200	100

16" Youth Model Carbine

A special walnut butt stock with 12" length of pull and 16.25" barrel. Short butt stock can be replaced with standard butt stock. Blue or stainless steel finish. Complete guns are offered in the same calibers as the 21" Carbine with the exception of the .375 Win. and the addition of the .45 Long Colt/.410 bore with vent rib barrel.

NIB	Exc.	V.G.	Good	Fair	Poor
350	300	250	200	150	100

TCR Hunter Model

This single shot top lever rifle is chambered for cartridges from .22 Long Rifle to .308 Win. Fitted with a 23" barrel. The finish is blue with walnut stock. Discontinued as a regular production rifle in 1993 but available from the TC custom shop as a special order.

NIB	Exc.	V.G.	Good	Fair	Poor
425	375	300	250	200	100

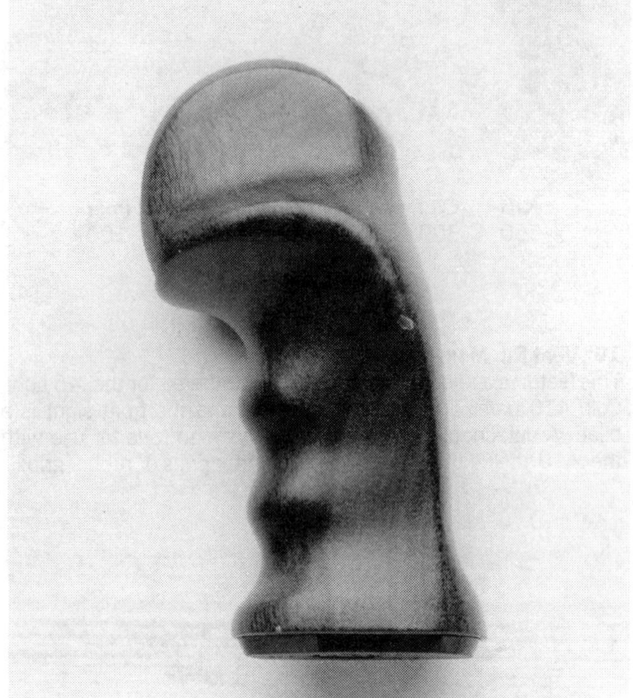

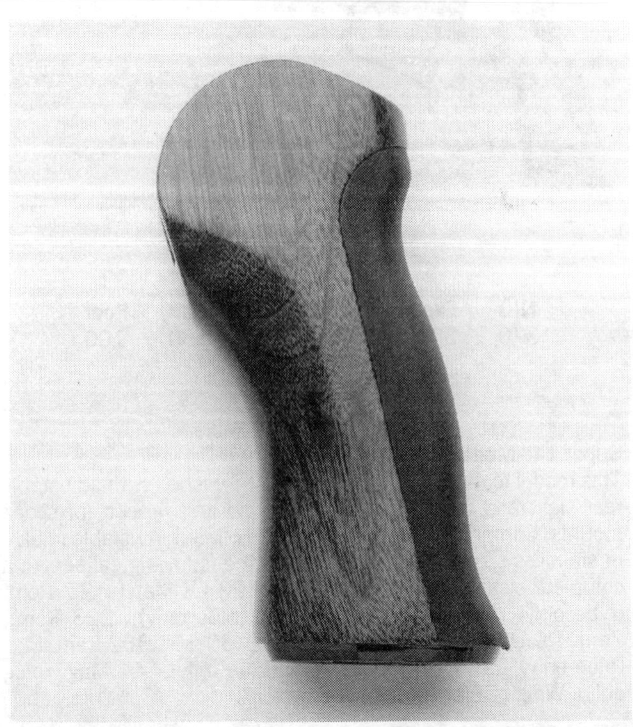

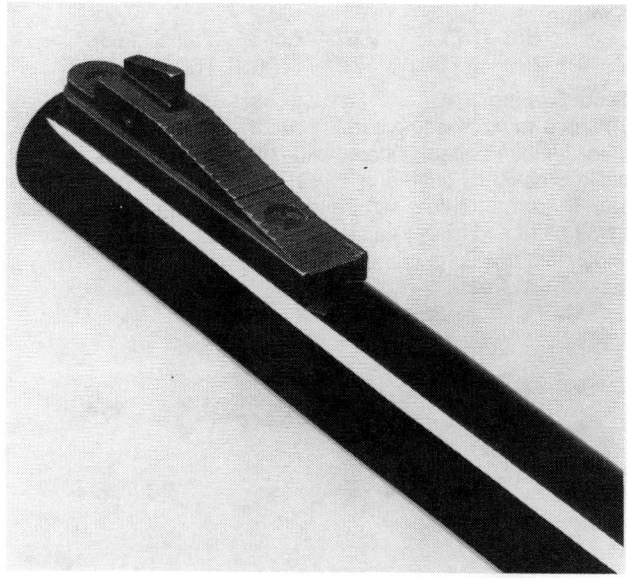

BLACK POWDER FIREARMS

Thunder Hawk

Introduced in 1993 this rifle features a .50 caliber Cap Lock in-line ignition with 21" round barrel. Rear sight is adjustable with ramp front sight. The stock is a plain American black walnut with rubber recoil pad. Trigger is adjustable. Weighs 6.75 lbs.

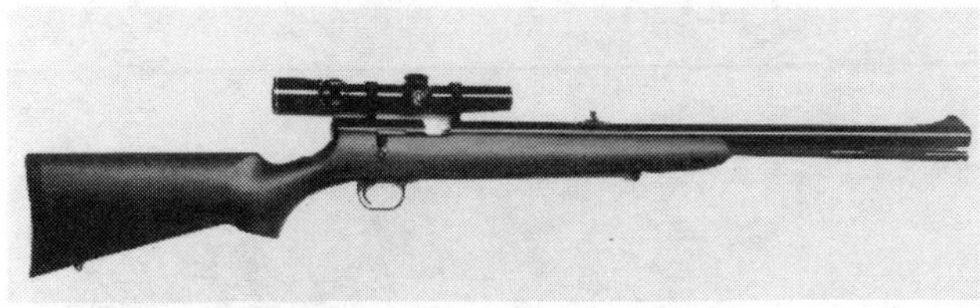

NIB	Exc.	V.G.	Good	Fair	Poor
225	200	175	150	100	75

Grey Hawk

This stainless steel composite stock rifle is a .50 caliber cap lock with 24" round barrel. It utilizes a hooked breech system. The lock is a heavy duty coil spring with floral engraving pattern. Adjustable rear sight and bead front sight are standard. Weighs about 7 lbs.

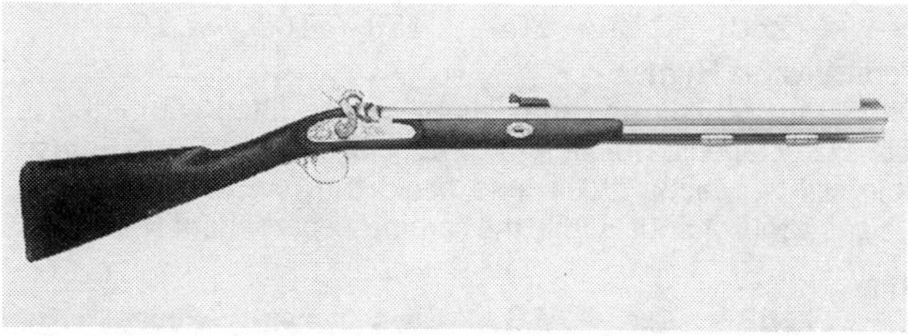

NIB	Exc.	V.G.	Good	Fair	Poor
225	200	175	150	100	75

Hawken Cap Lock Rifle

Available in .45, .50, and .54 caliber this rifle has a 28" octagon barrel and hooked breech system. Triggers are fully adjustable and can function as double set or single stage. Adjustable sights with bead front sight are standard. Trim is solid brass and stock is select American walnut with cheek piece. Weighs about 8.5 lbs.

NIB	Exc.	V.G.	Good	Fair	Poor
300	250	200	150	100	75

Hawken Flint Lock Rifle

Offered in .50 caliber with 28" octagon barrel. All other features are the same as above.

NIB	Exc.	V.G.	Good	Fair	Poor
310	260	200	150	100	75

Renegade Cap Lock Rifle

Offered in .50 or .54 caliber with 26" octagon barrel. Adjustable triggers which can function as double set or single stage. Adjustable sights with blue trim. Walnut stock. Offered in either right hand or left hand models. Weighs about 8 lbs.

NIB	Exc.	V.G.	Good	Fair	Poor
275	225	200	150	100	75

Renegade Flint Lock

Available in .50 caliber only and right hand only. Other features are the same as Cap Lock Model.

NIB	Exc.	V.G.	Good	Fair	Poor
275	250	200	150	100	75

Big Boar Rifle

This hooked breech model features the .58 caliber with 26" octagonal barrel. Single trigger and adjustable sights are standard. Trim is blued steel. American walnut stock with rubber pad. Weighs about 7.75 lbs.

NIB	Exc.	V.G.	Good	Fair	Poor
275	250	200	150	100	75

High Plains Sporter

This is a .50 caliber cap lock with a 24" round barrel. The lock is case-colored. Choice of adjustable open sights or tang sight. Trim is blued. The stock is walnut with rubber recoil pad, pistol grip, and sling swivel studs. Weighs about 7 lbs.

NIB	Exc.	V.G.	Good	Fair	Poor
275	250	200	150	100	75

Tree Hawk

Available in either .50 caliber Cap Lock or 12 gauge cap lock. The .50 caliber carbine has a 21" barrel and is offered in camo colors. The 12 gauge shotgun is fitted with a 27" barrel and also comes in camo colors. Weight is about 6.75 lbs.

Rifle

NIB	Exc.	V.G.	Good	Fair	Poor
275	250	200	150	100	75

Shotgun

NIB	Exc.	V.G.	Good	Fair	Poor
275	250	200	150	100	75

White Mountain Carbine

Available in either .45, .50, or 54 caliber cap lock or .50 flint lock. Fitted with a 20" 1/2 octagon barrel. The lock is case-colored and trim is blued. Stock is walnut with rubber recoil pad. Weighs about 6.5 lbs.

NIB	Exc.	V.G.	Good	Fair	Poor
250	225	200	150	100	75

Pennsylvania Hunter

Offered in .50 caliber cap or flint lock and fitted with either a 31" 1/2 octagon barrel or a 21" 1/2 octagon barrel. Fully adjustable sights, walnut stock, and blued trim are standard. Rifle weighs about 7.5 lbs. while the carbine weighs about 6.5 lbs.

Rifle

NIB	Exc.	V.G.	Good	Fair	Poor
250	225	200	150	100	75

Carbine

NIB	Exc.	V.G.	Good	Fair	Poor
250	225	200	150	100	75

New Englander Rifle

Offered in either .50 or .54 caliber cap lock with walnut stock and 26" round barrel. Adjustable sights. Weighs about 7 lbs. 15 ozs. A 12" barrel is optional.

NIB	Exc.	V.G.	Good	Fair	Poor
200	175	150	125	90	75

NOTE: Add $150 for interchangeable shotgun barrel.

New Englander Shotgun

Same as above, but fitted with a 27" 12 gauge barrel with screw in full choke. Weighs about 6 lbs. 8 ozs.

NIB	Exc.	V.G.	Good	Fair	Poor
230	200	175	150	100	75

New Englander Composite

Offered with composite stock. The .50 or .54 caliber rifle has a 24" barrel and the 12 gauge shotgun has a 27" barrel.

Rifle

NIB	Exc.	V.G.	Good	Fair	Poor
200	175	150	125	100	75

Shotgun

NIB	Exc.	V.G.	Good	Fair	Poor
225	200	175	150	100	75

Scout Carbine

This is a muzzleloading carbine of .50 or .54 caliber with an inline ignition system. Offered with either walnut stock or composite stock (first offered in 1993) it is fitted with a 21" round barrel. Adjustable rear sight and fixed blade front sight. Brass barrel band and trigger guard on walnut stock and blued barrel band and trigger guard on composite stock model. Weighs about 7 lbs. 4 ozs.

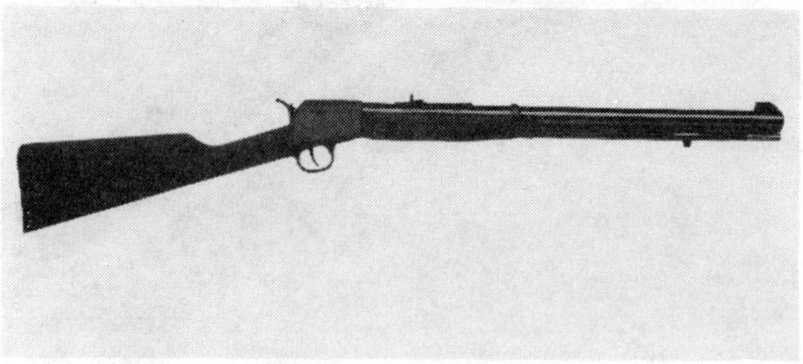

Walnut stock

NIB	Exc.	V.G.	Good	Fair	Poor
315	275	200	150	100	75

Composite stock

NIB	Exc.	V.G.	Good	Fair	Poor
240	220	185	150	100	75

Scout Pistol

The same design as the Scout carbine this single action pistol is available in .45, .50, or .54 caliber. Fitted with a 12" barrel, adjustable rear sight, and blue finish with brass trigger guard. Black walnut grips. Weighs 4 lbs. 6 ozs.

NIB	Exc.	V.G.	Good	Fair	Poor
250	225	200	175	100	75

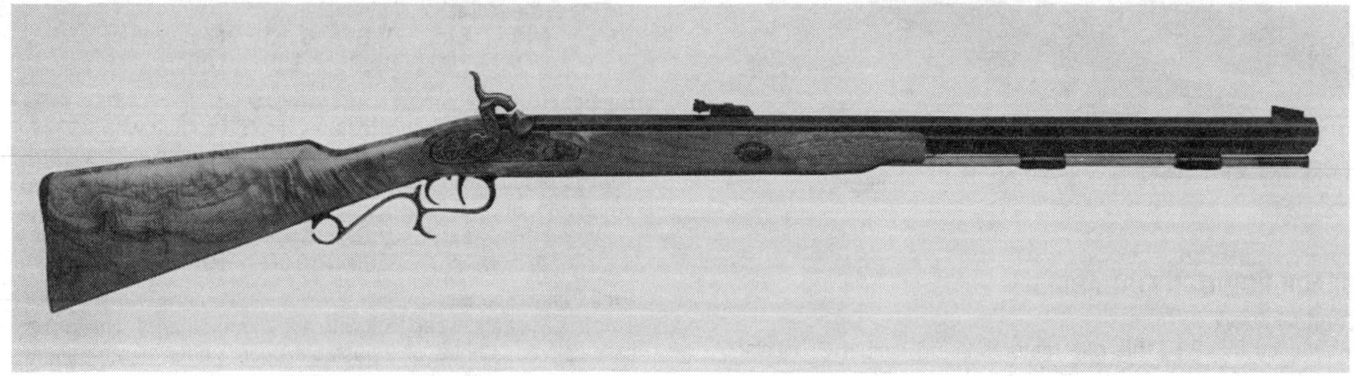

Thompson-Center Renegade Cap Lock Rifle.

Thompson-Center Renegade Cap Lock (lefthand).

Thompson-Center Renegade Hunter Model.

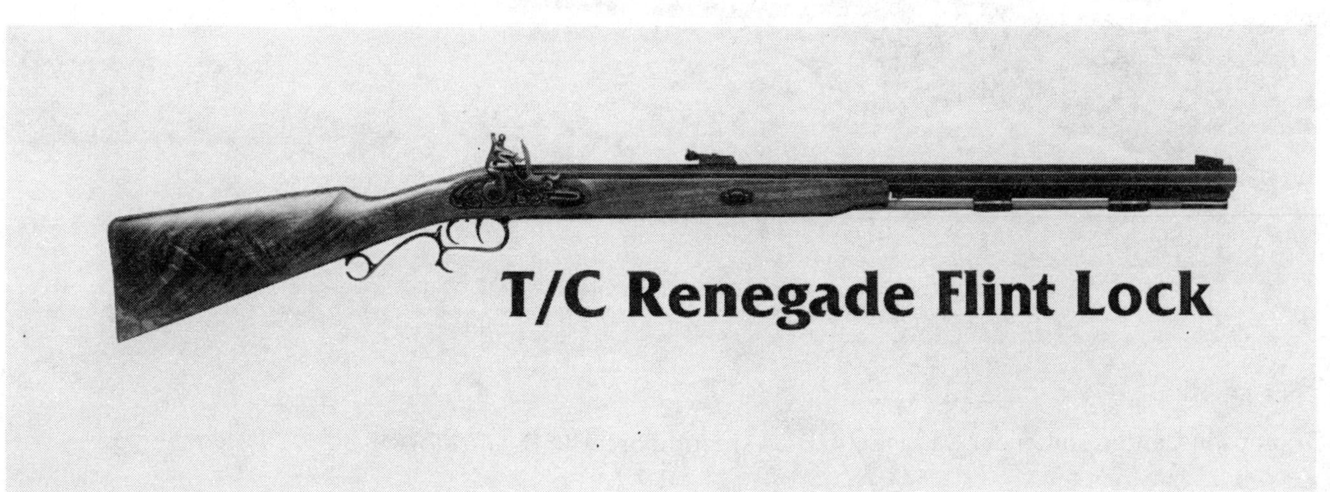

Thompson-Center Contender Carbine with Rynite stock.

Thompson-Center Contender Carbine /410 GA smoothbore with Rynite stock.

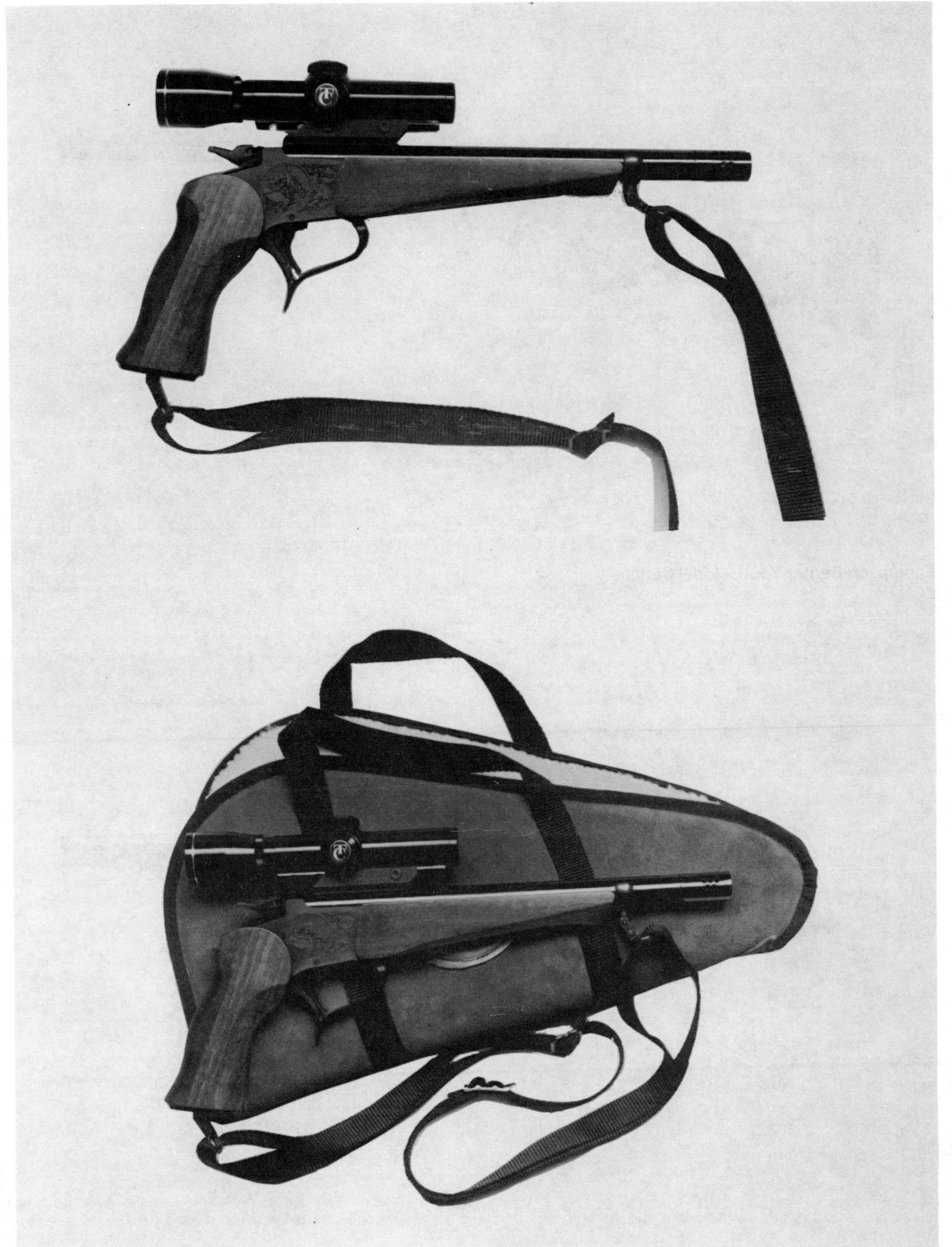

Thompson-Center Contender Hunter Package.

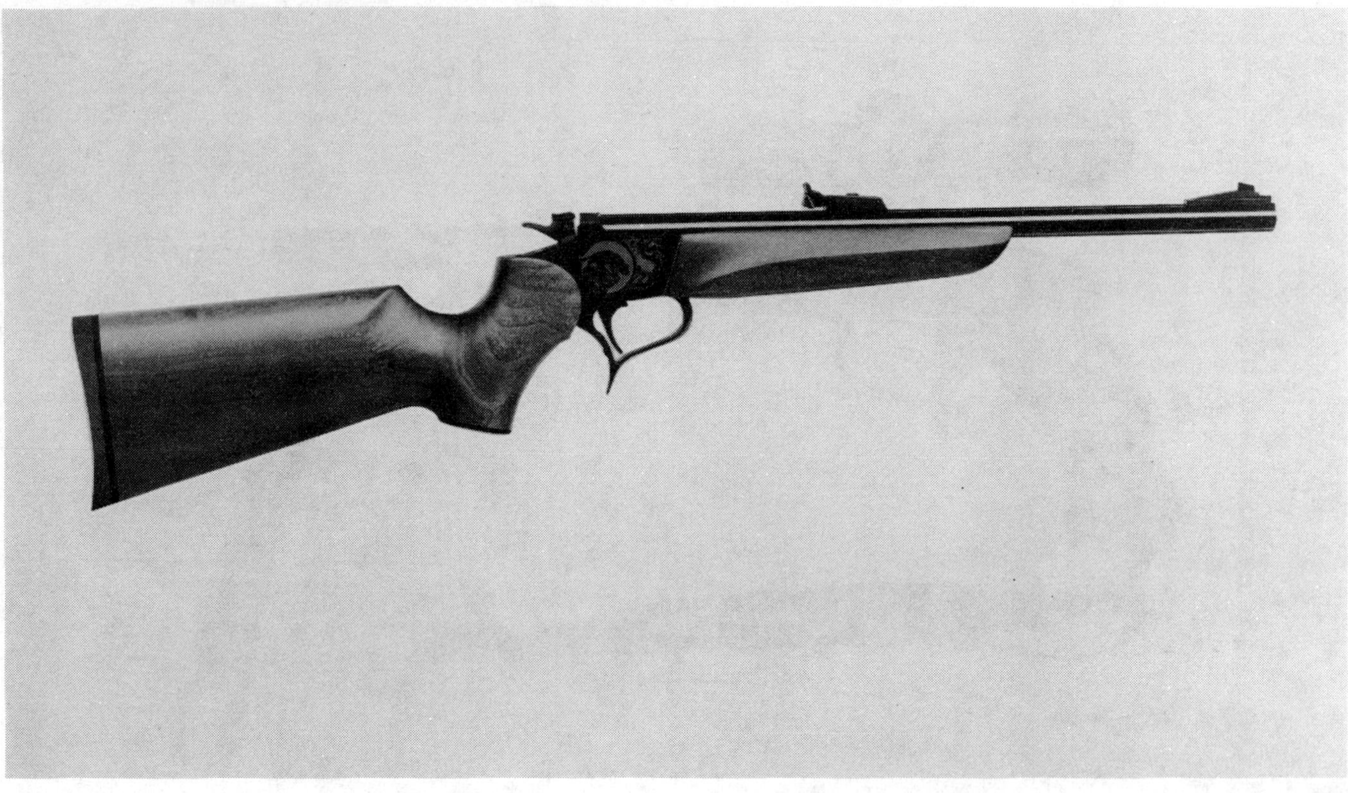

Thompson-Center Youth Model Carbine

Thompson-Center White Mountain Carbine .50 Cal. Cap Lock.

THUNDER FIVE

MIL Inc.
Piney Flats, Tennessee

Five shot, double action, 2" rifled barrel, matte finish, ambidextrous hammer block safety, Pacymayr grips, chambered in .45 Long Colt/.410 shotgun and 47-70 Gov.

NIB	Exc.	V.G.	Good	Fair	Poor
650	500	400	300	200	100

TIKKA

Tikkakoski, Finland
Importer—Stoeger Industries
South Hackensack, New Jersey

RIFLES

New Generation Rifles

This rifle features a hand checkered walnut stock with matte lacquer finish. These rifles are furnished without sights, but receiver is grooved. Magazine is detachable box type. Two action lengths are offered: medium and long. In medium action calibers the choices are: .223, .22-250, .243, and .308 with 22.4" barrels and weigh 7 lbs. The long action calibers are: .270 and .30-06 with 22.4" barrels and weigh 7.3 lbs., 7mm Rem. Mag., .300 and .338 Win. Mag. with 24.4" barrel and weigh 7.5 lbs.

NIB	Exc.	V.G.	Good	Fair	Poor
725	600	500	400	200	150

New Generation Premium Grade

Similar to standard model above but furnished with cheek piece, select walnut stock, rosewood pistol grip cap and forend tip. Metal surfaces are a highly polished blue. Same calibers as offered above.

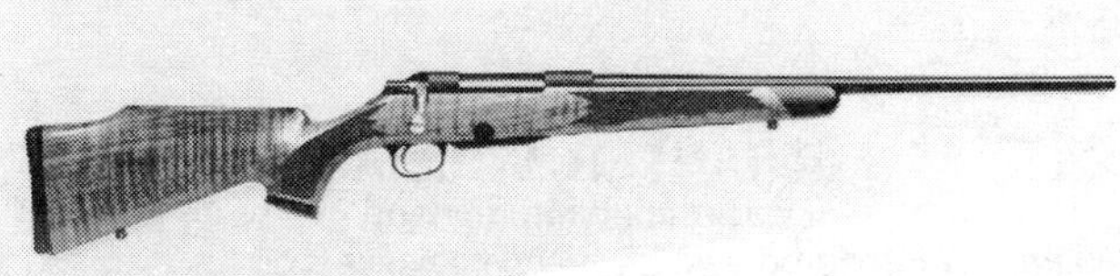

NIB	Exc.	V.G.	Good	Fair	Poor
875	700	600	400	200	150

Whitetail/Battue Rifle

This rifle was originally designed for the French market. The barrel is 20.5" long and is fitted with a raised quarter rib. The walnut is checkered with rubber recoil pad standard. In the medium action the only caliber is .308. In a long action the calibers are: .270, .30-06, 7mm Rem. Mag., .300 and .338 Win. Mag. All models weigh about 7 lbs.

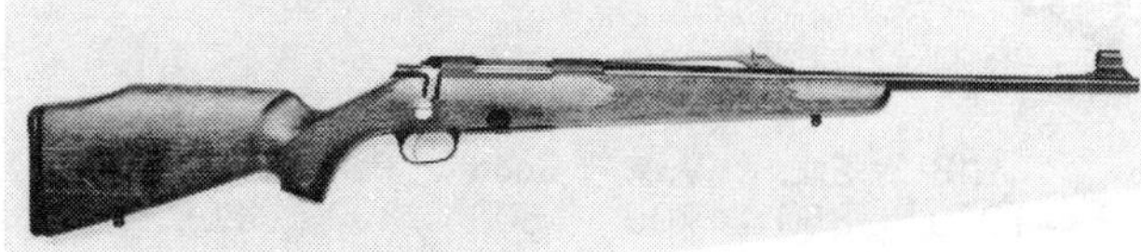

NIB	Exc.	V.G.	Good	Fair	Poor
750	600	500	400	200	150

Varmint/Continental Rifle

This model features a 23.5" heavy barrel without sights. The checkered walnut stock has a wide forend. Offered in .223, .22-250, .243, and .308. Weighs approximately 8.5 lbs.

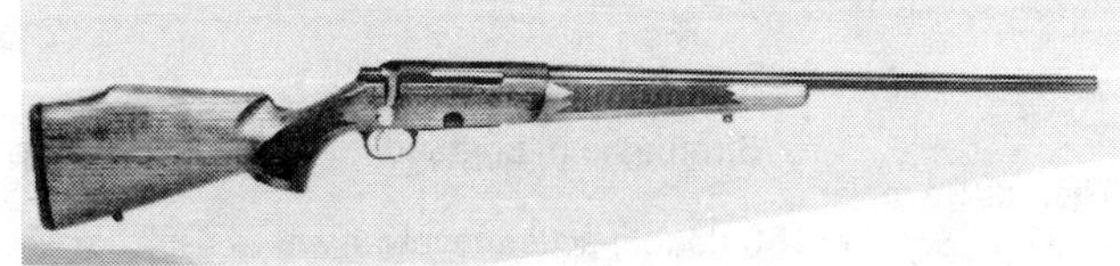

NIB	Exc.	V.G.	Good	Fair	Poor
875	700	600	400	200	150

SHOTGUNS/DOUBLE RIFLES (formerly Valmet)

Tikka, Valmet and Sako have been merged into one company, SAKO Ltd. These firearms are now manufactured under the brand name Tikka and are manufactured in Italy. Parts are interchangeable between the Valmet guns, made in Finland and the Tikka guns, made in Italy.

412S Shotgun

This Over/Under shotgun is available in 12 gauge only with 26" or 28" barrels. The stock is checkered European walnut. Weighs about 7.25 lbs.

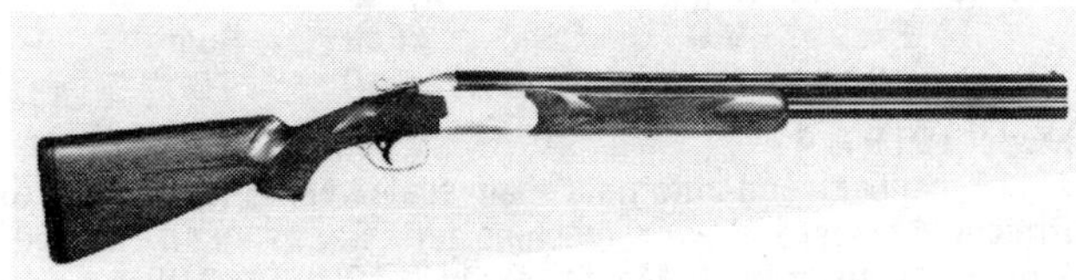

NIB	Exc.	V.G.	Good	Fair	Poor
950	800	650	500	300	200

412S Shotgun/Rifle

Same as above but with 12 gauge barrel and choice of .222 or .308 barrel. Barrel length is 24" and weighs 8 lbs.

NIB	Exc.	V.G.	Good	Fair	Poor
1000	850	700	500	300	200

412S Double Rifle

Same as above but fitted with a 24" Over/Under rifle barrel in 9.3x74R. Weighs about 8.5 lbs.

NIB	Exc.	V.G.	Good	Fair	Poor
1150	950	750	500	300	200

412S Sporting Clays
Introduced in 1993 this model is offered in 12 gauge with 28" barrels with choke tubes.

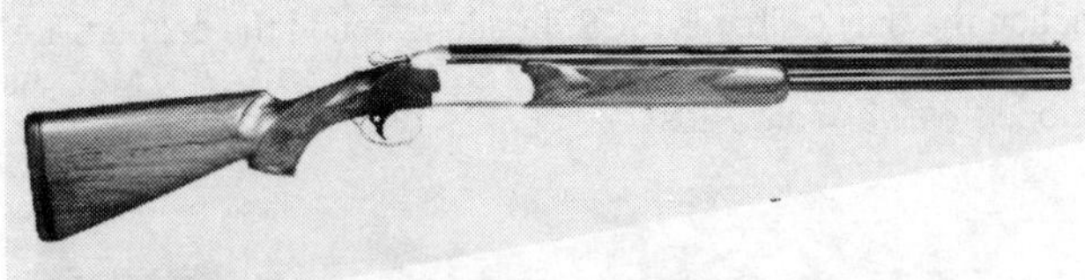

NIB	Exc.	V.G.	Good	Fair	Poor
1000	850	700	500	300	200

TIMBER WOLF
SEE—Action Arms

TIPPING & LAWDEN
Birmingham, England

Thomas Revolver
A .320, .380 or .450 double-action revolver with a 4.5" barrel and 5-shot cylinder, utilizing a cartridge extraction system designed by J. Thomas of Birmingham in which the barrel and cylinder may be moved forward. Manufactured from 1870 to 1877.

Exc.	V.G.	Good	Fair	Poor
550	450	400	300	175

TIPPMAN ARMS
Fort Wayne, Indiana

Model 1917
A .22 caliber semi-automatic half scale reproduction of the Browning Model 1917 water cooled machine gun. Barrel length 10". A tripod was sold with this model. Manufactured in 1986 and 1987.

Exc.	V.G.	Good	Fair	Poor
1700	1500	1250	950	750

Model 1919 A-4
A .22 caliber semi-automatic half scale reproduction of the Browning Model 1919 A-4 machine gun. Barrel length 11" and furnished with a tripod. Manufactured in 1986 and 1987.

Exc.	V.G.	Good	Fair	Poor
1200	1000	750	600	500

Model .50 HB
A .22 Magnum caliber semi-automatic half scale reproduction of the Browning .50 caliber machine gun. Barrel length 18.25", furnished with a tripod. Manufactured in 1986 and 1987.

Exc.	V.G.	Good	Fair	Poor
1800	1600	1350	1000	800

TODD, GEORGE H.
Montgomery, Alabama

Rifled Musket
A .58 caliber single shot percussion rifle with a 40" barrel and full-length stock secured by three barrel bands. Barrel and lock finished in the bright, brass furniture and walnut stock. The lock marked "George H. Todd/ Montgomery, Ala." Prospective purchasers are advised to secure a qualified appraisal prior to acquisition.

Exc.	V.G.	Good	Fair	Poor
6000	5000	4000	2500	1750

TOKAREV
Soviet State Arsenals

M 38 Rifle
A 7.62mm caliber gas-operated semi-automatic rifle with a 24" barrel and 10-shot magazine. Blued with a two-piece hardwood stock. Manufactured from 1938 to 1940.

Exc.	V.G.	Good	Fair	Poor
400	350	300	200	150

M 40 Rifle
As above, with a sheetmetal handguard and muzzle brake.

Exc.	V.G.	Good	Fair	Poor
400	350	300	200	150

TT30 & TT33
A 7.62mm semi-automatic pistol with a 4.5" barrel and 8-shot magazine. This model was produced in a number of communist countries.
TT30—Add 25%.

Exc.	V.G.	Good	Fair	Poor
450	400	300	250	175

TOMISKA, ALOIS
Pilsen, Czechoslovakia

Little Tom
A 6.35mm or 7.65mm caliber semi-automatic pistol with a 2.5" barrel. The slide marked "Alois Tomiska Plzen Patent Little Tom" and the grips inlaid with a medallion bearing the monogram "AT". Blued with checkered walnut grips. Manufactured from 1908 to 1918. Subsequently produced by the Wiener Waffenfabrik.

Exc.	V.G.	Good	Fair	Poor
475	425	350	250	175

TRADEWINDS
Tacoma, Washington

Model H-170
A 12 gauge semi-automatic shotgun with a 26" or 28" ventilated-rib barrel and 5-shot tubular magazine. Blued, anodized alloy receiver and walnut stock.

Exc.	V.G.	Good	Fair	Poor
300	250	225	150	100

Model 260-A
A .22 caliber semi-automatic rifle with a 22.5" barrel, open sights and 5-shot magazine. Blued with a walnut stock.

Exc.	V.G.	Good	Fair	Poor
200	175	125	100	75

Model 311-A
A .22 caliber bolt-action rifle with a 22.5" barrel, open sights and a 5-shot magazine. Blued with a walnut stock.

Exc.	V.G.	Good	Fair	Poor
175	150	100	75	50

Model 5000 "Husky"
A centerfire bolt-action rifle with a 24" barrel, adjustable sights and 4-shot magazine. Blued with a walnut stock.

Exc.	V.G.	Good	Fair	Poor
350	300	275	200	100

TRANTER, WILLIAM
Birmingham, England

William Tranter produced a variety of revolvers on his own and a number of other makers produced revolvers based upon his designs. Consequently, "Tranter's Patent" is to be found on revolvers made by such firms as Deane, Adams and Deane, etc.

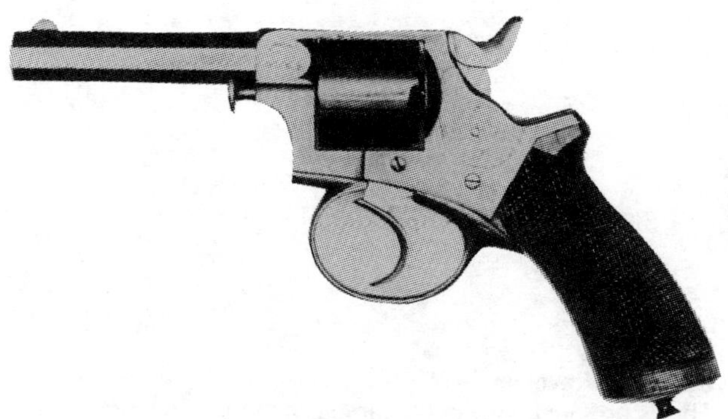

Courtesy Wallis & Wallis, Lewes, Sussex, England.

Model 1872

A .38 caliber double-action revolver with a 6" octagonal barrel and 6-shot cylinder. Blued with walnut grips.

Exc.	V.G.	Good	Fair	Poor
750	650	500	300	200

Model 1878

A .450 caliber double-action revolver with a 6" octagonal barrel. Blued with a walnut grip. Manufactured from 1878 to 1887.

Exc.	V.G.	Good	Fair	Poor
650	550	450	275	175

TRIPPLET & SCOTT MERIDAN MANUFACTURING COMPANY

Meridan, Connecticut

Repeating Carbine

A .50 caliber carbine with either a 22" or 30" round barrel and a 7-shot magazine located in the butt. This model is loaded by turning the barrel until it comes in line with the magazine. Blued, case-hardened with a walnut stock. Approximately 5,000 were made in 1864 and 1865.

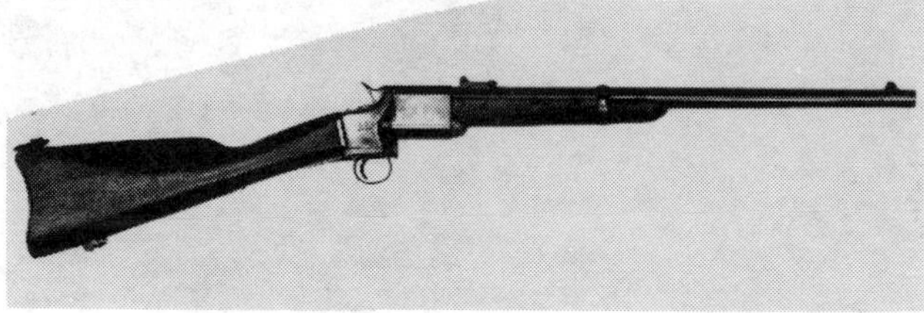

Courtesy Milwaukee Public Museum, Milwaukee, Wisconsin.

Exc.	V.G.	Good	Fair	Poor
950	850	700	550	400

TROCAOLA

Eibar, Spain

This maker produced a variety of .32, .38 and .44 caliber top break revolvers between approximately 1900 and 1936. These pistols can be identified by the monogram "TAC" stamped on the left side of the frame. The value of all these revolvers is as follows:

Exc.	V.G.	Good	Fair	Poor
150	125	100	75	50

TRYON, EDWARD K. & COMPANY

Philadelphia, Pennsylvania

Pocket Pistol

A .41 caliber single shot percussion pocket pistol with a 2" or 4" barrel, German silver mounts and a walnut stock. The lock marked "Tryon/Philada." Manufactured during the 1860s and 1870s.

Exc.	V.G.	Good	Fair	Poor
1250	1000	500	375	275

TUCKER SHERARD & COMPANY

Lancaster, Texas

Dragoon

A .44 caliber percussion revolver with a 7.75" round barrel fitted with a loading lever and a 6-shot cylinder. The barrel marked "Clark, Sherard & Co., Lancaster, Texas," and the cylinder etched in two panels with crossed cannons and the legend "Texas Arms." Approximately 400 revolvers of this type were made between 1862 and 1867. Prospective purchasers are advised to secure a qualified appraisal prior to acquisition.

Exc.	V.G.	Good	Fair	Poor
12500	10000	7500	5000	3000

TUFTS & COLLEY

New York, New York

Pocket Pistol

A .44 caliber single shot percussion pocket pistol with a 3.5" barrel, German silver mounts and walnut stock. The lock marked "Tufts & Colley" and the barrel "Deringer/Pattn." Manufactured during the 1860s.

Exc.	V.G.	Good	Fair	Poor
750	650	500	400	300

TURBIAUX, JACQUES

Paris, France

SEE—Ames

TURNER, THOMAS

Redding, England

Pepperbox

A .476 double-action percussion pepperbox having 6 barrels. Blued, case-hardened with walnut grips. The left side of the frame is engraved in an oval "Thomas Turner, Redding."

Courtesy Butterfield & Butterfield, San Francisco, California.

Exc.	V.G.	Good	Fair	Poor
3500	2500	1500	900	500

TYLER ORDNANCE WORKS

Tyler, Texas

This company produced 56 Austrian rifles, 508 Enfield rifles, 423 Hill rifles and 1,009 Texas rifles during the Civil War. Extreme caution is urged prior to purchasing any of these arms and a qualified appraisal should be sought.

Tyler Texas Rifle

A .57 caliber single shot rifle with a 27" barrel and a full stock secured by two barrel bands. The lock marked "Texas Rifle/Tyler/Cal. .57."

Exc.	V.G.	Good	Fair	Poor
9500	8500	7000	5000	3000

Hill Rifle

A .54 caliber single shot percussion rifle with a 27" barrel, full stock secured by two brass barrel bands and an iron triggerguard and buttplate. The lock marked "Hill Rifle/Tyler/Tex/Cal. .54."

Exc.	V.G.	Good	Fair	Poor
9500	8500	7000	5000	3000

USAS 12
DAEWOO PRECISION IND., LTD.
South Korea
Importer—Gilbert Equipment Company
Mobile, Alabama

USAS 12
A 12 gauge semi-automatic shotgun with a 18.25" cylinder bored barrel, and either a 10-shot box magazine or 20-shot drum magazine. Parkerized, with a composition stock. Because of pending legislation, no prices are quoted.

U.S. ARMS CO.
Riverhead, New York

Abilene .357 Magnum
A .357 Magnum single action revolver with a 4-5/8", 5-1/2" or 6-1/2" barrel, adjustable sights and transfer-bar safety. Blued with walnut grips. Manufactured from 1976 to 1983.
Stainless-Steel Version—Add 30%.

Exc.	V.G.	Good	Fair	Poor
250	225	200	150	100

Abilene .44 Magnum
As above, in .44 Magnum with a 7.5" or 8.5" barrel and a 6-shot unfluted cylinder.
Stainless-Steel Version—Add 30%.

Exc.	V.G.	Good	Fair	Poor
325	300	250	200	150

U.S. REPEATING ARMS CO.
SEE—Winchester

UBERTI, ALDO
Ponte Zanano, Italy
Importers—Cimarron Firearms
E.M.F., Inc.
Uberti USA

This company manufactures high-grade reproductions of famous Western-style American firearms. Their products have been imported over the years by a number of different companies. They produce both black powder guns and the cartridge firearms that are included in this section. This Italian manufacturer builds high quality firearms of the American West. Featured are Colt's, Winchester, and Remington. Each importer stamps its name on the firearm in addition to the Uberti address.

There may be small variations in stampings on the barrel address if requested by the importer. Perhaps the most noticeable difference between importers is the exclusive use of original stampings and patent dates on Colt single actions and Winchester rifles by Cimarron Arms. This firm also has a case hardened hammer on its Colt single action as well as a high polish charcoal blue.

The prices below represent the Uberti line as imported into the United States. Navy Arms also imports rifles and revolvers by Uberti and these are listed separately in the Navy Arms section.

Patterson Revolver
This is an exact copy of the famous and rare Colt pistol. Offered in .36 caliber with engraved 5 shot cylinder, the barrel is 7.5" long and octagonal forward of the lug. The frame is case hardened steel as is the backstrap. Grips are one piece walnut. Overall length is 11.5" and weight is about 2.5 lb.

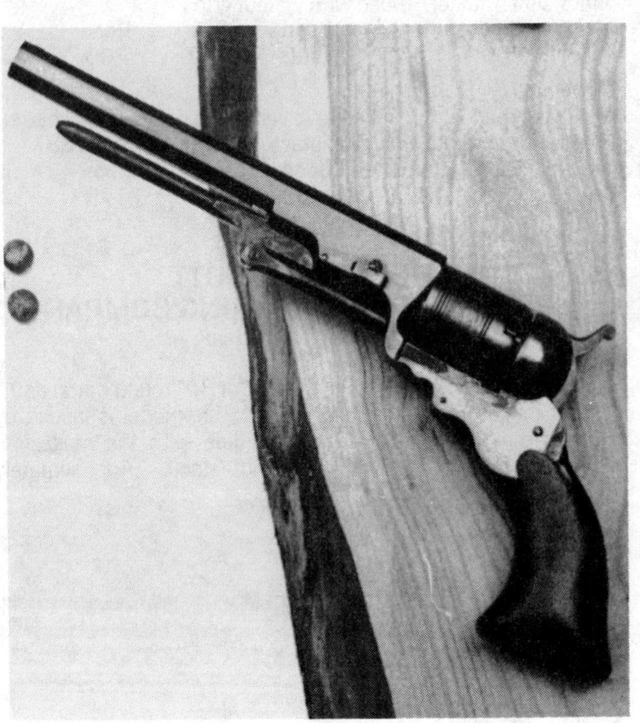

NIB	Exc.	V.G.	Good	Fair	Poor
225	200	150	125	100	75

Walker Colt Revolver
This is a faithful reproduction of the famous and highly sought after Colt's. Caliber is .44 and the round barrel is 9" in length. The frame is case hardened steel and the trigger guard is brass. The 6 shot cylinder is engraved with fighting Dragoons scene. Grip is one piece walnut. Overall length is 15.75" and weight is a hefty 70 oz.

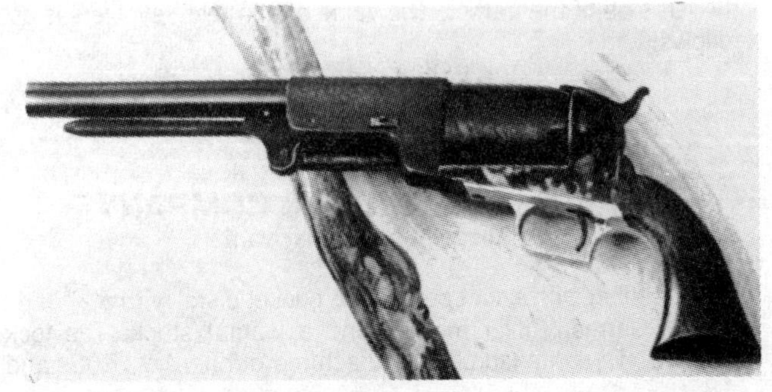

NIB	Exc.	V.G.	Good	Fair	Poor
250	225	200	125	100	75

Colt 1st Model Dragoon Revolver
This was a shorter version of the Walker and evolved directly from that original design. This model is a six shot .44 caliber with a 7.5" barrel. the frame is color case hardened steel while the backstrap and trigger guard are brass. Grips are one piece walnut. Overall length is 13.5" and weight is about 63 oz.

NIB	Exc.	V.G.	Good	Fair	Poor
225	200	175	125	100	75

Colt 2nd Model Dragoon Revolver
This differs from the 1st model in that the cylinder bolt slot is square instead of oval.

NIB	Exc.	V.G.	Good	Fair	Poor
225	200	175	125	100	75

Colt 3rd Model Dragoon Revolver
This model varies from the 2nd model as follows:

a: Loading lever taper is inverted.
b: Loading lever latch hook is different shape.
c: Loading lever latch.
d: Backstrap is steel and trigger guard is brass oval.
e: Frame is cut for a shoulder stock.

NIB	Exc.	V.G.	Good	Fair	Poor
225	200	175	125	100	75

Colt Model 1849 Wells Fargo
This model has no loading lever. Chambered for .31 caliber cartridge. The barrel is octagonal. The frame is case colored and hardened steel while the backstrap and trigger guard is brass. Cylinder is engraved and holds 5 rounds. Grip is one piece walnut. Overall length is 9.5" and weight is 34 oz.

NIB	Exc.	V.G.	Good	Fair	Poor
215	180	150	125	100	75

Colt Model 1849 Pocket Revolver
Same as the Wells Fargo with the addition of a loading lever.

NIB	Exc.	V.G.	Good	Fair	Poor
215	180	150	125	100	75

Colt Model 1848 Baby Dragoon
Similar is appearance to the Model 1849 but with a 4" tapered octagon barrel and a square back trigger guard. No loading lever. Weight is about 23 oz.

NIB	Exc.	V.G.	Good	Fair	Poor
215	180	150	125	100	75

The Model 1851 Navy Colt
Chambered for .36 caliber with an engraved 6 shot cylinder. The tapered octagonal barrel is 7.5". The frame is case colored steel and the backstrap and oval trigger guard are brass. Grips are one piece walnut. Overall length is 13" and weight is about 44 oz.

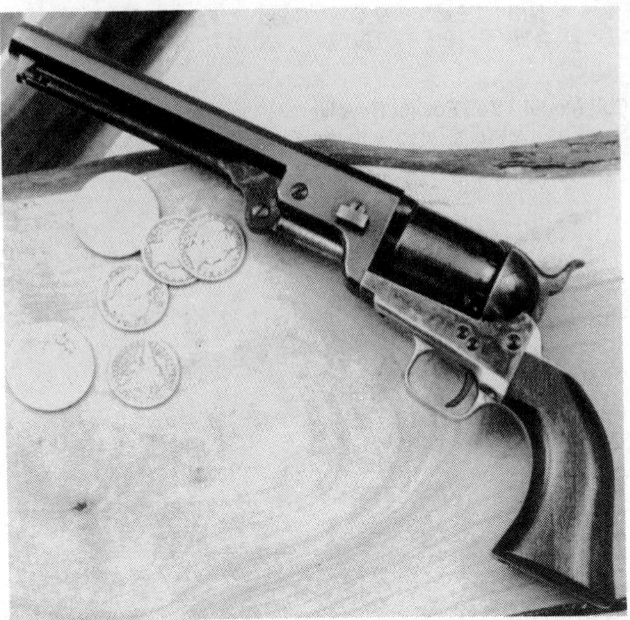

NIB	Exc.	V.G.	Good	Fair	Poor
200	175	150	125	100	75

Model 1861 Navy Colt

Sometime referred to as the "New Navy" this model is similar in appearance to the Model 1851. Offered in two variations. The military version has a steel backstrap and trigger guard and is cut for a shoulder stock. The civilian version has a brass backstrap and trigger guard and is not cut for a shoulder stock.

Military Model

NIB	Exc.	V.G.	Good	Fair	Poor
215	180	150	125	100	75

Civilian Model

NIB	Exc.	V.G.	Good	Fair	Poor
200	175	150	125	100	75

Colt Model 1860 Army

Chambered for the .44 caliber ball and fitted with a round tapered 8" barrel this revolver has a six shot engraved cylinder. Grips are one piece walnut. Overall length is 13.75" and weight is approximately 42 oz.

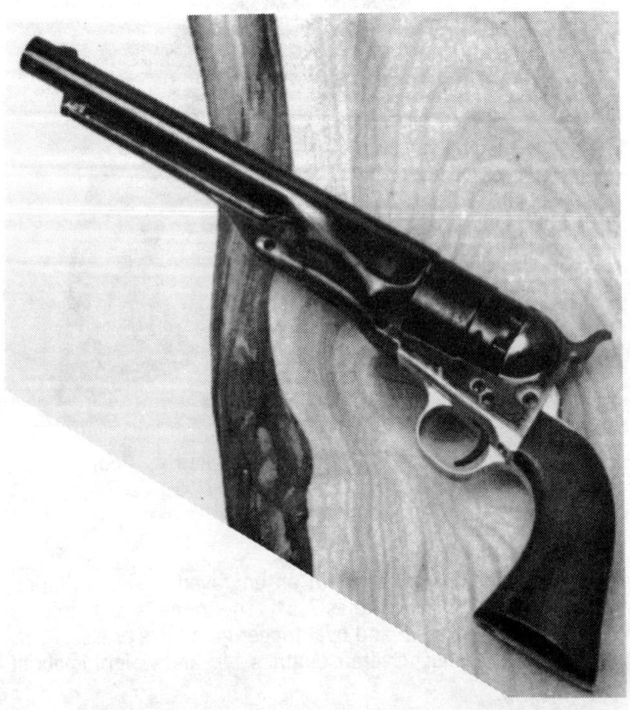

Military version has steel backstrap and brass trigger guard and is cut for a shoulder stock.

NIB	Exc.	V.G.	Good	Fair	Poor
200	175	150	125	100	75

Civilian version has brass backstrap and trigger guard and is not cut for a shoulder stock.

NIB	Exc.	V.G.	Good	Fair	Poor
200	175	150	125	100	75

Fluted Cylinder Version-Military

NIB	Exc.	V.G.	Good	Fair	Poor
210	185	160	125	100	75

Fluted Cylinder Version-Civilian

NIB	Exc.	V.G.	Good	Fair	Poor
185	150	125	100	80	65

Colt Model 1862 Police Revolvers

Chambered for .36 caliber and fitted with a round tapered barrel in 4.5", 5.5", or 6.5" barrel. The five shot cylinder is fluted, the frame color case-hardened, and the backstrap and trigger guard are brass. Grips are one piece walnut. Weight is about 25 oz.

NIB	Exc.	V.G.	Good	Fair	Poor
225	200	175	150	125	100

Colt Model 1862 Pocket Navy Revolver

Similar to the Model 1862 Police model but fitted with a five shot engraved non-fluted cylinder. Barrel lengths are 4.5", 5.5", and 6.5". Weight is about 27 oz.

NIB	Exc.	V.G.	Good	Fair	Poor
225	200	175	150	125	100

Remington Model 1858 New Army .44 Caliber
Chambered for .44 caliber and fitted with a tapered octagonal 8" barrel. Cylinder holds 6 shots and the frame is blued steel. Trigger guard is brass. Grips are two piece walnut. Overall length is 13.75" and weight is about 42 oz.

NIB	Exc.	V.G.	Good	Fair	Poor
200	175	150	125	100	75

Remington Model 1858 New Army .36 Caliber
Similar to above model but fitted with a 7 3/8" tapered octagonal barrel. Weight is approximately 40 oz.

NIB	Exc.	V.G.	Good	Fair	Poor
200	175	150	125	100	75

Remington Model 1858 New Army .44 Caliber Target
This version is fitted with a fully adjustable rear sight and ramp front sight.

NIB	Exc.	V.G.	Good	Fair	Poor
225	200	175	150	100	75

Remington Model 1858 New Army .44 Caliber Stainless Steel
All parts are stainless steel.

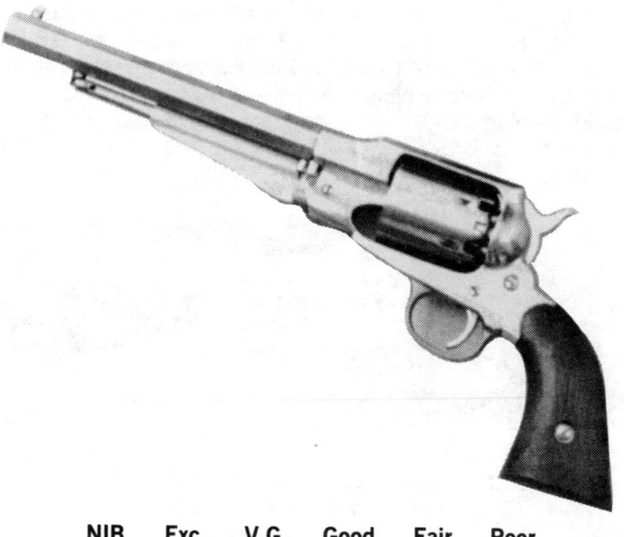

NIB	Exc.	V.G.	Good	Fair	Poor
225	200	175	150	100	75

Remington Model 1858 New Army .44 Cal. SS Target
Same as Target Model but all parts are stainless steel.

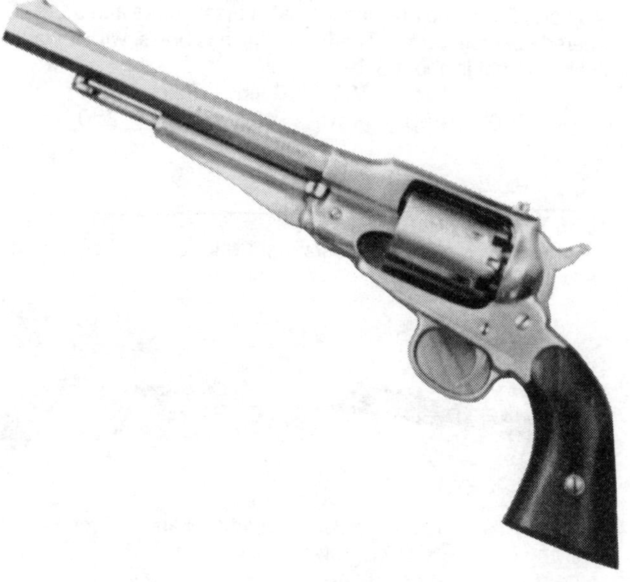

NIB	Exc.	V.G.	Good	Fair	Poor
250	225	200	175	100	75

Remington Model 1858 Target Revolving Carbine
Chambered for .44 caliber and fitted with an 18" octagon barrel. The frame is blued steel and the trigger guard is brass. Stock is select walnut. Overall length is 35" and weight is about 4.4 lb.

NIB	Exc.	V.G.	Good	Fair	Poor
300	250	200	150	100	75

1875 Remington "Outlaw"
This is a replica of the original Remington cartridge pistol chambered for .357 Magnum, .44-40, .45ACP, .45ACP/.45LC conversion,and .45 Colt. The frame is case-colored steel and the trigger guard is brass. It is offered with a 7.5" round barrel and is either blued or nickel-plated, with two piece walnut grips. Overall length is 13.75" and weight is about 44 oz.

NIB	Exc.	V.G.	Good	Fair	Poor
350	300	275	225	175	125

Remington Model 1890 Police
This is a 5.5"-barrelled replica of the original Remington Pistol. It is chambered for .357 Magnum, .44-40, .45ACP, .45ACP/.45LC conversion, and .45 Colt. The frame is case-

colored steel and the trigger guard is brass. It was available in either blue or nickel-plate. Grips are two piece walnut and are fitted with a grip ring. Overall length is 11.75" and weight is about 41 oz.

NIB	Exc.	V.G.	Good	Fair	Poor
400	350	300	275	225	175

Model 1871 Rolling Block Pistol
This is a single-shot target pistol chambered for .22 L.R., .22 Magnum, .22 Hornet, .222 Rem., 223 Rem., .45 Long Colt,or .357 Magnum. It has a 9.5" half-octagonal, half-round barrel and is blued, with a case-colored receiver and walnut grip and forearm. The trigger guard is brass. Overall length is 14" and weight is about 44 oz.

NIB	Exc.	V.G.	Good	Fair	Poor
300	250	225	200	150	100

Model 1371 Rolling Block Carbine
This Model is similar to the Pistol, with a 22.5" half-octagonal, half-round barrel and a full-length walnut stock. Trigger guard and butt plate are brass. Overall length is 35.5" and weight is approximately 4.8 lb.

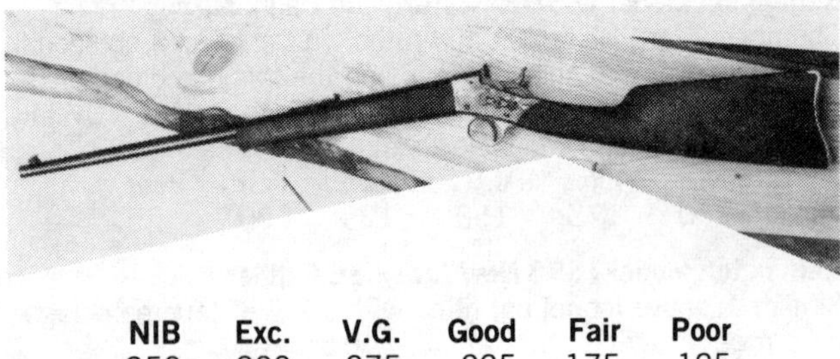

NIB	Exc.	V.G.	Good	Fair	Poor
350	300	275	225	175	125

Henry Rifle
This is a brass-framed reproduction of the famous Winchester/Henry Rifle. It is chambered for the .44-40 cartridge, and this is basically the only departure from being a true and faithful copy. The octagonal barrel is 24.25" on the rifle model and 22.25" on the carbine model. There is also two Trapper models offered; an 18.5" barrel and a 16.5" version. This is a high quality rifle and amazingly close to the original in configuration. There are three grades of engraving also available. Weights are as follows: rifle-9.2 lb., carbine-9 lb., 18.5" trapper-7.9 lb., 16.5" trapper-7.4 lb. Finish can be steel, standard blue or charcoal blue.
Grade A—Add $350.
Grade B—Add $450.
Grade C—Add $600.

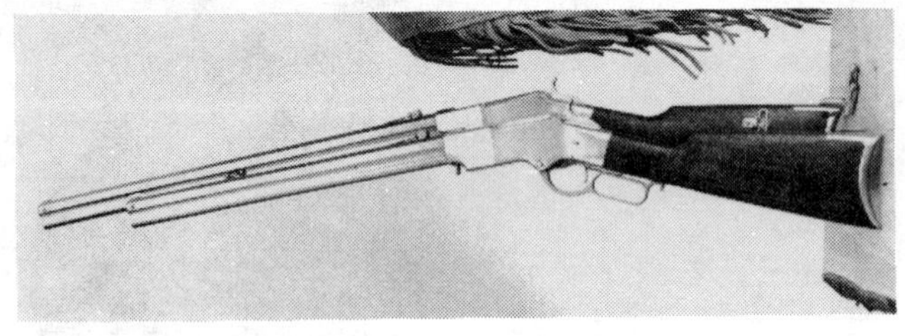

NIB	Exc.	V.G.	Good	Fair	Poor
750	650	550	450	350	275

Winchester Model 1866
This is a faithful replica of the Winchester 1866. It is chambered for .22 L.R., .22 Magnum, .38 Special, and .4440, and .45 Long Colt. The rifle version has a brass frame and a 24.25" tapered octagon barrel. The frame finish is brass, with a walnut stock. Weight is about 8 lb.

NIB	Exc.	V.G.	Good	Fair	Poor
600	550	450	400	300	250

1866 Yellowboy Carbine
This model is similar to the standard rifle, but is offered with a 19" round tapered barrel.

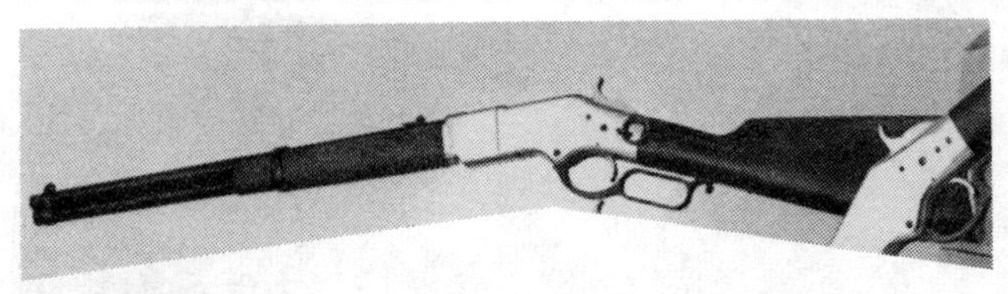

NIB	Exc.	V.G.	Good	Fair	Poor
700	600	500	450	350	300

Winchester Model 1873 Carbine

This is a reproduction of the Winchester 1873 chambered for .357 Magnum, .45 Long Colt, and .44-40. It has a case-colored steel receiver and a 19" round tapered barrel. The lever is also case-colored. The stock and forearm are walnut. Overall length is 38.25" and weight is about 7.4 lb.

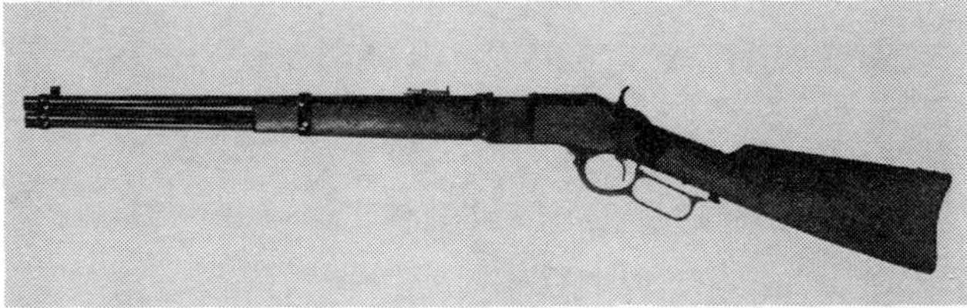

NIB	Exc.	V.G.	Good	Fair	Poor
700	600	500	450	350	300

Winchester Model 1873 Rifle

This model is similar to the Carbine, with a 24.25" octagonal barrel. Overall length is 43.25" and weight is approximately 8.2 Lb. NOTE: Extra barrel lengths from 30" to 20" in .45 LC and 44/40 are also offered at extra cost.

NIB	Exc.	V.G.	Good	Fair	Poor
750	650	550	450	350	300

Hawken Santa Fe

Based on the famous original rifle this reproduction is bored for .54 caliber and fitted with a 32" octagon barrel. A double set trigger and case-hardened lock plate are standard. The stock ferrule and wedge plates are German silver. The stock is walnut with cheekpiece. Overall length is 50" and weight is about 9.5 lb. Also available in kit form.

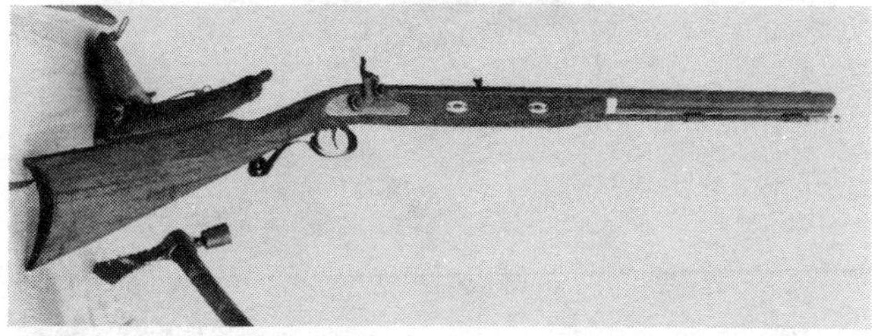

NIB	Exc.	V.G.	Good	Fair	Poor
350	300	250	200	150	100

Cattleman

This is a single-action revolver patterned very closely after the Colt Single-Action Army. It is chambered in various popular calibers; .357 Magnum, 44/40, .44 Special, .45 ACP, .45LC/.45 ACP convertible, and .45 Colt. It is offered with barrel lengths of 4.75", 5.5", and 7.5". It is offered with either a modern or black powder-type frame and brass or steel backstraps. The finish is blued, with walnut grips. A Sheriff's Model with a 3" barrel and no ejector rod chambered for .44-40 and .45 Colt is also available and is valued the same. Weight is approximately 38 oz. for 5.5" barrel gun.

NIB	Exc.	V.G.	Good	Fair	Poor
325	275	250	200	150	100

Cattleman Target Model

This model is similar to the standard Cattleman, with an adjustable rear sight.

NIB	Exc.	V.G.	Good	Fair	Poor
350	300	275	225	175	125

New Thunderer Model

Designed and imported exclusively by Cimarron Arms for single action shooting competition. Fitted with bird's head grip with hard rubber this model is chambered for the .357 Magnum, 44 Special, .44 WCF, and .45 Colt. Offered in barrel lengths of 3.5" and 7.5". Finish in nickel or blue with case-colored frame.

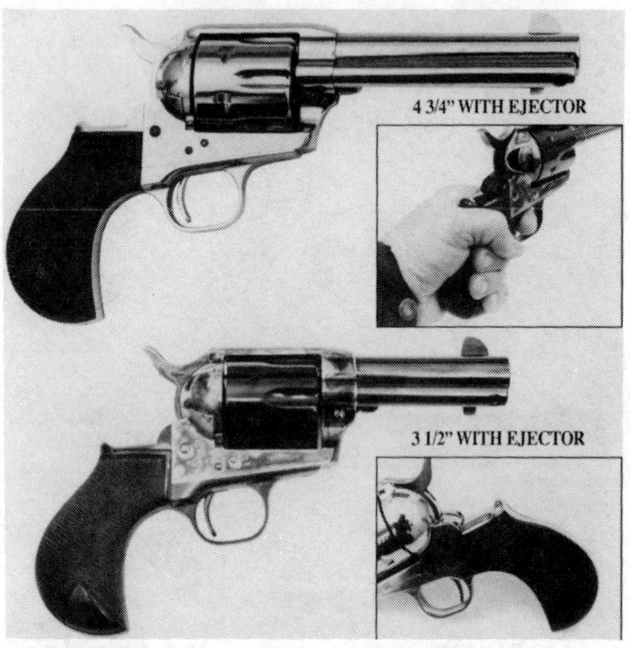

NIB	Exc.	V.G.	Good	Fair	Poor
400	350	300	250	200	100

Buckhorn Buntline

This version is chambered for the .44 Magnum. It has an 18" round barrel, and it is cut for attaching a shoulder stock. Steel backstrap and trigger guard. Overall length is 23" and weight is about 57 oz.

NOTE: Detachable Shoulder Stock--Add 25 Percent.

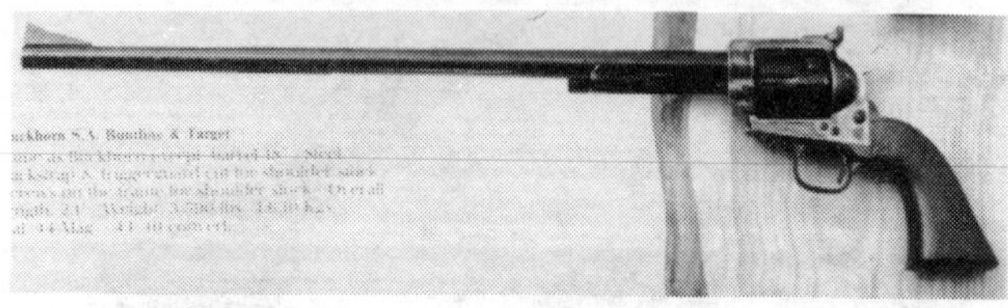

NIB	Exc.	V.G.	Good	Fair	Poor
350	325	300	250	200	100

Buckhorn Target

Same as above but fitted with an adjustable rear sight and ramp front sight. Has a flat upper frame.

NIB	Exc.	V.G.	Good	Fair	Poor
375	350	300	250	200	100

Phantom

Similar to the Buckhorn, but chambered for the .44 Magnum and the .357 Magnum. The barrel is a round 10.5" and the frame is blue with blue steel backstrap. One piece walnut grips with anatomic profile. Adjustable sight. Weight is approximately 53 oz.

NIB	Exc.	V.G.	Good	Fair	Poor
350	325	300	250	200	100

Buntline Carbine

This version has the 18" barrel but is fitted with a permanently mounted shoulder stock with a brass buttplate and sling swivel. Chambered for .44/40, .45 Long Colt, .357 Magnum, and .44 Magnum. Offered with fixed or adjustable sights.

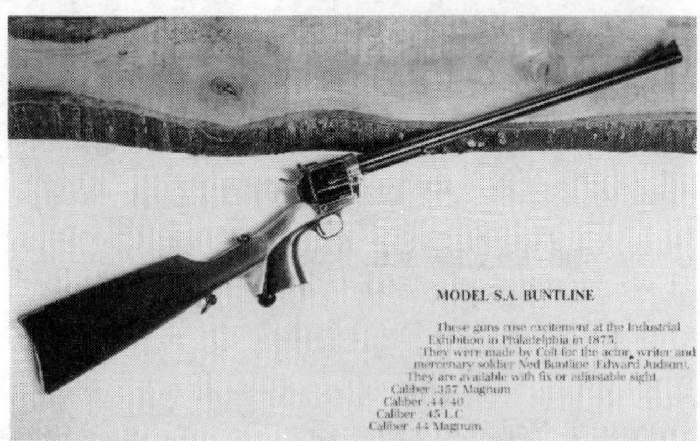

NIB	Exc.	V.G.	Good	Fair	Poor
450	400	350	300	250	200

1873 Stallion

This is a scaled-down version, chambered for .22 L.R./.22 Magnum. It is blued with a case-colored frame and features one-piece walnut grips.

NIB	Exc.	V.G.	Good	Fair	Poor
325	275	250	200	150	100

Inspector Model

This is a double action revolver built on the same general lines as the Colt Detective model. Cylinder holds 6 cartridges and is chambered for the .38 Special. Offered in the following barrel lengths with fixed sights: 2", 2.125", 2.5", 3", 4", 6" and also offered in 4" and 6" barrel lengths with adjustable sights. Grips are walnut and finish is blue or chrome. With the 3" barrel the weight is about 24 oz.

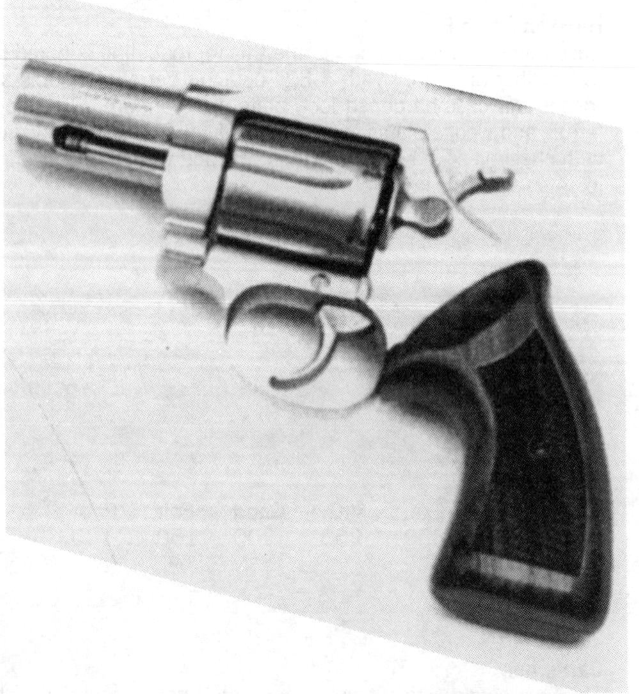

NIB	Exc.	V.G.	Good	Fair	Poor
250	200	150	125	100	75

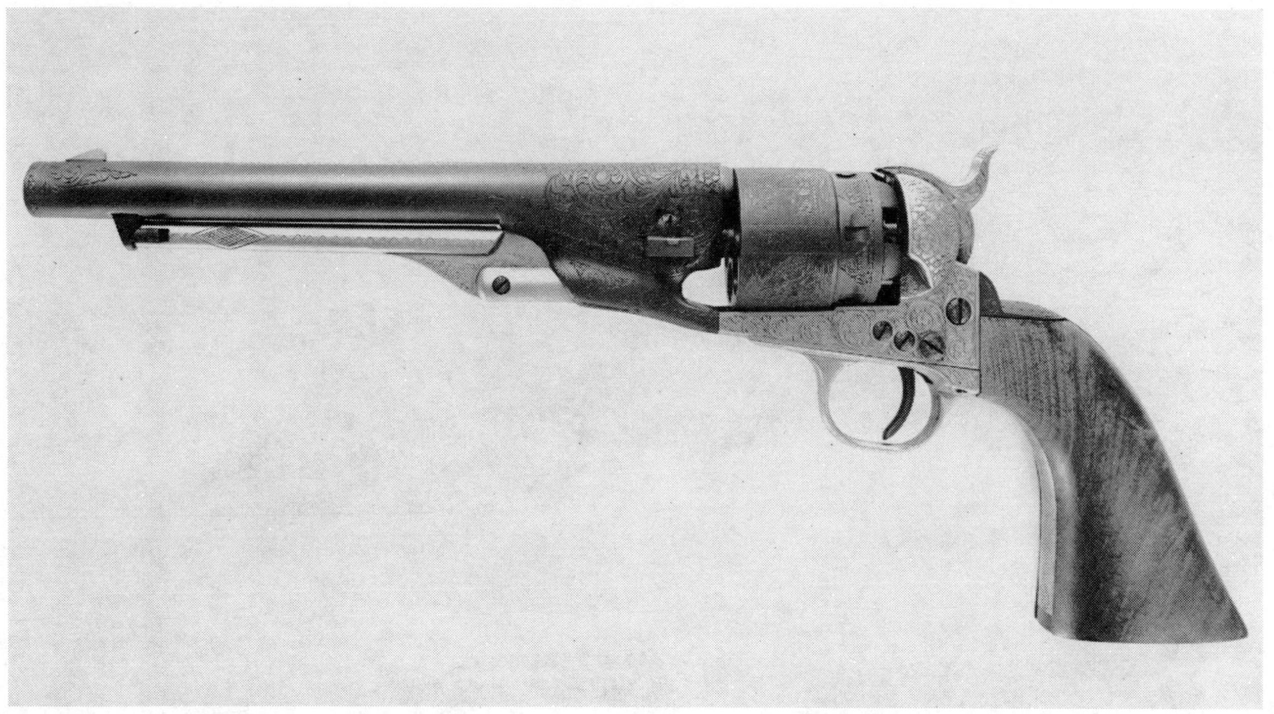

Uberti engraved 1860 Army Colt replica.

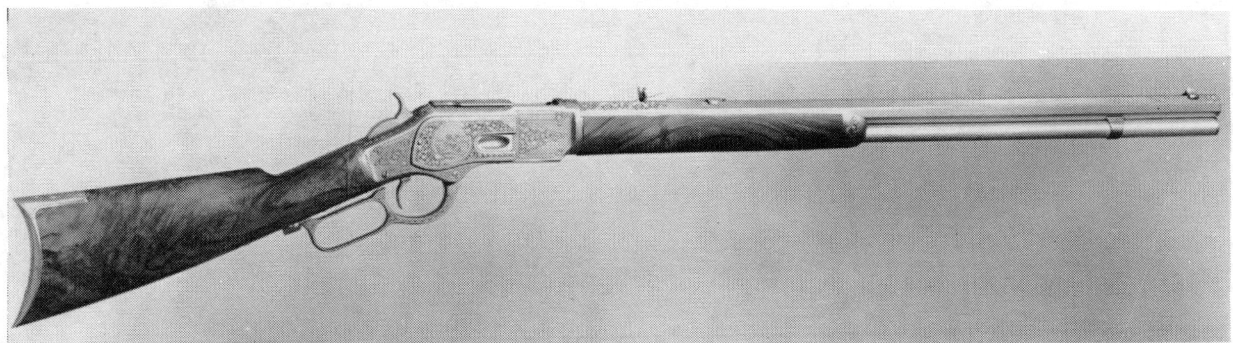

Uberti engraved 73 Winchester replica.

Uberti 1858 Remington replicas.

Uberti engraved 73 Winchester replica.

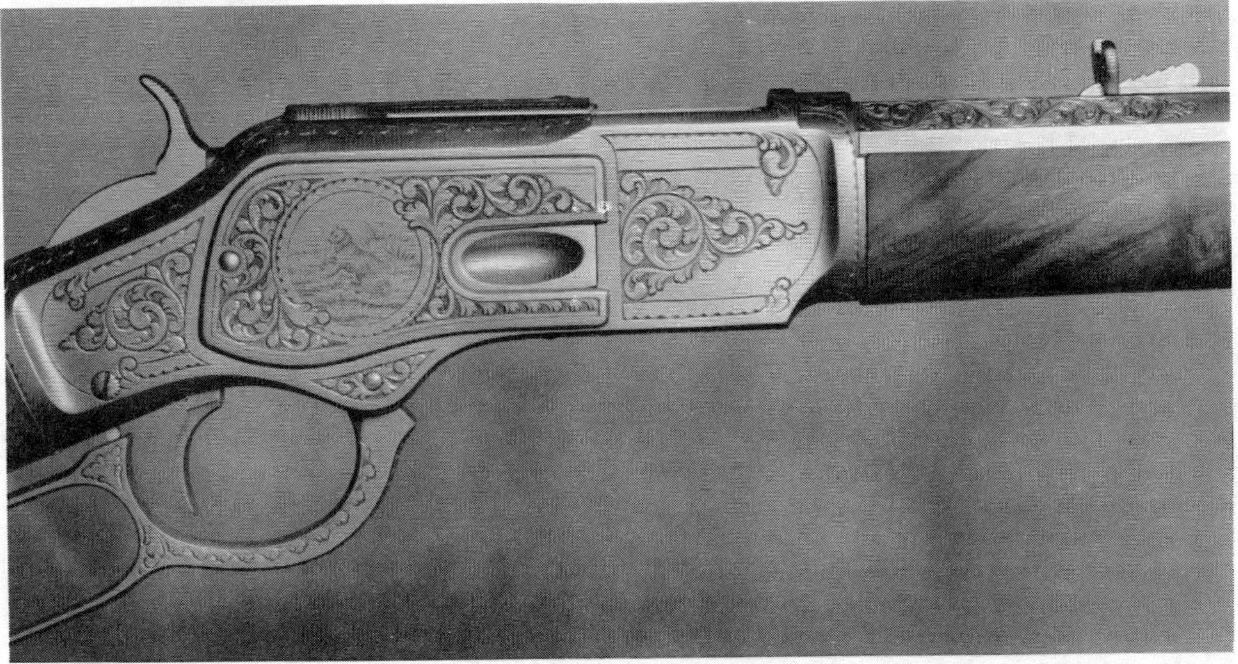

Uberti engraved 73 Winchester replica.

Uberti S.A.A. Colt replicas.

UHLINGER, WILLIAM P.

Philadelphia, Pennsylvania

Pocket Revolver

A .32 caliber spur trigger revolver with a 2.75" or 3" octagonal barrel and an unfluted 6-shot cylinder. Blued with rosewood or walnut grips. Manufactured during the late 1860s and early 1870s.

Note: Uhlinger manufactured pistols will often be found with retailer's names on them, such as: D.D. Cone, Washington, D.C.; J.P. Lower, and; W.L. Grant.

Long Cylinder (1-3/16")

Exc.	V.G.	Good	Fair	Poor
350	300	275	200	150

Short Cylinder (1")

Exc.	V.G.	Good	Fair	Poor
250	225	200	150	100

.32 Rimfire Model (5", 6", or 7" Barrel)

Exc.	V.G.	Good	Fair	Poor
300	250	225	175	125

ULTIMATE

SEE—Camex-Blaser

ULTRA LIGHT ARMS, INC.

Granville, West Virginia

This maker manufactures a variety of bolt action rifles fitted with Douglas barrels of varying lengths, custom triggers and reinforced graphite stocks. The values for standard production models are as follows:

Model 20 (Short Action)

NIB	Exc.	V.G.	Good	Fair	Poor
2000	1750	1500	1250	900	700

Model 24 (Long Action)

NIB	Exc.	V.G.	Good	Fair	Poor
2100	1850	1600	1350	900	700

Model 28 Magnum

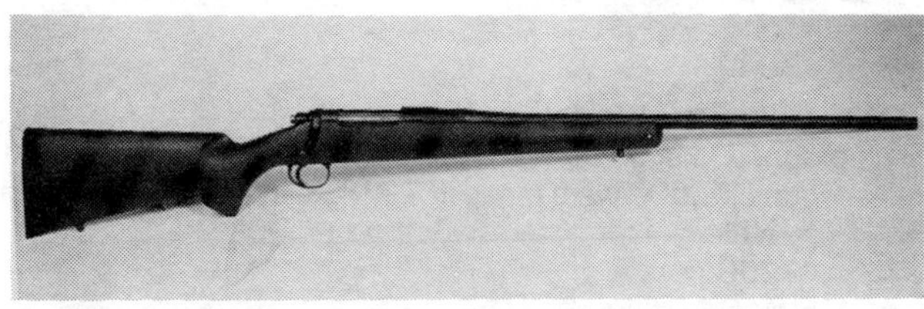

NIB	Exc.	V.G.	Good	Fair	Poor
2500	2250	1750	1500	1000	750

Model 20 Hunter's Pistol

A bolt-action repeating pistol designed with the serious hunter in mind. It is offered in various popular calibers with a 14", high quality, Douglas heavy barrel. It has a 5-shot magazine and is matte-blued, with a reinforced graphite Kevlar stock. It was introduced in 1987.

NIB	Exc.	V.G.	Good	Fair	Poor
1250	1000	850	750	600	500

UNCETA

SEE—Astra-Unceta SA

UNION FIRE ARMS COMPANY

Toledo, Ohio

This company was incorporated in 1902 and used the names of Union Fire Arms, Union Arms Co., Illinois Arms Co. (made for Sears) and Bee Be Arms Co. In 1917 the company was either bought up or absorbed by Ithaca Gun Co.

Model 24

Slide action, Model 25 Peerless which was fancy version of the Model 24 and the Model 25A which was a trap model, were manufactured from 1902 to 1913 in 12 or 16 gauge with 24", 26", 28" or 32" steel or Damascus barrels. This gun had a unique double trigger. The front trigger cocked and decocked and internal firing pin and the back trigger fired the gun. The gun is marked on the left side of the frame and the pump release is on the right side. This model had one very serious drawback, in that the slide that extracted a spent shell extended back over the comb of the stock. This often hit the shooters thumb knuckle and caused injury. In 1907 Union redesigned their slide by reducing its length and shielding it behind a steel plate that covered the rear half of the opening. These are the Model 24, 25 and 25A improved versions. Approximately 17,000 of all models combined were made.

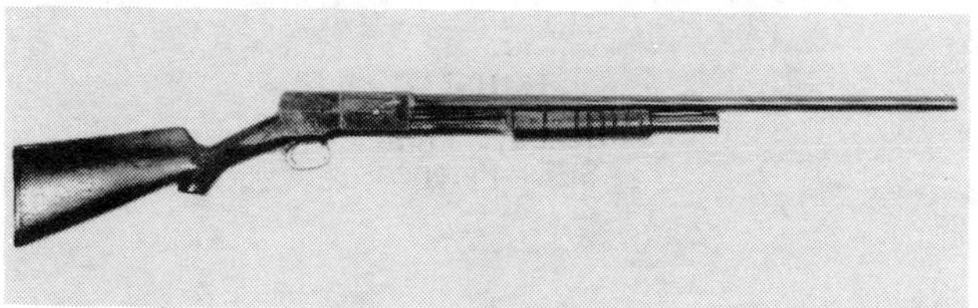

Exc.	V.G.	Good	Fair	Poor
500	400	300	200	100

Model 50

Manufactured 1911 to 1913. This was basically a redesign of the Model 24. The main distinguishing feature of the Model 50 was that the frame sloped down to meet the comb of the stock and the double trigger system was replaced by a single trigger. It came in 12 or 16 gauge with a 26", 28", 30" or 32" Krupp steel barrel. Fewer than 3,000 were made.

Exc.	V.G.	Good	Fair	Poor
600	500	400	300	200

Model 23

Hammerless double, manufactured between 1902 and 1913 with or without automatic ejectors. With some engraving, it came in both single and double trigger models; this was their top grade gun. Came in 12 and 16 gauge with 28", 30" or 32" steel, twist or Damascus barrels.

Exc.	V.G.	Good	Fair	Poor
200	175	150	125	100

Model 22
This was essentially a no frills Model 23. It had the same barrel length and steel options, but it had a plain walnut stock and no engraving. There were fewer than 10,000 Model 22 and 23's made.

Exc.	V.G.	Good	Fair	Poor
150	125	100	75	50

Diamond Grade
Single shot, manufactured between 1905 and 1910. It had a unique octagon breech in 12 gauge only with 30" steel, laminated or Damascus barrel. This was their premium grade single shot. Very few of these were made.

Exc.	V.G.	Good	Fair	Poor
150	125	100	75	50

Model 18
Single shot, manufactured 1906 to 1913 came in 12 or 16 gauge. 30", 32", 34" or 36" steel barrel. A plain single shot. Very few made.

Exc.	V.G.	Good	Fair	Poor
75	65	45	35	25

Reifengraber
A .32 or .38 S&W caliber gas operated semi-automatic pistol, with a 3" barrel. Blued with walnut grips, approximately 100 of these pistols were manufactured.

Exc.	V.G.	Good	Fair	Poor
900	750	650	500	350

Automatic Revolver
.32 S&W caliber, copy of the Webley Fosbery semi-automatic revolver with a 3" barrel. Blued with either walnut or plastic grips. The cylinder has zig-zag grooves.

Exc.	V.G.	Good	Fair	Poor
800	650	500	400	250

UNION
Unknown

Pocket Pistol
.22 caliber spur trigger single shot pistol with a 2.75" barrel marked "Union". Nickle-plated with walnut grips.

Exc.	V.G.	Good	Fair	Poor
250	200	150	100	75

UNIQUE
Hendaye, France
SEE—Pyrenees

UNITED SPORTING ARMS, INC.
Tucson, Arizona

Seville
A .357 Magnum, .41 Magnum, .44 Magnum or .45 caliber single action revolver with a 4-5/8", 5.5", 6.5" or 7.5" barrel having adjustable sights. Blued or stainless steel with walnut grips. Manufactured until 1986.

Exc.	V.G.	Good	Fair	Poor
375	350	300	250	200

Seville .357 Maxi
As above, in stainless steel and .357 Maximum caliber with a 5.5" or 7.5" barrel. Discontinued in 1986.

Exc.	V.G.	Good	Fair	Poor
550	500	450	350	300

Seville .375 USA
As above, in stainless steel and in .375 USA caliber. Discontinued in 1986.

Exc.	V.G.	Good	Fair	Poor
600	550	500	400	350

Seville .454 Magnum
As above, in stainless steel and .454 Magnum caliber with a 7.5" barrel and 5-shot cylinder. Discontinued in 1986.

Exc.	V.G.	Good	Fair	Poor
700	650	500	450	400

This series of revolvers was also available for silhouette shooting with 10.5" barrels and Pachmayr grips.

Sheriff's Model
Similar to the Seville Model with a 3.5" barrel. Blued or stainless steel with walnut grips. Discontinued in 1986.

Exc.	V.G.	Good	Fair	Poor
400	350	325	250	200

UNITED STATES ARMS
Otis A. Smith Company
Rockfall, Connecticut

Single Action Revolver
A .44 rimfire and centerfire single action revolver with a 7" barrel and integral ejector. The hammer nose is fitted with 2 firing pins so that rimfire or centerfire catridges can be used interchangeably. The barrel marked "United States Arms Company — New York," the top strap "No. 44." Blued with either hard rubber or rosewood grips. Manufactured in very limited quantities. Circa 1870 to 1875.

Exc.	V.G.	Good	Fair	Poor
750	650	550	400	300

UNITED STATES HISTORICAL SOCIETY
Richmond, Virginia

The following arms are manufactured by the Williamsburg Firearms Manufactory and the Virginia Firearms Manufactory.

George Washington
A reproduction of a flintlock pistol originally owned by George Washington. A total of 975 were made and were issued at a price of $2,500.

NIB
4000

Thomas Jefferson
A reproduction of a flintlock pistol originally owned by Thomas Jefferson. A total of 1,000 were made and were issued at a price of $1,900.

NIB
3000

Hamilton-Burr Dueling Pistols
Reproductions of the flintlock pistols used in the Hamilton-Burr Duel. A total of 1,200 sets were made and sold at an issue price of $2,100.

NIB
3000

Stonewall Jackson Pistol
A reproduction of a Colt Model 1851 Navy cased with accessories. Total of 2,500 were made in 1988.

NIB
2000

Texas Paterson Edition
A reproduction of a Colt Paterson revolver cased with accessories. Total of 1,000 were made in 1988.

NIB
2500

Buffalo Bill Centennial
A reproduction of a Colt Model 1860 Army revolver with acid etch scenes inlaid in gold, cased with accessories. Total of 2,500 were made in 1983 and issued at a price of $1,950.

NIB
2000

U.S. Calvary Model
A reproduction of a Colt Model 1860 Army revolver with a gold-plated cylinder and stag grips, cased with a brass belt buckle. Total of 975 were made beginning in 1988.

NIB
1500

Sam Houston Model
Reproduction of a Colt Model 1847 Army revolver with etched and gilt additions. Total of 2,500 were made.

NIB
2250

Robert E. Lee Model
Reproduction of the Colt Model 1851 Navy revolver with gilt additions and cased with accessories. A total of 2,500 were made.

NIB
2500

H. Deringer Set
Cased pair of reproduction .41 caliber Henry Deringer percussion pocket pistols available in three grades as follows:

Silver Mounted

NIB
2500

14 Kt. Gold Mounted

NIB
7500

18 Kt. Mounted with Gemstone
Issue Price—$25,000

UNIVERSAL FIREARMS
Sacksonville, Arkansas

Model 7312
A 12 gauge Over/Under shotgun with separated 30" ventilated-rib barrels, single selective trigger and automatic ejectors. The case-hardened receiver engraved. Blued with a walnut stock. Discontinued in 1982.

Exc.	V.G.	Good	Fair	Poor
1700	1500	1250	900	650

Model 7412
As above, with extractors. Discontinued in 1982.

Exc.	V.G.	Good	Fair	Poor
1500	1250	1000	750	500

Model 7712
As above, with 26" or 28" barrels, non-selective single trigger and extractors. Discontinued in 1982.

Exc.	V.G.	Good	Fair	Poor
450	400	350	250	200

Model 7812
As above, with more detailed engraving and automatic ejectors. Discontinued in 1982.

Exc.	V.G.	Good	Fair	Poor
600	550	450	350	250

Model 7912
As above, with a gold wash frame and single selective trigger. Discontinued in 1982.

Exc.	V.G.	Good	Fair	Poor
1200	1000	750	600	400

Model 7112
A 12 gauge double barrel boxlock shotgun with 26" or 28" barrels, double triggers and extractors. Blued, case-hardened with a walnut stock. Discontinued in 1982.

Exc.	V.G.	Good	Fair	Poor
350	300	250	200	100

Double Wing
A 10, 12, 20 or .410 bore boxlock double-barrel shotgun with 26", 28" or 30" barrels, double triggers and extractors. Blued with a walnut stock. Discontinued in 1982.

Exc.	V.G.	Good	Fair	Poor
350	300	250	200	100

Model 7212
A 12 gauge single barrel trap shotgun with a 30" ventilated-rib ported barrel, and automatic ejector. Engraved, case-hardened receiver and walnut stock. Discontinued in 1982.

Exc.	V.G.	Good	Fair	Poor
1000	850	650	450	300

Model 1000 Military Carbine
A copy of the U.S. M1 Carbine with an 18" barrel. Blued with a birch wood stock.

Exc.	V.G.	Good	Fair	Poor
250	225	200	100	75

Model 1003
As above, with a 16", 18" or 20" barrel.

Exc.	V.G.	Good	Fair	Poor
200	175	150	100	75

Model 1010
As above, but nickle-plated.

Exc.	V.G.	Good	Fair	Poor
275	225	175	125	100

Model 1015
As above, but gold-plated.

Exc.	V.G.	Good	Fair	Poor
300	250	200	150	125

Model 1005 Deluxe
As above, with a polished blue finish and Monte Carlo-style stock.

Exc.	V.G.	Good	Fair	Poor
250	225	150	100	75

Model 1006 Stainless
As the Model 1000, but in stainless steel.

Exc.	V.G.	Good	Fair	Poor
275	225	175	125	100

Model 1020 Teflon
As above, with a black or grey Dupont Teflon-S finish.

Exc.	V.G.	Good	Fair	Poor
275	225	175	125	100

Model 1256 Ferret
The Model 1000 in .256 Winchester Magnum caliber.

Exc.	V.G.	Good	Fair	Poor
225	200	175	125	100

Model 3000 Enforcer
A pistol version of the Model 1000 with an 11.25" barrel and 15- or 30-shot magazines.
Nickle Finish—Add 20%.
Gold-Plated—Add 40%.
Stainless Steel—Add 30%.
Teflon-S—Add 20%.

Blued

Exc.	V.G.	Good	Fair	Poor
250	225	200	150	100

Model 5000 Paratrooper
The Model 1000, with a 16" or 18" barrel and folding stock. This model, in stainless steel, is known as the Model 5006.

Exc.	V.G.	Good	Fair	Poor
225	200	175	125	100

1981 Commemorative Carbine
A limited production version of the Model 1000 cased with accessories. Produced in 1981.

NIB	Exc.	V.G.	Good	Fair	Poor
500	350	300	250	200	150

Model 2200 Leatherneck
A .22 caliber version of the U.S. M1 Carbine with an 18" barrel and blowback action. Blued with a birch wood stock

Exc.	V.G.	Good	Fair	Poor
250	225	200	150	100

U.S. M1 CARBINE

Various Manufacturers

This carbine was designed by William Roemer, Edwin Pugsley and others at the Winchester Repeating Arms Company in late 1940 and early 1941. The only feature which can be credited to David Marsh "Carbine" Williams is the short stroke piston design. The U.S. M1 Carbine was produced by a number of manufacturers as listed below. The M1 A1 version was produced by Inland. The selective fire version is known as the Model M2.

Inland

Exc.	V.G.	Good	Fair	Poor
350	300	250	200	150

Underwood

Exc.	V.G.	Good	Fair	Poor
350	300	250	200	150

S. G. Saginaw

Exc.	V.G.	Good	Fair	Poor
350	300	250	200	150

IBM

Exc.	V.G.	Good	Fair	Poor
375	325	275	225	175

Quality Hardware

Exc.	V.G.	Good	Fair	Poor
375	325	275	225	175

National Postal Meter

Exc.	V.G.	Good	Fair	Poor
375	325	275	225	175

Standard Products

Exc.	V.G.	Good	Fair	Poor
350	300	250	200	150

Rockola

Exc.	V.G.	Good	Fair	Poor
400	350	300	250	175

SG Grand Rapids

Exc.	V.G.	Good	Fair	Poor
450	400	350	300	250

Winchester

Exc.	V.G.	Good	Fair	Poor
450	400	350	300	250

Irwin Pedersen

Exc.	V.G.	Good	Fair	Poor
950	750	550	450	350

M1 A1 Paratrooper Model

The standard U.S. M1 Carbine fitted with a folding stock. Approximately 110,000 were manufactured by Inland between 1942 and 1945.

Exc.	V.G.	Good	Fair	Poor
700	650	600	500	300

URIZAR, TOMAS

Eibar, Spain

Celta, J. Cesar, Premier, Puma, and Union

A 6.35mm semi-automatic pistol with a 3" barrel. The slide marked with the tradenames listed above. Blued with black plastic grips, cast with a wildman carrying a club.

Exc.	V.G.	Good	Fair	Poor
175	150	125	90	75

Dek-Du

A 5.5mm folding trigger double-action revolver with a 12-shot cylinder. Later versions were made in 6.35mm. Manufactured from 1905 to 1912.

Exc.	V.G.	Good	Fair	Poor
125	100	75	50	25

Express

A 6.35mm semi-automatic pistol with a 2" barrel. The slide marked "The Best Automatic Pistol Express". Blued with walnut grips. A 7.65mm variety exists with a 4" barrel.

Exc.	V.G.	Good	Fair	Poor
150	125	100	75	50

Imperial

A 6.35mm caliber semi-automatic pistol with a 2.5" barrel. This model was actually made by Aldazabal. Manufactured circa 1914.

Exc.	V.G.	Good	Fair	Poor
150	125	100	75	50

Le Secours or Phoenix

A 7.65mm semi-automatic pistol marked with either of the tradenames listed above.

Exc.	V.G.	Good	Fair	Poor
150	125	100	75	50

Princeps

A 6.35mm or 7.65mm semi-automatic pistol marked on the slide "Made in Spain Princeps Patent."

Exc.	V.G.	Good	Fair	Poor
150	125	100	75	50

Venus

A 7.65mm semi-automatic pistol with the grips having the tradename "Venus" cast in them.

Exc.	V.G.	Good	Fair	Poor
150	125	100	75	50

UZI ISRAELI MILITARY INDUSTRIES

Importer—Action Arms, Ltd.
Philadelphia, Pennsylvania

Uzi Carbine Model B

A 9mm, .41 Action Express or .45 caliber semi-automatic carbine with a 16.1" barrel and 20-, 25- or 32-shot box magazines. A 50-shot drum magazine is available in 9mm caliber. Black parkerized finish, plastic grips and a folding stock. Because of the assault weapon problem in this country, we cannot accurately evaluate these weapons' values. Seek a qualified local appraisal.

Uzi Mini-Carbine

As above, in 9mm or .45 caliber with a 19.75" barrel.

Uzi Pistol

As above, with a 4.5" barrel, pistol grip, no rear stock and a 20-shot magazine.

VALMET, INC.
Jyvaskyla, Finland
Importer—Stoeger, Inc.
South Hackensack, New Jersey

M-625
A semi-automatic copy of the Finnish M-62 service rifle which is patterned after the Russian AK47. Fitted with a walnut or tubular steel stock. Manufactured after 1962.

M-715
As above, in 5.56mm caliber and available with a composition stock.

Model 76
As above, in 5.56mm, 7.62x39mm or 7.62x54mm with either a 16.75" or 20.5" barrel.

Model 78
As above, in 7.62x54mm with a 24.5" barrel, wood stock and integral bipod.

Lion
A 12 gauge Over/Under shotgun with 26", 28" or 30" barrels, single selective trigger and extractors. Blued with a walnut stock. Manufactured from 1947 to 1968.

Exc.	V.G.	Good	Fair	Poor
425	375	300	250	150

VALTION (LAHTI)
SEE—Lahti

VARNER SPORTING ARMS, INC.
Marietta, Georgia

The rifles listed below are all patterned after the Stevens Favorite model.

Hunter
.22 caliber single shot rifle with a 21.5" half-octagonal, takedown barrel fitted with an aperture rear sight. Blued with well figured walnut stocks. Introduced in 1988.

NIB	Exc.	V.G.	Good	Fair	Poor
375	325	275	225	150	100

Hunter Deluxe
As above, with a case-hardened receiver and a more finely figured stock.

NIB	Exc.	V.G.	Good	Fair	Poor
500	400	350	275	175	150

Presentation Grade
As above, with a target hammer and trigger, and a hand checkered stock.

NIB	Exc.	V.G.	Good	Fair	Poor
575	475	425	350	250	200

Engraved Presentation Grade

No. 1 Grade

NIB	Exc.	V.G.	Good	Fair	Poor
650	550	500	450	350	250

No. 2 Grade

NIB	Exc.	V.G.	Good	Fair	Poor
775	650	600	550	450	300

No. 3 Grade

NIB	Exc.	V.G.	Good	Fair	Poor
1100	950	750	650	550	400

VENUS WAFFENWERKE
Zella Mehlis, Germany

Venus
A 6.35mm, 7.65mm or 9mm semi-automatic pistol with a 3.5" barrel. Slide is marked "Original Venus Patent" and the grips bear the monogram "OW". Designed by Oskar Will. Blued, plastic grips. Manufactured from 1912 to 1914.

Exc.	V.G.	Good	Fair	Poor
600	500	400	250	175

VERNEY-CARRON
St. Etienne, France
Importer—Ventura
Seal Beach, California

Concours
A 12 gauge Over/Under boxlock shotgun with 26" or 28" ventilated-rib barrels, single selective triggers, automatic ejectors and profuse engraving. Blued, French case-hardened with checkered walnut stock. First imported in 1978.

Exc.	V.G.	Good	Fair	Poor
1000	850	750	600	450

Skeet Model
As above, with a 28" skeet chocked barrel and a pistol grip stock.

Exc.	V.G.	Good	Fair	Poor
1050	900	800	650	500

VETTERLI
Switzerland
Various Manufacturers
SEE—Swiss Military Section

VICKERS, LTD.
Crayford/Kent, England

Jubilee
A .22 caliber single shot Martini-action single shot rifle with a

28" barrel, adjustable sights and pistolgrip walnut stock. Blued. Manufactured prior to World War II.

Exc.	V.G.	Good	Fair	Poor
450	400	350	275	200

Empire

As above, with a 27" or 30" barrel and a straight stock.

Exc.	V.G.	Good	Fair	Poor
400	350	300	225	150

VICTORY ARMS COT., LTD.

North Hampton, England
Importer—Magnum Research, Inc.
Minneapolis, Minnesota

Model MC5

A 9mm, .38 Super, .41 Action Express, 10mm or .45 caliber semi-automatic pistol with a 4.25", 5.75" or 7.5" barrel, 10-, 12- or 17-shot magazine, decocking lever and Millett sights. Interchangeable barrels were available. Introduced in 1989.

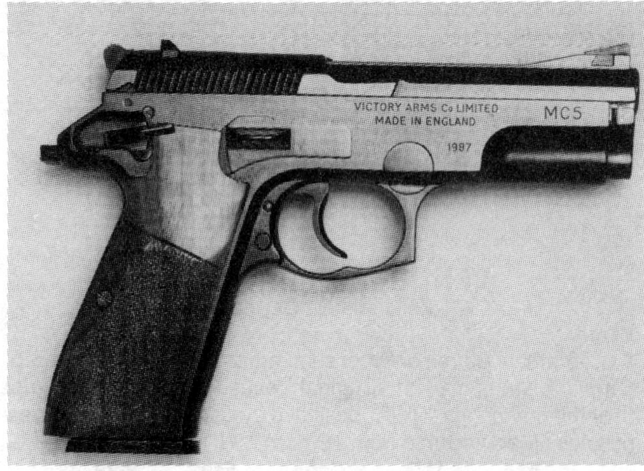

NIB	Exc.	V.G.	Good	Fair	Poor
500	450	400	300	250	200

VIRGINIAN

SEE—Interarms

VOERE

Kufstein, Austria

In 1987 this company was purchased by Mauser-Werke. Voere actions are used in rifles made and sold by KDF, Inc., of Seguin, Texas. Values for older-production rifles are as follows:

Bolt-Action Rifle

A bolt-action sporting rifle made in a variety of calibers with 22" or 24" barrels, 3- or 4-shot magazines and checkered walnut stock.

Exc.	V.G.	Good	Fair	Poor
350	300	250	200	100

Semi-Auto Rifle

A .22 caliber semi-automatic rifle with a 20" barrel, adjustable sights and a detachable magazine. Blued with a checkered walnut stock.

Exc.	V.G.	Good	Fair	Poor
250	200	150	100	75

VOLCANIC ARMS COMPANY

New Haven, Connecticut
SEE—Winchester Repeating Arms Co.

VOLUNTEER ENTERPRISES

Knoxville, Tennessee
SEE—Commando Arms

VOLKSPISTOLE

Various Makers
Germany

Volkspistole

Quite mysterious, as very few have ever been noted. It was designed as a cheaply manufactured, last-ditch weapon that was supposed to be used to flood the German countryside and cause casualties among the invaders at the close of WWII. It is chambered for the 9mm Parabellum cartridge and features a gas-operated, delayed blowback action. It has a 5.1" barrel with an 8-round, detachable box magazine. The construction is of steel stampings. It has no safety devices and no markings whatsoever. Examples noted are in the white, and there are no sights affixed to them. It appears that this weapon never actually went into production, and it would be impossible to estimate a value. Anyone encountering such a weapon would be wise to secure a qualified appraisal.

VOUZLAUD

Paris, France
Importer—Waverly Arms Co.
Suffolk, Virginia

Model 315 E

A 12, 16 or 20 gauge boxlock shotgun with 20" barrels, double triggers and straight gripped stock. Blued, case-hardened. Imported prior to 1988.

Exc.	V.G.	Good	Fair	Poor
7500	6500	5500	4000	2500

Model 315 EL

As above, with more engraving and also available in 28 or .410 bore which are worth approximately $1,000 more than the values listed below.

Exc.	V.G.	Good	Fair	Poor
10000	8500	6500	5000	3000

Model 315 EGL

As above, with a French case-hardened receiver. Discontinued in 1987.

Exc.	V.G.	Good	Fair	Poor
15000	12500	10000	7500	5000

Model 315 EGL-S

As above, with engraved hunting scenes. Discontinued in 1987.

Exc.	V.G.	Good	Fair	Poor
5500	4500	3500	2500	1750

WALCH, JOHN
New York, New York

Navy Revolver

A .36 caliber superimposed load percussion revolver with a 6" octagonal barrel and a 6-shot cylinder fitted with 12 nipples, 2 hammers and 2 triggers. The barrel marked "Walch Firearms Co. NY." and "Patented Feb. 8, 1859". Blued with walnut grips.

Exc.	V.G.	Good	Fair	Poor
3500	3000	2750	2000	1500

Pocket Revolver

A spur trigger .31 caliber 10-shot percussion revolver with either a brass or iron frame and walnut grips. The iron frame version is worth approximately 50% more than the brass variety.

Exc.	V.G.	Good	Fair	Poor
1750	1500	1250	750	500

WALDMAN
Germany

Waldman

A 7.65mm semi-automatic pistol with a 3.5" barrel and 8-shot magazine. The slide marked "1913 Model Automatic Pistol" and some examples are marked "American Automatic Pistol". Blued with checkered walnut grips inlaid with a brass insert marked "Waldman".

Exc.	V.G.	Good	Fair	Poor
250	225	200	150	100

WALLIS & BIRCH
Philadelphia, Pennsylvania

Pocket Pistol

A .41 caliber single shot percussion pocket pistol with a 2.5" or 3" barrel, German silver furniture and walnut stock. The barrels marked "Wallis & Birch Phila." Produced during the 1850s.

Exc.	V.G.	Good	Fair	Poor
650	600	500	400	300

WALTHER, CARL
Zella Mehilis and Ulm/Donau, Germany

In 1886 Carl Walther set up a workshop to make sporting arms. Until 1900 his operation remained very small. In 1907 he designed the 6.35mm blowback pistol. This design was offered for sale in 1908. In less than a year after the introduction of the first pistol the second model was introduced. Called the Model 2, this pistol was more advanced than the first design and became a very popular handgun in Germany prior to World War I. Two years later the Model 3 was introduced and successive models were designed and produced through 1921 when the Model 9 was announced. In 1929 Walther built the now famous Model PP, Polizei Pistole, which became synonymous with quality and advanced design. The Walther legend was born and has been maintained up to this date as a fine high quality German built pistol. After World War II the Walther company relocated in Ulm/Donau, Germany.

Editors Comment: There are a large number of Walther variations, especially during the WWII era that require years of experience to learn the subtleties of these variations. When dealing with expensive Walther pistols it is suggested that an expert appraisal be obtained before buying or selling these highly collectable handguns.

Model 1

A 6.35MM semi-automatic pistol barrel lengths of 2-6 inches. Blued with checkered hard rubber grips with the Walther logo on each grip. Introduced in 1908.

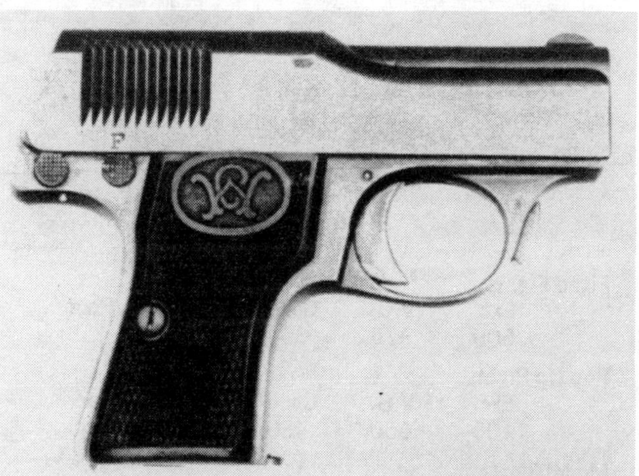

Courtesy James Rankin.

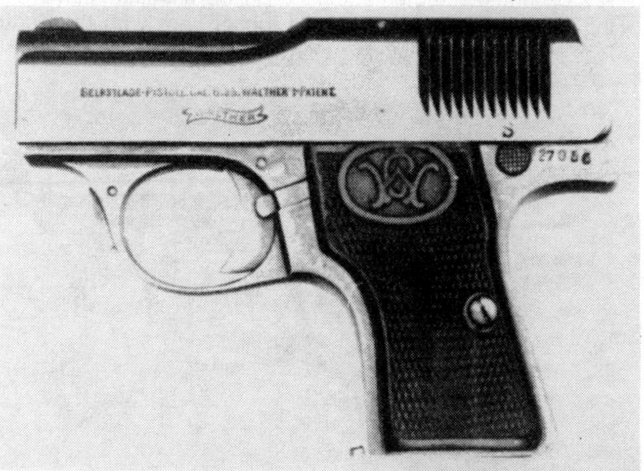

Courtesy James Rankin.

Exc.	V.G.	Good	Fair	Poor
600	375	300	200	150

Model 2

A 6.35MM semi-automatic pistol having a knurled bushing at the muzzle which retains the mainspring. There are two variations. One with a fixed rear sight, and one with a pop up rear sight. Blued with checkered hard rubber grips with the Walther logo on each grip. Introduced in 1909.

Courtesy James Rankin.

Courtesy James Rankin.

Fixed Sights

Exc.	V.G.	Good	Fair	Poor
500	375	300	200	150

Pop Up Sights

Exc.	V.G.	Good	Fair	Poor
1100	600	450	250	150

Model 3

A 7.65MM semi-automatic pistol having a smooth barrel bushing. Blued with checkered hard rubber grips with the Walther logo on each. Introduced in 1910.

Courtesy James Rankin.

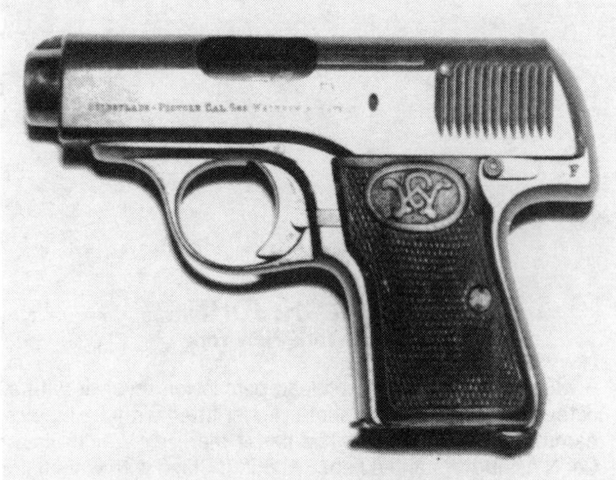

Courtesy James Rankin.

Exc.	V.G.	Good	Fair	Poor
1000	700	500	350	200

Model 4

A 7.65MM semi-automatic pistol larger than the preceding models. There were many variations of this model produced. Blued with checkered hard rubber grips with the Walther logo on each grip. Introduced 1910.

Courtesy James Rankin.

Courtesy James Rankin.

Exc.	V.G.	Good	Fair	Poor
450	375	300	200	150

Model 5

A 6.35MM semi-automatic pistol which is almost identical to the Model 2. Fixed sights. Blued with checkered hard rubber grips with the Walther logo on each grip.

Courtesy James Rankin.

Courtesy James Rankin.

Exc.	V.G.	Good	Fair	Poor
450	350	300	200	150

Model 6

A 9MM semi-automatic pistol. The largest of the Walther numbered pistols. Approximately 1500 manufactured. Blued with checkered hard rubber grips with the Walther logo on each grip. Sometimes seen with plain checkered wood grips. Introduced 1915.

Courtesy James Rankin.

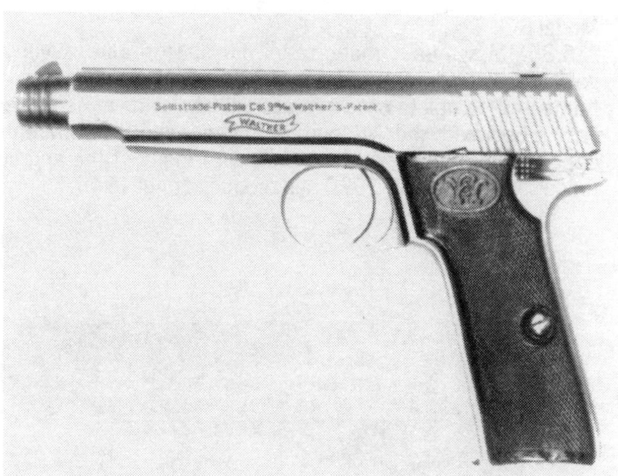

Courtesy James Rankin.

Exc.	V.G.	Good	Fair	Poor
4500	3000	2000	1000	700

Model 7

A 6.35MM semi-automatic pistol in the same style as the Model 4. Blued with checkered hard rubber grips with the Walther logo on each side. Introduced in 1917.

Courtesy James Rankin.

Courtesy James Rankin.

Exc.	V.G.	Good	Fair	Poor
500	375	300	200	150

Model 8

A 6.35MM semi-automatic pistol. Finishes in blue, silver and gold. Three types of engraving coverage; slide only, slide and frame and complete coverage overall. The grips are checkered hard rubber with the WC logo on one grip, and 6.35MM on the opposite side. Ivory grips are seen with many of the engraved models. Introduced in 1920 and produced until 1944.

Courtesy James Rankin.

Courtesy James Rankin.

Blue, silver and gold finish.

Exc.	V.G.	Good	Fair	Poor
500	375	300	200	150

Engraved slide.

Exc.	V.G.	Good	Fair	Poor
1000	700	500	300	200

Engraved slide and frame.

Exc.	V.G.	Good	Fair	Poor
1800	1400	850	450	300

Engraved, complete coverage.

Exc.	V.G.	Good	Fair	Poor
2000	1500	900	500	300

Model 9

A 6.35MM semi-automatic pistol. Smaller than the Model 8, but built as the Model 1 with exposed barrel. Same finishes and engraving as the Model 8. Introduced 1921 and produced until 1944.

Courtesy James Rankin.

Courtesy James Rankin.

All values the same as the Model 8.

Sport Model 1926
Walther Hammerless Target 22
Walther Standard Sport
Walther 1932 Olympia

Sport Model target, Special Stoeger Model

All of these 22 LR caliber semi-automatic pistols are the same target pistol introduced by Walther in 1926. A very well made pistol with a barrel length of between 6-16 inches. It has one-piece checkered wraparound wood grips. There was also a 22 short version of the Olympia model produced for rapid fire Olympic shooting. There was also a torpedo shape target weight available for shooters.

Courtesy Orville Reichert.

Courtesy Orville Reichert.

Exc.	V.G.	Good	Fair	Poor
750	550	450	350	250

Add $200 for target weight.
Add $500 for case.

Walther 1936 Olympia
This semi-automatic target pistol in 22 caliber resembled the earlier 1932 Olympia, but with many improvements. There were four standard models produced with many variations of each one. These variations included many barrel lengths, and both round and octagon barrels. There were duraluminum slides, frames and triggers. Various weight configurations to as many as four separate weights to one gun. One piece wrap around checkered wood grips in different configurations for the individual shooter. Produced until 1944. The four models were:

FunfklamphPentathlon
Jagerschafts-Hunter
Sport or Standard Model
Schnellfeur-Rapid Fire

Courtesy James Rankin.

Exc.	V.G.	Good	Fair	Poor
900	750	600	475	350

Add $250 for weights.

Model MP
A 9MM semi-automatic pistol which was the forerunner of the Model AP and P.38 series. Found in variations that resemble a large Model PP or the P.38. Blued finish with one piece wrap around checkered wood grips.

Courtesy James Rankin.

Exc.	V.G.	Good	Fair	Poor
35000	30000	25000	20000	15000

Model AP
A 9MM semi-automatic pistol which was the forerunner of the Model P.38. A hammerless pistol in various barrel lengths. Sometimes with duraluminum frames, and some with stocks. Blued finish with one piece wrap around checkered wood grips.

Exc.	V.G.	Good	Fair	Poor
28000	25000	20000	15000	10000

With stock, add $4000.

Model PP
A semi-automatic pistol in caliber 22, 25, 32 and 380. Introduced in 1928. It was the first successful commercial double-action pistol. It was manufactured in finishes of blue, silver and gold, and with three different types of engraving. Grips were generally two piece black or white plastic with the Walther Banner on each grip. Grips in wood or ivory are seen, but usually on engraved guns. There are many variations of the Model PP and numerous NSDAP markings seen on the pre-1946 models which were produced during the Nazi regime. All reflect various prices.

Courtesy Orville Reichert.

Courtesy Orville Reichert.

Courtesy Orville Reichert.

Model PP 22 Caliber

Exc.	V.G.	Good	Fair	Poor
700	500	350	250	150

Model PP 25 Caliber

Exc.	V.G.	Good	Fair	Poor
4500	3250	2500	1500	600

Model PP 32 Caliber High Polished Finish

Exc.	V.G.	Good	Fair	Poor
400	325	275	225	175

Model PP 32 Caliber Milled Finish

Exc.	V.G.	Good	Fair	Poor
375	275	250	200	125

Model PP 380 Caliber

Exc.	V.G.	Good	Fair	Poor
800	600	550	475	350

Model PP 32 Caliber with Duraluminum Frame

Exc.	V.G.	Good	Fair	Poor
800	675	550	400	200

Model PP 32 Caliber with Bottom Magazine Release

Exc.	V.G.	Good	Fair	Poor
850	700	600	400	200

Model PP 32 Caliber with Verchromt Finish

Exc.	V.G.	Good	Fair	Poor
1750	1350	1000	700	400

Model PP 32 Caliber in Blue, Silver or Gold Finish and Full Coverage Engraving

Blue

Exc.	V.G.	Good	Fair	Poor
3000	2500	2000	1200	700

Silver

Exc.	V.G.	Good	Fair	Poor
3500	3000	2500	1200	700

Gold

Exc.	V.G.	Good	Fair	Poor
4000	3500	3000	1200	700

Add $250 for ivory grips with any of the three above.
Add $700 for leather presentation cases.
Add $500 for 22 caliber.
Add $1000 for 380 caliber.

Model PP 32 Caliber, Allemagne Marked

Exc.	V.G.	Good	Fair	Poor
850	700	550	325	250

Model PP 32 Caliber, A.F. Stoeger Contract

Exc.	V.G.	Good	Fair	Poor
1800	1450	1050	700	400

Model PP 32 Caliber with Waffenampt Proofs. High Polished Finish.

Exc.	V.G.	Good	Fair	Poor
700	500	375	275	150

Model PP 32 Caliber with Waffenampt Proofs. Milled Finish.

Exc.	V.G.	Good	Fair	Poor
450	375	325	250	150

Model PP 32 Caliber. Police Eagle/C Proofed. High Polished Finish.

Exc.	V.G.	Good	Fair	Poor
650	475	375	250	150

Model PP 32 Caliber. Police Eagle/C and Police Eagle/F Proofed. Milled Finish.

Exc.	V.G.	Good	Fair	Poor
550	400	375	275	150

Model PP 32 Caliber. NSKK Marked On The Slide.

Exc.	V.G.	Good	Fair	Poor
2000	1500	850	550	300

Add $600 with proper NSKK DRGM AKAH holster.

Model PP 32 Caliber. NSDAP Gruppe Markings.

Exc.	V.G.	Good	Fair	Poor
1600	1000	750	500	300

Add $600 with proper SA DRGM AKAH holster.

Model PP 32 Caliber. PDM Marked with Bottom Magazine Release.

Exc.	V.G.	Good	Fair	Poor
850	700	550	475	300

Model PP 32 Caliber. RJ Marked.

Exc.	V.G.	Good	Fair	Poor
700	600	475	400	150

Model PP 32 Caliber. RFV Marked. High Polished or Milled Finish.

Exc.	V.G.	Good	Fair	Poor
700	600	475	400	150

Model PP 32 Caliber. RBD Munster Marked.

Exc.	V.G.	Good	Fair	Poor
2200	1750	1200	650	400

Model PP 32 Caliber. RpLt Marked.

Exc.	V.G.	Good	Fair	Poor
800	650	475	375	200

Model PP 32 Caliber. Statens Vattenfallsverk Marked.

Exc.	V.G.	Good	Fair	Poor
850	700	550	375	200

Model PP 32 Caliber. AC Marked.

Exc.	V.G.	Good	Fair	Poor
450	375	300	250	150

Model PP 32 Caliber. Duraluminum Frame.

Exc.	V.G.	Good	Fair	Poor
700	600	500	400	150

Model PP 380 Caliber. Bottom Magazine Release and Waffenampt Proofs.

Exc.	V.G.	Good	Fair	Poor
1200	900	700	500	300

Model PPK

A semi-automatic pistol in caliber 22, 25, 32 and 380. Introduced six months after the Model PP in 1929. A more compact version of the Model PP with one less round in the magazine and one piece wrap around checkered plastic grips in brown, black and white with the Walther Banner on each side of the grips. The Model PPK will be found with the same types of finishes as the Model PP as well as the same styles of engraving. Grips in wood or ivory are seen with some of the engraved models. As with the Model PP there are many variations of the Model PPK and numerous NSDAP markings seen on the pre-1946 models which were produced during the Nazi regime. All reflect various prices.

Courtesy Orville Reichert.

Courtesy Orville Reichert.

Model PPK 22 Caliber

Exc.	V.G.	Good	Fair	Poor
900	650	475	325	175

Model PPK 25 Caliber

Exc.	V.G.	Good	Fair	Poor
5000	3750	1850	1000	500

Model PPK 32 Caliber. High Polished Finish.

Exc.	V.G.	Good	Fair	Poor
500	400	325	250	150

Model PPK 32 Caliber. Milled Finish.

Exc.	V.G.	Good	Fair	Poor
425	375	325	250	150

Model PPK 380 Caliber

Exc.	V.G.	Good	Fair	Poor
2200	1750	1300	750	375

Model PPK 32 Caliber with Duraluminum Frame

Exc.	V.G.	Good	Fair	Poor
850	750	600	400	200

Model PPK 32 Caliber with Verchromt Finish.

Exc.	V.G.	Good	Fair	Poor
2000	1750	1200	700	350

Model PPK 32 Caliber in Blue, Silver or Gold Finish and Full Coverage Engraving.

Blue

Exc.	V.G.	Good	Fair	Poor
3500	3000	2500	1200	700

Silver

Exc.	V.G.	Good	Fair	Poor
3750	3250	2750	1200	700

Gold

Exc.	V.G.	Good	Fair	Poor
4500	3750	3000	1200	700

Add $750 for ivory grips with any of the three above.
Add $700 for leather presentation cases.
Add $500 for 22 caliber.
Add $1000 for 380 caliber.

Model PPK 32 Caliber Marked Mod. PP On Slide.

Exc.	V.G.	Good	Fair	Poor
3500	3000	2500	1500	1000

Model PPK 32 Caliber with Panagraphed Slide.

Exc.	V.G.	Good	Fair	Poor
650	550	450	300	200

Model PPK 32 Caliber. Czechoslovakian Contract.

Exc.	V.G.	Good	Fair	Poor
1850	1500	1000	550	300

Model PPK 32 Caliber. Allemagne Marked.

Exc.	V.G.	Good	Fair	Poor
800	700	600	400	250

Model PPK 32 Caliber with Waffenampt Proofs and A High Polished Finish.

Exc.	V.G.	Good	Fair	Poor
1050	750	550	400	250

Model PPK 32 Caliber with Waffenampt Proofs and A Milled Finish.

Exc.	V.G.	Good	Fair	Poor
675	500	375	300	175

Model PPK 32 Caliber. Police Eagle/C Proofed. High Polished Finish.

Exc.	V.G.	Good	Fair	Poor
675	575	450	300	175

Model PPK 32 Caliber. Police Eagle/C Proofed. Milled Finish.

Exc.	V.G.	Good	Fair	Poor
575	500	375	275	175

Model PPK 32 Caliber. Police Eagle/F Proofed. Duraluminum Frame. Milled Finish.

Exc.	V.G.	Good	Fair	Poor
850	700	550	350	225

Model PPK 22 Caliber. Late War, Black Grips.

Exc.	V.G.	Good	Fair	Poor
1000	750	600	450	300

Model PPK 32 Caliber. Party Leader Grips. Brown.

Exc.	V.G.	Good	Fair	Poor
2750	2550	2350	2250	2000

Model PPK 32 Caliber. Party Leader Grips. Black.

Exc.	V.G.	Good	Fair	Poor
3250	3000	2750	2550	2500

If grips are badly cracked or damaged on the two Party Leaders above, reduce $2000 each valuation.

Add $500 with proper Party Leader DRGM AKAH holster.

Model PPK 32 Caliber. RZM Marked.

Exc.	V.G.	Good	Fair	Poor
900	700	500	400	300

Model PPK 32 Caliber. PDM Marked with Duraluminum Frame and Bottom Magazine Release.

Exc.	V.G.	Good	Fair	Poor
2250	1750	1150	750	450

Model PPK 32 Caliber. RFV Marked.

Exc.	V.G.	Good	Fair	Poor
2000	1750	1150	650	400

Model PPK 32 Caliber. DRP Marked.

Exc.	V.G.	Good	Fair	Poor
800	650	550	450	275

Model PPK 32 Caliber. Statens Vattenfallsverk.

Exc.	V.G.	Good	Fair	Poor
1400	1200	700	450	300

WALTHER POST WORLD WAR II

Models PP and PPK

Manufactured by the firm of Manufacture de Machines du Haut-Rhin at Mulhouse, France under license by Walther.

Model PP Some with Duraluminum Frames.

Model PP 22 Caliber

Exc.	V.G.	Good	Fair	Poor
550	400	350	275	175

Model PP 32 Caliber

Exc.	V.G.	Good	Fair	Poor
500	375	350	275	175

Model PP 380 Caliber

Exc.	V.G.	Good	Fair	Poor
550	400	350	275	175

Model PP. All Three Calibers Finished In Blue, Silver and Gold With Full Coverage Engraving.

Blue

Exc.	V.G.	Good	Fair	Poor
1250	900	750	450	300

Silver

Exc.	V.G.	Good	Fair	Poor
1250	900	750	450	300

Gold

Exc.	V.G.	Good	Fair	Poor
1250	900	750	450	300

Model PP Mark II

These Walthers were manufactured under license by Walther and produced by the Manurhin Company. They were sold exclusively by Interarms, Alexandria, Virginia. The Mark II's were the same pistols as those above and have the same types of finish and engraving as well as the same value.

Model PP Manurhin

Manurhin Company manufactured with Manurhin logo and inscription. Usually "licensed by Walther" somewhere on the pistol. The same pistols as those above, bearing the same types of finish and engraving, and having the same values.

Model PP Sport, Manurhin

22 caliber. This is the same gun as the Model PP with different barrel lengths running from 5 - 7-3/4 inches. It is basically a target 22 with adjustable rear sights for elevation and windage. The front sight is also adjustable. There is a barrel bushing at the muzzle which attaches the front sight to the barrel. The grips are contoured checkered plastic and are either squared at the bottom of the grips or are in the shape of an inverted birds head.

Exc.	V.G.	Good	Fair	Poor
675	525	450	375	275

Model PP Sport C, Manurhin

22 caliber. This is the same gun as the Model PP Sport but in single action with a spur hammer. It has front and rear adjustable sights and squared target grips in checkered black, brown and plastic. Blued and silver finish.

Exc.	V.G.	Good	Fair	Poor
675	525	450	375	275

Model PP Sport, Walther

A 22 caliber Sport was manufactured by Manurhin, but sold by the Walther with the Walther logo and inscription. This is the same gun as the Model PP Sport, Manurhin. Only sold for a period of two years.

Exc.	V.G.	Good	Fair	Poor
675	525	450	375	275

Model PP Fiftieth Anniversary Commemorative Model

In 22 or 380 caliber. Blued with gold inlays and handcarved grips with oak leaves and acorns. Walther Banner carved into each side of the grips. Wood presentation case.

Exc.	V.G.	Good	Fair	Poor
1200	900	750	500	300

Model PPK. Some With Duraluminum Frames.

Model PPK. 22 Caliber.

Exc.	V.G.	Good	Fair	Poor
550	400	350	275	175

Model PPK. 32 Caliber.

Exc.	V.G.	Good	Fair	Poor
500	375	350	275	175

Model PPK. 380 Caliber.

Exc.	V.G.	Good	Fair	Poor
550	400	350	275	175

Model PPK. All Three Calibers Finished In Blue, Silver and Gold With Full Coverage Engraving.

Blue

Exc.	V.G.	Good	Fair	Poor
1250	900	750	450	300

Silver

Exc.	V.G.	Good	Fair	Poor
1250	900	750	450	300

Gold

Exc.	V.G.	Good	Fair	Poor
1250	900	750	450	300

Model PPK Mark II

These Walthers were manufactured under license by Walther and produced by the Manurhin Company. They were sold exclusively by Interarms, Alexandria, Virginia. The Mark II's were the same pistols as those above and have the same types of finish and engraving as well as the same value.

Model PPK Manurhin

Manurhin Company manufactured with Manurhin logo and inscription. Usually "Licensed by Walther" somewhere on the pistol. The same pistols as above, bearing the same types of finish and engraving, and having the same value.

Model PPK Fiftieth Anniversary Commemorative Model

In 22 or 380 caliber. Blued with gold inlays and handcarved grips with oak leaves and acorns. Walther Banner carved into each side of the grips. Wood presentation case.

Exc.	V.G.	Good	Fair	Poor
2100	1800	1250	1000	500

Model PPK/S

This Walther was manufactured in 22, 32 and 380 caliber for sale in the United States market after the introduction of the United States Gun Control Act of 1968. It is basically a Model PP with a cut off muzzle and slide. It has two piece black checkered plastic grips as seen on the Model PP. It was finished in blue, nickel, dull gold and verchromt.

Exc.	V.G.	Good	Fair	Poor
550	475	375	300	200

Model PPK American

In 1986 the Model PPK was licensed by the Walther Company to be manufactured in the United States. The finish is stainless steel. Caliber is 380.

Exc.	V.G.	Good	Fair	Poor
425	375	300	200	150

Model PPK/S American

Manufactured in the United States. The same as the German Model PPK/S. This pistol is finished in blue and stainless steel. Caliber is 380.

Exc.	V.G.	Good	Fair	Poor
425	375	300	200	150

Model TP

A Walther manufactured semi-automatic pistol in 22 and 25 calibers patterned after the earlier Model 9. Finish is blue and silver black plastic checkered grips with Walther Banner medallions in each grip.

Exc.	V.G.	Good	Fair	Poor
750	600	500	375	250

Model TPH

A Walther manufactured semi-automatic pistol in 22 and 25 calibers. This is a double-action pistol with a duraluminum frame. Finished in blue or silver. Two piece black checkered plastic grips. Full coverage engraving available.

Exc.	V.G.	Good	Fair	Poor
550	500	450	350	250

Add $300 for the engraved model.

Model TPH American

This semi-automatic is produced in both 22 and 25 calibers. It is licensed by Walther and manufactured in the United States. It is produced in stainless steel and has two piece black plastic checkered grips. It is a double-action pistol.

Exc.	V.G.	Good	Fair	Poor
330	250	200	150	100

Model PP Super

This is a 380 and 9x18 caliber, double-action semi-automatic manufactured by Walther. It is similar in design to the Model PP, but with a P. 38 type of mechanism. Finish is blue and the grips are wrap around black checkered plastic or a type of molded wood colored plastic.

Exc.	V.G.	Good	Fair	Poor
550	450	350	250	150

Model P-38

Following World War II, the P-38 was reintroduced in variety of calibers with a 5" barrel and alloy or steel frame.

.22 Caliber

NIB	Exc.	V.G.	Good	Fair	Poor
1000	800	650	500	350	200

Other Calibers

NIB	Exc.	V.G.	Good	Fair	Poor
600	500	450	400	300	200

Steel-Framed (Introduced 1987)

NIB	Exc.	V.G.	Good	Fair	Poor
1400	1250	1000	750	500	400

Factory-engraved versions of the P-38 pistol were blued, chrome, or silver or gold-plated. We suggest that a qualified appraisal be secured when contemplating purchase.

Model P-38K

As above, with a 2.8" barrel and front sight is mounted on the slide. Imported between 1974 and 1980.

Exc.	V.G.	Good	Fair	Poor
600	500	450	400	300

Model P-38 IV

A redesigned version of the above, with a 4.5" barrel and 8-shot magazine. Fitted with a decocking lever and adjustable sights. Imported prior to 1983.

Exc.	V.G.	Good	Fair	Poor
600	500	450	400	300

Model P 5

A 9MM semi-automatic pistol with a double-action firing mechanism. One of the first Walthers to have a decocker lever. Finish is a combination of black matte and high polish. It has black plastic checkered grips.

Exc.	V.G.	Good	Fair	Poor
700	600	500	400	300

Model P 5, Compact

A shorter version of the standard Model P 5.

Exc.	V.G.	Good	Fair	Poor
880	700	600	375	250

Model P 5 One Hundred Year Commemorative

Blued with gold inlays and hand carved grips with oak leaves and acorns. Walther Banner carved into each side of the grips. Wood presentation case.

Exc.	V.G.	Good	Fair	Poor
2000	1500	1000	700	400

Model P88

A 9MM semi-automatic in double-action with ambidextrous decocking lever. Fifteen shot magazine and two piece black checkered plastic grips. Combination of high polish and black matte finish.

Exc.	V.G.	Good	Fair	Poor
900	800	600	500	300

Model P88 Compact

A shorter version of the standard Model P88.

Exc.	V.G.	Good	Fair	Poor
900	800	600	500	300

Model FP

A 22 LR caliber, single shot target pistol which fires electrically. It has micro adjustable electric firing system along with micrometer sights and contoured wooden grips which are adjustable. The barrel is 11.7 inches and the finish is blue.

Exc.	V.G.	Good	Fair	Poor
1750	1350	900	500	400

Model GSP

A semi-automatic target pistol in 22 LR and 38 calibers. This target pistol has a 4-1/2 inch barrel, 5-shot magazine and contoured wood target grips. Blued finish and sold with attache case and accessories.

Exc.	V.G.	Good	Fair	Poor
1200	850	750	650	300

Model GSP-C

Almost the same pistol as the Model GSP, but in 32 cal. S&W Wadcutter.

Exc.	V.G.	Good	Fair	Poor
1200	850	750	650	300

Model OSP

A 22 short semi-automatic target pistol which is similar to the Model GSP. This pistol is made for rapid fire target shooting. Blued finish with contoured wood grips.

Exc.	V.G.	Good	Fair	Poor
1200	850	750	650	300

Free Pistol

A .22 caliber single shot target pistol with an 11.7" barrel, micrometer sights, adjustable grips and an electronic trigger. Blued.

NIB	Exc.	V.G.	Good	Fair	Poor
1800	1550	1200	900	700	550

Model B

A .30-06 caliber bolt-action rifle with a 22" barrel, 4-shot magazine and single or double set triggers. Double set triggers are worth approximately 20% more than the values listed below. Blued with a walnut stock.

Exc.	V.G.	Good	Fair	Poor
450	400	350	250	175

Olympic Single Shot

A .22 caliber bolt-action rifle with a 26" barrel, adjustable target sights and a walnut stock fitted with a palmrest and adjustable buttplate. Blued.

Exc.	V.G.	Good	Fair	Poor
950	850	700	500	400

Model V

A .22 caliber single shot bolt-action rifle with a 26" barrel and adjustable sights. Blued with a plain walnut stock. Manufactured before World War II.

Exc.	V.G.	Good	Fair	Poor
400	350	300	200	150

Model V Champion

As above, with a checkered walnut stock.

Exc.	V.G.	Good	Fair	Poor
450	400	350	250	200

Model KKM International Match

A .22 caliber single shot bolt-action rifle with a 28" barrel and adjustable sights. Blued with a walnut stock fitted for a palmrest and with an adjustable buttplate. Manufactured after World War II.

Exc.	V.G.	Good	Fair	Poor
900	800	650	450	350

Model KKM-S

As above, with an adjustable cheekpiece.

Exc.	V.G.	Good	Fair	Poor
950	850	700	500	400

Model KKW

As above, with a military-style stock.

Exc.	V.G.	Good	Fair	Poor
550	500	450	350	300

Model KKJ Sporter

A .22 caliber bolt-action rifle with a 22.5" barrel and 5-shot magazine. Blued with a checkered walnut stock. This model was available with double set triggers and their presence would add approximately 20% to the values listed below. Manufactured after World War II.

Exc.	V.G.	Good	Fair	Poor
550	500	450	350	300

Model KKJ-MA

As above, in .22 rimfire Magnum.

Exc.	V.G.	Good	Fair	Poor
550	500	450	350	300

Model KKJ-HO

As above, in .22 Hornet.

Exc.	V.G.	Good	Fair	Poor
750	700	600	450	350

Model SSV Varmint

A .22 caliber bolt-action single shot rifle with a 25.5" barrel not fitted with sights and Monte Carlo-style stock. Blued. Manufactured after World War II.

Exc.	V.G.	Good	Fair	Poor
600	550	475	375	300

Model UIT BV Universal

As above, with adjustable target sights and a walnut stock fitted with a palm rest and adjustable buttplate.

NIB	Exc.	V.G.	Good	Fair	Poor
1750	1500	1250	900	650	500

Model UIT Match

As above, with a stippled pistolgrip and forend. Also available with an electronic trigger which would add approximately $50.00 to the values listed below.

NIB	Exc.	V.G.	Good	Fair	Poor
1250	1000	750	600	450	400

GX 1

As above, with an adjustable Free Rifle stock.

NIB	Exc.	V.G.	Good	Fair	Poor
2250	2000	1750	1250	850	700

Prone Model 400

As above, with a prone position stock.

NIB	Exc.	V.G.	Good	Fair	Poor
750	700	600	450	350	300

Model KK/MS Silhouette

A .22 caliber bolt-action rifle with a 25.5" front-weighted barrel furnished without sights and a thumbhole stock having an adjustable buttplate. Introduced in 1984.

NIB	Exc.	V.G.	Good	Fair	Poor
1150	1000	850	700	550	400

Running Boar Model 500

As above, with a 23.5" barrel.

NIB	Exc.	V.G.	Good	Fair	Poor
1350	1150	950	750	600	450

Model WA-2000

A .300 Winchester Magnum or .308 caliber bolt-action sporting rifle produced on custom order. Prospective purchasers are advised to secure an appraisal prior to acquisition. Imported prior to 1989.

Exc.	V.G.	Good	Fair	Poor
6500	4750	3500	3000	2000

Model SF

A 12 or 16 gauge boxlock double-barrel shotgun fitted with double triggers and extractors. Blued with a checkered walnut stock fitted with sling swivels.

Exc.	V.G.	Good	Fair	Poor
500	450	350	250	200

Model SFD

As above, with the stock having a cheekpiece.

Exc.	V.G.	Good	Fair	Poor
650	600	525	425	350

WALTHER MANURHIN

Mulhouse, France

The Manurhin-manufactured Walther pistols are listed in the Walther section of this text under their respective model headings.

WANZEL

SEE—Austrian Military Firearms

WARNANT, L. AND J.

Ognee, Belgium

Revolver

Modeled after pistols manufactured by Smith & Wesson, the Warnants produced a variety of revolvers in .32, .38 or .45 caliber, between 1870 and 1890.

Exc.	V.G.	Good	Fair	Poor
125	100	75	60	50

Semi-Automatic Pistol

A 6.35mm semi-automatic pistol with a 2.5" barrel and 5-shot magazine. The slide marked "L&J Warnant Bte 6.35mm." Blued with black plastic grips bearing the monogram "L&JW" Manufactured after 1908.

Exc.	V.G.	Good	Fair	Poor
250	200	150	100	75

1912 Model

A 7.65mm caliber semi-automatic pistol with a 3" barrel and 7-shot magazine. The slide marked "L&J Warnant Brevetes Pist Auto 7.65mm." Manufactured prior to 1915.

Exc.	V.G.	Good	Fair	Poor
250	200	150	100	75

WARNER ARMS CORPORATION

Brooklyn, New York and Norwich, Connecticut

Established in 1912, this firm marketed revolvers, rifles, semi-automatic pistols and shotguns made for them by other companies (including N.R. Davis & Sons, Ithaca Gun Co. and so forth). In 1917, the company was purchased by N.R. Davis & Company. See also Davis-Warner.

The arms marketed by Warner Prior to 1917 are as follows:

SHOTGUNS

Single Trigger Hammerless Utica Special Double Barrel

In 12 gauge with 28", 30" or 32" barrels.

Double Trigger Hammerless Double Barrel

In 12 or 16 gauge with 28", 30" or 32" barrels.

Grade X, SF, XT, SFT, XD and XDF Hammer Guns

In 12, 16 or 20 gauge with 28", 30" or 32" barrels.

Field Grade Hammer Gun

In 12 or 16 gauge with 28" or 30" barrels.

Box Lock Hammerless

In 12 or 16 gauge with 28", 30" or 32" barrels.

RIFLES

Number 522

A .22 caliber single shot rifle with an 18" barrel.

Number 532

A .32 caliber single shot rifle with an 18" barrel.

REVOLVERS

Double Action

.32 and .38 caliber with 4" or 5" barrels.

Double Action Hammerless

.32 and .38 caliber with 4" or 5" barrels.

SEMI-AUTOMATIC PISTOLS

"Faultless": Warner-Schwarzlose Model C, .32 ACP.

WARNER, CHAS.

Windsor Locks, Connecticut

Pocket Revolver

A .31 caliber percussion revolver with a 3" round barrel and 6-shot unfluted cylinder. The cylinder marked "Charles Warner. Windsor Locks, Conn." Blued with walnut grips. Approximately 600 were made between 1857 and 1860.

Exc.	V.G.	Good	Fair	Poor
550	500	400	300	200

WARNER, JAMES

Springfield, Massachusetts

Revolving Carbines

A variety of revolving carbines were made by this maker. Nearly all of which are of .40 caliber, with octagonal barrels measuring 20" to 24" in length. The most commonly encountered variations are as follows:

Manually Revolved Grooved Cylinder

This model is fitted with two triggers one of which is a release so that the cylinder can be manually turned. Not fitted with a loading lever. The top strap marked "James Warner/Springfield, Mass." Approximately 75 were made in 1849.

Courtesy Milwaukee Public Museum, Milwaukee, Wisconsin.

Exc.	V.G.	Good	Fair	Poor
2000	1750	1500	1000	800

Retractable Cylinder Model

This version has a cylinder that fits over the breech, and it must be retracted before it can be manually rotated. The cylinder release is a button located in front of the trigger. It is marked "James Warner/Springfield Mass" and with an eagle over the letters "U.S." The cylinder is etched, and there is no loading lever. It also has a walnut stock with patchbox and no forearm. There were approximately 25 manufactured in 1849.

Exc.	V.G.	Good	Fair	Poor
4500	3750	3000	2000	1500

Automatic Revolving Cylinder

The cylinder is automatically turned when the hammer is cocked. This model is fitted with a loading lever and is marked "Warner's Patent/Jan. 1851" and "Springfield Arms Co." Approximately 200 were made during the 1850s.

Courtesy Milwaukee Public Museum, Milwaukee, Wisconsin.

Exc.	V.G.	Good	Fair	Poor
2000	1750	1500	1000	800

Belt Revolver

A .31 caliber double-action percussion revolver with a 4", 5" or 6" round barrel and 6-shot etched cylinder. Blued with walnut grips. No markings appear on this model except for the serial number. Manufactured in 1851.

Courtesy Milwaukee Public Museum, Milwaukee, Wisconsin.

Exc.	V.G.	Good	Fair	Poor
650	600	500	375	300

Pocket Revolver
A .28 caliber percussion revolver with a 3" octagonal barrel marked "James Warner, Springfield, Mass., USA,, and a 6-shot cylinder. Blued with walnut grips. Approximately 500 were made.

Exc.	V.G.	Good	Fair	Poor
600	550	450	400	350

Second Model
As above, with either a 3" or 4" barrel and marked "Warner's Patent 1857."

Courtesy Wallis & Wallis, Lewes, Sussex, England.

Exc.	V.G.	Good	Fair	Poor
500	450	400	300	250

Third Model
As above, but in .31 caliber.

Exc.	V.G.	Good	Fair	Poor
450	400	350	250	200

Single Shot Deringer
A .41 caliber rimfire single shot pocket pistol with a 2.75" round barrel, brass frame and walnut grips. As this model is unmarked, it can only be identified by the large breechblock which lifts upward and to the left for loading.

Exc.	V.G.	Good	Fair	Poor
3500	2750	2250	1500	1250

Pocket Revolver
A .30 caliber rimfire revolver with a 3" barrel marked "Warner's Patent 1857" and 5-shot cylinder. Blued or nickle-plated with walnut grips. Approximately 1,000 were made during the late 1860s.

Exc.	V.G.	Good	Fair	Poor
450	400	350	250	150

WEATHERBY
South Gate, California

This corporation was founded in 1945 by Roy Weatherby. He pioneered the high-velocity hunting rifle. His rifles were designed to fire cartridges that he also produced. They are examples of fine craftsmanship and have been used to take some of the top trophy animals from all around the world. Formerly these rifles were manufactured in West Germany. They are currently produced in Japan. Although the Japanese rifles are, in my opinion, every bit as fine a weapon as the German versions, collectors have dictated an approximate 25 percent premium assessed to the German-manufactured versions. The values given are for the current-production Japanese weapons. Simply add the premium for a German-manufactured rifle.

Mark V
This is a deluxe, bolt-action repeating rifle chambered for various popular standard calibers, as well as the full line of Weatherby cartridges from .240 Weatherby Magnum to .300 Weatherby Magnum. It is furnished with either a 24" or 26" barrel without sights. It has either a 3 or 5-round magazine, depending on the caliber. It has a deluxe, high-polish blued finish with a select, skip-line checkered walnut stock with a rosewood forearm tip and pistolgrip cap. This rifle is available with a lefthand action.

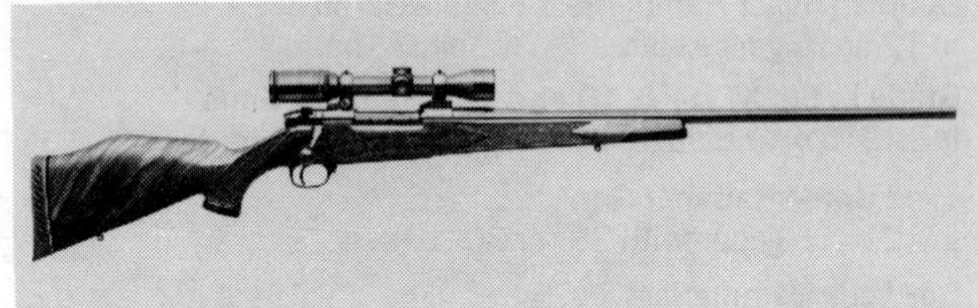

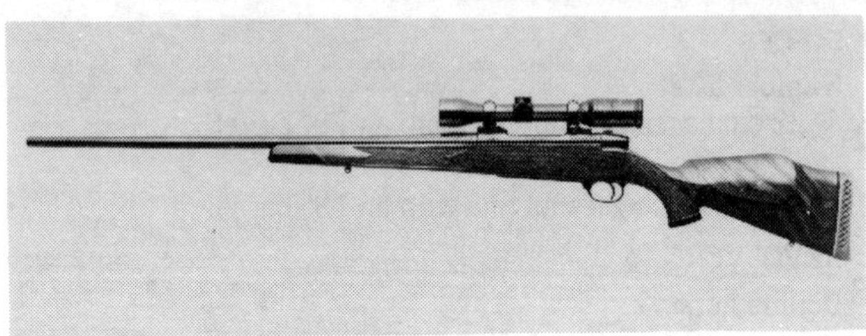

NIB	Exc.	V.G.	Good	Fair	Poor
1000	850	700	600	500	400

Mark V Sporter
Introduced in 1993 this model is identical to the Mark V Deluxe without the custom features. The metal is a low luster finish, the stock is Claro walnut with high gloss finish. A Monte Carlo comb with raised cheek piece and black 1" recoil pad are standard features on this model. Available in Weatherby calibers from .257 through .340 plus .270 Win., .30-06, 7mm Rem. Mag., .300 Win Mag., .338 Win. Mag. Weighs 8 to 8.5 lbs. depending on caliber.

NIB	Exc.	V.G.	Good	Fair	Poor
660	600	500	400	300	150

Mark V .340 Weatherby Magnum
This version is chambered for a larger magnum cartridge and is offered with the 26" barrel only.

NIB	Exc.	V.G.	Good	Fair	Poor
1050	900	750	650	550	200

Mark V .375 Weatherby Magnum
This version was manufactured in Germany only and is chambered for the currently obsolete .375 Weatherby Magnum cartridge. This version has become very collectible.

Exc.	V.G.	Good	Fair	Poor
1100	900	700	400	200

Mark V .378 Weatherby Magnum
This version is chambered for the .378 Weatherby Magnum cartridge and is considered to be one of the most powerful rifles currently available in the world. It is furnished with a 26" barrel only.

NIB	Exc.	V.G.	Good	Fair	Poor
1100	900	700	500	400	200

Mark V .416 Weatherby Magnum
This is an extremely powerful rifle suitable for hunting the biggest game. It is the first new caliber to be released by Weatherby since 1965. It was introduced in 1989.

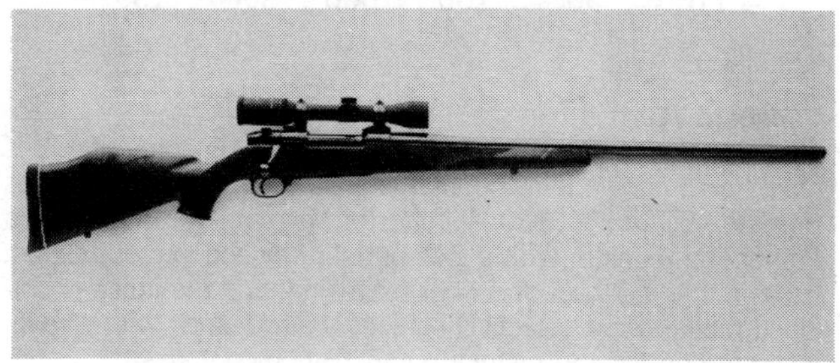

NIB	Exc.	V.G.	Good	Fair	Poor
1100	900	700	500	400	200

Mark V .460 Weatherby Magnum
This is the most powerful commercial rifle available in the world. It is considered to be overkill for any game except the largest and most dangerous creatures that roam the African continent. It is available with a 24" or 26" heavy barrel with an integral, recoil-reducing muzzle brake. It has a custom reinforced stock.

NIB	Exc.	V.G.	Good	Fair	Poor
1350	1200	1000	800	400	200

Mark V Varmint
This version is chambered for the .22-250 and the .224 Weatherby cartridge. It is offered with a 24" or 26" heavy barrel.

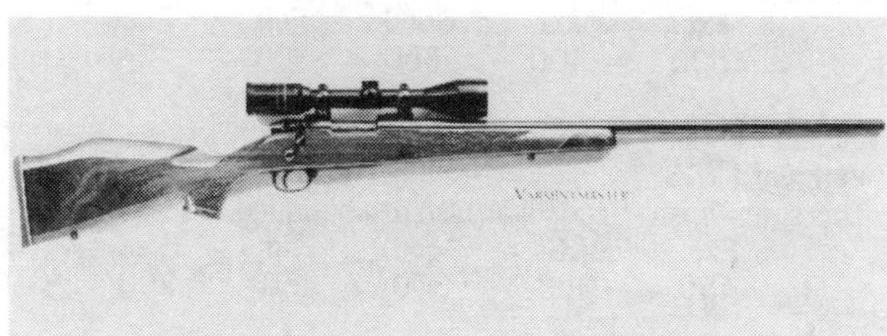

NIB	Exc.	V.G.	Good	Fair	Poor
975	800	750	550	400	200

Mark V Euromark
This model features a hand-checkered, oil-finished, claro walnut stock with an ebony forend tip and pistolgrip cap. It has a satin blued finish. It was introduced in 1986.

NIB	Exc.	V.G.	Good	Fair	Poor
1050	900	750	650	550	200

Mark V Lazermark
This version had a laser-carved pattern on the stock and forearm in place of the usual checkering. It was introduced in 1985.

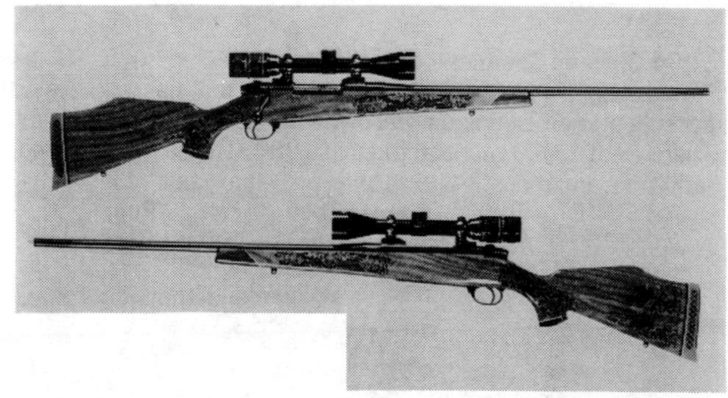

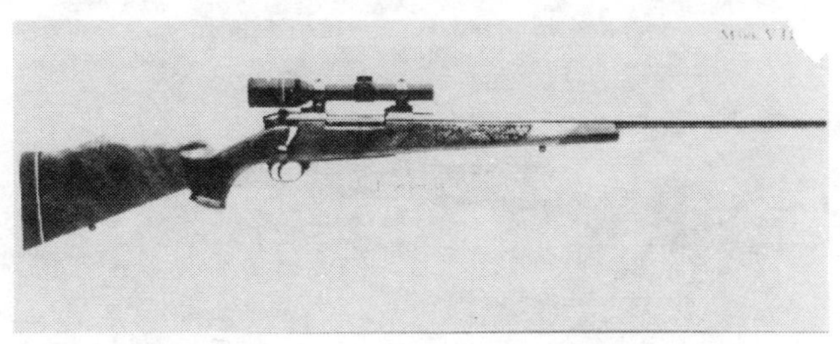

NIB	Exc.	V.G.	Good	Fair	Poor
1100	1000	800	700	400	200

Mark V Fibermark
This version has a matte blue finish and is furnished with a synthetic black, wrinkle-finished stock.

NIB	Exc.	V.G.	Good	Fair	Poor
1150	1000	850	750	400	200

Mark V Ultramark
This is a custom-finished version with a glass-bedded action and a special, high-polish blue. The action is hand-honed, and the walnut stock features basketweave checkering. It was introduced in 1989.

NIB	Exc.	V.G.	Good	Fair	Poor
1250	1150	900	750	400	200

35th Anniversary Commemorative Mark V
This specially embellished rifle that commemorated the 35th anniversary of the company. There were 1,000 produced in 1980. As with all commemoratives, it must be NIB with all furnished materials to be worth top dollar.

NIB	Exc.	V.G.	Good	Fair	Poor
1250	1150	900	750	400	300

1984 Olympic Commemorative Mark V
This is a specially embellished Mark V rifle that has gold-plated accents and an exhibition-grade walnut stock with a star inlay. There were 1,000 manufactured in 1984. This is a commemorative rifle and must be NIB to bring premium value.

NIB	Exc.	V.G.	Good	Fair	Poor
2200	1800	1500	1000	500	350

Safari Grade Mark V
This is a custom-order version that is available chambered from the .300 Weatherby Magnum through the .460 Weatherby Magnum. It is available with a number of custom options and can be ordered with an 8- to 10-month delivery delay.

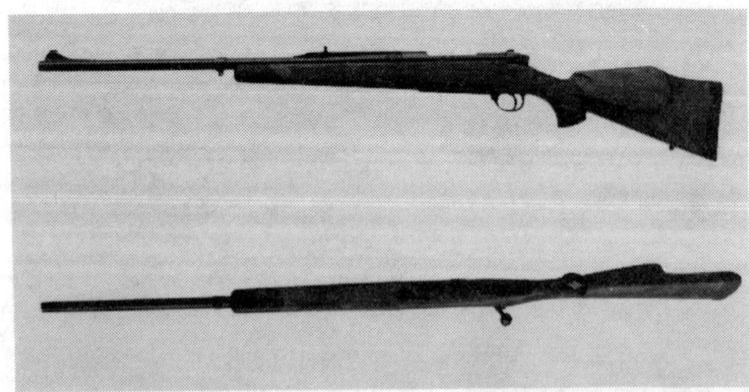

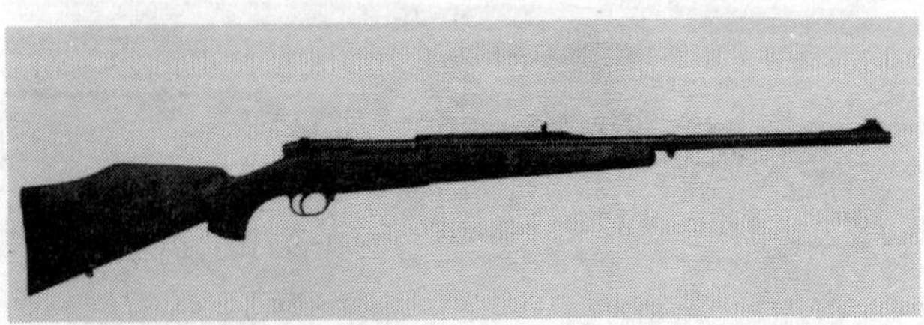

NIB	Exc.	V.G.	Good	Fair	Poor
3000	2750	2000	1200	600	300

Crown Grade Mark V
This is Weatherby's best-grade rifle and is available on a custom-order basis only. It features an engraved receiver and barrel with an exhibition-grade, hand-checkered walnut stock. It is also furnished with an engraved scope mount.

NIB	Exc.	V.G.	Good	Fair	Poor
4500	3500	2750	1500	750	300

.250 Savage Whitetail Deluxe Limited Edition
First introduced in 1993 this model features a select high grade Claro walnut stock with Monte Carlo and raised cheek piece. The contoured barrel is 22" without sights. The bolt and follower are jewelled, the stock is hand checkered with rosewood forend tip and pistol grip cap. The bolt knob is checkered and the floorplate is engraved. A rubber butt pad is standard. The rifle weighs 6 lbs.

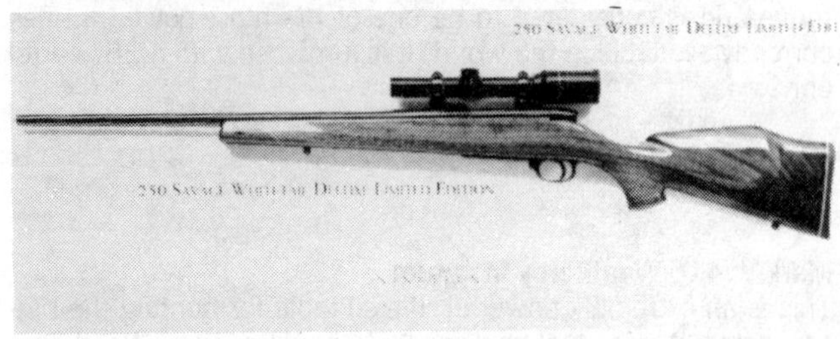

NIB	Exc.	V.G.	Good	Fair	Poor
1100	900	700	600	300	150

Vanguard VGX
This is Weatherby's Japanese-manufactured economy rifle. It is chambered for various popular standard American cartridges from .22-50 to the .300 Winchester Magnum cartridge. It is a bolt-action repeater with a 24" barrel furnished without sights. It has either a 3-shot or 5-shot magazine; and the finish is polished blue, with a select, checkered walnut stock with a rosewood forend tip and pistolgrip cap. This model was discontinued in 1988.

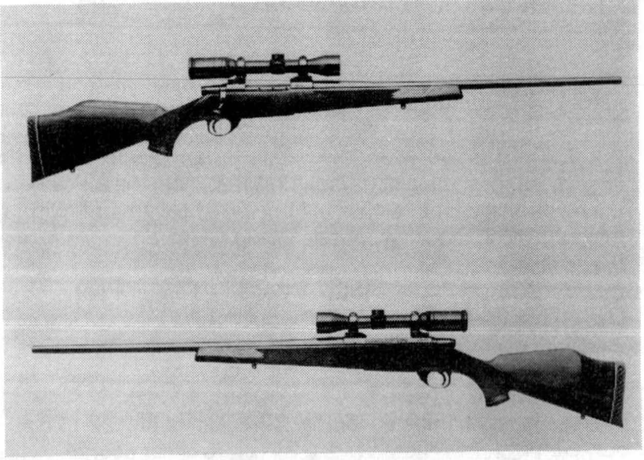

Exc.	V.G.	Good	Fair	Poor
500	400	350	300	250

Vanguard VGS
This satin-finish version was also discontinued in 1988.

Exc.	V.G.	Good	Fair	Poor
450	350	300	250	200

Vanguard VGL
This is a lightweight carbine version that has a 20" barrel. It was

discontinued in 1988.

Exc.	V.G.	Good	Fair	Poor
450	350	300	250	200

Fiberguard

This version has a matte-blued finish with a green fiberglass stock. It was discontinued in 1988.

Exc.	V.G.	Good	Fair	Poor
500	400	350	300	250

Vanguard Classic I

This version is chambered for various popular standard calibers and has a 24" barrel and either a 3- or 5-shot magazine. It has a satin blue finish and a select checkered, oil-finished walnut stock. It was introduced in 1989.

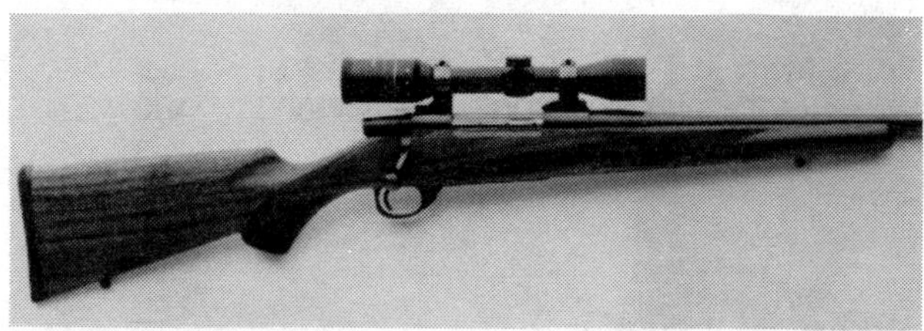

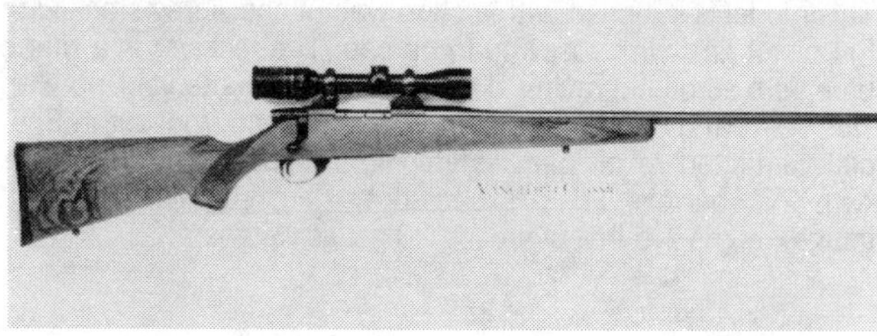

NIB	Exc.	V.G.	Good	Fair	Poor
475	400	375	300	250	200

Vanguard Classic II

This is a more deluxe version with a higher-grade walnut stock.

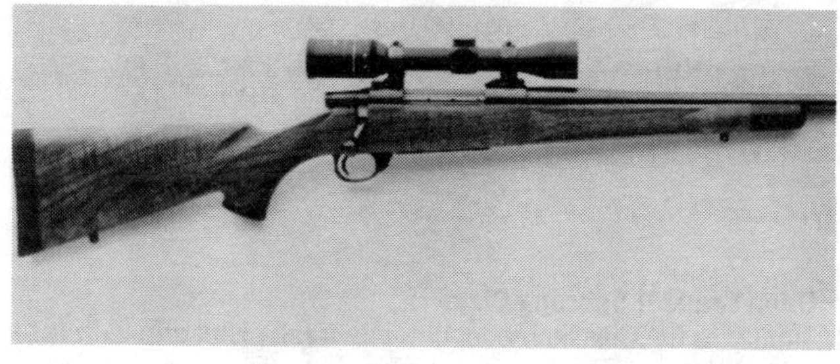

NIB	Exc.	V.G.	Good	Fair	Poor
600	550	475	400	300	250

Vanguard VGX Deluxe

This version has a high-gloss, Monte Carlo-type stock and a high-polished blued finish. It was introduced in 1989.

NIB	Exc.	V.G.	Good	Fair	Poor
600	550	475	400	300	250

Vanguard Weatherguard

This version has a wrinkle-finished, black synthetic stock. It was introduced in 1989.

NIB	Exc.	V.G.	Good	Fair	Poor
400	300	250	200	175	125

Weathermark

Introduced in 1993 this model features a checkered composite stock with matte blue metal finish. Available in Weatherby calibers from .257 through .340 and .270 Win., 7mm Rem. Mag., .30-06, .300 and .338 Win. Mag. Weighs 7.5 lbs.

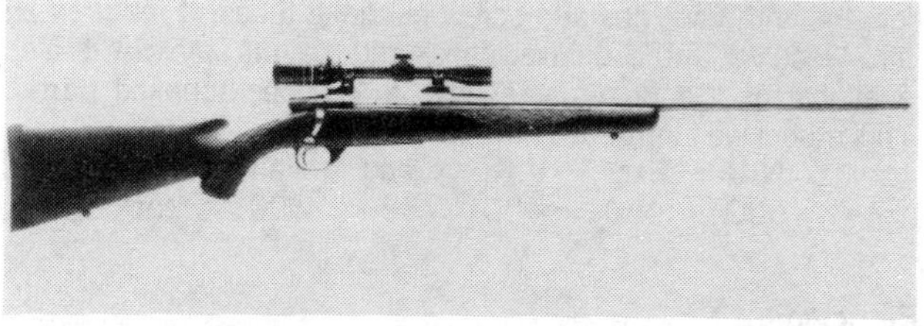

NIB	Exc.	V.G.	Good	Fair	Poor
550	450	350	300	200	150

Weathermark Alaskan

Similar to the Weathermark with checkered composite stock the barreled action is electriless nickel with non-glare finish. Muzzle brake is optional. Available in same calibers as Weathermark. Weighs 7.7 lbs.

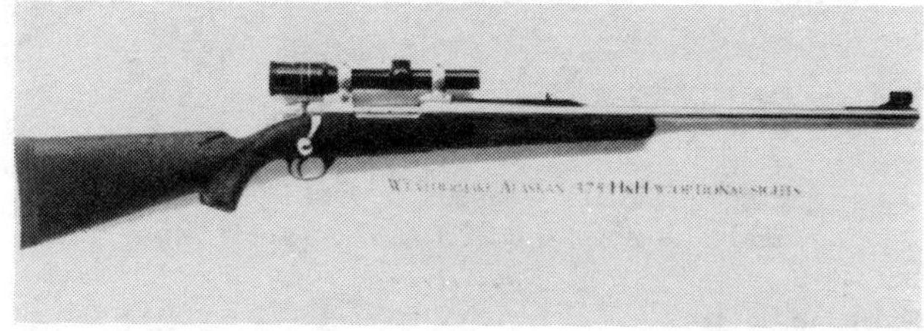

NIB	Exc.	V.G.	Good	Fair	Poor
725	600	500	400	300	150

Mark XXII

This is a semi-automatic rifle chambered for the .22 l.r. cartridge. There are two versions—one with a detachable magazine and the other with a tubular magazine. It has a 24" barrel with adjustable sights and a select checkered walnut stock with a rosewood forearm tip and pistolgrip cap. This model was originally produced in Italy and is currently manufactured in Japan.

NIB	Exc.	V.G.	Good	Fair	Poor
450	350	300	250	200	150

Centurion

This is a gas-operated semi-automatic shotgun chambered for 12 gauge. It is offered with various barrel lengths and chokes. It has a checkered walnut stock. It was manufactured between 1972 and 1981.

Exc.	V.G.	Good	Fair	Poor
350	300	250	200	150

Centurion Deluxe

This version is slightly engraved and features a vent-ribbed barrel and higher-grade wood.

Exc.	V.G.	Good	Fair	Poor
375	325	275	225	175

Model 82

This is a gas-operated semi-automatic shotgun chambered for 12 gauge with 2.75" or 3" chambers. It has various barrel lengths with vent ribs and screw-in choke tubes. It features an alloy receiver and a deluxe, checkered walnut stock. It is also available as the Buckmaster with a 22" open-choked barrel. This model was introduced in 1983.

NIB	Exc.	V.G.	Good	Fair	Poor
500	450	400	350	300	250

Patrician
This is a slide action shotgun chambered for 12 gauge. It is offered with various barrel lengths and choke combinations. It has a vent-rib barrel, a blued finish, and a checkered walnut stock. It was manufactured between 1972 and 1981.

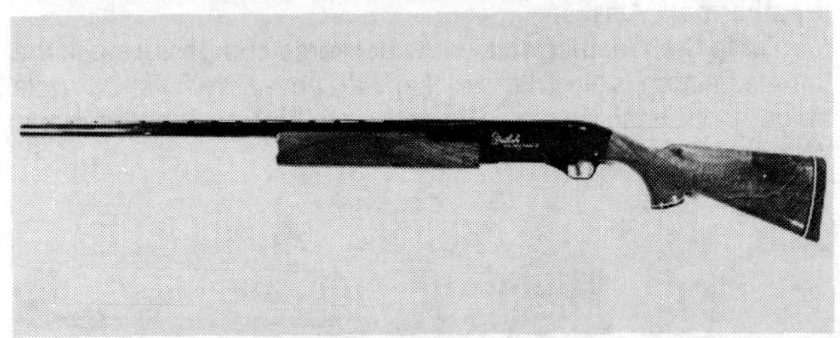

Exc.	V.G.	Good	Fair	Poor
300	250	225	175	125

Patrician Deluxe
This is a slightly engraved version with fancier-grade walnut.

Exc.	V.G.	Good	Fair	Poor
350	300	250	200	150

Model 92
This is a slide action shotgun chambered for 12 gauge with 2.75" or 3" chambers. It is offered with 26", 28", or 30" vent-rib barrels with screw-in choke tubes. It features a short, twin-rail slide action and an engraved alloy receiver. The finish is blued, with a deluxe checkered walnut stock. A Buckmaster model with a 22" open-choke barrel and rifle sights is also available.

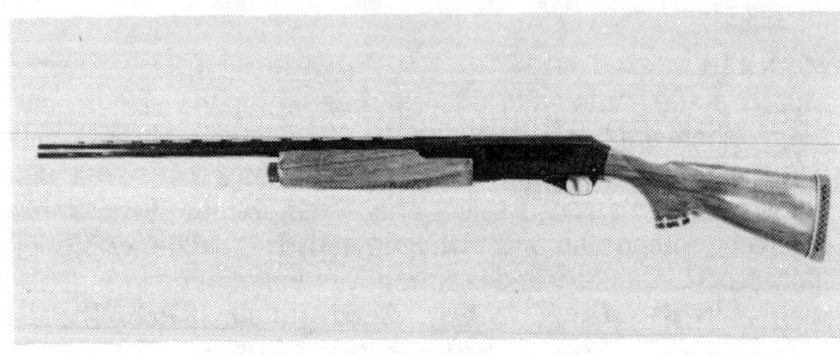

NIB	Exc.	V.G.	Good	Fair	Poor
350	300	250	200	175	125

Regency Field Grade
This is an Over/Under double-barrelled shotgun chambered for 12 or 20 gauge. It has various length vent-ribbed barrels and a boxlock action with engraved false sideplates. It features a single selective trigger and automatic ejectors. The finish is blued, with a checkered walnut stock. This model was imported from Italy between 1972 and 1980. It is also offered as a trap-grade with the same value.

Exc.	V.G.	Good	Fair	Poor
850	750	650	500	400

Olympian
This model is similar to the Regency, with less engraving. It was not imported after 1980. A skeet and a trap model, as well as a field-grade model, were available. The values were similar.

Exc.	V.G.	Good	Fair	Poor
800	700	600	450	400

Orion Grade I
This is an Over/Under double-barrel shotgun chambered for 12 or 20 gauge with 3" chambers. It is offered with 26" or 28" vent-rib barrels with screw-in chokes. It has a single selective trigger and automatic ejectors. The boxlock action features no engraving. The finish is blued, with a checkered walnut stock. It was introduced in 1989.

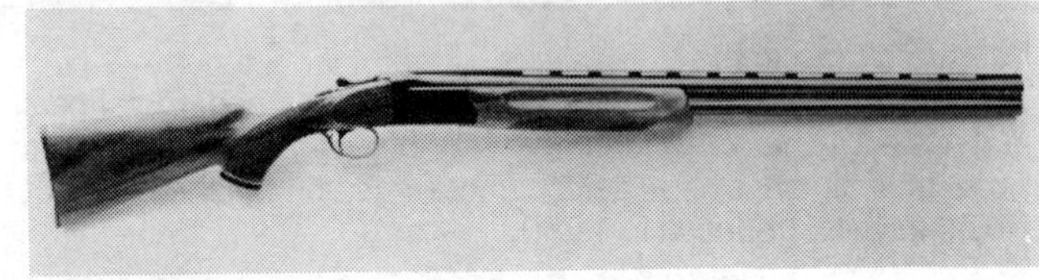

NIB	Exc.	V.G.	Good	Fair	Poor
850	750	700	600	500	400

Orion Grade II Skeet
This model is supplied with a claro walnut checkered stock with full pistol grip with rosewood grip cap. The receiver is a matte blue with scroll engraving. The barrel has a matte vent rib with side vents and mid-point head with white bead front sight. Special ventilated recoil pad. Offered in 12 gauge and 20 gauge with 26" barrels. Fixed skeet chokes are standard. The 12 gauge weighs 7.5 lbs. while the 20 gauge weighs 7.25 lbs.

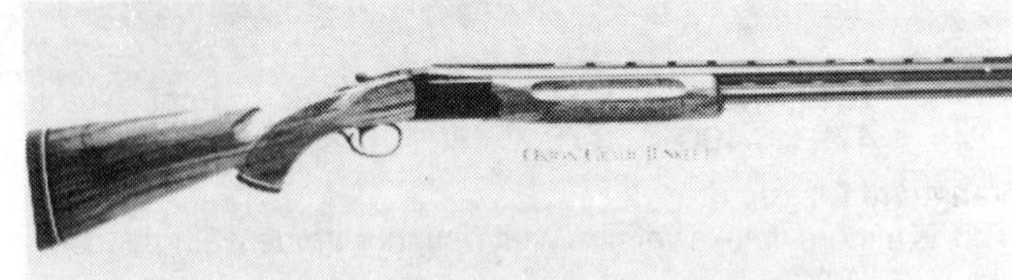

NIB	Exc.	V.G.	Good	Fair	Poor
950	800	700	550	300	150

Orion Grade II Sporting Clays
Similar to the Classic model but with a full pistol grip with rosewood grip cap. The receiver is silver gray with scroll engraving. The claro walnut stock is checkered with a high gloss finish. Offered in 12 gauge with 28" to 30" vent rib barrels. Supplied with 5 screw in choke tubes.

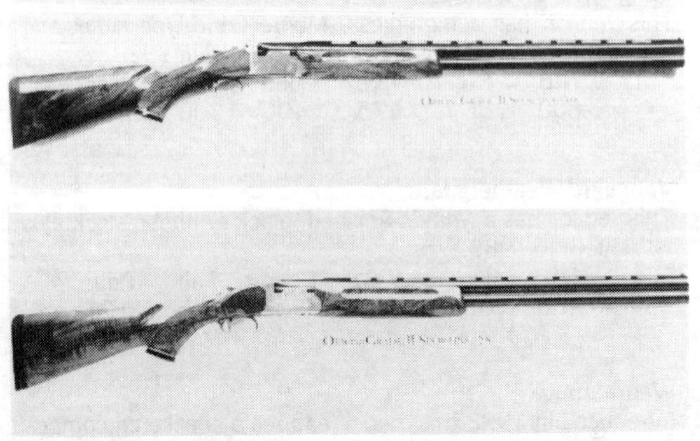

NIB	Exc.	V.G.	Good	Fair	Poor
1000	850	750	600	300	150

Orion Grade II Double Trap

This model featues an integral multi choke tube. The Monte Carlo stock has a rosewood pistol grip cap with diamond shaped inlay. The receiver is blue with scroll engraving. Available with 30" or 32" vent rib barrels. Weighs 8 lbs.

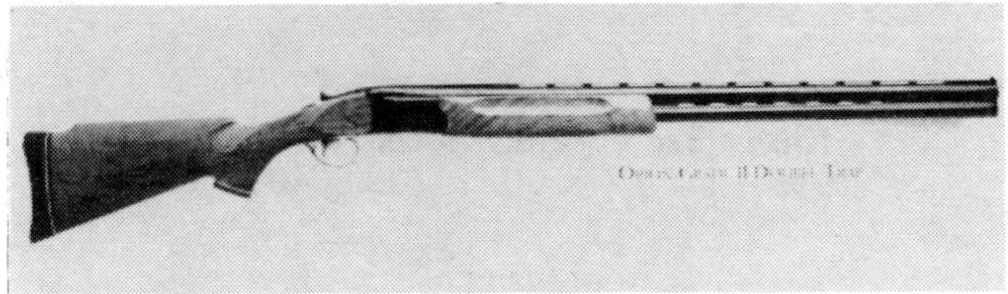

NIB	Exc.	V.G.	Good	Fair	Poor
950	800	700	550	300	150

Orion Grade II Single Trap

Similar to the Double Trap but furnished with a single 32" barrel. Weighs 8 lbs.

NIB	Exc.	V.G.	Good	Fair	Poor
950	800	700	550	300	150

Orion Grade II

This version is lightly engraved and has a high-gloss finish. Otherwise, it is similar to the Grade I.

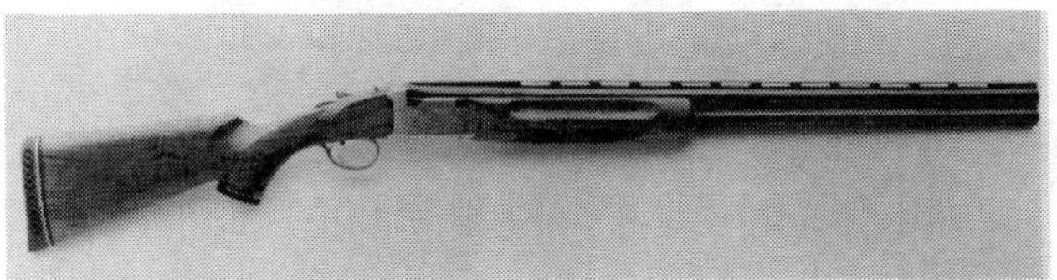

NIB	Exc.	V.G.	Good	Fair	Poor
1000	900	800	650	550	300

Orion Grade II Classic Field

Introduced in 1993 this model features a rounded pistol grip and slim forearm design. The walnut stock is oil finished. The receiver is blued with game scene engraving. A solid recoil pad is standard. Available in 12 gauge, 20 gauge, and 28 gauge with vent rib barrel lengths from 26" to 30" depending on gauge. Screw in choke tubes standard. Weighs 6.5 lbs. to 8 lbs. depending on gauge.

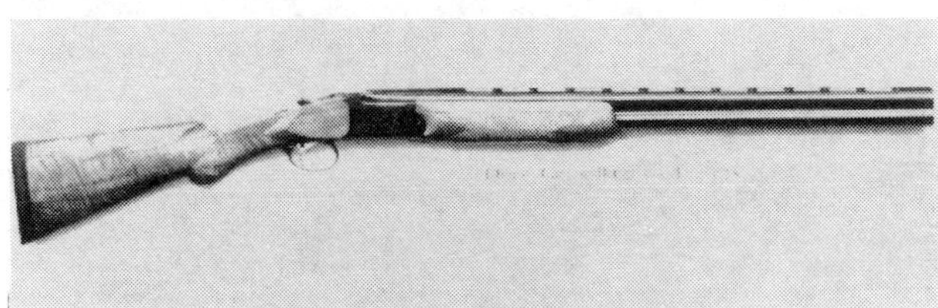

NIB	Exc.	V.G.	Good	Fair	Poor
900	800	700	550	300	150

Orion Grade II Classic Sporting Clays

Introduced in 1993 this model has a rounded pistol grip with slender forearm with an oil finished stock. The receiver is blued with scroll engraving. A stepped competition matte vent rib with additional side vents is supplied. The recoil pad has a special radisus heel. Offered in 12 gauge with 28" barrel. Furnished with 5 screw in choke tubes. Weighs 7.5 lbs.

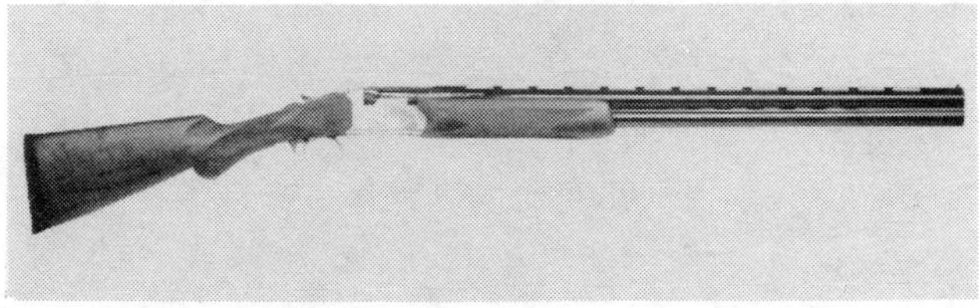

NIB	Exc.	V.G.	Good	Fair	Poor
1000	850	750	600	300	150

Orion Grade III

This version has a gamescene-engraved, coin-finished receiver and higher-grade walnut. It was introduced in 1989.

NIB	Exc.	V.G.	Good	Fair	Poor
1100	1000	900	750	650	350

Orion Grade III Classic Field

New for 1993 this model features a rounded pistol grip and slim forearm with oil finish Claro walnut with fine line checkering. The receiver is silver gray with scroll engraving and gold game bird overlays. Available in 12 gauge with 28" vent rib barrels and 20 gauge with 26" vent rib barrels. Screw in choke tubes standard.

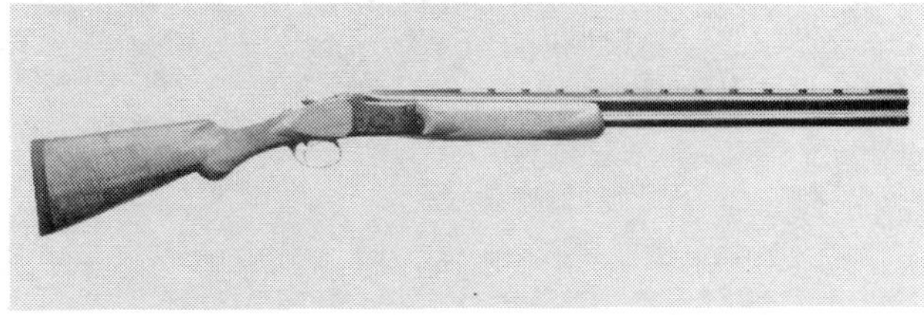

NIB	Exc.	V.G.	Good	Fair	Poor
1100	950	850	650	300	150

Athena Grade IV

This is an Over/Under double-barrel shotgun chambered for 12, 20, and 28 gauge, as well as .410. It has 3" chambers. It is offered with various barrel lengths with vent-ribs and screw-in choke tubes. It has a boxlock action with Greener crossbolt, single selective trigger, and automatic ejectors. It has engraved false sideplates and a satin nickle-plated action. The barrels are blued, with a select checkered walnut stock. This model was introduced in 1989.

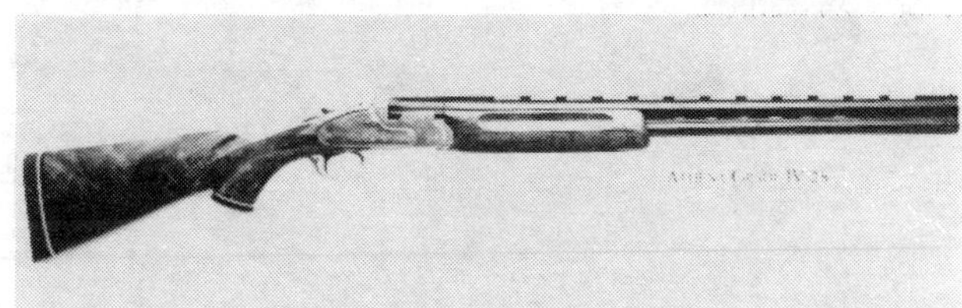

NIB	Exc.	V.G.	Good	Fair	Poor
2000	1750	1500	1200	950	750

Competition Model Athena

This is either a trap or skeet version with stock dimensions designed for either skeet or trap and competition-type ribs.

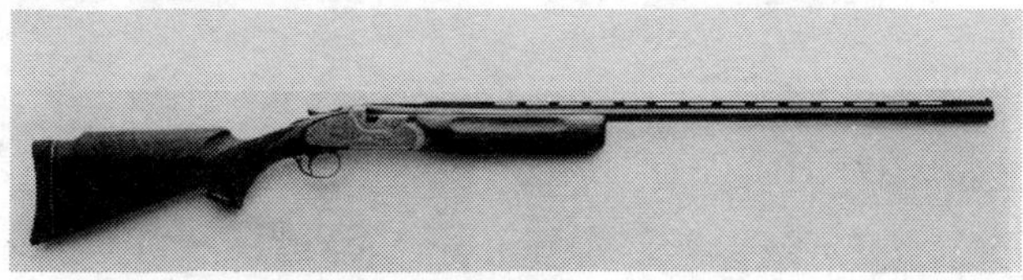

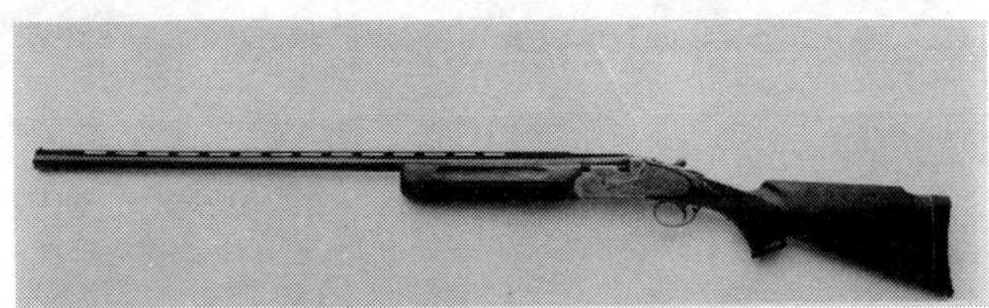

NIB	Exc.	V.G.	Good	Fair	Poor
1650	1400	1150	1000	600	300

Athena Grade V Classic Field

Introduced in 1993 this model features a rounded pistol grip with slender forearm. The high grade Claro walnut stock is oil finished with fine line checkering. The receiver has a side plate that is silver gray with rose and scroll engraving. The vent rib barrels also have side vents. A solid recoil is supplied. Offered in

12 gauge with 26", 28", or 30" barrels and 20 gauge with 26" and 28" barrels. Choke tubes are standard.

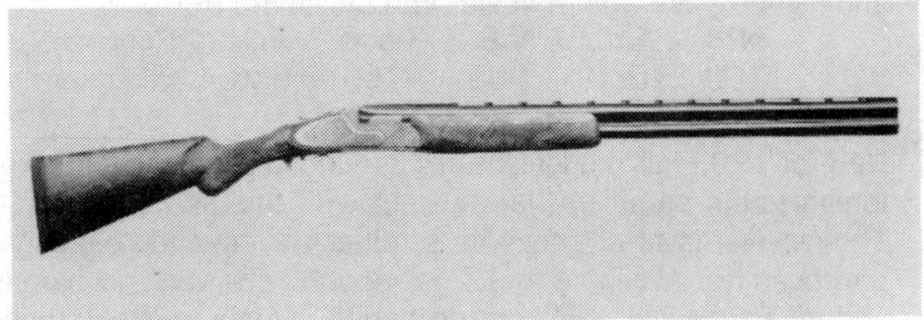

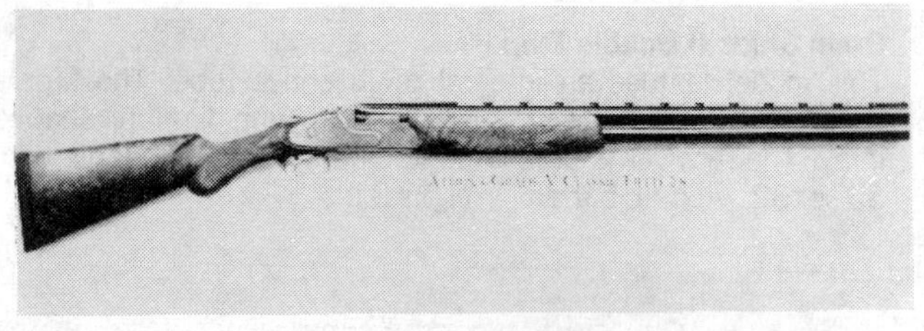

NIB	Exc.	V.G.	Good	Fair	Poor
1950	1750	1100	700	400	200

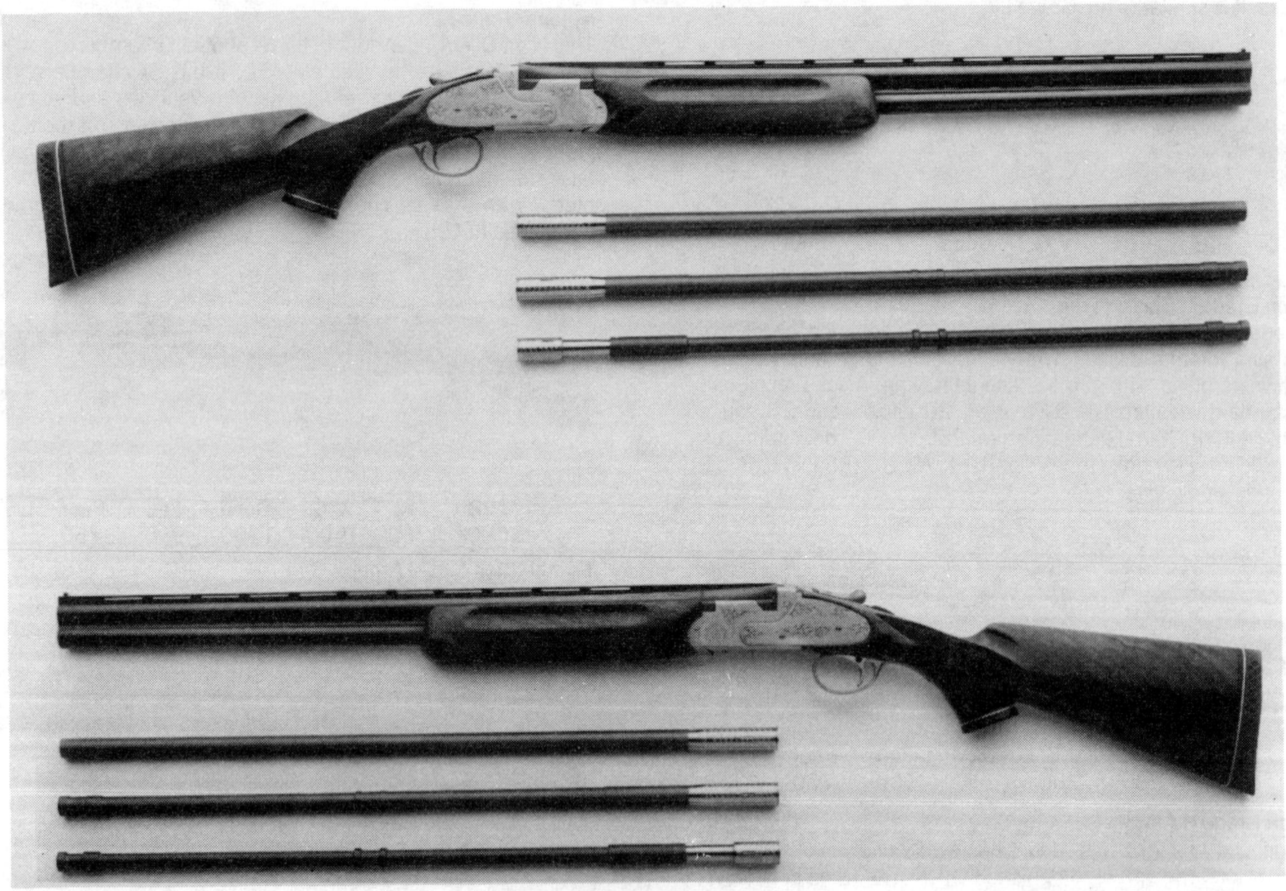

Weatherby Athena Master skeet tube set, 12 ga. 28'' skeet shotgun, plus two each 20, 28 and .410 ga. fitted, full length Briley tubes with integral extractors. Packed in custom fitted aluminum case (not shown).

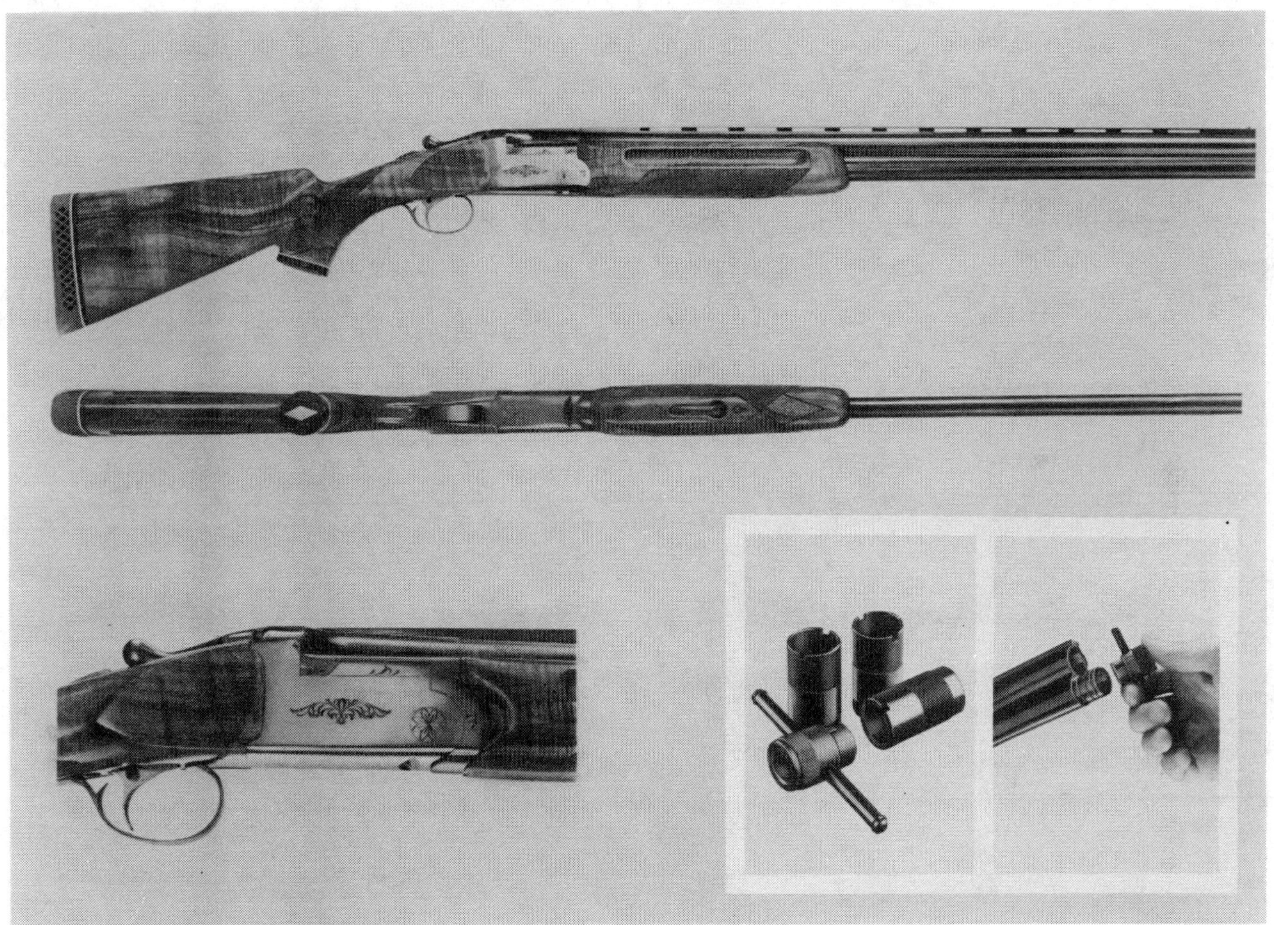

Weatherby Athena O/U Shotgun, IMC - Integral "Multi-choke" ⓣ flush-fitting interchangeable choke tubes.

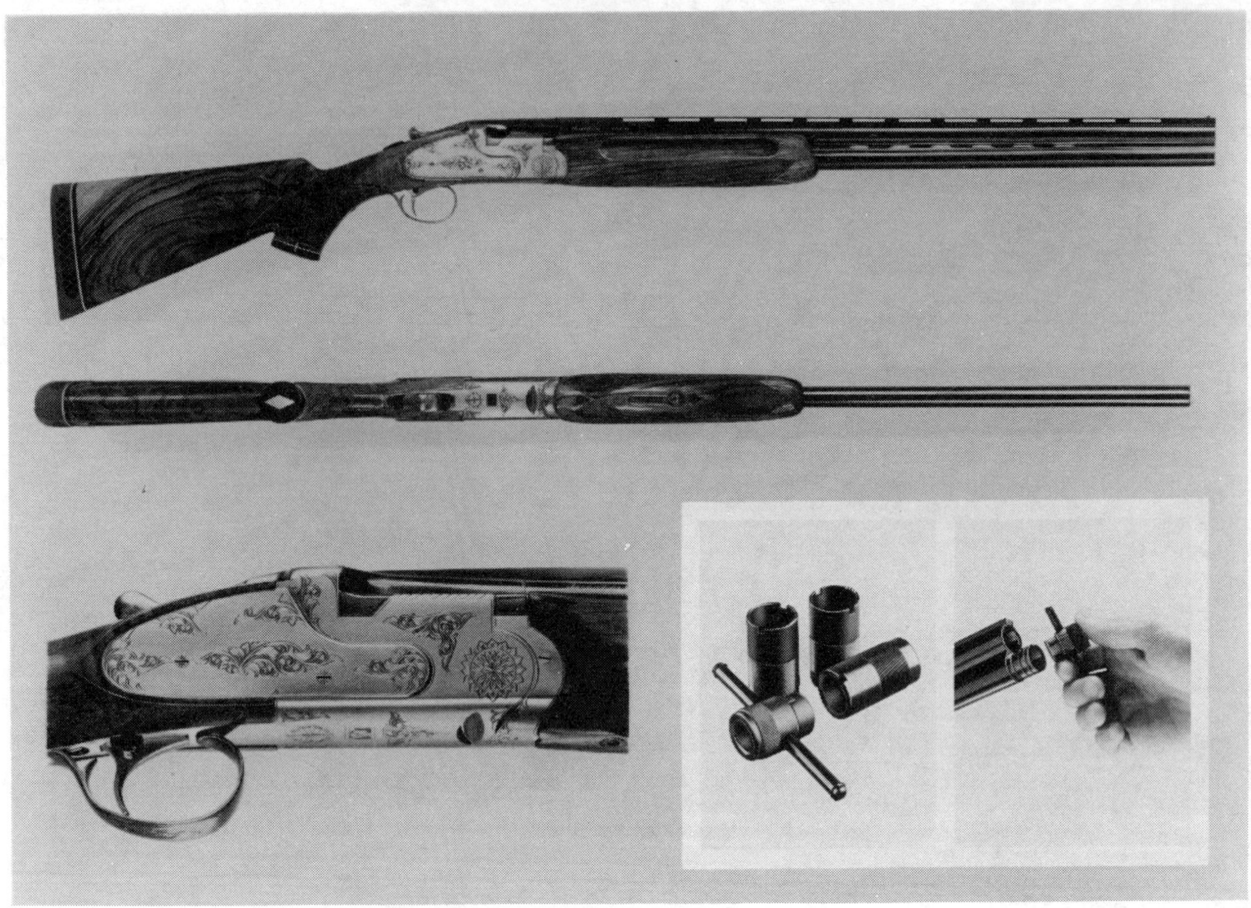

Weatherby Orion O/U Shotgun, IMC - Integral "Multi-choke" ® flush-fitting interchangeable choke tubes.

WEAVER ARMS
Escondido, California

Nighthawk Assault Pistol

A 9mm semi-automatic pistol with a 10" or 12" barrel, alloy receiver and ambidextrous safety. Blackened with plastic grips. Introduced in 1987.

Exc.	V.G.	Good	Fair	Poor
450	400	350	300	250

Nighthawk Carbine

As above, with a 16.1" barrel, retractable shoulder stock, 25-, 32-, 40- or 50-shot magazine. Introduced in 1984.

Exc.	V.G.	Good	Fair	Poor
550	500	450	400	350

WEBLEY & SCOTT, LTD.
Birmingham, England
Importer—New England Arms Co.
Kittery Point, Maine

Established in 1860, this firm has produced a wide variety of firearms over the years and has been known as Webley & Scott, Ltd. since 1906.

Model 1872 Royal Irish Constabulary

A .450 double-action revolver with a 3.25" barrel, 5-shot cylinder and rotating ejector. This model was also offered with 2.5" and 3.5" barrels. Blued with checkered walnut grips.

Exc.	V.G.	Good	Fair	Poor
350	300	250	200	150

Model 1880 Metropolitan Police

As above, with a 2.5" barrel and 6-shot cylinder.

Exc.	V.G.	Good	Fair	Poor
350	300	250	200	150

Model 1880 James Hill Revolver

As above, but chambered for the .430 Eley cartridge.

Exc.	V.G.	Good	Fair	Poor
350	300	250	200	150

New Model 1883 R.I.C.

Similar to the Model 1880, but in .455 caliber with a 4.5" barrel. Also made with a 2.5" barrel.

Exc.	V.G.	Good	Fair	Poor
250	200	175	125	100

Model 1884 R.I.C. Naval

As above, with a brass frame and oxidized finish. Barrel length 2.75" and of octagonal form.

Exc.	V.G.	Good	Fair	Poor
300	250	225	175	125

British Bulldog

Similar to the new Model 1883 R.I.C. blued, checkered walnut grips. Those engraved on the back strap "W.R.A. Co." were sold through the Winchester Repeating Arms Company's New York sales agency and are worth a considerable premium over the values listed below. Manufactured from 1878 to 1914.

Exc.	V.G.	Good	Fair	Poor
350	300	250	200	150

Model 1878 Army Express Revolver

A .455 caliber double-action revolver with a 6" barrel and integral ejector. Blued with one piece walnut grips.

Exc.	V.G.	Good	Fair	Poor
375	325	275	225	175

Webley Kaufmann Model 1880

A top-break, hinged-frame double-action revolver chambered for the .450 centerfire cartridge, with a 5.75" barrel and a curved birdshead butt. Blued, with walnut grips.

Exc.	V.G.	Good	Fair	Poor
475	425	350	275	200

Webley-Green Model

A double-action, top-break revolver chambered for the .455 cartridge, with a 6" ribbed barrel and a 6-shot cylinder. The cylinder flutes on this model are angular and not rounded in shape. Blued, with checkered walnut, squared-butt grips with a lanyard ring on the butt. Introduced in 1882 and manufactured until 1896.

Exc.	V.G.	Good	Fair	Poor
475	425	350	275	200

Mark I

A .442, .455 or .476 double-action top break revolver with a 4" barrel and 6-shot cylinder. Blued with checkered walnut grips. Manufactured from 1887 to 1894.

Exc.	V.G.	Good	Fair	Poor
250	200	175	125	100

Mark II

As above, with a larger hammer spur and improved barrel catch. Manufactured from 1894 to 1897.

Exc.	V.G.	Good	Fair	Poor
250	200	175	125	100

Mark III

As above, with internal improvements. Introduced in 1897.

Exc.	V.G.	Good	Fair	Poor
275	225	200	150	125

Mark IV

As above, with a .455 caliber 3", 4", 5" or 6" barrel.

Exc.	V.G.	Good	Fair	Poor
250	200	175	125	100

Mark V

As above, with a 4" barrel. Manufactured from 1913 to 1915.

Exc.	V.G.	Good	Fair	Poor
275	225	200	150	125

Mark VI

As above, with a 4" or 6" barrel and modified grip.

Courtesy Wallis & Wallis, Lewes, Sussex, England.

Exc.	V.G.	Good	Fair	Poor
350	300	250	175	125

Mark VI .22 Rimfire

A standard-size Mark V chambered for the .22 rimfire cartridge used as a training pistol. Manufactured in 1918 and quite scarce.

Exc.	V.G.	Good	Fair	Poor
475	425	350	250	200

Webley-Fosbery Automatic Revolver

A semi-automatic .38 or .455 caliber 6-shot revolver. An 8-shot variation is known and would command approximately a 100% premium over the values listed below. Blued with checkered walnut grips. Manufactured from 1901 to 1939.

Exc.	V.G.	Good	Fair	Poor
700	550	500	350	275

Model 1904

A .455 caliber semi-automatic pistol with a 5" barrel and 7-shot magazine. Blued with walnut grips. Manufactured from 1912 to 1939.

Exc.	V.G.	Good	Fair	Poor
750	650	500	400	300

Model 1906

A .32 or .380 semi-automatic pistol with a 3.5" barrel and 8-shot magazine. Blued with checkered plastic grips. Manufactured from 1906 to 1939.

Exc.	V.G.	Good	Fair	Poor
250	225	200	150	100

Model 1906 .25

As above, in .25 caliber with a 2" barrel and 6-shot magazine.

Exc.	V.G.	Good	Fair	Poor
200	175	150	100	75

Model 1909

As above, with an enclosed hammer.

Exc.	V.G.	Good	Fair	Poor
250	225	200	150	100

Model 1909 9mm

As above, in 9mm Browning caliber with a 5" barrel and external hammer. Manufactured from 1909 to 1930.

Exc.	V.G.	Good	Fair	Poor
450	400	350	275	200

Model 1912 Self-Loader

Similar to the Model 1904.

Exc.	V.G.	Good	Fair	Poor
450	400	350	275	200

Model 1915 Self-Loader

As above, with a special rear sight designed for targeting moving objects at ranges up to 200 yards. Adopted by the Royal Flying Corps in 1914. Discontinued in 1960.

Exc.	V.G.	Good	Fair	Poor
750	650	500	400	300

Model 1911 Target Pistol

A .22 caliber single shot pistol with a 4.5" or 9" barrel resembling a semi-automatic pistol.

Exc.	V.G.	Good	Fair	Poor
400	350	300	200	150

Model 700

A boxlock 12 or 20 gauge double-barrel shotgun available with either a single or double trigger. Blued, case-hardened with checkered walnut stock.

Exc.	V.G.	Good	Fair	Poor
1750	1500	1250	850	600

Model 702

As above, but more finely finished.

Exc.	V.G.	Good	Fair	Poor
2750	2500	2000	1500	1000

Model 701

As above, but heavily engraved with a finely figured, checkered walnut stock.

Exc.	V.G.	Good	Fair	Poor
3200	2750	2250	1750	1250

WEIHRAUCH, HANS HERMANN

Melrichstadt, West Germany
Importers—Beeman Precision Arms, Inc.
Santa Rosa, California
Helmut Hoffman
Placitas, New Mexico

Model HW 60M

A .22 caliber single shot bolt-action rifle with a 26.75" barrel and adjustable sights. Blued with a walnut stock.

NIB	Exc.	V.G.	Good	Fair	Poor
700	650	550	400	350	250

Model HW 66

A .22 Hornet or .222 Remington bolt-action rifle with a stainless steel 26" barrel and single or double set triggers. Blued with a walnut stock.

NIB	Exc.	V.G.	Good	Fair	Poor
600	550	500	350	300	200

Model HW-3

A double-action, solid-frame, swing-out cylinder revolver chambered for .22 l.r. or .32 Smith & Wesson long cartridges with a barrel length is 2.75", and a cylinder holding either seven or eight cartridges. Blued, with walnut grips. In America this revolver was known as the Dickson Bulldog. In Europe it was known as the Gecado.

Exc.	V.G.	Good	Fair	Poor
75	50	40	35	25

Model HW-5

As above, with a 4" barrel. Sold in the United States under the tradename "Omega".

Exc.	V.G.	Good	Fair	Poor
75	50	40	35	25

Model HW-7

As above, in .22 caliber with a 6" barrel and 8-shot cylinder. Sold in the United States as the "Herter's Guide Model". Also available with target sights and thumbrest grips as the Model HW-7S.

Exc.	V.G.	Good	Fair	Poor
75	50	40	35	25

Model HW-9

Similar to the HW-7, with a 6-shot cylinder and 6" ventilated-rib barrel fitted with target sights and target grips.

Exc.	V.G.	Good	Fair	Poor
75	50	40	35	25

These pistols all carry the Arminius trademark, a bearded head wearing a winged helmet. The model number will be found on the cylinder crane; the caliber, on the barrel; and the words "Made in Germany," on the frame.

WEISBURGER, A.
Memphis, Tennessee

Pocket Pistol

A .41 caliber percussion single shot pocket pistol with 2.5" barrel, German silver furniture and a walnut stock. Manufactured during the 1850s.

Exc.	V.G.	Good	Fair	Poor
750	650	500	400	300

WESSON, DAN ARMS
SEE—Wesson Firearms Co., Inc.

WESSON FIREARMS CO., INC.
Palmer, Massachusettes

The company was founded in 1968 by Daniel B. Wesson, the great grandson of D.B. Wesson, co-founder of Smith & Wesson. This line of handguns is unique for its barrel/shroud interchangeability. Dan Wesson revolvers have established themselves as champion metallic silhouette competition guns. The company offers a comprehensive line of handguns for almost every use. The company will also custom build a handgun to customer specifications. Dan Wesson Arms was re-structured on January 4, 1991 and is now identified as Wesson Firearms Co., Inc.. Wesson handguns made after this date will be stamped with this new corporate name.

Model 11

A .357 Magnum caliber double-action swing-out cylinder revolver with interchangeable 2.5", 4" or 6" barrels and a 6-shot cylinder. Blued with walnut grips. Manufactured in 1970 and 1971.

Extra Barrels—Add 25% per barrel.

Exc.	V.G.	Good	Fair	Poor
200	175	150	125	100

Model 12

As above, with adjustable target sights.

Exc.	V.G.	Good	Fair	Poor
250	225	200	175	125

Model 14

As above, with a recessed barrel locking nut and furnished with a spanner wrench. Manufactured from 1971 to 1975.

Exc.	V.G.	Good	Fair	Poor
225	200	175	150	100

Model 15

As above, with adjustable target sights.

Exc.	V.G.	Good	Fair	Poor
250	225	200	175	125

Model 8

As above, in .38 Special caliber.

Exc.	V.G.	Good	Fair	Poor
200	175	150	125	100

Model 9

As the Model 15, with adjustable sights and in .38 Special caliber. Manufactured from 1971 to 1975.

Exc.	V.G.	Good	Fair	Poor
250	225	200	175	125

.22 CALIBER REVOLVERS

Model 22

This is a double action target revolver chambered for the .22 Long Rifle cartridge. It is available in 2", 4", 6", and 8" barrel length with a choice of standard rib shroud, ventilated rib shroud, or ventilated heavy rib shroud. All variations feature an adjustable rear sight, red ramp interchangeable front sight and target grips. Offered in bright blue or stainless steel finish. For revolvers with standard barrel assembly weights are: 2"-36 oz., 4"-40 oz., 6"-44 oz., and 8"-49 oz.

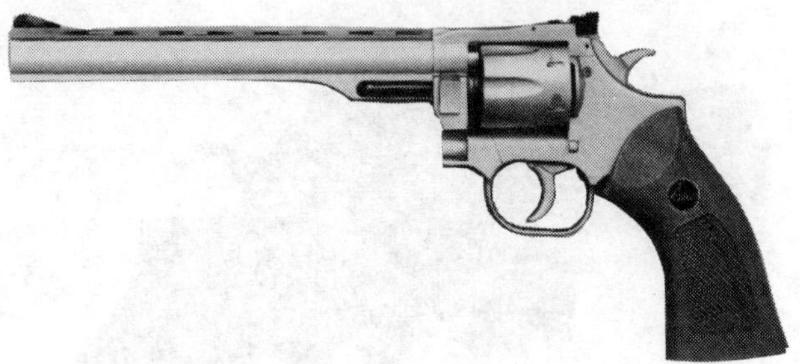

Model 722

Same as above but with stainless steel finish.

Model 22M

Same as above but chambered for .22 Magnum with blue finish.

Model 722M

Same as above but chambered for .22 Magnum with stainless steel finish.

Standard Rib Shroud

NIB	Exc.	V.G.	Good	Fair	Poor
280	250	200	150	100	75

Ventilated Rib Shroud

NIB	Exc.	V.G.	Good	Fair	Poor
300	275	225	150	100	75

Ventilated Heavy Rib Shroud

NIB	Exc.	V.G.	Good	Fair	Poor
330	280	240	200	125	100

NOTE: Add 10% to above prices for stainless steel finish.

P22 Pistol Pac

This model is also a target revolver similar to the Model 22 and its variations. Chambered for the .22 Long Rifle or .22 Magnum it is also offered with three types of barrel shrouds: standard , ventilated, or ventilated heavy. It is available in blue or stainless steel finish. The principal feature of the Pistol Pac is the 3 barrel assemblies in 2.5", 4", 6", and 8" with extra grips, 4 additional front sights, and a fitted carrying case.

Standard Rib Shroud

NIB	Exc.	V.G.	Good	Fair	Poor
500	450	400	350	300	150

Ventilated Rib Shroud

NIB	Exc.	V.G.	Good	Fair	Poor
600	550	500	450	350	150

Ventilated Heavy Rib Shroud

NIB	Exc.	V.G.	Good	Fair	Poor
650	600	550	475	350	150

NOTE: Add 10% to above prices for stainless steel finish.

HP22 Hunter Pac

This model is chambered for the .22 Magnum cartridge. The set includes a ventilated heavy 8" shroud, a ventilated 8" shroud only with Burris scope mounts and Burris scope in either 1.5x4X variable or fixed 2X, a barrel changing tool, and fitted carrying case. Finish is blue or stainless steel.

NOTE: Hunter Pac's are a special order item and should be evaluated at the time of sale.

.32 CALIBER REVOLVERS

Model 32

This model is a target revolver chambered for the .32 H&R Magnum cartridge. It is offered in 2", 4", 6", or 8" barrel lengths with choice of rib shrouds. All variations are fitted with adjustable rear sight, red ramp interchangeable front sight, and target grips. Available in blue or stainless steel finish. Weights depend on barrel length and shroud type but are between 35 oz. and 53 oz.

Model 732

Same as above but with stainless steel finish.

Model 322

Same as above but chambered for .32-20 cartridge with blue finish.

Model 7322

Same as above but chambered for .32-20 cartridge with stainless steel finish.

Standard Rib Shroud

NIB	Exc.	V.G.	Good	Fair	Poor
275	225	200	150	100	75

Ventilated Rib Shroud

NIB	Exc.	V.G.	Good	Fair	Poor
300	250	225	150	100	75

Ventilated Heavy Rib Shroud

NIB	Exc.	V.G.	Good	Fair	Poor
325	275	250	150	100	75

NOTE: Add 10% to above prices for stainless steel finish.

P32 Pistol Pac

This set offers the same calibers, barrel shrouds, and finishes as the above models but in a set consisting of 2", 4", 6", and 8" barrels with extra grips, 4 additional sights, and fitted case.

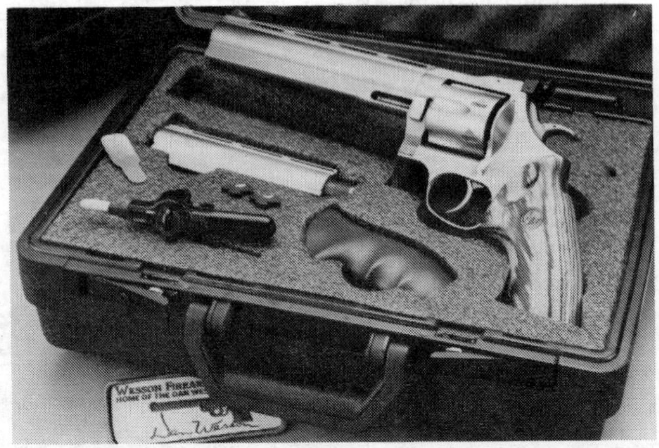

Standard Rib Shroud

NIB	Exc.	V.G.	Good	Fair	Poor
500	450	400	300	150	100

Ventilated Rib Shroud

NIB	Exc.	V.G.	Good	Fair	Poor
575	500	450	325	150	100

Ventilated Heavy Rib Shroud

NIB	Exc.	V.G.	Good	Fair	Poor
650	600	500	400	200	125

NOTE: Add 10% to above prices for stainless steel finish.

HP32 Hunter Pac

This model is chambered for the .32 H&R Magnum or .32-20 cartridge. The set includes a ventilated heavy 8" shroud, a ventilated 8" shroud only with Burris scope mounts and Burris scope in either 1.5x4X variable or fixed 2X, a barrel changing tool, and fitted carrying case. Finish is blue or stainless steel.

NOTE: Hunter Pac's are a special order item and should be evaluated at the time of sale.

.357 MAGNUM AND .38 CALIBER REVOLVERS

Model 14

This is a double action service revolver chambered for the .357 Magnum cartridge. Available with 2", 4", or 6" barrel with service shroud. It has fixed sights, service grip, and is offered in blue or stainless steel finish.

Model 714

Same as above but with stainless steel finish.

Model 8

Same as above but chambered for .38 Special cartridge with blue finish.

Model 708

Same as above but chambered for .38 Special with stainless steel finish.

NIB	Exc.	V.G.	Good	Fair	Poor
225	175	150	125	100	75

NOTE: Add 10% to above prices for stainless steel finish.

P14/8 Pistol Pac

This set consist of a 2", 4", and 6" barrel with service shroud and fixed sights. It has an extra grip and fitted carrying case. The P14 is chambered for the .357 Mag. and the P8 is chambered for the .38 Special.

NIB	Exc.	V.G.	Good	Fair	Poor
375	300	250	200	150	100

NOTE: Add 10% to above prices for stainless steel finish.

Model 15

This model is designed as a double action target revolver chambered for the .357 Magnum cartridge. It is available with 2", 4", 6", 8", and 10" barrels lengths with standard rib shroud. It features adjustable rear sight, red ramp interchangeable front sight, and target grips. Offered with blue finish. Weights according to barrel length are: 2"-32 oz., 4"-36 oz., 6"-40 oz., 8"-44 oz., 10"-50 oz.

Model 715

Same as above but with stainless steel finish.

Model 9

Same as above but chambered for .38 Special cartridge with blue finish.

Model 709

Same as above but with stainless steel finish.

Standard Rib Shroud

NIB	Exc.	V.G.	Good	Fair	Poor
275	225	200	150	100	75

Ventilated Rib Shroud

NIB	Exc.	V.G.	Good	Fair	Poor
300	250	225	150	100	75

Ventilated Heavy Rib Shroud

NIB	Exc.	V.G.	Good	Fair	Poor
325	275	250	150	100	75

NOTE: Add 10% to above prices for stainless steel finish.

P15/9 Pistol Pac

This model is a set with 2", 4", 6", and 8" barrels with standard rib shroud. Chambered for the .357 or .38 Special with standard rib shroud, 4 additional sights, and extra grip, and carrying case. The P15 is chambered for the .357 Mag. while the P9 is chambered for the .38 Special.

Standard Rib Shroud

NIB	Exc.	V.G.	Good	Fair	Poor
500	450	400	350	150	100

Ventilated Rib Shroud

NIB	Exc.	V.G.	Good	Fair	Poor
575	500	450	350	150	100

Ventilated Heavy Rib Shroud

NIB	Exc.	V.G.	Good	Fair	Poor
650	575	500	400	200	100

NOTE: Add 10% to above prices for stainless steel finish.

HP 15 Hunter Pac

This model is chambered for the .357 Magnum cartridge. The set includes a ventilated heavy 8" shroud, a ventilated 8" shroud only with Burris scope mounts and Burris scope in either 1.5x4X variable or fixed 2X, a barrel changing tool, and fitted carrying case. Finish is blue or stainless steel.

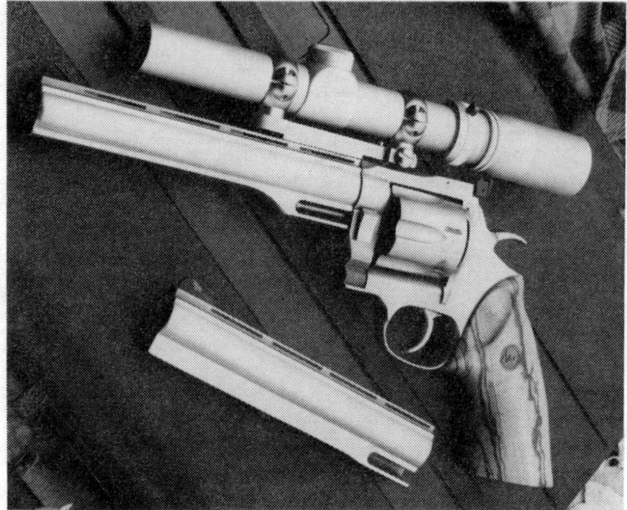

NOTE: Hunter Pac's are a special order item and should be evaluated at the time of sale.

Model 40/Supermag

This model is a target revolver chambered for the .357 Maximum cartridge. It has an adjustable rear sight, red ramp interchangeable front sight, ventilated rib shroud, and target grip. Barrel lengths are 4", 6', 8', or 10". A ventilated slotted shroud is available in 8" only. for 1993 a compensated barrel assembly, "CBA", as been added to the product line as a complete gun. Finish is blue. Weighs approximately 64 oz with ventilated rib shroud barrel.

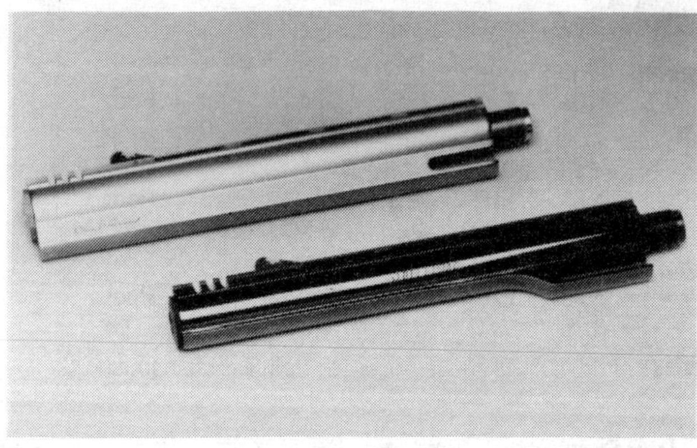

Model 740

Same as above but with stainless steel finish.

Ventilated Rib Shroud

NIB	Exc.	V.G.	Good	Fair	Poor
400	350	300	250	200	100

Ventilated Slotted Shroud-8" barrel only

NIB	Exc.	V.G.	Good	Fair	Poor
450	400	350	300	200	100

Ventilated Heavy Rib Shroud

NIB	Exc.	V.G.	Good	Fair	Poor
475	425	375	300	200	100

NOTE: Add 10% to above prices for stainless steel finish.

NOTE: For .357 Supermag with compensated barrel assembly add $30.

HP40 Hunter Pac

This model is chambered for the .357 Supermag cartridge. The set includes a ventilated heavy 8" shroud, a ventilated 8" shroud only with Burris scope mounts and Burris scope in either 1.5x4X variable or fixed 2X, a barrel changing tool, and fitted carrying case. Finish is blue or stainless steel.

NOTE: Hunter Pacs are a special order item and should be evaluated at the time of sale.

Model 375

This model, also known as the .375 Supermag, is chambered for the .357 Maximum cartridge, based on the .375 Winchester cartridge. Offered in 6", 8", 10" barrels in ventilated, ventilated heavy, or ventilated slotted rib barrels. Sights are interchangeable and adjustable. Available in bright blue finish only. Weighs approximately 64 oz. with ventilated rib shroud barrel.

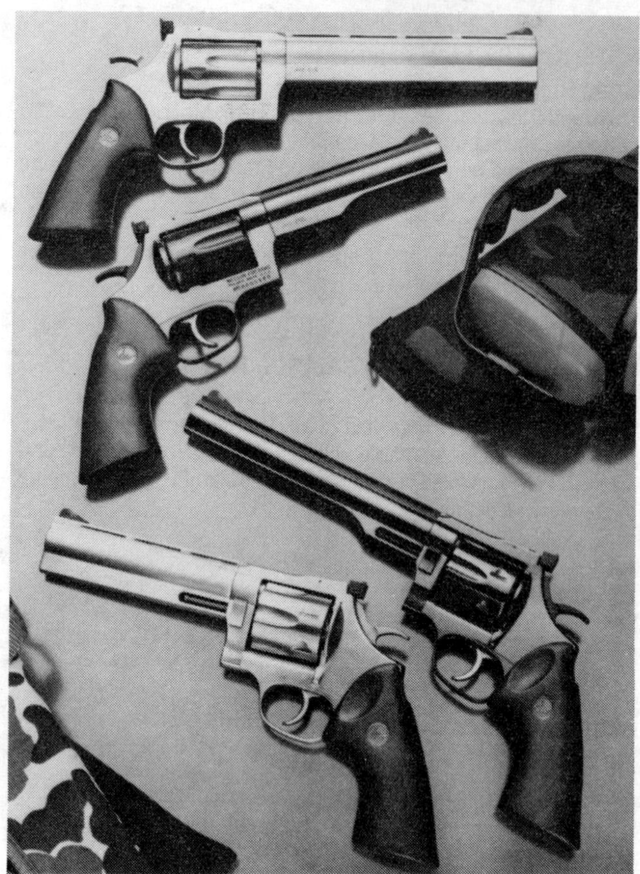

Ventilated Rib Shroud

NIB	Exc.	V.G.	Good	Fair	Poor
400	350	300	250	200	100

Ventilated Heavy Rib Shroud

NIB	Exc.	V.G.	Good	Fair	Poor
450	400	350	300	200	100

Ventilated Slotted Shroud-8" barrel only

NIB	Exc.	V.G.	Good	Fair	Poor
475	425	375	300	200	100

HP375 Hunter Pac

This model is chambered for the .375 Supermag cartridge. The set includes a ventilated heavy 8" shroud, a ventilated 8" shroud only with Burris scope mounts and Burris scope in either 1.5x4X variable or fixed 2X, a barrel changing tool, and fitted carrying case. Finish is blue or stainless steel.

NOTE: Hunter Pac's are a special order item and should be evaluated at the time of sale.

.41, .44 MAGNUM, AND 45 LONG COLT REVOLVERS

Model 44

This model is a target double action revolver chambered for the .44 Magnum. It has 4", 6", 8", or 10" barrels with ventilated rib shrouds. Other features include: adjustable rear sight, red ramp interchangeable front sight, and target grips. Finish is bright blue. Weights with 4" barrel-40 oz., 6"-56 oz., 8"-64 oz., and 10"-69 oz.

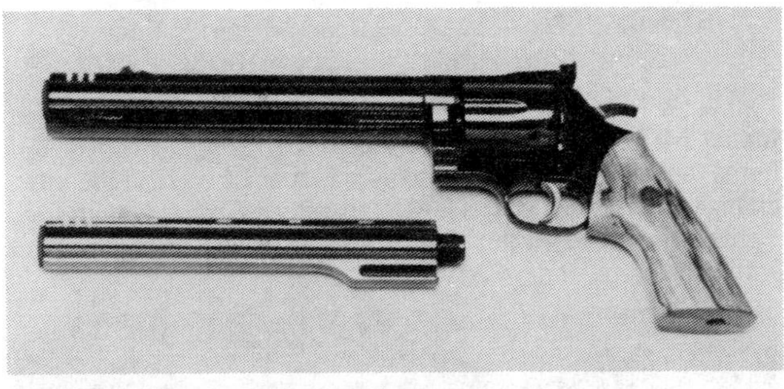

Model 744
Same as above but with stainless steel finish.

Model 41
Same as above but chambered for .41 Magnum with blue finish.

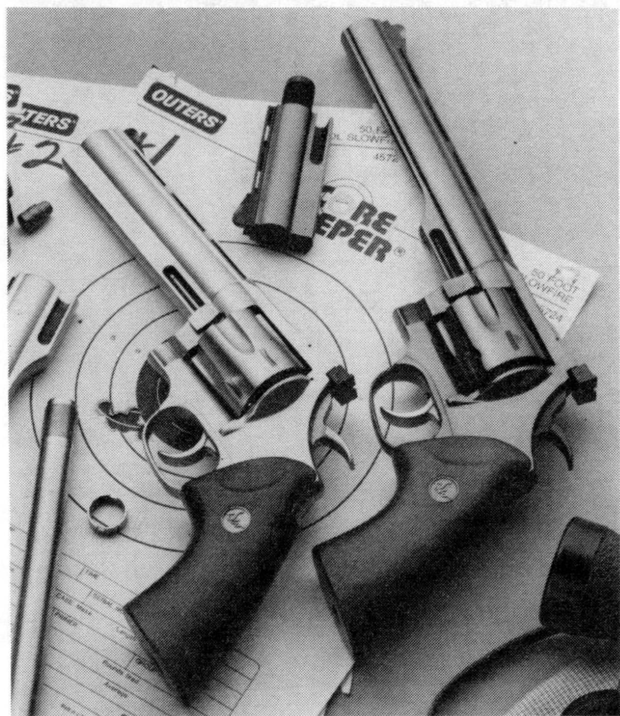

Model 741
Same as above but with stainless steel finish.

Model 45
Same as above but chambered for .45 Long Colt with bright blue finish.

Model 745
Same as above but with stainless steel finish.

Ventilated Rib Shroud

NIB	Exc.	V.G.	Good	Fair	Poor
350	300	250	200	100	75

Ventilated Heavy Rib Shroud

NIB	Exc.	V.G.	Good	Fair	Poor
375	325	275	200	100	75

NOTE: Add 10% to above prices for stainless steel finish.

P44/P41/P45 Pistol Pac
This set features a 6" and 8" barrel assembly with ventilated rib shroud, an extra grip, 2 additional front sights, and a fitted carrying case. Chambered for .41 Magnum, .44 Magnum, or .45 Long Colt.

Ventilated Rib Shroud

NIB	Exc.	V.G.	Good	Fair	Poor
525	475	400	300	200	100

Ventilated Heavy Rib Shroud

NIB	Exc.	V.G.	Good	Fair	Poor
575	525	425	300	200	100

NOTE: Add 10% to above prices for stainless steel finish.

HP41/44 Hunter Pac
This model is chambered for either the .41 or .44 Magnum cartridge. The set includes a ventilated heavy 8" shroud, a ventilated 8" shroud only with Burris scope mounts and Burris scope in either 1.5x4X variable or fixed 2X, a barrel changing tool, and fitted carrying case. Finish is blue or stainless steel.

NOTE: Hunter Pac s are a special order item and should be evaluated at the time of sale.

Model 445
This double action target revolver is chambered for the .445 Supermag cartridge. Barrel lengths offered are 8" with ventilated slotted rib shroud, 8" ventilated heavy slotted rib shroud, or 10" ventilated slotted rib shroud. Barrel lengths are also available in 4", 6", 8", and 10" with choice of ventilated rib or ventilated heavy rib shrouds. Introduced in 1993 is a compensated barrel assembly available as a complete gun. This is designated the "CBA". Fitted with adjustable rear sights, red ramp interchangeable front sight, and target grips. Finish is bright blue. Typical weight with 8" ventilated rib shroud barrel is about 62 oz.

Model 7445
Same as above but with stainless steel finish.

Ventilated Rib Shroud

NIB	Exc.	V.G.	Good	Fair	Poor
400	350	300	250	200	100

Ventilated Heavy Rib Shroud

NIB	Exc.	V.G.	Good	Fair	Poor
430	380	330	250	200	100

NOTE: Add 10% to above prices for stainless steel finish.

NOTE: For .44 Magnum and .445 Supermag with compensated barrel assembly add $30.

Model 7445 Alaskan Guide Special
This limited edition model, only 500 will be produced, is chambered for the .445 Supermag cartridge. It features a 4" ventilated heavy compensated shroud barrel assembly, synthetic grips, and a matte black Titanium nitride finish. Overall barrel length is 5.5" and the revolver weighs 56 oz.

NIB	Exc.	V.G.	Good	Fair	Poor
1100	800	600	350	200	100

HP455 Hunter Pac
This model is chambered for the .445 Supermag cartridge. The set includes a ventilated heavy 8" shroud, a ventilated 8" shroud only with Burris scope mounts and Burris scope in either 1.5x4X variable or fixed 2X, a barrel changing tool, and fitted carrying case. Finish is blue or stainless steel.

NOTE: Hunter Pac's are a special order item and should be evaluated at the time of sale.

FIXED BARREL HANDGUNS

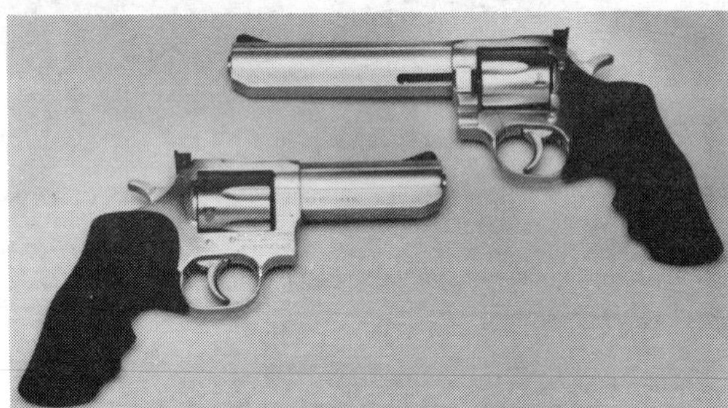

Model 38P
This model is a 5 shot double action revolver designed for the .38 Special P cartridge. Barrel is 2.5" with fixed sights. Choice of wood or rubber grips. Finish is blue. Weighs 24.6 oz.

Model 738P
Same as above but with stainless steel finish.

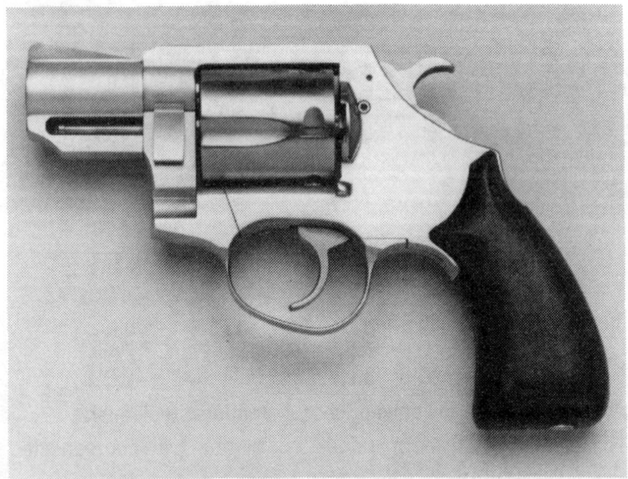

NIB	Exc.	V.G.	Good	Fair	Poor
225	200	175	150	100	75

NOTE: Add 10% to above prices for stainless steel finish.

Model 14/714 Fixed Barrel Service
Same features as the .357 Magnum Model 14 without the interchangeable barrels. Barrel length are either 2.5" or 4" with fixed sights. Offered in either blue or stainless steel. Weighs 30 oz with 2.5" barrel and 34 oz with 4" barrel.

NIB	Exc.	V.G.	Good	Fair	Poor
200	175	150	125	100	75

NOTE: Add 10% to above prices for stainless steel finish.

Model 15/715 Fixed Barrel Target
Same as the .357 magnum Model 15 with target sights and grips. Fixed barrel lengths are either 3" or 5". Available in blue or stainless steel. Weighs 37 oz with 3" barrel and 42 oz with 5" barrel.

NIB	Exc.	V.G.	Good	Fair	Poor
220	195	160	125	100	75

NOTE: Add 10% to above prices for stainless steel finish.

Model 45/745 Pin Gun
This model uses a .44 Magnum frame with 5" barrel with 2 stage compensator. Choice of ventilated or ventilated heavy rib shroud configuration. Chambered for .45ACP with or without half moon clips. Finish is blue or stainless steel. Weighs 54 oz.

Ventilated Rib Shroud

NIB	Exc.	V.G.	Good	Fair	Poor
550	500	450	400	200	100

Ventilated Heavy Rib Shroud

NIB	Exc.	V.G.	Good	Fair	Poor
600	550	500	400	200	100

NOTE: Add 10% to above prices for stainless steel finish.

Wesson Firearms Silhouette .22

This model is a 6 shot .22 Long Rifle single action only revolver with a 10" barrel. Fitted with compact style grips, narrow notch rear sight with choice of ventilated or ventilated heavy rib shroud. Finish is blue or stainless steel. Weighs 55 oz with ventilated rib shroud and 62 oz with ventilated heavy rib shroud.

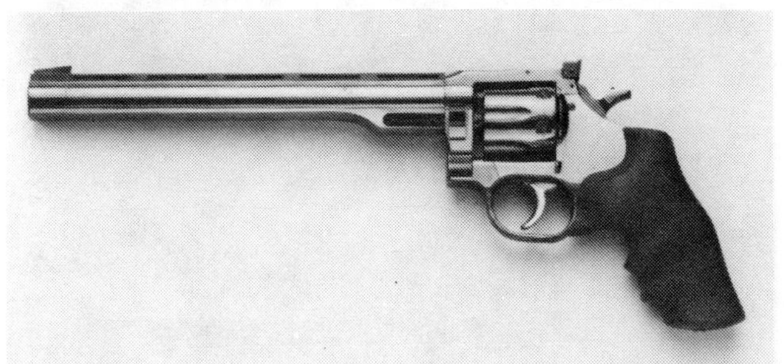

Ventilated Rib Shroud

NIB	Exc.	V.G.	Good	Fair	Poor
375	325	275	225	150	100

Ventilated Heavy Rib Shroud

NIB	Exc.	V.G.	Good	Fair	Poor
390	350	290	225	150	100

NOTE: Add 10% to above prices for stainless steel finish.

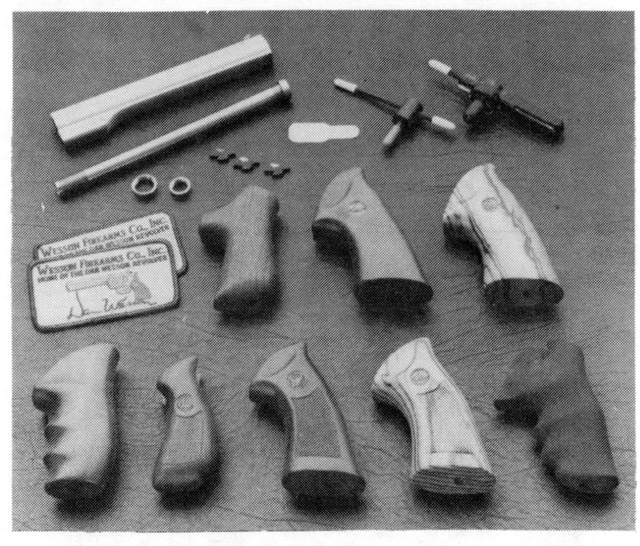

WESSON, EDWIN

Hartford, Connecticut

Dragoon

A .45 caliber percussion revolver with a 7" round barrel and 6-shot unfluted cylinder. The barrel blued, the frame case-hardened and the walnut grips fitted with a brass buttcap. Manufactured in 1848 and 1849.

Exc.	V.G.	Good	Fair	Poor
6000	5000	4000	3250	2500

WESSON, FRANK

Worcester, Massachusetts
Springfield, Massachusetts

Manual Extractor Model

A .22 caliber spur trigger single shot pistol with a 4" octagonal barrel and thin brass frame. The barrel release is located in the front of the trigger. No markings. Approximately 200 were made in 1856 and 1857.

Exc.	V.G.	Good	Fair	Poor
750	650	500	400	250

First Model Small Frame

As above, with a 3", 3.5" or 6" half-octagonal barrel. Blued with rosewood or walnut grips. The barrel marked "Frank Wesson Worcester Mass/Pat'd Oct. 25, 1859 & Nov. 11, 1862." Serial numbered from 1 to 2500.

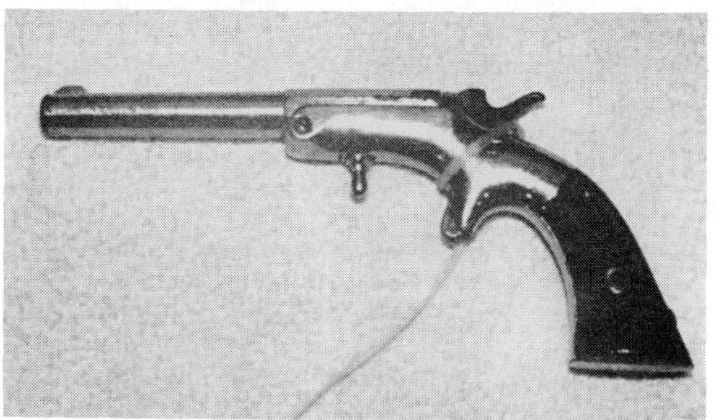

Exc.	V.G.	Good	Fair	Poor
650	550	450	300	150

Second Type

As above, with a flat sighted frame and a circular sideplate.

Exc.	V.G.	Good	Fair	Poor
550	450	350	250	125

First Model Medium Frame

As above, in .30 or .32 rimfire with a 4" half-octagonal barrel and an iron frame. Approximately 1,000 were made between 1859 and 1862.

Exc.	V.G.	Good	Fair	Poor
500	400	300	200	100

Medium Frame Second Model

As above, with a longer spur trigger and a slightly wider frame at the barrel hinge. Manufactured from 1862 to 1870.

Exc.	V.G.	Good	Fair	Poor
500	400	300	200	100

Small Frame Pocket Rifle

A .22 caliber spur trigger single shot pistol with a 6" half-octagonal barrel and narrow brass frame. This model is adopted for use with a detachable skeleton shoulder stock. The barrel marked "Frank Wesson Worcester, Mass." Manufactured from 1865 to 1875 with approximately 5,000 made.
Matching Shoulder Stock—Add 25%.

Pistol Only

Exc.	V.G.	Good	Fair	Poor
600	500	400	300	200

Medium Frame Pocket Rifle

As above, in .22, .30 or .32 rimfire with a 10" or 12" half octagonal barrel. Approximately 1,000 were made from 1862 to 1870.
Matching Shoulder Stock—Add 25%.

Pistol Only

Exc.	V.G.	Good	Fair	Poor
600	500	400	300	200

Model 1870 Small Frame Pocket Rifle

As above, in .22 caliber with a 10", 12", 15", or 18" or 20" half octagonal barrel which rotates to the side for loading. This model was made with either a brass or iron frame. It has a half cocked notch on the hammer.
Matching Shoulder Stock—Add 25%.

Pistol Only

Exc.	V.G.	Good	Fair	Poor
500	400	300	200	150

1870 Medium Frame Pocket Rifle First Type

As above, but with a slightly larger frame chambered for .32 rimfire. Approximately 5,000 were made from 1870 to 1893.
Matching Shoulder Stock—Add 25%.

Pistol Only

Exc.	V.G.	Good	Fair	Poor
550	450	350	250	200

1870 Medium Frame Pocket Rifle Second Type

As above, with an iron frame and a push button half cocked safety.
Match Shoulder Stock—Add 25%.

Pistol Only

Exc.	V.G.	Good	Fair	Poor
450	400	300	200	150

1870 Medium Frame Pocket Rifle Third Type

As above, with 3 screws on the left side of the frame.
Matching Shoulder Stock—Add 25%.

Pistol Only

Exc.	V.G.	Good	Fair	Poor
450	400	300	200	150

1870 Large Frame Pocket Rifle First Type

As above, in .32, .38, .42 or .44 rimfire with an octagonal barrel from 15" to 24" in length. The barrel marked "Frank Wesson Worcester, Mass Patented May 31, 1870." Less than 250 of these rifles were made between 1870 and 1880.
Matching Shoulder Stock—Add 25%.

Pistol Only

Exc.	V.G.	Good	Fair	Poor
850	750	650	500	300

1870 Large Frame Pocket Rifle Second Type

As above, with a sliding extractor.
Matching Shoulder Stock—Add 25%.

Pistol Only

Exc.	V.G.	Good	Fair	Poor
850	750	650	500	300

Small Frame Superposed Pistol

A .22 caliber spur trigger Over/Under pocket pistol with 2" or 2.5" octagonal barrels which revolve. Approximately 3,500 were made between 1868 and 1880. On occasion this pistol is found with a sliding knife blade mounted on the side of the barrels. The presence of this feature would add approximately 25% to the values listed below.

Exc.	V.G.	Good	Fair	Poor
800	650	550	400	275

Medium Frame Superposed Pistol

As above, in .32 rimfire with 2.5" or 3.5" barrels. As with the smaller version, this pistol is occasionally found with a sliding knife blade mounted on the barrels which would add 25% to the values listed below. Manufactured from 1868 to 1880.

First Type Marked "Patent Applied For"

Exc.	V.G.	Good	Fair	Poor
550	500	400	300	200

Second Type Marked "Patent December 15, 1868"

Exc.	V.G.	Good	Fair	Poor
600	550	450	350	250

Third Type Full-Length Fluted Barrels

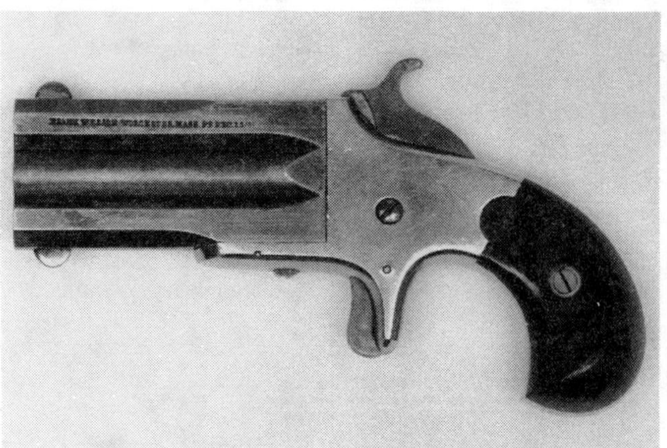

Courtesy W.P. Hallstein III and son Chip.

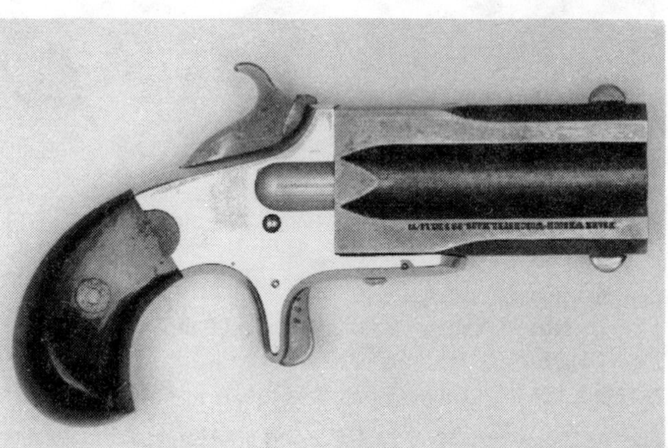

Courtesy W.P. Hallstein III and son Chip.

Exc.	V.G.	Good	Fair	Poor
650	550	350	250	150

Large Frame Superposed Pistol

As above, in .41 rimfire with a 3" octagonal barrel fitted with a sliding knife blade. Approximately 2,000 were made from 1868 to 1880.

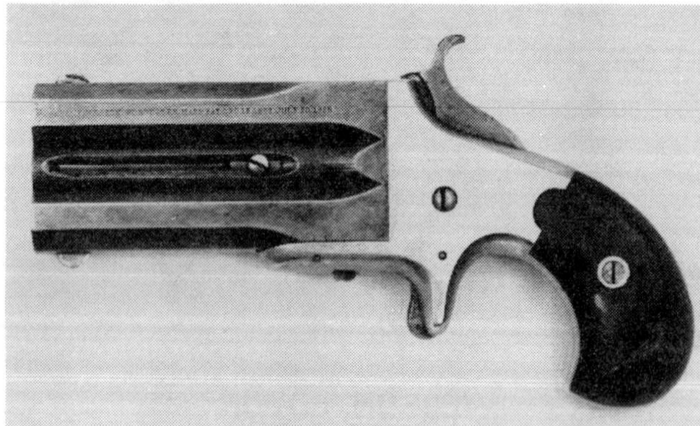

Courtesy W.P. Hallstein III and son Chip.

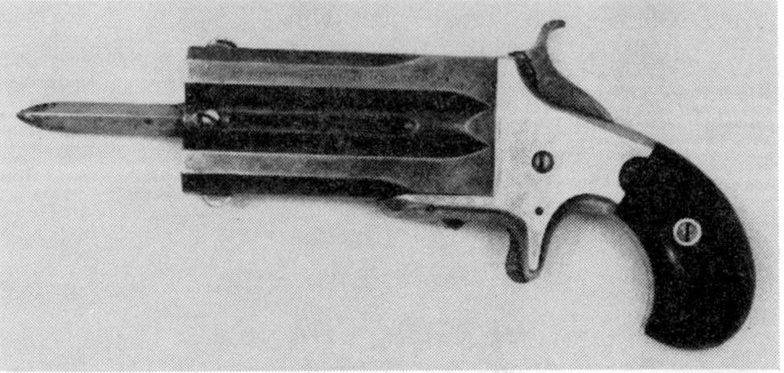

Courtesy W.P. Hallstein III and son Chip.

Exc.	V.G.	Good	Fair	Poor
850	750	650	500	300

No. 1 Long Range Rifle

A .44-100 or .45-100 caliber single shot dropping block rifle with a 34" octagonal barrel. Blued with a checkered walnut stock. The barrel marked "F. Wesson Mfr. Worcester, Mass. Long Range Rifle Creedmoor." Manufactured in 1876.

Exc.	V.G.	Good	Fair	Poor
5000	4500	3500	2500	1750

No. 2 Mid-Range or Hunting Rifle

Similar to the above, with the firing pin located in a bolster on the right side of the receiver. The triggerguard has a rear finger loop. Standard barrel length 28", 32" and 34" and marked "F. Wesson Maker Worcester, Mass." The 32" and 34" barrels are occasionally maked "Long Range Rifle Creedmoor." Approximately 100 were made.

Courtesy Buffalo Bill Historical Center, Cody, Wyoming.

Exc.	V.G.	Good	Fair	Poor
4500	3750	3000	2000	1500

No. 2 Sporting Rifle

A .38-100, .40-100 or .45-100 caliber single shot dropping barrel action rifle with barrels ranging from 28" to 34" in length. Approximately 25 were made.

Courtesy Buffalo Bill Historical Center, Cody, Wyoming.

Exc.	V.G.	Good	Fair	Poor
4750	4000	3250	2250	1750

WESSON & LEAVITT MASSACHUSETTS ARMS COMPANY

Chicopee Falls, Massachusetts

Revolving Rifle

A .40 caliber percussion revolving rifle with a 16" to 24" round barrel and 6-shot cylinder. Blued with a walnut stock. Approximately 25 were made in 1849.

Exc.	V.G.	Good	Fair	Poor
6000	5000	4000	3000	2000

Dragoon

A .40 caliber percussion revolver with a 6.25" or 7" round barrel and 6-shot cylinder. These pistols are marked "Mass. Arms Co./Chicopee Falls." Approximately 30 were made with the 6.25" barrel and 750 with the 7" barrel. Manufactured in 1850 and 1851.

Courtesy Milwaukee Public Museum, Milwaukee, Wisconsin.

Exc.	V.G.	Good	Fair	Poor
2000	1750	1500	1000	750

WESTERN ARMS

SEE—Bacon

WESTERN FIELD

Montgomery Ward

"Western Field" is the trade name used by Montgomery Ward & Company on arms which they retail. See Firearms Trade Names List at the end of this book.

WESTLEY RICHARDS & CO., LTD.

Birmingham, England
Importer—New England Arms Co.
Kittery Point, Maine

A wide variety of firearms have been produced by this company since its founding. Presently, it produces boxlock and sidelock double barrel shotguns of both side-by-side and Over/Under form, bolt-action rifles and double-barrel rifles. Prospective purchasers are advised to secure individual appraisals prior to acquisition.

ROBERT WHEELER

SEE—English Military Firearms

WHITE, ROLLIN

Lowell, Massachusetts

Pocket Pistol

A .32 or .38 rimfire spur trigger single shot pistol with a 3" or 5" octagonal barrel. Brass or iron frames with walnut grips. The .38 caliber version with the 5" barrel was not produced in large quantities and therefore is worth approximately 40% more than the values listed below. The barrels marked "Rollin White Arms Co., Lowell, Mass."

Exc.	V.G.	Good	Fair	Poor
650	550	450	300	200

Pocket Revolver

A .22 caliber spur trigger revolver with a 3.25" octagonal barrel and 7-shot cylinder. The brass frame silver-plated, barrel blued and grips of walnut. This revolver was marked in a variety of ways including "Rollin White Arms Co., Lowell, Mass.", "Lowell Arms Co., Lowell, Mass.", or "Made for Smith & Wesson by Rollin White Arms Co., Lowell, Mass." Approximately 10,000 were made during the late 1860s.

Exc.	V.G.	Good	Fair	Poor
500	450	400	300	200

WHITNEY ARMS CO.

New Haven, Connecticut

Whitney firearms are desirable from a collector's standpoint. Many are quite valuable. The number of different variations makes it advisable to secure a qualified appraisal if a transaction is contemplated.

Model 1841 Rifle

This is a muzzle-loading single shot rifle chambered for .54 caliber percussion. It has a 33" round barrel with a full-length walnut stock held on by two barrel bands. It has brass mountings and a patch box. The finish is brown with a blued trigger and barrel bands. The lock is case-colored. There is a steel ramrod mounted under the barrel. It is marked "E. Whitney" along with "U.S." military inspector's markings. There were approximately 22,500 manufactured between 1842 and 1854.

Exc.	V.G.	Good	Fair	Poor
1750	1500	1200	850	500

Model 1855 Rifle

This model is similar to the Model 1841 Rifle except that it is chambered for .58-caliber percussion with a 40" round barrel and a full-length stock held on by three barrel bands. It features iron mountings with a pewter forend tip. The lock is fitted with the Maynard Tape Primer device. The finish is in the white with a walnut stock. There were approximately 2,000 manufactured between 1858 and 1863.

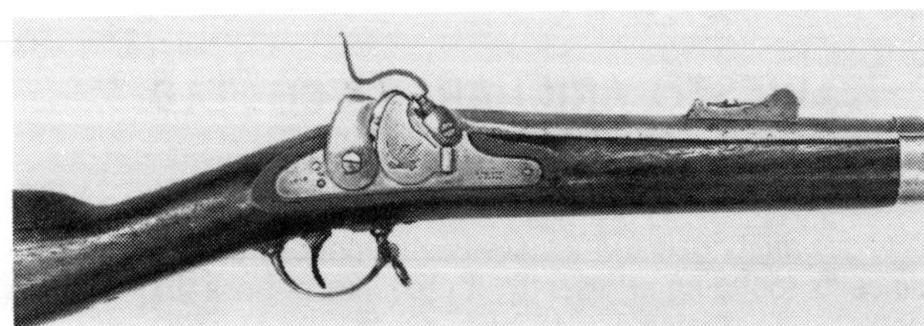

Courtesy Milwaukee Public Museum, Milwaukee, Wisconsin.

Exc.	V.G.	Good	Fair	Poor
1500	1250	1000	750	500

Model 1861 Rifle

This is a .69 caliber muzzleloader. It has a 34" round barrel and a full-length stock held on by two barrel bands. It has iron mountings and is U.S. marked. The finish is in the white with an oil-finished walnut stock. It is marked "U.S./ Whitneyville." The lock is dated. There were approximately 10,000 manufactured between 1861 and 1864.

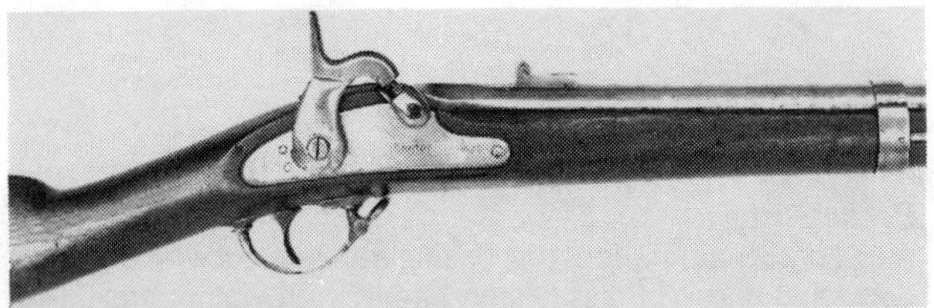

Courtesy Milwaukee Public Museum, Milwaukee, Wisconsin.

Courtesy Milwaukee Public Museum, Milwaukee, Wisconsin.

Exc.	V.G.	Good	Fair	Poor
1500	1250	1000	750	500

Single Barrelled Percussion Shotgun

This firearm was manufactured by Whitney out of surplus .58 caliber rifle barrels that were opened up and converted to smoothbore .60 caliber shotgun barrels. They are offered in lengths of 28" to 36" and are marked "Whitney Arms Co., Whitneyville, Conn. Homogeneous Wrought Steel." The finish is blued, with varnished walnut stocks that are crudely checkered. There were approximately 2,000 manufactured between 1866 and 1869. These guns are rarely encountered on today's market.

Exc.	V.G.	Good	Fair	Poor
850	750	600	450	250

Double Barrelled Percussion Shotgun

The specifications for this version are similar to that of the single barrel except that there are two side-by-side barrels with double locks and hammers and double triggers. They are slightly more common than the Single Barrelled version.

Exc.	V.G.	Good	Fair	Poor
800	700	550	400	200

Swing-Breech Carbine

This is a single shot breechloading carbine chambered for the .46-caliber rimfire cartridge. It has a 22" round barrel with a button-released breechblock that swings to the side for loading. The finish is blued, with a walnut stock. There were fewer than 50 manufactured in 1866.

Exc.	V.G.	Good	Fair	Poor
3000	2750	2250	1500	1100

Whitney-Cochran Carbine

This is a single shot breechloading carbine chambered for the .44 rimfire cartridge. It has a 28" round barrel with a lever-activated breechblock that raises upward for loading. It was manufactured under license from J. W. Cochran. The finish is blued, with a walnut stock. There is a saddle ring on the left side of the frame. It is marked "Whitney Arms Co.-Whitneyville, Conn." This gun was produced for the 1867 Government Carbine Trials. There were fewer than 50 manufactured in 1866 and 1867.

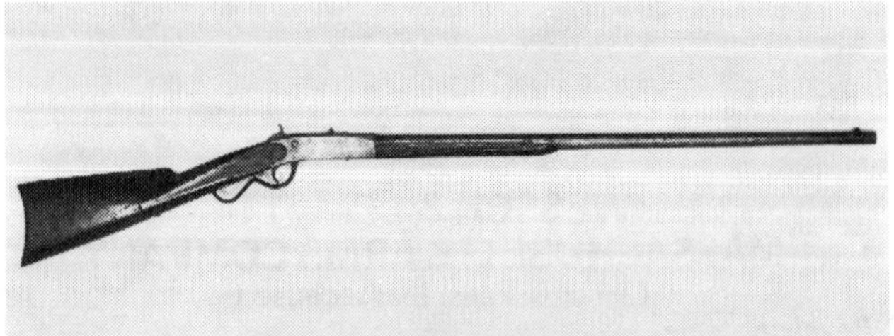

Courtesy Milwaukee Public Museum, Milwaukee, Wisconsin.

Exc.	V.G.	Good	Fair	Poor
1750	1500	1200	850	600

Excelsior

This is a single shot rifle chambered for the .38, .44, or .50 rimfire cartridges. It is found with various-length octagonal or round barrels. The finish is blued, with a walnut stock and forearm held on by one barrel band. The breechblock pivots downward for loading. There is a center-mounted hammer. It is marked "Whitney Arms Co. Whitneyville Conn." The shorter-barrelled carbine versions have a saddle ring on the frame. There were approximately 200 manufactured between 1866 and 1870.

Exc.	V.G.	Good	Fair	Poor
1500	1250	1000	750	500

Whitney-Howard Lever Action

This is a single shot breechloader that is chambered for the .44 rimfire cartridge. It has also been noted as a shotgun chambered for 20 gauge smoothbore with barrels from 30" to 40" in length. The rifle version has barrel lengths from 22" to 28". The breechblock is opened by means of a combination lever and triggerguard. There is also a carbine version with barrel lengths of 18.5" or 19". There were approximately 2,000 manufactured totally between 1866 and 1870. Values are as follows:

Shotgun

Courtesy Buffalo Bill Historical Center, Cody, Wyoming.

Exc.	V.G.	Good	Fair	Poor
650	600	500	350	250

Rifle

Courtesy Milwaukee Public Museum, Milwaukee, Wisconsin.

Exc.	V.G.	Good	Fair	Poor
750	700	600	450	300

Carbine

Courtesy Milwaukee Public Museum, Milwaukee, Wisconsin.

Exc.	V.G.	Good	Fair	Poor
850	800	700	550	400

Whitney Phoenix

There is very little known about the origin of this model. It is built on a patent issued to Whitney in 1874. There are a number of variations that are all marked "Phoenix, Patent May 24, 74." The Whitney name is not marked on any of the versions. They are all single shot breechloaders with a breechblock that lifts to the right side and upward for loading. The barrels are all blued, with either case-colored or blued receivers and walnut stocks. There were approximately 25,000 total manufactured between 1867 and 1881. The models and values are as follows:

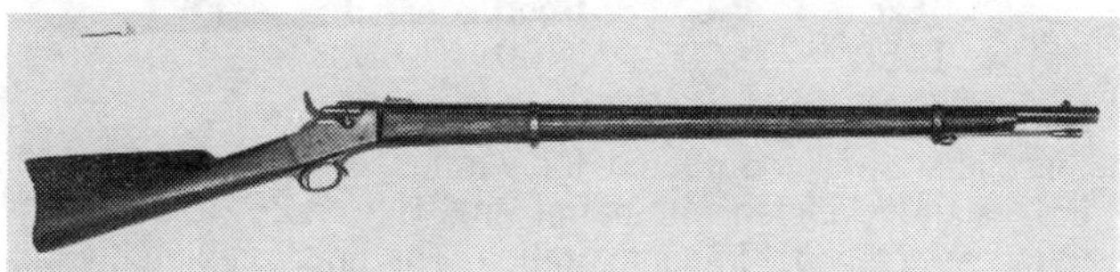

Courtesy Milwaukee Public Museum, Milwaukee, Wisconsin.

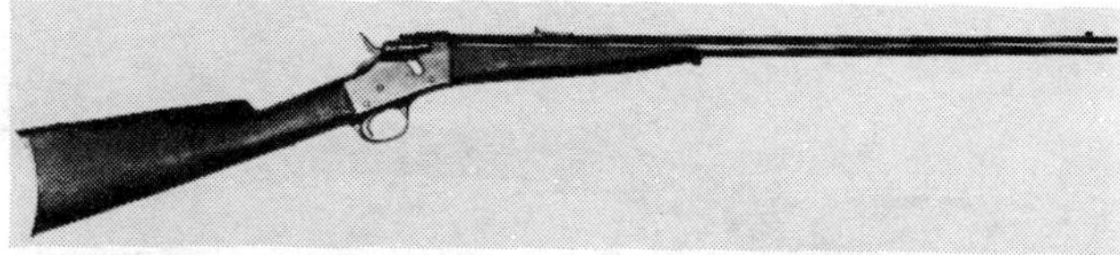

Courtesy Milwaukee Public Museum, Milwaukee, Wisconsin.

Gallery Rifle

This version is chambered for the .22 rimfire caliber and has a 24" half-octagonal barrel. Its production was quite limited.

Exc.	V.G.	Good	Fair	Poor
850	800	700	550	400

Shotgun

This is a smoothbore version chambered for 10, 12, 14, 16, or 22 gauge. It has smoothbore barrels between 26" and 32" in length. There were approximately 5,000 manufactured.

Exc.	V.G.	Good	Fair	Poor
600	550	450	300	200

Military Rifle

This version is chambered for the .433, .45 or .50 caliber centerfire cartridges. It has a 35" round barrel with a full-length, two-piece walnut stock held on by three barrel bands. There were approximately 15,000 manufactured. Many were sent to Central or South America.

Exc.	V.G.	Good	Fair	Poor
1250	1000	800	650	500

Schuetzen Rifle

This is a target-shooting version chambered for the .38, .40, or .44 centerfire cartridges. It has either a 30" or 32" octagonal barrel with a Schuetzen-type walnut stock and forearm that features handcheckering. It has a nickle-plated, Swiss-style buttplate and adjustable sights with a spirit level. This model has been noted with double-set triggers. There were very few manufactured.

Exc.	V.G.	Good	Fair	Poor
2000	1750	1250	850	650

Civilian Carbine

This version is chambered for the .44 caliber centerfire and has a 24" round barrel. The finish is blued, with a case-colored frame and a walnut stock and forearm held on by one barrel band. It has military-type sights, buttplate, and a saddle ring mounted on the frame. There were approximately 500 manufactured.

Courtesy Milwaukee Public Museum, Milwaukee, Wisconsin.

Exc.	V.G.	Good	Fair	Poor
2000	1750	1250	850	650

Military Carbine

This version is chambered for the .433, .45, or .50 centerfire cartridges. It has a 20.5" round barrel and was manufactured for Central and South America. It is very rarely encountered on today's market.

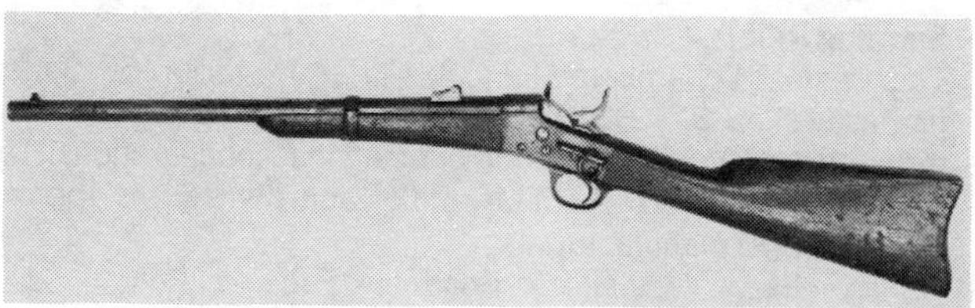

Courtesy Milwaukee Public Museum, Milwaukee, Wisconsin.

Courtesy Milwaukee Public Museum, Milwaukee, Wisconsin.

Exc.	V.G.	Good	Fair	Poor
2000	1750	1250	850	650

Whitney-Laidley Model 1 Rolling Block
Whitney acquired manufacturing rights for this model from the inventors T. Laidley and C. A. Emery, who had received the patent in 1866. Whitney immediately started to modify the action to become competitive with the Remington Rolling Block. There were approximately 50,000 manufactured total between 1871 and 1881. There are a number of variations of this model as follows:

Military Carbine
There were approximately 5,000 manufactured chambered for the .433, .45, or .50 centerfire cartridges. It has a 20.5" round barrel with military-type sights and a saddle ring on the receiver. The finish is blued, with a case-colored frame and a walnut stock. Most of them were shipped to Central or South America.

Exc.	V.G.	Good	Fair	Poor
1250	1000	800	550	350

Civilian Carbine
This version is chambered for .44 rimfire or centerfire and .46 rimfire. It has either an 18.5" or 19.5" barrel. It is blued, with a case-colored frame. The stock is walnut. A nickle-plated version is also available. There were approximately 1,000 of this version manufactured.

Exc.	V.G.	Good	Fair	Poor
1250	1000	800	550	350

Military Rifle
This version is chambered the same as the Military Carbine but has either a 32.5" or 35" round barrel with a full-length two-piece stock held on by three barrel bands. The finish is blued, with a case-colored receiver and a walnut stock. There were approximately 30,000 manufactured. Most were shipped to Central or South America.

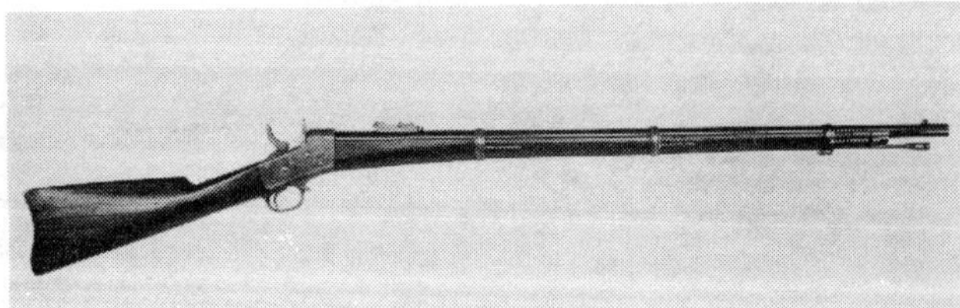
Courtesy Milwaukee Public Museum, Milwaukee, Wisconsin.

Exc.	V.G.	Good	Fair	Poor
1000	800	650	450	300

Gallery Rifle
This is a .22-caliber sporting-rifle version with a 24" octagonal barrel. The finish is similar to the Military Rifle. There were approximately 500 manufactured.

Exc.	V.G.	Good	Fair	Poor
900	800	600	400	300

Sporting Rifle
This version is chambered for .38, .40, .44, .45, or .50 centerfire, as well as .32, .38, or .44 rimfire. It features barrel lengths from 24" to 30" in either round or octagonal configurations. The finish is similar to the Military Rifle, and there were approximately 5,000 manufactured.

Exc.	V.G.	Good	Fair	Poor
1250	1000	800	550	350

Creedmoor No. 1 Rifle
This version is chambered for the .44 caliber cartridge and has a 32" or 34" barrel that is either round or octagonal in configuration. It has a blued finish with case-colored frame and a hand-checkered, select walnut stock and forearm. It features Vernier adjustable sights with a spirit level. It is marked "Whitney Creedmoor." There were fewer than 100 manufactured.

Exc.	V.G.	Good	Fair	Poor
3000	2500	2000	1250	750

Creedmoor No. 2 Rifle
This version is similar to the No. 1 Rifle except that it is chambered for the .40 caliber cartridge with either a 30" or 32" barrel.

Exc.	V.G.	Good	Fair	Poor
2750	2250	1750	1000	650

Whitney-Remington Model 2 Rolling Block
When Remington's patent for the Rolling Block action expired, Whitney was quick to reproduce the action, labeling it his "New Improved System." It is essentially quite similar to Remington's Rolling Block and is easily recognized when compared with the Model 1 because it has only two parts—the hammer and the breechblock. The frame is also rounded. The tang on this model is marked "Whitney Arms Company, New Haven Ct USA." There were approximately 50,000 total manufactured between 1881 and 1888. There are a number of variations as follows:

Shotgun
This is a smoothbore version chambered for 12, 14, 16, or 20 gauge. It is offered with barrel lengths between 26" and 30". Twenty-inch barrels have also been noted.

Exc.	V.G.	Good	Fair	Poor
650	550	450	300	200

Military Carbine
This version is chambered for the .433 and .45 centerfire cartridges. It has a 20.5" barrel and is blued, with a case-colored receiver and walnut stock. There were approximately 5,000 manufactured. Most were sent to South or Central America.

Exc.	V.G.	Good	Fair	Poor
1000	850	650	550	400

Civilian Carbine
This version is chambered for the .44 rimfire or centerfire cartridge with an 18.5" round barrel. The finish is similar to the Military Carbine. There were approximately 2,000 manufactured.

Exc.	V.G.	Good	Fair	Poor
1000	850	650	550	400

Military Rifle
This version is chambered for the .433, .45, or .50 centerfire cartridge. It has a 32.5" or 35" barrel. It is finished similarly to the Military Carbine. There were approximately 39,000 manufactured.

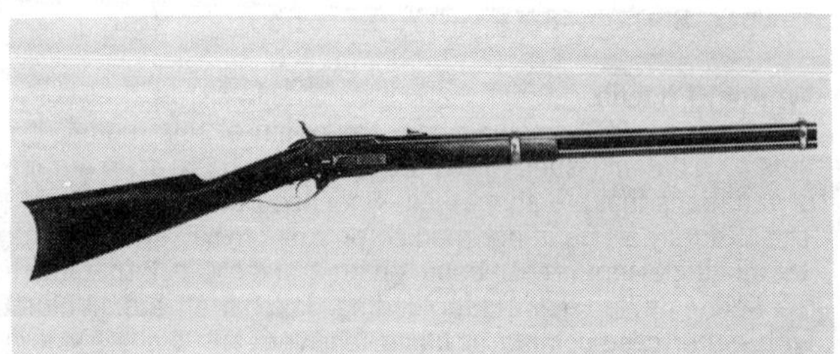
Courtesy Buffalo Bill Historical Center, Cody, Wyoming.

Exc.	V.G.	Good	Fair	Poor
1050	900	700	600	450

No. 1 Sporting Rifle
This version is chambered for various popular sporting cartridges and is offered with barrel lengths from 26" to 30", either round or octagonal in configuration. The finish is blued, with a case-colored receiver and a varnished walnut stock. There were

many options available that could radically affect the value, and a qualified appraisal would be advisable. There were approximately 3,000 manufactured.

Exc.	V.G.	Good	Fair	Poor
1100	950	750	650	500

No. 2 Sporting Rifle

This is a smaller version of the No. 1 Rifle, chambered for the .22 rimfire, .32, .38, and .44-40 centerfire cartridges. Again, a qualified appraisal would be helpful, as many options can affect the value.

Exc.	V.G.	Good	Fair	Poor
950	850	650	550	400

Whitney-Burgess-Morse Rifle

This is a lever-action repeating rifle chambered for the .45-70 Government cartridge. There are three variations. All have a magazine tube mounted beneath the barrel with blued finishes and walnut stocks. The barrels are marked "G. W. Morse Patented Oct. 28th 1856." The tang is marked "A. Burgess Patented Jan 7th 1873, Patented Oct 19th 1873." There were approximately 3,000 total manufactured between 1878 and 1882. The variations are as follows:

Sporting Rifle

This version has a 28" octagonal or round barrel. The magazine tube holds nine rounds. There are a number of options available that can increase the value drastically; and we recommend competent, individual appraisal. Value given is for a standard model.

Exc.	V.G.	Good	Fair	Poor
1250	1000	800	600	450

Military Rifle

This version has a 33" round barrel with a full-length forearm held on by two barrel bands. It features military sights and has an 11-round tubular magazine. It has a bayonet lug and sling swivels. This variation is also found chambered for the .43 Spanish and .42 Russian cartridges. There were approximately 1,000 manufactured.

Exc.	V.G.	Good	Fair	Poor
1500	1250	1000	800	550

Carbine

This version has a 22" round barrel with a full-length forearm held on by one barrel band. It has a 7-round tubular magazine and a saddle ring attached to the frame. There were approximately 500 manufactured.

Exc.	V.G.	Good	Fair	Poor
1750	1500	1250	1000	750

Whitney-Kennedy Rifle

This is a lever-action repeating rifle that was manufactured in two sizes. It has a magazine tube mounted under the barrel and a blued finish with a case-colored lever. The stock is walnut. The barrel is marked "Whitney Arms Co New Haven, Conn. U.S.A." Occasionally, the word "Kennedy" is marked after the Whitney name. There are two major variations. One features a standard-type action lever; and the other, the same "S"-shaped lever that is found on the Burgess model. This version would be worth approximately 10 percent additional. As with many of the rifles of this era, there were many options available that will affect the values. We strongly recommend securing a qualified appraisal for all but the standard models if a transaction is contemplated. There were approximately 15,000 manufactured between 1879 and 1886. The variations of the Whitney-Kennedy and their values are as follows:

Courtesy Buffalo Bill Historical Center, Cody, Wyoming.

Small Frame Sporting Rifle

This version is chambered for the .32-20, .38-40, and the .40-40 cartridges. It has a 24" barrel that is either round or octagonal in configuration. Examples will be noted with either a full-length or half-length tubular magazine.

Exc.	V.G.	Good	Fair	Poor
1500	1250	900	750	500

Large Frame Sporting Rifle

This version is chambered for the .40-60, .45-60, .45-75, and the .50-90 cartridges. The .50-caliber version is uncommon and will bring a 20 percent premium. The barrel lengths offered are 26" or 28".

Exc.	V.G.	Good	Fair	Poor
1750	1500	1200	900	650

Military Rifle

This is a large-frame model, chambered for the .40-60, .44-40, and the .45-60 cartridges. It has a 32.25" round barrel with either an 11- or 16-round tubular magazine. It has a full-length walnut forend held on by two barrel bands and features a bayonet lug and sling swivels. There were approximately 1,000 manufactured. Most were shipped to Central or South America.

Exc.	V.G.	Good	Fair	Poor
2250	1800	1500	1100	800

Military Carbine

This is built on either the small-frame or large-frame action and is chambered for the .38-40, .44-40, .40-60, or .45-60 cartridges. It has either a 20" or 22" round barrel and a 9- or 12-round tubular magazine, depending on the caliber. It has a short forend held on by a single barrel band. There were approximately 1,000 manufactured. Most were sent to Central or South America.

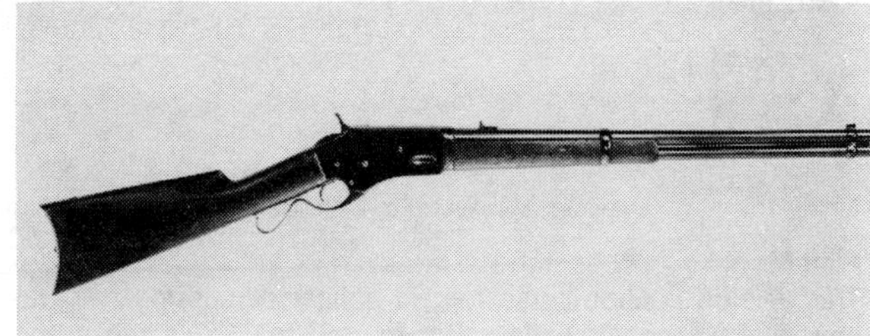

Courtesy Buffalo Bill Historical Center, Cody, Wyoming.

Exc.	V.G.	Good	Fair	Poor
2250	1800	1500	1100	800

Hooded Cylinder Pocket Revolver

This is an unusual revolver that is chambered for .28 caliber percussion. It has a manually rotated, 6-shot hooded cylinder that has etched decorations. The octagonal barrel is offered in lengths of 3" to 6". There is a button at the back of the frame that unlocks the cylinder so that it can be rotated. The finish is blued, with a brass frame and two-piece rounded walnut grips. It is marked "E. Whitney N. Haven Ct." There were approximately 200 manufactured between 1850 and 1853.

Exc.	V.G.	Good	Fair	Poor
2500	2000	1750	1250	900

Two Trigger Pocket Revolver

This is a conventional-appearing pocket revolver with a manually rotated cylinder. There is a second trigger located in front of the conventional triggerguard that releases the cylinder so that it can be turned. It is chambered for .32 caliber percussion and has an octagonal barrel from 3" to 6" in length. It has a 5-shot unfluted cylinder that is etched and a brass frame. The remainder is blued, with squared walnut two-piece grips. An iron-frame version is also available, but only 50 were produced. It would bring approximately 60 percent additional. There were approximately 650 total manufactured between 1852 and 1854.

Courtesy Milwaukee Public Museum, Milwaukee, Wisconsin..

Exc.	V.G.	Good	Fair	Poor
1500	1250	1000	750	550

Whitney-Beals Patent Revolver

This was an unusual, ring-trigger pocket pistol that was made in three basic variations.

Courtesy Milwaukee Public Museum, Milwaukee, Wisconsin..

First Model

This version is chambered for .31-caliber percussion and has barrels of octagonal configuration from 2" to 6" in length. It has a brass frame and a 6-shot cylinder. It is marked "F. Beals/New Haven, Ct." There were only 50 manufactured.

Exc.	V.G.	Good	Fair	Poor
2000	1750	1250	800	650

.31 Caliber Model

This version has an iron frame and a 7-shot cylinder. The octagonal barrels are from 2" to 6" in length. It is marked "Address E. Whitney/Whitneyville, Ct." There were approximately 2,300 manufactured.

Exc.	V.G.	Good	Fair	Poor
1000	850	650	500	350

.28 Caliber Model

Except for the caliber, this model is similar to the .31 Caliber Model. There were approximately 850 manufactured.

Exc.	V.G.	Good	Fair	Poor
1050	900	700	550	400

Whitney 1851 Navy

This is a faithful copy of the 1851 Colt Revolver. It is virtually identical. There is a possibility that surplus Colt parts were utilized in the construction of this revolver. There were approximately 400 manufactured in 1857 and 1858.

Exc.	V.G.	Good	Fair	Poor
1800	1650	1250	800	550

Whitney Navy Revolver

This is a single action revolver chambered for .36 caliber percussion. It has a standard octagonal barrel length of 7.5". It has an iron frame and a 6-shot unfluted cylinder that is roll-engraved. The finish is blued, with a case-colored loading lever and two-piece walnut grips. The barrel is marked either "E. Whitney/N. Haven" or "Eagle Co." There are a number of minor variations on this revolver, and we strongly urge competent appraisal if contemplating a transaction. There were 33,000 total manufactured between 1858 and 1862.

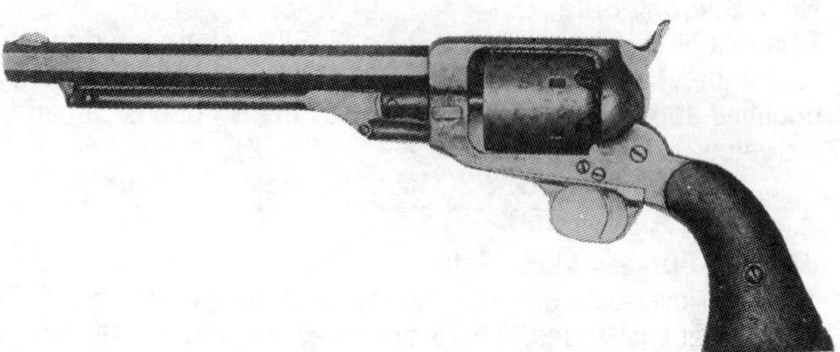

Courtesy Wallis & Wallis, Lewes, Sussex, England.

First Model

Nearly the entire production of the First Model is marked "Eagle Co." The reason for this marking is unknown. There are four distinct variations of this model. They are as follows:

First Variation

This model has no integral loading-lever assembly and has a very thin top strap. There were only 100 manufactured.

Exc.	V.G.	Good	Fair	Poor
1750	1500	1250	850	550

Second Variation

This version is similar to the First Variation, with an integral loading lever. There were approximately 200 manufactured.

Exc.	V.G.	Good	Fair	Poor
1250	1000	800	600	400

Third Variation

This is similar to the Second, with a three-screw frame instead of four screws. The loading lever is also modified. There were approximately 500 manufactured.

Exc.	V.G.	Good	Fair	Poor
1250	1000	800	600	400

Fourth Variation

This version has a rounded frame and a safety notch between the nipples on the rear of the cylinder. There have been examples noted marked "E. Whitney/N. Haven." There were approximately 700 manufactured.

Exc.	V.G.	Good	Fair	Poor
1250	1000	800	600	400

Second Model

First Variation

This version features a more robust frame with a brass trigger guard. The barrel is marked "E. Whitney/N. Haven." The cylinder pin is secured by a wing nut, and there is an integral loading lever. There were approximately 1,200 manufactured.

Exc.	V.G.	Good	Fair	Poor
800	650	500	400	300

Second Variation

This version has six improved safety notches on the rear of the cylinder. There were approximately 10,000 manufactured.

Exc.	V.G.	Good	Fair	Poor
750	600	450	350	250

Third Variation

This version has an improved, Colt-type loading-lever latch. There were approximately 2,000 manufactured.

Exc.	V.G.	Good	Fair	Poor
750	600	450	350	250

Fourth Variation

This is similar to the Third except the cylinder is marked "Whitneyville." There were approximately 10,000 manufactured.

Exc.	V.G.	Good	Fair	Poor
750	600	450	350	250

Fifth Variation

This version has a larger triggerguard. There were approximately

4,000 manufactured.

Exc.	V.G.	Good	Fair	Poor
750	600	450	350	250

Sixth Variation

This version has the larger triggerguard and five-groove rifling instead of the usual seven-groove. There were approximately 2,500 manufactured.

Exc.	V.G.	Good	Fair	Poor
750	600	450	350	250

Whitney Pocket Revolver

This is a single action revolver chambered for .31caliber percussion. It has octagonal barrels between 3" and 6" in length. It has a 5-shot unfluted cylinder that is roll-engraved and marked "Whitneyville." The frame is iron with a blued finish and a case-colored integral loading lever. The grips are two-piece walnut. The development of this model, as far as models and variations go, is identical to that which we described in the Navy Model designation. The values are different, and we list them for reference. Again, we recommend securing qualified appraisal if a transaction is contemplated. There were approximately 32,500 manufactured from 1858 to 1862.

Courtesy Buffalo Bill Historical Center, Cody, Wyoming.

First Model

First Variation

Exc.	V.G.	Good	Fair	Poor
950	850	700	550	400

Second Variation

Exc.	V.G.	Good	Fair	Poor
850	750	600	450	300

Third Variation

Exc.	V.G.	Good	Fair	Poor
750	650	500	350	250

Fourth Variation

Exc.	V.G.	Good	Fair	Poor
750	650	500	350	250

Fifth Variation

Exc.	V.G.	Good	Fair	Poor
750	650	500	350	250

Second Model

First Variation

Exc.	V.G.	Good	Fair	Poor
650	550	400	300	200

Second Variation

Exc.	V.G.	Good	Fair	Poor
650	550	400	300	200

Third Variation

Exc.	V.G.	Good	Fair	Poor
650	550	400	300	200

Fourth Variation

Exc.	V.G.	Good	Fair	Poor
750	650	500	350	250

New Model Pocket Revolver

This is a single action, spur-triggered pocket revolver chambered for .28-caliber percussion. It has a 3.5" octagonal barrel and a 6-shot roll-engraved cylinder. It features an iron frame with a blued finish and two-piece walnut grips. The barrel is marked "E. Whitney/N. Haven." There were approximately 2,000 manufactured between 1860 and 1867.

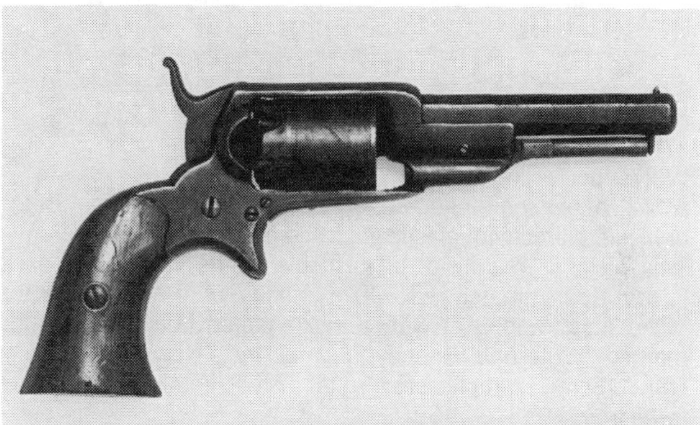

Courtesy Milwaukee Public Museum, Milwaukee, Wisconsin.

Exc.	V.G.	Good	Fair	Poor
750	650	500	350	250

Rimfire Pocket Revolver

This is a spur-trigger, single action, solid-frame pocket revolver that was produced in three frame sizes, depending on the caliber. It is chambered for the .22, .32, and .38 rimfire cartridges. The frame is brass, and it is found in a variety of finishes—nickle-plated or blued, or a combination thereof. The birdshead grips are rosewood or hard rubber; ivory or pearl grips are sometimes encountered and will bring a slight premium in value. The barrels are octagonal and from 1.5" to 5" in length. The barrels are marked "Whitneyville Armory Ct. USA." They have also been noted with the tradenames "Monitor," "Defender," or "Eagle." They were commonly referred to as the Model No. 1, No. 1.5, Model 2, or Model 2.5. The values for all are quite similar. There were approximately 30,000 manufactured of all types between 1871 and 1879.

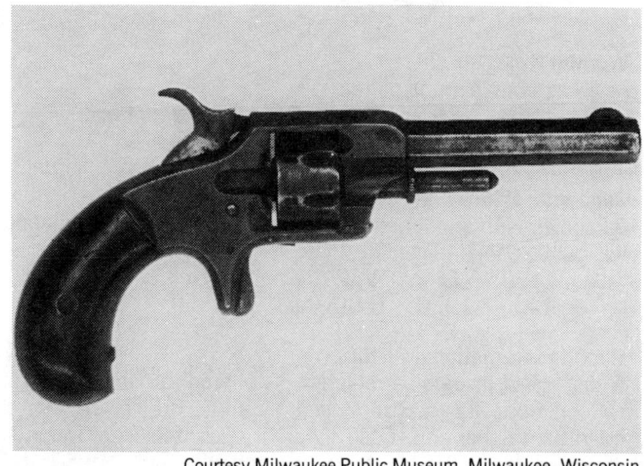

Courtesy Milwaukee Public Museum, Milwaukee, Wisconsin.

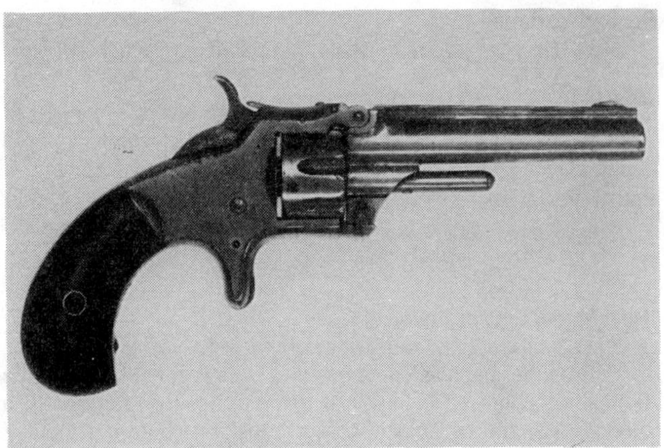
Courtesy Milwaukee Public Museum, Milwaukee, Wisconsin.

Exc.	V.G.	Good	Fair	Poor
350	300	250	200	150

WHITNEY FIREARMS COMPANY
Hartford, Connecticut

Wolverine

A .22 caliber semi-automatic pistol with a 4.75" barrel. Blued or nickle-plated with plastic grips and an aluminum alloy frame. This pistol is readily distinguishable by its very streamlined form. Approximately 13,000 examples were made with the blued finish and 900 with a nickle-plated finish. The slide marked "Wolverine Whitney Firearms Inc., New Haven, Conn USA." Some examples are also marked "Lightning." Manufactured from 1955 to 1962.

Blue Finish

Exc.	V.G.	Good	Fair	Poor
450	400	350	250	200

Nickle-Plated

Exc.	V.G.	Good	Fair	Poor
550	500	450	300	250

WHITWORTH
SEE—Interarms

WICHITA ARMS, INC.
Wichita, Kansas

Classic Rifle

A single shot bolt-action rifle produced in a variety of calibers with a 21" octagonal barrel. Offered with Canjar adjustable triggers. Blued with a checkered walnut stock.

NIB	Exc.	V.G.	Good	Fair	Poor
3000	2500	2250	1850	1250	1000

Varmint Rifle

As above, with a round barrel.

NIB	Exc.	V.G.	Good	Fair	Poor
2000	1750	1500	1250	1000	800

Silhouette Rifle

As above, with a 24" heavy barrel, grey composition stock and two ounce Canjar trigger.

NIB	Exc.	V.G.	Good	Fair	Poor
2200	1900	1700	1000	850	650

Wichita International Pistol

A single shot pivoted barrel target pistol produced in a variety of calibers from .22 to .357 Magnum with a 10.5" or 14" barrel fitted with either adjustable sights or telescopic sight mounts. Stainless steel with walnut forestock and grips.

NIB	Exc.	V.G.	Good	Fair	Poor
500	450	400	350	300	200

Wichita Classic Pistol

A bolt-action single shot pistol chambered for a variety of calibers up to .308, with a left hand action and 11.25" barrel. Blued with a walnut stock.

NIB	Exc.	V.G.	Good	Fair	Poor
3000	2500	2250	1850	1250	1000

Wichita Classic Engraved

As above, but embellished.

NIB	Exc.	V.G.	Good	Fair	Poor
5000	4250	3500	2500	2000	1500

Wichita Silhouette Pistol

As above, in 7mm HMSA or .308 with a 15" barrel. The walnut stock is made so that the pistolgrip is located beneath the foreward end of the bolt.

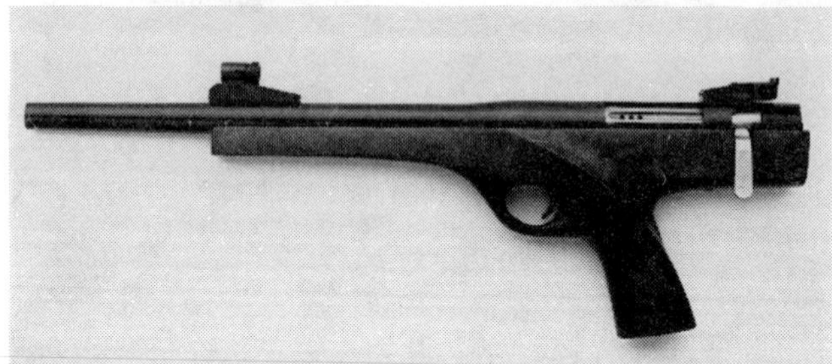

NIB	Exc.	V.G.	Good	Fair	Poor
1100	950	750	600	500	400

Wichita MK40

As above, with a 13" barrel having multi-range sights and either a composition or walnut stock. Standard finish is blued, however, this model was also made in stainless steel.

NIB	Exc.	V.G.	Good	Fair	Poor
1100	950	750	600	500	400

WICKLIFFE RIFLES
Triple S Development
Wickliffe, Ohio

Model 76

A single shot falling-block rifle produced in a variety of calibers from .22 Hornet to .45-70 with a 22" lightweight or 26" heavyweight barrel. Blued with a walnut stock. Introduced in 1976.

Exc.	V.G.	Good	Fair	Poor
400	350	300	250	175

Model 76 Deluxe

As above, with a nickle-silver pistolgrip cap, machine jewelled breechblock and more finely figured walnut stock. Introduced in 1976.

Exc.	V.G.	Good	Fair	Poor
450	400	350	300	200

Traditionalist

The Model 76 in .30-06 or .45-70 caliber with a 24" barrel having open sights and a checkered walnut buttstock. Introduced in 1979.

Exc.	V.G.	Good	Fair	Poor
400	350	300	250	175

Stinger

Similar to the Model 76, but chambered for .22 Hornet or .223 Remington with a 22" barrel fitted with a Burris 6X power telescope. Blued with a checkered Monte Carlo-style stock. Introduced in 1979.

Exc.	V.G.	Good	Fair	Poor
400	350	300	250	175

Stinger Deluxe

As above, with a superior grade of finish and more finely figured walnut stock.

Exc.	V.G.	Good	Fair	Poor
475	400	350	300	200

WIENER WAFFENFABRIK

Vienna, Austria

Little Tom

A 6.35mm or 7.65mm double-action semi-automatic pistol with a 2.5" barrel. The slide marked "Wiener Waffenfabrik Patent Little Tom", and the caliber. Blued with either walnut or plastic grips inlaid with a medallion bearing the company's trademark. Approximately 10,000 were made from 1919 to 1925.

Exc.	V.G.	Good	Fair	Poor
500	450	400	250	175

WILDEY FIREARMS CO., INC.

Cheshire, Connecticut
New Burg, New York
Brookfield, Connecticut

Wildey Auto Pistol

A gas-operated, rotary-bolt, double-action semi-automatic pistol chambered for the .357 Peterbuilt, the .45 Winchester Magnum, or the .475 Wildey Magnum cartridges. with 5", 6", 7", 8", or 10" ventilated-rib barrels. The gas-operated action is adjustable and features a single shot cutoff. The rotary bolt has three heavy locking lugs. Constructed of stainless steel with adjustable sights and wood grips. The values of this rarely encountered pistol are based on not only the condition, but the caliber—as well as the serial number range, with earlier-numbered guns being worth a good deal more than the later or current production models.

Cheshire CT Address

Produced in .45 Winchester Magnum only and is serial numbered from No. 1 through 2489.

Serial No. 1 through 200

NIB	Exc.	V.G.	Good	Fair	Poor
2000	1750	1500	1250	900	600

Serial Numbers Above 200 Would Be Worth Approximately $200 Less Respectively in Each Category of Condition.

Survivor Model

This pistol is presently manufactured in Brookfield, Connecticut.

NIB	Exc.	V.G.	Good	Fair	Poor
1100	950	800	600	500	400

Presentation Model

As above, but engraved and fitted with hand checkered walnut grips.

NIB	Exc.	V.G.	Good	Fair	Poor
2500	2000	1500	1250	850	700

WILKINSON ARMS CO.

Covina, California

Diane

A .25 caliber semi-automatic pistol with a 2.25" barrel and 6-shot magazine. Blued with plastic grips.

Exc.	V.G.	Good	Fair	Poor
150	125	100	75	50

Terry Carbine

A 9mm caliber semi-automatic carbine with a 16.25" barrel, adjustable sights and 30-shot magazine. Matte blued with either a black composition or maple stock.

Exc.	V.G.	Good	Fair	Poor
350	300	250	175	125

WILLIAMSON MOORE FIREARMS COMPANY

New York, New York

Derringer

A .41 caliber single shot pocket pistol with a 2.5" sliding barrel. Blued, with a silver-plated furniture and a checkered walnut grip. Barrel marked "Williamson's Pat. Oct. 2, 1866 New York." This pistol was fitted with an auxiliary percussion cap chamber adaptor. Manufactured from 1866 to approximately 1870.

Exc.	V.G.	Good	Fair	Poor
500	450	350	250	175

WILSON & CO.

SEE—English Military Firearms

WILSON, J. P.

Ilion, New York

Percussion Alarm Gun

This unusual little device is chambered for .22 caliber percussion. It consists of approximately a 1" rectangular brass block with a chamber bored into it that accepts a black-powder charge. There is no provision for a projectile. There is a spring-retained arm on top, that works as a hammer. As the device is activated by a door or a window, the hammer snaps closed, striking a percussion cap that causes the charge to fire, thereby creating an alarm notifying that the perimeter has been breached. It is marked "J. P. Wilson/Patented Feb. 8, 1859/Ilion., N.Y."

Exc.	V.G.	Good	Fair	Poor
250	200	175	100	50

WINCHESTER

WINCHESTER REPEATING ARMS COMPANY
New Haven, Connecticut

Winchester is a name that is identified with the Old West and the frontier days of America. Winchester rifles and shotguns are prized for their historical significance as well as their collectiblity. The Winchester Repeating Arms Company was formally established by Oliver F. Winchester on Feb. 20, 1866, and the first model to bear the name of the company was the Model 1866 lever action rifle chambered for the .44 caliber rimfire cartridge. As with any enterprise it is helpful to study the background and beginnings of the Winchester company so as to better understand the chronological sequence of various rifles and pistols that preceded the Winchester Model 1866.

The story begins with Walter Hunt of New York City who, in 1848, developed the Rocket Ball and Volition Repeater, a unique lever-action, breechloading, under-barrel magazine tube repeater. This rifle was the origin for future concepts. Hunt's business partner, George Arrowsmith, had as his machinist a man named Lewis Jennings, who improved and simplified Walter Hunt's original concept. Jennings' improvements were granted a U.S. patent in 1849. This 25-shot repeating rifle was promoted by Arrowsmith who found a willing investor in Courtland Palmer, a Connecticut merchant. Palmer bought both the Hunt and Jennings patents and had 5,000 Jennings rifles built by Robbins and Lawrence in Vermont in 1850. The foreman at Robbins and Lawrence was Benjamin Tyler Henry, a man who would play an important role in future repeating rifle developments. By 1851 two additional individuals would enter the Hunt-Jennings story: Daniel Wesson and Horace Smith. These two men improved on Lewis Jennings' design, and Smith was granted a patent in 1851, which he assigned to Palmer. Despite the initial achievements with the Jennings rifle, the action proved too complex and the cartridges too light for successful marketablity.

In 1854 Horace Smith and Daniel Wesson were granted a U.S. patent for a repeating firearm similar to earlier Horace Smith design. Courtland Palmer funded the experimental work on the new pistol, which featured a 4-inch barrel and a full-length under-barrel magazine. Palmer, Smith, and Wesson formed a partnership incorporating the Hunt, Jennings, Smith, and new Smith & Wesson patents. The pistols were made in Norwich, Connecticut under the name of Smith & Wesson. B. Tyler Henry was an employee of the new firm. Only about 1,000 of these pistols were produced before the company name was changed to Volcanic Repeating Arms Company, an incorporated firm, in 1855. The new company was formed by Palmer, Smith, and Wesson with the additional financial assistance of Oliver F. Winchester. Winchester was at the time a successful manufacturer of men's clothing in New Haven, Connecticut. The new company bought out Palmer and Smith, while Daniel Wesson stayed on as shop foreman to work on his metallic rimfire cartridge. Volcanic pistols and rifles were first built at the original Smith & Wesson factory in Norwich until 1856 when a new plant was located at New Haven. In 1857 the majority of stock in the Volcanic Repeating Arms Company was owned by Oliver Winchester.

The New Haven Arms Company was structured in April 1857 to assume the business of Volcanic Repeating Arms Company. This new company continued the production of Volcanic pistols and rifles, but these were now marked as "NEW HAVEN CONN. PATENT FEB. 14, 1854." These Volcanics received favorable reports as to their rapidity of fire and ease of operation, but they suffered from low velocity, energy, and small calibers. These difficulties affected sales, which remained slow. Perhaps this would be the end of the story had it not been for B. Henry Tyler, who was the shop foreman at New Haven Arms Company after the departure of Daniel Wesson. Tyler had been involved with the predecessors for the past 10 years and he received a patent in 1860 for the improvement in magazine firearms. The success of Henry's new design was twofold: First, the development of a new, more powerful .44 caliber metallic rimfire cartridge was sufficiently potent enough to compete with the single shot rifles of the day, and second, the advancement in the firing pin design, the addition of an extractor, and improvements in the bolt and feeding mechanisms all helped to make the Henry rifle a success. The first production Henry rifles were delivered in 1862. In 1866 the New Haven Arms Company name was changed to Winchester Repeating Arms Company.

The subsequent models offered by Winchester are highly prized by collectors. Winchester Repeating Arms Company went on to establish itself as one of the world's leading firearms manufacturers. Winchester provided repeating rifles that played an important role in this nation's history and will forever have a place as the company that built the guns that "Won the West." By the beginning of World War I, 1914, Winchester was the leading domestic firearms producer in the United States and also exported guns around the world. After World War I ended and beginning in the early 1920s, the company began to lose its dominant position in the firearms industry. The decade of the '20s marked a difficult financial period for Winchester with the company finally being forced into receivership by the end of the decade. In 1931, Winchester was purchased by the Western Cartridge Company owned by the Olin family. Because of the changing times, the company's focus was now on sporting arms, and the drive for new models and manufacturing techniques came from the vision and foresight of John M. Olin.

From 1931 until 1963, Winchester Repeating Arms regained its reputation for quality firearms, and the rifles and shotguns produced during this period in the company's history are as collectible as those guns that preceded it. In 1964, the company could no longer afford to mass produce firearms that in reality were hand fitted and hand machined. Production changes were implemented that reflected the mass production psychology that was becoming so commonplace in American industry. With the exception of the Model 21 and a few other select models of Winchester rifles and shotguns, many Winchester guns produced after 1963 are not viewed by collectors necessarily as collectibles. Nevertheless, they were excellent guns for the hunting fields and duck blinds. In 1981 Winchester Repeating Arms Company sold its firearms division to U.S. Repeating Arms Company. This new company continues to the present day to build rifles and shotguns under license from Winchester. U.S. Repeating Arms Company has itself been the object of several buyouts. Nevertheless, the Winchester legend lives on; collected and respected by many.

WINCHESTER CORPORATE AND DIVISIONAL NAME CHANGES

1931 - 1991

WINCHESTER REPEATING ARMS COMPANY
Dec. 22, 1931 - Dec. 31, 1938

WINCHESTER REPEATING ARMS COMPANY
A Division of Western Cartridge Company
Dec. 31, 1938 - Dec. 30, 1944

WINCHESTER REPEATING ARMS COMPANY
A Division of Olin Industries, Inc.
Dec. 30, 1944 - January 1952

WINCHESTER-WESTERN DIVISION
Olin Industries, Inc.
January 1952 - Aug. 31, 1954

WINCHESTER-WESTERN DIVISION
Olin Mathieson Chemical Corporation
Aug. 31, 1954 - Sept. 1, 1969

WINCHESTER-WESTERN DIVISION
OLIN CORPORATION
Sept. 1, 1969 - July 21, 1981

U.S REPEATING ARMS COMPANY
July 21, 1981 - Present

A brief guide to the Winchester Repeating Arms Company corporate and divisional name changes will be of help to the collector to establish the proper company name on various firearms and advertising materials.

The prices given here are for the most part standard guns without optional features that were so often furnished by the factory. These optional or extra cost features are too numerous to list and can affect the price of a shotgun or rifle to an enormous degree. In some cases these options are one of a kind. Collectors and those interested in Winchester firearms have the benefit of some of the orginial factory records. These records are now stored in the Cody Firearms Museum, Buffalo Bill Historical Center, P.O. Box 1000, Cody, Wyoming (307)-587-4771. For a $25 fee the museum will provide factory letters containing the original specifications of certain Winchester models using the original factory records.

MODEL	SERIAL NUMBER
1866	124995 to 170101
1873	1 to 720496 (N/A 497-610 and 199551-199598)
1876	1 to 63871
Hotchkiss	1 to 84555
1885 *	1 to 109999 (N/A 74459-75556)
1886	1 to 156599 (N/A 146000-150799)
1887 & 1901	1 to 72999
1890	1 to 329999 (N/A 20000-29999)
1906	1 to 79999
1892	1 to 379999
1893	1 to 34050
1897	1 to 377999
1894	1 to 353999
1895	1 to 59999
Lee	1 to 19999
1903	1 to 39999
1905	1 to 29078
1906	1 to 79999
1907	1 to 9999
21	1 to 35000

* Single Shot

Hunt Repeating Rifle

Walter Hunt described his repeating rifle as the Volition Repeater. Hunt was granted U.S. patent number 6663 in August 1849 for his repeating rifle which was to pave the way for future generations of Winchester repeating rifles. Hunt's rifle design was unique and innovative as was his patent number 5701 for a conical lead bullet that was to be fired in his rifle. This ingenious bullet had a hole in its base filled with powder and closed by a disc with an opening in the middle to expel the ignition from an independent priming source that used priming pellets made of fulminate of mercury. The rifle actually worked but only the patent model was built; it is now in the Cody Firearms Museum.

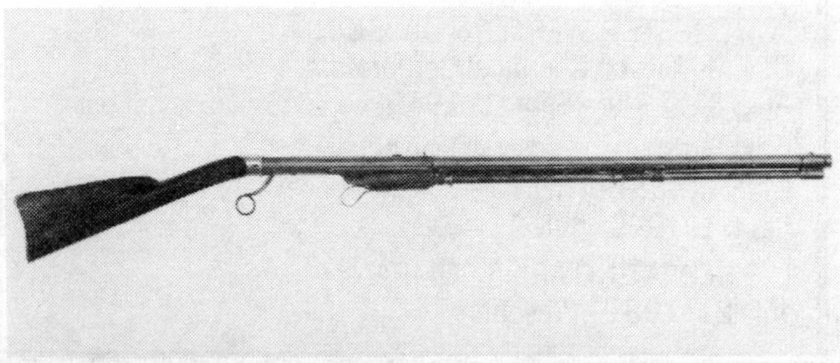

Jennings

Second in the evolutionary line of Winchester rifles is the Jennings. Made by Robbins & Lawrence of Windsor, Vermont, this rifle incorporated the original concept of the Hunt design with the additional improvements utilized by Lewis Jennings. The Jennings rifle is important not only as a link in the chain of repeating rifle development but also because it introduced Benjamin Henry Tyler to the concept of the tubular magazine lever action repeating rifle. The Jennings rifle was built in three separate and distinct models. While total production of the three types was contracted for 5,000 guns, it is probable that only about 1,000 were actually produced.

First Model

The First Model Jennings was built in a .54 caliber, breech-loading, single shot configuration with a ring trigger, oval trigger-guard, and 26-inch barrel. A ramrod was fixed to the underside of the barrel as well. This variation was made from 1850 to 1851.

Courtesy Milwaukee Public Museum, Milwaukee, Wisconsin.

Exc.	V.G.	Good	Fair	Poor
7500	5000	3500	2000	1000

Second Model

The Second Model Jennings was produced adopting the improvements made by Horace Smith. This Second Model is a breech-loading repeating rifle with an under-barrel magazine tube and a 26-inch barrel. The frame is sculptured, unlike the First Model. The ring trigger is still present, but the triggerguard was removed as part of the design change. The caliber remained a .54, and the rifle was fitted with a 25-inch barrel. The Second Model was produced in 1851 and 1852.

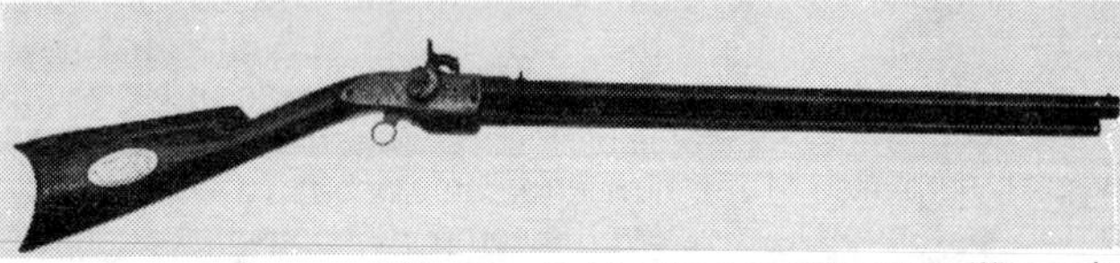

Courtesy Milwaukee Public Museum, Milwaukee, Wisconsin.

Exc.	V.G.	Good	Fair	Poor
10,000	8500	6500	3000	1500

Third Model

The Third Model represents an attempt by investors to use the remaining parts and close out production. The .54 caliber Third Model was a muzzle-loading rifle with a ramrod mounted under the barrel and a 26-1/2-inch barrel. The frame was the same as that used on the First Model, but the trigger was more of the conventional type. The triggerguard had a bow in the middle giving this model a distinctive appearance. This variation was produced in 1852 and marks the end of the early conceptual period in repeating rifle development.

Exc.	V.G.	Good	Fair	Poor
12,000	10,000	7500	5000	2500

Smith & Wesson Volcanic Firearms

An interesting connection in the evolution of the lever action repeating firearm is found in the production of a small group of pistols and rifles built in Norwich, Connecticut by Horace Smith and Daniel Wesson under the firm name of Smith & Wesson. The company built two types of Volcanic pistols. One was a large frame model with an 8-inch barrel and chambered in .41 caliber. About 500 of these large frames were produced. The other pistol was a small frame version with a 4-inch barrel chambered in .31 caliber. Slightly more of these small frame pistols were built, about 700, than the large frame version. In both variations the barrel, magazine, and frame were blued. Smith & Wesson also produced a lever-action repeating rifle. These rifles are exceedingly rare with less than 10 having been built. They were chambered for the .528 caliber and were fitted with 23-inch barrels. Because of the very small number of rifles built, no value is offered.

Courtesy Buffalo Bill Historical Center, Cody, Wyoming.

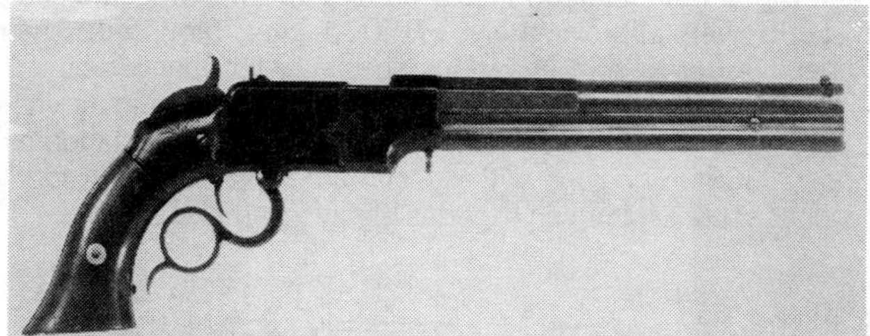

Courtesy Buffalo Bill Historical Center, Cody, Wyoming.

8" Pistol

Exc.	V.G.	Good	Fair	Poor
7500	6000	4000	2000	1000

Courtesy Buffalo Bill Historical Center, Cody, Wyoming.

4" Pistol

Exc.	V.G.	Good	Fair	Poor
5500	3500	2000	1500	1000

Volcanic Firearms (Volcanic Repeating Arms Company)

With the incorporation of the Volcanic Repeating Arms Company, a new and important individual was introduced who would have an impact on the American arms industry for the next 100 years: Oliver F. Winchester. This new company introduced the Volcanic pistol using the improvements made by Horace Smith and Daniel Wesson. Volcanic firearms are marked on the barrel, "THE VOLCANIC REPEATING ARMS CO. PATENT NEW HAVEN, CONN. FEB. 14, 1854." The Volcanic was offered as a .38 caliber breech-loading tubular magazine repeater with blued barrel and bronze frame. These pistols were available in three barrel lengths.

6" Barrel

Exc.	V.G.	Good	Fair	Poor
9000	7100	5500	3000	1500

8" Barrel

Exc.	V.G.	Good	Fair	Poor
9500	7700	6000	3500	2000

16" Barrel

Exc.	V.G.	Good	Fair	Poor
10,000	8500	7000	5000	2500

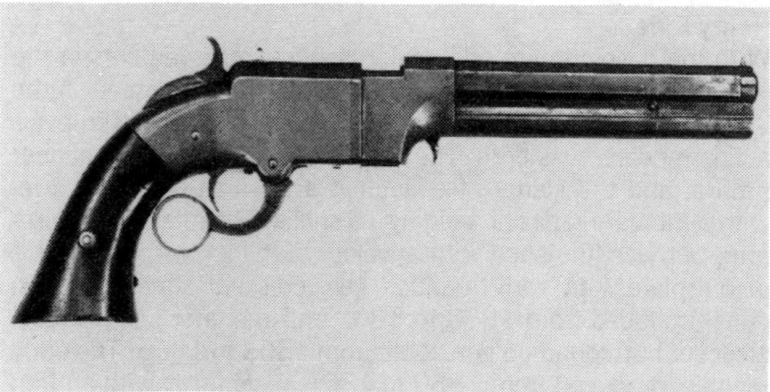

Courtesy Milwaukee Public Museum, Milwaukee, Wisconsin.

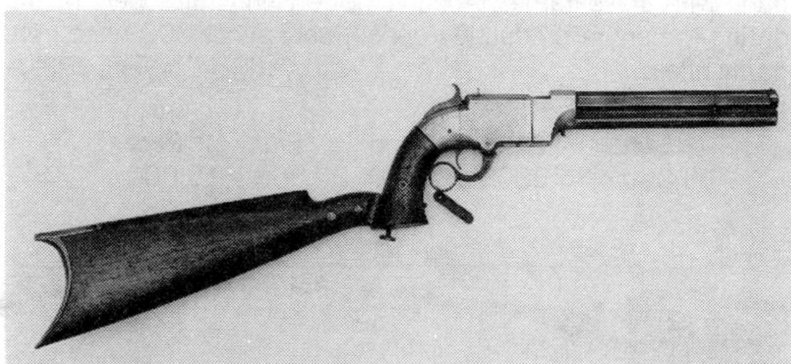

Courtesy Buffalo Bill Historical Center, Cody, Wyoming.

Note: A few Volcanic pistols were produced with detachable shoulder stocks. These are considered quite rare. For original guns with this option, the above prices should be increased by 50 percent.

Volcanic Firearms (New Haven Arms Company)

In 1857 the New Haven Arms Company was formed to continue the production of the former Volcanic Repeating Arms Company. Volcanic firearms continued to be built but were now marked on the barrel, "NEW HAVEN, CONN. PATENT FEB. 14, 1854." The Volcanic pistols produced by the New Haven Arms Company were built in .30 caliber and used the same basic frame as the original Volcanic. These pistols were produced in 3-1/2 inch and 6-inch barrel lengths.

3-1/2" Barrel

Exc.	V.G.	Good	Fair	Poor
8000	6000	5200	2000	1500

6" Barrel

Exc.	V.G.	Good	Fair	Poor
9000	7000	5500	2500	1250

Lever Action Carbine

New Haven Arms introduced, for the first time, a Volcanic rifle that featured a full length slotted magazine tube with a spring activated thumbpiece follower that moved along the entire length of the magazine tube. These rifles were chambered for .38 caliber cartridge and were offered in three barrel lengths; 16, 20, and 24 inches.

Courtesy Buffalo Bill Historical Center, Cody, Wyoming.

16" Barrel

Exc.	V.G.	Good	Fair	Poor
20,000	15,000	10,000	5000	3000

20" Barrel

Exc.	V.G.	Good	Fair	Poor
25,000	17,500	10,000	5000	3000

24" Barrel

Exc.	V.G.	Good	Fair	Poor
30,000	20,000	10,000	5000	3000

Henry Rifle

With the development of B. Tyler Henry's improvements in the metallic rimfire cartridge and his additional improvements in the Volcanic frame, the direct predecessor to the Winchester lever-action repeater was born. The new cartridge was the .44 caliber rimfire, and the Henry rifle featured a 24-inch octagon barrel with a tubular magazine holding 15 shells. The rifle had no fore-arm, but was furnished with a walnut buttstock with two styles of buttplates: an early rounded heel crescent shape seen on guns produced from 1860 to 1862 and the later sharper heel crescent butt found on guns built from 1863 to 1866. The early models, produced from 1860 to 1861, were fitted with an iron frame, and the later models, built from 1861 to 1866, were fitted with brass frames. About 14,000 Henry rifles were made during the entire production period; only about 300 were iron frame rifles.

Iron Frame Rifle

Exc.	V.G.	Good	Fair	Poor
40,000	35,000	25,000	20,000	15,000

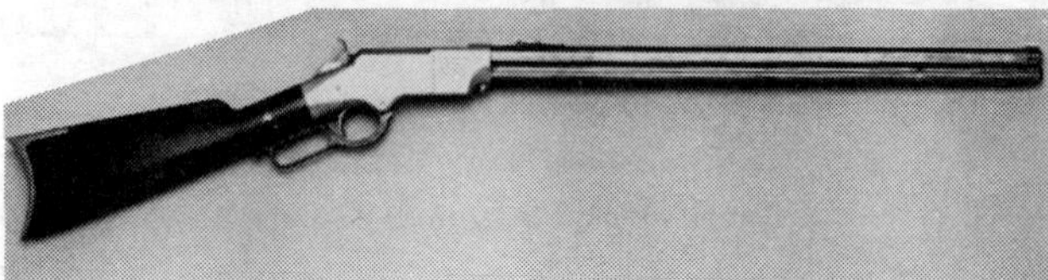

Courtesy Butterfield & Butterfield, San Francisco, California.

Courtesy Butterfield & Butterfield, San Francisco, California.

Brass Frame Rifle

Exc.	V.G.	Good	Fair	Poor
20,000	15,000	10,000	5000	3000

Model 1866

In 1866 the New Haven Arms Company changed its name to the Winchester Repeating Arms Company. The first firearm to be built under the Winchester name was the Model 1866. This first Winchester was a much improved version of the Henry. A new magazine tube developed by Nelson King, Winchester's plant superintendent, was a vast improvement over the slotted magazine tube used on the Henry and its predecessor. The old tube allowed dirt to enter through the slots and was weakened because of it. King's patent, assigned to Winchester, featured a solid tube that was much stronger and reliable. His patent also dealt with an improved loading system for the rifle. The rifle now featured a loading port on the right side of the receiver with a spring loaded cover. The frame continued to be made from brass. The Model 1866 was chambered for the .44 caliber Flat Rimfire or the .44 caliber Pointed Rimfire. Both cartridges could be used interchangeably.

The barrel on the Model 1866 was marked with two different markings. The first, which is seen on early guns up to serial number 23000, reads "HENRY'S PATENT-OCT. 16, 1860 KING'S PATENT-MARCH 29, 1866." The second marking reads, "WINCHESTER'S-REPEATING-ARMS.NEW HAVEN, CT. KING'S-IMPROVEMENT-PATENTED MARCH 29, 1866 OCTOBER 16, 1860." There are three basic variations of the Model 1866:

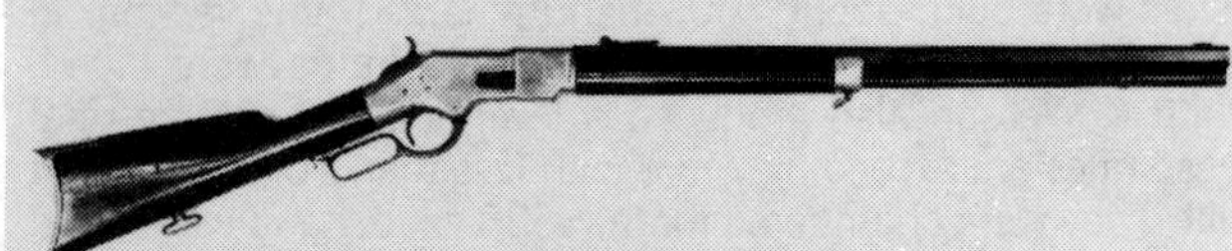

Courtesy Milwaukee Public Museum, Milwaukee, Wisconsin.

1. Sporting Rifle round or octagon barrel. Approximately 28,000 were produced.
2. Carbine round barrel. Approximately 127,000 were produced.
3. Musket round barrel. Approximately 14,000 were produced.

The rifle and musket held 17 cartridges, and the carbine had a capacity of 13 cartridges. Unlike the Henry, Model 1866s were fitted with a walnut forearm. The Model 1866 was discontinued in 1898 with approximately 170,000 guns produced. The Model 1866 was sold in various special order configurations, such as barrels longer or shorter than standard, including engraved guns. The prices listed below represent only standard Model 1866s. For guns with special order features, an independent appraisal from an expert is highly recommended.

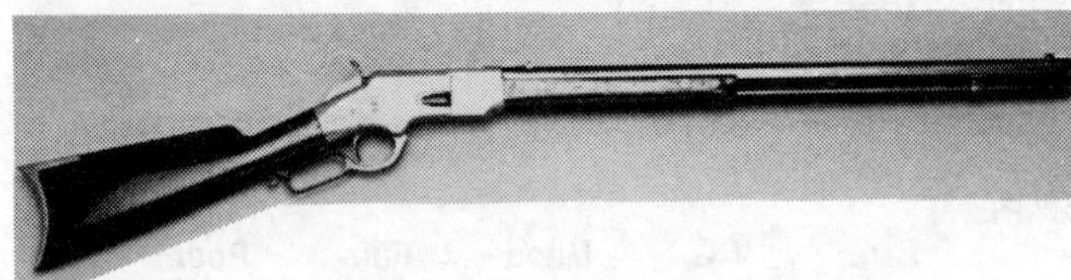

Courtesy Butterfield & Butterfield, San Francisco, California.

First Model

This first style has both the Henry and King patent dates stamped on the barrel, a flat loading port cover, and a two-screw upper tang. Perhaps the most distinctive feature of the First Model is the rapid drop at the top rear of the receiver near the hammer. This is often referred to as the "Henry Drop," a reference to the same receiver drop found on the Henry rifle. First Models will be seen up through the 15000 serial number range.

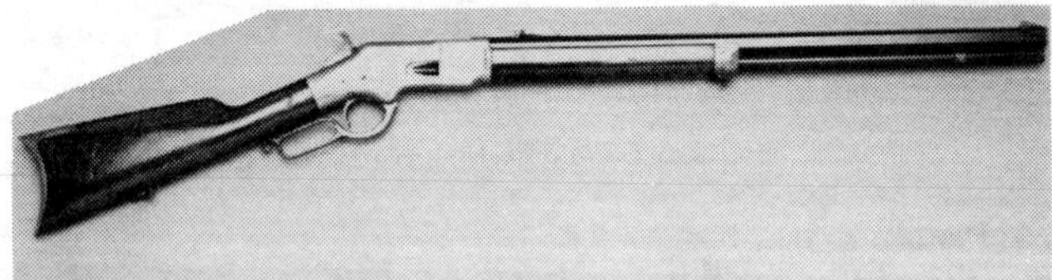

Courtesy Butterfield & Butterfield, San Francisco, California.

Rifle

Exc.	V.G.	Good	Fair	Poor
25,000	20,000	12,000	8000	5000

Carbine

Exc.	V.G.	Good	Fair	Poor
20,000	15,000	10,000	8000	4000

Second Model

The second style differs from the first most noticeably in its single screw upper tang and a flare at the front of the receiver to meet the forearm. The Second Model also has a more gradual drop at the rear of the receiver than the First Model. The second style Model 1866 appears through serial-number 25000.

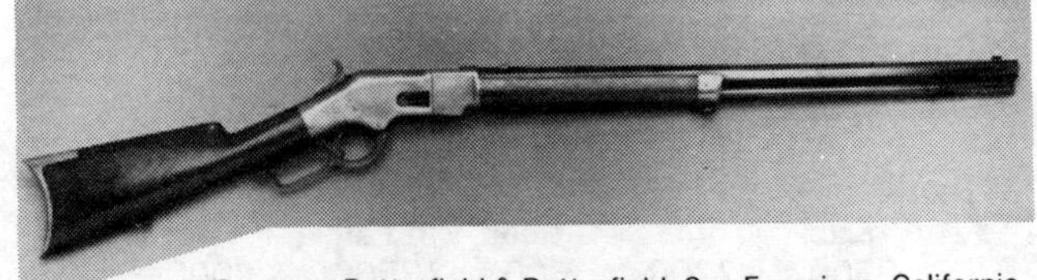

Courtesy Butterfield & Butterfield, San Francisco, California.

Rifle

Exc.	V.G.	Good	Fair	Poor
20,000	15,000	7500	4000	3000

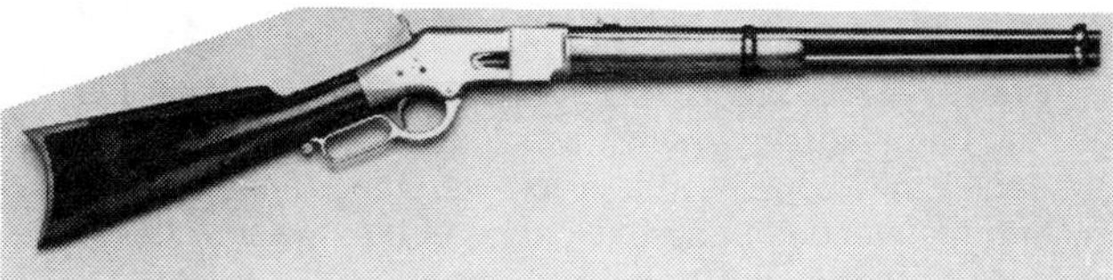

Courtesy Butterfield & Butterfield, San Francisco, California.

Carbine

Exc.	V.G.	Good	Fair	Poor
18,000	12,000	7500	5000	2000

Third Model

The third style's most noticeable characteristic is the more moderately curved receiver shape at the rear of the frame. The serial number is now stamped in block numerals behind the trigger thus allowing the numbers to be seen for the first time without removing the stock. The barrel marking is stamped with the Winchester address. The Third Model is found between serial-numbers 25000 and 149000. For the first time a musket version was produced in this serial number range.

Rifle

Exc.	V.G.	Good	Fair	Poor
18,000	12,000	7000	4000	2000

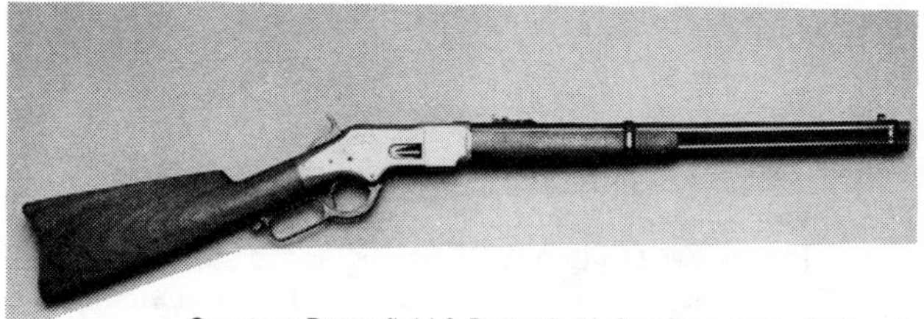

Courtesy Butterfield & Butterfield, San Francisco, California.

Carbine

Exc.	V.G.	Good	Fair	Poor
15,000	10,000	7500	3500	2000

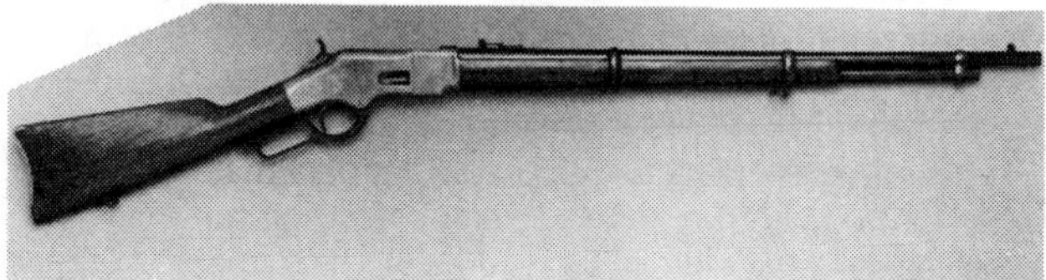

Courtesy Butterfield & Butterfield, San Francisco, California.

Musket

Exc.	V.G.	Good	Fair	Poor
12,000	8000	5000	2000	1000

Fourth Model

The fourth style has an even less pronounced drop at the top rear of the frame, and the serial number is stamped in script on the lower tang under the lever. The Fourth Model is seen between serial number 149000 and 170100 with the late guns having an iron buttplate instead of brass.

Rifle

Exc.	V.G.	Good	Fair	Poor
18,000	12,000	7500	3500	2000

Carbine

Exc.	V.G.	Good	Fair	Poor
15,000	10,000	5000	2000	1000

Musket

Exc.	V.G.	Good	Fair	Poor
12,000	8500	5000	1800	1000

Model 1873

This Winchester rifle was one of the most popular lever actions the company ever produced. This is the "gun that won the West" and with good reason. It was chambered for the more powerful centerfire cartridge, the .44-40. Compared to the .44 Henry, this cartridge was twice as good. With the introduction of the single action Colt pistol in 1878, chambered for the same cartridge, the individual had the convenience of a pistol for protection and the accuracy of the Winchester for food and protection. The .44-40 was the standard cartridge for the Model 1873. Three additional cartridges were offered but were not as popular as the .44. The .38-40 was first offered in 1879 and the .32-20 was introduced in 1882. In 1884 the Model 1873 was offered in .22 caliber rim fire, with a few special order guns built in .22 extra long rimfire. Approximately 19,552 .22 caliber Model 1873s were produced.

Early Model 1873s were fitted with an iron receiver until 1884, when a steel receiver was introduced. The Model 1873 was offered in three styles:

1. Sporting Rifle, 24-inch round, octagon, or half-octagon barrel. Equipped standard with a crescent iron buttplate, straight-grip stock and capped forearm.
2. Carbine, 20-inch round barrel. Furnished standard with a rounded iron buttplate, straight-grip stock, and carbine style forend fastened to the barrel with a single barrel band.
3. Musket, 30-inch round barrel. Standard musket is furnished with a nearly full-length forearm fastened to the barrel with three barrel bands. The buttstock has a rounded buttplate.

The upper tang was marked with the model designation and the serial number was stamped on the lower tang. Caliber stampings on the Model 1873 are found on the bottom of the frame and on the breech end of the barrel. Winchester discontinued the Model 1873 in 1919 after producing about 720,000 guns.

The Winchester Model 1873 was offered with a large number of extra cost options that greatly affect the value of the gun. For example, Winchester built two sets of special Model 1873s; the 1-of-100 and the 1-of-1000. Winchester sold only 8 1-of-100 Model 1873s, and 136 of the 1-of-1000 guns were built. In 1991 a few of these special guns were sold at auction and brought prices exceeding $75,000. The prices listed here are for standard guns only. For Model 1873 with special features, it is best to secure an expert appraisal. Model 1873s with case-colored receivers will bring a premium.

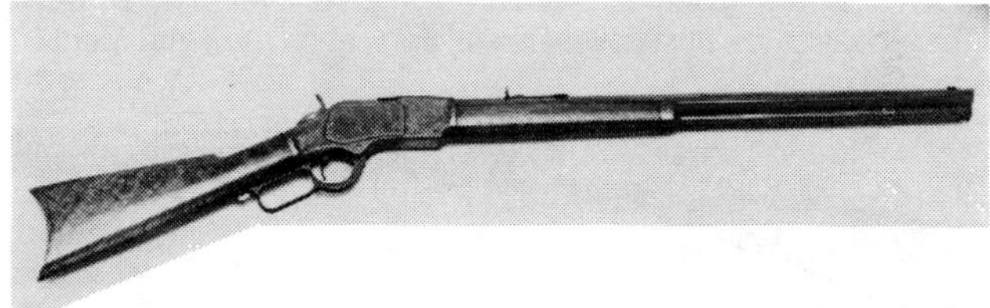

Courtesy Butterfield & Butterfield, San Francisco, California.

First Model

The primary difference between the various styles of the Model 1873 is found in the appearance and construction of the dust cover. The First Model has a dust cover held in place with grooved guides on either side. A checkered oval finger grip is found on top of the dust cover. The latch that holds the lever firmly in place is anchored into the lower tang with visible threads. On later First Models, these threads are not visible. First Models appear from serial number 1 to about 31000.

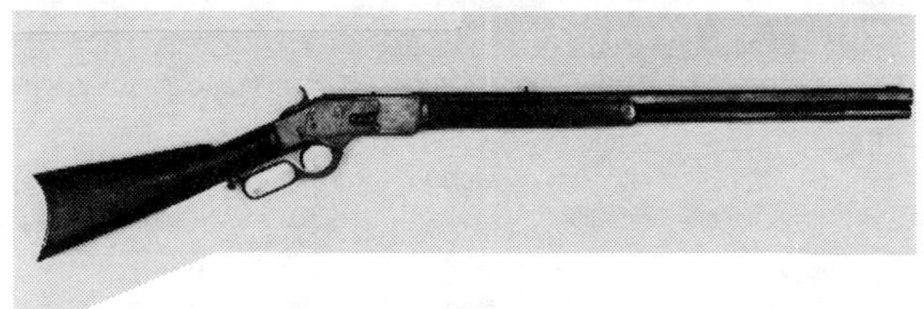

Courtesy Milwaukee Public Museum, Milwaukee, Wisconsin.

Rifle

Exc.	V.G.	Good	Fair	Poor
10,000	7500	4000	2000	750

Carbine

Exc.	V.G.	Good	Fair	Poor
15,000	10,000	5000	3000	1000

Musket

Exc.	V.G.	Good	Fair	Poor
5500	2500	1500	1000	500

Second Model

The dust cover on the Second Model operates on one central guide secured to the receiver with two screws. The checkered oval finger grip is still used, but on later Second Models this is changed to a serrated finger grip on the rear of the dust cover. Second Models are found in the 31000 to 90000 serial number range.

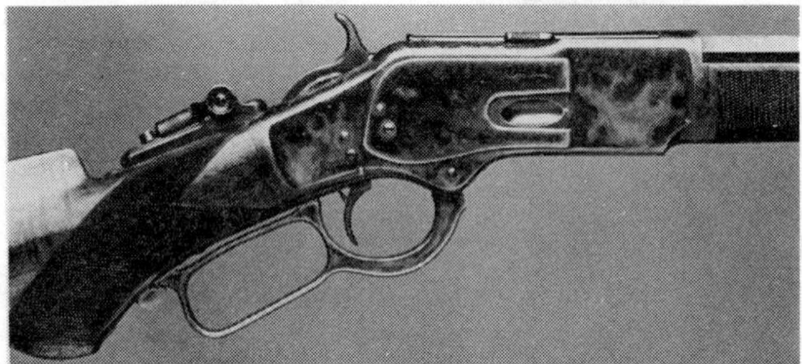

Courtesy Butterfield & Butterfield, San Francisco, California.

Rifle

Exc.	V.G.	Good	Fair	Poor
7500	5000	2500	1000	500

Carbine

Exc.	V.G.	Good	Fair	Poor
10,000	7500	4000	1500	800

Musket

Exc.	V.G.	Good	Fair	Poor
2500	1500	1000	750	500

Third Model

The central guide rail is still present on the Third Model, but it is now integrally machined as part of the receiver. The serrated rear edges of the dust cover are still present on the Third Model.

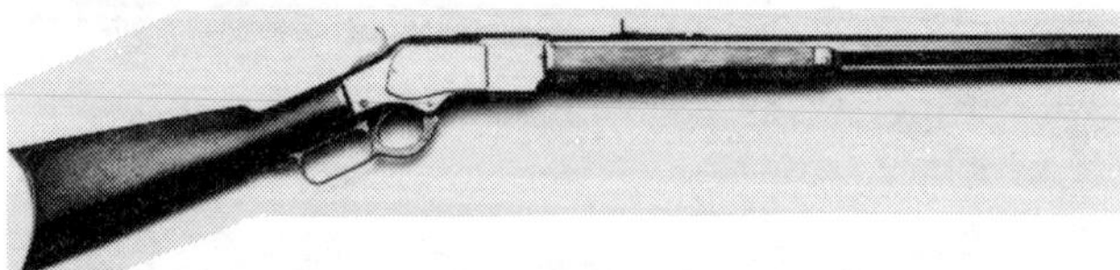

Courtesy Butterfield & Butterfield, San Francisco, California.

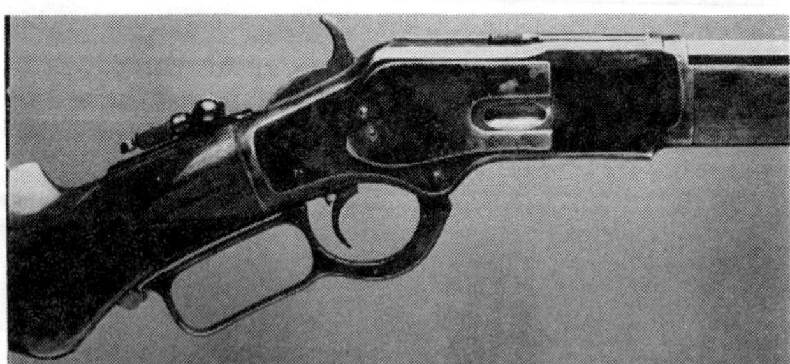

Courtesy Butterfield & Butterfield, San Francisco, California.

Rifle

Exc.	V.G.	Good	Fair	Poor
7500	4500	2000	800	400

Carbine

Exc.	V.G.	Good	Fair	Poor
10,000	6500	3500	1200	800

Musket

Exc.	V.G.	Good	Fair	Poor
2500	1500	1000	750	300

Model 1873 .22 Rimfire Rifle

Winchester's first .22 caliber rifle and the first .22 caliber repeating rifle made in America was introduced in 1884 and discontinued in 1904. Its drawback was the small caliber. The general preference during this period of time was for the larger caliber rifles. Winchester sold a little more than 19,000 .22 caliber Model 1873s.

Exc.	V.G.	Good	Fair	Poor
8000	4500	3000	1500	750

Model 1876

Winchester's Model 1876, sometimes referred to as the Centennial Model, was the company's response to the public's demand for a repeater rifle capable of handling larger and more potent calibers. Many single shot rifles were available at this time to shoot more powerful cartridges, and Winchester redesigned the earlier Model 1873 to answered this need. The principal changes made to the Model 1873 were a larger and stronger receiver to handle more powerful cartridges. Both the carbine and the musket had their forearms extended to cover the full length of the magazine tube. The carbine barrel was increased in length from 20 inches to 22 inches, and the musket barrel length was increased from 30 to 32 inches. The Model 1876 was the first Winchester to be offered with a pistolgrip stock on its special Sporting Rifle. The Model 1876 was available in the following calibers: 45-77 W.C.F., 50-95 Express, 45-60 W.C.F., 40-60 W.C.F. The Model 1876 was offered in four different styles:

1. Sporting Rifle, 28-inch round, octagon, or half-octagon barrel. This rifle was fitted with a straight grip stock with crescent iron butt plate. A special sporting rifle was offered with a pistol-grip stock.
2. Express Rifle, 26-inch round, octagon, or half-octagon barrel. The same sporting rifle stock was used.
3. Carbine, 22-inch round barrel with full length forearm secured by one barrel band and straight grip stock.
4. Musket, 32-inch round barrel with full-length forearm secured by one barrel band and straight grip stock. Stamped on the barrel is the Winchester address with King's patent date. The caliber marking is stamped on the bottom of the receiver near the magazine tube and the breech end of the barrel. Winchester also furnished the Model 1876 in 1-of-100 and 1-of-1000 special guns. Only 8 1-of-100 Model 1876s were built and 54 1-of-1000 76s were built. As with their Model 1873 counterparts, these rare guns often sell in the $75,000 range or more. Approximately 64,000 Model 1876s were built by Winchester between 1876 and 1897. As with other Winchesters, the prices given below are for standard guns.

First Model

As with the Model 1873, the primary difference in model types lies in the dust cover. The First Model has no dust cover and is seen between serial number 1 and 3000.

Courtesy Butterfield & Butterfield, San Francisco, California.

Rifle

Exc.	V.G.	Good	Fair	Poor
10,000	6500	3000	1500	1000

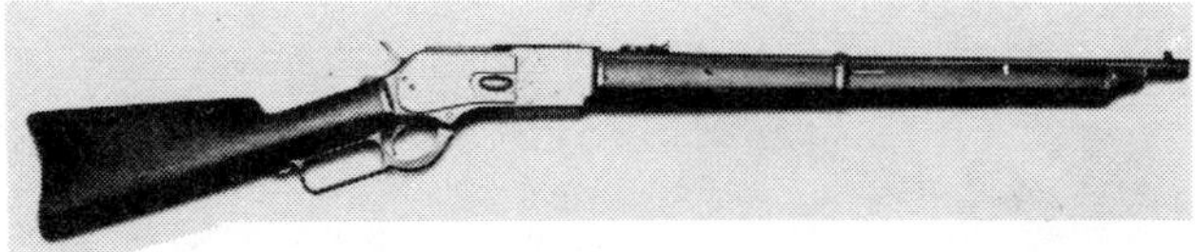

Courtesy Butterfield & Butterfield, San Francisco, California.

Carbine

Exc.	V.G.	Good	Fair	Poor
7500	5000	3000	1500	1000

Musket

Exc.	V.G.	Good	Fair	Poor
10,000	7000	4000	2000	1000

Second Model

The Second Model has a dust cover with guide rail attached to the receiver with two screws. On the early Second Model an oval finger guide is stamped on top of the dust cover while later models have a serrated finger guide along the rear edge of the dust cover. Second Models range from serial numbers 3000 to 30000.

Rifle

Exc.	V.G.	Good	Fair	Poor
5500	3500	2500	1000	500

Carbine

Exc.	V.G.	Good	Fair	Poor
6500	4500	2500	1500	700

Musket

Exc.	V.G.	Good	Fair	Poor
10,000	8000	5000	2000	1000

Third Model

The dust cover guide rail on Third Model 76s is integrally machined as part of the receiver with a serrated rear edge on the dust cover. Third Model will be seen from serial numbers 30000 to 64000.

Rifle

Exc.	V.G.	Good	Fair	Poor
5000	3500	2000	800	500

Carbine

Exc.	V.G.	Good	Fair	Poor
6000	4000	2500	1500	700

Musket

Exc.	V.G.	Good	Fair	Poor
10,000	8000	4500	2000	1000

Winchester Hotchkiss Bolt Action Rifle

This model is also known as the Hotchkiss Magazine Gun or the Model 1883. This rifle was designed by Benjamin Hotchkiss in 1876, and Winchester acquired the manufacturing rights to the rifle in 1877. In 1879 the first guns were delivered for sale. The Hotchkiss rifle was a bolt-action firearm designed for military and sporting use. It was the first bolt-action rifle made by Winchester. The rifle was furnished in 45-70-405 Government, and although the 1884 Winchester catalog lists a 40-65 Hotchkiss as being available, no evidence exists that such a chamber was ever actually furnished. The Model 1883 was available in three different styles:

1. Sporting Rifle, 26-inch round, octagon, or half-octagon barrel fitted with a rifle-type stock that included a modified pistol grip or straight grip stock.
2. Carbine, 24-inch round or 22-1/2 inch round barrel with military style straight grip stock.
3. Musket, 32- or 28-inch round barrel with almost full length military-style straight grip stock. Winchester produced the Model 1883 until 1899, having built about 85,000 guns.

First Model

This model has the safety and a turn button magazine cut-off located above the triggerguard on the right side. The Sporting Rifle is furnished with a 26-inch round or octagon barrel while the carbine has a 24-inch round barrel with a saddle ring on the left side of the stock. The musket has a 32-inch round barrel with two barrel bands, a steel forearm tip, and bayonet attachment under the barrel. The serial number range for the First Model is between 1 and about 6419.

Sporting Rifle

Exc.	V.G.	Good	Fair	Poor
5000	2500	1500	900	500

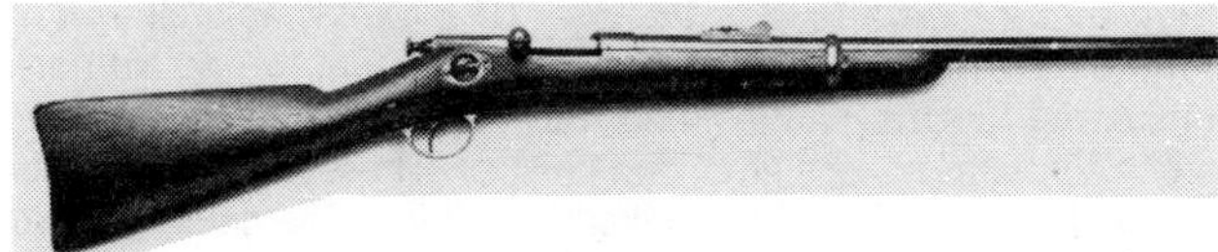

Courtesy Butterfield & Butterfield, San Francisco, California.

Carbine

Exc.	V.G.	Good	Fair	Poor
5000	2500	1500	900	500

Musket

Exc.	V.G.	Good	Fair	Poor
5000	2500	1500	900	500

Second Model

On this model the safety is located on the top left side of the receiver, and the magazine cutoff is located on the top right side of the receiver to the rear of the bolt handle. The sporting rifle remains unchanged from the First Model with the above exceptions. The carbine has a 22-1/2-inch round barrel with a nickeled forearm cap. The musket now has a 28-inch barrel. Serial-number range for the Second Model runs from 6420 to 22521.

Sporting Rifle

Exc.	V.G.	Good	Fair	Poor
4000	2500	1000	750	500

Courtesy Milwaukee Public Museum, Milwaukee, Wisconsin.

Carbine

Exc.	V.G.	Good	Fair	Poor
4000	2250	1000	750	500

Musket

Exc.	V.G.	Good	Fair	Poor
4000	2250	1000	750	500

Third Model

The Third Model is easily identified by the two-piece stock separated by the receiver. The specifications for the sporting rifle remain the same as before, while the carbine is now fitted with a 20-inch barrel with saddle ring and bar on the left side of the frame. The musket remains unchanged from the Second Model with the exception of the two-piece stock. Serial numbers of the Third Model range from 22552 to 84555.

Sporting Rifle

Exc.	V.G.	Good	Fair	Poor
3750	2200	1000	750	500

Carbine

Exc.	V.G.	Good	Fair	Poor
3750	2000	1000	700	400

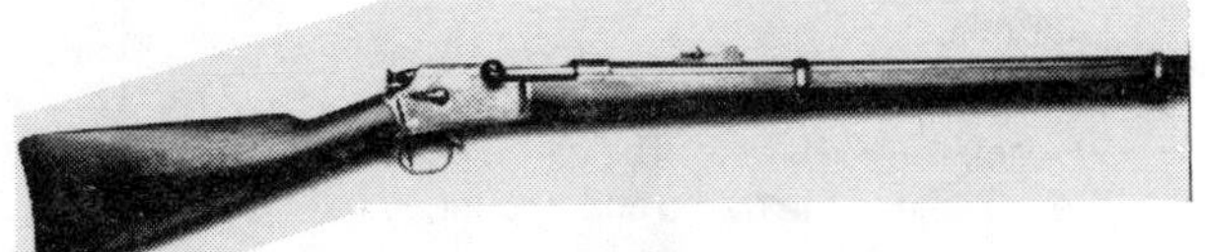

Courtesy Butterfield & Butterfield, San Francisco, California.

Musket

Exc.	V.G.	Good	Fair	Poor
3750	2000	750	500	300

Model 1885 (Single Shot)

The Model 1885 marks an important development between Winchester and John M. Browning. The Single Shot rifle was the first of many Browning patents that Winchester would purchase and provided the company with the opportunity to diversify its firearms line. The Model 1885 was the first single shot rifle built by Winchester. The company offered more calibers in this model than any other. A total of 45 centerfire calibers were offered from the .22 extra long to the 50-110 Express, as well as 14 rimfire caliber from .22 B.B. cap to the .44 Flat Henry. Numerous barrel lengths, shapes, and weights were available as were stock configurations, sights, and finishes. These rifles were also available in solid frame and takedown styles. One could almost argue that each of the 139,725 Model 1885s built are unique. Many collectors of the Winchester Single Shot specialize in nothing else. For this reason it is difficult to provide pricing that will cover most of the Model 1885s that the collector will encounter. However the prices given here are for standard guns in standard configurations.

The Model 1885 was offered in two basic frame types:

A. The High Wall was the first frame type produced and is so called because the frame covers the breech and hammer except for the hammer spur.

B. The breech and hammer are visible on the Low Wall frame with its low sides. This frame type was first introduced around the 5000 serial number range.

Both the High Wall and the Low Wall were available in two type frame profiles; the Thickside and the Thinside. The Thickside frame has flat sides which do not widen out to meet the stock. The Thickside is more common on the low wall rifle and rare on the High Walls.

The Thinside frame has shallow milled sides that widen out to meet the stock. Thinside frames are common on High Wall guns and rare on Low Wall rifles.

1. The standard High Wall rifle was available with octagon or round barrel with length determined by caliber. The buttstock and forearm was plain walnut with crescent buttplate and blued frame.
2. The standard Low Wall featured a round or octagon barrel with length determined by caliber and a plain walnut stock and forearm with crescent buttplate.
3. The High Wall musket most often had a 26-inch round barrel chambered for the .22 caliber cartridge. Larger calibers were available as were different barrel lengths. The High Wall Musket featured an almost full length forearm fastened to the barrel with a single barrel band and rounded buttplate.
4. The Low Wall musket is most often referred to as the Winder Musket named after the distinguished marksman, Colonel C.B. Winder. This model features a Lyman receiver sight and was made in .22 caliber.
5. The High Wall Schuetzen rifle was designed for serious target shooting and was available with numerous extras including a 30-inch octagon barrel medium weight without rear sight seat; fancy walnut checkered pistolgrip Schuetzen-style cheekpiece; Schuetzen-style buttplate; checkered forearm; double set triggers; spur finger lever, and adjustable palmrest.
6. The Low Wall carbine was available in 15-, 16-, 18-, and 20-inch round barrels. The carbine featured a saddle ring on the left side of the frame and a rounded buttplate.
7. The Model 1885 was also available in a High Wall shotgun in 20 gauge with 26-inch round barrel and straight grip stock with shotgun style rubber buttplate. The Model 1885 was manufactured between 1885 and 1920 with a total production of about 140000 guns.

Courtesy Butterfield & Butterfield, San Francisco, California.

Standard High Wall Rifle

Exc.	V.G.	Good	Fair	Poor
3500	3000	2250	1300	850

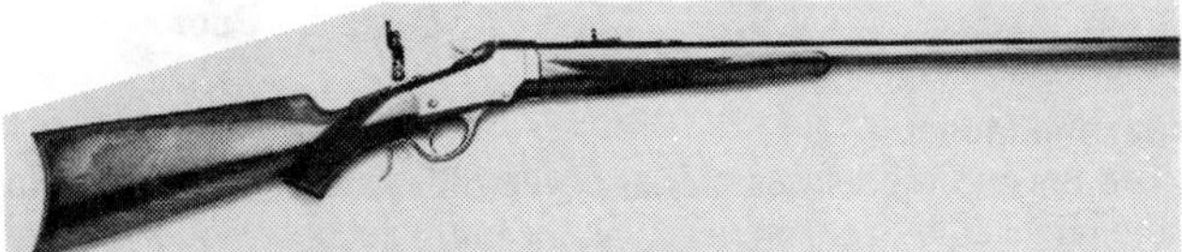

Courtesy Butterfield & Butterfield, San Francisco, California.

Standard Low Wall Rifle

Exc.	V.G.	Good	Fair	Poor
3000	2500	1750	1100	750

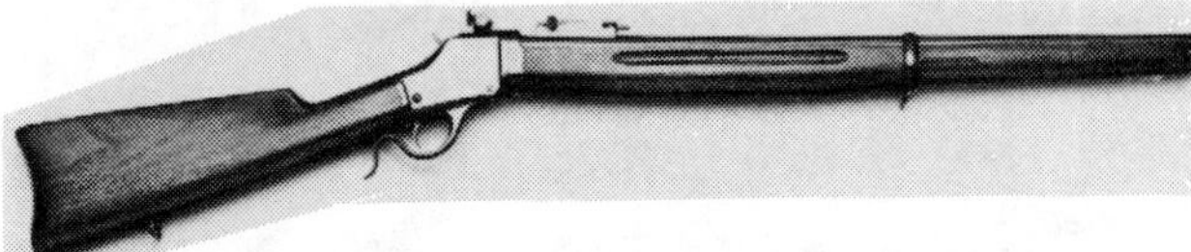

Courtesy Butterfield & Butterfield, San Francisco, California.

High Wall Musket

Exc.	V.G.	Good	Fair	Poor
2500	2000	1200	900	700

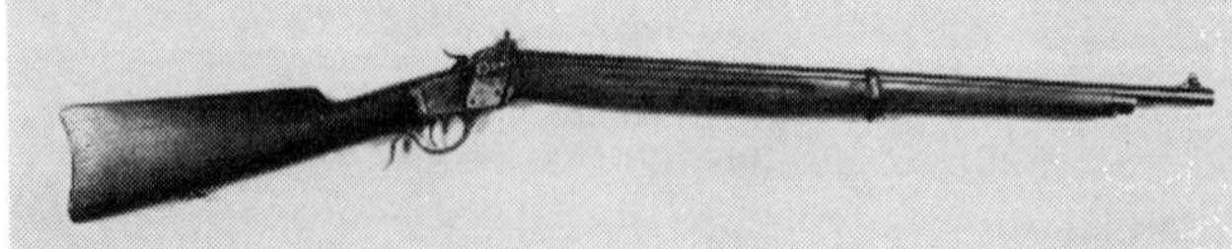

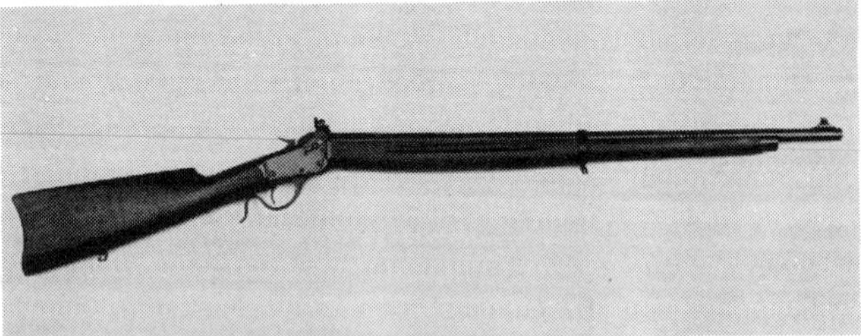

Courtesy Buffalo Bill Historical Center, Cody, Wyoming.

Low Wall Musket (Winder Musket)

Exc.	V.G.	Good	Fair	Poor
2500	2000	1200	900	700

High Wall Schuetzen Rifle

Exc.	V.G.	Good	Fair	Poor
9500	6000	4000	2000	1200

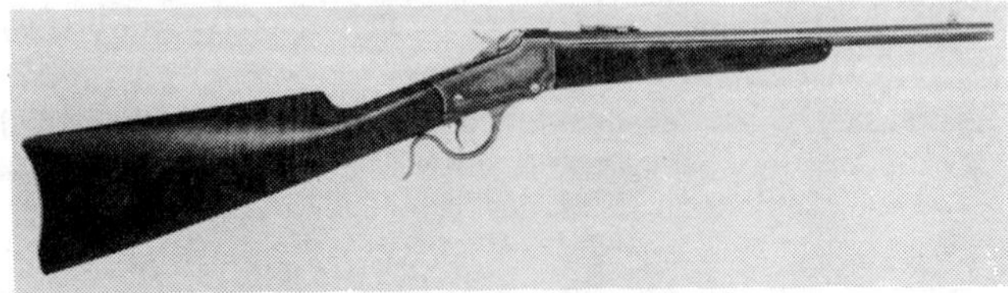

Low Wall Carbine

Exc.	V.G.	Good	Fair	Poor
15,000	10,000	7000	3000	1500

Courtesy Buffalo Bill Historical Center, Cody, Wyoming.

High Wall Shotgun

Exc.	V.G.	Good	Fair	Poor
3000	2500	1750	1250	850

NOTE: Model 1885s with case-colored frames bring a premium of 25 percent over guns with blued frames.

NOTE: Model 1885s in calibers 50-110 and 50-140 will bring a premium depending on style and configuration.

Model 1886

Based on a John Browning patent, the Model 1886 was one of the finest and strongest lever actions ever utilized in a Winchester rifle. Winchester introduced the Model 1886 in order to take advantage of the more powerful centerfire cartridges of the time. The rifle was available in 10 different chambers:

45-70 U.S. Government	50-110 Express
45-90 W.C.F.	40-70 W.C.F.
40-82 W.C.F.	38-70 W.C.F.
40-65 W.C.F.	50-100-450
38-56 W.C.F.	33 W.C.F.

The most popular caliber was the 45-70 Government. Prices of the Model 1886 are influenced by caliber, with the larger calibers bringing a premium. The 1886 was available in several different configurations.

1. Sporting Rifle, 26-inch, round, octagon, or half-octagon barrel, full or half magazine and straight grip stock with plain forearm.
2. Fancy Sporting Rifle, 26-inch, round or octagon barrel, full or half magazine and fancy checkered walnut pistolgrip stock with checkered forearm.
3. Takedown Rifle, 24-inch round barrel, full or half magazine with straight grip stock fitted with shotgun rubber buttplate and plain forearm.
4. Extra Light Weight Takedown Rifle, 22-inch round barrel, full or half magazine with straight grip stock fitted with shotgun rubber buttplate and plain forearm.
5. Extra Light Weight Rifle, 22-inch round barrel, full or half magazine with straight grip stock fitted with a shotgun rubber buttplate and plain forearm.
6. Carbine, 22-inch round barrel, full or half magazine, with straight grip stock and plain forearm.
7. Musket, 30-inch round barrel, musket style forearm with one barrel band. Military style sights. About 350 Model 1886 Muskets were produced.

Model 1886 rifles and carbines were furnished with walnut stocks, case-hardened frames, and blued barrels and magazine tubes. In 1901 Winchester discontinued the use of case-hardened frames on all its rifles and used blued frames instead. For this reason, case-hardened Model 1886 rifles will bring a premium. Winchester provided a large selection of extra cost options on the Model 1886, and for rifles with these options, a separate valuation should be made by a reliable source. The Model 1886 was produced from 1886 to 1935 with about 160,000 in production.

Courtesy Milwaukee Public Museum, Milwaukee, Wisconsin.

Sporting Rifle

Exc.	V.G.	Good	Fair	Poor
8500	5000	3000	1500	650

Courtesy Butterfield & Butterfield, San Francisco, California.

Fancy Sporting Rifle

Exc.	V.G.	Good	Fair	Poor
15,000	9000	5000	3500	2000

Takedown Rifle-Standard

Exc.	V.G.	Good	Fair	Poor
9500	6000	3500	1750	700

Extra Lightweight Takedown Rifle-.33 caliber

Exc.	V.G.	Good	Fair	Poor
4000	2500	1250	600	400

Extra Lightweight Takedown Rifle

Exc.	V.G.	Good	Fair	Poor
7500	4500	1500	1000	500

Extra Lightweight Rifle-.33 caliber

Exc.	V.G.	Good	Fair	Poor
3750	2250	1100	550	400

Extra Lightweight Rifle

Exc.	V.G.	Good	Fair	Poor
6000	4000	1500	750	500

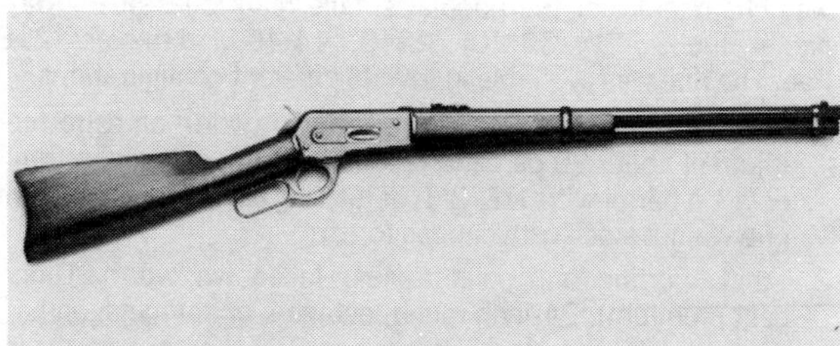
Courtesy Butterfield & Butterfield, San Francisco, California.

Carbine

Exc.	V.G.	Good	Fair	Poor
15,000	10,000	5000	2000	1000

Musket

Exc.	V.G.	Good	Fair	Poor
20,000	15,000	7500	3000	1500

NOTE: For .50 Express add a premium of 20 percent. Blued frame Model 1886 will bring 20 percent less than case-colored Model 1886s.

Model 71

When Winchester dropped the Model 1886 from its line in 1935 the company replaced its large bore lever-action rifle with the Model 71 chambered for the .348 caliber. The Model 71 is similar in appearance to the Model 1886 with some internal parts strengthened to handle the powerful .348 cartridge. The rifle was available in three basic configurations:

1. Standard Rifle, 24-inch round barrel, 3/4 magazine, plain walnut pistolgrip stock and semi-beavertail forearm.
2. Standard Rifle, 20-inch round barrel, 3/4 magazine, plain walnut pistolgrip stock and semi-beavertail forearm.
3. Deluxe Rifle, 24-inch round barrel, 3/4 magazine, checkered walnut pistolgrip stock and checkered semi-beavertail forearm. The frames and barrels were blued on all models of this rifle.

The Model 71 was produced from 1935 to 1957 with about 47,000 built.

Standard Rifle-24" Barrel

Exc.	V.G.	Good	Fair	Poor
950	800	600	400	300

Standard Rifle-20" Barrel (Carbine)

Exc.	V.G.	Good	Fair	Poor
3000	2000	1600	1200	650

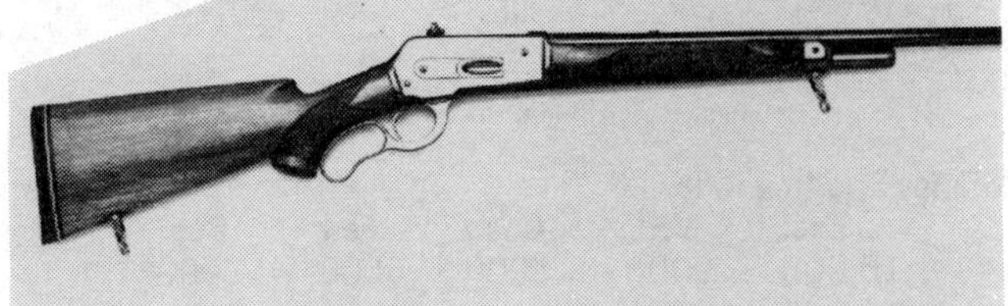

Courtesy Butterfield & Butterfield, San Francisco, California.

Deluxe Rifle-24" Barrel

Exc.	V.G.	Good	Fair	Poor
1400	950	700	525	425

Deluxe Rifle-20" Barrel (Carbine)

Exc.	V.G.	Good	Fair	Poor
3500	3000	2000	1250	700

NOTE: For pre-war Model 71s add a premium of 20 percent.

Model 1892

The Model 1892 was an updated successor to the Model 1873 using a scaled down version of the Model 1886 action. The rifle was chambered for the popular smaller cartridges of the day, namely the .25-20, .32-20, .38-40, .44-40, and the rare .218 Bee. The rifle was available in several different configurations:

1. Sporting Rifle, solid frame or takedown (worth an extra premium of about 20 percent), 24-inch round, octagon, or half-octagon barrel with 1/2, 2/3, or full magazines. Plain straight grip walnut stock with capped forearm.
2. Fancy Sporting Rifle, solid frame or takedown (worth 20 percent premium), 24-inch round, octagon, or half-octagon barrel with 1/2, 2/3, or full magazine. Checkered walnut pistolgrip stock with checkered capped forearm.
3. Carbine, 20-inch round barrel, full or half magazine, plain walnut straight grip stock with one barrel band forearm. Carbines were offered only with solid frames.
4. Trapper's Carbine, 18-, 16-, 15-, or 14-inch round barrel with the same dimensions of standard carbine. Federal law prohibits the possession of rifles with barrel lengths shorter than 16 inches. The Model 1892 Trapper's Carbine can be exempted from this law as a curio and relic with a federal permit.
5. Musket, 30-inch round barrel with full magazine. Almost full-length forearm held by two barrel bands. Buttstock is plain walnut with straight grip.

The Model 1892 was built between 1892 and 1932 with slightly more than 1 million sold. The Model 1892 carbine continued to be offered for sale until 1941.

Courtesy Butterfield & Butterfield, San Francisco, California.

Sporting Rifle

Exc.	V.G.	Good	Fair	Poor
3500	2500	900	600	300

Courtesy Butterfield & Butterfield, San Francisco, California.

Fancy Sporting Rifle

Exc.	V.G.	Good	Fair	Poor
5500	3750	2000	850	350

Courtesy Butterfield & Butterfield, San Francisco, California.

Carbine

Exc.	V.G.	Good	Fair	Poor
4000	3000	1750	900	350

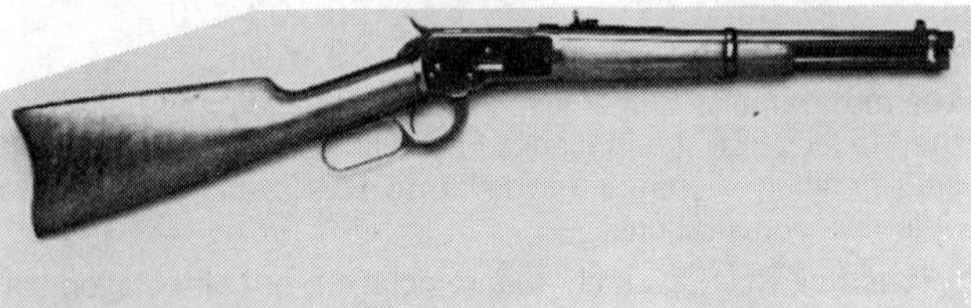

Courtesy Butterfield & Butterfield, San Francisco, California.

Trapper's Carbine

Exc.	V.G.	Good	Fair	Poor
7500	4800	3000	1250	400

Musket

Exc.	V.G.	Good	Fair	Poor
15,000	7500	3000	1500	750

Model 53

This model was in fact a slightly more modern version of the Model 1892 offered in the following calibers: .25-20, .32-20, and the .44-40. It was available in only one style: the Sporting Rifle, 22-inch round barrel, half magazine, straight or pistolgrip plain walnut stock with shotgun butt. It was available in solid frame or takedown with blued frame and barrel. The Model 53 was produced from 1924 to 1932 with about 25,000 built.

Sporting Rifle

Exc.	V.G.	Good	Fair	Poor
3500	2500	1000	500	300

Model 65

This model was a continuation of the Model 53 and was offered in three calibers: .25-20, .32-20, and .218 Bee. It had several improvements over the Model 53, namely the magazine capacity was increased to 7 cartridges, forged ramp for front sight, and a lighter trigger pull. The Model 65 was available only in solid blued frame with blued barrel and pistolgrip with plain walnut stock. Only about 5,700 of these rifles were built between 1933 and 1947.

Courtesy Butterfield & Butterfield, San Francisco, California.

Standard Rifle

Exc.	V.G.	Good	Fair	Poor
4000	3000	1250	750	450

Model 1894

Based on a John M. Browning patent, the Model 1894 was the most successful centerfire rifle Winchester ever produced. This model is still in production, and the values given here reflect those rifles produced before 1964, or around serial number 2550000. The Model 1894 was the first Winchester developed especially for smokeless powder and was chambered for the following cartridges: .32-40, .38-55, .25-35 Winchester, .30-30 Winchester, and the .32 Winchester Special. The rifle was available in several different configurations:

1. Sporting Rifle, 26-inch round, octagon, or half-octagon barrel, in solid frame or takedown. Full, 2/3 or 1/2 magazines were available. Plain walnut straight or pistolgrip stock with crescent buttplate and plain capped forearm.
2. Fancy Sporting Rifle, 26-inch round, octagon, or half-octagon barrel, in solid frame or takedown. Full, 2/3, or 1/2 magazines were available. Fancy walnut checkered straight or pistolgrip stock with crescent buttplate and checkered fancy capped forearm.
3. Extra Lightweight Rifle, 22-inch or 26-inch round barrel with half magazine. Plain walnut straight-grip stock with shotgun buttplate and plain capped forearm.
4. Carbine, 20-inch round barrel, half magazine, plain walnut straight grip stock with carbine style buttplate. Forearm was plain walnut uncapped with one barrel band. Carbines were available with solid frame only. Carbines made prior to 1925 were fitted with a saddle ring on the left side of receiver and worth a premium over carbines without saddle ring.
5. Trapper's Carbine, 18, 16, or 14 inches. Stock and saddle ring specifications same as standard carbine. All Model 1894s were furnished with blued frames and barrels, although case-hardened frames were available as an extra cost option. Case-colored Model 1894s are very rare and worth a considerable premium, perhaps as much as 1000 percent. Guns with extra cost options should be evaluated by an expert to determine proper value. Between 1894 and 1963, approximately 2,550,000 Model 1894s were sold.

Courtesy Butterfield & Butterfield, San Francisco, California.

Sporting Rifle

Exc.	V.G.	Good	Fair	Poor
2500	1600	1000	700	400

NOTE: Takedown versions are worth approximately 20 percent more.

Courtesy Butterfield & Butterfield, San Francisco, California.

Fancy Sporting Rifle

Exc.	V.G.	Good	Fair	Poor
4500	2500	1800	1000	700

NOTE: Takedown versions are worth approximately 20 percent more. Fancy Sporting Rifles were also engraved at the customer's request. Check factory where possible and proceed with caution. Factory engraved Model 1894s are extremely valuable.

Extra Lightweight Rifle

Exc.	V.G.	Good	Fair	Poor
3500	2500	1500	850	500

Courtesy Butterfield & Butterfield, San Francisco, California.

Carbine

Exc.	V.G.	Good	Fair	Poor
2500	1500	800	500	350

NOTE: Above values are for guns with saddle rings. For carbines without saddle rings deduct 35 percent.

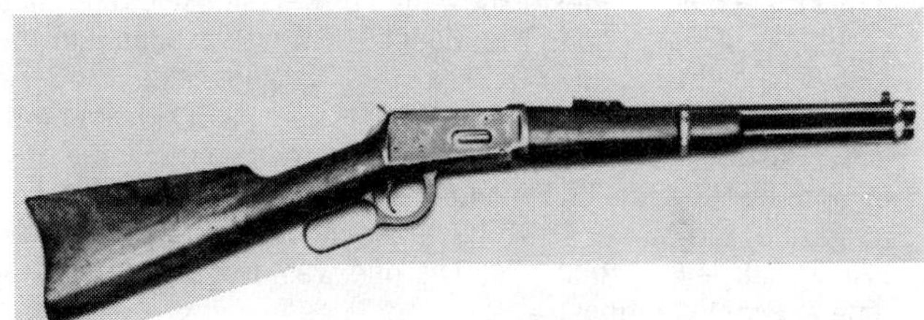

Courtesy Butterfield & Butterfield, San Francisco, California.

Trappers Carbine

Exc.	V.G.	Good	Fair	Poor
5500	3500	2000	1000	500

Model 55

This model was a continuation of the Model 1894 except in a simplified version. Available in the same calibers as the Model 1894, this rifle could be ordered only with a 24-inch round barrel, plain walnut straight-grip stock with plain forend and shotgun butt. Frame and barrel were blued with solid or takedown features. This model was produced between 1924 and 1932 with about 21,000 sold. Serial numbers for the Model 55 were numbered separately until serial number 2870; then the guns were numbered in the Model 1894 sequence.

Standard Rifle

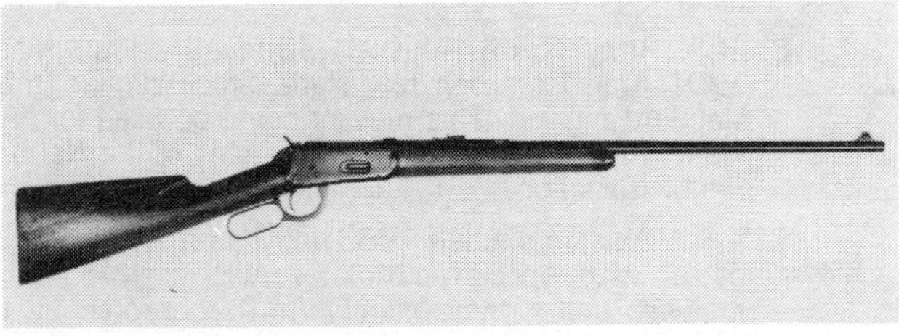

Exc.	V.G.	Good	Fair	Poor
1500	1000	800	600	350

NOTE: .25-35 caliber will bring about a 50 percent premium.

Model 64

An improved version of the Model 55, this gun featured a larger magazine, pistolgrip stock, and forged front sight ramp. The trigger pull was also improved. Frame and barrel were blued. Serial number of the Model 64 was concurrent with the Model 1894. Built between 1933 and 1957, approximately 67,000 were sold. This model was reintroduced in 1972 and discontinued in 1973. The values listed below are for the early version only.

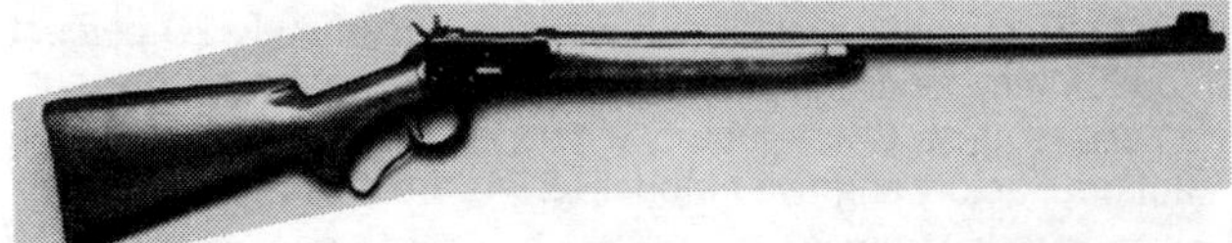

Courtesy Butterfield & Butterfield, San Francisco, California.

Standard Rifle

Exc.	V.G.	Good	Fair	Poor
1800	1350	800	400	300

Carbine-20" Barrel

Exc.	V.G.	Good	Fair	Poor
1950	1300	850	600	400

NOTE: For Deluxe model add 25 percent to above prices. For Carbine model add 25 percent to above prices.

Model 1895

The Model 1895 was the first non-detachable box magazine rifle offered by Winchester. Built on a John M. Browning patent, this rifle was introduced by Winchester to meet the demand for a rifle that could handle the new high power, smokeless hunting cartridges of the period. The Model 1895 was available in the following calibers: .30-40 Krag, .38-72 Winchester, .40-72 Winchester, .303 British, .35 Winchester, .405 Government, 7.62 Russian, .30-03, and .30-06. The rifle gained fame as a favorite hunting rifle of Theodore Roosevelt. Because of its box magazine, the Model 1895 has a distinctive look like no other Winchester lever-action rifle. The rifle was available in several different configurations:

1. Sporting Rifle, 28-inch or 24-inch (depending on caliber) round barrel, plain walnut straight-grip stock with plain forend. The first 5,000 rifles were manufactured with flat sided receivers, and the balance of production were built with the receiver sides contoured. After serial-number 60000 a takedown version was available.
2. Fancy Sporting Rifle, 28-inch round barrel, fancy walnut checkered straight grip stock and fancy walnut checkered forearm. Rifles with serial numbers below 5000 had flat sided frames.
3. Carbine, 22-inch round barrel, plain walnut straight-grip stock with military style handguard forend. Some carbines are furnished with saddle rings on left side of receiver.
4. Musket:
   - A. Standard Musket, 28-inch round, plain walnut straight-grip stock with musket style forend with two barrel bands.
   - B. U.S. Army N.R.A. Musket, 30-round barrel, Model 1901 Krag-Jorgensen rear sight. Stock similar to the standard musket. This musket could be used for "Any Military Arm" matches under the rules of the National Rifle Association.
   - C. N.R.A. Musket, Models 1903 and 1906, 24-inch round barrel with special buttplate. Also eligible for all matches under "Any Military Arm" sponsored by the N.R.A.. This musket was fitted with the same stock as listed above.
   - D. U.S. Army Musket, 28-inch round barrel chambered for the .30-40 Krag. Came equipped with or without knife bayonet. These muskets were furnished to the U.S. Army for use during the Spanish-American War and are "US" marked on the receiver.
   - E. Russian Musket, similar to standard musket but fitted with clip guides in the top of the receiver and with bayonet. Approximately 294,000 Model 1895 Muskets were sold to the Imperial Russian Government between 1915 and 1916. The first 15,000 Russian Muskets had 8-inch knife bayonets, and the rest were fitted with 16-inch bayonets.

The Model 1895 was produced from 1895 to 1931 with about 426,000 sold.

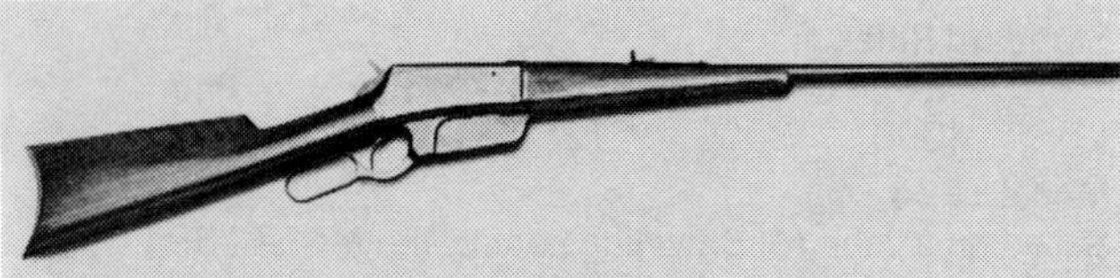

Courtesy Butterfield & Butterfield, San Francisco, California.

Sporting Rifle

Exc.	V. G.	Good	Fair	Poor
5000	3000	1500	900	400

NOTE: Flat side rifles will bring a premium of 100 percent. Takedown rifles will add an additional 15 percent.

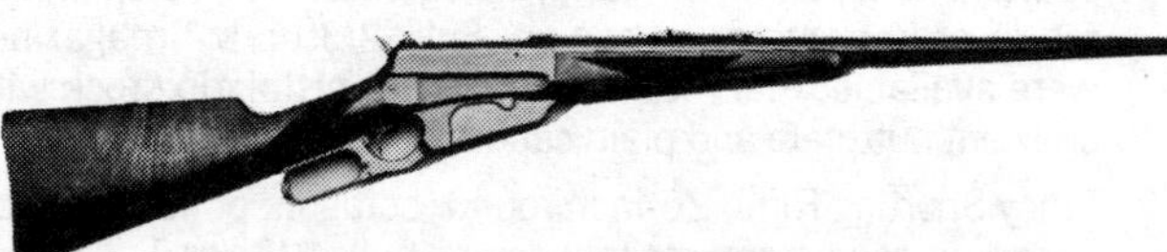

Courtesy Butterfield & Butterfield, San Francisco, California.

Fancy Sporting Rifles

Exc.	V.G.	Good	Fair	Poor
6500	4500	2000	1500	1000

NOTE: Flat side rifles will bring a premium of 100 percent. Takedown rifles will add an additional 15 percent.

Courtesy Butterfield & Butterfield, San Francisco, California.

Carbine

Exc.	V.G.	Good	Fair	Poor
2500	1750	1300	800	600

Standard Musket

Exc.	V.G.	Good	Fair	Poor
2500	2000	1000	700	350

U.S. Army N.R.A. Musket

Exc.	V.G.	Good	Fair	Poor
3500	2000	1500	1000	500

N.R.A. Musket, Model 1903 and 1906

Exc.	V.G.	Good	Fair	Poor
3500	2500	1500	1000	500

U.S. Army Musket

Exc.	V.G.	Good	Fair	Poor
5000	3000	2000	1000	750

Russian Musket

Exc.	V.G.	Good	Fair	Poor
2250	1600	1100	650	350

Breechloading Double Barrel Shotgun

Winchester imported an English made shotgun sold under the Winchester name between 1879 and 1884. The gun was available in 10 and 12 gauge with 30- or 32-inch Damascus barrels. It was sold in 5 separate grades referred to as "classes." The lowest grade was the "D" and the best grade was called the "Match Grade." These were marked on the sidelocks. The center rib was stamped "Winchester Repeating Arms Co., New Haven, Connecticut, U.S.A." About 10,000 of these guns were imported by Winchester.

Class A,B,C, and D

Exc.	V.G.	Good	Fair	Poor
2500	2250	1750	1400	1000

Match Gun

Exc.	V.G.	Good	Fair	Poor
2500	2250	1750	1400	1000

Model 1887 Shotgun

Winchester enjoyed a great deal of success with its imported English shotgun, and the company decided to manufacture a shotgun of its own. In 1885 it purchased the patent for a lever-action shotgun designed by John M. Browning. By 1887 Winchester had delivered the first model 1887 in 12 gauge and shortly after offered the gun in 10 gauge. Both gauges were offered with 30- or 32-inch full choked barrels, with the 30-inch standard on the 12 gauge and 32-inches standard on the 10 gauge. A Riot Gun was offered in 1898 both in 10, and 12 gauge with 20-inch barrels choked cylinder. Both variations of the Model 1887 were offered with plain walnut pistolgrip stocks with plain forend. The frame was case-hardened and the barrel blued. Between 1887 and 1901 Winchester sold approximately 65,000 Model 1887 shotguns.

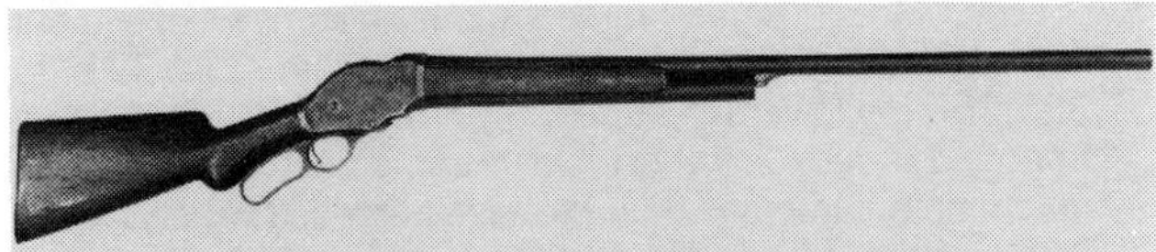

Courtesy Milwaukee Public Museum, Milwaukee, Wisconsin.

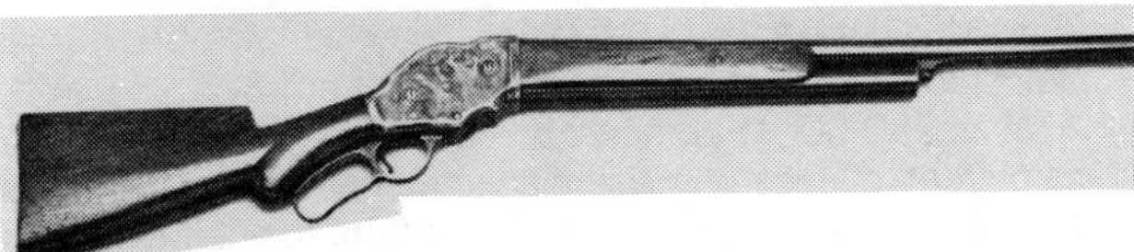

Courtesy Butterfield & Butterfield, San Francisco, California.

Standard Shotgun

Exc.	V.G.	Good	Fair	Poor
1700	1200	850	500	300

Riot Shotgun

Exc.	V.G.	Good	Fair	Poor
2000	1500	950	600	400

Model 1901 Shotgun

This model is a redesign of the Model 1887 shotgun and was offered in 10 gauge only with a 32-inch barrel choked full, modified, or cylinder. The barrel was reinforced to withstand the new smokeless powder loads and the frame was blued instead of case-hardened. The stock was of plain walnut with a modified pistolgrip and plain forearm. The Model 1901 was built between 1901 and 1920 with about 65,000 guns sold.

Standard Shotgun

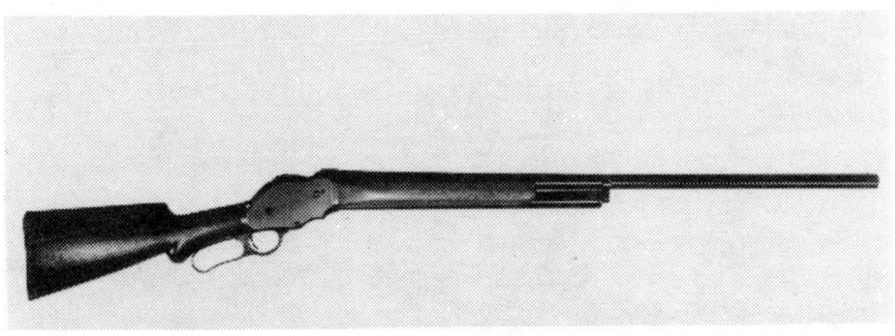

Exc.	V.G.	Good	Fair	Poor
1200	800	600	400	250

Model 1893

This was the first slide action repeating shotgun built by Winchester. It featured an exposed hammer and side ejection. Based on a John M. Browning patent this model was not altogether satisfactory. The action proved to be too weak to handle smokeless loads even though the gun was designed for black powder. The gun was offered in 12 gauge with 30- or 32-inch barrels choked full. Other chokes were available on special order and will command a premium. The stock was plain walnut with a modified pistolgrip, grooved slide handle, and hard rubber buttplate. The receiver and barrel were blued. Winchester produced the Model 1893 between 1893 and 1897, selling about 34,000 guns.

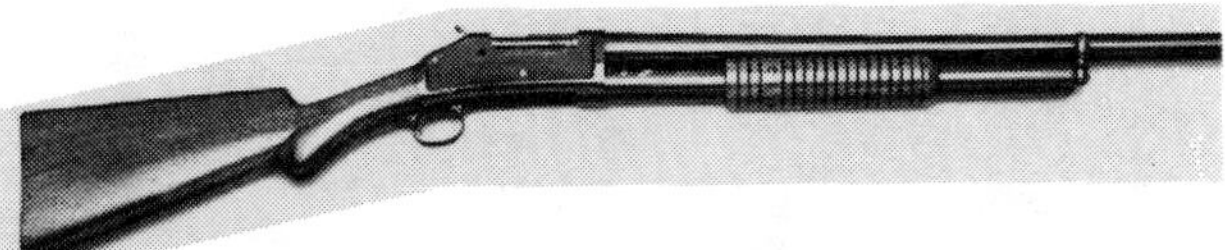

Courtesy Butterfield & Butterfield, San Francisco, California.

Standard Shotgun

Exc.	V.G.	Good	Fair	Poor
1000	700	500	325	150

Model 1897

The Model 1897 replaced the Model 1893, and while similar to the Model 1893, the new model had several improvements such as a stronger frame, chamber made longer to handle 2-3/4 inch shells, frame top was covered to force complete side ejection, the stock was made longer and with less drop. The Model 1897 was available in 12 or 16 gauge with the 12 gauge offered either in solid or takedown styles and the 16 gauge available in takedown only. The Model 1897 was available with barrel lengths of 20-, 28-, and 30-inches and in practically all choke options from full to cylinder. The shotgun could be ordered in several different configurations:

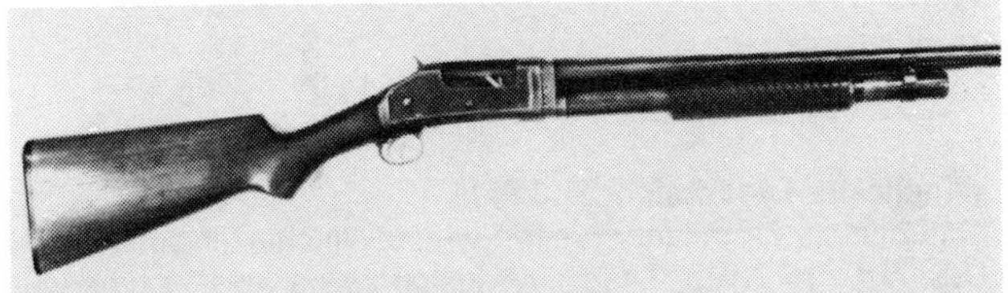

1. Standard Gun, 12 or 16 gauge, 30-inch barrel in 12 gauge and 28-inch barrel in 16 gauge, with plain walnut modified pistolgrip stock and grooved slide handle. Steel buttplate standard.
2. Trap Gun, 12 or 16 gauge, 30-inch barrel in 12 gauge and 28-inch barrel in 16 gauge, fancy walnut stock with oil finish checkered pistolgrip or straight-grip stock with checkered slide handle. Marked "TRAP" on bottom of frame.
3. Pigeon Gun, 12 or 16 gauge, 28-inch barrel on both 12 and 16 gauge, straight or pistolgrip stock same as Trap gun, receiver hand engraved.
4. Tournament Gun, 12 gauge only with 30-inch barrel, select walnut checkered straight grip stock and checkered slide handle, top of receiver is matted to reduce glare.
5. Brush Gun, 12 or 16 gauge, 26-inch barrel, cylinder choke, has a slightly shorter magazine tube than standard gun, plain walnut modified pistolgrip stock with grooved slide handle.
6. Brush Gun, Take Down, same as above with takedown feature and standard length magazine tube.
7. Riot Gun, 12 gauge, 20-inch barrel bored to shoot buckshot, plain walnut modified pistolgrip stock with grooved slide handle. Solid frame or takedown.
8. Trench Gun, same as Riot Gun but fitted with barrel hand guard and bayonet.

The Winchester Model 1897 was a great seller for Winchester. During its 60 year production span 1,025,000 guns were sold.

Standard Gun

Exc.	V.G.	Good	Fair	Poor
600	400	300	200	125

Trap Gun

Exc.	V.G.	Good	Fair	Poor
850	550	400	325	250

Pigeon Gun

Exc.	V.G.	Good	Fair	Poor
2700	2200	1600	1250	1000

Tournament Gun

Exc.	V.G.	Good	Fair	Poor
900	600	450	350	250

Brush Gun

Exc.	V.G	Good	Fair	Poor
850	550	400	325	250

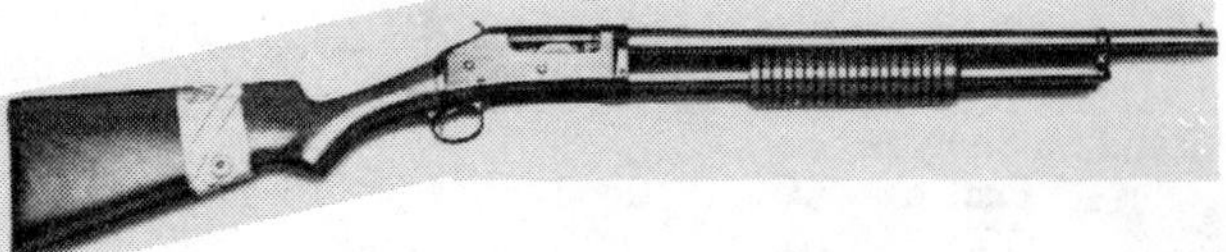

Courtesy Butterfield & Butterfield, San Francisco, California.

Riot Gun

Exc.	V.G.	Good	Fair	Poor
700	600	500	350	200

Courtesy Butterfield & Butterfield, San Francisco, California.

Trench Gun

Exc.	V.G.	Good	Fair	Poor
1500	1200	800	500	300

Winchester-Lee Straight Pull Rifle

This rifle was a military firearm which Winchester built for the U.S. Navy in 1895. The Navy version was a musket type with 28 inch round barrel and musket style forearm and plain walnut pistol grip stock. In 1897 Winchester offered a commercial musket version for public sale as well as a Sporting Rifle. All of these guns were chambered for the 6mm Lee (236 Caliber) cartridge. The Sporting Rifle featured a 24-inch round barrel with plain walnut pistolgrip stock and finger grooves in the forearm. Built from 1895 to 1905, Winchester sold about 20,000 Lee rifles; 15,000 were sold to the U.S. Navy, 3,000 were sold in the commercial version, and 1,700 were Sporting Rifles.

U.S. Navy Musket

Exc.	V.G.	Good	Fair	Poor
1200	900	650	550	375

Commercial Musket

Exc.	V.G.	Good	Fair	Poor
1500	1100	750	600	400

Sporting Rifle

Exc.	V.G.	Good	Fair	Poor
1000	800	550	450	300

Model 1890

The Model 1890 was the first slide action rifle ever produced by Winchester. Designed by John and Matthew Browning, this rifle was chambered for the .22 Short, Long, and Winchester Rimfire cartridges (the WRf cartridge was developed by Winchester specifically for the Model 1890) not on an interchangeable basis. In 1919 the .22 Long Rifle cartridge was offered as well. The rifle was a slide action top ejecting rifle with an 18-inch under barrel magazine tube. All Model 1890s were furnished standard with plain walnut straight stocks with crescent buttplate and 12 groove slide handle. This rifle was one of the company's best selling small caliber firearms and was in world wide use. The Model 1890 came in three separate and distinct variations which greatly affect its value:

1. First Model, solid frame, 24-inch octagon barrel, casehardened frame, and fixed rear sight. Approximately 15,552 of these First Model guns were produced, and their distinctive feature is concealed locking lugs and solid frame. Serial numbered on the lower tang only. Built from 1890 to 1892.
2. Second Model, takedown, 24-inch octagon barrel, casehardened frame, and adjustable rear sight. Serial numbered from 15,553 to 112,970 (on lower tang only) these Second Model guns feature the same concealed locking lugs but with the added takedown feature. A Deluxe version was offered with fancy walnut checkered straight or pistolgrip stock and grooved slide handle.

2A. Second Model (Blued Frame Variation), same as above but with blued frame. Serial-numbered from 112,971 to 325,250 (on lower tang until 232,328, then also on bottom front end of receiver) these blued frame Second Models are much more numerous than the case-hardened variety. A Deluxe version was offered with fancy walnut checkered straight or pistolgrip stock and grooved slide handle.

3. Third Model, takedown, 24-inch octagon barrel, blued frame, adjustable rear sight. Serial-numbered from 325,251 to as high as 853,000 (numbered on both the lower tang and bottom front of receiver) the distinctive feature of the Third Model is the locking cut made on the front top of the receiver to allow the breech bolt to lock externally. A Deluxe version was offered with fancy walnut checkered stock, straight or pistolgrip with grooved slide handle. Winchester offered many extra cost options for this rifle that will greatly affect the value. Secure an expert appraisal before proceeding. The Model 1890 was produced from 1890 to 1932 with approximately 775,000 guns sold.

First Model-Standard Grade

Exc.	V. G.	Good	Fair	Poor
6500	3500	1500	1000	350

Second Model-Casehardened Frame

	Exc.	V.G.	Good	Fair	Poor
Standard	3000	2000	1000	500	200
Deluxe	4500	3000	1500	900	600

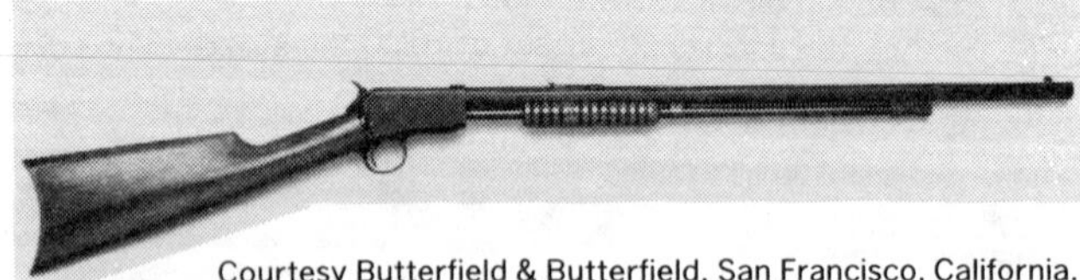

Courtesy Butterfield & Butterfield, San Francisco, California.

Courtesy Butterfield & Butterfield, San Francisco, California.

Second Model-Blued Frame

	Exc.	V.G.	Good	Fair	Poor
Standard	2250	1550	850	450	200
Deluxe	3500	2550	1300	850	600

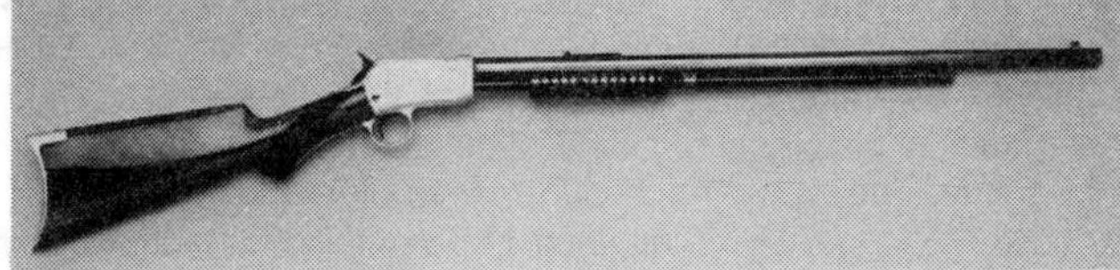

Courtesy Butterfield & Butterfield, San Francisco, California.

Third Model

	Exc.	V.G.	Good	Fair	Poor
Standard	1500	900	600	400	200
Deluxe	2500	1500	900	750	600

Note: For Third Models chambered for .22 Long Rifle add 20 percent premium.

Model 1906

In 1906 Winchester decided to offer a lower cost version of the Model 1890. The Model 1906 used the same receiver but was fitted with a 20-inch round barrel and plain gumwood straight grip stock. When the Model 1906 was first introduced, it sold for two-thirds of the price of the Model 1890. For the first two years the gun was chambered for the .22 Short cartridge only. In 1908 the rifle was modified to shoot .22 Short, Long, and Long Rifle cartridges interchangeably. This modification insured the Model 1906's success, and between 1906 and 1932 about 800,000 were sold. All Model 1906s were of the takedown variety. The Model 1906 is available in three important variations:

1. .22 Short Only, 20-round barrel, straight-grip gumwood stock and smooth slide handle. These were built from serial-number 1 to around 113000.
2. Standard Model 1906, 20-inch round barrel, straight-grip gumwood stock with 12 groove slide handle. Serial numbered from 113000 to 852000.
3. Model 1906 Expert, 20-inch round barrel, pistolgrip gumwood stock with fluted smooth slide handle. Expert was available from 1918 to 1924 and was offered in three different finishes: regular blued finish, half nickle (receiver, guard and bolt), and full nickle (receiver, guard, bolt, and barrel nickled).

Courtesy Butterfield & Butterfield, San Francisco, California.

Model 1906 .22 Short Only

Exc.	V.G.	Good	Fair	Poor
2000	1200	600	400	150

Courtesy Butterfield & Butterfield, San Francisco, California.

Standard Model 1906

NIB	Exc.	V.G.	Good	Fair	Poor
3000	1000	700	400	250	150

Courtesy Butterfield & Butterfield, San Francisco, California.

Model 1906 Expert

Exc.	V.G.	Good	Fair	Poor
1250	900	500	375	200

Note: Prices are for all blued Experts. Add 25 percent for half nickle and 100 percent for full nickle.

Model 62 and 62A

When the Model 1890 and Model 1906 were dropped from the Winchester product line in 1932, the company introduced the Model 62 to take their place. An updated version of the earlier slide action .22 rifles, the Model 62 was fitted with a 23-inch round barrel and was capable of shooting .22 Short, Long, and Long Rifle cartridges interchangeably. Winchester offered a Gallery version of the Model 62 which was chambered for .22 Short only. Some of these Gallery guns have "Winchester" stamped on the left side of the receiver. A change in the breech bolt mechanism brought about a change in the name designation from Model 62 to Model 62A. This occurred around serial-number 98000. The letter "A" now appears behind the serial-number. This model stayed in production until 1958, and collectors will concede a premium for guns built prior to World War II with small slide handles. The stock was of plain walnut with straight grip and grooved slide handle. Both the receiver and barrel were blued. All Model 62 and 62As were takedown. Approximately 409,000 guns were sold.

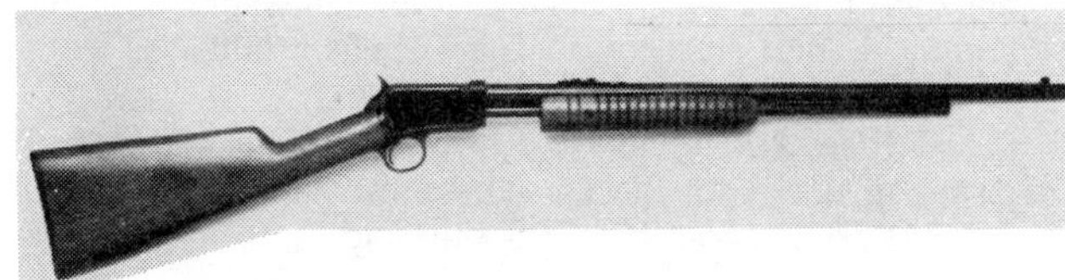

Courtesy Butterfield & Butterfield, San Francisco, California.

Prewar Model 62

NIB	Exc.	V.G.	Good	Fair	Poor
1750	1250	600	300	200	100

NOTE: Barrels marked with Model 62 are worth more than barrels marked with Model 62A by approximately 15 percent. Gallery models will bring a premium of 400 percent.

Postwar Model 62

NIB	Exc.	V.G.	Good	Fair	Poor
1000	550	350	225	175	100

NOTE: Gallery models will bring a premium of 400 percent.

Model 61

Winchester developed the Model 61 in an attempt to keep pace with its competitors' hammerless .22 rifles. The Model 61 featured a 24-inch round or octagon barrel and could be ordered by the customer in a variety of configurations. Collector interest in this rifle is high because of the fairly large number of variations. The following is a list of chamber and barrel variations found in this model:

1. 24-inch round barrel, .22 Short, Long, Long Rifle
2. 24-inch octagon barrel, .22 Short only.
3. 24-inch octagon barrel, .22 Long Rifle only.
4. 24-inch octagon barrel, .22 W.R.F. only.
5. 24-inch round barrel, .22 Long Rifle Shot only.
6. 24-inch round barrel, .22 W.R.F. only.
7. 24-inch round barrel, .22 Long Rifle only.
8. 24-inch round barrel, .22 Winchester Magnum.
9. 24-inch round barrel, .22 Short only.

The Model 61 was fitted with a plain walnut pistol grip stock with grooved slide handle. All Model 61s were of the take down variety. Prewar models will have a short slide handle. Manufactured between 1932 and 1963, approximately 342,000 guns were sold.

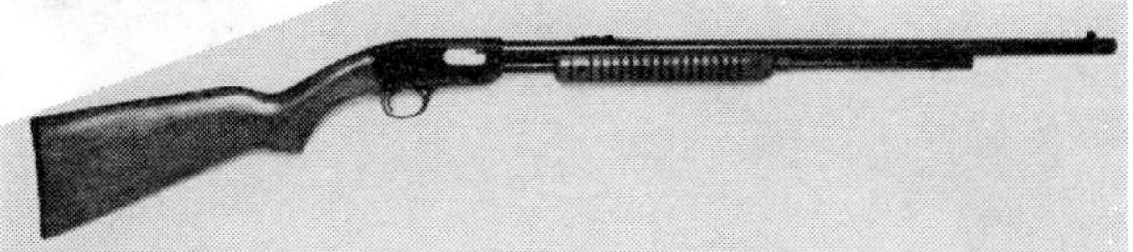

Courtesy Butterfield & Butterfield, San Francisco, California.

Prewar Model 61

NIB	Exc.	V.G.	Good	Fair	Poor
1800	800	400	300	225	100

NOTE: Single caliber models will command a premium of 50 percent depending on caliber. Octagon barrel models will command a premium of 100 percent. Shot only models will bring a premium of 200 percent.

Postwar Model 61

NIB	Exc.	V.G.	Good	Fair	Poor
1300	600	350	250	175	100

Model 61 Magnum

NIB	Exc.	V.G.	Good	Fair	Poor
1500	750	400	300	225	100

NOTE: This variation was produced from 1960 to 1963.

Model 1903

The first semi-automatic rifle produced by Winchester was designed by T.C. Johnson. This rifle was offered in a takedown version only and was available in a 20-inch round barrel chambered for the .22 Winchester Automatic Rimfire. The tubular magazine is located in the buttstock and holds 10 cartridges. The rifle was available in two different configurations:

1. Standard Rifle, 20-inch round barrel, plain walnut straight-grip stock with plain forend. Steel shotgun butt was standard.
2. Deluxe Rifle, 20-inch round barrel, fancy checkered walnut pistolgrip stock with checkered forearm. Manufactured from 1903 to 1932, about 126,000 were sold.

Standard Rifle

Exc.	V.G.	Good	Fair	Poor
700	450	350	250	100

Courtesy Butterfield & Butterfield, San Francisco, California.

Deluxe Rifle

Exc.	V.G.	Good	Fair	Poor
2500	1000	700	500	250

NOTE: The first 5,000 guns were built without safeties, and the first 15,000 guns were furnished with bronze firing pins instead of steel. These early Model 1903s will bring a premium of 50 percent.

Model 63

The Model 63 took the place of the Model 1903 in 1933 in an attempt by Winchester to solve the problem of having to use a special .22 caliber cartridge in the gun to operate the blowback system. The Model 63 was chambered for the .22 Long Rifle cartridge and was available in a 20-inch barrel for the first 4 years or until about serial number 9800. Thereafter, the model was offered with a 23-inch round barrel for the remainder of the production period. The gun was fitted with a plain walnut pistolgrip stock and forearm. The tubular magazine was located in the buttstock which came with a steel buttplate. The last 10,000 Model 63s were sold with a grooved receiver top to make the addition of a scope easier. Manufactured between 1933 and 1958, about 175,000 guns were sold.

Courtesy Butterfield & Butterfield, San Francisco, California.

20" Barrel Model 63

NIB	Exc.	V.G.	Good	Fair	Poor
2750	1200	800	600	500	250

Courtesy Butterfield & Butterfield, San Francisco, California.

23" Barrel Model 63

NIB	Exc.	V.G.	Good	Fair	Poor
1500	800	450	350	300	200

NOTE: Grooved top receivers command a premium of 15 percent.

Model 1905

The Model 1905 was a larger version of the Model 1903, developed by T.C. Johnson to handle the more powerful centerfire cartridges. It was chambered for the .32 Winchester Self-Loading and .35 Self-Loading cartridges, loading by means of a detachable box magazine. Available in takedown only, this model was offered in two different styles:

1. Sporting Rifle, 22-inch round barrel, plain walnut straight-grip (changed to pistolgrip in 1908) stock with plain forend.
2. Fancy Sporting Rifle, 22-inch round barrel, fancy walnut checkered pistolgrip stock with checkered forend. This model was the first Winchester semi-automatic rifle to fire centerfire cartridges. Produced from 1905 to 1920 with about 30,000 rifles sold.

Sporting Rifle

Exc.	V.G.	Good	Fair	Poor
500	350	250	175	125

Fancy Sporting Rifle

Exc.	V.G.	Good	Fair	Poor
600	400	300	200	150

Model 1907

The Model 1907 was an improved version of the Model 1905 and chambered for the new .351 Winchester Self-Loading cartridge. Outward appearance was the same as Model 1905 except for 20-inch round barrel. This rifle was available in three different styles:

1. Sporting Rifle, 20-inch round barrel, plain walnut pistolgrip stock with plain forend. Discontinued in 1937.
2. Fancy Sporting Rifle, 20-inch round barrel, fancy walnut checkered pistolgrip stock and checkered forend.
3. Police Rifle, 20-inch round barrel, plain walnut pistolgrip stock and beavertail forend. This version was fitted with a leather sling and with or without knife bayonet. First introduced in 1937. Winchester discontinued this model in 1957 after having sold about 59,000 guns.

Sporting Rifle

Exc.	V.G.	Good	Fair	Poor
400	300	250	175	125

Fancy Sporting Rifle

Exc.	V.G.	Good	Fair	Poor
550	400	300	200	150

Police Rifle

Exc.	V.G.	Good	Fair	Poor
450	350	275	200	150

Model 1910

This model was similar to the Model 1907 but the action was made stronger to handle the new Winchester .401 Self-Loading cartridge. The specifications for this model are the same as the Model 1907. Built between 1907 and 1936, only about 21,000 of these guns were sold.

Courtesy Butterfield & Butterfield, San Francisco, California.

Sporting Rifle

Exc.	V.G.	Good	Fair	Poor
400	300	250	175	125

Fancy Sporting Rifle

Exc.	V.G.	Good	Fair	Poor
550	400	300	200	150

Model 55 (Rimfire Rifle)

Not to be confused with the lever-action model, this .22 caliber rifle was a semi-automatic single shot with a 22-inch round barrel. Fitted with a plain walnut pistolgrip one piece stock and forend. This model was not serial numbered and was produced from 1957 to 1961 with about 45,000 guns sold.

Standard Rifle

Exc.	V.G.	Good	Fair	Poor
200	150	125	90	60

Model 74

This was a semi-automatic chambered for either the .22 Short or the .22 Long Rifle. The rifle has a tubular magazine in the buttstock and a 24-inch round barrel. The bolt on this rifle was designed to be easily removed for cleaning or repair. The stock was plain walnut pistolgrip with semi-beavertail forend. A Gallery Special was offered which was chambered for the .22 Short and fitted with a steel shell deflector. This gallery model was also available with chrome trimmings at extra cost.

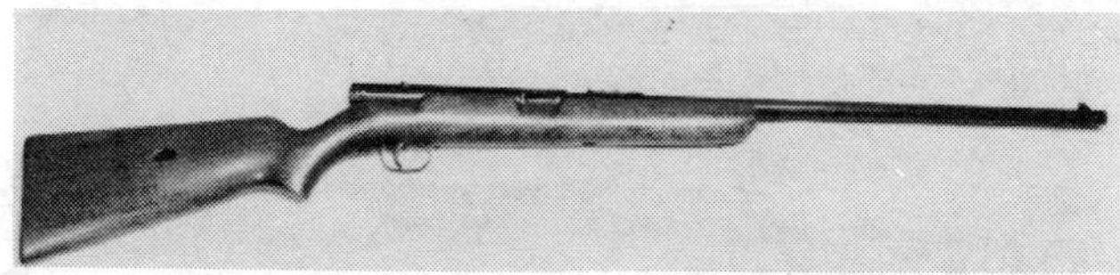

Courtesy C.H. Wolfersberger.

Sporting Rifle

Exc.	V.G.	Good	Fair	Poor
350	250	175	125	100

Gallery Special

Exc	V.G.	Good	Fair	Poor
400	300	250	200	150

NOTE: For Gallery models with chrome trimmings, add a premium of 50 percent.

Model 77

This rifle was built on the blow-back design for semi-automatic rifles and is chambered for the .22 Long Rifle. It features a 22-inch round barrel and either a detachable box magazine or under barrel tubular magazine. The rifle has a triggerguard made of nylon. It has a plain walnut pistolgrip stock with semi-beavertail forend and composition buttplate. Built between 1955 and 1963, Winchester sold about 217,000 of these rifles.

Standard Rifle

Exc.	V.G.	Good	Fair	Poor
200	175	125	90	75

Note: Models with tubular magazines will bring a slight premium of 10 percent.

Model 100

This rifle is gas operated, semi-automatic and chambered for the .243, .308, and 284 caliber center cartridges. It was available in a rifle version with a 22-inch round barrel and a carbine version with a 19-inch barrel. Both were furnished with a detachable box magazine. The stock was a one-piece design with pistolgrip and was offered in either hand cut checkering or pressed basketweave checkering. Rifles were introduced in 1961 and the carbine in 1967. The Model 100 was last produced in 1973 with about 263,000 guns sold.

Model 100 Rifle

Exc.	V.G.	Good	Fair	Poor
475	400	300	250	200

Model 100 Carbine

Exc.	V.G.	Good	Fair	Poor
575	475	375	325	225

Note: Pre-1964 models 15 percent premium. Cut checkered add 10 percent. Prices given are for .308 caliber; for .243 add 15 percent, for .284 add 20 percent.

Model 88

The Model 88 was a modern short stroke lever-action chambered for the .243, .308, 284, and .358 calibers. It was available in a rifle version with 22-inch round barrel and a carbine version with 19-inch round barrel. Both were furnished with a detachable box magazine. The stock was a one-piece design with pistolgrip and was offered with either hand cut checkering or pressed basketweave checkering. The rifle was introduced in 1955 and the carbine was first offered in 1968. Both versions were discontinued in 1973 with about 284,000 sold.

Model 88 Rifle

Exc.	V.G.	Good	Fair	Poor
400	300	225	160	140

Model 88 Carbine

Exc.	V.G.	Good	Fair	Poor
525	425	325	225	200

Note: Pre-1964 models add 15 percent premium. Hand cut checkering add 10 percent. Prices above are for .308 caliber., for .243 add 15 percent, for .284 add 20 percent, and for .358 add 100 percent.

Model 1900

This single shot bolt-action .22 caliber rifle was based on a John M. Browning design. The rifle was furnished with an 18-inch round barrel and chambered for the .22 Short and Long interchangeably. The stock was a one piece plain gumwood straight grip without a buttplate. The rifle was not serial-numbered. It was produced from 1899 to 1902 with about 105,000 sold.

Courtesy Buffalo Bill Historical Center, Cody, Wyoming.

Model 1900

Exc.	V.G.	Good	Fair	Poor
2500	1250	750	500	300

Model 1902

Also a single shot, this model was of the same general design as the Model 1900 with several improvements: a special shaped metal triggerguard was added, a shorter trigger pull, a steel buttplate, a rear peep sight, and the barrel was made heavier at the muzzle. The rifle was chambered for the .22 Short and Long cartridges until 1914 when the .22 Extra Long was added. In 1927 the .22 Extra Long was dropped in favor of the more popular .22 Long Rifle. All of these cartridges were interchangeable. The stock was a one piece plain gumwood with straight grip (the metal triggerguard added a pistolgrip feel) and steel buttplate which was changed to composition in 1907. This model was not serial numbered. About 640,000 Model 1902s were sold between 1902 and 1931 when it was discontinued.

Model 1902

Exc.	V.G.	Good	Fair	Poor
850	600	400	225	125

Model 99 or Thumb Trigger

This rifle was a modification of the Model 1902 without a traditional trigger. The rifle was fired by depressing the trigger with the thumb which was part of the sear and extractor located behind the bolt. The rifle was chambered for the .22 Short and Long until 1914 when it was also chambered for the .22 Extra Long. All cartridges could be shot interchangeably. The stock was the same as the Model 1902 without the trigger or trigerguard. This model was not serial numbered. Built between 1904 and 1923. Winchester sold about 76,000 rifles.

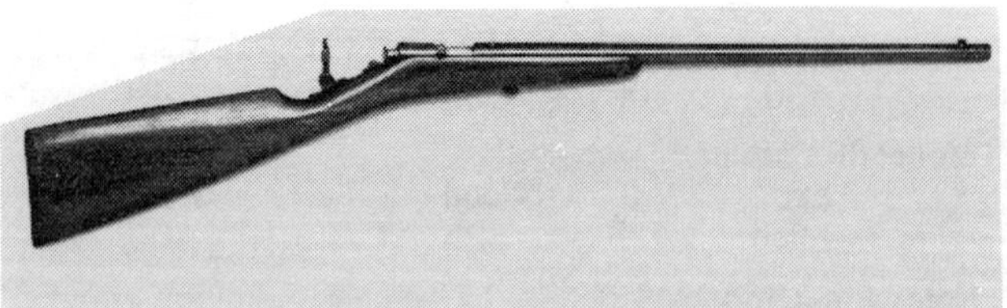

Courtesy Butterfield & Butterfield, San Francisco, California.

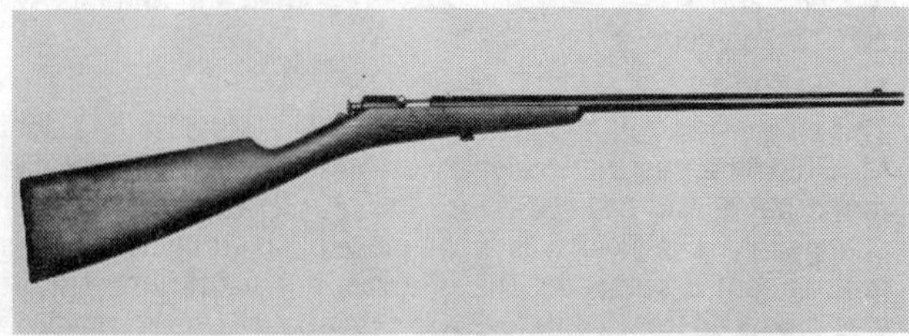

Model 99 or Thumb Trigger

Exc.	V.G.	Good	Fair	Poor
2500	1250	750	450	250

Model 1904

This model was a slightly more expensive version of the Model 1902. It featured a 21-inch round barrel, a one piece plain gumwood straight grip stock (the metal triggerguard gave the rifle a pistolgrip feel) with a small lip on the forend. Rifle was chambered for the .22 Short and Long until 1914 when the .22 Extra Long was added. The .22 Long Rifle cartridge was added in place of the Extra Long in 1927. This model was not serial numbered. Produced between 1904 and 1931, about 303,000 rifles were sold.

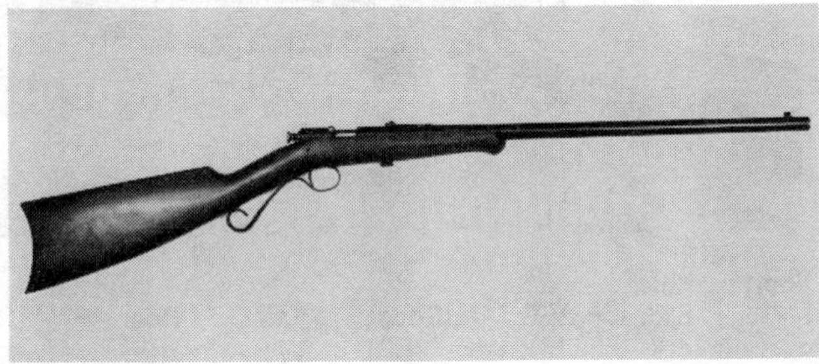

Model 1904

Exc.	V.G.	Good	Fair	Poor
600	400	300	200	100

Model 43

Introduced in 1949, this rifle was chambered for the .218 Bee, .22 Hornet, .25-20 Winchester, and the .32-20 Winchester. The rifle was a bolt-action with detachable box magazine, fitted with a 24-inch round barrel and front sight ramp forged integrally with barrel. This model was available in two styles:

1. Standard Rifle, 24-inch round barrel, plain walnut pistolgrip stock and forend. One inch sling swivels are standard.
2. Special Rifle, 24-inch round barrel, select walnut checkered pistolgrip stock and checkered forend. Furnished with either open sporting rear sight or Lyman 57A micrometer receiver sight.

The Model 43 was produced from 1949 to 1957 with about 63,000 sold.

Standard Rifle

Exc.	V.G.	Good	Fair	Poor
550	475	400	300	200

Special Rifle

Exc.	V.G.	Good	Fair	Poor
650	575	500	400	300

Model 47

This model was a single shot bolt-action rifle chambered for the .22 Short, Long, and Long Rifle interchangeably. The rifle was furnished with a 25-inch round barrel, plain walnut pistolgrip stock and forend. The bolt, bolt handle, and trigger are chrome plated. This model was not serial numbered. Produced between 1948 and 1954, Winchester sold about 43,000 guns.

Courtesy Buffalo Bill Historical Center, Cody, Wyoming.

Model 47

Exc.	V.G.	Good	Fair	Poor
300	250	200	150	100

Model 52

One of the finest small caliber bolt-action rifles ever built , the Model 52 was Winchester's answer to the increased demand for a military style target rifle following World War I. The Model 52 was a well made quality built bolt-action rifle. The rifle was chambered for the .22 Long Rifle cartridge. Designed by T.C. Johnson, this rifle was built in several different configurations over its production life:

1. Model 52 Target Rifle, 28-inch round standard weight or heavyweight barrel, plain walnut modified pistolgrip stock with finger groove in forend and one barrel band. Produced from 1920 to 1929.
2. Model 52 Target Rifle, same as above but without finger groove in forend and has first speed lock. Made from 1929 to 1932.
3. Model 52A Target Rifle, same as above with addition of reinforced receiver and locking lug. Made from 1932 to 1935.
4. Model 52B Target Rifle, same as above with addition of adjustable sling swivel and single shot adaptor. Made from 1935 to 1947.
5. Model 52C Target Rifle, same as above with addition of an easily adjustable vibration-free trigger mechanism. Made from 1947 to 1961.
6. Model 52D Target Rifle, this is a single shot rifle with free-floating barrel and new design stock with adjustable handstop channel.
7. Model 52 Bull Gun, same as target rifle but fitted with extra heavyweight barrel. Made from 1939 to 1960.
8. Model 52 International Match, a free style stock with thumbhole and adjustable buttstock and forend introduced in 1969 and an International Prone model with no thumbhole or adjustable buttplate and forend was introduced in 1975. Both discontinued in 1980.
9. Model 52 Sporter, 24-inch round barrel, select walnut checkered pistolgrip stock with cheekpiece and forend with black plastic tip. Pistolgrip was furnished with hard rubber grip cap. The Model 52 Sporter was introduced in 1934 and discontinued in 1958. It went through the same improvements as the Target Rifle, thus the designation Model 52A Sporter etc.

Model 52 Target

Exc.	V.G.	Good	Fair	Poor
450	375	300	275	225

Model 52 Target-Speed Lock

Exc.	V.G.	Good	Fair	Poor
500	425	350	300	250

Model 52A Target

Exc.	V.G.	Good	Fair	Poor
450	375	300	275	225

Model 52B Target

Exc.	V.G.	Good	Fair	Poor
550	450	375	325	250

Model 52C Target

Exc.	V.G.	Good	Fair	Poor
700	600	500	400	300

Model 52D Target

Exc.	V.G.	Good	Fair	Poor
600	500	400	325	275

Model 52 Bull Gun

Exc.	V.G.	Good	Fair	Poor
650	550	450	350	300

Model 52 International Match

Exc.	V.G.	Good	Fair	Poor
750	650	500	350	300

Model 52 Sporter

Exc.	V.G.	Good	Fair	Poor
2350	1650	1300	1100	900

NOTE: Model 52A Sporters will being a 20 percent premium.

Editors Comment: According to Winchester factory records, Model 52 barrels were, "originally drilled and tapped for Winchester telescope bases designed for use with the Winchester 3A, 5A, and Lyman telescopes. These bases had a 6.2-inch center to center spacing . . . a change in the bases and the spacing to be used was authorized on January 11, 1933. These new bases had a specially shaped Fecker type notch added on the right hand side of both bases. They are known as Winchester Combination Telescope Sight Bases and are satisfactory for use with Winchester, Lyman, Fecker, and Unertl telescopes. Bases are spaced 7.2 inches center to center . . .". This should help solve some of the controversy surrounding whether or not the Model 52 was drilled and tapped for telescopes at the factory.

Model 54

The Model 54 was to centerfire cartridges what the Model 52 was to rimfire cartridges. The Model 54 was also a quality made bolt-action rifle with a non-detachable box magazine and was chambered for a variety of calibers: .270, .30-06, .30-30, 7mm, 7.65, 9.mm, .250-3000, .22 Hornet., .220 Swift, and .257 Roberts. This was Winchester's first bolt-action rifle built for heavy, high velocity ammunition. The rifle was available in several different styles:

1. Standard Rifle, 24- or 20-inch round barrel (except .220 Swift which was 26-inches), plain walnut checkered pistolgrip stock and forend.
2. Carbine, 20-inch round barrel, plain walnut pistolgrip stock with finger groove on each side of forend.
3. Sniper's Rifle, 26-inch round heavyweight barrel, plain walnut pistolgrip stock and forend.
4. N.R.A. Rifle, 24-inch round barrel, select walnut checkered pistolgrip stock and forend.
5. Super Grade Rifle, 24-inch round barrel, select walnut checkered pistolgrip stock with cheekpiece and checkered forend

with black plastic tip. Pistolgrip was capped with hard rubber cap. Super Grade was equipped with 1-inch detachable sling swivels.

6. Target Rifle, 24-inch round heavyweight barrel, plain walnut checkered pistolgrip stock and forend.
7. National Match Rifle, 24-inch round barrel, plain walnut special target stock and forend.

The Model 54 was introduced in 1925 and was discontinued in 1936 with about 50,000 guns sold.

Standard Rifle

Exc.	V.G.	Good	Fair	Poor
650	550	400	300	225

Carbine

Exc.	V.G.	Good	Fair	Poor
700	600	450	350	275

Sniper's Rifle

Exc.	V.G.	Good	Fair	Poor
900	750	600	500	350

N.R.A. Rifle

Exc.	V.G.	Good	Fair	Poor
900	750	600	500	350

Super Grade Rifle

Exc.	V.G.	Good	Fair	Poor
900	750	600	450	375

Target Rifle

Exc.	V.G.	Good	Fair	Poor
900	750	600	450	375

National Match Rifle

Exc.	V.G.	Good	Fair	Poor
900	750	600	450	375

Note: The rare calibers are the 7.65 and the .30-30 which bring considerable premiums in some cases as much as 250 percent over standard calibers. Proceed with caution on Model 54s with rare caliber markings.

Model 56

This model was designed to be a medium priced bolt-action rim fire rifle. It featured a detachable box magazine and was chambered for the .22 Short or .22 Long Rifle cartridges. The rifle was offered in two styles;

1. Sporting Rifle, 22-inch round barrel, plain walnut pistolgrip stock and forend.
2. Fancy Sporting Rifle, 22-inch round barrel, fancy walnut checkered pistolgrip stock and forend.

Both styles had a forend with a distinctive lip on the forend tip. The rifle was introduced in 1926 and was discontinued in 1929 with about 8,500 rifles sold.

Sporting Rifle

Exc.	V.G.	Good	Fair	Poor
1500	1000	750	525	400

Fancy Sporting Rifle

Exc.	V.G.	Good	Fair	Poor
3000	2000	1500	900	750

Model 57

The Model 57 was very close in appearance to the Model 56 with the addition of a heavier stock, target sights, and swivel bows attached to the stock. The rifle was chambered for the .22 Short or .22 Long Rifle and featured a 22-inch round barrel with detachable box magazine. The stock was plain walnut with pistolgrip and plain forend. The rifle was introduced in 1927 and dropped from the Winchester line in 1936 having sold only about 19,000 guns.

Model 57

Exc.	V.G.	Good	Fair	Poor
750	600	450	325	250

Model 58

This model was an attempt by the company to market a low priced .22 caliber rimfire rifle in place of its Models 1902 and 1904. This was a single shot bolt-action, cocked by pulling the firing pin head to the rear. It had an 18-inch round barrel and was chambered for the .22 Short, Long, and Long Rifle interchangeably. The stock was a one piece plain wood with straight-grip. This model was not serial-numbered. The Model 58 was introduced in 1928 and discontinued in 1931. About 39,000 were sold.

Model 58

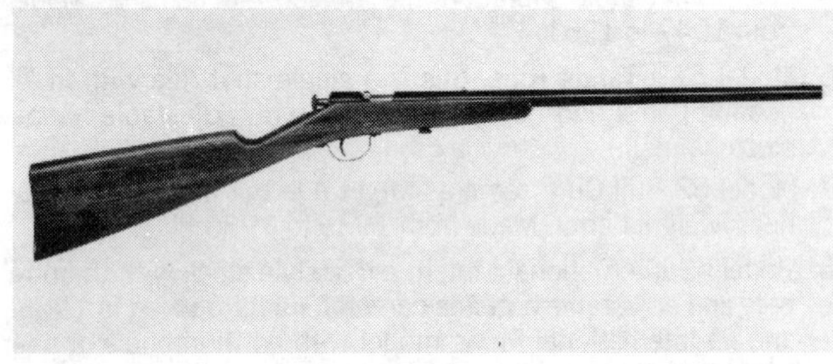

Exc.	V.G.	Good	Fair	Poor
750	600	425	250	125

Model 59

The Model 59 was essentially a Model 58 with the addition of a pistolgrip stock and a 23-inch round barrel. Introduced in 1930, it was dropped from the product line in the same year with a total sales of about 9,000 guns.

Courtesy Olin Corporation.

Model 59

Exc.	V.G.	Good	Fair	Poor
600	475	350	200	125

Model 60 and 60A

This rifle used the same action as that of the Model 59. When the rifle was first introduced in 1931, it was furnished with a 23-inch round barrel which was changed to 27 inches in 1933. Several other mechanical improvements were included with this model, perhaps the most noticeable was the chrome-plated bolt, bolt handle, and trigger. The stock was plain wood with pistolgrip. In 1933 the Model 60A was added which was the same rifle but in a target configuration. The front sight was a square top military blade with a Lyman 55W receiver sight. The Model 60 was discontinued in 1934 with about 166,000 rifles sold. The Model 60A was dropped in 1939 with only about 6,100 rifles sold.

Courtesy Buffalo Bill Historical Center, Cody, Wyoming.

Model 60

Exc.	V.G.	Good	Fair	Poor
400	325	275	175	125

Model 60A

Exc.	V.G.	Good	Fair	Poor
550	400	325	250	200

Model 67

Winchester again upgraded and improved the Model 60 with an expansion of the styles offered to the shooting public. The standard chamber for the rifle was .22 Short, Long, and Long Rifle interchangeably with the W.R.F. only added in 1935:

1. Sporting Rifle, 27-inch round barrel, stock similar to the Model 60.
2. Smoothbore Rifle, 27-inch barrel, chambered for the .22 Long Shot or .22 Long Rifle Shot.
3. Junior Rifle, 20-inch round barrel and shorter stock.
4. Rifle with miniature target boring, 24-inch round barrel, chambered for .22 Long Rifle Shot.

Model 67s were not serial numbered for domestic sales but were numbered for foreign sales. Introduced in 1934 the gun was dropped from the line in 1963 having sold about 384,000. Many of these models were fitted at the factory with telescopes, and the bases were mounted on the rifle and the scope was packed separately.

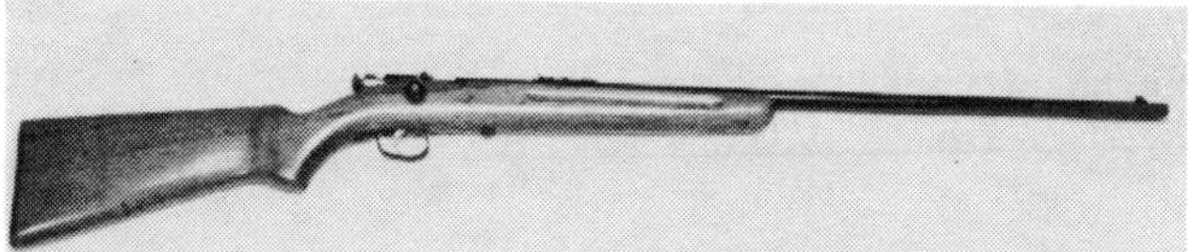
Courtesy C.H. Wolfersberger.

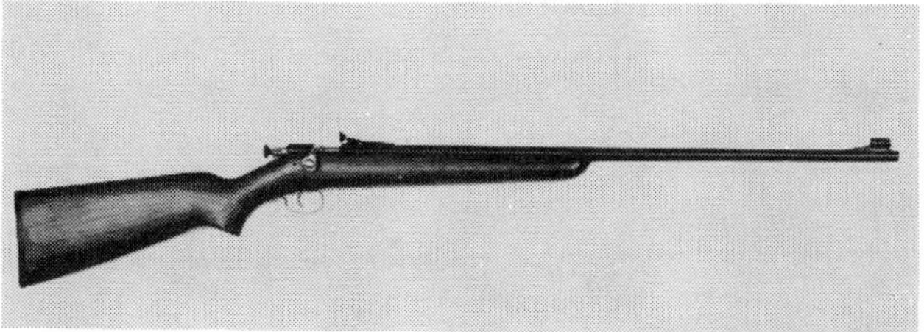
Courtesy Buffalo Bill Historical Center, Cody, Wyoming.

Sporting Rifle

Exc.	V.G.	Good	Fair	Poor
200	150	125	100	75

Smoothbore Rifle

Courtesy Buffalo Bill Historical Center, Cody, Wyoming.

Exc.	V.G.	Good	Fair	Poor
450	350	300	250	200

Junior Rifle

Exc.	V.G.	Good	Fair	Poor
2540	200	175	150	125

Model 677

This model looked the same as the Model 67 but was manufactured without iron sights and therefore will have no sight cuts in the barrel. The rifle was furnished with either 2 3/4 power scopes or 5 power scopes. This model was not serial numbered. Introduced in 1937 and discontinued in 1939.

Model 677

Exc.	V.G.	Good	Fair	Poor
1500	900	600	400	200

Model 68

Another take-off on the Model 67, this model differed only in the sight equipment offered. Winchester fitted this rifle with its own 5 power telescopes. First sold in 1934 the Model 68 was dropped in 1946 with sales of about 101,000.

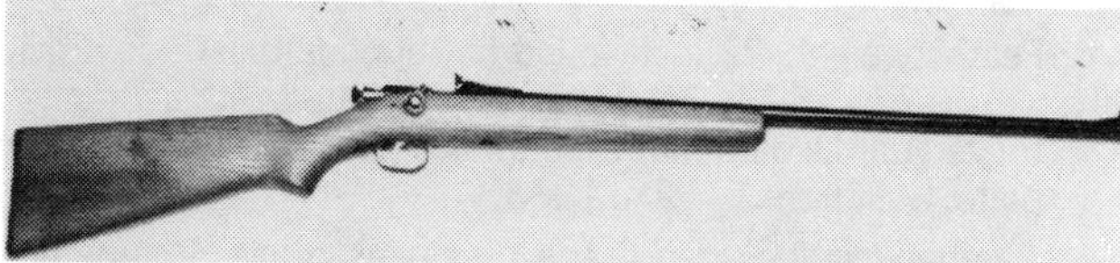
Courtesy C.H. Wolfersberger.

Model 68

Exc.	V.G.	Good	Fair	Poor
800	700	500	375	150

Model 69 and 69A

This model was designed by Winchester to answer the demand for a medium priced hunting and target .22 rimfire bolt-action rifle. The rifle had a detachable box magazine, and many were offered with factory-installed telescopes in 2-3/4 and 5 power. The stock was plain walnut with pistolgrip and plain forend. This model was not serial numbered. The 69A version was introduced in 1937 and featured an improved cocking mechanism. Introduced in 1935 as the Model 69, this gun was dropped in 1963 with sales of about 355,000 guns.

Model 69 and 69A

Exc.	V.G.	Good	Fair	Poor
250	200	175	150	125

Model 697

The Model 697 was similar in appearance to the Model 69 except it was equipped exclusively for a telescope. Winchester offered either a 2-3/4 or 5 power scope with the bases attached at the factory and the scope packed separately. Built between 1937 and 1941 with very small sales, this model was not serial numbered.

Model 697

Exc.	V.G.	Good	Fair	Poor
800	650	500	450	400

Model 70

Considered by many as the finest bolt-action rifle ever built in the United States, the pre-1964 Model 70 is highly sought after by shooters and collectors alike. Its smooth, strong action has no peer. It is often referred to as "The Riflemen's Rifle." The Model 70 is an updated and improved version of the Model 54 and features a hinged floorplate, new speed locks, new safety design that does not interfere with telescope, manually releasable bolt stop, more attractive buttstock and forend, and forged steel triggerguard. Like many Winchesters, the Model 70 was available with several extra cost options which should be evaluated by an expert. The values listed below are given for pre-1964 Model 70s with serial numbers from 1 to 581471. This rifle was available in several different styles:

1. Standard Grade, 24-inch round barrel (except 26-inch round barrel for .220 Swift and .300 H&H Magnum - 25-inch round barrel for .375 H&H Magnum after 1937), plain walnut checkered pistol stock and forend. Built from 1936 to 1963.
2. Standard Grade Carbine, 20-inch round barrel, chambered for .22 Hornet, .250-3000, .257 Roberts, .270, 7mm, and 30-06, same stock as Standard Grade. Built from 1936 to 1946.
3. Super Grade Rifle, same barrel and calibers as Standard Grade, select walnut checkered and capped pistolgrip stock with cheekpiece and checkered forend with plastic tip. Built from 1936 to 1960.
4. Featherweight, 22-inch round barrel chambered for .243, .264, .270, .308, .30-06, and .358. Fitted with aluminum triggerguard, aluminum buttplate, and aluminum floor plate. Built from 1952 to 1963.
5. Featherweight Super Grade, same as above except not chambered for the .358 cartridge, but fitted with Super Grade stock. Built from 1952 to 1960.
6. National Match, same as Standard Grade but fitted with target type stock and telescope bases. Chambered for .30-06 only. Discontinued in 1960.
7. Target, 24-inch round medium-weight barrel with same stock as National Match in .243 and 30-06 calibers. Discontinued in 1963.
8. Varmint, 26-inch round heavy barrel, with heavier stock, chambered for .243 and .220 Swift. Built from 1956 to 1963.
9. Westerner, 26-inch round barrel with Standard Grade stock, chambered for .264 Winchester Magnum. Built from 1960 to 1963.
10. Alaskan, 25-inch round barrel, with Standard Grade stock, chambered for .338 Winchester Magnum and .375 H&H Magnum. Built from 1960 to 1963.
11. Bull Gun, 28-inch round barrel, same stock as National Match, chambered for .30-06 and .300 H&H Magnum. Built from 1936 to 1963.

The standard calibers offered for the Model 70 are as follows in order of rarity: .300 Savage, .35 Rem., .458 Win Magnum, 7mm, .358 Win., .250-3000 Savage, .300 Win Magnum, .338 Win. Magnum, .375 H&H Magnum, .257 Roberts, .220 Swift, .22 Hornet, .264 Win. Magnum, .300 H&H Magnum, .308 Win., .243 Win., .270 W.C.F., .30-06.

Prices for the Model 70 are, in many cases, based on the caliber of the rifle; the more rare the caliber, the more premium the gun will command.

Standard Rifle

Exc.	V.G.	Good	Fair	Poor
700	600	400	350	275

NOTE: Above prices are for rifles in .30-06 and .270. Below are prices for calibers with respect to rarity:

.243. Win.

Exc.	V.G.	Good	Fair	Poor
1000	850	600	400	300

.308 Win.

Exc.	V.G.	Good	Fair	Poor
750	650	450	400	300

.300 H&H Magnum

Exc.	V.G.	Good	Fair	Poor
800	700	500	450	350

.264 Win. Magnum

Exc.	V.G.	Good	Fair	Poor
800	700	600	550	350

.22 Hornet

Exc.	V.G.	Good	Fair	Poor
950	800	550	475	375

.220 Swift

Exc.	V.G.	Good	Fair	Poor
950	800	550	475	375

.257 Roberts

Exc.	V.G.	Good	Fair	Poor
950	800	550	475	375

.375 H&H Magnum

Exc.	V.G.	Good	Fair	Poor
1500	1100	700	550	400

.338 Win. Magnum

Exc.	V.G.	Good	Fair	Poor
1200	900	600	500	375

.300 Win. Magnum

Exc.	V.G.	Good	Fair	Poor
1200	900	600	500	375

.250-3000 Savage

Exc.	V.G.	Good	Fair	Poor
1700	1250	700	600	400

7MM

Exc.	V.G.	Good	Fair	Poor
2500	1750	1250	950	600

.35 Rem.

Exc.	V.G.	Good	Fair	Poor
3500	2500	1750	1200	900

.300 Savage

Exc.	V.G.	Good	Fair	Poor
3000	2500	1750	1200	900

Standard Grade Carbine

Exc.	V.G.	Good	Fair	Poor
1500	1250	800	650	600

NOTE: For calibers other than standard add a premium of 100 percent to Standard Grade prices.

Super Grade

Exc.	V.G.	Good	Fair	Poor
1250	950	700	500	400

NOTE: For Super Grade rifles in .375 H&H add 75 percent. For Super Grade rifles in .458 Win. Mag. add 125 percent.

For calibers other than standard add a premium of 70 percent to Standard Grade prices.

Featherweight

Exc.	V.G.	Good	Fair	Poor
850	700	600	500	400

NOTE: Add 50 percent for .358 Win.

Relative Caliber Rarity*
Model 70
1936 - 1963

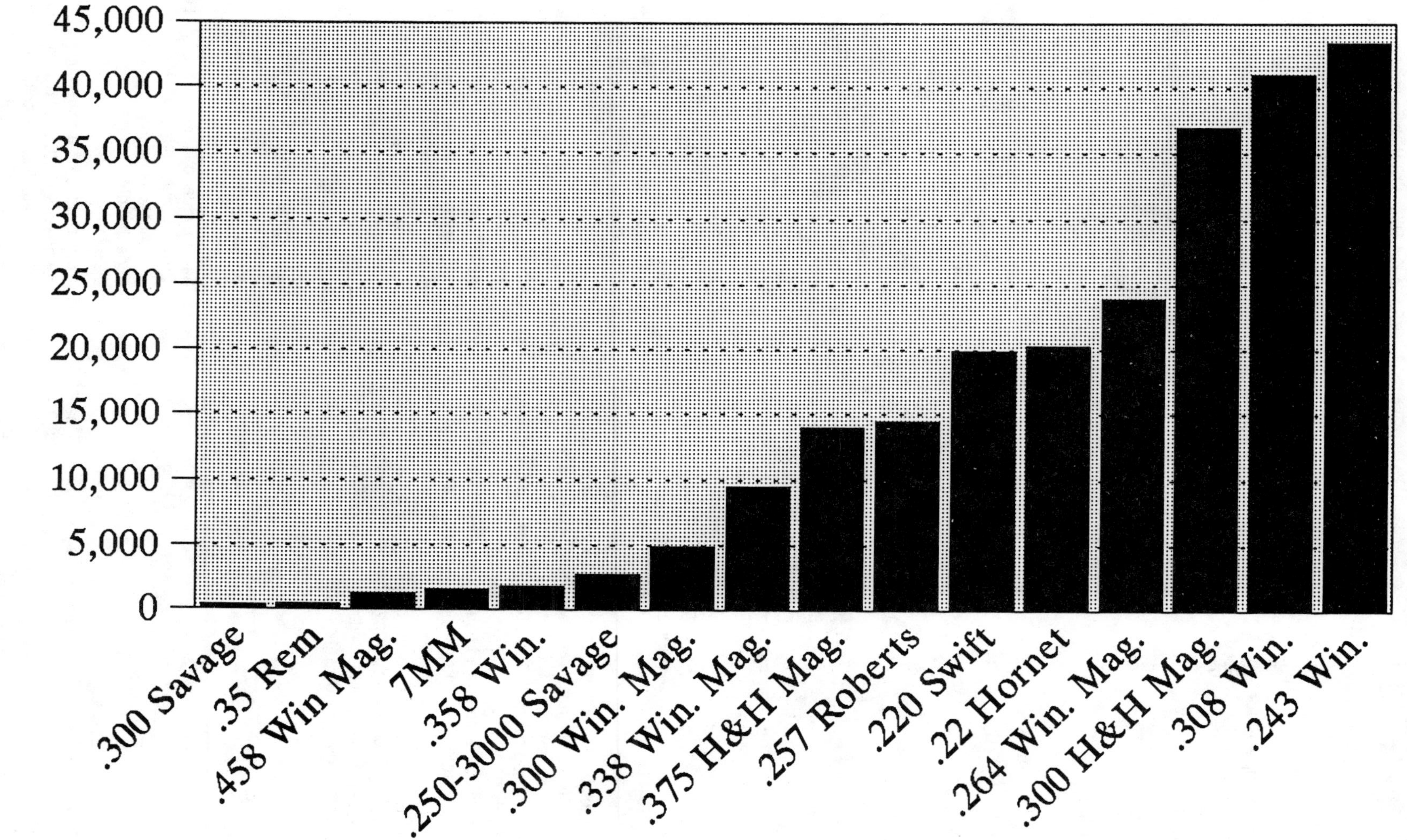

* Excluding the .270 W.C.F.(approx. 100,000) and 30-06 (approx. 200,000) which were the most common.

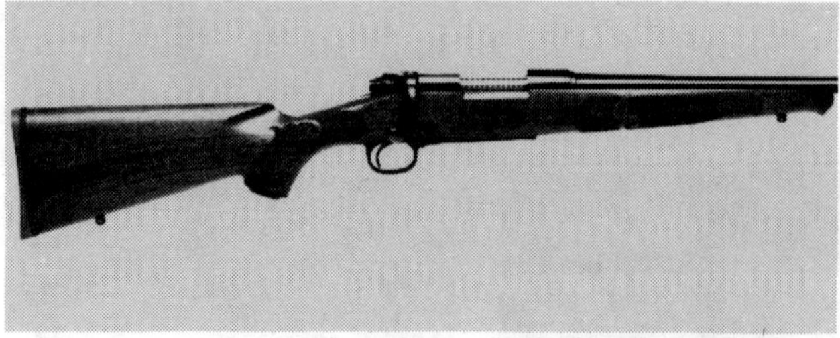

Featherweight Super Grade

Exc.	V.G.	Good	Fair	Poor
1750	1250	950	750	500

National Match

Exc.	V.G.	Good	Fair	Poor
1000	750	600	500	400

Target

Exc.	V.G.	Good	Fair	Poor
1000	750	600	500	400

Varmint

Exc.	V.G.	Good	Fair	Poor
800	700	550	450	325

Bull Gun

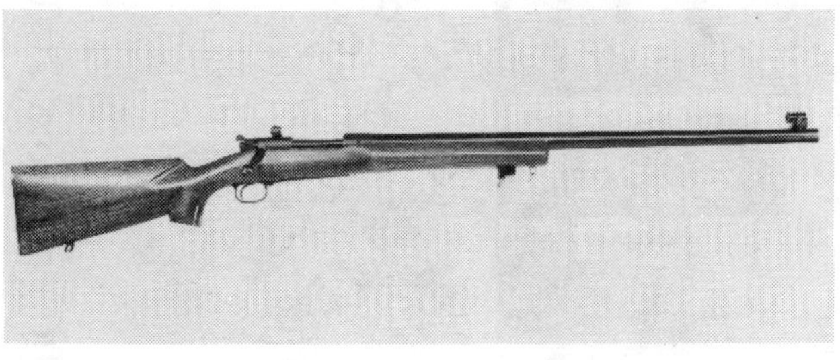

Exc.	V.G.	Good	Fair	Poor
1500	1200	850	650	500

Model 72

This model is a bolt-action rifle with tubular magazine. It is chambered for the .22 Short, Long, and Long Rifle cartridges interchangeably. Early rifles were available with 2-3/4 or 5 power telescopes, but the majority were furnished with either open sights or peep sights. This rifle was available in two different configurations:

1. Sporting Rifle, 25-inch round barrel, chambered for the .22 Short, Long, and Long Rifle cartridges, one piece plain walnut pistolgrip stock and forend.
2. Gallery Special, 25-inch round barrel, chambered for .22 Short only, stock same as Sporting Rifle.

This model was not serial numbered. It was built between 1938 and 1959 with about 161,000 rifles sold.

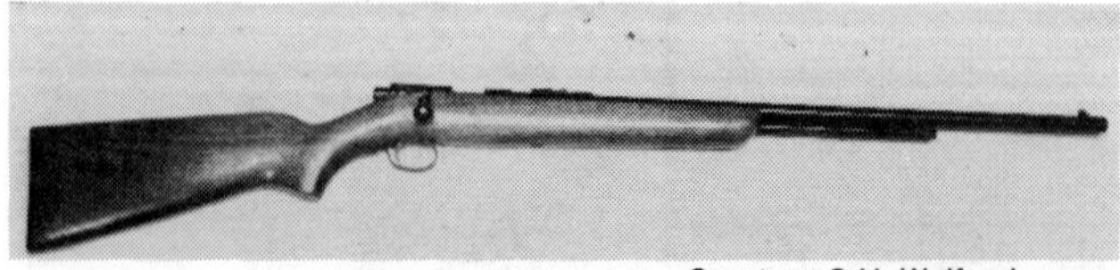

Courtesy C.H. Wolfersberger.

Model 72

Exc.	V.G.	Good	Fair	Poor
300	250	200	150	125

NOTE: Gallery Special will command a premium of 100 percent.

Model 75

Introduced in 1938, Winchester hoped that the Model 75 could meet the demand for a medium-priced target rifle for those who could not afford the more expensive Model 52. This bolt-action rifle featured a detachable box magazine and was offered in two styles:

1. Sporting Rifle, 24-inch round barrel, chambered for .22 Long Rifle, select walnut checkered pistolgrip stock and forend. This rifle was furnished with either open rear sights or a Lyman 57E receiver sight.
2. Target Rifle, 28-inch round barrel, chambered for .22 Long Rifle, plain walnut pistolgrip stock and forend. The Target Rifle was furnished with either a Winchester 8 power telescope or a variety of target sights.

This model was discontinued in 1958 with about 89,000 sold.

Model 75 Sporter

NIB	Exc.	V.G.	Good	Fair	Poor
1500	750	600	450	350	200

Model 75 Target

Exc.	V.G.	Good	Fair	Poor
500	400	325	250	200

Model 12

This model was designed by T.C. Johnson and was the first slide action hammerless shotgun built by Winchester. The Model 12 has enjoyed great success in its 51-year history, and over 1,900,000 were sold. This was a high quality, well-made shotgun that is still in use in the hunting and shooting fields across the country. All Model 12s were of the takedown variety. The Model 12 was dropped from regular product line in 1963, but a special model was produced in the Custom Shop until 1979. In 1972 Winchester resurrected the Model 12 in its regular production line in 12 gauge only and ventilated-rib. This reintroduced Model 12 was dropped in 1980. The prices listed below are for guns made prior to 1964 or for guns with serial numbers below 1968307. This shotgun was offered in several different styles:

1. Standard Grade, 12, 16, 20, and 28 gauge, with plain, solid rib, or vent-rib round barrels of standard lengths (2611, 2811, 3011, 3211), plain walnut pistolgrip stock with grooved slide handle. Built from 1912 to 1963.
2. Featherweight, same as above with lightweight alloy trigger guard. Built between 1959 and 1962.
3. Riot Gun, in 12 gauge only with 20-inch round choked cylinder, stock same as Standard Grade. Built between 1918 and 1963.
4. Trench Gun, chambered for 12 gauge only with 20-inch round barrel with ventilated handguard over barrel, fitted with bayonet lug. All metal surfaces are "Parkerized," and these shotguns should be U.S. marked as a military firearm. Introduced in 1918 and built for U.S. Armed Forces on special order.
5. Skeet Grade, chambered for 12, 16, 20, and 28 gauge with 26-inch round barrel with solid or ventilated-rib, select walnut checkered pistol stock and special checkered extension slide handle (longer than standard). Built from 1933 to 1963.
6. Trap Grade, chambered for 12 gauge only with 30-inch round barrel with solid rib or ventilated-rib, select walnut pistol or straight grip stock, checkered extension slide handle. Built from 1914 to 1963.
7. Heavy Duck Gun, chambered in 12 gauge only with 30-inch round barrel with plain, solid, or ventilated-rib, plain walnut pistol grip stock fitted with Winchester rubber recoil pad, plain grooved slide handle. Built from 1935 to 1963.

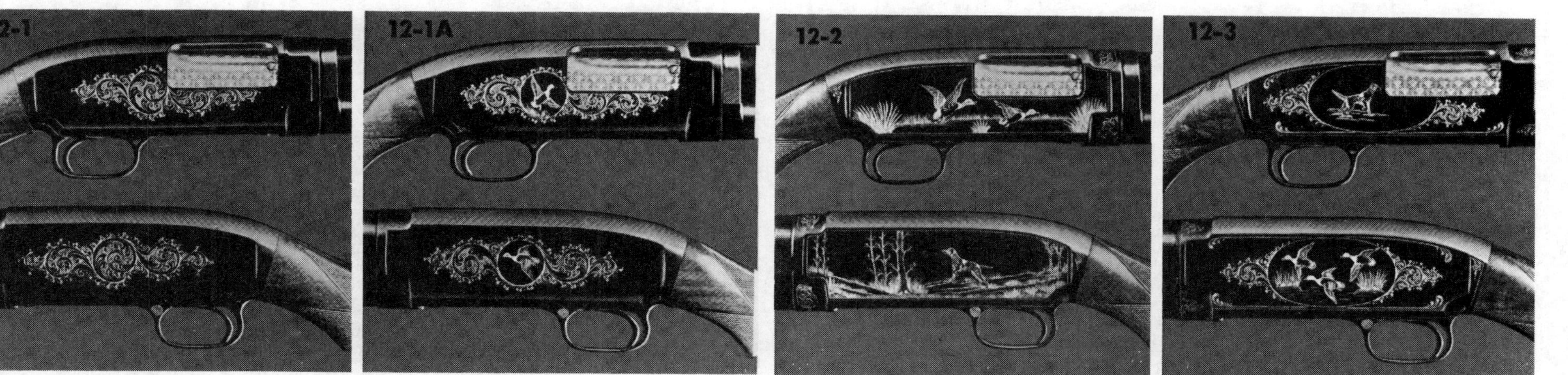

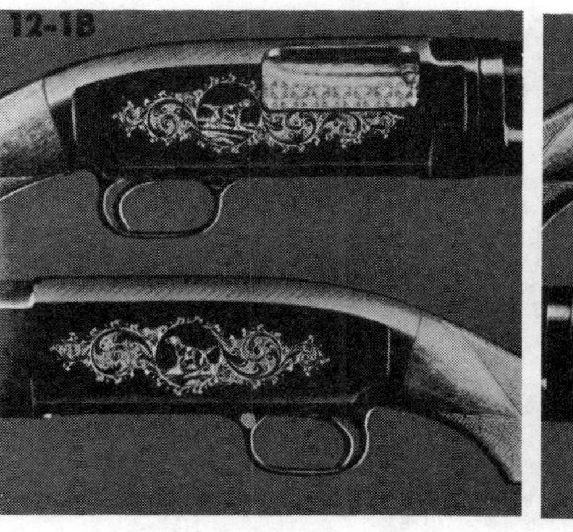

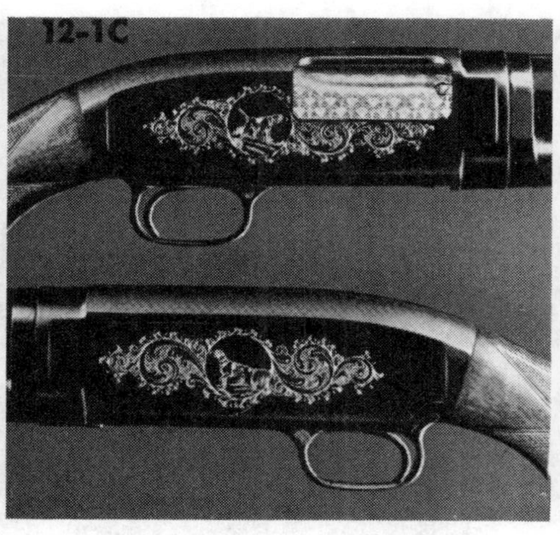

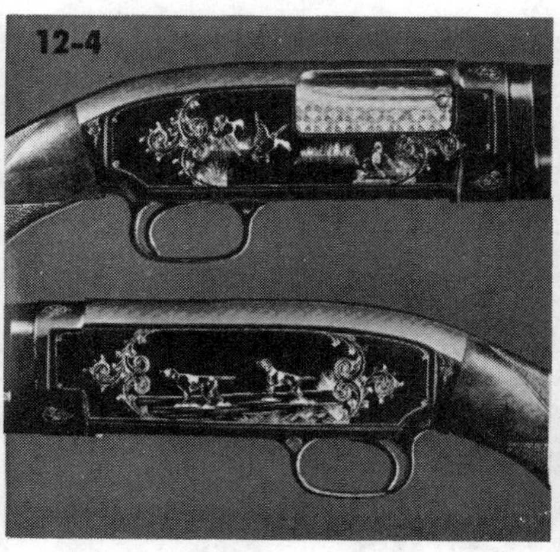

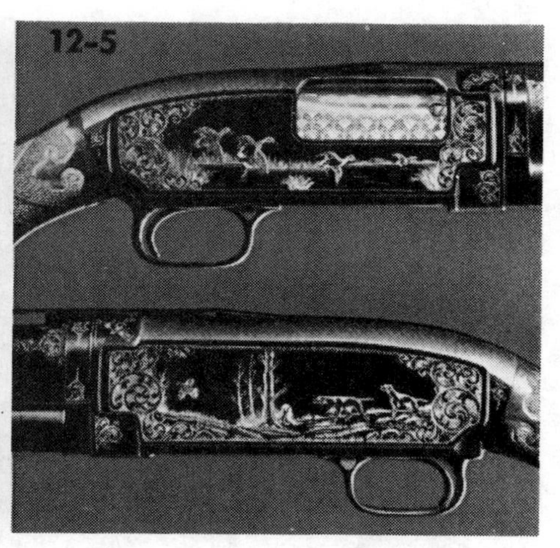

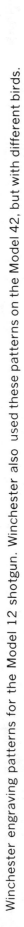

Winchester engraving patterns for the Model 12 shotgun. Winchester also used these patterns on the Model 42, but with different birds.

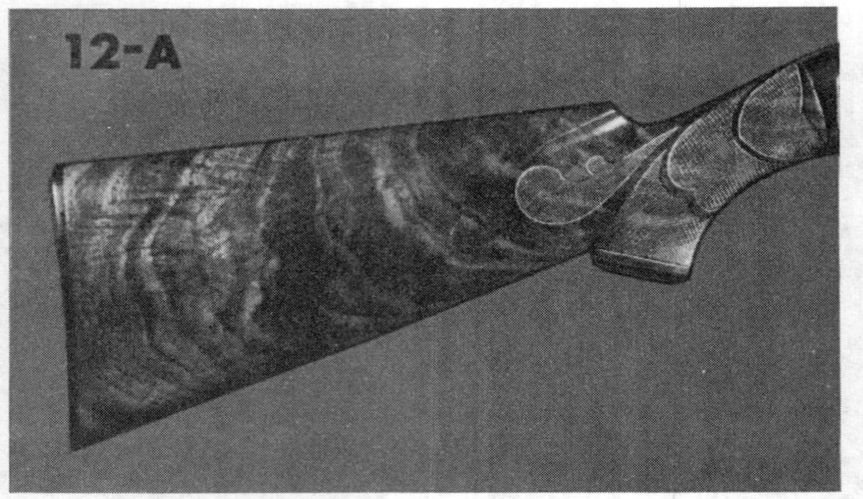

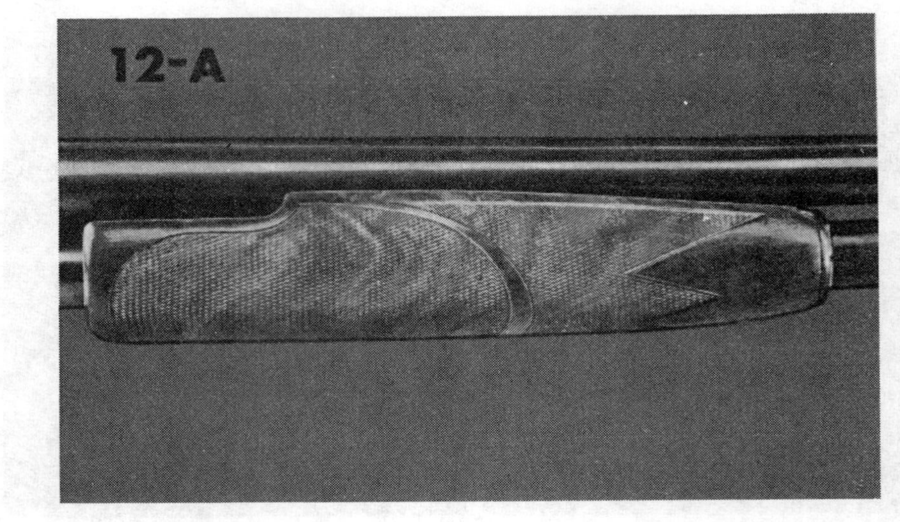

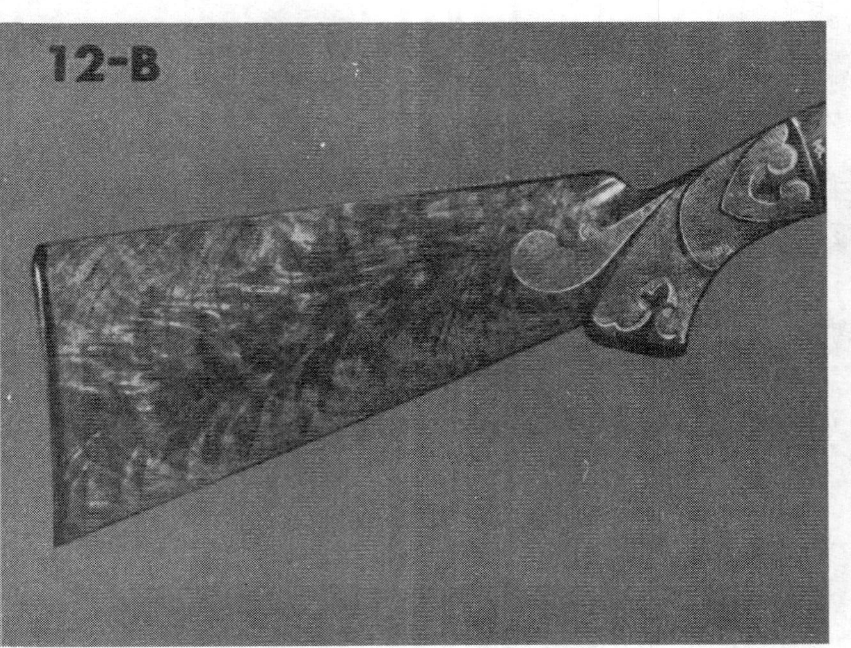

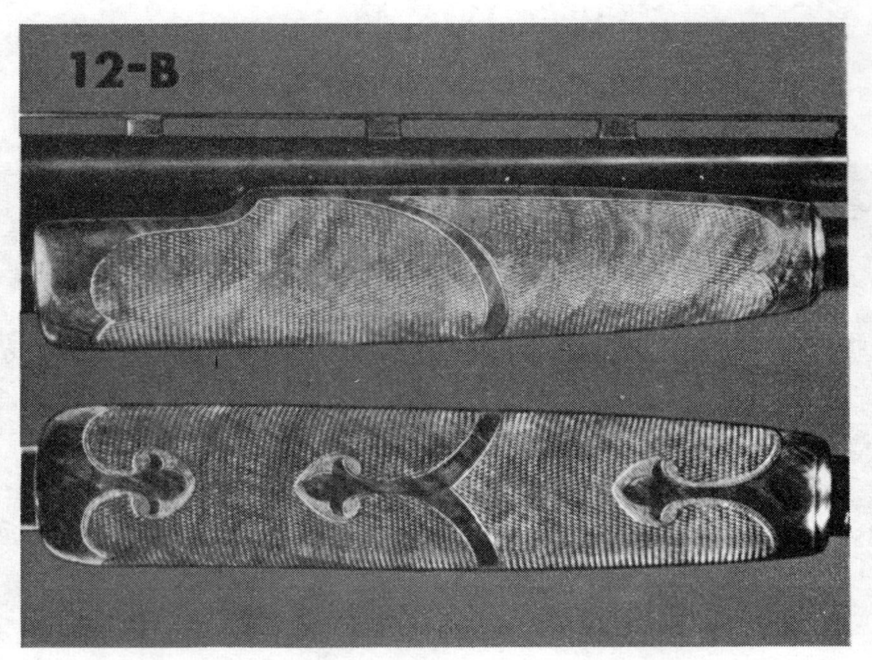

Winchester also provided optional factory stock carving for the Model 12 as well as the Model 42.

8. Pigeon Grade, chambered for 12, 16, 20, and 28 gauges with standard barrel lengths and chòice of ribs. This was a special order shotgun and will be seen in many different variations, most of these guns were factory engraved. Built 1914 to 1963.

The Model 12 shotgun will be seen in many different combinations of gauges, barrel lengths, ribs, and stocks, all of which determine value. The more rare a particular combination, the higher the price. The buyer is urged to be extremely cautious before purchasing the more rare combinations, such as a 28 gauge. The best advice is to seek assistance from an expert and get as many opinions as possible. The prices listed below are for guns in standard configurations.

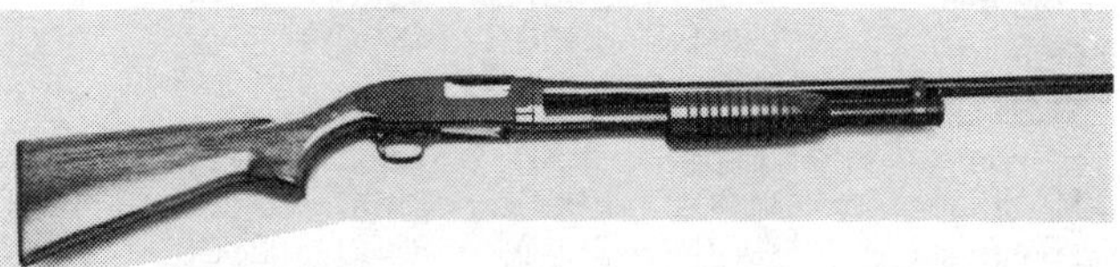

Courtesy Butterfield & Butterfield, San Francisco, California.

Standard Grade-12 gauge

Exc.	V.G.	Good	Fair	Poor
650	425	350	300	250

Featherweight

Exc.	V.G.	Good	Fair	Poor
450	400	325	275	250

Riot Gun

Exc.	V.G.	Good	Fair	Poor
750	650	550	400	250

Trench Gun

Exc.	V.G.	Good	Fair	Poor
1100	900	700	500	350

Skeet Grade

Exc.	V.G.	Good	Fair	Poor
750	550	450	400	350

Trap Grade

Exc.	V.G.	Good	Fair	Poor
750	650	550	450	400

Heavy Duck Gun

Exc.	V.G.	Good	Fair	Poor
550	425	350	325	300

Pigeon Grade

Exc.	V.G.	Good	Fair	Poor
1500	1100	850	650	500

Note: For 16 Gauge add 15 percent. For 20 gauge add 20 percent. For 28 gauge add 600 percent. For guns with Solid rib add 20 percent. For guns with Winchester Special Ventilated-Rib add 30 percent. For guns with Milled Rib add 40 percent.

Model 25

This model is similar in appearance to the Model 12 but does not have the takedown feature. All guns were solid frame. The Model 25 was furnished in 12 gauge only with 26- or 28-inch plain round barrel, plain walnut pistolgrip stock with grooved slide handle. This was an attempt by Winchester to introduce a less expensive version of the Model 12. Introduced in 1949 it was dropped from the product line in 1954 having sold about 88,000 guns.

Model 25

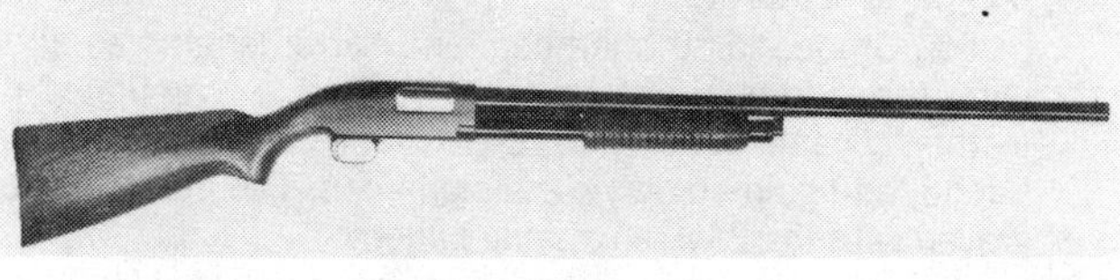

Exc.	V.G.	Good	Fair	Poor
350	250	225	175	150

Model 20

In order to utilize the expanded production facilities left over from World War I, Winchester introduced a series of three different models of single shot shotguns; the Model 20 was the first of the three. This model has a visible hammer and a top lever frame. It was the first Winchester to have this type of breakdown action. It was chambered for the .410, 2-1/2 inch shell. The barrel is 26-inch round choked full, plain walnut pistolgrip stock with hard rubber buttplate. The forend has a small lip on the front end. The Model 20 was dropped from the product line in 1924 having sold about 24,000 guns.

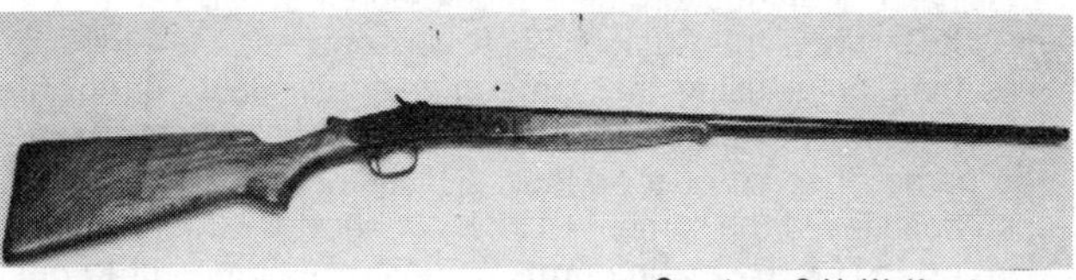

Courtesy C.H. Wolfersberger.

Model 20

Exc.	V.G.	Good	Fair	Poor
600	500	350	200	150

Model 36

The Model 36 was the second of the single shot shotguns to be introduced in 1920. This model features a bolt-action which is cocked by pulling the firing pin head to the rear. It is fitted with an 18-inch round barrel, chambered for the 9MM Long Shot, 9MM Short Shot, and 9MM Ball interchangeably, plain gumwood straight-grip stock with special metal pistolgrip triggerguard. Winchester referred to this model as the "Garden Gun" for use against birds and pests around the house and barn. This model was not serial numbered. It was dropped from the product line in 1927 having sold about 20,000 guns.

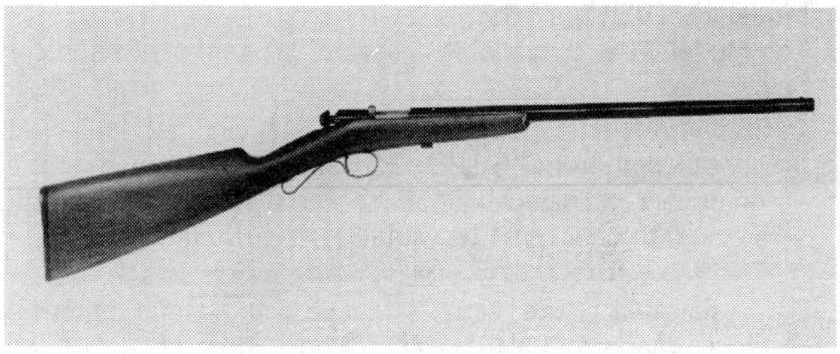

Model 36

Exc.	V.G.	Good	Fair	Poor
750	475	375	300	225

Model 41

This was the third of the low-priced single shot shotguns to be announced in 1920. Like the Model 36, the Model 41 was a bolt-action arrangement but of much stronger construction and design. It features a 24-inch round barrel, chambered for the .410 2-1/2 inch shell, plain walnut pistolgrip stock and forend. Straight-grip stock were furnished at no extra charge. This model was not serial numbered. It was discontinued in 1934 having sold about 22,000 guns.

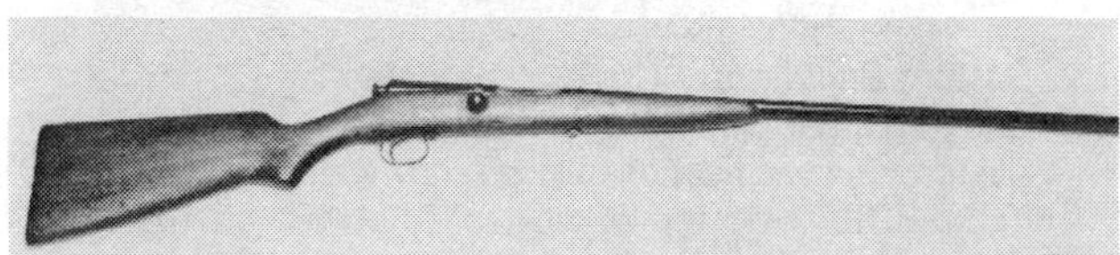

Courtesy C.H. Wolfersberger.

Model 41

Exc.	V.G.	Good	Fair	Poor
1000	750	600	400	300

Model 21

The Model 21 was Winchester's finest effort with regard to quality, reliability, and strength. Developed in the late 1920s the introduction of this fine side by side shotgun was delayed by the company's financial troubles. When Winchester was purchased by the Olin family, the Model 21 was assured the attention it richly deserved due to John M. Olin's love for the gun. Despite the Model 21 being offered as a production gun it was, in fact, a hand-built custom made shotgun. Almost each Model 21 built has a personality of its own because each shotgun is slightly different with regard to chokes, barrel lengths, stock dimensions, and embellishments. The gun was introduced in 1931 and is still in production by U.S. Repeating Arms Co. under license from Winchester. From 1931 to 1959 the Model 21 was considered a production line gun and about 30,000 were sold. In 1960, when the Custom Shop was opened, the Model 21 was built there using the same procedures. Sales during the Custom Shop era were about 1,000 guns. Winchester changed the name of some of the Model 21 styles but the production methods stayed the same. In 1981 Winchester sold its firearms division to U.S. Repeating Arms Co. including the right to build the Model 21. Again the production procedures stayed the same as did many of the former employees. U.S. Repeating Arms expanded and changed some of the style designations for the Model 21. No sales figures are available for this time period. Collectors and shooters will be given the price breakdown for all three eras of production separately.

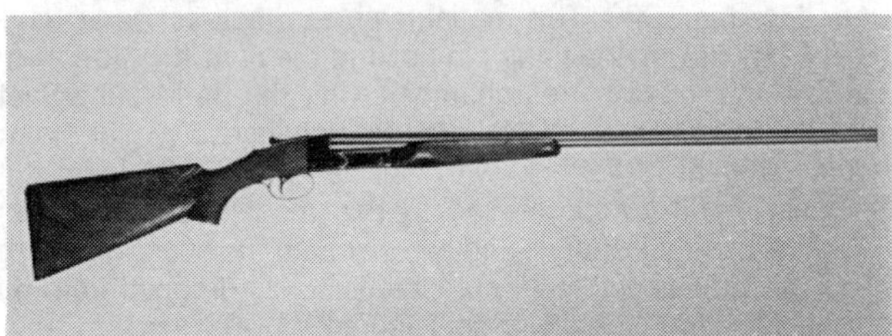

Model 21-1931 to 1959

The Model 21 was available in several different styles and configurations:

1. Standard Grade, chambered in 12, 16, and 20 gauge with barrel length from 26-, 28-, 30-, and 32-inches with matted rib or vent-rib, select walnut checkered pistol or straight-grip stock with checkered beavertail forend. Built from 1931 to 1959.
2. Tournament Grade, same as above with special dimension stock. Marked "TOURNAMENT" on bottom of triggerplate. Built from 1933 to 1934.
3. Trap Grade, same as above with slightly better grade wood and stock made to customers' dimensions. Marked "TRAP" on triggerplate. Built from 1940 to 1959.
4. Skeet Grade, same as above with the addition of the 28 gauge, stock furnished with checkered butt. Marked "SKEET" on triggerplate. Built from 1936 to 1959.
5. Duck Gun, chambered for 12 gauge 3" magnum shells, 30- or 32-inch barrels, Standard Grade stock except for shorter length of pull. Marked "DUCK" on triggerplate. Built from 1940 to 1952.
6. Magnum Gun, chambered for 3-inch 12 or 20 gauge, same stock as Duck Gun. Not marked on triggerplate. Built from 1953 to 1959.
7. Custom Built/Deluxe Grade, chambered for 12, 16, 20, 28, and .410, barrel lengths from 26 to 32 inches, stock built to customers specifications using fancy walnut. Marked "CUSTOM BUILT" on top of rib or "DELUXE" on triggerplate. These grades are frequently but not always engraved. Built from 1933 to 1959.

NOTE: Some early Model 21s were furnished with double triggers, extractors, and splinter forends. This combination reduces the price of the gun regardless of grade. Deduct about 25 percent.

Standard Grade

	Exc	V.G.	Good	Fair	Poor
12 gauge	3300	2800	2400	2000	1700
16 gauge	3800	3400	3100	2500	2000
20 gauge	4800	4400	4100	3500	2900

Tournament Grade

	Exc.	V.G.	Good	Fair	Poor
12 gauge	3500	3000	2500	2100	1800
16 gauge	4000	3600	3300	2600	2100
20 gauge	5000	4600	4300	3600	3000

Trap Grade

	Exc.	V.G.	Good	Fair	Poor
12 gauge	3700	3200	2700	2200	1800
16 gauge	3400	3900	3500	2700	2100
20 gauge	5300	4900	4500	3700	3000

Skeet Grade

	Exc.	V.G.	Good	Fair	Poor
12 gauge	3400	2900	2500	2100	1800
16 gauge	3900	3500	3300	2500	2100
20 gauge	4900	4500	4300	3600	3000

Duck/Magnum Gun

Exc	V.G.	Good	Fair	Poor
3500	2800	2400	2200	1800

NOTE: Add 50 percent for 20 gauge Magnum.

NOTE: Factory ventilated-ribs command a premium of about $300 on 12 gauge guns and $700 on 20 and 16 gauge guns. Models 21s with factory furnished extra barrels will bring an additional premium of about $1,500.

NOTE: Refinished and restored Model 21s are in a somewhat unique category of American made collectable shotguns. A gun that has been professionally refurnished by a master craftsman will come close to the value of factory original guns.

Custom Built/Deluxe Grade

The prices paid for guns of this grade are determined by gauge, barrel and choke combinations, rib type, stock specifications, and engraving. Seek expert appraisal on this grade Model 21 before proceeding. It is best to secure a factory letter from the Cody Firearms Museum. With respect to such letter it is important to note that these records are incomplete and may be inaccurate in a few cases. Records for Model 21s built during the 1930s may be missing. Special order guns may have incomplete records. In such cases a written appraisal from an authoritative collector or dealer may be helpful.

Custom Built-.410 Bore

Exc.	V.G.	Good	Fair	Poor
35,000	25,000	20,000	17,500	15,000

NOTE: Less than 50 .410 Model 21s were built between 1931 and 1959 in all grades. The number of 28 gauge Model 21s built is unknown but the number is probably no greater than the .410 bore.

Custom Shop Model 21s-1960 to 1981

When Winchester moved the production of the Model 21 into the Custom Shop the number of styles was greatly reduced. There were now three distinct styles:

1. Custom Grade, chambered in 12, 16, 20, 28 gauge, and .410 bore in barrel lengths from 26 to 32 inches. Matted rib, fancy walnut checkered pistol or straight grip stock with checkered forend. Guns with pistolgrips furnished with steel grip cap. A small amount of scroll engraving was provided on the frame of this grade.
2. Pigeon Grade, same chambers and barrel lengths as above with the addition of choice of matted or ventilated-rib, leather covered recoil pad, style "A" carving on stock and forend, and gold engraved pistolgrip cap. The frame was engraved with the 21-6 engraving pattern.
3. Grand American Grade, same chambers and barrel lengths as Pigeon Grade with the addition of "B" carving on the stock and forend, 21-6 engraving with gold inlays, extra set of in-

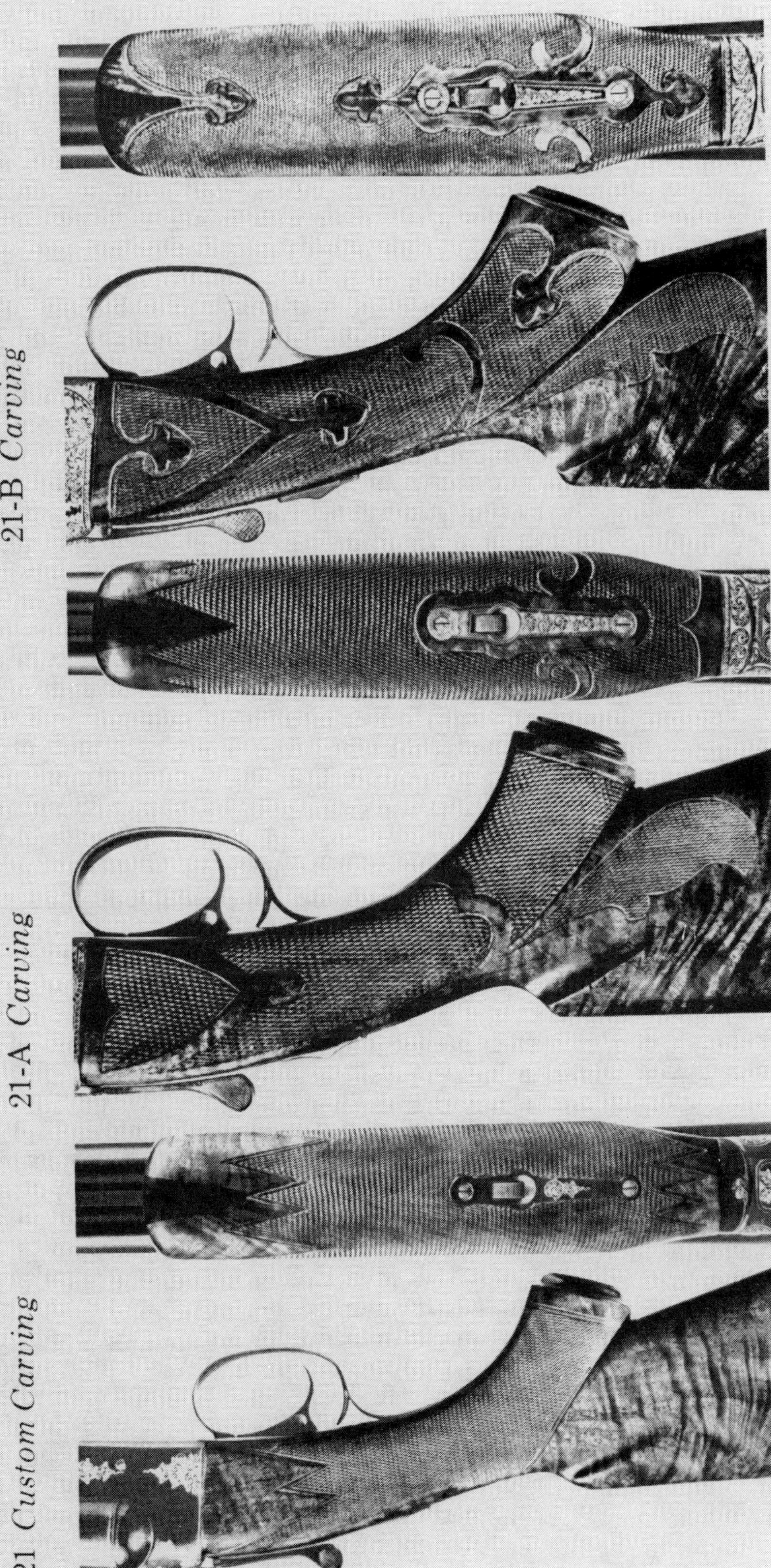

Winchester factory stock carvings for the Model 21.

Engravings for Model 21 Shotguns

THE lines of a double gun are particularly suited to tasteful ornamentation through genuine hand engraving. The six styles shown here and on the following pages have been executed by WINCHESTER custom engravers and designed exclusively for the Model 21. Other designs to meet a desire for something more elaborate can be submitted to our Custom Gun Department. For personalized engraving we will work from sketches or ideas offered by the purchaser.

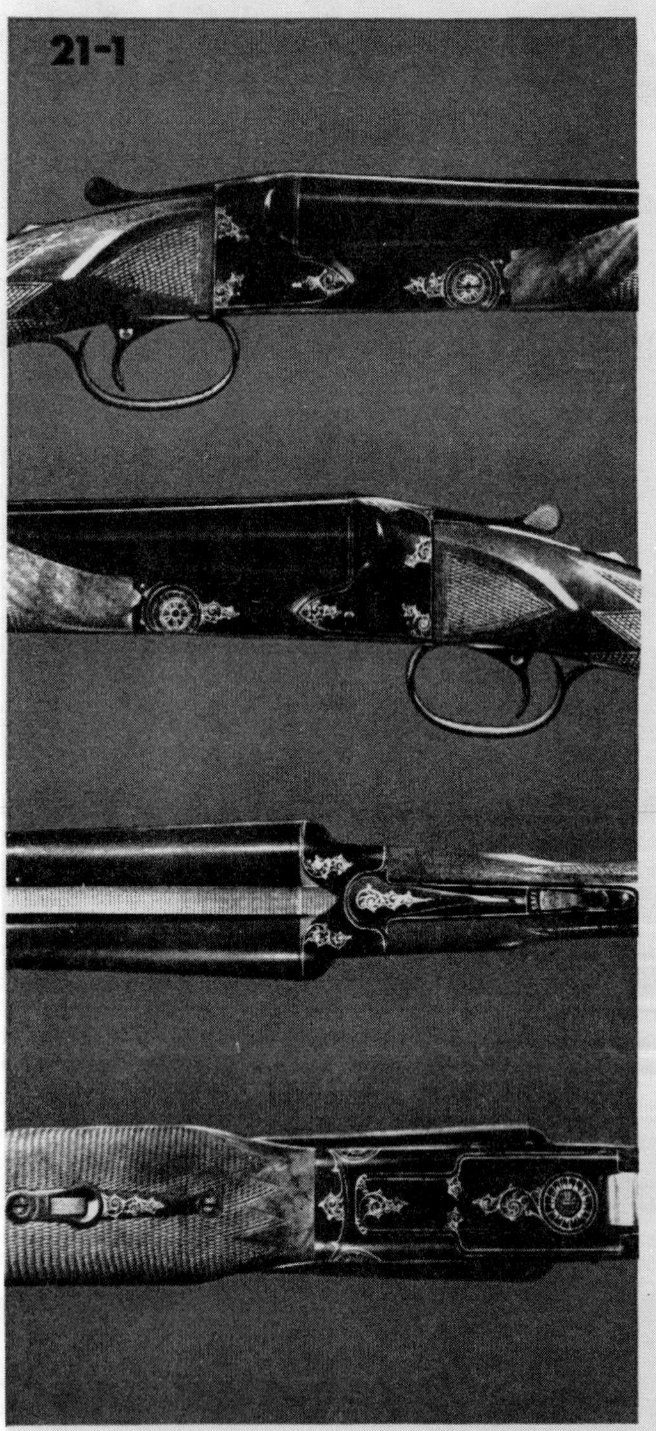

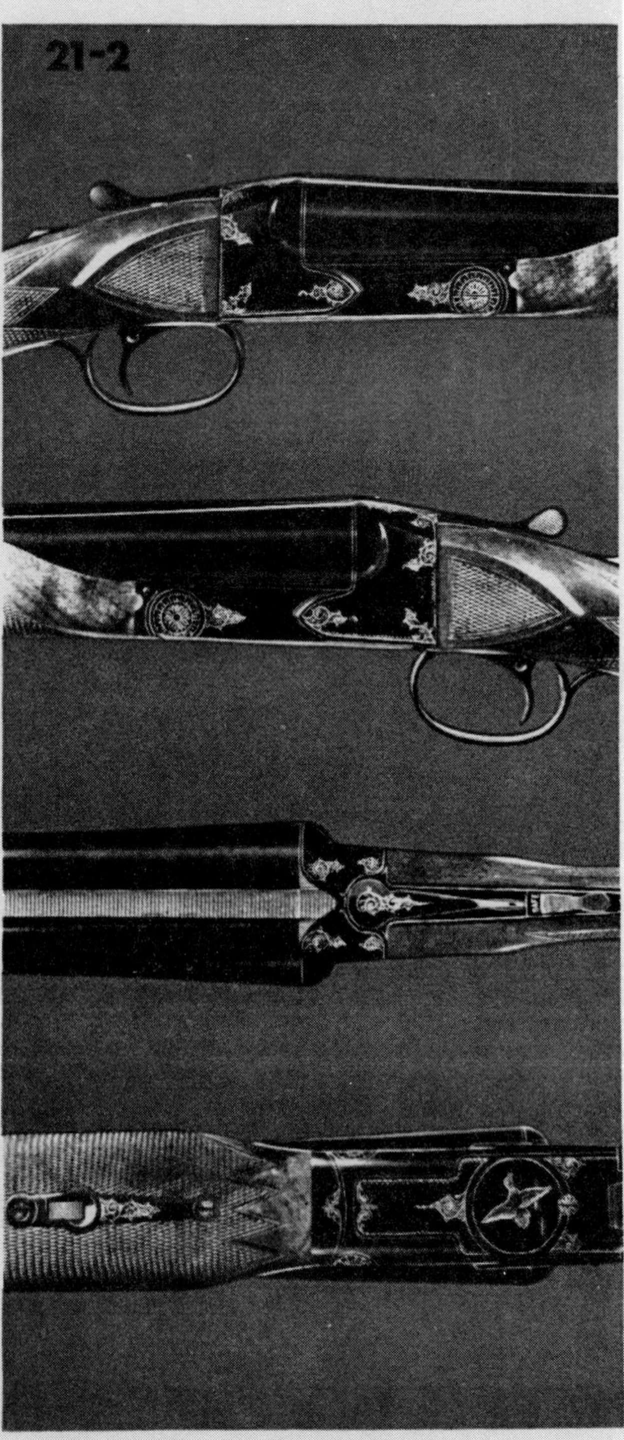

Engraving patterns used by Winchester for the Model 21 between 1932 and 1959.

Engravings for Model 21 Shotguns

WINCHESTER custom engravers have specialized for many years in executing high fidelity game scenes; game animals and birds; hunting dogs; beautiful floral designs and artistic pattern or scroll work; as well as monogrammed shields or nameplates in the stock. Techniques range from very fine flat designs to heavy relief work and all types of inlay work in gold, silver or platinum.

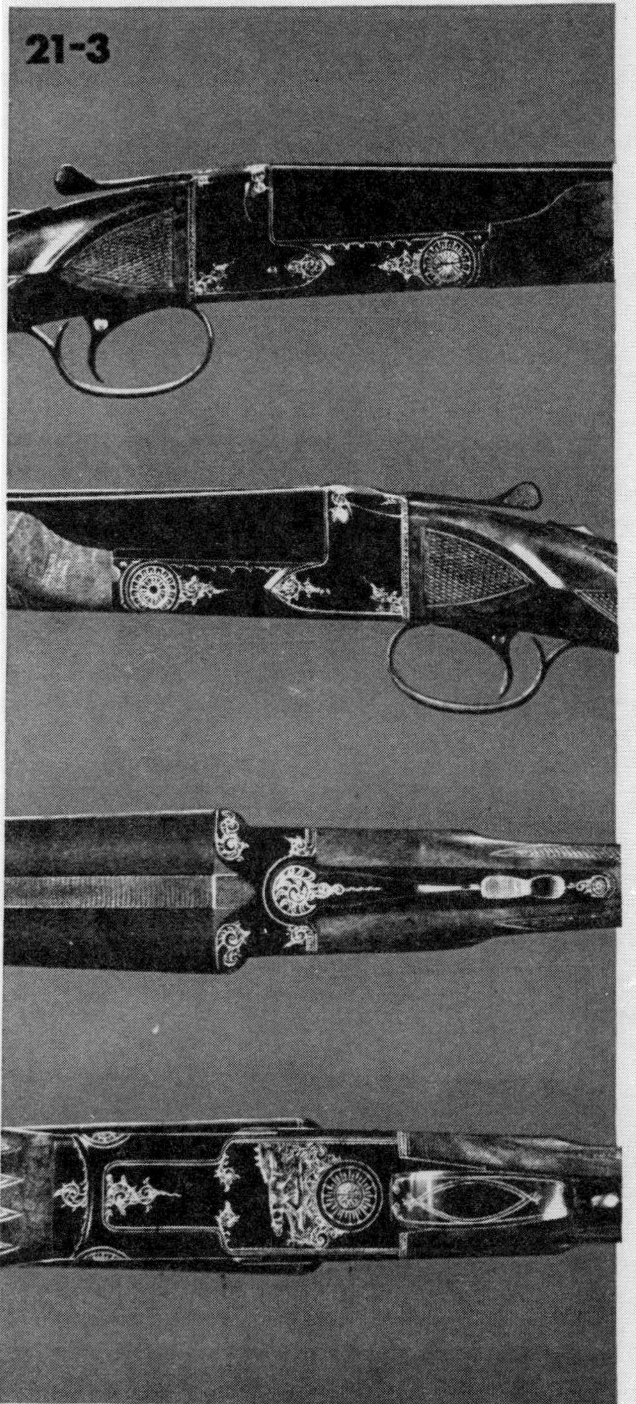

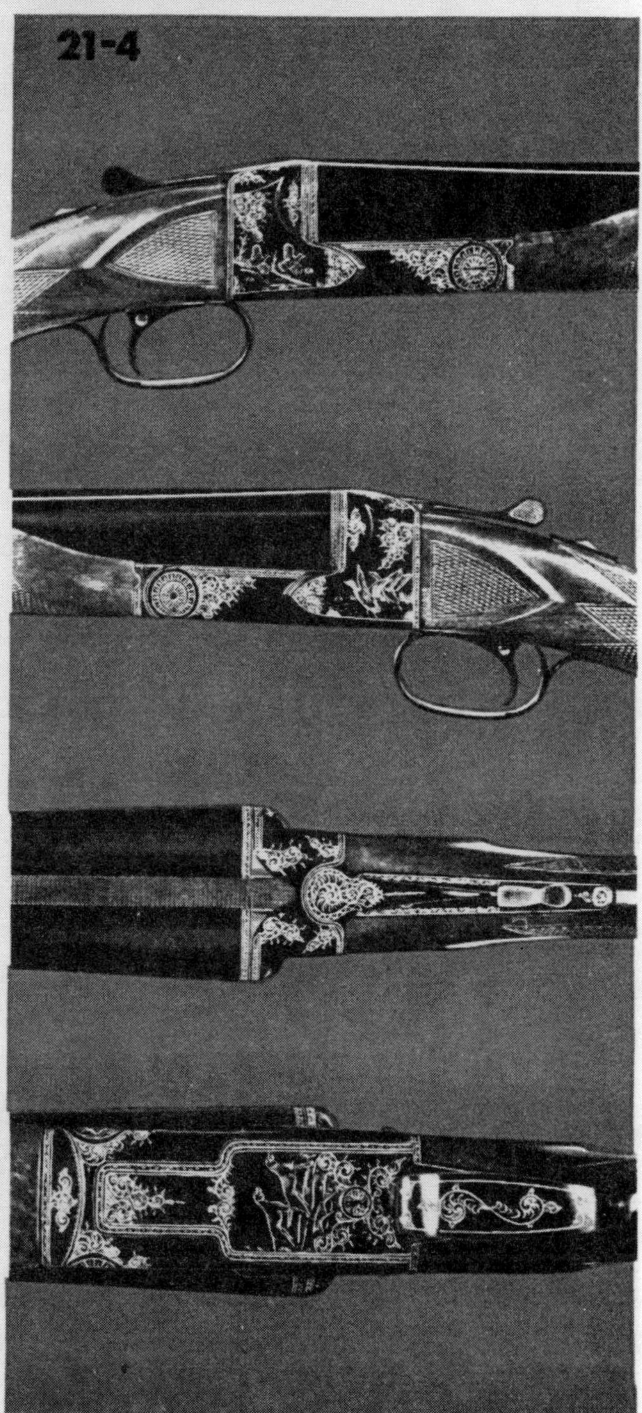

Engraving patterns used by Winchester for the Model 21 between 1932 and 1959.

Engravings for Model 21 Shotguns

AMONG the parts of the Model 21 which lend themselves to a suitable distribution of ornamentation are the frame, trigger guard, fore-end shoe and catch plate, barrels at the breech and muzzle, top lever, tang and safety slide. Trigger may be checkered and either partly or fully gold-plated.

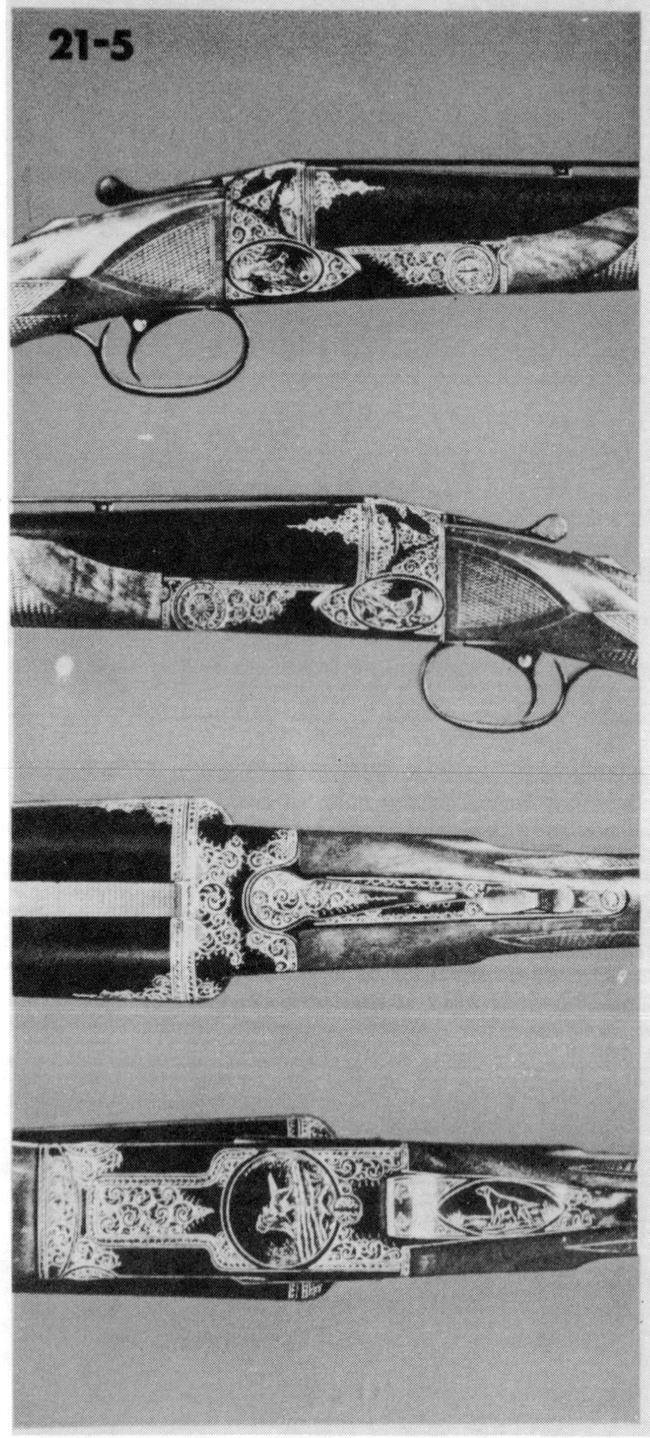

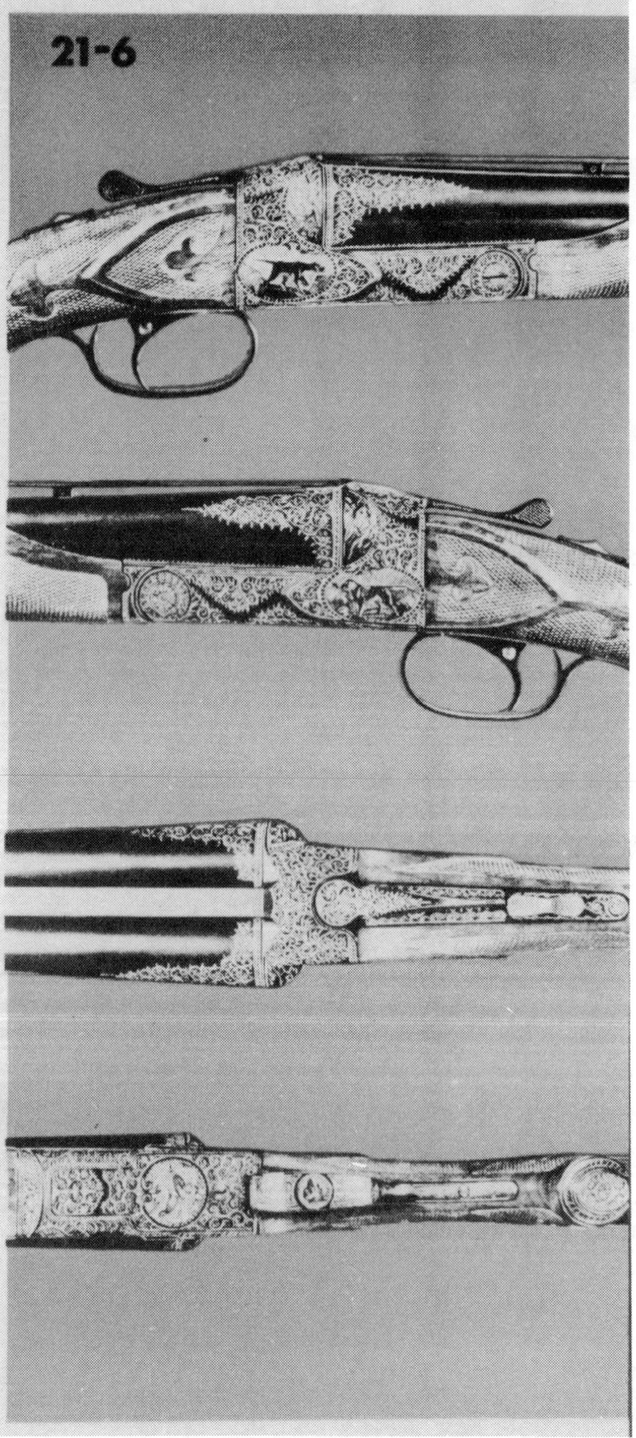

Engraving patterns used by Winchester for the Model 21 between 1932 and 1959.

Engravings for Winchester Model 21 Double Barrel Shotguns

21 *Custom Engraving*

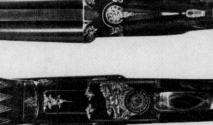

21-3 *Engraving*

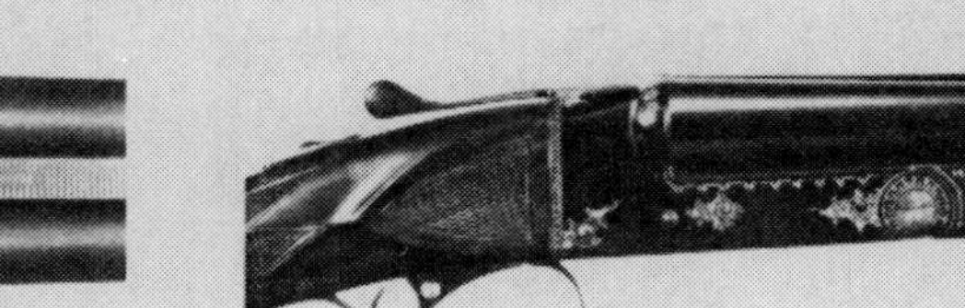

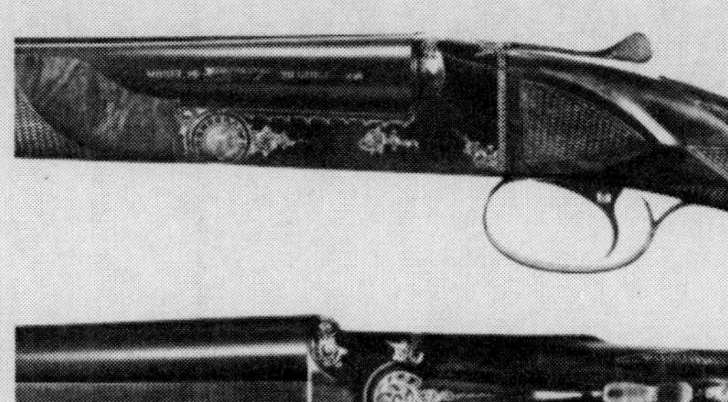

These engraving patterns were used by the factory on the Model 21 from 1960 to the present time.

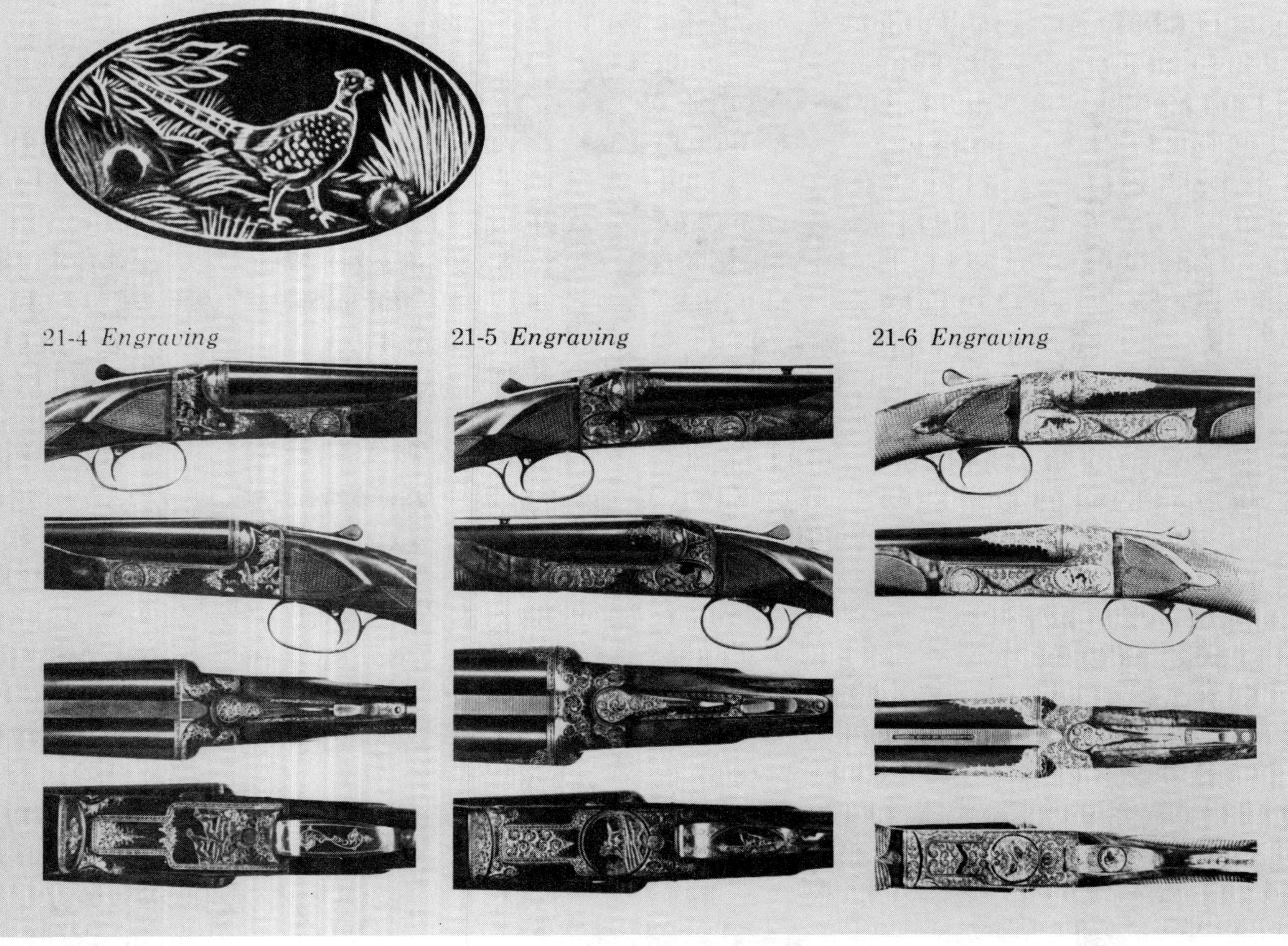

These engraving patterns were used by the factory on the Model 21 from 1960 to the present time.

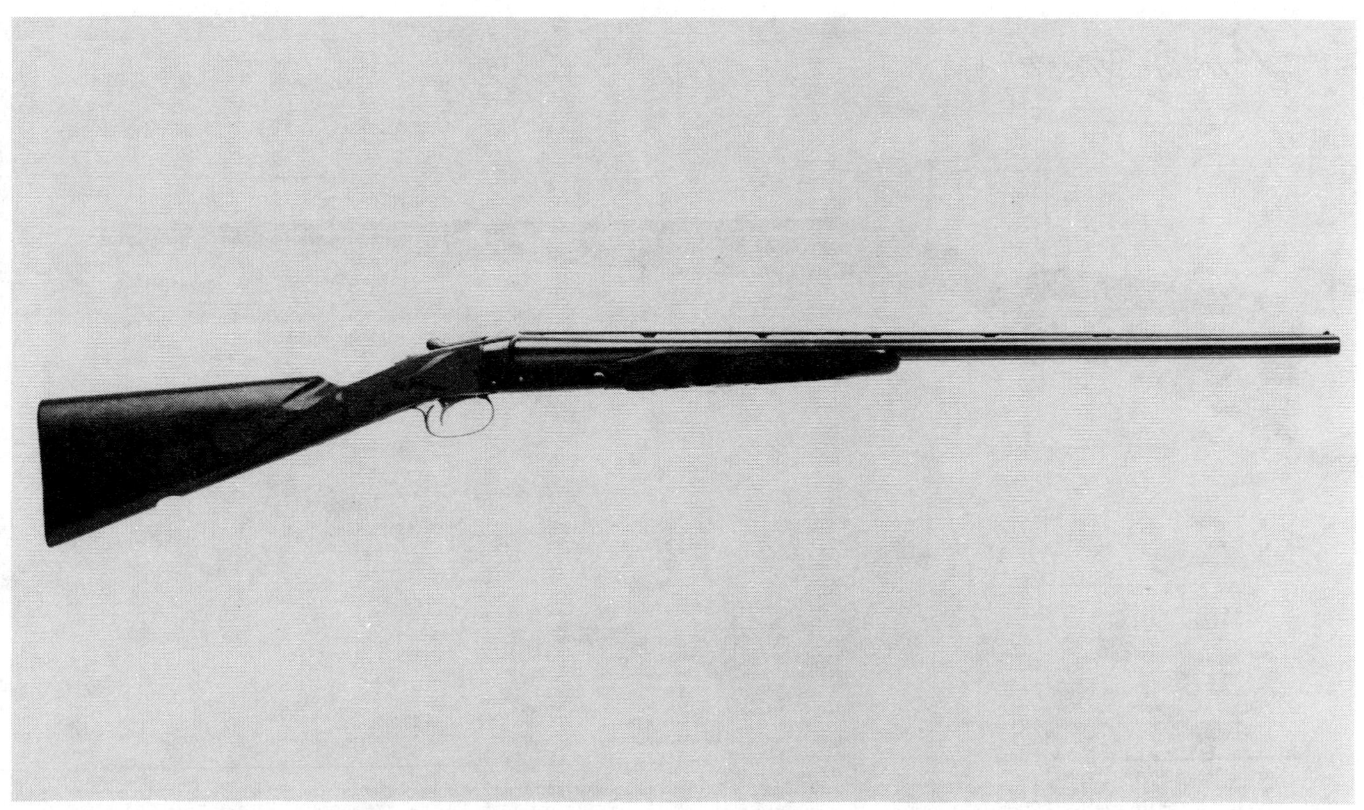

A Custom Grade Model 21 with straight grip stock and ''A'' carved wood. This Model 21 has no engraving which was not standard on Custom Grade guns.

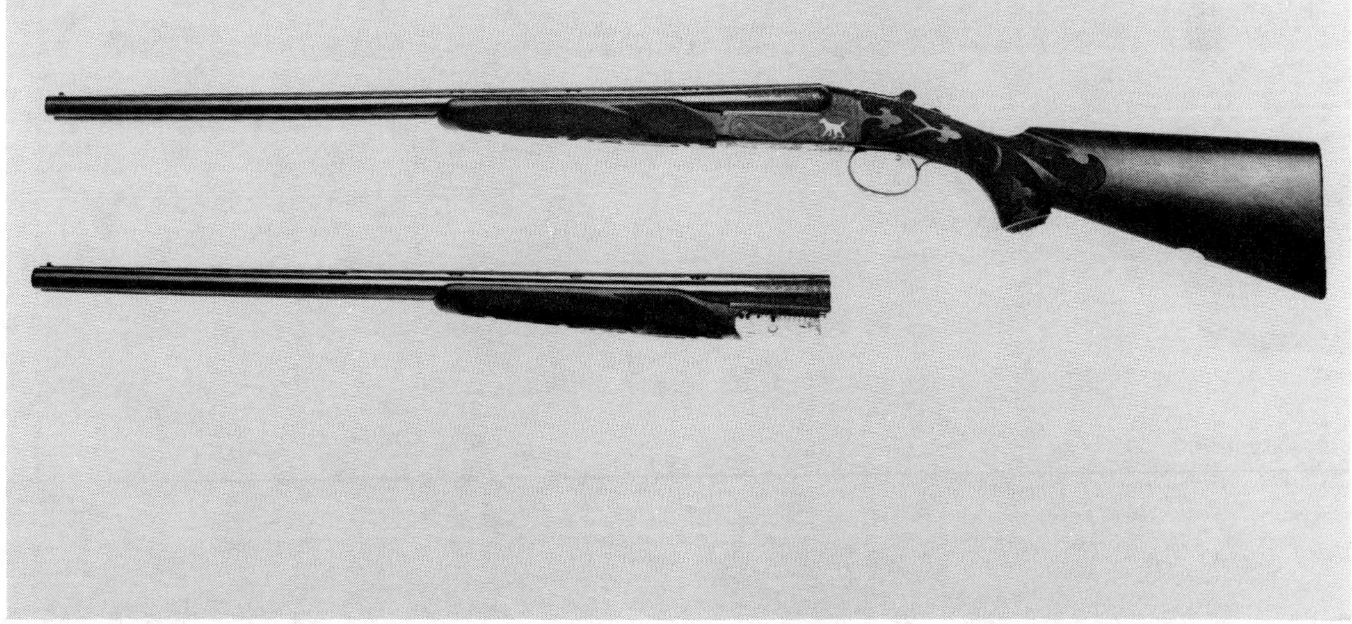

A typical Model 21 Grand American. All Grand Americans were sold with two sets of barrels and a leather trunk style case.

Pigeon Grade

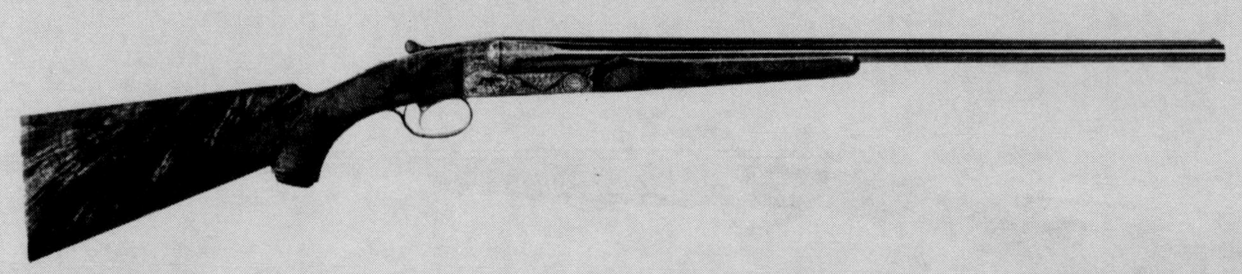

1. *Choice of Gauge (12—16—20)*
2. *Choice of Barrel Length*
   12 gauge—32", 30", 28", 26"
   16 gauge—30", 28", 26"
   20 gauge—30", 28", 26"
3. *Choice of Choke Combination*
4. *Matted Rib or Ventilated Rib*
5. *2¾ or 3" Chamber (3" Chamber not available in 16 ga.)*
6. *Stock and Beavertail Forearm of Grade AA Full-Fancy American Walnut*
7. *Style "A" carving on stock and beavertail forearm. (Style B available at extra cost—see page 8)*
8. *Stock built to individual specifications (within manufacturing limits). Straight or Pistol Grip—includes Cheekpiece, Monte Carlo and/or Offset*
9. *Choice of Forearm—Field, Skeet or Trap*
10. *Black insert in forearm tip*
11. *Gold Inlaid Pistol Grip Cap*
12. *Choice of composition buttplate, recoil pad, checkered butt or leather covered recoil pad*
13. *Panel in top rib inscribed "Custom Built by Winchester for (Customer's Name)"*
14. *Automatic or non-automatic safety (optional)*
15. *Choice of bead sights—front and middle*
16. *Engine turned standing breech, frame, barrel flats, barrel lug, extractors, barrel breech, forearm retainer and inside upper surfaces of forearm shoe*
17. *Gold plated trigger*
18. *Gold oval name plate or 3 initials gold inlaid on trigger guard*
19. *Choice of three (3) initials engraved on name plate*
20. *#6 engraving on frame and barrels*
21. *Leather trunk style gun case with canvas cover available at extra cost, (both case and cover embossed with 3 initials in gold or black)*

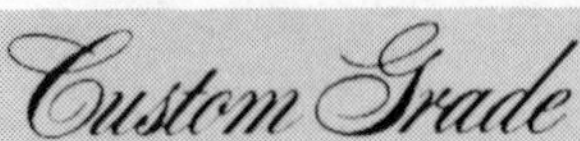

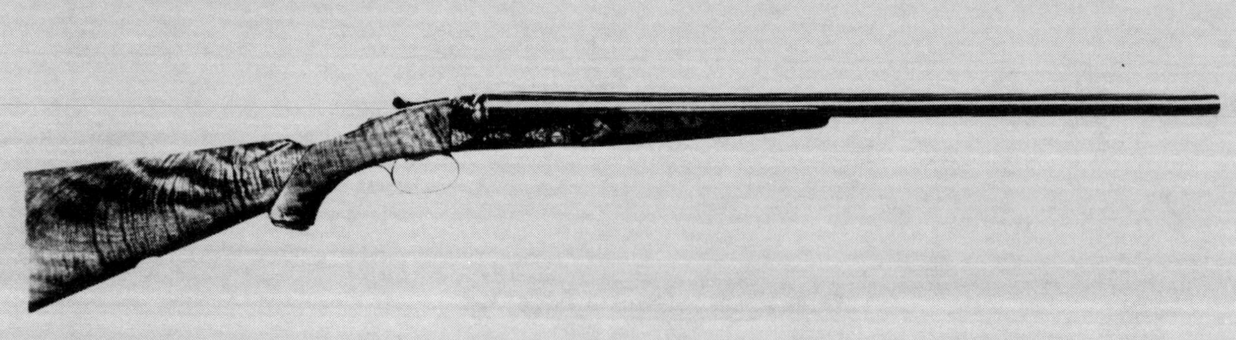

1. *Choice of Gauge (12—16—20)*
2. *Choice of Barrel Length*
   12 gauge—32", 30", 28", 26"
   16 gauge—30", 28", 26"
   20 gauge—30", 28", 26"
3. *Choice of Choke Combination*
4. *Matted Rib*
5. *2¾" Chamber*
6. *Stock and Beavertail Forearm of Grade AA Full-Fancy American Walnut*
7. *Stock built to individual specifications (within manufacturing limits). Straight or Pistol Grip—includes Cheekpiece, Monte Carlo and/or Offset*
8. *Choice of Forearm—Field, Skeet or Trap*
9. *Black insert in forearm tip*
10. *Custom Style Checkering on stock and forearm (Style A or B available at extra cost—see page 8)*
11. *Steel Pistol Grip Cap*
12. *Choice of composition buttplate, recoil pad or checkered butt*
13. *Panel in top rib inscribed "Custom Built by Winchester for (Customer's Name)"*
14. *Automatic or non-automatic safety (optional)*
15. *Choice of bead sights—front and middle*
16. *Engine turned standing breech, frame, barrel flats, barrel lug, extractors, barrel breech, forearm retainer and inside upper surfaces of forearm shoe*
17. *Custom style ornamentation*
    Additional engraving available at extra cost—see patterns 3, 4 and 5 on pages 6 and 7
18. *Gold plated trigger*
19. *Gold oval name plate (optional)*
20. *Choice of three (3) initials engraved on name plate*
21. *Leather trunk style gun case with canvas cover available at extra cost, (both case and cover embossed with 3 initials in gold or black)*

terchangeable barrels with extra forend. All of this was enclosed in a leather trunk case.

Custom Grade-12 Gauge

Exc.	V.G.	Good	Fair	Poor
5700	4500	3800	3000	2500

NOTE: Add $4,000 for 16 gauge. Add $3,000 for 20 gauge.

Pigeon Grade-12 Gauge

Exc.	V.G.	Good	Fair	Poor
9000	7500	5000	2500	1500

NOTE: Add $5,000 for 16 gauge. Add $4,000 for 20 gauge.

Grand American-12 Gauge

Exc.	V.G.	Good	Fair	Poor
14,000	10,000	8000	5000	3000

NOTE: Add $10,000 for 16 gauge. Add $4,000 for 20 gauge.

Editor's Comment: There were eight 28 gauge Model 21s built during this period and 5 .410 bores built. These guns obviously command a very large premium. Factory letters are available on these guns.

Custom Shop Model 21s 1982 to Present

When U.S. Repeating Arms Co. took over the production of the Model 21 the Pigeon Grade was dropped from the line. The Grand American Grade was retained with all the features of its predecessor but with the addition of a small bore set featuring a 28 gauge and .410 bore set of barrels. Two new grades were introduced in 1983; the Standard Custom Grade and the Special Custom Built. In addition to these grades the factory would undertake to build for its customers whatever was desired. Due to the unique nature of these guns it is advised that an expert appraisal be sought to establish a value. While the change over from Winchester to U.S. Repeating Arms was a transfer of business assets and the craftsmen and personel remained the same, collectors are reluctant to assign the same values to U.S. Repeating Arms Model 21s as those produced by Winchester. No official production figures are available for U.S.R.A. Model 21s but the number is most likely very small; perhaps areound 200 guns.

Standard Custom Built

NIB	Exc.	V.G.	Good	Fair	Poor
8000	4550	3500	3000	2400	2000

Grand American

NIB	Exc.	V.G.	Good	Fair	Poor
22500	11000	8000	6500	4000	2500

Grand American-Small Gauge Set-28 or .410 bore

NIB	Exc.	V.G.	Good	Fair	Poor
39000	22000	17500	8000	6000	4000

Model 24

The Model 24 was Winchester's attempt to develop a medium-priced double barrel shotgun. Like the Model 21, it was a top lever breakdown model that was available in 12, 16, and 20 gauge in various barrel lengths from 26 to 30 inches. Offered in a Standard model only with double triggers, raised matted rib, plain walnut pistol or straight-grip stock with semi-beavertail forend, the Model 24 was introduced in 1939 and was discontinued in 1957 with about 116,000 guns sold.

Model 24

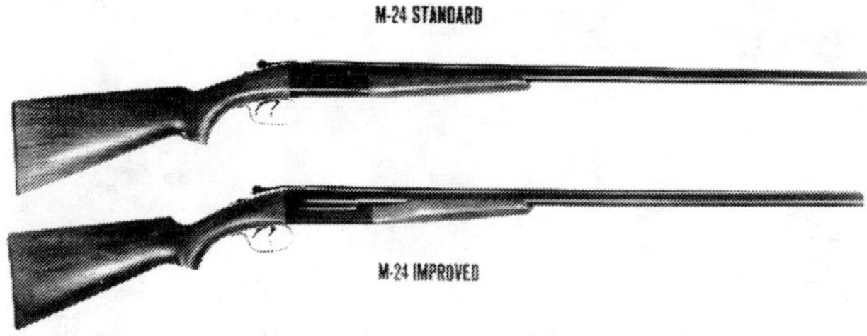

Exc.	V.G.	Good	Fair	Poor
500	400	350	250	200

Model 37

This model was developed to keep pace with Winchester's competitors in the low-price single barrel exposed hammer shotgun market. The shotgun was available in 12, 16, 20, 28 gauge, and .410 bore with barrel lengths from 26 to 30 inches. The stock was plain walnut with pistolgrip and semi-beavertail forend. This model was not serial numbered. Introduced in 1936 it stayed in the company line until 1963 having sold slightly over 1,000,000 guns.

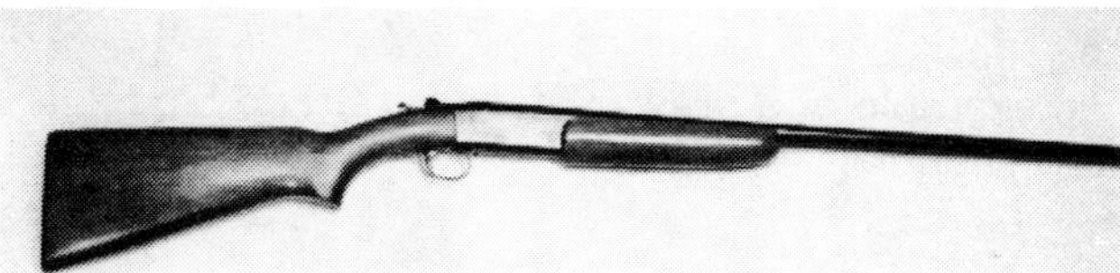

Courtesy C.H. Wolfersberger.

Model 37

	Exc.	V.G.	Good	Fair	Poor
12 gauge	200	150	125	100	50
16 gauge	225	175	150	125	60
20 gauge	250	200	175	150	90
28 gauge	1200	900	675	525	450
410 bore	300	225	200	175	100

Model 42

This was the first slide action shotgun ever developed exclusively for the .410 bore. Invented by William Roemer, the Model 42 was in effect, at least in outward appearance, a miniature Model 12. This shotgun was a quality built, fast handling, racy looking shotgun that many refer to as "Everybody's Sweetheart." The Model 42 was offered in several different configurations throughout its production:

1. Standard Grade, 26- or 28-inch plain or solid rib barrel, plain walnut pistolgrip stock with grooved slide handle, fitted with composition buttplate. Built from 1933 to 1963.
2. Skeet Grade, 26- or 28-inch plain, solid rib, or ventilated-rib barrel, select walnut checkered pistol or straight-grip stock with checkered extension slide handle. The Skeet Grade was offered in chokes other than skeet. Skeet Grade Model 42s are seen in full, modified, cylinder, improved cylinder, and skeet chokes. Built from 1933 to 1963.
3. Trap Grade, 26- or 28-inch plain or solid rib barrel, fancy walnut special checkered pistol or straight-grip stock with special checkered extension slide handle. The Trap Grade checkering pattern has one closed diamond on each side of the pistolgrip or, in the case of the straight-grip, the diamond is located on the underside of the grip. The extension slide handle has two diamonds on each side. Stamped "TRAP" on the bottom of the receiver. Built from 1934 to 1939.
4. Deluxe Grade, same as above, available with ventilated-rib in 1954. Some early models stamped "DELUXE" on bottom of receiver. Built from 1940 to 1963.
5. Pigeon Grade, same as above Deluxe Grade but engraved with a Pigeon on the lower magazine tube. Very few of this grade were built by Winchester, and the majority were done in the late 1940s.

Engraved Model 42s will occasionally be seen. Collectors are urged to seek expert advice on these very rare and expensive guns. The Model 42 was produced from 1933 to 1963. About 160,000 were sold.

Standard Grade

NIB	Exc.	V.G.	Good	Fair	Poor
1500	850	600	425	325	275

NOTE: For guns with solid ribs add 50 percent.

Skeet Grade-Solid Rib

Exc.	V.G.	Good	Fair	Poor
2300	1500	900	500	350

An example of a prewar Standard Grade Model 42. Notice the distinctive grip on the butt stock and the round slide handle.

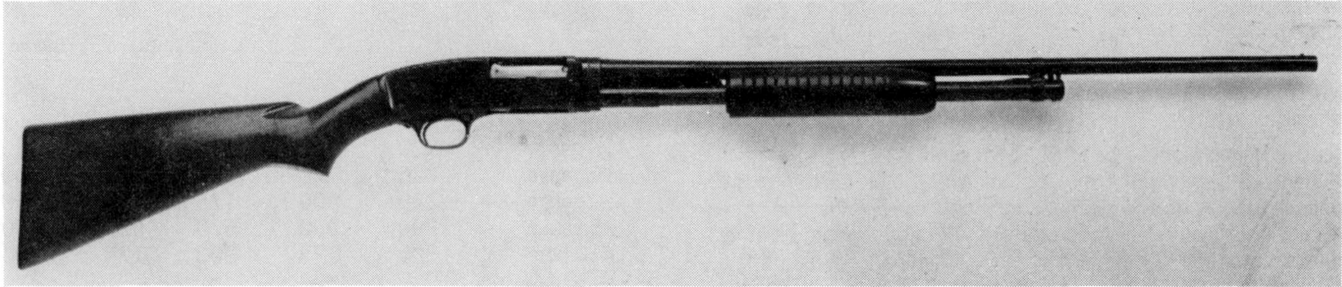

A postwar Standard Grade Model 42. The pistol grip has a new shape as does the flat bottom slide handle.

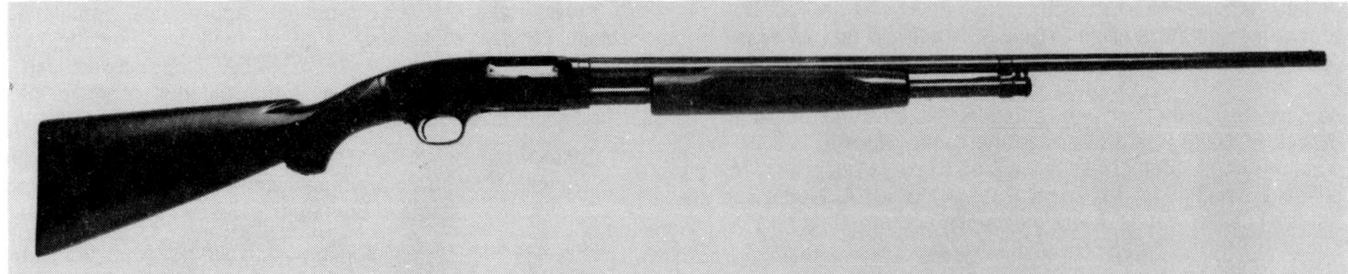

A Skeet Grade Model 42 with solid rib. Notice the extension slide handle which was used on all Model 42 Skeet Grades. The pistol grip is fitted with a grip cap.

A Skeet Grade with factory ventilated rib. Winchester began to install ventilated ribs on the Model 42 in 1954 and continued until the end of production in 1963.

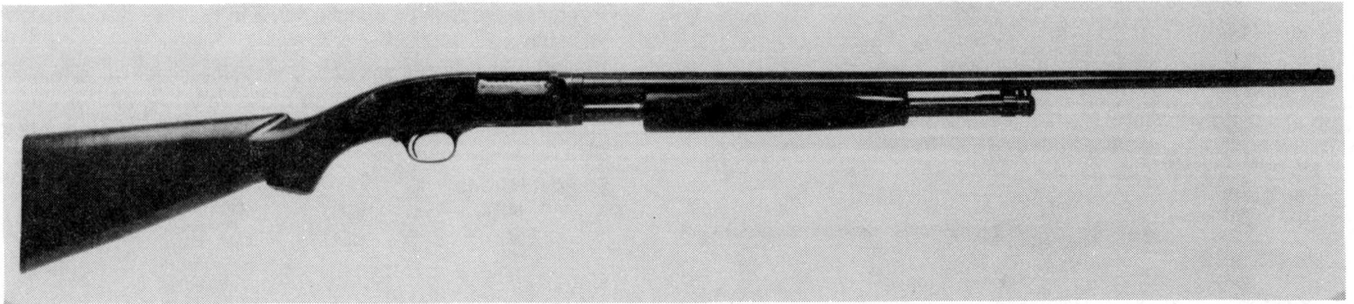

An example of a Deluxe Grade Model 42. Notice the single diamond in the pistol grip and the two diamonds on the extension slide handle. This particular gun has a solid rib, but Winchester build Deluxe Grades with ventilated ribs as well.

NOTE: Add 25 percent of guns chambered for 2-1/2-inch shells.

Skeet Grade-Ventilated Rib

Exc.	V.G.	Good	Fair	Poor
3000	2500	1250	850	600

NOTE: Add 25 percent of guns chambered for 2-1/2-inch shells.

Editor's Comment: Contrary to traditional views, Winchester did install factory ventilated-ribs on its Model 42. Former employees and factory drawings substantiate this fact. However, the subject of what is a factory rib and what is not has been covered in great detail in an excellent book on the Model 42. Seek expert advice before selling or purchasing any Model 42 with a ventilated-rib.

Trap Grade

Exc.	V.G.	Good	Fair	Poor
7500	5500	3500	1750	700

Deluxe Grade-Solid Rib

Exc.	V.G.	Good	Fair	Poor
4000	2750	1500	750	300

Deluxe Grade-Ventilated Rib

Exc.	V.G.	Good	Fair	Poor
5500	4000	2250	900	400

NOTE: For Pigeon Grade Model 42s add 100 percent.

Model 1911

This was Winchester's first self-loading shotgun and was developed by T.C. Johnson in order to keep pace with the Remington Auto-Loading Shotgun Model 11 which was developed by John M. Browning with help from T.C. Johnson. Because of the delays involved in developing a brand new design, the Model 1911 was introduced on Oct. 7, 1911. The shotgun was a recoil operated mechanism, had a tubular magazine and had the takedown feature. The shotgun was available in two styles:

1. Plain Model 1911, 26- or 28-inch barrel, 12 gauge, choked full, modified, or cylinder, plain birch laminated pistolgrip stock and forend with hard rubber buttplate.
2. Fancy Model 1911, same as above with fancy birch laminated stock.

Because of the hurry in getting the model ready for production, the shotgun demonstrated design weakness and never proved satisfactory. It was discontinued in 1925 with about 83,000 guns sold.

Model 1911-Plain

Exc.	V.G.	Good	Fair	Poor
550	375	300	250	200

Model 1911-Fancy

Exc.	V.G.	Good	Fair	Poor
800	500	400	300	250

Model 40

This model represents Winchester's second attempt to build a self-loading long recoil-operated repeating shotgun. This shotgun was a hammerless tubular magazine gun without the hump at the rear of the receiver. Available in 12 gauge only with barrel lengths from 28 to 30 inches. The Standard Grade had plain walnut pistolgrip stock and forend. The Skeet Grade was fitted with select walnut checkered pistolgrip stock and checkered forend. The Model 40 suffered from the same design problems as the Model 11, and sales were small. Introduced in 1940 and discontinued in 1941, Winchester sold about 12,000 guns.

Standard Grade

Exc.	V.G.	Good	Fair	Poor
600	500	400	275	200

Skeet Grade

Exc.	V.G.	Good	Fair	Poor
800	600	500	300	250

Model 50

The Model 50 was the company's third attempt to produce a satisfactory self-loading repeating shotgun. Winchester went to the short recoil system, utilizing a floating chamber design. This model was available in several different styles:

1. Standard Grade, 12 or 20 gauge with plain or ventilated-rib in lengths from 26 to 30 inches, plain walnut checkered pistol grip stock and forend.
2. Skeet Grade, 12 or 20 gauge with 26-inch ventilated-rib barrel. Walnut checkered pistolgrip stock and forend.
3. Trap Grade, 12 gauge with 30-inch ventilated-rib barrel, walnut checkered Monte Carlo stock and forend.
4. Pigeon Grade, 12 or 20 gauge with barrel lengths to customers' specifications. Fancy walnut checkered stock and forend. Made on special orders only.
5. Featherweight, a lighter version of all the above except Trap Grade.

This model begins with serial-number 1000. This model was successful and was built between 1954 and 1961. Winchester sold about 200,000 guns.

Standard Grade

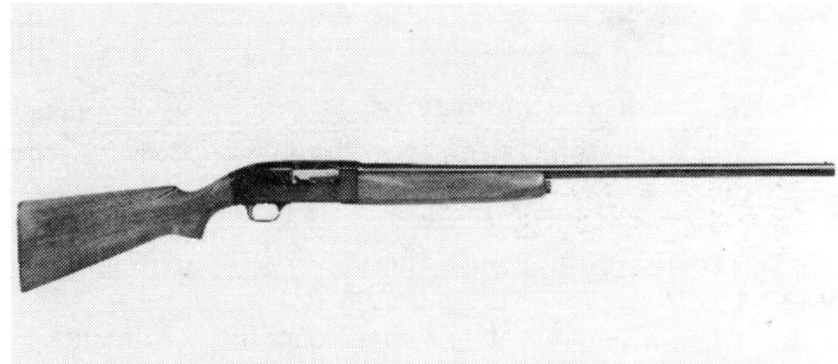

Exc.	V.G.	Good	Fair	Poor
450	375	300	200	125

Skeet Grade

Exc.	V.G.	Good	Fair	Poor
500	425	360	250	150

Trap Grade

Exc.	V.G.	Good	Fair	Poor
500	425	360	250	150

Pigeon Grade

Exc.	V.G.	Good	Fair	Poor
1250	900	750	450	250

Featherweight

Exc.	V.G.	Good	Fair	Poor
475	400	325	225	125

Model 59

The fourth and final pre-1964 Winchester self-loading shotgun featured a steel and fiberglass barrel with aluminum alloy receiver. The gun was available in 12 gauge only with barrel lengths from 26 to 30 inches with a variety of chokes. In 1961 Winchester introduced the "Versalite" choke tube which gave the shooter a choice of full, modified, or improved cylinder chokes in the same barrel. This model was available in two different styles:

1. Standard Grade, plain walnut checkered pistolgrip stock and forend.
2. Pigeon Grade, select walnut checkered pistolgrip and forend.

Winchester sold about 82,000 of these guns between 1960 and 1965.

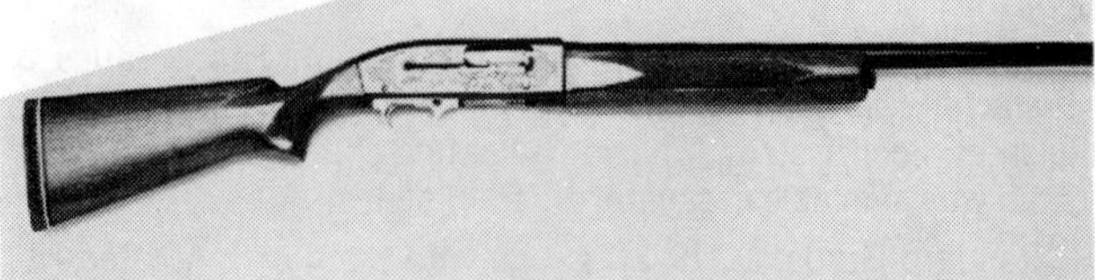
Courtesy Butterfield & Butterfield, San Francisco, California.

Standard Grade

Exc.	V.G.	Good	Fair	Poor
500	375	325	225	150

Pigeon Grade

Exc.	V.G.	Good	Fair	Poor
1500	1100	850	600	300

POST-1963 RIFLES AND SHOTGUNS

Model 121

This is a single shot, bolt-action rifle chambered for the .22 rimfire cartridge. It has a 20.75" barrel with open sights. The finish is blued, with a plain walnut stock. It was manufactured between 1967 and 1973. A youth model with a shorter stock was designated the 121Y and is valued the same.

Courtesy Buffalo Bill Historical Center, Cody, Wyoming.

Exc.	V.G.	Good	Fair	Poor
125	100	80	60	40

Model 131

This is a bolt-action repeater chambered for the .22 rimfire cartridge. It has a 20.75" barrel with open sights and a 7-round, detachable magazine. The finish is blued, with a plain walnut stock. It was manufactured between 1967 and 1973. A tubular magazine version was designated the Model 141 and is valued the same.

Exc.	V.G.	Good	Fair	Poor
140	110	90	75	50

Model 310

This is a single shot, bolt-action rifle chambered for the .22 rimfire cartridge. It features a 22" barrel with open sights. The finish is blued, with a checkered walnut stock. It was manufactured between 1972 and 1975.

Courtesy Buffalo Bill Historical Center, Cody, Wyoming.

Exc.	V.G.	Good	Fair	Poor
200	150	125	100	75

Model 320

This is a bolt-action repeating rifle that is similar in configuration to the Model 310 single shot. It has a 5-round, detachable box magazine. It was manufactured between 1972 and 1974.

Exc.	V.G.	Good	Fair	Poor
350	300	250	175	125

Model 250

This is a lever-action repeating rifle with a hammerless action. It is chambered for the .22 rimfire cartridge and has a 20.5" barrel with open sights and a tubular magazine. The finish is blued, with a checkered pistolgrip stock. It was manufactured between 1963 and 1973.

Exc.	V.G.	Good	Fair	Poor
125	100	80	60	40

Model 250 Deluxe

This version is similar to the Model 250 and is furnished with select walnut and sling swivels. It was manufactured between 1965 and 1971.

Exc.	V.G.	Good	Fair	Poor
150	125	100	75	50

Model 255

This version is simply the Model 250 chambered for the .22 WMR cartridge. It was manufactured between 1964 and 1970.

Exc.	V.G.	Good	Fair	Poor
145	120	90	70	50

Model 255 Deluxe

This version was offered with select walnut and sling swivels. It was manufactured between 1965 and 1973.

Exc.	V.G.	Good	Fair	Poor
175	150	125	100	75

Model 270

This is a slide action rifle chambered for the .22 rimfire cartridge. It has a 20.5" barrel and a tubular magazine. The finish is blued, with a checkered walnut stock. It was manufactured between 1963 and 1973.

Exc.	V.G.	Good	Fair	Poor
125	100	75	50	35

Model 490

This is a blowback-operated, semi-automatic rifle chambered for the .22 l.r. cartridge. It has a 22" barrel with open sights and a 5-round, detachable magazine. The finish is blued, with a checkered stock. It was manufactured between 1975 and 1980.

Exc.	V.G.	Good	Fair	Poor
250	200	150	100	75

Model 94

This is the post-'64 lever-action carbine chambered for the .30-30, 7-30 Waters, and the .44 Magnum cartridges. It is offered with a 20" or 24" barrel and has a 6- or 7-round, tubular magazine depending on barrel length. The round barrel is offered with open sights. The forearm is held on by a single barrel band. The finish is blued, with a straight-grip walnut stock. In 1982 it was modified to angle ejection to simplify scope mounting. It was introduced as a continuation of the Model 94 line in 1964.

NIB	Exc.	V.G.	Good	Fair	Poor
275	225	175	125	100	75

Model 94 Ranger-Base Model

NIB	Exc.	V.G.	Good	Fair	Poor
240	200	175	150	100	75

Model 94 Deluxe—Checkered Stock

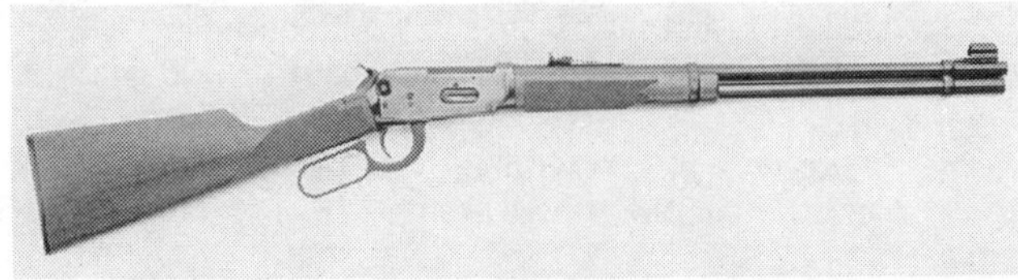

NIB	Exc.	V.G.	Good	Fair	Poor
300	250	200	150	125	100

Model 94 Win-Tuff—Laminated Stock

NIB	Exc.	V.G.	Good	Fair	Poor
300	250	200	150	125	100

Model 94 XTR—Select, Checkered Walnut Stock—Disc. 1988

Exc.	V.G.	Good	Fair	Poor
275	225	150	100	85

Model 94 XTR Deluxe—Fancy Checkering

Exc.	V.G.	Good	Fair	Poor
350	300	200	150	110

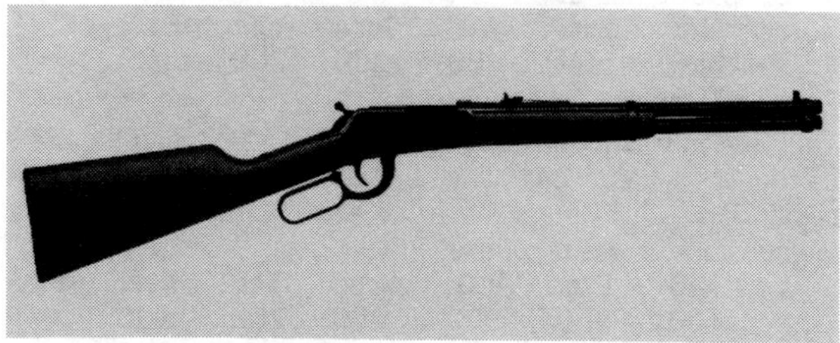

Model 94 Trapper—16" Barrel

NIB	Exc.	V.G.	Good	Fair	Poor
285	225	175	125	100	75

Model 94 Antique Carbine—Gold-plated Saddle Ring

Exc.	V.G.	Good	Fair	Poor
250	200	175	125	90

Model 94 Wrangler—.32 Win. Special

Exc.	V.G.	Good	Fair	Poor
325	275	175	125	100

Model 94 Wrangler II—Loop Lever

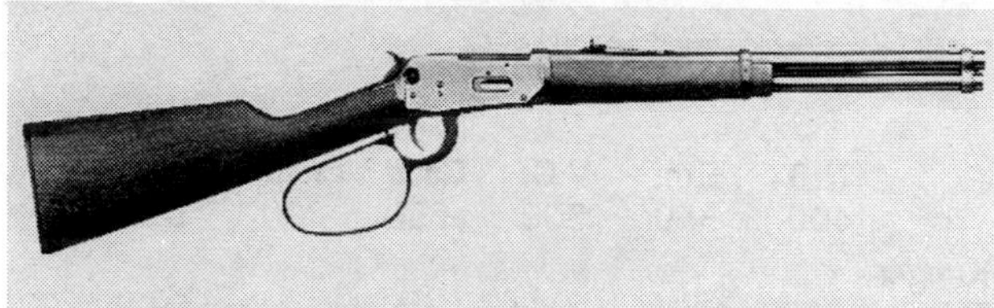

Exc.	V.G.	Good	Fair	Poor
250	200	150	100	85

Model 94 XTR Big Bore

This version is chambered for the .307, .356, or the .375 Win. cartridges. It features the angle-ejection and is blued with a walnut, Monte Carlo-type stock and recoil pad. The round barrel is 20" in length. It has a 6-round, tubular magazine. It was introduced in 1978.

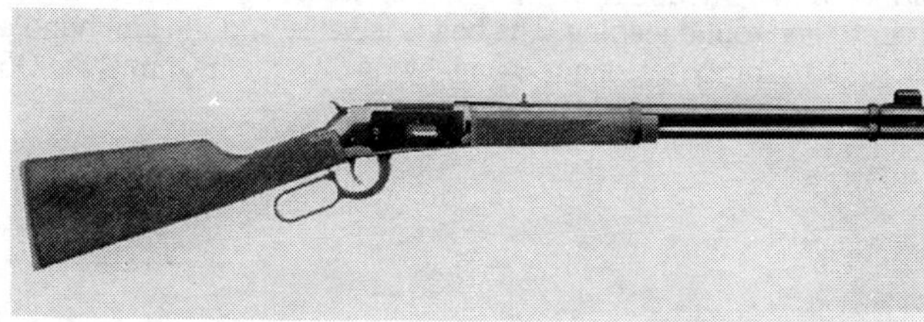

NIB	Exc.	V.G.	Good	Fair	Poor
300	250	200	150	125	100

Model 9422 XTR

This is a deluxe lever-action rifle chambered for the .22 rimfire cartridges. It is a takedown rifle with a 20.5", round barrel and a tubular magazine. The finish is blued with a checkered, high-gloss, straight-grip walnut stock. It was introduced in 1922. A .22 Magnum version is also available and would be worth approximately $10 additional.

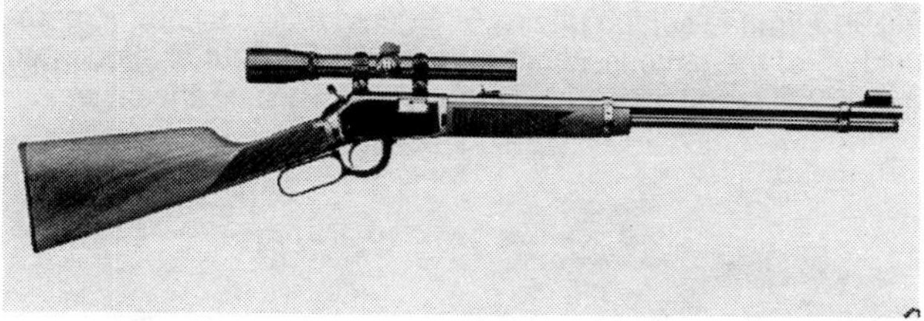

NIB	Exc.	V.G.	Good	Fair	Poor
325	275	225	175	125	100

Model 9422 XTR Classic

This version is similar to the standard Model 9422 XTR except that it features a 22.5" barrel and a satin-finished, plain, pistolgrip walnut stock. It was manufactured between 1985 and 1987.

Exc.	V.G.	Good	Fair	Poor
350	300	250	200	125

Model 9422 WinTuff

This model features an uncheckered laminated wood stock that is brown in color. Chambered for both the .22 Rimfire and the .22 Winchester Magnum Rimfire. Weighs 6.25 lbs. Other features are the same as the standard Model 9422.

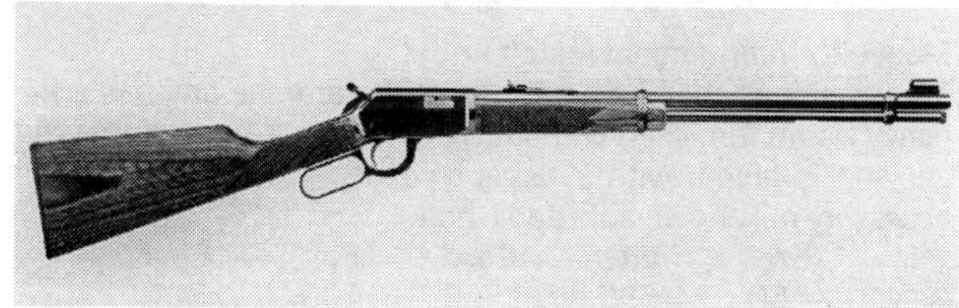

NIB	Exc.	V.G.	Good	Fair	Poor
300	250	200	150	100	75

Model 9422 WinCam

This model is chambered only for the .22 Winchester Magnum Rimfire. The laminated stock is a green color. Weighs 6.25 lbs.

NIB	Exc.	V.G.	Good	Fair	Poor
315	260	200	150	100	75

Model 64

This is a post-1964 version of the lever-action Model 64. It is chambered for the .30-30 cartridge and has a 24", round barrel with open sights and a 5-round, two-thirds-length tubular magazine. The finish is blued with a plain walnut, pistolgrip stock. It was manufactured between 1972 and 1974.

Exc.	V.G.	Good	Fair	Poor
250	200	150	100	85

Model 52B Sporting Rifle

A 1993 limited edition rifle (6,000 guns) that is a faithful reproduction of the famous Winchester Model 52 Sporter. Equipped with a 24" barrel, adjustable trigger, and "B" style cheekpiece.

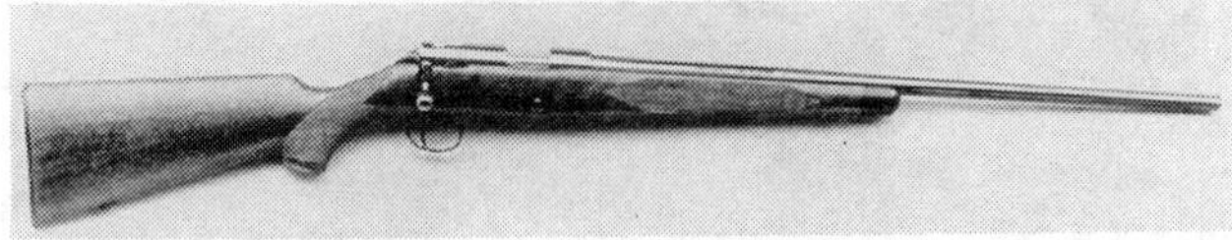

NIB	Exc.	V.G.	Good	Fair	Poor
460	400	350	300	200	100

Post-'64 Model 70

This is a bolt-action sporting rifle chambered for various popular calibers between .22-250 and .30-06. It features a 22" barrel with open sights and a 5-round, integral box magazine. The finish is blued with a Monte Carlo-type stock furnished with sling swivels. It was manufactured between 1964 and 1980.

Exc.	V.G.	Good	Fair	Poor
350	325	250	200	125

Model 70 Mannlicher

This is a full-length, Mannlicher-type stocked version of the Model 70 bolt-action rifle that is chambered for the .243, .270, .308, and the 30-06 cartridges. It features a 19" barrel with open sights. The finish is blued. It was discontinued in 1972.

Exc.	V.G.	Good	Fair	Poor
400	375	350	275	150

Model 70 Target Rifle

This version is chambered for the .308 or the .30-06 cartridges. It was offered with a 24" heavy barrel without sights. It is furnished with bases for a target scope. The finish is blued with a heavy walnut target stock with a palmrest.

Exc.	V.G.	Good	Fair	Poor
650	550	450	350	250

Model 70 International Match Army

This version is chambered for the .308 cartridge and has a 24" heavy barrel furnished without sights. It has an adjustable trigger and is blued, with a target-type heavy stock that had an accessory rail and an adjustable butt.

Exc.	V.G.	Good	Fair	Poor
750	650	500	400	300

Model 70A

This is a utility version of the bolt-action Post-'64 Model 70. It was furnished without a hinged floorplate. The finish is blued, with a walnut stock. It was manufactured between 1972 and 1978.

Exc.	V.G.	Good	Fair	Poor
300	275	225	175	100

Model 70 XTR Featherweight

This gun was built after the takeover by the U.S.R.A. Company. It is a bolt-action sporting rifle chambered for various calibers from .22-250 up to the .30-06 cartridges. It has a 22" barrel that is furnished without sights and features either a short- or medium-length action. It has a 5-round, integral magazine. The finish is blued, with a checkered walnut stock. It was introduced in 1981.

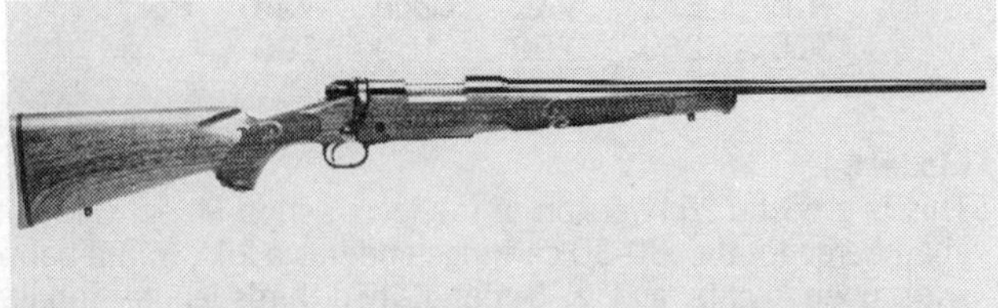

NIB	Exc.	V.G.	Good	Fair	Poor
450	400	325	300	250	200

Model 70 Fiftieth Anniversary Model

This is a commemorative version of the Post-'64 Model 70 bolt-action rifle. It is chambered for the .300 Win. Mag. and is offered with a 24" barrel. It is engraved and high-gloss blued with a deluxe, checkered walnut stock. There were 500 manufactured in 1987. In order to realize collector potential, it must be NIB with all supplied materials.

NIB	Exc.	V.G.	Good	Fair	Poor
1000	800	600	450	350	250

Model 70 XTR Super Express

This is a heavy-duty version of the Post-'64 Model 70 chambered for the .375 H&H and the .458 Win. Mag. cartridges. It is offered with a 22" or 24" heavy barrel and a 3-round, integral box magazine. This version has extra recoil lugs mounted in the stock and is blued with a select, straight-grain walnut stock and a recoil pad standard.

NIB	Exc.	V.G.	Good	Fair	Poor
650	500	400	300	200	100

Model 70 XTR Varmint

This version is chambered for the .22-250, .223, and the .243 cartridges. It has a 24" heavy barrel and is furnished without sights. It has a 5-round magazine and is blued with a heavy walnut stock. It was introduced in 1972.

NIB	Exc.	V.G.	Good	Fair	Poor
400	350	300	250	200	100

Model 70 Winlight

This version is offered in various calibers between .270 and the .338 Win. Mag. It features a matte-blue finish and a fiberglass stock. It is offered with a 22" or a 24" barrel and a 3- or 4-round magazine. It was introduced in 1986.

NIB	Exc.	V.G.	Good	Fair	Poor
400	350	300	250	200	100

Ranger

This is a utility-grade, bolt-action rifle chambered for the .270 Win., .30-06, and the 7mm Rem. Mag. cartridges. It is offered with a 22" or a 24" barrel with open sights and has a 3- or 4-round box magazine. The finish is blued with a plain hardwood stock.

NIB	Exc.	V.G.	Good	Fair	Poor
350	300	275	225	150	100

POST-1964 WINCHESTER

Model 70 Featherweight Classic

A U.S.R.A. model with 22" barrel, walnut stock, and claw-controlled round feeding. The bolt is jeweled and the bolt handle knurled. Comb is straight. Available in .270, .280, and 30-06 calibers. Rifle weighs about 7.25 lbs.

NIB	Exc.	V.G.	Good	Fair	Poor
600	450	350	250	200	100

Model 70 Super Grade
Another U.S.R.A. rilfe that features a select walnut stock, claw-controlled round feed, a single reinforced cross bolt, 24" barrel shipped with bases and rings. The butt stock has a straight comb with classic cheekpiece and deep cut checkering. Available in .270, 30-06, 7MM Rem. Mag., .300 Win. Mag., .338 Win. Mag. Rifle weighs approximately 7.75 lbs. Currently in production.

NIB	Exc.	V.G.	Good	Fair	Poor
800	650	550	450	300	150

Model 70 Super Express
A U.S.R.A. version of the post-1964 XTR Super Express. Specifications are the same as the earlier model. Rifle weighs 8.5 lbs. Introduced in 1993.

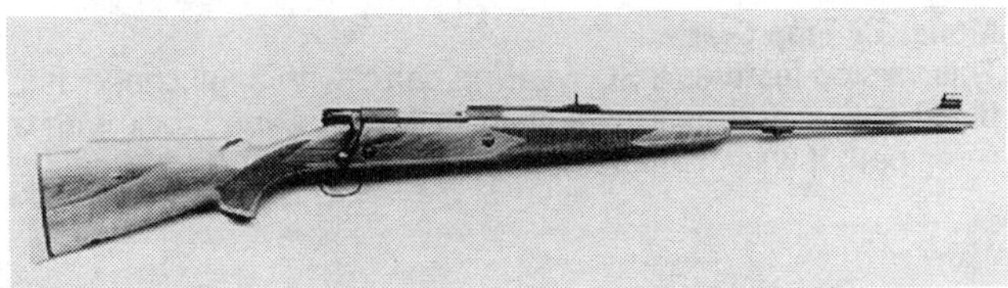

NIB	Exc.	V.G.	Good	Fair	Poor
650	500	400	300	200	100

Model 70 Custom Sharpshooter
A U.S.R.A. Custom Shop gun. This model is fitted with a stainless steel Schneider barrel with hand honed action and hand fitted. The stock is a custom McMillan A-2 glass bedded stock. Offered in .223 Rem., .22-250 Rem., .308 Win. and .300 Win. Mag. omes from the factory with a hard case. Currently in production.

NIB	Exc.	V.G.	Good	Fair	Poor
1300	950	750	500	300	150

Model 70 Custom Sporting Sharpshooter
Essentially a take off on the Custom Sharpshooter but configured for hunting. Fitted with a McMillan sporter style gray stock and Schneider stainless steel barrel. Offered in .270 Win., .300 Win., and 7MM STW. Introduced in 1993.

Winchester Model 70
Grey Sporting Sharpshooter

NIB	Exc.	V.G.	Good	Fair	Poor
1250	900	750	500	300	150

Model 70 Custom Grade
This custom built Model 70 is hand finished, polished, and fitted in the Custom Shop. Internal parts are hand honed while the barrel is lead lapped. The customer can order individual items to his or her own taste, including engraving, special stock dimensions and carvings etc. Each Custom Grade Model 70 should be priced on an individual basis.

Model 70 Custom Express
Also built in the Custom Shop this model features figured walnut, hand honed internal parts, bolt and follower are engined turned. A special 3-leaf rear sight is furnished also. Offered in .375 H&H Mag., .375 JRS, .416 Rem. Mag., .458 Win. Mag., and .470 Capstick.

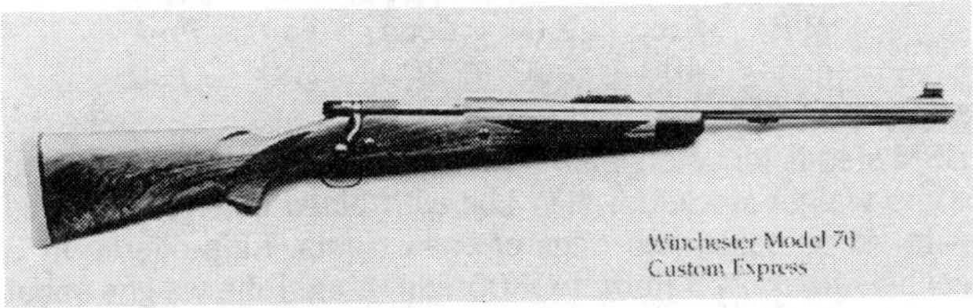
Winchester Model 70
Custom Express

NIB	Exc.	V.G.	Good	Fair	Poor
1700	1400	900	500	300	150

Model 70 Heavy Varmint
Introduced by U.S.R.A. in 1993 this rifle features a fiberglass/graphite stock with heavy 26" stainless steel barrel. Offered in .223, .22-250, .243, and .308. Rifle weighs about 10.75 lbs.

NIB	Exc.	V.G.	Good	Fair	Poor
550	475	400	300	200	100

Model 70 Stainless
All metal parts are stainless steel, including the barrel, with synthetic stock. Available with 24" barrel and chambered for: .270, 30-06, 7MM Rem. Mag., .300 Win. Mag., and .338 Win. Mag. Weighs about 7.5 lbs. Currently in production.

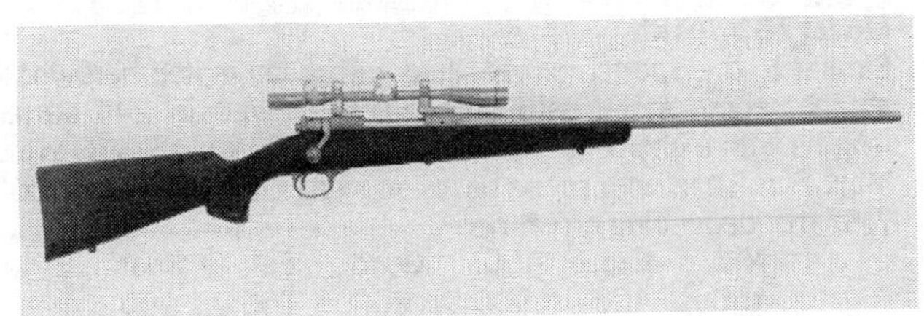

NIB	Exc.	V.G.	Good	Fair	Poor
485	425	375	300	200	100

Model 70 SM
This rifle features a synthetic stock with black matte finish. Barrel length is 24". Available in 10 calibers from .223 Rem. to .375 H&H Mag. Depending on caliber rifle weighs between 7 and 8 lbs. Currently in production.

NIB	Exc.	V.G.	Good	Fair	Poor
475	400	300	200	150	100

Model 70 DBM-S
Similar to the Model 70 SM but fitted with a detachable box magazine. The metal parts are blued and the stock is synthetic. Offered in 8 calibers from .223 Rem. to .338 Win. Mag. Furnished with scope bases and rings are open sights. Rifle weighs about 7.25 lbs. depending on caliber. Introduced in 1993.

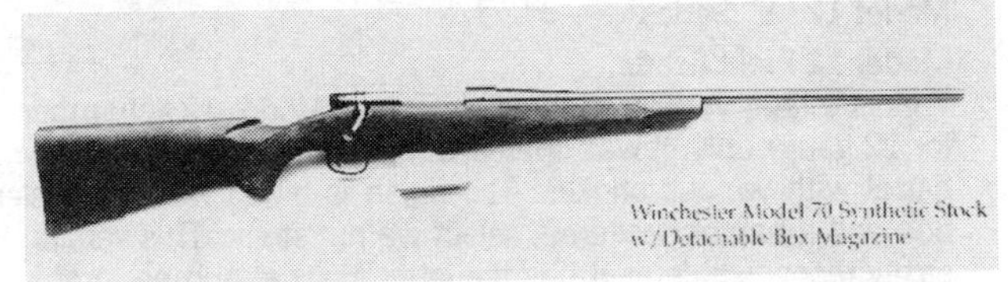
Winchester Model 70 Synthetic Stock
w/Detachable Box Magazine

NIB	Exc.	V.G.	Good	Fair	Poor
500	425	325	225	150	100

Model 70 Varmint

Similar to the Model 70 Heavy Varmint but furnished with a traditional walnut stock and 26" medium heavy barrel. Offered in .223 Rem., .22-250, .243, and .308. Weighs 9 lbs.

NIB	Exc.	V.G.	Good	Fair	Poor
465	400	300	200	150	100

Model 70 DBM

DBM stands for detachable box magazine. Fitted with a straight comb walnut stock. Jeweled bolt with blued receiver. Shipped with scope bases and rings or open sights. Rifle offered in 8 calibers from .223 Rem. to .300 Win. Mag. Rifle weighs about 7.35 lbs. depending on caliber. Introduced in 1993.

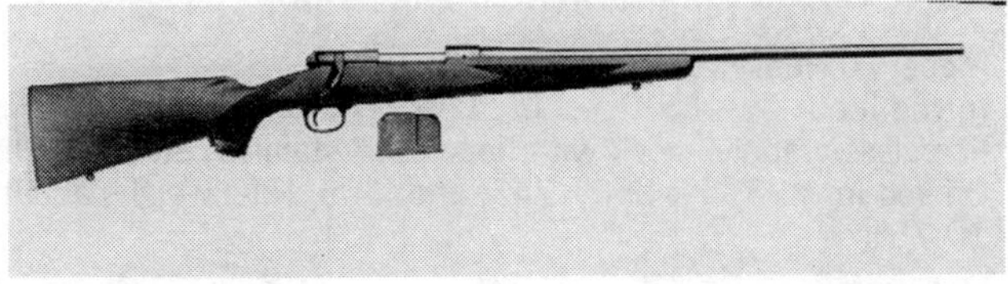

NIB	Exc.	V.G.	Good	Fair	Poor
480	425	325	225	150	100

Model 70 Sporter

U.S.R.A.'s basic Model 70 offering. Straight comb walnut stock with checkering, jeweled bolt and blue receiver and barrel are standard. Available in 12 calibers from .223 Rem. to .338 Win. Mag. including .250-6 and .300 Weatherby Mag. Barrel length is 24" and is available with either scope bases and rings or open sights. Rifle weighs about 7.5 lbs.

NIB	Exc.	V.G.	Good	Fair	Poor
450	400	300	200	150	100

Model 70 WinTuff

Similar to the Sporter except fitted with a laminated hardwood straight comb stock with cheekpiece. Offered in 24" barrel lengths with a choice of 6 calibers from .270 Win. to .338 Win. Mag. Furnished with scope bases and rings. Rifle weighs about 7.65 lbs. depending on caliber.

NIB	Exc.	V.G.	Good	Fair	Poor
450	400	300	200	150	100

Model 70 Lightweight

Similar to the Model 70 Winlight. Offered with straight comb checkered walnut stock with knurled bolt and blued receiver and barrel. The barrel is 22" without sights. Offered in 5 calibers: .223, .243, .270, .308, and 30-06. Rifle weighs about 7 lbs. depending on caliber.

NIB	Exc.	V.G.	Good	Fair	Poor
400	350	300	200	150	100

Model 70 Ladies/Youth Ranger

A scaled down version of the Ranger. Length of pull is 1" shorter than standard. Rifle weighs 6.5 lbs. Chambered in .243 and .308.

NIB	Exc.	V.G.	Good	Fair	Poor
375	350	300	200	150	100

POST-1964 SHOTGUNS

Model 12 "Y" Series

Model 12 Field Grade

This is a later version of the slide action Model 12, chambered for 12 gauge only. It was offered with a 26", 28", or 30" vent-rib barrel with various chokes. The finish is blued with a jeweled bolt and a hand-checkered, select walnut stock. This version is easily recognizable as it has the letter Y serial number prefix. It was manufactured between 1972 and 1976.

Exc.	V.G.	Good	Fair	Poor
650	550	400	350	275

Model 12 Super Pigeon Grade

This is a deluxe version that features extensive engraving and fancy checkering. It was offered with a tuned action and select, fancy-grade walnut. It was a limited-production item produced between 1964 and 1972. It was briefly re-introduced in 1984 and discontinued again in 1985.

Exc.	V.G.	Good	Fair	Poor
3000	2500	1850	1400	950

Model 12 Skeet

This version is similar to the Field Grade but is offered with a 26", vent-rib, skeet-bored barrel. The finish is blued, with a skeet-type stock and recoil pad. It was manufactured between 1972 and 1975.

Exc.	V.G.	Good	Fair	Poor
700	650	550	350	300

Model 12 Trap Grade

This version features a 30" vent-rib barrel with a full choke. It is blued with a trap-type, standard or Monte Carlo stock with a recoil pad. It was manufactured between 1972 and 1980.

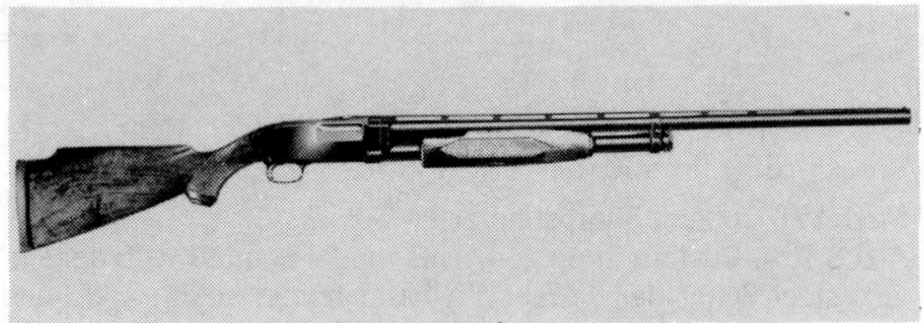

Exc.	V.G.	Good	Fair	Poor
650	600	500	300	200

Model 12 (Limited Edition)

Available in 20 gauge only. Furnished with a 26" vent rib barrel choked Improved Cylinder. The walnut stock is checkered with pistol grip. Introduced in 1993 and available in three different grades.

Grade I (4,000 guns)

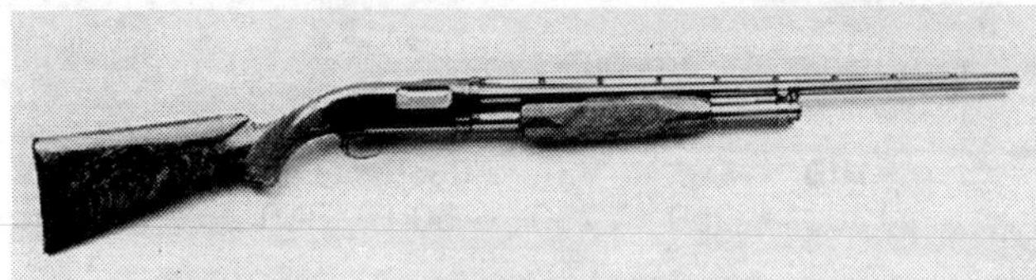

NIB	Exc.	V.G.	Good	Fair	Poor
700	600	450	350	200	100

Grade IV (1,000 guns) Gold highlights

NIB	Exc.	V.G.	Good	Fair	Poor
1150	900	650	400	200	100

Ducks Unlimited Model

Available through Ducks Unlimited chapters. An independent appraisal is suggested.

Model 42 (Limited Edition)

A reproduction of the famous Winchester Model 42 .410 bore slide action shotgun. Furnished with a 26" ventilated rib barrel choked full. The receiver is engraved with gold border. Introduced in 1993 and limited to 850 guns.

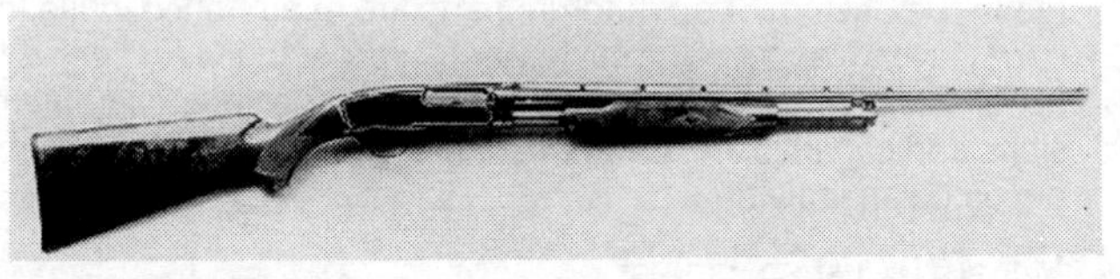

NIB	Exc.	V.G.	Good	Fair	Poor
1250	900	600	400	300	150

Model 1200

This is a slide-action shotgun chambered for 12, 16, or 20 gauge. It was offered with a 26", 28", or 30", vent-rib barrel with various chokes. It has an alloy receiver and is blued, with a checkered walnut stock and recoil pad. It was manufactured between 1964 and 1981. This model was offered with the plastic Hydrocoil stock, and this would add approximately 35 percent to the values given.

Exc.	V.G.	Good	Fair	Poor
225	175	150	100	75

Model 1300 XTR

This is the current slide action shotgun offered by Winchester. It is chambered for 12 and 20 gauge with 3" chambers. It is a takedown gun that is offered with various-length vent-rib barrels with screw-in choke tubes. It has an alloy frame and is blued with a walnut stock. It was introduced in 1978.

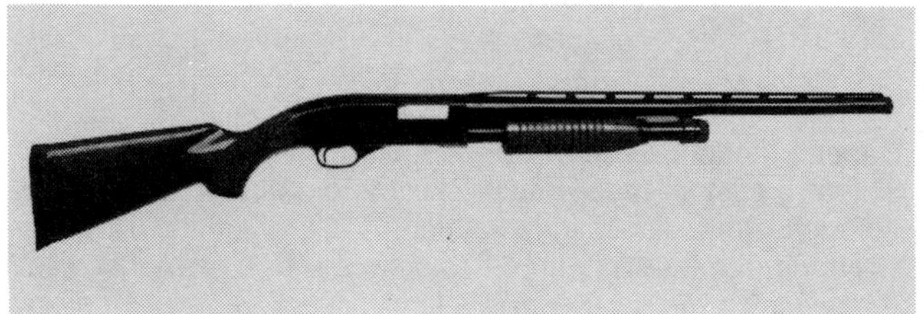

Exc.	V.G.	Good	Fair	Poor
300	250	200	150	100

Model 1300 Waterfowl

This version is chambered for 12 gauge, 3" only. It has a 30" vent-rib barrel with screw-in choke tubes. It is matte-blued, with a satin-finished walnut stock and a recoil pad. It was introduced in 1984. A laminated Win-Tuff stock was made available in 1988 and would add $10 to the value.

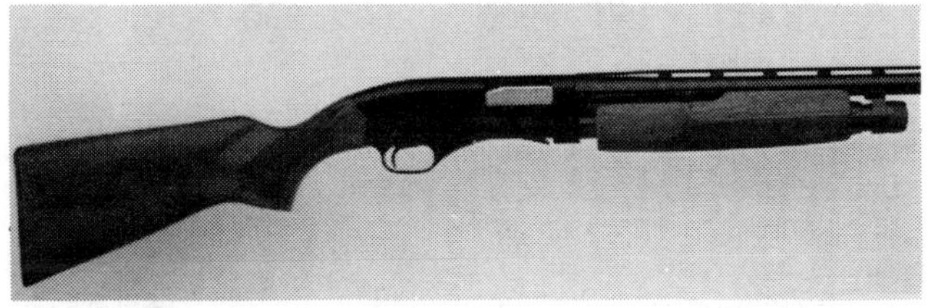

NIB	Exc.	V.G.	Good	Fair	Poor
350	300	250	200	150	100

Model 1300 Win-Cam Turkey Gun

This version is similar to the Model 1300 Turkey Gun, with a green, laminated hardwood stock. It was introduced in 1987. A Win-Tuff version is also available and would add $20 to the values given.

NIB	Exc.	V.G.	Good	Fair	Poor
375	325	250	200	150	125

Model 1300 Stainless Security

This version is chambered for 12 or 20 gauge and is constructed of stainless steel. It has an 18" cylinder-bore barrel and a 7- or 8-shot tubular magazine. It is available with a pistolgrip stock, which would add approximately 50 percent to the values given.

NIB	Exc.	V.G.	Good	Fair	Poor
250	225	200	150	125	100

Model 1300 Turkey

This slide action model features a 22" vent rib barrel chambered for 3" 12 gauge shells. Supplied with choke tubes. Gun weighs 7.25 lbs.

NIB	Exc.	V.G.	Good	Fair	Poor
350	300	250	200	150	100

Model 1300 National Wild Turkey Federation Series III

Engraved receiver, Camo stock, open sights on a 22" plain barrel, and all metal and wood parts are non-glare. Comes with a quick detachable sling. Offered in 12 gauge only. Gun weighs 7.25 lbs.

NIB	Exc.	V.G.	Good	Fair	Poor
370	320	250	200	150	100

Model 1300 National Wild Turkey Federation Series IV

Introduced in 1993 this model is similar to the Series II with the additional of a 22" vent rib barrel. Stock is black laminated. Comes with quick detachable sling. Gun weight 7 lbs.

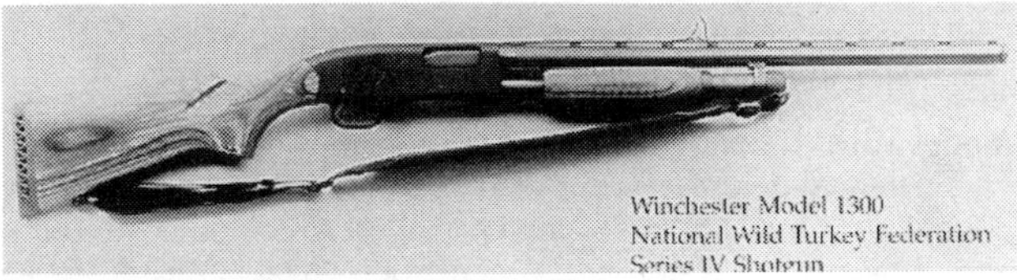
Winchester Model 1300 National Wild Turkey Federation Series IV Shotgun

NIB	Exc.	V.G.	Good	Fair	Poor
370	320	250	200	150	100

Model 1300 Whitetails Unlimited Slug Hunter

This slide action model features a full length rifle barrel chambered for 3" 12 gauge shells. Barrel is choked cylinder. Fitted with a checkered walnut stock with engraved receiver. Receiver is drilled and tapped for bases and rings which are included. Comes equipped with camo sling. Weighs 7.25 lbs.

NIB	Exc.	V.G.	Good	Fair	Poor
350	300	250	200	150	100

Model 1300 Slug Hunter

Similar to the Whitetails Unlimited model, but without the engraved receiver.

NIB	Exc.	V.G.	Good	Fair	Poor
350	300	250	200	150	100

Model 1300 Slug Hunter Sabot (Smooth Bore)

Similar to the Slug Hunter but furnished with a smooth bore barrel with a special extended screw in choke tube that is rifled.

NIB	Exc.	V.G.	Good	Fair	Poor
275	250	200	175	150	100

Model 1300 Ranger

This slide action shotgun is a lower cost version of the Model 1300. Furnished with a hardwood stock and available in 12 or 20 gauge with 26" or 28" vent rib barrel. Win. chokes are included.

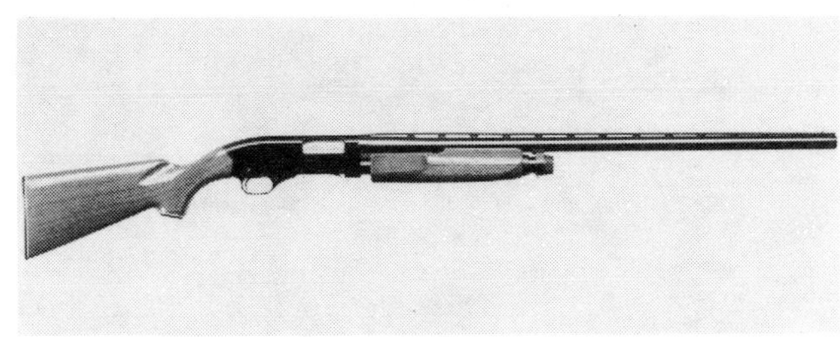

NIB	Exc.	V.G.	Good	Fair	Poor
235	200	175	150	125	100

Model 1300 Ranger Ladies/Youth

Available in 20 gauge only this model has a 1" shorter than standard length of pull and a 22" vent rib barrel. Choke tubes are included. Gun weighs 6.75 lbs.

NIB	Exc.	V.G.	Good	Fair	Poor
250	200	175	150	125	100

Model 1300 Ranger Deer Slug

Comes in two principal configurations: a 12 gauge 22" smooth barrel with cylinder choke; and a 12 gauge 22" rifled barrel. Both are chambered for 3" shells and weighs 6.75 lbs.

NIB	Exc.	V.G.	Good	Fair	Poor
250	200	175	150	125	100

Model 1300 Ranger Deer Combo

The Model 1300 Ranger Deer Combos are available in three different configurations. One: 12 gauge 22" smooth barrel and 28" vent rib barrel with WinChokes. Two: 12 gauge 22" rifled barrel with 28" vent rib barrel with WinChokes. Three: 20 gauge 22" smooth barrel with 28" vent rib barrel with WinChokes.

12 Gauge Combo

NIB	Exc.	V.G.	Good	Fair	Poor
300	250	200	175	150	100

20 Gauge Combo

NIB	Exc.	V.G.	Good	Fair	Poor
300	250	200	175	150	100

Model 1300 Defender Combo

This personal defense slide action shotgun features a 18" cylinder choked barrel and a 28" vent rib barrel with Mod. WinChoke and an accessory pistol grip. A hardwood stock comes fitted to the gun.

NIB	Exc.	V.G.	Good	Fair	Poor
300	250	200	175	150	100

Model 1300 Defender 5-Shot

Same as above but furnished with a hardwood stock only and 18" barrel.

NIB	Exc.	V.G.	Good	Fair	Poor
220	200	175	150	125	100

Model 1300 Defender 8-Shot

Same as above but furnished with a 18" barrel with extended magazine tube.

NIB	Exc.	V.G.	Good	Fair	Poor
220	200	175	150	125	100

Model 1300 Defender Synthetic Stock

Same as above but fitted with a black synthetic full stock. Available in either 12 or 20 gauge.

NIB	Exc.	V.G.	Good	Fair	Poor
220	200	175	150	125	100

Model 1300 Defender Pistol Grip

Same as above but fitted with a black synthetic pistol grip and extended magazine tube.

NIB	Exc.	V.G.	Good	Fair	Poor
220	200	175	150	125	100

Model 1300 Stainless Marine

This 12 gauge slide action shotgun comes with a black synthetic full stock with all metal parts chrome plated. Barrel is 18" and magazine tube holds 7 rounds. Gun weighs 6.75 lbs.

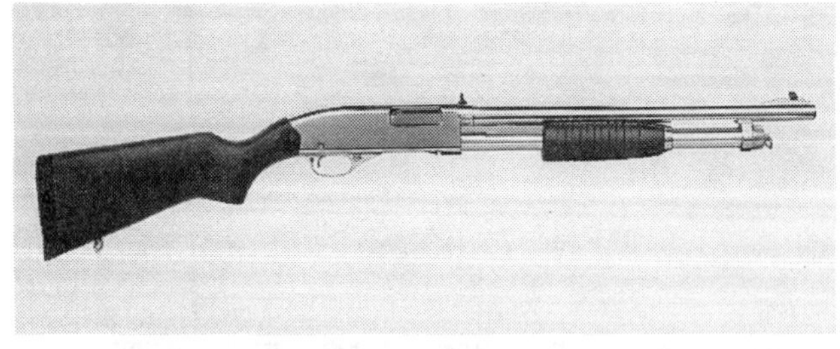

NIB	Exc.	V.G.	Good	Fair	Poor
350	300	250	200	150	100

Model 1300 Stainless Marine with Pistol Grip

Same as above with black synthetic pistol grip in place of full butt stock. Gun weighs 5.75 lbs.

NIB	Exc.	V.G.	Good	Fair	Poor
350	300	250	200	150	100

Model 1400

This is a gas-operated, semi-automatic shotgun chambered for 12, 16, or 20 gauge. It was offered with a 26", 28", or 30" vent-rib barrel with various chokes. The finish is blued, with a checkered walnut stock. It was manufactured between 1964 and 1981. The Hydrocoil plastic stock was available on this model and would add approximately 35 percent to the values given.

Exc.	V.G.	Good	Fair	Poor
250	225	200	150	100

Model 1500 XTR

This is a gas-operated, semi-automatic shotgun chambered for 12 or 20 gauge, with a 28" vent-rib barrel with screw-in chokes. The finish is blued, with a walnut stock. It was manufactured between 1978 and 1982.

Exc.	V.G.	Good	Fair	Poor
300	250	225	175	125

Super X Model 1

This is a self-compensating, gas-operated,semi-automatic shotgun chambered for 12 gauge. It was offered with a 26", 28", or 30" vent-rib barrel with various chokes. It features all-steel construction and is blued, with a checkered walnut stock. It was manufactured between 1974 and 1981.

Exc.	V.G.	Good	Fair	Poor
400	325	250	200	150

Super X Model 1 Custom Competition

This is a custom-order trap or skeet gun that features the self-compensating, gas-operated action. It is available in 12 gauge only from the Custom Shop. It is offered with a heavy degree of engraving on the receiver and a fancy, checkered walnut stock. Gold inlays are available and would add approximately 50 percent to the values given. This model was introduced in 1987.

NIB	Exc.	V.G.	Good	Fair	Poor
1300	1000	850	700	600	450

New Model 1400

This is a gas-operated, semi-automatic shotgun chambered for 12 or 20 gauge. It is offered with a 22" or 28" vent-rib barrel with screw-in chokes. The finish is blued, with a checkered walnut stock. It was introduced in 1989.

NIB	Exc.	V.G.	Good	Fair	Poor
400	350	300	250	200	125

Model 1400 Ranger

This is a utility-grade, gas-operated, semi-automatic shotgun chambered for 12 or 20 gauge. It is offered with a 28" vent-rib barrel with screw-in chokes, as well as a 24" slug barrel with rifle sights. The finish is blued, with a checkered stock. A combination two-barrel set that includes the deer barrel would be worth approximately 20 percent additional. This model was introduced in 1983 and is currently produced.

NIB	Exc.	V.G.	Good	Fair	Poor
340	300	250	200	150	100

Model 1400 Quail Unlimited

This 12 gauge semi-automatic shotgun model was introduced in 1993. It features compact engraved receiver with 26" vent rib barrel supplied with WinChoke tubes. Stock is checkered walnut. Gun weighs 7.25 lbs.

Winchester Model 1400 Quail Unlimited Shotgun

NIB	Exc.	V.G.	Good	Fair	Poor
340	300	250	200	150	100

Model 1400 Ranger Deer Combo

This model features a 12 gauge 22" smooth barrel and a 28" vent rib barrel with three WinChokes.

NIB	Exc.	V.G.	Good	Fair	Poor
340	300	250	200	150	100

Model 23 XTR

This is a side-by-side, double-barrel shotgun chambered for 12 or 20 gauge. It is offered with 25.5", 26", 28", or 30" vent-rib barrels with 3" chambers and various choke combinations. It is a boxlock gun that features a single trigger and automatic ejectors. It is scroll-engraved with a coin-finished receiver, blued barrels, and a checkered, select walnut stock. It was introduced in 1978. This model is available in a number of configurations that differ in the amount of ornamentation and the quality of materials and workmanship utilized in their construction. These models and their values are as follows:

Grade I—Discontinued

Exc.	V.G.	Good	Fair	Poor
900	750	650	500	400

Pigeon Grade—With Winchokes

Exc.	V.G.	Good	Fair	Poor
1000	850	750	600	500

Pigeon Grade Lightweight—Straight Stock

Exc.	V.G.	Good	Fair	Poor
1300	1000	900	750	600

Golden Quail

This series was available in 28 gauge and .410, as well as 12 or 20 gauge. It features 25.5" barrels that are choked improved cylinder/modified. It features a straight-grip, English-style stock with a recoil pad. The .410 version would be worth approximately 10 percent more than the values given. This series was discontinued in 1987.

Exc.	V.G.	Good	Fair	Poor
1500	1250	1100	850	750

Model 23

Model 23 Light Duck

This version is chambered for 20 gauge and was offered with a 28" full and full-choked barrel. There were 500 manufactured in 1985.

Exc.	V.G.	Good	Fair	Poor
1500	1250	1100	850	750

Model 23 Heavy Duck

This version is chambered for 12 gauge with 30" full and full-choked barrels. There were 500 manufactured in 1984.

Exc.	V.G.	Good	Fair	Poor
1500	1250	1100	850	750

Model 21

This is a very high-quality, side-by-side, double-barrel shotgun that features a boxlock action and is chambered for 12, 16, 20, and 28 gauges, as well as .410. It is featured with various barrel lengths and choke combinations. Since 1960 the Model 21 has been available on a custom-order basis only. It is available in five basic configurations that differ in the options offered, the amount of ornamentation, and the quality of materials and workmanship utilized in their construction. See previous Model 21 entry.

Model 101 Field Grade

This is an Over/Under, double-barrel shotgun chambered for 12, 20, and 28 gauge, as well as .410. It was offered with 26", 28", or 30" vent-rib barrels with various choke combinations. As of 1983 screw-in chokes have been standard, and models so furnished would be worth approximately $50 additional. This is a boxlock gun with a single selective trigger and automatic ejectors. The receiver is engraved; the finish, blued with a checkered walnut stock. It was manufactured between 1963 and 1987.

28 Gauge—Add 40%.

.410—Add 50%.

Exc.	V.G.	Good	Fair	Poor
750	650	500	375	300

Waterfowl Model

This version of the Model 101 is chambered for 12 gauge with 3" chambers. It has 30" or 32" vent-rib barrels and a matte finish.

Exc.	V.G.	Good	Fair	Poor
1250	1000	850	650	500

Model 101 Magnum

This version is similar to the Field Grade, chambered for 12 or 20 gauge with 3" Magnum chambers. It was offered with 30" barrels with various chokes. The stock is furnished with a recoil pad. It was manufactured between 1966 and 1981.

Exc.	V.G.	Good	Fair	Poor
775	675	525	400	325

Model 101 Skeet Grade

This version was offered with 26" skeet-bored barrels with a competition rib and a skeet-type walnut stock. It was manufactured between 1966 and 1984.

Exc.	V.G.	Good	Fair	Poor
950	850	750	500	400

Model 101 Three-Gauge Skeet Set

This combination set was offered with three barrels, chambered for 20 and 28 gauge, as well as .410. It was furnished with a fitted case and manufactured between 1974 and 1984.

Exc.	V.G.	Good	Fair	Poor
1850	1450	1000	750	650

Model 101 Trap Grade

This version is chambered for 12 gauge only and was offered with 30" or 32" competition ribbed barrels, choked for trap shooting. It is furnished with a competition-type stock. It was manufactured between 1966 and 1984.

Exc.	V.G.	Good	Fair	Poor
1250	1000	850	650	500

Model 101 Pigeon Grade

This is a more deluxe engraved version of the Model 101, chambered for 12, 20, or 28 gauge, as well as .410. It features a coin-finished receiver with a fancy checkered walnut stock. It was introduced in 1974.

Exc.	V.G.	Good	Fair	Poor
1500	1250	1000	800	700

Super Pigeon Grade

This is a very deluxe version of the Model 101, chambered for 12 gauge. It is heavily engraved with several gold inlays. The receiver is blued, and it features a high-grade walnut stock with fleur-de-lis checkering. It was imported between 1985 and 1987.

Exc.	V.G.	Good	Fair	Poor
4000	3500	2750	2000	1650

Model 101 Diamond Grade

This is a competition model, chambered for all four gauges. It was offered in either a trap or skeet configuration with screw-in chokes, an engraved matte-finished receiver, and a select checkered walnut stock. The skeet model features recoil-reducing muzzle vents.

Exc.	V.G.	Good	Fair	Poor
1600	1250	1000	750	600

Model 501 Grand European

This is an Over/Under, double-barrel shotgun chambered for 12 or 20 gauge. It was available in trap or skeet configurations and was offered with a 27", 30", or 32" vent-rib barrel. It is heavily engraved and matte-finished, with a select checkered walnut stock. It was manufactured between 1981 and 1986.

Exc.	V.G.	Good	Fair	Poor
1500	1150	950	700	550

Model 501 Presentation Grade

This is a deluxe version chambered in 12 gauge only. It is ornately engraved and gold-inlaid. The stock is made out of presentation-grade walnut. It was furnished with a fitted case. It was manufactured between 1984 and 1987.

Exc.	V.G.	Good	Fair	Poor
3000	2500	2000	1500	1250

Combination Gun

This is an Over/Under rifle/shotgun combination chambered for 12 gauge over .222, .223, .30-06, and the 9.3x74R cartridges. It features 25" barrels. The shotgun tube has a screw-in choke. It is engraved in the fashion of the Model 501 Grand European and features a select checkered walnut stock. It was manufactured between 1983 and 1985.

Exc.	V.G.	Good	Fair	Poor
2250	2000	1750	1250	1000

Express Rifle

This is an Over/Under, double-barrelled rifle chambered for the .257 Roberts, .270, 7.7x65R, .30-06, and the 9.3x74R cartridges. It features 23.5" barrels with a solid rib and express sights. It is engraved with gamescenes and has a satin-finished receiver. The stock is checkered select walnut. It was manufactured in 1984 and 1985.

Exc.	V.G.	Good	Fair	Poor
1750	1500	1250	1000	750

Model 96 Xpert

This is a utility-grade, Over/Under, double-barrel shotgun that is mechanically similar to the Model 101. It is chambered for 12 or 20 gauge and was offered with various barrel lengths and choke combinations. It has a boxlock action with single selective trigger and automatic ejectors. The plain receiver is blued, with a checkered walnut stock. It was manufactured between 1976 and 1982. A competition-grade model for trap or skeet was also available and would be worth approximately the same amount.

Exc.	V.G.	Good	Fair	Poor
650	550	450	350	275

Model 1001 Field

A new addition to the U.S.R.A. product line for 1993. This Over/Under shotgun is available in 12 gauge only, with a 28" ventilated rib barrel furnished with WinPlus choke tubes. A walnut checkered pistol stock is standard. The finish is blued with scroll engraving on the receiver. The receiver top has a matte finish. The gun weighs 7 lbs.

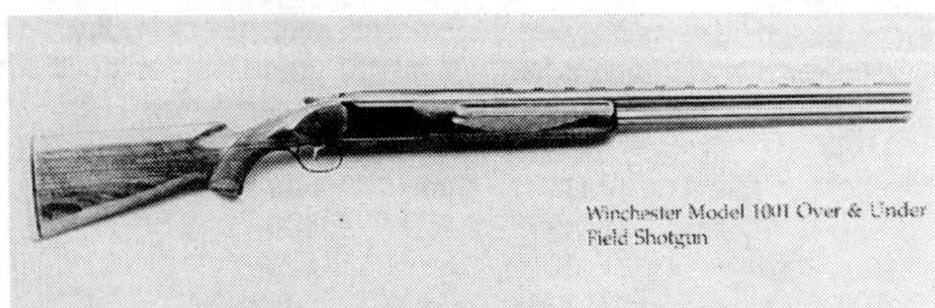

Winchester Model 1001 Over & Under Field Shotgun

NIB	Exc.	V.G.	Good	Fair	Poor
875	750	650	500	300	150

Model 1001 Sporting Clays I & II

This model features different stock dimensions, a fuller pistol grip, a raduised recoil pad, and a wider vent rib fitted on a 28" barrel (Sporting Clays I model, the Sporting Clays II features a 30" barrel). Comes complete with choke tubes. The frame has a silver nitrate finish and special engraving featuring a flying clay target. Introduced in 1993. Gun weighs 7.75 lbs.

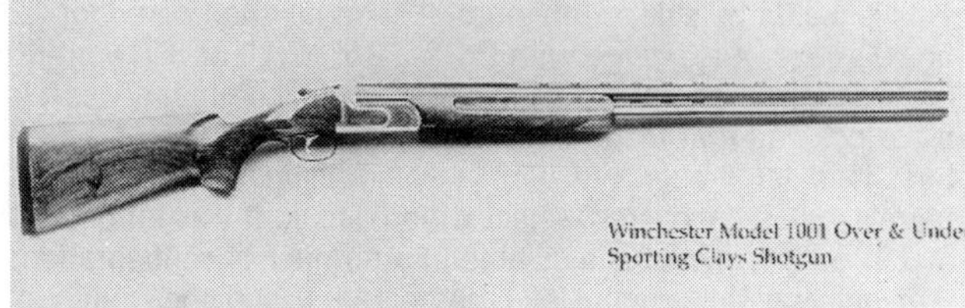

Winchester Model 1001 Over & Under Sporting Clays Shotgun

NIB	Exc.	V.G.	Good	Fair	Poor
1000	800	700	550	300	150

WINCHESTER COMMEMORATIVE RIFLES

Since the early 1960s, Winchester has produced a number of special Model 1894 rifles and carbines that commemorated certain historic events, places, or individuals. In some cases they are slightly embellished and in others are quite ornate. The general liquidity of these commemoratives has not been as good as would be expected. In some cases they were produced in excessive amounts and could not, in all honesty, be considered limited-production items. In any case, in our opinion one should purchase weapons of this nature for their enjoyment factor as the investment potential is not sufficient reason for their purchase. As with all commemoratives, in order to realize the collector potential they must be NIB with all supplied materials including, in the case of Winchester, the colorful outer sleeve that encased the factory carton. If a Winchester commemorative rifle has been cocked leaving a line on the hammer or the lever, many collectors will show little or no interest in its acquisition. If they have been fired, they will realize little premium over a standard, Post-'64 Model '94. A number of commemoratives have been ordered by outside concerns and are technically not factory issues. Most have less collectibility than the factory-issued models. There are a number of concerns that specialize in marketing the total range of Winchester commmemorative rifles. We list the factory-issue commemoratives with their current value, their issue price, and the number manufactured.

1964 Wyoming Diamond Jubilee—Carbine

NIB	Issue	Amt. Mfg.
1295	100	1,500

1966 Centennial—Rifle

NIB	Issue	Amt. Mfg.
395	125	—

1966 Centennial—Carbine

NIB	Issue	Amt. Mfg.
395	125	102,309

1966 Nebraska Centennial—Rifle

NIB	Issue	Amt. Mfg.
1295	100	2,500

1967 Canadian Centennial—Rifle

NIB	Issue	Amt. Mfg.
350	125	—

1967 Canadian Centennial—Carbine

NIB	Issue	Amt. Mfg.
350	125	90,301

1967 Alaskan Purchase Centennial—Carbine

NIB	Issue	Amt. Mfg.
1495	125	1,500

1968 Illinois Sesquicentennial—Carbine

NIB	Issue	Amt. Mfg.
350	110	37,648

1968 Illinois Sesquicentennial—Rifle

NIB	Issue	Amt. Mfg.
350	110	37,648

1968 Buffalo Bill—Carbine

NIB	Issue	Amt. Mfg.
375	130	112,923

1968 Buffalo Bill—Rifle

NIB	Issue	Amt. Mfg.
375	130	—

1968 Buffalo Bill "1 or 300"—Rifle

NIB	Issue	Amt. Mfg.
2250	1000	300

1969 Theodore Roosevelt—Rifle

NIB	Issue	Amt. Mfg.
375	135	—

1969 Theodore Roosevelt—Carbine

NIB	Issue	Amt. Mfg.
375	135	52,386

1969 Golden Spike Carbine

NIB	Issue	Amt. Mfg.
350	120	69,996

1970 Cowboy Commemorative Carbine

NIB	Issue	Amt. Mfg.
450	125	27,549

1970 Cowboy Carbine "1 of 300"

NIB	Issue	Amt. Mfg.
2350	1000	300

1970 Northwest Territories (Canadian)

NIB	Issue	Amt. Mfg.
850	150	2,500

1970 Northwest Territories Deluxe (Canadian)

NIB	Issue	Amt. Mfg.
1100	250	500

1970 Lone Star—Rifle

NIB	Issue	Amt. Mfg.
425	140	—

1970 Lone Star—Carbine

NIB	Issue	Amt. Mfg.
425	140	38,385

1971 NRA Centennial—Rifle

NIB	Issue	Amt. Mfg.
350	150	21,000

1971 NRA Centennial—Musket

NIB	Issue	Amt. Mfg.
350	150	23,400

1972 Yellow Boy (European)

NIB	Issue	Amt. Mfg.
1195	250	500

1973 Royal Canadian Mounted Police (Canadian)

NIB	Issue	Amt. Mfg.
750	190	9,500

1973 Mounted Police (Canadian)

NIB	Issue	Amt. Mfg.
750	190	5,100

1974 Texas Ranger—Carbine

NIB	Issue	Amt. Mfg.
695	135	4,850

1974 Texas Ranger Presentation Model

NIB	Issue	Amt. Mfg.
2350	1000	150

1974 Apache (Canadian)

NIB	Issue	Amt. Mfg.
750	150	8,600

1975 Commanche (Canadian)

NIB	Issue	Amt. Mfg.
750	230	11,500

1975 Klondike Gold Rush (Canadian)

NIB	Issue	Amt. Mfg.
750	240	10,500

1975 Klondike Gold Rush—Dawson City Issue (Canadian)

NIB	Issue	Amt. Mfg.
8500	—	25

1976 Sioux (Canadian)

NIB	Issue	Amt. Mfg.
750	280	10,000

1976 Little Bighorn (Canadian)

NIB	Issue	Amt. Mfg.
750	300	11,000

1976 U.S. Bicentennial Carbine

NIB	Issue	Amt. Mfg.
595	325	19,999

1977 Wells Fargo

NIB	Issue	Amt. Mfg.
450	350	19,999

1977 Legendary Lawman

NIB	Issue	Amt. Mfg.
450	375	19,999

1977 Limited Edition I

NIB	Issue	Amt. Mfg.
1395	1500	1,500

1977 Cheyenne—.22 Cal. (Canadian)

NIB	Issue	Amt. Mfg.
595	320	5,000

1977 Cheyenne—.44-40 Cal. (Canadian)

NIB	Issue	Amt. Mfg.
750	300	11,225

1978 Cherokee—.22 Cal. (Canadian)

NIB	Issue	Amt. Mfg.
595	385	3,950

1978 Cherokee—.30-30 Cal. (Canadian)

NIB	Issue	Amt. Mfg.
750	385	9,000

1978 "One of One Thousand" (European)

NIB	Issue	Amt. Mfg.
7500	5000	250

1978 Antler Game Carbine

NIB	Issue	Amt. Mfg.
450	375	19,999

1979 Limited Edition II

NIB	Issue	Amt. Mfg.
1395	1500	1,500

1979 Legendary Frontiersman Rifle

NIB	Issue	Amt. Mfg.
450	425	19,999

1979 Matched Set of 1,000

NIB	Issue	Amt. Mfg.
2250	3000	1,000

1979 Bat Masterson (Canadian)

NIB	Issue	Amt. Mfg.
750	650	8,000

1980 Alberta Diamond Jubilee (Canadian)

NIB	Issue	Amt. Mfg.
750	650	2,700

1980 Alberta Diamond Jubilee Presentation (Canadian)

NIB	Issue	Amt. Mfg.
1495	1900	300

1980 Saskatchewan Diamond Jubilee (Canadian)

NIB	Issue	Amt. Mfg.
750	695	2,700

1980 Saskatchewan Diamond Jubilee Presentation (Canadian)

NIB	Issue	Amt. Mfg.
1495	1995	300

1980 Oliver Winchester

NIB	Issue	Amt. Mfg.
550	375	19,999

1981 U.S. Border Patrol

NIB	Issue	Amt. Mfg.
550	1195	1,000

1981 U.S. Border Patrol—Member's Model

NIB	Issue	Amt. Mfg.
595	695	800

1981 Calgary Stampede (Canadian)

NIB	Issue	Amt. Mfg.
1250	2200	1,000

1981 Canadian Pacific Centennial (Canadian)

NIB	Issue	Amt. Mfg.
550	800	2,000

1981 Canadian Pacific Centennial Presentation (Canadian)

NIB	Issue	Amt. Mfg.
1100	2200	300

1981 Canadian Pacific Employee's Model (Canadian)

NIB	Issue	Amt. Mfg.
550	800	2,000

1981 John Wayne (Canadian)

NIB	Issue	Amt. Mfg.
995	995	1,000

1982 John Wayne

NIB	Issue	Amt. Mfg.
795	600	49,000

1982 Duke

NIB	Issue	Amt. Mfg.
2950	2250	1,000

1982 John Wayne "1 of 300" Set

NIB	Issue	Amt. Mfg.
6500	10000	300

1982 Great Western Artist I

NIB	Issue	Amt. Mfg.
1195	2200	999

1982 Great Western Artist II

NIB	Issue	Amt. Mfg.
1195	2200	999

1982 Annie Oakley

NIB	Issue	Amt. Mfg.
650	699	6,000

1983 Chief Crazy Horse

NIB	Issue	Amt. Mfg.
450	600	19,999

1983 American Bald Eagle

NIB	Issue	Amt. Mfg.
595	895	2,800

1983 American Bald Eagle—Deluxe

NIB	Issue	Amt. Mfg.
1995	2995	200

1983 Oklahoma Diamond Jubilee

NIB	Issue	Amt. Mfg.
1400	2250	1,001

1984 Winchester-Colt Commemorative Set

NIB	Issue	Amt. Mfg.
2000	3995	2,300

1985 Boy Scout 75th Anniversary—.22 Cal.

NIB	Issue	Amt. Mfg.
450	615	15,000

1985 Boy Scout 75th Anniversary—Eagle Scout

NIB	Issue	Amt. Mfg.
1995	2140	1,000

Texas Sesquicentennial Model—Rifle—.38-55 Cal.

NIB	Issue	Amt. Mfg.
2400	2995	1,500

Texas Sesquicentennial Model—Carbine—.38-55 Cal.

NIB	Issue	Amt. Mfg.
550	695	15,000

Texas Sesquicentennial Model Set with Bowie Knife

NIB	Issue	Amt. Mfg.
6250	7995	150

1986 Model 94 Ducks Unlimited

NIB	Issue	Amt. Mfg.
650	—	2,800

1986 Statue of Liberty

NIB	Issue	Amt. Mfg.
7000	6500	100

1986 120th Anniversary Model—Carbine—.44-40 Cal.

NIB	Issue	Amt. Mfg.
850	995	1,000

1986 European 1 of 1,000 Second Series (European)

NIB	Issue	Amt. Mfg.
7000	6000	150

1987 U.S. Constitution 200th Anniversary-44-40

NIB	Issue	Amt. Mfg.
13000	12000	17

1990 Wyoming Centennial-30-30

NIB	Issue	Amt. Mfg.
995	895	500

1991 Winchester 125th Anniversary

NIB	Issue	Amt. Mfg.
4995	4995	61

1992 Arapaho-30-30

NIB	Issue	Amt. Mfg.
995	895	500

1992 Ontario Conservation-30-30

NIB	Issue	Amt. Mfg.
1195	1195	400

1992 Kentucky Bicentennial-30-30

NIB	Issue	Amt. Mfg.
995	995	500

1993Nez Peaze-30-30

NIB	Issue	Amt. Mfg.
995	995	600

Winchester 120th Commemorative Anniversary carbine.

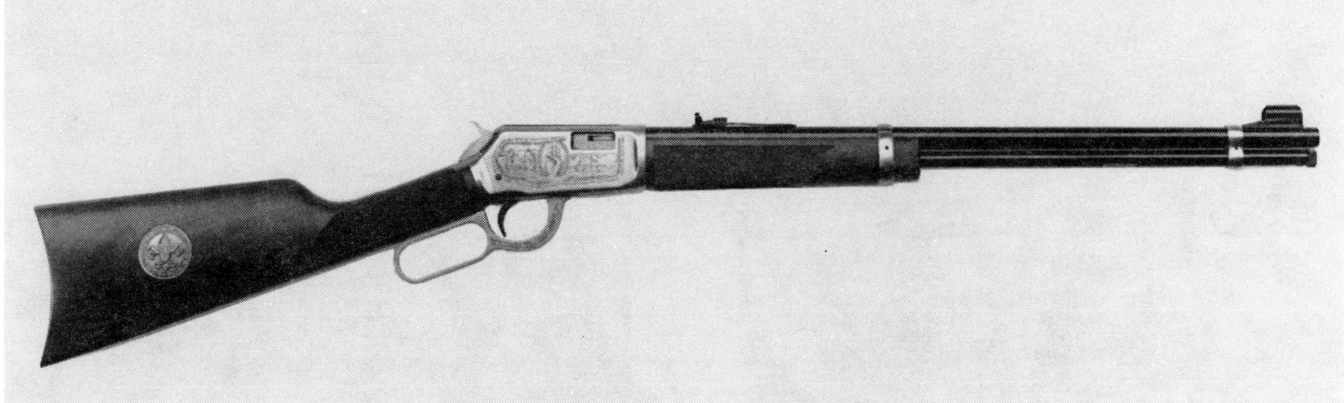

Winchester Model 9422 Boy Scouts of America Commemorative.

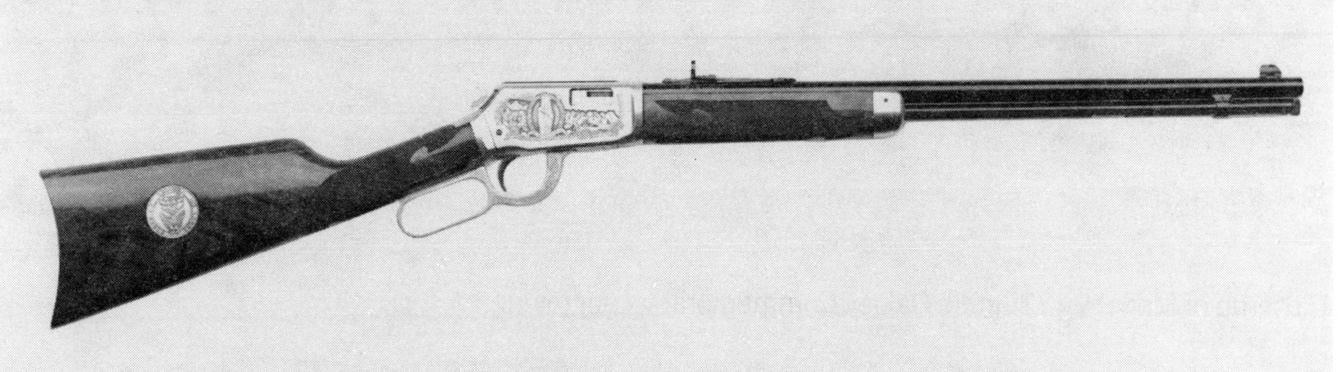

Winchester Model 9422 Eagle Scout Limited Edition Commemorative.

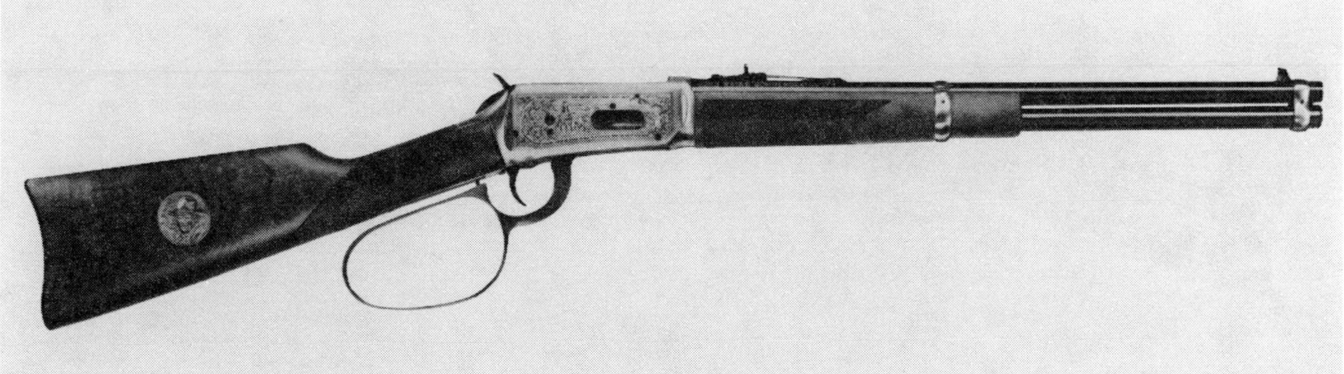

John Wayne Commemorative Gun.

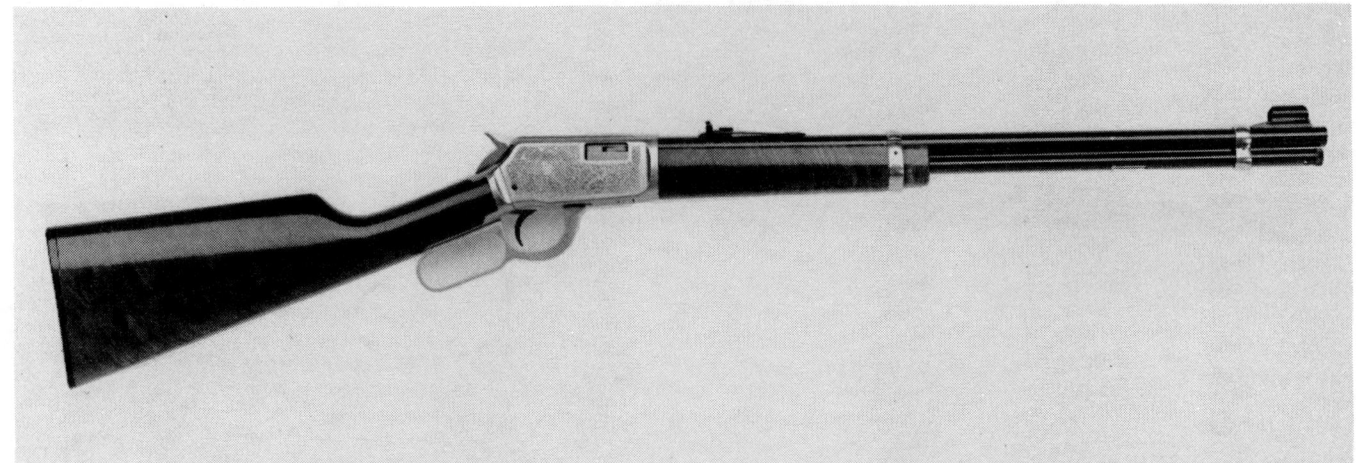

Winchester Model 9422 Annie Oakley Commemorative.

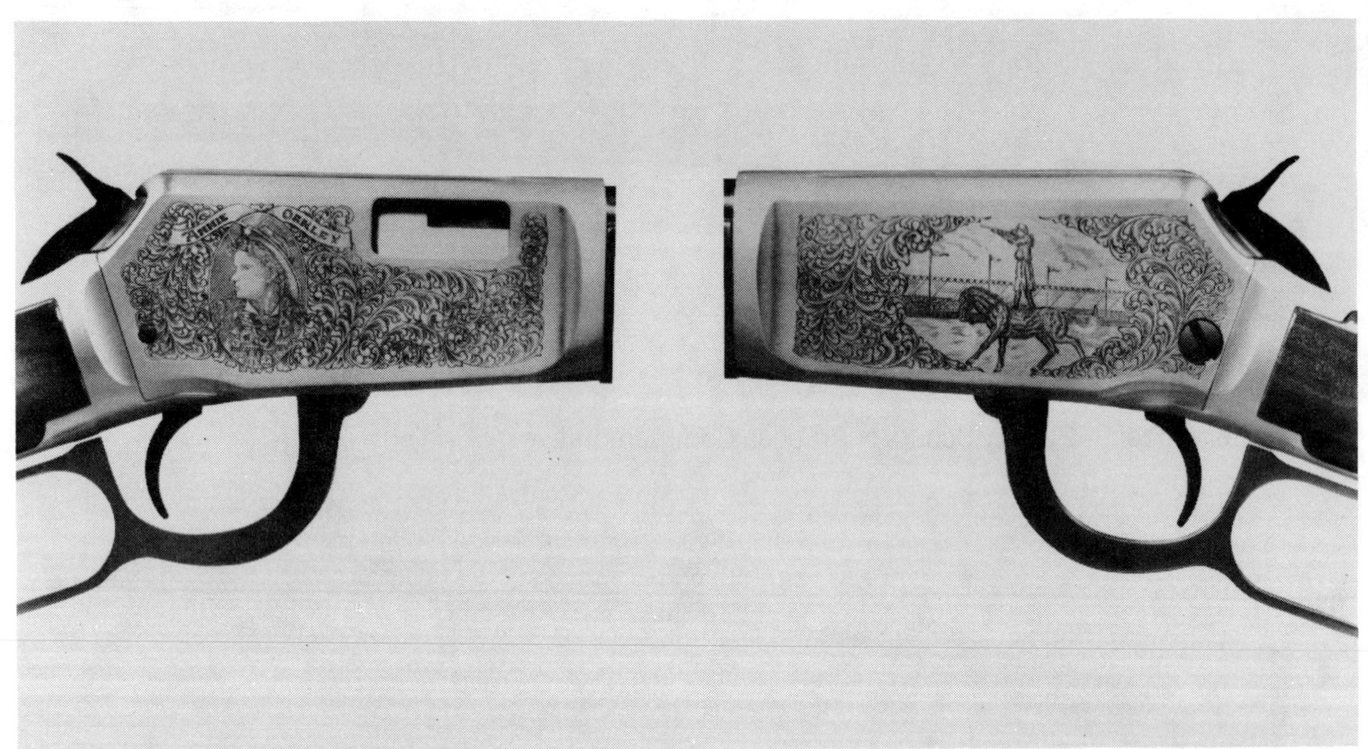

Close-up of Model 9422 Annie Oakley Commemorative engraving.

Winchester Chief Crazy Horse Commemorative.

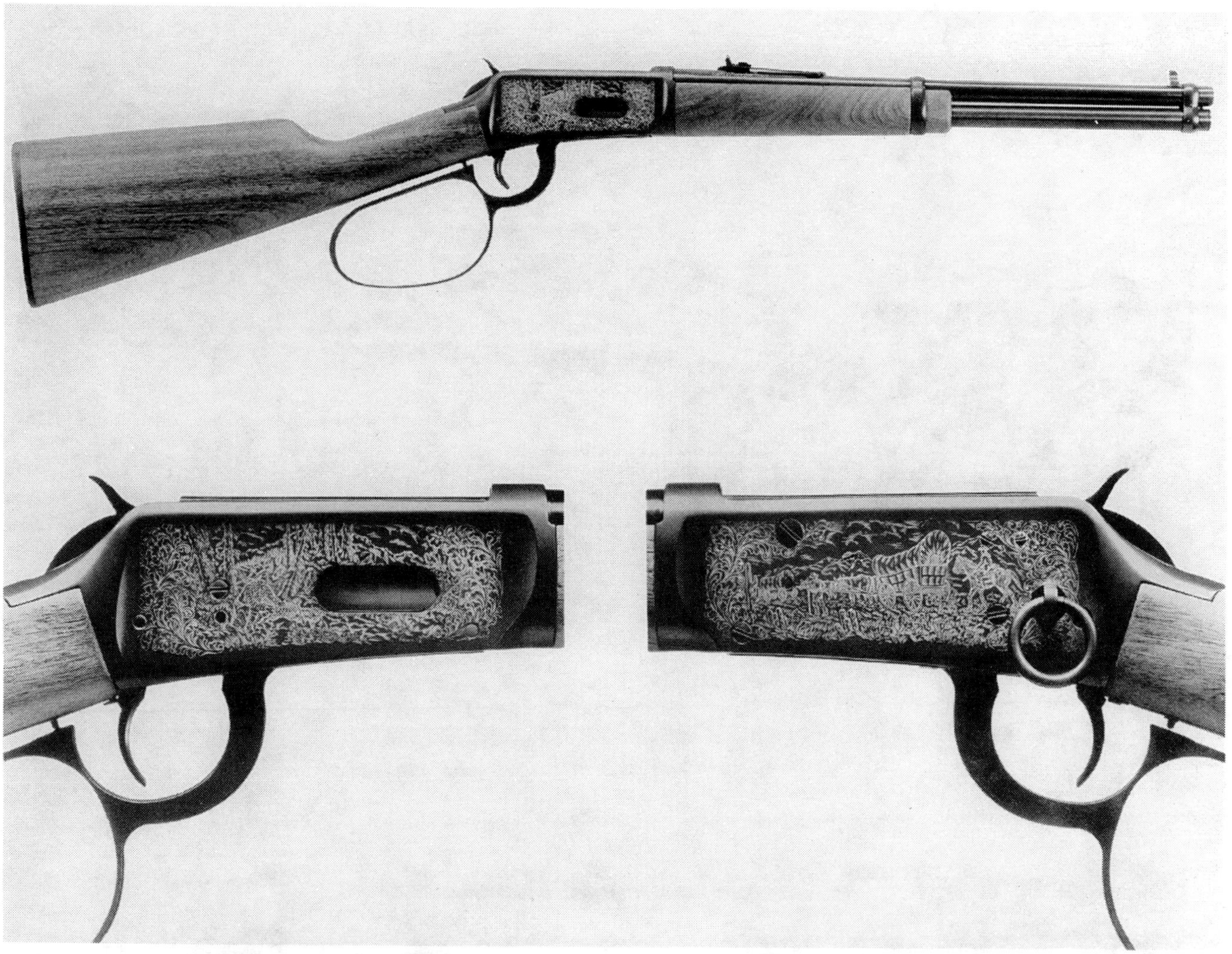

Winchester Texas Ranger Commemorative.

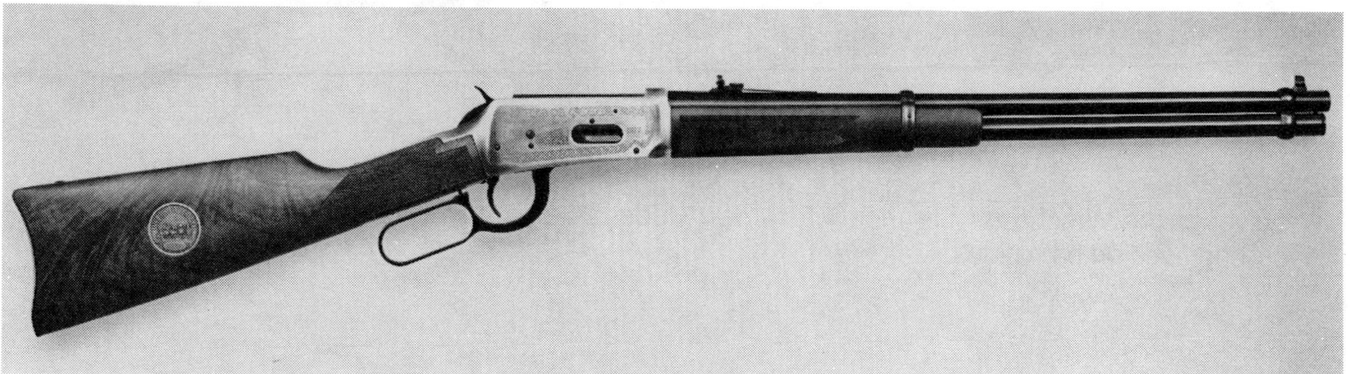

Winchester Wells Fargo & Co. Commemorative carbine.

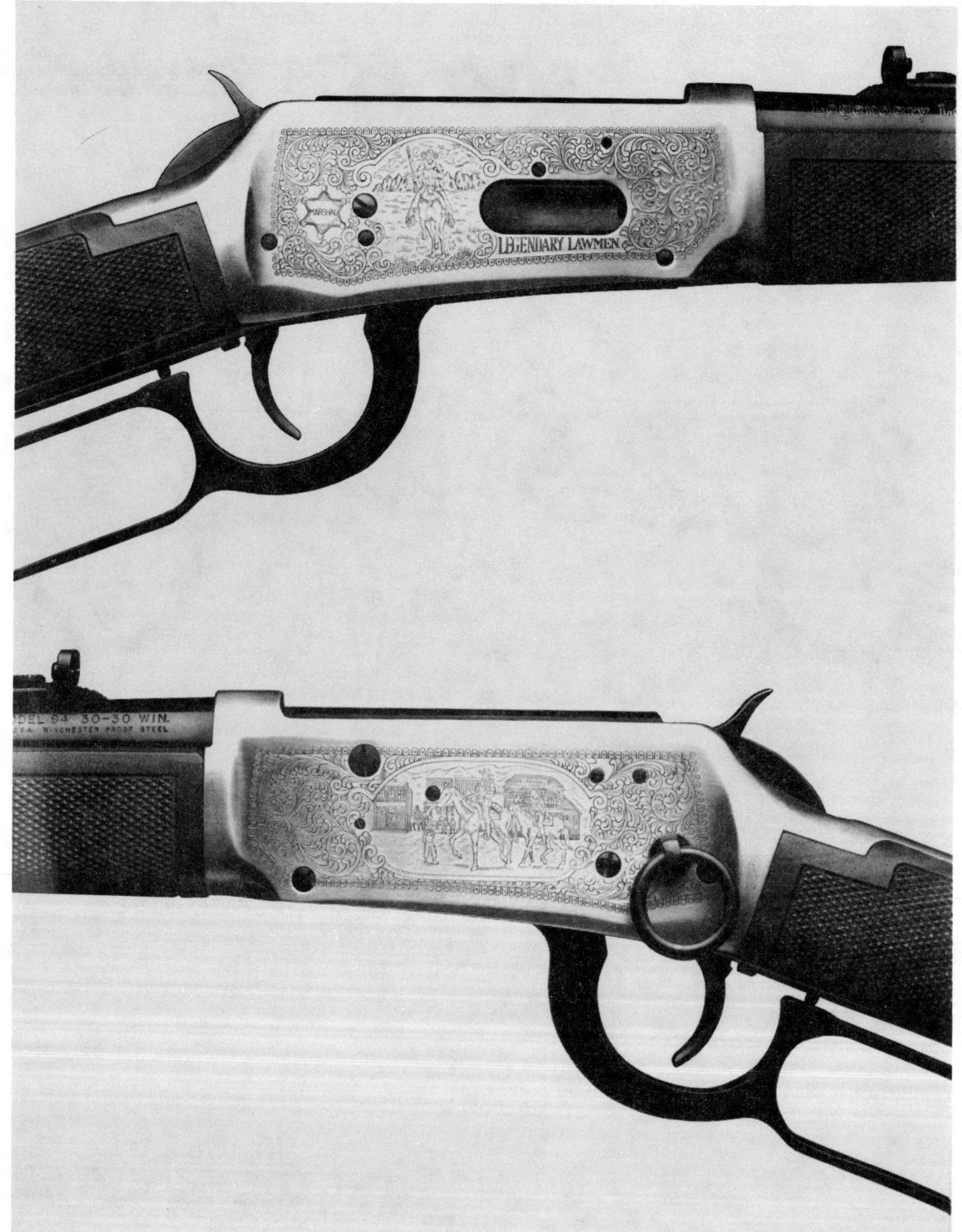

Receiver of the Winchester Legendary Lawmen Model 94 carbine. The antique silver finish is decoratively engraved on both sides.

Winchester Serial Numbers

Records at the factory indicate the following serial numbers were assigned to guns at the end of the calendar year.

MODEL 100

Year	Serial	Year	Serial
1961—	1 to 32189	1968—	210053
62—	60760	69—	A210999
63—	78863	70—	A229995
64—	92016	71—	A242999
65—	135388	72—	A258001
66—	145239	73—	A262833
67—	209498		

Records at the factory indicate the following serial numbers were assigned to guns at the end of the calendar year.

MODEL 88

Year	Serial	Year	Serial
1955—	1 to 18378	1965—	162699
56—	36756	66—	192595
57—	55134	67—	212416
58—	73512	68—	230199
59—	91890	69—	H239899
60—	110268	70—	H258229
61—	128651	71—	H266784
62—	139838	72—	H279014
63—	148858	73—	H283718
64—	160307		

Records at the factory indicate the following serial numbers were assigned to guns at the end of the calendar year.

MODEL 74

Year	Serial	Year	Serial
1939—	1 to 30890	1948—	223788
40—	67085	49—	249900
41—	114355	50—	276012
42—	128293	51—	302124
43—	None	52—	328236
44—	128295	53—	354348
45—	128878	54—	380460
46—	145168	55—	406574
47—	173524		

Records at the factory indicate the following serial numbers were assigned to guns at the end of the calendar year.

MODEL 71

Year	Serial	Year	Serial
1935—	1 to 4	1947—	25758
36—	7821	48—	27900
37—	12988	49—	29675
38—	14690	50—	31450
39—	16155	51—	33225
40—	18267	52—	35000
41—	20810	53—	37500
42—	21959	54—	40770
43—	22048	55—	43306
44—	22051	56—	45843
45—	22224	57—	47254
46—	23534		

Records at the factory indicate the following serial numbers were assigned to guns at the end of the calendar year.

MODEL 70

Year	Serial	Year	Serial
1935—	1 to 19	1950—	173150
36—	2238	51—	206625
37—	11573	52—	238820
38—	17844	53—	282735
39—	23991	54—	323530
40—	31675	55—	361025

Year	Serial	Year	Serial
41—	41753	56—	393595
42—	49206	57—	425283
43—	49983	58—	440792
44—	49997	59—	465040
45—	5 0921	60—	504257
46—	58382	61—	545446
47—	75675	62—	565592
48—	101680	63—	581471
49—	131580		

All post-64 Model 70s began with the serial number 700000

Year	Serial	Year	Serial
1964—	740599	1973—	G1128731
65—	809177	74—	G1175000
66—	833795	75—	G1218700
67—	869000	76—	G1266000
68—	925908	77—	G1350000
69—	G941900	78—	G1410000
70—	G957995	79—	G1447000
71—	G1018991	80—	G1490709
72—	G1099257	81—	G1537134

Records at the factory indicate the following serial numbers were assigned to guns at the end of the calendar year.

MODEL 63

Year	Serial	Year	Serial
1933—	1 to 2667	1946—	61607
34—	5361	47—	71714
35—	9830	48—	80519
36—	16781	49—	88889
37—	25435	50—	97259
38—	30934	51—	105629
39—	36055	52—	114000
40—	41456	53—	120500
41—	47708	54—	127000
42—	51258	55—	138000
43—	51631	56—	150000
44—	51656	57—	162345
45—	53853	58—	174692

Factory records indicate the following serial numbers were assigned to guns at the end of the calendar year.

MODEL 62

Year	Serial	Year	Serial
1932—	1 to 7643	1946—	183756
33—	10695	47—	219085
34—	14090	48—	252298
35—	23924	49—	262473
36—	42759	50—	272648
37—	66059	51—	282823
38—	80205	52—	293000
39—	96534	53—	310500
40—	116393	54—	328000
41—	137379	55—	342776
42—	155152	56—	357551
43—	155422	57—	383513
44—	155425	58—	409475
45—	156073		

Records at the factory indicate the following serial numbers were assigned to guns at the end of the calendar year.

MODEL 61

Year	Serial	Year	Serial
1932—	1 to 3532	1948—	115281
33—	6008	49—	125461
34—	8554	50—	135641
35—	12379	51—	145821
36—	20615	52—	156000
37—	30334	53—	171000
38—	36326	54—	186000
39—	42610	55—	200962
40—	49270	56—	215923
41—	57493	57—	229457
42—	59871	58—	242992
43—	59872	59—	262793
44—	59879	60—	282594
45—	60512	61—	302395

46—	71629	62—	322196
47—	92297	63—	342001

This model was discontinued in 1963. For some unknown reason there are no actual records available from 1949 through 1963. The serial number figures for these years are arrived at by taking the total production figure of 342,001, subtracting the last known # of 115281, and dividing the difference equally by the number of remaining years available, (15).

Records at the factory indicate the following serial numbers were assigned to guns at the end of the calendar year.

MODEL 55 CENTERFIRE

1924—	1 to 836	1929—	12258
25—	2783	30—	17393
26—	4957	31—	18198
27—	8021	32—	19204
28—	10467	33—	Clean-up 20580

Records at the factory indicate the following serial numbers were assigned to guns at the end of the calendar year.

MODEL 54

1925—	1 to 3140	1931—	36731
26—	8051	32—	38543
27—	14176	33—	40722
28—	19587	34—	43466
29—	29104	35—	47125
30—	32499	36—	50145

Records at the factory indicate the following serial numbers were assigned to guns at the end of the calendar year.

MODEL 53

In the case of the Model 53 the following list pertains to the number of guns produced each year rather than a serial number list.

The Model 53 was serially numbered concurrently with the MODEL 92.

MODEL 53s PRODUCED

1924—	1488	1929—	1733
25—	2861	30—	920
26—	2531	31—	621
27—	2297	32—	206
28—	1958		

This model was discontinued in 1932, however, a clean up of production continued for 9 more years with an additional 486 guns.

TOTAL PRODUCTION APPROXIMATELY — 15100

Records at the factory indicate the following serial numbers were assigned to guns at the end of the calendar year.

MODEL 52

1920—	None indicated	1950—	70766
21—	397	51—	73385
22—	745	52—	76000
23—	1394	53—	79500
24—	2361	54—	80693
25—	3513	55—	81831
26—	6383	56—	96869
27—	9436	57—	97869
28—	12082	58—	98599
29—	14594	59—	98899
30—	17253	60—	102200
31—	21954	61—	106986
32—	24951	62—	108718
33—	26725	63—	113583
34—	29030	64—	118447
35—	32448	65—	120992
36—	36632	66—	123537
37—	40419	67—	123727
38—	43632	68—	123917
39—	45460	69—	E124107
40—	47519	70—	E124297
41—	50317	71—	E124489
42—	52129	72—	E124574
43—	52553	73—	E124659
44—	52560	74—	E124744
45—	52718	75—	E124828
46—	56080	76—	E125019
47—	60158	77—	E125211
48—	64265	78—	E125315
49—	68149		

This model was discontinued in 1978. A small clean up of production was completed in 1979 with a total of 125,419.

Records at the factory indicate the following serial numbers were assigned to guns at the end of the calendar year.

MODEL 50

1954—	1 to 24550	1958—	122750
55—	49100	59—	147300
56—	73650	60—	171850
57—	98200	61—	196400

Records at the factory indicate the following serial numbers were assigned to guns at the end of the calendar year.

MODEL 42

1933—	1 to 9398	1949—	81107
34—	13963	50—	87071
35—	17728	51—	93038
36—	24849	52—	99000
37—	30900	53—	108201
38—	34659	54—	117200
39—	38967	55—	121883
40—	43348	56—	126566
41—	48203	57—	131249
42—	50818	58—	135932
43—	50822	59—	140615
44—	50828	60—	145298
45—	51168	61—	149981
46—	54256	62—	154664
47—	64853	63—	159353
48—	75142		

Records at the factory indicate the following serial numbers were assigned to guns at the end of the calendar year.

MODEL 24

1939—	1 to 8118	1944—	33683
40—	21382	45—	34965
41—	27045	46—	45250
42—	33670	47—	58940
43—	None recorded	48—	64417

There were no records kept on this model from 1949 until its discontinuance in 1958. The total production was approximately 116,280.

Records at the factory indicate the following serial numbers were assigned to guns at the end of the calendar year.

MODEL 12

1912—	5308	1938—	779455
13—	32418	39—	814121
14—	79765	40—	856499
15—	109515	41 –	907431

16—	136412	42 —	958303
17—	159391	43 —	975640
18—	183461	44 —	975727
19—	219457	45 —	990004
20—	247458	46—	1029152
21—	267253	47—	1102371
22—	304314	48—	1176055
23—	346319	49—	1214041
24—	385196	50—	1252028
25—	423056	51—	1290015
26—	464564	52—	1328002
27—	510693	53—	1399996
28—	557850	54—	1471990
29—	600834	55—	1541929
30—	626996	56—	1611868
31—	651255	57—	1651435
32—	660110	58—	1690999
33—	664544	59—	1795500
34—	673994	60—	1800000
35—	686978	61—	1930029
36—	720316	62—	1956990
37—	754250	63—	1962001

A clean up of production took place from 64 through 66 with the ending serial # 1970875

New Style M / 12

1972 –	Y200 0100-Y2006396
73 –	Y2015662
74 –	Y2022061
75 –	Y2024478
76 –	Y2025482
77 –	Y2025874
78 –	Y2026156
79 –	Y2026399

Records at the factory indicate the following serial numbers were assigned to guns at the end of the calendar year.

MODEL 1911 S.L.

1911—	1 to 3819	1919—	57337
12—	27659	20—	60719
13—	36677	21—	64109
14—	40105	22—	69132
15—	43284	23—	73186
16—	45391	24—	76199
17—	49893	25—	78611
18—	52895		

The model 1911 was discontinued in 1925. However, guns were produced for three years after that date to clean up production and excess parts. When this practice ceased there were approximately 82,774 guns produced.

Records at the factory indicate the following serial numbers were assigned to guns at the end of the calendar year.

MODEL 1910

1910—	1 to 4766	1924—	17030
11—	7695	25—	17281
12—	9712	26—	17696
13—	11487	27—	18182
14—	12311	28—	18469
15—	13233	29—	18893
16—	13788	30—	19065
17—	14255	31—	19172
18—	14625	32—	19232
19—	15665	33—	19281
20—	No # Available.	34—	19338
21—	15845	35—	19388
22—	16347	36—	19445
23—	16637		

A clean up of production continued into 1937 when the total of the guns were completed at approximately 20786 ...

Records at the factory indicate the following serial numbers were assigned to guns at the end of the calendar year.

MODEL 1907

1907—	1 to 8657	1933—	44806
08—	14486	34—	44990
09—	19707	35—	45203
10—	23230	36—	45482
11—	25523	37—	45920
12—	27724	38—	46419
13—	29607	39—	46758
14—	30872	40—	47296
15—	32272	41—	47957
16—	36215	42—	48275
17—	38235	43—	None
18—	39172	44—	None
19—	40448	45—	48281
20—	No # Available	46—	48395
21—	40784	47—	48996
22—	41289	48—	49684
23—	41658	**49—	50662
24—	42029	**50—	51640
25—	42360	**51—	52618
26—	42688	**52—	53596
27—	43226	**53—	54574
28—	43685	**54—	55552
29—	44046	**55—	56530
30—	44357	**56—	57508
31—	44572	**57—	58486
32—	44683		

** Actual records on serial-numbers stops in 1948. The serial numbers ending each year from 1948 to 1957 were derived at by taking the last serial number recorded (58486) and the last number from 1948, (49684) and dividing the years of production, (9), which relates to 978 guns each year for the nine year period.

Records at the factory indicate the following serial numbers were assigned to guns at the end of the calendar year.

MODEL 1906

1906—	1 to 52278	1920—	None
07—	89147	21—	598691
08—	114138	22—	608011
09—	165068	23—	622601
10—	221189	24—	636163
11—	273355	25—	649952
12—	327955	26—	665484
13—	381922	27—	679692
14—	422734	28—	695915
15—	453880	29—	711202
16—	483805	30—	720116
17—	517743	31—	725978
18—	535540	32—	727353
19—	593917		

A clean up of production took place for the next few years with a record of production reaching approximately 729,305.

Records at the factory indicate the following serial numbers were assigned to guns at the end of the calendar year.

MODEL 1905

1905—	1 to 5659	1913—	25559
06—	15288	14—	26110
07—	19194	15—	26561
08—	20385	16—	26910
09—	21280	17—	27297
10—	22423	18—	27585
11—	23503	19—	28287
12—	24602	20—	29113

Records at the factory indicate the following serial numbers were assigned to guns at the end of the calendar year.

MODEL 1903

Year	Serial No.	Year	Serial No.
1903—	# Not Available	1918—	92617
04—	6944	19—	96565
05—	14865	20—	# Not Available
06—	23097	21—	97650
07—	31852	22—	99011
08—	39105	23—	100452
09—	46496	24—	101688
10—	54298	25—	103075
11—	61679	26—	104230
12—	69586	27—	105537
13—	76732	28—	107157
14—	81776	29—	109414
15—	84563	30—	111276
16—	87148	31—	112533
17—	89501	32—	112992

This model was discontinued in 1932, however, a clean up of parts was used for further production of approximately 2,000 guns. Total production was stopped at serial number 114962 in 1936.

Records at the factory indicate the following serial numbers were assigned to guns at the end of the calendar year.

MODEL 1901 SHOTGUN

Year	Serial No.	Year	Serial No.
1904—	64856 to 64860	1913—	72764
05—	66483	14—	73202
06—	67486	15—	73509
07—	68424	16—	73770
08—	69197	17—	74027
09—	70009	18—	74311
10—	70753	19—	74872
11—	71441	20—	77000
12—	72167		

Records at the factory indicate the following serial numbers were assigned to guns at the end of the calendar year.

MODEL 1897

Year	Serial No.	Year	Serial No.
1897—	to 32335	1928—	796806
98—	64668	29—	807321
99—	96999	30—	812729
1900—	129332	31—	830721
01—	161665	32—	833926
02—	193998	33—	835637
03—	226331	34—	837364
04—	258664	35—	839728
05—	296037	36—	848684
06—	334059	37—	856729
07—	377999	38—	860725
08—	413618	39—	866938
09—	446888	40—	875945
10—	481062	41—	891190
11—	512632	42—	910072
12—	544313	43—	912265
13—	575213	44—	912327
14—	592732	45—	916472
15—	607673	46—	926409
16—	624537	47—	936682
17—	646124	48—	944085
18—	668383	49—	953042
19—	691943	50—	961999
20—	696183	51—	970956
21—	700428	52—	979913
22—	715902	53—	988860
23—	732060	54—	997827
24—	744942	55—	1006784
25—	757629	56—	1015741
26—	770527	57—	1024700
27—	783574		

Records on this model are incomplete. The above serial-numbers are estimated from 1897 thru 1903 and again from 1949 thru 1957. The actual records are in existence from 1904 through 1949.

Records at the factory indicate the following serial numbers were assigned to guns at the end of the calendar year.

MODEL 1895

Year	Serial No.	Year	Serial No.
1895—	1 to 287	1914—	72082
96—	5715	15—	174233
97—	7814	16—	377411
98—	19871	17—	389106
99—	26434	18—	392731
1900—	29817	19—	397250
01—	31584	20—	400463
02—	35601	21—	404075
03—	42514	22—	407200
04—	47805	23—	410289
05—	54783	24—	413276
06—	55011	25—	417402
07—	57351	26—	419533
08—	60002	27—	421584
09—	60951	28—	422676
10—	63771	29—	423680
11—	65017	30—	424181
12—	67331	31—	425132
13—	70823	32—	425825

Records at the factory indicate the following serial numbers were assigned to guns at the end of the calendar year.

MODEL 94

Year	Serial No.	Year	Serial No.
1894—	1 to 14579	1939—	1101051
95—	44359	40—	1142423
96—	76464	41—	1191307
97—	111453	42—	1221289
98—	147684	43—	No Record Avail.
99—	183371	44—	No Record Avail.
1900—	204427	45—	No Record Avail.
01—	233975	46—	No Record Avail.
02—	273854	47—	No Record Avail.
03—	291506	48—	1500000
04—	311363	49—	1626100
05—	337557	50—	1724295
06—	378878	51—	1819800
07—	430985	52—	1910000
08—	474241	53—	2000000
09—	505831	54—	2071100
10—	553062	55—	2145296
11—	599263	56—	2225000
12—	646114	57—	2290296
13—	703701	58—	2365887
14—	756066	59—	2410555
15—	784052	60—	2469821
16—	807741	61—	2500000
17—	821972	62—	2551921
18—	838175	63—	2586000
19—	870762	*1964—	
20—	880627		2700000-2797428
21—	908318	65—	2894428
22—	919583	66—	2991927
23—	938539	67—	3088458
24—	953198	68—	3185691
25—	978523	69—	3284570
26—	997603	70—	3381299
27—	1027571	71—	3557385
28—	1054465	72—	3806499
29—	1077097	73—	3929364
30—	1081755	74—	4111426
31—	1084156	75—	4277926
32—	1087836	76—	4463553
33—	1089270	77—	4565925
34—	1091190	78—	4662210
35—	1099605	79—	4826596
36—	1100065	80—	4892951

37—	1100679	81—	5024957
38—	1100915	62—	5103248

* The post-64 Model 94 began with serial number 2700000.

Serial number 1000000 was presented to President Calvin Coolidge in 1927.
Serial number 1500000 was presented to President Harry S. Truman in 1948.
Serial number 2000000 was presented to President Dwight D. Eisenhower in 1953.
Serial numbers 2500000 and 3000000 were presented to the Winchester Gun Museum, now located in Cody, Wyoming.
Serial number 3500000 was not constructed until 1979 and was sold at auction in Las Vegas, Nevada.
Serial numbers 4000000 — whereabouts unknown at this time.
Serial numbers 4500000 — shipped to Italy by Olin in 1978. Whereabouts unknown.
Serial numbers 5000000 — in New Haven, not constructed as of March 1983.

Records at the factory indicate the following serial numbers were assigned to guns at the end of the calendar year.

MODEL 1892

1892—	1 to 23701	1913—	742675
93—	35987	14—	771444
94—	73508	15—	804622
95—	106721	16—	830031
96—	144935	17—	853819
97—	159312	18—	870942
98—	165431	19—	903649
99—	171820	20—	906754
1900—	183411	21—	910476
01—	191787	22—	917300
02—	208871	23—	926329
03—	253935	24—	938641
04—	278546	25—	954997
05—	315425	26—	973896
06—	376496	27—	990883
07—	437919	28—	996517
08—	476540	29—	999238
09—	522162	30—	999730
10—	586996	31—	1000727
11—	643483	32—	1001324
12—	694752		

Records on the Model 1890 are somewhat incomplete. Our records indicate the following serial numbers were assigned to guns at the end of the calendar year beginning with 1908. Actual records on the firearms which were manufactured between 1890 and 1907 will be available from the "Winchester Museum," located at The "Buffalo Bill Historical Center" P.O. Box 1020, Cody, WY 82414

MODEL 1890

1908— 330000 to	363850	1920—	None
09—	393427	21—	634783
10—	423567	22—	643304
11—	451264	23—	654837
12—	478595	24—	664613
13—	506936	25—	675774
14—	531019	26—	687049
15—	551290	27—	698987
16—	570497	28—	711354
17—	589204	29—	722125
18—	603438	30—	729015
19—	630801	31—	733178
		32—	734454

The Model 1890 was discontinued in 1932, however, a clean up of the production run lasted another 8+ years and included another 14 to 15,000 guns. Our figures indicate approximately 749,000 gun were made.

Records at the factory indicate the following serial numbers were assigned to guns at the end of the calendar year.

MODEL 1887

1887—	1 to 7431	1993—	54367
88—	22408	94—	56849
89—	25673	95—	58289
90—	29105	96—	60175
91—	38541	97—	63952
92—	49763	98—	64855

According to these records no guns were produced during the last few years of this model and it was therefore discontinued in 1901.

Records at the factory indicate the following serial numbers were assigned to guns at the end of the calendar year.

MODEL 1886

1886—	1 to 3211	1905—	138838
87—	14728	06—	142249
88—	28577	07—	145119
89—	38401	08—	147322
90—	49723	09—	148237
91—	63601	10—	150129
92—	73816	11—	151622
93—	83261	12—	152943
94—	94543	13—	152947
95—	103708	14—	153859
96—	109670	15—	154452
97—	113997	16—	154979
98—	119192	17—	155387
99—	120571	18—	156219
1900—	122834	19—	156930
01—	125630	20—	158716
02—	128942	21—	159108
03—	132213	22—	159337
04—	135524		

No further serial numbers were recorded until the discontinuance of the MODEL which was in 1935 — at — 159994.

Records at the factory indicate the following serial numbers were assigned to guns at the end of the calendar year.

MODEL 1885 SINGLE SHOT

1885—	1 to 375	1900—	88501
86—	6841	01—	90424
87—	18328	02—	92031
88—	30571	03—	92359
89—	45019	04—	92785
90—	None	05—	93611
91—	53700	06—	94208
92—	60371	07—	95743
93—	69534	08—	96819
94—	None	09—	98097
95—	73771	10—	98506
96—	78253	11—	99012
97—	78815	12—	None
98—	84700	13—	100352
99—	85086		

No further serial numbers were recorded until the end of 1923. The last number recorded was: 139700

Records at the factory indicate the following serial numbers were assigned to guns at the end of the calendar year.

MODEL 1876

1876—	1 to 1429	1988—	63539
77—	3579	89—	None
78—	7967	90—	None
79—	8971	91—	None
80—	14700	92—	63561

81—	21759	93—	63670
82—	32407	94—	63678
83—	42410	95—	None
84—	54666	96—	63702
85—	58714	97—	63869
86—	60397	98—	63871
87—	62420		

Records at the factory indicate the following serial numbers were assigned to guns at the end of the calendar year.

MODEL 1873

1873—	1 to 126	1897—	513421
74—	2726	98—	525922
75—	11325	99—	541328
76—	23151	1900—	554128
77—	23628	01—	557236
78—	27501	02—	564557
79—	41525	03—	573957
80—	63537	04—	588953
81—	81620	05—	602557
82—	109507	06—	613780
83—	145503	07—	None
84—	175126	08—	None
85—	196221	09—	630385
86—	222937	10—	656101
87—	225922	11—	669324
88—	284529	12—	678527
89—	323956	13—	684419
90—	363220	14—	686510

91—	405026	15—	688431
92—	441625	16—	694020
93—	466641	17—	698617
94—	481826	18—	700734
95—	499308	19—	702042
96—	507545		

No last # available — 20, 21, 22, 23 720609

Records at the factory indicate the following serial numbers were assigned to guns at the end of the calendar year.

MODEL 1866

1866—	12476 to 14813	1883—	162376
67—	15578	84—	163649
68—	19768	85—	163664
69—	29516	86—	165071
70—	52527	87—	165912
71—	88184	88—	167155
72—	109784	89—	167401
73—	118401	90—	167702
74—	125038	91—	169003
75—	125965	92—	None
76—	131907	93—	169007
77—	148207	94—	169011
78—	150493	95—	None
79—	152201	96—	None
80—	154379	97—	169015
81—	156107	98—	170100
82—	159513	99—	Discontinued

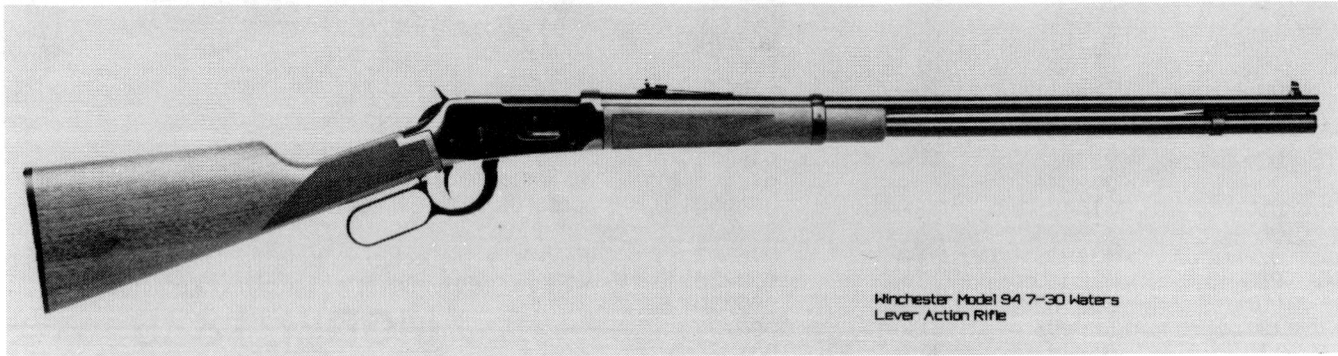
Winchester Model 94 7-30 Waters Lever Action Rifle

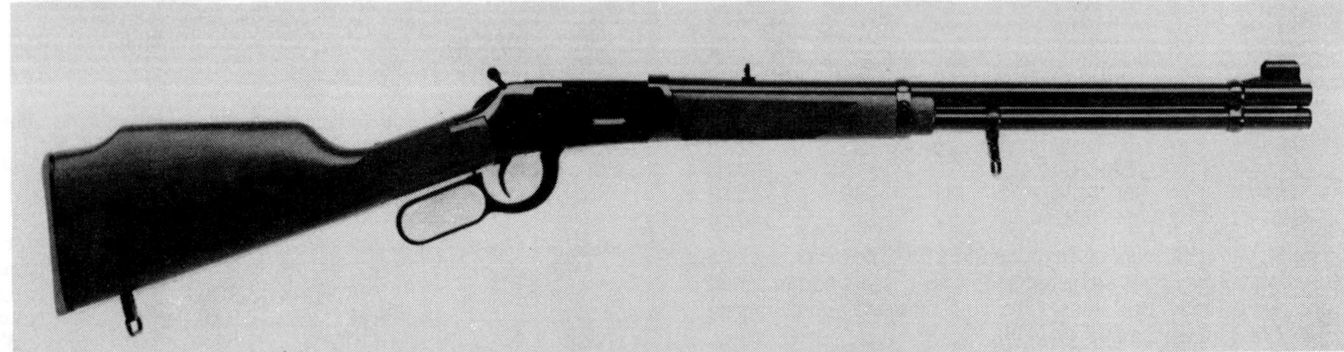

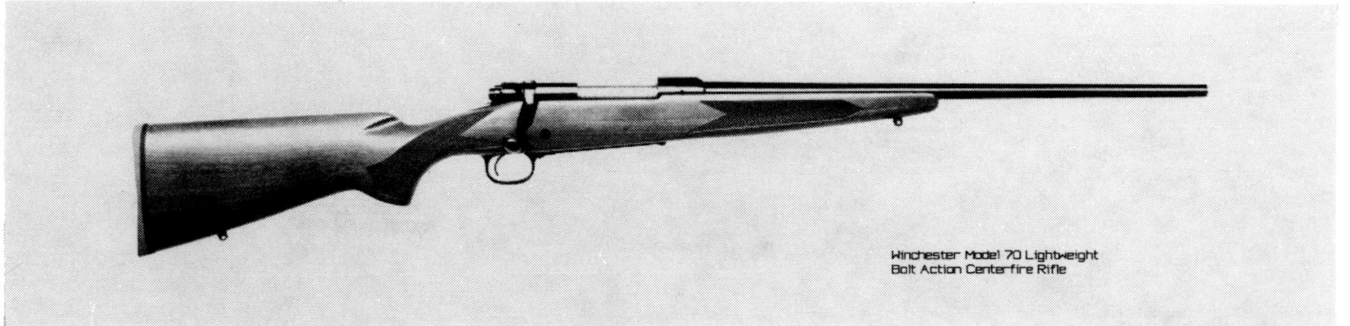

Winchester Model 70 lightweight bolt action centerfire rifle.

Winchester Ranger lever action rifle.

Winchester Model 9422 walnut.

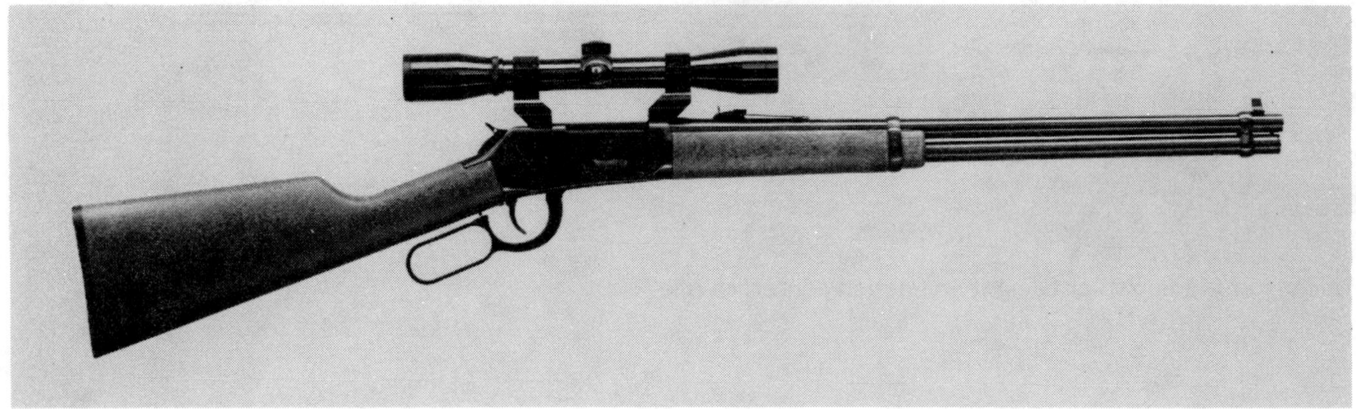

Winchester Model 94 Ranger with Bushnell Sportview 4 power scope and see-through mounts.

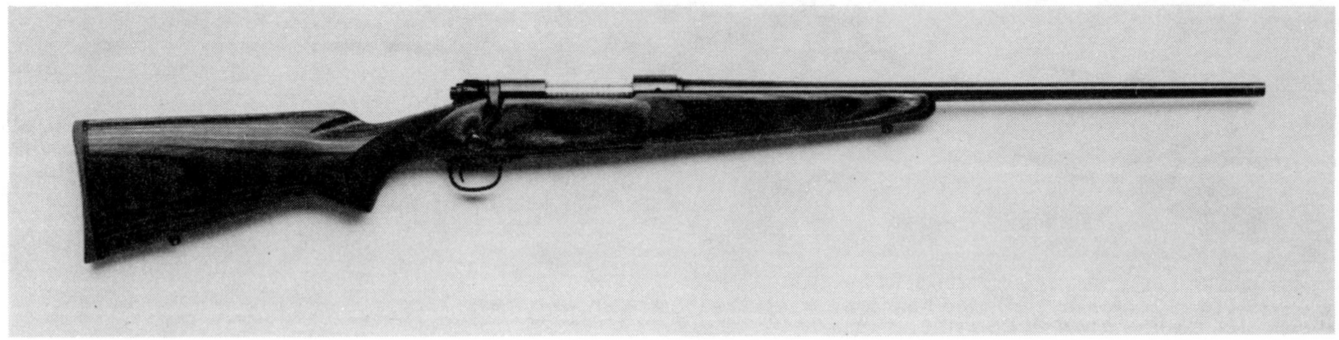

Winchester Model 70 lightweight Win-Tuff, laminated stock.

WINDSOR
Windsor, Vermont
Robbins & Lawrence
Hartford, Connecticut

Windsor Rifle
A .577 caliber single shot percussion rifle with a 39" round barrel secured by three barrel bands. The lock marked "Windsor". Rifles of this pattern were contracted for by the British Government. The lock and barrel finished in the white, brass furniture and a walnut stock. Approximately 16,000 were made from 1855 to 1858.

Exc.	V.G.	Good	Fair	Poor
1500	1250	1000	750	500

WINSLOW ARMS CO.
Camden, South Carolina

Bolt-Action Rifle
A high-grade, semi-custom sporting rifle built upon a number of actions and offered in all popular calibers from .17 Remington to the .458 Winchester Magnum with a 24" barrel and a 3-shot magazine. The larger Magnum models have a 26" barrel and a 2-shot magazine. Two basic stocks are offered—the Conventional Bushmaster which features a standard pistolgrip and a beavertail forearm; and also the Plainsmaster which has a full-curled, hooked pistolgrip and a wide, flat beavertail forearm. Both have Monte Carlo-style stocks with recoil pads and sling swivels. Offered in a choice of popular woods with rosewood forend tips and pistolgrip caps. Eight different grades of this rifle are available and the following lists the values applicable for each.

Commander Grade

Exc.	V.G.	Good	Fair	Poor
500	450	400	350	300

Regal Grade

Exc.	V.G.	Good	Fair	Poor
600	550	450	375	325

Regent Grade

Exc.	V.G.	Good	Fair	Poor
750	700	500	450	350

Regimental Grade

Exc.	V.G.	Good	Fair	Poor
950	850	650	550	450

Crown Grade

Exc.	V.G.	Good	Fair	Poor
1400	1250	1000	750	600

Royal Grade

Exc.	V.G.	Good	Fair	Poor
1550	1400	1150	850	700

Imperial Grade

Exc.	V.G.	Good	Fair	Poor
3500	3000	2500	2000	1450

Emperor Grade

Exc.	V.G.	Good	Fair	Poor
6000	5000	4000	3000	2000

WISEMAN, BILL & CO.
Bryan, Texas

Rifle
A custom order bolt-action rifle utilizing a Sako action, McMillan stainless steel barrel and laminated stock. The action components Teflon coated. It is made in four styles: the Hunter, Hunter Deluxe, Maverick and the Varminter.

Exc.	V.G.	Good	Fair	Poor
1500	1250	1000	750	600

Silhouette Pistol
A custom made single shot pistol produced in a variety of calibers with a 14" fluted stainless steel barrel and laminated pistolgrip stock. Furnished without sights. Introduced in 1989.

Exc.	V.G.	Good	Fair	Poor
1300	1000	800	600	500

WITNESS
SEE—European American Armory

WOODWARD, JAMES & SONS
London, England

Prior to World War II, this company produced a variety of boxlock and sidelock shotguns which are regarded as some of the best made. Prospective purchasers should secure a qualified appraisal prior to acquisition.

WURFFLEIN, ANDREW & WILLIAM
Philadelphia, Pennsylvania

Pocket Pistol
A .41 caliber percussion single shot pocket pistol with either a 2.5" or 3" barrel, German silver furniture and checkered walnut stock. The lock marked "A. Wurfflein/Phila." Manufactured during the 1850s and 1860s.

Exc.	V.G.	Good	Fair	Poor
750	650	500	400	300

Single Shot Target Pistol
A .22 caliber single shot pistol with half-octagonal barrels measuring from 8" to 16" in length. The barrel pivots downward for loading and is marked "W. Wurfflein Philad'a Pa. U.S.A. Patented June 24th, 1884." Blued with walnut grips. This model is also available with a detachable shoulder stock which if present would add approximately 35% to the values listed below. Manufactured from 1884 to 1890.

Exc.	V.G.	Good	Fair	Poor
550	450	400	300	200

Single Shot Rifle
A single shot rifle produced in a variety of calibers with octagonal barrels of 24" to 28" length. This rifle was available with a wide variety of optional features and a qualified appraisal should be sought if any features are in doubt.

Exc.	V.G.	Good	Fair	Poor
600	500	450	350	250

Mid-range Model
As above, with a 28" or 30" half-octagonal barrel.

Exc.	V.G.	Good	Fair	Poor
850	800	700	500	400

Model No. 25
The highest grade rifle manufactured by Wurfflein.

Exc.	V.G.	Good	Fair	Poor
1000	900	800	600	500

XL
HOPKINS & ALLEN
Norwich, Connecticut

Derringer

A .41 caliber spur trigger single shot pistol with a 2.75" octagonal barrel and either iron or brass frame. Blued, nickle-plated with rosewood grips. The barrel marked "XL Derringer". Manufactured during the 1870s.

Exc.	V.G.	Good	Fair	Poor
400	350	300	250	150

Vest Pocket Derringer

As above, in .22 caliber with a 2.25" round barrel and normally full nickle-plated. The barrel marked "XL Vest Pocket". Manufactured from 1870s to 1890s.

Exc.	V.G.	Good	Fair	Poor
350	300	250	200	100

XPERT
HOPKINS & ALLEN
Norwich, Connecticut

Xpert Derringer

A .22 or .30 caliber spur trigger single shot pistol with round barrels, 2.25" to 6" in length and a nickle-plated finish with rosewood grips. The breechblock pivots to the left side for loading. The barrel marked "Xpert—Pat. Sep. 23. 1878." Manufactured during the 1870s.

Exc.	V.G.	Good	Fair	Poor
300	250	200	150	100

Z

Z-B RIFLE CO.
Brno, Czechoslovakia

Varmint Rifle
A Mauser bolt-action rifle chambered for the .22 Hornet cartridge. It has a 23" barrel with a three-leaf, folding rear sight. It is offered standard with double-set triggers. The finish is blued, with a select walnut checkered stock.

Exc.	V.G.	Good	Fair	Poor
850	750	650	500	400

ZANOTTI, FABIO
Brescia, Italy
Importer—New England Arms Co.
Kittery Point, Maine

Model 625
A 12 to .410 bore boxlock double-barrel shotgun with automatic ejectors and single selective trigger. Blued with checkered walnut stock.

Exc.	V.G.	Good	Fair	Poor
3000	2500	2000	1500	1000

Model 626
As above, engraved with either scroll work or hunting scenes.

Exc.	V.G.	Good	Fair	Poor
3700	3200	2500	1550	1100

Giacinto
An external hammer boxlock shotgun produced in a variety of gauges with double triggers.

Exc.	V.G.	Good	Fair	Poor
5000	4500	3750	2500	1500

Maxim
Similar to the Model 625, but fitted with detachable sidelocks.

Exc.	V.G.	Good	Fair	Poor
7500	6500	5000	3500	2250

Edward
As above, but more intricately engraved.

Exc.	V.G.	Good	Fair	Poor
10000	8000	6500	5000	3500

Cassiano I
As above, with exhibition grade engraving.

Exc.	V.G.	Good	Fair	Poor
11000	9000	7000	6000	4000

Cassiano II
As above, with gold inlays.

Exc.	V.G.	Good	Fair	Poor
12500	10000	8500	7000	5000

Cassiano Executive
A strictly custom made shotgun produced to the client's specifications. Prospective purchasers should secure a qualified appraisal prior to acquisition.

Exc.	V.G.	Good	Fair	Poor
15000	12500	10000	8500	6500

ZEHNER, E. WAFFENFABRIK
Suhl, Germany

Zehna
A 6.35mm semi-automatic pistol with a 2.5" barrel and 5-shot magazine. The slide marked "Zehna DRPa," and the caliber on later production models. Blued with a black plastic grips bearing the monogram "EZ". Approximately 20,000 were made from 1921 to 1927.

Exc.	V.G.	Good	Fair	Poor
350	300	250	175	100

ZEILINGER
SEE—Austrian Military Firearms

ZEPHYR
Eibar, Spain
Importer—Stoegers

Woodlander II
A 12 or 20 gauge boxlock shotgun with varying length barrels, double triggers and extractors. Blued with a walnut stock.

Exc.	V.G.	Good	Fair	Poor
500	450	400	300	200

Uplander
A 12, 16, 20, 28 or .410 bore sidelock double-barrel shotgun with varying length barrels, double triggers and automatic ejectors. Blued with a walnut stock.

Exc.	V.G.	Good	Fair	Poor
600	550	500	400	300

Upland King
As above, in 12 or 16 gauge with ventilated-rib barrels.

Exc.	V.G.	Good	Fair	Poor
800	700	600	500	400

Vandalia
A 12 gauge single barrel trap gun with a 32" full choked barrel. Blued with a walnut stock.

Exc.	V.G.	Good	Fair	Poor
700	600	550	450	350

Sterlingworth II
Identical to the Woodlander, but with sidelocks.

Exc.	V.G.	Good	Fair	Poor
700	600	550	450	350

Victor Special
A 12 gauge boxlock double-barrel shotgun with 25", 28" or 30" barrels, double triggers and extractors. Blued with a walnut stock.

Exc.	V.G.	Good	Fair	Poor
450	400	300	250	175

Thunderbird
A 10 gauge Magnum boxlock double-barrel shotgun with 32" full choked barrels, double triggers and automatic ejectors. Blued with a walnut stock.

Exc.	V.G.	Good	Fair	Poor
800	700	600	500	400

Honker
A 10 gauge Magnum single barrel shotgun with a 36" full choked and ventilated-rib barrel. Blued with a walnut stock.

Exc.	V.G.	Good	Fair	Poor
500	450	400	300	200

ZOLI USA, ANGELO

Brescia, Italy
Importer—Same
Addison, Illinois

Slide Action Shotgun

A 12 gauge Magnum slide action shotgun produced with a variety of barrel lengths with detachable choke tubes. Blued with a walnut stock.

NIB	Exc.	V.G.	Good	Fair	Poor
325	300	250	200	150	100

Diano I

A 12, 20 or .410 bore single shot folding barrel shotgun. Produced in a variety of barrel lengths. Blued with a walnut stock.

NIB	Exc.	V.G.	Good	Fair	Poor
125	100	90	80	60	40

Diano II

As above, but with a bottom lever instead of a top release lever.

NIB	Exc.	V.G.	Good	Fair	Poor
125	100	90	80	60	40

Apache

A 12 gauge Magnum lever action shotgun with a 20" barrel fitted with detachable choke tubes. Blued with a walnut stock.

NIB	Exc.	V.G.	Good	Fair	Poor
475	425	350	300	250	150

Quail Special

A .410 Magnum bore double-barrel shotgun with 28" barrels and a single trigger. Blued with a walnut stock.

NIB	Exc.	V.G.	Good	Fair	Poor
250	225	200	175	125	100

Falcon II

As above with 26" or 28" barrels and double triggers.

NIB	Exc.	V.G.	Good	Fair	Poor
250	225	200	175	125	100

Pheasant

A 12 gauge Magnum double-barrel shotgun with 28" barrels, single trigger and automatic ejectors. Blued with a walnut stock.

NIB	Exc.	V.G.	Good	Fair	Poor
425	375	325	300	250	200

Classic

As above, with 26" to 30" barrels fitted with detachable choke tubes, single selective trigger and automatic ejectors. Blued with a walnut stock.

NIB	Exc.	V.G.	Good	Fair	Poor
700	650	600	500	350	250

Snipe

A .410 bore Over/Under shotgun with 26" or 28" barrels and a single trigger.

NIB	Exc.	V.G.	Good	Fair	Poor
275	250	225	175	150	100

Dove

Similar to the above.

NIB	Exc.	V.G.	Good	Fair	Poor
300	275	250	200	175	125

Texas

A 12, 20 or .410 bore Over/Under shotgun with 26" or 28" barrels, double triggers and a bottom barrel release lever.

NIB	Exc.	V.G.	Good	Fair	Poor
300	275	250	200	175	125

Field Special

A 12 or 20 gauge Magnum double-barrel shotgun produced in a variety of barrel lengths with a single trigger and extractors. Blued with a walnut stock.

NIB	Exc.	V.G.	Good	Fair	Poor
325	300	275	225	200	150

Pigeon Model

As above, but more finely finished.

NIB	Exc.	V.G.	Good	Fair	Poor
400	350	300	250	225	175

Standard Model

Similar to the above.

NIB	Exc.	V.G.	Good	Fair	Poor
450	400	350	300	275	200

Special Model

As above, with detachable choke tubes and a single selective trigger.

NIB	Exc.	V.G.	Good	Fair	Poor
525	475	400	350	325	250

Deluxe Model

As above, but engraved and with better quality walnut.

NIB	Exc.	V.G.	Good	Fair	Poor
750	675	575	500	400	300

Presentation Model

As above, with false sidelocks and finely figured walnut stock.

NIB	Exc.	V.G.	Good	Fair	Poor
850	750	650	575	450	350

St. George's Target

A 12 gauge Over/Under shotgun trap or skeet board with various length barrels, single selective trigger and automatic ejectors. Blued with a walnut stock.

NIB	Exc.	V.G.	Good	Fair	Poor
1050	900	700	600	550	450

Express Rifle

A .30-06, 7x65Rmm or 9.3x74Rmm Over/Under double barrel rifle with single triggers and automatic ejectors. Blued with a walnut stock.

NIB	Exc.	V.G.	Good	Fair	Poor
4000	3500	3000	2500	1850	1450

Express EM

As above, but more finely finished.

NIB	Exc.	V.G.	Good	Fair	Poor
4500	4000	3500	3000	2250	1750

Savana E

As above, with double triggers.

NIB	Exc.	V.G.	Good	Fair	Poor
6000	5250	4500	3500	2750	2000

Savana Deluxe

As above, but engraved with hunting scenes.

NIB	Exc.	V.G.	Good	Fair	Poor
8000	7000	6000	4750	3500	3000

AZ 1900

A .243, .270, 6.5x55mm, .308 or .30-06 bolt-action rifle with a 24" barrel having open sights. Blued with a walnut stock.

NIB	Exc.	V.G.	Good	Fair	Poor
500	450	400	350	250	200

AZ 1900 Deluxe

As above, but more finely finished.

NIB	Exc.	V.G.	Good	Fair	Poor
550	500	450	400	300	250

AZ 1900 Super Deluxe

As above, but engraved with a finely figured walnut stock.

NIB	Exc.	V.G.	Good	Fair	Poor
800	700	600	500	400	300

Patricia Model

As above, in .410 Magnum bore with 28" ventilated-rib barrels, various chokes, single selective trigger and automatic ejectors. Engraved, blued with finely figured walnut stock.

NIB	Exc.	V.G.	Good	Fair	Poor
1350	1100	950	750	650	550

Condor

A .30-06 or .308 and 12 gauge Over/Under combination shotgun rifle with double triggers, extractors and sling swivels. Blued with a walnut stock.

NIB	Exc.	V.G.	Good	Fair	Poor
750	700	650	550	450	400

Airone

As above, with false sidelocks.

NIB	Exc.	V.G.	Good	Fair	Poor
800	750	700	600	500	450

Leopard Express

A .30-06, .308, 7x65Rmm or .375 Holland & Holland Over/Under double barrel rifle with 24" barrels having express sights, double triggers and extractors. Blued with a walnut stock.

NIB	Exc.	V.G.	Good	Fair	Poor
1500	1250	950	750	600	500

ZOLI, ANTONIO

Brescia, Italy
Importer—Antonio Zoli USA, Inc.
Fort Wayne, Indiana

Silver Hawk

A 12 or 20 gauge boxlock double-barrel shotgun produced in a variety of barrel lengths and chokes with a double trigger. Engraved, blued with walnut stock.

Exc.	V.G.	Good	Fair	Poor
450	400	350	300	250

Ariete M3

A 12 gauge boxlock double-barrel shotgun with 26" or 28" barrels, non-selective single trigger and automatic ejectors. Engraved, blued with a walnut stock.

NIB	Exc.	V.G.	Good	Fair	Poor
600	500	450	400	350	300

Empire

As above, in 12 or 20 gauge with 27" or 28" barrels. Engraved, French casehardened, blued with a walnut stock.

NIB	Exc.	V.G.	Good	Fair	Poor
1650	1450	1200	1000	750	600

Volcano Record

A 12 gauge sidelock double-barrel shotgun with 28" barrels available in a variety of chokes, single selective trigger and automatic ejectors. Engraved, French case-hardened, blued with a walnut stock.

NIB	Exc.	V.G.	Good	Fair	Poor
6000	5250	4000	3000	2500	2000

Volcano Record ELM

This model is strictly a custom ordered shotgun produced to the purchaser's specifications. A qualified appraisal is suggested prior to acquisition.

NIB	Exc.	V.G.	Good	Fair	Poor
14500	12500	10000	8500	7000	5500

Silver Snipe

A 12 or 20 gauge Over/Under shotgun produced with varying lengths, ventilated-rib barrels, single trigger and extractors. Engraved, blued with a walnut stock.

Exc.	V.G.	Good	Fair	Poor
500	450	400	325	275

Golden Snipe

As above, but more finely finished and fitted with automatic ejectors.

Exc.	V.G.	Good	Fair	Poor
550	500	450	375	300

Delfino

As above, in 12 or 20 gauge Magnum with 26" or 28" ventilated-rib barrels, non-selective single trigger and automatic ejectors. Engraved, blued with walnut stock.

NIB	Exc.	V.G.	Good	Fair	Poor
425	375	325	275	250	200

Ritmo Hunting Gun

As above, in 12 gauge Magnum with 26" or 28" separated ventilated-rib barrels, single selective trigger and automatic ejectors. Engraved, blued with a walnut stock.

NIB	Exc.	V.G.	Good	Fair	Poor
600	550	500	400	350	275

Condor Model

As above, in 12 gauge with 28" skeet bored barrels having a wide competition rib, single selective trigger and automatic ejectors. Engraved, French case-hardened, blued with a walnut stock.

NIB	Exc.	V.G.	Good	Fair	Poor
900	800	650	550	400	300

Angel Model

As above, in a field grade version.

NIB	Exc.	V.G.	Good	Fair	Poor
900	800	650	550	400	300

Ritmo Pigeon Grade IV

As above, with 28" separated ventilated-rib barrels, single selective trigger, automatic ejectors and extensively engraved. French case-hardened, blued with a finely figured walnut stock.

NIB	Exc.	V.G.	Good	Fair	Poor
1800	1600	1250	900	750	650

Model 208 Target

As above, with 28" or 30" trap or skeet bored barrels fitted with a wide ventilated-rib.

NIB	Exc.	V.G.	Good	Fair	Poor
1000	850	700	600	500	400

Model 308 Target

As above, but more finely finished.

NIB	Exc.	V.G.	Good	Fair	Poor
1600	1400	1050	750	550	450

Combinato

A .222 or .243 and 12 or 20 gauge Over/Under combination rifle/shotgun with an engraved boxlock action, double triggers and a folding rear sight. French case-hardened, blued with a walnut stock.

NIB	Exc.	V.G.	Good	Fair	Poor
700	625	550	450	375	300

Safari Deluxe

As above, but with false sidelocks which are engraved with scrolls or hunting scenes.

NIB	Exc.	V.G.	Good	Fair	Poor
2800	2250	1850	1500	1200	950

ZULAICA, M.

Eibar, Spain

Zulaica

A solid-frame .22 caliber revolver having a 6-shot cylinder that has zigzag grooves on its exterior surface. It is fired by an external hammer and the frame is hollow with a rod inside of it that connects to the breechblock. There is a serrated cocking piece connected to this rod that is found at the top rear of the frame. When fired, the cartridge case blows from the cylinder and activates the breechblock similar to a semi-automatic pistol.

Exc.	V.G.	Good	Fair	Poor
750	600	500	350	250

Royal

The name Royal was applied to a number of pistols produced by this company, as noted below.

Royal

A 6.35mm or 7.65mm semi-automatic pistol which is normally marked on the slide "Automatic Pistol 6.35 Royal" or "Automatic Pistol 7.65 Royal".

Exc.	V.G.	Good	Fair	Poor
150	125	100	75	50

Royal

As above, in 7.65mm caliber with a 5.5" barrel and 12-shot magazine.

Exc.	V.G.	Good	Fair	Poor
175	150	125	100	75

Royal

A rather poor copy of the Mauser Model C/96 semi-automatic pistol with fixed lockwork.

Exc.	V.G.	Good	Fair	Poor
750	650	600	400	250

Vincitor

A 6.35mm or 7.65mm caliber semi-automatic pistol patterned after the Model 1906 Browning. The slide marked "SA Royal Vincitor." Blued with plastic grips.

Exc.	V.G.	Good	Fair	Poor
175	150	125	100	75

Firearms Trade Names

A.A. Co.: Inexpensive pocket revolvers of unknown manufacture.

Acme: a) Trade name used by the W.H. Davenport Firearms Company on shotguns.
b) Trade name used by the Hopkins and Allen Company on revolvers produced for the Merwin, Hulbert and Company and the Herman Boker Company of New York.
c) Trade name used by the Maltby, Henley and Company of New York on inexpensive pocket revolvers.

Acme Arms Company: Trade name used by the J. Stevens Arms and Tool Company on pistols and shotguns produced for the Cornwall Hardware Company of New York.

N.R. Adams: Trade name used by the N. R. Davis and Company on shotguns.

Aetna: Trade name used by the firm of Harrington and Richardson on inexpensive pocket revolvers.

Alamo Ranger: The name found on inexpensive Spanish revolvers.

Alaska: Trade name used by the Hood Firearms Company on inexpensive pocket revolvers.

Alert: Trade name used by the Hood Firearms Company on inexpensive pocket revolvers.

Alexander Gun Company: Trade name believed to have been used by E.K. Tryon of Philadelphia on imported shotguns.

Alexis: Trade name used by the Hood Firearms Company on inexpensive pocket revolvers.

Allen 22: Trade name used by the Hopkins and Allen Company on inexpensive pocket revolvers.

America: Trade name used by the Crescent Firearms Company on inexpensive pocket revolvers.

American: Trade name used by the Ely and Wray on inexpensive pocket revolvers.

American Barlock Wonder: Trade name used by the H. & D. Folsom Arms Company on Shotguns made for the Sears, Roebuck Company of Chicago.

American Boy: Trade name used on firearms retailed by the Townley Metal and Hardware Company of Kansas City, Missouri.

American Bulldog: Trade name used by the Iver Johnson Arms and Cycle Works on inexpensive pocket revolvers.

American Bulldog Revolver: Trade name used by Harrington and Richardson Arms Company on an inexpensive pocket revolver.

American Eagle: Trade name used by the Hopkins and Allen Company on inexpensive pocket revolvers.

American Gun Company: Trade name used by H. & D. Folsom Arms Company on pistols and shotguns that firm retailed.

American Gun Barrel Company: Trade name used by R. Avis of West Haven, Connecticut between 1916 and 1920.

American Nitro: Trade name used by H. & D. Folsom Arms Co. on shotguns.

Americus: Trade name used by the Hopkins and Allen Company on inexpensive pocket revolvers.

Angel: Trade name found on inexpensive pocket revolvers of unknown manufacture.

The Arab: Trade name used by the Harrington and Richardson Arms Company on shotguns.

Aristocrat: a) Trade name used by the Hopkins and Allen Company on inexpensive pocket revolvers.
b) Trade name used by the Supplee - Biddle Hardware Company of Philadelphia on firearms they retailed.

Armory Gun Company: Trade name used by H. & D. Folsom Arms Co. on shotguns.

Aubrey Shotgun: Trade name found on shotguns made for the Sears, Roebuck and Company of Chicago by Albert Aubrey of Meriden, Connecticut.

Audax: Trade name used by the Manufacture d'Armes Pyrenees on semi-automatic pistols.

Aurora: Trade name found on inexpensive Spanish semi-automatic pistols.

Autogarde: Trade name used by the Societe Francaise des Munitions on semi-automatic pistols.

Automatic: a) Trade name used by the Forehand and Wadsworth Company on inexpensive pocket revolvers.
b) Trade name used by the Harrington and Richardson Arms Company on inexpensive pocket revolvers.
c) Trade name used by the Iver Johnson Arms and Cycle Works on inexpensive pocket revolvers.

Auto Stand: Trade name used by the Manufacture Francaise d'Armes et Cycles, St. Etiene on semi-automatic pistols.

Avenger: Trade name found on inexpensive pocket revolvers of unknown manufacture.

Baby Hammerless: Trade mark used successively by Henry Kolb and R.F. Sedgley on pocket revolvers they manufactured.

Baby Russian: Trade name used by the American Arms Company on revolvers they manufactured.

Baker Gun Company: Trade name used by the H. & D. Folsom Arms Company on shotguns they retailed.

Baker Gun and Forging Company: Trade name used by the H. & D. Folsom Arms Company on shotguns they retailed.

Bang: Trade name found on inexpensive pocket revolvers of unknown manufacture.

Bang Up: Trade name used on inexpensive pocket revolvers retailed by the Graham and Haines Company of New York.

T. Barker: Trade name used by the H. & D. Folsom Arms Company of New York on shotguns they retailed.

Bartlett Field: Trade name used on shotguns retailed by Hibbard, Spencer, Bartlett and Company of Chicago.

Batavia: Trade name used on shotguns produced by the Baker Gun Company.

Batavia Leader: Trade name used on shotguns produced by the Baker Gun Company.

Bay State: Trade name used by the Harrington and Richardson Arms Company on both inexpensive pocket revolvers and shotguns.

Belknap: Trade name used by the Belknap Hardware Company of Louisville, Kentucky on shotguns made by the Crescent Fire Arms Company, which they retailed.

Bellmore Gun Company: Trade name used by the H. & D. Folsom Arms Company on shotguns made for them by the Crescent Fire Arms Company.

Berkshire: Trade name used by the H. & D. Folsom Arms Company on shotguns made for the Shapleigh Hardware Company of St. Louis, Missouri.

Bicyle: Trade name used on firearms made by the Harrington and Richardson Arms Company.

Big All Right: Trade name used on shotguns manufactured by the Wright Arms Company.

Big Bonanza: Trade name found on inexpensive pocket revolvers of unknown manufacture.

Bismarck: Trade name found on inexpensive pocket revolvers of unknown manufacture.

Black Beauty: Trade name used by the Sears, Roebuck and Company on imported shotguns they retailed.

Black Diamond: Trade name found on Belgian made shotguns retailed by an unknown American wholesale house.

Black Diana: Trade name used by the Baker Gun Company on shotguns.

Blackfield: Trade name used by the Hibbard, Spencer, Bartlett and Company of Chicago on shotguns they retailed.

Blackhawk: Trade name found on inexpensive pocket revolvers of unknown manufacture.

Black Prince: Trade name used by the Hopkins and Allen Company on inexpensive pocket revolvers.

Bliss: Trade name believed to have been used by the Norwich Arms Company.

Blood Hound: Trade name found on inexpensive pocket revolvers of unknown manufacture.

Bluefield: Trade name used by the W.H. Davenport Firearms Company on shotguns.

Bluegrass: Trade name used by the Belknap Hardware Company of Louisville, Kentucky on shotguns they retailed.

Bluegrass Arms Company: Trade name of shotguns made by H. & D. Folsom Arms Co. for Belknap Hardware of Louisville, KY.

Blue Jacket: Trade name used by the Hopkins and Allen Company on inexpensive pocket revolvers they made for the Merwin, Hulbert and Company of New York.

Blue Leader: Trade name found on inexpensive pocket revolvers of unknown manufacture.

Blue Whistler: Trade name used by the Hopkins and Allen Company on inexpensive pocket revolvers they made for the Merwin, Hulbert and Company of New York.

Bogardus Club Gun: Trade name found on Belgian made shotguns retailed by an unknown American wholesaler (possibly B. Kittredge and Company of Cincinnati, Ohio).

Boltun: Trade name used by F. Arizmendi on semi-automatic pistols.

Bonanza: Trade name used by the Bacon Arms Company on inexpensive pocket revolvers.

Boom: Trade name used by the Shattuck Arms Company on inexpensive pocket revolvers.

Daniel Boone Gun Company: Trade name used by the Belknap Hardware Company of Louisville, Kentucky on firearms they retailed.

Boone Gun Company: Trade name used by the Belknap Hardware Company of Louisville, Kentucky on firearms they retailed.

Boss: a) Trade name used by E.H. and A.A. Buckland of Springfield, Mass., on single shot derringers designed by Holt & Marshall.

b) Trade name used on inexpensive pocket revolvers of unknown American manufacture.

Boys Choice: Trade name used by the Hood Firearms Company on inexpensive pocket revolvers.

Bride Black Prince: Trade name used by H. & D. Folsom Arms Co. on shotguns.

Bridge Gun Company: Registered trade name of the Shapleigh Hardware Company, St. Louis, Missouri.

Bridgeport Arms Company: Trade name used by H. & D. Folsom Arms Co. on shotguns.

Bright Arms Company: Trade name used by H. & D. Folsom Arms Company

British Bulldog: Trade name found on inexpensive pocket revolvers of unknown American and English manufacture.

Brownie: a) Trade name used by the W.H. Davenport Firearms Company on shotguns.

b) Trade name used by the O.F. Mossberg Firearms Company on a four-shot pocket pistol.

Brutus: Trade name used by the Hood Firearms Company on inexpensive pocket revolvers.

Buckeye: Trade name used by the Hopkins and Allen Company on inexpensive pocket revolvers.

Buffalo: Trade name used by Gabilongo y Urresti on semi-automatic pistols.

Buffalo: Trade name found on bolt action rifles made in France.

Buffalo: Trade name used by the Western Arms Company on an inexpensive pocket revolver.

Buffalo Bill: Trade name used by the Iver Johnson Arms and Cycle Works on an inexpensive pocket revolver.

Buffalo Stand: Trade name used by the Manufacture Francaise d'Armes et Cycles on target pistols.

Bull Dog: Trade name used by the Forehand and Wadsworth Company on inexpensive pocket revolvers.

Bull Dozer: a) Trade name used by the Norwich Pistol Company on inexpensive pocket revolvers.

b) Trade name used by the Forehand and Wadsworth Company on inexpensive pocket revolvers.

c) Trade name on Hammond Patent pistols made by the Connecticut Arms and Manufacturing Company.

Bull Frog: Trade name used by the Hopkins and Allen Company on rifles.

Bulls Eye: Trade name used by the Norwich Falls Pistol Company (O.A. Smith) on inexpensive pocket revolvers.

Burdick: Trade name used by the H. & D. Folsom Arms Company on shotguns made for the Sears, Roebuck and Company of Chicago.

General Butler: Trade name found on inexpensive pocket revolvers of unknown manufacture.

Cadet: Trade name used by the Crescent Firearms Company on rifles.

Canadian Belle: Trade name used by H. & D. Folsom Arms Co. on shotguns.

Cannon Breech: Trade name used by the Hopkins and Allen Company on shotguns.

Captain: Trade name used by Manufacture d'Armes de Pyrenees on semi-automatic pistols.

Captain Jack: Trade name used by Hopkins & Allen on inexpensive pocket revolvers.

Carolina Arms Company: Trade name used by the H. & D. Folsom Arms Company on shotguns produced for the Smith, Wadsworth Hardware Company of Charlotte, North Carolina.

Caroline Arms: Trade name used by the H. & D. Folsom Arms Co.

Caruso: Trade name used by the Crescent Firearms Company on shotguns made for the Hibbard, Spencer, Bartlett and Company of Chicago.

Centennial 1876: a) Trade name used by the Deringer Pistol Company on inexpensive pocket revolvers.
b) Trade name used by the Hood Firearms Company on inexpensive pocket revolvers.

Central Arms Company: Trade name used by the W.H. Davenport Firearms Company on shotguns made for the Shapleigh Hardware Company of St. Louis, Missouri.

Century Arms Company: Trade name used by the W.H. Davenport Firearms Company on shotguns made for the Shapleigh Hardware Company of St. Louis, Missouri.

Challenge: a) Trade name found on inexpensive pocket revolvers of unknown manufacture.
b) Trade name used by the Sears, Roebuck and Company of Chicago on shotguns made by Albert Aubrey of Meriden, Connecticut.

Challenge Ejector: Trade name used by the Sears, Roebuck and Company of Chicago on shotguns made by Albert Aubrey of Meriden, Connecticut.

Champion: a) Trade name used by H.C. Squires on shotguns.
b) Trade name used by J.P. Lovell on shotguns.
c) Trade name used by the Iver Johnson Arms and Cycle Works on shotguns and inexpensive pocket revolvers.
d) Trade name used by the Norwich Arms Company on inexpensive pocket revolvers.

Chantecler: Trade name used by Manufacture d'Armes de Pyrenees on semi-automatic pistols.

Chatham Arms Company: Trade name used by H. & D. Folsom Arms Company used on shotguns.

Cherokee Arms Company: Trade name used by the H. & D. Folsom Arms Company on shotguns made for C.M. Mclung and Company of Knoxville, Tennessee.

Chesapeake Gun Company: Trade name used by the H. & D. Folsom Arms Company of New York.

Chicago: Trade name found on shotguns retailed by the Hibbard, Spencer, Bartlett and Company of Chicago.

Chicago Ledger: Trade name used by the Chicago Firearms Company on inexpensive pocket revolvers.

Chicago Long Range Wonder: Trade name used by the H. & D. Folsom Arms Company on shotguns made for the Sears, Roebuck and Company of Chicago.

Chichester: Trade name used by Hopkins & Allen on inexpensive pocket revolvers.

Chicopee Arms Company: Trade name used by the H. & D. Folsom Arms Company of New York.

Chieftan: Trade name found on inexpensive pocket revolvers of unknown manufacture.

Christian Protector: Trade name found on inexpensive pocket revolvers of unknown manufacture.

Climax XL: Trade name used by Herman Boker and Company of New York on revolvers, rifles and shotguns.

Club Gun: Trade name used by B. Kittredge and Company of Cincinnati, Ohio on shotguns they retailed.

Cock Robin: Trade name used by the Hood Firearms Company on inexpensive pocket revolvers.

Colonial: Trade name used by Manufacture d'Armes de Pyrenees on semi-automatic pistols.

Colonial: Trade name used by H. & D. Folsom Company on shotguns.

Columbian Automatic: Trade name used by Foehl & Weeks on inexpensive pocket revolvers.

Colton Arms Company: Trade name used by the Shapleigh Hardware Company of St. Louis, Missouri on imported shotguns they retailed.

Colton Firearms Company: Trade name used by the Sears, Roebuck and Company of Chicago on shotguns they retailed.

Columbia: a) Trade name found on inexpensive pocket revolvers of unknown manufacture.
b) Trade name used by H.C. Squires on shotguns.

Columbia Arms Company: Registered trade name of Henry Keidel, Baltimore, Maryland.

Columbian: Trade name found on inexpensive pocket revolvers of unknown manufacture.

Columbian Firearms Company:
a) Trade name used by the Maltby, Henly and Company on inexpensive pocket revolvers.
b) Trade name used by the Crescent Firearms Company on shotguns.

Comet: Trade name used by the Prescott Pistol Company on inexpensive pocket revolvers.

Commander: Trade name used by the Norwich Arms Company on inexpensive pocket revolvers.

Commercial: Trade name used by the Norwich Falls Pistol Company (O.A. Smith) on inexpensive pocket revolvers.

Compeer: Trade name used by the H. & D. Folsom Arms Company on firearms made for the Van Camp Hardware and Iron Company of Indianapolis, Indiana.

Competition: Trade name used by John Meunier of Milwaukee, Wisconsin on rifles.

Conestoga Rifle Works: Trade name of Henry Leman, Philadelphia, Pennsylvania.

Connecticut Arms Company: Trade name used by H. & D. Folsom Arms Company on shotguns.

Constable: Trade name used by Astra on semi-automatic pistols.

Constabulary: Trade name used by L. Ancion-Marx of Liege on revolvers.

Continental: Trade name used by the Great Western Gun Works of Pittsburgh, Pennsylvania on firearms they retailed.

Continental Arms Company: Trade name used by the Marshall-Wells Company of Duluth, Minnesota on firearms they retailed.

Cotton King: Trade name found on inexpensive pocket revolvers of unknown manufacture.

Cowboy: Trade name used by the Hibbard, Spencer, Bartlett and Company of Chicago on imported, inexpensive pocket revolvers they retailed.

Cowboy Ranger: Trade name used by the Rohde Spencer Company of Chicago on inexpensive pocket revolvers.

Crack Shot: Trade name used by the J. Stevens Arms and Tool Company on rifles.

Cracker Jack: Trade name used by the J. Stevens Arms and Tool Company on pistols.

Creedmoore: a) Trade name used by the Hopkins and Allen Company on inexpensive pocket revolvers.
b) Trade name used by the Chicago Firearms Company on inexpensive pocket revolvers.
c) Trade name used by William Wurflein on rifles.

Creedmoore Armory: Trade name used by A.D. McAusland of Omaha, Nebraska on rifles.

Creedmoore Arms Company: Trade name found on imported shotguns retailed by an unknown American wholesaler.

Crescent: Trade name used by the Crescent Arms Company on inexpensive pocket revolvers.

Crescent International 1XL: Trade name used by Herman Boker and Company of New York on shotguns.

Creve Coeur: Trade name used by the Isaac Walker Hardware Company of Peoria, Illinois on imported shotguns they retailed.

Crown: Trade name used by the Harrington and Richardson Arms Company on inexpensive pocket revolvers.

Crown Jewel: Trade name used by the Norwich Arms Company on inexpensive pocket revolvers.

Cruso: Trade name used by the H. & D. Folsom Arms Company on shotguns made for Hibbard, Spencer, Bartlett and Company of Chicago.

Cumberland Arms Company: Trade name used by the H. & D. Folsom Arms Company on shotguns made for the Gray and Dudley Hardware Company of Nashville, Tennessee.

Czar: a) Trade name used by the Hopkins and Allen Company on inexpensive pocket revolvers.

b) Trade name used by the Hood Firearms Company on inexpensive pocket revolvers.

Daisy: a) Trade name used by the Bacon Arms Company on inexpensive pocket revolvers.

b) Registered proprietary trade name engraved on firearms made by the Winchester Repeating Arms Company for the F. Lassetter and Company, Limited of Sydney, Australia.

Daniel Boone Gun Company: Trade name used by H. & D. Folsom Arms Company on shotguns made for Belknap Hardware Company of Louisville, Ky.

Daredevel: Trade name used by Lou J. Eppinger of Detroit, Michigan on pistols.

Dash: Trade name found on inexpensive pocket revolvers of unknown manufacture.

Davis Guns: Trade names used successively by N.R. Davis, Davis Warner and the Crescent — Davis Arms Company on various firearms.

Dead Shot: a) Trade name found on inexpensive pocket revolvers of unknown manufacture.

b) Trade name used by the Meriden Firearms Company on rifles.

Deer Slayer: Trade name used by J. Henry and Son of Boulton, Pennsylvania on rifles.

Defender: a) Trade name used by the Iver Johnson Arms and Cycle Works on inexpensive pocket revolvers.

b) Trade name used by the U.S. Small Arms Company on knife pistols.

Defiance: Trade name used by the Norwich Arms Company on inexpensive pocket revolvers.

Delphian Arms Company:

a) Trade name used by the Supplee — Biddle Hardware Company of Philadelphia, Pennsylvania on shotguns they retailed which were supplied by the H. & D. Folsom Company of New York.

b) Trade name used by the H. & D. Folsom Arms Company of New York on shotguns.

Delphian Manufacturing Company: Trade name used by the H. & D. Folsom Arms Company of New York on shotguns.

Demon: Trade name used by Manufacture d'Armes de Pyrenees on semi-automatic pistols.

Demon Marine: As above.

Dexter: Trade name found on inexpensive pocket revolvers of unknown manufacture.

Diamond Arms Company: Trade name used by the Shapleigh Hardware Company of St. Louis, Missouri on imported shotguns they retailed.

Dictator: Trade name used by the Hopkins and Allen Company on inexpensive pocket revolvers.

Dominion Pistol: Trade name found on inexpensive pocket revolvers of unknown manufacture.

Double Header: Trade name used by E.S. Renwick on Perry and Goddard Patent derringers.

Douglas Arms Company: Trade name used by the Hopkins and Allen Company on shotguns.

Dreadnought: Trade name used by the Hopkins and Allen Company on shotguns and inexpensive pocket revolvers.

Duchess: Trade name used by the Hopkins and Allen Company on inexpensive pocket revolvers.

Duke: Trade name found on inexpensive pocket revolvers which may have been made by the Hopkins and Allen Company.

Dunlop Special: Trade name used by the Davis Warner Arms Company on shotguns made for the Dunlop Hardware Company of Macon, Georgia.

Duplex: Trade name used by the Osgood Gun Works of Norwich, Connecticut.

E.B.A.C.: Trade name used by Manufacture d'Armes de Pyrenees on semi-automatic pistols.

Eagle: Trade name used by the Iver Johnson Arms and Cycle Works on inexpensive pocket revolvers.

Eagle Arms Company: Trade name used by the Iver Johnson Arms and Cycle Works on inexpensive pocket revolvers.

Earlhood: Trade name used by E.L. Dickinson on inexpensive pocket revolvers.

Earnest Companion: Trade name found on inexpensive pocket revolvers of unknown manufacture.

Earthquake: Trade name used by E.L. Dickinson on inexpensive pocket revolvers.

Eastern Arms Company: Trade name used by the Sears, Roebuck and Company of Chicago on both shotguns and inexpensive revolvers made by the Iver Johnson Arms and Cycle Works.

Eclipse: a) Trade name found on single shot derringers of unknown manufacture.

b) Trade name used by E.C. Meacham on imported shotguns.

Electric: Trade name found on inexpensive pocket revolvers of unknown manufacture.

Electric City Single Hammer: Trade name found on single shot shotguns retailed by the Wyeth Hardware and Manufacturing Company of St. Joseph, Missouri.

Elector: Trade name found on inexpensive pocket revolvers of unknown manufacture.

Elgin Arms Company: Trade name used by the H. & D. Folsom Arms Company on shotguns made for the Strauss and Schram Company of Chicago.

Elita: Trade name used by the W.H. Davenport Fire Arms Company on shotguns.

Empire: a) Trade name used by the Rupertus Patented Pistol Manufacturing Company on inexpensive pocket revolvers.

b) Trade name used by the Crescent Firearms Company on shotguns.

Empire Arms Company: Trade name used by the H. & D. Folsom Arms Company on firearms made for the Sears, Roebuck and Company of Chicago.

Enders Royal Shotgun: Trade name used by the Crescent — Davis Firearms Company on shotguns made for the Simmons Hardware Company of St. Louis, Missouri.

Enders Special Service: Trade name used by the Crescent — Davis Firearms Company on shotguns made for the Simmons Hardware Company of St. Louis, Missouri.

Enterprise: Trade name used by the Enterprise Gun Works on inexpensive pocket revolvers.

Essex Gun Works: Trade name used by the Crescent — Davis Firearms Company on shotguns made for the Belknap Hardware Company of Louisville, Kentucky.

Eureka: Trade name used by the Iver Johnson Arms and Cycle Works on inexpensive pocket revolvers.

Excel: Trade name used by both the H. & D. Folsom Arms Company and the Iver Johnson Arms and Cycle Works on shotguns made for the Montgomery Ward and Company of Chicago.

Excelsior: a) Trade name found on inexpensive pocket revolvers of unknown manufacture.
b) Trade name used by the Iver Johnson Arms and Cycle Works on shotguns.

Expert: a) Trade name found on single shot derringers of unknown manufacture.
b) Trade name used by the W.J. Davenport Firearms Company on shotguns made for the Witte Hardware Company of St. Louis, Missouri.

Express: Trade name used by the Bacon Arms Company on inexpensive pocket revolvers.

Express: Trade name used by Tomas de Urizar on a variety of semi-automatic pistols.

Farwell Arms Company: Trade name used by the Farwell, Ozmun, Kirk and Company of St. Paul, Minnesota on shotguns.

Fashion: Trade name found on inexpensive pocket revolvers of unknown manufacture.

Faultless: Trade name used by the H. & D. Folsom Arms Company on shotguns made for the John M. Smythe Merchandise Company of Chicago.

Faultless Goose Gun: Trade name used by the H. & D. Folsom Arms Company on shotguns made for the John M. Smythe Merchandise Company of Chicago.

Favorite: a) Trade name used by the J. Stevens Arms and Tool Company on rifles.
b) Trade name used by the Iver Johnson Arms and Cycle Works on inexpensive pocket revolvers.

Favorite Navy: Trade name used by the Iver Johnson Arms and Cycle Works on inexpensive pocket revolvers.

Featherlight: Trade name used by the Sears, Roebuck and Company of Chicago on firearms they retailed.

Federal Arms Company: Trade name used by Meriden Firearms Company.

Folks Gun Works: Trade name of William and Samuel Folk of Bryan, Ohio on rifles and shotguns.

Freemont Arms Company: Trade name found on shotguns distributed by an unknown retailer.

Frontier: Trade name used by the Norwich Falls Pistol Company (O.A. Smith) on inexpensive pocket revolvers made for the firm of Maltby, Curtis and Company of New York.

Fulton: Trade name used by the Hunter Arms Company on shotguns.

Fulton Arms Company: Trade name used by the W.H. Davenport Firearms Company on shotguns.

Furor: Trade name used by Manufacture d'Armes de Pyrenees on semi-automatic pistols.

Gallia: Trade name used by Manufacture d'Armes de Pyrenees on semi-automatic pistols.

Game Getter: Registered trade mark of the Marble Arms and Manufacturing Company on combination rifle — shotguns.

Gaulois: Trade name used by Manufacture d'Armes et Cycles on squeezer type pistols (see also Mitrailleuse).

Gem: a) Trade name used by the J. Stevens Arms and Tool Company on single shot pocket pistols.
b) Trade name used by the Bacon Arms Company on inexpensive pocket revolvers.

General: Trade name used by the Rupertus Patented Pistol Manufacturing Company on inexpensive pocket revolvers.

Gerrish: Trade name of G.W. Gerrish of Twin Falls, Idaho used on shotguns.

Gibralter: Trade name of Albert Aubrey on shotguns made for the Sears, Roebuck and Company of Chicago.

Gladiator: Trade name of Albert Aubrey on shotguns made for the Sears, Roebuck and Company of Chicago.

Gold Field: Trade name found on inexpensive pocket revolvers of unknown manufacture.

Gold Hibbard: Trade name used by Hibbard, Spencer, Bartlett and Company of Chicago on firearms they retailed.

Gold Medal Wonder: Trade name used by H. & D. Folsom Arms Co. on shotguns.

Governor: Trade name used by the Bacon Arms Company on inexpensive pocket revolvers.

Guardian: Trade name used by the Bacon Arms Company on inexpensive pocket revolvers.

Gut Buster: Trade name found on inexpensive pocket revolvers of unknown manufacture.

Gypsy: Trade name found on inexpensive pocket revolvers of unknown manufacture.

Half Breed: Trade name found on inexpensive pocket revolvers of unknown manufacture.

Hamilton Arms: Registered trade name of the Wiebusch and Hilger Company, New York.

Hammerless Auto Ejecting Revolver: Trade name of the Meriden Firearms Company used on revolvers made for the Sears, Roebuck and Company of New York.

Hanover Arms Co.: If no foreign proofmarks then trade name used by H. & D. Folsom Arms Company.

Hard Pan: Trade name used by Hood Arms Company on inexpensive pocket revolvers.

S.H. Harrginton: If no foreign proofmarks then trade name used by H. & D. Folsom Arms Company.

Frank Harrison Arms Company: Trade name used by the Sickles and Preston Company of Davenport, Iowa on firearms they retailed.

Hart Arms Company: Trade name used by a Cleveland, Ohio wholesaler (possibly the George Worthington Company).

Hartford Arms Company: Trade name used by the H. & D. Folsom Arms on shotguns made for the Simmons Hardware Company of St. Louis, Missouri.

Harvard: Trade name used by the H. & D. Folsom Arms Company on shotguns made for the George Worthington Company of Cleveland, Ohio.

Hercules: Trade name used by the Iver Johnson Arms and Cycle Works on shotguns made for the Montgomery Ward and Company of Chicago.

Hermitage Arms Company: Trade name used by the H. & D. Folsom Arms Company on shotguns made for the Gray and Dudley Hardware Company of Nashville, Tennessee.

Hero: a) Trade name used by the American Standard Tool Company on percussion pistols.
b) Trade name used by the Manhattan Firearms Manufacturing Company on percussion pistols.

Hexagon: Trade name used by the Sears, Roebuck and Company of Chicago on shotguns they retailed.

Hinsdale: Trade name used by the Hopkins and Allen Company on inexpensive pocket revolvers.

S. Holt Arms Company: Trade name used by the Sears, Roebuck and Company of Chicago on shotguns they retailed.

Hornet: Trade name used by the Prescott Pistol Company on inexpensive pocket revolvers.

Howard Arms Company: Trade name used by the H. & D. Folsom Arms Company on shotguns they distributed.

Hudson: Trade name used by the Hibbard, Spencer, Bartlett and Company of Chicago on shotguns they retailed.

Hunter: Trade name used by the H. & D. Folsom Arms Company on shotguns made for the Belknap Hardware Company of Louisville, Kentucky.

The Hunter: Trade name used by the Hunter Arms Company on shotguns.

Hurricane: Trade name found on inexpensive pocket revolvers of unknown manufacture.

Illinois Arms Company: Trade name used by the Rohde, Spencer Company of Chicago on firearms they retailed.

Imperial: Trade name used by the Lee Arms Company on inexpensive pocket revolvers.

Imperial Arms Company: Trade name used by the Hopkins and Allen Company on inexpensive pocket revolvers.

Infallible: Trade name used by the Lancaster Arms Company of Lancaster, Pennsylvania on shotguns they retailed.

Infallible Automatic Pistol: Trade name used by the Kirtland Brothers Company of New York on inexpensive pistols they retailed.

International: a) Trade name found on inexpensive pocket revolvers of unknown manufacture.
b) Trade name used by E.C. Meacham on shotguns.

Interstate Arms Company: Trade name used by the H. & D. Folsom Arms Company on shotguns made for the Townley Metal and Hardware Company of Kansas City, Missouri.

I.O.A.: Trade name used by the Brown, Camp Hardware Company of Des Moines, Iowa on firearms they retailed.

Invincible: Trade name used by the Iver Johnson Arms and Cycle Works on both shotguns and inexpensive pocket revolvers.

I.X.L.: a) Trade name used by B.J. Hart on percussion revolvers.
b) Trade name used by the W.H. Davenport Firearms Company on shotguns made for the Witte Hardware Company of St. Louis, Missouri.

Ixor: Trade name used by Manufacture d'Armes de Pyrenees on semi-automatic pistols.

J.S.T. & Company: Trade name used by the Iver Johnson Arms and Cycle Works on inexpensive pocket revolvers.

Jackson Arms Company: Trade name used by the H. & D. Folsom Arms Company on shotguns made for C.M. Mclung and Company of Knoxville, Tennessee.

Jewel: Trade name used by the Hood Fire Arms Company on inexpensive pocket revolvers.

Joker: Trade name used by the Marlin Firearms Company on inexpensive pocket revolvers.

Joseph Arms Company (Norwich, Conn.): Trade name used by H. & D. Folsom Arms Company.

Judge: Trade name found on inexpensive pocket revolvers of unknown manufacture.

Jupitor: Trade name used by Fabrique d'Armes de Grand Precision, Eibar, Spain on semi-automatic pistols.

K.K.: Trade name used by the Hopkins and Allen Company on shotguns made for the Shapleigh Hardware Company of St. Louis, Missouri.

Keno: Trade name found on inexpensive pocket revolvers of unknown manufacture.

Kentucky: Trade name used by the Iver Johnson Arms and Cycle Works on inexpensive pocket revolvers.

Keystone Arms Company: Trade name used by the W.H. Davenport Firearms Company on shotguns made for the E.K. Tryon Company of Philadelphia, Pennsylvania.

Kill Buck: Trade name of the Enterprise Gun Works (James Bown), Pittsburgh, Pennsylvania.

Killdeer: Trade name used by the Sears, Roebuck and Company of Chicago on firearms bearing their trade name Western Arms Company.

King Nitro: Trade name used by the W.H. Davenport Firearms Company on shotguns made for the Shapleigh Hardware Company of St. Louis, Missouri.

King Pin: Trade name found on inexpensive single shot and revolving pocket pistols.

Kingsland Gun Company: Trade name used by the H. & D. Folsom Arms Company on shotguns made for the Geller, Ward and Hasner Company of St. Louis, Missouri.

Kirk Gun Company: Trade name used by Farwell, Ozmun, and Kirk Company of St. Paul, Minnesota.

Knickerbocker: Trade name used by the Crescent-Davis Firearms Company on shotguns.

Knickerbocker Club Gun: Trade name used by Charles Godfrey of New York on imported shotguns he retailed.

Knockabout: Trade name used by the Montgomery Ward and Company of Chicago on shotguns they retailed.

Knox-All: Trade name used by the Iver Johnson Arms and Cycle Works on firearms they made for the H. & D. Folsom Arms Company of New York.

L'Agent: Trade name used by Manufacture Francaises d'Armes et Cycles on revolvers.

Lakeside: Trade name used by the H. & D. Folsom Arms Company on firearms they made for the Montgomery Ward and Company of Chicago.

Leader: a) Trade name used by the Shattuck Arms Company on inexpensive pocket revolvers.
b) Trade name used by the Harrington and Richardson Arms Company on inexpensive pocket revolvers.

Leader Gun Company: Trade name used by the H. & D. Folsom Arms Company on shotguns they made for the Charles Williams Stores, Inc. of New York.

Le Colonial: Trade name used by Manufacture Francaises d'Armes et Cycles on revolvers.

Le Colonial: As above.

Lee's Hummer: Trade name used by the H. & D. Folsom Arms Company on firearms they made for the Lee Hardware Company of Salina, Kansas.

Lee's Special: Trade name used by the H. & D. Folsom Arms Company on firearms they made for the Lee Hardware Company of Salina, Kansas.

Le Francais: Trade name used by Manufacture Francaises d'Armes et Cycles on semi-automatic pistols.

Le Francais: As above on semi-automatic pistols.

Le Petit Forminable: Trade name used by Manufacture Francaises d'Armes et Cycles on revolvers.

Le Petit Forminable: As above on revolvers.

Le Protecteur: Trade name used by J.E. Turbiaux of Paris on squeezer pistols of the type later made by the Ames Sword Company.

Le Terrible: Trade name used by Manufacture Francaises d'Armes et Cycles on revolvers.

Liberty: Trade name used by the Norwich Falls Pistol Company (O.A. Smith) on inexpensive pocket revolvers.

Liege Gun Company: Trade name used by the Hibbard, Spencer, Bartlett and Company of Chicago on imported shotguns they retailed.

Lion: Trade name used by the Iver Johnson Arms and Cycle Works on inexpensive pocket revolvers.

Lion: Trade name used by the Iver Johnson Arms and Cycle Works on inexpensive pocket revolvers.

Little Giant: Trade name used by the Bacon Arms Company on inexpensive pocket revolvers.

Little John: Trade name used by the Hood Firearms Company on inexpensive pocket revolvers.

Little Joker: Trade name found on inexpensive pocket revolvers of unknown manufacture.

Little Pal: Registered trade name for knife pistols made by L.E. Pulhemus.

Little Pet: Trade name used by the Sears, Roebuck and Company of Chicago on inexpensive pocket revolvers they retailed.

London Revolver: Trade name found on inexpensive pocket revolvers of unknown manufacture.

Lone Star: Trade name found on inexpensive pocket revolvers of unknown manufacture.

Long Range Winner: Trade name used by the Sears, Roebuck and Company of Chicago on shotguns they retailed.

Long Range Wonder: Trade name used by the Sears, Roebuck and Company of Chicago on shotguns they retailed.

Long Tom: Trade name used by the Sears, Roebuck and Company of Chicago on shotguns they retailed.

Looking Glass: Trade name used on semi-automatic pistols of unknown Spanish manufacture.

Marquis of horne: Trade name used by Hood Arms Company on inexpensive pocket revolvers.

Mars: Trade name used by Manufacture d'Armes de Pyrenees on semi-automatic pistols.

Marshwood: Trade name used by the H. and D. Folsom Arms Company on shotguns they made for the Charles Williams Stores Inc. of New York.

Marvel: Trade name used by the J. Stevens Arms and Tool Company on various firearms.

Massachusetts Arms Company: Trade name used by both the J. Stevens Arms and Tool Company and the H. & D. Folsom Arms Company on firearms made for the Blish, Mizet and Silliman Hardware Company of Atchinson, Kansas.

Maximum: Trade name found on inexpensive pocket revolvers of unknown manufacture.

Metropolitan: Trade name used by the H. & D. Folsom Arms Company on firearms they made for the Siegal-Cooper Company of New York.

Metropolitan Police:

a) Trade name used by the Maltby, Curtiss and Company on inexpensive pocket revolvers.
b) Trade name used by the Rohde-Spencer Company of Chicago on inexpensive pocket revolvers.

Midget Hammerless: Trade name used by the Rohde - Spencer Company of Chicago on inexpensive pocket revolvers.

Mikros: Trade name used by Manufacture d'Armes de Pyrenees on semi-automatic pistols.

Minnesota Arms Company: Trade name used by the H. & D. Folsom Arms Company on shotguns they made for the Farwell, Ozmun, Kirk and Company of St. Paul, Minnesota.

Missaubi Arms Company: Trade name used by the Hunter Arms Company, possibly for the Farwell, Ozmun, Kirk and Company of St. Paul, Minnesota.

Mississippi Arms Company: Trade name used by the H. & D. Folsom Arms Company on firearms made for the Shapleigh Hardware Company of St. Louis, Missouri.

Mississippi Valley Arms Company: Trade name used by the H. & D. Folsom Arms Company on firearms made for the Shapleigh Hardware Company of St. Louis, Missouri.

Mitrailleuse: Alternate trade name of the Gauluis squeezer pistol.

Mohawk: Trade name used by the H. & D. Folsom Arms Company on firearms made for the Blish, Mizet and Silliman Hardware Company of Atchinson, Kansas.

Mohegan: Trade name used by the Hood Firearms Company on inexpensive pocket revolvers.

Monarch: a) Trade name used by the Hopkins and Allen Company on inexpensive pocket revolvers.
b) Trade name used by the Osgood Gun Works on Duplex revolvers.

Monitor: a) Trade name used by the Whitneyville Armory on inexpensive pocket revolvers.
b) Trade name used by the H. & D. Folsom Arms Company on firearms made for the Paxton and Gallagher Company of Omaha, Nebraska.

Montgomery Arms Company: Trade name used by the H. & D. Folsom Arms Company on a variety of firearms.

Mountain Eagle: Trade name used by the Hopkins and Allen Company on inexpensive pocket revolvers.

Mount Vernon Arms Company: Trade name used by the H. & D. Folsom Arms Company on firearms made for the Carlin, Hullfish Company of Alexandria, Virginia.

My Companion: Trade name found on inexpensive pocket revolvers of unknown manufacture.

My Friend: Trade name used by James Reid of New York.

Napoleon: Trade name used by the Thomas J. Ryan Pistol Manufacturing Company of Norwich, Connecticut on inexpensive pocket revolvers.

National Arms Company: Trade name used by the H. & D. Folsom Arms Company on firearms made both for the May Hardware Company of Washington, D.C., and the Moskowitz and Herbach Company of Philadelphia, Pennsylvania.

Nevermiss: Trade name used by the Marlin Firearms Company on single shot pocket pistols.

New Aubrey: Trade name used by Albert Aubrey of Meriden, Connecticut on both revolvers and shotguns made for the Sears, Roebuck and Company of Chicago.

New Britain Arms Company: Trade name used by H. & D. Folsom Arms Company.

New Defender: Trade name used by Harrington & Richardson on revolvers.

New Elgin Arms Company: Trade name used by H. & D. Folsom Arms Company.

New Empire: Trade name used by H. & D. Folsom Arms Company.

New England Arms Company: Trade name believed to have been used by Charles Godfrey on shotguns made for the Rohde, Spencer Company of Chicago.

New Era Gun Works: Trade name used by the Baker Gun Company on firearms made for an unknown retailer.

New Haven Arms Company: Trade name found on Belgian shotguns imported by either E.K.Tryon of Philadelphia or the Great Western Gun Works of Pittsburgh, Pennsylvania.

New Liberty: Trade name used by the Sears, Roebuck and Company of Chicago on inexpensive pocket revolvers they retailed.

Newport: a) Trade name found on inexpensive pocket revolvers of unknown manufacture.
b) Trade name used by the H. & D. Folsom Arms Company on shotguns made for Hibbard, Spencer, Bartlett and Company of Chicago.

New Rival: Trade name used by the H. & D. Folsom Arms Company on firearms made for the Van Camp Hardware and Iron Company of Indianapolis, Indiana.

New Worcester: Trade name used by the Torkalson Manufacturing Company of Worcester, Massachusetts.

New York Arms Company: Trade name used by the H. & D. Folsom Arms Company on firearms made for the Garnet Carter Company of Chattanooga, Tennessee.

New York Gun Company: Trade name used by the H. & D. Folsom Arms Company on firearms made for the Garnet Carter Company of Chattanooga, Tennessee.

New York Club: Trade name used by the H. & D. Folsom Arms Company on rifles.

New York Machine Made: Trade name used by the H. & D. Folsom Arms Company.

New York Pistol Company: Trade name used by the Norwich Falls Pistol Company (O.A. Smith) on inexpensive pocket revolvers.

Nightingale: Trade name found on inexpensive pocket revolvers of unknown manufacture.

Nitro Bird: Trade name used by the Richards and Conover Hardware Company of Kansas City, Missouri.

Nitro Hunter: Trade name used by the H. & D. Folsom Arms Company on shotguns made for the Belknap Hardware Company of Louisville, Kentucky.

Nitro King: Trade name used by the Sears, Roebuck and Company of Chicago on shotguns of unknown manufacture.

Nitro Special: Trade name used by the J. Stevens Arms and Tool Company on shotguns.

Northfield Knife Company: Trade name used by the Rome Revolver and Novelty Works of Rome, New York on inexpensive pocket revolvers.

Norwich Arms Company:
a) Trade name used by the Hood Firearms Company on inexpensive pocket revolvers.
b) Trade name found on shotguns retailed by the Marshall, Wells Company of Duluth, Minnesota and Winnipeg, Manitoba, Canada.

Norwich Falls Pistol Company: Trade name used by the O.A. Smith Company on inexpensive pocket revolvers made for Maltby, Curtis and Company of New York.

Norwich Lock Manufacturing Company: Trade name used by F.W. Hood Firearms Company on inexpensive pocket revolvers.

Not-Nac Manufacturing Company: Trade name used by the H. & D. Folsom Arms Company on firearms made for the Canton Hardware Company of Canton, Ohio.

Novelty: Trade name used by D.F. Mossberg & Sons on Shattuck Unique pistols.

OK: a) Trade name used by the Marlin Firearms Company on single shot pocket pistols.
b) Trade name used by Cowles and Son of Chicopee Falls, Massachusetts on single shot pocket pistols.
c) Trade name found on inexpensive pocket revolvers of unknown manufacture.

Old Hickory: a) Trade name found on inexpensive pocket revolvers of unknown manufacture.
b) Trade name used by the Hibbard, Spencer, Bartlett and Company of Chicago on shotguns they retailed.

Old Reliable: Trade name used by the Sharps Rifle Company.

Olympic: a) Trade name used by the J. Stevens Arms and Tool Company on rifles and pistols.
b) Trade name used by the Morley and Murphy Hardware Company of Green Bay, Wisconsin on firearms they retailed (possibly made by the J. Stevens Arms and Tool Company).

Osprey: Trade name used by Lou J. Eppinger of Detroit, Michigan on firearms he made.

Our Jake: Trade name used by E.L. and J. Dickinson of Springfield, Massachusetts on inexpensive pocket revolvers.

Oxford Arms Company: Trade name used by the H. & D. Folsom Arms Company on firearms made for the Belknap Hardware Company of Louisville, Kentucky.

Pagoma: Trade name used by the H. & D. Folsom Arms Company on firearms made for the Paxton and Gallagher Company of Omaha, Nebraska.

Peoria Chief: Trade name found on inexpensive pocket revolvers.

Perfect: Trade name used by the Foehl and Weeks Firearms Manufacturing Company of Philadelphia, Pennsylvania on inexpensive pocket revolvers.

Perfect: Trade name used by Manufacture d'Armes de Pyrenees on semi-automatic pistols.

Perfection: a) Trade name used by the H. & D. Folsom Arms Company on firearms made for the H.G. Lipscomb and Company of Nashville, Tennessee.
b) Trade name used by the John M. Smythe Merchandise Company of Chicago on firearms they retailed.

Pet: Trade name found on inexpensive pocket revolvers of unknown manufacture.

Petrel: Trade name found on inexpensive pocket revolvers of unknown manufacture.

Phenix: Trade name used by J. Reid of New York on revolvers.

Phoenix: a) Trade name used by J. Reid of New York on revolvers.
b) Trade name used by the Whitneyville Armory on percussion revolvers.

Piedmont: Trade name used by the H. & D. Folsom Arms Company on firearms made for the Piedmont Hardware Company of Danville, Pennsylvania.

Pinafore: Trade name used by the Norwich Falls Pistol Company (O.A. Smith) on inexpensive pocket revolvers.

Pioneer: Trade name found on inexpensive pocket revolvers of unknown manufacture.

Pioneer Arms Company: Trade name used by the H. & D. Folsom Arms Company on firearms made for the Kruse and Baklmann Hardware Company of Cincinnati, Ohio.

Pittsfield: Trade name used by the Hibbard, Spencer, Bartlett and Company of Chicago on firearms probably made by the H. & D. Folsom Arms Company.

Plug Ugly: Trade name found on inexpensive pocket revolvers of unknown manufacture.

Plymouth: Trade name used by Spear and Company of Pittsburgh, Pennsylvania on firearms they retailed.

Pocahontas: Trade name found on inexpensive pocket revolvers of unknown manufacture.

Pointer: Trade name found on single shot pocket pistols of unknown manufacture.

Prairie Fire: Trade name found on inexpensive pocket revolvers of unknown manufacture.

Prairie King: a) Trade name used by the Bacon Arms Company on inexpensive pocket revolvers.
b) Trade name used by the H. & D. Folsom Arms company on inexpensive pocket revolvers.

Premier: a) Trade name used by the Thomas E. Ryan Company on inexpensive pocket revolvers.
b) Trade name used by the Harrington and Richardson Arms Company on revolvers.
c) Trade name used by the Montgomery Ward and Company of Chicago on firearms they retailed.
d) Registered trade name of Edward K. Tryon and Company of Philadelphia, Pennsylvania.

Premium: Trade name used by the Iver Johnson Arms and Cycle Works on inexpensive pocket revolvers.

John W. Price: Trade name used by the Belknap Hardware Company of Louisville, Kentucky on firearms they retailed.

Princess: Trade name found on inexpensive pocket revolvers of unknown American manufacture.

Progress: Trade name used by Charles J. Godfrey of New York on shotguns.

Protection: Trade name used by the Whitneyville Armory on revolvers.

Protector: a) Trade name found on inexpensive pocket revolvers of unknown manufacture.
b) Trade name used by the Chicago Firearms company on inexpensive pocket revolvers.

Protector Arms Company: Trade name used by the Rupertus Patented Pistol Manufacturing Company on inexpensive pocket revolvers.

Providence: Trade name found on inexpensive pocket revolvers of unknown manufacture.

Puppy: Trade name found on inexpensive pocket revolvers made by several European makers.

Quail: Trade name used by the Crescent-Davis Arms Company on shotguns.

Queen: a) Trade name used by the Hood Firearms Company on inexpensive pocket revolvers.
b) Trade name used by the Hyde and Shattuck Company on inexpensive single shot pocket pistols.

Queen City: Trade name used by the H. & D. Folsom Arms Company on firearms made for the Elmira Arms Company of Elmira, New York.

Ranger: a) Trade name found on inexpensive pocket revolvers of unknown manufacture.
b) Trade name used by the Eastern Arms Company on various firearms made for the Sears, Roebuck and Company of Chicago.
c) Trade name of the Sears, Roebuck and Company of Chicago on a wide variety of firearms marketed by that firm.

Rapid-Maxim: Trade name used by Manufacture d'Armes de Pyrenees on semi-automatic pistols.

Reassurance: Trade name found on inexpensive pocket revolvers of unknown manufacture.

Red Chieftan: Trade name used by the Supplee Biddle Hardware Company of Philadelphia, Pennsylvania on inexpensive pocket pistols they retailed.

Red Cloud: Trade name used by the Ryan Pistol Manufacturing Company on inexpensive pocket revolvers.

Red Hot: Trade name found on inexpensive pocket revolvers of unknown manufacture.

Red Jacket: a) Trade name used by the.Lee Arms Company on inexpensive pocket revolvers.
b) Trade name used by the Hopkins and Allen Company on inexpensive pocket revolvers.

Reliable: Trade name found on inexpensive pocket revolvers of unknown manufacture.

Reliance: Trade name used by John Meunier of Milwaukee, Wisconsin on rifles.

Rev-O-Noc: Trade name used by the H. & D. Folsom Arms Company on firearms made for the Hibbard, Spencer, Bartlett and Company of Chicago.

Rich-Con: Trade name used by the H. & D. Folsom Arms Company for shotguns made for Richardson & Conover Hardware Company.

Richmond Arms Company: Trade name used by the H. & D. Folsom Arms Company on firearms made for an unknown retailer.

Charles Richter Company: Trade name used by the H. & D. Folsom Arms Company on firearms made for the New York Sporting Goods Company of New York.

Rickard Arms Company: Trade name used by the H. & D. Folsom Arms Company on firearms made for the J.A. Rickard Company of Schenectady, New York.

Rip Rap: Trade name used by the Bacon Arms Company on inexpensive pocket revolvers.

Rival: Trade name used by the H. & D. Folsom Arms Company on firearms made for the Van Camp Hardware and Iron Company of Indianapolis, Indiana.

Riverside Arms Company: Trade name used by the J. Stevens Arms and Tool Company on various types of firearms.

Robin Hood: Trade name used by the Hood Firearms Company on inexpensive pocket revolvers.

Rocky Hill: Trade name found on inexpensive cast iron percussion pocket pistols made in Rocky Hill, Connecticut.

Rodgers Arms Company: Trade name used by the Hood Firearms Company on firearms made for an unknown retailer.

Royal Gun Company: Trade name used by the Three Barrel Gun Company.

Royal Service: Trade name used by the Shapleigh Hardware Company of St. Louis, Missouri on firearms they retailed.

Rummel Arms Company: Trade name used by the H. & D. Folsom Arms Company on firearms made for the A.J. Rummel Arms Company of Toledo, Ohio.

Russel Arms Company: Registered trade name of the Wiebusch and Hilger Company of New York.

Russian Model: Trade name used by the Forehand and Wadsworth Company on inexpensive pocket revolvers.

S.A.: Trade mark of the Societe d'Armes Francaises.

Safe Guard: Trade name found on inexpensive pocket revolvers of unknown manufacture.

Safety Police: Trade name used by the Hopkins and Allen Company on inexpensive pocket revolvers.

St. Louis Arms Company: Trade name used by the H. & D. Folsom Arms Company on firearms made for the Shapleigh Hardware Company of St. Louis, Missouri.

Scott: Trade name used by the Hopkins and Allen Company on inexpensive pocket revolvers.

Secret Service Special: Trade name used by the Rohde, Spencer Company of Chicago on inexpensive pocket revolvers.

Selecta: Trade name used by Manufacture d'Armes de Pyrenees on semi-automatic pistols.

Senator: Trade name found on inexpensive pocket revolvers of unknown manufacture.

Sentinal: Trade name found on inexpensive pocket revolvers of unknown manufacture.

The Sheffield: Trade name used by the A. Baldwin and Company, Limited of New Orleans, Louisiana on shotguns they retailed.

Sickels-Arms Company: Trade name used by the Sickels and Preston Company of Davenport, Iowa on firearms they retailed.

Simson: Trade name used by the Iver Johnson Arms and Cycle Works on firearms made for the Iver Johnson Sporting Goods Company of Boston, Massachusetts.

Sitting Bull: Trade name found on inexpensive pocket revolvers of unknown manufacture.

Skue's Special: Trade name used by Ira M. Skue of Hanover, Pennsylvania on shotguns.

Smoker: Trade name used by the Iver Johnson Arms and Cycle Works on inexpensive pocket revolvers.

John M. Smythe & Company: Trade name used by H. & D. Folsom Arms Company for shotguns made for John M. Smythe Hardware Company of Chicago.

Southern Arms Company: Trade name used by the H. & D. Folsom Arms Company on firearms made for an unknown retailer.

Southerner: a) Trade name used by the Brown Manufacturing Company and the Merrimac Arms Manufacturing Company on single shot pocket pistols.
b) Registered trade name of Asa Farr of New York on pistols.

Southron: Trade name found on inexpensive pocket pistols of unknown manufacture.

Special Service: Trade name used by the Shapleigh Hardware Company of St. Louis, Missouri on inexpensive pocket revolvers.

Spencer Gun Company: Trade name used by the H. & D. Folsom Arms Company.

Splendor: Trade name found on inexpensive pocket revolvers of unknown manufacture.

The Sportsman: Trade name used by the H. & D. Folsom Arms Company on firearms made for the W. Bingham Company of Cleveland, Ohio.

Springfield Arms Company: Trade name used by the J. Stevens Arms and Tool Company.

Spy: Trade name found on inexpensive pocket revolvers of unknown manufacture.

Square Deal: Trade name used by the H. & D. Folsom Arms Company on firearms made for the Stratton, Warren Hardware Company of Memphis, Tennessee.

Standard: Trade name used by the Marlin Firearms Company on revolvers.

Stanley Arms: Registered trade name of the Wiebusch and Hilger Company of New York on firearms they retailed.

Stanley Double Gun: Trade name used by the H. & D. Folsom Arms Company on shotguns they retailed.

Star: a) Trade name found on inexpensive single shot pocket pistols of unknown manufacture.
b) Trade name used by the Prescott Pistol Company on inexpensive pocket revolvers.
c) Trade name used by Johnson & Bye on single shot cartridge derringers.

State Arms Company: Trade name used by the H. & D. Folsom Arms Company on firearms made for the J.H. Lau and Company of New York.

Sterling: a) Trade name used by E.L. and J. Dickinson of Springfield, Massachusetts on single shot pistols.
b) Trade name used by the H. & D. Folsom Arms Company on shotguns they retailed.

Stinger: Registered proprietary trade name engraved on firearms made by the Winchester Repeating Arms Company for the Perry Brothers Limited of Brisbane, Australia.

Stonewall: a) Trade name used by the Marlin Firearms Company on single shot derringers.
b) Trade name used by T.F. Guion of Lycoming, Pennsylvania on single shot percussion pistols he retailed.

Striker: Trade name found on inexpensive pocket revolvers of unknown manufacture.

Sullivan Arms Company: Trade name used by the H. & D. Folsom Arms Company on firearms made for the Sullivan Hardware Company of Anderson, South Carolina.

Superior: Trade name of the Paxton and Gallagher Company of Omaha, Nebraska on revolvers and shotguns.

Super Range: Trade name of the Sears, Roebuck and Company of Chicago on shotguns.

Sure Fire: Trade name found on inexpensive pocket revolvers of unknown manufacture.

Swamp Angel: Trade name used by the Forehand and Wadsworth Company on inexpensive pocket revolvers.

Swift: Trade name used by the Iver Johnson Arms and Cycle Works on firearms made for the John P. Lovell & Sons, Boston, Massachusetts.

Syco: Trade name used by the Wyeth Hardware Company of St. Joseph, Missouri on firearms they retailed.

Sympathique: Trade name used by Manufacture d'Armes de Pyrenees on semi-automatic pistols.

Ten Star: Trade name used by the H. & D. Folsom Arms Company on firearms made for the Geller, Ward and Hasner Company of St. Louis, Missouri.

Terrier: Trade name used by the Rupertus Patented Pistol Manufacturing Company on inexpensive pocket revolvers.

Terror: Trade name used by the Forehand and Wadsworth Company on inexpensive pocket revolvers.

Texas Ranger: Trade name used by the Montgomery Ward and Company of Chicago on inexpensive pocket revolvers they retailed.

Thames Arms Company: Trade name used by the Harrington and Richardson Arms Company on firearms they made for an unknown wholesaler.

Tiger: a) Trade name used by the Iver Johnson Arms and Cycle Works on inexpensive pocket revolvers.
b) Trade name used by the J.H. Hall and Company of Nashville on shotguns they retailed.

Tobin Simplex: Trade name used on shotguns of unknown manufacture which were retailed by the G.B. Crandall Company, Limited of Woodstock, Ontario, Canada.

Toledo Firearms Company:
a) Trade name used by the Hopkins and Allen Company on inexpensive pocket revolvers.
b) Trade name used by E.L. and J. Dickinson on inexpensive pocket revolvers.

Toronto Belle: Trade name found on inexpensive pocket revolvers of unknown manufacture.

Touriste: Trade name used by Manufacture d'Armes de Pyrenees on semi-automatic pistols.

Tower's Police Safety: Trade name used by Hopkins & Allen on inexpensive pocket revolvers.

Townley's Pal and Townley's American Boy: Trade name used by H. & D. Folsom Arms Company for shotguns made for Townley Metal and Hardware Company of Kansas City, Missouri.

Tramps Terror: Trade name used by the Forehand and Wadsworth Company on inexpensive pocket revolvers.

Traps Best: Trade name believed to have been used by the H. & D. Folsom Arms Company on firearms made for the Watkins, Cottrell Company of Richmond, Virginia.

Triumph: Trade name used by the H. & D. Folsom Arms Company on shotguns.

Trojan: Trade name found on inexpensive pocket revolvers of unknown manufacture.

True Blue: Trade name found on inexpensive pocket revolvers of unknown manufacture.

Tryon Special: Trade name used by the Edward K. Tryon Company of Philadelphia, Pennsylvania on shotguns they retailed.

Tycoon: Trade name used by the Iver Johnson Arms and Cycle Works on inexpensive pocket revolvers.

Uncle Sam: Trade name used by Johnson & Bye on percussion pocket pistols.

Union: a) Trade name found on inexpensive single shot pocket pistols of unknown manufacture.
b) Trade name used by the Hood Firearms Company on inexpensive pocket revolvers.
c) Trade name used by the Prescott Pistol Company on inexpensive pocket revolvers.

Union Arms Company: Trade name used by the H. & D. Folsom Arms Company on firearms made for the Bostwick, Braun Company of Toledo, Ohio.

Union Jack: Trade name found on inexpensive pocket revolvers of unknown manufacture.

Union N.Y.: Trade name used by the Whitneyville Armory on inexpensive pocket revolvers.

Unique: Trade name used by the C.S. Shattuck Arms Company on revolvers and four barrel pocket pistols.

United States Arms Company: Trade name used by Norwich Falls Pistol Company (O.A. Smith) on inexpensive pocket revolvers.

U.S. Arms Company: Trade name used successively by the Alexander Waller and Company (1877), the Barton and Company (1878) and the H. & D. Folsom Arms Company (1879 forward) on a variety of firearms.

U.S. Revolver: Trade name used by the Iver Johnson Arms and Cycle Works on inexpensive pocket revolvers.

U.S. Single Gun: Trade name used by the Iver Johnson Arms and Cycle Works on single barrel shotguns.

Universal: Trade name used by the Hopkins and Allen Company on inexpensive pocket revolvers.

Utica Firearms Company: Trade name used by the Simmons Hardware Company of St. Louis, Missouri on firearms they retailed.

Valient: Trade name used by the Spear and Company of Pittsburgh, Pennsylvania on firearms they retailed.

Veiled Prophet: Trade name used by the T.E. Ryan Pistol Manufacturing Company on inexpensive pocket revolvers.

Venus: Trade name used by the American Novelty Company of Chicago on inexpensive pocket revolvers.

Veteran: Trade name found on inexpensive pocket revolvers of unknown manufacture.

Veto: Trade name found on inexpensive pocket revolvers of unknown manufacture.

Victor: a) Trade name used by the Marlin Firearms Company on single shot pocket pistols.
b) Trade name used by the Harrington and Richardson Arms Company on inexpensive pocket revolvers.
c) Trade name used by the H. & D. Folsom Arms Company on inexpensive pocket pistols and revolvers.

Victor Arms Company: Trade name used by the H. & D. Folsom Arms Company on firearms made for the Hibbard, Spencer, Bartlett and Company of Chicago.

Victor Special: Trade name used by the H. & D. Folsom Arms Company on firearms made for the Hibbard, Spencer, Bartlett and Company of Chicago.

Victoria: Trade name used by the Hood Firearms Company on inexpensive pocket revolvers.

Vindix: Trade name used by Manufacture d'Armes de Pyrenees on semi-automatic pistols.

Viper: Trade name used on inexpensive pocket revolvers of unknown American manufacture.

Virginia Arms Company: Trade name used by the H. & D. Folsom Arms Company and later the Davis-Warner Arms Company on firearms made for the Virginia-Carolina Company of Richmond, Virginia.

Volunteer: Trade name used by the H. & D. Folsom Arms Company on inexpensive pocket revolvers made for the Belknap Hardware Company of Louisville, Kentucky.

Vulcan: Trade name used by the H. & D. Folsom Arms Company on firearms made for the Edward K. Tryon Company of Philadelphia, Pennsylvania.

Walnut Hill: Trade name used by the J. Stevens Arms and Tool Company on rifles.

Warner Arms Corporation: Trade name used by the H. & D. Folsom Arms Company on firearms made for the Kirtland Brothers, Inc. of New York.

Wasp: Trade name found on inexpensive pocket revolvers of unknown manufacture.

Wautauga: Trade name used by the Whitaker, Holtsinger Hardware Company of Morristown, Tennessee on firearms they retailed.

Western: Trade name used by the H. & D. Folsom Arms Company on firearms made for the Paxton and Gallagher Company of Omaha, Nebraska.

Western Arms Company:
a) Trade name used by the Bacon Arms on various types of firearms.
b) Trade name used by W.W. Marston on revolvers.
c) Trade name used by Henry Kolb and later R.F. Sedgly of Philadelphia, Pennsylvania on Baby Hammerless revolvers.
d) Trade name used by the Ithaca Gun Company on shotguns believed to have been made for the Montgomery Ward and Company of Chicago.

Western Field: Trade name used by Montgomery Ward and Company of Chicago on shotguns of various makes which they retailed.

Western Field: Trade name used by Manufacture d'Armes de Pyrenees on revolvers.

J.J. Weston: Trade name used by the H. & D. Folsom Arms Company on shotguns.

Whippet: Trade name used by the H. & D. Folsom Arms Company on firearms made for the Hibbard, Spencer, Bartlett and Company of Chicago.

Whistler: Trade name used by the Hood Firearms Company on inexpensive pocket revolvers.

White Powder Wonder: Trade name used by Albert Aubrey of Meriden, Connecticut on shotguns made for the Sears, Roebuck and Company of Chicago.

Wildwood: Trade name used by the H. & D. Folsom Arms Company for shotguns made for Sears, Roebuck & Company.

Wilkinson Arms Company: Trade name used by the H. & D. Folsom Arms Company on firearms made for the Richmond Hardware Company of Richmond, Virginia.

Wiltshire Arms Company: Trade name used by the H. & D. Folsom Arms Company on firearms made for the Stauffer, Eshleman and Company of New Orleans, Louisiana.

Winfield Arms Company: Trade name used by the H. & D. Folsom Arms Company on various types of firearms.

Winner: Trade name found on inexpensive pocket revolvers of unknown manufacture.

Winoca Arms Company: Trade name used by the H. & D. Folsom Arms Company on firearms made for the N. Jacobi Hardware Company of Wilmington, North Carolina.

Witte's Expert: Trade name used by the Witte Hardware Company of St. Louis, Missouri on shotguns they retailed.

Witte's IXL: Trade name used by the Witte Hardware Company of St. Louis, Missouri on shotguns they retailed.

Wolverine Arms Company: Trade name used by the H. & D. Folsom Arms Company on firearms made for the Fletcher Hardware Company of Wilmington, North Carolina.

Woodmaster: Trade name found on Belgian shotguns imported by an unknown wholesaler.

Worlds Fair: Trade name used by the Hopkins and Allen Company on shotguns.

Worthington Arms Company: Trade name used by the H. & D. Folsom Arms Company on various types of firearms.

Wyco: Trade name used by the Wyeth Hardware and Manufacturing Company of St. Joseph, Missouri on firearms they retailed.

XL: a) Trade name used by the Hopkins and Allen Company on inexpensive pocket revolvers.
b) Trade name used by the Marlin Firearms Company on single shot pocket pistols.

XPERT: a) Trade name used by the Hopkins and Allen Company on inexpensive pocket revolvers.
b) Trade name used by the Iver Johnson Arms and Cycle Works on inexpensive single shot pocket pistols.

XXX Standard: Trade name used by the Marlin Firearms Company on revolvers.

You Bet: Trade name used on inexpensive pocket revolvers of unknown American manufacture.

Young America: Trade name used by J.P. Lindsay of New York on superimposed - load percussion pistols.

Young American: Trade name used by the Harrington and Richardson Arms Company on revolvers.

FIREARMS MANUFACTURERS AND IMPORTERS

Action Arms, Ltd.
P.O.Box 9573
Philadelphia, PA 19124

AMAC, Inc.
2202 Redmond Road
Jacksonville, AR 72076

American Arms, Inc.
715 E. Armour Road
N. Kansas City, MO 64116

American Derringer Corp.
127 N. Lacy Drive
Waco, TX 76705

American Historical Foundation
1142 West Grace St.
Richmond, VA 23220

Anschutz-Precision Sales, Inc.
P.O. Box 1776
Westfield, MA 01086

Armes De Chasse
P.O. Box 827
Chadds Ford, PA 19317

Arminex Ltd.
7127 E. Sahuaro Drive
#107A
Scottsdale, AZ 85254

Armscorp of America
4424 John Avenue
Baltimore, MA 21227

Auto-Ordnance Corp.
Williams Lane
West Hurley, NY 12491

Bailons Gunmakers, Ltd.
94-95 Bath Street
Birmingham, England B4 6HG

Barrett Firearms Mfg.
8211 Manchester Highway
P.O.Box 1077
Murfreesboro, TN 37130

Beretta USA Corp.
17601 Beretta Drive
Accokeek, MD 20607

Charles Boswell Gunmakers
212 East Morehead Street
Charlotte, NC 28202

Browning
Route 1
Morgan, UT 84050

Calico
405 East 19th Street
Bakersfield, CA 93305

Caspian Arms, Ltd.
14 North Main Street
Hardwick, VT 05843

Century Arms
P.O. Box 714
St. Albans, VT 05478

Champlin Firearms
P.O. Box 3191/Woodring Airport
Enid, OK 73702

Charter Arms
26 Beaver Street
Ansonia, CT 06401

Charter Arms Corp.
430 Sniffens Lane
Stratford, CT 06497

China Sports, Inc.
P.O. Box 3250
Ontario, CA 91761

Chipmunk Mfg., Inc.
114 East Jackson
Medford, OR 97501

E. J. Churchill, Ltd.
Ockley Road, Dorking
Surrey, England RH5 4PU

Cimarron Arms
P.O. Box 906
Fredericksburg, TX 78624

Colt Firearms
P.O. Box 1868
Hartford, CT 06101

Connecticut Shotgun Manufacturing Co.
A.H. Fox Shotguns
35 Woodland Street
Box 1692
New Britain, CT 06051

Coonan Arms
830 Hampden Avenue
St. Paul, MN 55114

Dakota Arms, Inc.
HC55, Box 326
Sturgis, SD 57785

Davis Industries
15150 Sierra Bonita Lane
Chino, CA 91710

New Detonics Mfg. Corp.
21438 N. 7th Avenue
Suite F
Phoenix, AZ 85027

DuBiel Arms Co.
1800 West Washington Avenue
#205
Sherman, TX 75090-5359

Eagle Imports
1907 Highway 35
Ocean, NJ 07712

Ellett Bros.
P.O. Box 128
Chapin, SC 29036

EMF Co., Inc.
1900 E. Warner Avenue
1-D
Santa Ana, CA 92705

European American Armory
P.O. Box 3498
Hialeah, FL 33013

F.N. Manufacturing, Inc.
P.O. Box 104
Columbia, SC 29202

Falcon Firearms Mfg. Corporation
P.O. Box 3748
Granada Hills, CA 91344

Feather Industries
2300 Central Avenue
Boulder, CO 80301

Federal Ordnance, Inc.
1443 Potrero Avenue
S. El Monte, CA 91733

F.I.E. Corporation
4530 N.W. 135th Street
Opa-Locka, FL 33054

Fiocchi Of American
Route 2, Box 90-8
Ozark, MO 65721

Freedom Arms
P.O. Box 1776
Freedom, WY 83120

Furr Arms
91 North 970 West
Orem, UT 84057

Galaxy Imports
P.O. Box 3361
Victoria, TX 77903

Renato Gamba
Via Michelangelo, 64
Gardone, Italy 1-25063

Gibbs Guns, Inc.
Route 2, 411 Highway
Greenback, TN 37742

Glock, Inc.
6000 Highlands Parkway
Smyrna, GA 30082

Goncz Company
11526 Burbank
#18
N. Hollywood, CA 91601

Grendel, Inc.
P.O. Box 560908
Rockledge, FL 32956

Griffin & Howe
36 West 44th Street
#1011
New York, NY 10036

Griffin & Howe, Inc.
33 Claremont Road
Bernardsville, NJ 07924

GSI, Inc.
108 Morrow Ave.
Trussville, AL 35173

Hatfield International
224 North 4th
St. Joseph, MO 64501

Heckler & Koch, Inc.
21480 Pacific Boulevard
Sterling, VA 22170

Heym America Inc.
1426 East Tillman Road
Fort Wayne, IN 46816

Holmes Firearms
Route 6, Box 242
Fayetteville, AR 72703

Lew Horton Distributing Co., Inc.
15 Walkup Drive
Westboro, MA 01581

Hyper Single, Inc.
520 East Beaver
Jenks, OK 74037

Illinois Arms
2300 Central Avenue, Suite K
Boulder, CO 80301

Interarms
10 Prince Street
Alexandria, VA 22313

Intratec
12405 SW 130th Street
Miami, FL 33186

Ithaca Gun/Ithaca Acq. Corp.
891 Route 34 B
King Ferry, NY 13081

Jennings Firearms
3680 Research Way
Carson City, NV 89706

K.B.I. Inc.
P.O. Box 11933
Harrisburg, PA 17108

KDF
2485 Highway 46 North
Seguin, TX 78155

Kimber of Oregon, Inc.
9039 SE Jannsen Road
Clackamas, OR 97015

Krieghoff International
P.O. Box 549
Ottsville, PA 18942

L.A.R. Manufacturing
4133 West Farm Road
West Jordan, UT 84084

Law Enforcement Ordnance Corp.
P.O. Box 336
Ridgeway, PA 15853

Ljutic Industries
732 North 16th Avenue
Suite 22
P.O. Box 2117
Yakima, WA 98907

Lorcin Engineering Co., Inc.
6471 Mission Boulevard
Riverside, CA 92509

Magnum Research, Inc.
7110 University Avenue N.E.
Minneapolis, MN 55432

Marlin Firearms
100 Kenna Drive
North Haven, CT 06473

Maverick Arms Inc.
P.O. Box 586
Industrial Boulevard
Eagle Pass, TX 78853

G. McMillan & Co.
21438 North 7th Avenue
Phoenix, AZ 85027

Military Armament Corp.
P.O.Box 1156
Stephenville, TX 76401

Mitchell Arms Inc.
3400 W. MacArthur Blvd. #1
Santa Ana, CA 92704

M.O.A. Corp.
175 Carr
Brookville, OH 45309

William Larkin Moore & Co.
31360 Via Colinas #109
Westlake Village, CA 91301

O. F. Mossberg & Sons, Inc.
Seven Grasso Avenue
North Haven, CT 06473

Navy Arms Co.
689 Bergen Blvd.
Ridgefield, NJ 07657

New England Arms Co.
Lawrence Lane
Kittery Point, ME 03905

North American Arms
1800 N 300 W
Spanish Fork, UT 84660

Para-Ordnance
3411 McNicoll Avenue
Scarborough, Ontario M1V 2V6

Parker Reproductions
124 River Road
Middlesex, NJ 08846

Perazzi USA Inc.
1207 South Shamrock Avenue
Monrovia, CA 91016

Precision Imports
5040 Space Center Dr.
San Antonio, TX 78218

P.S.M.G. Gun Co.
10 Park Avenue
Arlington, MA 02174

Raven Arms
1300 Bixby Drive
City of Industry, CA 91745

Remington Arms Co., Inc.
1007 Market Street
Wilmington, DE 19898

Seecamp, L.W.C.
301 Brewster Rd.
Milford, CT 06460

Savage Arms
Springdale Road
Westfield, MA 01085

SGS Importers International
1750 Brielle Ave. Unit B-1
Wanamassa, NJ

Shiloh Rifle Mfg. Co., Inc.
P.O. Box 279
Ind. Park
Big Timber, MT 59011

SigArms, Inc.
Industrial Drive
Exeter, NH 03833

Sile Distributors
7 Centre Market Place
New York, NY 10013

Smith & Wesson
2100 Roosevelt Road
Springfield, MA 01102

Sokolovsky Inc.
P.O. Box 70113
Sunnyvale, CA 94086

Specialty Shooters
3325 Griffin Road
Suite 9M/M
Fort Lauderdale, FL 33312

Springfield Armory, Inc.
420 West Main Street
Geneseo, IL 61254

SSK Industries
721 Woodvue Lane
Wintersville, OH 43952

Steyr-Mannlicher GmbH
108 Morrow Avenue
Trussville, AL 35173

Stoeger Industries
55 Ruta Court
South Hackensack, NJ 07606

Sturm Ruger & Co., Inc.
10 Lacey Place
Southport, CT 06490

Taurus International
4563 SW 71st Avenue
Miami, FL 33155

Texas Longhorn Arms
P.O. Box 703
Richmond, TX 77469

Thompson/Center Arms Co.
Farmington Road
Rochester, NH 03867

Uberti USA, Inc.
P.O. Box 469
Lakeville, CT 06039

Ultra Light Arms, Inc.
P.O. Box 1270
Granville, WV 26534

U.S. Repeating Arms/Winchester
275 Winchester Ave.
New Haven, CT 06511

Varner Sporting Arms Inc.
1004-F Cobb Parkway North
Marietta, GA 30062

Weatherby, Inc.
2781 Firestone Boulevard
South Gate, CA 90280

Westley Richards & Co. Ltd.
40 Grange Road, Bournbrook
Birmingham, England B29 5A

Dan Wesson
293 Main Street
Monson, MA 01057

Wichita Arms
444 Ellis
Wichita, KS 67211

Wildey, Inc.
P.O. Box 475
Brookfield, CT 06804

Wilkinson Arms
26884 Pearl Road
Parma, ID 83660

Winchester/U.S. Repeating Arms Co. Inc.
275 Winchester Avenue
New Haven, CT 06511

Winslow Arms
P.O. Box 783
Camden, SC 29020

Antonio Zoli USA Inc.
P.O. Box 6190
Fort Wayne, IN 46896

GUN COLLECTORS ASSOCIATIONS

Alaska Gun Collectors Association
P.O. Box 101522
Anchorage, Alaska 99510

Ark-La-Tex Gun Collectors Association
919 Hamilton Road
Bossier City, LA 71111

Bay Colony Weapons Collectors, Inc.
47 Homer Road
Belmont, MA 02178

Boardman Valley Collectors Guild
County Road 600
Manton, MI 49663

Browning Collectors Association
1306 Walcott Drive
Ogden, UT 84402

Collectors Arms Dealers Association
P.O. Box 427
Thomson, IL 61285

California Rifle & Pistol Association, Inc.
12062 Valley View Street
Garden Grove, CA 92645

Central Illinois Gun Collectors Assn., Inc.
Box 875
Jacksonville, IL 62651-0875

Central Penn Antique Arms Association
978 Thistle Road
Elizabethtown, PA 17022

Chisholm Trail Antique Gun Association
1906 Richmond
Wichita, KS 67203

Colt Collectors Association
17694 Isleton Court
Lakeville, MN 55044

The Corpus Christi Antique Gun Collectors Association
P.O. Box 9392
Corpus Christi, TX 78410

Dallas Arms Collectors Association, Inc.
Rt. 1, Box 282-B
DeSoto, TX 75115

Fort Lee Arms Collectors
P.O. Box 1716
South Hackensack, NJ 07606

Hawaii Historic Arms Association
Box 1733
Honolulu, HI 96806

Houston Gun Collectors Association
P.O. Box 53435
Houston, TX 77052

Indianhead Firearms Association
Route 9, Box 186
Chippewa Falls, WI 54729

Indian Territory Gun Collectors Association
Box 4491
Tulsa, OK 74159

Iroquois Arms Collectors Association
214 70th Street
Niagara Falls, NY 14304

Jefferson State Arms Collectors
521 South Grape
Medford, OR 97501

Jersey Shore Antique Arms Collectors
P.O. Box 100
Bayville, NJ 08721

Kentuckiana Arms Collectors Association
P.O. Box 1776
Louisville, KY 40201

Kentucky Gun Collectors Association
P.O. Box 64
Owensboro, KY 42376

Lehigh Valley Military Collectors Association
P.O. Box 72
Whitehall, PA 18052

Long Island Antique Gun Collectors Association
35 Beach Street
Farmingdale, L.I., NY 11735

Maryland Arms Collectors Association
P.O. Box 20388
Baltimore, MD 21284-0388

Memphis Antique Weapons Association
4672 Barfield Road
Memphis, TN 38117

Minnesota Weapons Collectors Association
P.O. Box 662
Hopkins, MN 55343

Smith & Wesson Collectors Association
P.O. Box 321
Bellevue, WA 98009

Tampa Bay Arms Collectors Association
2461 67th Avenue South
St. Petersburg, FL 33712

Washington Arms Collectors, Inc.
P.O. Box 7335
Tacoma, WA 98407

Weapons Collectors Society of Montana
3100 Bancroft
Missoula, MT 59801

Weatherby Collectors Association, Inc.
P.O. Box 128
Moira, NY 12957

Willamette Valley Arms Collectors Association, Inc.
P.O. Box 5191
Eugene, OR 97405

Winchester Arms Collectors Association
P.O. Box 6754
Great Falls, MT 59406

Ye Connecticut Gun Guild
U.S. Route 7
Kent Road
Cornwall Bridge, CT 06754

Zumbro Valley Arms Collectors, Inc.
Box 6621
Rochester, MN 55901

Missouri Valley Arms Collectors Association
P.O. Box 33033
Kansas City, MO 64114

Montana Arms Collectors Association
308 Riverview Drive
East Great Falls, MT 59404

National Automatic Pistol Collectors Association
Box 15738-TOGS
St. Louis, MO 63163

National Rifle Association
1600 Rhode Island Avenue N.W.
Washington, D.C. 20036

New Hampshire Arms Collectors, Inc.
P.O. Box 6
Harrisville, NH 03450

Northeastern Arms Collectors Association, Inc.
P.O. Box 185
Amityville, NY 11701

Ohio Gun Collectors Association
P.O. Box 24F
Cincinnati, OH 45224

Oregon Arms Collectors
P.O. Box 25103
Portland, OR 97225

Pelican Arms Collectors Association
P.O. Box 747
Clinton, LA 70722

Pennsylvania Antique Gun Collectors Association
28 Fulmer Avenue
Havertown, PA 19083

Pikes Peak Gun Collectors Guild
406 E. Uintah
Colorado Springs, CO 80903

Potomac Arms Collectors Association
P.O. Box 2676
Laurel, MD 20811

Remington Society of America
380 South Tustin Avenue
Orange, CA 92666

Ruger Collectors Association, Inc.
P.O. Box 1778
Chino Valley, AZ 86323

Sako Collectors Association, Inc.
1725 Woodhill Lane
Bedford, TX 76021

Santa Barbara Antique Arms Collectors Association
P.O. Box 6291
Santa Barbara, CA 93160-6291

San Bernardino Valley Arms Collectors
1970 Mesa Street
San Bernardino, CA 92405

Santa Fe Gun Collectors Association
1085 Nugget
Los Alamos, NM 87544

San Fernando Valley Arms Collectors Association
P.O. Box 65
North Hollywood, CA 91603

Shasta Arms Collectors Association
P.O. Box 3292
Redding, CA 96049

BIBLIOGRAPHY

Bady, Donald *Colt Automatic Pistols.* Alhambra, California: Borden Publishing Company, 1973.

Baer, Larry L. *The Parker Gun.* Los Angeles, California: Beinfeld Publications, 1980.

Bailey, D. and Nie, D. *English Gunmakers.* London: Arms and Armour Press, 1978.

Belford, James & Dunlap, Jack *The Mauser Self-Loading Pistol.* Alhambra, California: Borden Publishing, 1969.

Bishop, Chris and Drury, Ian *Combat Guns.* Secaucus, New Jersey: Chartwell Books, 1987.

Blackmore, H. *Gunmakers of London.* York, Pennsylvania: Geo. Shumway, 1986.

Blackmore, H. *Guns and Rifles of the World.* New York, New York: Viking Press, 1965.

Blair, C. *Pistols of the World.* London: B.T. Batsford, Ltd., 1968.

Bogdanovic & Valencak *The Great Century of Guns.* New York, New York: Gallery Books, 1986.

Bowen, T.G. *James Reid and his Catskill Knuckledusters.* Lincoln, Rhode Island: Andrew Mowbray, Inc., 1989.

Breathed, J. and Schroeder, J. *System Mauser.* Glenview, Illinois: Handgun Press, 1967.

Brophy, Lt. Col. William S., USAR, Ret. *The Krag Rifle.* Los Angeles, California: Beinfeld Publications, 1980.

Brophy, Lt. Col. William S., USAR, Ret. *L.C. Smith Shotguns.* Los Angeles, California: Beinfeld Publications, 1977.

Brophy, W. *Marlin Firearms.* Harrisburg, Pennsylvania: Stackpole Books, 1989.

Browning, J. and Gentry, C. *John M. Browning; American Gunmaker.* Ogden, Utah: Browning, 1989.

Butler, David F. *The American Shotgun.* New York, New York: Winchester Press, 1973.

Buxton, Warren *The P 38 Pistol.* Dallas, Texas: Taylor Publishing Company, 1978.

Carr, J. *Savage Automatic Pistols.*

Chant, Christopher *The New Encyclopedia of Handguns.* New York, New York: Gallery Books.

Conley, F.F. *The American Single Barrel Trap Gun.* Carmel Valley, California: F.F. Conley, 1989.

Cope, K.L. *Stevens Pistols and Pocket Rifles.* Ottawa, Ontario: Museum Restoration Service.

Cormack, A.J.R. *Small Arms, a Concise History of Their Development.* Profile Publications, Ltd.

Cormack, A.J.R. *Small Arms in Profile, Volume 1.* Garden City, New York: Doubleday & Company, Inc., 1973.

de Hass, Frank *Bolt Action Rifles.* Northfield, Illinois: Digest Books, Inc., 1971.

de Hass, Frank *Single Shot Rifles and Actions.* Northfield, Illinois: Digest Books, Inc., 1969.

Eberhart, L. D. & Wilson, R. L. *The Deringer in America: Volume Two - The Cartridge Era.* Lincoln, RI: Andrew Mowbray Inc., Publishers, 1993.

Goddard, W. H. D. *The Government Models.* The Development of the Colt Model of 1911. Lincoln, Rhode Island: Andrew Mowbray Inc., 1988.

Graham, R., Kopec, J., Moore, C. *A Study of the Colt Single Action Army Revolver.* Dallas, Texas: Taylor Publishing Co., 1978.

Greener, W. *The Gun and Its Development.* Secaucus, New Jersey: Chartwell Books, 1988.

Gun Digest 1967 through 1989 Editions. Northfield, Illinois: DBI Books.

Guns of the World Los Angeles, California: Petersen Publishing Company, 1972.

Dunlap, J. *Pepperbox Firearms.* Palo Alto, California: Pacific Books, 1964.

Ezell, Edward C. *Small Arms Today.* Harrisburg, Pennsylvania: Stackpole Books.

Frasca & Hill *The .45-70 Springfield.* Northridge, California: Springfield Publishing Company, 1980.

Fuller, C. *The Whitney Firearms.* Huntington, West Virginia: Standard Pub., Inc., 1946.

Hayward, J.F. *Art of the Gunmaker,* Vol. 1. London: Barrie & Rockliff, 1962; Vol. 2. London: Barrie & Rockliff, 1963.

Henshaw, Thomas, et. al., *The History of Winchester Firearms 1866-1992, 6th Ed.* Winchester Press, 1993.

Hinman, Bob *The Golden Age of Shotgunning,* New York, N.Y., Winchester Press, 1975.

Hoff, A. *Airguns and Other Pneumatic Arms.* London: Barrie & Jenkins, 1972.

Hoffschmidt, E.J. *Know Your .45 Auto Pistols Models 1911 & A1.* Southport, Connecticut: Blacksmith Corporation, 1974.

Hoffschmidt, E.J. *Know Your Walther PP & PPK Pistols.* Southport, Connecticut: Blacksmith Corporation, 1975.

Hogg, Ian V. *German Pistols and Revolvers 1871-1945.* Harrisburg, Pennsylvania: Stackpole Books, 1971.

Hogg, Ian V. and Weeks, John *Military Small Arms of the 20th Century.* Fifth Edition. Northfield, Illinois: DBI Books, 1985.

Hogg, Ian V. and Weeks, John *Pistols of the World. Revised Edition.* Northfield, Illinois: DBI Books, 1982.

Honeycutt, Fred L., Jr. *Military Pistols of Japan.* Lake Park, Florida: Julin Books, 1982.

Houze, H. *The Sumptuous Flaske.* Cody, Wyoming: Buffalo Bill Historical Center, 1989.

Houze, H.G. *To The Dreams Of Youth: Winchester .22 Caliber Single Shot Rifle.* Iola, WI: Krause Publications, 1993.

Jamieson, G. Scott *Bullard Arms.* Erin, Ontario: Boston Mills Press, 1988.

Jinks, R.G. *History of Smith A. Wesson.* Beinfeld Pub., Inc., 1977.

Karr, C.L. and C.R. *Remington Handguns.* Harrisburg, Pennsylvania: Stackpole Co., 1956.

Kenyon, C. *Lugers at Random.* Glenview, Illinois: Handgun Press, 1990.

Kindig, J., Jr. *Thoughts on the Kentucky Rifle in its Golden Age.* New York, New York: Bonanza Books, 1964.

Larson, Eric *Variations of the Smooth Bore H&R Handy-Gun.* Takoma Park, Maryland: 1993.

Leithe, Frederick E. *Japanese Handguns.* Alhambra, California: Borden Publishing Company, 1968.

Lenk, T. *The Flintlock, Its Origins and Development.* New York, New York: Bramhall House, 1965.

Lugs, J. *Firearms Past and Present.* London: Grenville, 1975.

Madis, George *The Winchester Model 12.* Brownsboro, Texas: Art & Reference House, 1982.

Madis, George *The Winchester Book.* Brownsboro, Texas: Art & Reference House, 1977.

Marcot, R. *Spencer Repeating Firearms.* Irvine, California: Northwood Heritage Press, 1990.

Markham, George *Japanese Infantry Weapons of World War Two.* New York, New York: Hippocrene Books, Inc., 1976.

McDowell, R. *Evolution of the Winchester.* Tacoma, Washington: Armory Pub., 1985.

McIntosh, Michael *A.H. Fox; The Finest Gun in the World.* Countrysport Press, 1992.

Moller, G. D. *American Military Shoulder Arms, Volume I, Colonial and Revolutionary War Arms.* Niwot, CO: University Press of Colorado, 1993.

Murphy, J. M.D. *Confederate Carbines & Musketoons.* J. Murphy, M.D., n.p.: 1986.

Murray, Douglas P. *The 99: A History of the Savage Model 99 Rifle.* Murray, 1976.

Myatt, Major Frederick, M.D. *Pistols and Revolvers.* New York, New York: Crescent Books, 1980.

Nutter, W.E. *Manhattan Firearms.* Harrisburg, Pennsylvania: Stackpole Co., 1958.

Olson, Ludwig *Mauser Bolt Rifles.* Third Edition. Montezuma, Iowa: Brownell & Sons, 1976.

Parsons, J.E. *Henry Deringer's Pocket Pistol.* New York, New York: Wm. Morrow & Co., 1952.

Pender, Roy G. III *Mauser Pocket Pistols 1910-1946.* Houston, Texas: Collectors Press, 1971.

Peterson, H.L. *Arms and Armor in Colonial America.* New York, New York: Brandhall House, 1956.

Rankin, J. *Walther Models PP and PPK.* Coral Gables, Florida: Rankin, 1989.

Rankin, J. *Walther Volume III, 1908-1980.* Coral Gables, Florida: Rankin, 1981.

Reese, Michael II *Luger Tips.* Union City, Tennessee: Pioneer Press, 1976.

Reilly, R. *United States Martial Flintlocks.* Lincoln, Rhode Island: Andrew Mowbray, Inc., 1986.

Reilly, R. *United States Military Small Arms 1816-1865.* Baton Rouge, Louisiana: Eagle Press, Inc., 1970.

Renneberg, R.C. *The Winchester Model 94: The First 100 Years.* Iola, WI: Krause Publications, 1992.

Riling, R. *The Powder Flask Book.* New York, New York: Bonanza Books, 1953.

Rosenberger, R. F. & Kaufmann, C. *The Long Rifles of Western Pennsylvania - Allegheny and Westmoreland Counties.* Pittsburgh, PA: University of Pittsburgh Press, 1993.

Rule, R. *The Rifleman's Rifle: Winchester's Model 70, 1936-1963.* Northridge, California: Alliance Books, 1982.

Ruth, L. *War Baby! Comes Home - The U.S. Caliber .30 Caliber Carbine Volume II.* Toronto, Ontario: Collector Grade Publications, Inc., 1993.

Ruth, L. *War Baby! The U.S. Caliber .30 Carbine.* Toronto, Ontario: Collector Grade Publications, Inc., 1992.

Schroeder, Joseph J. *Gun Collector's Digest, Volume II.* Northfield, Illinois: Digest Books, Inc., 1977.

Schwing, N. *Winchester's Finest, The Model 21.* Iola, Wisconsin: Krause Pub., 1990.

Schwing, N. *The Winchester Model 42.* Iola, Wisconsin: Krause Pub., 1990.

Schwing, N. *Winchester Slide Action Rifles, Vol. I: Model 1890 and Model 1906.* Iola, WI: Krause Publications, 1992.

Schwing, N. *Winchester Slide Action Rifles, Vol. II: Model 61 and Model 62.* Iola, WI: Krause Publications, 1993.

Sellers, F. *Sharps Firearms.* North Hollywood, California: Beinfeld Pub., Inc., 1978.

Sellers, F. *American Gunsmiths.* Highland Park, New Jersey: Gun Room Press, 1983.

Sellers, F. and Smith, S. *American Percussion Revolvers.* Ottawa, Ontario: Museum Restoration Service, 1971.

Serven, James E. *200 Years of American Firearms.* Chicago, Illinois: Follett Publishing Company, 1975.

Serven, J. *Collecting of Guns.*

Sharpe, P. *The Rifle in America.* Funk and Wagnalls Co., 1953.

Sheldon, Douglas G. *A Collector's Guide to Colt's .38 Automatic Pistols.* Sheldon, 1987.

Smith, W. *The Book of Pistols and Revolvers.* Harrisburg, Pennsylvania: Stackpole Co., 1962.

Stadt, R.W. *Winchester Shotguns and Shotshells.* Tacoma, Washington: Armory Publications, 1984.

Stevens, R. *The Browning High Power Automatic Pistol.* Toronto, Canada: Collector Grade Publications, 1990.

Stoeger's Catalog & Handbook. 1939 Issue. Hackensack, New Jersey: Stoeger Arms Corporation.

Sutherland, R.Q. & Wilson, R.L. *The Book of Colt Firearms.* Kansas City, Missouri: R.Q. Sutherland, 1971.

Tivey, T. *The Colt Rifle, 1884-1902.* N.S.W. Australia: Couston & Hall, 1984.

Vorisek, Joleph T *Shotgun Markings:* 1865 to 1940, Canton, CT: Armsco Press 1990.

Wahl, Paul *Wahl's Big Gun Catalog/1.* Cut And Shoot, Texas: Paul Wahl Corporation, 1988.

Walter, John *The German Rifle.* Ontario, Canada: Fortress Publishing, Inc., 1979.

Whitaker, Dean H. *The Winchester Model 70 1937-1964.* Dallas, Texas: Taylor Publishing Company, 1978.

Wilkerson, Don *The Post War Colt Single Action Army Revolver.* Dallas, Texas: Taylor Publishing Company, 1978.

Wilson, R.L. *Colt An American Legend.* New York, New York: Abbeville Press, 1985.

Wilson, R.L. *Colt Engraving.* Beinfeld Publishing, Inc., n.p., 1982.

Wilson, R.L. *Winchester Engraving.* Palm Springs, California: Beinfeld Books, 1989.

Wilson, R.L. *The Colt Heritage.* New York, New York: Simon & Schuster, 1979.

Wilson, R.L. *Winchester An American Legend.* New York, New York: 1991.

Winant, L. *Early Percussion Firearms.* New York, New York: Wm. Morrow & Co., 1959.

Winant, L. *Firearms Curiosa.* New York, New York: Greenburg Pub., 1955.

About the Editors

Ned Schwing's historical interest in firearms spans five decades. Beginning in 1950, with the purchase of his first rifle, Ned has researched a wide variety of firearms topics. Trained as a historian with an undergraduate and Master's degree in history, Mr. Schwing taught history at the University of Houston for several years. He has combined his capabilities as a working historian with those of a firearms collector to impart his knowledge to the collecting and shooting public.

Mr. Schwing has authored several books on Winchester firearms including: *The Winchester Model 42* (1989), *Winchester's Finest: the Model 21* (1990), and, more recently, the two volume work *Winchester Slide Action Rifles, Volume I: The Model 1890 and 1906* (1992) and *Winchester Slide Action Rifles, Volume II: The Model 61 and Model 62* (1993). His articles have appeared in the *American Rifleman* and other firearms publications.

Herbert G. Houze received his bachelor of arts degree from McMaster University in Hamilton, Ontario and master of education degree from George Peabody College of Vanderbilt University in Nashville, Tenn.

Mr. Houze has a long history in firearms involvement. He served as curator of weapons and military history for the Chicago Historical Society (1973-'76), is a consultant to the Royal Military College of Canada Museum in Kingston, Ontario (1977 to date), was curator of the Cody Firearms Museum, Buffalo Bill Historical Center, in Cody, Wyo., (1983-1991), and is currently the managing director of Lynham Sayce Co. Inc. of Cody, Wyoming.

He is affiliated with the Arms and Armour Society of England, Armor and Arms Club of New York and Les mis du Musee d'Armes de Liege, Belgium. Published works to his credit include *The Sumptuous Flaske* (1989), *American Sporting Arms of the Eighteenth and Nineteenth Centuries* (1975), *The Cody Firearms Museum* (1991), *To The Dreams Of Youth* (1993) plus more than 30 articles for various journals and magazines.

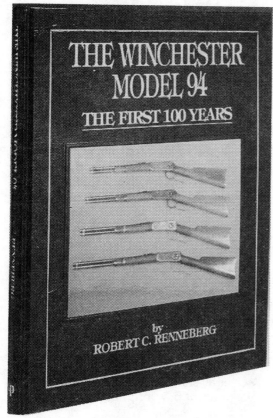

Gun List provides a service and stands beside it.

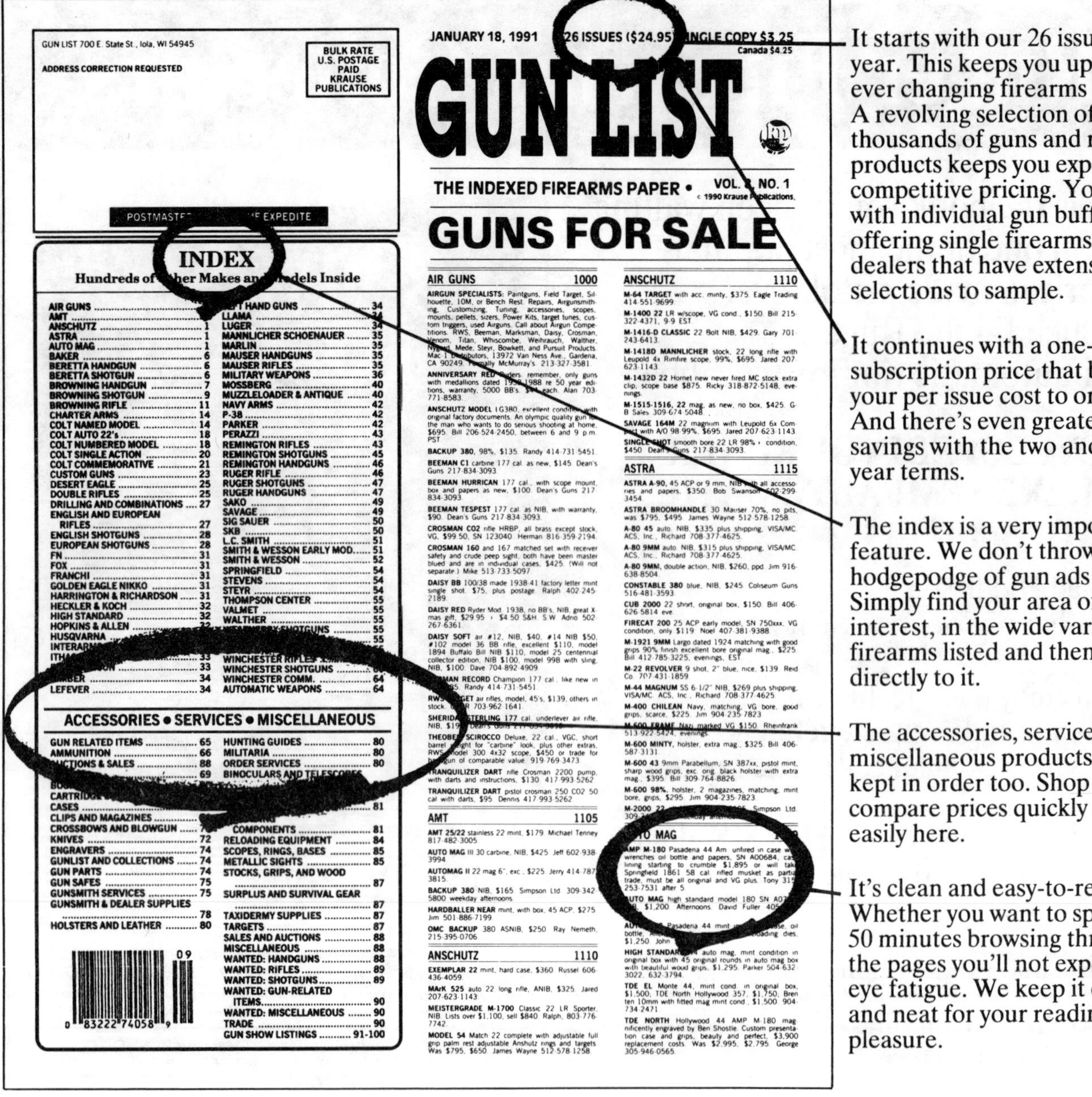

GUN LIST 700 E. State St., Iola, WI 54945

ADDRESS CORRECTION REQUESTED

BULK RATE
U.S. POSTAGE
PAID
KRAUSE
PUBLICATIONS

POSTMASTE… …E EXPEDITE

INDEX

Hundreds of …her Makes an… …dels Inside

0 83222 74058 9 09

JANUARY 18, 1991 26 ISSUES ($24.95) SINGLE COPY $3.25 Canada $4.25

GUN LIST

THE INDEXED FIREARMS PAPER • VOL. 8, NO. 1 © 1990 Krause Publications.

GUNS FOR SALE

AIR GUNS 1000

AIRGUN SPECIALISTS: Paintguns, Field Target, Silhouette, 10M, or Bench Rest. Repairs, Airgunsmithing, Customizing, Tuning, accessories, scopes, mounts, pellets, sizers, Power Kits, target tunes, custom triggers, used Airguns. Call about Airgun Competitions. RWS, Beeman, Marksman, Daisy, Crosman, Venom, Titan, Whiscombe, Weihrauch, Walther, Nygard, Mede, Steyr, Bowkett, and Pursuit Products. Mac-1 Distributors, 13972 Van Ness Ave., Gardena, CA 90249. Formally McMurray's. 213-327-3581.

ANNIVERSARY RED Ryders: remember, only guns with medallions dated 1938-1988 re 50 year editions, warranty, 5000 BB's. $… each. Alan 703-771-8583.

ANSCHUTZ MODEL LG380, excellent condition with original factory documents. An olympic quality gun for the man who wants to do serious shooting at home, $695. Bill 206-524-2450, between 6 and 9 p.m. PST.

BACKUP 380, 98%, $135. Randy 414-731-5451.

BEEMAN C1 carbine 177 cal. as new, $145. Dean's Guns 217-834-3093.

BEEMAN HURRICAN 177 cal., with scope mount, box and papers as new, $100. Dean's Guns 217-834-3093.

BEEMAN TESPEST 177 cal. as NIB, with warranty, $90. Dean's Guns 217-834-3093.

CROSMAN CO2 rifle HRBP, all brass except stock, VG, $99.50, SN 123040. Herman 816-359-2194.

CROSMAN 160 and 167 matched set with receiver safety and crude peep sight, both have been master blued and are in individual cases. $425. (Will not separate.) Mike 513-733-5097.

DAISY BB 100/38 made 1938-41 factory letter mint single shot. $75, plus postage. Ralph 402-245-2189.

DAISY RED Ryder Mod. 1938, no BB's, NIB, great X-mas gift, $29.95 + $4.50 S&H. S.W. Adrio 502-267-6361.

DAISY SOFT air #12, NIB, $40, #14 NIB $50, #102 model 36 BB rifle, excellent $110, model 1894 Buffalo Bill NIB $110, model 25 centennial collector edition, NIB $100, model 998 with sling, NIB, $100. Dave 704-892-4909.

…MAN RECORD Champion 177 cal., like new in …85. Randy 414-731-5451.

RWS …GET air rifles, model, 45's, $139, others in stock. …R 703-962-1641.

SHERIDA… STERLING 177 cal. underlever air rifle, NIB, $19… Dean's Guns …

THEOBE… SCIROCCO Deluxe, 22 cal., VGC, short barrel …ight for "carbine" look, plus other extras, RWS …odel 300 4x32 scope, $450 or trade for …gun of comparable value. 919-769-3473.

…RANQUILIZER DART rifle Crosman 2200 pump, with darts and instructions, $130. 417-993-5262.

TRANQUILIZER DART pistol crosman 250 CO2 50 cal with darts, $95. Dennis 417-993-5262.

AMT 1105

AMT 25/22 stainless 22 mint, $179. Michael Tenney 817-482-3005.

AUTO MAG III 30 carbine, NIB, $425. Jeff 602-938-3994.

AUTOMAG II 22 mag 6", exc., $225. Jerry 414-787-3815.

BACKUP 380 NIB, $165. Simpson Ltd. 309-342-5800 weekday afternoons.

HARDBALLER NEAR mint, with box, 45 ACP, $275. Jim 501-886-7199.

OMC BACKUP 380 ASNIB, $250. Ray Nemeth, 215-395-0706.

ANSCHUTZ 1110

EXEMPLAR 22 mint, hard case, $360. Russel 606-436-4059.

MArK 525 auto 22 long rifle, ANIB, $325. Jared 207-623-1143.

MEISTERGRADE M-1700 Classic 22 LR Sporter, NIB. Lists over $1,100, sell $840. Ralph, 803-776-7742.

MODEL 54 Match 22 complete with adjustable full grip palm rest adjustable Anshutz rings and targets. Was $795, $650. James Wayne 512-578-1258.

ANSCHUTZ 1110

M-64 TARGET with acc. minty, $375. Eagle Trading 414-551-9699.

M-1400 22 LR w/scope, VG cond., $150. Bill 215-322-4371, 9-9 EST.

M-1416-D CLASSIC 22 Bolt NIB, $429. Gary 701-243-6413.

M-1418D MANNLICHER stock, 22 long rifle with Leupold 4x Rimfire scope, 99%, $695. Jared 207-623-1143.

M-1432D 22 Hornet new never fired MC stock extra clip, scope base $875. Ricky 318-872-5148, evenings.

M-1515-1516, 22 mag, as new, no box, $425. G-B Sales 309-674-5048.

SAVAGE 164M 22 magnum with Leupold 6x Compact with A/O 98-99%, $695. Jared 207-623-1143.

SINGLE SHOT smooth bore 22 LR 98% + condition, $450. Dean's Guns 217-834-3093.

ASTRA 1115

ASTRA A-90, 45 ACP or 9 mm, NIB with all accessories and papers, $350. Bob Swanson 602-299-3454.

ASTRA BROOMHANDLE 30 Mauser 70%, no pits, was $795, $495. James Wayne 512-578-1258.

A-80 45 auto. NIB, $335 plus shipping, VISA/MC. ACS, Inc., Richard 708-377-4625.

A-80 9MM auto. NIB, $315 plus shipping, VISA/MC. ACS, Inc., Richard 708-377-4625.

A-80 9MM, double action, NIB, $260, ppd. Jim 916-638-8504.

CONSTABLE 380 blue, NIB, $245. Coliseum Guns 516-481-3593.

CUB 2000 22 short, original box, $150. Bill 406-626-5814 eve.

FIRECAT 200 25 ACP early model, SN 750xxx, VG condition, only $119. Noel 407-381-9388.

M-1921 9MM Largo dated 1924 matching with good grips 90% finish excellent bore original mag., $225. Bill 412-785-3225, evenings, EST.

M-22 REVOLVER 9 shot, 2" blue, nice, $139. Reid Co. 707-431-1859.

M-44 MAGNUM SS 6-1/2" NIB, $269 plus shipping, VISA/MC. ACS, Inc., Richard 708-377-4625.

M-400 CHILEAN Navy, matching, VG bore, good grips, scarce, $225. Jim 904-235-7823.

M-600 FRAME Nazi marked VG $150. Rheinfrank 513-922-5424, evenings.

M-600 MINTY, holster, extra mag., $325. Bill 406-587-3131.

M-600 43 9mm Parabellum, SN 387xx, pistol mint, sharp wood grips, exc. orig. black holster with extra mag., $395. Bill 309-764-8826.

M-600 98%, holster, 2 magazines, matching, mint bore, grips, $295. Jim 904-235-7823.

M-2000 22 … Simpson Ltd. 309-…

…O MAG

…MP M-180 Pasadena 44 Am unfired in case w… wrenches oil bottle and papers, SN A00684, ca… lining starting to crumble $1,895 or will tak… Springfield 1861 58 cal. rifled musket as parti… trade, must be all original and VG plus. Tony 315-253-7531 after 5.

…UTO MAG high standard model 180 SN A07… …B, $1,200. Afternoons. David Fuller 405…

AU… Pasadena 44 mint … …se, oil bottle, … …oading dies, $1,250. John …

HIGH STANDAR… auto mag, mint condition in original box with 45 original rounds in auto mag box with beautiful wood grips, $1,295. Parker 504-632-3022, 632-3794.

TDE EL Monte 44, mint cond. in original box, $1,500; TDE North Hollywood 357, $1,750; Bren ten 10mm with fitted mag mint cond., $1,500. 904-734-2471.

TDE NORTH Hollywood 44 AMP M-180 magnificently engraved by Ben Shostle. Custom presentation case and grips, beauty and perfect, $3,900 replacement costs. Was $2,995, $2,795. George 305-946-0565.

It starts with our 26 issues per year. This keeps you up on the ever changing firearms market. A revolving selection of thousands of guns and related products keeps you exposed to competitive pricing. You'll deal with individual gun buffs offering single firearms and dealers that have extensive selections to sample.

It continues with a one-year subscription price that brings your per issue cost to only 96¢. And there's even greater savings with the two and three year terms.

The index is a very important feature. We don't throw a hodgepodge of gun ads at you. Simply find your area of interest, in the wide variety of firearms listed and then go directly to it.

The accessories, services and miscellaneous products are kept in order too. Shop and compare prices quickly and easily here.

It's clean and easy-to-read. Whether you want to spend 5 or 50 minutes browsing through the pages you'll not experience eye fatigue. We keep it clean and neat for your reading pleasure.

You'll return again and again to these helpful pages to find special buys and to see what's happening in the gun buying, selling and trading world.

GUN LIST - the indexed firearms paper

It's your best source for quality and service.
Get thousands of firearms bargains every two weeks.

Gun List
700 E. State St.
Iola, WI 54990-0001
Business Phone 1-715-445-2214

(Prices subject to change, call for current subscription price information)

VISA and MASTERCARD users: 1-800-258-0929. Hours: 6:30 a.m. to 8 p.m. CST Monday-Friday; 8 a.m. to 2 p.m. Saturday